HUMAN ANATOMY

AND PHYSIOLOGY

HUMAN ANATOMY

AND
PHYSIOLOGY

Alvin Silverstein
Chairman, Department of Biological Sciences,
College of Staten Island,
City University of New York

paintings by Howard Friedman

JOHN WILEY & SONS
new york
chichester
brisbane
toronto

This book was designed by Edward A. Butler.

This book was set in Times Roman by Rocappi and printed and bound by Kingsport Press. The drawings were designed and executed by John Balbalis with the assistance of the Wiley Illustration department. Rosemary Wellner was the copyeditor. Picture research was done by Kathy Bendo. Claire Egielski supervised production.

Library of Congress Cataloging in Publication Data:

Silverstein, Alvin.
   Human anatomy and physiology.

   Includes index.
   1. Human physiology. 2. Anatomy, Human. I. Title.
[DNLM: 1. Anatomy. 2. Physiology. QS4.3 S587h]
QP34.5.S54   612   79–13053
ISBN 0-471-79166-0

Printed in the United States of America

10 9 8 7 6 5 4 3 2 1

PREFACE

Today progress in science and technology is moving faster than ever before. The biomedical sciences are in a particular ferment. New discoveries and advances are announced almost daily. These advances in basic biomedicine are frequently translated into new treatments and techniques in the health science arena.

The rapidly rising national medical bill attests to the critical importance of the allied health sciences, not only in our national economy but also in the health and well being of our citizens. The training of new doctors, nurses, and other health science personnel is crucial to the future well being of people throughout the world.

This book attempts to provide a foundation of basic knowledge of human anatomy and physiology in an accessible form that will facilitate learning. The anatomical structures and physiological mechanisms of the major organ systems of the body are treated in detail. In addition, the book covers the modern status of several fields of great importance to health science students: development, growth, and aging; nutrition; disease and the body's defenses; and the biomedical frontiers that are transforming medical practice. Advances in medical electronics, prosthetics, germfree research, biochemical engineering, and genetic engineering are described. The concluding chapter, "The Health Sciences and Society," discusses some major problems in the contemporary health sciences, such as the role of the FDA in the assessment of drugs and food additives, problems of drug abuse, pollution, the issues associated with death and dying, and questions of national priorities in the biomedical arena.

The writing of a textbook may be a lonely quest, but its publication requires the collaboration of a small army of skilled professionals. I would like to take this opportunity to thank those who have done so much to aid in bringing this book to its final, printed form: Gail Blair, John Harley, Elaine N. Marieb, E. D. Mickelberg, John D. Palmer, and Robert L. Shipp, whose careful reading of the manuscript and thoughtful comments were of invaluable help; my Wiley editors, Bob Rogers, Fred Corey, and Rosemary Wellner, whose enthusiasm, skilled coordination, and guidance kept the project moving smoothly; Howard Friedman, Russell Peterson, and the Wiley staff artists, who helped to convey concepts and information in a vivid graphic form; designer Edward A. Butler; photo researcher Peggy Simsarian Striegel; and members of the Wiley staff who have helped to bring it all together—Kathy Bendo, Ed Burke, Claire Egielski, Jerry McCarthy, Ron Nelson, Ann Renzi, and Ed Starr. Warm thanks are also due to my typist,

June Hardenburg; to my children, Robert, Glenn, Carrie, Sharon, Laura, and Kevin, for their patient understanding; and to my wife, Virginia, without whose encouragement and aid this book could not have been written.

Alvin Silverstein

CONTENTS

HUMAN ANATOMY

AND PHYSIOLOGY

INTRODUCTION 1

THE HEALTH SCIENCES
THE STUDY OF THE BODY

Science and technology have shaped our world. And these molding forces continue to have a profound effect on our lives. Jet planes, color TV, the ubiquitous computers, synthetics, and a host of other artificial creations have become commonplace.

At first there may seem to be little connection between today's technological marvels and the study of anatomy and physiology. Yet each facet of our modern world affects the human body and its health, sometimes obviously and directly, and sometimes far more subtly. Modern means of transportation have created a revolution in our way of life, dramatically increasing mobility and bringing with them a host of new problems affecting the health sciences—from the huge toll of accident victims to pollution, and even the "jet exhaustion" that may result from too rapid crossing of time zones. Modern means of communication are having far-reaching psychological effects on humans that are just beginning to be assessed, and there is growing concern about the effects on the body of the radio waves that permeate our atmosphere. The clothes we wear, the houses we live in, various articles of daily use, and even the foods we eat contain chemical substances that did not exist a century ago. Computers are creating and solving problems in nearly every aspect of our lives.

Under the hectic and rapidly changing conditions of modern life, the health professions have taken on an importance never before equalled. Yet science and technology have also provided means to a more profound knowledge of the body and have armed health scientists with an unprecedented arsenal of weapons in the fight against disease and death.

THE HEALTH SCIENCES

Humankind has always been prey to a variety of accidents and ills. Indeed, fossil remains of the earliest humans show evidence of such ailments as tooth decay, arthritis, broken bones, and congenital abnormalities, millennia before the dawn of recorded history. Then, as now, there were those who attempted to study and treat the disorders of the body. Thousands of years ago, for example, physicians in ancient Egypt were practicing trephining (opening of the skull) and other sophisticated medical and surgical techniques.

In our modern civilization, the needs for health care have grown explosively. The sheer numbers of people and the complexity of their interactions have contributed to the problem. Rising standards of living have brought with them a revolution of expectations: more and more, a minimum standard of health has become recognized as a right for all, not a privilege for the favored few. Paradoxically, the very progress in medical science has further contributed to the problem; increasing numbers of people are surviving to old age, when organs and systems of the body may become less efficient or break down entirely. All these factors contribute to the growing need for people trained in the health sciences.

The thought of medicine and health care evokes dramatic pictures: the noted surgeon performing a life-saving operation; the friendly family doctor who tries to know and treat the whole person; the dedicated nurse providing efficient and compassionate care to a ward of hospital patients. Yet these highly trained professionals are supported by an army of others, whose knowledge and services are equally vital. Today, the health sciences encompass not only doctors and nurses and dentists, but also people in such fields as radiology, rehabilitation, mental health counseling, genetic counseling, laboratory technology, biomedical engineering and instrumentation, environmental control, dietary service, and the processing and correlation of medical information. Basic to the training of all these health care personnel is a thorough knowledge of the human body in sickness and health.

THE STUDY OF THE BODY

This is a textbook of anatomy and physiology. Here, at the beginning of the book, it might be a good idea to pause briefly for some basic definitions, to give you a more precise idea of just what you will be studying over the coming months.

Anatomy and physiology are both subdivisions of the science of **biology,** the study of living organisms. The term **anatomy** is derived from Greek words meaning literally "a cutting up," and it refers to the study of the structure of the body. **Physiology,** from Greek roots meaning "the study of nature," deals with the functions of the body, the activities characteristic of living matter. Anatomy is essentially a descriptive science; indeed, it is most often studied by the dissection ("cutting apart") of dead specimens. Physiology is a dynamic science, reaching into the areas that are the essence of life and often gaining knowledge by active experimentation. Because the study of function is meaningless without a knowledge of the structures involved, and these structures to some extent determine the nature of functions—and vice versa—anatomy and physiology are thus inextricably interrelated, and both are essential to students of the life sciences. The terms "anatomy" and "physiology" can be used to refer to any organism; in this book, however, we will concentrate on the organism with the greatest interest to the health sciences: the human being.

Anatomy and physiology, subdivisions of biology, can in turn be subdivided into narrower disciplines.

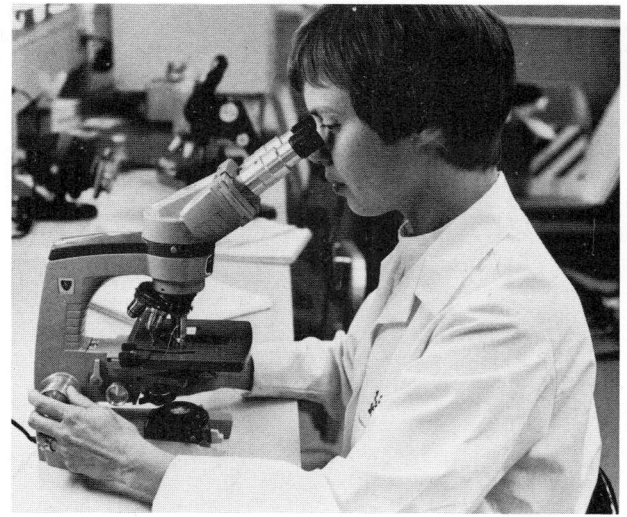

A

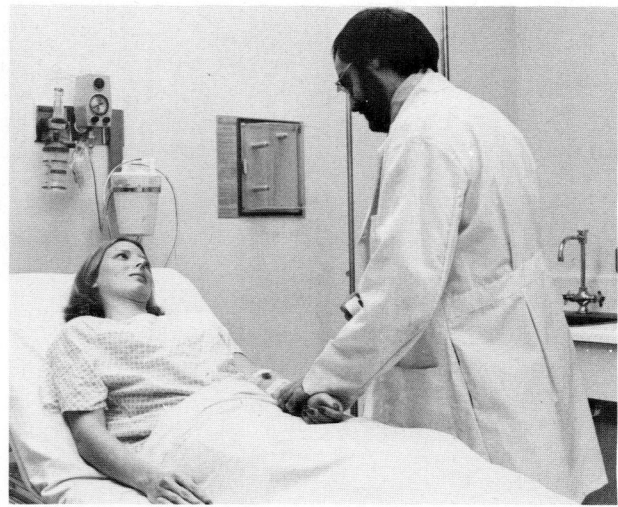

B

C

FIGURE 1-1 Modern health care personnel deal with patients and an array of sophisticated instruments and devices.

D

Gross anatomy deals with macroscopic structure—that which can be seen with the naked eye. It may be studied either regionally (focusing on the interrelationships of the various organs and structures in a particular region of the body) or systemically (tracing all the structures of the body associated with a particular function, regardless of their location in the body). Its principal technique is dissection.

Microscopic anatomy deals with structures too small to be seen with the naked eye and that can be viewed only through the magnification provided by a microscope. The development of the optical microscope produced a revolution in biology; microscopes, for example, revealed the existence of cells and permitted their roles to be fathomed. The development of electron microscopes, providing far greater magni-

fication than possible with an optical microscope, has yielded equally dramatic additions to our knowledge, revealing details of structures within cells. One area of microscopic anatomy, that dealing with cells, is called **cytology.** The study of the structure of tissues (groups of similar cells performing a common function) is **histology.**

Human anatomy deals with the structure of the human body. **Comparative anatomy** is the study of the

FIGURE 1-2 "The Anatomy Lesson," by Rembrandt.

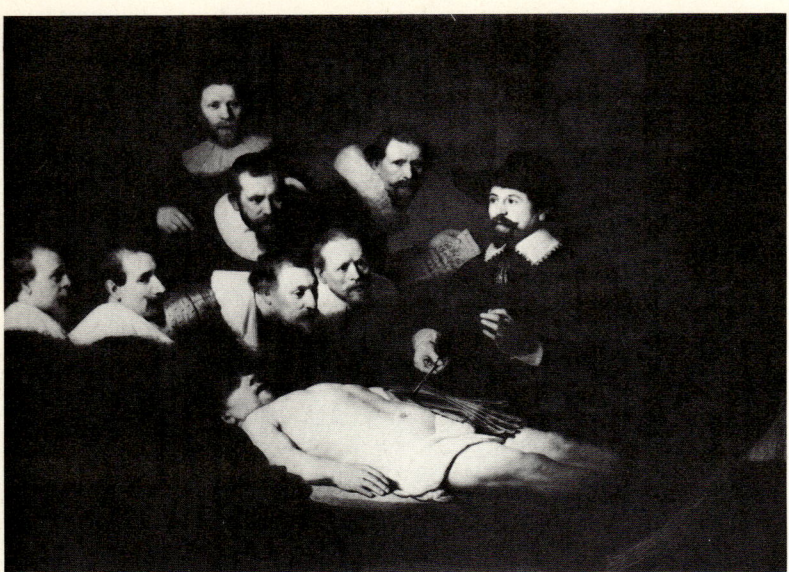

similarities and differences in the structures of various kinds of animals, with emphasis on their evolutionary history.

Developmental anatomy is the study of the development of body structures, from conception to birth (**embryology**) and on through childhood and various stages of maturity.

Pathological anatomy deals with the structural changes caused by disease and their effects on the body.

Human physiology deals with the functions of the body as a whole; **cellular physiology** treats the activities of the individual cells, which live their own lives on the micro-level and perform many of the same functions as the organism: respiration, intake of food, excretion, movement, and so on. Comparative, developmental, and pathological physiology may also be distinguished, with meanings analogous to the corresponding divisions of anatomy.

We are living in the midst of an unparalleled information revolution. It has been estimated that 90 percent of all the scientists who have ever lived are alive and working today. They are turning out such a mountain of new data that the modern scientist or physician finds it virtually impossible to keep up to date on all the literature even in a small area of knowledge. This vast outpouring of facts and theories has led to increasingly narrow specialization in nearly every field, including the health sciences. Yet even specialists must have a firm grounding in certain basic general information and must constantly guard against focusing so closely on their own specialties that they lose sight of the overall picture. In the health sciences, the body of general information that all must master includes the fundamental principles of human anatomy and physiology.

SUMMARY

Our technological society has brought new health problems and provided new tools for combatting them.

Although accident and disease have always been factors in human life, population growth, a technology-based way of life, rising living standards, and medical advances have produced an unprecedented need for health care services and trained personnel to deliver them.

The study of the human body is fundamental to the health sciences.

Anatomy is the study of the structures of the body.

Physiology is the study of the functions of the body.

Divisions of anatomy include:

Gross anatomy

Microscopic anatomy (histology, cytology)

Human anatomy

Comparative anatomy

Developmental anatomy

Pathological anatomy

Divisions of physiology include:

Human physiology

Cellular physiology

Comparative physiology

Developmental physiology

Pathological physiology

QUESTIONS FOR REVIEW AND THOUGHT

1 Discuss ways in which the following aspects of modern life might affect human health: (a) automobiles; (b) food additives; (c) aerosol sprays; (d) rock and roll music; (e) sedentary occupations.

2 How well is our society fulfilling the goal of maintaining minimum standards of health for all? What improvements might be desirable?

3 In discussions of the interrelationship of anatomy and physiology, it has often been stated that "form follows function." Yet to some degree anatomical structure can also provide and limit opportunities for the development of physiological functions. Discuss the relationship of structure and function for the example of the human hand.

4 Why must health science personnel, who deal with the sick body, have a firm knowledge of the anatomy and physiology of the healthy human?

THE ORGANIZATION OF THE BODY

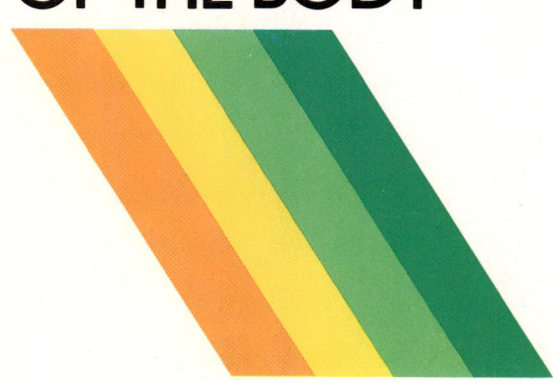

2

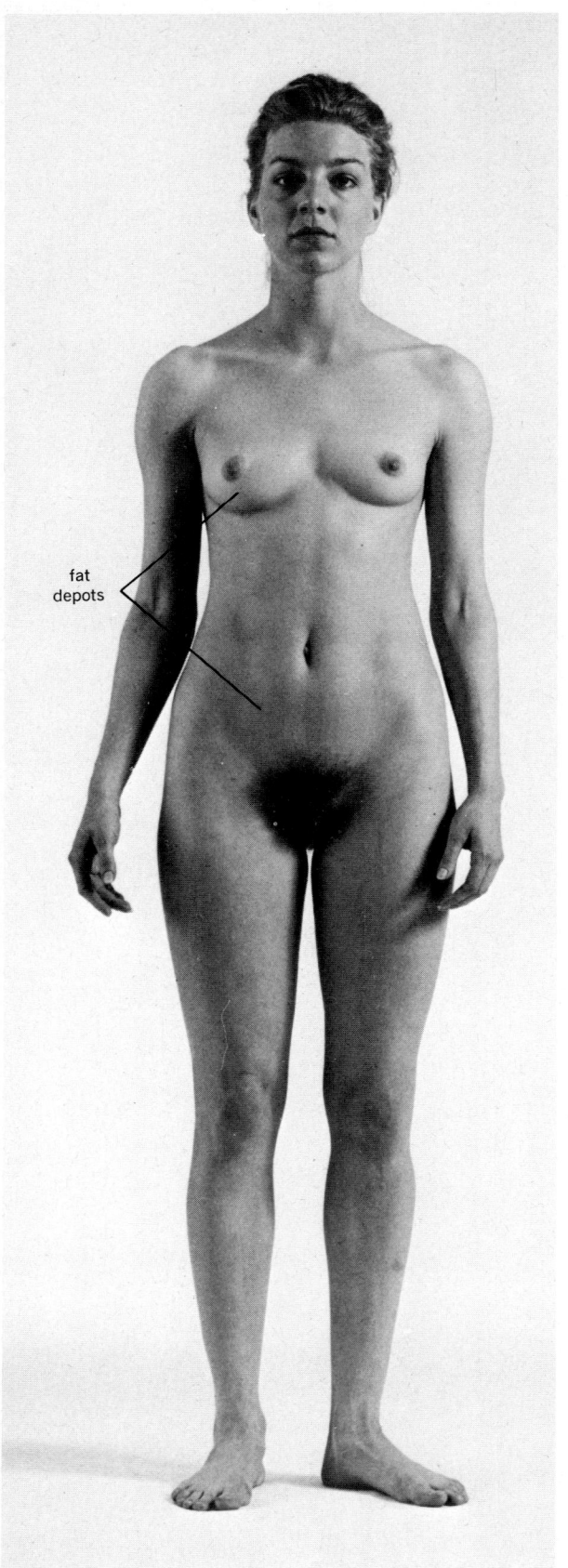

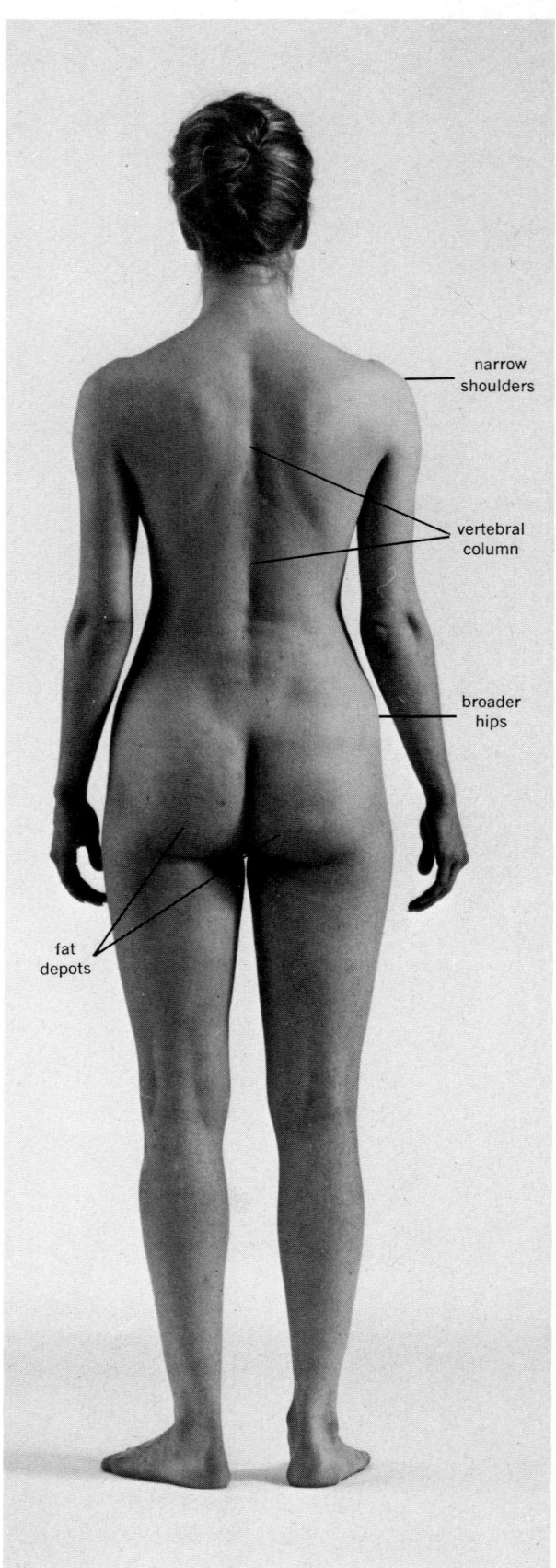

A

B

FIGURE 2-1 The human body: female (A,B) and male (C,D).

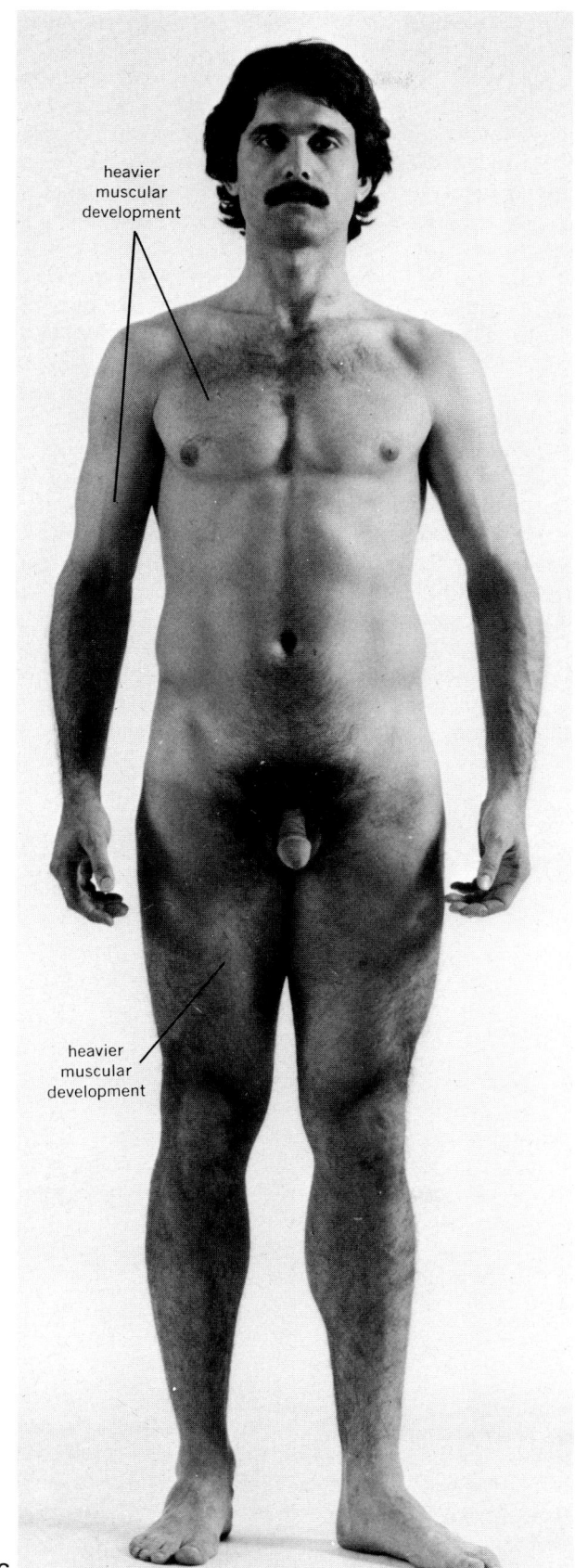

heavier
muscular
development

heavier
muscular
development

C

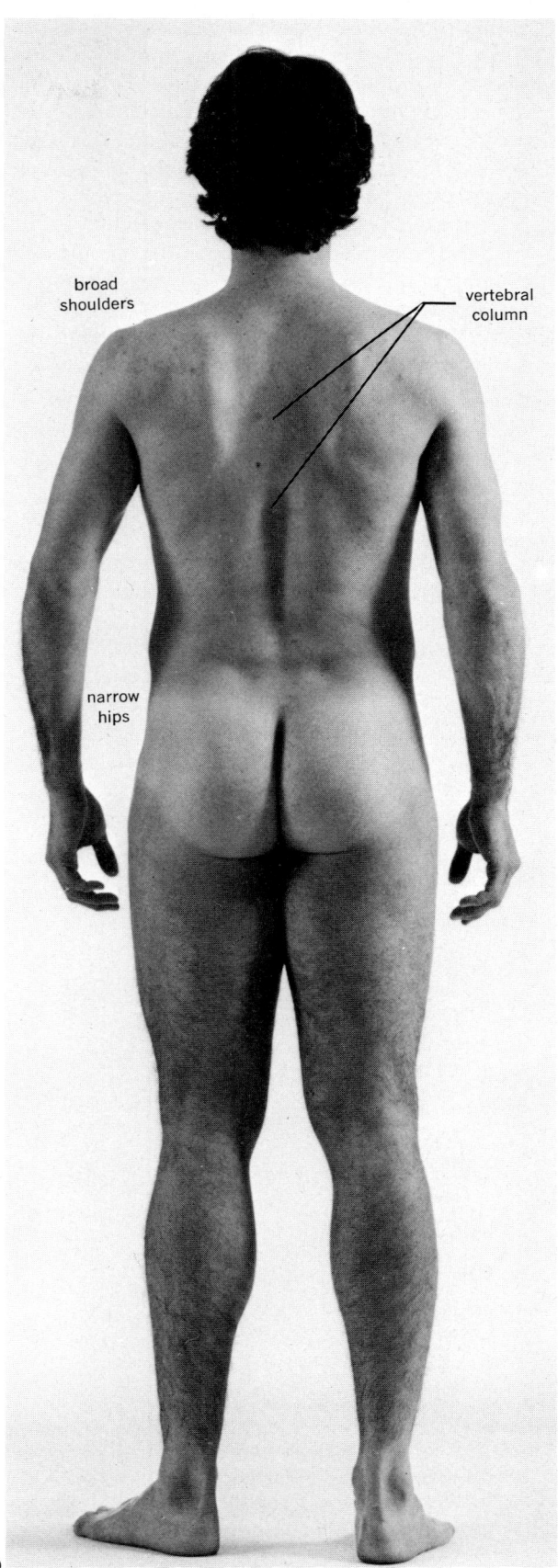

broad
shoulders

vertebral
column

narrow
hips

D

Careers in the health sciences require an intimate knowledge of the structure and functions of the human body, both in health and in disease. In anatomy and physiology, most of the time is devoted to studies of specific parts or systems of the body, and it is often all too easy to think of each part in isolation, without relation to other parts and systems and the body as a whole. Yet each part of the body is dependent for its survival and proper functioning upon the coordinated functioning of all the other body systems. The complex structure that is the human body is a prime example of the maxim, "the whole is greater than the sum of its parts." It is thus appropriate to begin the study of the human body with a brief overview of the body as a whole, with some basic generalizations on its overall organization.

THE HUMAN BODY AS A WHOLE

We belong to the group of vertebrates, and thus a prominent structural characteristic of the human body is the flexible rodlike spine or **vertebral column** that runs through the long axis of the body. This vertebral column is part of a well-developed internal framework or skeleton, which makes up about 20 percent of the total body weight and is composed of more than 200 separate bones. Soft tissues molded over the bony framework give the body its basic shape.

As Figure 2-1 makes strikingly evident, there are considerable differences in body form between men and women. A man is more heavily built in general, with broader shoulders but proportionately narrower hips than a woman. Strategic fat deposits give a woman a more rounded, curving appearance, while a man's body is more angular. The body form also varies with age, with diet, amount of physical exercise, and is to a large extent determined by heredity. A child's head and abdomen are disproportionately large in comparison with the adult figure; middle age may bring the deposition of fat pads (the typical "paunch"), while a depletion of underlying fat in old age causes the skin to sag. Heavy physical activity can lead to growth of muscle and bone; a sedentary life, combined with a food intake that exceeds the energy expenditures, can produce obesity. Some anatomists classify general body structure in several basic types: endomorph (plump, stocky), ectomorph (thin), and mesomorph (heavy muscular build).

A human being, like other vertebrates, is characterized by **bilateral symmetry:** an imaginary plane, passing through the spine from front to back, would divide the body into two halves that are roughly mirror

FIGURE 2-2 Humans, like many (but not all) members of the animal kingdom, have a bilaterally symmetrical body plan.

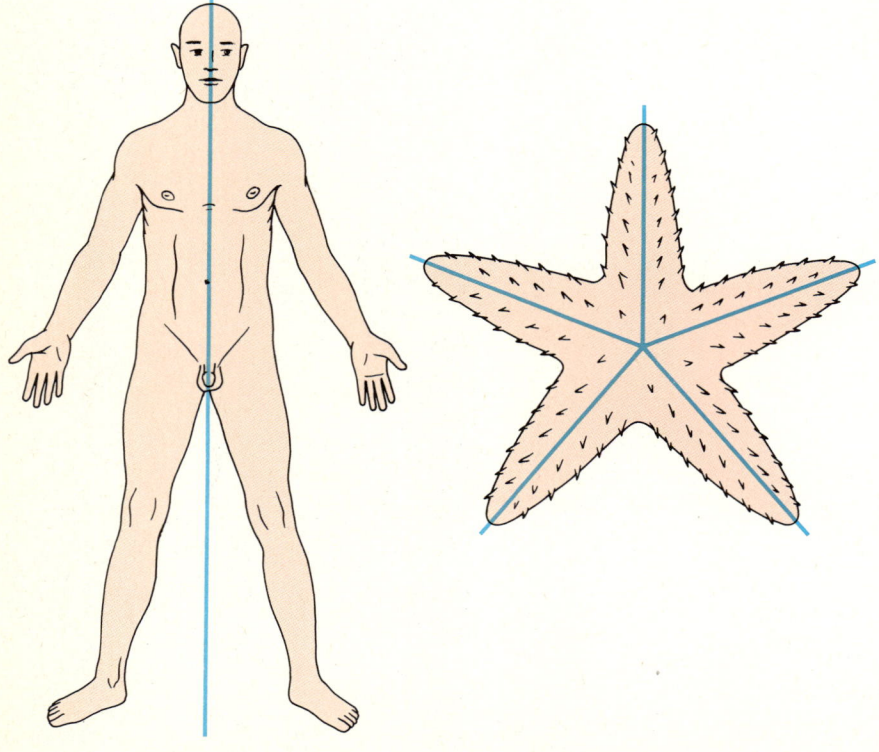

bilateral symmetry

radial symmetry

images of each other. Thus, many body parts and organs occur in pairs—two eyes, two ears, two arms, two legs, two lungs, two kidneys, and so forth. Single organs and parts are usually relatively centrally located along the long axis of the body—the mouth, the heart, the stomach, and the urethra, for example. The mirror symmetry is not perfect; the heart, for example, is tipped somewhat to the left, and the left lung is correspondingly smaller than the right to accommodate the differential within the close confines of the chest. Even in body functions, the symmetry is not precise—there is usually a pronounced "handedness" and even a corresponding dominance of one leg over the other and one eye over the other. But despite these discrepancies, the human body is built basically on a bilateral plan, in contrast to some lower organisms such as the jellyfish and starfish, which are characterized by radial symmetry (Figure 2-2).

Among the vertebrates, humans belong to the group of mammals, which are characterized by several salient features. The structure that gives this class of animals its name is the **mammary glands,** which produce milk to feed the young. (Both the female and the male of the species have mammary glands, but only those of the female are functional.) Mammals are **homoiothermic** (warm-blooded), which means they are able to maintain a relatively constant internal body temperature over a wide range of variation of environmental conditions. The characteristic body temperature varies slightly according to the species; for humans it is 98.6°F, or 37°C. The mammalian body, in general, is covered with a coat of fur, the amount of which varies with the species. Humans are among the more hairless of mammals; our "fur coat" is reduced to a sparse covering of body hairs, plus a few characteristic patches of longer, thicker hair, which are more decorative than functional. The amount and distribution of hair varies among the races of man, as do the pigmentation of the skin and certain distinctive facial features (Figure 2-3). Despite these superficial differences, however, all the humans living today belong to the same species, *Homo sapiens.*

THE BODY REGIONS

The division of an ant's body into head, thorax, and abdomen (together with the various appendages) is so sharp that it looks like an assembly of three beads on a string. The divisions of the human body are much less extreme, but anatomists find it convenient to con-

FIGURE 2-3   We all belong to the same species, but differences in skin pigmentation, type and distribution of hair, and facial features are the basis of classification of three major human races: Caucasoid (A), Negroid (B), and Mongoloid (C).

sider the body as divided into several basic regions: the head and neck, the trunk, and the extremities or limbs (Figure 2-4). As in an insect, the extremities are attached to the central portion of the body (the trunk). Thus, the head, neck, and trunk together can be viewed as the **axial portion** of the body, while the extremities make up the **appendicular portion.** ("Appendicular" comes from a root meaning "to hang".)

The Axial Portion

The Head and Neck.
The human head has an importance quite out of proportion to its small size. Through the sense organs of the head (eyes, ears, and organs of taste and smell) the person receives a continual flow of information about the outside world. This information is perceived and evaluated, and appropriate actions are initiated in the brain. Without a functioning brain, life itself ceases. The head also contains the entrance for food intake, without which the body could not continue to function, as well as key parts of the apparatus for speech, the basis of human social interactions.

The neck serves as a connecting link through which nerves, blood vessels, and the major food and air passages run. The spinal cord, continuous with the brain, passes through the neck. Such structures as the thyroid and parathyroid glands and the larynx (voice box) are located entirely in the neck. The existence of a narrow, flexible neck also permits rotation of the head, which would not be possible if it were fused with the trunk.

The Trunk.
The trunk or torso is the largest region of the body, including everything except the head, neck, and extremities. As indicated in Figure 2-4, it can be subdivided into the thorax, abdomen, and pelvis. The major organs involved in respiration and digestion, the heart that pumps blood through the vessels of the circulatory system, and the reproductive organs are all concentrated in the trunk.

The Appendicular Portion

The Upper Extremity.
Some anthropologists believe that the adoption of an upright posture, freeing the hands for manipulative activities, provided the impetus that sparked the development of our apelike ancestors into the first men. The upper extremities of man are multiply jointed, permitting great flexibility of movement. Each upper limb is divided into the **upper arm,** extending from the shoulder to the elbow; the **forearm,** from elbow to wrist; and the **hand.** The **armpit** or **axilla** is located at the point of attachment of the upper extremity to the trunk. The front of the

elbow is known as the **antecubital fossa;** it is a favored site for the withdrawal of blood and the intravenous injection of drugs or nutrients because major blood vessels of the arm pass close to the surface here.

The Lower Extremity.
The lower extremities in man are larger and more heavily built than the upper extremities, as befits their function in supporting the entire weight of the body. Each lower limb consists of the **thigh,** extending from the hip to the knee; the **leg,** the portion between the knee and the ankle; and the **foot.** The **inguinal region** or **groin** is located at the front of the body, at the junction of the lower extremity and the trunk. The back of the knee is called the **popliteal fossa,** and is comparable to the antecubital fossa of the upper extremity.

THE LANGUAGE OF ANATOMY
People in the health sciences who deal with the body and its functions must be able to describe the regions of the body in precise terms, which cannot be misunderstood. Anatomists have therefore developed a standardized vocabulary, with terms relating to directions and locations on the body, planes of reference, specific features such as body cavities, and types of movement of the body and its parts.

The language of anatomy can be a bit tricky for the beginning student, for many of the words used are also part of the normal vocabulary, either with a similar or with a somewhat different meaning. If you remarked to a nonscience friend, for example, that "The hip is superior to the knee," you would probably be greeted with a puzzled stare. Yet to an anatomist, you would simply be stating the obvious fact that the hip is higher or closer to the head than the knee.

Anatomical terms are used throughout this book, in describing various structures of the body. It is important that you learn the basic descriptive terms now, so that you will feel easy and familiar with them when they appear. As you read the sections that follow, mentally relate each term to your own body. When you are with other people, mentally describe their body parts and movements in anatomical terms. (You may find that your practice sessions can enliven a lunchroom conversation.)

Direction and Location
Everything is relative, it is said, and the human body is no exception. Directions along the body and locations of body parts are described in relation to other body parts. If confusion is to be avoided, the position of the body is crucial. If you were lying on your back with your knees bent, for example, your knees would be higher than your hips—yet anatomists regard the

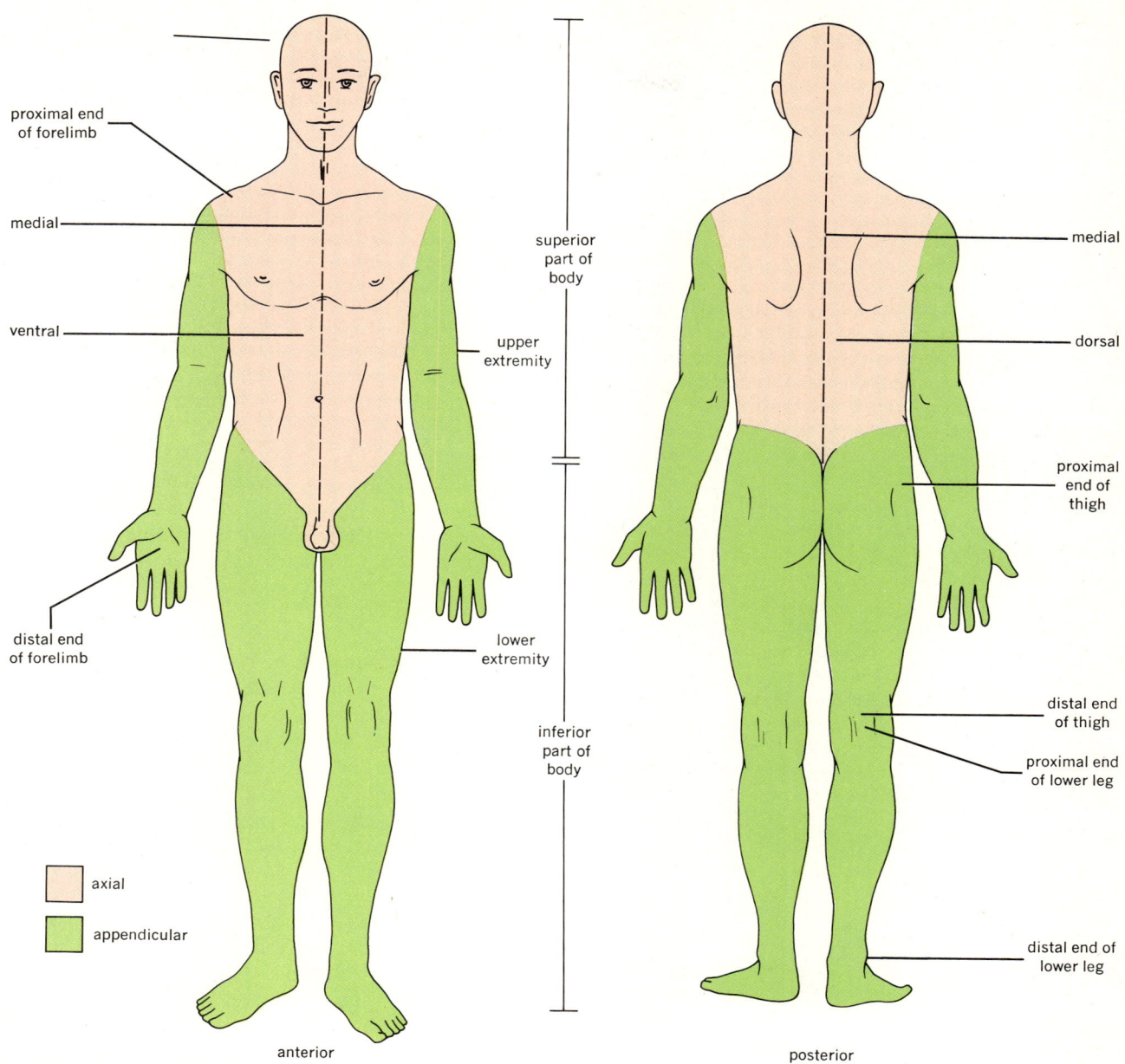

FIGURE 2-4   The anatomical position and the basic regions of the body.

hips as "superior" to the knees.

Anatomists have avoided ambiguities in terms describing directions and locations on the body by adopting a standardized **anatomical position,** which is shown in Figure 2-4. In this convention, the body is always considered in an erect position, with the head facing forward, the feet on the floor and slightly apart, and the arms hanging at the sides with the palms turned forward.

Following are some of the basic terms used for anatomical direction and location. Their meanings are also depicted in Figure 2-4.

Anterior: toward the front of the body or body part. The term **ventral** (derived from a root meaning "belly") is often used as a synonym.

Posterior: toward the back of the body or body part. The term **dorsal** (derived from a root meaning "back") is also used.*

Superior: upward or toward the head end. Synonyms are **cranial** and **cephalad.**

* Comparative anatomists, dealing with four-footed animals, use these terms somewhat differently. Since a quadruped does not normally stand upright, its standard anatomical position is a side view. *Ventral* is used for the belly surface, but since "front" is not synonymous with it for a four-footed animal, *anterior* is reserved for the meaning "toward the head end." *Dorsal* refers to the animal's back surface, while *posterior* means toward the rear or tail end.

Inferior: downward or below, that is, farther from the head or toward the feet. **Caudal** is used as a synonym. (The terms *superior* and *inferior* in anatomy do not have the connotation they have in common speech. For instance, the superior vena cava is not "better" than the inferior vena cava in any way; the descriptive terms simply refer to the fact that these two major veins return blood to the heart from the upper and lower portions of the body, respectively.)

Medial: nearer to the midline of the body (an imaginary vertical line dividing the body into right and left halves). It is sometimes referred to as **mesial.**

Lateral: farther from the midline of the body. The ears are on the lateral aspects of the head, for example, while the nose is medial to each eye. Note that in the anatomical position, the big toe is on the medial side of the foot, but the thumb is on the lateral side of the hand.

Superficial: at or nearer to the surface of the body. Synonyms that are sometimes used are **external** and **peripheral.** Peripheral is generally used in the sense of extensions from the principal part. For example, the peripheral nervous system is comprised of the nerves that go out from and into the brain and spinal cord. Together, the brain and spinal cord are referred to as the central nervous system.

Deep: the opposite of superficial, lying deeper inward, farther from the body surface than some other structure. **Internal** and **central** are also used with a similar meaning.

Proximal: nearer the origin of a part.

Distal: farther from the origin of a part. Proximal and distal are often used to refer to the extremities (e.g., the elbow is distal to the shoulder and proximal to the hand), as well as to internal structures (e.g., the proximal and distal convoluted tubules of the kidneys).

Parietal: referring to the walls of a cavity.

Visceral: referring to the organs within a cavity. (The viscera are the organs within the body cavities.)

Planes and Sections

A medical student learns human anatomy firsthand by dissecting a cadaver. The body must be cut or sectioned in order to study the deep structures in relation to one another. Even in dealing with the structures of the living body, it is convenient to use standard sections or planes of reference as a means of orientation.

The human body is three-dimensional. As might be expected, therefore, there are three standard planes of reference, depicted in Figure 2-5.

Sagittal: a lengthwise plane, running from front to back, which divides the body vertically into right and left portions. The sagittal plane passing precisely through the midline of the body is called a **midsagittal** or **median sagittal** plane and divides the body into two equal halves.

Coronal: a lengthwise plane at right angles to the sagittal plane, dividing the body vertically into anterior and posterior portions. This plane is also called a **frontal** plane.

Transverse: any plane that divides the body into superior and inferior portions. It is at right angles to both the sagittal and coronal planes. Since in the anatomical position such a plane is horizontal, it is also called a **horizontal** plane. In a dissection of a body or organ, a transverse section may also be referred to as a **cross section.**

The Body Cavities

The head and trunk contain a number of cavities. In general, these cavities are not empty, but are filled with organs and fluid. There are two major body cavities, each subdivided into two parts (Figure 2-6). The **dorsal cavity** consists of the **cranial** and **spinal cavities**, and thus is situated partly in the head and partly in the trunk. The **ventral cavity**, entirely in the trunk, is partitioned by the diaphragm into the **thoracic cavity** and the **abdominopelvic cavity**, which is further subdivided into the abdominal and pelvic cavities. These major cavities are closed; but other, smaller cavities such as the nasal cavity, open to the body surface. The alimentary canal, which runs from the buccal (mouth) cavity through the esophagus, stomach, and intestines to the anus, actually opens only to the outside—it is completely separated from the major body cavities and does not communicate with them.

The Dorsal Cavity Encased within the protection of the bony skull, and lined with membranes called meninges, the **cranial cavity** houses the brain. The cranial cavity is continuous with the **spinal cavity** or **vertebral canal**, housing the spinal cord. The two meet at the **foramen magnum**, an opening in the base of the skull. The brain and spinal cord together make up the central nervous system, the master control system that, along with the endocrine system, coordinates the body's activities.

The Ventral Cavity A number of vitally important organs are neatly packed into the ventral cavity, which is sometimes referred to as the body cavity or **celom.** The upper portion of the celom, the **thoracic cavity,** is bounded below by the muscular partition of the diaphragm. It is in turn subdivided into the two **pleural cavities,** each of which encloses a lung, and the area between them, the **mediastinum.** Within the mediastinum lie the **pericardial cavity** (which encloses the heart) and the trachea, esophagus, and thymus, along with assorted large blood vessels, lymphatic vessels and nodes, and nerves.

The **abdominal cavity** is inferior to the diaphragm. In it are packed the stomach, the small intestine, most of the large intestine, the liver, the gallbladder, the spleen, the pancreas, the kidneys, the adrenal glands, and the ureters. The inner abdominal wall is lined with a membrane, the **parietal peritoneum.** The potential space between this membrane layer and the **visceral peritoneum,** the membrane covering the abdominal organs, is called the **peritoneal cavity.** (Peritonitis, an infection of the peritoneal cavity, may

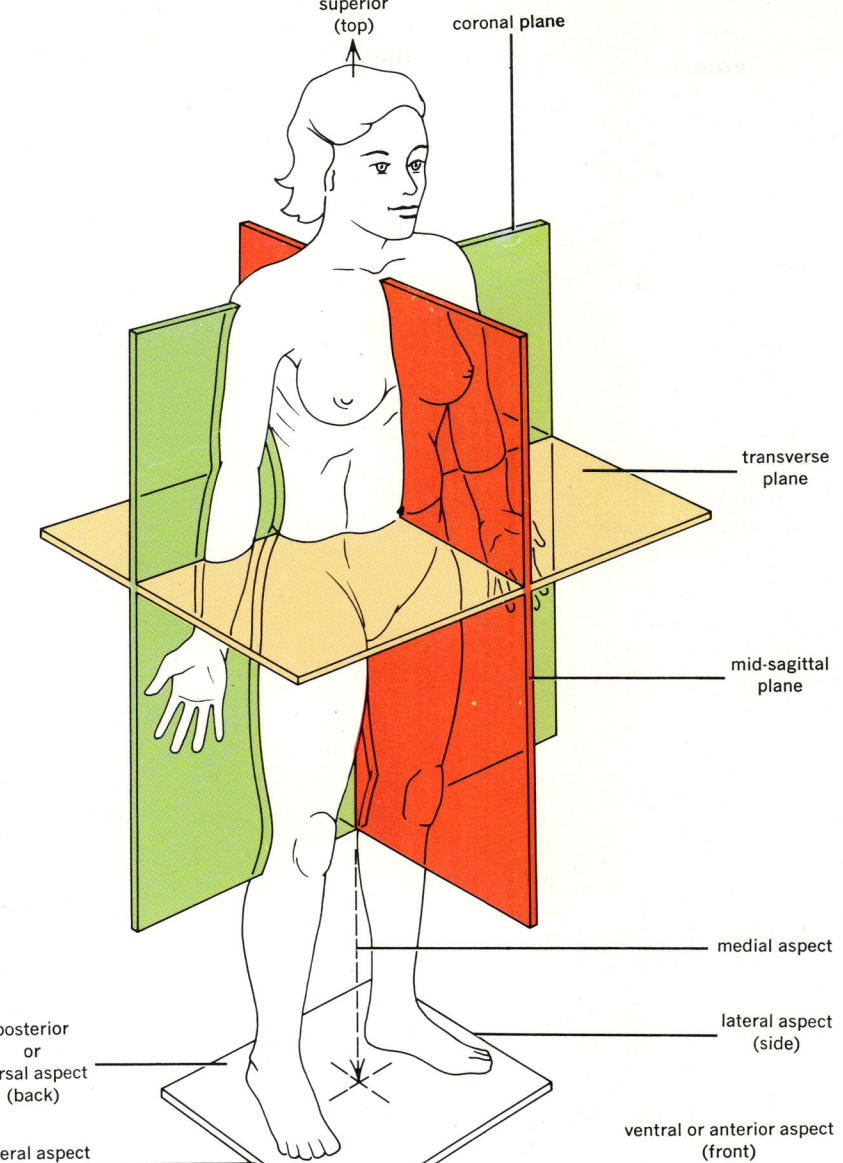

superior
(top)

coronal plane

FIGURE 2-5 Anterior view in the anatomical position, showing planes of reference and some directional terms.

transverse plane

mid-sagittal plane

medial aspect

lateral aspect (side)

posterior or dorsal aspect (back)

lateral aspect (side)

ventral or anterior aspect (front)

inferior (bottom)

result from the accidental introduction of contaminated material into the cavity. This may occur after a perforation of the alimentary canal, perhaps due to an ulcer, or via a wound that pierces the parietal peritoneum from outside the body. It can be a dangerous complication following abdominal surgery, and all possible efforts are made to avoid contamination.)

The lowest portion of the abdominal cavity is called the **pelvic cavity.** It is the region lying below an imaginary line drawn across the crests of the hip bones. The pelvic cavity contains the urinary bladder, the rectum (the last section of the large intestine), and some of the reproductive organs.

For convenience in locating abdominal organs, anatomists further divide the abdominal region into nine imaginary regions, bounded by the arbitrary grid of lines depicted in Figure 2-7.

THE ORGANIZATION OF THE BODY

Many microscopic pond organisms, such as *Amoeba* and *Paramecium,* consist of just a single cell. This cell is able to get and take in nutrients, generate energy, move, and reproduce itself. The human body, by contrast, is made up of literally trillions of cells. Although

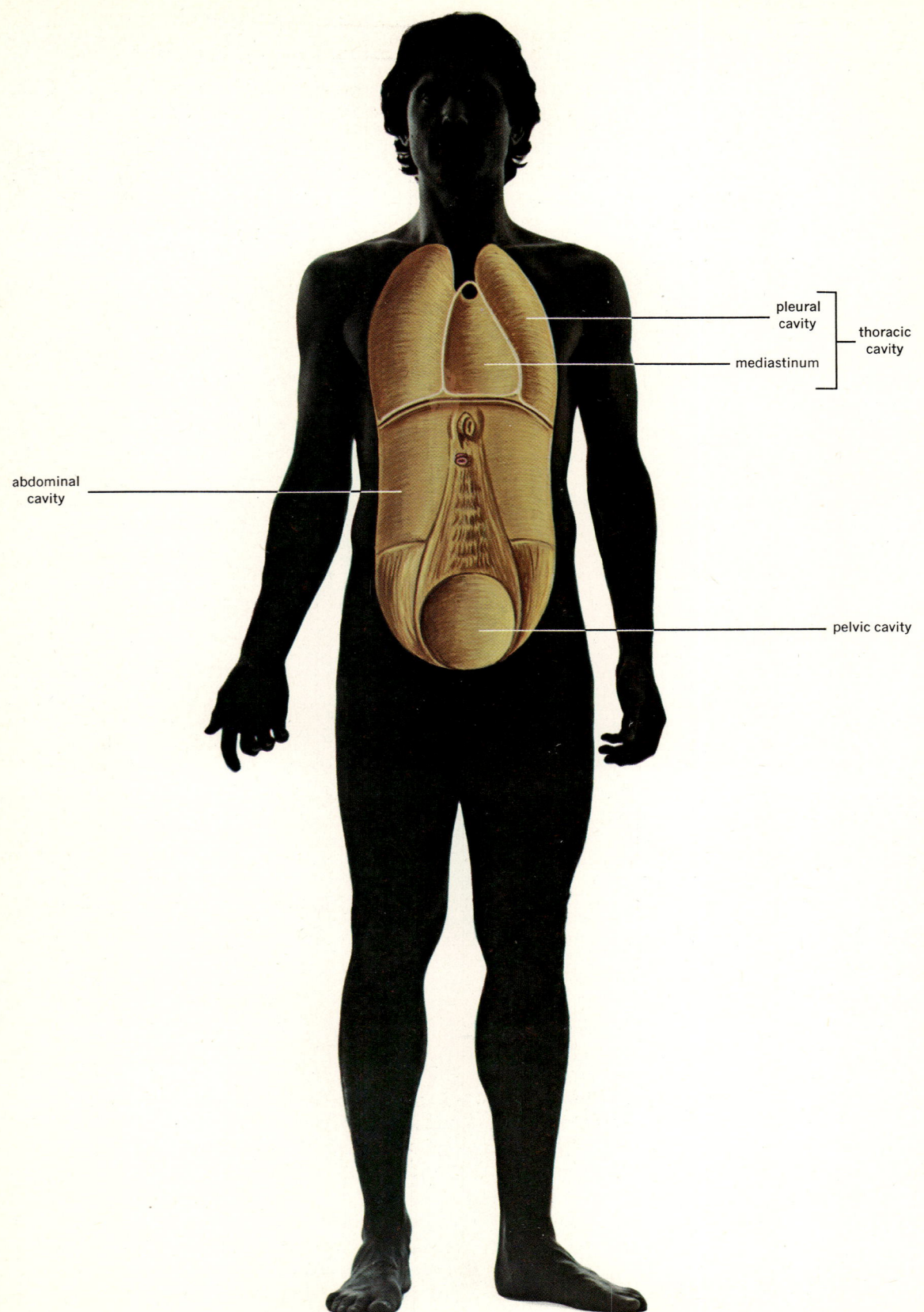

A

FIGURE 2-6 The body cavities: frontal (A) and lateral (B) views.

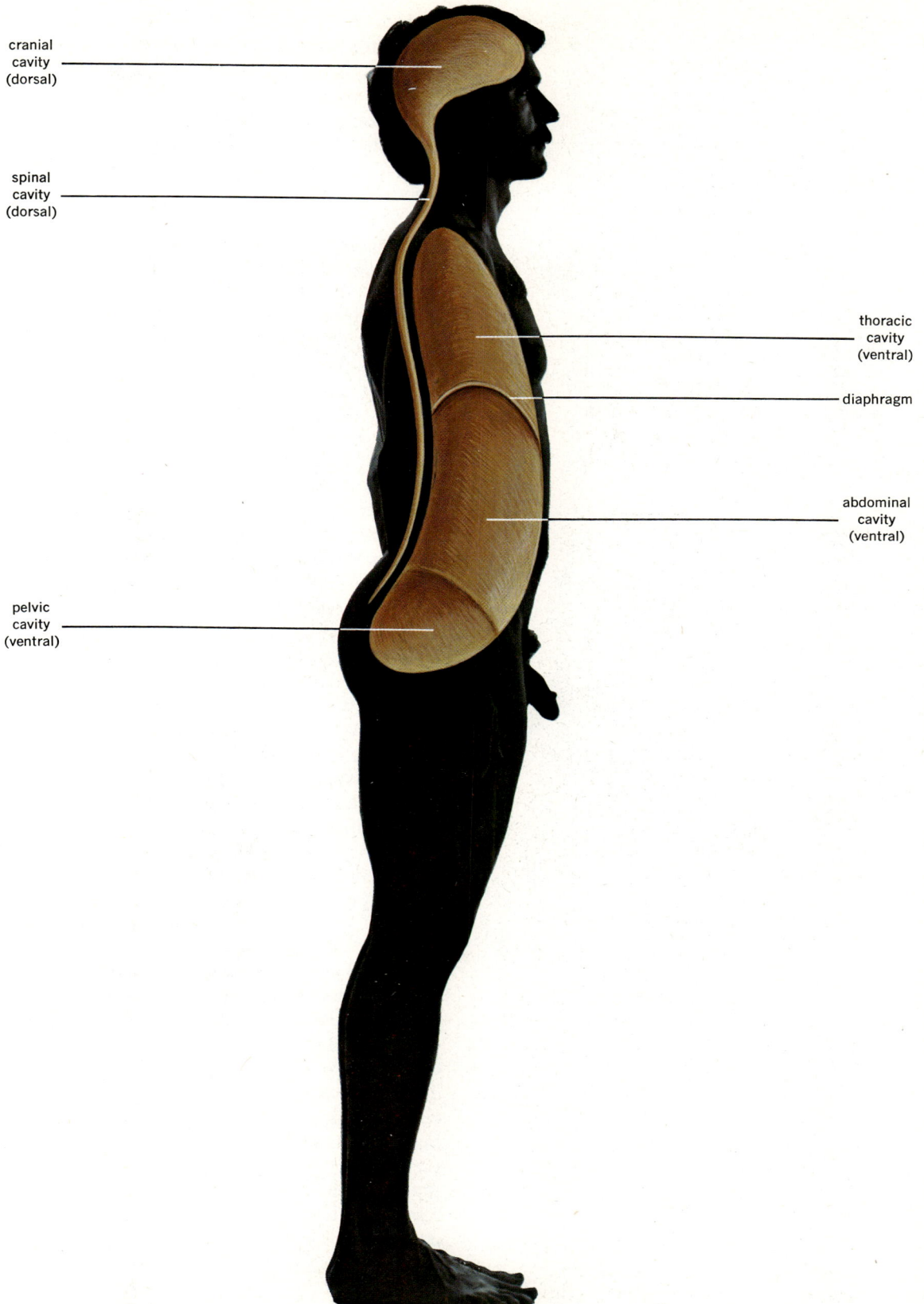

cranial
cavity
(dorsal)

spinal
cavity
(dorsal)

thoracic
cavity
(ventral)

diaphragm

abdominal
cavity
(ventral)

pelvic
cavity
(ventral)

B

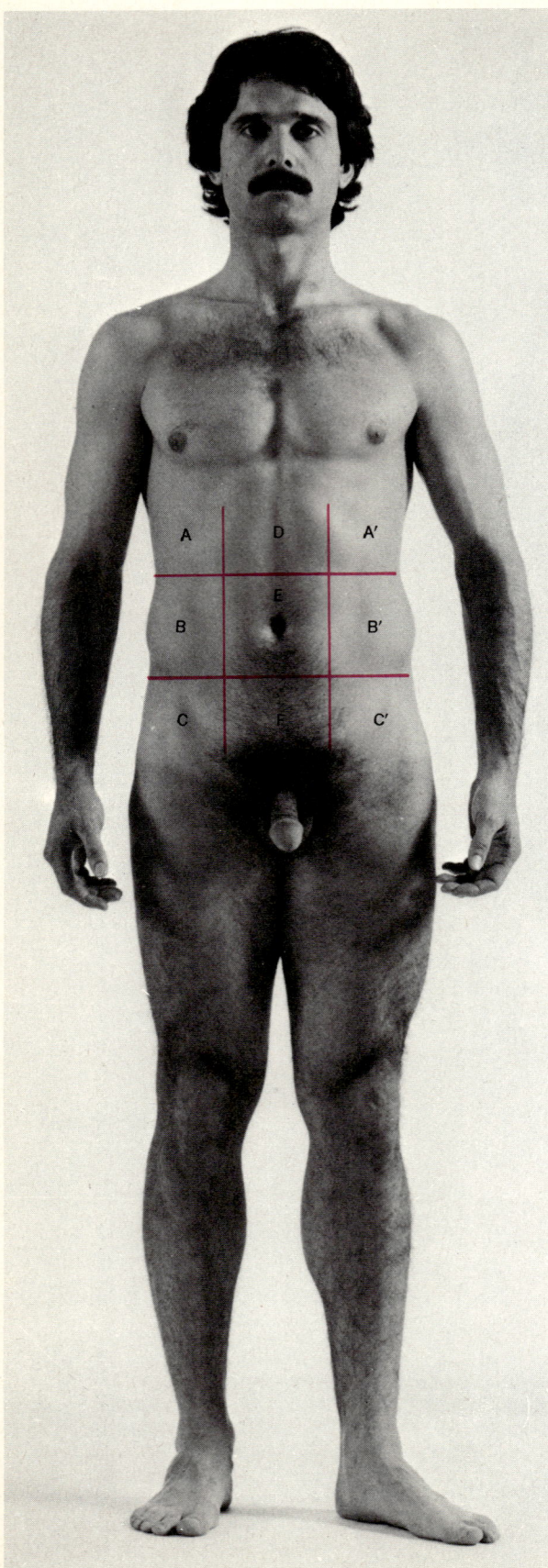

each of the body cells is capable of many of the same vital functions as an *Amoeba* or *Paramecium,* the body cells are not capable of independent existence. In the evolution of multicellular organisms, independence has been sacrificed for the benefits of cooperation. The body cells are specialized for specific functions and are supported and nourished by other cells through the integrated systems of the body.

The keynote of the human body is organization. Cells are grouped into organ systems, and the integrated sum of these systems is the body as a whole (Figure 2-8). This organization is maintained through a constant struggle against **entropy** (the general tendency of things to degenerate into randomness), and the struggle involves continual expenditures of energy.

Cells   The cell is the smallest structural unit of the body capable of carrying on all the vital functions. Yet it is one of the most complex structures in the universe. Within its confines, thousands of chemical reactions take place. Its basic building material, **protoplasm,** is essentially a colloidal suspension of proteins, lipids, carbohydrates, other organic substances, and inorganic salts in water. The membranes that enclose the cell and honeycomb its interior organize these seemingly simple constituents into functioning aggregates. The structures of the body cells are highly specialized for their characteristic functions. Thus, there is far more diversity among the cells of the human body than there is, for example, between human nerve cells and the nerve cells of a mouse. Each individual cell of the body leads a life that in some respects mirrors, in miniature, the life of the body as a whole. Human cells, however, cannot live alone. They have traded independence for the benefits of mutual cooperation with the other cells of the body.

Tissues   In recent decades, science has been characterized by an ever increasing degree of specialization. But the concept of specialization itself is not a recent invention. It has been a hallmark of living systems for millions of years. In the human body, specialization of structure and function is dramatically demonstrated at the level of tissues. Groups of cells with a similar structure, together with the nonliving material (intercellular substance or matrix) between them, form a tissue. The cells of a particular tissue share certain basic characteristics of structure and function with those of other tissues, but they are specialized for the performance of specific functions. For

FIGURE 2-7   Anatomical regions of the abdomen: right and left hypochondriac (A,A'), right and left lumbar (B,B'), right and left inguinal (C,C'), epigastric (D), umbilical (E), and hypogastric (F).

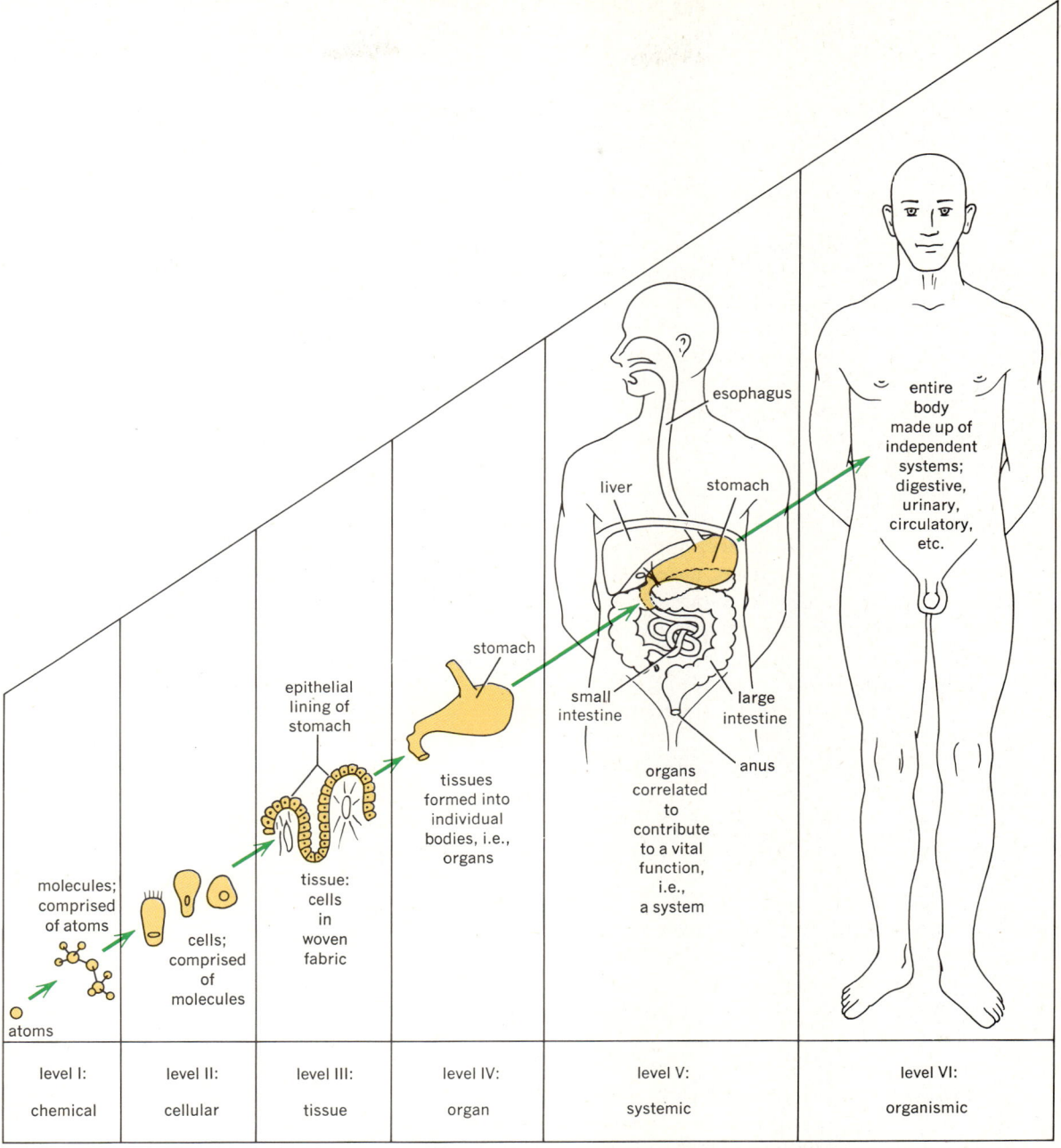

FIGURE 2-8 From the chemical level up to the level of the whole organism, the body's structural organization shows increasing degrees of complexity and specialization.

example, all cells can contract to some extent, but the cells of muscle tissue exhibit an especially high degree of contractility; all cells show some electrical activity, but the cells of nerve tissue are specialized for the conduction of electrochemical impulses. The varied tissues of the body can be classified in the following major categories: **epithelial,** or covering tissue; **connective** tissue, which connects, supports, and fills out body structures; **muscle** tissue, the contractions of which permit movement of body structures; and **nerve** tissue, which provides the body with an effective communication and control system.

Organs   Tissues performing a common function or functions are grouped into organs. Often several or all of the major types of tissues are represented in a single organ. The human heart, for example, is one of the most remarkable structures in nature. It works as a pump, circulating blood through the blood vessels of the body. During the average lifetime, this prodigious pump beats 2.5 billion times and pumps a total of 400,000 tons of fluid. Highly specialized muscle tissue is a key component of this workhorse of the body, but epithelial, connective, and nerve tissues also contribute to its structure and function. But the heart is only one of the many vital organs of the body. Brain, lungs, liver, and all the other organs also contribute to the functioning of the body as a whole.

Systems Teamwork is an essential ingredient for survival in the living body. Cooperation and coordination is especially evident within the systems of the body. A system is a group of organs that work together to perform a series of functions. Some systems, such as the circulatory and nervous systems, have components distributed throughout the body. Others, such as the respiratory and digestive systems, are somewhat more localized. But their functions are equally as important for the body as a whole. The human body is generally considered to include ten systems: **skeletal, muscular, integumentary, digestive, circulatory, respiratory, excretory, nervous, endocrine,** and **reproductive.** (Some anatomists recognize fewer systems, omitting, for example, the integumentary system as a separate entity.)

The skeletal system consists of bones and the connective tissues that bind them together. It provides the basic framework that supports the body and protects such vital but vulnerable structures as the brain and spinal cord.

The muscular system consists of striated (skeletal and cardiac) muscles and nonstriated (smooth) muscles. It works with the bones of the skeleton to provide support and produce movement of body parts.

The integumentary system, the skin, covers and protects the body. It prevents the loss of the fluids that bathe the cells, helps in the elimination of body wastes, and plays a key role in the body's temperature-regulating mechanisms.

The digestive system includes the mouth, esophagus, stomach, intestines, and various accessory organs and glands. It is concerned with the intake, breakdown, and absorption of food materials and the elimination of solid wastes.

The circulatory system comprises the heart, blood vessels, and lymph vessels. It distributes nutrients and oxygen to all the body cells and carries away their waste products.

The respiratory system includes the nasal passages, pharynx, larynx, trachea, bronchi, and lungs. It provides the means for bringing oxygen into the body and eliminating carbon dioxide.

The excretory system includes mainly the kidneys, ureters, bladder, and urethra (which function in the production and voiding of urine). It works to eliminate the waste products of cell activity. The lungs, glands of the skin, and the intestines also participate in excretory functions.

The nervous system consists of the brain and spinal cord, the nerves that connect them to all parts of the body, and the associated sense receptors (in the eyes, ears, nose, mouth, skin, etc.). It receives and evaluates information about the outside world and controls and coordinates the body's activities.

The endocrine system includes the pituitary gland, the thyroid gland, the parathyroids, the adrenals, the thymus gland, pineal, and portions of the pancreas, ovaries, and testes. It produces chemical substances (hormones) that affect other cells and organs and help to control and coordinate their activities.

The reproductive system consists of the testes, seminal vesicles, penis, urethra, and prostate in the male; and the ovaries, uterine tubes, uterus, vagina, and vulva in the female. It functions in the continuation of the species.

The basic structural and functional components of the body, from the chemicals of life through cells and tissues, will be discussed in greater detail in the chapters that follow. The remainder of the book is devoted largely to the structure and functions of the major organ systems of the body.

SUMMARY

Human beings are vertebrates and are characterized by a flexible, rodlike vertebral column.
    The internal framework (skeleton) is covered with soft tissues, which give the body its basic shape.
    The body shape varies with sex, age, diet, physical activity, and heredity.
The human body is characterized by bilateral symmetry.
Humans are mammals and share the typical mammalian characteristics:
    Mammary glands
    Homoiothermy
    Hair
Despite differences in hair, pigmentation, and facial features, all the currently living human races belong to the species *Homo sapiens.*
The human body is divided into regions:
    Axial portion
        Head and neck
        Trunk (thorax, abdomen, and pelvis)
    Appendicular portion
        Upper extremity (upper arm, forearm, and hand)
        Lower extremity (thigh, leg, and foot)
In the anatomical position, the body is considered in an erect position, with the head facing forward, the feet on the floor and slightly apart, and the arms hanging at the sides with palms turned forward.
Terms describing direction and location:
    Anterior, ventral: toward the front of the body or body part.
    Posterior, dorsal: toward the back of the body or body part.
    Superior, cranial, cephalad: upward or toward the head end.
    Inferior, caudal: downward or below; farther from the head or toward the feet.
    Medial, mesial: nearer to the midline of the body.

Lateral: farther from the midline of the body.

Superficial, external, peripheral: at or nearer to the surface of the body.

Deep, internal, central: lying deeper inward, farther from the surface of the body.

Proximal: nearer the origin of a part.

Distal: farther from the origin of a part.

Parietal: referring to the walls of a cavity.

Visceral: referring to the organs within a cavity.

Planes and sections of the body:

Sagittal: a lengthwise plane, running from front to back, which divides the body vertically into right and left portions.

Midsagittal or median sagittal plane: the sagittal plane passing precisely through the midline of the body.

Coronal, frontal: a lengthwise plane at right angles to the sagittal plane, dividing the body vertically into anterior and posterior portions.

Transverse, horizontal: any plane that divides the body into superior and inferior portions.

The body cavities:

Dorsal cavity

Cranial cavity

Spinal cavity

Ventral cavity

Thoracic cavity (pleural cavities, mediastinum, pericardial cavity)

Abdominal cavity (peritoneal cavity)

Pelvic cavity

Organization of the body:

Cells are the basic units of structure and function in the body.

Tissues are composed of groups of cells of similar structure, together with the nonliving material (matrix) between them.

Organs are groups of tissues performing a common function or functions.

Organ systems are groups of organs, which work together to perform a series of functions.

Systems of the human body:

Skeletal system

Muscular system

Integumentary system

Digestive system

Circulatory system

Respiratory system

Excretory system

Nervous system

Endocrine system

Reproductive system

QUESTIONS FOR REVIEW AND THOUGHT

1 List the body structures that correspond to bilateral symmetry of the human body and those that deviate from bilateral symmetry.

2 Discuss the advantages and disadvantages of the following organs and systems in the human body:

(a) sense receptors in the head

(b) food intake apparatus in the head

(c) brain in the head

(d) heart in the trunk

(e) digestive organs in the trunk

(f) respiratory organs in the trunk

(g) manipulative organs (hands) on the upper extremities

If you were designing a new model, *Homo superior*, would you suggest any changes in localization of structures?

3 Why are precise terms for body structures and their positions essential for health science workers?

4 Give at least *three* answers for each of the following:

(a) The nose is medial to the _____.

(b) The elbow is proximal to the _____.

(c) The umbilicus ("belly button") is inferior to the _____.

(d) The umbilicus is ventral to the _____.

(e) Surface structures may be referred to as _____.

5 If you swallow a marble and it ultimately emerges in your feces, it can be said that the marble was never truly "inside" your body. Explain in terms of body cavities.

6 If a doctor asks you if you have had any epigastric pains, to what region is he or she referring?

7 Compare an *Amoeba* with a human from the standpoint of benefits and disadvantages of specialization and cooperation of cells.

8 Define: tissue, organ, organ system, organism.

THE CHEMISTRY OF LIFE

3

The past few decades have witnessed a revolution in the study of life. The current ferment in the biomedical sciences is actually the latest in a series of revolutions, which have enabled scientists to probe deeper and deeper into the mysteries of how the body works.

A major breakthrough in the study of life came during the Renaissance, when anatomists began to dissect the bodies of animals and even humans and could thus progress from observations of the body as a whole to precise knowledge of organs and systems. For example, the landmark work by Harvey in the seventeenth century, on the nature of the circulation of blood, was based on careful dissections.

With the formulation of the cell theory, popularized by Schleiden and Schwann in the nineteenth century, anatomists and physiologists plunged into a new level of understanding. Studies of microscopic cells, tiny living units, began to cast light on the mysteries of organs, systems, and the body as a whole.

The latest revolution in the biomedical sciences has focused the attention of researchers on another level, still deeper into the mysteries of life. Increasingly, the emphasis has been inside the cell, beyond the reach of even the most powerful optical microscopes, at the level of the chemicals of life themselves.

Each living cell contains thousands of different kinds of chemicals. These chemicals are not an inert mixture, but are constantly acting upon and interacting with one another. The blueprints of heredity are encoded in chemical form. The structures of the body are built up from chemical constituents, and differences in chemical composition distinguish one type of tissue from another. The contraction of a muscle, the conduction of nerve impulses, the digestion of food—these and all the other processes that go on in the human body are based on chemical reactions.

Electron microscopy, X-ray diffraction study, gas chromatography and other methods of micro- and ultramicroanalysis, and other techniques of modern technology are yielding a wealth of new information each year. Although we still have barely scratched the surface of all there is to know about the chemistry of life, researchers have built up a fairly coherent picture of its broad outlines. The more that is learned, the more evident it becomes that a knowledge of the chemistry of life is basic to an understanding of the human body and its functions. This chapter presents some basic chemical background, with emphasis on the aspects relevant to the interactions that occur in living systems.

MATTER AND ENERGY

The batter in the box waits tensely for the pitch. As the ball speeds toward him, he swings the bat in a powerful arc. Bat meets ball with an explosive *Crack!*

and the ball speeds out again for a clean single into left field. Dropping the bat, the batter dashes down the base path.

Matter

This brief vignette illustrates some basic facts of the world around us. The bat and ball, the batter's body, and the ground on which he stood are all examples of what scientists call **matter.** So were the water he sipped in the dugout before his turn at bat, the sweat trickling down his back, and the air he drew into his lungs. Matter can be defined as something that *occupies space and has mass (weight).* The earth and everything on it, both living and nonliving, are all matter.

Matter can exist in any of three states: solid, liquid, or gas. A **solid,** such as a ball or bat, has a fixed shape and maintains a constant volume even if great pressure is applied to it. Many substances of biological importance are solids—most of the foods we eat, for example. A **liquid** maintains a constant volume, but it flows to assume the shape of its container. The most common liquid in our world—and one of the most important constituents of the human body—is water. A **gas** can expand to fill a container, or it can be compressed (reduced in volume) if pressure is applied. Our planet earth is wrapped in an envelope of gases, the atmosphere. It seems strange to think of the invisible air of the atmosphere as matter—yet balloons and automobile tires are common proofs of its existence and properties. (Air only seems to lack substance because its individual particles are packed far less densely than those of liquids and solids.) Man and nearly all the other living things of our world utilize one of the gases of the atmosphere: oxygen, which constitutes about one-fifth of the mixture that is air. Deprived of oxygen, we would quickly die.

The states of matter are not fixed and immutable. Substances can pass more or less readily from one state into another. Liquid water, poured into an ice cube tray and placed in the freezer, quickly turns into a solid form, ice. The same water, boiled on the stove in a pot, will turn into a gas form, steam. Despite these changes in physical states, however, the *chemical* composition of water remains unchanged.

Energy

Changes of state, as well as various other changes that matter can undergo, involve an input or release of **energy.** Energy is usually defined as *a capacity to do work.* It can exist in a variety of forms (Figure 3-1). A hurtling ball and a swinging bat possess an energy of motion called **kinetic energy.** So does the blood flowing through the batter's arteries and veins. The raised bat also possesses another type of energy, by virtue of its position. This type of energy, called **potential energy,** is converted to kinetic energy when the batter lets go of the bat, and it falls to the ground. The muscle contractions that power the batter's swing and his dash to first base are products of another type of energy, **chemical energy.** A by-product of muscle contraction is still another form of energy, **heat.** The human body has an intricate complex of mechanisms that cope with excess heat. Part of it is radiated out through the surface of the body into the surrounding atmosphere, and part is carried out of the body through the sweat pores by water and water vapor. Other forms of energy of great importance to us are **light energy** (which not only permits us to perceive our surroundings but is the ultimate source of food on our planet) and **electrical energy.** Forms of energy can be interconverted to one another, and can produce changes in matter.

Temperature Measurements

A measure of the heat energy contained in a substance is its **temperature.** Temperature is a vital factor in the lives of living organisms. The temperature of the external environment tends to fluctuate, more or less depending on the distance from the equator. For the lower ("cold-blooded") animals, body temperature roughly approximates the environmental temperature. Yet the complex chemical reactions that occur within the living body have a relatively narrow range of optimum temperature conditions. If the temperature falls too low, a cold-blooded animal becomes sluggish and inert. Too high an environmental temperature can also have ill effects. Humans and the other mammals, as well as the birds, have evolved a complex of mechanisms, linking the nervous and circulatory systems, as well as such skin structures as the sweat glands, to maintain a relatively constant body temperature regardless of the external temperature. (These mechanisms of "warm-blooded animals" have their limits, of course: it is possible for an unprotected man to freeze to death or suffer from heat prostration if the environmental conditions are too extreme.)

Temperature is commonly measured with a mercury column thermometer. There is currently some confusion concerning the scales used to express temperature values. Most of the world now uses the **Centigrade** or **Celsius scale,** which has as its reference points the freezing point (0°C) and boiling point (100°C) of water. But in the United States, the traditional **Fahrenheit scale** is still in common use, both among the general public and in clinical practice. (American researchers, however, generally use the Centigrade scale in scientific work.) This situation will gradually change, as the general switch to the Metric System is phased in throughout the United States. But until the changeover is complete, there will be the need for inconvenient interconversions of temperature values from one scale to the other. It is

FIGURE 3-1 Forms of energy: (1) kinetic; (2) potential; (3) heat and light; (4,5) electrical and light; (6) chemical.

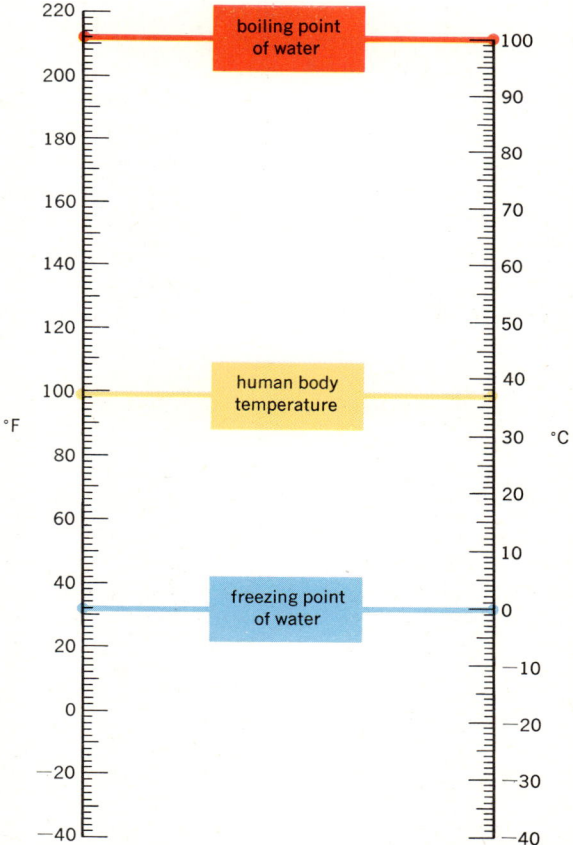

FIGURE 3-2 Comparison of the Fahrenheit and centigrade (Celsius) temperature scales.

handy to remember as a general rule of thumb that a Centigrade degree is not quite twice as large as a Fahrenheit degree, and to recall the following reference points (Figure 3-2):

Freezing point of water	$= 0°C$	$= 32°F$
Human body temperature	$= 37°C$	$= 98.6°F$
Boiling point of water	$= 100°C$	$= 212°F$

The exact conversion formulas are:

$$°C = {}^5/_9 (°F - 32)$$

$$°F = {}^9/_5 (°C) + 32$$

ATOMS AND ELEMENTS

What do a man and a mountain, a mouse and a house, a tree and a lake all have in common? They are all made of matter, and the body of each is composed of an enormous number of tiny chemical building blocks, far too small to be seen by the naked eye. (Some of them, indeed, are still invisible to the best electron microscopes.) These tiny building blocks of matter are called **atoms.** Their name comes from a word meaning "indivisible," and although in this Atomic Age this meaning is no longer precisely accurate, an atom is the smallest unit of matter that can be obtained by ordinary chemical means.

A living organism such as a man is quite different, however, from an inanimate object such as a mountain or a lake. And even living organisms, such as men, mice, and trees, differ greatly from one another. How can this be if they are all composed of atoms of matter? Part of the answer lies in the fact that there are many different kinds of atoms, which form a variety of chemical **elements.** An element may be defined as a substance that cannot be decomposed by ordinary chemical means. Men and mountains contain somewhat different assortments of elements, present in different proportions. A total of ninety-two elements occur in nature, and another dozen or so have been produced in the laboratory. The most abundant elements in the human body are carbon, hydrogen, oxygen, and nitrogen, together with smaller amounts of phosphorus, sulfur, iron, copper, and a host of others, some present in very minute amounts.

The key to the differences among the chemical ele-

ments lies in the internal structure of their atoms. Each atom is composed of three kinds of smaller particles: **protons, neutrons,** and **electrons.** The protons and neutrons are far larger than the electrons. (Their masses are 1836 and 1837 times as great, respectively.) They are concentrated in a central core of the atom, the **nucleus,** while the tiny electrons travel around them in precisely defined paths or **orbitals** (Figure 3-3A).*

The atom itself is electrically neutral. However, protons and electrons carry an electrical charge; protons are positively charged, and electrons are negatively charged. The old adage "opposites attract" may not always hold true in human relationships, but in the physical world it is law. The equal but opposite electrical charges of the electrons and protons attract one another and provide the main force that holds the electrons to the atom. As would be expected from the electrical neutrality of the atom, the number of protons it contains is always exactly equal to the number of its electrons. (The number of electrically neutral neutrons may vary.)

The chemical elements differ from one another in the number of protons in the atomic nucleus (and thus in the number of electrons as well). The total number of protons in the nucleus of each atom of a particular element is called its **atomic number.** The sum of the protons and neutrons in the nucleus is called the **atomic mass.** (The mass of the electrons is so small in comparison with the proton and neutron that it can be neglected.)

You may notice that the chart of the elements in Figure 3-4 lists atomic *weights,* some of which are not whole numbers. This does not mean that the atomic

---

* The depiction of the "planetary" atom in Figure 3-3A, which somewhat resembles the sun and the planets of the solar system, is actually a simplification. In more precise work, electron orbitals are depicted in the form of density maps, representing the probability of finding an electron in any particular place at a particular time. For some electrons, the regions of greatest probability density trace out a sphere, for others a set of dumbbells, or an even more complex geometrical figure (Figure 3-3B).

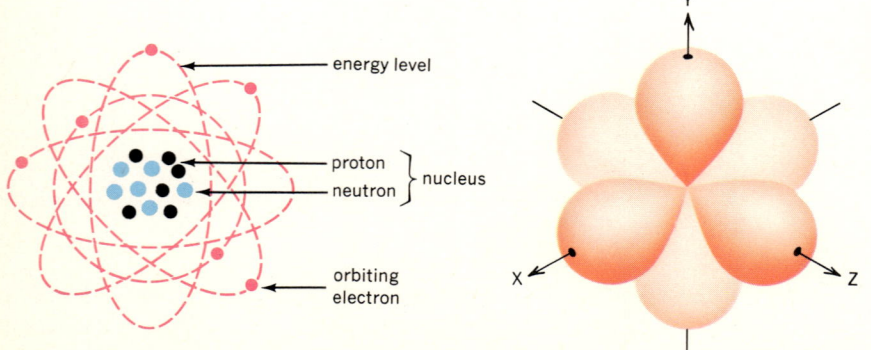

FIGURE 3-3 Bohr's "planetary" model of the atom (A) has been supplemented by more complex electron density models such as the one in (B), depicting dumbbell-like *p*-orbitals, each of which can accommodate two electrons.

nucleus contains fractions of neutrons or protons. Rather, it reflects the fact that many elements occur in nature in a mixture of several forms, or **isotopes,** each of which has the same number of protons but a different number of neutrons, and thus a different atomic mass. The **atomic weight** is a weighted average of the mass numbers of all the isotopes of an element, which takes into account the relative abundance of the various isotopes. (The isotopes of any particular element all have the same chemical properties, de-

Key (atomic number / symbol for element (here, Carbon) / atomic weight):

6
C
12.011

Elements essential for living organisms

IA	IIA	IIIB	IVB	VB	VIB	VIIB	VIII	VIII	VIII	IB	IIB	IIIA	IVA	VA	VIA	VIIA	0
1 H 1.00797																	2 He 4.0026
3 Li 6.939	4 Be 9.012											5 B 10.811	6 C 12.011	7 N 14.007	8 O 15.9994	9 F 18.998	10 Ne 20.183
11 Na 22.990	12 Mg 24.312											13 Al 26.98	14 Si 28.086	15 P 30.97	16 S 32.064	17 Cl 35.453	18 Ar 39.95
19 K 39.102	20 Ca 40.08	21 Sc 44.96	22 Ti 47.90	23 V 50.94	24 Cr 52.00	25 Mn 54.94	26 Fe 55.85	27 Co 58.93	28 Ni 58.71	29 Cu 63.54	30 Zn 65.37	31 Ga 69.72	32 Ge 72.59	33 As 74.92	34 Se 78.96	35 Br 79.91	36 Kr 83.80
37 Rb 85.47	38 Sr 87.62	39 Y 38.91	40 Zr 91.22	41 Nb 92.91	42 Mo 95.94	43 Tc 99	44 Ru 101.07	45 Rh 102.91	46 Pd 106.4	47 Ag 107.87	48 Cd 112.40	49 In 114.82	50 Sn 118.69	51 Sb 121.75	52 Te 127.60	53 I 126.90	54 Xe 131.30
55 Cs 132.90	56 Ba 137.34	7-71 La series* 138.91	72 Hf 178.49	73 Ta 180.95	74 W 183.85	75 Re 186.2	76 Os 190.2	77 Ir 192.2	78 Pt 195.1	79 Au 196.97	80 Hg 200.59	81 Tl 204.37	82 Pb 207.19	83 Bi 208.98	84 Po 210	85 At 210	86 Rn 222
87 Fr 223	88 Ra 226	89- Ac series† 227															

*Lanthanide series

57 La 138.91	58 Ce 140.12	59 Pr 140.91	60 Nd 144.24	61 Pm 147	62 Sm 150.35	63 Eu 151.96	64 Gd 157.25	65 Tb 158.92	66 Dy 162.50	67 Ho 164.93	68 Er 167.26	69 Tm 168.93	70 Yb 173.04	71 Lu 174.97

†Actinide series

89 Ac 227	90 Th 232.04	91 Pa 231	92 U 238.03	93 Np 237	94 Pu 239	95 Am 241	96 Cm 242	97 Bk 249	98 Cf 252	99 Es 254	100 Fm 253	101 Md	102 No	103 Lw

FIGURE 3-4 The Periodic Table. The elements are arranged horizontally according to the number of electrons in the outermost shell. Because these outer valence electrons determine many of the chemical properties of elements, the elements in each period (vertical column) tend to be chemically similar to one another.

spite their differences in atomic mass, since each has the same number of electrons, which are the parts of the atom that take part in chemical reactions.)

The lightest of all the elements is hydrogen. The atoms of its most abundant isotope have just one proton in the nucleus (and one electron outside it) and contain no neutrons at all. The atomic mass of hydrogen is thus 1. (The relative abundance of the other isotopes—deuterium with one proton and one neutron and a mass of 2, and tritium with one proton and two neutrons and a mass of 3—is so low that the atomic weight of hydrogen is very close to 1.) The carbon atom contains six protons, six neutrons, and six electrons in its principal isotope, and its atomic mass is 12. Nitrogen has an atomic mass of 14 (7 p + 7 n), while oxygen has an atomic mass of 16 (8 p + 8 n). Indeed, as can be seen from the chart in Figure 3-4, these and all the other elements found in the human body are among the lightest of the elements that occur in nature.

More than a century ago, the Russian chemist Dmitri Mendeleev discovered that if the chemical elements are arranged in order of increasing atomic weight, certain patterns begin to emerge. Elements that resemble one another chemically—and to some extent physically as well—occur at definite intervals along the list. Mendeleev arranged the similar elements one under another in families that he called periods. The chart in Figure 3-4 is a modern modification of the **Periodic Table** of the elements that Mendeleev devised.

Not enough was known about the inner structure of the atom in Mendeleev's time to satisfactorily explain the pattern he had discovered. But now it is known that the electrons of an atom are arranged in a series of concentric shells, something like the rings of an onion. Each successive shell can hold up to a definite number of electrons: going out from the nucleus, the capacities of the electron shells are 2, 8, 18, 32, and so on. The properties of an element are determined by the number of electrons in the outermost shell of its atoms. Elements with one or two electrons in the outer shell are generally metals, and can give these outer electrons to other atoms, forming chemical bonds of a type called **ionic bonds** (Figure 3-5). Elements lacking just one or two electrons to fill the outermost shell are generally nonmetals and can receive electrons from other atoms in forming bonds. (The added electrons are held in the appropriate orbitals by the attractive force of the positive nucleus and become indistinguishable from the electrons that the atom originally possessed.) Elements with an intermediate number of electrons in the outer shell tend to share electrons with other atoms in forming bonds of a type called **covalent bonds** (Figure 3-6).

An atom that has donated or accepted one or more

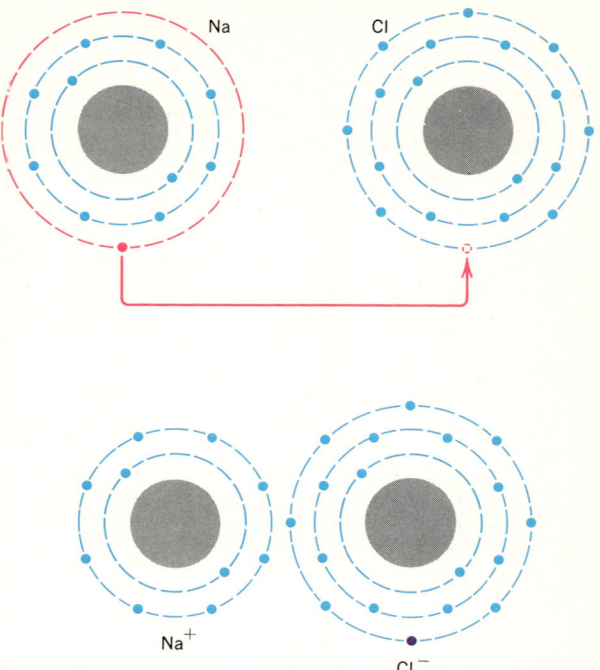

FIGURE 3-5 The ionic bond: a sodium atom donates a valence electron to a chlorine atom to form the salt NaCl. The transferred electron travels exclusively around the chlorine nucleus and is indistinguishable from the other electrons in its outermost shell.

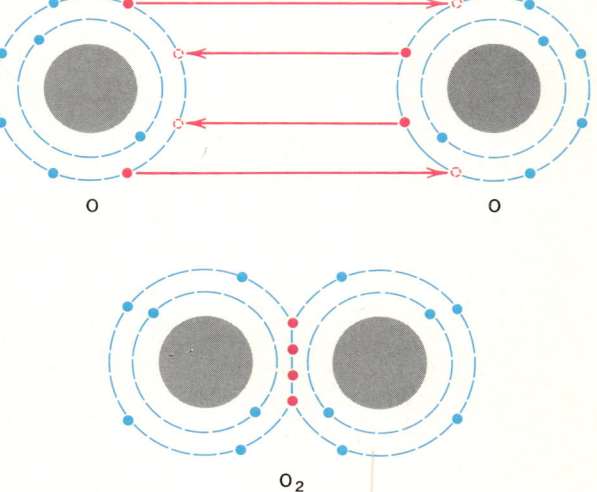

FIGURE 3-6 The covalent bond: two oxygen atoms share electrons to form the oxygen molecule. The shared electrons (two contributed by each original atom) are held in common and travel around each nucleus in a molecular orbital.

electrons loses its electrical neutrality and becomes a charged particle called an **ion.** If electrons have been donated, the atom is left with more protons in the nucleus than there are electrons in the orbitals around it and thus acquires an overall positive charge. An atom that has accepted one or more electrons is negatively charged. Positive ions are referred to as **cations,** and negative ions as **anions.**

MOLECULES AND COMPOUNDS

Our 26-letter alphabet can be used to spell a virtually infinite number of words. It should not be surprising then that with the 105-"letter" alphabet of the chemical elements, a virtually limitless number of different combinations is possible. Not every possible combination is used, however. Just as our language has a set of spelling rules, chemical elements combine according to specific rules and in definite proportions.

A chemical **compound** is made up of two or more elements, present in a definite proportion by weight. The properties of a compound are often quite different from those of the elements that formed it. Hydrogen and oxygen are both gases, for example, while the compound that they form—water—is a liquid. Another common compound, table salt, is a combination of sodium and chlorine. Sodium is a soft, shiny metal, so reactive that it explodes if it comes in contact with water. Chlorine is a viciously corrosive, poisonous gas. Yet sodium chloride (salt) is a solid that crystallizes in shiny white cubes, uneventfully dissolves in water, is nonpoisonous when consumed in reasonable amounts, and is absolutely essential to life.

The smallest unit of a compound that still retains the properties of the compound is called a **molecule.** A molecule is made up of atoms, joined by chemical bonds. (A molecule can be broken down to its component atoms, but then these atoms no longer retain the physical and chemical properties of the compound.) Just as each element has a characteristic atomic weight, each compound has its own characteristic **molecular weight.** This quantity is simply the sum of the atomic weights of the elements that comprise the compound, each multiplied by a factor to take into account its proportion in the compound. For example, there are two atoms of hydrogen and one atom of oxygen in each water molecule. The molecular weight of water is:

$$
\begin{array}{llll}
2 \times \text{atomic weight of hydrogen} & = 2 \times 1 & = & 2 \\
1 \times \text{atomic weight of oxygen} & = 1 \times 16 & = & 16 \\
\hline
\text{molecular weight of water} & & = & 18
\end{array}
$$

Chemists are just as lazy as anyone else, and it certainly would be cumbersome to have to spell out the name of every element in a compound and its relative proportion in words. Therefore, a chemical shorthand notation is used instead. Each chemical element is given a one- or two-letter symbol, usually the first letter(s) of its name. Thus, water can be denoted as H_2O. (The subscript 2 following the H means that there are two hydrogen atoms to every one oxygen atom.) A few of the chemical symbols may seem rather mysterious at first: for example, Na for sodium, and Fe for iron. Usually these are cases in which the symbol was taken from the element's Latin

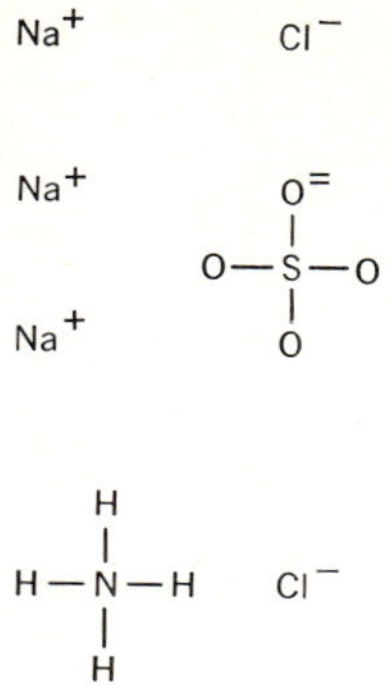

FIGURE 3-7 Some common salts: (A) sodium chloride, NaCl; (B) sodium sulfate, Na_2SO_4; (C) ammonium chloride, NH_4Cl. Note that the positive and negative electrical charges are balanced in each case. (A line between two atoms indicates a covalently shared pair of electrons.)

name (e.g., *natrium* and *ferrum* in the examples mentioned).

The weight of a single atom is infinitesimal. A carbon atom, for instance, weighs about 0.00000000000000000000000199 gram, while a hydrogen atom weighs only 0.000000000000000000000000017 gram. Even the most complex molecules of life, containing millions of atoms, weigh only a small fraction of a gram. If scientists had to deal with the weights of single atoms and molecules, they would constantly be juggling astronomical numbers. Instead, they have found it convenient to express the molecular weight of each compound in grams. Such a gram molecular weight, called a **mole,** contains 6.02×10^{23} molecules of the compound and thus can be equated to a mole of any other compound. The mole is a much less unwieldy unit to work with than the weights of single molecules, and it provides a means for readily calculating equivalent concentrations of various compounds in solutions, starting with either percentages or weight in grams.

Acids, Bases, and Salts

If you mention "salt" to a chemist, he will not necessarily think of the white crystals you sprinkle on your food to make it taste better. To him, table salt (NaCl) is only one of a much larger class of chemical compounds. A **salt** in the chemical sense is an electrically neutral combination of a metal (or metal-like group of atoms) and a nonmetal (or nonmetal-like group of atoms). The components of a salt are joined together by an ionic bond: electrons are actually donated from one atom or group to the other (Figure 3-7). This leaves a positive charge on the metal part and a negative charge on the nonmetal portion; the two are held together by the force of their mutual electrical attraction. But when a salt is dissolved in water (most salts are water-soluble), the charged particles (ions) are separated by water molecules. The presence of electrically charged particles in a salt solution permits it to conduct an electric current; salts thus belong to the class of **electrolytes,** current-conducting substances. In addition to sodium chloride, there are numerous other salts in the body, mostly in aqueous (water) solution in the blood and body fluids.

Another important class of electrolytes is the acids. An **acid** is a substance that can liberate hydrogen ions (H^+), or donate a proton (H), or combine with hydroxyl ions (OH^-). Acids are generally sour to the taste and turn litmus paper red. A common strong acid, hydrochloric acid (HCl), is a key constituent of the gastric juice in the stomach and helps to digest food. Another common acid of interest to man is acetic acid (CH_3COOH), the principal constituent of vinegar. Carbonic acid (H_2CO_3) is a weak acid that does not liberate hydrogen ions as readily and plays a key role in the transport of carbon dioxide (CO_2) in the body fluids.

The lye used in making soaps is an example of a third major class of electrolytes, the bases. A **base** may be defined as a substance that can liberate hydroxyl ions (OH^-) or accept a proton. A base turns litmus paper blue, has a slippery feel, and is generally bitter to the taste. (The latter two items should not be checked out firsthand with a concentrated base: strong bases such as lye, NaOH, are extremely caustic and can produce a severe alkali burn.)

Acids and bases can react to neutralize one another, producing a salt and water, for example:

$$HCl + NaOH \rightarrow NaCl + H_2O$$

Hydrogen and hydroxyl ions play a key role in many chemical reactions, including those of living organisms. Indeed, the human body is extremely sensitive to relatively minor changes in hydrogen ion concentration. Even a small excess of acid **(acidosis)** or alkali **(alkalosis)** can produce changes in cell permeability (determining what substances can pass into and out of the cells) and inactivate the enzymes that play a crucial role in the chemical reactions in the cells. Death of cells, and ultimately of the organism, may result.

A convenient scale has been devised for expressing the strength of acids. This scale, the **pH scale,** is based on the negative logarithm of the hydrogen ion concentration:

$$pH = -\log[H^+], \text{ or } pH = \log \frac{1}{[H^+]}$$

It has been found experimentally that one liter (a little over a quart) of pure water contains 0.0000001 gram of hydrogen ions.* The neutral pH value (nei-

* These ions come from a partial dissociation of the water molecules:
$$H_2O \rightleftharpoons H^+ + OH^-$$
Since water is electrically neutral, a liter of water also contains 0.0000001 gram of hydroxyl ions. It is also evident that only a small fraction of the water molecules are dissociated into ions, since a liter of water weighs 1000 grams.

ther an excess of hydrogen ions nor one of hydroxyl ions) is therefore 7. The pH of human blood is normally slightly alkaline, about 7.4. The pH of the fluid inside the cells (intracellular fluid) is closer to neutral, averaging about 7.1. The pH of gastric juice is quite acid, from 1 to 3.5. (Note that the pH scale is an inverse scale—as the acidity *increases,* the pH *decreases.*)

With the crucial importance of pH to the body and its cells, it is not surprising that the body has a number of mechanisms for adjusting the pH to the optimum range whenever small deviations arise. The most rapid acting of these mechanisms is the action of **buffer systems,** substances capable of reacting with either hydrogen or hydroxyl ions and thus tying up any excess. In the blood, for example, dissolved carbon dioxide combines with water to form a weak acid, carbonic acid (H_2CO_3). This acid can dissociate to yield hydrogen ions and bicarbonate ions (HCO_3^-). Both H_2CO_3 and HCO_3^- are thus present in the blood, and together they can take care of any excess of either hydrogen or hydroxyl ions:

$$H_2CO_3 + OH^- \rightarrow HCO_3^- + H_2O$$
$$HCO_3^- + H^+ \rightarrow H_2CO_3$$

Organic Compounds

Acids, bases, and salts are all ionic compounds. But chemical compounds can also be produced by covalent bonds. These bonds involve a sharing of electrons, rather than an outright gift. The shared electrons move in a new, molecular orbital that encompasses both of the atoms involved. Thus, two hydrogen atoms each contribute an electron to a shared molecular orbital when they combine to form a hydrogen molecule (Figure 3-8).

A chemical compound may contain both ionic and covalent bonds. In acetic acid (CH_3COOH), for example, the last H is bonded to the adjacent O by an ionic bond, and can dissociate in solution $(CH_3COO^-$

FIGURE 3-8 The hydrogen molecule. The two shared electrons are held in common and travel around each nucleus in a molecular orbital.

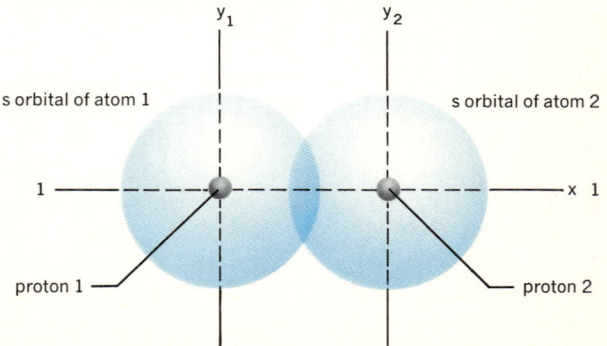

+ H$^+$). But all the atoms in the CH_3COO portion of the molecule are bonded to one another by covalent bonds.

The champion of all covalent bond formers is the carbon atom. It possesses a total of six electrons, two in the innermost shell and four in the outer shell (which has a total capacity of eight electrons). Even the outer shell of the carbon atom is rather close to the nucleus. The pull of the positive protons is so strong that carbon does not normally give away any of its electrons. But it will readily share electrons with other atoms that have electrons of their own to contribute to complete carbon's electron shell.

Often carbon forms bonds with four separate atoms, in each of which a pair of electrons is shared. Such bonds are called **single** or **saturated bonds.** Such bonds are the basis of the methane molecule, CH_4 (Figure 3-9). In other cases, two or more pairs of electrons may be shared between a carbon atom and another atom, forming bonds called **multiple** or **unsaturated bonds.** The carbon dioxide molecule, CO_2, for example, contains two $C=O$ double bonds (Figure 3-

10). Unsaturated bonds are usually highly reactive; other atoms with electrons to share may be added at the site of an unsaturated bond, forming new, saturated bonds.

Carbon atoms readily form bonds with other carbon atoms, linking themselves into intricate chains, rings, and more complex structures like a microscopic tinkertoy. This versatility of carbon is so unique that it has formed the basis for the complex chemical structures of living organisms. The chemistry of life may be called the chemistry of carbon compounds.

At one time it was thought that the chemicals of life were somehow qualitatively different from those that occurred in the nonliving world or could be produced in the laboratory. The chemicals of nonliving things were called **inorganic compounds,** while the term **organic compounds** was used for the substances that were products of or isolated from living organisms. But in 1828 the German chemist Friedrich Wöhler synthesized the compound urea, a common metabolic waste product. Since then numerous other "chemicals of life" have been synthesized artificially,

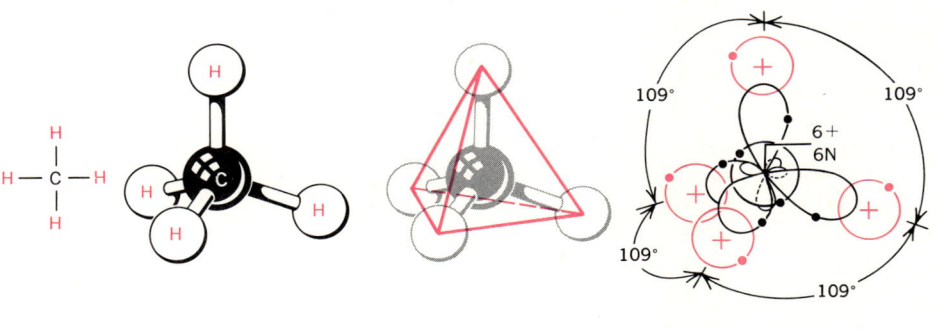

109°   109°

6+
6N

109°

109°

methane, CH_4

FIGURE 3-9 The methane molecule. The covalent bonds of the carbon atom form a tetrahedron.

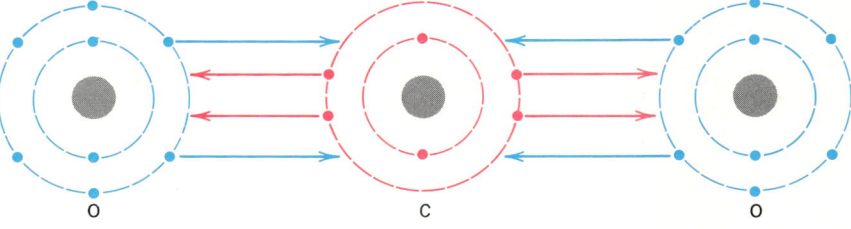

O   C   O

FIGURE 3-10 The carbon dioxide molecule, CO_2 or $O=C=O$.

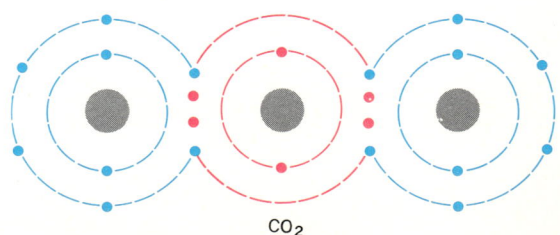

CO_2

and some scientists are even speculating on the possibility of synthesizing living cells. Therefore, the term "organic chemistry" is now used for the chemistry of carbon compounds, no matter what their origin.

MIXTURES

Nothing in our world is pure. The air we breathe is a mixture of gases: mainly nitrogen and oxygen, with smaller amounts of carbon dioxide, water vapor, traces of sulfur and nitrogen compounds, suspended dust particles, and so forth. The water that runs out of the tap is not pure H_2O, but contains a variety of dissolved salts. (Most people find distilled water, relatively pure H_2O, rather flat-tasting and unpleasant.) The human body itself is one of the most complex mixtures of all, containing thousands of different substances.

In general, the most interesting and important mixtures from the biological standpoint are those in which the major component is a liquid. Depending on the size of the particles dispersed in the liquid, such mixtures may be classified as either suspensions, colloidal dispersions, or solutions (Figure 3-11).

Sea water after the bottom sand has been stirred up by a storm is an example of a **suspension,** a mixture in which the size of the dispersed particles exceeds 100 mµ (about 0.000004 inch). If a suspension is allowed to stand, eventually the dispersed phase settles out.

When the dispersed particles are in the size range from 1 to 100 mµ (invisible under an optical microscope but visible under an electron microscope), the mixture is known as a **colloidal dispersion.** The particles are kept suspended indefinitely by the motions of the molecules of the suspending liquid, as well as by chemical and electrical interactions. The matter of living cells is largely in the form of colloidal dispersions.

When the size of the dispersed particles is significantly below 1 mµ, that is, when individual molecules or ions are dispersed in a liquid, the resulting mixture is known as a **solution.** The dissolved molecules or ions may be those of a gas, liquid, or solid, and they are capable of remaining uniformly dispersed indefinitely. In a solution, the dissolved substance is referred to as the **solute,** while the medium in which they are dissolved is called the **solvent.** Human blood is an example of a solution in which a variety of substances are dissolved: gases such as oxygen, nitrogen, and carbon dioxide; and solids such as chlorides, sulfates, nitrates, and other inorganic salts, together with a variety of organic compounds.

The most common solvent, both in the world outside us and in the microcosm within our bodies, is water. This relatively simple substance, H_2O, is uniquely fitted for the role of an efficient solvent, particularly for electrolytes. It has been found that the

hydrogens are joined to the single oxygen atom in the water molecule in such a way as to form an obtuse angle, so that the whole molecule looks something like an Australian boomerang (Figure 3-12A). The nucleus of the oxygen atom has eight protons, while each hydrogen nucleus contains only one. The attractive force of the positive oxygen nucleus is thus considerably more powerful than that of hydrogen. Although the oxygen and hydrogen atoms in water share electrons, they do not share as equals. The mutually shared electrons spend most of their time closer to the oxygen nucleus than to the hydrogen nuclei. As a result, the oxygen end of the water molecule acquires a slight positive charge, while the hydrogen end is slightly negatively charged. A molecule of this kind, with oppositely charged ends, is referred to as a **polar molecule.**

When an electrolyte is mixed with water, the polar water molecules congregate around the individual ions, with the negative ends turned inward toward the positive ions and the positive ends oriented toward the negative ions. The water molecules thus form **solvate shells** (Figure 3-12B), which effectively shield the oppositely charged ions from one another and help to keep them dispersed.

Other polar molecules, such as alcohols and ammonia, also possess solvating powers and are good solvents for salts and other electrolytes. Nonpolar organic substances, however, such as fats and oils, usually do not dissolve in water and other polar sol-

FIGURE 3-11 Three types of mixtures: solution (A), colloidal dispersion (B), and suspension (C). The tiny solute particles of a solution will remain dispersed in the solvent indefinitely. The intermediate-sized particles of a colloid will remain dispersed under normal conditions. The large particles of a suspension will settle out upon standing.

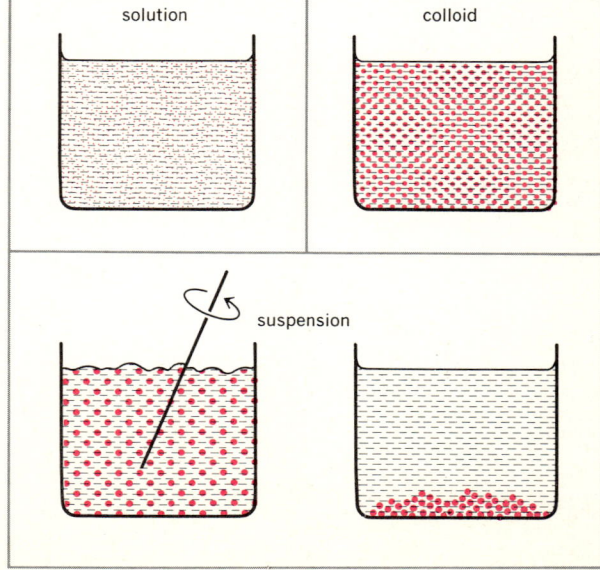

vents. They do dissolve in such nonpolar solvents as ether or gasoline. In terms of the body, substances are usually thought of as either water-soluble or fat-soluble.

The study of solutions is particularly important, both for chemistry in general and for the chemistry of life in particular, because many chemical reactions take place only in solution.

CHEMICAL REACTIONS

At this very second, thousands of chemical reactions are taking place in your body. Molecules and atoms are joining or being split apart or undergoing intricate exchanges and rearrangements. All these diverse reactions share certain general properties and obey certain general laws.

First of all, if there is more than one **reactant** (participant in a reaction), the reactants must be brought together, with sufficient energy and in the proper orientation to react. According to the **kinetic theory of matter,** atoms and molecules are in a ceaseless, random motion. In gases, the atoms or molecules are so sparsely distributed that they may travel great distances without colliding either with one another or with the walls of their container. In solids, on the contrary, the atoms, ions, or molecules are so closely packed that their motions are greatly restricted. In liquids, such as the fluids of the human body, the kinetic motions of atoms, ions, and molecules and the intermediate density of their packing combine to provide for an optimum number of fruitful collisions that

may lead to reactions. When a solid surface is in contact with a liquid, particularly if it is able to selectively hold certain solute molecules by physical or chemical forces, the potential for chemical reactions may be further enhanced (Figure 3-13). This is the underlying principle of the action of **catalysts,** substances that increase the rate and effectiveness of chemical reactions while remaining unchanged themselves. Such substances as finely divided platinum are used as industrial catalysts, but synthetic catalysts are generally far less efficient than the organic catalysts in the bodies of living organisms: complicated proteins called **enzymes.** Many chemical reactions in living organisms actually take place at the surface of solid membranes, bathed by the fluid medium, and are catalyzed by enzymes.

A variety of factors affect the rate and direction of chemical reactions. One factor, as we have seen, is the presence of a solvent. Water, incidentally, not only plays the role of a solvent, but also is an active participant in many reactions of the body, either as a reactant or as a product. Neutralization reactions, for example, produce a salt and water. The reactions of digestion of food materials, on the other hand, are generally **hydrolysis reactions,** in which a complex molecule is split, and a hydrogen from water is added to one fragment and a hydroxyl to the other.

Temperature is another key factor influencing the rate and direction of chemical reactions. Usually an input of energy is necessary to start a reaction going. Energy is stored in chemical bonds and, as bonds are

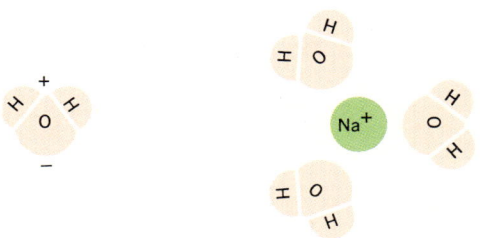
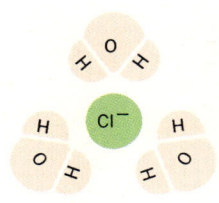

FIGURE 3-12 The polarized water molecule (A) can solvate ionic substances (B,C). The charged ions, surrounded by shells of water molecules, are shielded from the electrical effects of ions of opposite charge and thus kept in a state of dispersion in solution.

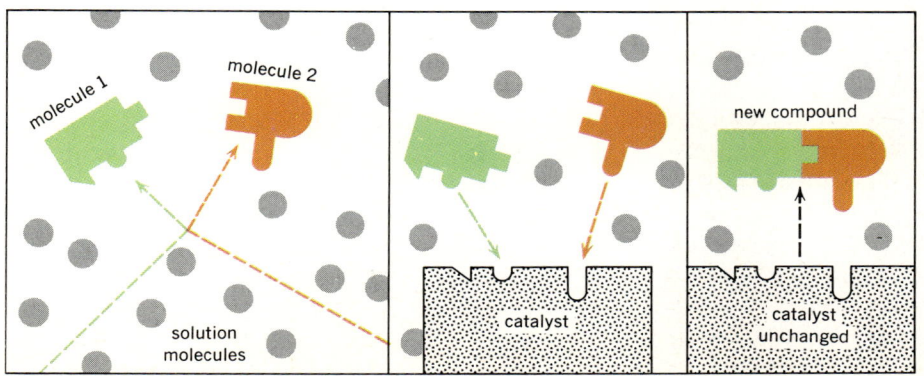

FIGURE 3-13 A catalyst helps other molecules to react. Two molecules randomly colliding in solution (A) may or may not be appropriately oriented; a catalyst temporarily holds the reactants in suitable orientation to form reaction products (B,C).

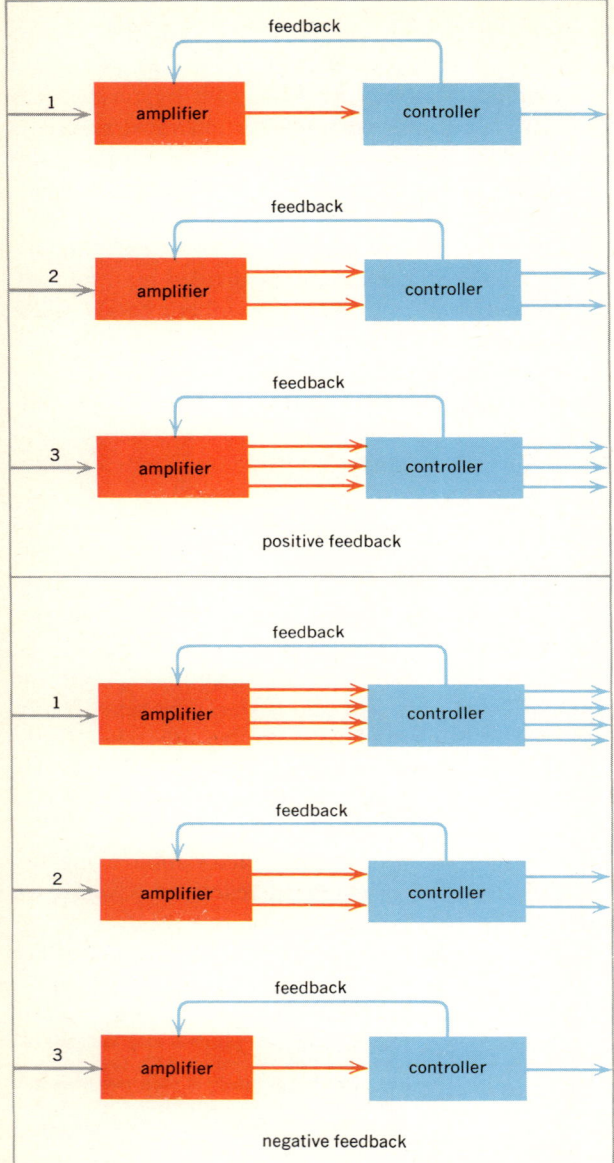

FIGURE 3-14 Processes in living organisms are controlled by positive and negative feedback interrelationships. In positive feedback (A), the reaction product enhances the reaction and thus stimulates further accumulation of the product. In negative feedback (B), the reaction product has an inhibiting effect on the reaction; as it accumulates, the reaction tends to come to a halt, thus imposing a self-limiting regulation.

broken and new bonds are formed, there may actually be a net release of energy that keeps the reaction going. The initial "energy push," however, may be provided by the kinetic energy of the ceaselessly moving atoms and molecules. When the temperature is raised, these movements speed up, and the energy content of the system increases. Thus, the rates of chemical reactions usually increase with increasing temperature. As a general rule of thumb, a doubling of the reaction rate is observed with each 10° C temperature rise. However, in living systems there are usually effective temperature limits for chemical reactions. If the temperature falls too low, reactions cannot proceed effectively. Too high a temperature inactivates and ultimately destroys the delicate enzymes. In the human body, chemical reactions generally proceed optimally at about 37° C.

The concentrations of the reactants also affect the rate of chemical reactions. Living organisms have developed elaborate **feedback systems** of control (Figure 3-14), in which the increased concentration of a reaction product either stimulates the reaction or series of reactions to proceed further **(positive feedback)** or acts as a damper, causing the reaction to come to a halt **(negative feedback).** Negative feedback mechanisms are common in the healthy body and help to maintain its dynamic equilibria. Positive feedback mechanisms may generate a runaway process or "vicious cycle" and may lead to disease or death.

The nature of the reactants themselves is another important factor affecting chemical reactions. They must have a suitable structure, electrical charge, and so forth. The laws that govern the reactivity of atoms and molecules are beyond the scope of this book. However, we should mention one other class of reactions of particular importance both in the nonliving world and in living organisms. This is the class of **oxidation–reduction** or **redox reactions,** in which one reactant is **oxidized** (loses electrons) and the other is **reduced** (gains electrons). Oxygen is a frequent participant in redox reactions. (It acts as an oxidizing agent, and is itself reduced.) The rusting of iron is an oxidation–reduction reaction in which iron reacts with oxygen molecules of the air to form iron oxide. Molecular oxygen from the inhaled air participates in the sequence of reactions of energy metabolism, which provide the energy for the body's activities.

The sum total of all the chemical reactions that go on in the living organism is called **metabolism.** Some of these reactions result in a buildup of body structures; they form the category of **anabolic reactions. Catabolic reactions,** on the other hand, are the breakdown reactions of the body. Both types go on constantly, building up and breaking down substances in a bewildering interplay that is vital to life.

CHEMICAL CONSTITUENTS OF THE BODY

A number of years ago, it was computed that the actual worth of the elements composing a human body was less than a dollar. Inflation has since brought that figure up substantially—to $5.60 according to recent estimates. This is for the elements in their elemental form. But the chemical elements of the body are combined into compounds that are worth far more. The blood of an individual alone has a market value of hundreds of dollars, and some of the human hormones would sell for many thousands of dollars a gram.

People have long dreamed of creating life, of building humanlike androids that could function like them. Such a feat would require a profound knowledge of the chemical constituents of the human body, and how they are put together and interact. So far we have barely scratched the surface of such knowledge. We are far from being able to duplicate even the simplest living cell, for any price, much less the pittance of the "market value" of its elemental constituents. However, life scientists have learned and are learning a great deal about the chemistry of life.

The substance of life, **protoplasm,** is a complex mixture of inorganic and organic compounds. None of its elements is unique to living things. This is evident from Table 3-1, which compares the elementary composition of the human body with the abundance of the same elements in the earth's crust. As is also evident from the table, however, the distribution of the elements in the living and nonliving worlds is quite different. And even more important is that the elements in living organisms are combined into an assortment of complex compounds, many of which have no counterpart in the nonliving world. The main constituents of protoplasm are water, inorganic salts, proteins, carbohydrates, lipids, and nucleic acids.

Water

Water is the most abundant compound on the face of the earth. It is also the most abundant compound in the body, constituting more than 65 percent of the total body weight. Water is one of the simplest compounds in the body, yet it is one of the most important. A human being can survive for only a few days without taking in water.

Water serves a great variety of functions in the body. It provides the fluid medium in which the chemical reactions of the cells take place. In the blood, water furnishes the major transport medium for distributing oxygen, nutrients, and such other substances as hormones to the body cells, as well as for carrying away their waste products. Water is important in the excretion of wastes, through the kidneys, intestines, and sweat glands. The water that is eliminated through the sweat glands also plays a key role in the body's temperature-control mechanisms, eliminating excess heat from the body.

The water content of the tissues is continuously monitored in the brain. A control center in the hypothalamus triggers a sensation of thirst if more water must be taken in to meet the body's needs. Too much water in the tissues triggers hormone-mediated con-

TABLE 3-1 Elementary composition of the human body, compared with the earth's crust (in percent by weight)

ELEMENT	PERCENTAGE IN HUMAN BODY	PERCENTAGE IN EARTH'S CRUST
Oxygen (O)	65.0	46.6
Carbon (C)	18.5	0.03
Hydrogen (H)	9.5	0.1
Nitrogen (N)	3.3	Trace
Calcium (Ca)	1.5	3.6
Phosphorus (P)	1.0	0.1
Potassium (K)	0.4	2.6
Sulfur (S)	0.3	0.05
Chlorine (Cl)	0.2	0.05
Sodium (Na)	0.2	2.9
Magnesium (Mg)	0.1	2.1
Iron (Fe)	0.004	5.0
Iodine (I)	0.00004	Trace
Silicon (Si)	Trace	25.7
Fluorine (F)	Trace	0.03
Copper (Cu)	Trace	0.01
Manganese (Mn)	Trace	0.1
Zinc (Zn)	Trace	Trace
Selenium (Se)	Trace	Trace
Cobalt (Co)	Trace	Trace
Molybdenum (Mo)	Trace	Trace
Boron (B)	Trace	Trace

trol mechanisms that promptly restore the balance by increasing fluid elimination.

Inorganic Salts

We tend to think of the human body as made up of organic chemicals. Yet the "chemicals of life" include nearly two-thirds water, and another 4.4 percent of the weight of the human body is comprised of inorganic salts. These salts are found partly in dissolved form, dissociated into ions, and partly in combination with organic compounds.

Sodium and chloride ions are the most abundant inorganic ions in the body fluids; within the cells, potassium and phosphate ions are the major inorganic constituents. Calcium phosphate is the major constituent of bones. Various other ions are present in smaller amounts, some in barely detectable traces. Yet there is a growing awareness of the importance even of these "trace elements." Some of them are constituents of key enzyme systems, without which the normal reactions in the body could not take place.

Inorganic salts play an important role in the regulation of osmotic conditions, determining the passage of substances through membranes; in the acid-base balance, the coagulation of blood (calcium), the transport of oxygen and carbon dioxide (iron in hemoglobin); in nerve conductivity and muscle contraction (sodium, potassium, and calcium chlorides); and in the coordination of metabolic activities (iodine in the thyroid hormone).

A number of glands of internal secretion contribute to maintaining the salt balance of the body, including the adrenal cortex and the posterior lobe of the pituitary.

Carbohydrates

Candy, cake, and most "snack foods" contain large amounts of a group of compounds called **carbohydrates.** This class of compounds includes sugars and starches, which are the major sources of energy for the body. Carbohydrates contain the three elements carbon, hydrogen, and oxygen, combined in the ratio $C_xH_{2y}O_y$.

Glucose, a simple sugar with six carbons in its molecule, is the form that is carried in the blood. It is an essential nutrient for all the body cells; brain cells are avid consumers of glucose and are especially sensitive to a lack of it.

Starch, the major form of stored food in plants, consists of glucose units, linked together into large molecules. It is digested to glucose in the body. Whatever glucose is not immediately needed by the body is then synthesized into an "animal starch," **glycogen,** which is stored mainly in the liver and muscle cells.

The utilization of glucose, its conversion to glycogen, and the mobilization of the glycogen reserves to yield glucose to meet the body's needs are controlled by various glands, particularly through the two hormones of the pancreas.

Lipids

Fats have acquired a bad reputation in our society. Obese people are exhorted to go on a diet, and fatty deposits in the arteries are a major factor in heart disease. Yet fats and the other fatty-like substances that also fall under the general category of lipids do play some valuable roles in the body.

Fat deposits serve as a source of reserve energy. Although they are not as readily oxidized as carbohydrates, gram for gram, fats yield more than twice as many calories and are thus a more economical means of energy storage. (The lipids in the body are not all derived from fats in the diet; they can be produced from carbohydrates as well.) Superficial fat deposits also act as insulators, cutting down heat loss from the body. Women, who tend to have more fat deposits than men, are thus better equipped to withstand cold weather.

Lipids are a major constituent of the cell membranes and play an important role in maintaining normal cell permeability; they thus help to regulate the flow of materials into and out of the cell. Lipids aid in the transport of fat-soluble vitamins.

The neutral fats and oils in fatty foods are combi-nations of **fatty acids,** RCOOH (where R is a long hydrocarbon chain, which may be saturated or unsaturated), and **glycerol,** $CH_2(OH)CH(OH)CH_2OH$. Lipids in the living body may contain phosphorus and nitrogen or may be linked with carbohydrates. The class of lipids also includes **cholesterol** and the **steroid** hormones. All the lipids share the general property of insolubility in water, due to the influence of the large nonpolar hydrocarbon groups in their molecules.

Proteins

There are about 100,000 different kinds of proteins in the human body. The assortment of "human" proteins differs from those of other species, and there are even differences from one person to another. The peculiarities of protein content are undoubtedly an important contributing factor in the differences between individuals and species.

Proteins are high-molecular-weight substances, formed by the linking together of smaller units called **amino acids** (Figure 3-15). There are about twenty naturally occurring amino acids. An amino acid,

$$\overset{NH_2}{\underset{|}{}}$$

which can be symbolized as $R{-}\overset{|}{C}H{-}COOH$, has two highly reactive chemical groups, the **amino (NH_2) and carboxyl (COOH) groups.** When the amino group of one amino acid reacts with the carboxyl group of another to form a linkage called a **peptide bond,** a molecule of water is eliminated. Proteins are built up from amino acids, joined by peptide bonds. Some are huge, with molecular weights in the millions.

Next to water, proteins are the most abundant substance in most cells—from 10 to 20 percent of the cell mass. They serve a great variety of functions in the body, but most can be categorized in one of two main classes: structural proteins and functional proteins, which include enzymes and hormones that regulate the body's activities.

Structural proteins are present in the various membranes of the cells and hold the cell structures together. Hair is almost pure structural protein. Most of the structural proteins are fibrillar, that is, the individual molecules are in the form of long, fibrous threads. These threads provide tensile strength for the cell structures.

Enzymes are the organic catalysts, without which most of the chemical reactions in the body would not proceed. Their molecules are generally coiled, folded, and twisted into a globular form. They may be found dissolved in various fluids of the body or attached to the surface of the cell membranes. Their shape is intricate and highly specific, possessing various reactive sites that can attract and temporarily hold the molecules (**substrates**) on which they act. The most striking feature of enzyme action is specificity; many enzymes catalyze only a single chemical reaction with a single set of reactants, and do not act even on somewhat similar compounds. The enzyme-substrate interaction has been characterized as a "lock and key" relationship: the characteristic conformation of the enzyme with its active sites provides a "lock," which only a highly specific substrate "key" with just the right corresponding structure can fit. Enzymes are fantastically efficient catalysts. The enzyme catalase, for example, catalyzes the decomposition of hydrogen peroxide, and one catalase molecule can act on as many as five million hydrogen peroxide molecules each minute at the temperature of ice water (0° C). Usually the enzyme proteins exist in a complex with one or more **cofactors,** such as vitamins and metal ions.

Other important proteins in the body include **hormones,** * which control and coordinate the activities of the cells, tissues, and organs of the body; and **nucleoproteins,** complexes of proteins and nucleic acids, which carry the hereditary blueprints for all the body's structures and activities.

Growth of new tissue and repair of old tissue require a continuous supply of available protein. The proteins taken in as foods are not used as such: they are first digested (hydrolyzed) into their constituent amino acids, which are then built up into the characteristic proteins of the body.

Nucleic Acids

How many blueprints and directions would be necessary to build and operate a human being, from conception to old age? Perhaps a thousand books of 500 pages each? That is the amount of information that has been estimated to be contained in the chromosomes of a single human cell. How could so much information be crammed into such a tiny package? It is encoded in nucleic acid molecules, spelled out in a four-letter alphabet of units called nitrogen bases.

The name of the nucleic acids came from the fact that they were first discovered in the cell nucleus. But actually nucleic acids are found in the cytoplasm of the cell, outside the nucleus, as well. In the past few decades, they have been objects of avid investigation, and much progress has been made. More than a dozen Nobel Prize winners have received their awards for work in the field of molecular genetics, the study of the chemicals of heredity.

It is now known that there are several kinds of nucleic acids, each with its own functions in the cell. The master plans are carried in **DNA (deoxyribonu-**

* Some hormones are proteins or smaller, proteinlike substances (peptides); others are steroids, which are classed in the general group of lipids.

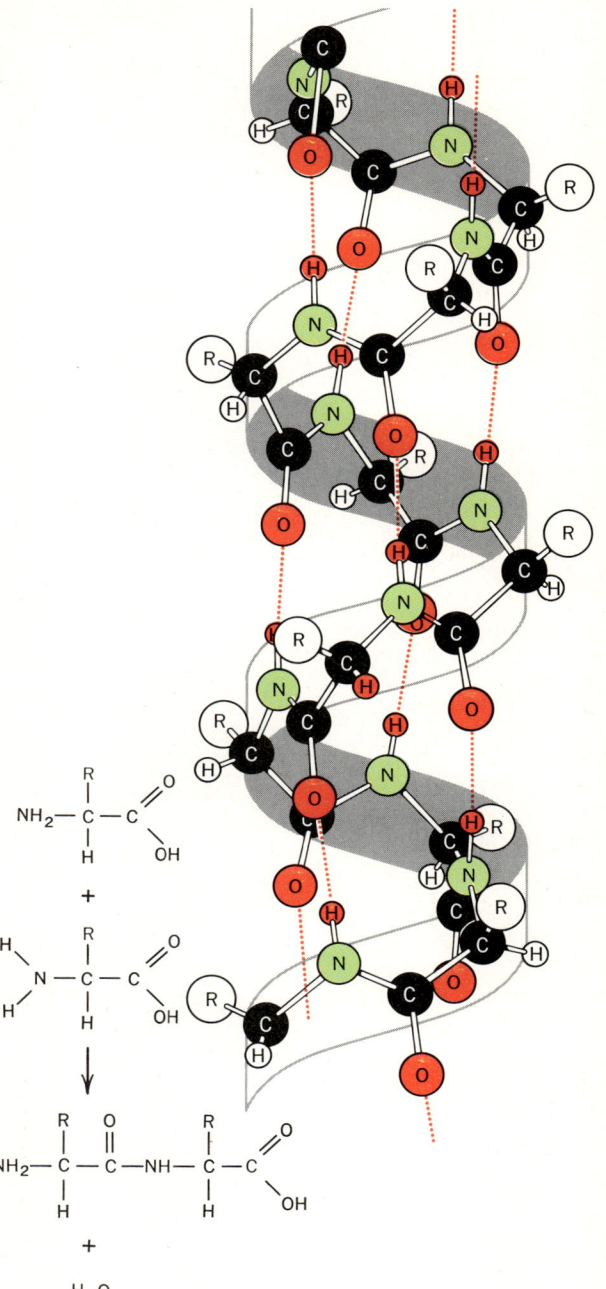

FIGURE 3-15 Protein structure: peptide bonds link amino acids into long chains, coiled into an alpha helix.

cleic acid) molecules, whose molecular weights run into the billions. Working parts of the plans are passed on through several types of **RNA (ribonucleic acid),** and ultimately translated into proteins.

The DNA molecule is built in the form of a double helix, somewhat like a spiral staircase (Figure 3-16). Each of the two strands of the double helix has a backbone of alternating **sugar** and **phosphate** groups. The sugar is a five-carbon sugar, **deoxyribose.** (The

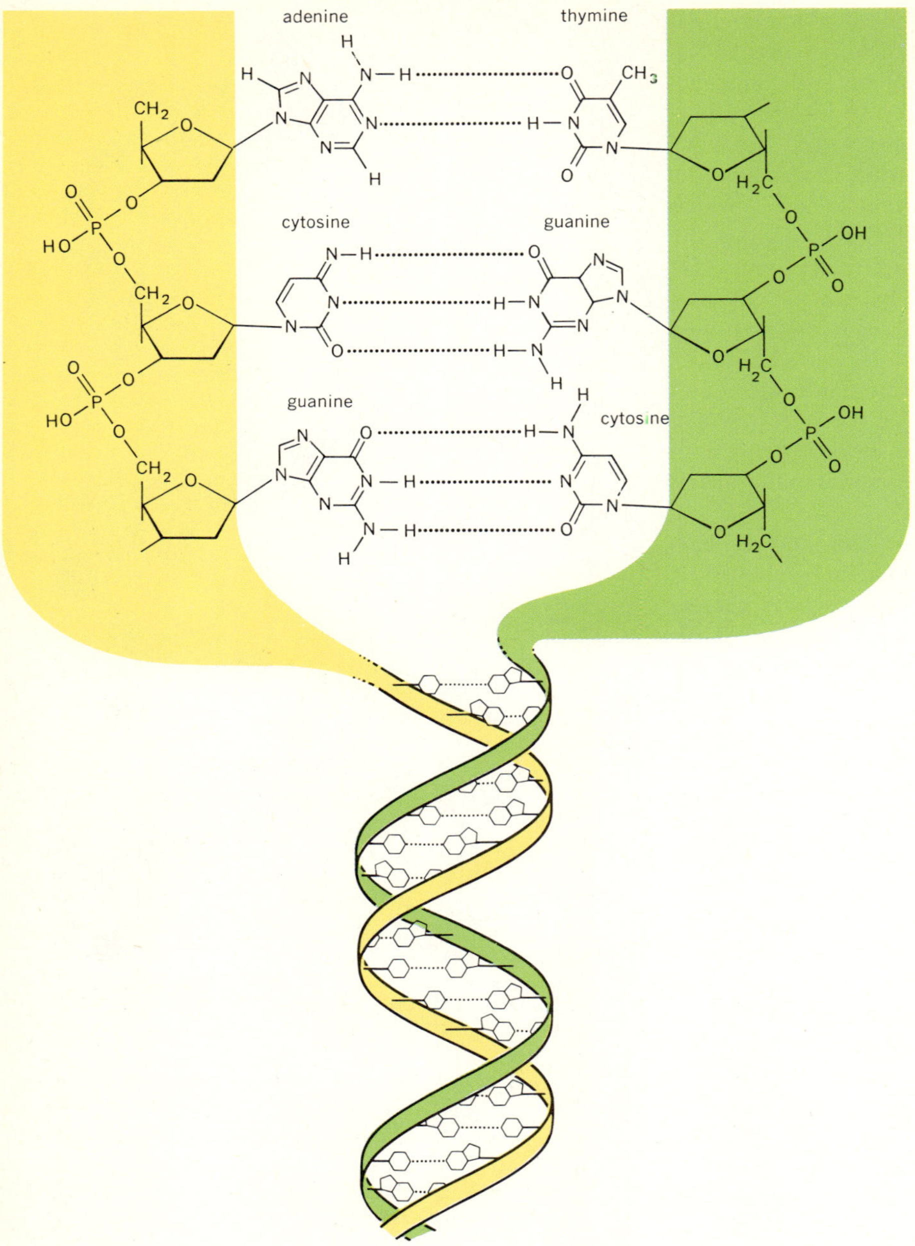

FIGURE 3-16 DNA structure: a double helix of sugar phosphates and nitrogen bases. Hydrogen bonds hold the two chains together.

molecule of blood sugar, glucose, has six carbons.) Nitrogen bases of four types are attached to the sugar components: **adenine, thymine, cytosine,** and **guanine.**

Weak chemical bonds called hydrogen bonds link the nitrogen bases of the two DNA strands together, maintaining the double helix. Because of their chemical structure, the bases obey specific pairing rules in forming these bonds. Adenine pairs only with thymine, for example, and cytosine with guanine. The sequence of bases along the DNA strands carries the genetic information, parts of which are "read out" in the synthesis of RNA and subsequently protein.

There are three main types of RNA: **messenger RNA, transfer RNA,** and **ribosomal RNA** (Figure 3-

17). All are synthesized within the cell, using parts of the DNA strands as a pattern or **template.** Messenger RNA carries the DNA "message" out of the nucleus into the cytoplasm. At the ribosomes, which have their own ribosomal RNA, messenger RNA molecules are joined by a number of much smaller transfer RNA molecules. Each transfer RNA molecule has the ability to pick up a specific amino acid molecule from the cell medium and deliver it to the ribosomes. (There is at least one specific transfer RNA molecule for each kind of amino acid.) At the ribosomes, the messenger RNA molecule provides the pattern for protein synthesis. Its message is read out in groups of three bases, each of which is complementary to a

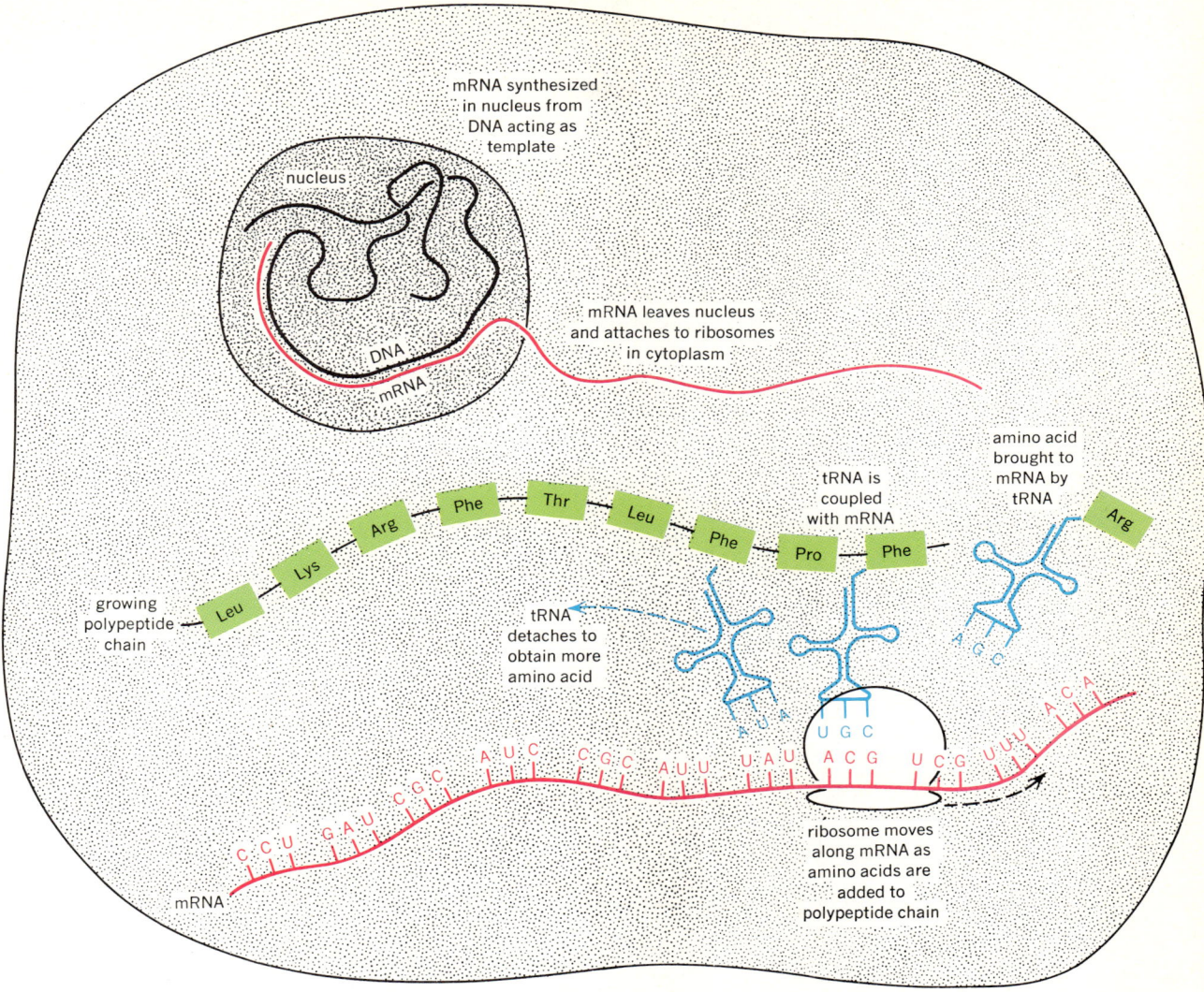

FIGURE 3-17   Protein synthesis: messenger RNA, transfer RNA, and ribosomal RNA cooperate in the assembly of amino acids according to the DNA blueprint, spelled out in triplet "codons" of bases.

group of three bases on one of the transfer RNA molecules. Each transfer RNA molecule takes its place in turn and adds its activated amino acid molecule to the growing peptide chain.

RNA molecules are structurally similar to DNA in some respects and different in others. Like DNA, they are constructed from sugar, phosphate, and nitrogen base components. But the sugar in RNA is a slightly different five-carbon sugar, **ribose.** Three of the nitrogen bases contained in RNA molecules are the same as those in DNA: adenine, guanine, and cytosine. But instead of thymine, RNA contains **uracil.** (Uracil acts like thymine in forming base pairs; thus, when RNA is synthesized on the DNA template, a uracil is incorporated opposite each adenine on the DNA strand.) RNA molecules are helical, but unlike DNA they form a single-stranded helix.

Like proteins, the nucleic acids in foods are not utilized as such, but are digested into their constituents. The characteristic nucleic acids of the body are synthesized as needed.

SUMMARY

Observable phenomena in living systems are based on chemical reactions within the cells.

Matter occupies space and has mass (weight).

A solid has a fixed shape and maintains a constant volume.

A liquid maintains a constant volume but flows to assume the shape of its container.

A gas can expand to fill a container or can be compressed if pressure is applied.

Changes of state of matter involve an input or release of energy.

Energy is a capacity to do work. Types of energy include:

kinetic
potential
chemical
heat
light
electrical

Temperature is a measure of heat energy
$$°C = \tfrac{5}{9}(°F - 32) \text{ (Centigrade scale)}$$
$$°F = \tfrac{9}{5}(°C) + 32 \text{ (Fahrenheit scale)}$$
An element is a substance that cannot be decomposed by ordinary chemical means.
  92 elements occur in nature, and about a dozen more have been produced in the laboratory.
Elements are composed of atoms, the units of matter.
  Atoms contain protons, electrons, and neutrons.
  Protons have a positive electrical charge; electrons have a negative electrical charge; the number of protons in a particular atom is exactly equal to the number of electrons, so that the atom is electrically neutral.
  The atomic number of an element is the number of protons in its nucleus.
  The atomic mass of an element is the sum of its protons and neutrons.
  Isotopes of an element have the same number of protons (atomic number) but different numbers of neutrons (atomic mass).
  The atomic weight of an element is a weighted average of the atomic masses of its isotopes.
Atoms can donate, accept, or share electrons to form chemical bonds.
  In an ionic bond, electrons are completely transferred.
  In a covalent bond, electrons are shared.
  An atom that has donated or accepted one or more electrons and acquired a positive or negative charge is called an ion.
A chemical compound is made up of two or more elements, joined by chemical bonds, in a definite proportion by weight.
  The smallest unit of a compound that still retains the properties of the compound is called a molecule.
  The molecular weight of a compound is the sum of the atomic weights of the elements that comprise it, each in proportion to its representation in the compound.
  The molecular weight expressed in grams is called a mole.
A salt is an electrically neutral combination of a metal and a nonmetal, joined by an ionic bond.
An acid is a substance that can liberate hydrogen ions, or donate a proton, or combine with hydroxyl ions.
A base is a substance that can liberate hydroxyl ions or accept a proton.
Acids, bases, and salts are electrolytes (can conduct an electric current in solution).
An acid and a base can neutralize one another, producing a salt and water.
Acidity is measured on the pH scale, based on the negative logarithm of the hydrogen ion concentration.
  Buffer systems react with excess hydrogen or hydroxyl ions, maintaining a relatively constant pH.
Organic compounds are compounds containing carbon atoms.
  Carbon atoms can form covalent bonds with one another and with other atoms, producing a variety of chains, rings, and so forth.
Depending on the size of the dispersed particles, mixtures can be classified as:
  Suspensions (particle size > 100 mμ; dispersed phase settles out upon standing).
  Colloidal dispersions (particle size from 1 to 100 mμ; particles kept in suspension by motions of molecules of suspending liquid).
  Solutions (particle size < 1 mμ; dissolved molecules or ions can remain uniformly dispersed indefinitely).
    Dissolved substance is solute; dissolving medium is solvent.
    Water possesses effective solvating properties due to its polar structure.

Chemical reactions are affected by various factors including:
  The nature of the reactants
  The concentrations of the reactants
  Temperature
  The presence of catalysts (substances that increase the rate and effectiveness of chemical reactions while themselves remaining unchanged)
In oxidation-reduction (redox) reactions, one reactant is oxidized (loses electrons) and the other is reduced (gains electrons).
Metabolism is the sum total of all the chemical reactions that go on in the living organism.
  Anabolic reactions result in a buildup of body structures.
  Catabolic reactions are breakdown reactions.
Protoplasm, the substance of life, is a complex mixture, including mainly:
  water
  inorganic salts
  proteins
  carbohydrates
  lipids
  nucleic acids
Carbohydrates include sugars and starches.
Lipids include fats and steroids.
Proteins are built up from amino acids and include structural proteins, enzymes, some hormones, and nucleoproteins.
Nucleic acids, carriers of genetic information, include DNA and several types of RNA: messenger, transfer, and ribosomal. They are built up from sugar, phosphate, and nitrogen base units.

QUESTIONS FOR REVIEW AND THOUGHT

1 Characterize several of your daily activities (such as eating breakfast, climbing stairs, or watching television) from the standpoint of matter and energy transformations.
2 Convert the following to °C: −140° F; 0° F; 32° F; 70° F; 100° F; 212° F; 1000° F. Convert to °F: −273° C; 0° C; 20° C; 50° C; 100° C; 200° C; 1000° C.
3 Sodium has an atomic mass of 23 and tends to donate one electron in forming chemical bonds. How many protons and how many neutrons would you expect the nucleus of a sodium atom to contain?
4 Naturally occurring chlorine has an atomic weight of 35.5 and consists mainly of two isotopes, 75.5 percent chlorine-35 and 24.5 percent chlorine-37. In chemical reactions it tends to accept an electron. How many electrons does each of its orbitals contain?
5 Silicon is directly below carbon in the Periodic Table, and its outer orbital contains four electrons. What kind of chemical bond would you expect it to form most readily? Why does it not form as great a variety of compounds as carbon?
6 The molecule of a soap contains a polar salt portion and a nonpolar hydrocarbon portion. Use the concepts of solubility to explain its action in washing away oily dirt particles.
7 Discuss the effects of temperature on chemical reactions. What advantages do the temperature-control mechanisms of warm-blooded animals confer?
8 Why is a continual intake of water essential to life?
9 Could a synthetic diet of appropriate proportions of water, carbohydrates, proteins, and lipids support human life? If not, what key ingredients are missing?
10 How many different sequences could be formed from 20 different amino acid residues, linked together into a peptide chain? Now picture the possibilities for a protein molecule containing thousands of amino acid residues of these same 20 types.
11 Diagram the sequence by which the "code" inscribed in DNA molecules is translated into the protein products of the cell.

CELLS

4

At what level can we draw the line between "life" and "nonlife"? There is no question that the whole organism is alive. A thinking brain, a beating heart, a hand capable of deft manipulations—all these portions of the living body have characteristics that readily distinguish them from nonliving matter, although they themselves are not capable of independent existence. Yet could blood or bone be thought of as "alive?"

The human body and its parts are made up of trillions of microscopic structures called cells, plus intercellular material (matrix) that the cells produce, and body fluids. Of these three types of ingredients, only the cells have the characteristics that are generally recognized as distinguishing life from nonlife: growth, metabolism, irritability (responsiveness to stimuli), and reproduction. Cells are thus the smallest living units of the body.

Single cells hold within them the answers to thousands of problems confronting the life scientist. The past few decades have brought a revolution in the study of cells, through the development of new techniques for probing into their depths. Before the electron microscope, for example, the living cell was usually thought of as a tiny membranous bag, within which various structures or organelles floated in a liquid "soup" of protoplasm. The development of the electron microscope (Figure 4-1) brought a hundredfold increase in magnifying power and revealed finer details of cell structure for the first time. Then it was discovered that the inside of the cell is just as highly structured as the body as a whole, with each organelle having its own characteristic location and functions. In addition to electron microscopy, other modern techniques such as phase microscopy (which can be used to study unstained living cells), histochemistry (revealing not only characteristic chemicals within cells, but also the sites of various enzymatic reactions), ultracentrifugation (separating the various cell structures so that they can be further studied), autoradiography (in which radioisotopes reveal details of cell structures and reactions), and micrurgy (micromanipulation of cells and their organelles in the field of a microscope) are yielding floods of new information each year.

CELL SIZE AND SHAPE

Textbooks of anatomy and physiology generally contain a diagram and discussion of the structures of a "typical cell." (This text is no exception.) Yet, strictly speaking, there is no such thing as a "typical cell." Nerve cells are long, threadlike structures, while cells carefully scraped from the inside of the cheek look like flat paving stones under a microscope. Some body cells are nearly spherical, others like tiny cubes, still others column-shaped. The cells of the heart mus-

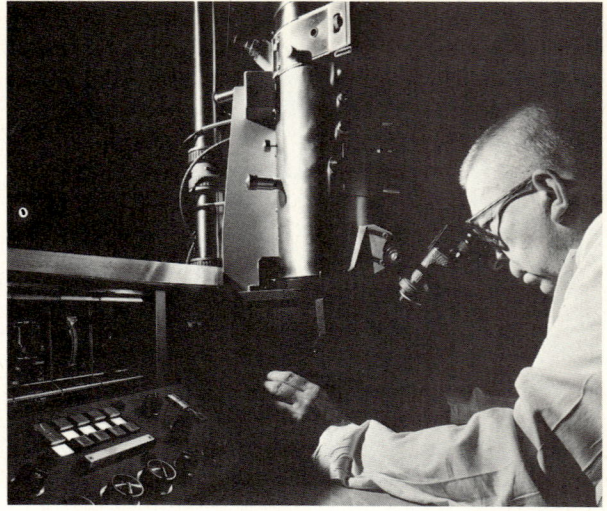

A

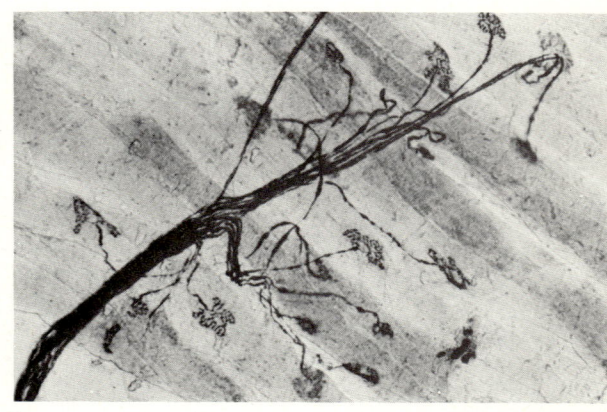

B

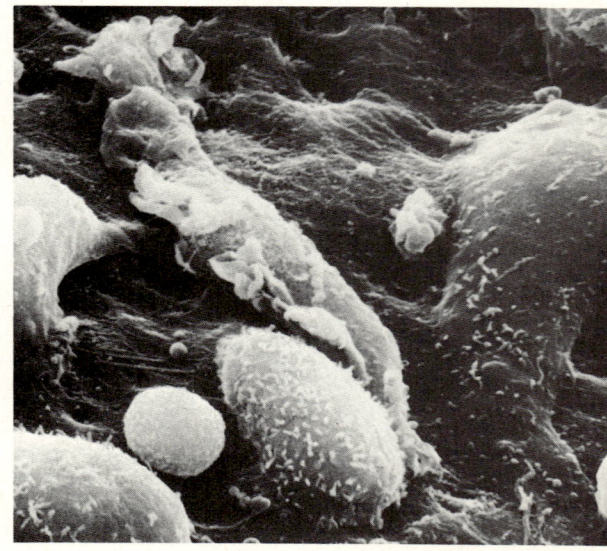

C

FIGURE 4-1 The electron microscope has revolutionized biology and medicine. (A) An electron microscope in action; (B) electron micrograph of motor end plates; (C) scanning EM of a macrophage crawling over the surface of the diaphragm. ((B) courtesy Carolina Biological Supply Co.)

cle are actually fused so that they can scarcely be thought of as individual units.

With all this diversity of cell size and shape, some basic generalizations can still be made. First of all, with a single exception, all the cells of the human body are microscopic—too small to be seen with the naked eye. (The single exception is the ovum, the female reproductive cell, which is a barely visible speck.) Red blood cells, among the smallest cells in the body, are only about 7.5 microns in diameter. A cigar-shaped muscle cell may be an inch long or more, but only about 50 microns in diameter. Some of the peripheral nerves, running to or from the legs, may stretch through much of the length of the body— three feet or more. Yet these cells still could not be seen without a microscope, for their diameter is only about 10 microns.

Another important factor in cell size and shape is the ratio of surface area to volume. In general, for a given volume, a spherical cell would have the smallest surface area; the more irregular a cell, the greater its surface (Figure 4-2). A nerve cell, in which extremely long, thin fibers (processes) branch out from the cell body, exposes a huge surface area to the surrounding body fluids in comparison to its minute volume. This structural peculiarity becomes understandable when viewed in functional terms: the nerve cell contains very little stored food; its extensive surface provides maximum opportunities for receiving food supplies from the body media.

The human ovum is an example of a cell that is perfectly spherical. But it is a rarity in the human body. Most body cells are pressed and squeezed by the other cells that surround them, so that they assume an irregular, many-sided shape.

The variations of cell size and shape are correlated with variations in their internal structure (organelles and their arrangement) and in their functions. A liver cell, a nerve cell, and a skin cell not only look quite different, but they do different things for the body. Yet with all this diversity, nearly all the body cells share certain features of structure and function in common. This is the rationale for the hypothetical "typical cell" we now discuss.

STRUCTURE OF THE CELL

It is hard to believe that a structure too small to see with the naked eye should be as complex as a city. Yet this is exactly the case with the living cell. A typical cell (Figure 4-3) is bounded by a delicate **cell membrane** or **plasma membrane** that encloses the living substance **protoplasm.** Far from the random "soup" that was originally imagined, the protoplasm of the cell is intricately structured, in part by a complicated maze of twisting, folded membranes that divide the cell into compartments. This system of inter-

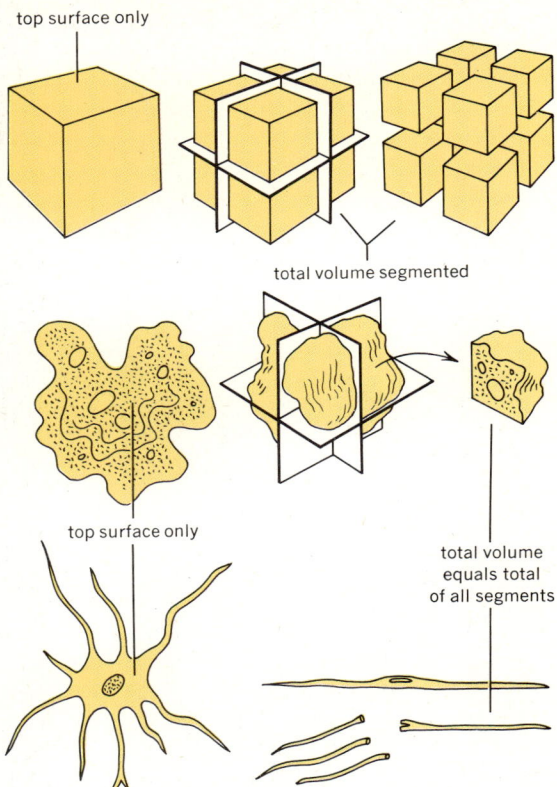

FIGURE 4-2 Irregular cells have a far larger surface area than a cube of equivalent volume.

nal membranes is called the **endoplasmic reticulum.** Roughly at the center of the cell is the **nucleus,** enclosed in its own membrane. The nucleus is the heart of the cell, the control center, without which a cell cannot long continue to exist. The protoplasm of the nucleus is referred to as **nucleoplasm,** while the living matter outside the nucleus is called **cytoplasm.**

The microscope reveals numerous tiny structures or **organelles** dispersed in the cytoplasm, some free-lying and others associated with parts of the endoplasmic reticulum. Some cell organelles, such as the **mitochondria, lysosomes,** and **Golgi apparatus,** each have their own membrane covering. Other cytoplasmic organelles include the **ribosomes, centrosomes,** and **fibrils.**

When a cell divides in two, yielding two smaller copies of itself, all its characteristic organelles are reproduced. Thus, each daughter cell receives a full set of mitochondria, ribosomes, and so forth. However, cells also typically contain inclusions of nonliving materials, such as stored food substances, pigments, and crystals. Such **cytoplasmic inclusions** are not reproduced.

The number, appearance, and arrangement of the various organelles and inclusions vary with the type of cell and are correlated with the functions of the cell as a whole.

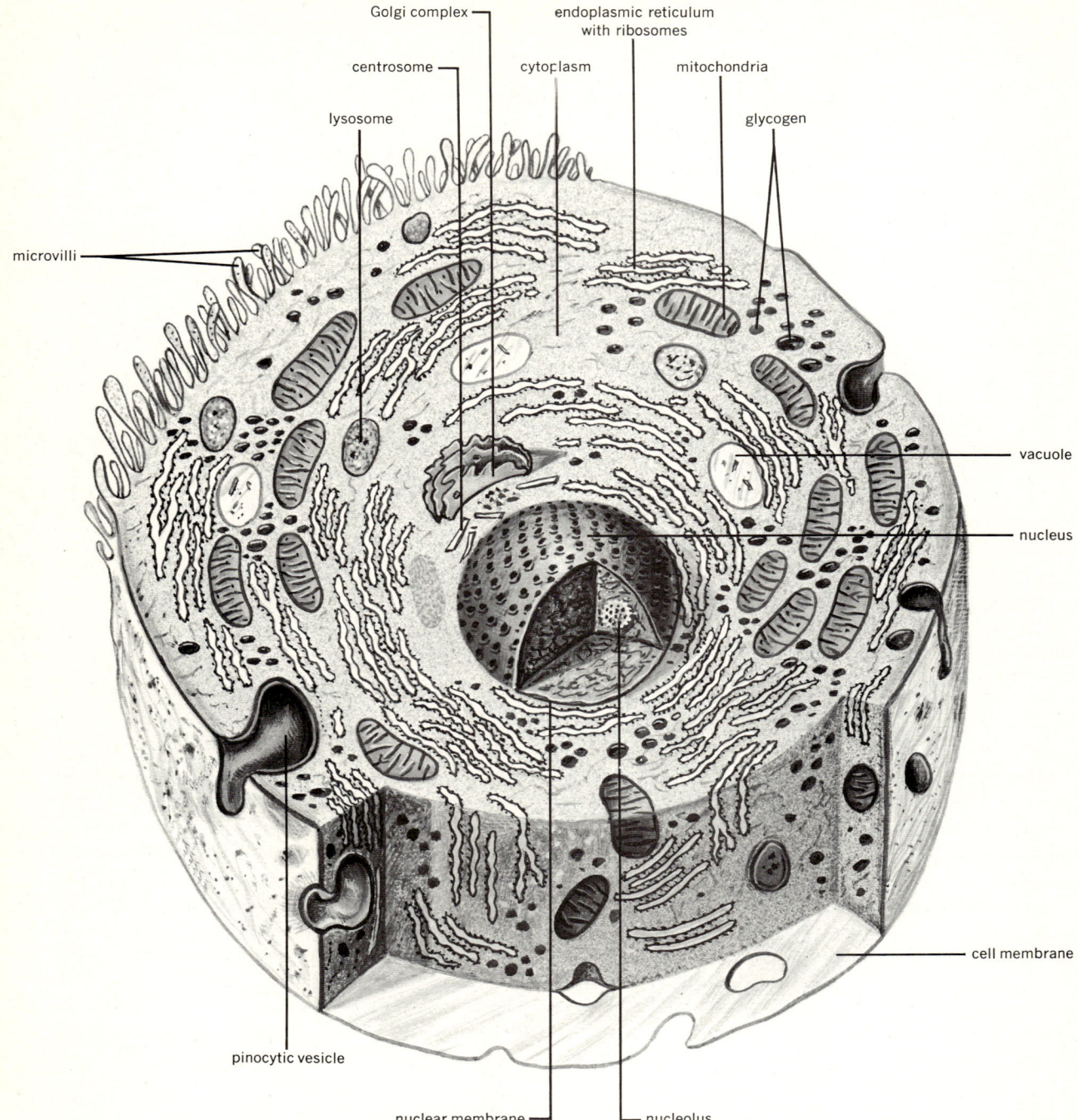

Golgi complex

centrosome

lysosome

cytoplasm

endoplasmic reticulum
with ribosomes

mitochondria

glycogen

microvilli

vacuole

nucleus

cell membrane

pinocytic vesicle

nuclear membrane

nucleolus

A

FIGURE 4-3   The diagram shows the structure of a generalized, "typical" cell, as revealed by the electron microscope; the electron micrograph was taken of a liver parenchymal cell, ×8000.

THE CELL MEMBRANE

Numerous mysteries surround the nature and composition of the structures of life. But few are under more active scrutiny than the cell membrane. The huge numbers of scientists now engaged in studying the structure and functions of the cell membrane reflect the enormous importance they ascribe to this envelope. It is expected that studies of the cell surface will be of critical importance in our war against cancer,

since one of the key distinctions between cancer cells and normal cells is the failure of the cancer cell to obey the usual "stop" signals it encounters when its surface comes in contact with the surface of another body cell.

Electron micrographs of cell sections (Figure 4-4A) show each cell is bounded by a double line of dark material, with a layer of light material between the two dark lines. Thus, the membrane appears to have

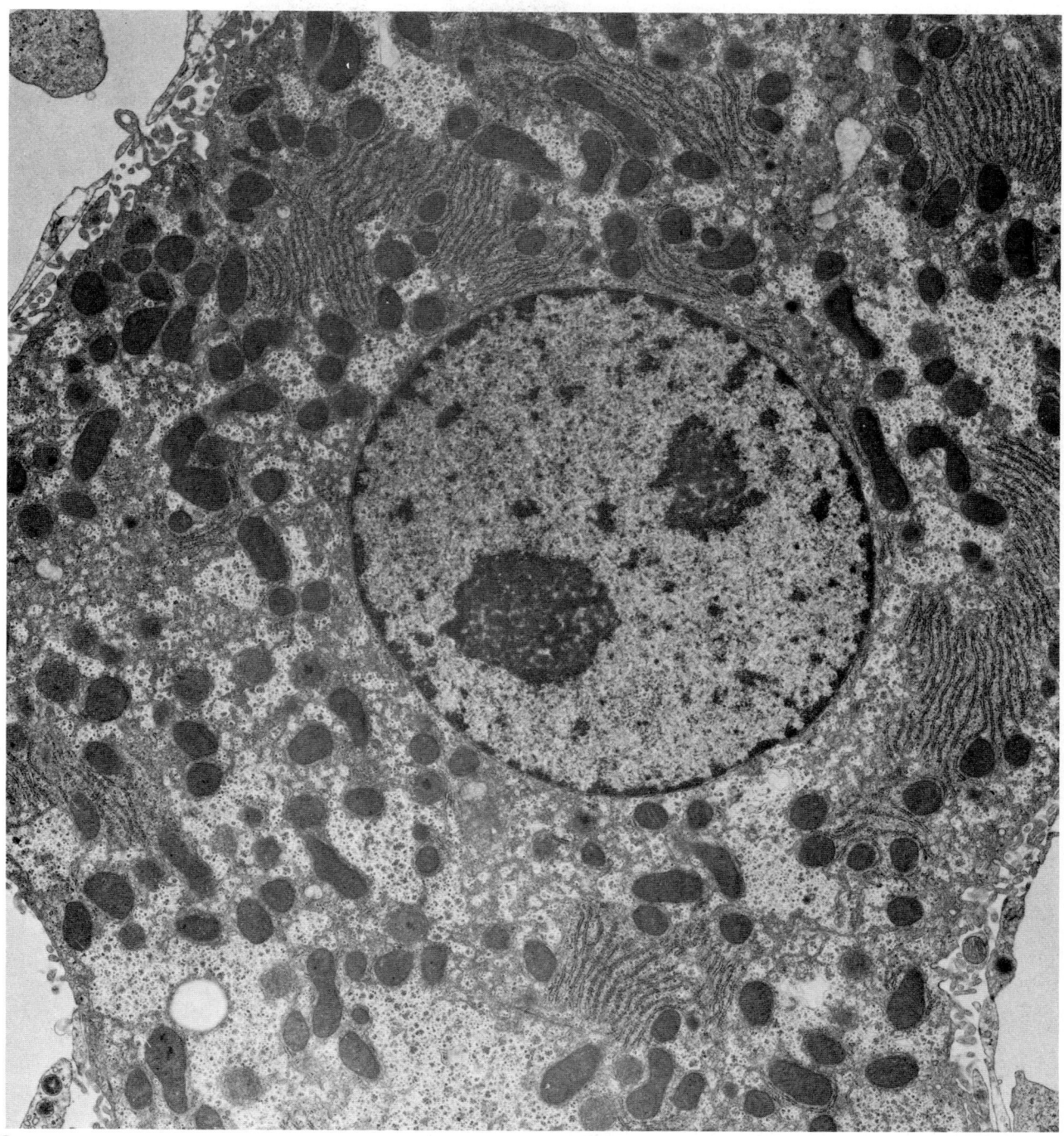

B

three layers, each about 25 Å thick, for an overall thickness of 75 Å (about 3/10,000,000 of an inch). In a simplified form, the cell membrane has been pictured as a "sandwich," like a cheese sandwich with two slices of bread enclosing two slices of American cheese. The bread layers correspond to protein molecules, while the cheese filling is represented in the cell membrane by two layers of phospholipid molecules, arranged at right angles to the surface of the membrane. X-ray diffraction studies have revealed that each phospholipid molecule in the lipid bilayer consists of a distinct phosphate "head" and a fatty acid "tail." The molecules are oriented with their "heads" facing the outside of the membrane and their "tails" facing inward.

An actual cell membrane is not as simple as the sandwich model of its structure might suggest. Its thickness may vary in places, and at some sites pores

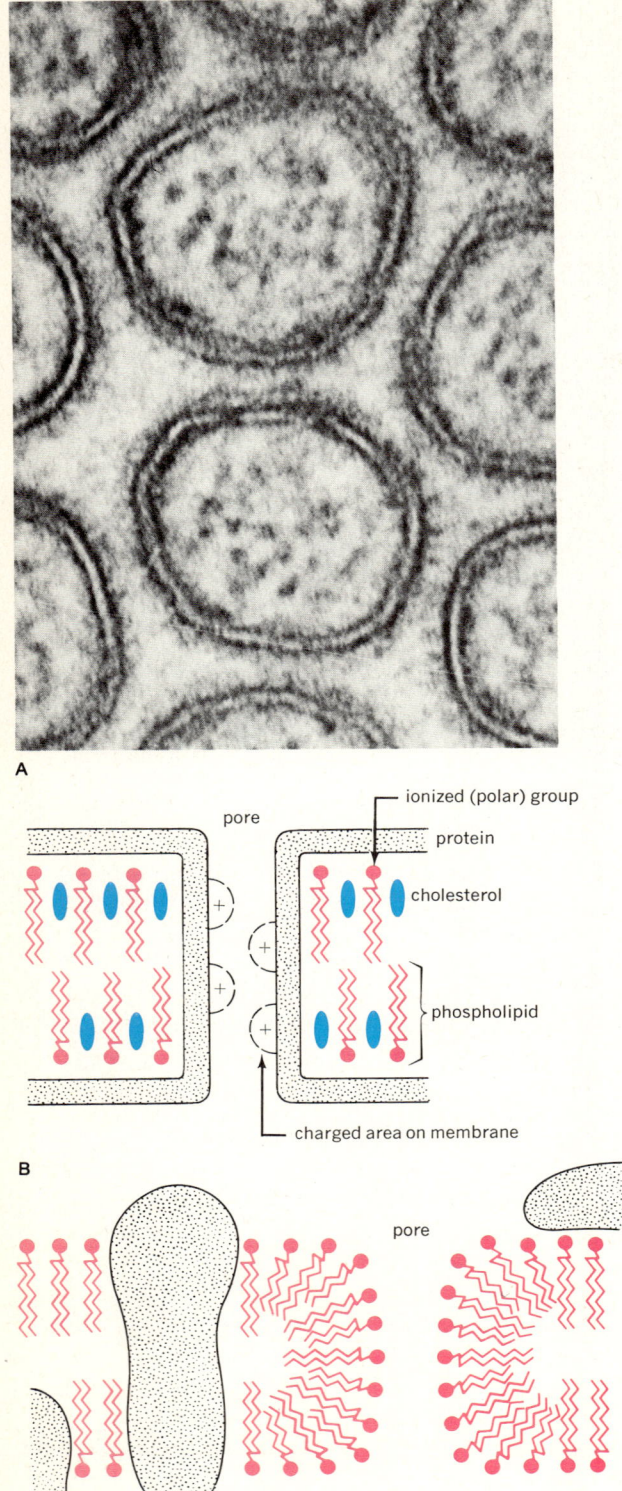

FIGURE 4-4 (A) Cross-sectioned epithelial cells in microvilli reveal a distinct unit membrane structure. ×352,000. The diagrams show two theories of the membrane structure: the "sandwich" model (B) and the newer fluid mosaic model (C). In the fluid mosaic, protein molecules may partially or entirely penetrate the phospholipid bilayer or may lie on its outer or inner surface.

may be seen to penetrate the membrane (Figure 4-4B). More recent theories suggest that the protein layers do not actually extend continuously over the inner and outer surfaces of the cell membrane. Instead, it is now believed that the arrangement of the protein molecules is much less regular than that of the phospholipids and forms a **fluid mosaic** (Figure 4-4C); some proteins lie at various points on the membrane surfaces, others penetrate the membrane to various depths, and still others extend through the entire thickness of the membrane. In simplified form, the cell membrane might thus be visualized according to the latest evidence not as a cheese sandwich, but rather as a slice of raisin bread, where the bread represents the lipid bilayer, and the raisins the proteins.

The outer surface of the cell membrane contains a number of tiny inpocketings, **pinocytotic vesicles.** These structures function in bringing selected particles into the cell, in a manner that is described in Chapter 6. In other places, the surface of the membrane may be raised into numerous minute fingerlike projections, called **microvilli,** which greatly increase the total surface area exposed to the surrounding medium. The cell membrane may also be modified for attachment to other cells either **overlapping** with a portion of an adjacent cell, or fusing with a portion of the adjacent cell membrane in a **tight junction,** or forming an intercellular bridge of fine filaments through the action of specialized structures called **desmosomes.** Numerous infoldings of the cell membrane are continuous with the endoplasmic reticulum that interlaces the interior of the cell.

The cell membrane is far from a passive "bag," holding in the cell contents. It is **semipermeable:** it permits certain substances to pass into or out of the cell, while barring the way to others. Very small molecules, such as water and oxygen, can diffuse readily through the cell membrane, while fats are soluble in the membrane and are thus enabled to pass through it. Other substances are carried into or out of the cell by active, energy-requiring processes. (These modes of transport of substances through membranes are discussed in greater detail in Chapter 6.)

The cell membrane is a scene of frenetic activity. Enzymes in the protein layers provide active sites for chemical interactions with the cell's environment, and the structural peculiarities of the membrane largely determine the immunological properties of the cell and its responses to drugs, invading microbes, and neighboring body cells.

THE NUCLEUS

The very name of the nucleus implies a strategic or important structure, and this is precisely what the nucleus of the cell is. If the nucleus of a cell is removed by delicate micromanipulation or destroyed with a finely focused laser beam, leaving the rest of the cell intact, that cell is doomed. It may die immediately, or it may go on for awhile, seeming to function normally. But it will not reproduce itself by dividing, and eventually it dies.

Most of the body cells have a single nucleus, which appears under the microscope as a round or oval body, sharply distinguished from the surrounding, clearer cytoplasm (Figure 4-5). (Exceptions are the striated muscle cells, which are generally multinucleated, and mature red blood cells, which lack a nucleus.) The nucleus is surrounded by an envelope consisting of two membranes, each of which is similar in structure to the cell membrane. The nuclear envelope is perforated by numerous circular pores, through which materials can pass into and out of the nucleus, and it appears to be continuous with the endoplasmic reticulum. Like the cell membrane, the nuclear envelope is a site of active interaction with the environment (in this case, the cytoplasm).

The nucleus of each cell contains a complete set of the materials of heredity, the complete DNA blueprints for all of the structures and functions of the whole body. In the nondividing cell, this hereditary material is found in the form of long threads of **chromatin;** in suitably stained cell preparations, it may show up as irregular clumps. As a cell begins to divide, the chromatin strands coil into compact, dense, rodlike particles called **chromosomes.** Each human **somatic** or body cell has a characteristic set of 46 chromosomes, which can be recognized on stained specimens by their typical shapes and grouped into 23 matching pairs. The human **gametes** or **germ cells** (the sperm and ova) contain just one of each pair of chromosomes, with a total set of 23 chromosomes.

Another organelle of the nucleus is the **nucleolus.** This is a tiny, spherical, darkly staining body that consists of about 95 percent protein and 5 percent RNA. A cell nucleus may contain one or more nucleoli. The nucleolus is involved in the synthesis of ribosomal RNA and its packaging with protein to form ribosomes. It may also be involved in the modification of messenger RNA. The nucleolus is generally very large in growing cells, where it is associated with specific regions of certain chromosomes, then disappears temporarily during cell division.

The organelles of the nucleus are suspended in a clear fluid nuclear sap, which is a site of great metabolic activity.

THE CYTOPLASM

A living cell might be thought of as a miniature factory complex, which receives a variety of raw materials and supplies and processes them, some for internal consumption and other products for distribution to customers outside. In these manufacturing processes,

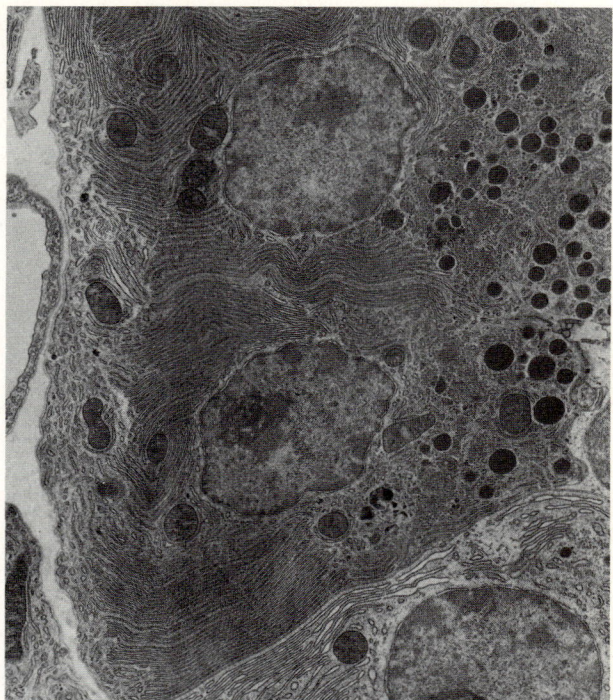

FIGURE 4-5 These pancreatic exocrine cells each have a large, clearly delineated nucleus. ×4200.

energy is consumed, and wastes are produced and disposed of. Deep within the factory complex is the "inner sanctum," the boss's office, where information is received, major decisions are made, and orders are sent out to the employees. In the cell, this "inner sanctum" is the nucleus. Outside in the cytoplasm are numerous organelles, specialized "departments" where specific jobs are done.

The actual assortment of organelles may vary from one type of cell to another—cells specialized for a particular function, such as the secretion of a hormone or the transmission of nerve impulses, may have a heavy accumulation of certain organelles, while lacking another type entirely. However, the characteristic functions of each type of organelle are constant from one cell to another. Ribosomes, for example, function in protein synthesis, whether they are found in nerve cells or in liver cells. Many unanswered questions about the cell organelles still remain, but modern research techniques are gradually revealing more and more of their secrets.

The Endoplasmic Reticulum

Probably more than any other structure in the cell, the endoplasmic reticulum is a symbol of the revolution that the electron microscope brought to the study of life. When only optical microscopes were available to peer into the cell's interior, it was assumed that the cell contents was an amorphous sort of colloidal dispersion, in which various organelles were suspended.

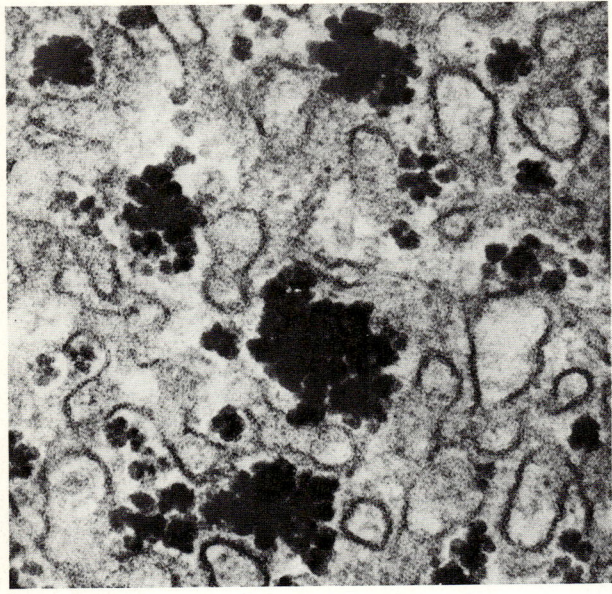

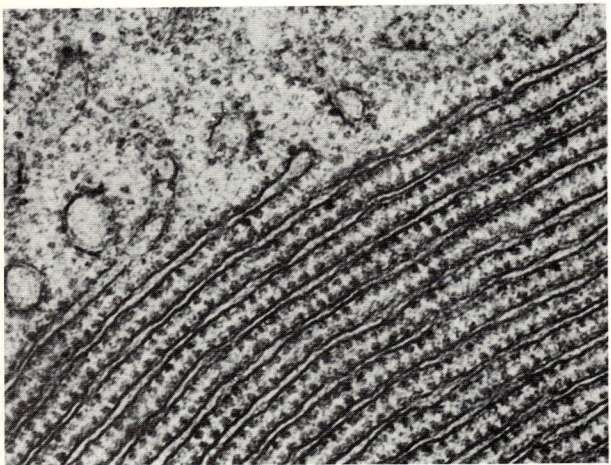

A

B

FIGURE 4-6 Electron micrographs of smooth ER, ×116,200 (A) and rough ER, ×35,000 (B).

But electron microscopy revealed that each living cell is crisscrossed by an intricate system of membranes, which provide continuous channels of communication between the cell's environment and its nucleus and divide the cell into numerous compartments. These membranes, the endoplasmic reticulum or ER, bring order to the cell. Reactions that occur at the surface of the ER and in the organelles associated with it are vital to the life of the cell and of the body as a whole.

The ER is continuous with the cell membrane and has a similar protein-lipid-protein structure. Its lacy networks enclose numerous interconnected membrane-lined spaces, or vesicles. There are two distinct structural types of ER, each with its own characteristic functions. **Smooth ER** appears under the electron microscope as a network of smooth-surfaced tubules (Figure 4-6A). It is especially prominent in such structures as the adrenal cortex, liver, and striated muscle. The smooth ER is thought to function in the synthesis and metabolism of steroids and glycogen.

Rough ER is so called as a result of its microscopic appearance (Figure 4-6B); its surface is studded with granular ribosomes, which are sites of protein synthesis. As might be expected, rough ER is particularly abundant in cells engaged in active protein synthesis. It often takes the form of flattened vesicles, or **cisternae,** which may be stacked together in a parallel array.

The endoplasmic reticulum not only varies from cell to cell, but may also change its appearance in the same cell, depending on the phases of its activity. At times it may be a loose irregular network, at others a highly ordered arrangement of vesicles. Sometimes the ER is greatly distended, taking up a large fraction of the cell volume; at other times it becomes packed with lipid droplets, granules, or protein crystals. The ER is thus a dynamic system, capable of rapid modifications of structure and function, depending on the activities and needs of the cell.

The Ribosomes

The ribosomes are the "translation centers" of the cell. Here the language of the nucleic acids is translated into the proteins of life.

On an electron micrograph, the ribosomes appear as numerous small, dark granules, from 100 to 150 Å in diameter. Studies show that the ribosomes are especially rich in RNA, containing as much as 60 percent of all the RNA in the cell. Many of the ribosomes can be seen on electron micrographs to be associated with the ER and, in ultracentrifugation studies, the bulk of the ribosomes sediment with fragments of ER. But other ribosomes can be seen lying free in the cytoplasm, sometimes linked into chains or clusters called **polysomes** (Figure 4-7). It appears that the ribosomes associated with the ER synthesize proteins for export, while the free-lying ribosomes produce proteins for use within the cell. (In such glands as the pancreas, which produce protein hormones that are exported to other parts of the body, the amounts of rough ER and associated ribosomes are greatly increased.)

The Golgi Apparatus

One of the problems cytologists face in their attempts to unravel the mysteries of the cell is that the techniques they use to study cell structures sometimes change these structures, so that what they view under the microscope does not correspond to reality. Staining techniques, in particular, may introduce so-called artifacts, apparent structures visible on prepared

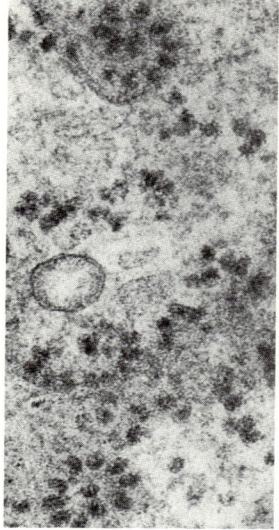

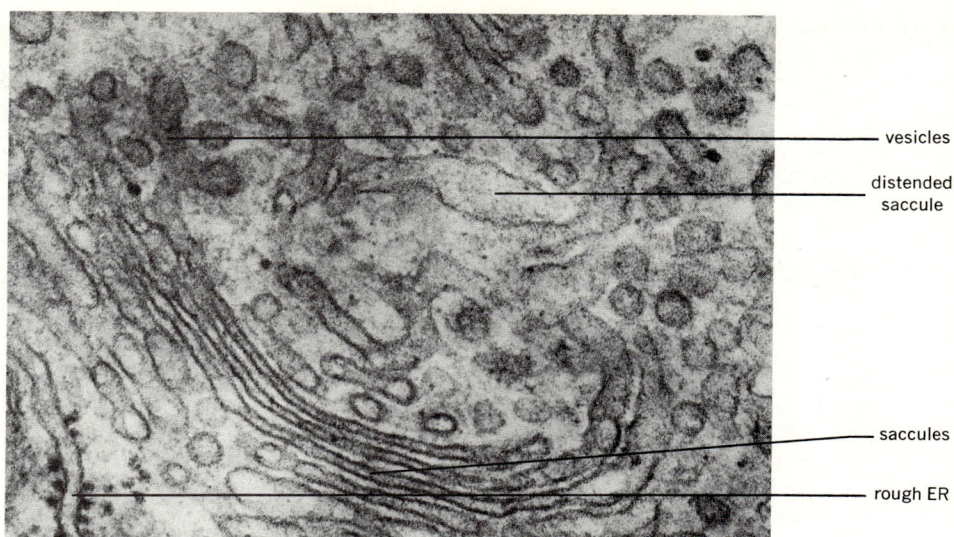

vesicles

distended
saccule

saccules

rough ER

FIGURE 4-7   Polysomes in a rat
liver cell, ×99,200.

FIGURE 4-8   Golgi apparatus in a rat macrophage, ×89,000.

specimens that do not really exist in the living cell. Thus, when the Italian physician Camillo Golgi announced in 1898 that he had discovered a new cell organelle, he unleashed a storm of controversy. Many scientists insisted that the "Golgi bodies" were merely artifacts introduced by Golgi's silver staining technique. The electron microscope ultimately resolved the debate, revealing that the Golgi apparatus does indeed exist.

In electron micrographs, the Golgi apparatus or Golgi complex appears as an array of tightly packed, smooth vesicles, stacked in a parallel or semicircular arrangement (Figure 4-8). It might actually be considered as part of the endoplasmic reticulum, but its organization, location in the cell (close to the nucleus), and functions are characteristic enough to warrant classifying the Golgi apparatus as a distinct cell organelle.

In secretory cells, proteins synthesized at the ribosome "factories" of the rough ER are discharged into the Golgi apparatus, where they may be combined with a carbohydrate component, packaged in microvesicles, and stored until they are secreted. In cells specialized for absorption, such as those of the intestinal lining, the Golgi vesicles become filled with lipids. The Golgi apparatus may also play a key role in enzyme-catalyzed biochemical reactions.

The Mitochondria

Energy shortages have become a continuing problem for the nations of the world. The decades to come will witness intensified searches for new energy sources to replace our dwindling reserves of fossil fuels and power the activities of modern life. The cell, too, has a continuing need for energy, to power its metabolic

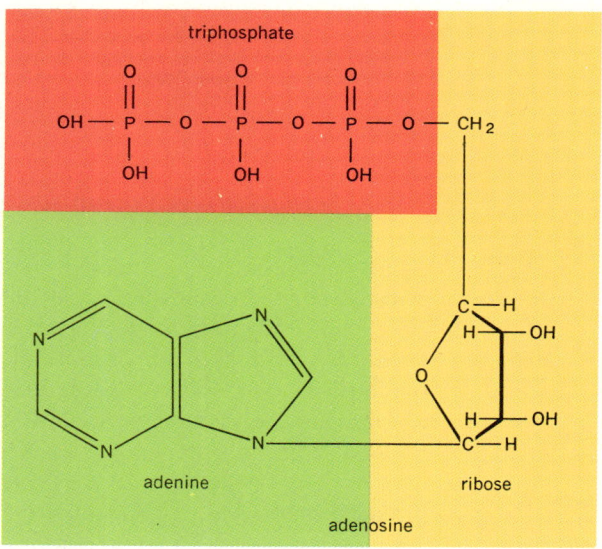

triphosphate

adenine

ribose

adenosine

FIGURE 4-9   ATP, the energy currency of the cell. Energy is stored in phosphate bonds, which can be broken one by one. Note the similarity to the nucleotide units of the nucleic acids.

activities. Energy sources for the human body are the energy-rich chemical bonds of foodstuffs. The breakdown of the complex organic compounds of food, with a controlled release of the energy they contain, is a long and intricate process. The immediate energy needs of the cell are satisfied by an intermediate storage form of energy, which can be quickly broken down to supply small energy packets as they are needed for specific metabolic reactions. This intermediate "energy currency" of the living cell is the chemical compound ATP (adenosine triphosphate), which contains energy-rich phosphate bonds (Figure 4-9). ATP is produced in the reactions of cellular respira-

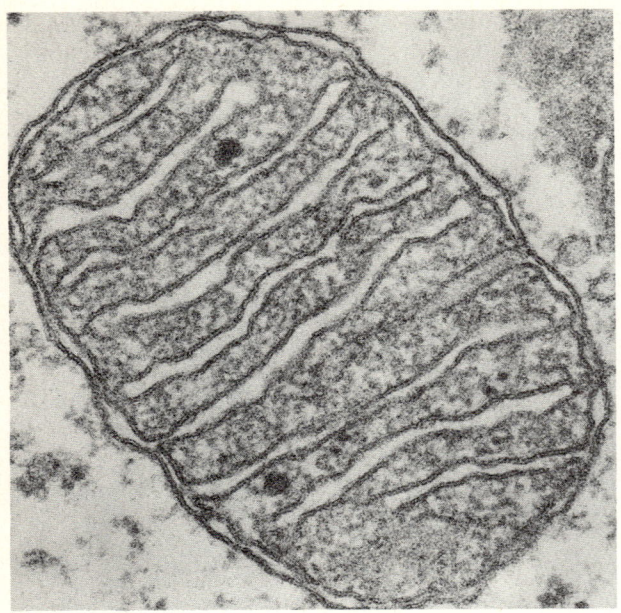

A

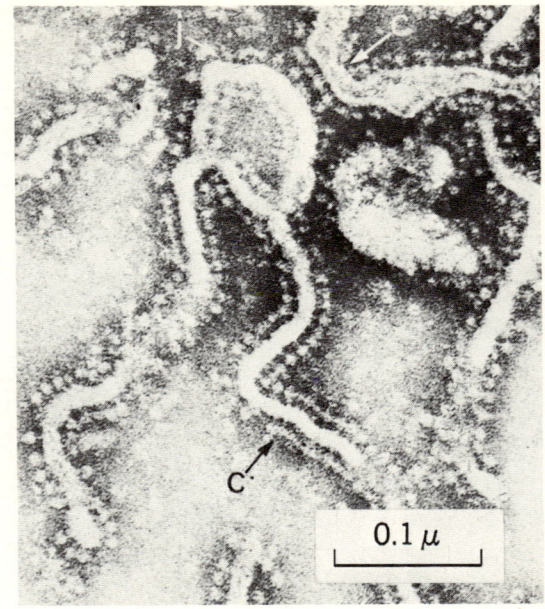

B

FIGURE 4-10 (A) Mitochondrion from a guinea pig pancreas, ×135,000; (B) negatively stained preparation of osmotically swollen mitochondria; (C) diagram of the internal structure of the mitochondrion, showing its two-layered structure and the folded membranes that compartmentalize its interior.

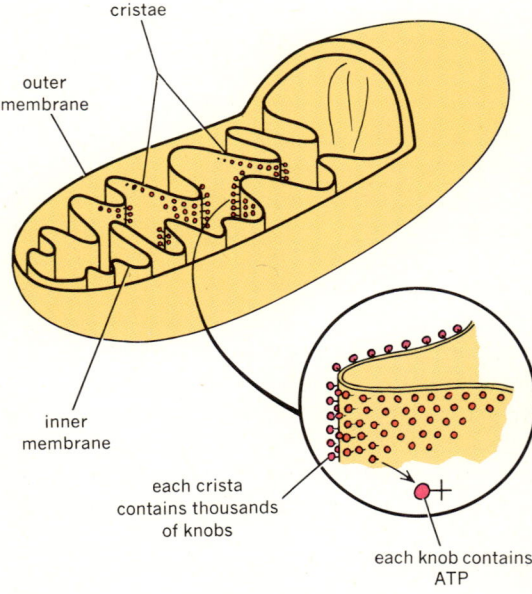

C

tion, which take place in organelles of the cell called mitochondria.

Mitochondria, the "powerhouses of the cell," are typically large, sausage-shaped organelles, about 0.5 micron in diameter and 4 microns long (Figure 4-10A). They are readily visible even under the light microscope, particularly when stained with the vital dye, Janus green. The shape, size, number, and distribution of the mitochondria vary, depending on the kind of the cell and its activity. The average cell contains a few hundred mitochondria, while a liver cell may contain a thousand or more; mature erythrocytes (red blood cells), on the other hand, have no mitochondria at all. Within the cell, mitochondria tend to congregate in areas of the greatest cell activity.

The mitochondrion is surrounded by two membranes, each of which has the typical protein-lipid-protein unit membrane structure. The inner membrane of the mitochondrion is extensively folded, with the folds (**cristae**) projecting like shelves into the interior of the mitochondrion and vastly increasing the surface area of the membrane (Figure 4-10C). In highly magnified electron micrographs, both the outer and the inner membranes of the mitochondria have a pimpled appearance (Figure 4-10B). They are covered with thousands of tiny particles, which are thought to be enzymes.

The interior of the mitochondrion is filled with fluid. Enzymes floating in the fluid and other enzymes associated with the inner membrane catalyze the various reactions of the cell's respiratory cycles; the energy released in these reactions is stored in the form of ATP.

Studies have shown that the mitochondria contain not only RNA, but also DNA, and thus carry blueprints for their own replication and growth, independent of the DNA in the nucleus. Indeed, it has even been suggested that the mitochondria had their origin in independent microbes, which joined forces with early forms of living cells in a mutually beneficial association.

The Lysosomes

The researchers who first discovered the lysosomes nicknamed them "suicide bags." Indeed, these organelles contain more than a dozen powerful hydrolytic enzymes capable of digesting the very substance of the cell. The living cell is protected from this disastrous result by the membrane of the lysosome, which in some way not yet understood holds in the lytic enzymes without itself being digested. At death, the lysosome membranes rupture, their enzymes spill out, and self-digestion or autolysis of the body cells ensues.

Despite their potential danger, the lysosomes perform important functions in the cell. They are the cell's digestive organelles. Their appearance varies greatly according to the phase of their activity. (Indeed, lysosomes are so variable that they cannot be identified by appearance alone, but rather by the presence of lytic enzymes.) Particles taken into the cell, as well as various complex chemical compounds synthesized within the cell, are broken down in the lysosomes into smaller fragments that can pass through the mitochondrial membrane and be utilized in the cell's energy metabolism. Broken-down mitochondria and other bits of cell debris are dispensed with by digestion in lysosomes. In phagocytes, which are white blood cells that engulf microbes and other invading foreign particles, lysosomes are particularly active. The lytic enzymes of ruptured lysosomes are the key factor in the breakdown of individual cells that have died, clearing the way for their replacement.

The lysosomes are currently objects of lively speculation and study, with particular emphasis on agents that strengthen or weaken the lysosome membrane. It has been suggested that the anti-inflammatory effect of the hormones of the adrenal cortex is due to their ability to stabilize the lysosome membrane. Substances that cause the lysosome membrane to rupture, on the other hand, might prove valuable in the treatment of cancer. It is thought that a decrease in the efficiency of the lysosomes may also be an important factor in the effects of aging.

The Centrosome

The cell has a pair of tiny, cylindrical structures called **centrioles,** which can be seen only when the cell is dividing. The two centrioles, which together form the centrosome, are arranged at right angles to one another (Figure 4-11). They are found in the cytoplasm, near the nucleus. During cell division, they act like the conductors of an orchestra, organizing and directing the activities within the cell.

Early in cell division, the centrioles are duplicated. The two pairs of centrioles then seem to start the process of division by moving apart, forming a series

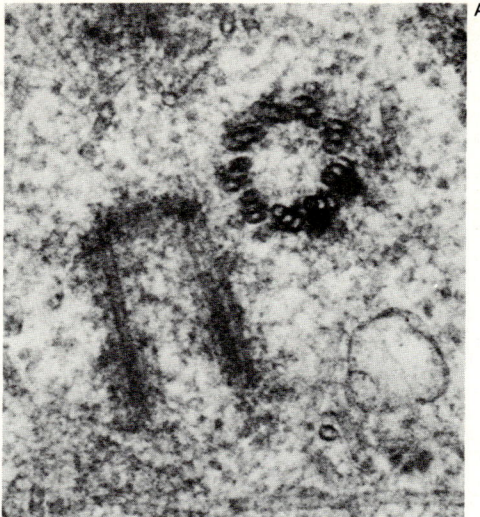

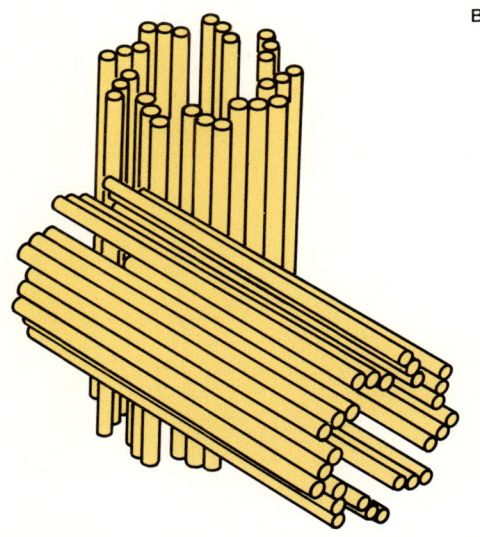

FIGURE 4-11 Centrioles: the electron micrograph shows two centrioles at right angles to each other, one cut transversely, the other parallel to its longitudinal axis. The organization of these cylindrical structures is shown schematically in the diagram.

of extremely thin filaments between them. Ultimately these filaments form a football-shaped structure, the **spindle,** with one pair of centrioles at each end. The filaments, or spindle fibers, then serve as points of attachment for the chromosomes as cell division proceeds.

In addition to the centrioles that participate in cell division, centriole-like structures are sometimes found in nondividing cells, at the base of cilia and flagella.

Fibrils

Thin, threadlike fibrils are a prominent feature of both muscle and nerve cells. In muscle cells, the fibrils are highly contractile and serve as contracting units. In nerve cells, the fibrils function in the conduction of nerve impulses. But to some extent, fibrils are also found in many other types of body cells. They are

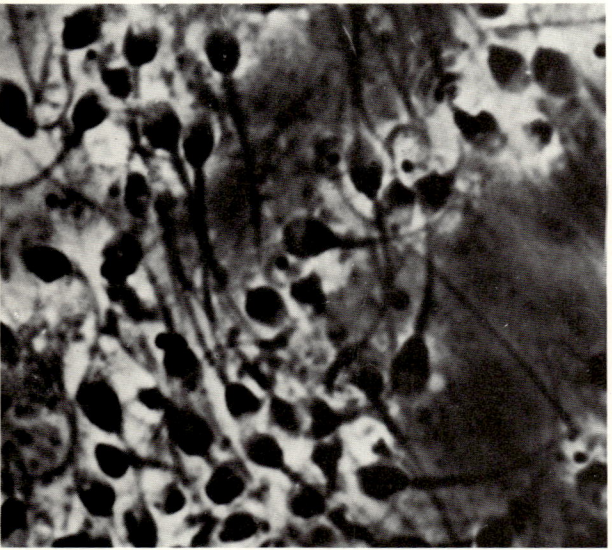

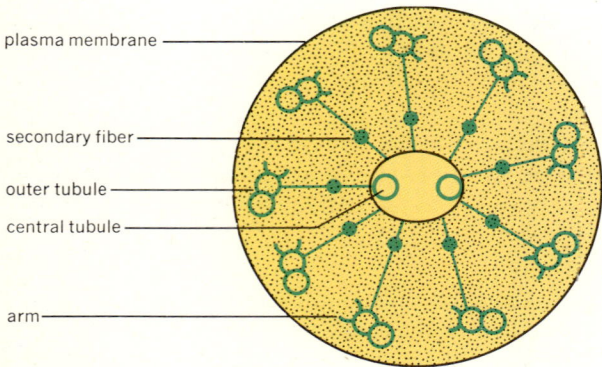

plasma membrane

secondary fiber

outer tubule

central tubule

arm

C

FIGURE 4-12 Ciliated epithelium (A) and human sperm, each equipped with a single flagellum (B). The diagram (C) shows the internal structure of a cilium of flagellum in cross section.

believed to lend support to the cell and aid in its organization.

Cilia

Back in the seventeenth century, the Dutch lensmaker Anton van Leeuwenhoek entertained the scientific community of the time with a series of reports on the microscopic "animalcules" that he found swimming around in drops of water from rain barrels, puddles, and even samples of his own saliva. One of the "animalcules" he described was a slipper-shaped creature, which moved through the water by the motions of numerous tiny "legs." (Later researchers with better microscopes named the hairlike locomotive organelles of one-celled pond organisms cilia.) Leeuwenhoek and his contemporaries never dreamed that some of the cells of their own bodies were equipped with cilia very similar to those of the "animalcules."

Cilia on the surface of the cells lining the respiratory passageways (Figure 4-12A) wave back and forth in a rhythmic motion, setting up a streaming movement in the mucus coating that helps to carry dust particles and other foreign matter upward into the throat, where they can be coughed out or swallowed. Cilia lining the tubes of the female reproductive system help to transport the ovum (the female reproductive cell) to the uterus. The sperm, the male reproductive cells, swim through the fluids in the female reproductive tract, propelled by the lashings of a single long, hairlike "tail," a **flagellum** (Figure 4-12B).

Electron micrographs of both cilia and flagella reveal the same characteristic structure (Figure 4-12C): a hollow extension of the cell membrane, filled with cytoplasm; two single fibrils running through the center of the shaft, and nine groups of fibrils arranged around the periphery. At the base of each cilium or flagellum is a bulblike basal body, anchored in the cytoplasm of the cell. Generally the term cilia is used for numerous short organelles of this type; flagellum refers to one or several long and whiplike structures.

Cytoplasmic Inclusions

The organelles discussed thus far are more or less permanent parts of the cell. They have a characteristic structure and location, and when a cell divides, its organelles are faithfully reproduced and transmitted to the daughter cells as part of their inheritance. But living cells usually contain more transient and variable inclusions as well, which are not replicated when the cell divides. The term cytoplasmic inclusions is used for particles suspended in the cytoplasm. They include a variety of substances, such as pigments, fat droplets, and stored food materials such as glycogen. Some are produced within the cells (e.g., hemoglobin, melanin); others are taken in from the surrounding medium (e.g., carotene, minerals). Some cells contain precursors of enzymes, stored in the form of **zymogen granules,** which become active when they are released from the cell. The types and amounts of cytoplasmic inclusions vary not only according to the type of cell (e.g., adipose cells are almost wholly occupied by their huge fat inclusions), but also during the lifetime of the cell, changing with its changing needs and activities.

SUMMARY

Cells are the structural and functional units of the body.

Cells are microscopic structures, with great diversity of size and shape.

For a given volume, a spherical cell has the smallest surface area.

Variations of cell size and shape are correlated with variations of internal structure and function.

Structural elements of the cell include:

Cell membrane

Cytoplasm

Endoplasmic reticulum

Mitochondria

Lysosomes

Golgi apparatus

Ribosomes

Centrosomes

Fibrils

Cytoplasmic inclusions

Nucleus

Nuclear membrane

Nucleolus

Chromosomes

The cell membrane has a three-layered protein-lipid-protein structure.

Surface features include pinocytotic vesicles, microvilli, and desmosomes.

The cell membrane is semipermeable, permitting the selective passage of substances in and out of the cell.

The nucleus (usually one per cell) controls and coordinates the cell's activities. It contains a complete set of hereditary information, encoded in the DNA of the chromatin.

During cell division, the chromatin strands coil into rodlike chromosomes.

Each human somatic cell has a characteristic set of 46 chromosomes (23 pairs).

Each human gamete (sperm or ova) contains 23 chromosomes (one of each pair).

The nuclear membrane, continuous with the endoplasmic reticulum and perforated by numerous pores, is a site of active interaction with the cytoplasm.

The nucleolus is an organelle of the nucleus associated with RNA synthesis and storage.

The cytoplasm of the cell is highly structured and compartmented and contains numerous organelles, each with specific functions.

The endoplasmic reticulum (ER) is a branching system of membranes that compartmentalizes the cytoplasm, provides channels of communication between cell membrane and nuclear membrane, and with its attached organelles is the site of numerous chemical reactions.

Smooth ER is involved in the synthesis and metabolism of steroids and glycogen.

Rough ER is associated with ribosomes and functions in protein synthesis and the storage of lipids, proteins, and other cell products.

The ribosomes are small granular organelles, containing up to 60 percent of the RNA in the cell. They are the site of assembly of amino acids into proteins.

Ribosomes may be associated with rough ER or may lie free in the cytoplasm.

They are sometimes linked into chains or clusters called polysomes.

The Golgi apparatus is an array of vesicles that functions in the packaging and storage of proteins and lipids.

The mitochondria are large sausage-shaped organelles, which are the site of cellular respiration, in which energy is stored in ATP.

Each mitochondrion is surrounded by two membranes. The inner membrane is extensively folded into cristae.

Mitochondria contain both RNA and DNA and are replicated independently of the nucleus.

The lysosomes are digestive organelles, containing more than a dozen hydrolytic enzymes.

The lysosome membrane protects the living cell from damage by the lytic enzymes. At death, the membrane ruptures, and lysis of the cell results.

The centrosome consists of two cylindrical centrioles, which function in cell division, producing the spindle.

Fibrils are especially prominent in muscle and nerve cells, where they are specialized for contractility and impulse conduction, respectively.

Cilia and flagella are locomotive orgenelles. Ciliated cells in the linings of the respiratory and reproductive tracts set up currents in the mucus coating and help to expel foreign particles and propel the ovum to the uterus. The human sperm swims with a single flagellum.

Transient and variable inclusions in cells include pigments, fat droplets, stored food materials such as glycogen, and zymogen granules.

QUESTIONS FOR REVIEW AND THOUGHT

1 Discuss similarities and differences of body cells. Is there justification for discussions of the "typical cell"?

2 Contrast the fluid mosaic model of the cell membrane with the "sandwich" model initially proposed on the basis of electron micrographs. Are the two models mutually exclusive?

3 A mature red blood cell lacks a nucleus. What activities would you expect it to be unable to perform?

4 What are the functions of the endoplasmic reticulum? What advantages does the ER confer, in comparison with the early concept of the cytoplasm as an amorphous fluid suspension?

5 Discuss the roles of the ribosomes and Golgi apparatus in protein synthesis and processing.

6 What features of the internal structures of the mitochondrion are specially adapted for its function as the "powerhouse" of the cell?

7 Why is the lysosome membrane of crucial importance to the cell?

8 Distinguish between: protoplasm and cytoplasm; nucleus and nucleolus; rough and smooth ER; cilia and flagella; organelles and cytoplasmic inclusions.

TISSUES

5

A single-celled pond organism such as a paramecium is a jack-of-all-trades. This single cell, too small to be seen without a microscope, can move, respond to stimuli, take in food, and reproduce itself. But, as the old saying concludes, such a single cell is master of none of its "trades." It cannot contract as efficiently as a human muscle cell, nor conduct impulses as well as a nerve cell, nor is it as sensitive to light as a cell in the retina of the human eye. The individual cells of humans and other multicellular organisms lack the independence of a paramecium, but each is efficiently specialized for the tasks it performs and benefits from the coordinated activities of all the other cells of the body.

As we saw in Chapter 2, a group of cells of similar structure and function, together with the nonliving intercellular substance that fills any spaces between them, is called a tissue. Despite the great differences among tissues in different organs and parts of the body, there are also numerous basic similarities.

Thus, **histologists** (scientists who study the microscopic structure of tissues) generally classify all the tissues of the body in four major groups: **epithelial, connective, muscular,** and **nervous tissues.** These basic types of tissues differ in the structure of the cells that form them, and also in the amount and kind of intercellular substance. Some tissues, such as the epithelium of the skin, contain very little intercellular material; others, such as bone (a connective tissue), present the appearance of a nonliving matrix, in which occasional cells are embedded. The intercellular substance may be fibrous, or an amorphous gel; it may contain large quantities of mineral deposits, or may be wholly fluid. Various minor differences cause the basic categories of tissues to be subdivided further. For example, squamous and columnar epithelium may be distinguished, and squamous epithelium may be further differentiated as simple or stratified. The basic types of tissues are summarized in Table 5-1.

TABLE 5-1   Types of tissues

TISSUE	EXAMPLES
Epithelial	
Simple squamous	Linings of alveoli, of blood and lymph vessels (endothelium), and of serous membranes of body cavities (mesothelium); in parts of kidneys, testes, and ears
Stratified squamous	Epidermis (skin); linings of mouth, esophagus, and vagina
Transitional	Lining of bladder and urinary tract
Cuboidal	Covering of ovaries, lining of kidney tubules; follicles of glands; pigmented epithelium of retina
Simple columnar	Lining of stomach and intestines, bronchioles, and uterus and uterine tubes
Pseudostratified columnar	Lining of nasal cavity, trachea, bronchi
Stratified columnar	Lining of pharynx and larynx
Connective	
Loose:	
Areolar	Between organs and muscles; supporting blood vessels and nerves
Adipose	Subcutaneous fat; packing around organs, muscles, nerves, and blood vessels; breasts
Reticular	Framework of liver, spleen, lymph nodes, and bone marrow

TISSUE	EXAMPLES
Dense:	
Regular	Tendons, ligaments, aponeuroses
Irregular	Dermis of skin, sheaths, capsules, septa
Cartilage:	
Hyaline	Fetal skeleton; articulating surfaces of bones; tip of nose, trachea, larynx
Fibrous	Discs between vertebrae; symphysis pubis; knee and hip joints
Elastic	External ear; epiglottis
Bone	Skeleton
Dentin	Teeth
Blood, lymph	Fluid in vessels of circulatory system
Muscle	
Striated (skeletal)	Skeletal muscles; muscles of tongue, pharynx; extrinsic eye muscles
Smooth	Muscular walls of digestive tract, urinary tract, and blood vessels; intrinsic eye muscles; arrector muscles of hairs
Cardiac	Muscular wall of heart
Nerve	
Neurons and neuroglia	Brain, spinal cord, nerves

EPITHELIAL TISSUE

When a young child swallows a small object, the worried parents' first thoughts are of operations or stomach probes. But usually the doctor advises them to watch and wait, and in due course the intruding object emerges unchanged from the other end of the child's digestive tract. During all this time, in a sense, the object actually has not been *inside* the child's body. Through its entire trip down the digestive tract, it has been walled off from the body proper by a lining of epithelial tissue.

The category of epithelial tissue includes all the coverings and linings of the body: the outer portion of the skin and the linings of the blood vessels, those of the body cavities, and of the digestive, urinary, and reproductive tracts. The delicate epithelial cells are packed closely, glued together firmly by a viscous substance called hyaluronic acid, and arranged in sheets, which are anchored to a **basement membrane** composed of connective tissue (Figure 5-1). The epithelium itself is avascular—it has no blood-vessel supply of its own. However, the basement membrane is richly supplied with blood vessels, which nourish the overlying epithelial tissues as well.

Epithelial tissues serve a number of important functions in the body. As coverings and linings of surfaces, both of the body and of its structures, epithelium provides **protection** from microbes, from physical injury, from various irritants, and from drying out. In the intestines, the thin epithelial lining provides an avenue for **absorption,** permitting nutrients to pass into the body from the digestive tract. In the kidneys, epithelium acts as a membrane for **filtration** and **dialysis,** permitting the selective passage of certain types of molecules while retaining others. In the lungs, the epithelium lining the tiny air sacs (alveoli) is a site of gas exchange, as carbon dioxide and oxygen pass through the membrane by **diffusion.** In the stomach and certain other organs, specialized glandular epithelial cells produce **secretions,** such as the watery mucus that coats the inner surfaces of the digestive tract.

The varied functions of epithelial tissues are correlated with variations of structure. The protective epithelium of the skin, for example, is **stratified:** it consists of a number of layers of cells. The outermost layers of the skin are actually dead, and contain a horny substance called **keratin.** The cells in the deepest layers continue to divide actively, producing new layers that are gradually displaced outward while the old, dead cells are sloughed off. The epithelium involved in absorption and filtration, on the other hand, is generally **simple** epithelium, consisting of just a single layer of cells. The number of layers of cells present (simple vs. stratified) is one way of classifying epithe-

lial tissues; another commonly used criterion is the shape of the cells at the surface: **squamous** (flattened, **cuboidal** (cube-shaped), and **columnar** (column-shaped) (Figures 5-1 and 5-2).

Squamous Epithelium

Simple squamous epithelium is composed of a single thin layer of flat, scalelike cells, fitted together like a mosaic. This type of tissue is ideally suited for diffusion and filtration. Simple squamous epithelium lines the air sacs of the lungs, the blood and lymph vessels, and the serous membranes of the closed body cavities. It is also found in parts of the testes, kidneys, and ears. The simple squamous epithelium lining the blood and lymph vessels is sometimes referred to as **endothelium;** that covering the surfaces of serous membranes such as the pleura, pericardium, and peritoneum is called **mesothelium.**

Stratified squamous epithelium is also composed of flat cells, but they are arranged in layers. This type of tissue is found both on wet and on dry surfaces of the body. The linings of the mouth, esophagus, and vagina are kept wet by secretions from glands, and the outer layer of cells does not become keratinized. In the skin, the surface of which also consists of stratified squamous epithelium, the outer layer is tough and horny (keratinized), as befits its protective role. Stratified squamous epithelium, with its actively dividing lower layer, has a great capacity for self-repair.

Transitional epithelium is a peculiar type of squamous epithelium, which is found in organs such as the bladder that are periodically stretched and contracted. When the bladder is distended, the cells of its epithelial lining look like typical flat squamous cells. But when the bladder is empty, its epithelial cells are round and plump. This special modification permits the lining to be stretched without tearing apart.

Cuboidal Epithelium

In **simple cuboidal epithelium,** the cells are medium-sized and look rather like a tray of tiny ice cubes. This type of tissue covers the surface of the ovaries and lines the kidney tubules and the follicles of the thyroid gland.

Columnar Epithelium

Columnar epithelium is the most varied of all the epithelial tissues, though all its cells share the characteristic of being taller than they are wide. **Simple columnar epithelium** lines the stomach and intestines, parts of the respiratory tract, and the uterus and uterine tubes. Some of the cells of this tissue type are modified structurally for special functions. **Goblet cells,** for example, take their name from their characteristic shape. They secrete mucus, which covers the surface of the epithelium with a moist, slippery coating. In

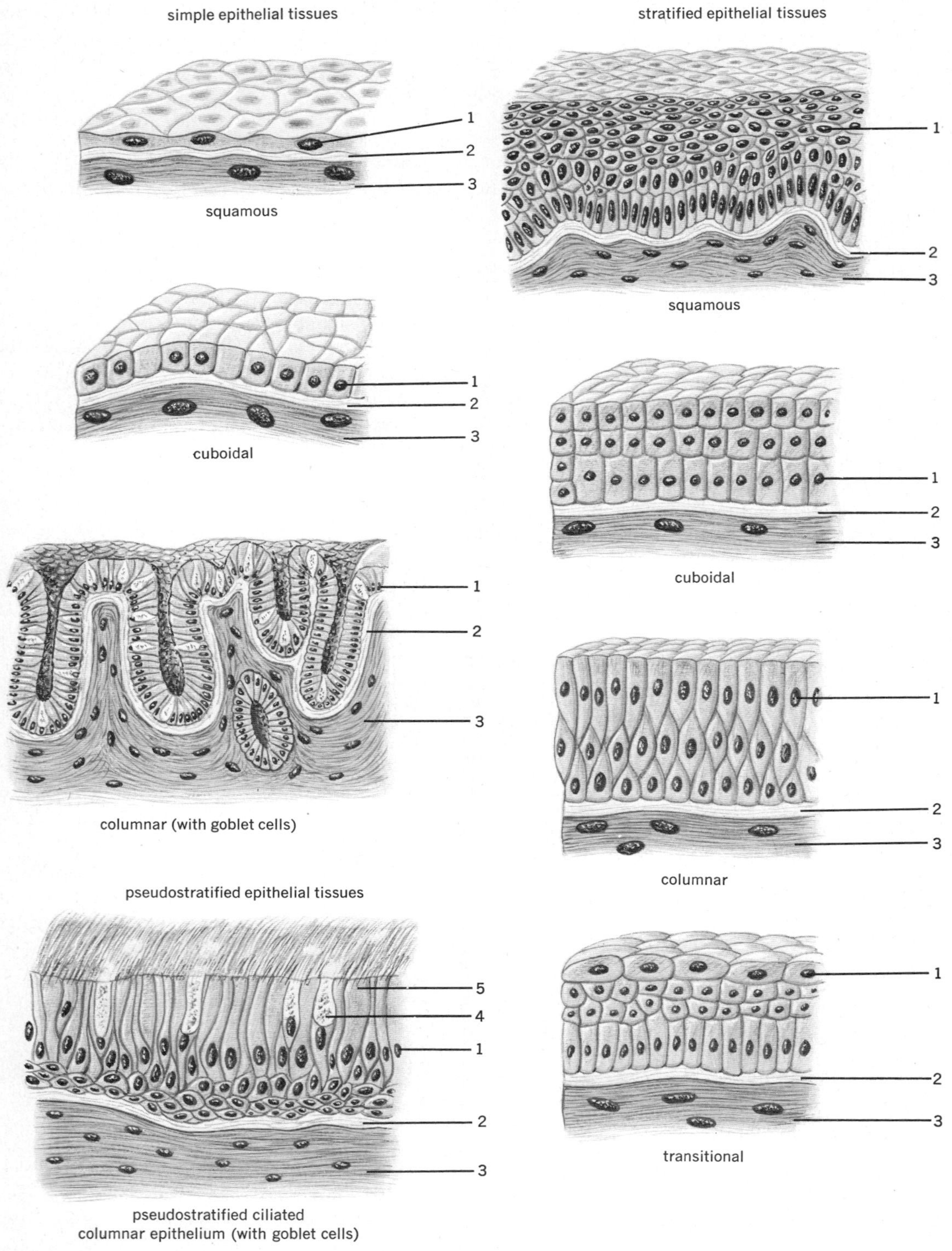

simple epithelial tissues

squamous

cuboidal

columnar (with goblet cells)

pseudostratified epithelial tissues

pseudostratified ciliated
columnar epithelium (with goblet cells)

stratified epithelial tissues

squamous

cuboidal

columnar

transitional

FIGURE 5-1 **Types of epithelial tissue. Simple epithelium contains a single layer of epithelial cells. Stratified epithelium consists of two or more layers of cells. Pseudostratified epithelium may appear to consist of more than one layer of cells in places, but it is not a true stratified tissue. Transitional epithelium resembles stratified squamous epithelium, but the superficial cells are larger and more rounded.**
(1) nucleus; (2) basement membrane; (3) connective tissue layer; (4) goblet cell; (5) ciliated cell.

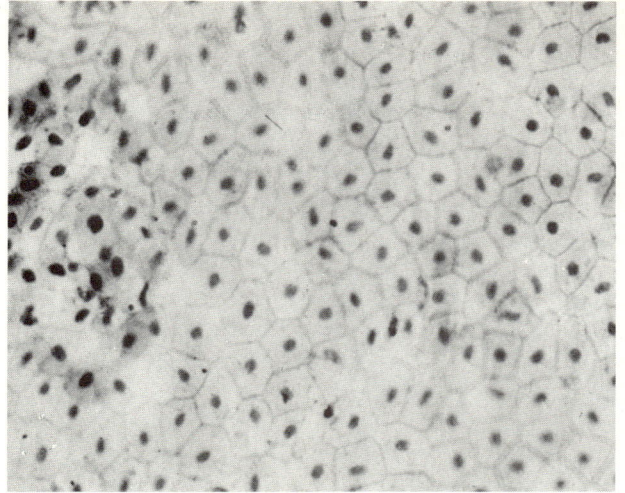

A

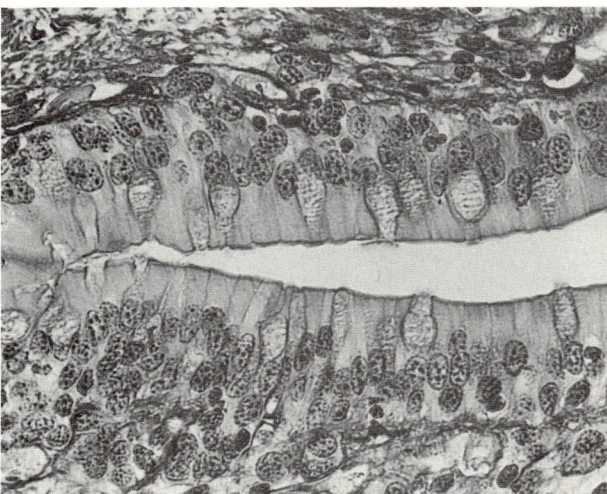

B

C

FIGURE 5-2 Micrographs of some representative types of epithelium: simple squamous (A); simple cuboidal (B); columnar with goblet cells (C). (Courtesy Carolina Biological Supply Company.)

the intestines, many of the epithelial cells are specially modified for efficient absorption: their surface is covered with minute projections called **villi,** which are in turn covered with even smaller **microvilli**—as many as 3000 on one cell. Together they produce an enormous increase in effective surface area. The columnar epithelial cells lining the respiratory tract and uterine tubes are **ciliated:** the surface of each cell is studded with about 270 cilia, which stick out like microscopic eyelashes. The cilia beat rhythmically, bending over and straightening up again in unison. The rhythm of their beating is closely coordinated and spreads in waves over the surface of the epithelium. The movement of the cilia sets up currents in the slimy mucus that covers the lining membrane. In the passages of the respiratory tract, the movements of the cilia help to bring up inhaled particles to where they can be expelled from the body by a cough or sneeze; this ciliary action is temporarily paralyzed by contact with cigarette smoke, thwarting the clearing of the respiratory passages. In the uterine tubes, the currents generated by the ciliated epithelium help to propel the ovum along.

In some columnar epithelium, particularly the ciliated varieties, some of the cells in contact with the basement membrane do not reach the surface of the tissue, although most do. In some tissue sections, such epithelium may appear to be stratified, although this is not actually the case. This type of epithelium is referred to as **pseudostratified columnar epithelium.**

Glandular Epithelium

The term epithelium normally calls to mind a covering or a lining. But in some parts of the body, epithelial cells specialized for secretion have invaded the underlying connective tissue to form accumulations called **glands.**

Exocrine glands retain a connection to the surface, through a tubelike duct. Clusters of cells at the ends of the ducts produce the secretions, which are emptied out to the surface through the ducts. The sebaceous glands of the skin, the apocrine sweat glands, and the mammary glands are all examples of exocrine glands. The salivary glands and the pancreatic glands that produce digestive juices are also exocrine glands.

Endocrine glands are like islands scattered through the body: during the process of development, they lost their connection with the epithelial surface entirely. Their secretions (hormones) pass out into the bloodstream or lymph and are carried to the appropriate target site through the waterways of the body. The endocrine glands, which are discussed in detail in Chapter 32, form a finely coordinated system, with the secretions of one gland profoundly influencing and controlling the activities of others.

CONNECTIVE TISSUE

If a person were somehow stripped of all but connective tissue, he would be eerily similar to his former self. The epithelial covering would be gone, it is true; so would the muscles that move the parts of the body and help to support them through numerous postural adjustments. Gone would be the nerves that control thoughts and movements. But the basic body shape

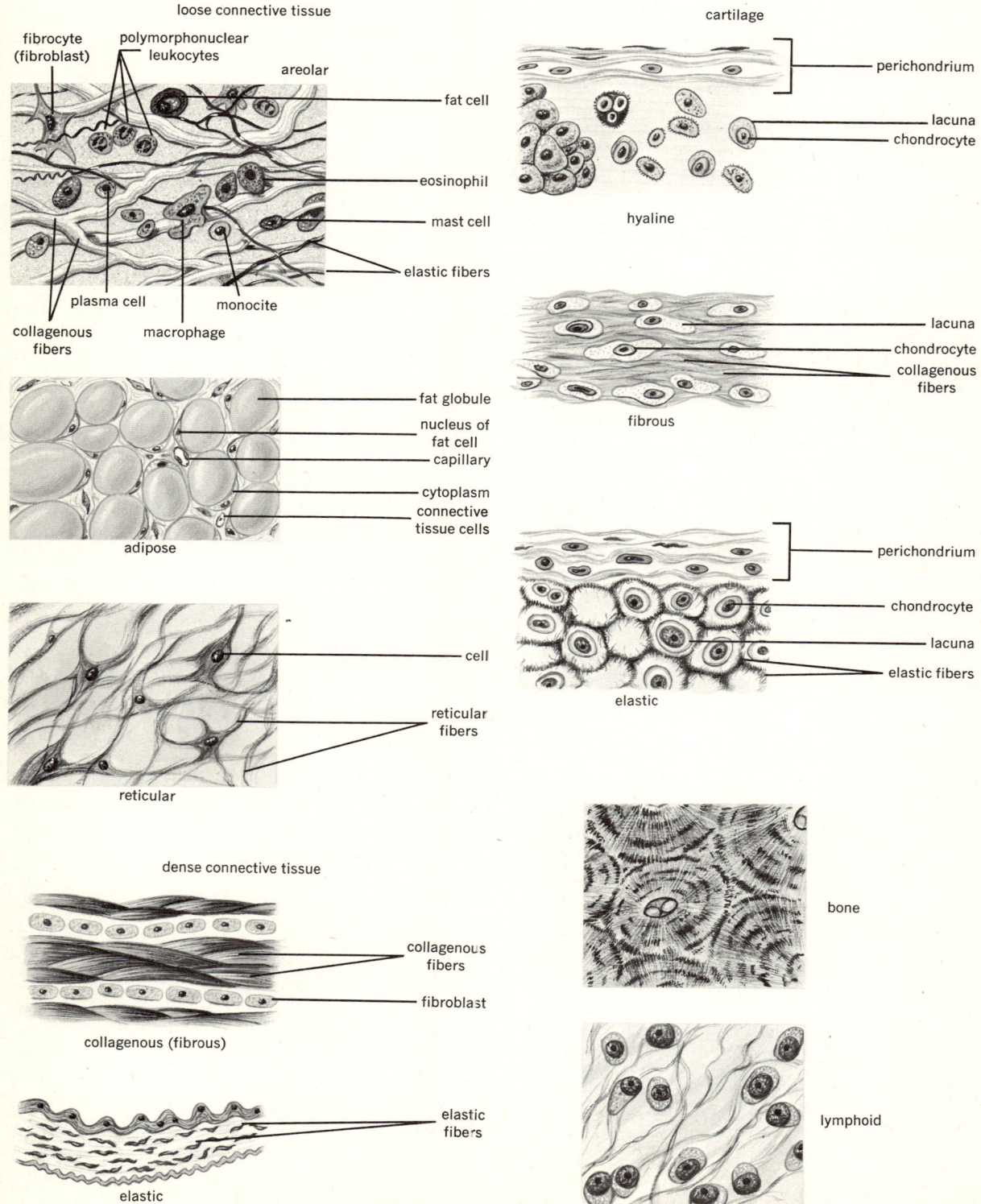

FIGURE 5-3 Types of connective tissue differ in constituent cells and ground substance, in density, and in regularity of fiber orientation.

would remain, little changed. For connective tissue is the most widespread and abundant tissue in the body.

Connective tissue is not only the most abundant of all the tissue types, but also the most varied (Figure 5-3). It includes sturdy bones and thin, delicate webs, tough tendons and soft fatty masses, and even a fluid suspension, blood. Varied as they are, connective tissues share an important feature in common: unlike epithelial tissues, which are composed mainly of cells, with very little intercellular material, connective tissues contain considerably more intercellular material (matrix) than cells. Indeed, it is the matrix rather than the cells that gives the various types of connective tissues their distinguishing characteristics.

The connective tissue matrix generally consists of **fibers,** embedded in an amorphous **ground substance,** the state of which varies from a fluid to a semisolid gel. Three types of fibers are found in connective tissues: white **collagenous fibers,** composed of the protein collagen; yellow **elastic fibers,** long threads that contain a protein elastin, which permits them to stretch to one and a half times their original length and snap back to their former size like a rubber band; and **reticular fibers,** thin, short threads that branch and join to form a delicate network, or reticulum. Collagenous fibers are the most common; reticular fibers form a meshlike **stroma** or framework that supports the functional cells of glands. Both the ground substance and the fibers are produced by the connective tissue cells.

The cells of connective tissues are also quite varied, but most of them fall into two main categories: **fibroblasts** and **macrophages** (Figure 5-4). The fibroblasts, as might be guessed from their name, produce the connective tissue fibers. They have a characteristic star shape, with a flattened nucleus. (In dense connective tissue, such as tendons, the cells are so compressed that only their small, dark nuclei are visible.) Macrophages, or **histiocytes,** are the body's "clean-up squad." They may have a stellate shape like the fibroblasts, or may be oval or round; but all can act as phagocytes, engulfing particles of foreign matter and cell debris. They swarm in loose connective tissue, where they may be as numerous as the fibroblasts, but they are usually absent in dense connective tissue.

Other cells that may be present in loose connective tissue include **fat cells,** which may be so swollen with stored fat that they look like a signet ring under the microscope; various **white blood cells; pigment cells,** mainly those containing the dark pigment melanin; **mast cells,** which can release active substances such as heparin, histamine, and serotonin, which may have profound effects on surrounding tissues; and **plasma cells,** a key link in the body's antibody production system.

The functions of connective tissues are just as varied as their structures. Indeed, the implications of their name may be somewhat misleading. Although they do **connect** (e.g., muscles to bones and bones to other bones), connective tissues also **support** the body and its structures; serve as depots for **fat storage;** produce blood cells, thus serving a **hemopoietic** function; play a key role in the body's **defense** mechanisms; and help to **nourish** the tissues they support, surround, or permeate.

Though epithelium is classified according to the

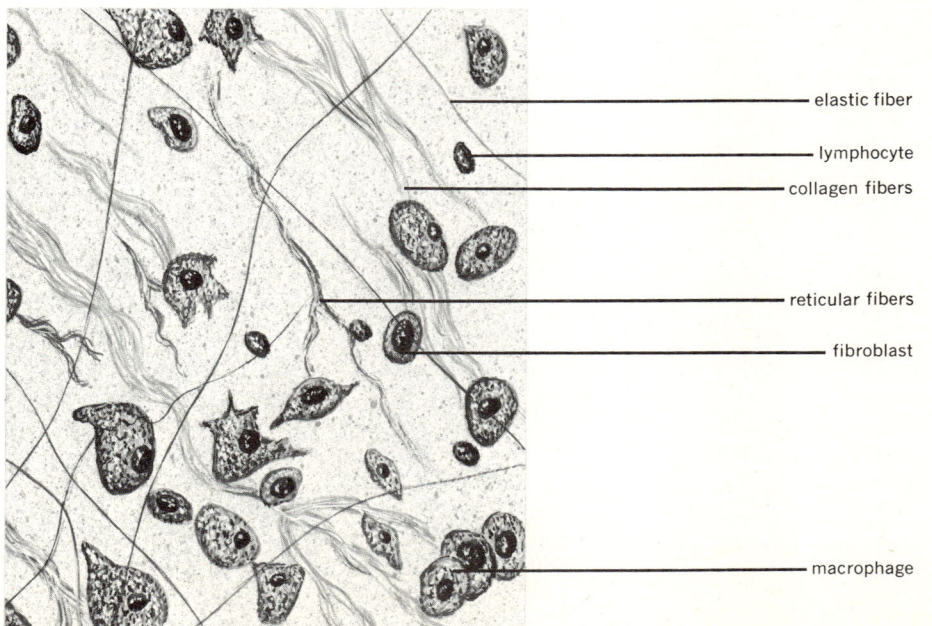

FIGURE 5-4 Loose areolar connective tissue, showing fibroblasts, macrophages, and a variety of fibers.

elastic fiber

lymphocyte

collagen fibers

reticular fibers

fibroblast

macrophage

types and arrangement of cells it contains, histologists have found it more convenient to classify connective tissue mainly according to the nature of the matrix and the fibers that it contains. The following main types of connective tissue are distinguished (see Figure 5-3): loose connective tissue; dense connective tissue; compact connective tissue, including bone, cartilage, and the dentin of teeth; and fluid tissue (blood and lymph).

Loose Connective Tissue

Loose connective tissue forms the "internal environment" of the body. It is one of the most ubiquitous of all tissues. Distributed throughout the body—as packing around and between organs and as basement membrane under sheets of epithelial tissues—it acts as a sort of elastic glue, holding adjacent structures together. (Another name for this tissue, **areolar tissue,** literally means "like a small space" and refers to the bubbles that appear when loose connective tissue is pulled apart during dissections.)

The semifluid matrix of loose connective tissue, called **tissue fluid,** contains about 11 percent of all the body fluid. It brings nourishment to the body cells, delivers their metabolic products to the blood and lymph, and serves as a temporary storage place for water, salts, and glucose. Suspended in the tissue fluid are loosely interwoven networks of collagenous and elastic fibers, which make loose connective tissue somewhat elastic and highly resistant to tearing. A variety of cells are also found here (Figure 5-5A): fibroblasts, which produce both the fibers and the ground substance, predominate; macrophages are often a close second. Plasma cells and mast cells are commonly found in loose connective tissue, while various types of white blood cells from the blood and lymph are transient residents, moving freely through the tissues.

Adipose tissue (Figure 5-5B), a specialized variety of loose connective tissue, is one of the most maligned tissues in the body. Many millions of dollars are spent each year on reducing pills, exercise devices, and diet books, in the hope of eliminating deposits of fat in the adipose tissues of the body. Indeed, excess adipose tissue can be both unsightly and unhealthy, putting a strain on the heart and increasing the chances of an early death. But a certain amount of adipose tissue is essential to a healthy body. It acts as a firm but resilient packing around and between organs, bundles of muscle fibers, nerves, and blood vessels, protecting them from injury. Adipose tissue also acts as a heat insulator, protecting the body from excessive heat loss or extreme temperature rise, and as an emergency reserve of food materials, including fat-soluble vitamins. (Unfortunately, the body's adipose tissue can also retain environmental pollutants, for example,

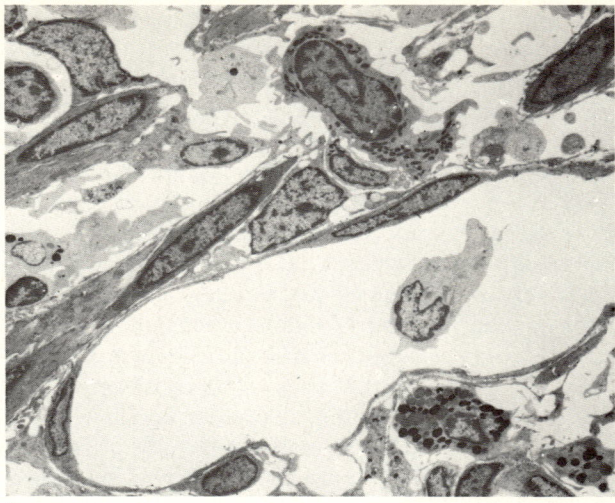

A

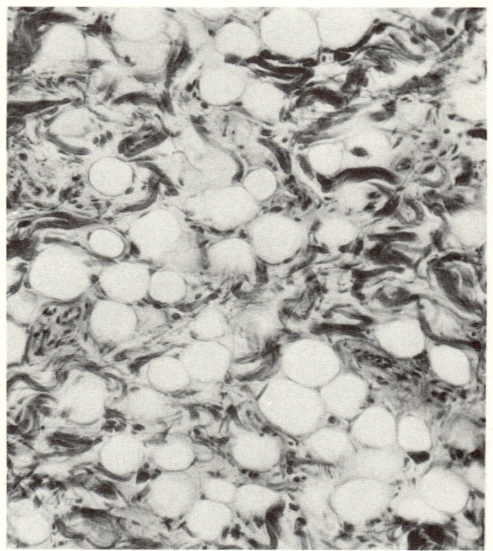

B

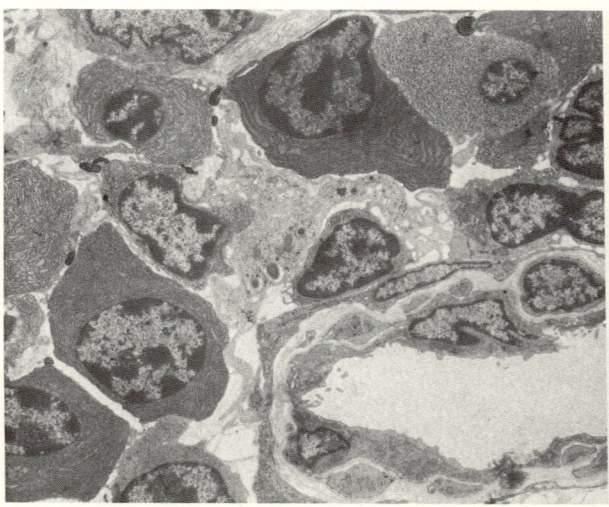

C

FIGURE 5-5 Micrographs of loose connective tissue: areolar (A), adipose (B), and reticular (C).

pesticide residues and industrial by-products such as PCB's.) It is distributed through the body in characteristic fat depots (Figure 5-6). Adipose tissue differs from ordinary loose connective tissue in that it contains mainly fat cells, and fewer fibroblasts, macrophages, and mast cells.

Reticular tissue (Figure 5-5C) is still another specialized type of loose connective tissue, permeated by a network of finely branching fibers. Reticular tissue forms the framework of the liver, spleen, lymph nodes, and bone marrow. It produces lymphocytes and macrophages and plays an important role in the body's system of defense against bacteria. (The connective tissue macrophages, reticuloendothelial cells in the linings of tiny blood vessels in the liver, spleen, and bone marrow and in the lining of lymph channels in the lymph nodes, along with microglia of the central nervous system, form the **reticuloendothelial system,** or RES. The role of the RES in the body's defenses is discussed in detail in Chapter 37.)

Dense Connective Tissue

According to Greek myths, the mother of the great hero Achilles gained invulnerability for her son by dipping him into the river Styx while he was an infant. But unfortunately, she held him by the heel as she lowered him into the water, and the one portion of his body that was untouched by the water was the "Achilles heel" that ultimately sustained a fatal blow many years later. Today this myth is commemorated in the name of the Achilles tendon, a powerful cord at

the back of the heel that attaches the triceps surae muscle to the calcaneus (heel bone). Damage to this tendon, while not fatal, can be crippling.

Tendons are one type of dense connective tissue. They contain mainly collagenous fibers, arranged in parallel bundles, which impart great tensile strength to the tissue. This strength is needed, for tendons anchor muscles to bones and must withstand the tremendous forces generated by muscle contraction.

Ligaments are also connective-tissue cords; they bind bones to other bones. In this case, a little stretchability is a desirable feature—in ligaments, unlike tendons, bundles of elastic fibers predominate.

Aponeuroses are flat sheets of white fibrous tissue that anchor muscles to other structures. Structurally, they are rather like flattened tendons, with parallel fiber bundles gathered in sheets, arranged so that the fibers in one sheet run crosswise to those of the sheet above or below.

Tendons, ligaments, and aponeuroses are examples of regular fibrous tissue (Figure 5-7A). There are also dense fibrous tissues in which the fibers are arranged irregularly, running in different directions or in different planes. **Dense irregular fibrous tissue** (Figure 5-7B) is a sort of condensed areolar tissue, with compact layers of collagen and elastic fibers. It is found in the dermis of the skin, in the sheaths around muscles and nerves, in capsules around organs, and in septa that divide some organs into lobes. An example of such connective tissue can be seen when a cut or burn produces a temporary breach in the skin. Under the

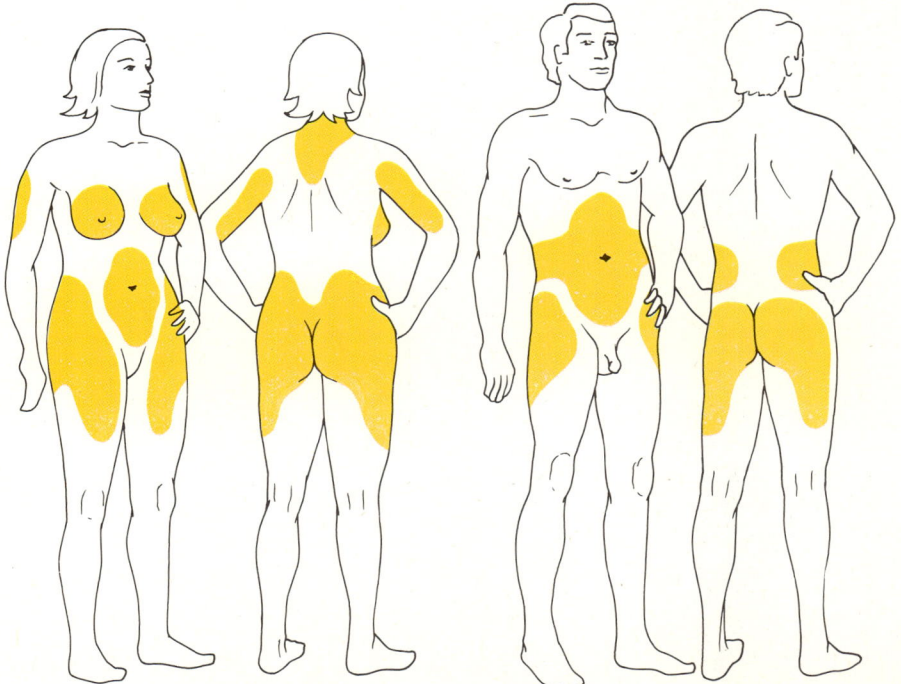

FIGURE 5-6 Stored lipids are deposited in characteristic subcutaneous fat depots.

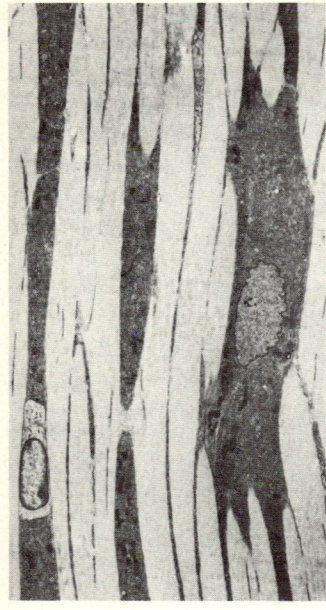 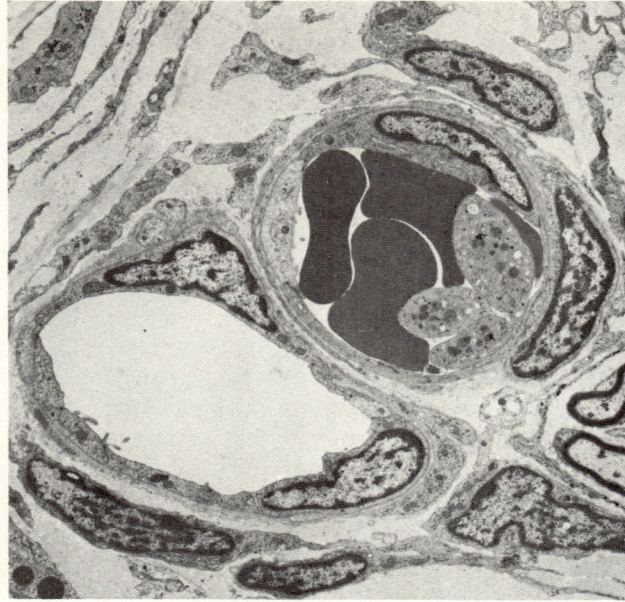

A   B

FIGURE 5-7 Regular fibrous tissue from a tendon (A) and subepithelial connective tissue (B), intermediate between loose and dense connective tissue. This tissue is rich in cells, and irregular fibers completely fill the intercellular spaces.

protective scab that forms over the wound, cells from the surrounding tissues migrate in and proliferate, filling the damaged area with new skin. But after the scab falls off, it can be seen that the new tissue—scar tissue—has a different appearance from the surrounding skin. It lacks the characteristic pigments, hairs, and other typical features. For this new tissue is not epithelium; the cells that formed it migrated from the underlying layers of connective tissue. (In time, if the scar is not too extensive, epithelial cells may gradually invade the fibrous connective tissue and replace it with more normal-appearing skin.)

Cartilage

New parents are often alarmed to discover that their baby's head is noticeably lopsided. The condition usually corrects itself rapidly, and the infant's head assumes more symmetrical proportions. The distortion of an infant's skull under the powerful compressive forces experienced during the birth process and its subsequent reshaping are vivid results of the fact that during the early stages of life the human skeleton is actually composed of flexible cartilage, which is gradually replaced by rigid bone.

Cartilage is a tough but resilient, pliable form of compact connective tissue. Like other types of connective tissue, cartilage contains more intercellular material than cells. The matrix of cartilage consists of a firm gel, in which collagenous fibers are embedded. Cartilage is an avascular tissue, and thus its cells **(chondrocytes)** must be nourished by the diffusion of nutrients from adjoining tissues. Cartilage is surrounded by a fibrous membrane, the **perichondrium,**

consisting of an outer layer of collagenous fibers and an inner vascular layer containing cells called **chondroblasts.** This inner layer not only nourishes the cartilage, but gives rise to new chondrocytes for the growth and repair of the cartilage.

Three main types of cartilage are distinguished according to the types of fibers embedded in the matrix (Figure 5-8). In **hyaline cartilage,** the collagenous fibers are so fine that they cannot be seen with the ordinary microscope. As a result, the cartilage has a clear, glassy appearance. ("Hyaline" is derived from a Greek root meaning "glass.") Hyaline cartilage is the most common type. It makes up the entire skeleton in the early fetus, and is gradually replaced by bone. In the adult, vestiges of the hyaline cartilage remain in a thin layer covering all the articulating surfaces of bones. There it functions to cushion the bones from jolts. Hyaline cartilage also forms the framework of the nose and respiratory passageways.

Fibrous cartilage contains a large number of collagenous bundles embedded in its matrix, and very few cells, arranged in rows between the bundles. The fibrous bundles give it the greatest tensile strength of all the types of cartilage. The cushioning discs of fibrous cartilage between the vertebrae and the internal cartilages of the knee joints are enabled by their structure to stand up under the continuous heavy pressure to which they are subjected. (Actually, the intervertebral discs, which make up about a fourth of the total length of the vertebral column, are somewhat compacted by the pressures of a day of sitting, standing, and walking, and return to their original state after a night's rest. As a result, you are slightly

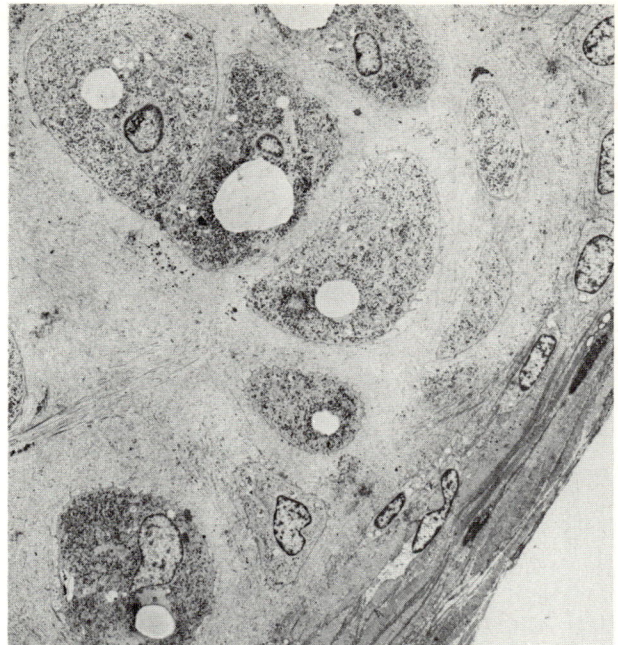

A

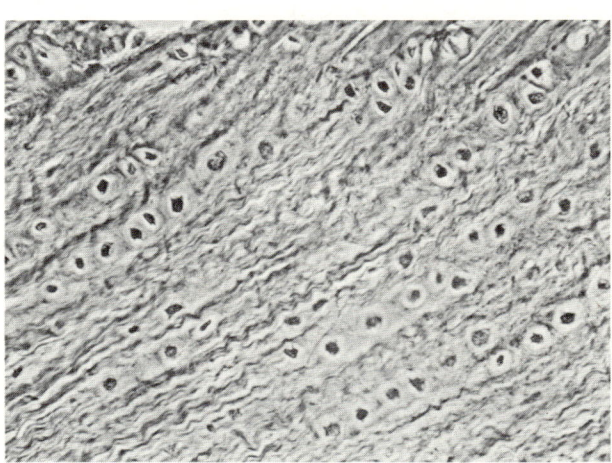

B

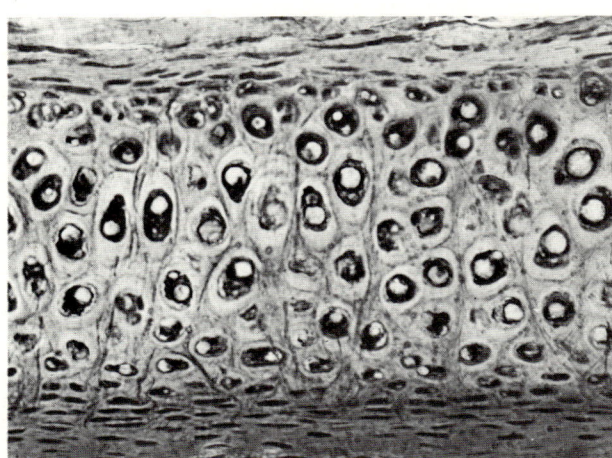

C

FIGURE 5-8 Hyaline (A), fibrous (B), and elastic (C) cartilage.

FIGURE 5-9 Micrograph of a bone cross-section (human femur, ×800), showing a Haversian system.

taller in the morning than you are in the evening. Aging brings a gradual flattening of the discs that is not reversible.)

Elastic cartilage contains elastic fibers in addition to the collagenous fibers, and consequently is more resilient than either hyaline or fibrous cartilage. It is found in structures that are subjected to continual bending, such as parts of the external ear and epiglottis.

Bone

Bone is commonly thought of as a solid and inert substance. This view is not accurate. Bone is a living tissue. Its structure is rigid, yet it provides for a rich vascular supply (bone bleeds when it is cut) and is the site of considerable metabolic activity.

The hardness and rigidity of bone results from deposits of inorganic **calcium salts.** Numerous collagenous fibers, embedded in this calcified matrix, help to maintain the structure. If a long bone is placed in a weak acid, the calcium salts are dissolved away. The bone retains its basic shape, but it becomes flexible—it can be bent, twisted, and even tied in a knot.

Under a microscope, bone (which histologists refer to as **osseous tissue**) has a highly characteristic structure (Figure 5-9). The calcified matrix is arranged in concentric cylindrical layers, called lamellae, enclosing a central channel, the **Haversian canal,** along which small blood vessels and lymphatics run. The spider-shaped bone cells **(osteocytes)** are found in small spaces called **lacunae,** between the lamellae. Numerous microscopic canals **(canaliculi)** radiate out from the Haversian canal, providing channels through which nourishment can reach all the bone cells. (No osteocyte is more than a tenth of a millimeter from a Haversian canal.) Each unit of lamellae, together with the canal they enclose, constitutes a **Haversian system.**

Two types of bone are distinguished on the basis of the arrangement of the lamellae: compact or dense and cancellous or spongy. In **compact bone,** adjacent Haversian systems are fitted tightly together, with any intervening spaces filled in with interstitial lamellae. **Cancellous bone** has a much lighter structure, with numerous open spaces interspersed by thin bony struts. In the long bones of the body, the shaft is formed by cancellous bone, surrounded by a dense outer layer of compact bone.

Despite their large inorganic component, bones are far from static. Inactivity can cause bones of the body to atrophy, while continual stress on a particular bone can result in hypertrophy (an increase in the bone mass). Cavities within the bones contain the bone marrow; in certain bones the marrow is a site of active blood cell production.

The **dentin** of teeth is structurally very similar to bone, although it is harder and denser than bone. Before the teeth erupt from the gums, epithelial cells secrete an even harder coating of enamel onto the dentin framework.

Blood

When we think of a tissue, we generally tend to visualize a solid mass. Yet blood and lymph also satisfy the criteria of a tissue: groups of cells, together with their intercellular material, associated in a common function or functions. In this case the matrix is entirely fluid, without suspended fibers. (Blood still retains the potential for forming fibers, however, as can be seen whenever a clot is formed.) Histologists have various reasons for classifying blood and lymph as connective tissues: the blood cells share a common embryological origin with other connective tissue cells; the pattern of cells suspended in a large proportion of matrix is similar to that of other connective tissues; and, in a sense, blood and lymph connect all the regions of the body.

The fluid matrix of blood is called **plasma.** The cells or **corpuscles** suspended in it include the **erythrocytes** (red blood cells) and a variety of **leukocytes** (white blood cells), along with the **platelets,** not-quite-cells that are produced by fragmentation of leukocytes (Figure 5-10). The red blood cells contain the red pigment **hemoglobin,** which is capable of combining reversibly with dissolved gases and plays a key role in the oxygen- and carbon dioxide-carrying function of the red cells. The red blood cells are unique in that, in their mature form, they do not contain a nucleus. The less numerous white blood cells, active in the body's defense system, are amorphous cells that resemble the pond-dwelling amebas and are capable of the same sort of slithering, oozing motion.

Unlike the other tissues of the body, the blood is in constant motion. However, this movement through the body occurs within fixed channels—the blood vessels.

Lymph is mostly water. It contains some leukocytes but no erythrocytes. It is formed by the continual draining of fluid from the intercellular spaces of the cells into the lymph vessels, which ultimately empty into the bloodstream via two veins at the base of the neck.

MUSCLE TISSUE

The amount of muscle tissue found in even the "weakest" of us is surprising: close to half of the body mass is muscle.

Muscle tissue consists of elongated cells, often referred to as muscle fibers, and a small amount of intercellular substance, which attaches the cells to the framework of connective tissue in which they are embedded. Muscle cells are specialists: they have perfected contractility, a property shared to some extent by all cells, to an unparalleled degree. The contractions of muscle cells move body structures, and the forces they can exert are phenomenal: the human calf muscle, for example, can withstand forces exceeding a ton.

The number of muscle cells remains unchanged

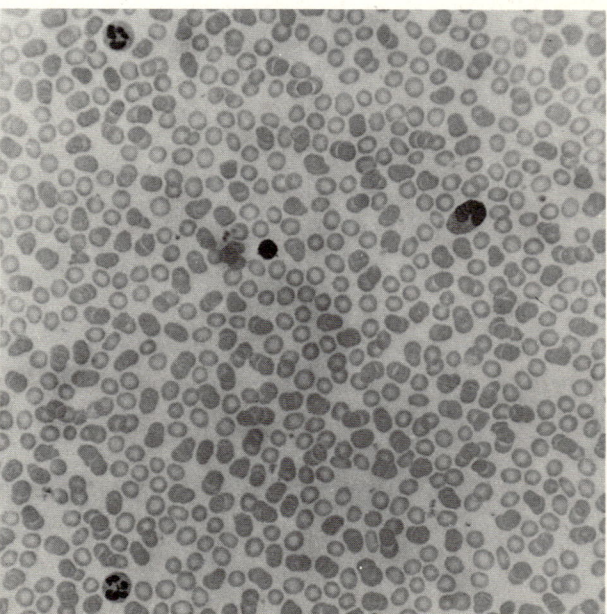

FIGURE 5-10 Blood smear, showing erythrocytes, leukocytes, and platelets.

from birth onward—no new muscle cells are added. How, then, can a "98 pound weakling" develop into a broad-shouldered, muscle-bound lifeguard after an intensive program of exercise? The answer is that each muscle cell has the capacity to expand considerably in volume when demands are placed on it by repeated strenuous use.

The "muscles" that come immediately to mind when the word is mentioned are those that move the bones of the skeleton. However, such muscles are only one of three major types, which are distinguished on the basis of the criteria of location, microscopic structure, and nervous control. These three types are **skeletal** or **striated muscle, smooth muscle,** and **cardiac muscle** (Figure 5-11).

Striated Muscle Tissue

A microscopic view of striated muscle tissue reveals a unique picture. The first feature that strikes the eye is the pattern of cross-banding, or striation that gives these muscle fibers one of their names. Then a closer look reveals that instead of the customary one nucleus per cell, each muscle cell has many nuclei, distributed at random along its surface, just under the cell membrane. Technically, such a multinucleated mass of protoplasm is referred to as a **syncytium.**

Each striated muscle cell is spindle shaped, between 1 and 40 mm long and only 0.01 to 0.15 mm in diameter. It contains close-packed **myofibrils,** thin fibers that run the length of the muscle cell (Figure 5-12). The myofibrils are composed of the contractile

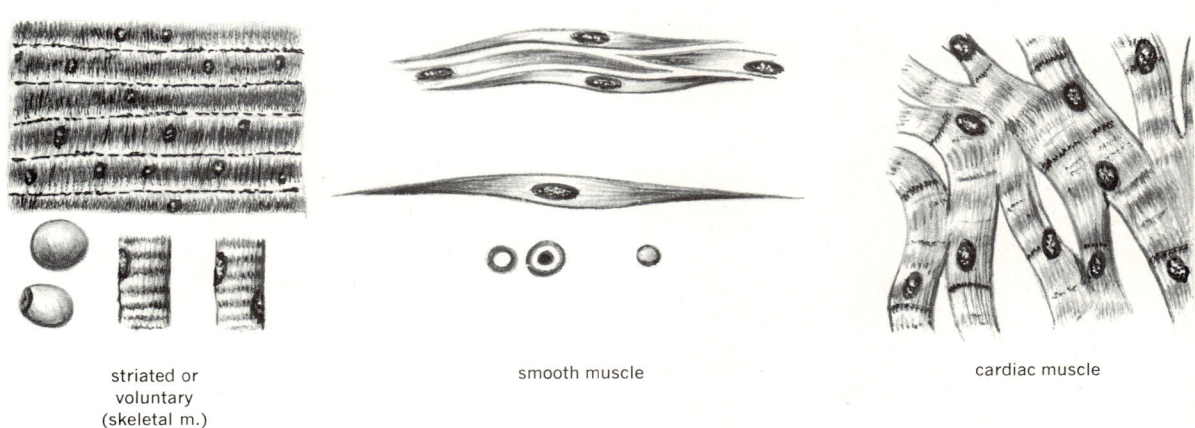

| striated or voluntary (skeletal m.) | smooth muscle | cardiac muscle |

FIGURE 5-11   Types of muscle tissue: skeletal, smooth, and cardiac.

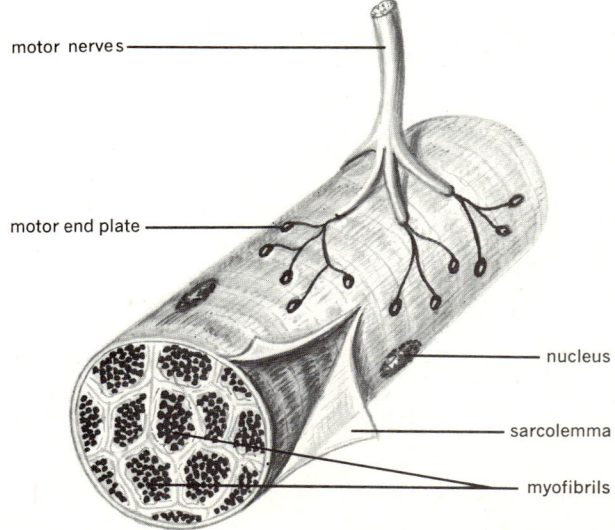

motor nerves

motor end plate

nucleus

sarcolemma

myofibrils

FIGURE 5-12   The skeletal muscle cell, a bundle of myofibrils, is supplied with motor nerve fibers that permit voluntary control of its contrac-

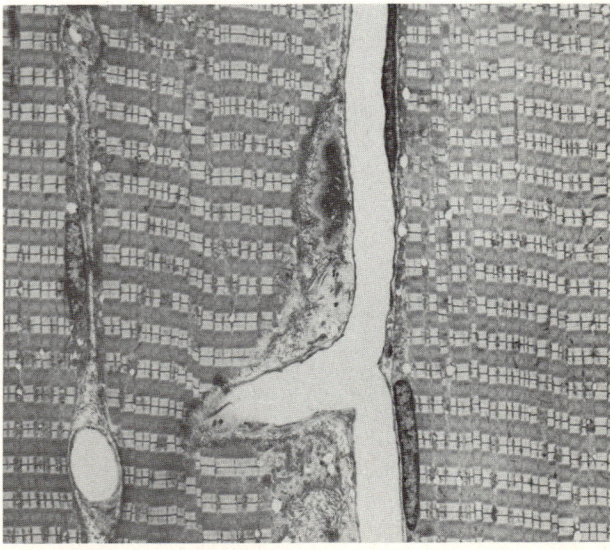

tions. The electron micrograph shows a longitudinal section of rat skeletal muscle cells, ×1470. (The white spaces are lumina of capillaries.)

proteins **actin** and **myosin.** The cytoplasm of muscle cells is given a special name, **sarcoplasm.** Each striated muscle cell is wrapped in its sheathlike cell membrane, the **sarcolemma.** Groups of muscle cells are bound together by thicker, tougher membranes, to form bundles **(fasciculi),** which are bound together in turn to form larger and larger bundles, until the familiar whole muscle is enveloped in a connective tissue sheath.

Striated muscles are also called **skeletal muscles,** because they are attached to bones of the skeleton. Another term that is used for them is **voluntary muscle:** they are supplied with nerve fibers from the cerebrospinal nervous system, and their contractions can be controlled voluntarily. Striated muscle contracts very rapidly.

Smooth Muscle Tissue

A rumbling stomach and the abdominal cramps that accompany a severe case of diarrhea are manifestations of the action of smooth muscle tissue. But normally the smooth muscle of the body does its work

silently, and we are unaware of its action.

The name "smooth muscle" comes from the fact that this muscle tissue lacks the cross-striations and multiple nuclei that characterize striated muscle tissue (Figure 5-13). The spindle-shaped cells of smooth muscle are smaller than those of striated muscle—about 0.015 to 0.5 mm long and 0.002 to 0.02 mm in diameter. The single oval nucleus is situated near the center of the cell.

Smooth muscle is sometimes called **visceral muscle,** because it is found in the walls of visceral organs such as the stomach, intestines, urinary bladder, and uterus. It is also contained in the walls of blood vessels, the bile ducts, and the hair follicles of the skin. Usually smooth muscle cells are arranged in two main layers: an inner, thick, circular coat and an outer, thin, longitudinal coat.

Smooth muscle contracts very slowly and can maintain a state of contraction longer than skeletal muscle. Its action may be initiated by hormonal or nervous influences. It is innervated by fibers from the autonomic nervous system, and thus its contractions are not normally under voluntary control. Thus, another name for this type of muscle tissue is **involuntary muscle.**

Cardiac Muscle Tissue

About a month after you were conceived, your heart muscle began to contract in a rhythmic beating. Since then it has continued to function continuously, and will continue to function until the moment you die.

The heart or cardiac muscle is a unique type, found nowhere else in the body. In microscopic structure, it is intermediate between the striated and smooth muscle tissue. It has striations visible under a microscope, but they are not as dark as those of striated muscle. Each cardiac muscle cell has a single oval nucleus, located deep within the cell. As can be seen from Figure 5-14, the cardiac muscle fibers seem to branch and merge with others, and it was thought that they form a syncytium. However, electron microscopic studies have revealed that each cell is completely bounded by its own cell membrane. A prominent feature of microscopic preparations of cardiac muscle tissue is the presence of dark bands, called **intercalated discs,** which cross the fibers at intervals. These bands are formed by the two layers of cell membrane of adjacent cardiac muscle cells.

Cardiac muscle is also unique in that its contractions (which are involuntary) are initiated within the heart muscle itself. A heart completely removed from the body can continue to beat for a time; even a small piece of heart muscle tissue can maintain a rhythmic beating. The rate of the heartbeat, however, is regulated by nervous and hormonal influences. Impulses can pass over the network of cardiac muscle fibers. As

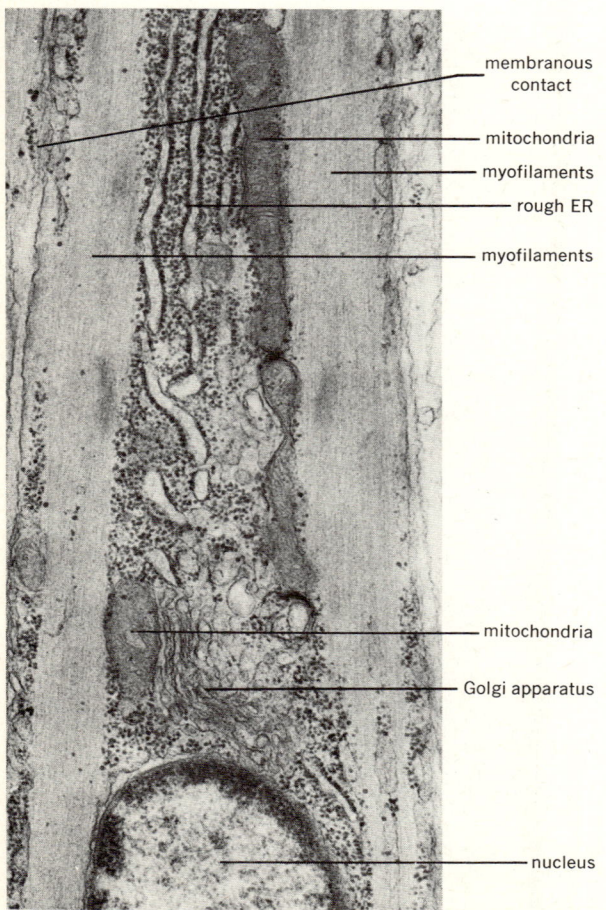

membranous contact

mitochondria

myofilaments

rough ER

myofilaments

mitochondria

Golgi apparatus

nucleus

FIGURE 5-13   Electron micrograph of smooth muscle tissue, ×22,400. Note the membranous contact between two smooth muscle cells.

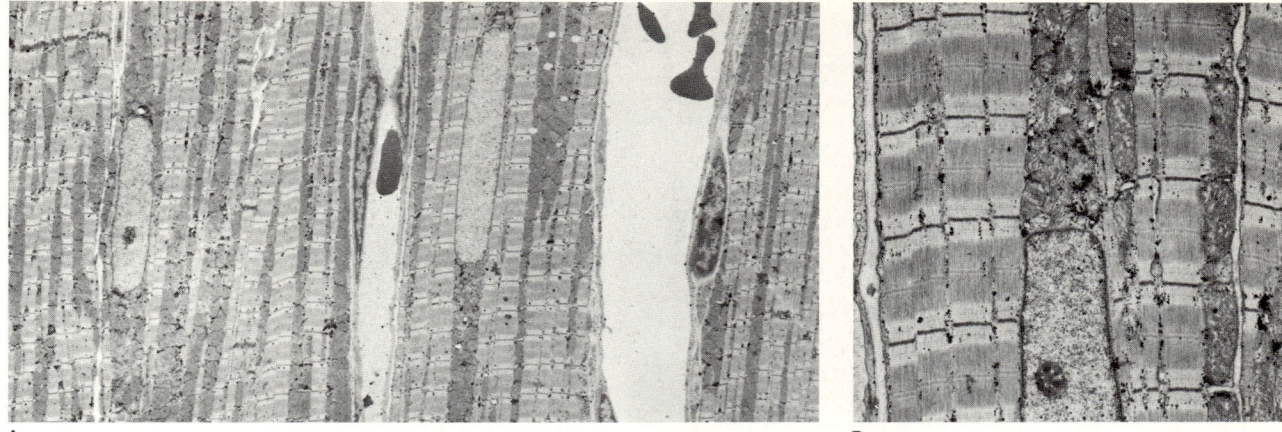

A   B

FIGURE 5-14 Electron micrograph of rat cardiac muscle, ×1425, showing an apparent syncytium (A); higher magnification, ×5625, reveals distinct cell boundaries (B).

a result, a single impulse can induce all of the cardiac muscle cells in a given area to contract simultaneously, producing a single powerful contraction.

Cardiac muscle has little or no capacity to regener-

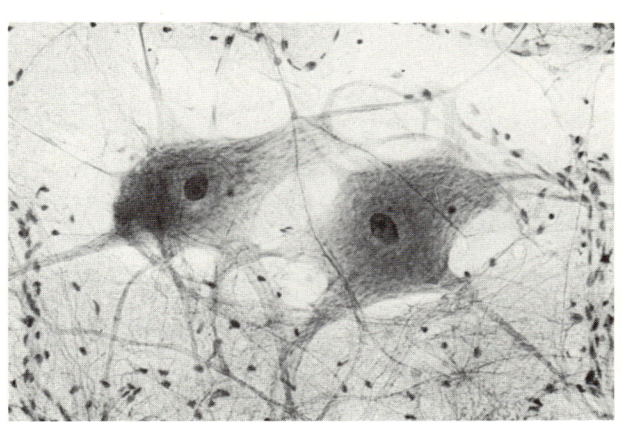

ate fibers. Damage produced by a heart attack or trauma is healed by the formation of scar tissue, which cannot function in the work of the heart.

NERVE TISSUE

Our perception of the world around us and our responses to the environment are all mediated through the nervous system. The cells of nerve tissue are specialized in two key areas: **irritability,** or responsiveness to stimuli, and **conductivity,** the ability to transmit impulses.

The cell units of nerve tissue are the **neurons,** or nerve cells, billions of which extend to almost every region of the body. There are several types of neurons in the body, differing somewhat in structure and ranging in size from several thousandths of an inch to several feet long. Yet all the nerve cells of the body have certain basic characteristics (Figure 5-15). Each

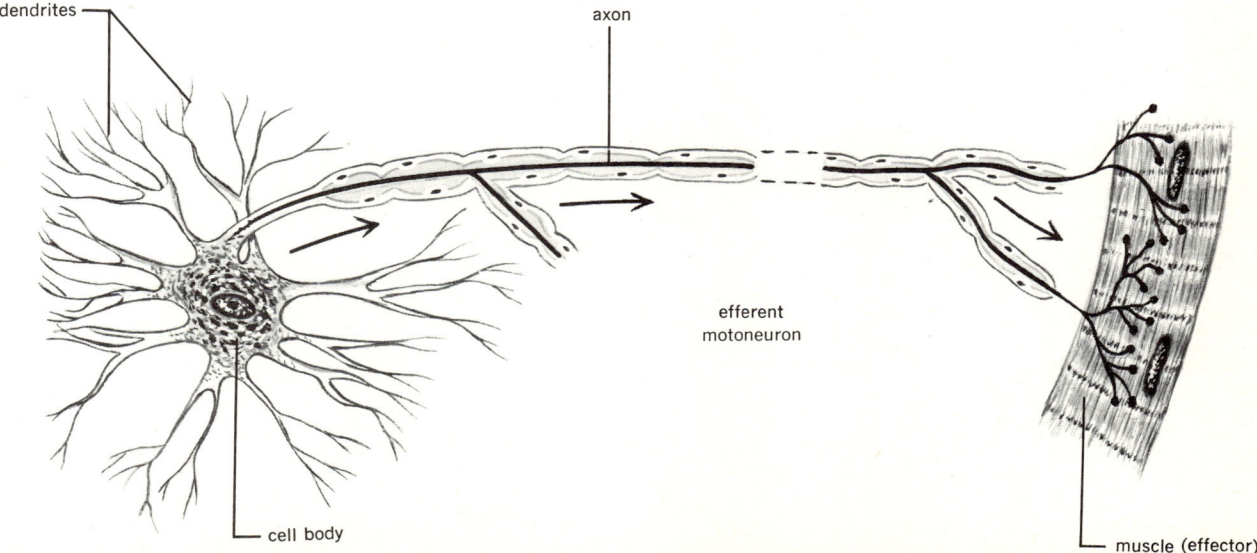

dendrites   axon

efferent
motoneuron

cell body   muscle (effector)

FIGURE 5-15 Nerve tissue: the drawing shows the structure of a typical motor neuron; a synapse between two neurons can be seen in the micrograph.

includes a **cell body,** containing a nucleus and various organelles, an extension or **process** called the **axon,** which carries impulses away from the cell body, and several processes called **dentrites,** which carry impulses to the cell body.

Impulses are transmitted along chains of neurons. However, there is no direct protoplasmic connection between one neuron and the next in the chain. A gap called a **synapse** separates them. Chemical neurotransmitters carry the impulse across the synapse from one neuron to another.

In addition to the neurons, nerve tissue includes interstitial cells, the **neuroglia,** which support and nourish the neurons.

SUMMARY

Tissues are classified as epithelial, connective, muscular, and nervous.
Epithelial tissue composes the coverings and linings of the body.
    It consists of sheets of closely packed cells, with little ground substance, on a basement membrane.
    Functions include protection, absorption, filtration and dialysis, diffusion, and secretion.
    Subdivisions of epithelial tissue are:
        Simple squamous
        Stratified squamous
        Transitional
        Simple cuboidal
        Simple columnar
        Pseudostratified columnar
        Stratified columnar
    Structural modifications for speicalized functions include:
        Goblet cells for secretion
        Villi and microvilli for absorption
        Cilia for directed flow of fluids
    Glandular epithelium comprises exocrine and endocrine glands.
Connective tissue is the most abundant and varied.
    It contains more matrix than cells.
    Connective tissue matrix consists of an amorphous ground substance, in which fibers are embedded:
        Collagenous fibers
        Elastic fibers
        Reticular fibers
    Connective tissue cells include:
        Fibroblasts
        Macrophages (histiocytes)
        Fat cells
        White blood cells
        Pigment cells
        Mast cells
        Plasma cells
    Functions of connective tissue include:
        Connecting body structures
        Support
        Fat storage
        Hemopoiesis
        Defense of body
        Nourishment of tissues
    Subdivisions of connective tissue are:
        Loose
            Areolar
            Adipose
            Reticular
        Dense
            Regular (tendons, ligaments, aponeuroses)
            Irregular
        Cartilage
            Hyaline
            Fibrous
            Elastic
        Bone (and dentin)
        Blood
    Bone (osseous tissue) contains a calcified matrix, arranged in concentric cylindrical layers comprising Haversian systems.
    Types of bone:
        Compact (dense)
        Cancellous (spongy)
    Blood consists of a fluid matrix (plasma) with suspended cells (corpuscles):
        Erythrocytes (red blood cells)
        Leukocytes (white blood cells)
        Platelets
    Lymph is mostly water, with some leukocytes but no erythrocytes.
Muscle tissue constitutes nearly half of the body mass
    It consists of elongated cells (muscle fibers) and a small amount of intercellular substance.
    Muscle cells are highly specialized for contractility.
    Types of muscle tissue are:
        Striated (skeletal, voluntary)
        Smooth (visceral, involuntary)
        Cardiac (heart)
    The myofibrils of muscle cells are composed of the contractile proteins actin and myosin.
    Striated muscle contracts rapidly and can be controlled voluntarily.
    Smooth muscle contracts slowly, can maintain a state of contraction longer than striated muscle, and is normally not under voluntary control.
    Cardiac muscle contractions are self-initiated and involuntary.
Nerve tissue includes neurons (nerve tissue proper) and neuroglia (supporting cells).
    Neurons are specialized for irritability and conductivity.
    A neuron consists of a cell body, axon, and dendrites.
        Impulses are conducted across synapses (gaps) between adjacent neurons.

QUESTIONS FOR REVIEW AND THOUGHT

1 Characterize and contrast the major types of epithelial and connective tissues with respect to cell types, intercellular substance, and functions.
2 Describe specialized modifications found in certain types of epithelium and discuss their functions.
3 What do such diverse tissues as adipose tissue, tendons, bones, and blood have in common?
4 Applications of the enzyme collagenase, which breaks down collagen, have been suggested as a means of removing unsightly scars. How would this treatment work?
5 Discuss possible adaptive advantages of having a cartilage skeleton in infancy and a skeleton of bone as an adult.
6 Compare skeletal, smooth, and cardiac muscle with respect to cell types, nature of contraction, and means of initiation of contraction.
7 What characteristics do different types of nerve cells have in common?

BASIC BIOLOGICAL PRINCIPLES

Man and other living organisms are often regarded as qualitatively distinct from the nonliving world, and indeed, there are a number of important characteristics that set life apart from nonlife. Yet living organisms are still made up of matter and consume energy. At all levels of organization, from the molecular up to the whole organism, they are governed by the same physical laws that govern the nonliving world—the laws of motion, the interconversions of forms of energy, the chemical properties of the elements, and so on. The functioning of the human body, like other living organisms, is also profoundly affected by some unique biological laws, which are not operative in the nonliving world. One of the most important of these is the set of principles determining the transmission of genetic information—the essence of a living organism—from one generation to the next. A knowledge of these fundamental laws, both physical and biological, is essential to a clear understanding of the systems of the human body and their functioning. Some basic principles have already been discussed in Chapter 3. In this chapter we shall explore some more fundamental laws that govern the functioning of the human body, and the characteristics that distinguish life from the nonliving world.

THE TRANSPORT OF MATTER AND CELL PERMEABILITY

The human body needs a continuing influx of nutrients and oxygen, to fuel its varied activities. But a mouthful of food, chewed and swallowed, is not yet really *in* the body for all practical purposes. Nor is a breath of air drawn into the lungs really *in* the body. To be used by the body, food materials must first pass through the membranes of cells lining the digestive tract; then they pass into the vessels of the circulatory system, again crossing membrane barriers, are transported through the body by the bloodstream, and then enter the individual cells, again by passing through cell membranes. Oxygen drawn into the lungs must also pass through a series of membranes and be transported through the body via the blood supply before reaching the individual body cells. Some of the substances needed by the body cells are produced within the body. Even if they are to be used within the cell in which they were formed, they may have to be transported from one part of the cell to another, possibly passing through membranes en route. If they are hormones or other products for "export," or waste products that must be dispensed with, the transport mechanisms of the body again come into play. For the right substance is useless or even harmful to the body unless it is in the right place at the right time.

There is a continual interchange of materials be-

tween the **intracellular fluid** (the fluid within the cells) and the **extracellular fluid** (which includes the blood and lymph and the interstitial fluid within the tissue spaces). This constant traffic into and out of the cells is regulated by the cell membrane, which is far from an absolute barrier. Instead, it is **differentially** or **selectively permeable:** it permits some substances to pass through while holding back others. In some respects it works like a sieve; small molecules, such as water (H_2O) molecules, pass readily through the cell membrane, while large molecules, such as proteins, are held back. But cell permeability is not so simple. Under certain conditions, large molecules or even sizeable solid particles can be transported into a cell. In general, the transport of matter in the body occurs through the basic mechanisms outlined in Figure 6-1: **diffusion, osmosis, filtration, active transport, pinocytosis,** and **phagocytosis.**

Diffusion

If a bottle of ionone (a synthetic chemical with the odor of violets) were poured out over home plate in the Houston Astrodome, after awhile the fans in the farthest reaches of the stands would be smelling violets—even though the stadium is shielded from winds that might disperse the chemical by the huge dome that covers it. If a spoonful of sugar is dropped into a cup of hot coffee, the shiny crystals will quickly dissolve, and then, even if the coffee is not stirred, ultimately every sip of the coffee will be flavored with sugar.

The cause of these and other seemingly puzzling phenomena lies in the kinetic theory of matter. As mentioned in Chapter 3, this law states that the molecules of matter are engaged in a ceaseless, random motion. In the course of their motion, molecules collide from time to time with other molecules and with the walls of their container; in such collisions, a molecule may gain or lose kinetic energy, and the direction of its motion may be changed. Thus, if a particular molecule would be followed by time-lapse photography, it would trace out a haphazard, zigzag path. In a gas, molecules are relatively far apart, and any individual molecule might travel a considerable distance between collisions. In a liquid, the molecules are somewhat closer and are more subject to the influence of neighboring molecules and ions. In a solid, the molecules are so closely packed that their kinetic movements are more like the oscillations of a ball attached to a spring, the other end of which is fixed.

Although the motions of the individual molecules are random, when a system is observed for a time a general pattern emerges: there is a trend of movement from regions of greater concentration to regions of lesser concentration (Figure 6-2A). This trend continues until the difference is eliminated, and all regions

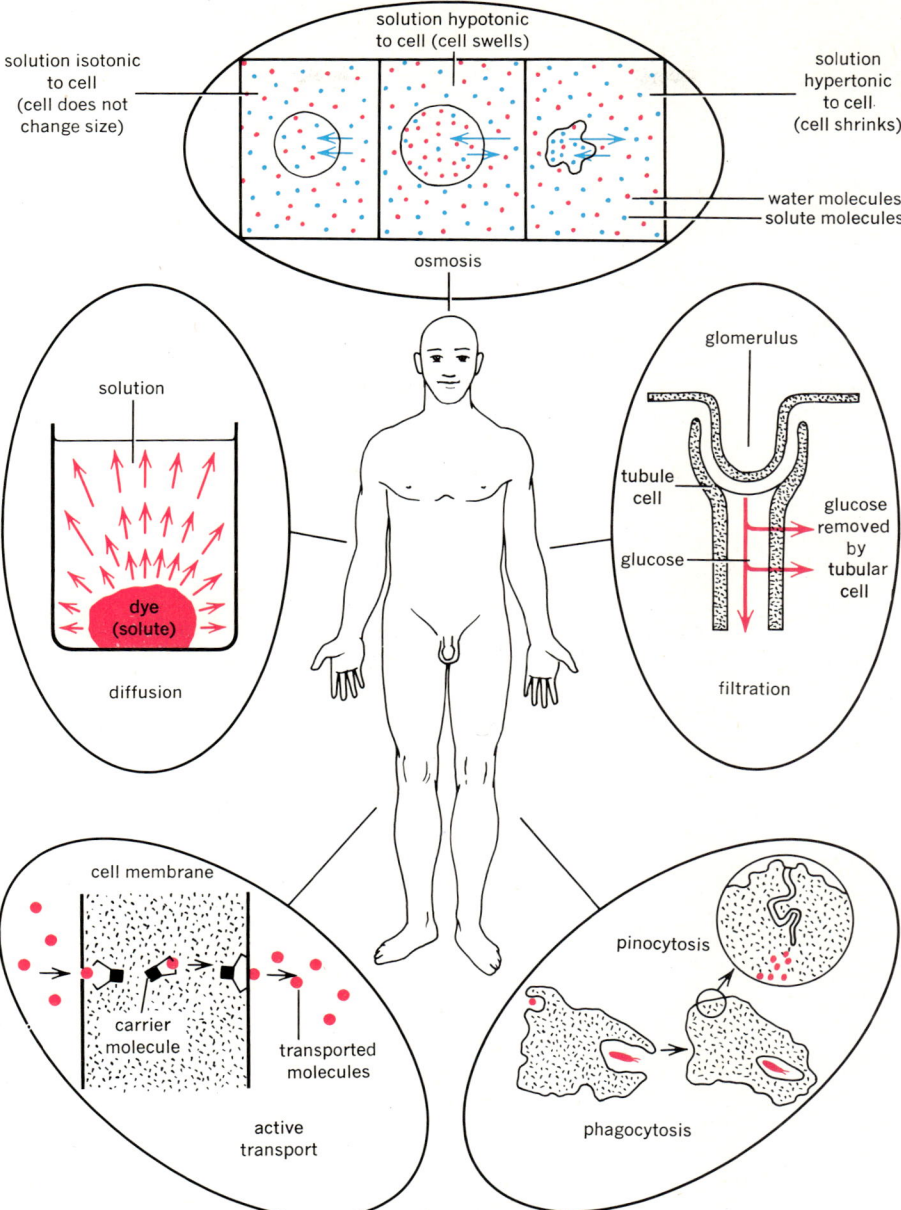

FIGURE 6-1 Mechanisms of transport of matter in the body: diffusion, osmosis (diffusion through a semipermeable membrane), filtration, active transport, pinocytosis, and phagocytosis.

have the same concentration of molecules. This observation seems to be a paradox—how can *random* movement be *directed* along a concentration gradient? The paradox does not really exist. No individual molecule experiences directed movement as a result of its kinetic motions. The net flow of molecules along the concentration gradient is simply the result of the fact that at any particular moment there are more molecules available to move out of a region of high concentration than there are to move into it. When conditions of uniform concentration are eventually reached, this is not a static situation, but rather a dynamic equilibrium. At any moment, the number of molecules leaving a particular area is exactly equal to the number of molecules that happen to be arriving there from other regions.

The movement of molecules or ions along a **concentration gradient** (i.e., from regions of higher to lower concentrations) is called **diffusion.** Diffusion is influenced by a number of factors in addition to concentration. An increase in the temperature speeds up processes of diffusion, because it increases the energy content of the molecules and consequently increases the speed of their kinetic motions. In the diffusion of ions, their electrical charge may play a role: positive ions tend to move toward a region of concentration of negative electrical charge, while negative ions move toward a positively charged region. Thus,

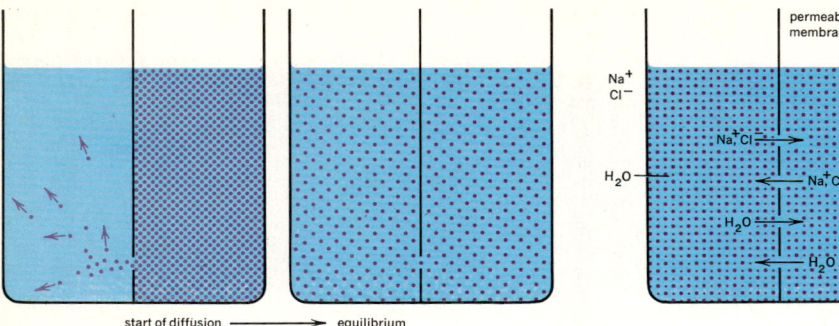

FIGURE 6-2 (A) Diffusion: random movements of individual particles result in a net redistribution, equalizing the concentrations in the communicating compartments. (B) Both NA$^+$ and Cl$^-$ ions and water molecules diffuse freely through a permeable membrane, equalizing the concentrations at equilibrium.

diffusion may also occur along an **electrical gradient.**

Diffusion plays a key role in many transport processes in the body. Products of digestion diffuse through the walls of the intestine and capillaries into the blood; these nutrients are then transported by the blood in a dissolved state until they diffuse through the membranes of body cells. Oxygen in the alveoli of the lungs diffuses through the walls of these air sacs and the capillaries that surround them into the blood. (The blood delivered to the lungs has a lower oxygen concentration than the alveoli.) The oxygen is carried in the blood to oxygen-poor body cells, which it enters by diffusing through their membranes. Waste products of the cells diffuse out into the blood, where their concentration is lower.

As can be seen from the examples mentioned, diffusion in the human body frequently occurs through a membrane. If the membrane is permeable to both solvent and solute, molecules pass freely through it in both directions. For example, suppose a container is divided into two compartments by a permeable membrane, and a concentrated salt solution is poured into one compartment and pure water into the other (Figure 6-2B). Ions of the salt and water molecules will diffuse freely through the membrane, until the salt concentrations in both compartments are equal. (The final concentration on both sides of the membrane, of course, will be lower than that of the original salt solution.)

In speaking of diffusion through membranes thus far, we have been implicitly regarding the cell membrane as a sort of sieve, perforated by numerous minute holes, through which small molecules can pass. To some extent this picture seems to be correct. The surface that the cell presents to its surroundings is a layer of lipid, which behaves as though it contains numerous round holes, about 8 Å in diameter, through which small molecules and ions can pass. (The exact nature of these "pores" is still unknown.) But this is not the whole story. Lipid-soluble substances can dissolve in the cell membrane and diffuse

through the lipid into the cell. Oxygen, which is very soluble in lipids, passes readily through the cell membrane in this way. Glucose, which is not soluble in lipids, can nonetheless pass through the cell membrane by a process of **facilitated diffusion:** it combines with a carrier substance at the outer surface of the membrane. The carrier then diffuses, or, if it is a very large molecule, simply rotates, carrying the glucose molecule to the inner surface of the membrane, where it is discharged into the cell.

The term **dialysis** is sometimes used for processes of diffusion in which molecules or ions of the *solute* move through a membrane.* But what if the membrane is only **semipermeable**—if it is permeable to molecules of the solvent, but impermeable to solute molecules? Then special effects result, the phenomenon of **osmosis.**

Osmosis

If human red blood cells are placed in a test tube of distilled water, a dramatic sequence of events ensues. A spreading red stain emerges from the mound of cells, until the water in the tube is uniformly colored. If the process is watched under a microscope, it can be seen that when the cells come in contact with the pure water, their biconcave shape begins to bulge and swell, stretching and straining the cell membrane until it bursts, spilling out the cell contents (Figure 6-3A). If, on the other hand, red blood cells are placed in a test tube containing a concentrated salt solution, the cells will shrivel and shrink (Figure 6-3B). The first process (bursting) is called **hemolysis;** the second (shriveling) is referred to as **crenation.** Both are examples of osmosis, the diffusion of solvent molecules through a semipermeable membrane.

When two solutions, separated by a semipermeable membrane, have the same concentrations of the same

---

* In cases of impaired kidney function, modern dialysis setups perform the life-saving function of artificially removing poisonous cell wastes from the patient's blood by diffusion.

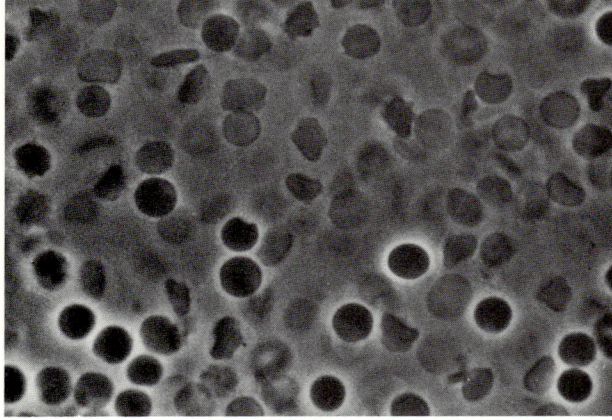

A

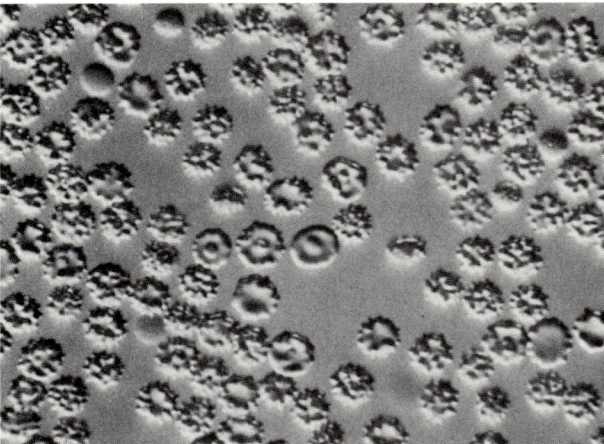

B

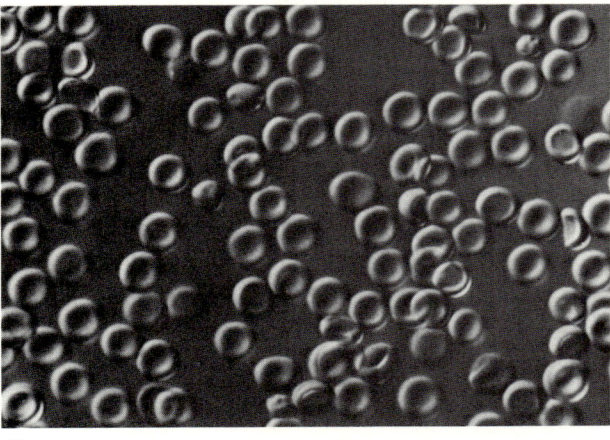

C

FIGURE 6-3 Hemolysis (A) and crenation (B). When red cells are placed in a hypotonic solution, diffusion of water causes the cells to swell, burst, and lose their cell contents. The micrograph (A) shows many empty, distorted membranes and some round, swollen cells that are not yet completely hemolyzed. Placing red cells in hypertonic medium results in diffusion of water out of the cells, producing the distortions of the crenated cells shown in (B). In (C) normal red cells in isotonic medium (blood plasma) are shown for comparison.

solute and solvent, they are said to be **isoosmotic,** or **isotonic.** Although solvent molecules will continually pass through the membrane in both directions, there will be no *net* diffusion in either direction. If two solutions have different concentrations of the same solute, a concentration gradient is established, and osmosis occurs (a net diffusion of solvent molecules into the solution with a lower concentration of the solvent and a higher concentration of the solute). The solution with a higher solute concentration is said to be **hypertonic** to the other, while the less concentrated solution is said to be **hypotonic** to the more concentrated one. Thus, osmosis occurs from a hypotonic solution to a hypertonic solution.

This is exactly what happened in the red blood cell examples cited at the beginning of the section. In the case of hemolysis, the water in the test tube was hypotonic to the red blood cells, and water diffused into the cells until their membranes could hold no more—so they burst. In the case of crenation, the concentrated salt solution was hypertonic to the cells, and water diffused out of them into the solution. These two cases are of great practical importance in the body. When a substance is injected into the body, it is injected in a medium isotonic to the body cells, to avoid damage to the cells by osmosis. The two solutions most commonly used for injections are isotonic solutions of 0.9 percent sodium chloride (physiological saline) and 5.5 percent glucose.

The principles of osmosis are usually demonstrated in the laboratory with a sugar solution, using a thistle tube setup. A semipermeable membrane separates the concentrated sugar solution in the thistle tube from the water in the beaker. If gravity were the only factor operating, the level of the solution in the thistle tube would be expected to fall until it was equalized with the level of liquid in the beaker. But instead, the level of the solution in the thistle tube *rises,* while the level of liquid in the beaker falls. What has happened is that water molecules have diffused from the beaker through the membrane into the thistle tube, along the concentration gradient. (In the beaker, the concentration of water is higher than in the thistle tube; for sugar, the concentration gradient is the reverse. However, sugar molecules cannot pass through the membrane, and thus there is a diffusion only of solvent molecules.) Since there is no sugar in the beaker, the concentrations on both sides of the membrane can never be equalized. The water might therefore be expected to go on diffusing through the membrane indefinitely. But at some point, the level of liquid in the thistle tube stops rising—at the point at which its **osmotic pressure** (a measure of the tendency for osmosis to proceed) exactly balances the pressure exerted by the column of sugar solution (**hydrostatic pressure**). The more concentrated the solution, the higher the osmotic pressure, and the higher the liquid in the this-tle tube will rise before it stops.

Filtration

One of the commonest techniques used in the chemistry laboratory is filtration: a liquid suspension is poured onto a paper fiber or sintered glass filter, and the liquid component drips through, while the solid component is retained on the filter. But filtration in the laboratory can sometimes be a slow and frustrating process. The chemist often speeds it up by placing the filter on a specially adapted flask, attached to a suction line that reduces the pressure under the filter below the atmospheric pressure above it. The resultant pressure difference literally pushes the molecules through the filter.

Filtration is just as common and important in the human body as it is in the chemistry lab. For example, fluid continuously filters out through the thin walls of the capillaries into the surrounding tissue spaces. Here the pressure difference that drives the process is produced by the pumping action of the heart, which raises the pressure of the blood inside the blood vessels. Filtration of this kind plays a key role in the work of the kidneys. (Fluid continuously filters out of the glomerulus into the tubule.)

In one respect, filtration is similar to diffusion: only molecules or ions that are small enough pass through the filter; larger molecules are retained. But there is an important distinction between filtration and diffusion: diffusion is an effect purely of the inherent kinetic motions of molecules and ions; filtration, on the other hand, requires an external force.

Active Transport

Can you imagine a ball rolling uphill? It will not do so, unless someone actually rolls it, investing a certain amount of energy in the process. In the body, molecules and ions left to their own devices will tend to move along a concentration gradient, just as a ball, unpushed, will tend to roll downhill. Yet there are numerous examples of molecules and ions in the body being transported *against* a concentration gradient, from regions of lower concentration into regions of higher concentration. For example, sodium ions continually diffuse into cells, yet their concentration does not build up beyond a certain level, which is lower than that of the extracellular fluid. Obviously there must be some other process, working counter to normal diffusion, to "pump" the excess sodium ions out of the cell. This "sodium pump" and similar processes that transport molecules and ions through cell membranes against the concentration gradient are called **active transport,** to distinguish them from the passive processes of diffusion and osmosis, which proceed according to the laws of physics, without any external

input of energy. Active transport, on the other hand, is an energy-requiring process powered by the energy generated in cell metabolism.

Active transport has been a subject of intense interest and study in recent years. As yet, little is known with certainty about how it works, but hypotheses have been developed that are in good agreement with the experimental observations thus far. It is believed that the molecule or ion to be transported through the cell membrane combines in a temporary complex with some carrier molecule (perhaps a protein or lipoprotein) at the cell surface (Figure 6-4). The carrier molecule then either travels through the membrane, or rotates, transferring the attached molecule or ion to the inner surface of the membrane, or perhaps slides the complexed molecule or ion along from one active site to another. The carrier systems of the cell membrane are quite specific, combining only with a certain substance or substances. The carrier system that pumps sodium out of the cell, for example, also transports potassium into the cell (likewise against the concentration gradient). A different carrier system transports sugars through the membranes of certain cells, while still others are responsible for the active transport of specific amino acids. Enzymes and perhaps hormones are believed to be involved in the processes of active transport. The energy required for these processes is supplied in the form of ATP, produced in the mitochondria. (If a cell is treated with a poison that interferes with cell respiration, the sodium pump stops working, water diffuses into the cell, and the cell promptly swells.)

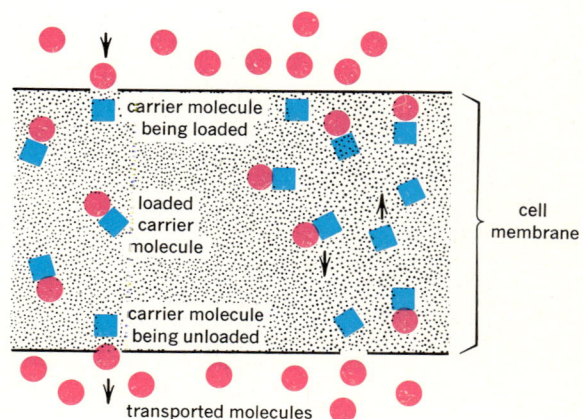

FIGURE 6-4 Active transport across the cell membrane. A currently accepted hypothesis explains transport against the concentration gradient by the functioning of fat-soluble carrier molecules, which combine with molecules or ions at the cell surface. The loaded carrier molecules diffuse through the membrane from a region of high concentration at the outer surface to a region of lower concentration at the inner surface, then discharge their load into the cell and diffuse back to the outer surface, where they can be reloaded. Both the "loading" and the "unloading" reactions are catalyzed by enzymes and consume energy.

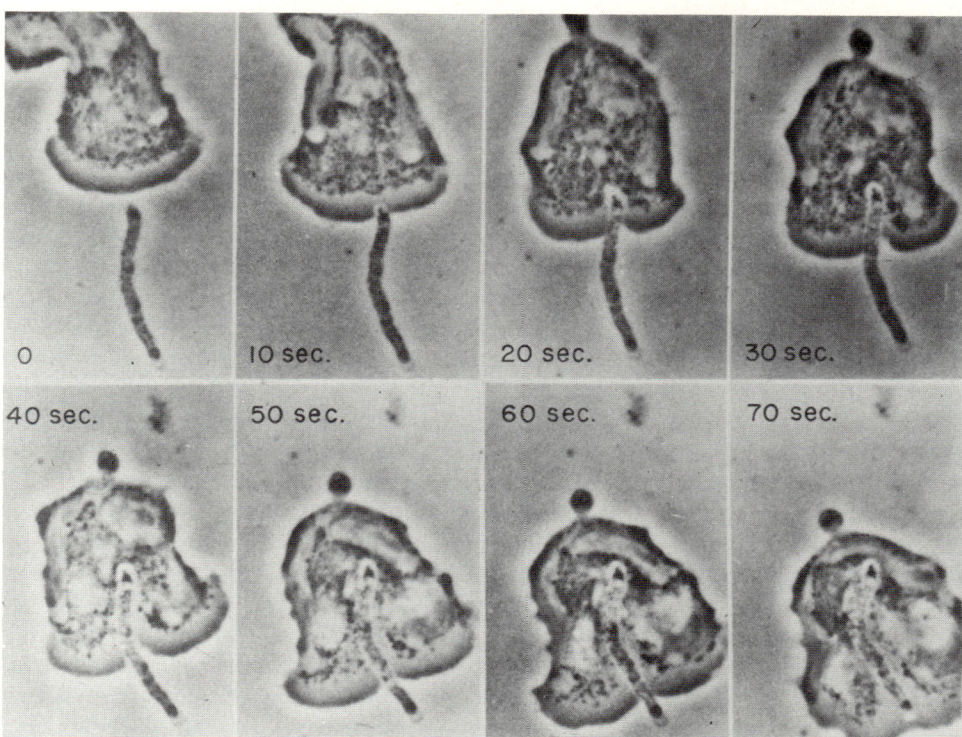

FIGURE 6-5 Phagocytosis: the photo sequence shows a white blood cell ingesting a bacillus.

0   10 sec.   20 sec.   30 sec.

40 sec.   50 sec.   60 sec.   70 sec.

Phagocytosis and Pinocytosis

On the microscopic level, a cut finger presents the scene of a violent battlefield. Macrophages, attracted by chemical distress signals given off by the damaged tissues, swarm about, gobbling up invading bacteria that have slipped in through the cut and scavenging bits of debris. Oozing along, the amorphous macrophage sends out bulging pseudopods that surround its prey and engulf it, enclosing it in a vacuole inside the cell (Figure 6-5), where it is ultimately digested. This process of engulfing of bacteria or other fairly substantial solid particles by a cell is called **phagocytosis,** which literally means "cell eating." In amebas (microscopic pond dwellers that somewhat resemble the phagocytes of the human body) phagocytosis is actually used for the purpose of "eating." In some lower animals, such as sponges, amebalike cells in the lining of the digestive cavity similarly serve a function of ingestion. In man, however, phagocytosis is mainly utilized as one of the body's defense mechanisms, for coping with invading microbes and clearing up cell debris.

Another process of cell ingestion with a rather anthropomorphic name is **pinocytosis,** literally "cell drinking." A minute incupping forms at the surface of the cell membrane (Figure 6-6). Liquid droplets, adhering to the surface, are pulled down through the membrane as the infolding deepens, carrying along any suspended particles they may contain. The invagination closes about the droplets to form a vesicle;

finally the membrane enclosing the vesicle disappears, and the droplets are inside the cell. Pinocytosis, like phagocytosis, is a means of transporting substances

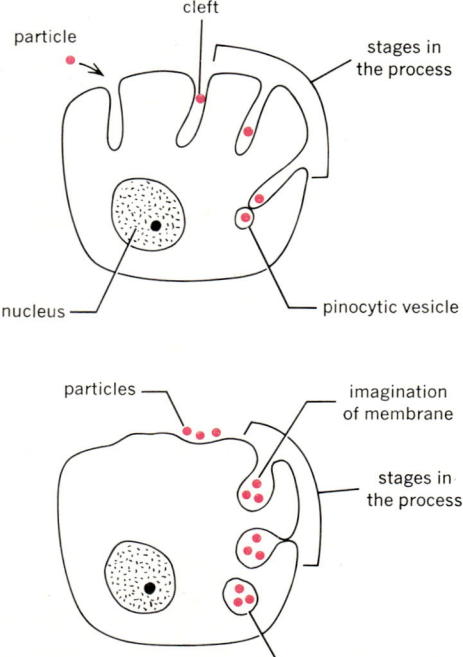

FIGURE 6-6 Two mechanisms of pinocytosis: (A) a particle enters a cleft and becomes enclosed in a vesicle; (B) particles adsorbed on the cell membrane become enclosed in a vesicle as the cell membrane enfolds it.

into the cell, to which the membrane would normally be impermeable.

HOMEOSTASIS

The life forms of our planet are subjected to continual changes in the conditions of the external environment—alternations of light and darkness, heat and cold, variations of the quantity of water available and its content of minerals, changes in the availability and type of food materials. As life developed on the earth, most organisms developed mechanisms for maintaining a relatively constant internal environment, despite changes in the external world. In the warm-blooded animals, including man, such mechanisms have been perfected to a high degree: not only are the pH and chemical composition of the internal body fluids well controlled, but even the temperature of the internal environment is kept constant within a relatively narrow tolerance, in the face of wide fluctuations of the external conditions.

Physiologists call the constancy of the internal environment of living organisms **homeostasis,** and it is perhaps the central theme of all their studies. Indeed, in a sense, virtually everything in this book relates to homeostasis in one way or another. The structures and mechanisms for getting, digesting, absorbing, and assimilating food supply the needed raw materials. The respiratory system provides for a continual new supply of oxygen and removal of the waste carbon dioxide produced in cellular respiration. The circulatory system is essential in distributing nutrients and oxygen and also functions in the body's temperature-control mechanisms. The kidneys continuously act as a quality control monitor, adjusting any deviations from the normal physiological conditions of the body fluids. The integrating and control functions of the nervous and endocrine systems also play a key role in the maintenance of homeostasis.

Homeostasis is not a static condition, once achieved and preserved unchanged forever more. It is a dynamic equilibrium, a matter of continual adjustments, of modifying small changes before they have a chance to grow into large ones, of nudging processes back in the right direction before they can go too far astray.

Throughout this book, you will find numerous references to normal values, or normal ranges of values, of various body indices. These are characteristics of the healthy body. But in disease, the homeostatic mechanisms may become less efficient. The body temperature may rise, or specific components of the blood may be higher or lower than normal. Such deviations are important clinical clues to the diagnosis of diseases, and an understanding of the body's homeostatic mechanisms can aid in taking measures to restore the constancy of the internal environment that is essential to life and health.

CHARACTERISTICS OF LIVING MATTER

The search for life on other worlds has focused attention on the problem of defining just what life is. On earth, in most cases, the distinction between the living and the nonliving does not require much thought, and indeed can readily be made intuitively even by a small child. But the possibility of some day discovering life forms totally outside our experience has called for a reexamination of the characteristics of living matter. Such a reexamination may aid not only in recognizing alien life forms if we ever meet them, but also in better understanding ourselves and the life forms that share our own planet.

We have already seen that there is nothing intrinsically unique about the chemical composition of protoplasm. What, then, provides the qualitative difference that distinguishes life from nonlife? It was once commonly believed that living organisms were animated by a mysterious "vital force." Later the philosophical school of mechanism held sway, maintaining that all phenomena, both living and nonliving, can ultimately be explained by definite physical laws. To a large extent, the concepts of mechanism predominate in scientific circles today, and it is hoped that one day the synthesis of a living cell in the laboratory from nonliving raw materials will be achieved. Meanwhile, it is most convenient to define a living organism as one possessing a certain complex of attributes. Some of them may be superficially similar to attributes possessed by nonliving matter, but in the aggregate they are unmistakably "life."

Organization   A living organism might be thought of as an island of order, surrounded on all sides by chaos. It is a general principle in the physical world that processes tend toward a state of ever increasing disorder and randomness. (A physical scientist might phrase this principle in terms of an increase in the **entropy** of the system.) Life is a continual struggle against entropy, the creation of organization out of randomness. This struggle has a heavy cost—it requires a continual supply of energy. Living organisms obtain the energy they need to maintain their organization from the external environment: plants trap and utilize the energy radiated by the sun, while animals obtain energy from food materials. The organization of living organisms includes varying degrees of differentiation and specialization for the performance of particular functions.

Excitability   A living organism does not exist in isolation. It is immersed in an environment and, in order to survive, it must be able to respond appropriately to changes in its environment. Even at the single-cell level there is some degree of excitability, or responsiveness to changes in the environment. An ameba will retreat if it is touched with a sharp object, while a euglena (another single-celled pond organism) will swim toward a light of moderate intensity. In higher organisms such as man, the responses to **stimuli** (changes in the environment) are far more complex and may be greatly modified by experience and learning. But the interaction with the environment made possible by excitability is just as vital to survival for a human as for an ameba. An important aspect of physiology is the study of the responses of the various systems of the body to stimuli.

Conductivity   Reaching across the stove, your arm accidentally brushes against a hot pot. If your awareness of the heat stimulus stopped at the skin of your arm, its inherent excitability would not do you much good. You are enabled to respond effectively to the stimulus by pulling your arm away and (if you know something about first aid) quickly running cold water on the burn, by means of another characteristic of living matter: conductivity, or the ability to transmit a wave of excitation. In the human body, nerve and muscle cells are highly specialized for this attribute (Figure 6-7).

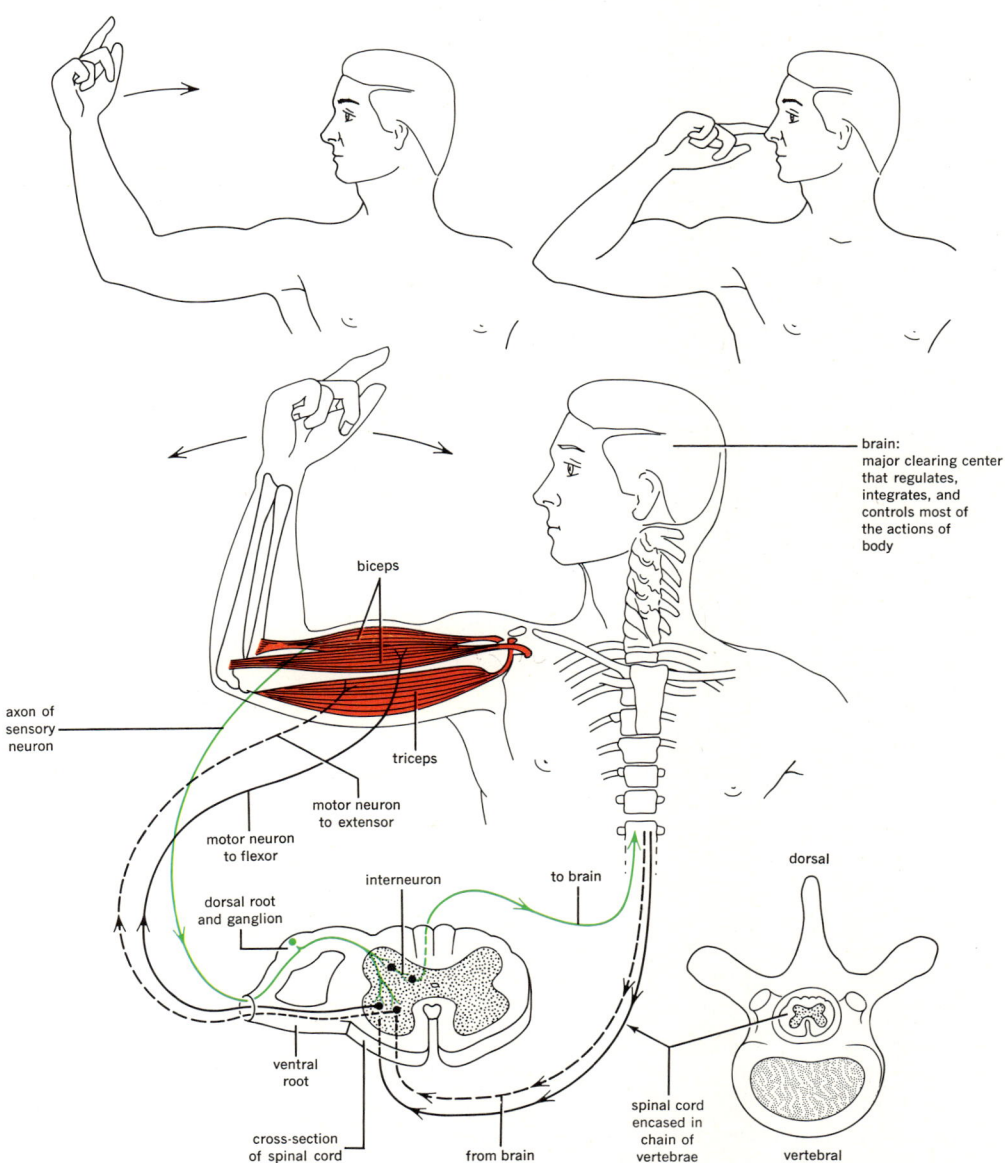

FIGURE 6-7   The smooth, coordinated movements of the arm involve nerves and muscles, which are highly specialized for the properties of excitability, conductivity, and contractility.

Contractility Responses to stimuli often involve movement of one kind or another. Movement is produced through another attribute of living matter: contractility, the ability of cells to undergo a shortening. In higher organisms, muscle cells are the specialists in contractility. But this attribute is not a monopoly of higher organisms. The pond-dwelling euglena swims by contractions of its one-celled body and lashings of its long, whiplike flagellum that are powered by contractile chemicals very similar to those in human muscle cells.

Metabolism In a universe where progressive randomization is the rule, a living organism must constantly conduct an uncountable number of activities and interactions merely to hold its own, much less to gain ground in its ceaseless quest for order. Food materials must be broken down for the energy they contain or built up into new structural materials for the body. Waste products must be eliminated or converted to substances that can be utilized. All of the myriad chemical processes that go on in a living organism are grouped under the general term of metabolism. In the buildup phase of metabolism, called **anabolism,** complex compounds are synthesized from simpler units. Anabolic reactions are essential for all growth and repair. **Catabolism,** the breakdown phase of metabolism, is equally important to the body. These are the reactions that make stored chemical energy available for the body's activities. Processes of digestion and respiration are key aspects of catabolism.

Growth and Reproduction A snowball rolling downhill gathers more snow and increases in size. If it happens to hit an obstacle, it may break apart, yielding two snowballs. The growing snowball has some superficial similarities to the attributes of a living organism, but there are important distinctions. Growth in the nonliving world generally occurs by **accretion:** the addition of new material to the outside of the object. Growth of a living organism, on the other hand, occurs by a process called **intussusception:** the intake and assimilation of materials from the outside environment, which are transformed into the substance of the organism (Figure 6-8). All living organisms grow, at least at some time during their life cycle. Their growth generally includes both an increase in size and a progressive differentiation. Even after overall growth of the body has ceased, growth still occurs at the cell and tissue level, providing for the replacement of worn-out or damaged structures.

Living organisms perpetuate their kind from one generation to another through reproduction. This is more than a random fragmentation, such as that of a snowball. It is a careful duplication and transmission of characteristics from parent to offspring. In single-celled organisms, reproduction is often a simple matter of division of cells, producing two copies of the parent. In higher organisms such as man, the concept of sex comes into operation. Reproduction requires two parents, who provide complementary legacies of hereditary material to each offspring. Sexual reproduction permits the combining of divergent heritages into new assortments and thus supplies a greater pool of variability from which potentially valuable new adaptations to the environment may arise.

CELL DIVISION

You began life as a single cell. This cell, the fertilized egg or **zygote,** contained a complete set of hereditary blueprints for the formation of a functioning human being. But as a single cell, it was only a potential human being. In order to reach the trillions of cells that form a recognizable human, it had to reproduce itself again and again. Reproduction at the cellular level occurs by a process of cell division, or **mitosis,** in which the original parent cell splits into two daughter cells. The "parent-child" relationship at the cellular level is quite different from the type with which we are familiar in human society. The parent cell ceases to exist at the instant of formation of its two daughters. Before dividing, it has carefully duplicated its entire genetic legacy; each daughter cell, receiving half of this hereditary material, is thus a faithful copy of the original parent.

You have already completed, or nearly completed, the phase of active overall body growth in your life cycle. Yet mitosis still continues actively. Each *min-*

FIGURE 6-8 A snowball grows by accretion; if it splits, it forms two fragments. A chick grows by intussusception and reproduces to form new individuals.

ute, more than 200 million new cells are being "born" in your body—about as many cells as there are people in the entire United States. These new cells replace worn-out or damaged old cells, and thus mitosis is an integral and vital part of the processes of healing and the maintenance of normal body function. In addition, another kind of cell division is taking place in your reproductive organs. This is a special, reductive variant of cell division called **meiosis,** in which only *half* of the hereditary information (one chromosome of each pair) is transmitted to each daughter cell. The resultant **gametes** are potentially capable of combining with their counterparts from a person of the opposite sex to form a zygote.

Mitosis

Mitosis is a continuous process, with characteristic sequences of events following one another as one cell becomes two. However, it is convenient for cytolo-

gists to divide the process into a series of discrete stages, keyed to salient features that appear on micrographs and to the occurrence of important events. In general, a particular tissue specimen will contain individual cells in many different phases of cell division. Using certain chemicals such as colchicine, it is sometimes possible to "stop the clock" of cell division temporarily and synchronize all the cells in a culture, so that subsequently all the cells pass through each successive stage of mitosis at the same time. Piecing together information obtained from synchronized cell cultures and from observations of appropriately stained sections of normal, unsynchronized cells, cytologists have built up the following general outline of mitosis, depicted in Figure 6-9.

Interphase   The interphase, the stage during which micrographs show no visible signs of cell division, is sometimes referred to as the "resting phase." But this

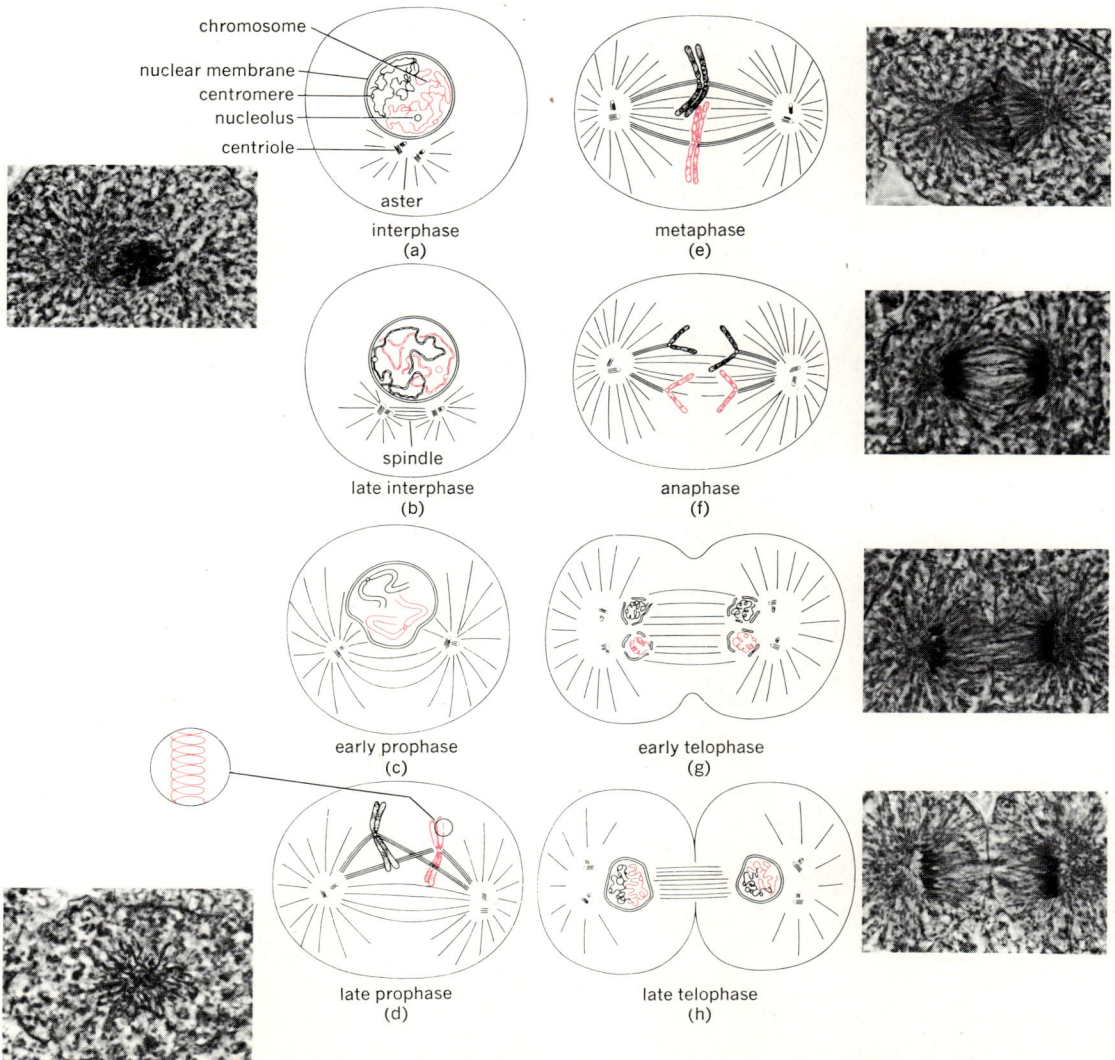

FIGURE 6-9   Mitosis: stages of mitotic cell division in a simplified animal cell (diagrams) and in the whitefish embryo (photos).

is a misnomer. Far from being at rest, the interphase cell is a seething cauldron of metabolic activity, carrying on its normal functions and growing in size. During a restricted portion of the interphase, referred to as the S-period, the DNA of the nucleus is replicated (Figure 6-10). This is not evident at this stage, however, for the genetic material is seen as a granular-appearing mass, consisting of long, thin, tangled strands of chromatin. During the interphase, the nucleus is a prominent, membrane-bounded organelle, with one or more distinct nucleoli.

Prophase This is the beginning of the visible manifestations of cell division. Within the nucleus, the thin, tangled chromatin strands gradually become shortened and thickened into discrete, rodlike particles. High magnification reveals that each chromosome in a prophase nucleus actually consists of two separate strands, called sister **chromatids,** joined together by a small body called a **centromere.** While the chromosomes are becoming more distinct, the nucleolus is gradually fading away, and by the end of the prophase it is no longer visible. The nuclear mem-

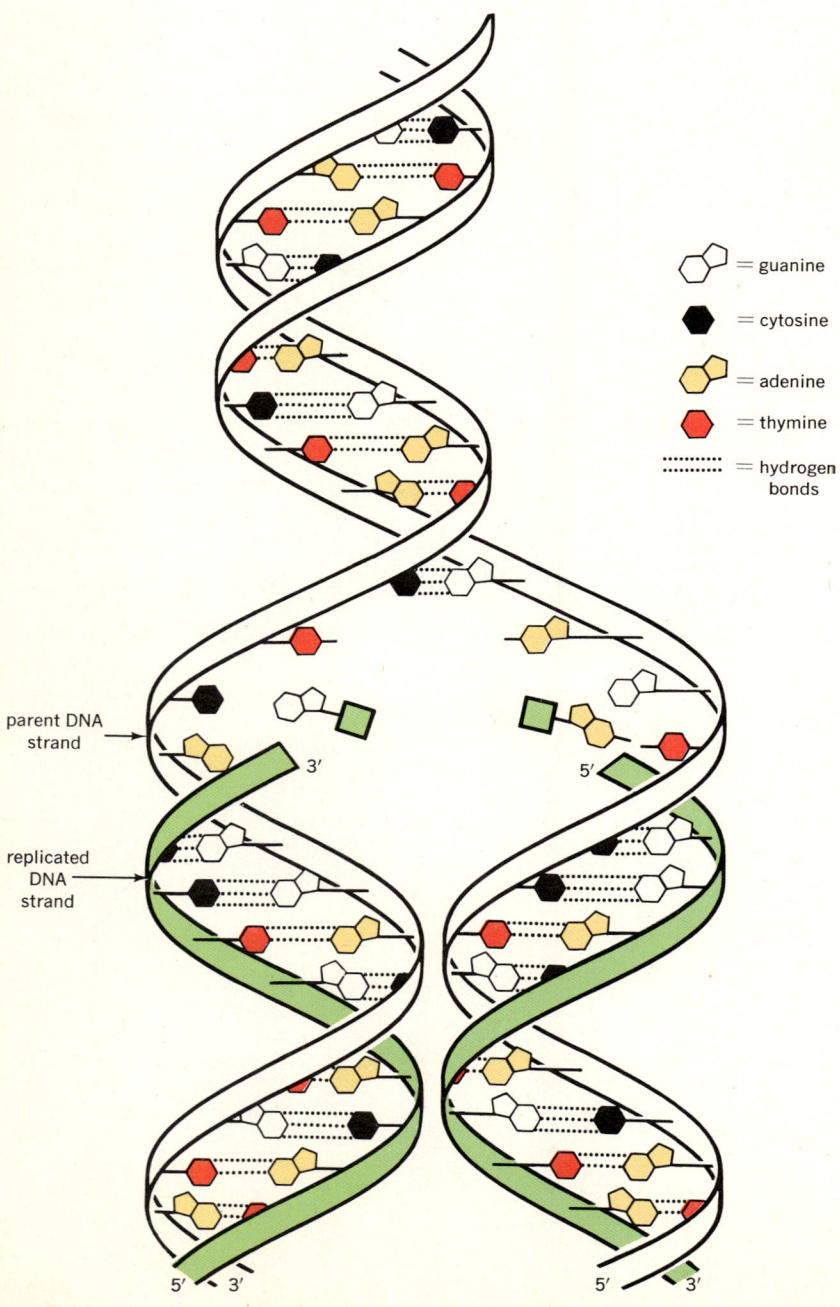

parent DNA strand

replicated DNA strand

FIGURE 6-10 DNA replication according to the Watson-Crick model. Assembly of daughter strands proceeds on the exposed template of the unwinding DNA double helix. When the process reaches the end of the double helix, there will be two complete, separate DNA molecules. Barring mutations, the two daughter helices will have an identical base sequence; each will contain one strand of "old" DNA and one newly synthesized strand.

= guanine

= cytosine

= adenine

= thymine

= hydrogen bonds

brane also gradually disappears as the prophase progresses.

Meanwhile, in the cytoplasm, other significant events are occurring. The centrioles move apart, one pair to each pole of the cell, on opposite sides of the nucleus. As they move, a starlike structure of thin fibrils, the **aster,** forms about each pair of centrioles. Some of the fibrils link up and are drawn out into a spindle-shaped formation (the **spindle**), spanning the nucleus, as the centrioles move apart.

Metaphase   Now the chromosomes begin to move, marking the end of the prophase and the beginning of the next phast of mitosis, the metaphase. Independently, the chromosomes align themselves with the centromere of each attached to the center of one of the spindle fibers. When the alignment is complete, all the centromeres are lined up at the equatorial plane, an imaginary plane passing through the middle of the cell, perpendicular to the axis of the spindle. The arms of the chromosomes dangle randomly in all directions from the aligned centromeres. At this stage the nuclear membrane has disappeared entirely. The metaphase ends with another important nuclear event: the centromere of each double-stranded chromosome divides, converting the former sister chromatids to two single-stranded **daughter chromosomes.**

Anaphase   Now the actual separation of the nuclear material is beginning. During the anaphase, the divided centromeres begin to move toward the poles of the cell, dragging their chromosomes like dangling tails behind them. One of each pair of formerly joined chromosomes moves toward one pole of the cell, while the other moves toward the opposite pole. Thus, by the end of the anaphase, each half of the cell contains one complete assortment of chromosomes, which have nearly reached the respective poles.

Telophase   Viewing the nuclear events of the telophase is very much like watching a movie of the prophase run backward. The spindle disappears, and the chromosomes again become enclosed within a nuclear membrane, assembled from the endoplasmic reticulum. (Only now there are *two* separate nuclei, one in each half of the cell.) The nucleolus reappears as a distinct structure (one or more in each of the new nuclei), and, as it emerges into view, the chromosomes begin to lose their discrete shapes, reforming the tangled mass of chromatin. Out in the cytoplasm there is a pinching in of the cell membrane along the equator of the old cell. The furrows deepen progressively until the old cell has been transformed into two separate daughter cells, each surrounded by its own complete cell membrane. Meanwhile, the various cytoplasmic organelles have been distributed and the

centrioles have been duplicated late in the telophase. Thus, when **cytokinesis** (the division of the cytoplasm) is completed, two fully equipped, functioning interphase cells have been formed, ready to grow and perhaps ultimately to divide again.

Meiosis

If *all* cell division occurred by mitosis, an absurd situation would quickly be reached. If human gametes were formed by mitosis, then the gametes of the first man and woman would each have possessed 46 chromosomes, just like their parent cells. Then, when they combined, the resultant zygote would have had 92 chromosomes. Dividing by mitosis, it would have passed a legacy of 92 chromosomes on to each of its cell progeny. The human being who developed from the zygote would in time have produced 92-chromosome gametes, which would ultimately have yielded children whose chromosome number again would have doubled. In fifteen generations the human chromosome number would have risen to more than a million. If that seems a mind-boggling number of chromosomes to fit into the nucleus of one cell, then consider that in the long ages that have passed since the days of the first humans, mitosis would have packed so many chromosomes into each of your cells that their combined weight would far exceed the total weight of the universe! Obviously, some other variation of cell division than mitosis must be involved in the formation of gametes. This variation is meiosis, a form of cell division in which the chromosome number of the resultant daughter cells is only half that of the original parent cell.

The sequence of stages of meiosis is diagramed in a generalized form in Figure 6-11. (The specific peculiarities of meiosis in the formation of the human gametes, sperm and ova, are discussed in greater detail in Chapters 33 and 34.) As can be seen from the diagram, meiosis actually includes a sequence of two cell divisions, following one after the other.

Meiosis begins quite similarly to mitosis. During the interphase, the DNA of the chromatin is duplicated. During the first prophase of meiosis, just as in mitosis, the chromatin condenses into discrete chromosomes. But the chromosomes do not move independently, as they do in mitosis. Instead, the chromosomes of each pair (**homologous chromosomes**) come together and move as a unit. This pairing process is called **synapsis.**

In the first metaphase of meiosis, the chromosomes line up at the equatorial plane, as in mitosis, but both members of each homologous pair (i.e., a total of four chromatids) are attached to the same spindle fiber.

As anaphase I of meiosis begins, the centromeres of the chromosomes do not divide. Instead, one of each homologous pair (i.e., two sister chromatids, still at-

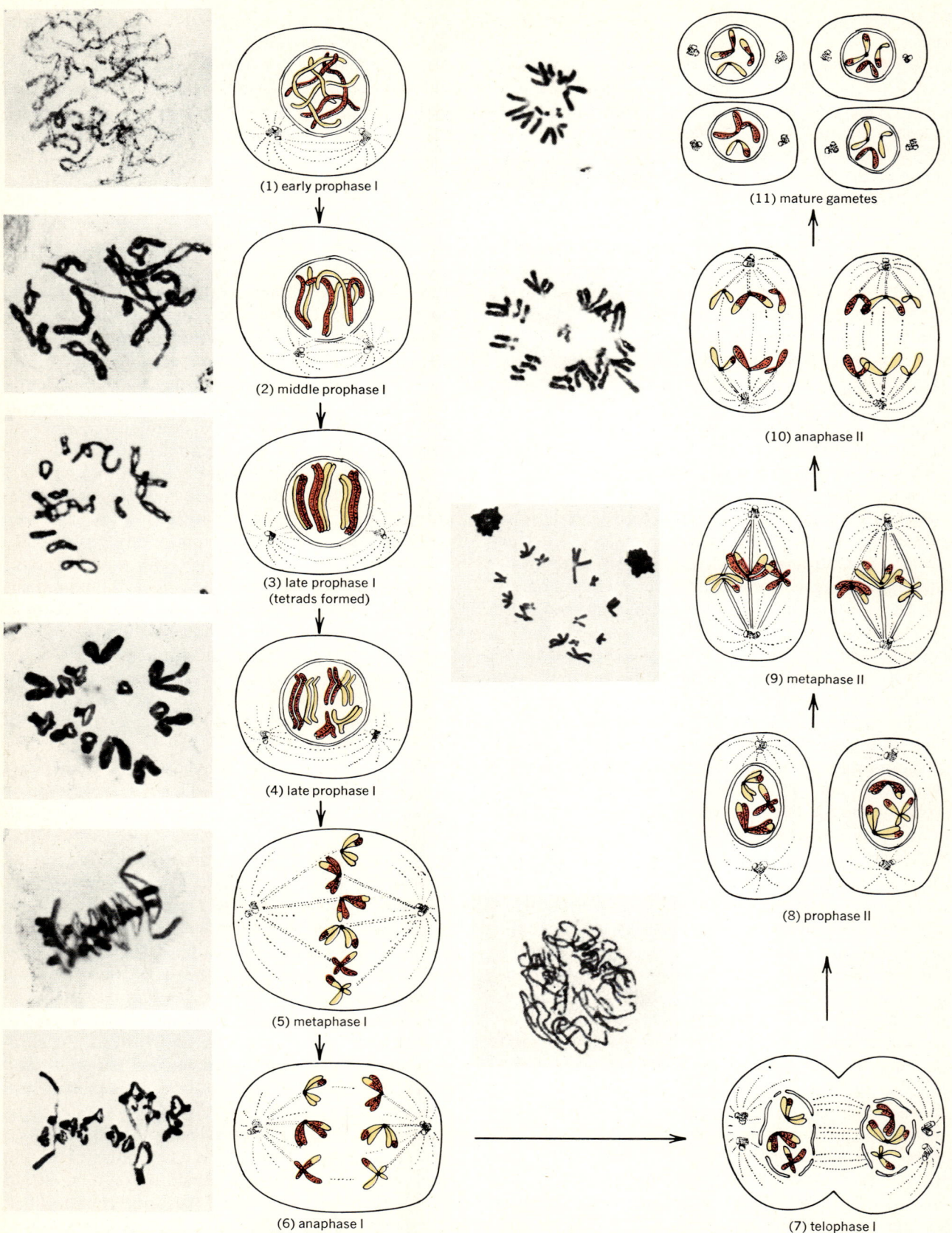

(1) early prophase I

(2) middle prophase I

(3) late prophase I (tetrads formed)

(4) late prophase I

(5) metaphase I

(6) anaphase I

(7) telophase I

(8) prophase II

(9) metaphase II

(10) anaphase II

(11) mature gametes

FIGURE 6-11   Meiosis: the diagrams outline the process in simplified form for an animal with a chromosome number of six. The photos illustrate stages of the meiotic sequence of spermatogenesis in Amphiuma.

tached) moves toward one pole of the cell, while the other moves toward the opposite pole.

Telophase I of meiosis produces two new nuclei and ultimately two separate cells, just like the telophase of mitosis. But the daughter cells of mitosis contain single-stranded chromosomes, the same number as the parent cell. The daughter cells resulting from the first division of meiosis, on the other hand, contain only half the original number of chromosomes, and they are double-stranded. Since each daughter cell has received only one of each pair of homologous chromosomes, and since homologous chromosomes, although basically similar, are rarely completely identical, the daughter cells differ in their sets of genetic information, both from each other and from the original parent. (The situation is analogous to dealing out a deck of cards to two players, giving each of them one of the black aces, one of the red aces, one of the black kings, one of the red fours, and so forth. Each player winds up with one card of every number and color. But neither has the complete assortment that was contained in the original deck.)

The first telophase of meiosis is followed by a brief period called **interkinesis,** which is similar to the interphase. But during interkinesis there is no duplication of DNA. (Remember that the chromosomes are still double-stranded.)

The second division of meiosis is essentially a mitotic division. The chromosomes move independently, the centromeres divide, the daughter chromosomes move apart to their respective poles, and the resultant nuclei contain single-stranded chromosomes.

In reductive division, or meiosis, a single parent cell gives rise to a total of four daughter cells. Each has just half the original number of chromosomes, including one of each type. (This is the **haploid** chromosome set.) In mitosis, one parent cell produces two daughter cells. Each daughter cell has the same number of chromosomes as its parent, and its assortment consists of homologous pairs, that is, two of each type. (This is the **diploid** chromosome set.) The unique features of meiosis play an important role in the transfer of hereditary information from one generation to another.

GENETICS

The field of genetics is one of the most actively researched areas of biology today. More than a dozen winners of Nobel Prizes in recent years have been working on various aspects of genetic studies. Their work has already had important practical applications in the health sciences and promises to have an even greater impact in the future. Today genetic counseling permits a realistic assessment of the hazard of bearing a mentally or physically impaired child before it is even conceived. The first tentative steps

have already been taken toward detecting and correcting hereditarily determined metabolic imbalances even before birth. It is hoped that in the not-too-distant future, scientists will be able to intervene actively in the mechanisms of heredity, to insert genes made to order to correct a specific defect, and perhaps to activate at will the genetic controls that could transform malignant cancer cells back into a normal cell.

Genetics is a subject in which a great deal of progress has been made in a relatively short time. Of course, people were applying the principles of heredity long before any really scientific studies of genetics were conducted. Farmers have capitalized on chance variations in their stock to breed desirable traits into domesticated animals and cultivated plants, probably for thousands of years. Observations that certain traits seem to run in particular human families have long been common. But the first really quantitative studies of heredity were not made until the late nineteenth century, by an obscure Austrian monk named Gregor Mendel. Working in his monastery garden, Mendel grew thousands of peas. He carefully arranged crosses between strains with different characteristics—different-colored flowers or seeds, tall plants and dwarf plants, and so on. Painstakingly tabulating his results, Mendel found that the various types of progeny were generally present in roughly whole-number ratios. At a time when little was known about the behavior of the chromosomes, or their role in heredity, Mendel derived laws of heredity that agree beautifully with modern theories and experimental findings.

Mendel's first law of heredity was called the **law of segregation.** From his observations, Mendel deduced that each adult organism possesses two distinct units or factors of heredity for each trait. In the formation of gametes, this pair of hereditary units is separated, or segregated. But at the time of fertilization, when two gametes unite, the paired relationship is restored. Current knowledge of the behavior of homologous chromosomes during meiosis now provides a firm physical foundation for Mendel's first law.

In his studies of peas, Mendel found that when there are two or more alternate variations of a particular trait, one of them is generally **dominant:** that is, when pure strains of two different varieties are crossed, the first-generation progeny show the characteristics of only one of the parent strains. But then, when these mixed-bred or **hybrid** plants are crossed with one another, the "hidden" or **recessive** trait reappears in some of the second-generation progeny (Figure 6-12).

Mendel's second law, the **law of independent assortment,** dealt with the inheritance of two or more unrelated traits. According to Mendel's findings with peas,

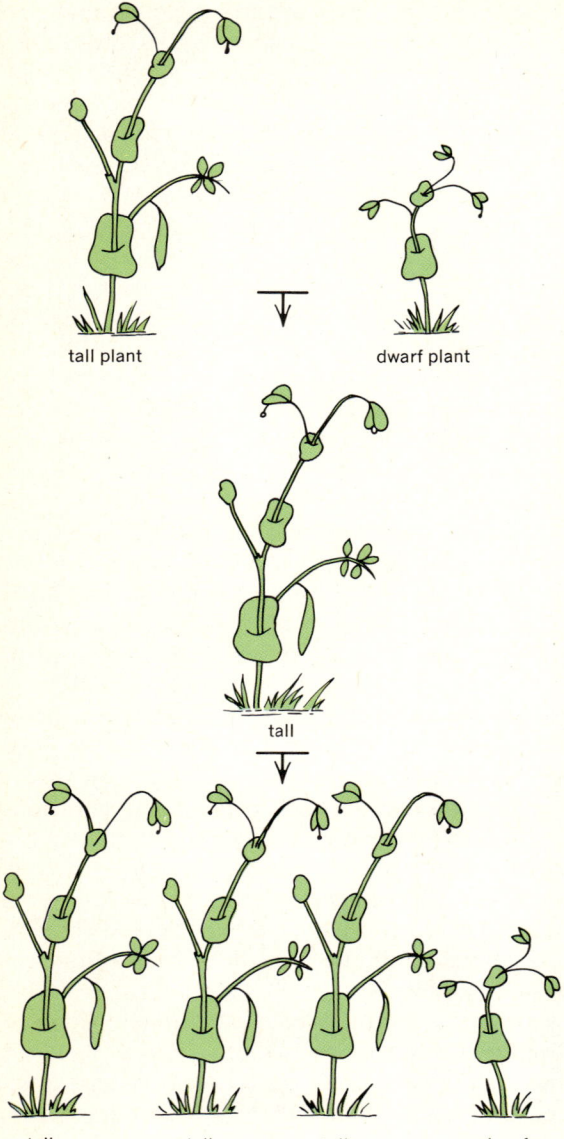

tall plant

dwarf plant

tall

tall   tall   tall   dwarf

FIGURE 6-12 One of Mendel's experiments: crossing tall plants with dwarfs yielded all tall plants in the first-generation progeny, but self-pollination of the hybrid plants gave a 3:1 ratio of tall to dwarf plants in the second generation. (In humans the hereditary determination of height is more complicated, and shortness is dominant.)

term **gene** was coined for Mendel's units of heredity, and the term **allele** came to be used for alternate variations of a particular gene (e.g., the genes for blue eyes and brown eyes, or the A and B blood types). It was determined that the genes are small regions of the chromosomes; much later, after it was realized that DNA is the carrier of the hereditary information, it was computed that each human gene contains about a thousand nucleotide pairs. (Since the average length of a human chromosome is about 175 million nucleotide pairs, and there are 46 chromosomes in the human set, each of your cells contains about eight million genes!) Each gene carries the information for the synthesis of one cell protein, either an enzyme or a structural protein.

Look back at Figure 6-12 for a moment. If you think about the sequence of parents and progeny, you will notice that the **phenotype** (the overt expression of a particular trait) may be quite different from the **genotype** (the hereditary information—that is, genes—determining the expression of that trait). The F_1 (first-generation) progeny looked just like one of their parents, but their genetic heritage was quite different, since it included both dominant and recessive genes. What do you think the genotypes of the tall plants in the F_2 (second-generation) progeny were? Were they all the same?

In genetic experiments, an unknown genotype can be determined through carefully arranged crosses of parents with particular phenotypes. In humans, whose matings cannot be arranged to suit the convenience of the geneticist, the inheritance of traits is laboriously traced through pedigrees, records of the transmission of a particular trait through the generations in a particular family. Much information about the genotypes of individuals can be deduced from such studies. A simple device called the Punnett square was invented by the English geneticist R. C. Punnett to predict the results of crosses. Its use is illustrated in Figure 6-13, which diagrams the inheritance of brown hair and blond hair. Notice that only a person with blond hair genes on each of the corresponding pair of homologous chromosomes can show the blond hair phenotype. The person is said to be **homozygous** for the blond hair trait. A person with brown hair may be either homozygous (two brown hair genes) or **heterozygous** for the hair color trait (carrying both blond and brown hair genes, one on each of the homologous chromosomes). (As might be imagined, the principles of the inheritance of human hair color were worked out before the use of hair dyes became so prevalent—today the human phenotype is fast becoming as difficult to discover as the genotype.)

As Mendel's laws were refined and expanded in later studies, it was discovered that to some extent they are oversimplifications. From the genetic stand-

two or more pairs of hereditary factors may assort at random during the formation of gametes, and each pair is distributed independently of the others. If a pea plant with yellow round seeds, for example, is crossed with a plant with green wrinkled seeds, all the first-generation progeny will have yellow round seeds. But then the second-generation progeny will include four variations: yellow round, yellow wrinkled, green round, and green wrinkled, in a ratio of approximately 9:3:3:1.

After the turn of the century, there was a burgeoning of scientific interest in the field of heredity. The

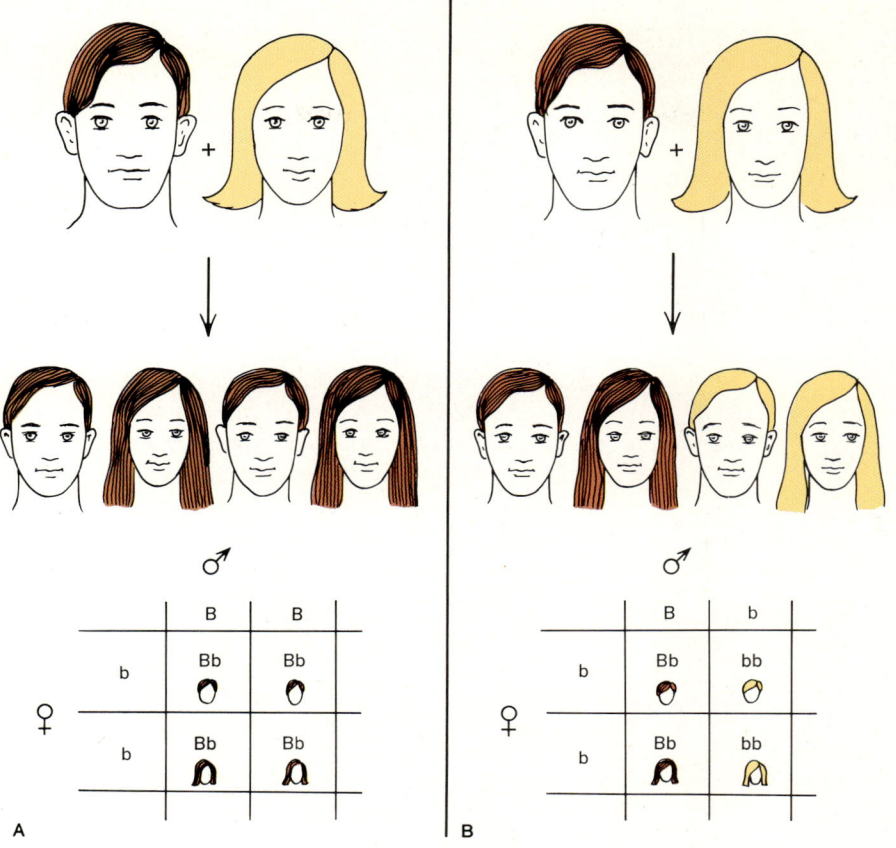

FIGURE 6-13 The inheritance of brown and blond hair: the brown hair gene is dominant to its blond allele. In (A) the brown-haired parent is homozygous and all children will be brown-haired. In (B) the brown-haired parent is heterozygous and the children are likely to be half brown-haired, half blond. (Actual ratios obtained may differ greatly because of variations from statistical probability in small samples.)

point, the pea is a rather simple organism. It has only 14 chromosomes (seven pairs) and, as it turned out, the seven traits that Mendel selected for study happen to be governed by seven genes, located one on each of the seven kinds of chromosomes. Studies of other organisms have revealed important exceptions to Mendel's laws.

First of all, although dominance-recessiveness is still a key concept in genetics, it is not always complete. Mendel might have arrived at quite different conclusions if he had worked with the four-o'clock instead of the pea. In this plant, if a parent with red flowers is crossed with a parent with white flowers, all the F_1 progeny have pink flowers. (In the F_2 progeny, red, pink, and white flowers appear in a ratio of about 1:2:1, so Mendel's law of segregation is still obeyed.) In human heredity there are numerous examples of **incomplete dominance,** such as the M and N blood groups (if both alleles are present, the blood type is MN) and the inheritance of curly hair (a combination of curly and straight hair alleles results in a wavy hair phenotype).

If Mendel had happened to study two traits controlled by genes on the same chromosome, he never would have derived his law of independent assortment. For such traits are generally inherited together, and in genetic parlance are said to be **linked.**

An important class in the category of linked characters is formed by the **sex-linked** traits—those that appear far more often in members of one sex than in the other. Up to now, we have spoken of the human chromosome set as consisting of 23 matching pairs. This is not strictly correct. Although the homologous pairs of chromosomes in the female chromosome set are all matching pairs (Figure 6-14A), in the chromosome set from the cells of a human male (Figure 6-14B) it can be seen that in one pair the chromosomes do not "match"—one is much shorter than the other. The 23rd pair of human chromosomes is called the sex chromosomes. They contain various genes associated with the reproductive organs and their functions, and they determine the sex of an individual: the female genotype is XX (two of the longer sex chromosomes), while the male genotype is XY (one of each type).

The sex chromosomes, particularly the X chromosome, also contain numerous genes controlling traits that are not associated with reproduction. These genes are sex-linked, inherited along with the sex chromosomes. For example, genes determining blood clotting factors are found on the human X chromosome. A defect of these genes results in hemophilia, the "bleeders' disease." People with hemophilia may die from a relatively minor cut or a routine surgical

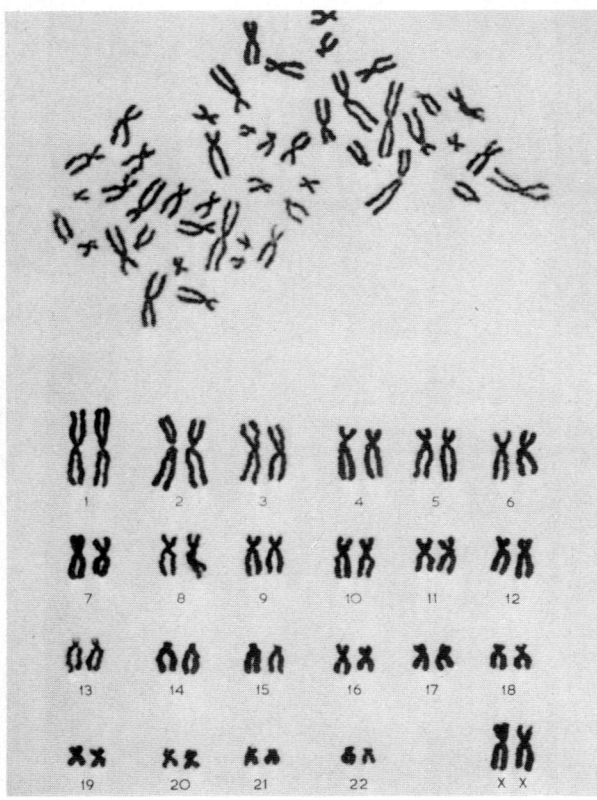

A

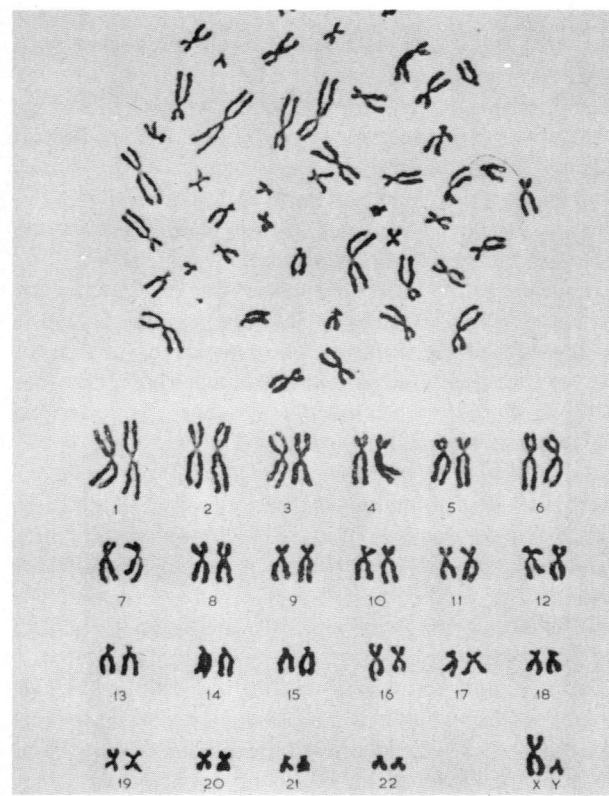

B

FIGURE 6-14 Human karyotypes: female (A) and male (B). Chromosome smears are shown above, and the idiograph below.

procedure, because their blood does not clot normally. If a recessive gene, such as the hemophilia gene, appears on one of the X chromosomes of a female, there may be a corresponding dominant allele on her other X chromosome to mask its presence. The female is thus heterozygous for the trait; in the case of hemophilia, since the defective gene is recessive, such a person's blood will clot normally. But if this recessive gene is passed on to a son, he will have no homologous X chromosome, and the recessive allele will be expressed in his phenotype—a boy or man carrying the hemophilia gene will be a "bleeder." Sex-linked characteristics, inherited with the X chromosome, often tend to "skip over" the women in a line of descent (who are carriers of the gene) and are expressed only in the male members of the family. (Each son of a woman carrying one recessive allele on an X chromosome has a 50 percent chance of inheriting the trait, since he can receive either one or the other of his mother's X chromosomes.) The trait can be expressed in a female only if she had inherited a "double dose" of the allele, one on an X chromosome from each parent—that is, if she is homozygous for the trait. The most famous example of hemophilia occurred in the past century in the royal families of Europe. According to the pedigree compiled later (see Figure 19-20 on page 000), Queen Victoria of England apparently passed a hemophilia gene on to some of her children, and the cases of the disease that popped up in succeeding generations had a profound effect on the history of the world. In looking at the pedigree, you may notice that nearly all the male hemophilia sufferers died young, and no women in the family suffered from the disease, although there were a number of carriers. Now that at least limited supplies of clotting factors are available for treating hemophilia patients, the disease is not necessarily so rapidly fatal. As more boys with hemophilia survive to adulthood and marry, the incidence of the disease among women will probably rise. Indeed, in the case of color blindness, a sex-linked defect that is far less disadvantageous from the standpoint of survival, the trait is observed in women in just about the expected percentage of cases (far less than in men).

Just as the existence of linkage was found to be an exception to Mendel's second law, it has subsequently been found that there are exceptions to the concept of gene linkage. Two genes located on the same chromosome are generally inherited together, but in a small yet statistically significant percentage of cases they are found to assort independently, just as though they were on different chromosomes. The explanation for this paradox has been found in the phenomenon of **crossing-over.** During synapsis in meiosis, the homologous chromosome pairs are closely associated, often with the arms of the chromosomes intertwined.

At this time it is possible for a breakage and rejoining to occur at the point where one chromosome crosses over the other (Figure 6-15). Afterward, the end of the arm of one chromosome may be attached to the homologous chromosome, and vice versa. Through this exchange of genetic material between the homologous chromosomes, linked genes are separated and are subsequently inherited independently. As might be expected, crossing-over occurs more frequently the farther apart two genes are along the chromosome. As a result, geneticists have been able to compile detailed gene maps of individual chromosomes on the basis of the relative frequencies of crossing-over between pairs of linked genes.

One of the most important concepts of genetics that has been formulated in this century is that of **mutation.** It had long been known that occasional "sports" arose in pure lines of animals or plants—offspring that showed a sudden and discontinuous change of some trait from the parental form. Twentieth-century geneticists found that such sudden changes or mutations may be caused by a variety of factors, including X rays and other radiations, high temperatures, and certain chemicals **(mutagens).** As more was learned about the nature of the genetic material, it was found that mutations can arise in various ways.

There may be a change in the number of chromosomes. For example, if cytokinesis did not occur on schedule and the DNA were replicated again before the cell finally divided, the resultant gametes would be diploid, and the progeny would have one-and-a-half or two times the normal number of chromosomes. Such cases, referred to as **polyploidy,** are very rare in animals, although they do occur commonly in plants. In animals (including man), there are numerous instances in which the chromosome number is one more or less than the normal complement (e.g., 47 or 45 in man). This effect would be produced if something went wrong in the movement of the chromosomes to their respective poles during cell division—if one chromosome went the wrong way. In humans this phenomenon, called **nondisjunction,** occurs more frequently with increasing age of the mother, which is one of the reasons why birth defects are more frequent in children of older mothers. One

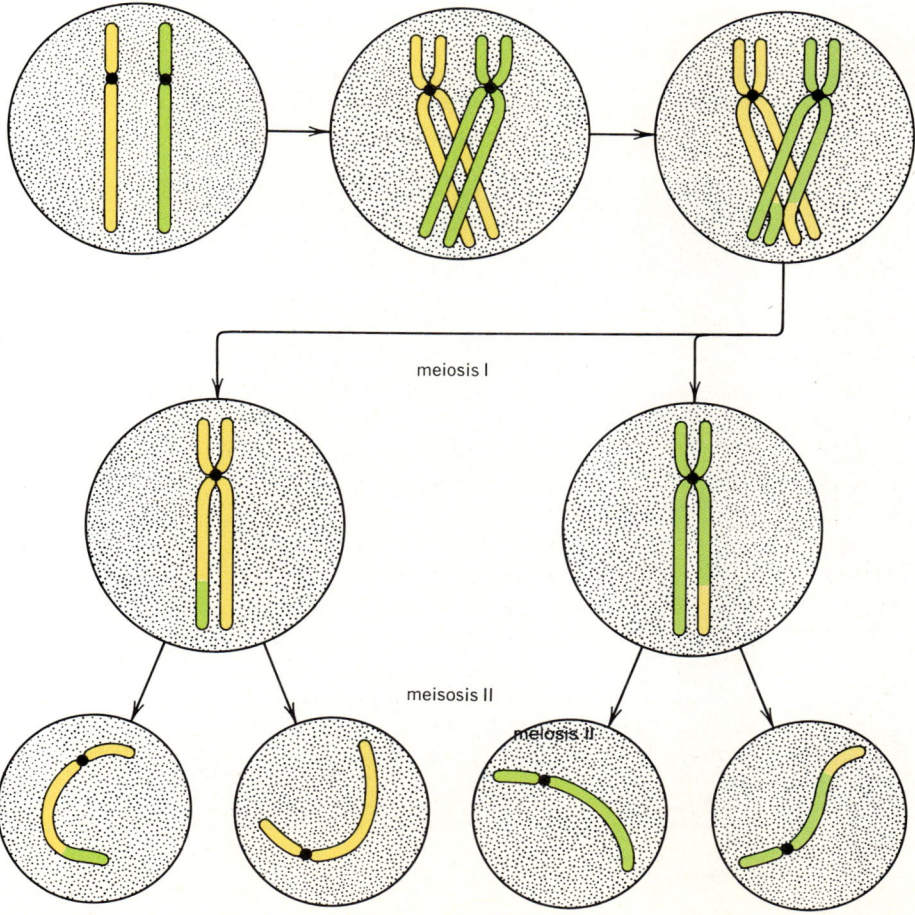

FIGURE 6-15 Crossing-over: portions of homologous chromosomes are exchanged during meiosis, resulting in a redistribution of linked genes.

meiosis I

meiosis II

meiosis II

common result of nondisjunction in humans is Down's syndrome (Figure 6-16), characterized by the presence of an extra chromosome 21, and expressed in mental retardation and a characteristic constellation of physical characteristics. Nondisjunction may also affect the sex chromosomes. Individuals with an XO genotype (only one X chromosome and no Y chromosomes) have been observed: they are sterile, rather undeveloped females. The XXY genotype produces a male with somewhat feminized characteristics. There was a brief flurry of publicity in the press when it was discovered that a number of murderers and other violent criminals had an XYY genotype. But although this excess of "maleness" may be a predisposing factor to aggressive behavior, the XYY genotype is also possessed by numerous law-abiding citizens who show no obvious deviations from the norm.

Other mutations might arise through damages to the chromosomes. Various influences, such as chemicals or radiations, can produce breaks in chromosomes. They may remain broken, or the cell's repair systems may neatly rejoin the broken pieces. But they may not be rejoined correctly (Figure 6-17). A chromosome fragment might be reattached backward, or joined to a different chromosome. In the case of multiple breaks, a fragment might be omitted when the ends of the chromosome are rejoined, or an extra fragment might be added. All these types of chromosome damage and their mutant effects have been observed in lower organisms and humans.

Even a change in a single nitrogen base in DNA might give rise to a mutation. The blood disease sickle-cell anemia, for example, has been traced to a change in just one amino acid residue in the hemoglobin molecule: the replacement of glutamic acid by valine. This insignificant-seeming change—in only one out of about 300 amino acids—happens to be in a key spot and changes the properties of the hemoglobin molecule, so that a sickle-cell anemia patient's red blood cells may suddenly assume a half-moon shape, stick together in clumps, and block small blood vessels, causing pain, illness, and even death. Each amino acid in a protein is assembled according to precise instructions spelled out in the base sequences of nucleic acids, and thus the sickle-cell mutation can be traced back to a single change in a portion of the gene containing the blueprints for hemoglobin synthesis.

The focus of attention in genetics in recent years has been precisely at this molecular level. One of the greatest achievements in molecular genetics was the cracking of the genetic code in the early 1960s, through the studies of Marshall Nirenberg, Severo Ochoa, and others. Although their work was done on material from microorganisms, it has subsequently been shown that the **genetic code,** relating the "four-letter alphabet" of the nitrogen bases of nucleic acids to the "twenty-letter alphabet" of amino acids in proteins, is a general phenomenon, applicable to all earth's organisms, including humans.

It was mentioned in Chapter 3 that messenger

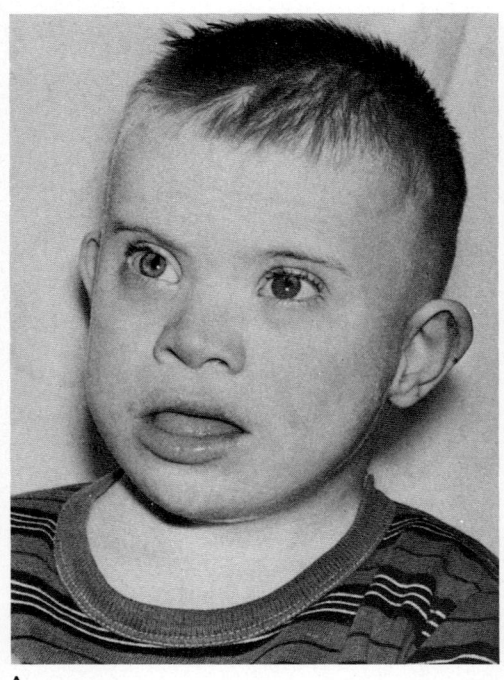
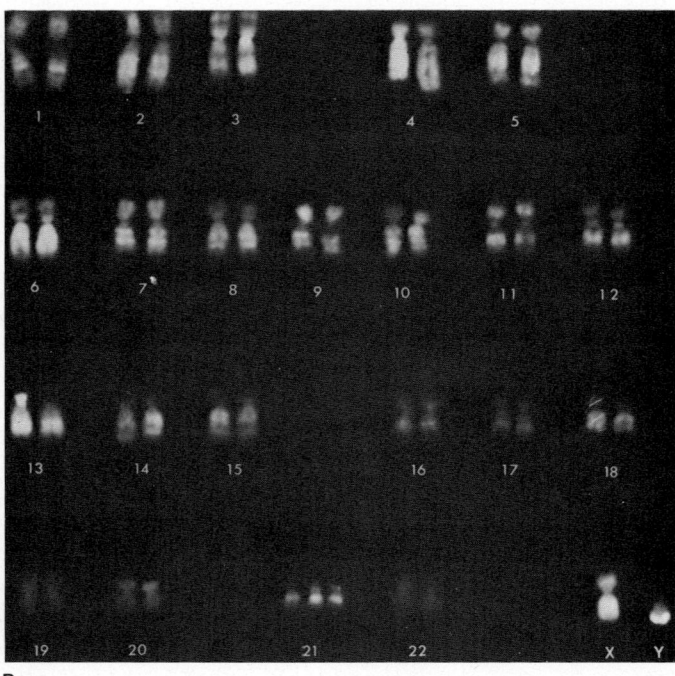

A   B

FIGURE 6-16 A child with Down's syndrome (A) and a karyotype showing the 21 trisomy responsible for the condition (B).

RNA, synthesized on a portion of the DNA molecule, in turn serves as a pattern or template for the assembly of amino acids into proteins at the ribosomes. Each successive amino acid is determined by a sequence of three nucleotides along the RNA strand. This is the "code," and the three-nucleotide sequences are called **codons.** The first breakthrough in cracking the genetic code came when Nirenberg added a synthetic polynucleotide containing only one of the nitrogen bases, polyuridylic acid, to a system containing the components for protein synthesis. Although all twenty amino acids were present, the polypeptide formed on the polyuridylic acid template contained only one of them, phenylalanine. The codon for phenylalanine was thus UUU. In an ingenious series of experiments, Nirenberg, Ochoa, and other researchers worked out the codons corresponding to all the amino acids and compiled a complete "dictionary" of the genetic code (Table 6-1).

Current research in molecular genetics is pursuing a number of exciting avenues. Genes have been synthesized in the laboratory from mixtures of nucleotides, together with suitable enzymes, without the intervention of living organisms. Each year brings more information about the nature of the "on–off switches" that control the development of the organism; their mastery may ultimately make it possible to stop cancer cells from proliferating and to regenerate limbs and organs to replace lost body parts. In the budding field of genetic engineering, scientists are striving to

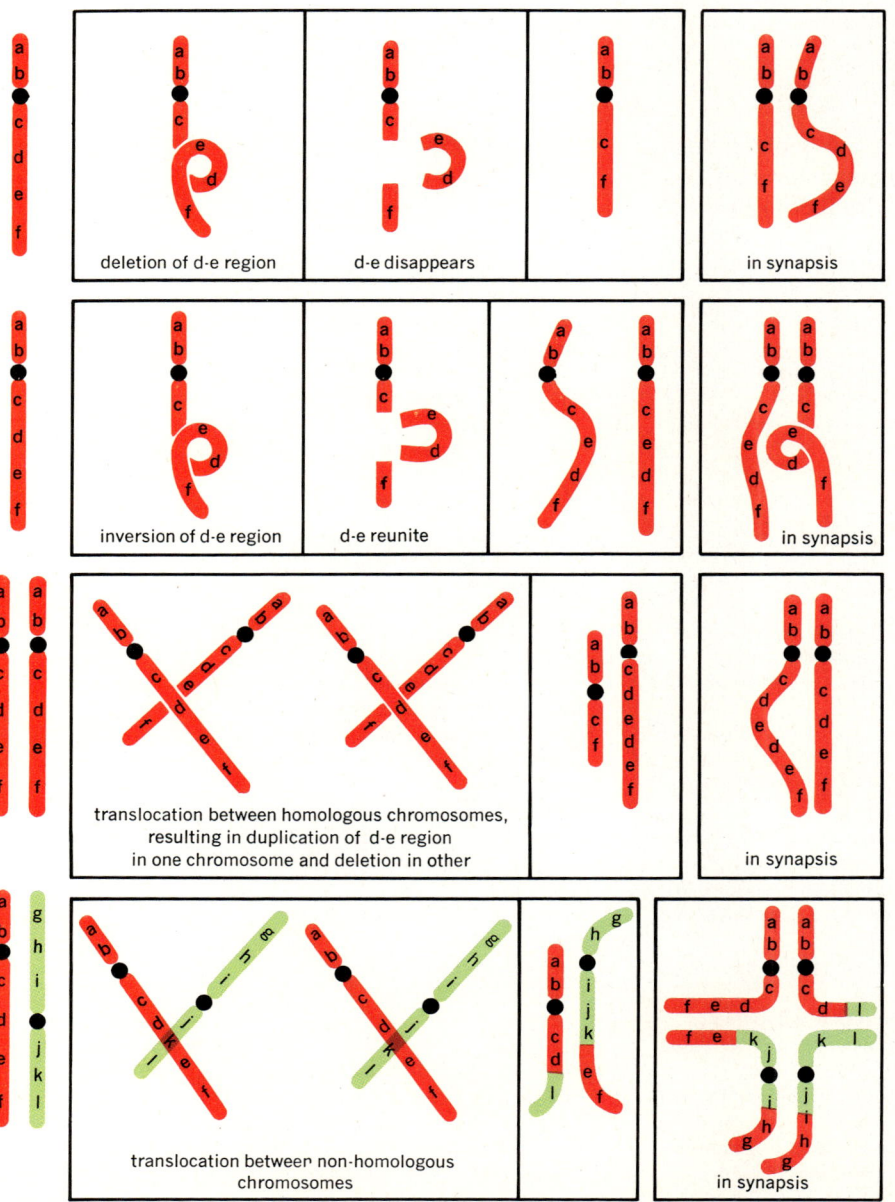

FIGURE 6-17 Various types of chromosome mutations. In synapsis (the pairing of homologous chromosomes), each type presents a characteristic picture in electron micrographs.

deletion of d-e region

d-e disappears

in synapsis

inversion of d-e region

d-e reunite

in synapsis

translocation between homologous chromosomes, resulting in duplication of d-e region in one chromosome and deletion in other

in synapsis

translocation between non-homologous chromosomes

in synapsis

TABLE 6-1 The genetic code

AAU }	Asparagine	GAU }	Aspartic acid	CAU }	Histidine	UAU }	Tyrosine
AAC }		GAC }		CAC }		UAC }	
AAA }	Lysine	GAA }	Glutamic acid	CAA }	Glutamine	UAA }	Stop signals
AAG }		GAG }		CAG }		UAG }	
AGU }	Serine	GGU }	Glycine	CGU }	Arginine	UGU }	Cysteine
AGC }		GGC }		CGC }		UGC }	
AGA }	Arginine	GGA }		CGA }		UGA	Stop signal
AGG }		GGG }		CGG }		UGG	Tryptophan
AUU }	Isoleucine	GUU }	Valine	CUU }	Leucine	UUU }	Phenylalanine
AUC }		GUC }		CUC }		UUC }	
AUA }		GUA }		CUA }		UUA }	Leucine
AUG	Methionine	GUG }		CUG }		UUG }	
ACU }	Threonine	GCU }	Alanine	CCU }	Proline	UCU }	Serine
ACC }		GCC }		CCC }		UCC }	
ACA }		GCA }		CCA }		UCA }	
ACG }		GCG }		CCG }		UCG }	

find ways to repair defective genes or replace them with new genes, made to order. These and other new techniques may ultimately provide millions of people suffering from genetic disorders with a chance to lead a normal life.

SUMMARY

The continual exchange of materials between the intracellular fluid and the extracellular fluid is regulated by the cell membrane.

The transport of matter in the body occurs by the mechanisms:

Diffusion
Osmosis
Filtration
Active transport
Pinocytosis and phagocytosis

Diffusion is the movement of molecules or ions along a concentration gradient.

It requires no external input of energy; it is driven by the inherent random kinetic movements of the molecules or ions.

Diffusion can occur through a permeable or semipermeable membrane.

Dialysis is the diffusion of solute molecules or ions through a membrane.

Osmosis is the diffusion of solvent molecules through a membrane that is impermeable to the solute.

Facilitated diffusion involves carrier substances but proceeds along the concentration gradient.

Two solutions, separated by a semipermeable membrane, are isotonic if they have the same concentrations of the same solute and solvent.

If one solution has a higher solute concentration, it is hypertonic to the other.

The solution with a lower solute concentration is hypotonic.

In a hypertonic medium, osmosis produces crenation of blood cells.

In a hypotonic medium, osmosis produces hemolysis of blood cells.

Filtration is driven by a pressure difference across a membrane.

Active transport is the transport of molecules or ions through a cell membrane against the concentration gradient.

It is an energy-requiring process, powered by ATP produced in cell respiration.

The mechanism of active transport involves a carrier substance.

Examples of active transport include the sodium pump, which transports sodium ions out of cells, and the potassium pump, which transports potassium ions into cells.

Phagocytosis is a mode of ingestion of large particles, bacteria, and so forth, by the cell by means of engulfing.

Pinocytosis is a mode of ingestion of liquids and suspended particles by the cell through the formation of a vesicle.

Homeostasis refers to constancy of the internal environment of living organisms.

Various body mechanisms maintain constant pH, temperature, and so on.

Deviations from normal values of body indices may signal disease.

Characteristics of living organisms include:

Organization
Excitability (irritability)
Conductivity
Contractility
Metabolism (anabolism and catabolism)
Growth and reproduction

Mitosis is a process of cell division in which the two daughter cells formed are exact copies of the parent cell, with a diploid chromosome set.

Meiosis is a reductive variant of cell division in which each daughter cell receives only half the hereditary information of the parent cell (a haploid chromosome set); gametes are formed by meiosis.

The phases of mitosis include:

Interphase
Prophase
Metaphase
Anaphase
Telophase

DNA replication occurs during the interphase.

As mitosis proceeds, the thin, tangled chromatin strands condense into discrete, rodlike chromosomes, which are precisely distributed between the two daughter cells forming.

The division of the cytoplasm is called cytokinesis; the division of the nucleus is called karyokinesis.

The phases of meiosis include:
Interphase
Prophase I
Metaphase I
Anaphase I
Telophase I
Interkinesis
Prophase II
Metaphase II
Anaphase II
Telophase II
The process of meiosis consists of two successive cell divisions, without any DNA replication in the interkinesis.
During prophase I of meiosis, the homologous chromosomes pair up and move as a unit (synapsis).
In anaphase I of meiosis, the members of each homologous pair of chromosomes move toward opposite poles.
The foundation of modern genetics (the science of heredity) was laid by the studies of Gregor Mendel on garden peas.
Mendel's contributions include:
The law of segregation
The law of independent assortment
The concepts of dominance and recessiveness
A gene is the unit of heredity; alleles are alternate variations of a particular gene.
Each gene carries the information for the synthesis of one cell protein.
The phenotype is the overt expression of a trait; the genotype is the hereditary information determining the expression of a trait.
A person homozygous for a trait carries only one type of gene (identical alleles) for that trait; a person heterozygous for the trait carries two different alleles.
Some important concepts of genetics formulated after Mendel are:
Incomplete dominance
Linkage of genes (including sex linkage)
Crossing-over
Mutation
Mutations (sudden hereditary changes) may be caused by radiations, high temperature, and chemical mutagens.

Types of mutations include polyploidy, nondisjunction, chromosome breakage and rejoining, and chemical changes in the nitrogen bases of DNA.
The genetic code translates from the "four-letter alphabet" of nitrogen bases in nucleic acids to the "twenty-letter alphabet" of amino acids in proteins by means of three-nucleotide codons.
Current genetic research is focused on the synthesis and analysis of genes and their "on-off switches." Genetic engineering aims to repair or replace defective genes.

QUESTIONS FOR REVIEW AND THOUGHT

1 Why is a *semipermeable* cell membrane essential to the effective functioning of the cell? Discuss in terms of metabolism and entropy.

2 Distinguish among: diffusion, osmosis, dialysis, filtration.

3 Why are diffusion processes alone inadequate for all the cell's transport needs?

4 Discuss the concept of homeostasis and the body's homeostatic mechanisms.

5 You are the exobiologist of Starship *Santa Maria*. The survey team has just brought in several objects that look like furry purple pincushions. What criteria can you use to determine whether they are alive?

6 Trace the sequences of events in mitosis and meiosis. How do they differ?

7 Follow the changes in human chromosome number during: (a) a mitotic cycle, from interphase to interphase; (b) a complete process of meiosis.

8 Blue eyes are recessive and brown eyes dominant. A blue-eyed woman marries a brown-eyed man. Can they have blue-eyed children? Do the phenotypes of the parents provide enough information to give a definite answer? Explain.

9 A normal man marries a woman carrying a gene for the sex-linked trait of color blindness. Use a Punnett square to diagram the possible inheritance of the trait by their sons and daughters.

10 On the basis of the genetic code shown in Table 6-1, what single substitution of a nitrogen base could result in the replacement of glutamic acid by valine in the hemoglobin of sickle-cell anemia patients?

THE SKIN

7

Would you be tempted by an ad for a coat that was waterproof, stretchable, washable, needed no ironing, automatically repaired small cuts, rips, and burns with "invisible mending," and was guaranteed to last a lifetime with reasonable care? Such advertising would probably sound too good to be true. Yet you already have such a "coat"—the skin that covers every square inch of your outer body surface.

The skin, or **integument,** is far more than just a covering for the body. It **protects** the body from invasion by microbes, from injury to delicate underlying tissues, from the injurious effects of chemicals, and from damage by ultraviolet radiation of the sun, thus serving as both a **mechanical and** a **chemical barrier** between the body and the environment. The skin is a **waterproof coating,** protecting the body from dehydration due to excessive loss of water. The skin also plays a key role in **temperature regulation,** helping to retain body heat in a cold environment and dissipate excess heat when the body needs cooling. Skin contains numerous **sense organs,** which signal sensations of heat and cold, touch, pressure, and pain. When skin is exposed to sunlight, it **synthesizes vitamin D,** thus providing an essential substance for the body. The skin acts as an **excretory organ,** eliminating water, sodium chloride, and urea through the sweat glands. It also serves as a site of **storage** of fat, water, glucose, and sodium chloride.

With all these varied functions, the skin is also one of the most self-sufficient of the body organs. It is self-lubricating through the secretions of the sebaceous (oil) glands, and it is constantly self-renewing, with an extraordinary potential for healing.

Normally the surface of the skin is inhabited by a characteristic **microflora,** an assortment of generally harmless microorganisms. Certain diseases or poor habits of personal hygiene may upset the skin's natural "ecology" and promote the proliferation of pathogenic (disease-causing) bacteria and fungi, especially in such potential trouble spots as the genital and anal regions and between the toes.

STRUCTURE OF THE SKIN

If the skin of an average adult human were stretched out flat, it would completely cover a large dinner table, three by seven feet. With a total surface area of about 1.75 square meters (3000 square inches), human skin weighs about six pounds—nearly twice as much as the brain. On a living human, of course, skin is not a flat oblong, but is supply fitted over all the curves and appendages of the body. The relative distribution of skin-covered body surface area breaks down roughly as follows:

Head and neck	9%
Trunk	36%
Upper extremity	18%
Lower extremity	36%
Perineum	1%

Skin is not uniform; it is actually a two-layered covering, made up of two different types of tissues. The outer layer, the **epidermis,** is composed of epithelial tissue. The inner, thicker layer, the **dermis,** consists of dense connective tissue. The two layers are cemented together at a boundary that is not pancake-flat, but instead presents a wavy appearance, with numerous indentations (Figure 7-1). As seen from the figure, both the epidermis and the dermis are further subdivided into layers, which show up distinctly in sections of thick skin, such as that of the back or the soles of the feet. Bundles of collagenous fibers extending downward from the dermis firmly anchor the skin in the underlying tissue, the **superficial fascia.**

The skin contains several types of accessory organs, which are derived from the epidermis: sweat and sebaceous glands, and hair; nails are another appendage of the skin, restricted to the ends of the fingers and toes. It has been calculated that a single square inch of human skin contains an average of 20 blood vessels, 65 hairs, 100 sebaceous glands, 650 sweat glands, 28 nerves, 13 sense receptors for cold, 78 for heat, 165 for pressure, and 1300 for pain.

EPIDERMIS

Beauty, it is said, is only skin deep. This proverb reflects the fact that the skin is the portion of the body that each of us presents to the view of the world. Technically speaking, not all of the skin is seen, but just the outermost layer of the epidermis. And surprisingly, the skin cells that are visible—whether on the petal-soft skin of a baby or the dry, wrinkled skin of the aged—are dead!

On reflection, it is really not too surprising that the outer layer of the epidermis is composed of dead cells. The living cells of the body are bathed in a fluid environment, in which the pH, chemical content, and various other factors are carefully controlled. Yet the outer cells of the skin are in direct contact with the uncontrollable external environment. Instead of tissue fluid, they are bathed in air. Living cells could not survive under such conditions.

Depending on the thickness of the skin, the epidermis contains from two to four zones of stratified squamous epithelium. The outermost layers contain increasing amounts of a horny protein, **keratin.** In thick skin, the four zones of the epidermis are (from the outside in): the **stratum corneum** ("horny layer"), **stratum lucidum** ("clear layer"), **stratum granulosum** ("granular layer"), and **stratum germinativum** ("growing layer").

The stratum corneum is the major portion of the

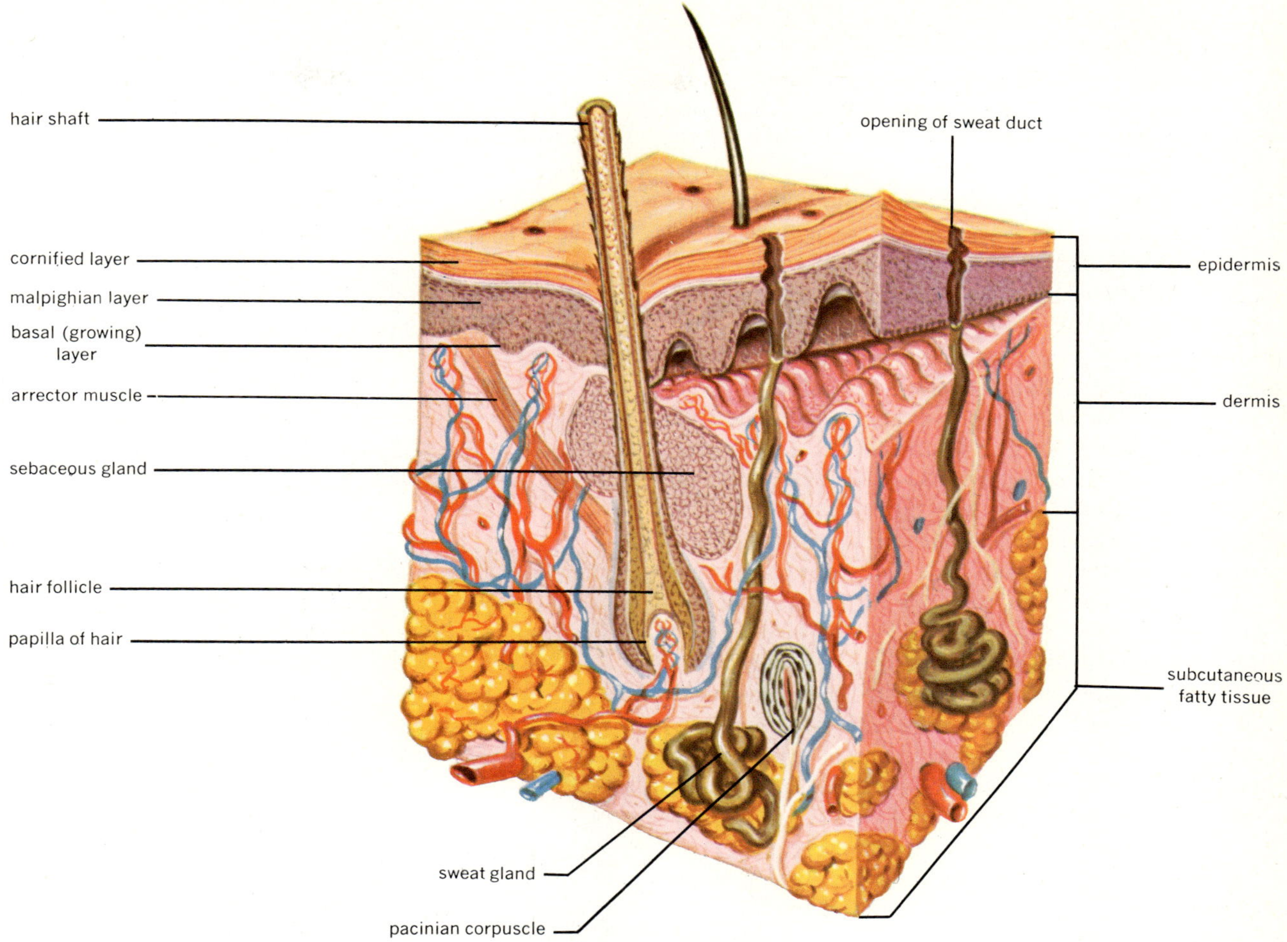

hair shaft

opening of sweat duct

cornified layer

epidermis

malpighian layer

basal (growing) layer

dermis

arrector muscle

sebaceous gland

hair follicle

papilla of hair

subcutaneous fatty tissue

sweat gland

pacinian corpuscle

FIGURE 7-1 Microscopic sections of the skin. In the artist's rendering, a portion of the epidermis is shown raised to expose the dermal papillae. The micrograph shows a section through thick skin of the palm of the hand.

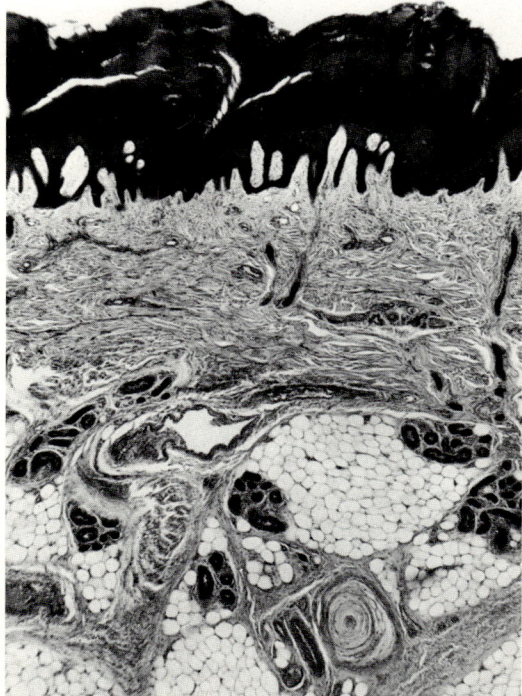

barrier that the skin presents to the outside world. Its cells are dead and highly keratinized; they contain only 20 percent water (compared to 70 percent in most living cells). The thickness of the stratum corneum varies over the parts of the body; it is thickest in regions that receive the greatest stimulation by abrasion and weight bearing, such as the soles of the feet. The keratin of the stratum corneum imparts its waterproof properties. The cells of this layer are poor conductors of heat; they not only aid in retaining body heat, but provide some protection from burns. The outermost cells of the epidermis have an acid pH, which apparently helps to destroy certain microorganisms.

The stratum lucidum is a thin layer of flattened cells, which appear translucent in stained sections. They contain a keratinlike substance called **eleidin.** These cells are dead—no nuclei are present, and no mitosis can be seen.

The stratum granulosum is a layer of dying cells. Some cell nuclei can be seen, but the most conspicuous feature of these cells is the granules of dark-staining **keratohyalin.**

The deepest layer of the epidermis, the stratum germinativum, is the living layer. It is subdivided into the spiny layer and, beneath it, the basal layer. The spiny layer consists of polygonal, flattened cells, with tiny spinelike projections connecting them with other cells. The basal layer is composed of columnar or cuboidal epithelium, resting on a basement membrane. Cells of the stratum germinativum multiply actively. They give rise to the other layers of epidermis in a continuous progression. Outer cells of the stratum corneum are continually being sloughed or rubbed off. (You may have noticed whitish flakes of "dead skin" when you rub yourself after a bath; the process is accelerated in the case of "peeling" after a sunburn.) Meanwhile, as the outermost layers are lost, cells in the lower layers of the epidermis undergo progressive changes, losing their living structures and becoming keratinized as they are displaced outward toward the surface.

Some of the cells of the stratum germinativum, called **melanocytes,** are specialized for the production of the dark pigment **melanin.** The amount of melanin in the skin is the major determinant of the varying shades of skin color. (It produces the black and brown shades; the pinkish color of "white" skin is an effect of the blood vessels in the underlying dermis. Yellow tones are imparted by another pigment, **carotene,** found in the stratum corneum and the fatty regions of the dermis.) The activity of the melanocytes is genetically determined. More melanin is produced among certain population groups than in others; this is the basis of color differences among races (Figure 7-2). The activity of the melanocytes is also stimulated by exposure to sunlight. The resultant "suntan" is a protective response: the additional melanin produced screens out potentially harmful ultraviolet rays from sunlight, protecting the underlying tissues. Dark-skinned people have a greater natural protection from sun rays, but the shielding effect of melanin limits the amount of vitamin D that their skin can produce.* This adaptation to regions of intense sunlight gives rise to an increased need for dietary sources of vitamin D among dark-skinned people living in temperate regions of the world.

If you have ever accidentally stitched your finger while sewing, you may have discovered firsthand another characteristic of epidermis: it has no blood vessels and is very sparsely supplied with nerves. It is possible to prick the epidermis with a needle without drawing any blood or even feeling any pain.

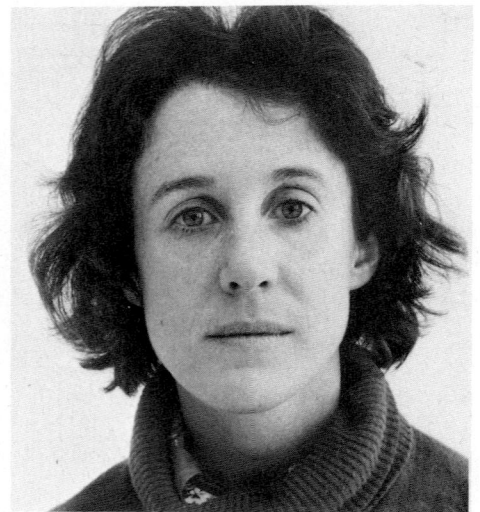

A

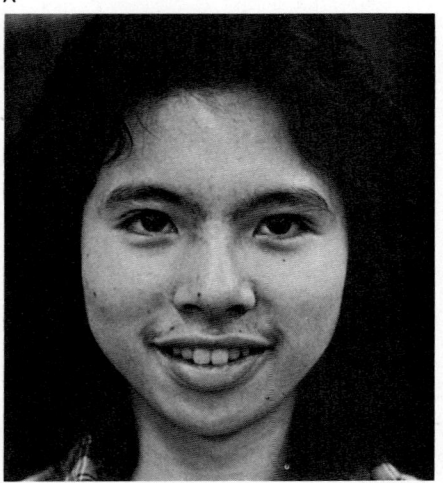

B

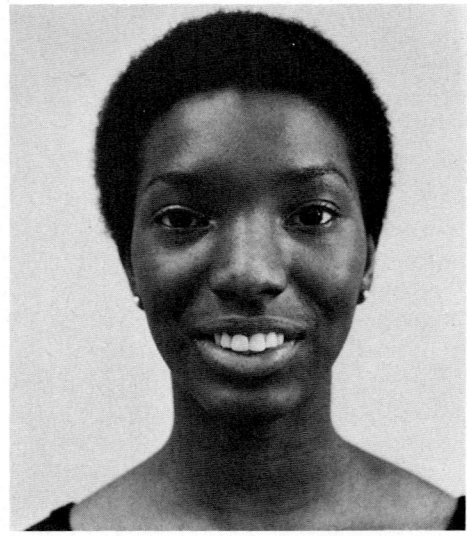

C

FIGURE 7-2 **Skin color differences among races are due to genetically determined differences in melanin production. Note the gradation in typical representatives of the Caucasoid (A), Mongoloid (B), and Negroid (C) races.**

---

* The active form of the vitamin is produced when solar radiation interacts with steroid compounds in the skin. The synthetic vitamin D (calciferol) found in vitamin supplements is a slightly different compound.

DERMIS

You are unique. There has never been another human being on the earth exactly like you. You can see one evidence of your uniqueness if you spread your hand and examine the patterns of grooves and ridges on your palm and fingertips. The idea of using fingerprints to identify people dates back to 1880. Since then, fingerprints have been classified into a number of basic types (Figure 7-3), but—with the exception of identical twins—no two people have exactly the same set of prints. The ridges and grooves on the fingers and palms serve a function for the body in addition to their serendipitous use for identification: they increase the resistance between contact surfaces and thus make gripping more effective. (Similar patterns on the soles of the feet serve the same function; other grooves and ridges in the skin correspond to folds produced by movements of body parts.) The patterns of grooves and ridges we see are in the epidermis, but they do not originate there. They are produced by variations of folds and ridges in the underlying dermis. The wrinkles that appear in the skin with increasing age or overexposure to sunlight also originate in the dermis.

The dermis, sometimes called the **corium** or true skin, is a thick layer of dense connective tissue, containing mainly white collagenous fibers, with some yellow elastic fibers and reticular fibers. Blood and lymph vessels, nerves, hair follicles, sweat and sebaceous glands are embedded in the dermis, though hair and glands are actually products of the epidermis.

The dermis can be divided into two layers: the su-

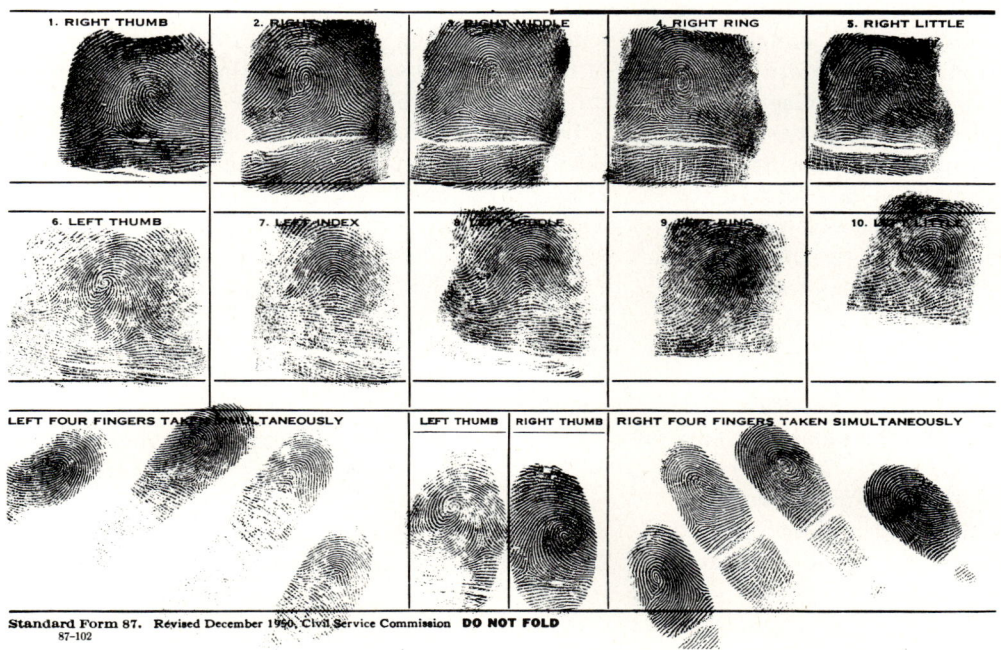

A

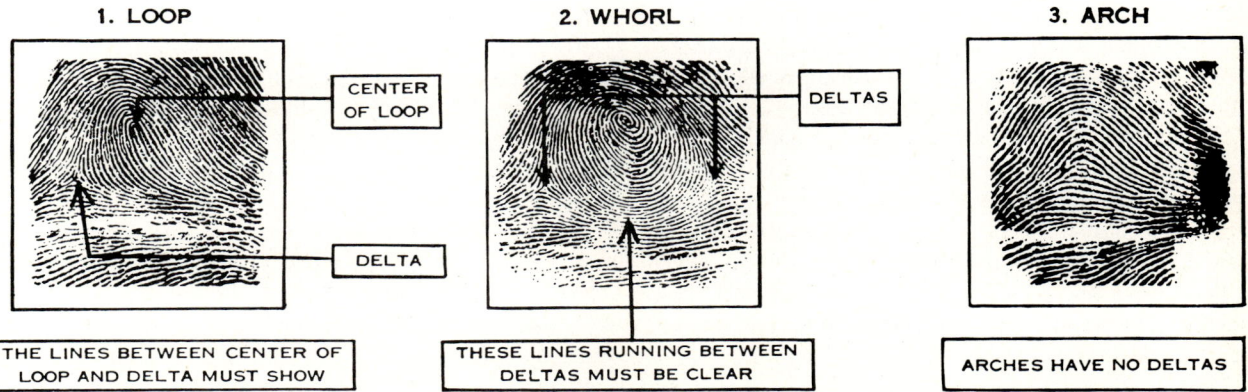

B

FIGURE 7-3 (A) A typical (yet unique) set of fingerprints. (B) The patterns of dermal ridges have been classified into four main types: loops, whorls, arches, and composites (combinations of loops and forks).

perficial **papillary layer** and the deeper **reticular layer.**

The striking feature of the papillary layer is the **papillae,** conical mounds or folds that project up into the epidermis. The papillae contain small bundles of fibrils, arranged parallel to the long axis of the papillae, and a loop of capillaries. Indeed, the papillary layer is extremely vascular, and nourishes both the dermis and the stratum germinativum of the epidermis lying just above. In regions of the skin where the sense of touch is particularly acute (such as the palmar surfaces of the hands and fingers), many of the papillae contain tactile corpuscles.

The reticular layer, as its name implies, contains an interlacing mesh of fibers (mainly collagenous, with some elastic fibers). This fibrous network imparts toughness to the skin.

The structure of the dermis contributes great strength, distensibility, and elasticity to the skin. Most movements of body parts involve some stretching or wrinkling of skin; young skin is able to return quickly to its normal smooth condition. In advancing age, the resiliency of the skin decreases, and wrinkles become permanently set. Even in young skin there are some limits to its elasticity. When skin is stretched too greatly, as in pregnancy, or in the case of large tumors or extreme obesity, tiny tears may be produced in the tautly stretched skin and remain as silvery white "stretch marks" or **striae albicantes.**

The dermis is attached to the underlying structures by a sheet of areolar connective tissue, called **subcutaneous tissue** or **superficial fascia.** In all but a few parts of the body, the subcutaneous layer contains fat. Subcutaneous injections are made into this layer, the structure of which is loose enough to accommodate a large volume of liquid. Although it is closely related to the skin, the subcutaneous layer is not considered an actual part of the skin.

Blood Vessels and Lymphatics

An embarrassing situation can cause a sudden flush of warmth to spread over your skin, as you turn rosy red in a blush. Fright, on the other hand, may cause your skin suddenly to turn pale. Both these effects are reflections of the skin's rich blood supply.

Networks of arteries in the subcutaneous connective tissue send branches out into the dermis, forming abundant capillary beds in the papillary layer, and around the hair follicles and the sweat and sebaceous glands. Several networks of veins lie at different levels in the dermis and subcutaneous tissue, especially just beneath the papillae, sweat glands, and the tips of hair follicles and sebaceous glands.

The blood in the vessels of the skin gives it its rosy tones. Dilation of the skin blood vessels produces a reddish flush. When the skin capillaries are distended, they can hold a substantial fraction of all the blood in the body. The redness of a blush is most noticeable in people who are normally fair-skinned. Melanin tends to mask the effects of dilation of the skin capillaries. Constriction of the skin capillaries restricts the amount of blood flowing through the skin and produces pallor. Aside from the indication of emotional reactions, dilation and constriction of the skin capillaries play an important role in the maintenance of homeostasis. Dilation of the superficial cutaneous (skin) blood vessels enhances the loss of body heat by radiation from the body surface. Constriction of these vessels helps to conserve body heat. In addition, the constriction of superficial cutaneous blood vessels is part of the body's "fight or flight" mechanism, preparing for an emergency situation. (The diversion of much of the blood flow from the skin provides extra nourishment for the brain, heart, and muscles, which may be called on for extraordinary efforts to cope with the impending emergency.) All these responses of the skin blood vessels are controlled and mediated through the central nervous system.

In addition to its arteries, capillaries, and veins, the skin is abundantly supplied with lymphatic vessels, arranged in both superficial and deep networks. These networks communicate with each other and with the lymphatics of the subcutaneous tissue and drain excess fluid from the skin.

Nerves and Sense Organs

Even with your eyes closed, you can form a fairly detailed picture of an object by touching it. You can estimate its size, shape, and texture, whether it is rigid or yielding, hot or cold, wet or dry, and its relative weight. The skin is one of the brain's important "windows on the world," through which it receives information about the environment and its impact on the body.

As with any part of the body, there is a two-way traffic of messages between the skin and the central nervous system. An abundance of afferent nerve fibers carry information to the central nervous system from specialized receptors in the skin. Each of these modified nerve endings is responsive to one type of sensation: cold, warmth, touch, or pressure. Their distribution over the surface of the body is quite nonuniform: certain areas such as the lips and fingertips are especially richly supplied with sense receptors, while in other areas they are sparse. For example, if someone pokes you in the back with two or three fingers, you will be quite unable to distinguish how many separate pressures are being exerted—there are so few sense receptors in the skin of the back that even three fingers will be perceived as a single pressure. Yet on the skin of the hand, much finer distinctions can be made. Damage to peripheral nerves or to the central nervous system may produce **anesthesia** (loss of sensation) in parts of the skin.

Efferent nerves, carrying impulses from the central nervous system to the skin, terminate in the smooth muscle of the blood vessel walls (and can stimulate them to dilate or contract) or regulate the activity of the sweat and sebaceous glands and the smooth muscles around the hair follicles.

ACCESSORY ORGANS OF THE SKIN

The skin is far more than a mere covering for the body, and its varied functions are abetted by a number of appendages and accessory organs. The most prominent of these are the hair and nails. Less visible, but even more important are the cutaneous glands, embedded within the skin and connected to the surface by narrow ducts. These multitudinous microscopic glands are of two main types: sebaceous, or oil glands, and sudoriferous, or sweat glands.

Hair

A trip to the beach graphically demonstrates the wide spectrum of hair distribution on the human body: some men sport a thick mat of hair on the chest, and perhaps on the arms and legs as well, while others have only a sparse sprinkling; some women seem practically hairless, except for a luxuriant crop of hair on the head, sharply stenciled eyebrows, and improbably long lashes. (The women who favor a more natural look still typically have considerably less body hair than the average man.) Even allowing for such modifications of the phenotype as introduced by cutting, shaving, depilatories, and so on, there is a great variation of the amount of hair among human individuals. But humans are genuine mammals: no member of their species is totally hairless. Indeed, with the exception of a few restricted regions—the palms of the hands, the soles of the feet, and the last phalanges of the fingers and toes—human skin is entirely covered with hairs, or **pili.**

The hairs over most of the body are very short and fine, but longer, coarser hair grows in characteristic patches. A prominent one of these is the hair of the scalp, which, if uncut, can grow to a length of about three feet (even longer in some rare cases). The coarse hair of the armpits and pubic region and (in males) facial and chest hair appear at puberty and are signs of sexual maturation. The coarse, stiff hairs of the eyebrows and eyelashes, as well as those inside the nostrils, serve a protective function, helping to screen out dust particles, small insects, and other potential irritants.

Hair is a modification of the epidermis, and their life histories have many features of similarity. Hair growth begins in the hair follicle, a sheath-like structure embedded in the dermis (see Figure 7-1). The **hair follicle** has an outer connective tissue sheath and an inner epithelial membrane, continuous with the stratum germinativum. It is nourished by a loop of capillaries enclosed in connective tissue at the bottom of the follicle, the hair **papilla.** The epithelial cells lying just above the papilla reproduce actively and give rise to the hair. As long as these cells are undamaged, a hair can regrow, even if it is cut, shaved, or plucked out.

The actual hair consists of a **root,** enclosed in the hair follicle, and a **shaft,** the visible portion. Micro-

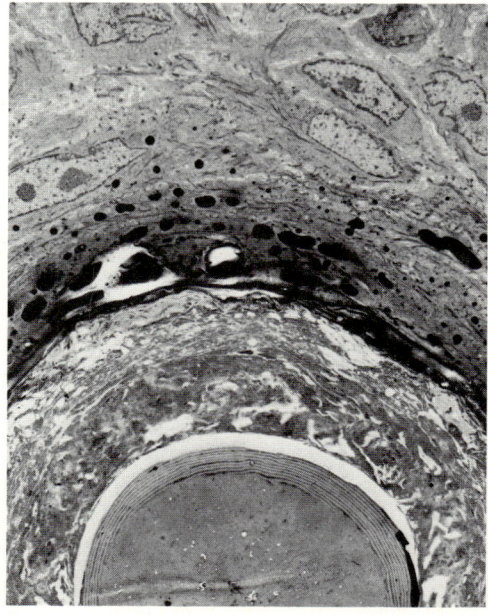

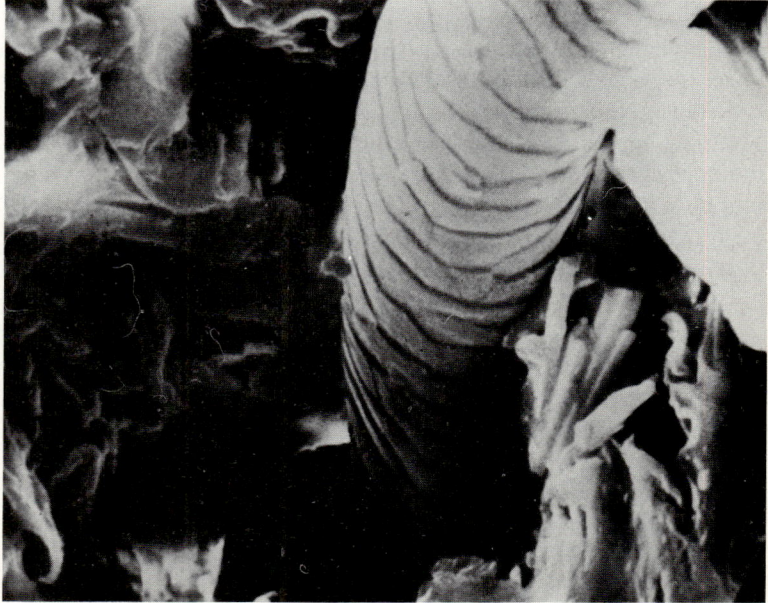

A B

FIGURE 7-4 (A) Cross section of a hair shaft (×1386) inside its root sheath. (B) SEM of a hair (×912) extending from its follicle. Note the scale-like cuticle.

scopically, the hair shaft is found to have a complex structure (Figure 7-4). The outermost layer, the **cuticle,** consists of transparent flattened, overlapping scalelike cells. Just within the cuticle is the **cortex,** the principal portion of the shaft, which consists of several layers of keratinized cells, joined to form flattened fibers. Hair color is determined by the pigments contained in the cortex layer. (The type and amount of the pigments is inherited.) The absence of pigment results in gray hair, while white hair is produced by a combination of lack of pigment and the presence of air bubbles in the hair shaft. The innermost layer of the hair shaft, the **medulla,** is composed of cuboidal cells, interspersed with numerous air spaces. Note that the hair, like the epidermis from which it is formed, has no blood vessels or nerves of its own.

The form of the hair shaft and the curvature of the follicle determine another characteristic of hair: if the hair shaft is cylindrical and the hair follicle straight, the hair is straight; if the hair shaft is flattened, and the follicle is bent, the hair is curly. This characteristic is also inherited, but there are ways to modify the phenotype artificially. The keratin of the cortex is a protein that is cross-linked into a characteristic folded configuration (alpha-keratin) that imparts considerable elasticity. When hair is stretched, the keratin is pulled out into a more linear form (beta-keratin), and indeed, wet hair can be stretched out to one-and-a-half times its usual length. Normally it snaps right back to the alpha-configuration as soon as it is released. But "permanent wave" sets utilize chemical agents to break the cross-links and form new ones, after the hair has been molded into the desired waves.

Hair passes through regular cycles of growth and rest. During the growing phase, the root is elongated. As new cells from the **matrix** (the actively growing lower portion of the bulb) move upward, they increase in volume and gradually become keratinized. The hair of the head can grow as fast as 12 mm a month, perhaps five inches in a year. Body hair grows more slowly, although an occasional "rogue hair" may rapidly outstrip its neighbors. But this growth does not go on indefinitely. After a time (usually two

to six years for the head hair), the actively growing hair is transformed into a dead **club hair,** with a short, bulblike root (Figure 7-5). The dead hair is soon shed, and is replaced by a new, actively growing hair. Perhaps you worry when you find loose hairs in your hairbrush. Although shedding hair may be a sign of incipient baldness,* in young people it is more likely just a manifestation of the normal cycle of hair development. The next time you clean your hairbrush, you might take comfort from the thought that you have plenty of hairs to spare: the average human scalp contains about 100,000 hairs.

Two or more sebaceous glands open into each hair follicle and secrete an oily **sebum** that keeps the hair soft and pliable. The follicle is also associated with a bundle of involuntary muscle fibers, the **arrector pili muscles.** The hair follicles are set into the skin somewhat at a slant. Thus, the hairs emerge at an oblique angle. When the arrector pili muscles contract, they pull the hairs up straight, making them "stand on end." In animals with a thick coat of fur, arrector pili muscles serve several important protective functions. They are stimulated by cold to raise the hairs, providing a thicker and more effective insulating layer of trapped air around the body. Fright can also stimulate the arrector pili muscles, with two effects. First, the raised hairs make the animal appear larger (this effect is strikingly evident in an alarmed housecat) and may cause an enemy to have second thoughts about attacking. In addition, the raised hairs give a greater scope to the tactile senses. (Hairs act as levers, transmitting touch sensations to sensitive nerve endings around the follicle.) In sparsely-haired man, though the functional significance has been lost, the reflexes still remain, and cold or fright can stimulate the arrector pili muscles to contract, producing characteristic "goose bumps."

---

* Pattern baldness, in which the hair is lost from a characteristic sequence of regions of the scalp, is hereditary. Although it can occur in both men and women, it is far more common in men and is classified as a sex-limited trait: it seems to act as a dominant in men, and a recessive in women. The predisposing factor is the male sex hormone—despite a spate of advertising claims, the only effective "cure" for developing baldness that has yet been discovered is castration.

FIGURE 7-5   The life cycle of a hair.

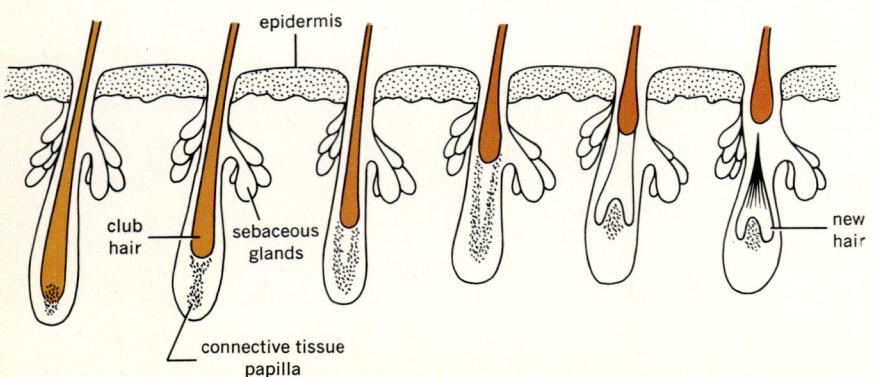

epidermis

club hair

sebaceous glands

new hair

connective tissue papilla

Human hair does serve some functions. The scalp hair helps to cushion and protect the skull, both from mechanical injury and from the rays of the sun. (It also provides a natural "head-warmer" in cold weather.) The greater surface area provided by the body hair aids in the evaporation of sweat from the body surface. Hair in the armpits and groin traps and holds secretions of skin glands, enhancing characteristic body odors. This is often considered a negative effect in humans, but in many animals it serves an important sexual attractant function.

Nails

The longest fingernails ever recorded were possessed by a Chinese priest in Shanghai, who took 27 years to grow nails more than 22 inches long. Few people could lead the kind of life of extreme manual inactivity necessary to keep fingernails that long from breaking, but the nails of each of us do grow at a rate of about a tenth of a millimeter each day. (At that rate, an entire fingernail can be replaced in several months.)

Nails are translucent horny plates, derived from the epidermis and composed of keratin. Each nail consists of a **root** and a **body,** lying on an epithelial **nail bed.** The nail bed is richly supplied with blood vessels, the pink color of which shows through the nail plate. (An exception is the crescent-shaped white region at the base of each nail. This portion of the nail plate is called the **lunula,** or "little moon." Its white color is produced by air spaces mixed in the keratin matrix.) The nail root is hidden under a fold of skin called the cuticle. Actively reproducing cells in the stratum germinativum are transformed as they move outward, into hard, dry scales, which join to form a solid plate. The nail slides along the nail bed and projects beyond the end of the finger. The movement of the nail is so slow as to be imperceptible, but its progress can be watched when there are small white spots or black-and-blue marks (signs of past mechanical trauma to the nail root) on the nail plate. As the days and weeks pass, such marks are steadily carried away from the root and are ultimately lost. If an entire nail is ripped off, it can be regenerated as long as the cells of the stratum germinativum remain.

Nails provide some protection to the dorsal surfaces of the fingertips, and their appearance may give an indication of general body health. A bluish color of the nail beds (cyanosis) results from improper oxygenation of the blood and may indicate a circulatory disorder; evidence of nail biting may be a hint of emotional problems.

Sebaceous Glands

Acne sufferers know the misery of clogged and inflamed sebaceous glands. These microscopic pear-shaped structures are generally associated with hair follicles. (In a few hairless regions, such as the eyelids, sebaceous glands open directly to the surface of the skin.) Their secretion, **sebum,** is an oily substance containing fats, soaps, cholesterol, albuminous material, inorganic salts, and the remains of epithelial cells. (The actual secretory cells themselves are converted to the secretion of the glands, and are then replaced by a constant proliferation of new cells. Glands of this type are referred to as **holocrine** glands.) Sebum spreads out to form a protective film over hair and skin, which keeps them from becoming dry and brittle.

The secretion of the sebaceous glands is controlled by the endocrine system. At puberty and late in pregnancy there is a spurt in sebaceous gland activity, caused by the elevated hormone levels. In adolescence the enhanced sebaceous secretion often produces excessively oily skin and hair and may give rise to "blackheads" and pimples. A blackhead is produced when the fatty material at the orifice of a sebaceous gland becomes discolored as a result of oxidation by the air. When sebaceous glands are plugged, the secretions serve as a growth medium for pus-producing bacteria, thus giving rise to pimples and boils. The prominence of unsightly blackheads and pimples on the face during adolescent acne results from the presence of the largest sebaceous glands on the nose and other parts of the face.

With advancing age, falling hormone levels result in reduced activity of the sebaceous glands, producing problems of dry skin and lusterless hair.

Sweat Glands

Each year, hundreds of millions of dollars are spent by Americans in an attempt to control the effects of their sweat glands. Sweat or **sudoriferous glands** are distributed over most of the body surface, but are most abundant in the axillae (armpits), the palms of the hands, the soles of the feet, and the forehead. It has been estimated that there are 3000 sweat glands in each square inch of skin surface on the palms. Each sweat gland is a single long, coiled tube, with a lining of epithelial cells that secrete a thin, watery fluid. The coiled basal portion of the gland, embedded in the lower dermis or in the superficial fascia, is surrounded by a mesh of capillaries. Its secretions are emptied through a long, coiled duct.

There are two main kinds of sweat glands: **eccrine** and **apocrine** (Figure 7-6). Eccrine sweat glands, which are smaller, empty their secretions at tiny pores at the skin surface. They produce their secretion, a clear, watery fluid, under control by the nervous system. Heat stimuli are transmitted to a control center in the hypothalamus, which in turn triggers activity of eccrine sweat glands. The sweat glands on the fore-

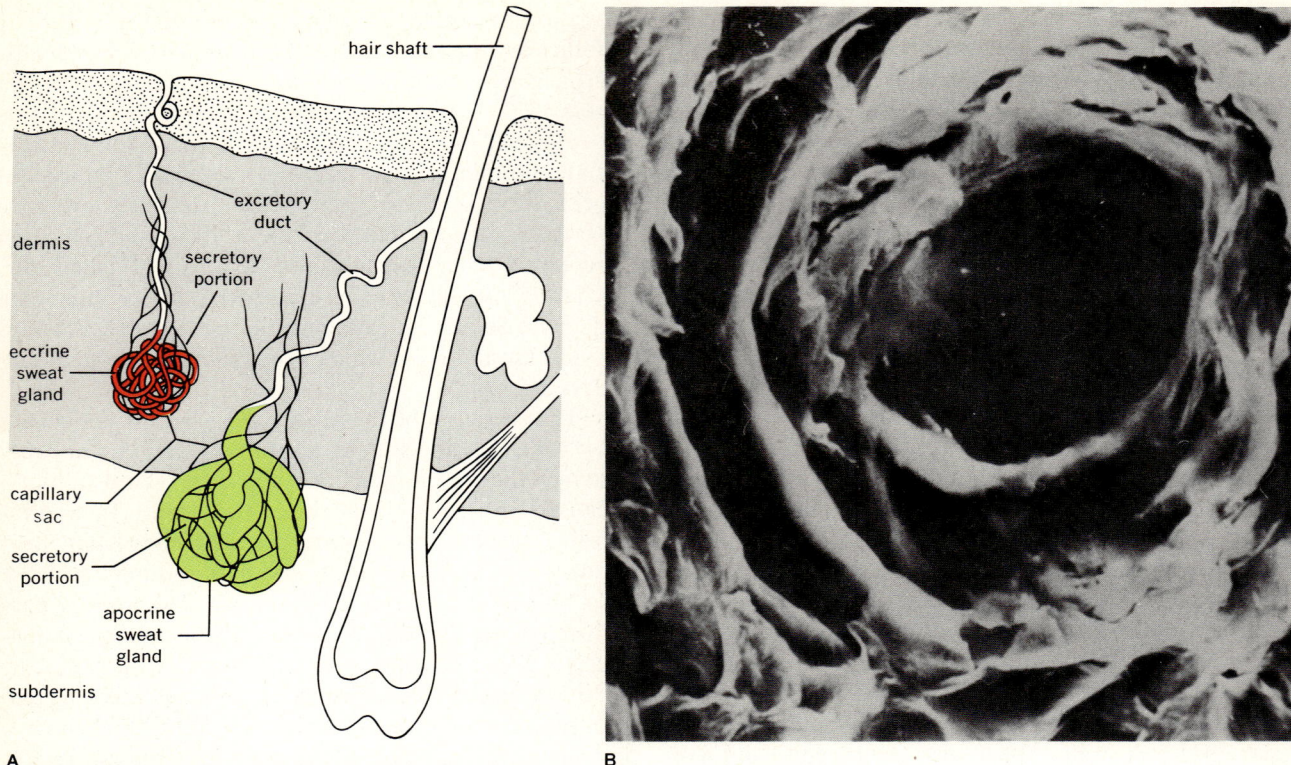

FIGURE 7-6 (A) Eccrine and apocrine sweat glands; (B) the SEM shows an eccrine sweat pore, magnified 300 ×.

head, the neck, the back and front of the trunk, and the backs of the hands are very responsive to thermal stimuli. The abundant eccrine sweat glands in the palms of the hands and soles of the feet respond very little to heat stimuli, but respond strongly to emotional stimuli. (That is why nervousness is usually accompanied by sweating of the palms.) Their action is mediated through the cerebral cortex.

Apocrine sweat glands have a similar structure to the eccrine glands, but are much larger, and they generally empty into a hair follicle. They are not uniformly distributed over the body, but instead are found mainly in the axillae, around the nipples of the breast, around the anus, and around the vagina (in females) or in the prepuce and scrotum (in males). It is the apocrine secretion that is the main object of underarm deodorants and antiperspirants, vaginal sprays, and other commercial preparations. The apocrine secretion is a sticky whitish, gray, or yellowish fluid, containing various odorous chemicals that become even more odorous when sweat is trapped in the body hairs and subjected to bacterial action. (Bacteria multiply rapidly on the nutrients contained in apocrine secretions.) The combination of these and other skin secretions produces a characteristic body odor that is highly individual. Animals such as dogs, with a better developed sense of smell, can use individual body odors as a means of identification.

Ceruminous Glands

Excessive wax in the ears is a frequent problem among children. Although an accumulation of hardened **cerumen** (ear wax) deep in the auditory canal can cause earache and interfere with hearing, a normal secretion of this waxy substance keeps the surface of the canal and the eardrum lubricated.

The yellow, waxy cerumen is secreted by modified sweat glands called ceruminous glands, located in the skin lining the external auditory canal. Their ducts open directly onto the skin surface or into the ducts of large sebaceous glands.

THE SKIN AS AN EXCRETORY ORGAN

Routine screenings of children in urban areas for lead poisoning include analyses of hair clippings for traces of the metal. Murder cases sometimes hinge on the results of tests of the hair of an exhumed corpse for arsenic. The excretion of heavy elements through the hair is one way the body gets rid of unwanted substances. But the bulk of the work of the skin as an excretory organ occurs through the sweat glands.

Up to an environmental temperature of about 88 to 90° F, the sweat glands secrete continuously but so slowly that the droplets of moisture evaporate before they can become visible. This type of sweating is referred to as **insensible perspiration,** and amounts to about a pint of fluid a day. If the environmental temperature rises above the critical value, there is a sharp increase in the number of sweat glands functioning and the volume of sweat they produce. Drops of visible moisture break out over the skin surface and are spoken of as **sensible perspiration.** When heavy labor is performed under extremely hot conditions, as much as three gallons of sweat may be produced in 24 hours.

Thus, sweat is a major means of eliminating fluid from the body. (Through feedback mechanisms mediated through the hypothalamus, the elimination of fluids through the kidneys is cut back when sweating is particularly heavy, to prevent dehydration of the body.) Salts and other dissolved solids are carried out with the sweat. Indeed, eccrine sweat somewhat resembles a very dilute urine. It consists of about 99 percent water, with about half the remaining 1 percent sodium chloride and the rest organic substances, including mainly urea, along with uric acid, ammonia, creatinine, glucose, lactic acid, amino acids, fatty acids, and traces of vitamins B and C. The various acids in sweat give it a pH ranging from 4 to 6.

The composition of sweat depends on the material carried in the bloodstream (though it is not a simple filtrate, but rather a product of active secretion by the cells of the sweat glands). Its exact constituents are determined partly by heredity (particularly the apocrine sweat) and to some degree by the content of the diet. Both these factors contribute to a real but often unconsidered problem of international relations: people of different races or cultures sometimes smell offensive to one another.

THE SKIN AND TEMPERATURE REGULATION

On a cold winter day, the temperature difference between the air flowing past your face and the interior of your body may be as much as 100°F or more. If homeostasis is to be maintained under such conditions, the need for efficient heat-retention mechanisms is obvious. Less obvious but equally important is the need for efficient cooling mechanisms. It seems paradoxical that the body must be constantly cooled even when the temperature of the environment is considerably below the body temperature. ("Room temperature" of 70°F, or about 21°C, feels comfortable, while an environmental temperature of 90°F—still below the body's 98.6°F—seems unpleasantly hot.) The reason for this situation is that heat is continually being produced as a by-product of muscle contractions and various oxidative reactions of cell metabolism.

The skin, as the portion of the body in direct contact with the environment, fittingly plays a key role in the body's systems of temperature regulation. Skin acts as an insulator, and it also helps to raise or lower the body temperature as needed (Figure 7-7). The

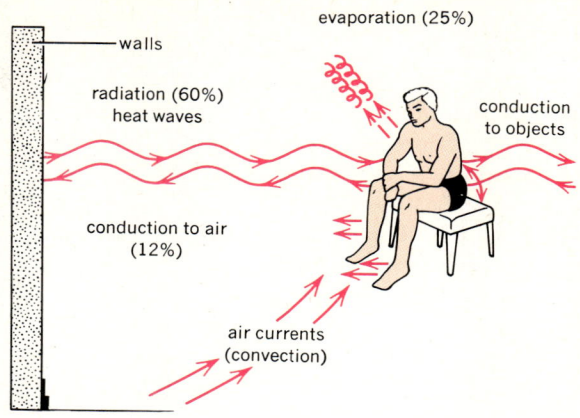

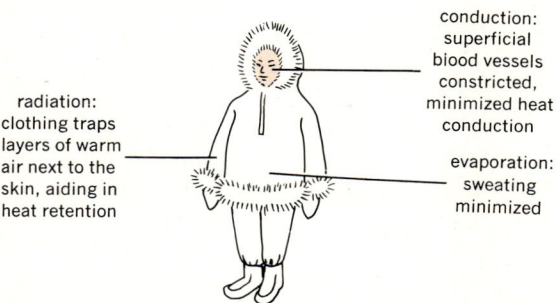

FIGURE 7-7   At the interface with the environment, the skin participates in the body's mechanisms of temperature regulation.

skin acts as a **radiator** surface, from which body heat, carried through the abundant skin capillaries, is radiated out into the surrounding medium. When the air over the body surface is moving, **convection** increases the heat loss through the skin. The continual secretion of insensible perspiration carries off substantial amounts of heat. Water can hold considerable heat, and more energy is consumed (and removed from the body) in the process of **evaporation** of sweat. (The change from liquid to gas is an energy-requiring process.)

The body's internal temperature, as reflected by the flowing blood, is continuously monitored by the hypothalamus. Thermal sense receptors in the skin transmit information to the brain about changes in the temperature of the environment.

When heat retention is needed, impulses are transmitted along nerves to **arteriovenous anastomoses** (muscular-walled connections between arteries and veins) in the skin, which constrict, reducing the blood flow to the surface. The reduced blood flow effectively cuts down heat radiation. Meanwhile, the arrector pili muscles are stimulated to contract, erecting the hairs and enhancing the insulating layer, and shivering is initiated in the muscles, increasing heat production. These mechanisms keep the internal body temperature relatively constant, even though the skin itself may be quite cool.

When the body needs cooling, impulses transmitted to the anastomoses cause the blood vessels to dilate, increasing the flow to the surface and enhancing radiation. At environmental temperatures above about 88°F, a general sweating reaction is produced. Exercise elicits profuse sweating even at lower temperatures, in response to the stimulation of deeper thermal receptors in the skin by internally produced heat. Sweating is an efficient thermoregulatory mechanism only when the humidity of the environment is low enough to permit the sweat to evaporate.

ABSORPTION THROUGH THE SKIN

In the early 1960s it was accidentally discovered that a common chemical solvent, dimethyl sulfoxide (DMSO), penetrates readily and rapidly through unbroken skin. The initial discovery sparked tests of DMSO's drug potential, and at first it seemed literally too good to be true. Early reports noted that this substance kills pain, speeds healing of wounds and burns, reduces inflammation, acts as a tranquilizer, relaxes muscles, purges poisons from the body, relieves arthritis and bursitis, and carries other drugs (such as insulin and anticancer drugs) into the body. Then, after two years of worldwide testing, animal studies indicated that DMSO might produce changes in the eyes of users, and the FDA abruptly withdrew approval of all clinical uses of the substance. The decision sparked a controversy that raged until 1966, when it was decided to permit the use of DMSO again, but only in carefully controlled tests.

For a long time it was believed that the skin is a virtually impenetrable barrier to nearly all chemical substances. But now it is known that gases and lipid-soluble substances can pass through skin with relative ease. Electrolytes do not penetrate human skin in appreciable amounts; they are held back not by the stratum corneum (which acts as a gross sieve), but by an "electrical double layer" of H^+ and OH^- ions that exists at the junction between the cornified and non-cornified layers of the skin.

Some of the substances capable of penetrating through skin into the body are of great practical importance. The fat-soluble vitamins A, D, and K, as well as carotenes, are readily absorbed through skin. So are various steroid hormones, including estrogens, progesterone, testosterone, and deoxycorticosterone. Various phenolic compounds are also readily absorbed through the skin. One of them, methyl salicylate (oil of wintergreen), is a common ingredient of liniments. When rubbed onto the surface of the skin, it rapidly penetrates to the sore muscles on which it acts.

Salts of lead, tin, copper, arsenic, bismuth, antimony, and mercury can penetrate through skin and in some cases may cause accidental poisoning. The salts themselves are not lipid soluble, but become so when they combine with fatty acids of the sebum at the skin surface.

Such gases as oxygen, carbon dioxide, hydrogen sulfide, nitrogen, ammonia, and hydrogen cyanide are also readily absorbed through the skin. (Fortunately, carbon monoxide is an exception and does not penetrate the skin.) In frogs, earthworms, and some other animals with thin, moist skin, a significant fraction of the respiratory gas exchange occurs through the skin. (A hibernating frog at the bottom of a pond does not use its lungs at all; "breathing" through its skin takes care of its reduced respiratory needs.) There is some evidence to indicate that the passage of oxygen through the skin provides for a small part of the human body's oxygen needs, but the amounts of oxygen and carbon dioxide that can be transmitted through the skin are far below those required for human respiration.

SKIN DISORDERS AND OTHER CLINICAL CONSIDERATIONS

With the thousands of new chemicals that humans have added to their environment, there has been a substantial rise in the incidence of puzzling rashes and other skin disorders. Some of these conditions have been traced to sensitivity to artificial fibers and elastics (some people are allergic to natural fibers such as wool), "enzyme" detergents, metals, and various foods, food additives, and drugs. Such allergic skin reactions commonly take the form of **urticaria** (hives), in which a vascular reaction of the skin suddenly produces raised edematous patches (**wheals**) that itch intolerably.

In addition to hives, the skin is subject to a variety of other ills and abnormalities, including (Figure 7-8):

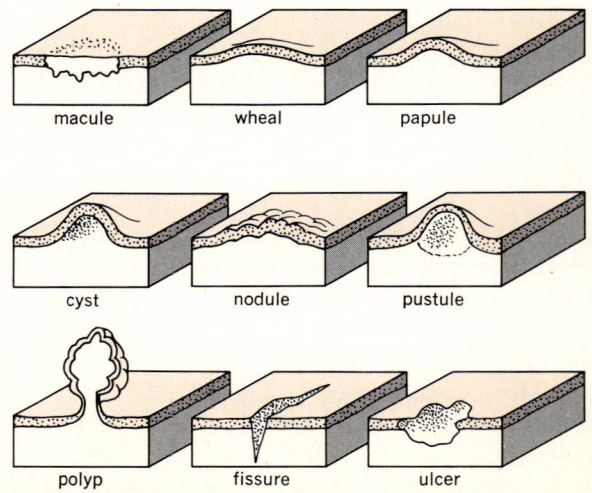

FIGURE 7-8 Types of skin abnormalities.

acne vulgaris (pimples), an inflammation of sebaceous glands; **boils** and **carbuncles,** bacterial infections of hair follicles; **macules,** discolored spots on the skin; **papules** (solid elevations of the skin) and **nodules** (small, solid, irregular-shaped nodes); **cysts** (fluid-filled sacs) and **pustules** (pus-filled elevations); **ulcers,** open sores that do not heal (**decubitus ulcers,** or bed sores, may develop in patients confined to bed for long periods, in sites where the skin covering bony prominences such as the elbows or hips is pressed against the mattress); **corns** and **calluses,** thickened areas of epidermis produced in response to repeated friction or pressure on a particular spot; and **fissures,** cracks or clefts in the skin. When a cleft due to a cut or incision in the skin heals, the ridge of new tissue formed (mainly connective tissue) may produce a visible **scar.**

One of the commonest skin disorders is **sunburn,** produced by the ultraviolet portion of solar radiation. Overexposure to sunlight (especially when the rays are reflected by white snow or sand) produces first an **erythema** (reddening) of the skin, and then a rise in the skin temperature. In severe cases, fever, chills, nausea, and prostration may follow. Repeated overexposure to sunlight can also cause skin cancer. In moderation, sunlight can have beneficial effects, stimulating the production of vitamin D and preventing bacterial and fungus infections. The commonsense approach to sunbathing is to gradually increase exposure over a period of many days, permitting the skin to build up its natural ultraviolet-screen of melanin.

Anesthesia (loss of feeling) of the skin may result from injury to the peripheral nerves or central nervous system. Special care must be taken in caring for patients suffering from anesthesia of the skin, for they do not have the protective skin senses that warn of potential danger from heating pads and other devices.

Careful observation of the skin can be valuable to the doctor, who makes use of characteristic **skin signs** in forming a diagnosis. Extremely pale skin may suggest anemia, while a bluish skin (cyanosis) may indicate severe heart disease or pneumonia. A yellow skin (jaundice) is caused by the presence of bile pigments in the blood and is commonly associated with liver diseases; patients with Addison's disease (underactivity of the adrenal glands) have a characteristic bronzed skin. **Dermatitis** (a generalized term referring to inflammation of the skin) is sometimes associated with vitamin deficiencies. (In such cases the skin is rough, with cracked and scaly patches around the corners of the mouth.) Characteristic skin rashes are diagnostic aids in common childhood diseases such as measles, chicken pox, and scarlet fever; venereal diseases such as syphilis and type 2 herpes virus are frequently accompanied by skin **lesions** (sores) in the region of the genital organs, while another type of herpes virus produces characteristic cold sores around the mouth. Fungus diseases such as ringworm and athlete's foot also produce characteristic skin lesions.

HEALING

Some tissues of the body—for example, the nervous tissue of the brain—cannot be replaced once they are damaged. It is fortunate that the skin is not one of these nonreplaceable tissues, for it is constantly get-

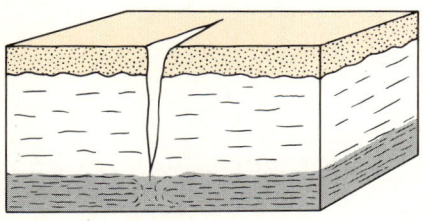
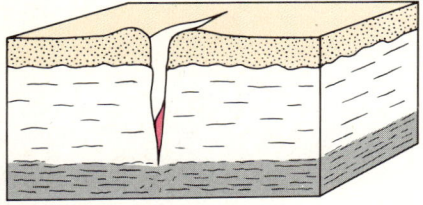
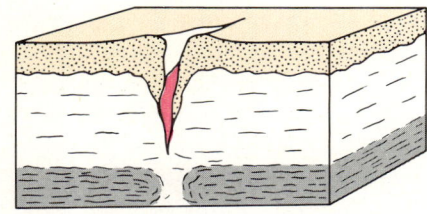
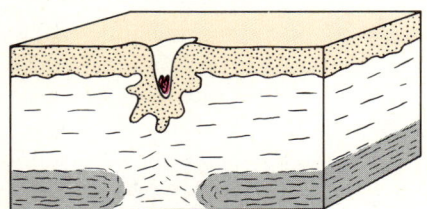
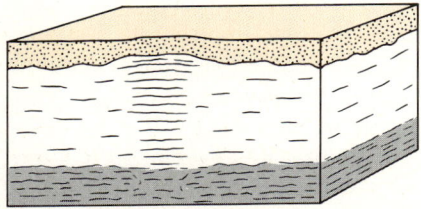

FIGURE 7-9 Successive stages in the healing of a wound. (A) An early clot has formed, but there is still some bleeding in the subcutaneous tissue; (B) the clot lines the walls of the wound, the epidermis thickens, and the subcutaneous tissues show an inflammatory reaction; (C) epidermis migrates down the walls of the wound and phagocytes remove debris; (D) epidermis has covered the defect and the scab is ready to be sloughed off; (E) a raised, thin epidermis covers a dense maturing scar.

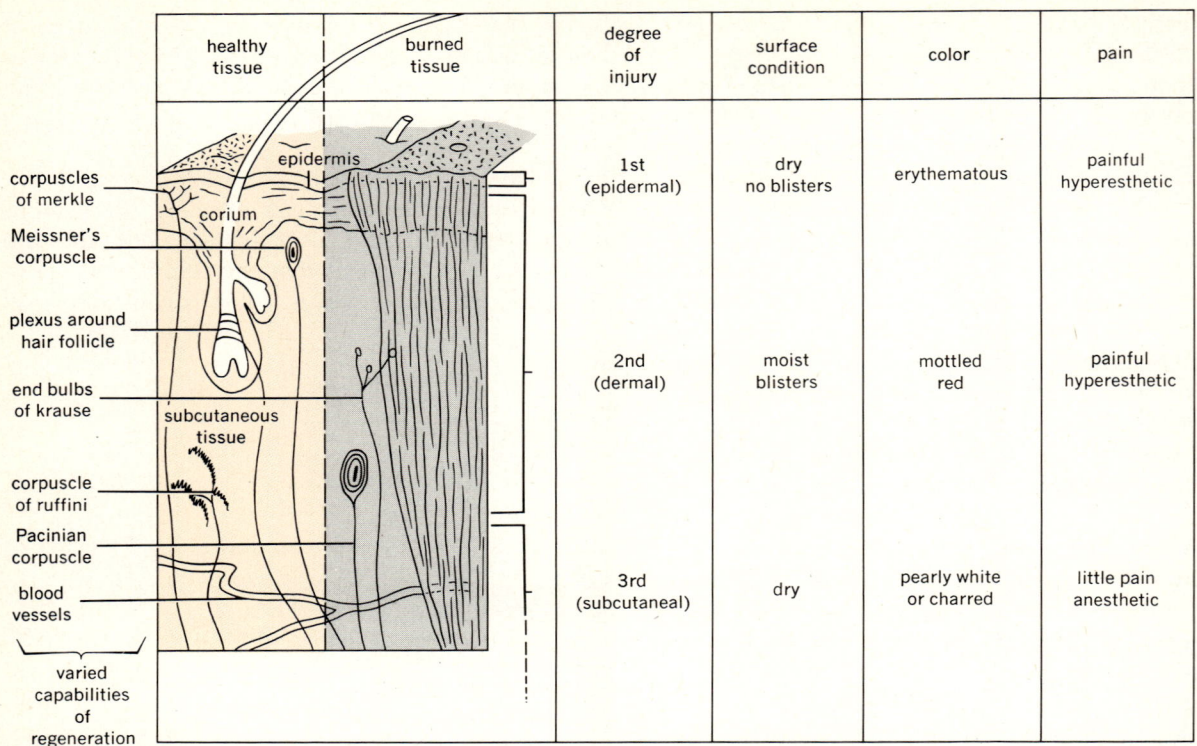

healthy tissue	burned tissue	degree of injury	surface condition	color	pain
epidermis		1st (epidermal)	dry no blisters	erythematous	painful hyperesthetic
corium		2nd (dermal)	moist blisters	mottled red	painful hyperesthetic
subcutaneous tissue		3rd (subcutaneal)	dry	pearly white or charred	little pain anesthetic

Labels on diagram (left side): corpuscles of merkle, Meissner's corpuscle, plexus around hair follicle, end bulbs of krause, corpuscle of ruffini, Pacinian corpuscle, blood vessels, varied capabilities of regeneration

FIGURE 7-10 Burn injuries are classified as first, second, or third degree according to their depth. A first-degree burn affects only the epidermis; a second-degree burn extends into the dermis; a third-degree burn extends through the full thickness of the skin, down into the subcutaneous tissue.

ting cut, abraded, burned, and subjected to various other accidental traumas in the course of a person's normal activities. Peeling an apple, pouring coffee, even licking an envelope could be fraught with deadly danger if it were not for the fantastic abilities of the skin for self-renewal and repair.

The first step in wound healing follows the initial trauma immediately. Bleeding into the wound results in the formation of a clot, which plugs the gap and provides a temporary mechanical protection. If the injury involves only the skin, it is rapidly repaired by the multiplication of cells in the deep layer of stratified squamous epithelium. A small defect may be entirely covered within 48 hours. In deeper and more extensive wounds, involving underlying tissues, fibroblasts from the connective tissue begin multiplying within hours and migrate from the edges toward the central portion of the wound (Figure 7-9). Vascular buds develop and grow across the wound, forming new capillaries. These, together with the growing connective tissue, form **granulation tissue,** which gradually builds up on the wound surface. The granulation tissue has a characteristic pebbly appearance. As the fibroblasts proliferate and produce collagenous fibers, the wound is entirely filled with scar tissue.

Maintaining good general health is important for promoting rapid wound healing. In the case of extensive injuries, particularly burns, considerable blood plasma may be lost, along with its proteins and electrolytes, upsetting the body's fluid balance; these fluids must be replaced. Proteins are needed in ample amounts for building new tissues. Vitamins play a key role, both in healing and in preventing infections. Vitamin A is especially important in the repair of epithelial tissues.

SKIN GRAFTS

A sudden splash of scalding water, a flash fire, or an explosion can produce extensive burns that severely tax the skin's potential for regeneration. Burns can vary in severity, from the transient erythema of a sunburn (a first degree burn, in which only the epidermis is injured) to the deep tissue damage of a third degree burn, in which epidermis, dermis, and even subcutaneous tissue may be seared and charred (Figure 7-10). When a significant fraction of the body is covered with third-degree burns, it is literally a race against death for the patient. There is a potential for replacing all the lost skin, but the new skin is formed slowly, as cells migrate out from the edges of the undamaged portions. Meanwhile, vital fluids are continuously lost from the unprotected regions, which are also particularly vulnerable to infection.

Victims of burns and other injuries can be helped by the technique of grafting skin from one part of the body to another. This can be a slow and tedious process, requiring repeated operations, spread out over a period of many months. For only suitable skin can be used (burns on a woman's face, for example, could not be effectively repaired with grafts of hairy skin from her legs without the danger of subsequent psychological problems), and adequate skin must be left to permit regeneration in the site from which it was taken. A number of promising lines of research are being pursued, in efforts to make skin grafting techniques more effective. Sheets of pigskin or a mesh of collagen are often used as temporary coverings for exposed regions of burned skin. Strips of skin for a graft may be cut into a mesh (Figure 7-11) and spread out to cover a much larger area before they are affixed in place. The skin mesh provides so many edges from which cells can migrate, that the gaps are quickly filled in with new skin. Eventually the mesh pattern disappears. In another recently developed technique, skin for transplants is first minced and grown on a base of pigskin, then grafted (pigskin and all) onto the injured site. The pigskin dries up and sloughs off, while living skin covers the damaged area.

Successful skin grafting has thus far been confined to transplants of a person's own skin from one body site to another. The special problems encountered in attempts to transplant tissues from one person to an-

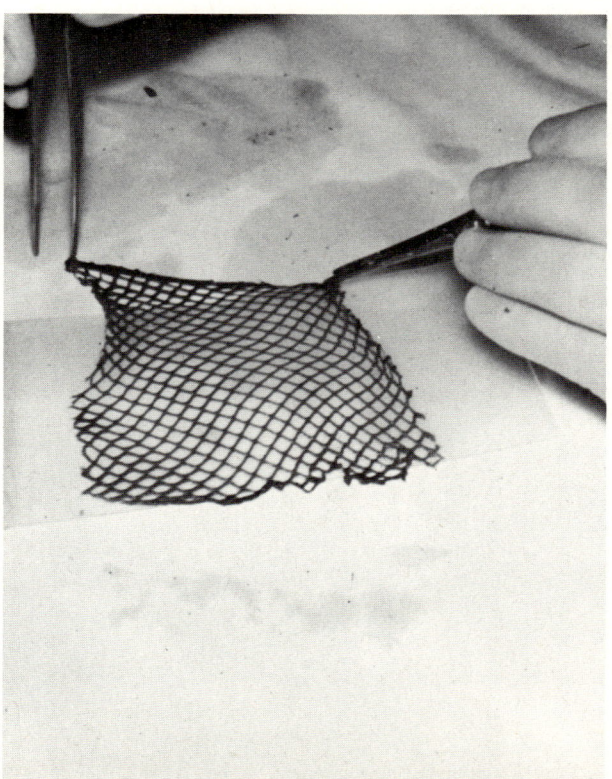

FIGURE 7-11 Skin for grafting can be cut into a filigree to greatly expand the area effectively covered by the graft.

other are discussed in Chapter 37.

SUMMARY

The covering of the body is the skin, or integument. Its functions include:
Mechanical and chemical barrier between the body and the environment, providing protection from:
Microbes
Mechanical injury
Chemicals
Ultraviolet radiation
Waterproof coating, preventing excessive water loss
Temperature regulation
Sense reception
Synthesis of vitamin D
Excretion
Storage site for fat, water, glucose, and sodium chloride
The skin surface is inhabited by a characteristic microflora.
The skin structure is subdivided into:
Epidermis (outer layer)
Dermis (inner layer)
Accessory organs (sweat and sebaceous glands, hair, and nails)
Epidermis contains up to four zones of stratified squamous epithelium, the outer layers of which contain increasing amounts of keratin:
stratum corneum (outermost layer)
stratum lucidum
stratum granulosum
stratum germinativum (innermost layer)
The stratum germinativum is the living layer, in which cells reproduce actively.
Epidermal cells are progressively displaced outward, keratinized, and ultimately sloughed off.
Melanocytes in the stratum germinativum are specialized for the production of melanin, which imparts a dark color to skin and acts an an ultraviolet shield.
Dermis, or corium, includes two layers:
Papillary layer
Reticular layer
The dermis contributes strength and resiliency to skin.
Its blood vessels (in papillae) nourish the overlying epidermis and give skin a rosy color.
Characteristic fingerprints and other ridges and grooves in the epidermis originate in folds and ridges in the dermis.
The dermis is attached to underlying structures by the subcutaneous tissue or superficial fascia.
The skin contains abundant specialized sense receptors, responsive to sensations of cold, warmth, touch, and pressure.
Messages from the sense receptors are carried to the central nervous system via afferent nerves; efferent nerves regulate the activity of the skin blood vessel walls, sweat and sebaceous glands, and arrector pili muscles.
As mammals, humans are characterized by a coat of hair, ranging from short, fine body hairs to long, coarse scalp hairs and stiff eyebrows and eyelashes.
At puberty, patches of coarse hair appear in the armpits, pubic region, and (in men) on the chest and face.
Each hair grows within a sheathlike follicle, embedded in the dermis, and includes a shaft (keratinized) and a root.
Hairs experience regular cycles of growth and rest and are periodically shed and replaced.
Hairs are lubricated by the secretions of sebaceous glands and can be elevated by the action of arrector pili muscles.
They transmit touch sensations to sensitive nerve endings.
Nails are keratinized plates, consisting of a root and a body and growing on an epithelial nail bed.

They are restricted to the ends of the fingers and toes.

Sebaceous glands (oil glands) are holocrine glands, in which the secretory cells are converted to the secretion of the glands.

Their secretion, sebum, keeps hair and skin moist and pliable.

Sebaceous glands generally empty into hair follicles.

Bacterial infections of sebaceous glands produce pimples and boils.

Sweat glands (sudoriferous glands) are most abundant in the axillae, the palms of the hands, the soles of the feet, and the forehead.

There are two kinds of sweat glands:

Eccrine sweat glands (smaller) secrete a clear, watery fluid and empty their secretions at pores at the skin surface.

They are responsive to thermal and emotional stimuli.

Apocrine sweat glands (larger) are found mainly in the axillae, around the anus, and in the pubic region; they secrete a sticky, cloudy fluid, containing odorous substances, and generally empty into hair follicles.

Ceruminous glands are modified sweat glands that produce ear wax (cerumen).

Sweat glands serve an excretory function. (Sweat contains about 99 percent water, and the remainder sodium chloride and organic substances, mainly urea.)

Insensible perspiration refers to sweat that evaporates as quickly as it is formed.

Sensible perspiration refers to sweat produced more rapidly than it can evaporate and appearing as visible drops of moisture on the skin.

The skin plays a key role in body-temperature regulation.

Heat is lost from the skin surface by radiation, convection, and evaporation of sweat.

Links with the central nervous system permit reflex regulation of the blood vessel diameter, enhancing or minimizing heat loss by radiation.

Thermal receptors in the skin relay information about the environment to the central nervous system.

Although the skin generally acts as a barrier to electrolytes, gases and fat-soluble substances can be absorbed through unbroken skin.

Salts of lead, tin, copper, arsenic, bismuth, antimony, and mercury combine with fatty acids of sebum and can then pentrate the skin.

Skin disorders and abnormalities include urticaria, acne vulgaris, macules, papules, nodules, cysts, pustules, ulcers, and fissures.

The condition and appearance of skin may provide important clues in diagnosing diseases.

Skin has a high potential for regeneration and can heal wounds effectively.

Healing of extensive wounds proceeds through the formation of granulation tissue.

Extensive skin damage due to burns or other injuries may be repaired by grafting skin from one part of the body to another.

QUESTIONS FOR REVIEW AND THOUGHT

1 Discuss the adaptive advantages of having the body's outermost covering consist of a layer of dead cells.

2 Describe the structure of the skin and its accessory organs.

3 Discuss the factors determining skin color (including temporary changes in skin color).

4 What functions does human hair serve?

5 Distinguish between: epidermis and dermis; sweat glands and sebaceous glands; eccrine and apocrine sweat glands; sensible and insensible perspiration.

6 Why does "room temperature" of about 70° F (21° C) feel comfortable although it is so far below the normal body temperature of 98.6° F (37° C)?

7 What kinds of substances can penetrate unbroken skin? Which cannot? Discuss the skin's effectiveness as a barrier and the factors that contribute to this function.

8 Why does a patient with extensive burns have such vastly increased requirements for fluids and nutrients?

THE SKELETAL SYSTEM

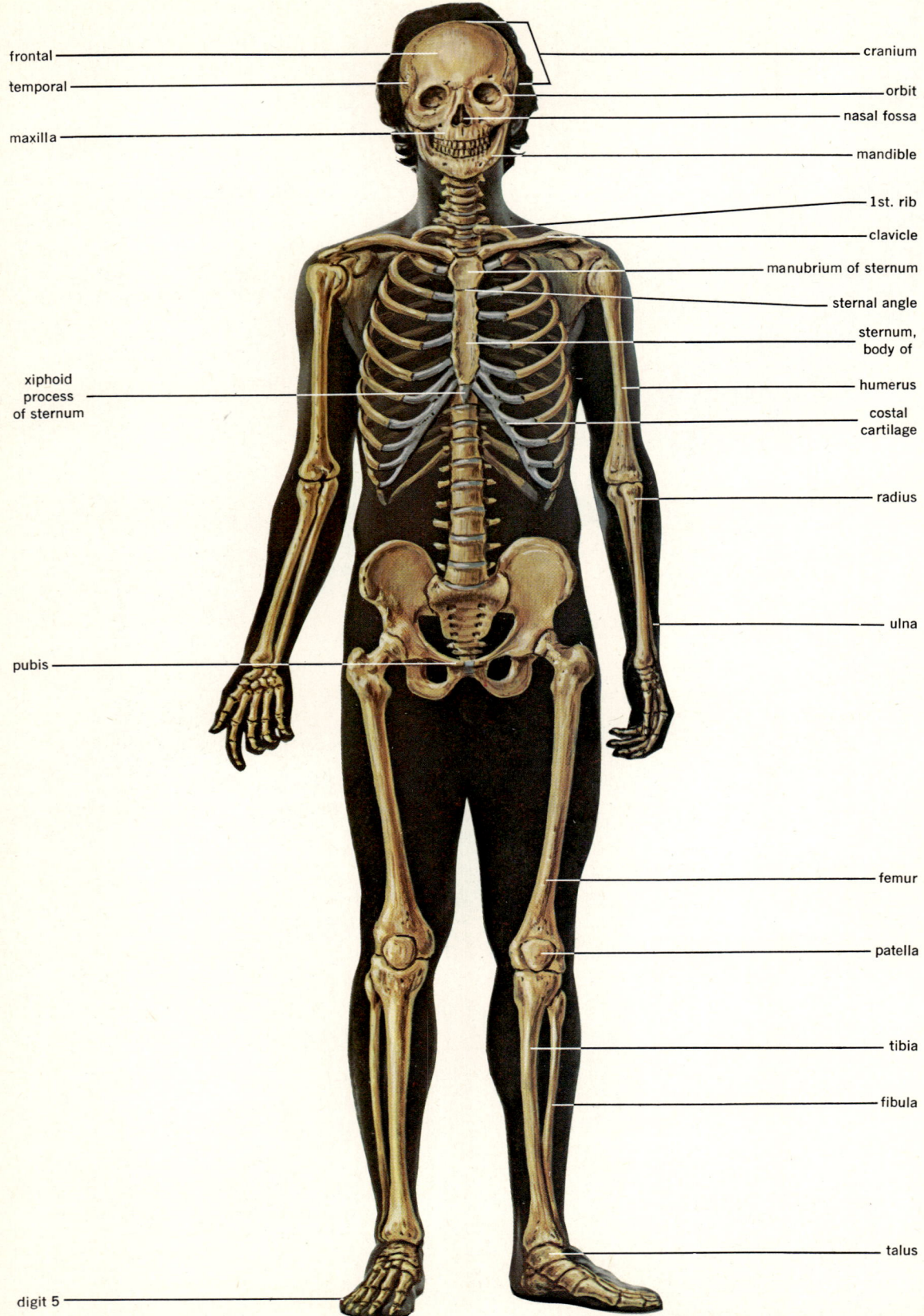

frontal

temporal

maxilla

cranium

orbit

nasal fossa

mandible

1st. rib

clavicle

manubrium of sternum

sternal angle

sternum, body of

xiphoid process of sternum

humerus

costal cartilage

radius

ulna

pubis

femur

patella

tibia

fibula

talus

digit 5

A

FIGURE 8-1   The human skeleton: anterior (A) and posterior (B) views.

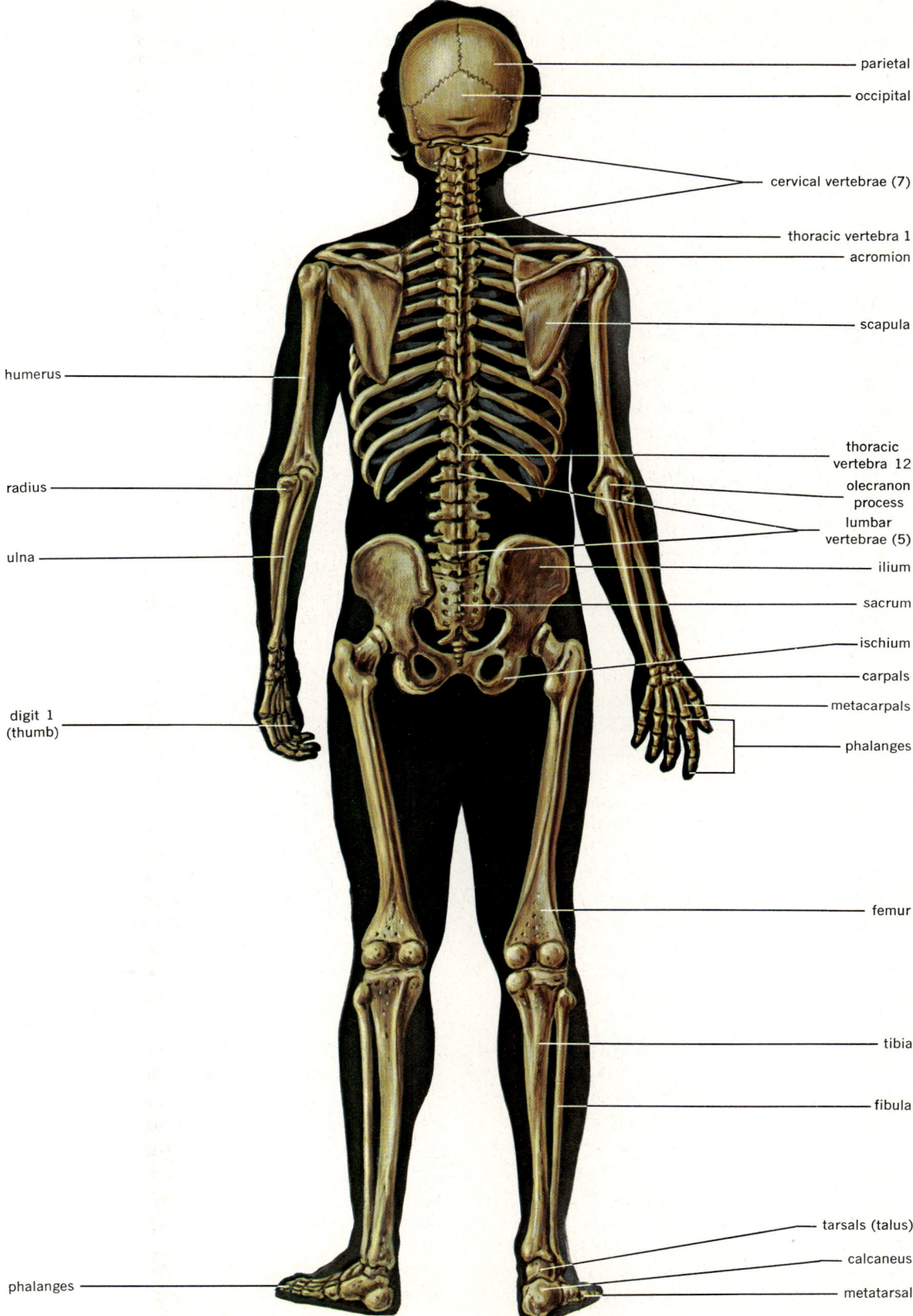

parietal

occipital

cervical vertebrae (7)

thoracic vertebra 1

acromion

scapula

humerus

thoracic
vertebra 12

olecranon
process

radius

lumbar
vertebrae (5)

ilium

sacrum

ulna

ischium

carpals

metacarpals

digit 1
(thumb)

phalanges

femur

tibia

fibula

tarsals (talus)

calcaneus

phalanges

metatarsal

B

In a house or office building, the outer and inner walls are fastened to a sturdy framework of wood or metal, which provides the needed support and stability. The human body, too, has a strong and sturdy inner framework, made up of bones and cartilage. This is the skeletal system, and it differs from the framework of a building in a number of important respects. The joints at which bones are held together by ligaments are not fixed and rigid, as in the frame of a building, but permit movement. Thus, the bones of the skeleton not only provide support for the structures of the body, but also act as levers for movements of body parts. (The motive force is provided by muscles, firmly anchored to the bones.) Bones are often thought of as inert and unchanging, like the building materials with which a house is constructed and, indeed, bones are the most enduring of all human structures. A human skeleton reconstructed by the Belgian physician Andreas Vesalius as an anatomical demonstration back in the 1500s can still be observed today. In the living body, however, bone is a dynamic substance, capable of growth or atrophy, repair, and a constant interchange of materials with the surrounding body media.

The skeletal system serves a number of important functions in the body in addition to the obvious one of **support.** As mentioned above, it **aids in movement,** providing anchorage for the muscles and leverage to enhance the effects of their actions. Bones **protect** vital body organs and other soft tissues. The hard casings provided by the skull and the rib cage are important examples of this function. Cavities within bones house red bone marrow, in which the crucial function of **hemopoiesis,** or the formation of blood cells, takes place. Each day billions of red blood cells and millions of white blood cells are produced in your bone marrow and take the place of those that have worn out and died. Finally, the bones of the body act as an important **storage depot for minerals,** especially calcium and phosphorus. In times of increased mineral needs, for example, during pregnancy, salts may be withdrawn from the bones.

There are about 206 bones in the skeleton of an adult human (Figure 8-1). Indeed, the bones are often considered a particular bane by health science students because there are so many of them, and each has a name of its own. The bones of the skeleton can be briefly categorized as follows:

Cranium (skull)	8
Face	14
Ear	6
Hyoid	1
Spine (vertebral column)	26
Sternum and ribs	25
Upper extremities	64
Lower extremities	62

Not included in the total are variable numbers of **sesamoid bones,** which are embedded in the tendons covering the bones of the knee, hand, and foot, and **wormian bones,** small isolated bones that are found in cranial sutures.

BONE STRUCTURE

The next time you have chicken for dinner, save one of the long leg bones and place it in a jar of vinegar for a few days. There will be little change in the bone's external appearance, but it will gradually become rubbery rather than stiff, and ultimately it will be so pliable that it can be tied into a knot. The weak acid (acetic acid) in the vinegar gradually dissolves out the calcium salts of the bone, leaving the tough, collagenous fibers that were embedded in the salt matrix.

Structurally, bone is rather similar to reinforced concrete. Its great hardness is imparted by the deposits of mineral salts in the matrix. These consist chiefly of a complex of calcium carbonate ($CaCO_3$) and calcium phosphate [$Ca_3(PO_4)_2$], which resembles a naturally occurring mineral, **hydroxyapatite.** Strength is imparted to the hard bone matrix by the reinforcing fibers of bone collagen, or **ossein.** In addition to the nonliving matrix, bone contains numerous living bone cells, **osteocytes,** which are nourished by blood vessels that lie in a complex of interconnected channels that permeate the bone.

The microscopic structure of bone (Figure 8-2A) was described in Chapter 5. The concentric cylindrical **lamellae** of the haversian systems look in cross section like a collection of annual rings on a cut tree trunk. **Canaliculi,** tiny channels running at right angles to the haversian canals and connecting the **lacunae,** are filled with tissue fluid, which thus permeates the solid bone matrix and bathes the osteocytes. Oxygen and nutrients diffuse through the tissue fluid from the blood vessels, and cell waste products are carried off from the osteocytes through the bathing fluid. Thus, these cells can remain vigorously alive even within the "dry," hard substance of bone.

TYPES OF BONES

Though bones are all made of the same basic substance, they come in many different sizes and shapes. The long, heavy thighbone (femur) looks quite different from the flattened ribs and the tiny hammer, anvil, and stirrup within the ear. Despite this diversity, however, bones can be conveniently classified in four major groups: long, short, flat, and irregular.

Long Bones

Long bones are found in the extremities. Each consists of a rodlike shaft with knoblike ends. This category includes the femur, the longest bone in the body, as well as a number of much smaller bones, such as

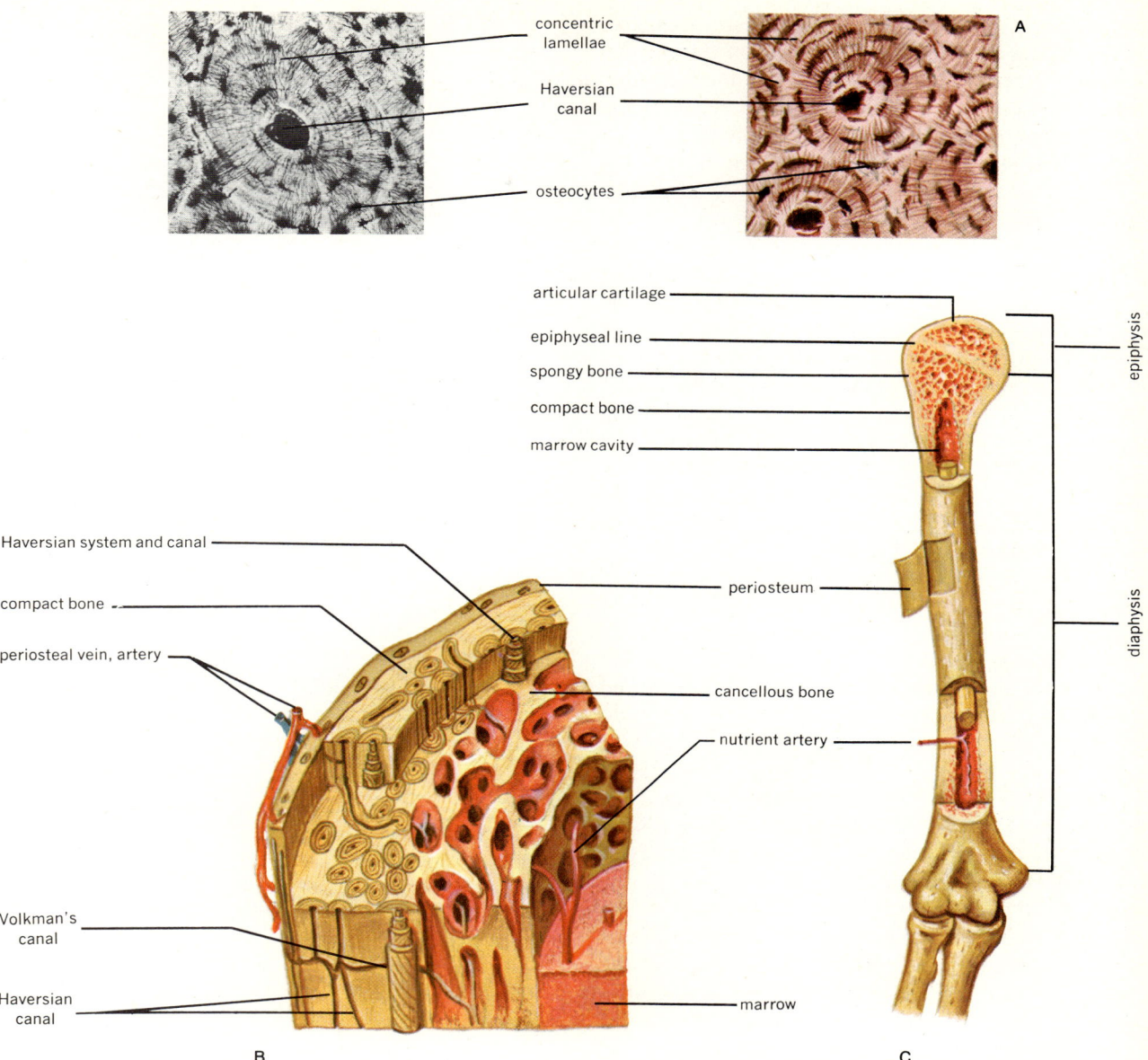

FIGURE 8-2   Bone is a living tissue with an intricate internal structure. (A) Cross section of bone showing Haversian systems and osteocytes. (B) Structure of compact and cancellous bone. (Haversian systems and lamellae have been magnified out of proportion.) (C) Structure of a long bone. The micrograph (×1000) shows a cross section through the compact bone of the femur, showing a Haversian system.

the terminal phalanx of the little finger. Yet no matter how short a long bone may be, it still has a basically elongated shape.

The gross structure of a typical long bone is shown in Figure 8-2B and C. The shaft, called the **diaphysis,** is a cylinder consisting mainly of compact bone. The innermost layer is composed of cancellous (spongy) bone, and within the diaphysis there is a large cavity (the **medullary** or **marrow cavity**), filled with bone marrow. The hollow cylindrical shape of the shafts of the long bones provides great strength with far less weight than a comparable solid cylinder, and thus they are especially well suited to weight bearing.

The ends of the long bones, called **epiphyses,** have

a somewhat bulbous shape, which provides roomy areas for muscle attachment and gives stability to joints. The knobby epiphyses are lighter than they look, for they consist mainly of porous cancellous bone, with only a thin outer layer of compact bone. The spaces in the spongy bone are filled with bone marrow.

The bones are wrapped in a dense white fibrous membrane, the **periosteum.** This membrane is supplied with blood and lymph vessels and nerves, and in growing bones its inner layer contains **osteoblasts** (bone-forming cells). The periosteum is thus important in nourishing the bone cells, and it also provides a site for the attachment of tendons and ligaments. In long bones, the periosteum does not form a complete covering: the articular (joint) surfaces of the epiphyses are covered with a thin layer of resilient hyaline cartilage, the **articular cartilage,** which cushions the ends of the bones in their contacts in the joints.

The marrow cavity, the spaces in cancellous bone, and the haversian canals are lined with another type of membrane, the **endosteum.** Its cells can become osteoblasts in times of need.

The bones of adults contain two types of bone marrow: **red bone marrow** and **yellow bone marrow.** Blood cells are produced in the red bone marrow, while the yellow bone marrow contains a large proportion of fat cells. In infants and young children, red bone marrow is found in numerous bones, but it is gradually replaced by yellow bone marrow. In the adult, the marrow cavities of the long bones contain yellow bone marrow, while the red marrow is confined mainly to the cancellous bone of the ribs, vertebrae, sternum, and bones of the pelvis.

Short Bones

Short bones are cube-shaped bones, which consist of cancellous bone enclosed in a thin shell of compact bone. Examples are the carpal bones of the wrists and the tarsals of the ankles.

Flat Bones

Flat bones are exactly what their name implies. They consist of two plates of compact bone, enclosing a layer of cancellous bone between them in a sort of sandwich. The ribs, the scapula (shoulder blade), the sternum (breastbone), and most of the bones of the skull are flat bones. Flat bones provide broad surfaces for muscle attachment, protect soft structures of the body, and in some instances (e.g., the ribs and sternum) are important sites of blood cell manufacture.

Irregular Bones

The irregular bones are a catch-all category, including all the bones of the skeleton whose shapes do not fit into the other groups. The vertebrae and the ossicles of the ear are typical examples. Their internal structure is generally similar to that of short bones: a thin layer of compact bone covering cancellous bone.

BONE FORMATION

The formation of the skeleton begins early in life, long before birth. Indeed, by three months after conception, the fetus already possesses a complete skeleton (Figure 8-3)—but there is not yet a single bone in its body. The fetal skeleton is initially composed mainly of hyaline cartilage, with some of the "bones" of the skull and face consisting of fibrous membrane. During the months that follow, there is a progressive **ossification:** a replacement of the cartilaginous struc-

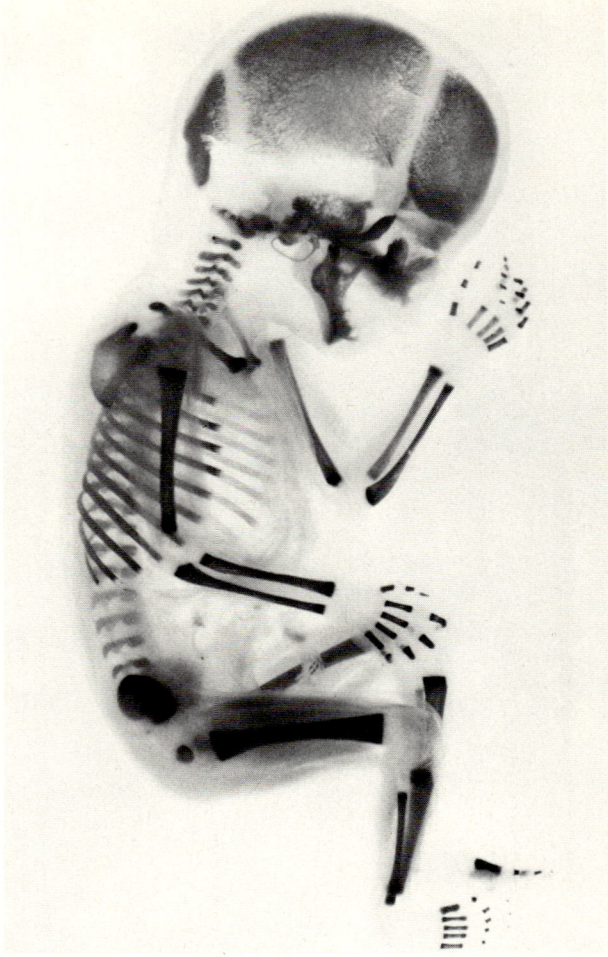

FIGURE 8-3 A human fetus, cleared and stained to show the developing bone. (Courtesy Carolina Biological Supply Company.)

tures with bone. This process follows a fairly consistent timetable; indeed, when an obstetrician is trying to decide on the advisability of inducing a birth before term, a standard test of "fetal maturity" is to take X rays and observe how far the ossification of certain key bones has progressed. But the ossification of the skeleton is far from complete at birth. Bone maturation, modification, and growth continue until about the age of 21.

It is sometimes said that the cartilage of the early skeleton "turns into" bone. This statement is not really accurate, although most of the cartilaginous fetal "bones" do resemble the bones of the adult. Instead, the cartilage serves as an environment in which new bone is formed, and is ultimately replaced by bone as ossification proceeds.

Bone formation may occur in two ways: **intramembranous ossification,** in which bone develops within membranes; and **endochondral ossification,** in which bones are formed within a cartilage model of their final form.

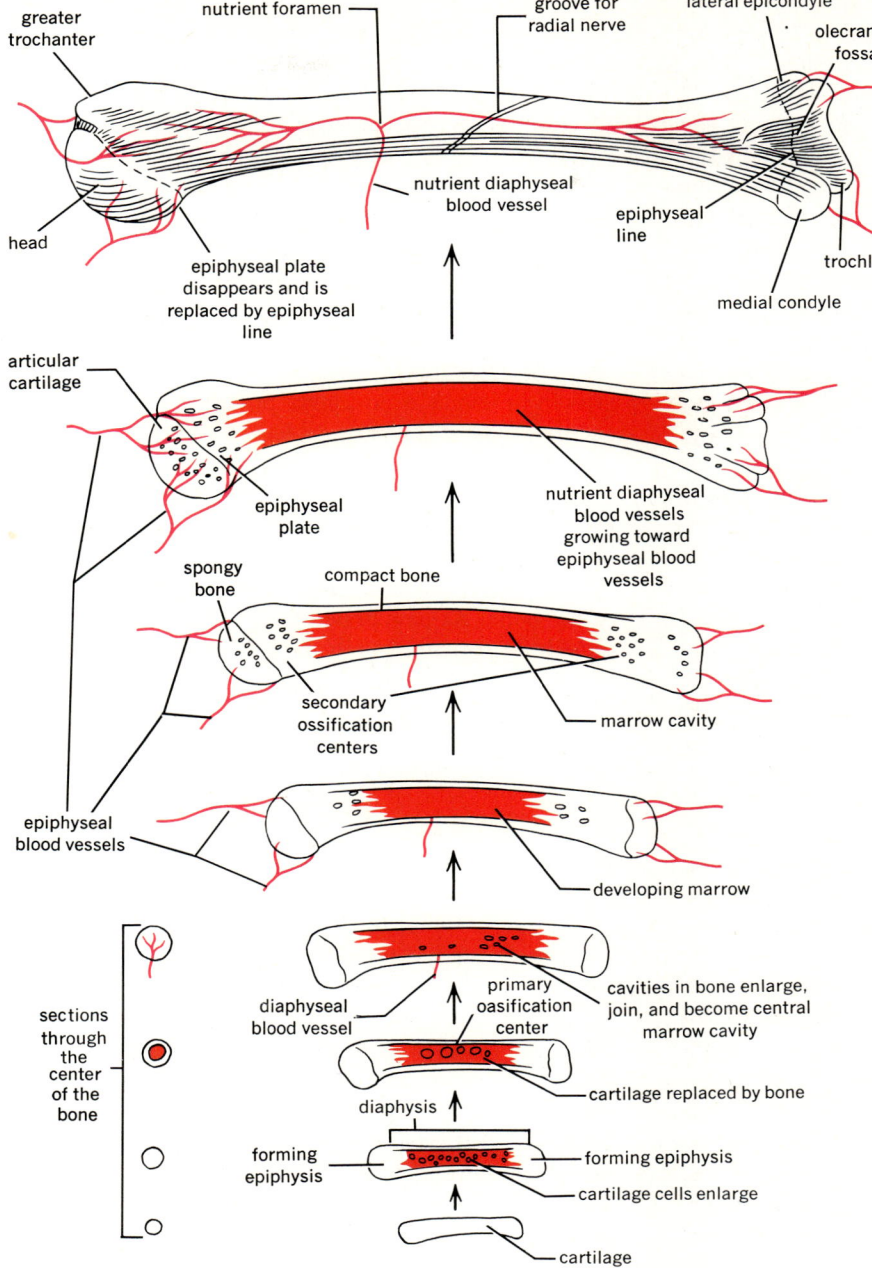

FIGURE 8-4 Successive stages in the formation of a long bone from a cartilage "model."

Intramembranous Ossification

The bones of the skull are formed by intramembranous ossification. Within each membrane in the prototype skeleton of the fetus, bone-forming cells called **osteoblasts** begin to secrete the organic intercellular substance of bone, and immediately **calcification** (the deposition of calcium salts in the intercellular substance) occurs. From this center of ossification, small bone spicules are built up in a radiating network. Osteoblasts swarm on the free margins and surfaces of the spicules; as the spicules interlace and coalesce, some of the osteoblasts are trapped in small spaces

(lacunae) and become osteocytes. Gradually, the bone takes shape, and the osteoblasts cover the spongy bone with layers of compact bone.

Endochondral Ossification

Most of the bones of the body are formed by the process of endochondral ossification, (Figure 8-4), and indeed, further growth of the bones in length occurs at a growth plate consisting of layers of cartilage. The formation of true bones in the cartilage "bones" of the fetus begins with an enlargement of the cartilage cells in certain areas. In the long bones, these areas are in the center of the shaft (diaphysis) and in each end (epiphysis). Soon the enlarged cartilage cells begin to degenerate and ultimately disappear, leaving spaces that are invaded by blood vessels from the **perichondrium,** a fibrous membrane that covers the cartilage model. Osteoblasts move in along with the blood vessels and begin to secrete the organic components of bone: collagenous fibers and cementing substances. Calcium salts are deposited, and blood vessels ramify through the growing bone. Bone spicules (called **trabeculae**) are formed and are loosely joined into a spongy network. The bone formation spreads out from the centers of ossification and, keeping pace with it, the destruction of cartilage continues in adjacent regions. Finally, only two thin strips of cartilage remain, between the diaphysis and each epiphysis (Figure 8-5). These plates of cartilage, called **epiphyseal plates,** are ultimately replaced by bone when the growth of the bones is completed, at which time the epiphyses are said to be closed.

As the cartilage model is gradually replaced from within by spongy bone, marrow begins to form in the spaces within the spongy network. The spaces in the center of the shaft coalesce, and the marrow cavity is formed. Meanwhile, at the outside of the cartilage model, osteoblasts between the cartilage and the enveloping perichondrium begin to lay down layers of compact bone that form a sleeve around the diaphysis. The perichondrium becomes the **periosteum,** and the bone gradually grows in circumference as additional layers of compact bone are laid down.

BONE GROWTH

The growth of bones, through prenatal life, childhood, and adolescence, proceeds according to a precisely regulated individual timetable, governed by the person's heredity and by environmental factors, especially diet. The hormones of the endocrine system play a key role in promoting or inhibiting bone growth. The growth hormone of the pituitary gland has dramatic effects: a deficiency of this hormone may result in a dwarf, while an excess of growth hormone can produce a giant. (Even after the epiphyses have closed, and growth in length is no longer possible, an excess of pituitary growth hormone can still stimulate abnormal bone growth, producing the skeletal distortions of acromegaly.) Other hormones, such as the thyroid and parathyroid hormones, insulin, and the sex hormones, also have profound effects on growth. Normally, all these chemical messengers interact harmoniously, bringing the body through the sequence of growth and development leading to the adult form.

After the bones are formed, growth can still occur for varying periods, depending on the type of bone and the body's individual "timetable," both in length and in circumference (Figure 8-6). At the epiphyseal plates of the long bones, ossification occurs at the side adjacent to the shaft, while new cartilage is formed at the distal side. Thus, the shaft gradually grows longer. As ossification proceeds, the epiphyseal plates gradually grow thinner, an effect that can be observed on X rays of the ends of the long bones. A child's "bone age" can be determined; it will match his or her chronological age more or less closely, depending on personal growth rate. Large discrepancies between bone age and chronological age may indicate an endocrine disorder. When the epiphyses have closed (i.e., the epiphyseal plates have been completely ossified), growth in length is no longer possible. This generally occurs at about 18 years in females and 20 in males.

The growth of bones in length is paralleled by an increase in their circumference. This aspect of bone growth occurs by the deposition of layers of new bone by osteoblasts in the inner surface of the periosteum. Meanwhile, a curious thing is occurring in the interior of the bone. As new bone layers are deposited on the outside of the bone, cells called **osteoclasts** (literally, "bone breakers") are busily dissolving away bony tissue adjacent to the marrow cavity. In this way, the marrow cavity is gradually enlarged, and its increase in size keeps pace with the overall growth of the bone.

BONE PHYSIOLOGY

It might seem that once the bones have been formed, they are set for life. And indeed, there is often very little apparent change in the bones after their growth has ceased; they seem the most "lifeless" of all the tissues of the body. Yet the apparent changelessness of the bones is not at all the true situation. Throughout life, processes of reabsorption of bone by osteoclasts and its deposition by osteoblasts go on constantly. During childhood and adolescence, the processes of deposition are more active than those of reabsorption, and there is a net growth of the bone. Later in life, reabsorption and deposition are generally in balance, so that in the midst of constant change, the bones remain essentially the same. Yet even at this time, excessive stress on a bone can give rise to hypertrophy, while disuse may cause the bones to atrophy. (A loss of calcium from the body and weakening of the bones is an important problem faced by astronauts during space missions involving long periods of weightlessness. It is combatted by specially designed physical exercises to keep the processes of bone building and destruction in better balance.)

The bones of children contain more organic matter and less inorganic salts than those of older people. As a result, children's bones are more flexible and less brittle, and therefore less susceptible to fracture. Often in old age, there is a generalized loss of bone

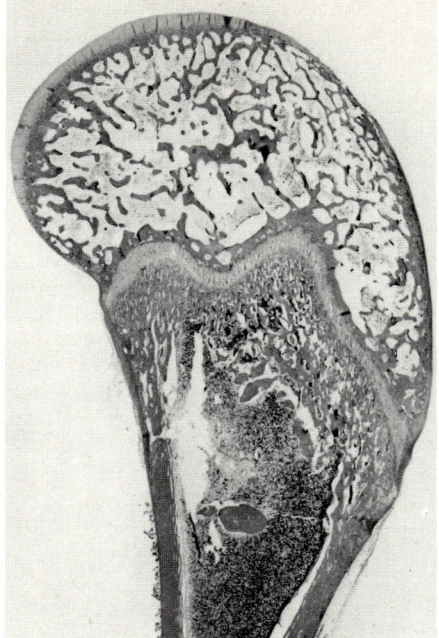

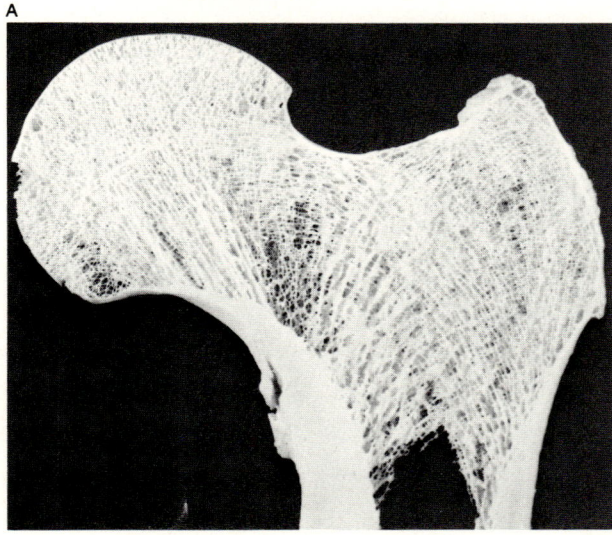

FIGURE 8-5 (A) Sagittal section of femoral condyle of a young rabbit, showing the epiphyseal cartilage plate. In the section of an adult human femur (B), the epiphyseal plate has disappeared.

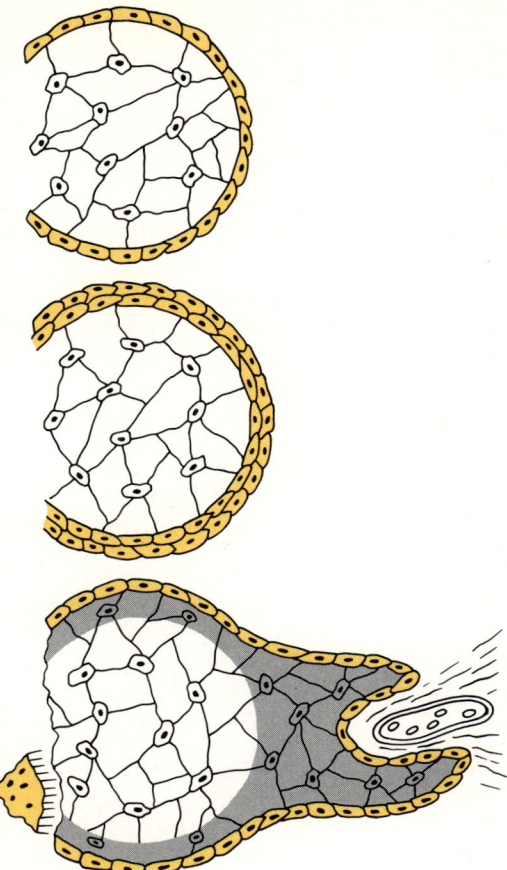

FIGURE 8-6 Stages in the growth of bone in circumference: (A) a layer of osteoblasts covers the bone surfaces; (B) the osteoblasts proliferate; (C) the inner layer of osteoblasts is secreting bone matrix; some osteoclasts at lower left are destroying bone; on the right osteoblasts are growing around a capillary, which provides a source of nutrition. (Modified from Ham, A.W.: Some histophysiological problems peculiar to calcified tissues. *J. Bone Joint Surg.,* **34A:** 707, 1952.)

substance, producing a condition known as **osteoporosis.** The bones may become painful and are extremely brittle and easily broken. Osteoporosis is due mainly to excessive bone resorption, probably as a result of an inadequate intake of calcium in the diet.

The balance of resorption and deposition in the bones is another aspect of homeostasis and is an important part of the body's calcium metabolism. About 99 percent of all the calcium in the body is stored in the bones. The remaining, very important 1 percent is found in the blood plasma and the interstitial fluid. Calcium ions participate in such vital processes as nerve transmission, muscle contraction, and blood clotting. Normally the calcium level in the blood is regulated by the parathyroid glands, and a balance is maintained between the blood calcium, the calcium in the bones, and the calcium excreted through the kidneys and bowel. If the calcium level in the blood falls (perhaps as a result of an inadequate intake of new supplies of the mineral with food), there is a rise in the secretion of parathyroid hormone, and reabsorption of the bones is increased. The calcium salts removed from the bone pass into the extracellular fluid and thence into the blood, protecting the vital functions of the body. (If the calcium concentration in the blood falls to half its normal value, the ensuing extreme nerve and muscle irritability can lead to convulsions and death.) But a price is paid in a weakening of the bones.

BONE MARKINGS

A paleontologist, given a few bones (or even fragments of bones), can not only identify the type of animal they came from, but can reconstruct its skeleton, deducing the position of each bone and its functional relationships to other bones, muscles, and the body structure as a whole. Each bone has its own characteristic assortment of markings—bumps and hollows, grooves and ridges, and so forth. To the trained eye these surface features of bone structure provide a wealth of information on functional interrelationships—sites of attachment of tendons and ligaments, surfaces of articulation with other bones, passageways for blood vessels and nerves.

There are two basic classes of bone markings: projections of various kinds (which are referred to in general as **processes**) and **depressions** or **cavities.** Following are the anatomical terms for the most common types.

Head. An expanded end portion beyond a constricted region called a **neck.**

Condyle. A rounded projection, found at a point of articulation with another bone. For example, the distal end of the femur (thigh bone) has large condyles, which articulate with the tibia at the knee joint.

Crest. A narrow ridge on a bone. A prominent example is the flaring upper border of the ilium (hip bone).

Line. A bone ridge that is not as prominent as a crest.

Spine. A sharp, slender process. There is a spinous process on the posterior portion of each vertebra.

Trochanter. A very large process with a rough appearance, which serves as a site for muscle attachment.

Tuberosity. A large, rounded process with a roughened surface, to which muscles are attached. The largest tuberosities of the body are found on the ischium (part of the hip bone). They bear the weight of your body when you sit down.

Tubercle. A small, rounded process for muscle attachment. The upper end of the humerus (arm bone) contains the greater and lesser tubercles.

Trochlea. A process shaped like a pulley (which is what its name means in Latin). The lower end of the humerus contains a trochlea.

Fossa. A depression or cavity that does not go all the way through the bone.

Fovea. A shallow depression.

Foramen. A hole in a bone, through which blood vessels and/or nerves pass. For example, the spinal cord passes through the foramen magnum in the occipital bone of the skull.

Fissure. A narrow slit, often between two bones.

Meatus or **canal.** A long, tubelike passageway. The external auditory meatus is a canal leading to the eardrum.

Sulcus or **groove.** A long, shallow depression.

Sinus. An air-filled cavity within a bone. (The term *sinus* has some alternate meanings in anatomy; it can refer to a narrow tract through tissues, leading from the surface to a cavity, or it can refer to a large vein.)

DIVISIONS OF THE SKELETON

When children draw a "stick figure" to represent a person, they are demonstrating an intuitive grasp of some basic principles of the human structure. Simpli-

fied to its essentials, the skeleton is basically a central axis (represented by the skull and spinal column) with a variety of other bones attached or appended to it, suspended from two main "hangers," the shoulder and pelvic girdles. Thus, it seems logical to divide the skeleton into two main parts (Figure 8-7): the **axial skeleton,** comprising the bones of the skull, the thorax, and the vertebral column; and the **appendicular skeleton,** consisting of the bones of the shoulder, the upper extremities, the hips, and the lower extremities.

The 206 bones of the skeleton can be classified as follows:

Axial skeleton: 80 bones, including:
  Head or skull: 29 bones
    Cranium: 8
    Face: 14
    Ossicles (ear bones): 6
    Hyoid: 1
  Vertebral column: 26 bones
  Thorax: 25 bones
    Sternum: 1
    Ribs: 24

Appendicular skeleton: 126 bones, including:
  Shoulder girdle: 4
  Upper extremities: 60
    Humerus: 2
    Ulna: 2
    Radius: 2
    Carpals: 16
    Metacarpals: 10
    Phalanges: 28
  Pelvic girdle: 2
  Lower extremities: 60
    Femur: 2
    Fibula: 2
    Tibia: 2
    Patella: 2
    Tarsals: 14
    Metatarsals: 10
    Phalanges: 28

Learning about 206 bones (plus a variable number of extras: the sesamoid and wormian bones) may seem like a tiresome chore. You will find the task both easier and more interesting if you continually take time out to follow various points of the discussion on the anatomical specimen you have with you at all times—your own body. Although your skeleton is covered by layers of soft tissues and wrapped in skin, you will be able to explore by feel a surprising number of details of the bones within you. This process of self-discovery will help to make the descriptions you read more meaningful.

THE AXIAL SKELETON

The main function of the appendicular skeleton is to support body parts and to work in conjunction with

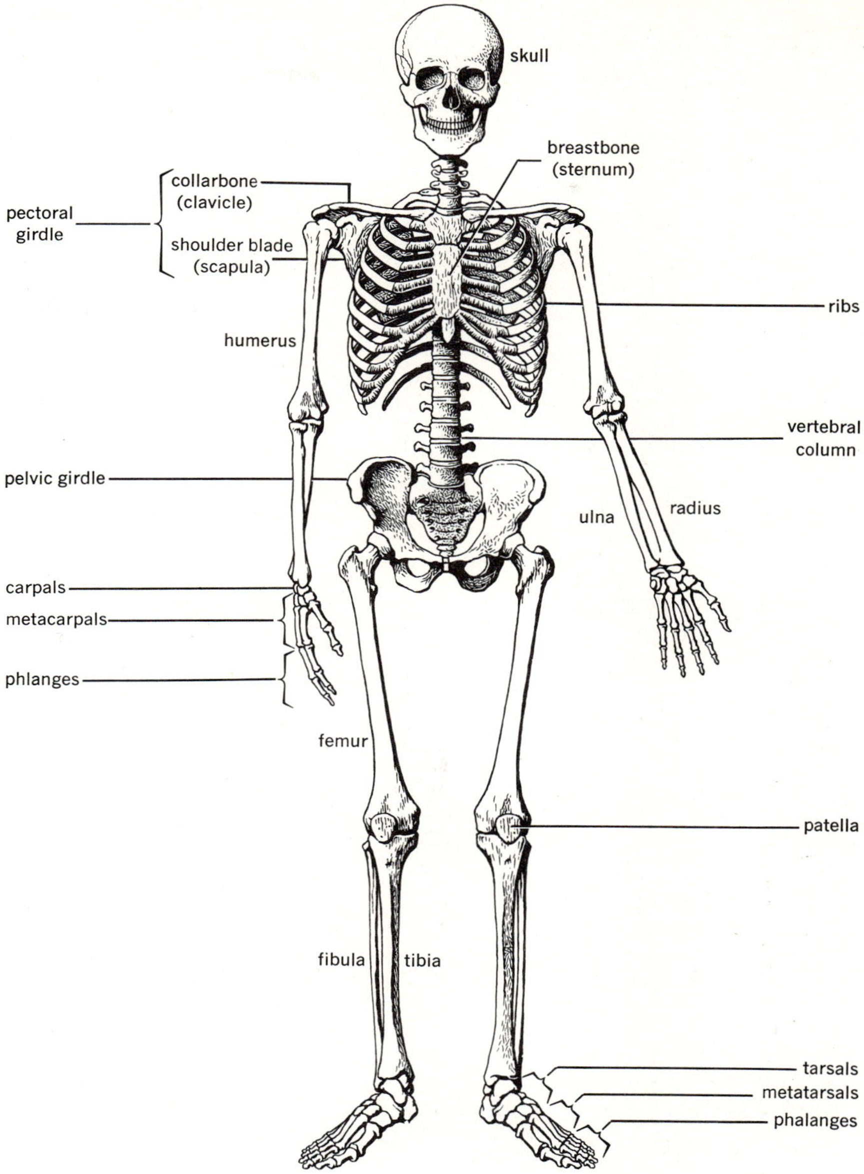

FIGURE 8-7 Bones of the head and trunk
form the axial skeleton; those of the extremities
form the appendicular skeleton.

skull

collarbone
(clavicle)

pectoral
girdle

shoulder blade
(scapula)

breastbone
(sternum)

humerus

ribs

vertebral
column

pelvic girdle

carpals

metacarpals

phlanges

ulna

radius

femur

patella

fibula tibia

tarsals
metatarsals
phalanges

skeletal muscles to provide for movement. The axial skeleton, however, in addition to a supporting role, has an even more important function: to protect the most crucial organs of the body. The skull, the vertebral column, and the rib cage are essentially appropriately shaped "boxes," which house such vital and vulnerable organs as the brain, the spinal cord, the heart, and the lungs.

THE SKULL

Skulls and skull fragments, preserved for thousands and even millions of years, have provided anthropologists with a wealth of evidence on man's origins and evolutionary development. A progression can be traced from apelike ancestors, with heavy jawbones and a small cranial capacity (and therefore a small

brain) to more recent manlike forebears with a high, vaulting cranium and a much reduced jaw. To the trained eye, a skull presents a far larger picture than mere bones. From various bone markings, an anthropologist can reconstruct the probable outlines of muscles, subcutaneous tissues, and ultimately a realistic model of the full head (Figure 8-8). Similar deductions can be made from a modern skull, a skill that has proved helpful in solving a number of murder cases.

The skull of an adult consists of 28 bones, most of them flat bones, fused together so that only one of them (the lower jaw or mandible) is freely movable. (The ear bones, or ossicles, move only slightly in response to sound vibrations transmitted by the eardrum.) The 29th bone mentioned in the list on p. 118

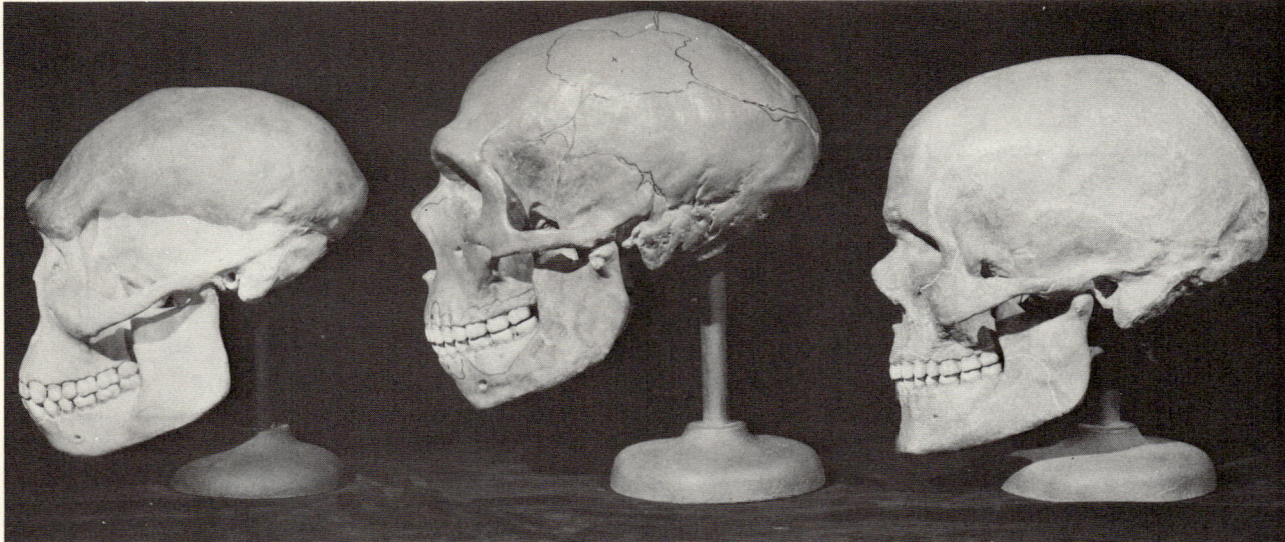

A

B

FIGURE 8-8 Working with skulls of prehistoric men (A), anthropologists can reconstruct their appearance (B). From left to right: Pithecanthropus ("ape-man"), Neanderthal, and Cro-Magnon.

is the hyoid bone, which supports the tongue. It is not really part of the skull proper, since it does not articulate with any other bones, but it is generally considered with the skull because of its location in the upper part of the neck.

The skull as a whole can be conveniently divided into two main parts: the cranium, or brain case, and the face (Figure 8-9). As already mentioned, ossification of the skull begins in about the third month of fetal development but is not entirely completed at

birth. The bones of a newborn infant's skull have not yet fused to form the firm, continuous structure characteristic of the adult; in six regions, called fontanels, there are gaps between the infant's cranial bones, and the brain is covered by a tough membrane rather than bone. As ossification proceeds, the fontanels close, and ultimately the bones of the skull are fully joined in solid articulations called sutures. There is also a change in the relative proportions of the skull with age. The infant's skull is disproportionately large in

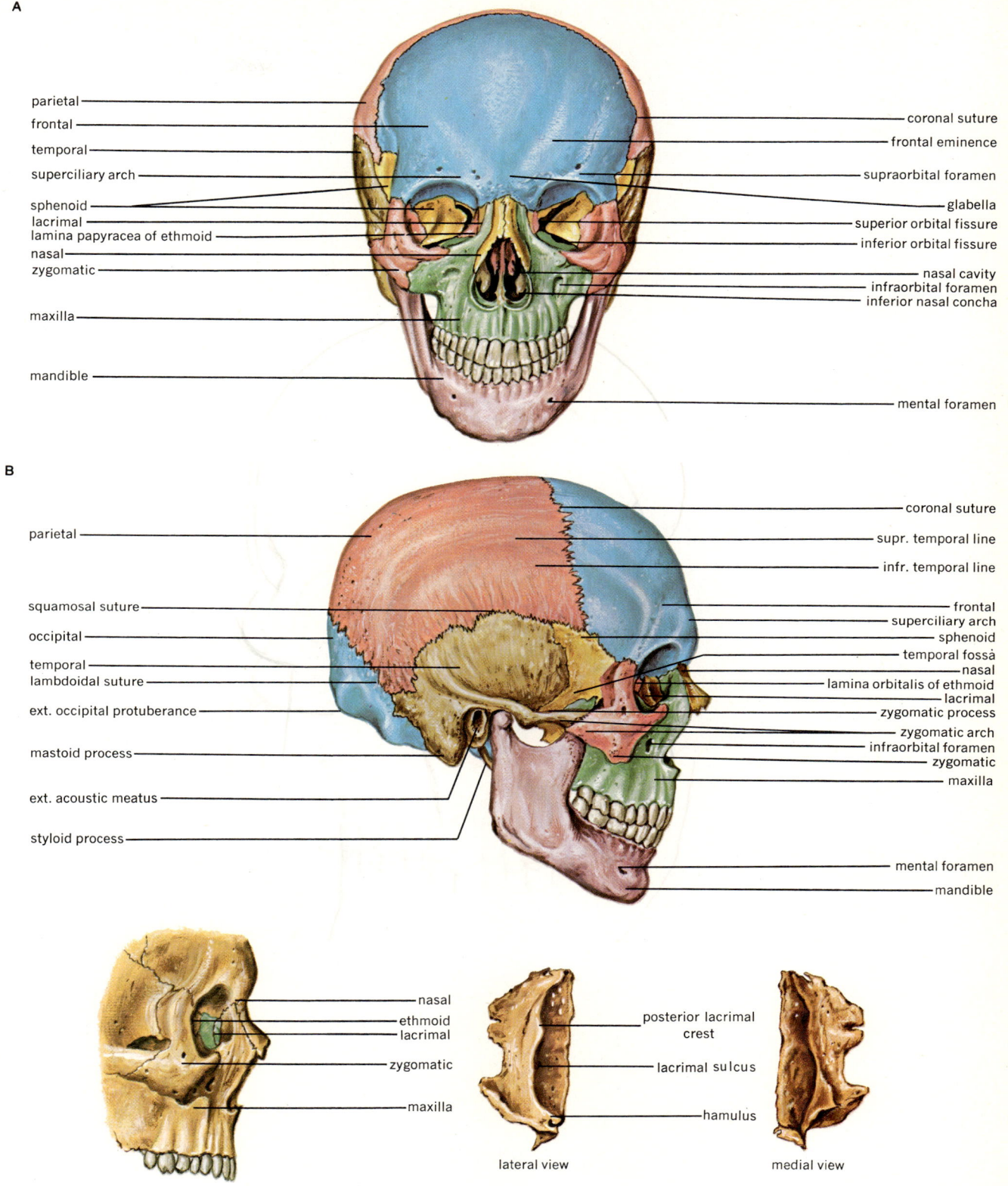

A

parietal
frontal
temporal
superciliary arch
sphenoid
lacrimal
lamina papyracea of ethmoid
nasal
zygomatic

maxilla

mandible

coronal suture
frontal eminence
supraorbital foramen
glabella
superior orbital fissure
inferior orbital fissure
nasal cavity
infraorbital foramen
inferior nasal concha

mental foramen

B

parietal

squamosal suture

occipital

temporal
lambdoidal suture

ext. occipital protuberance

mastoid process

ext. acoustic meatus

styloid process

coronal suture
supr. temporal line
infr. temporal line
frontal
superciliary arch
sphenoid
temporal fossa
nasal
lamina orbitalis of ethmoid
lacrimal
zygomatic process
zygomatic arch
infraorbital foramen
zygomatic
maxilla

mental foramen
mandible

nasal
ethmoid
lacrimal
zygomatic

maxilla

posterior lacrimal crest
lacrimal sulcus
hamulus

lateral view

medial view

lacrimal bone

FIGURE 8-9 Anterior (A) and right lateral (B) views of the skull and details of some of the bones that compose it.

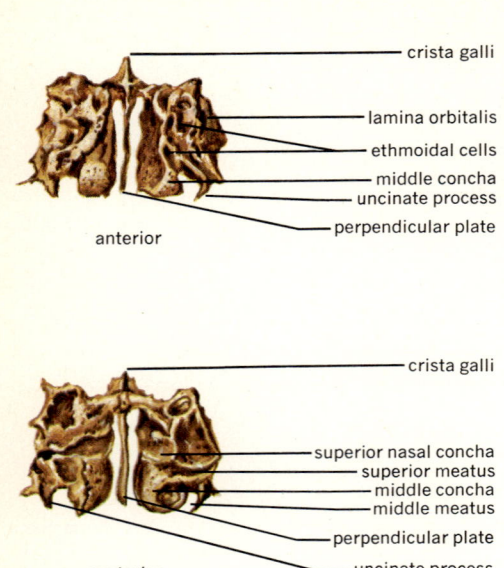

crista galli

lamina orbitalis

ethmoidal cells

middle concha
uncinate process

perpendicular plate

anterior

crista galli

superior nasal concha
superior meatus
middle concha
middle meatus

perpendicular plate

uncinate process

posterior

ethmoid

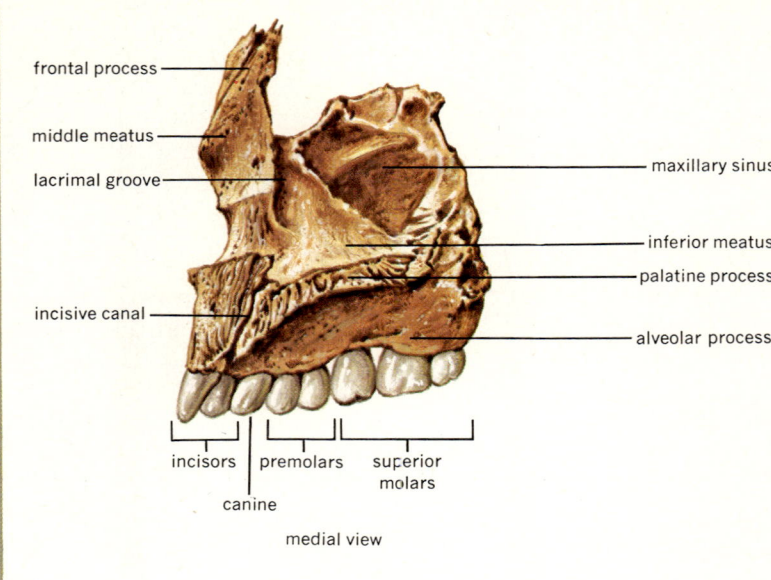

frontal process

middle meatus

lacrimal groove

maxillary sinus

inferior meatus

palatine process

alveolar process

incisive canal

incisors   premolars   superior
molars

canine

medial view

maxilla

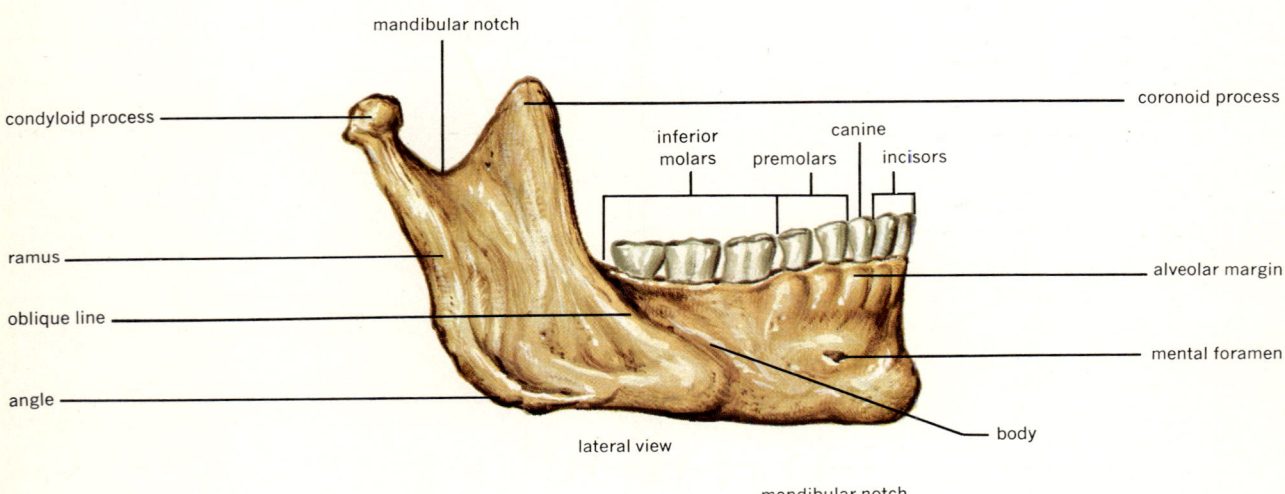

mandibular notch

condyloid process

coronoid process

inferior
molars   premolars   canine   incisors

ramus

alveolar margin

oblique line

mental foramen

angle

body

lateral view

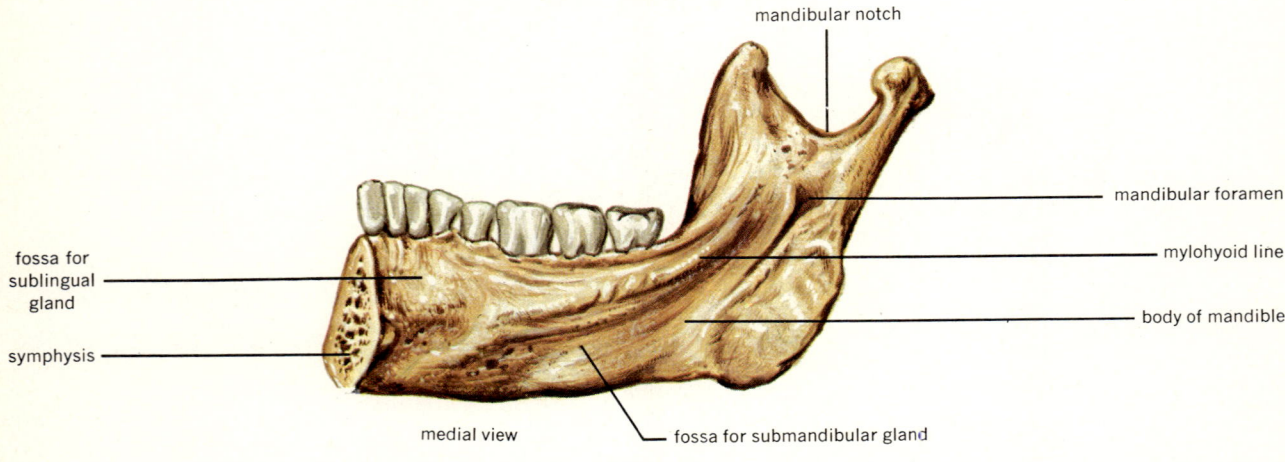

mandibular notch

mandibular foramen

mylohyoid line

fossa for
sublingual
gland

body of mandible

symphysis

medial view

fossa for submandibular gland

mandible

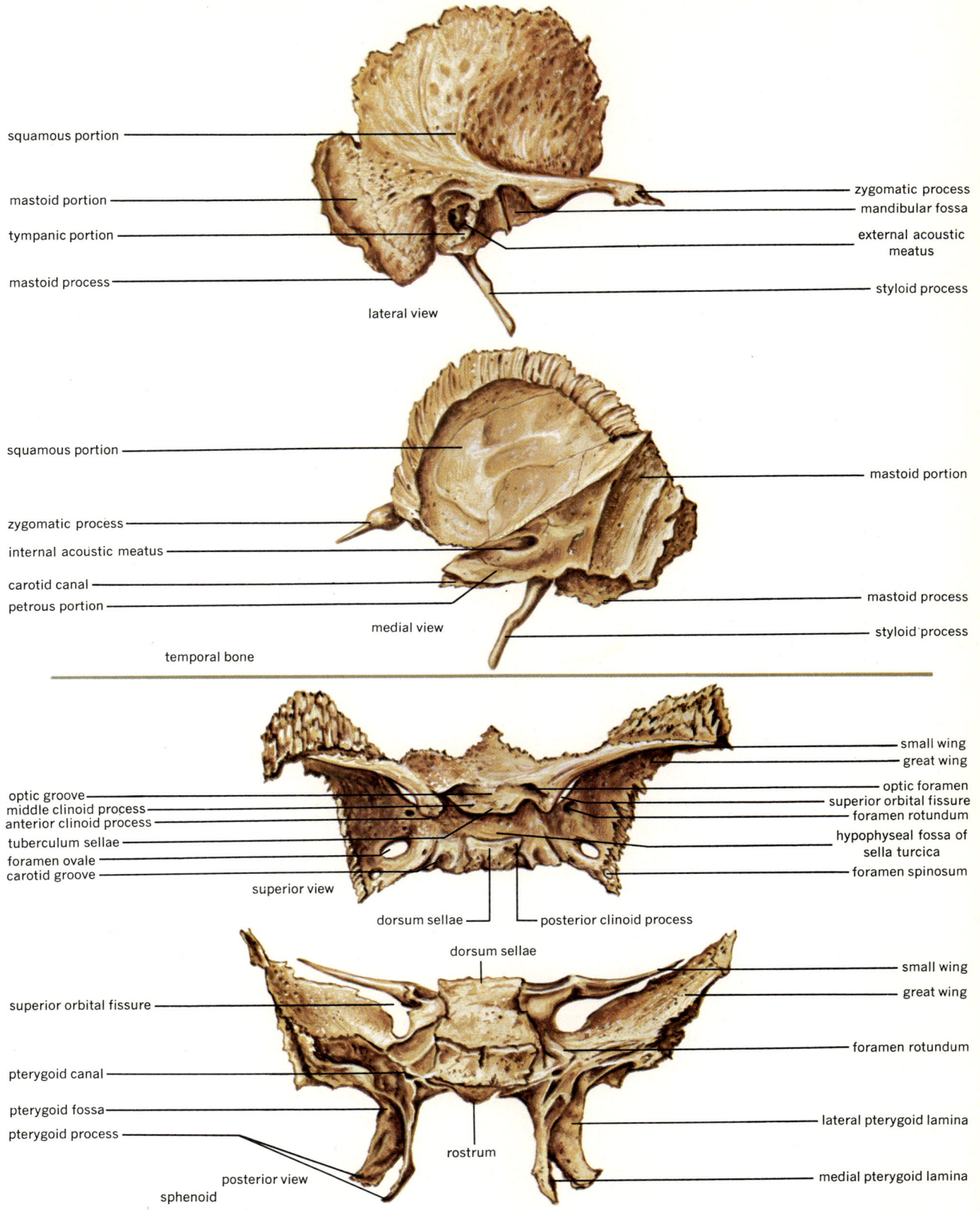

squamous portion

mastoid portion

tympanic portion

mastoid process

zygomatic process

mandibular fossa

external acoustic meatus

styloid process

lateral view

squamous portion

zygomatic process

internal acoustic meatus

carotid canal

petrous portion

mastoid portion

mastoid process

styloid process

medial view

temporal bone

small wing

great wing

optic groove

middle clinoid process

anterior clinoid process

tuberculum sellae

foramen ovale

carotid groove

optic foramen

superior orbital fissure

foramen rotundum

hypophyseal fossa of sella turcica

foramen spinosum

superior view

dorsum sellae

posterior clinoid process

dorsum sellae

small wing

great wing

superior orbital fissure

foramen rotundum

pterygoid canal

pterygoid fossa

pterygoid process

lateral pterygoid lamina

medial pterygoid lamina

rostrum

posterior view

sphenoid

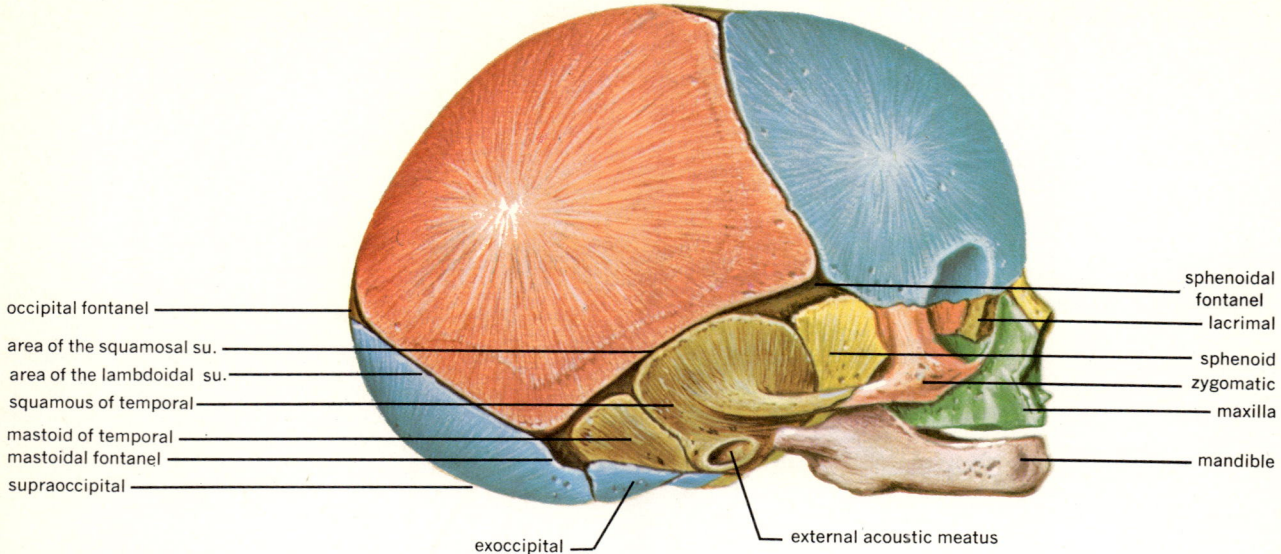

occipital fontanel

area of the squamosal su.

area of the lambdoidal su.

squamous of temporal

mastoid of temporal

mastoidal fontanel

supraoccipital

exoccipital

external acoustic meatus

sphenoidal
fontanel

lacrimal

sphenoid

zygomatic

maxilla

mandible

FIGURE 8-10   Skull of a newborn (lateral view).

comparison with the rest of the skeleton, and the cranium is large in proportion to the face (Figure 8-10). Pronounced enlargements of the face and jaws occur with the eruption of the first and second sets of teeth. Premature ossification of the sutures results in the condition of **microcephaly,** in which the cranial capacity is abnormally small while the face is of normal size. Since the growth of the brain is stunted by this bony confinement, such individuals are usually mentally deficient.* In old age, the skull again acquires somewhat childlike proportions, as teeth are lost and bony material from the jaws is reabsorbed.

The bones of the skull contain a number of foramina, accommodating the passage of nerves, blood vessels, and other structures. Certain bones are modified to accommodate sensory organs: the two orbital cavities for the eyes and the nasal cavity for the nose (serving both olfactory and respiratory functions) are prominent features of the facial bones, while on the lateral aspects of the skull the external auditory meatus provides a conducting channel leading to the eardrum. The skull rests on the vertebral column, into which the spinal cord passes through a large opening at the base of the skull, called the **foramen magnum.**

The bones of the skull include eleven pairs of bones and six single bones (plus the hyoid bone and a variable number of small irregular bones along the sutures, called Wormian bones):

Cranium: 8 bones
 Frontal: 1
 Parietal: 2

Temporal: 2
Occipital: 1
Sphenoid: 1
Ethmoid: 1

Face: 14 bones
 Nasal: 2
 Maxillary: 2
 Zygomatic (malar): 2
 Mandible: 1
 Lacrimal: 2
 Palatine: 2
 Inferior conchae (turbinates): 2
 Vomer: 1

Ossicles (ear bones): 6 bones
 Malleus (hammer): 2
 Incus (anvil): 2
 Stapes (stirrup): 2

Hyoid bone: 1 bone

Wormian bones: variable number (not included in 206 total for skeleton)

The Cranium

The terms "skull" and "cranium" are sometimes loosely used as synonyms. Used correctly, the cranium refers only to the rounded bony case enclosing and protecting the brain, while the skull includes both the cranial and the facial bones.

Viewed from the outside, the cranium looks a little like a patchwork quilt (see Figure 8-9). The eight individual "patches" (bones) that form it are joined together, edge-to-edge, in jagged seams (sutures).

Frontal Bone   This bone is a large and prominent part of the skull. It is the bone that forms the forehead, as well as the roof of the nasal cavity and the upper portions of the orbits (the bony sockets that

---

* The normal cranial capacity for human adults ranges from 1200 to 1600 cc. On the average men tend to have a cranial capacity about 150 cc greater than women. However, despite variations within the normal range, there is no scientific evidence to indicate any inherent differences in intelligence either among races or between the sexes.

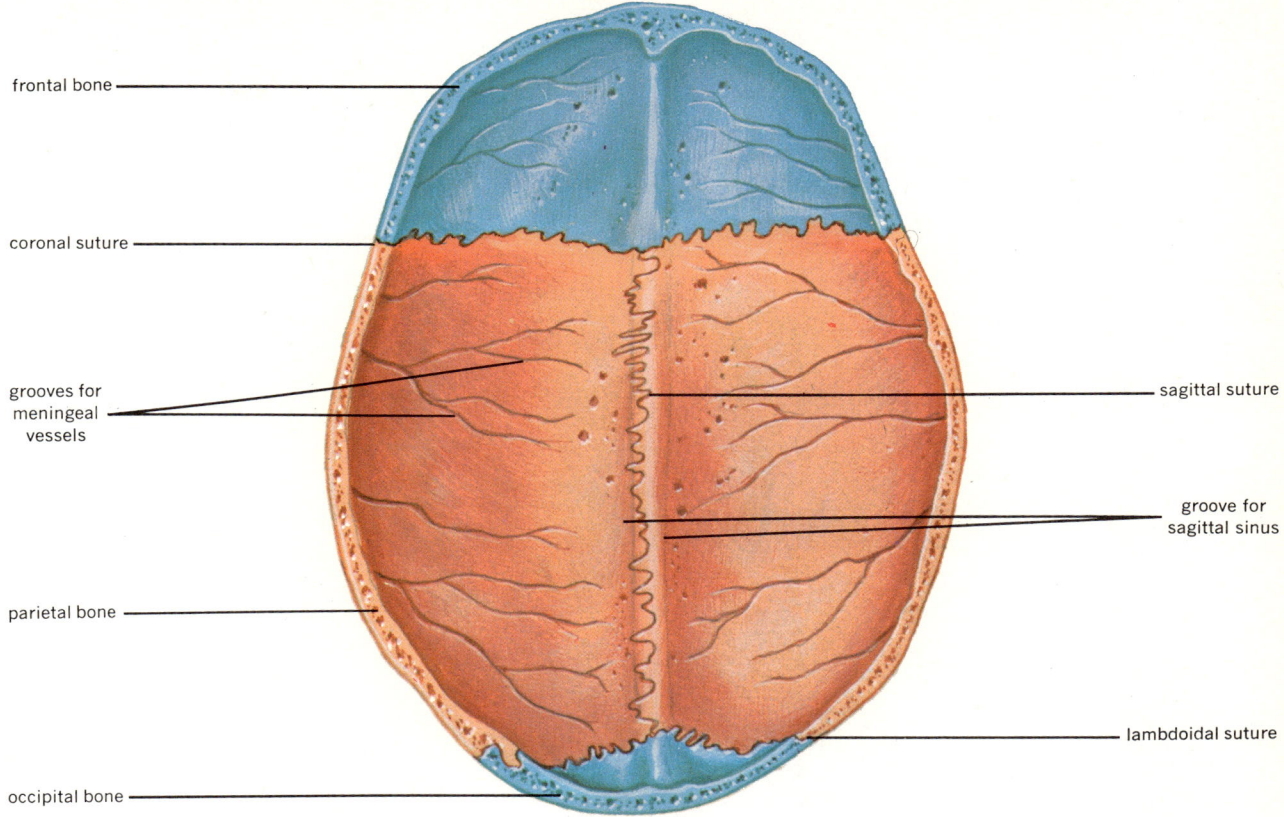

frontal bone

coronal suture

grooves for
meningeal
vessels

parietal bone

occipital bone

sagittal suture

groove for
sagittal sinus

lambdoidal suture

FIGURE 8-11   Interior surface of the vault of the cranium.

contain the eyes). Above the orbital margins (the upper edges of the orbits), a pair of ridgelike prominences jut out. These are the **superciliary arches.** In a living person, these ridges are decorated at the surface of the skin with a pair of eyebrows. The skull of modern man has modest brow ridges in comparison with the beetling brows of the modern anthropoid apes and of some of the apelike ancestors of humans and their anthropoid relatives.

Inside the frontal bone, beneath the superciliary arches, lie a pair of air cavities, the **frontal sinuses.** These cavities are lined with a mucous membrane that serves as a combination membrane and periosteum. The frontal sinuses communicate directly with the nasal cavity, as do similar sinuses in the ethmoid and sphenoid bones of the cranium and the maxillary bones of the face. These sinuses serve two main functions: they help to lighten the skull, and they act as resonating chambers for the sounds of the voice.

A baby starts out in life with a pair of frontal bones, one on each side of the forehead, which join at the center in the **frontal suture.** But usually these two halves fuse completely during early childhood, so that no trace of the former separation remains. (Occasionally a complete suture persists in an adult. It is then referred to as a **metopic suture,** and may be mistaken for a skull fracture if it shows up on an X ray of an

accident victim.) The frontal bone is joined with the two parietal bones at the **coronal suture.**

Parietal Bones   The two parietal bones form the roof of the skull. Along with the frontal bones, they comprise the bulk of the "skullcap," or **calvaria.** They house the all-important cerebrum, the seat of man's memory and thought. The outer surface of the parietal bones is smooth and convex. But the concave inner surface, like that of other parts of the cranium, is marked by numerous grooves and depressions (Figure 8-11), which accommodate the convolutions of the brain and the blood vessels that deliver its rich blood supply. The two parietal bones are joined together along the midline in the **sagittal suture.**

Occipital Bone   If you run your fingers up and down the back of your head, you will feel a pronounced bony projection. This is the end of the occipital bone, which forms the back and base of the cranium. It is joined to the parietal bones in the **lambdoid suture.** The inferior portion of the occipital bone contains a large, roughly circular opening, the **foramen magnum** (which literally means "large opening"). The spinal cord passes through this opening and merges into the medulla oblongata of the brain at about the level of the foramen magnum. The **external**

A

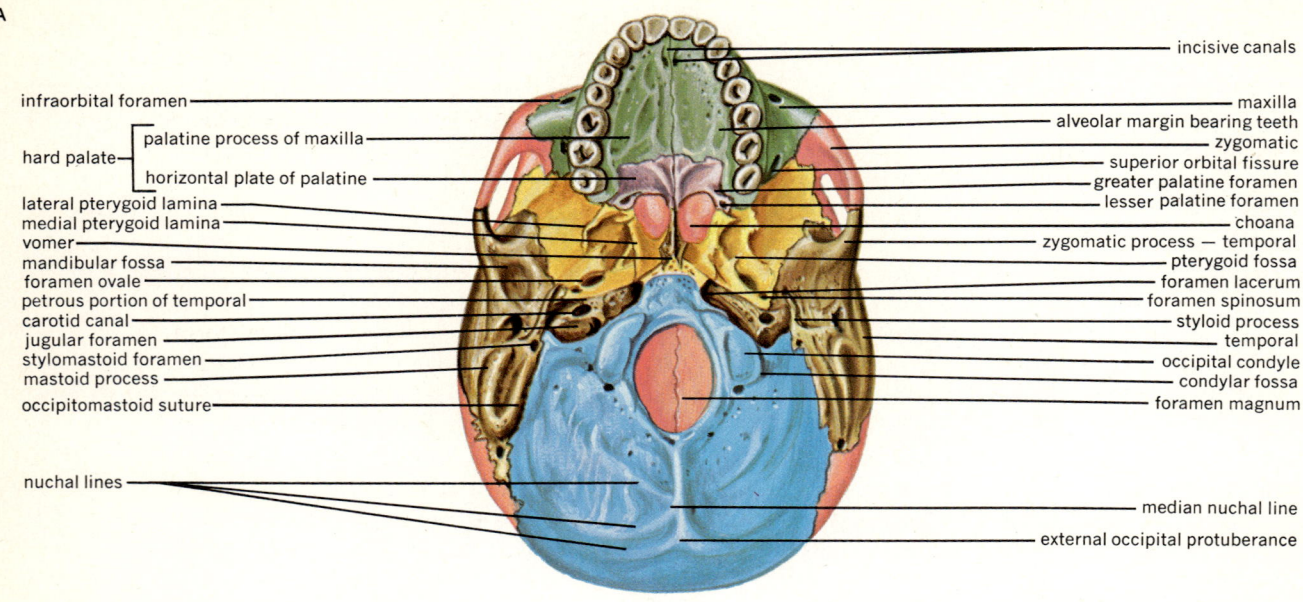

incisive canals
infraorbital foramen
maxilla
alveolar margin bearing teeth
palatine process of maxilla
zygomatic
hard palate
superior orbital fissure
horizontal plate of palatine
greater palatine foramen
lateral pterygoid lamina
lesser palatine foramen
medial pterygoid lamina
choana
vomer
zygomatic process — temporal
mandibular fossa
pterygoid fossa
foramen ovale
foramen lacerum
petrous portion of temporal
foramen spinosum
carotid canal
styloid process
jugular foramen
temporal
stylomastoid foramen
occipital condyle
mastoid process
condylar fossa
occipitomastoid suture
foramen magnum
nuchal lines
median nuchal line
external occipital protuberance

B

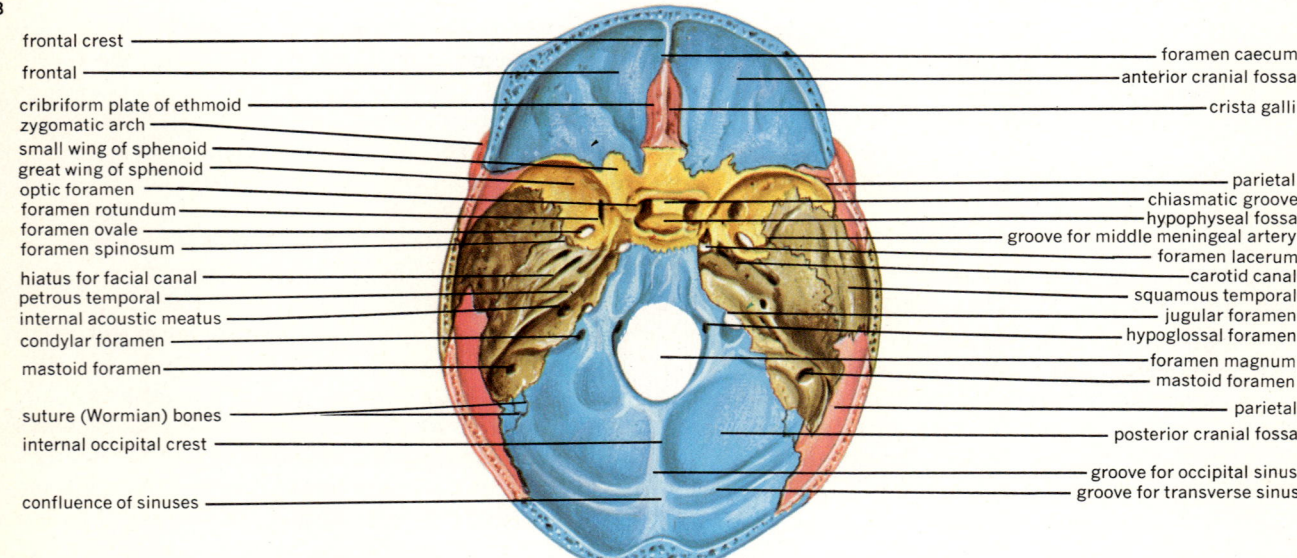

frontal crest
foramen caecum
frontal
anterior cranial fossa
cribriform plate of ethmoid
crista galli
zygomatic arch
small wing of sphenoid
great wing of sphenoid
parietal
optic foramen
chiasmatic groove
foramen rotundum
hypophyseal fossa
foramen ovale
groove for middle meningeal artery
foramen spinosum
foramen lacerum
hiatus for facial canal
carotid canal
petrous temporal
squamous temporal
internal acoustic meatus
jugular foramen
condylar foramen
hypoglossal foramen
foramen magnum
mastoid foramen
mastoid foramen
suture (Wormian) bones
parietal
internal occipital crest
posterior cranial fossa
groove for occipital sinus
confluence of sinuses
groove for transverse sinus

FIGURE 8-12   **Floor of the cranial cavity: exterior surface viewed from below (A) and interior surface viewed from above (B).**

occipital protuberance (the projection you can feel though the scalp at the back of your head) and the **external occipital crest** are important sites of attachment for muscles and ligaments. On each lower side of the occipital bone there is an **occipital condyle** (see Figure 8-12); these two bony processes articulate with the atlas, the first of the vertebrae. When you nod your head, you are utilizing the movement of this joint.

Temporal Bones   The two temporal bones are rather complicated bones, which form part of the sides and base of the cranium. They are situated in the region of the temples, and each encloses an ear. Each temporal bone consists of four parts: squamous, petrous, mastoid, and tympanic (see figure 8-9).

The **squamous portion** is named for its shape; it is a scalelike plate of bone at the side of the cranium. It is the largest portion of the temporal bone. From its lower lateral surface, the **zygomatic process** projects forward and joins with the temporal process of the zygomatic bone (cheek bone), together forming the **zygomatic arch.** The lower surface of the squamous portion contains the **mandibular fossa,** which forms a socket for the condyle of the mandible (lower jaw). Movement at this articulation permits the lower jaw to flap up and down like a trap door on hinges and permits such activities as eating and speaking.

The **petrous portion** is a pyramid-shaped mass of bone, wedged in at the base of the cranium. A series of cavities in this portion of the temporal bone contains the inner ear. The **styloid process,** a pointed spike of bone to which muscles and ligaments of the tongue are attached, projects downward from the undersurface of the petrous portion and is often lost in laboratory skeletons.

The **mastoid portion** projects downward immediately behind the external auditory meatus. It contains a number of air spaces called **mastoid cells** or **sinuses,** which communicate with the middle ear. Only a thin bony partition separates the mastoid spaces from the brain. As a result, ear infections involving the mastoid cells (**mastoiditis**) are potentially dangerous, since they may spread to the brain membranes, giving rise to meningitis. If you feel your skull just behind the ear, you can locate the rounded projection of the **mastoid process.**

The **tympanic portion** is a curved plate below the squamous portion, anterior to the mastoid process. It forms part of the external auditory meatus, the canal that is closed by the tympanic membrane (eardrum).

The temporal bones articulate with the occipital bone (**occipitomastoid suture**), the parietal bones (**squamous suture**), and the sphenoid bone (**sphenosquamous suture**).

Sphenoid Bone The sphenoid bone looks very much like a large butterfly with its wings outspread (see Figure 8-9). It forms the anterior portion of the base of the cranium and serves as a keystone, binding the other cranial bones together. On the upper surface of the sphenoid bone, in the interior of the cranium, there is a saddle-shaped depression, the **sella turcica** (literally, "Turkish saddle"), in which the pituitary gland rests. Two pairs of wings spread out laterally: the large **greater wings** form part of the floor and side walls of the brain case. The **lesser wings** of the sphenoid bone are somewhat anterior to the greater wings and on a higher plane; they form part of the floor of the brain case and part of the roof of the orbits. A pair of **pterygoid processes** project downward from the sphenoid bone (like the spikes on the wings of some butterflies) and help to form the side walls of the nasal cavity. The body of the sphenoid bone contains two large air spaces, the **sphenoid sinuses,** which drain into the nasal cavity.

Ethmoid Bone The ethmoid bone is the lightest of all the cranial bones. It is a cancellous bone, and its lateral portions are referred to as **labyrinths,** for they are masses of air cells (**ethmoid sinuses**) that open into the nasal cavity. A horizontal portion of the ethmoid bone, the **cribriform plate,** forms the roof of the nasal cavities and part of the base of the cranium (see Figures 8-9 and 8-13). A triangular projection on the upper surface of the plate, the **crista galli** (literally, "cock's comb"), provides a point of attachment for the membrane covering of the brain. Numerous small openings in the horizontal plate, the **olfactory foramina,** permit the passage of the sensory nerves for smell from the nasal cavity into the brain. The **perpendicular plate,** a portion of the ethmoid projecting down from the horizontal plate, forms part of the nasal septum. Two pairs of thin, scroll-shaped bones, the **superior and middle nasal conchae,** project down into the nasal cavity from the ethmoid labyrinths. These processes, together with the **inferior turbinate bones** (which are bones of the face, not part of the ethmoid bone), act as baffles and help to circulate and filter the inhaled air on its way to the lungs.

Wormian Bones These small, irregularly shaped bones were named for Olaus Worm, a Danish anatomist, rather than for any resemblance to a worm in shape. Variable numbers of them are frequently found in some of the cranial sutures.

Auditory Ossicles
The middle ear contains an efficient amplifying system for sound vibrations. After striking the tympanic membrane, such vibrations are transmitted along a sequence of three tiny bones: the **malleus,** the **incus,** and the **stapes.** The names of the ear bones, or auditory ossicles, are very graphic: *malleus* means "hammer," *incus* means "anvil," and *stapes* means "stirrup," and these are exactly what the ossicles look like (see Figure 18-3). The malleus is attached by its "handle" to the tympanic membrane. Its head articulates in a freely movable joint with the incus, which in turn articulates with the stapes. The stirrup is joined to the oval window, a membranous partition between the middle and inner ear chambers. Vibrations transmitted by the ear bones to the oval window thrust against the fluid inside the inner ear and are perceived with the aid of special sensory structures in the inner ear, which is discussed in Chapter 18. Occasionally calcium deposits may "freeze" the joints of the auditory ossicles, preventing them from transmitting sound vibrations. The deafness that results can be cured by a surgical operation, freeing the movement of the joints.

Facial Bones
Faces play a disproportionately important role in human relationships. Even though we may know better, we tend to form initial impressions of people from the appearance of their faces. We may think that one person looks honest, another sly; a person whose face

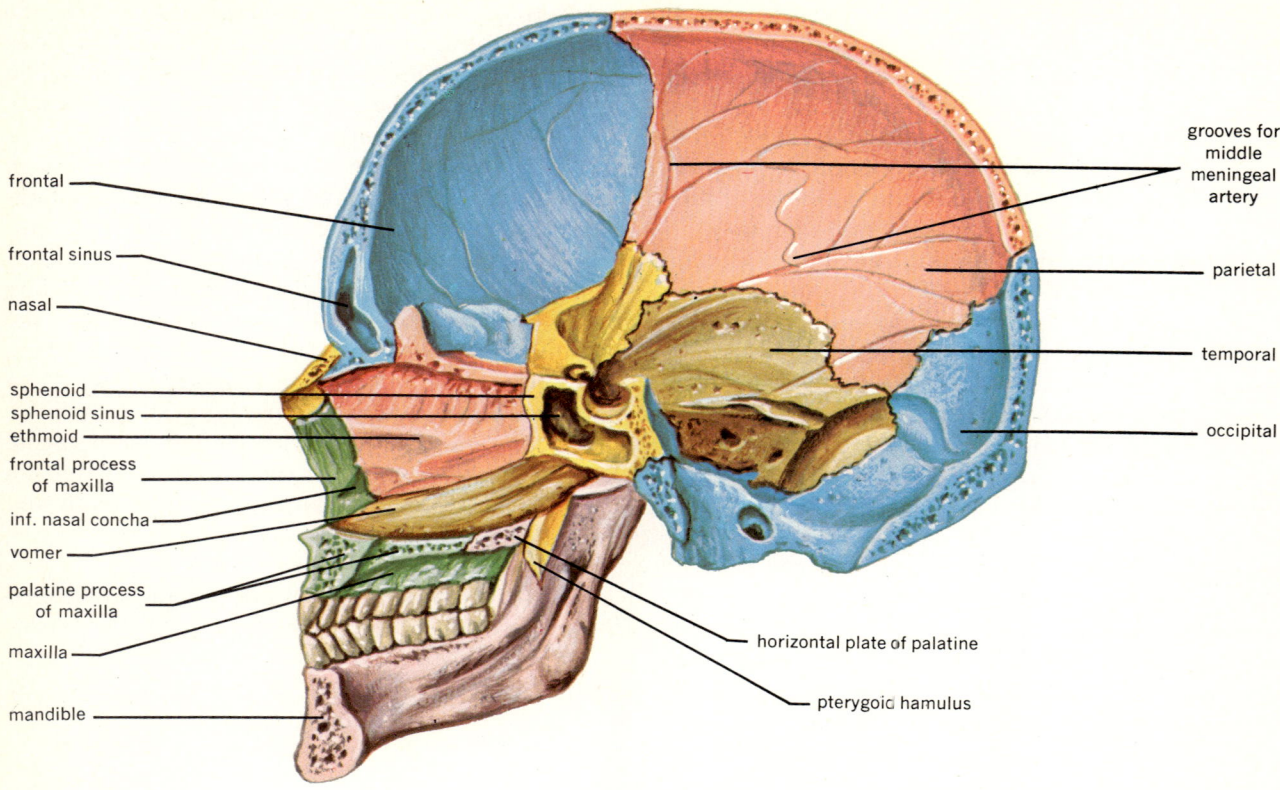

frontal

frontal sinus

nasal

sphenoid
sphenoid sinus
ethmoid
frontal process
of maxilla

inf. nasal concha

vomer

palatine process
of maxilla

maxilla

mandible

grooves for
middle
meningeal
artery

parietal

temporal

occipital

horizontal plate of palatine

pterygoid hamulus

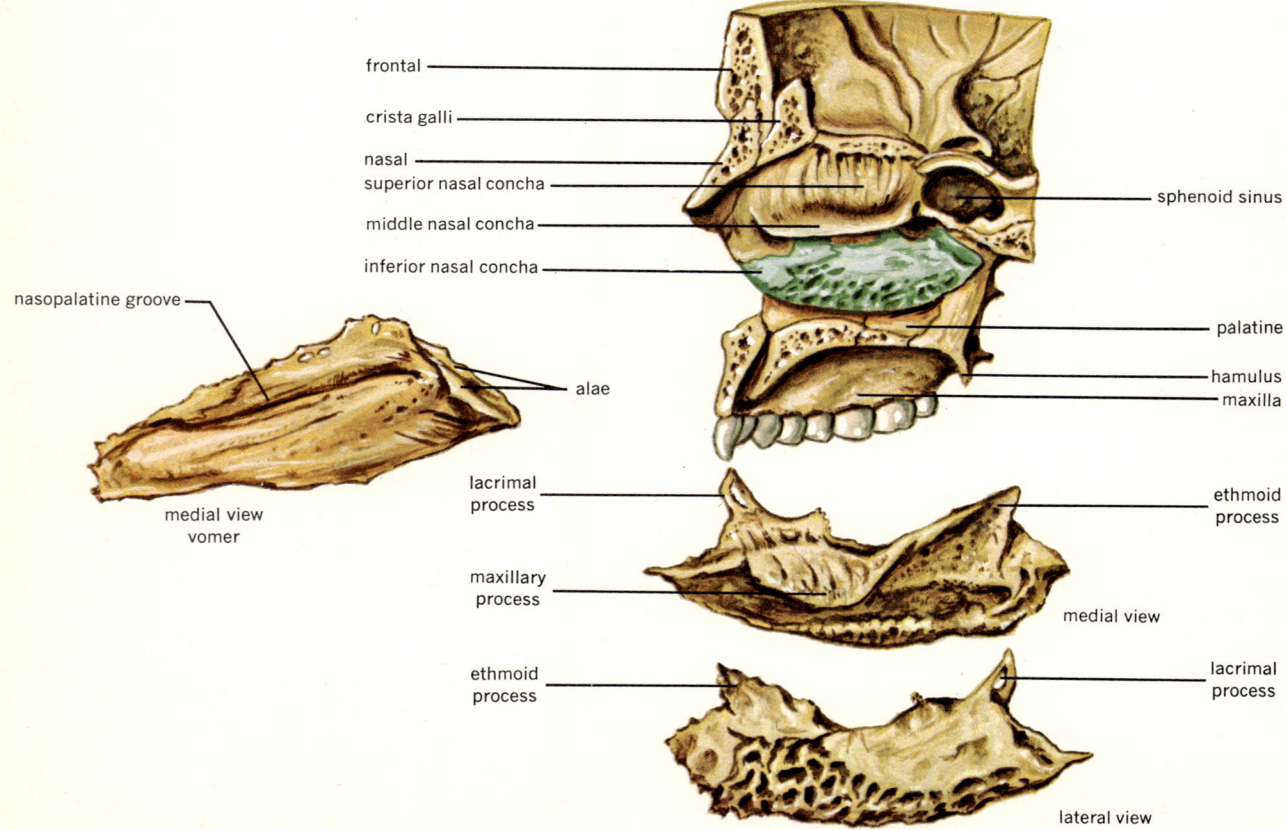

frontal

crista galli

nasal
superior nasal concha

middle nasal concha

inferior nasal concha

sphenoid sinus

palatine

hamulus
maxilla

nasopalatine groove

alae

medial view
vomer

lacrimal
process

maxillary
process

ethmoid
process

medial view

ethmoid
process

lacrimal
process

lateral view

inferior nasal concha

FIGURE 8-13   Sagittal section of the skull and details of the nasal cavity.

conforms to the current standards of beauty may find it much easier to attract friends or get a job than someone who is less well favored. Indeed, plastic surgery has proven to be a promising approach in rehabilitating certain criminals whose antisocial attitudes were partly shaped by the reactions of others to their appearance. Although some aspects of beauty or disfigurement are literally only "skin deep," the appearance of the face is determined to a large degree by the underlying structure of facial bones.

We have already seen that a number of the cranial bones contribute to the formation of the face, in addition to protecting and supporting the brain. The forehead and parts of the orbits, nasal cavity, and cheekbones are formed by cranial bones. The remainder of the facial structure is shaped by 14 facial bones, of which twelve are paired and two are single, and only one (the mandible) is movable.

Nasal Bones

When you look at a skull, one of the most striking features is that the face seems to be lacking a nose. Instead of the prominent projection that often dominates the living face, there is only a gaping cavity, with a suggestion of a framework at the top and a portion of a septum dividing the cavity vertically down the middle. The two nasal bones are small, oblong flat bones, side by side, which are joined to form the bridge of the nose. They articulate with the frontal bone above and with the perpendicular place of the ethmoid bone inside the skull. In the living face, most of the structure of the nose is formed by cartilage. (Feeling your own nose, you can easily differentiate the hard, bony portion of its internal structure from the readily pliable cartilaginous portion.) In human populations, noses show a wide range of variations on the basic functional shape, determined both by heredity and by vulnerability to falls, punches, and impacts with thrown balls. Alterations of the shape of the nose are among the leading types of cosmetic surgery.

Inferior Nasal Conchae

Also called the inferior turbinate bones, these are a pair of thin, scroll-shaped bones on the lateral walls of the nasal cavity. They are very similar to the superior and middle conchae, processes of the ethmoid bone located above them (see Figure 8-13). But the inferior conchae are larger, separate bones. One projects into each nostril. In the living body, they are covered with mucous membrane and help to warm, moisten, and filter the inhaled air.

Vomer

The vomer is a thin single bone, shaped something like a plow, and its name comes from a Latin word meaning "plowshare." It forms the lower part of the nasal septum (see Figure 8-13), merging with the perpendicular plate of the ethmoid bone at its upper anterior border. Its lower anterior border is fitted with grooves, to which the cartilage septum of the nose is attached. Often the vomer turns to one side or the other, making one nasal passage larger than the other.

Lacrimal Bones

The paired lacrimal bones are the smallest and most fragile bones of the face. About the size of a fingernail, they form part of the orbits, just lateral and posterior to the nasal bones. *Lacrimal* comes from a word meaning "tears"; the lateral surface of each lacrimal bone contains a fossa that holds the **lacrimal sac** and a groove along which the **lacrimal** or **tear duct** passes from the orbit to the nasal cavity (refer back to Figure 8-9).

Maxillary Bones

The two **maxillae** are large bones, composing the upper jaw and a substantial part of the facial structure (see Figure 8-9). They form much of the floor of the orbits, part of the floor and outer wall of the nasal cavity, the **hard palate** (roof of the mouth), and much of the anterior portion of the face below the temples. These two bones articulate with all of the other facial bones *except* for the mandible (lower jaw). The maxillae each contain a large **maxillary sinus,** lateral to the nose, which connects with the nasal cavity. These upper jaw bones contain the sockets for the upper teeth. The two maxillae are joined along the midline. The portions that form the anterior part of the hard palate and part of the floor of the nasal cavity are called the **palatine processes.** If the two palatine processes fail to join during prenatal development, the condition known as **cleft palate** results. In addition to the opening in the roof of the mouth, communicating with the nasal cavity, cleft palate may also be associated with a cleft in the lip, referred to as **harelip.** (The cleft lip, however, is to one side, not medial.) The **zygomatic processes** of the maxillae extend laterally and articulate with the zygomatic bones, forming the cheeks.

Zygomatic Bones

In addition to the eyes, nose, and mouth, the cheekbones are often a prominent feature in the basic shape of the face. The zygomatic bones, also called the **malar bones,** form part of the outer border and floor of the orbits. The **frontal process** extends upward to articulate with the frontal bone. The **temporal process** joins with the zygomatic process of the temporal bone and the zygomatic process of the maxilla to form the **zygomatic arch** (refer back to Figure 8-9). In the living face, the region below the cheekbones is filled in to some degree with soft tissues, but the outline of the arches is easily traced by pressing gently along and under the cheekbones.

Palatine Bones Despite their name, the palatine bones form only a small, posterior portion of the hard palate, the roof of the mouth. (Most of the palate is formed by the palatine processes of the maxillary bones.) Each of the palatine bones is roughly L-shaped, but the bones are oriented so that one of the "L's" is the mirror image of the other. The horizontal portion, or foot of the "L" contributes to the roof of the mouth and floor of the nasal cavity (see Figure 8-13), while the vertical portion forms part of the lateral walls of the nasal cavity, and the orbital process at the top of the "L" contributes a small part to the floor of the orbit.

Mandible One of the "last resorts" for an extremely obese person desperately eager to lose weight is to have the jaws wired shut. Without the ability to move the lower jaw, the crash dieter must then subsist on liquids. The total food intake is generally greatly reduced under such conditions, and pounds and inches gradually melt away. Fortunately, few people ever experience such a vivid demonstration of the importance of the lower jaw, or mandible. It is the largest bone of the face, and the only movable one. It consists of a horseshoe-shaped horizontal body with two perpendicular portions, the **rami** (see Figure 8-9). Like the frontal bone, the mandible starts out as a pair of bones, but the two parts fuse early in childhood into a single continuous structure.

Each ramus of the mandible bears two processes: the **coronoid process,** to which the temporal muscle is attached, and a condyle that articulates with the temporal bone. (Note that the mandible is *not* attached in any way to the maxillae, or upper jaw.) In addition to its up-and-down hinge-type movements, the mandible can be moved forward (protruded) and backward (retracted) and from side to side. Such movements are useful in chewing. You can feel the condyle of the mandible sliding back and forth if you place your fingers on each side of your face, just in front of the openings of the external ears, and move your jaw in various ways. Then follow the line of the jawbone downward to the sharp angle where the ramus joins the horizontal portion of the mandible. This region is referred to as the **angle of the jaw** (i.e., that term does not refer to the articulation with the temporal bone).

The **alveolar border** of the mandible bears the lower teeth, which are embedded in individual sockets just like the upper teeth in the maxillae. The teeth of the lower jaw are slightly smaller than those of the upper jaw. If development has proceeded normally, the projections and indentations of the upper and lower teeth mesh neatly when the jaws are closed, providing good opposition for biting and chewing. In old age, if teeth are lost, the alveoli of both the mandible and the maxillae are partly resorbed, and the chin appears more prominent. (The stereotype of an "old witch" exaggerates this age change in the facial bone structure.)

Orbits The eyes are such a prominent feature in the living face that their absence in the empty eye sockets of a skull have an unsettling effect on the viewer. As we have seen, the orbits are rather complicated cavities, pierced by openings for nerves, blood vessels, and muscles, and formed by portions of a number of cranial and facial bones (Figure 8-14). In the living body, the optic nerve and ophthalmic artery pass through the optic foramen, at the apex of the cavity. Following is a brief summary of the bones contributing to each orbit:

Region of orbit	Bones
roof	frontal
	sphenoid

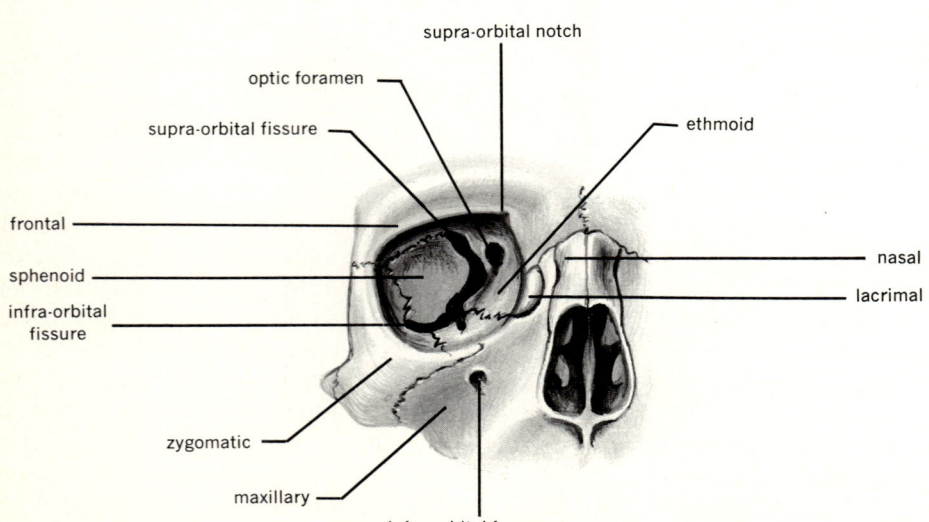

FIGURE 8-14 A number of cranial bones fit together to form the orbits (eye sockets).

supra-orbital notch

optic foramen

supra-orbital fissure

ethmoid

frontal

sphenoid

nasal

infra-orbital fissure

lacrimal

zygomatic

maxillary

infra-orbital foramen

Region of orbit	Bones
floor	maxillary
	zygomatic
lateral wall	zygomatic
	sphenoid (greater wing)
medial wall	maxillary
	lacrimal
	ethmoid
upper rim	frontal
	sphenoid (lesser wing)
lateral rim	sphenoid (lesser wing)
medial rim	frontal
	zygomatic
	maxillary

Nasal Cavity   The bony structure of the nose is another complex formation (see Figure 8-13), to which bones of the cranium and face contribute:

Region of nose	Bones
roof	ethmoid (cribriform plate)
	frontal
	sphenoid
floor	maxillary
	palatine
lateral wall	maxillary
	palatine
	sphenoid (pterygoid processes)
	lacrimal
	ethmoid (superior and middle conchae)
	inferior nasal conchae
septum (medial wall)	ethmoid (perpendicular plate)
	vomer
	nasal
bridge	nasal

The Hyoid Bone

The hyoid bone is the only bone in the axial skeleton that does not articulate with any other bone. It is a horseshoe-shaped bone, with a distinct body and two pairs of "horns": the **greater cornua** (the arms of the horseshoe) and the **lesser cornua** (two small projec-

tions) (Figure 8-15). It is found in the throat region just above the larynx; it supports the tongue and serves as a point of attachment for some of the muscles of the tongue.

Although it does not articulate directly with other bones, the hyoid bone is not totally isolated from the rest of the skeleton. It is suspended from the styloid processes of the temporal bones by the **stylohyoid ligaments.**

THE VERTEBRAL COLUMN

Has anyone ever told you to straighten up your spine? To put some stiffening into your backbone? Actually, the vertebral column is neither stiff nor straight. It is a marvel of efficient engineering: a cylindrical column consisting of a series of disclike bones **(vertebrae),** stacked one upon the other, strong enough to provide support for the body, yet flexibly articulated to provide for bending, stooping, twisting, and a variety of other body motions. Instead of a straight rod, the adult vertebral column is shaped into a sort of double-S curve (Figure 8-16A). In the region of the neck, the **cervical curvature** is slightly convex anteriorly. Proceeding downward, there is a concave curvature in the chest region **(thoracic curvature);** then the spine swings forward again in the **lumbar curvature;** and finally, in the pelvic region, there is another concave curvature, the **sacral curvature.** We are not born with all these curves in the vertebral column. A newborn infant has a rather C-shaped spine (convex posteriorly). At about three months, when it begins to hold its head up, the cervical curve appears and becomes more pronounced when the baby learns to sit up. The lumbar curve does not develop until about a year, when the child begins to walk upright. The curves help to provide resilience and spring to the vertebral column. Injury, disease, or poor posture may distort the normal spinal curvature (Figure 8-16C). An accentuation of the thoracic curvature results in the condition called **kyphosis,** or hunchback. An exaggerated lumbar curvature is known as **lordosis,** or "swayback." A lateral curvature, involving rotation of the vertebrae, is called **scoliosis.**

FIGURE 8-15   The hyoid bone (anterior view).

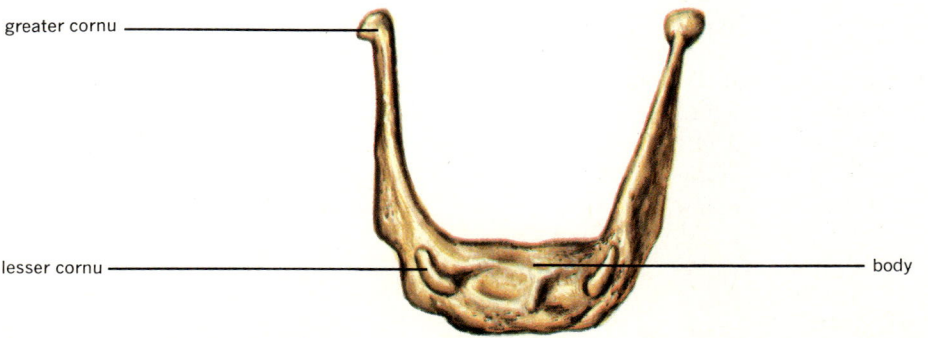

greater cornu

lesser cornu — — — — body

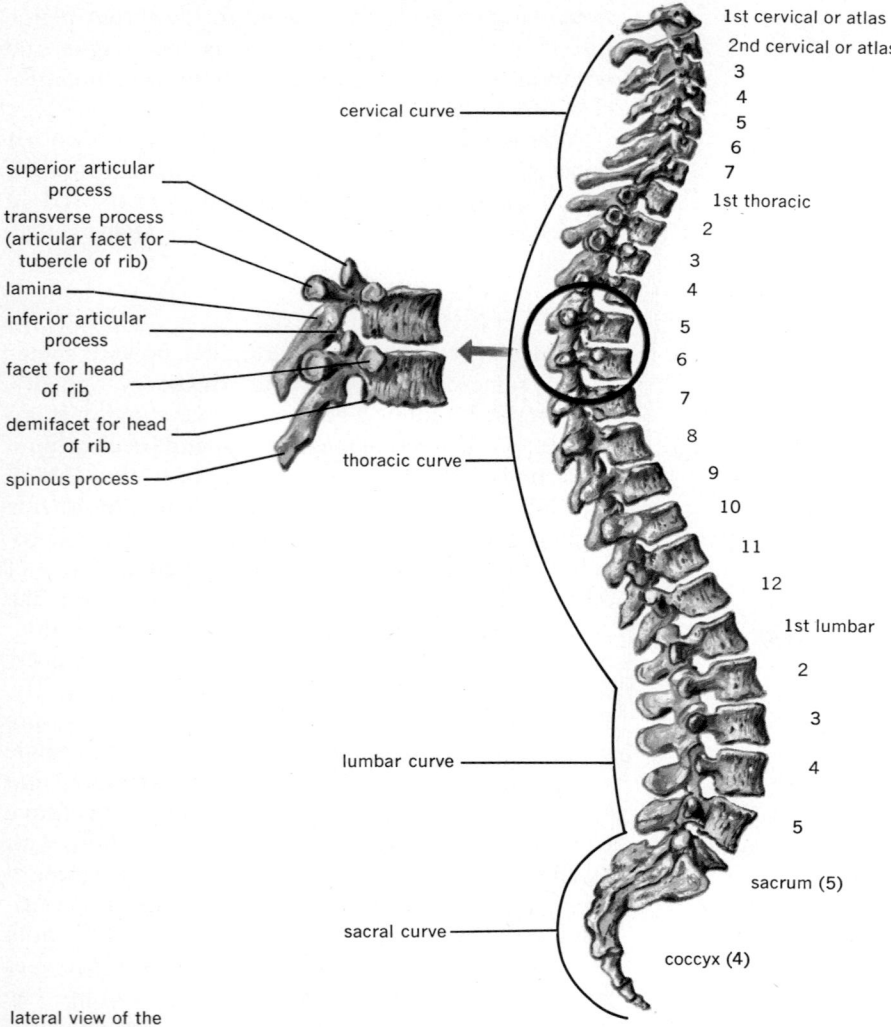

A

1st cervical or atlas
2nd cervical or atlas
3
4
5
6
7
1st thoracic
2
3
4
5
6
7
8
9
10
11
12
1st lumbar
2
3
4
5
sacrum (5)
coccyx (4)

cervical curve

superior articular
process
transverse process
(articular facet for
tubercle of rib)
lamina
inferior articular
process
facet for head
of rib
demifacet for head
of rib
spinous process

thoracic curve

lumbar curve

sacral curve

lateral view of the
vertebral column

FIGURE 8-16 The interlocking bones of the vertebral column provide support with flexibility. (A) Lateral view of the vertebral column. (B) Structure of the axis and atlas; typical cervical, thoracic, and lumbar vertebrae; and the sacrum and coccyx. (C) The X ray shows the abnormal condition of scoliosis, a lateral curvature of the spine.

In an adult, the vertebral column, or backbone, consists of 26 bones, classified into groups according to their location: 7 **cervical vertebrae** in the neck, 12 **thoracic vertebrae** in the thorax, and 5 **lumbar vertebrae** in the loin, along with the **sacrum** and the **coccyx** in the pelvis. The latter two bones are the result of fusion of a number of separate vertebrae (5 and 4, respectively). Thus, a child has a total of 33 vertebrae, which are gradually contracted to the 26 of the adult as fusion of the sacrum and coccyx proceeds.

Despite characteristic differences among bones in each of the groups of vertebrae, each vertebra has roughly the same general structure (Figure 8-16B). It consists of an anterior **body,** a central **vertebral foramen** (except in the coccyx), and a posterior **vertebral arch.** Except for the first two cervical vertebrae, the body is roughly drum-shaped and is the basic weight-bearing component of the bone. An **intervertebral disc** of compressible fibrous cartilage is sandwiched

between each two adjacent vertebrae, cushioning the joint. With this structure, the vertebral column can withstand forces of compression many times the weight of the body—a capacity that is essential if the bones of the spine are to be undamaged by the sudden shocks of jumps and falls. The shock-absorbing intervertebral discs also help to protect the brain from injury by reducing the force of jarring impacts transmitted along the spine.

The vertebral arch, surrounding the vertebral foramen, is composed of several parts: two **pedicles,** short thick projections that extend posteriorly from the sides of the body of the vertebra, and two **laminae,** broad bony plates that arise from the pedicles and meet and fuse posteriorly. (If the laminae fail to fuse during prenatal development, the condition of **spina bifida** results; a portion of the spinal cord or its coverings may protrude through the opening in the bone.) Each pedicle bears a superior and an inferior notch.

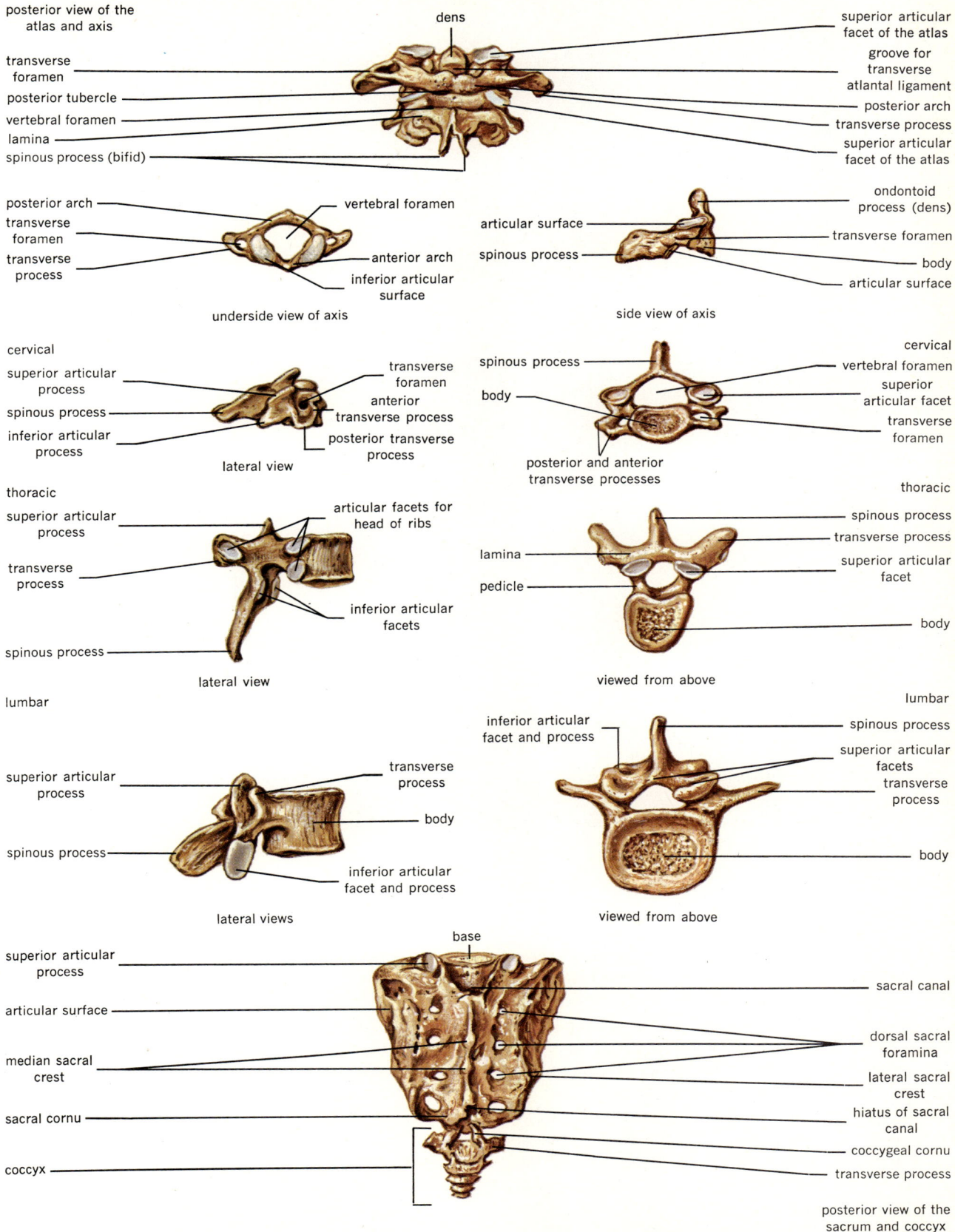

posterior view of the atlas and axis

dens

superior articular facet of the atlas

groove for transverse atlantal ligament

posterior arch

transverse process

superior articular facet of the atlas

transverse foramen

posterior tubercle

vertebral foramen

lamina

spinous process (bifid)

posterior arch

transverse foramen

transverse process

vertebral foramen

anterior arch

inferior articular surface

underside view of axis

articular surface

spinous process

ondontoid process (dens)

transverse foramen

body

articular surface

side view of axis

cervical

superior articular process

spinous process

inferior articular process

transverse foramen

anterior transverse process

posterior transverse process

lateral view

spinous process

body

cervical

vertebral foramen

superior articular facet

transverse foramen

posterior and anterior transverse processes

thoracic

superior articular process

transverse process

spinous process

articular facets for head of ribs

inferior articular facets

lateral view

lamina

pedicle

thoracic

spinous process

transverse process

superior articular facet

body

viewed from above

lumbar

superior articular process

spinous process

transverse process

body

inferior articular facet and process

lateral views

inferior articular facet and process

lumbar

spinous process

superior articular facets

transverse process

body

viewed from above

base

superior articular process

articular surface

median sacral crest

sacral cornu

coccyx

sacral canal

dorsal sacral foramina

lateral sacral crest

hiatus of sacral canal

coccygeal cornu

transverse process

posterior view of the sacrum and coccyx

B

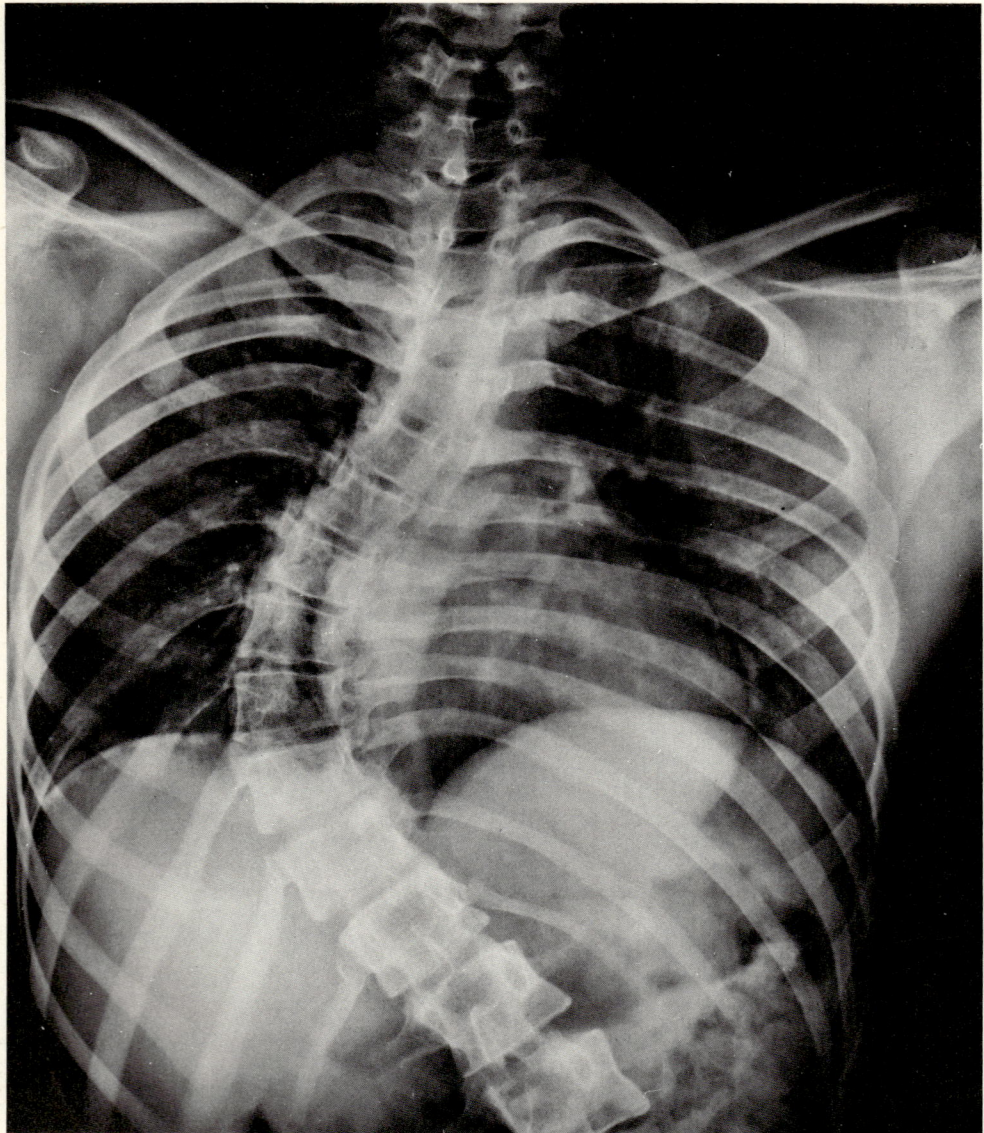

c

The corresponding notches of adjacent vertebrae form **intervertebral foramina,** which accommodate the passage of spinal nerves.

The vertebrae are lined up in sequence in the vertebral column so that the adjacent vertebral foramina form a continuous **vertebral canal,** which surrounds and protects the spinal cord. Most of the vertebrae bear a sharp or blunt **spinous process,** which projects posteriorly, and two **transverse processes,** projecting laterally. The spinous processes of the vertebrae can be seen as a series of "bumps" down the middle of the back. (They are more prominent, the thinner the person is.) Strong, somewhat extensible ligaments bind adjacent vertebrae together into a continuous series and resist displacement of individual vertebrae while permitting considerable flexibility. Between the extensibility of the ligaments and the compressibility of the intervertebral discs, the spine is capable of backward, forward, sideways, and twisting movements.

In addition to their features in common, the groups of vertebrae also possess certain distinctive variations.

Cervical Vertebrae

According to Greek myths, Atlas was a giant who held up the world on his shoulders. Your body contains an **atlas** named for the mythical Greek: the first cervical vertebra, which supports the head. The atlas (see Figure 8-16B) is a rather atypical vertebra. It has no body, nor any spinous process. It is in essence just a bony ring, which articulates, on its upper surface, with the condyles of the occipital bone. (When you nod your head, you are utilizing the movement of this joint.) The atlas does share one characteristic peculiarity with the other cervical vertebrae: its transverse processes each contain a hole, the **transverse foramen,** through which the vertebral arteries pass on their way to the brain.

The second cervical vertebra also has an individual name: it is the **axis,** and it provides an axis for the rotation of the head. A large, toothlike structure, the **dens** ("tooth") or **odontoid process,** projects upward from the body of the axis and fits into the anterior part of the atlas to form a pivot (Figure 8-16B). The dens is actually the "missing" body of the atlas, which became detached during our evolutionary development and fused with the next vertebra in line.

The following cervical vertebrae are more "typical." They are all rather small (the cervical vertebrae, in general, are smaller than the thoracic and lumbar vertebrae), have transverse foramina, and the third, fourth, and fifth cervical vertebrae have a forked spinous process, which accommodates the strong ligaments supporting the head. The seventh cervical vertebra has a long, unforked spinous process, which can be seen and felt at the back of the neck.

Thoracic Vertebrae

Moving down the spine, the thoracic vertebrae grow progressively larger. All of them are larger and stronger than the cervical vertebrae. Their long spinous processes are directed downward, and those of adjacent vertebrae overlap one another like the shingles on a roof. Unlike the cervical vertebrae, the thoracic vertebrae do not have transverse foramina. The distinguishing feature of these twelve vertebrae of the chest region is the presence of six **facets,** or smooth areas (three on each side), which articulate with the ribs. A typical thoracic vertebra is shown in Figure 8-16B.

Lumbar Vertebrae

Standing upright involves a constant struggle against gravity. The skeleton bears the brunt of this struggle, since it must support the weight of the body. The task increases progressively down the spine, as the weight of additional overlying structures is added. It is not surprising, therefore, that the progressive increase in size and strength of the vertebrae continues, and the lumbar vertebrae are the largest and strongest of all. Their spinous and transverse processes are proportionately short and thick. They have neither transverse foramina nor rib facets, but the spinous processes are modified for the attachment of the powerful back muscles and do not overlap each other as do the spines of thoracic vertebrae. A typical lumbar vertebra is depicted in Figure 8-16B.

The Sacrum

The cervical, thoracic, and lumbar vertebrae are the movable bones of the vertebral column. The sacrum, which articulates with the fifth lumbar vertebra, has a quite different appearance (Figure 8-16B). It is a triangular bone, wedged in between the two ossa coxae (hipbones). The remains of spinous processes (the **median sacral crest**) on the posterior surface and the transverse ridges on the anterior surface betray its origin as five separate vertebrae, which fuse into a single bone during childhood. The sacral canal is continuous with the vertebral canal and contains spinal nerves; but the spinal cord proper does not extend down this far, ending at the second lumbar vertebra. The bony structure of the vertebral canal on the posterior surface is incomplete at the level of the last two sacral vertebrae, forming an irregular opening into the canal, the **sacral hiatus.**

The ear-shaped **auricular surfaces** on the sides of the sacrum articulate with the iliac portion of the hipbones, forming the sacroiliac joint that has been made famous in jokes and songs. Strong sacroiliac ligaments hold up the sacrum between the ilia against the weight of the body. Repeated pregnancies place a strain on this joint and may weaken the sacroiliac ligaments, resulting in chronic low back pain. A prominent lip at the upper anterior surface of the sacrum protrudes into the pelvic cavity, forming the **sacral promontory;** this is one of the important landmarks an obstetrician uses in measuring the pelvis for childbirth.

The Coccyx

Occasionally a baby is born with a small but distinct tail. Usually this superfluous structure is discreetly snipped off by the attending physician. Most of us do not have such an obvious vestige of our evolutionary descent from tailed vertebrate ancestors, but we do carry a bit of evidence hidden under our flesh: the small "tailbone" or coccyx at the end of the spine. The coccyx is formed from the fusion of four rudimentary vertebrae and is attached to the tip of the sacrum (Figure 8-16B). The slight movement possible at this joint can help to increase the size of the birth canal during delivery. But in later life the coccyx and sacrum may fuse.

Some of the muscles that move the tail in lower animals are attached to the human coccyx, but normally the human tailbone is incapable of wagging. Its chief importance is in a negative aspect: it may be fractured in a fall, and then gives rise to severe pain.

BONES OF THE THORAX

Take a deep breath. Then try to imagine what the effect would be if the internal organs of your chest were enclosed in a solid case of fused, immovable bones like the skull that protects your brain. Such a design would hardly be practical, since the heart and lungs continually expand and contract as they func-

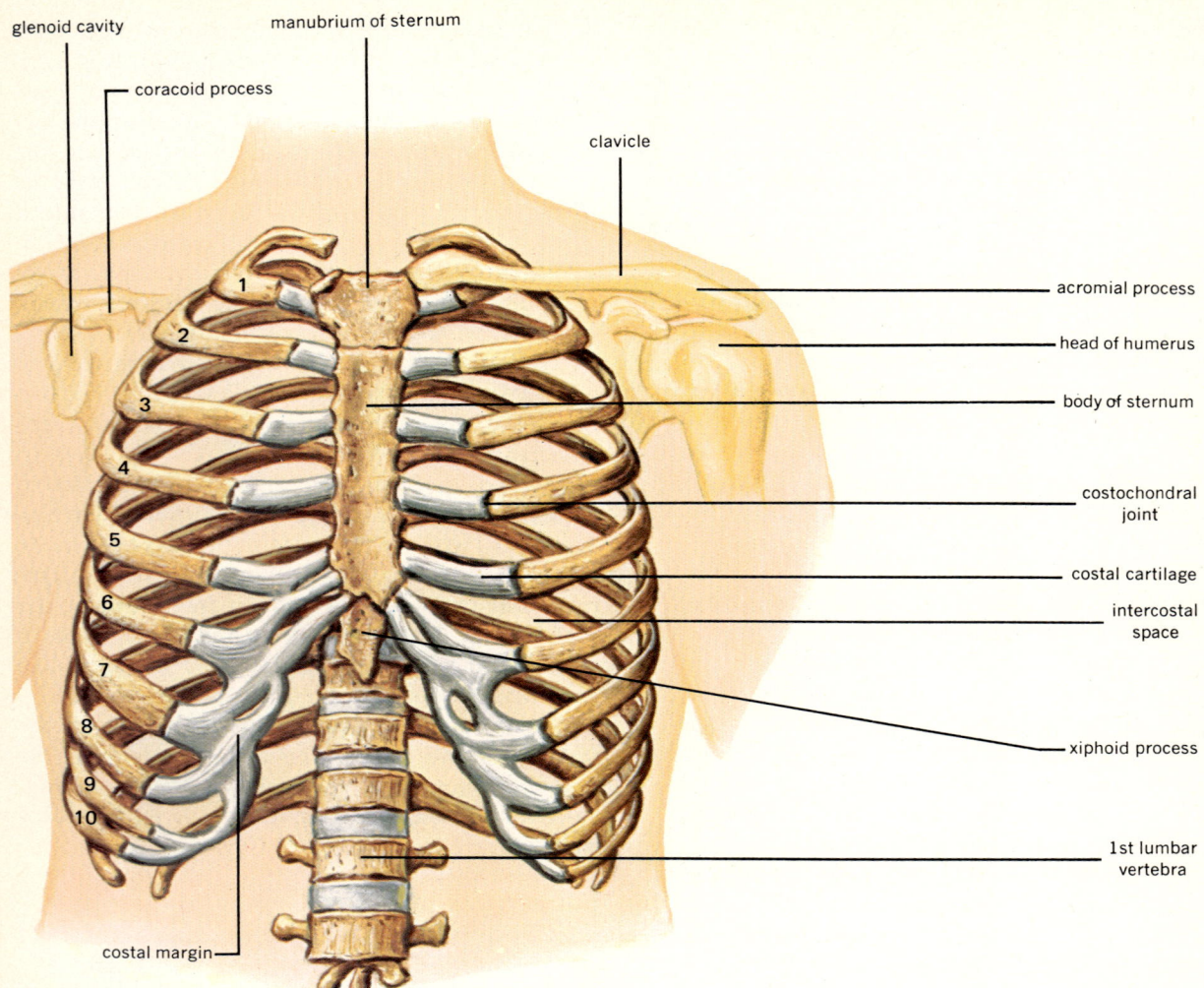

glenoid cavity

coracoid process

manubrium of sternum

clavicle

1
2
3
4
5
6
7
8
9
10

acromial process

head of humerus

body of sternum

costochondral joint

costal cartilage

intercostal space

xiphoid process

1st lumbar vertebra

costal margin

FIGURE 8-17   Bones of the thorax (anterior view): the rib cage, shoulder girdle, and vertebral column.

tion. Yet these vital organs need protection and support. The bones of the thorax represent an effective compromise: they form a roughly cone-shaped bony cage, which supports and protects the soft organs within it while still allowing for expansion and contraction.

The thorax consists of the rib cage, formed by twelve pairs of **ribs,** the solid, dagger-shaped **sternum** (breastbone) in front, and the twelve thoracic vertebrae at the back (Figure 8-17). The floor of the thorax is formed by a dome-shaped muscle, the **diaphragm.** The liver and stomach, situated in the upper part of the abdominal cavity just below the diaphragm, can thus share in the protection provided by the thorax.

In addition to protecting the internal organs of the chest, the thorax plays an important role in the process of breathing and helps to support the bones of the shoulder girdle.

The Sternum

The dagger-shaped sternum forms a solid plate of armor down the middle of the anterior wall of the chest cavity. It consists of three distinct segments: the uppermost portion, the **manubrium;** the largest, middle portion, the **body** or **gladiolus;** and the small lowest portion, the **xiphoid process.** Both the manubrium and the body of the sternum contain notches for the attachment of ribs via cartilage. No ribs are attached to the xiphoid process, but it is a site of attachment for some abdominal muscles. In later life, usually after 40, the xiphoid process becomes fused with the body of the sternum.

The junction of the manubrium with the body of the sternum is called the **sternal angle.** It can be clearly felt at the base of the neck and is an important clinical landmark: the second rib joins the sternum at this point, and the sternal angle is commonly taken as

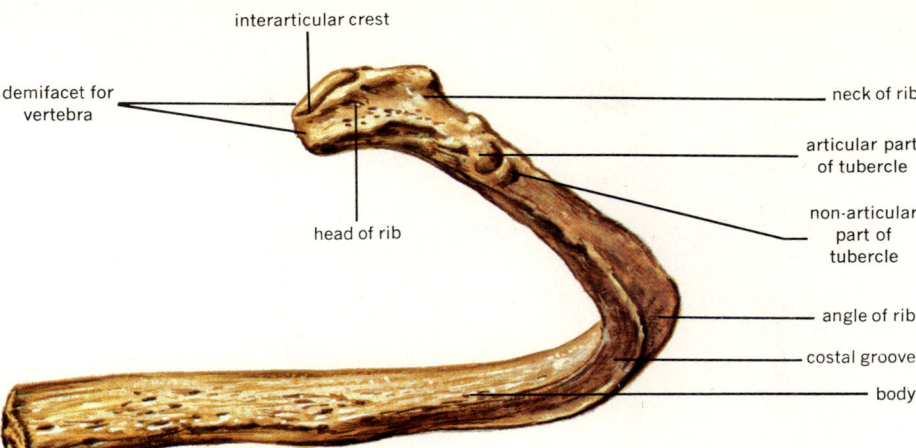

FIGURE 8-18 Structure of a rib (posterior view).

interarticular crest

demifacet for vertebra

head of rib

neck of rib

articular part of tubercle

non-articular part of tubercle

angle of rib

costal groove

body

the starting point for counting a patient's ribs.

The marrow cavity of the sternum is filled with red bone marrow throughout life and is a major site of blood cell production. Because of its accessibility, this bone is a favorite site for obtaining samples of blood-forming tissue in the diagnosis of blood disorders. The cortex of the sternum is punctured with a large needle called a trocar, and a marrow specimen is withdrawn.

The Ribs

The myth that a man has one less rib than a woman is poetic but inaccurate. The normal human set of ribs—in both sexes—consists of 12 pairs, although individual variations are seen, and occasionally 11, 13, or even 14 pairs of ribs may be observed.

The ribs are elongated, curving, flattened bones. All of them articulate posteriorly with the thoracic vertebrae. (Each vertebra accommodates two ribs, one on each side.) From the vertebra, the rib curves laterally downward, then swings anteriorly, forming a sharp angle. The first seven pairs of ribs are attached to the sternum by bands of hyaline cartilage, the **costal cartilages.** The eighth, ninth, and tenth pairs of ribs are indirectly attached to the sternum: a cartilage binds the end of each of these ribs to the cartilage of the rib just superior to it. But the last two pairs of ribs have no firm anterior attachment at all. They are often referred to as **floating ribs.** (They do not really "float" in the living body; they are firmly embedded in the muscles of the abdominal wall.)

A typical rib (Figure 8-18) has a rounded **head** on its posterior end, containing two flattened facets that articulate with corresponding facets on the body of a thoracic vertebra. Then follows a **neck,** and just below it, a lateral bulge or **tubercle,** which articulates with the facet of a transverse process on the corresponding vertebra. The lower ribs are progressively

longer than the upper ones (with the exception of the last two pairs, the "floating ribs"), giving the rib cage its basically conical shape. Grooves along the upper and lower edges of the ribs accommodate nerves and blood vessels. The spaces between the ribs, called intercostal spaces, contain the intercostal muscles. The red marrow of the ribs is another important site of blood cell formation.

THE APPENDICULAR SKELETON

All the bones we have discussed so far are part of the axial skeleton, lying along the central axis of the body. But some of the structures most important in our daily lives are supported by bones of the appendicular skeleton (literally "hanging onto" or suspended from the axial skeleton). Each time you take a step or raise a bit of food or drink to your mouth, you are utilizing bones of your appendicular skeleton and the muscles associated with them. Life is possible without appendages, as victims of accidents, disease, and birth defects have demonstrated; but it is a far more difficult life than most of us enjoy.

A child's stick figure representation of the human body often misses a crucial detail. The arms and legs are not attached directly to the axial skeleton. Instead, the bones of the extremities are suspended from yoke-like structures, the **pectoral** (shoulder) and **pelvic** (hip) **girdles,** which in turn articulate with the axial skeleton.

THE UPPER EXTREMITIES

Each of your arms contains 30 separate bones (32, counting the shoulder girdle). This total is larger than all the bones of the skull, or all the vertebrae, or all the bones of the thorax. The bones of the upper extremity can be divided conveniently into five main groups: the shoulder girdle, the arm, the forearm, the wrist, and the hand (Figure 8-19). In each upper

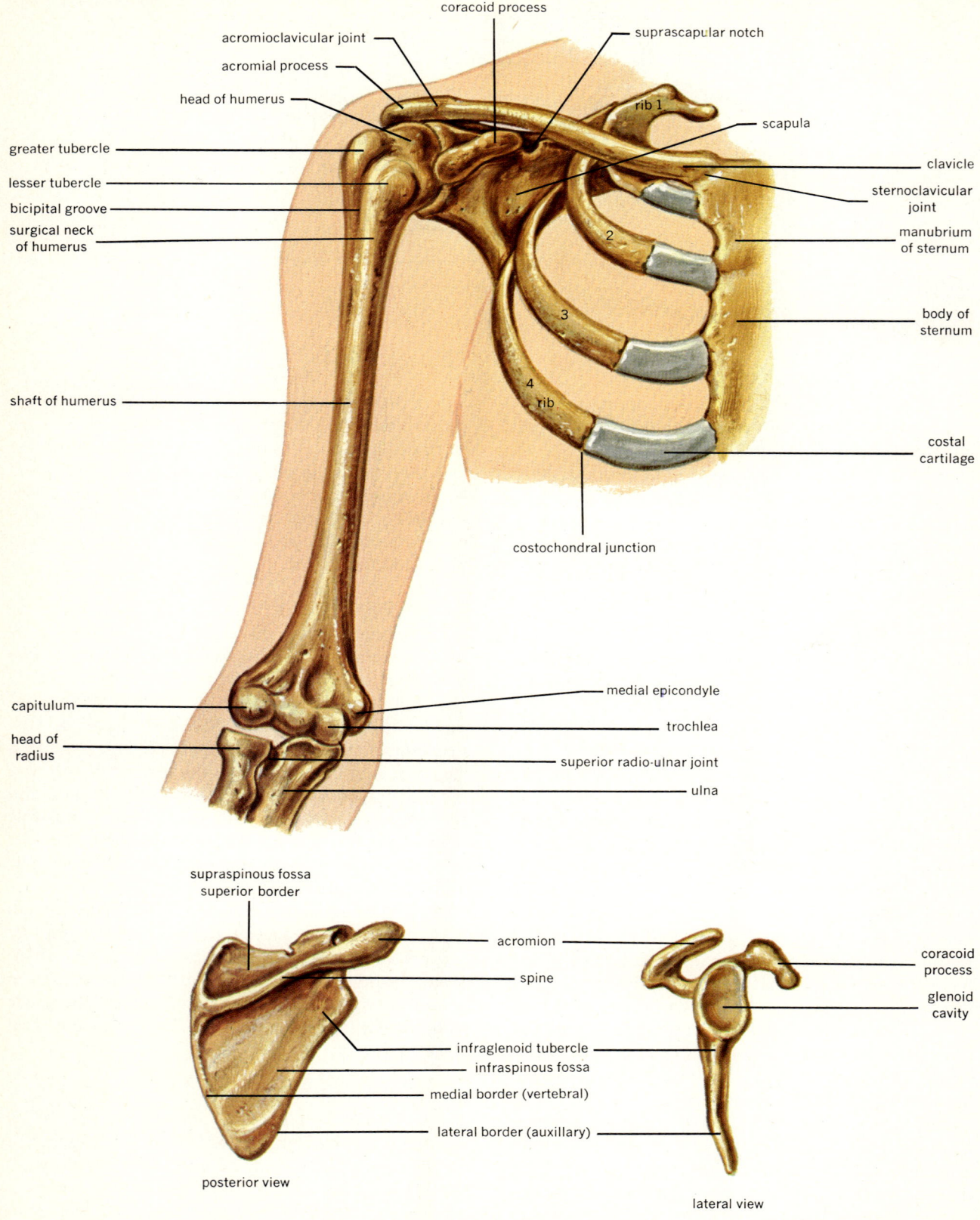

coracoid process

acromioclavicular joint

acromial process

head of humerus

suprascapular notch

rib 1

scapula

greater tubercle

clavicle

lesser tubercle

sternoclavicular joint

bicipital groove

surgical neck of humerus

2

manubrium of sternum

3

body of sternum

shaft of humerus

4
rib

costal cartilage

costochondral junction

capitulum

medial epicondyle

trochlea

head of radius

superior radio-ulnar joint

ulna

supraspinous fossa
superior border

acromion

spine

coracoid process

glenoid cavity

infraglenoid tubercle

infraspinous fossa

medial border (vertebral)

lateral border (auxillary)

posterior view

lateral view

scapula

A

FIGURE 8-19 Bones of the upper extremity: shoulder and arm (A) and forearm and hand (B).

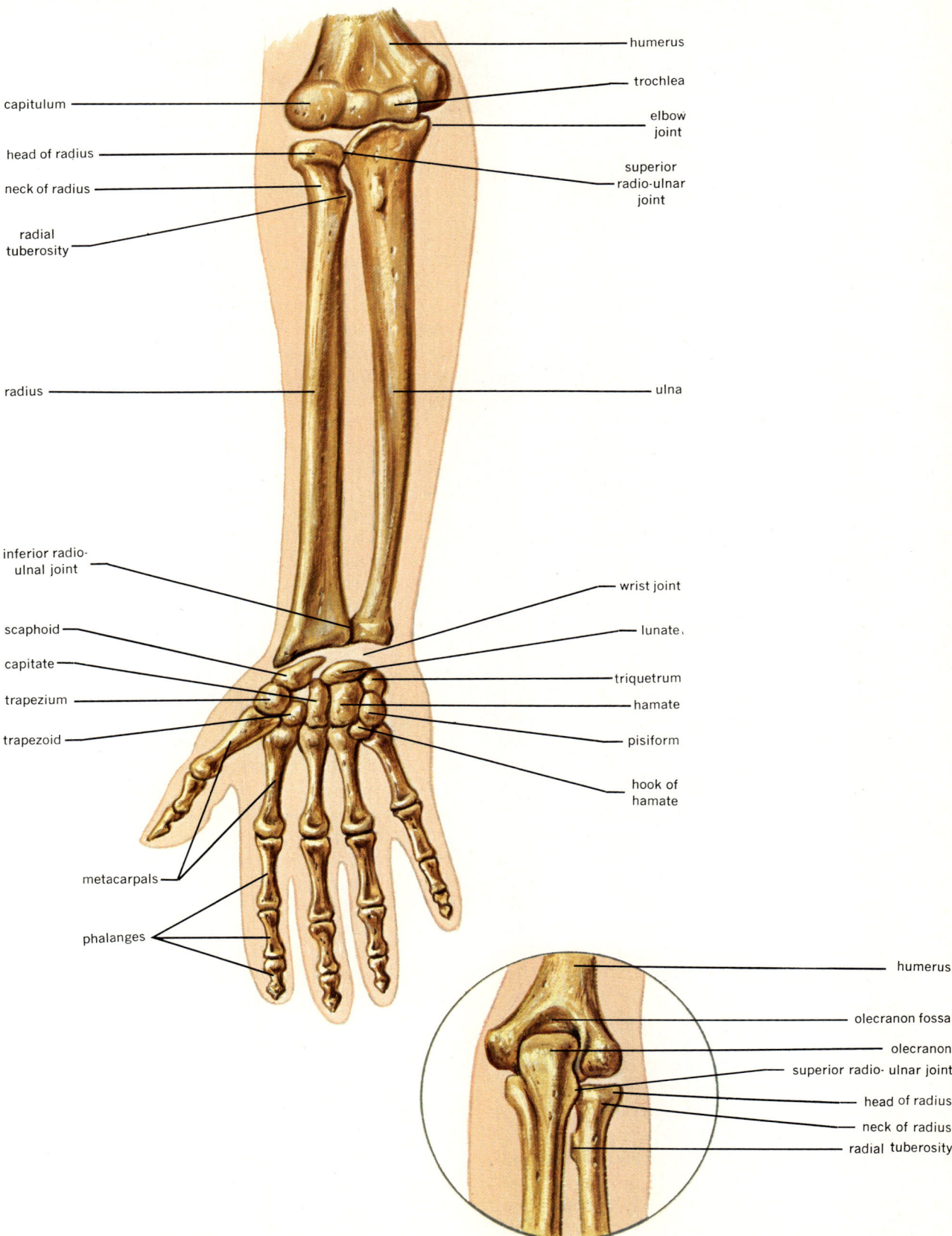

humerus

trochlea

elbow joint

capitulum

head of radius

neck of radius

radial tuberosity

superior radio-ulnar joint

radius

ulna

inferior radio-ulnal joint

wrist joint

lunate

scaphoid

capitate

triquetrum

trapezium

hamate

trapezoid

pisiform

hook of hamate

metacarpals

phalanges

humerus

olecranon fossa

olecranon

superior radio- ulnar joint

head of radius

neck of radius

radial tuberosity

B

extremity, these groups include:

Shoulder	1 clavicle (collarbone)
	1 scapula (shoulder blade)
Arm	1 humerus
Forearm	1 radius
	1 ulna
Wrist	8 carpal bones
Hand	5 metacarpal bones
	14 phalanges

The Shoulder Girdle

The term "girdle" usually calls to mind a beltlike object that wraps around the body and is joined into a complete ring. The shoulder girdle does not completely fulfill this expectation. It consists of the two clavicles and the two scapulae, one of each on each side of the body. On the anterior portion, the clavicles are joined to the sternum. But the scapulae fail to close the ring, for there is a substantial gap between the medial edge of each scapula and the vertebral column. In the living body, these gaps are filled by some of the muscles that move the scapula; the arrangement contributes to the exceptional mobility of the arms. When you shrug your shoulders, you are elevating your shoulder girdle.

Clavicle
The clavicle, or collarbone, is shaped like an elongated S (see Figure 8-19). You can readily see and feel your clavicles curving outward on the anterior surface of the trunk, just below the neck. The articulation of the clavicles with the manubrium of the sternum is the only bony attachment of the entire upper extremity to the trunk.

The clavicles act as anterior braces or struts, helping to prevent dislocation of the shoulder. But these slender bones are in an exposed position, and they are very vulnerable to fracture in falls and in contact sports such as football.

If you are not too well padded with adipose tissue, you can trace the entire course of the clavicle from the midline toward the shoulder joint, as it curves first anteriorly then posteriorly. The lateral end of the clavicle is called the acromial end, for it articulates with the acromial process of the scapula.

Scapula
The "wings" that can be seen protruding from the back of a thin person are part of the scapulae, or shoulder blades. Each scapula is a large, flat, triangular bone, situated on the upper back portion of the thorax and extending over the levels of the second to seventh ribs (see Figure 8-19). A prominent **spine** on the upper posterior surface of the scapula ends in a large, flat process, the **acromion,** which articulates with the clavicle at the tip of the shoulder. A beaklike process on the upper anterior surface, the **coracoid process,** serves as the origin for some of the muscles that move the arm. The head of the **humerus,** or arm bone, fits into a shallow socket on the lateral surface of the scapula, the **glenoid cavity.**

Both the clavicle and the scapula are sites of attachment for many muscles (21 for the scapula alone), which help to bind the upper extremity to the trunk, providing a degree of stability to the shoulders in spite of their minimal bony attachment.

The Arm

When you use the word "arm," you are probably referring to the entire upper extremity. But an anatomist usually reserves the term for the upper arm, between the shoulder and elbow joints. This portion of the upper extremity contains a single bone, the **humerus,** which is the largest and longest bone of the upper extremity.

The humerus is a typical long bone, with a cylindrical shaft (diaphysis) and a knobby epiphysis at each end (see Figure 8-19). The rounded **head** at the upper end of the humerus articulates with the scapula, forming a ball-and-socket joint at the glenoid cavity. A constricted area between the head and the shaft is called the **anatomic neck.** Two prominences near the anatomic neck, the **greater tubercle** on the lateral side and the **lesser tubercle** on the anterior side, serve as sites of muscle attachment. The portion of the shaft just below the tubercles is called the **surgical neck,** because it is often a site of fractures.

About midway down the long and narrow shaft of the humerus there is a roughened area on the lateral surface. This is the **deltoid tuberosity,** the site of insertion of the deltoid muscle. The shaft of the humerus is slightly twisted, so that the axis of the elbow joint is at an angle to the axis of the head.

The distal end of the humerus is broadened. It articulates with the two separate bones of the forearm: with the ulna at a pulley-shaped area called the **trochlea,** and with the head of the radius at a rounded process, the **capitulum.** Two depressions on the distal end of the humerus play an important role in the functioning of the elbow joint: the **coronoid fossa,** on the anterior surface, accommodates the coronoid process of the ulna when the forearm is flexed; the **olecranon fossa,** on the posterior surface, provides room for the olecranon process of the ulna when the forearm is extended. The distal end of the humerus has two more prominent features: two projections from the margins, on a line with the depressions. These are the **medial** and **lateral epicondyles.** You can feel them readily on your own elbow, just above the articulation. The medial epicondyle of the humerus is the "funnybone." A large nerve passes just below this projection and may be pinched if you bump your elbow, resulting in a painful tingling sensation—hitting your funnybone is not a humorous experience!

The Forearm

Two separate long bones, the radius and ulna, form the framework of the forearm. Bend your arm upward at the elbow, with the palm of your hand facing you, and run the fingers of your other hand along the forearm, from the little-finger side of the wrist to the bony projection at the elbow. The bone you have just traced is the **ulna.** The **radius** can be felt if you follow the bone that runs from the thumb side of the wrist to the elbow joint. Now rotate your hand so that the palm is facing away from you, and again trace the radius and ulna. Their attachments remain the same, but because of the rotation of the hand, the two forearm bones are no longer parallel; instead, they form an X (Figure 8-20).

Ulna   The ulna is the longer of the two bones of the forearm, and lies on the medial side. Its slender shaft is somewhat triangular. The enlarged upper end has a hook-shaped projection, the **olecranon process,** which forms the point of the elbow. When the arm is ex-

tended, the olecranon process fits into the olecranon fossa of the humerus and lies on a straight line with the medial and lateral epicondyles; when the forearm is flexed, these three landmarks form the points of a triangle. A concave surface in front of the olecranon process, the **semilunar notch,** articulates with the trochlea of the humerus.

The distal end of the ulna is much smaller than the proximal end. It contains a knobby **head** and, posterior to it, a downward projection, the **styloid process.** Small, smooth areas on the lateral side articulate with the radius. The ulna does not articulate directly with the wrist bones, from which it is separated by a fibrocartilaginous disc.

Radius   The radius is shorter than the ulna, and where the ulna is considerably larger at its upper end than its lower end, the radius is just the reverse. This bone lies at the lateral, or thumb side of the forearm. It is somewhat more difficult to feel in your own forearm (except at the wrist) because it is more padded with muscles.

The proximal end of the radius bears a disclike **head,** which articulates with the capitulum of the humerus and with the side of the ulna. The annular ligament around the constricted **neck** of the radius binds it tightly to the ulna, preventing displacement of the head. Below the neck there is a projection on the medial side of the shaft, the **radial tuberosity,** which is the site of insertion of the biceps muscle.

The expanded distal end of the radius contains a **styloid process** that is larger than that of the ulna. The head of the ulna fits into the **ulnar notch** at the distal end of the radius. A smooth surface on the underside of the distal end articulates with two of the wrist bones.

Throughout most of their length, the radius and ulna are bound together by the **interosseous membrane.**

A break in the lower third of the radius, called **Colles' fracture,** is one of the most common fractures. It results from a fall on the palm of the hand, when the radius must suddenly bear the weight of the body. Fractures of the styloid processes of both radius and ulna are also frequent.

The Wrist

Wristwatches are worn on the forearm, rather than on the wrist. Anatomically speaking, the term *wrist* pertains to the group of eight small **carpal bones,** situated in what people usually think of as part of the hand (Figure 8-21). One of these bones, the **pisiform bone,** is readily identifiable, for it projects posteriorly to form a prominent bump on the little-finger side. The other carpals are hard to distinguish from outside; they are crowded together like two rows of inter-

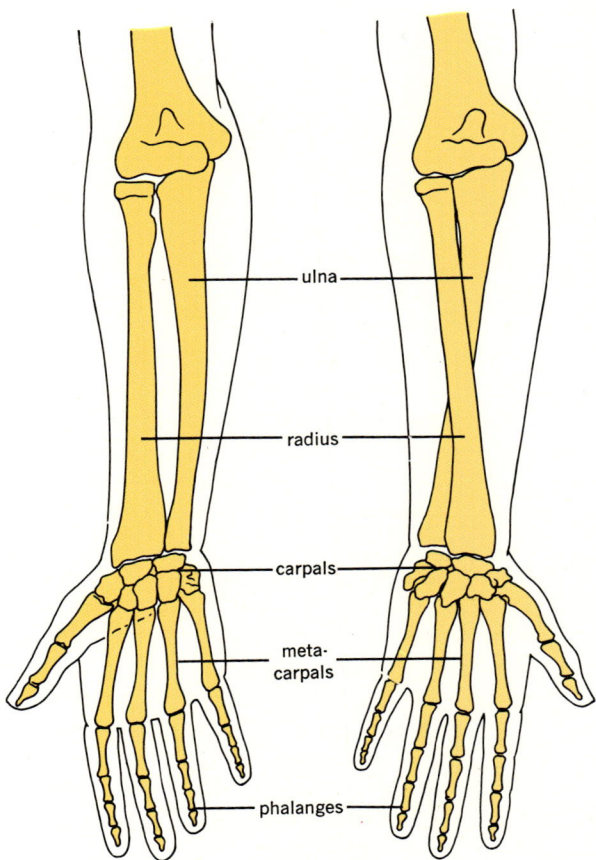

ulna

radius

carpals

meta-carpals

phalanges

FIGURE 8-20   Bones of the forearm: the radius and ulna change from a parallel arrangement to an X as the forearm is rotated.

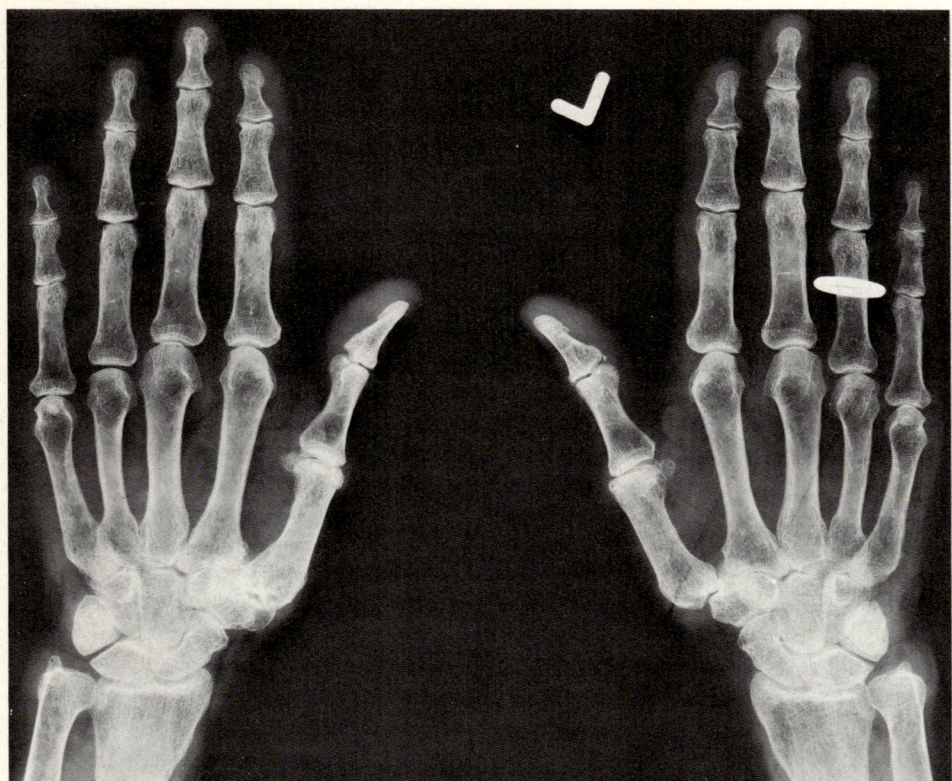

FIGURE 8-21 X ray of the hands, dorsal surface. Note the position of the ring, corresponding to the base of the finger. (If it looks "wrong," count the phalanges.)

locking pebbles, bound together by ligaments. Though the individual carpal bones are capable of only slight displacements relative to one another, the wrist as a whole is extremely flexible and supple.

The wrist is referred to anatomically as the **carpus.** The eight carpal bones that support it are arranged in two irregular rows (starting from the lateral, or thumb side, in each row):

Proximal row	Distal row
Scaphoid	Trapezium
Lunate	Trapezoid
Triquetral (or triangular)	Capitate
Pisiform	Hamate

The Hand

Evolutionary theorists are still debating which came first and precipitated the evolution of humans from their apelike ancestors—the explosive expansion of the forebrain or the development of an upright posture, freeing the hands for manipulation. Whichever the case may be, the human hand is amazingly versatile. It is capable of the crude force of a karate chop and of the deft skill involved in painting a portrait or performing delicate surgical operations on a microscopic living cell. Such complexity of performance would be impossible without a corresponding complexity of internal structure: each hand has a supporting structure consisting of 19 separate bones, in addi-

tion to the eight carpals. The bones of the hand are divided into two main groups: the five **metacarpal bones** (bones of the palm) and the 14 **phalanges,** or finger bones.

Metacarpals The hand of a skeleton appears to have much longer fingers than a living hand. In life, the metacarpals and part of the first phalanges are buried in layers of flesh. The five metacarpals are miniature long bones, each with a cylindrical shaft and two rounded ends. They are not parallel, but instead radiate out from the wrist like the spokes of a wheel. The proximal ends of the metacarpals articulate with the distal row of carpal bones. The distal ends of the metacarpals (the heads) articulate with the proximal phalanges of the fingers. The knuckles of the hand are formed by the heads of the metacarpals.

The metacarpals are customarily numbered from 1 to 5, starting from the lateral side of the hand, rather than being given individual names. Thus, the metacarpal of the thumb is numbered 1, while that of the little finger is the fifth metacarpal.

Phalanges One of the keys to the versatility of the human hand is the opposable thumb: the hand is constructed in such a way that the thumb can be brought up to meet any of the other digits (fingers) in a pincer grasp. The thumb has another distinguishing structural feature, which is evident both on your own hands and in the skeleton (Figure 8-21: each of the digits has three phalanges, except for the thumb, which has only two.

Like the metacarpals, the phalanges are miniature long bones, with cylindrical shafts and rounded ends. The three rows of phalanges are referred to as the **proximal** or first, the **middle** or second, and the **distal** or third phalanges. (The thumb has only proximal and distal phalanges.) Each proximal phalanx articulates with the corresponding metacarpal bone, and with a middle phalanx. The middle phalanges articulate with the proximal and distal phalanges, while the distal phalanges articulate only with the middle phalanges, since they are at the ends of the digits. Like the metacarpals, the phalanges are numbered from 1 to 5, starting with the thumb.

THE LOWER EXTREMITIES

The lower extremities support the entire weight of the body in standing and walking. Indeed, they are sometimes called upon to support far greater forces, as in running and leaping. It is not surprising that the bones of the lower extremities are generally larger and heavier than those of the upper extremities.

The lower extremities are both simpler and more specialized than the upper extremities. The keynote of the hands and arms is versatility. The bones are light, the joints are articulated for maximum mobility, the muscles function mainly to move the hands from place to place, and the hands themselves are able to perform such a variety of tasks precisely because they are basically unspecialized. The lower extremities, on the other hand, are highly modified for weight bearing and locomotion. The basic skeletal design (Figure 8-22) is similar—a bony girdle, on which the limb bones are suspended, a single long bone in the upper leg, a pair of long bones in the lower leg, and the tarsals, metatarsals, and phalanges of the ankle and foot roughly corresponding to the carpals, metacarpals, and phalanges of the hand. However, whereas the shoulder girdle moves freely on the trunk, the pelvic girdle is fixed by some of the strongest and tightest ligaments in the body. The hip joints have traded a degree of mobility for greater strength and stability. The two bones of the lower leg cannot be rotated around one another, as the radius can rotate around the ulna. And the bones of the foot are modified for support and balance, with a concomitant loss of prehensile (grasping) capabilities.

The 62 bones of the lower extremities can be classified as follows (the numbers in the list are given for one side of the pelvic girdle and one leg):

Hip	1 os coxae (hipbone)
Thigh	1 femur (thigh bone)
Knee	1 patella (kneecap)
Leg	1 tibia (shinbone)
	1 fibula (calfbone)
Ankle	7 tarsal bones
Foot	5 metatarsal bones
	14 phalanges

The Pelvis

The pelvis performs two key functions in the body. It not only provides attachment for the legs, but also supports the soft organs of the abdominal cavity. It is essentially a bony basin (its name comes from a Latin word meaning "basin") formed by the two hip bones, the **ossa coxae,** and the sacrum and coccyx of the vertebral column.

Most of the bones of the skeleton are basically similar in both men and women. (The bones of men are usually somewhat larger and heavier, but this is generally a matter of degree rather than a qualitative difference, and there is considerable individual variability.) But the male and female pelves are so strikingly different that an anatomist, on seeing a complete skeleton or even a fragment of the pelvis, can state immediately whether it came from a man or a woman (Figure 8-23). The modifications of the female pelvis are associated with the woman's role in childbearing. Not only must this bony basin support her enlarged abdomen while she is carrying the child, but it must also provide a large enough opening for a full-sized infant to slip smoothly out of the mother's body during childbirth. The bones of the female pelvis are lighter and smoother than the male's. Her pelvis is shallower, but broader, with a greater total capacity, and it is tilted forward (the male pelvis is tilted backward). The opening in the female pelvis is broader and more oval, and the pubic arch is also broader and more rounded.

In the adult, the ossa coxae (sometimes called the **innominate bones**) are a pair of large bones that articulate anteriorly with each other at the midline of the body in a semimovable joint called the **symphysis pubis.** Posteriorly each hipbone is joined with a side of the sacrum, completing the ring.

Each os coxae starts out as three separate bones, the **ilium,** the **ischium,** and the **pubis.** These unite by late adolescence to form a single bone, but their names are retained to refer to the corresponding parts of the hipbone. The lines of fusion of the three bones can be seen in the **acetabulum,** the cup-shaped socket on the lateral aspect of the hipbone into which the head of the femur fits in a ball-and-socket joint (Figure 8-24).

Ilium   The upper, flaring portion or prominence of the hipbone is the ilium. It is the largest of the three portions, and its somewhat concave inner surface

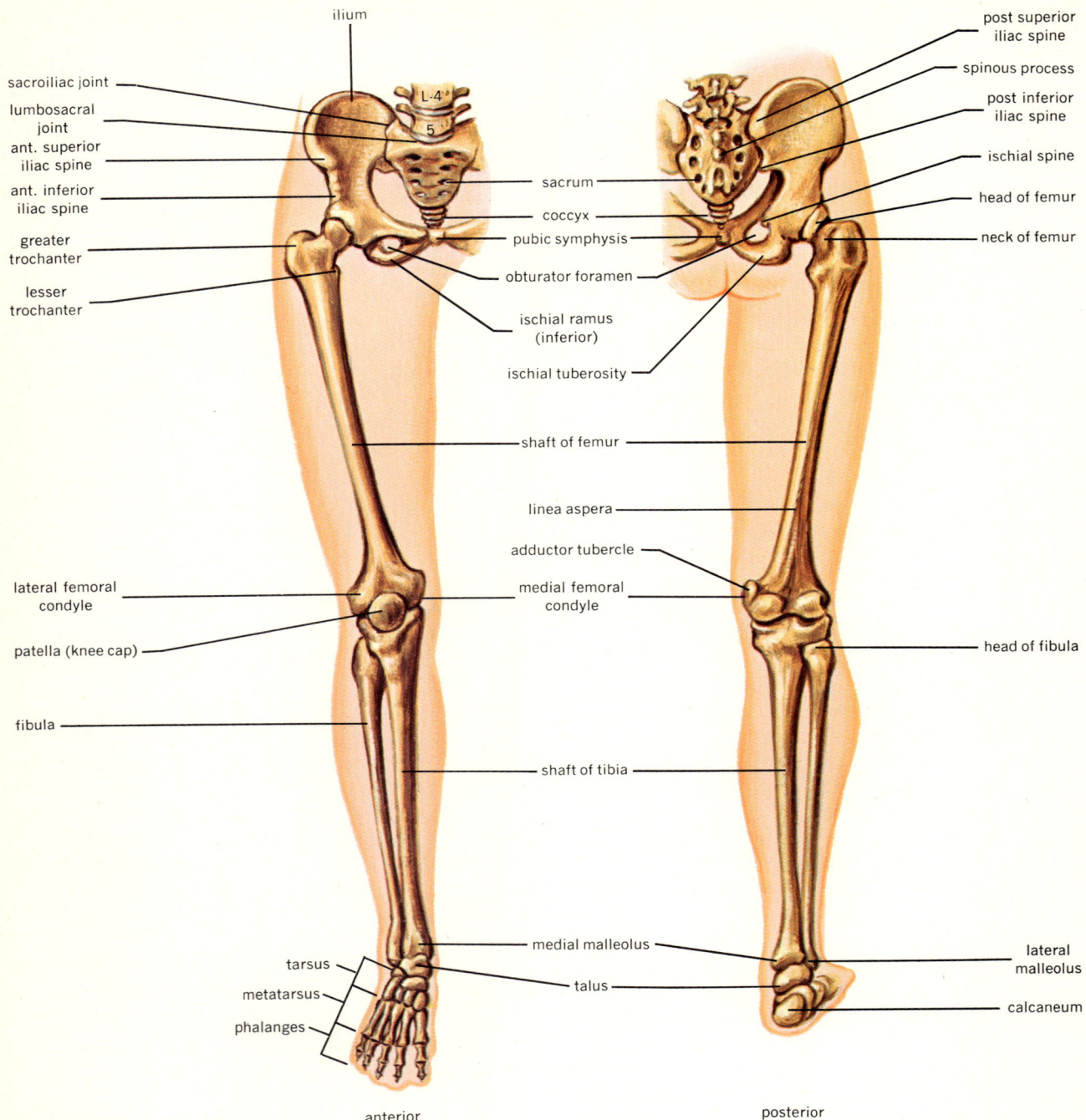

ilium

sacroiliac joint

lumbosacral joint

ant. superior iliac spine

ant. inferior iliac spine

greater trochanter

lesser trochanter

L-4

5

sacrum

coccyx

pubic symphysis

obturator foramen

ischial ramus (inferior)

ischial tuberosity

shaft of femur

linea aspera

adductor tubercle

medial femoral condyle

lateral femoral condyle

patella (knee cap)

fibula

shaft of tibia

tarsus

metatarsus

phalanges

medial malleolus

talus

anterior

post superior iliac spine

spinous process

post inferior iliac spine

ischial spine

head of femur

neck of femur

head of fibula

lateral malleolus

calcaneum

posterior

FIGURE 8-22 Bones of the lower extremity.

contributes to the basinlike appearance of the pelvis. The curved upper rim of the ilium, the **iliac crest,** can be felt in the region of the waist as the "hipbone." Bony projections at the ends of the iliac crest are called the **anterior** and **posterior superior iliac spines;** along with the inferior spines, they serve as sites of attachment for abdominal muscles. The articulation of the ilium with the sacrum is the **sacroiliac joint.** Torn ligaments in this region (which may result from lifting heavy objects with improper body mechanics)

can be a source of great pain. The **sciatic nerve,** the largest nerve in the body, passes through the **greater sciatic notch** of the ilium as it descends into the thigh.

Ischium The lower, posterior portion of the hipbone is formed by the ischium, which is the strongest portion of the os coxae. Its most outstanding feature is the large tuberosity, which bears the weight of the body in a sitting position. A ramus (branch) of the ischium curves forward and joins with the pubis.

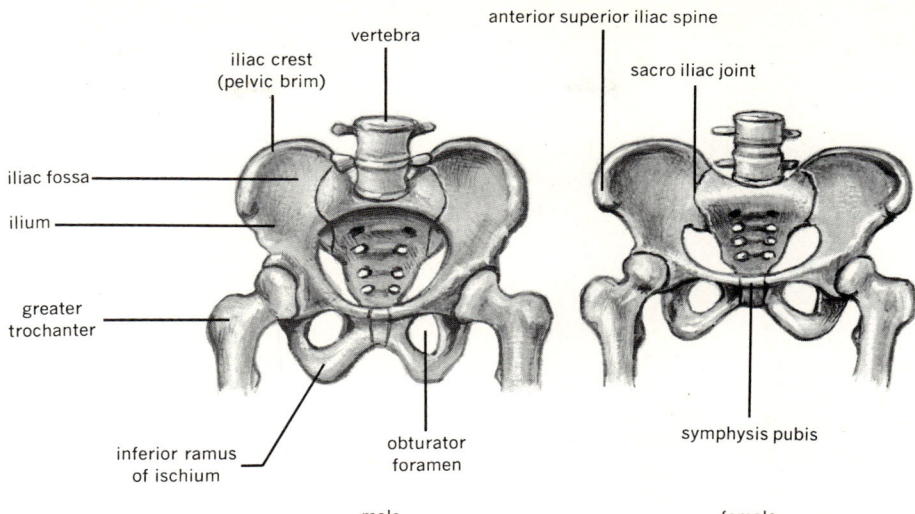

iliac crest (pelvic brim)

vertebra

anterior superior iliac spine

sacro iliac joint

iliac fossa

ilium

greater trochanter

inferior ramus of ischium

obturator foramen

symphysis pubis

male

female

FIGURE 8-23 Comparison of the male and female pelves: note the broader, shallower shape of the female pelvis and the heavier male pelvis.

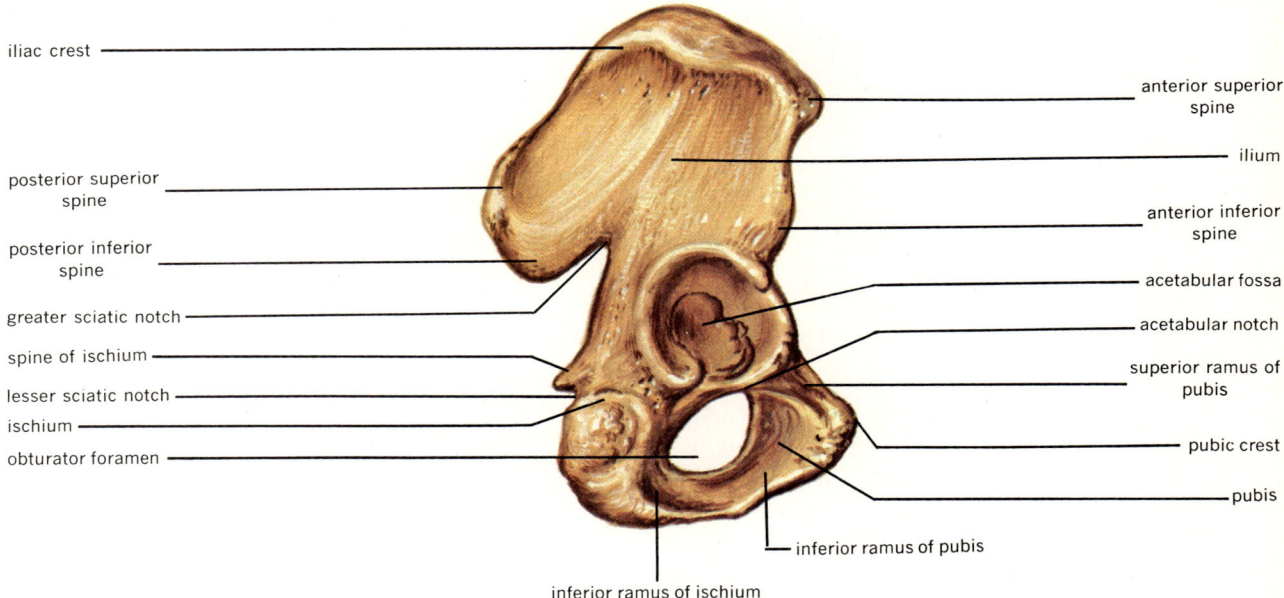

iliac crest

posterior superior spine

posterior inferior spine

greater sciatic notch

spine of ischium

lesser sciatic notch

ischium

obturator foramen

anterior superior spine

ilium

anterior inferior spine

acetabular fossa

acetabular notch

superior ramus of pubis

pubic crest

pubis

inferior ramus of pubis

inferior ramus of ischium

FIGURE 8-24 Lateral view of the right hipbone (os coxae).

Pubis The two pubic bones form the anterior portion of the pelvis. Their bodies join at the symphysis pubis. One ramus of each pubic bone passes upward to join with the corresponding ilium. The other curves downward and merges with the ramus of the ischium. Their junction results in a bony loop that extends down from each side of the pelvis, enclosing an opening called the **obturator foramen.** In the living body this opening is almost completely covered by the dense obturator membrane. The angle formed by the inferior rami of the two pubic bones is called the **pubic arch,** and it is one of the most obvious distinguishing features between the male and female skeletons: in the male pelvis, the pubic angle is usually less than 90 degrees, while in the female it is usually greater than 90 degrees.

The pelvis as a whole is commonly divided into two main parts: the greater, or **false pelvis,** and the lesser, or **true pelvis.** The division is marked by the **pelvic brim,** a curved line passing from the sacral promontory, downward and forward on each side along the ilia, to the upper margin of the symphysis pubis. The true pelvis is of crucial importance during childbirth. It consists of an inlet (the pelvic brim), a cavity (a short, curved canal), and an outlet (the space bounded by the coccyx, the ischial tuberosities, and the pubic arch). A child must pass through its mother's true pelvis in order to be born normally. An

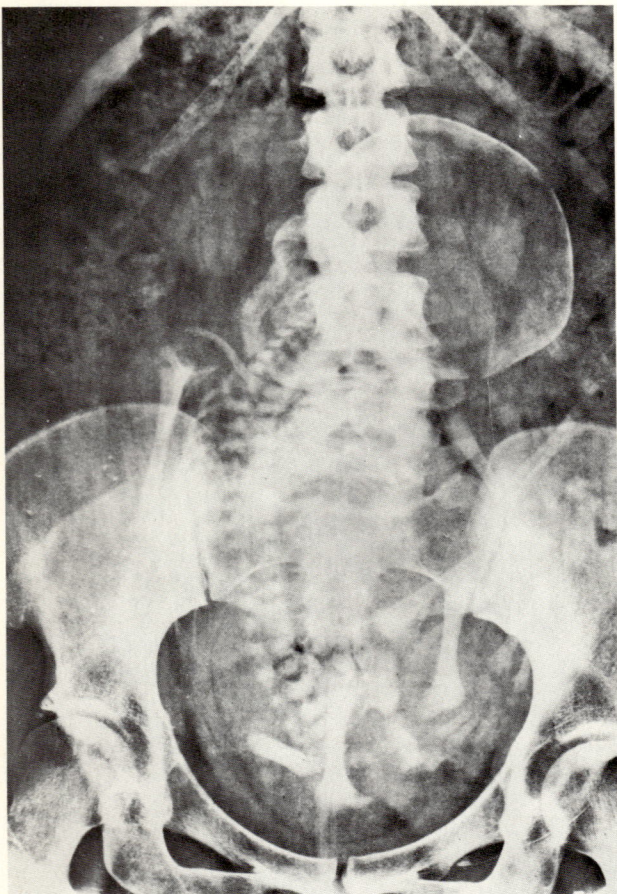

FIGURE 8-25 This pelvic X ray of a pregnant woman shows a full-term infant in utero.

ter (on the lateral aspect) and the **lesser trochanter** (on the medial side of the bone). The **interotrochanteric crest,** running between the two trochanters, and the **linea aspera,** a narrow ridge running down the posterior surface of the shaft of the femur, also are sites of muscle attachment.

The two thigh bones do not hang straight down from the hips. Instead, they slant inward, forming a rough V. Because the female pelvis is much broader than the male's, the inclination of the femurs is correspondingly greater in women.

At the lower end of the femur there are two large bony prominences, the **lateral and medial condyles,** which articulate with the tibia to form the hinge joint of the knee. A smooth surface on the anterior aspect, between the condyles, articulates with the **patella** (kneecap). On the posterior aspect there is a deep depression between the condyles, called the **intercondyloid notch.** The patella becomes fixed against this depression in the femur when the knee is bent.

Fracture of the femur is a rather common and serious accident, particularly in old people whose bones are somewhat brittle. This fracture (often referred to as a "broken hip") usually occurs at the neck of the femur, which is inherently weakened by the angular junction with the shaft of the bone. Modern surgical techniques, employing metal pins, plates, and screws to fasten the broken bones together, have been a tremendous advance in speeding recovery from this painful and debilitating condition.

The Knee

The **patella,** or kneecap, is a flat, somewhat teardrop-shaped bone, lying at the front of the knee joint (refer back to Figure 8-22). It is classified as a sesamoid bone, for it is entirely enveloped within the tendon of the quadriceps femoris muscle, which passes over the front of the knee and inserts on the tibia. It is the largest of the sesamoid bones (about 2 inches broad and equally long), and the two patellas (one in each knee) are included in the total for the skeleton because they occur universally and are more consistent in their location and form than other sesamoid bones.

The patella articulates with the femur, but it is essentially a "floating" bone. If you relax your quadriceps femoris muscle, you can actually move your kneecap about slightly with your thumb and finger. The main function of this bone is to protect the knee joint, but its exposed position makes it vulnerable to dislocation or fracture. (The structure of the knee joint and the varied ills to which it is prone are discussed in more detail in the next chapter.)

The Leg

The lower leg, like the forearm, is supported by two long bones with shafts that are approximately parallel. The radius and ulna of the forearm, however, are

obstetrician measures various dimensions of the openings and may decide on a caesarian delivery if the pelvis is too narrow. Diameters may be determined by palpation through the vagina or (more accurately) by actual measurements of X rays of the pelvis (Figure 8-25). The size of the baby's head can also be determined in this way.

The Thigh

Like the upper arm, the upper segment of the leg is supported by a single long bone, the **femur.** This is the longest, heaviest, and strongest bone in the body. You will find it rather difficult to feel in your own leg, except at the ends, because it is thickly covered by muscles. (Females also have substantial fat pads in the thigh region.)

The head of the femur fits into a lateral depression in the os coxae, the acetabulum, forming a ball-and-socket joint. It is held in place by a ligament and by the tough fibrous capsule surrounding the joint. The constricted neck of the femur forms an obtuse angle with the shaft of the bone. At the junction of the neck and shaft, two roughened prominences provide sites for muscle attachment. These are the **greater trochan-**

approximately the same size; the two bones of the lower leg are grossly different (see Figure 8-22). The **fibula,** or calfbone, seems toothpick-thin in comparison with the heavy **tibia** (the shinbone).

Tibia   The shinbone or tibia, on the medial side of the leg, is the second longest bone in the body. It is a strong bone, and it must be, for the tibias bear the full weight of the body, transmitted through them to the feet from the femurs. The broad upper end of the tibia bears two large bony masses, the **medial and lateral condyles.** Their surfaces are concave and articulate with the respective condyles of the femur. The lateral condyle also articulates with the head of the fibula. Just below the head of the tibia, on the anterior surface, there is a knobby tuberosity, which can be distinctly felt on the front of the leg. Indeed, the entire anterior surface of the tibia is covered by only a thin layer of flesh and is often painfully bruised when we bump our shins.

The lower end of the tibia is broadened (though not as large as the upper end) and has smooth surfaces for articulation with the fibula (laterally) and the **talus,** a tarsal bone (below). A knobby prominence on the lower end of the tibia, the **medial malleolus,** can readily be felt on the inside of the ankle, just under the skin. (This is another favorite site for bumps and bruises.)

Fibula   The fibula is a long, slender, twisted bone, on the lateral side of the tibia. Its upper end does not articulate with the femur, and indeed does not even reach the knee joint; its head articulates with the lateral aspect of the upper end of the tibia. Thus, the fibula is not a weight-bearing bone.

The lower end of the fibula projects down below the end of the tibia and ends in a pointed process, the **lateral malleolus.** This is the outer "ankle bone," which can be clearly seen and felt on the outside of the ankle. A sudden sharp turn of the ankle can fracture the fibula a few inches above the ankle and split off the medial malleolus of the tibia. The popularity of high heels and platform shoes has taken a predictable toll in this type of broken ankle, which is referred to as **Pott's fracture.**

At its distal end, the fibula articulates both with the tibia and with the talus.

The Foot

The bones of the feet show many similarities to those of the hands, but also some important differences, associated with their specialization for weight bearing and locomotion. The bones of the ankle (**tarsal bones,** corresponding to the carpals of the wrists) are larger and heavier, since the heels of the feet bear the brunt of the initial impact with each step we take. The toes have **metatarsal bones** and **phalanges** precisely analogous to the metacarpals and phalanges of the fingers, but their mobility is greatly limited, and the great toes are not opposable to the other digits of the feet. Our monkey and ape relatives are far better endowed in this respect—their feet are also equipped with fully functional opposable thumbs. Indeed, humans still retain the potential for far more agile use of the feet. People born without arms have successfully learned to use their feet to feed themselves, paint pictures, use a typewriter, and even play the piano. But in most humans, feet quickly develop into specialized drudges, which are not only walked on but are often abused by being jammed into ill-fitting shoes that cramp the toes, with high heels that throw the body's weight forward onto the metatarsals, which were never designed to bear the full load.

Tarsus   The seven tarsal bones are basically homologous to the eight carpal bones of the wrist, but they are arranged somewhat differently (Figure 8-26).

The **talus** is a rather large bone, with a head, a neck, and a body. Its head articulates with the distal ends of the tibia and fibula. Below, it articulates with two of the other tarsal bones, the calcaneus (heel bone) and the navicular.

The **calcaneus** is the largest and strongest of the tarsal bones. It receives the weight of the body, transmitted from the tibia through the talus. Its posterior end is the heel of the foot, and its roughened posterior surface provides attachment for the Achilles tendon. (You can readily feel this thick, cordlike tendon running up the posterior surface of the ankle.)

The **navicular,** on the medial side of the foot, is just anterior to the talus.

The **cuboid** is a roughly cube-shaped bone on the lateral side of the foot, just anterior to the calcaneus. It articulates with the calcaneus, the navicular, the lateral cuneiform, and with the fourth and fifth metatarsals.

The **cuneiforms** are three wedge-shaped bones anterior to the cuboid. They are referred to as the lateral, intermediate, and medial cuneiforms, according to their position in the foot, and articulate anteriorly with the third, second, and first metatarsals, respectively.

Metatarsal Bones   The five metatarsal bones of the foot are similar to the metacarpals, but they are larger than their homologs in the hand. The enlarged heads of the metatarsals (on their distal ends) form the ball of the foot. The arrangement of the metatarsals is more parallel than that of the metacarpals of the hand.

The metatarsals and tarsals together form three major arches in the foot: the **lateral and medial longitudinal arches,** which run lengthwise along the foot, and the **transverse** arch, which runs across the foot.

right foot viewed from above

FIGURE 8-26   Bones of the foot.

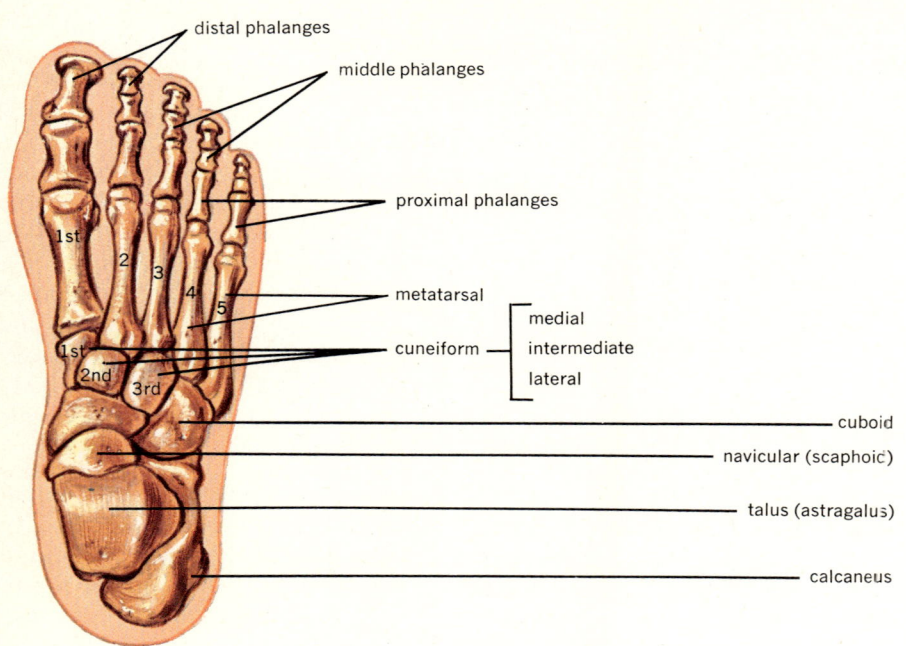

distal phalanges

middle phalanges

proximal phalanges

1st
2
3
4
5

metatarsal

cuneiform ⎯ medial
intermediate
lateral

1st
2nd
3rd

cuboid

navicular (scaphoid)

talus (astragalus)

calcaneus

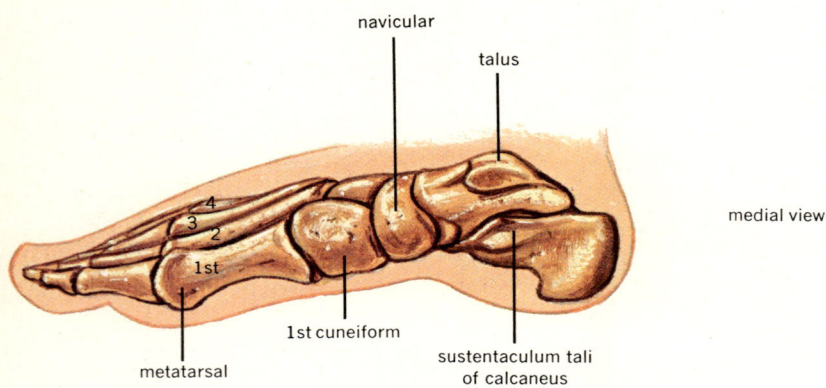

navicular

talus

4
3
2
1st

1st cuneiform

metatarsal

sustentaculum tali
of calcaneus

medial view

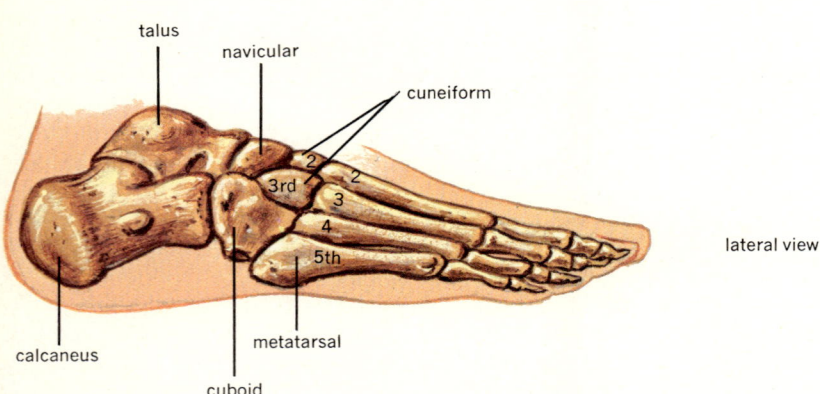

talus

navicular

cuneiform

2
3rd
3
4
5th

calcaneus

cuboid

metatarsal

lateral view

Architects have long known that the arch is an extremely effective weight-bearing construction. The arches of the foot provide great strength, yet the tendons and ligaments that bind the bones together al-

low a certain degree of "give"; thus, the feet can also provide spring and lift for movements. Small sesamoid bones in the tendons on the plantar (sole) surface of the foot provide additional support at the dis-

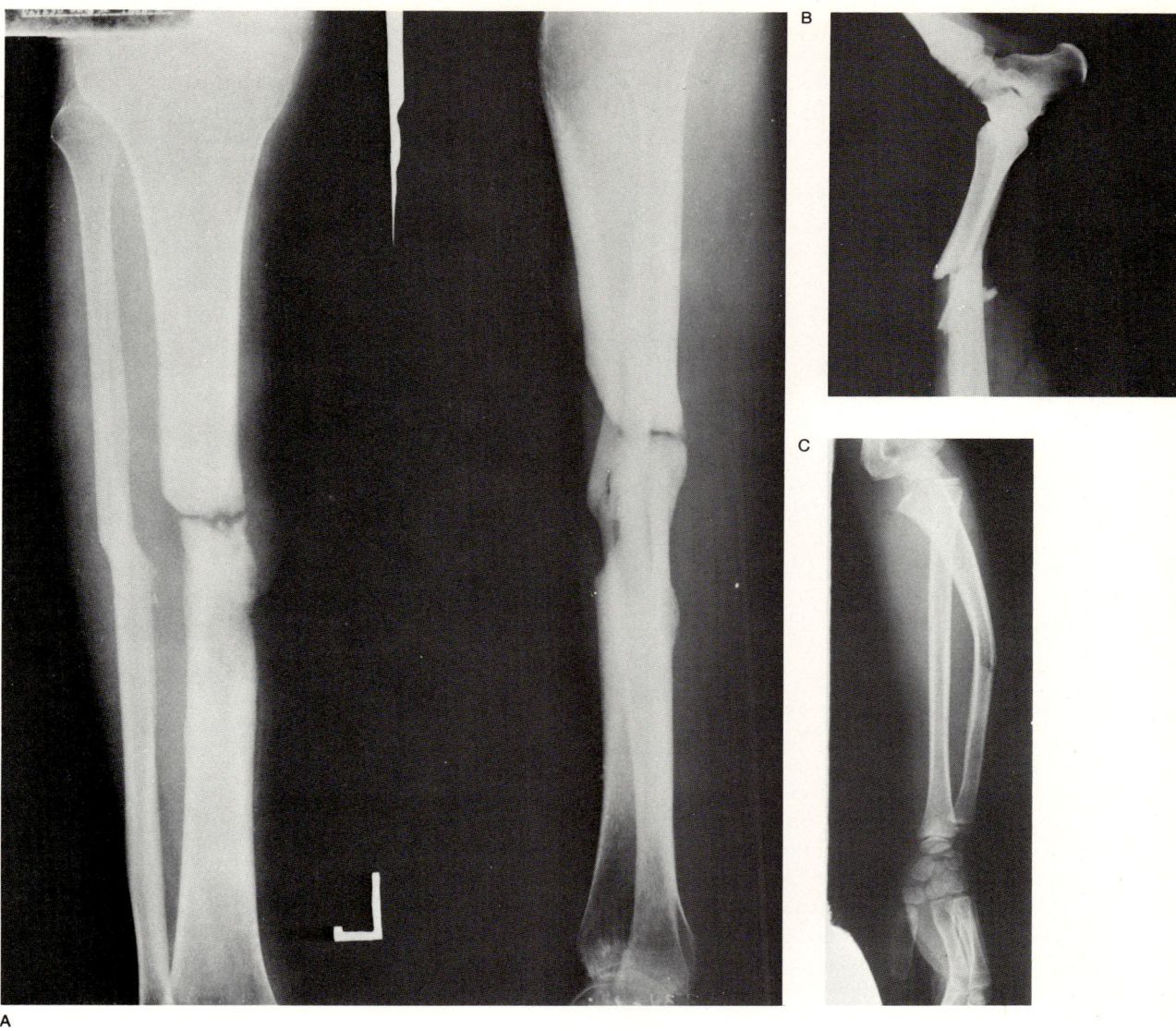

FIGURE 8-27 X rays reveal bone fractures: simple (A), compound (B), and greenstick (C) fractures.

tal ends of the longitudinal arches. **Flatfoot,** a condition of decreased height of the longitudinal arches, may be inherited or can result from a weakness of the foot muscles.

Phalanges   The arrangement of the 14 phalanges of the toes is exactly the same as that of the phalanges of the fingers: three in each digit, except for two in the great toe (on the medial side of the foot). The phalanges of the toes are generally smaller than those of the fingers (but they are still classified as long bones, even though some are extremely short). Except in unusual circumstances, they provide far more limited movement than their homologs in the fingers.

BONE DISEASES AND DISORDERS

With their "reinforced concrete" structure, bones are amazingly strong. But they can and do break—in contact sports, skiing accidents, falls, automobile accidents, and other mishaps. In addition, certain diseases, hormone imbalances, and dietary deficiencies may give rise to abnormalities of various bones of the skeleton. These effects may occur at any phase of life, from early prenatal development through old age.

Fractures and Healing

A **fracture** is the breaking or cracking of a bone (Figure 8-27). If a bone is broken, but the skin at the fracture site is unbroken, the injury is referred to as a **simple fracture.** In a **compound fracture,** the broken ends of the bone actually protrude through the skin. Severe skull fractures are often **depressed fractures,** in which the broken bone is driven inward and may press on and damage the soft organs underneath. In a **comminuted fracture,** the bone is splintered into small fragments. A **fatigue fracture** is an incomplete fracture resulting from mechanical stress or strain. (This type is commonly seen in the metatarsals in people who spend long periods of time walking or marching.) In **pathological fracture,** on the other hand, a bone breaks as a result of destruction by disease, without any significant external stress.

Have you noticed that some people seem to break one bone after another, while others seem able to survive falls and other accidents with all their bones intact? Whether an accident will result in a broken bone or merely a bruise, and the type of fracture, depend on a number of factors, including the person's diet, general health, and especially age. Children's bones are rather soft and resilient. Generally, when they break they splinter rather than breaking completely; such a fracture is termed a **greenstick fracture,** because it resembles the way a green tree branch breaks. With increasing age, there is a progressive decrease in the relative proportion of organic matter in the bone and an increase in the proportion of inorganic salts. Complete fractures occur more readily. In old age, there is frequently a generalized resorption of bone tissue, due to dietary deficiencies and perhaps to hormonal influences (or their lack) as well. In this condition, **osteoporosis,** the bones become extremely porous and so fragile that they may break without much provocation.

The body has the capacity to repair broken bones, knitting the fragments together into a continuous whole again. But unless the fragments are brought into proper alignment and immobilized there until a firm joining has been formed, healing may be delayed, and the bone may be permanently deformed. The realignment of the bone fragments is called **reduction of the fracture.** In some cases it can be accomplished simply by pulling on the ends of the broken bone; sometimes an operation is necessary to expose the bone surgically, and pins, screws, or plates may have to be fastened to the bone fragments to stabilize them. In any case, bone setting is not a do-it-yourself project—it requires the skill and experience of a physician to avoid causing the patient greater harm. Commonly, X rays are taken to determine the positions of the bone fragments before and after setting, and the injured body part may be immobilized in a cast for weeks or even months.

Healing of a bone begins at the very moment of the injury. In addition to the bone break, the periosteum is ruptured at the site, blood vessels are torn, and nerves and muscles are often damaged. A large blood clot forms at the site of the fracture and is gradually infiltrated by fibroblasts, ultimately converting it to granulation tissue. Collagen fibers produced by the fibroblasts bridge the gap between the broken ends of bone with a fibrous **callus.** Cells in the periosteum and endosteum of the adjacent undamaged bone begin to form new bone trabeculae, and eventually the fibrous callus is entirely replaced by bone.

In the healing of bones, again children are better off than adults, for the rate of healing decreases progressively with age. Certain bones heal faster than others: a fractured radius or ulna may heal completely in a month or so, while a fractured femur may take as long as six months to heal. Promising results have been obtained from the application of weak electric currents to broken bones. (The original studies were sparked by the discovery that the growing ends of bones carry a small negative charge, while the shafts are electrically neutral or positively charged; when a bone is broken, however, the entire outer surface of the bone acquires a negative charge, which is strongest at the site of the break.) The technique reduces the time of healing of fractures in half, and the decreased time of immobilization also means less muscle atrophy.

Other Bone Disorders

Congenital malformations, or errors of prenatal development account for many types of skeletal deformities. Certain bones may fail to form in the developing fetus, or may be formed abnormally. Such conditions as spina bifida and cleft palate, mentioned earlier in the chapter, are the result of failures of bones to fuse on schedule. **Talipes,** or "clubfoot," is a common malformation in which the foot is twisted out of shape or position (Figure 8-28A). Congenital malformations may be caused by a genetic disorder in the child, or by a disease suffered or drug taken by the mother during pregnancy. The tragedy that resulted from the use of the sedative drug Thalidomide by pregnant women focused attention on the potential effects of drugs during pregnancy and sparked a major reexamination of our drug regulation and testing procedures in general. Thalidomide taken during certain stages of pregnancy caused an arrested development of the bones of the arms or legs, resulting in the formation of tiny flipperlike appendages instead of normal extremities (Figure 8-28B). The condition is called **phocomelia** (from words meaning "seal limb"), and the task of tracing the cause of its sudden outbreak was made easier by the fact that it is normally an extremely rare birth defect.

Rickets is a metabolic disorder in children in which the calcification of the bones does not take place normally; the bones remain soft and are readily bent out of shape by the body's weight, resulting in bowlegs, knock-knees, pigeon breast (a protrusion of the sternum), and other distortions of the skeleton (Figure 8-28C). Rickets is commonly caused by a vitamin D deficiency; without adequate supplies of the vitamin, the body cannot metabolize calcium and phosphorus properly, even if these minerals are present in ade-

FIGURE 8-28   Some skeletal abnormalities: talipes or clubfoot (A); phocomelia (B); rickets (C); acromegaly (D).

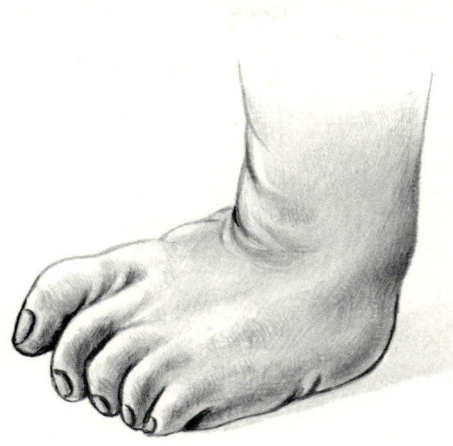

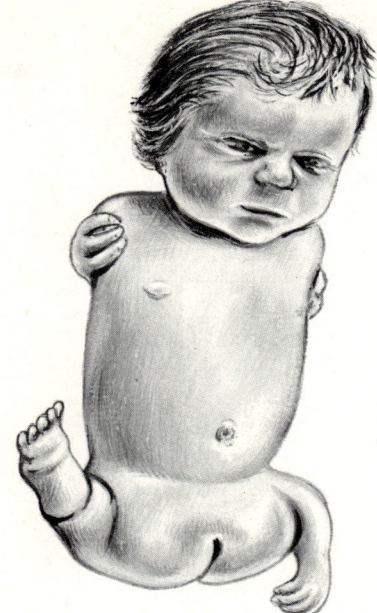

A   talipes (clubfoot)

B   phocomelia

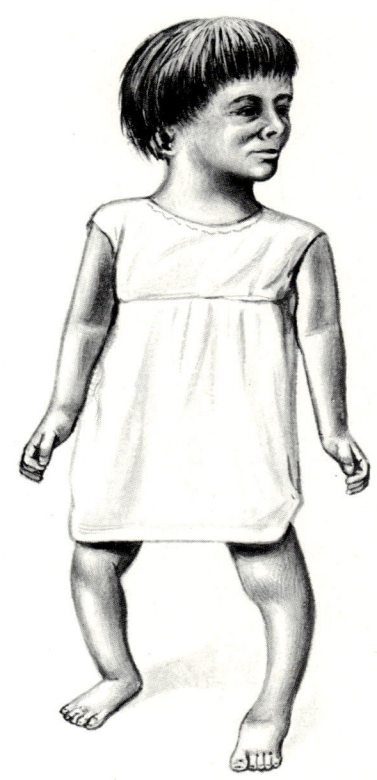

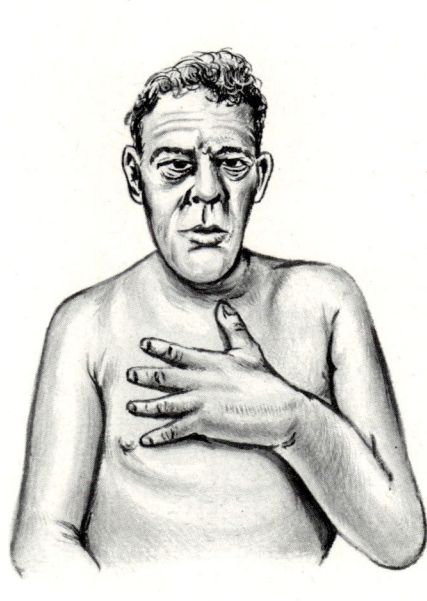

D   acromegaly

C   rickets

quate amounts. Rickets is treated and prevented by supplying ample amounts of dietary calcium, phosphorus, and vitamin D. A similar condition in adults, resulting from vitamin D deficiency and characterized by bone softening and demineralization, is called **osteomalacia.**

Hormonal disorders can produce distortions of the skeleton. **Acromegaly,** characterized by hypertrophy (enlargement) of bones of the face, hands, and feet (Figure 8-28D), is caused by hypersecretion of growth hormone by the anterior lobe of the pituitary. **Osteitis,** an inflammation of bones, may be caused by an excess of parathyroid hormone.

Diseases can also affect the skeleton. **Osteomyelitis,**

an inflammation of the bone marrow, may spread to the bone and on to the periosteum. It is caused by pyogenic (pus-forming) microorganisms. **Tuberculosis** may produce an inflammation of the vertebrae, causing them to degenerate and resulting in abnormal curvatures of the spine.

Old age brings degenerative changes to the skeleton. In addition to the increased brittleness of bones, there may be an atrophy of certain bones, such as the mandible. **Kyphosis,** or a stoop-shouldered appearance frequently develops, and there is a flattening and loss of resiliency of the intervertebral discs, which results in an actual small decrease in height in old age. Sesamoid bones may form within tendons of muscles such as the gastrocnemius and under the great toe. Bony deposits may also form in and around the joints, with a painful and crippling effect. These and other disorders of the joints are discussed in more detail in the next chapter.

SUMMARY

The functions of the skeleton system include:
  Support
  Movement
  Protection
  Hemopoiesis
  Storage of minerals
Bone consists of:
  Mineral salts, chiefly a complex of $CaCO_3$ and $Ca_3(PO_4)_2$ (hydroxyapatite)
  Collagen fibers
  Bone cells (osteocytes)
Bones can be classified in four types:
  Long bones
  Short bones
  Flat bones
  Irregular bones
A typical long bone consists of a shaft (diaphysis) enclosing a marrow cavity, bulbous ends (epiphyses), and an outer covering membrane (periosteum); cavities and spaces are lined with endosteum.
Bone-forming cells are called osteoblasts.
Bone formation can occur by:
  Intramembranous ossification (e.g., bones of skull)
  Endochondral ossification (e.g., long bones)
During bone growth, osteoclasts dissolve away bone to enlarge the marrow cavity.
The epiphyses close and growth of bones in length stops in late adolescence, but processes of one deposition and resorption continue throughout life. Calcium may be withdrawn from bones to meet body needs.
Characteristic bone markings include:
  Process: a projection.
  Head: an expanded end beyond a constricted neck.
  Condyle: a rounded projection at a point of articulation.
  Crest: a narrow ridge.
  Line: a ridge less prominent than a crest.
  Spine: a sharp, slender process.
  Trochanter: a large, rough-surfaced process.
  Tuberosity: a large, rounded, rough-surfaced process for muscle attachment.
  Tubercle: a small, rounded process for muscle attachment.

  Trochlea: a pulley-shaped process.
  Fossa: a depression or cavity.
  Fovea: a shallow depression.
  Foramen: a hole through a bone.
  Fissure: a narrow slit, often between two bones.
  Meatus or canal: a long, tubelike passageway.
  Sulcus or groove: a long, shallow depression.
  Sinus: an air-filled cavity in a bone.
The axial skeleton includes the bones of the skull, vertebral column, and thorax (total 80 bones).
The appendicular skeleton includes the shoulder girdle, upper extremities, pelvic girdle, and lower extremities (total 126 bones).
The 206 bones of the human skeleton are summarized below:

AXIAL SKELETON

SKULL	Protects brain; supports sense organs
Cranium (8)	Braincase
Frontal bone (1)	Anterior of cranium (forehead)
Parietal bone (2)	Roof of skull
Temporal bone (2)	Sides and base of cranium (temples and ears)
Occipital bone (1)	Back and base of cranium
Sphenoid bone (1)	Anterior base of cranium; articulates with all other cranial bones
Ethmoid bone (1)	Nasal cavity and base of cranium
Face (14)	
Nasal bones (2)	Bridge of nose
Inferior nasal conchae (2)	Projecting into nostrils
Vomer (1)	Nasal septum
Lacrimal bones (2)	Oribits; hold lacrimal sacs and tear ducts
Maxillary bones (2)	Upper jaw and much of facial structure; articulate with all the facial bones except the mandible
Zygomatic bones (2)	Cheekbones (joined with processes of temporal and maxillary bones)
Palatine bones (2)	Part of hard palate (remainder is formed by maxillae)
Mandible (1)	Lower jaw; the only movable bone of the skull
Auditory ossicles (6)	Resonating bones in middle ear
Malleus (2)	"Hammer"
Incus (2)	"Anvil"
Stapes (2)	"Stirrup"
Hyoid bone (1)	In throat; does not articulate directly with any other bones
Wormian bones	Variable number of small irregular bones in cranial sutures
VERTEBRAL COLUMN	Protects spinal cord and supports trunk
Cervical vertebrae (7)	Neck region; characterized by transverse foramen and spinous process (except atlas)
Atlas	First cervical vertebra; holds up head; lacks body and spinous process
Axis	Second cervical vertebra; odontoid process articulates with atlas

Thoracic vertebrae (12)	Chest region; characterized by six facets for articulation with ribs; have spinous process but no transverse foramen
Lumbar vertebrae (5)	Abdominal region; large and heavy; have no rib facets or transverse foramina
Sacrum (1)	Pelvis; formed from 5 fused vertebrae
Coccyx (1)	Pelvis ("tailbone"); formed from 4 fused vertebrae
THORAX	Protects heart and lungs; participates in breathing
Sternum (1)	Breastbone; attachment for ribs; contains red bone marrow
Ribs (24)	12 pairs of long, flat, curving bones; all attached to thoracic vertebrae; pairs 1–7 attached to sternum directly; pairs 8–10 attached indirectly; pairs 11–12 "floating"

APPENDICULAR SKELETON

SHOULDER GIRDLE	Attachment for upper extremities
Clavicle (2)	Collarbone; only direct attachment of upper extremities to axial skeleton
Scapula (2)	Shoulder blades; socket for humerus is glenoid cavity
ARM	Upper arm, between shoulder and elbow
Humerus	Arm bone
FOREARM	Between elbow and wrist
Ulna (2)	Bone on medial (little-finger) side of forearm
Radius (2)	Bone on lateral (thumb) side of forearm
WRIST	
Carpus (carpal bones) (16)	Small bones in proximal part of hand
Scaphoid Lunate Triquetral (triangular) Pisiform	Proximal row, from lateral to medial side
Trapezium Trapezoid Capitate Hamate	Distal row, from lateral to medial side
HAND	Capable of varied movements and manipulations
Metacarpal bones (10)	Miniature long bones of hand; heads of metacarpals (distal ends) form knuckles; numbered from 1 to 5, starting with thumb
Phalanges (28)	Finger bones; 3 in each digit (proximal, middle, distal) except for 2 in thumb (proximal, distal)

PELVIC GIRDLE	Support for trunk; attachment for lower extremities
Os coxae (2)	Hipbone; formed from 3 fused bones; ilium, ischium, and pubis; head of femur fits into socket called acetabulum; female pelvis is broader and shallower than male
THIGH	Upper leg, from hip to knee
Femur (2)	Thigh bone; longest, heaviest, and strongest bone in the body
KNEE	Joint between upper and lower leg
Patella (2)	Kneecap: a sesamoid bone (enveloped in a tendon)
LEG	Lower leg, from knee to ankle
Tibia (2)	Shinbone, on medial side of leg; bears weight of body
Fibula (2)	Calfbone, on lateral side of leg; a thin, non-weight-bearing bone
FOOT	Homologous to hand but highly specialized for weight bearing and locomotion
Tarsus (tarsal bones) (14)	Foot bones
Talus (2)	Articulates with tibia and fibula in ankle joint
Calcaneus (2)	Heel bone
Navicular (2) Cuboid (2) Cuneiforms (6)	Bones of foot; form arches with metatarsals
Metatarsal bones (10)	Bones of foot; heads of metatarsals (distal ends) form ball of foot
Phalanges (28)	Toe bones; 3 in each toe, except for 2 in great toe

The bones of the cranium are joined in nonmovable articulations called sutures.

The spinal cord passes through the foramen magnum, a large opening at the base of the skull.

Sinuses in the frontal, ethmoid, sphenoid, and maxillary bones communicate with the nasal cavity and act as resonating chambers.

The orbits, or eye sockets, are formed by portions of the frontal, sphenoid, ethmoid, maxillary, zygomatic, and lacrimal bones.

The adult vertebral column has four curvatures: cervical, thoracic, lumbar, and sacral, which provide resilience and spring.

Adjacent vertebrae are separated by a compressible fibrocartilage intervertebral disc.

The pelvis is formed by the ossa coxae, sacrum, and coccyx; the ossa coxae are joined anteriorly at the symphysis pubis.

The basin-shaped pelvis is divided by the pelvic brim into the upper, false pelvis, and the lower, true pelvis.

The dimensions of the inlet, cavity, and outlet of the true pelvis are of importance in childbirth.

An important characteristic of the human hand is the opposable thumb; the foot lacks an opposable thumb, and the movements of the toes are normally much more restricted than those of the fingers.

Accidents or disease may result in fracture (breaking or cracking) of bones.

Types of fractures include:

Simple fracture: skin at fracture site is unbroken.

Compound fracture: broken ends of bone protrude through skin.

Depressed fracture: broken bone is driven inward.

Comminuted fracture: bone is splintered into small fragments.

Fatigue fracture: incomplete fracture resulting from mechanical stress or strain.

Pathological fracture: break resulting from disease-caused bone destruction.

Greenstick fracture: incomplete fracture in the form of splintering; characteristic of young bones.

The realignment of fragments of a broken bone is referred to as reduction of the fracture.

If broken bones are aligned properly, they can heal completely, through the formation of granulation tissue and a fibrous callus.

Congenital malformations of the skeleton may be caused by faulty heredity, disease, or drugs taken by the mother during pregnancy.

Talipes or clubfoot is a condition in which the foot is twisted out of shape or position.

Phocomelia is characterized by undeveloped, flipperlike extremities.

Rickets is a condition in children due to vitamin D deficiency and characterized by softening of bones and skeletal distortions resulting from inadequate calcification.

Osteomalacia is a similar condition in adults.

Acromegaly is caused by pituitary hypersecretion.

Osteitis is an inflammation of bones.

Osteomyelitis is an inflammation of bone marrow, which may spread to bone and periosteum.

Tuberculosis may cause inflammation of vertebrae and abnormal curvature of the spine.

Osteoporosis, a generalized resorption of bone resulting in brittleness and fragility, is commonly seen in old age and may be due to dietary deficiency.

QUESTIONS FOR REVIEW AND THOUGHT

1 In designing prostheses (artificial replacements for bones), what characteristics and functions of bones must be taken into account? Assuming suitable materials could be devised and implanted, could a completely artificial skeleton perform all the functions of living bone? Discuss.

2 What are the advantages of long bones containing cavities and porous cancellous bone, rather than entirely solid structures?

3 Give examples of: long bones; short bones; flat bones; irregular bones.

4 Describe the processes of bone growth in (a) length and (b) circumference.

5 You are a physical anthropologist, acting as a part-time consultant to the local police department. A human skeleton with a hole in its skull has just been dug up from a shallow grave in the woods. Describe how you would go about reconstructing details of the victim's age, sex, and physical appearance.

6 Discuss the supportive and protective roles of the axial skeleton. From the standpoint of design efficiency, do you think the human plan of immovable skull and movable vertebral column and rib cage could use improvements?

7 List the similarities and differences of: (a) the shoulder girdle and the pelvic girdle; (b) the bones of the upper and lower extremities.

8 Distinguish among: (a) simple, compound, depressed, comminuted, and greenstick fractures; (b) osteomalacia, osteitis, osteomyelitis, and osteoporosis.

THE ARTICULAR SYSTEM

The robots in science fiction stories generally move with stiff, jerky motions. Their apparent awkwardness results partly because their bodies and limbs have fewer joints than the human body, and those joints that they do have permit more restricted movements than the joints of their human prototype. The numerous and varied movements made possible by the joints or **articulations** of the human body permit the sinuous grace of a ballet dancer or an athlete, as well as such mundane activities as walking, sitting, eating, talking, and writing. If the skeleton were one continuous structure, rather than being composed of more than two hundred bones connected in joints, we would be as immobile as statues.

An articulation is the junction between two or more bones, regardless of how much, if any, actual movement is permitted. Although most of the joints of the body permit various degrees of bending or rotation of body parts (the shoulder joint is one of the most mobile), there are also bone junctions that do not permit any movement at all. Such immovable joints include the sutures of the adult skull, at which flat bony plates are held together rigidly in interlocking junctions. The joints of the body are commonly classified according to the degrees and types of movement they permit (Figure 9-1): **synarthroses*** (immovable joints), **amphiarthroses** (slightly movable articulations), and **diarthroses** (freely movable articulations). The latter group has a number of subdivisions such as ball-and-socket, pivot, and hinge joints, determined by the structure of the articulation.

The principal joints of the body, the bones that compose them, and the types of movements they permit are summarized in Table 9-1.

SYNARTHROSES

At certain articulations, a degree of rigidity can be quite desirable. If the junctions of the bones of the skull provided mobility, for example, a blow to the head might jar the bones inward, damaging the delicate brain structures beneath them. Instead, the cranial bones are fused into rigid, immovable joints, synarthroses, and act as an efficient "hard hat," protecting the brain from injury. Special care must be taken to protect the head of an infant, for in babies the fusion of the skull bones has not yet taken place. The gaps between the bones form six separate soft spots, called **fontanels,** which gradually become covered by protective bone. The last of the fontanels usually has disappeared by about two years.

The articulations of the cranial bones are typical of a type of synarthrosis called **sutures.** The bones that form such a joint are united by a thin layer of fibrous tissue, and held in place by a series of interlocking processes (projections) and indentations, so that the junction line looks rather like a roughly sewed seam.

Synchondroses represent another type of immovable joint. These are articulations in which two bony surfaces are connected by cartilage. A synchondrosis is a temporary joint, which is ultimately replaced by bone. Examples are the joints between the epiphysis and diaphysis of the long bones. This, too, is a case in which immobility is a desirable feature.

AMPHIARTHROSES

The soft skull of a fetus can undergo great distortions during the process of birth without suffering any permanent harm. Yet even with the pliability of the infant head, labor would be more difficult—if not fruitless—if the mother's pelvis remained completely rigid. Fortunately, the symphysis pubis, the articulation of the pubic bones, is a partially movable joint. A disc of fibrocartilage is sandwiched between the surfaces of the two bones (see Figure 9-1). During pregnancy fluid accumulates in the cartilage, allowing some extra movement during childbirth.

The symphysis pubis is a typical example of one type of amphiarthrosis, or slightly movable articulation. A **symphysis** is a joint in which bones are covered with hyaline cartilage and connected by an intervening disc of fibrocartilage. The fibrogelatinous pulp filling the center of the disc acts as a shock-absorbing cushion. Other examples of symphyses are the intervertebral discs between the bodies of the vertebrae.

The **syndesmosis** is another type of slightly movable joint, in which the bones are connected by ligaments. Examples of syndesmoses are the articulations of the radius and the ulna, the fibula and tibia, and the scapula and clavicle. In each case, a small degree of movement is permitted by twisting and slight stretching of the binding ligaments.

DIARTHROSES (SYNOVIAL JOINTS)

When two moving parts rub against each other, the friction that results can generate heat and produce abrasive wear. The lubricating oil used in automobile engines and other motors coats the surfaces of moving parts, permitting them to slip more easily past one another and thus reducing friction, heat production, and wear. The harmful effects of friction could also develop in the movable joints of the body, if there were no means of reducing friction. Coatings of hyaline cartilage on the bone surfaces in contact help to provide a smooth gliding surface. Lubrication of the joint is provided by a viscous fluid called **synovial fluid.** (Its name comes from Greek words meaning "with egg," for its consistency somewhat resembles egg white.) The presence of synovial fluid is the basis for a commonly used alternate name for diarthroses: **synovial joints.**

---

* *Arthro-* is a combining form commonly used to refer to joints. *Arthr*itis, for example, is an inflammation of the joints. *Arthro*logy is the study of joints.

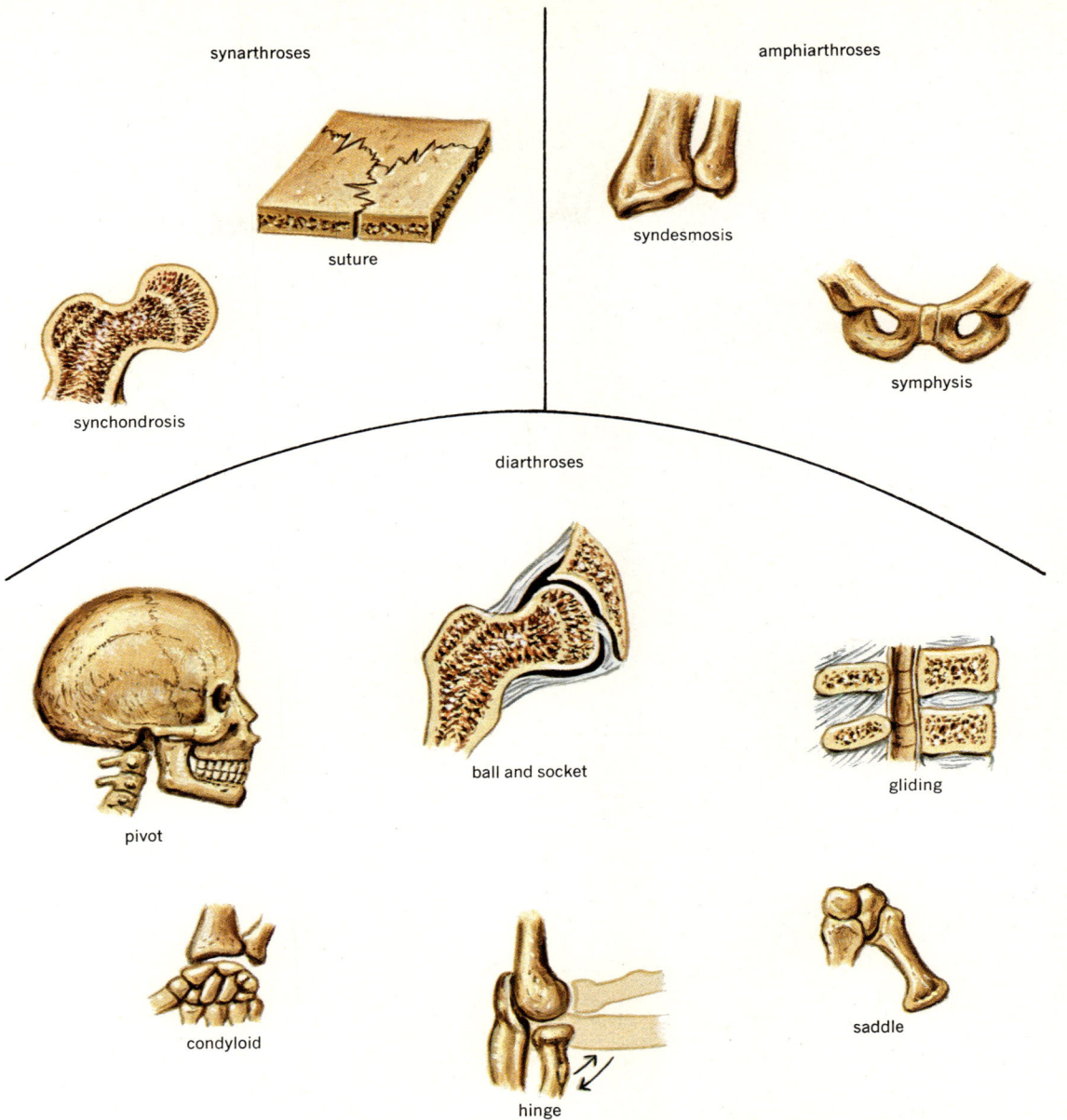

FIGURE 9-1 Types of joints: synarthroses (immovable joints), amphiarthroses (slightly movable joints), and diarthroses (freely movable joints). Different joint structures permit different kinds and degrees of motion.

TABLE 9-1 Principal joints of the body

NAME OF JOINT	ARTICULATING BONES	TYPE OF JOINT	MOVEMENTS PERMITTED
Sutures of skull	Cranial bones, e.g., temporal, occipital, parietal, frontal	Synarthrotic	None
Atlantoepistropheal	Atlas and axis (epistropheus)	Diarthrotic (pivot)	Partial rotation of head
Vertebral	Between bodies of vertebrae Between articular processes of vertebrae	Amphiarthrotic (symphysis) Diarthrotic (gliding)	Slight movement between any two vertebrae, but considerable mobility for vertebral column as a whole
Sacroiliac	Sacrum and ilia	Diarthrotic (gliding)	None or slight (e.g., during late pregnancy and delivery)

TABLE 9-1 (Continued)

NAME OF JOINT	ARTICULATING BONES	TYPE OF JOINT	MOVEMENTS PERMITTED
		(joint cavity gradually obliterated)	
Clavicular:			
Sternoclavicular	Clavicle (medial end) and sternum (manubrium)	Diarthrotic (gliding)	Gliding
Acromioclavicular	Clavicle (distal end) and scapula (acromion)	Diarthrotic (gliding)	Gliding, elevation, depression, protraction, retraction
Thoracic	Ribs (heads) and vertebrae (bodies)	Diarthrotic (gliding)	Gliding
	Ribs (tubercles) and vertebrae (transverse processes)	Diarthrotic (gliding)	Gliding
Shoulder	Humerus (head) and scapula (glenoid cavity)	Diarthrotic (ball and socket)	Free movement: flexion, extension, abduction, adduction, rotation, and circumduction of arm
Elbow	Humerus (trochlea) and ulna (semilunar notch); radius (head) and humerus (capitulum)	Diarthrotic (hinge)	Flexion and extension
	Radius (head) and ulna (radial notch)	Diarthrotic (pivot)	Supination and pronation of forearm and hand; rotation of forearm
Wrist	Scaphoid, lunate, and triquetral bones with radius and articular disc	Diarthrotic (condyloid)	Flexion, extension, abduction, and adduction of hand
Carpal	Between various carpals	Diarthrotic (gliding)	Gliding
Hand:			
Thumb	First metacarpal and trapezium	Diarthrotic (saddle)	Flexion, extension, abduction, adduction, and circumduction of thumb and opposition to the fingers
Finger:	Metacarpals and proximal phalanges	Diarthrotic (hinge)	Flexion, extension, and limited abduction and adduction of fingers
	Between phalanges	Diarthrotic (hinge)	Flexion and extension of finger sections
Symphysis pubis	Pubic bones	Amphiarthrotic (symphysis)	Slight (especially during pregnancy and delivery)
Hip	Femur (head) and os coxae (acetabulum)	Diarthrotic (ball and socket)	Flexion, extension, abduction, adduction, rotation, and circumduction
Knee	Femur and tibia	Diarthrotic (hinge)	Flexion and extension; slight rotation of tibia
Tibiofibular	Tibia (head) and fibula (lateral condyle)	Diarthrotic (gliding)	Gliding
Ankle	Tibia and fibula with talus	Diarthrotic (hinge)	Flexion and extension
Foot	Between tarsals	Diarthrotic (gliding)	Gliding; inversion and eversion
	Metatarsals and proximal phalanges	Diarthrotic (hinge)	Flexion, extension, slight abduction and adduction
	Between phalanges	Diarthrotic (hinge)	Flexion and extension

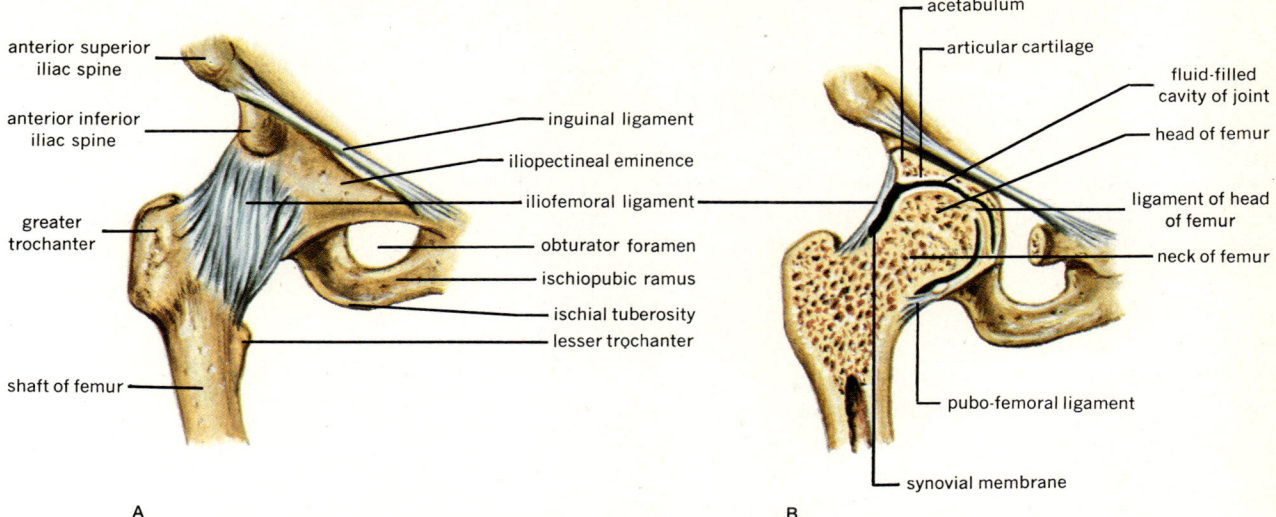

anterior superior
iliac spine

anterior inferior
iliac spine

greater
trochanter

shaft of femur

inguinal ligament

iliopectineal eminence

iliofemoral ligament

obturator foramen

ischiopubic ramus

ischial tuberosity

lesser trochanter

acetabulum

articular cartilage

fluid-filled
cavity of joint

head of femur

ligament of head
of femur

neck of femur

pubo-femoral ligament

synovial membrane

A

B

FIGURE 9-2   The hip joint, a synovial joint. (A) Intact hip joint, showing the ligaments between femur and pelvic bone; (B) section of hip joint showing the ball-in-socket fit of the bones and the atricular capsule, filled with synovial fluid.

Typically, a diarthrosis (Figure 9-2) is enclosed in an encircling band of fibrous tissue called the **articular capsule.** The outer layer of the capsule is a strong, tough ligament, while the inner lining is smooth, slippery synovial membrane. The **articular cavity** enclosed by the capsule is filled with synovial fluid and separates the bones of the joint so that their surfaces do not come into direct contact. The synovial fluid is about 95 percent water and has a protein content from 1 to 2 percent.

In some diarthroses, **articular discs,** consisting of fibrocartilage, are found between the articular cartilages. These discs act as shock absorbers and are supplied with sensory nerve fibers that relay information on pressure changes within the joint cavity. In certain cases when additional strength of the joint is needed, such as in knee and hip joints, interosseous ligaments are found within the joint and bind one bone to another.

The tendons of muscles pass over synovial joints and play a major role in maintaining the stability of the joints. In paralysis, when the forces of the muscles are no longer operative, the joints are slack and permit a far greater range of movement than normal.

Types of Diarthroses

Diarthroses are commonly defined as freely movable joints. Yet you yourself have undoubtedly noticed that the movements of certain joints are limited in various ways. The shoulder joints are quite mobile: you can easily raise and lower your arms and swing them around in a full circle. (With practice the same can be done with the legs.) Yet knees and elbows bend in only one direction, and the finger joints like-

wise cannot be bent backward. Even for the most "doublejointed," there are distinct limitations to joint mobility.

Movements at joints are limited by several factors: (1) the shape of the bones forming the joint; (2) the tautness of the ligaments binding the bones together and the articular capsule surrounding the joint; and (3) the arrangement and action of the muscles associated with the joint. The synovial joints of the body are classified in six main types according to their structure and the kinds of motion they permit (see Figure 9-1):

Ball-and-socket Joints

As their name implies, these are joints in which a ball-shaped head of one bone fits into a cup-shaped cavity of another. Ball-and-socket joints permit the freest movement, in almost any direction or plane. Examples are the shoulder and hip joints.

Condyloid Joints

This is a limited variation on the ball-and-socket joint, in which an oval-shaped articular surface fits into an elliptical cavity. Movement is possible in two planes at right angles to each other, but the articulation does not permit rotation. Examples are the wrist joint between the radius and carpal bones, and the joints between the metacarpals and the first phalanges of the fingers.

Hinge Joints

This type of joint permits movement in only one plane, like the hinges on a door. The surface of one bone of the joint is convex, the other concave, and they fit smoothly together. The joints of the knees and elbows, those of the ankles, and the articulations of the phalanges are all hinge joints.

Pivot Joints

This is a special type of hinge joint, in which a ring rotates around a pivot. When you turn your head, the atlas rotates around a pivot-like projection on the axis, called the odontoid process. In the proximal articulation of the radius and ulna there is a pivot joint, in which the head of the radius rotates inside a ring formed by the radial notch of the ulna and the annular ligament. This joint permits twisting movements of the lower arm, such as those used in turning a doorknob or a screwdriver.

Saddle Joints

This type, as its name implies, is shaped roughly like a saddle: the articular surface of one bone is concave in one direction and convex in the other, while the other articular surface is just the reverse, so that the two bones fit together neatly. A saddle joint permits a considerable range of movement, in two planes at right angles to each other, although it does not permit rotation. An example is the carpometacarpal joint at the base of the thumb.

Gliding Joints

In gliding joints, the opposing bone surfaces are flattened or slightly curved, permitting sliding movements in all directions (including rotation). Relatively little movement takes place in comparison to other types of diarthroses. Examples are the joints of the carpal bones of the wrist and the tarsal bones of the feet, as well as the intervertebral joints.

Movements Permitted by Joints

The standard anatomical position that was described in Chapter 2 depicts the human body frozen in a fixed stance. But the living body is in almost constant motion. Legs move in walking and running. Hands and arms move in a bewildering variety of activities. Jaws open and close, eyes dart back and forth. Even while asleep, a person tosses and turns and shifts position hundreds of times in a night. The movements of body parts are mainly the result of movements of bones at synovial joints. In devising a system of standard terminology for describing the movements of the body (Figure 9-3), anatomists generally consider the movements of body parts in relation to specific axes: either the central axis of the body as a whole, or the long axis of a particular extremity.

Movements at joints may be **gliding movements,** producing relative displacements of bones; **angular movements,** which change the angle between two bones; or **rotation,** a twisting of a body part around its own longitudinal axis. Specific types of movements include the following.

Flexion: a movement in which the two ends of an extremity are brought closer together—for example, bending the arm up at the elbow. The term is also used to describe a bending of the neck or spine forward.

Extension: moving the two ends of an extremity apart; the opposite of flexion. An example is straightening the arm from a flexed position. Extension can also refer to bending the neck or spine backward.

Abduction: lateral movement of an extremity, away from the median plane of the body. For example, abduction occurs at the shoulder joints when the arms are raised to the sides.

Adduction: movement of an extremity toward the median plane of the body; the opposite of abduction. (The prefix *ab-* means "away from," while *ad-* means "toward.")

Abduction and adduction have special meanings in relation to the fingers and toes. In the hand, these terms relate to movement away from or toward an imaginary plane passing through the middle finger; in the foot, the reference plane passes through the second toe. Thus, spreading the fingers would be classified as abduction, regardless of their relation to the median plane of the body as a whole.

Circumduction: a movement in which an extremity describes the surface of a cone, while its distal end describes a circle. Swinging the arms around in a circle is an example of circumduction, and it is a complex movement, involving elements of flexion, extension, abduction, and adduction.

Elevation: a raising—for example, closing the mouth involves elevation of the mandible (lower jaw), while shrugging the shoulders elevates the scapulae.

Depression: a lowering; the opposite of elevation.

Protraction: moving a part forward, for example, sticking out your tongue.

Retraction: drawing a part back.

A rotation is a movement in which a body part is partially revolved about its long axis. For example, turning the upper part of the trunk to either side without moving the feet involves a rotation of the vertebral column. The following special terms are used for rotation of the hands and feet:

Supination: turning the palm of the hand forward (in the anatomical position, the hands are already supinated).

Pronation: turning the hands so that the palms face backward. Notice in Figure 9-3 that the radius and ulna change their relative positions when the hand is supinated and pronated. You can feel this for yourself by grasping your right forearm with your left hand and then turning the right palm back and forth.

Inversion: turning the feet so that the soles face one another.

Eversion: turning the feet so that the soles face outward (the opposite of inversion).

Most people walk with a slight degree of inversion or eversion. You can discover what category you fit

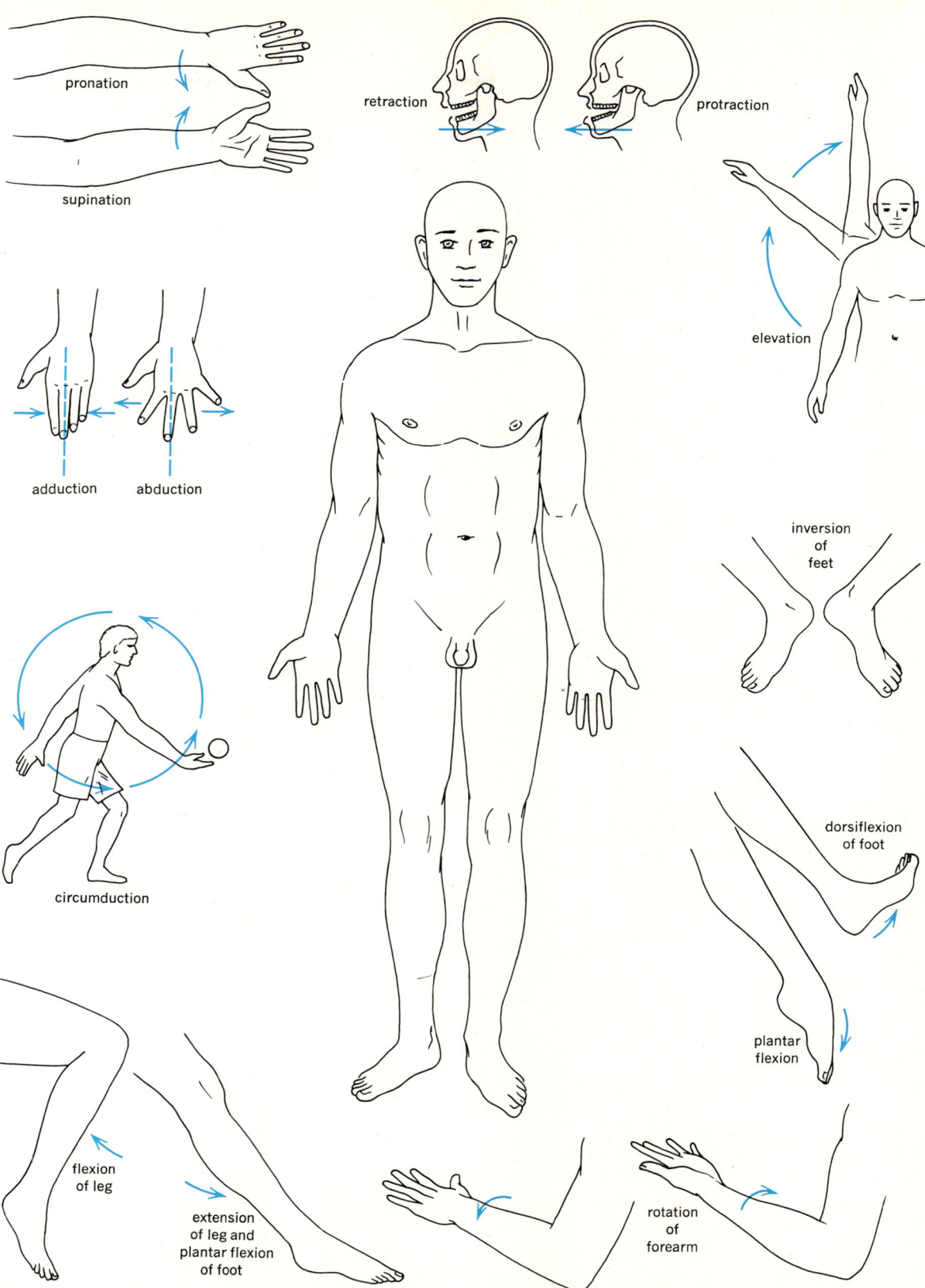

FIGURE 9-3 The articulated skeleton permits a variety of movements of body parts.

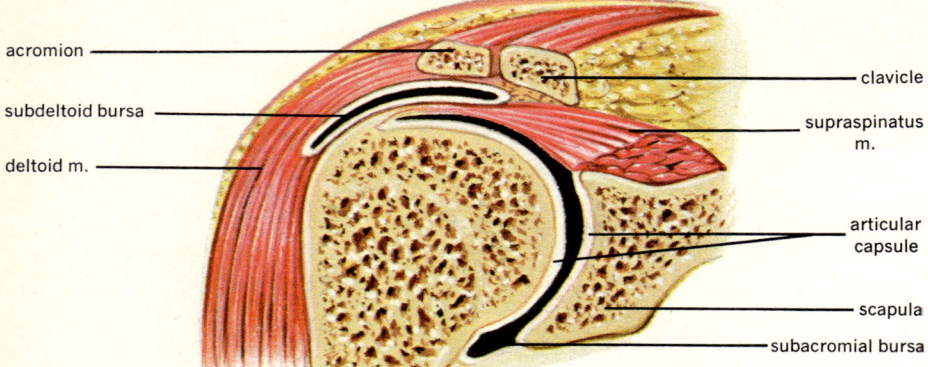

FIGURE 9-4 Bursae of the shoulder joint.

acromion
subdeltoid bursa
deltoid m.
clavicle
supraspinatus m.
articular capsule
scapula
subacromial bursa

into by examining the soles of your shoes. If you walk with your feet everted, the soles will be more worn on the inner edge; greater wear on the outer edge indicates a tendency for inversion.

BURSAE

With modern conveniences, most homemakers of today are spared an ailment that used to plague the women of a generation ago: "housemaid's knee." This is a painful swelling in the region of the patella, which may develop when a person works for long periods in a kneeling position on a hard surface. "Housemaid's knee" actually is not a disorder of the knee joint itself but rather of a fluid-filled sac in the subcutaneous tissue between the skin and the patella. This sac is one of numerous bursae found in various parts of the body.

The term **bursa** comes from a word meaning "wineskin" or "bag." (The French *bourse,* meaning "purse" and by extension referring to the stock exchange, is derived from the same Latin root.) In the body, a bursa is a small enclosed cavity, lined with synovial membrane and filled with synovial fluid (Figure 9-4). Bursae are generally found between structures that move against each other—for example, tendons, ligaments, and bones. They function to reduce friction between moving parts, very much like the articular capsules. Indeed, some bursae located in the region of joints actually communicate with the joint capsules. In addition to the bursae of the knees, prominent bursae are found at the elbows, hips, and heels. **Bursitis,** an inflammation of the bursae, is a common affliction of the shoulders. ("Tennis elbow" is a form of bursitis.) A **bunion** is a swelling of a bursa at the metatarso-phalangeal joint of the great toe, which may be caused by pressure or friction from improperly fitted shoes.

THE KNEE JOINT

Active sports such as basketball and football are extremely hard on the knees. Not only must these joints help to support the full weight of the body in the sudden jars that accompany running and leaping, but they are frequently subjected to twisting and wrenching movements as a basketball player shifts and dodges, or a football player is tackled at the lower legs. It is small wonder that knee injuries are among the most frequent sports problems. Indeed, the fact that athletes' knees stand up as well as they do is a tribute to the efficient engineering of these joints.

In many ways, the knee joints are typical of the diarthroses; in view of this, as well as their special importance to the body, we shall examine them in greater detail.

The knee joint (Figure 9-5) has not one, but three separate articulating surfaces. It includes the articulations of the rounded condyles of the femur with the relatively flat surface of the tibia, as well as the femoropatellar joint. This construction provides for a large degree of movement: though the knee joint is basically a hinge joint, it also permits slight pivotal movement, as well as some gliding movement. But the "mismatch" of the articulating bone surfaces makes the knee joint inherently unstable. Both internal and external structures help to stabilize the joint. Two C-shaped discs of fibrocartilage, called the **medial and lateral menisci** or **semilunar cartilages,** deepen the articulating surface of the tibia. Within the joint, two exceptionally strong ligaments, the **anterior and posterior cruciate ligaments,** bind the head of the tibia to the femur. (The term "cruciate" comes from the way these ligaments cross one another to form an X shape.) The tough fibrous capsule that surrounds the knee joint is the strongest of all the articular capsules of the body. Strong ligaments lash the femur to the tibia (**medial collateral ligament**) and to the fibula (**lateral collateral ligament**). The common tendon of the muscles of the front of the thigh passes over the anterior surface of the knee joint and forms the **patellar ligament.** (The patella, embedded in this ligament, is a sesamoid bone.) A posterior reinforcement of the articular capsule, the **oblique popliteal ligament,** and the attachments of the thigh muscles to the tibia and fibula further strengthen the knee joint.

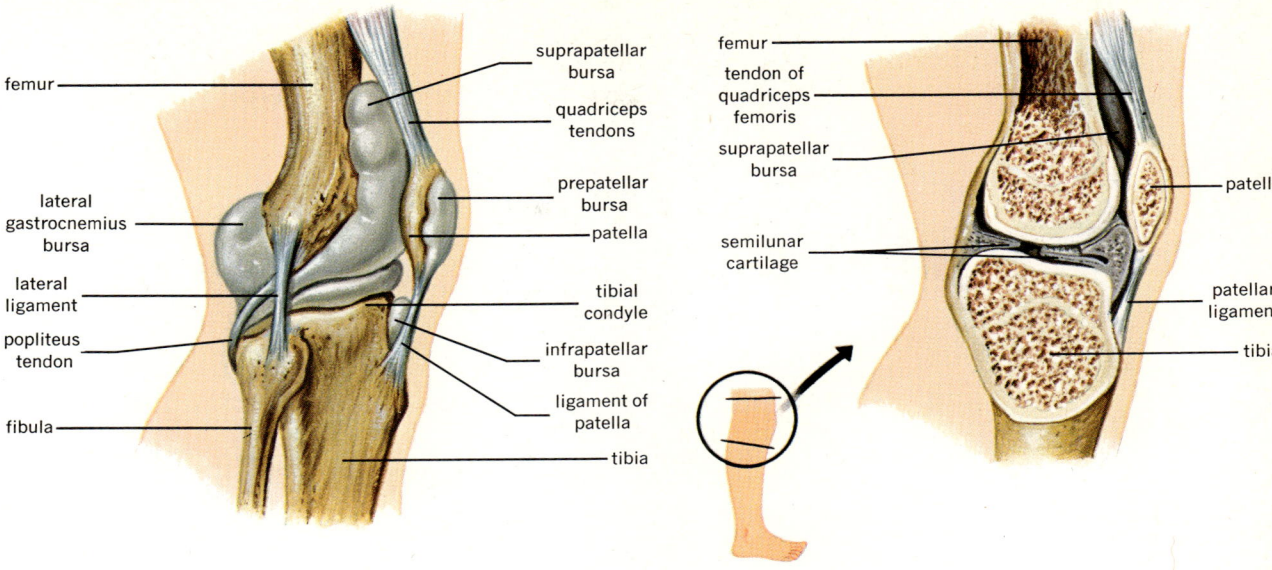

FIGURE 9-5 Lateral view of the right knee joint (A) and the same joint in sagittal section (B).

The joint cavity of the knee is large and complex and communicates with numerous bursae. Fat-filled folds in the synovial membrane help to reduce open spaces in the joint cavity during movements.

DISORDERS OF THE JOINTS

The "creaking joints" that are one of the common cliches in descriptions of old age are often not merely a figurative expression; the movements of elderly joints may be accompanied by clearly audible clicks, snaps, and creakings. Degenerative changes in the joints that develop with age include a reduction of the secretion of lubricating synovial fluid, the replacement of cartilage by bone, and the formation of bony spurs around joints, which can make movements quite painful. In addition, the joints at any age are vulnerable to a variety of injuries and ills.

Sprain

A sudden twisting or wrenching of a joint may tear or stretch its attachments. If no bones are displaced, the injury is classified as a sprain and is accompanied by swelling, redness, and pain.

Dislocation

A displacement of one of the bones of a joint or an internal derangement of the parts that compose the joint is a more serious condition than a sprain; it is classified as a dislocation. The shoulder and knee joints are among the most vulnerable to dislocation. The socket of the scapula is rather shallow, and the head of the humerus may be pulled out of it, resulting in a shoulder dislocation. This sort of displacement can usually be reduced by a physician by pulling the arm away from the trunk and rotating it suitably. In the case of the knee, the most common injury is a

crushing or tearing of one of the semilunar cartilages, resulting from a twisting injury. Not only is the condition extremely painful, but the knee may have a tendency to lock suddenly. Often surgery involving removal of the damaged cartilage is the only effective treatment. (The knee joint can still function efficiently with the cartilage removed.) Jarring blows from the front or side can also damage the knee joint, tearing the ligaments that lash the bones together. Such injuries often leave football players and other athletes with a "trick knee," which may unexpectedly give way. An elastic bandage may be used to provide support to the joint; surgical repair may be necessary.

An incomplete or partial dislocation of a joint is called a **subluxation.** (The technical term for a dislocation is a **luxation.**) Dislocation or subluxation of the hip joint is a common type of birth defect. It can be spotted early by an alert pediatrician, verified by X rays, and treated by immobilization of the hip joints in a brace or cast so as to stimulate suitable bone growth, forming a more normal and fully functional ball-and-socket fit of the femur and os coxae.

Herniated Disc

Between each pair of vertebrae there is an intervertebral disc, a compressible, cushionlike pad composed of tough fibrous tissue and cartilage and filled with a protein solution. Although each vertebra is bound to the adjacent vertebrae by strong ligaments, damage to the surrounding tissues may cause a disc to bulge or slip out of its normal position (Figure 9-6). The resultant slipped or herniated disc causes back pain. If the disc presses on the sciatic nerve, pains in the legs (**sciatica**) will also be experienced. Treatment with bed rest and pain killers is generally prescribed; traction and remedial exercises may also be used. If

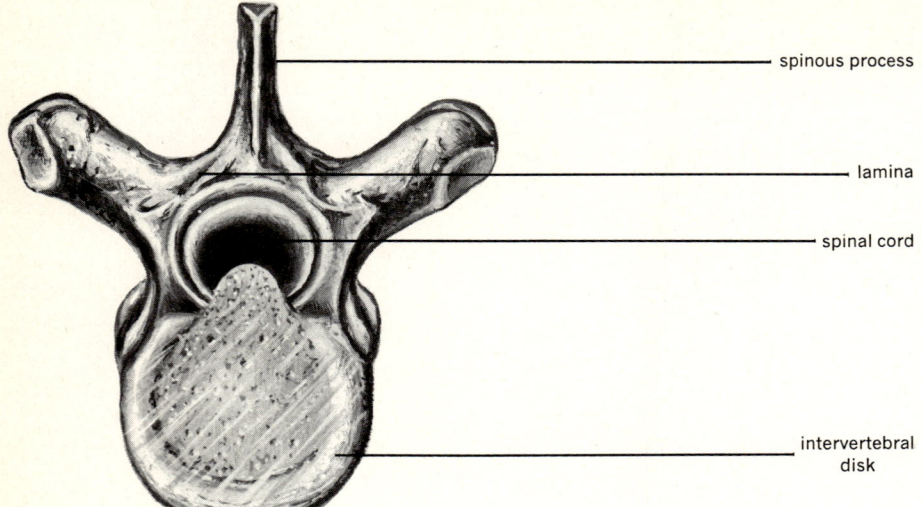

FIGURE 9-6 A herniated disc. The soft, central portion of the disc is protruding into the vertebral canal, where it exerts pressure on the spinal cord.

spinous process

lamina

spinal cord

intervertebral disk

the pain persists, an operation called **laminectomy** may be performed, in which the herniated disc is removed and the adjacent vertebrae are fused. In this procedure, a loss of movement is conceded in exchange for stability. An ingenious, though still controversial, alternate treatment is the injection of the enzyme chymopapain (a variation of the enzyme papain used as a meat tenderizer) into the disc. The enzyme breaks down the protein of the ground substance, permitting it and the water to escape and be absorbed by the body. The disc shrinks back into place, easing the pressure on the surrounding nerves.

Bursitis

Although bursitis is an inflammation of a synovial bursa, rather than of a joint itself, it may affect a joint, since many of the bursae are situated in the region of joints. The inflammation may be caused by excessive stress on the bursa or by a local or systemic inflammatory process. A frequent site is the subacromial bursa, which lies close to the shoulder joint. Pain from the inflamed bursa limits movement at the shoulder joint. Calcium deposits may be formed in the supraspinatus tendon, further limiting motion. If the condition becomes chronic, the muscles may atrophy and the shoulder may become stiff.

Rheumatic Fever

The initial symptoms of rheumatic fever, a bacterial disease caused by *Streptococcus pyogenes,* involve the joints, but this disease rarely causes any lasting damage to the articular system. It begins with a sudden intense inflammation of the synovial tissues, tendons, and other connective tissues around the joints. After a short time, the pain and inflammation of the joints subside, but the disease may cause permanent dam-

age to the heart valves, which is later manifested as rheumatic heart disease.

Rheumatism

"Rheumatism" is a common, rather loosely used term, which usually refers to the condition of **primary fibrositis,** an inflammation of the fibrous connective tissue. The joints involved are usually tender and stiff, and movements may be limited. Many structures may be involved simultaneously, or the fibrositis may travel from one part of the body to another. There is no permanent damage to the joints, and recovery can be complete.

In a related condition, called **tenosynovitis,** the sheaths of tendons are inflamed. When the flexor tendons of the hand are affected, the hand may become locked into a clawlike position, with the patient unable to extend the fingers.

Arthritis

Arthritis, an inflammation of the joints, is probably the most widespread crippling disease. Fifty varieties of arthritis are known; the most common are rheumatoid arthritis, osteoarthritis, and gouty arthritis.

Rheumatoid arthritis is a systemic disease, the cause of which is still unknown. It begins with inflammation of the synovial membrane, the tissue of which becomes thickened. The thickened synovial tissue **(pannus)** damages the joint cartilage, and then becomes invaded by tough fibrous material, which limits motion in the joint. This stage, called **fibrous ankylosis** (the term *ankylosis* refers to immobility of a joint), may degenerate further: the fibrous tissue may become calcified and converted to bone **(bony ankylosis),** resulting in fusion of the bones of the joint and a total loss of mobility.

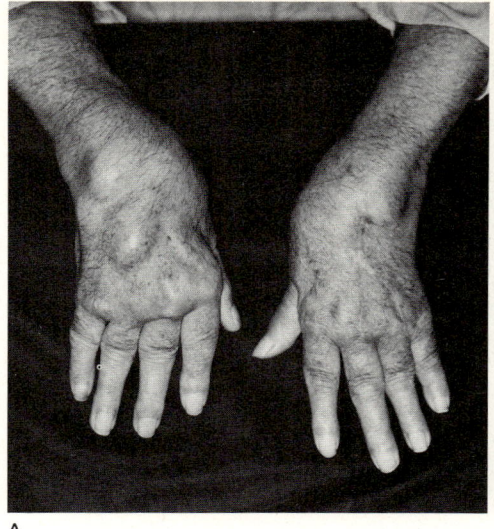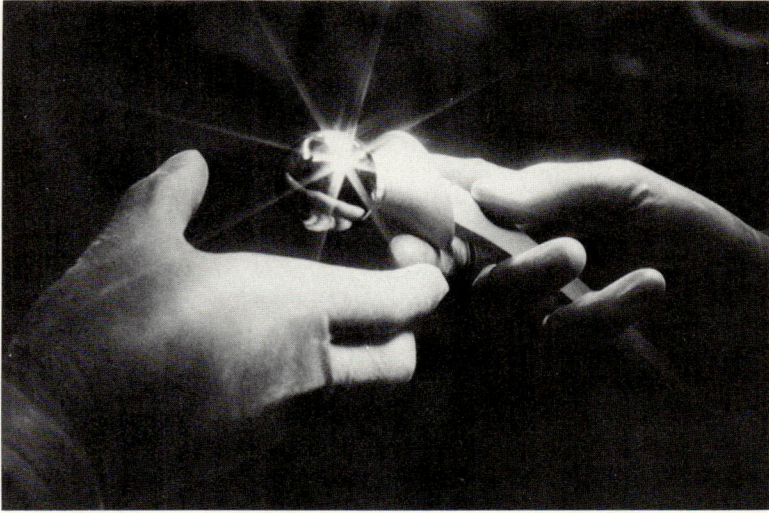

FIGURE 9-7 (A) The gnarled joints typical of the crippling effects of arthritis. (B) Hip prostheses have restored mobility to arthritis victims.

Osteoarthritis is a degenerative disease, which occurs in middle and old age. The constant wear and tear on weight-bearing joints produces a softening, thinning, and ultimate disintegration of the joint cartilages. Increased friction irritates the periosteum, stimulating proliferation of bony growths on the joint surfaces (Figure 9-7A).

Gout is a disturbance of the body's purine metabolism, characterized by an increase in the uric acid level of the blood and the formation of deposits of urates in the joints. Inflammation of the joints and damage to the articular cartilages result.

Although no cure for arthritis has yet been found, considerable progress has been made in the surgical repair of arthritic joints. For example, when a hip joint is crippled by osteoarthritis, the head of the femur can be replaced with an artificial part **(prosthesis)** of stainless steel, while the hip socket is replaced with a prosthesis made of high-density polyethylene (Figure 9-7B). With this combination, full mobility of the joint is restored.

SUMMARY

An articulation or joint is the junction between two or more bones.
Joints are classified according to the degrees and types of movement they permit:
Synarthroses (immovable joints)
Amphiarthroses (slightly movable joints)
Diarthroses (freely movable joints)
Types of synarthroses include:
Sutures (e.g., articulations of cranial bones)
Synchondroses (e.g., between epiphysis and diaphysis of long bones)
Types of amphiarthroses include:
Symphyses (e.g., symphysis pubis and intervertebral discs)
Syndesmoses (e.g., articulation of radius and ulna)
A diarthrosis is enclosed in an articular capsule, the cavity of which is filled with synovial fluid.
Types of diarthroses include:
Ball-and-socket joints (e.g., shoulder and hip joints)
Condyloid joints (e.g., wrist joint)
Hinge joints (e.g., knee and elbow joints)
Pivot joints (e.g., articulations of atlas and axis and radius and ulna)
Saddle joints (e.g., joint at base of thumb)
Gliding joints (e.g., joints of carpals, tarsals, and intervertebral joints)
Movements permitted by joints include gliding movements, angular movements, and rotations.
Terms describing body movements:
Flexion: a bending movement in which the two ends of an extremity are brought closer together.
Extension: moving the two ends of an extremity apart.
Abduction: lateral movement of an extremity, away from the median plane of the body.
Adduction: movement of an extremity toward the median plane of the body.
Circumduction: a movement in which an extremity describes the surface of a cone.
Elevation: a raising.
Depression: a lowering.
Protraction: moving a part forward.
Retraction: drawing a part back.
Rotation: movement in which a body part is partially revolved around its long axis.
Supination: turning the palm of the hand forward.
Pronation: turning the palm of the hand backward.
Inversion: turning the feet so that the soles face one another.
Eversion: turning the feet so that the soles face outward.
A bursa is a small enclosed cavity, lined with synovial membrane and filled with synovial fluid.
Bursae are found between moving parts (e.g., tendons, ligaments, bones) and reduce friction.
They may communicate with joint capsules.
The inherent instability of the knee joint is compensated for by an exceptionally strong joint capsule, internal and external liga-

ments, tendons, and the semilunar cartilages.

Disorders of the joints include:

Sprain: a tearing or stretching of joint attachments due to wrenching.

Dislocation: a displacement of one of the bones of a joint or an internal derangement of its components.

Herniated disc: bulging or displacement of an intervertebral disc.

Bursitis: inflammation of a synovial bursa (e.g., "housemaid's knee," bunion).

Rheumatic fever: a systemic disease causing temporary inflammation of joint tissues and possible permanent impairment of heart valves.

Rheumatism: primary fibrositis, an inflammation of the fibrous connective tissue, which does not permanently damage the joints.

Arthritis: an inflammation of the joints. Varieties include rheumatoid arthritis, osteoarthritis, and gouty arthritis.

QUESTIONS FOR REVIEW AND THOUGHT

1 Distinguish among synarthroses, amphiarthroses, and diarthroses, with respect to structure of joint and degree of movement permitted.

2 What would happen if bone surfaces in movable joints were in direct contact, without intervening cartilage or fluid?

3 Which type of diarthrosis permits: (a) the freest movement? (b) movement in one plane only? (c) rotating movement? (d) sliding movement?

4 Distinguish between: (a) flexion and extension; (b) abduction and adduction; (c) protraction and retraction.

5 What is a bunion?

6 Which knee ligaments would be likely to be torn by a blow from the (a) medial side? (b) lateral side? (c) front?

7 Distinguish among: (a) arthritis, rheumatism, and bursitis; (b) rheumatoid arthritis and osteoarthritis.

THE STRUCTURE OF THE MUSCLES

10

It would be hard to think of any activity of a human being that does not involve the action of muscles. Walking, dancing, playing the piano, and throwing a ball are all made possible by the contractions of muscles that move the arms and legs. While you are sitting quietly reading a book, it might seem that you are motionless except when you need to turn a page or jot down a marginal note. Yet an observer would notice your eyes darting back and forth in little jerks, successively focusing across each line of print; muscles move your eyeballs and help to accommodate the lenses of your eyes. Meanwhile, numerous tiny adjustments of skeletal muscles in your body help to keep you erect. You are barely conscious of these muscle actions, if at all, and even more unaware of the rhythmic beating of your heart, pumping blood around your body; of the contractions of your diaphragm as you breathe; and of the ceaseless work of smooth muscles in your internal organs, adjusting the blood vessel diameters, and sending waves of peristalsis rippling down your intestines. Waking and sleeping, the muscles of the body continue to contract and relax, producing movement of body parts and contributing to the functioning of internal organs.

The work of the muscles begins long before birth and continues throughout life. Near the end of the third week of your life before birth, when your mother was barely realizing that she had missed a menstrual period, your heart had already begun to beat, and it has not paused in its rhythmic contractions ever since. In the seventh week after conception, when you were just an inch long, your skeletal muscles were already well enough developed to produce movements of your body—though it was another two months or more before your mother felt the first flutterings of life. After birth, the strength of your skeletal muscles and your control over them gradually increased, and you learned to sit, stand, walk, and perform increasingly delicate manipulations with your hands.

Muscles can be looked upon as the machines of the body: they transform chemical energy into a directed force and generally produce **movement**—of the body as a whole (locomotion); of body parts (from the winking of an eye to the kick of a leg and the expansion of the chest cavity during breathing); and of various fluids and other materials through the channels of the body (blood through the circulatory system; food through the digestive tract; urine through the urinary tract, and so on).

Muscle cells are highly specialized in one common property of living matter: **contractility.** Muscles do their work by contracting. On the microscopic level, the structure of muscles is uniquely suited to this function. On the macroscale, the arrangement of the muscles of the body (Figure 10-1) permits them to work either together or in opposition to achieve a variety of movements.

As we have already seen in Chapter 5, there are three types of muscle tissue in the body, differing in structure, mode of action, and function: skeletal muscle, smooth muscle, and cardiac muscle.

Skeletal muscles are usually attached to bones, and their contractions permit movement of the arms, legs, head, and other body parts (Figure 10-1). Skeletal muscles surround the mouth cavity and form the body of the tongue; they surround the body cavities and separate the thoracic and abdominal cavities; and skeletal muscles attached to the outer layer of the eyeball permit movement of the eyes. Skeletal muscles have a capacity for tremendous power: the force exerted in the uncontrolled contractions of skeletal muscles during a convulsion can snap bones. But, like a high-speed engine, a skeletal muscle cannot keep up its exertions for long; after a short time it must rest.

Smooth muscles are found in the walls of the viscera. Sheets of smooth muscle are present in the walls of the blood vessels and lymphatic vessels, the gastrointestinal tract, the urinary and reproductive tracts, the respiratory passages, and in various internal organs such as the spleen and gall bladder. Contractions of smooth muscle in the walls of the uterus propel a baby on its one-way trip out into the world; smooth muscle is also found around the hair follicles of the skin and within the skin connective tissue, as well as within the eyeball. If the skeletal muscle is like the hare in Aesop's fable, the smooth muscle is more like the tortoise—slow and steady. Like a heavy-duty engine, it cannot summon the huge surges of power that skeletal muscles can, but smooth muscle can go on contracting in its steady manner day after day, without the need for frequent rests.

Cardiac muscle is the muscle that forms the walls of the heart. In some ways it is like both skeletal and smooth muscles, yet different from either. It goes on rhythmically contracting day after day, from a few weeks after conception to the last moments of life. But it does get a brief rest between beats. Though it normally works along steadily, cardiac muscle is capable of "shifting into high gear" for brief periods when extra stress calls for a vigorous response—when you race to catch a bus, for example, or run up the stairs.

Some of the main differences among the three types of muscles are summarized in Table 10-1. In this chapter we examine the structure of muscle tissue in general and of the major skeletal muscles of the body. The following chapter explores various aspects of the functioning of muscles, from the molecular level up to the gross effects observed in the body as a whole.

TABLE 10-1   Comparison of muscle types

CHARACTERISTIC	SKELETAL MUSCLE	CARDIAC MUSCLE	SMOOTH MUSCLE
Location	Usually attached to bones	Heart wall	Walls of internal organs
Cell type	Long cylindrical fibers (1–40 mm) arranged in bundles	Short fibers (0.05–0.1 mm), forming branched network	Elongated tapering fibers (0.015–0.5 mm) arranged in bundles or sheets
Cell membrane	Distinct double-layered sarcolemma	Sarcolemma forms intercalated discs	Delicate sarcolemma fused with adjacent fibers
Cytoplasm	Sarcoplasm limited, organelles numerous	Large amount of sarcoplasm, organelles numerous	Small amount of sarcoplasm, fewer organelles
Myofibrils	Striated, fill cell	Striated, fewer than in skeletal muscle	Nonstriated, fill cell
Nuclei	Multiple flattened nuclei scattered over cell periphery just under sarcolemma	One (usually) or two oval nuclei at center of cell	One oval or rod-shaped nucleus at center of cell
Vascular supply	Good blood supply; lymph capillaries restricted to epimysium and perimysium	Dense blood capillary beds; some lymph capillaries	Fair supply of blood and lymph capillaries
Nerve supply	Motor and sensory nerve endings	Parasympathetic and sympathetic innervation (motor); sensory nerves report on oxygen supply	Parasympathetic and sympathetic innervation (motor); sensory nerves (stretch receptors)
Type of contraction	Voluntary, often vigorous, short duration; fibers contract independently	Involuntary, rhythmic (inherent); contractions of fibers coordinated	Involuntary, sluggish, often rhythmic; contractions of fibers coordinated

MICROSCOPIC STRUCTURE OF MUSCLE TISSUE

It may seem surprising that the various types of muscle tissue look so different from one another under the microscope, when we consider that each performs basically the same function. Skeletal, smooth, and cardiac muscle cells are all specialized for contractility, a property that is imparted to them by thin strands of the contractile proteins **actin** and **myosin.** All muscle cells are more or less elongated, and as a result they are often referred to as muscle *fibers.* But there are considerable differences among the three types of muscles, both in size and shape of the cells and their arrangement, and in their internal structure (Figure 10-2).

As mentioned in Chapter 5, a specialized terminology is used for muscle cells: the cell membrane is referred to as the **sarcolemma,** while the cytoplasm is called the **sarcoplasm.** (The prefix comes from the Greek word *sarkos,* meaning "flesh.")

Skeletal Muscle

Looking at a slide of a skeletal muscle preparation such as that in Figure 10-2A, the most striking feature is the regular pattern of cross-banding or transverse striation that covers the muscle cells. It looks almost as though someone with artistic inclinations had decided to decorate each muscle fiber with alternating light and dark stripes, repeating in a regular pattern. These striations give skeletal muscle tissue an alternate name, **striated muscle tissue** (which is actually a more appropriate name, for all skeletal muscles are striated, while not all are attached to bones of the skeleton).

The striations of skeletal muscle fibers are clearly visible in the light microscope, and histologists studied and named their various features long before there was any knowledge of what caused these unique markings. The dark bands were designated as **A bands** (anisotropic), while the light bands were referred to as **I bands** (isotropic). A thin dark line can clearly be seen running across the muscle fiber precisely in the middle of each light I band; this is the **Z line** (from the German word *zwischen,* meaning "between"). A somewhat lighter zone, the **H zone,** runs through the middle of each A band; and the pale H zone, in turn, is bisected by a dark line, the **M line** (Figure 10-3). A skeletal muscle fiber can be viewed as a series of repeating units, each with the same characteristic banded structure. The unit, extending from one Z line to the next, is called a **sarcomere;** as we shall see later, it is not only the structural unit, but

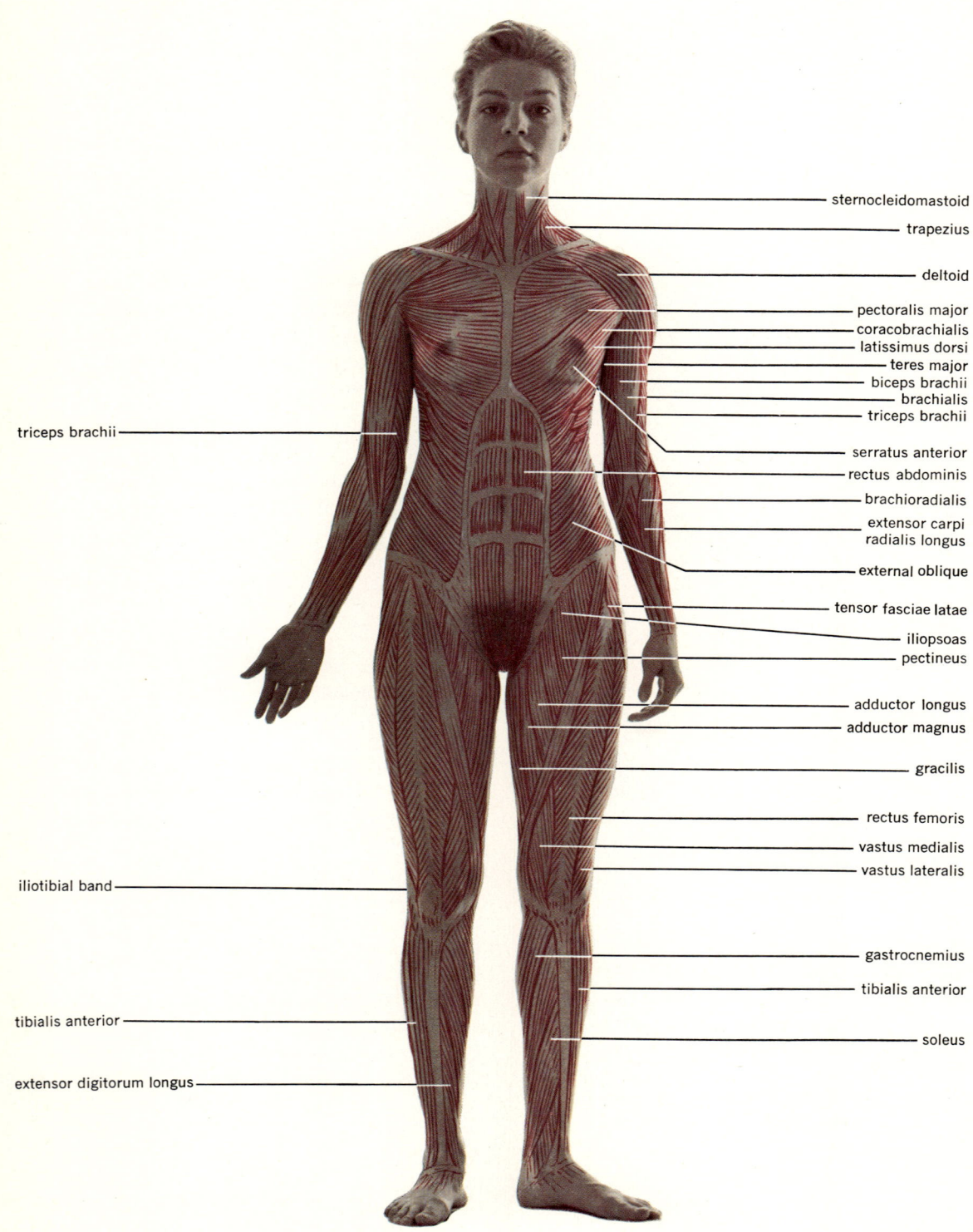

sternocleidomastoid
trapezius
deltoid
pectoralis major
coracobrachialis
latissimus dorsi
teres major
biceps brachii
brachialis
triceps brachii
serratus anterior
rectus abdominis
brachioradialis
extensor carpi
radialis longus
external oblique
tensor fasciae latae
iliopsoas
pectineus
adductor longus
adductor magnus
gracilis
rectus femoris
vastus medialis
vastus lateralis
gastrocnemius
tibialis anterior
soleus

triceps brachii

iliotibial band

tibialis anterior

extensor digitorum longus

A

FIGURE 10-1   Principal superficial skeletal muscles: anterior (A) and posterior (B) views.

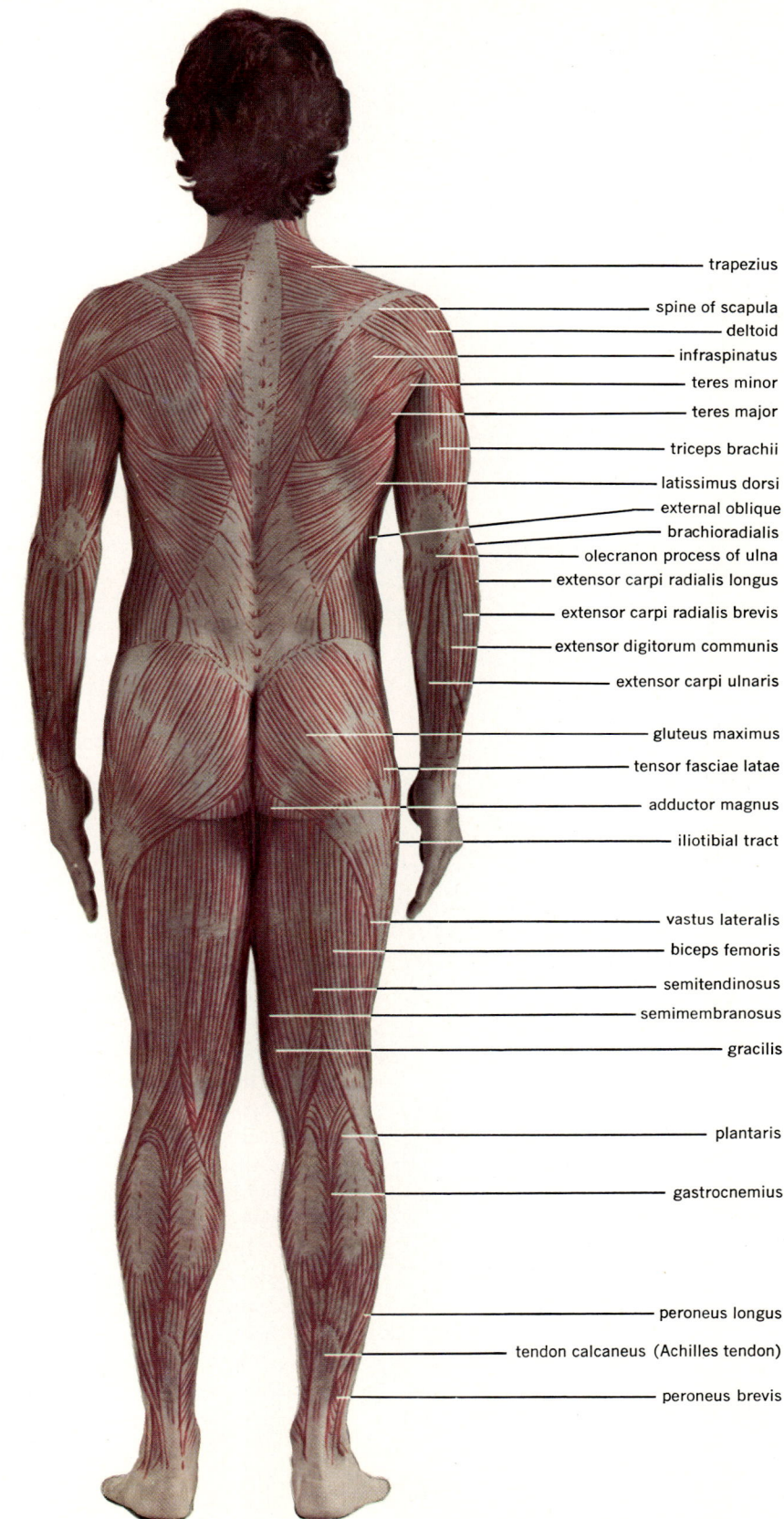

trapezius

spine of scapula

deltoid

infraspinatus

teres minor

teres major

triceps brachii

latissimus dorsi

external oblique

brachioradialis

olecranon process of ulna

extensor carpi radialis longus

extensor carpi radialis brevis

extensor digitorum communis

extensor carpi ulnaris

gluteus maximus

tensor fasciae latae

adductor magnus

iliotibial tract

vastus lateralis

biceps femoris

semitendinosus

semimembranosus

gracilis

plantaris

gastrocnemius

peroneus longus

tendon calcaneus (Achilles tendon)

peroneus brevis

B

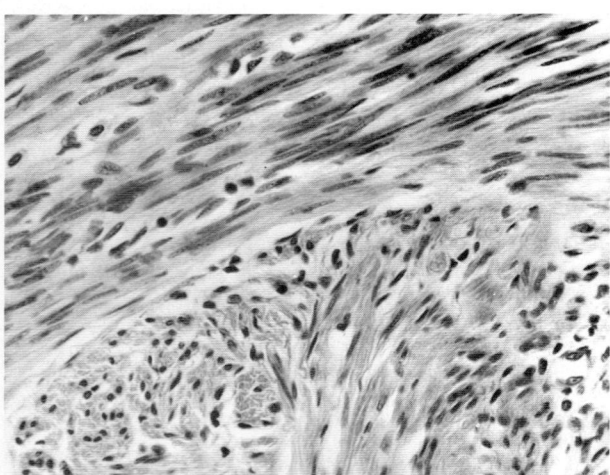

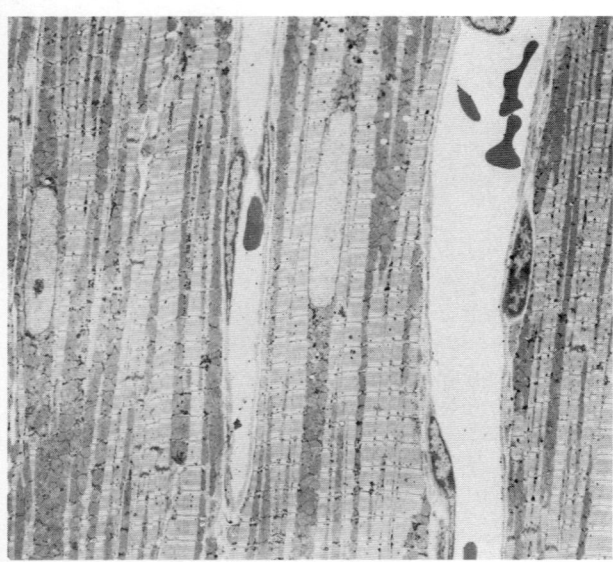

FIGURE 10-2 Skeletal (A), smooth (B), and cardiac (C) muscle tissue.

also the contracting unit of a muscle fiber.

In the light microscope, it can be seen that the skeletal muscle fiber contains numerous thinner fibers called **myofibrils.** These are oriented lengthwise and closely packed in the sarcoplasm, and they are marked by the pattern of banding that gives the typical striated appearance to the skeletal muscle cell as a whole. Electron micrographs reveal that the myofibrils have a fine structure of their own, which explains the striations. Each myofibril is composed in turn of 1000 to 2000 still more delicate fibers, called **myofilaments.** There are two types of myofilaments, which differ in length, diameter, and composition, and are arranged in a regular pattern. **Thick myofilaments** (about 100 Å thick) are composed of the contractile protein **myosin.** They are concentrated in the dense A bands; each thick myofilament has a swelling of the middle of the strand (together these swellings produce the M line in the middle of the A band), and, in addition, a number of peglike lateral projections, which stick out at an angle of about 60°. **Thin myofilaments** (about 50 Å thick) are composed of the contractile protein **actin,** associated with two other proteins, **tropomyosin** and **troponin.** As Figure 10-3 shows, the two types of myofilaments have an alternating, partly overlapping arrangement, held together by cross-bridges formed by the lateral projections of the thick myofilaments. The dark portions of the A bands are regions in which both myosin and actin filaments are found. The paler H zones are areas between the ends of successive actin filaments, containing only the thicker myosin filaments. (When a muscle cell contracts, the ends of successive actin filaments move toward one another, and the H zone disappears.) The I bands appear so light in skeletal muscle preparations because they are the regions of the gaps between the ends of the thick myosin filaments and contain only the thin actin filaments. The Z line is believed to be formed by the dense intertwinings of the ends of actin filaments (i.e., two actin strands, joined end-to-end, form each thin filament). During muscle contraction, the thick and thin myofilaments seem to slide over one another, decreasing the overall length of the sarcomere (Figure 10-4).

In addition to their characteristic striations, skeletal muscle cells possess a number of other prominent features. Unlike nearly all the other cell types of the body, skeletal muscle cells are multinucleated, each with over a hundred oval, flattened nuclei scattered randomly over the periphery of the cell, just beneath the sarcolemma. Outside the sarcolemma, the muscle fiber is wrapped in a delicate sheet of connective tissue called the **endomysium.** Inside the cell, the sarcolemma is continuous with the **sarcoplasmic reticulum,** a complex network of tubules and sacs that is analogous to the endoplasmic reticulum of other cells. The

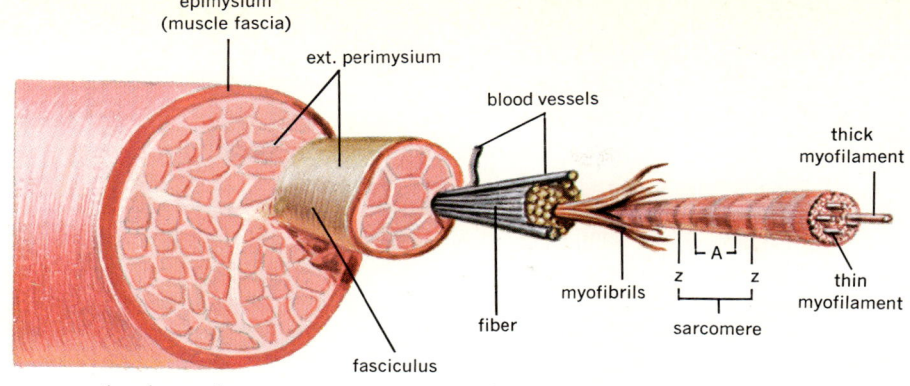

epimysium
(muscle fascia)

ext. perimysium

blood vessels

thick
myofilament

myofibrils

fiber

thin
myofilament

fasciculus

Z   Z

A

sarcomere

section of a muscle

FIGURE 10-3   Muscle structure: the muscle is made up of bundles of muscle fibers, which in turn are composed of myofibrils, made up of thick myofilaments (myosin) and thin myofilaments (actin).

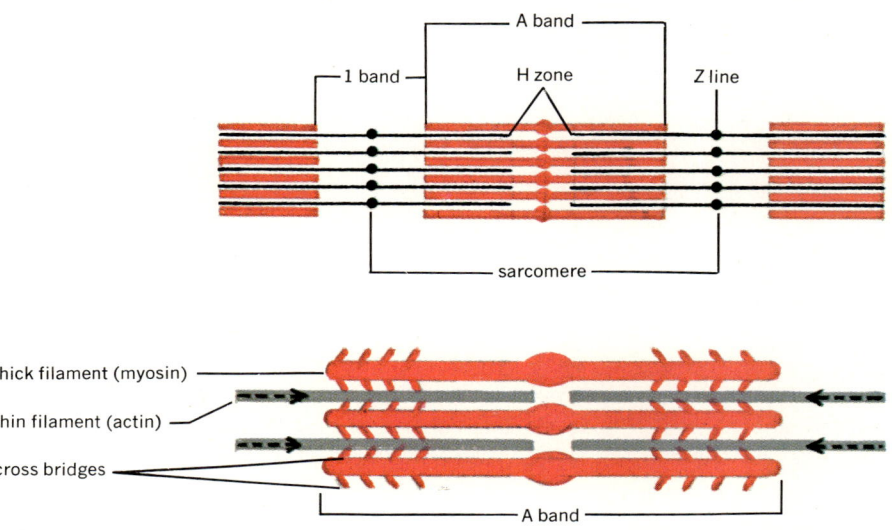

A band

1 band

H zone

Z line

sarcomere

thick filament (myosin)

thin filament (actin)

cross bridges

A band

FIGURE 10-4   The changes in the banded structure of striated muscle in successive stages of contraction, shown in the micrograph (A), can be explained by the sliding-filament hypothesis, shown schematically in (B).

transverse tubules of the sarcoplasmic reticulum are structures unique to the skeletal muscle cells. Often referred to as the **T-system,** these tubules begin as funnellike invaginations in the sarcolemma and lead inward to the myofibrils. Thus they provide a direct connection between the myofibrils and the exterior of the cell and act as a conduction pathway in spreading the impulse that excites a muscle contraction.

Skeletal muscle cells are abundantly supplied with organelles, particularly mitochondria, the cell's energy generators. Other organelles include ribosomes and small Golgi complexes. Lipid droplets and glycogen granules are common cell inclusions. **Myoglobin,** a hemoglobinlike pigment, is present in many skeletal muscle cells and transports oxygen from blood capillaries to the mitochondria. Like hemoglobin, myoglobin is an iron-containing protein and gives a red color to cells that contain it. In the human body, both **red fibers** (myoglobin-containing) and **white fibers** (myoglobin-deficient) are normally intermingled, so that the muscle tissue overall has a rich red color. In some animals, however, the two types of fibers are separated—for example, in the "white meat" and "dark meat" of a chicken. White fibers are large cells, with abundant myofibrils, an extensive sarcoplasmic reticulum, and few mitochondria; they can contract rapidly for long periods and are sometimes referred to as **fast muscle.** Red fibers are smaller cells, with fewer myofibrils and numerous mitochondria, and they have a richer blood supply. They contract slowly and powerfully, and thus are called **slow muscle.** White fibers are abundant in such muscles as the biceps and the muscles that move the eyeball; white muscles are involved in delicate and skilled movements. Red fibers predominate in the muscles of respiration and mastication; red fibers are also important in maintaining posture, which requires long, slow contractions.

Smooth Muscle

Like striated muscles, smooth muscles get their name from their microscopic appearance. The pronounced pattern of cross-banding is absent in micrographs of smooth muscle cells (see Figure 10-2B), and their delicate cell membrane usually cannot be seen with a light microscope. The individual smooth muscle cells are elongated and spindle-shaped, with a single oval or rod-shaped nucleus embedded in the center of the cell. The cells are arranged with their tapered ends overlapping, and form cords, bundles, or sheets. Short, fingerlike projections from the cell surface make contact with (and may be connected to) adjacent smooth muscle cells. Connective tissue ensheaths the individual smooth muscle cells.

The sarcolemma of the smooth muscle cell is dimpled by numerous micropinocytotic invaginations and surface vesicles, but there are no tubelike T-systems such as are found in skeletal muscle cells. (Tubules are present in the sarcoplasmic reticulum, but they are not continuous with the sarcolemma.) Like skeletal muscle cells, smooth muscle cells contain numerous myofibrils, oriented parallel to the long axis of the muscle fiber. The myofibrils are composed of myofilaments of three types: thick filaments (about 150 Å thick), which apparently contain myosin; intermediate-size filaments (about 100 Å thick) of undetermined protein structure; and thin filaments (about 50 Å thick). The arrangement of the myofilaments in smooth muscle cells does not produce a pattern of striation; instead, two or three rows of thin filaments may be arranged around a single thick filament to form a rosettelike pattern. (Generally there is a high proportion of thin filaments in comparison with the thick filaments; there are few intermediate-size filaments.) The thin filaments pass through dense oval bodies, which hold them close together. They are also attached to dense bodies on the inner surface of the sarcolemma.

Mitochondria are rather scarce in smooth muscle cells, but Golgi complexes, numerous free ribosomes, lipid droplets, and glycogen granules are present.

Cardiac Muscle

The unique tasks imposed upon the heart, which continues to beat rhythmically throughout life, are reflected in a number of special features of its microscopic structure. Cardiac muscle tissue is actually composed of two types of cells: cardiac muscle fibers and specialized cells of the conducting system.

In some respects a cardiac muscle fiber resembles a cross between skeletal and smooth muscle (see Figure 10-2). It is striated, with the characteristic A, I, and Z bands, but the pattern of striations is less distinct than in skeletal muscle fibers. Like smooth muscle fibers, a cardiac muscle cell has a single cigar-shaped nucleus (or perhaps two), positioned at the center of the cell. Unlike either of the other two types, cardiac muscle fibers branch, bifurcate, and anastomose (merge) freely to form an interconnected network. The fibers and their branches are joined end-to-end at **intercalated discs,** formed by the sarcolemmas of adjacent cells, linked together by short interdigitating cell processes. Each cell is wrapped in a thin endomysium, which, however, does not penetrate into the intercalated discs. The cardiac muscle fibers are arranged in thin layers, parallel to each other within each layer.

Like skeletal muscle cells, the cardiac muscle fibers of the ventricles of the heart contain a T-system of tubular invaginations from the sarcolemma; in the atria, however, the T-system is absent. There are fewer myofibrils than in skeletal muscle fibers, but they have the same internal structure of thick myosin and thin actin filaments. Mitochondria are especially abundant; the Golgi zone is small. Glycogen granules and lipid droplets are numerous. In addition, brown to yellow granules of the pigment **lipofuscin** are deposited at the poles of the nucleus. Lipofuscin is sometimes called the "aging pigment," for its deposits in the heart muscle increase progressively with age, and it is thought that they may ultimately interfere with the functioning of the heart.

The specialized cells of the conducting system of the heart are slightly modified cardiac muscle cells, collected into small nodes or strands, which are encased in a connective tissue sheath. The cells of the nodes are spindle-shaped and smaller than the usual cardiac muscle cells and form a compact, branching network. Often they are interconnected into cordlike clusters, joined mainly side-to-side. Their microstructure is basically similar to that of the ordinary cardiac muscle cells, except that they lack the T-system and intercalated discs. These specialized cardiac muscle cells help to distribute the contraction impulse throughout the heart and coordinate the contraction of the four chambers of the heart; they serve as pace-makers for the heart beat.

GROSS STRUCTURE OF THE MUSCLES

The muscular system of the body is composed of hundreds of muscles, each of which may be considered as an organ. A muscle contains numerous muscle cells or fibers, which are its functional units. But muscle fibers are not the only components of a muscle, by any means. Connective tissue and nerve tissue components are an important part of a muscle, as are vascular elements that carry blood and lymph. We have already seen that there are striking differences among the three types of muscle fibers. There are equally striking differences in the shape, composition, and organization of skeletal, smooth, and cardiac muscles, and indeed, considerable variation within each type.

Skeletal Muscles

If you bend your arm up at the elbow and clench your fist, you will notice a number of muscles bulging just under the skin of your hand and arm. These are all skeletal muscles.

The skeletal muscles of the body show a great variation of shape (Figure 10-5). Some are like long cords, others like flat sheets. Many of the skeletal muscles (e.g., the biceps) are long and tapering at the ends, with a middle portion thickened into a distinct **belly.** Some skeletal muscles are shaped like a triangle (e.g., the deltoid muscle); the various sphincter muscles are ring-shaped. The individual muscle fibers are arranged in distinct patterns in muscles of different shapes. In flat sheets of muscle, the fibers have a parallel orientation. In **fusiform,** or tapering muscles, the fibers are parallel to the long axis of the muscle. In muscles such as the deltoid, the individual fibers converge toward a narrow attachment. In some muscles, the arrangement of the fibers resembles a feather, either one-sided (**pennate**) or two-sided (**bipennate**). The "midrib" of the feathery structure is a tendon, a

tough cord of fibrous connective tissue in which the muscle fibers are anchored. In **sphincter** muscles, found at various openings of the body, the muscle fibers are arranged circularly around a central opening.

Each individual skeletal muscle fiber is encased in a connective tissue sheath, the **endomysium.** Groups of skeletal muscle cells are gathered into bundles, called **fasciculi,** which are in turn wrapped in a sheet of connective tissue, the **perimysium.** The muscle itself is a bundle of bundles (see Figure 10-3 on page 173)—a group of fasciculi, wrapped in a layer of dense connective tissue, the **epimysium.** This compartmentalized structure of a skeletal muscle has considerable functional importance: the fasciculi can contract independently of their neighbors, and in general, the more separate bundles a muscle contains, the more finely graded movements it can produce. In some parts of the body, different groups of muscles are encased in envelopes of connective tissue called **septa.** For example, septa in the thigh separate the extensor, flexor, and adductor groups of muscles.

The epimysium, perimysium, and endomysium are continuous with the strong, tough tendons and aponeuroses that bind muscles firmly to bones or other muscles. (A **tendon** is a cord of fibrous connective tissue, while an **aponeurosis** is a broad, flat sheet of fibrous connective tissue.)

Tendons are usually found at the ends of muscles, but they may also be found in the middle, producing a muscle with two fleshy bellies. Tendinous patches may develop in regions of the muscle surface that are subjected to friction; such patches may form an extensive smooth, glistening surface. (Perhaps you have noticed such tendinous sheets on cuts of meat. Steaks, roasts, and chops are mainly muscle tissue.) When two muscles pass over one another or over a bone in a moving joint, friction may be further reduced by the interposition of a **bursa,** a tough, fluid-filled sac. Where a tendon is subjected to constant friction be-

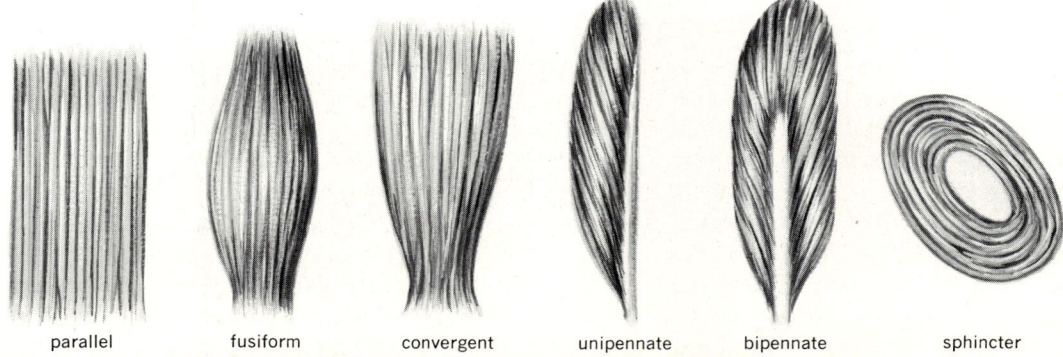

parallel   fusiform   convergent   unipennate   bipennate   sphincter

FIGURE 10-5 Types of skeletal muscles, classified according to the arrangement of the fibers.

cause it runs through a tight tunnel, such as in the wrist and ankle, it may be surrounded by a **tendon sheath,** which is a kind of modified bursa. In some cases, friction may stimulate ossification in a tendon, so that a **sesamoid bone** forms.

As a person ages, the skeletal muscles undergo a process called **fibrosis.** Skeletal muscle fibers gradually degenerate and are progressively replaced by fibrous connective tissue. The loss of contractility results in a gradual decrease in muscular strength.

With the prodigious amount of work that they do, muscles need large amounts of energy, and a bountiful supply of oxygen is necessary for the energy-yielding reactions of cell respiration. Oxygen is carried to the muscles in the blood. Arteries carrying oxygen-rich blood from the heart branch to form numerous blood capillaries, which run along the individual muscle fibers and branch and anastomose to form a meshlike network. Lymphatic vessels carry excess fluid back to the heart; they are not present in the endomysium of skeletal muscles, but are found in the epimysium and perimysium.

Nerves are another important constituent of a skeletal muscle. **Afferent** or **sensory nerves** carry messages to the brain, keeping it informed of the degree of contraction of the skeletal muscles. This information is important for coordinating muscular movements. Messages are carried from the brain to the muscles over **somatic efferent** or **motor nerves.** The axons of these nerves branch profusely, terminating in tiny buttonlike nerve endings called **motor end plates,** each of which is lodged in a trenchlike hollow on the surface of a muscle fiber. The junction between the nerve ending and the muscle fiber is called a **myoneural** (or **neuromuscular**) **junction,** and a single neuron, together with the group of muscle fibers with which it is in contact is called a **motor unit.** A single nerve cell may innervate as many as a hundred muscle fibers; in this case, impulses along the nerve fiber stimulate all the muscle fibers of the motor unit to contract, and a gross movement is produced. Some neurons innervate only one or a very few muscle cells and produce fine movements.

Smooth Muscles

Although skeletal muscles are found more or less as independent structures, smooth muscle, for the most part, is situated *within* other structures—generally within the walls of internal organs and the tubular vessels and ducts of the body.

Smooth muscle tissue is arranged in cords, bundles, and sheets. In the walls of a tubular organ, the smooth muscle fibers may run circularly around the central opening (lumen) of the tube, or they may be aligned longitudinally, along the length of the tube.

Often a layer of smooth muscle tissue has fibers running at right angles to those of an adjacent layer: circular muscle next to longitudinal muscle (Figure 10-6). The intestines are a prime example of this type of arrangement. There is an outer longitudinal layer and an inner circular layer. Actually, the fibers of both the outer and the inner muscle coats of the intestines are arranged in spirals: the spiral of the circular layer is very tightly wound, while the spiral of the longitudinal layer is so loosely wound that the fibers are oriented practically along the long axis of the tube. These arrangements of the muscle fibers explain the wavelike contractions of peristalsis, which periodically course down the length of the intestines. When a particular site is stimulated by stretching (e.g., when a portion of semidigested food is squirted into the intestines from the stomach), a wave of contraction starts down both muscle layers. In the tightly wound spiral of the circular muscle coat, the contraction must negotiate so many turns that it travels rather slowly down the length of the tube, constricting each successive region in turn. Meanwhile, the contraction wave is traveling more rapidly down the loosely wound longitudinal coat, pulling it up toward the source of the stimulation. The net effect is to relax the tension in the walls and permit the intestine to bulge in the region that is not being constricted by the circular muscles.

The smooth muscle layer in the wall of an organ is firmly bound to the other components of the wall by connective tissue. Connective tissue fibers separate layers and bundles of smooth muscle cells, but no tendons occur in smooth muscle.

Both blood and lymphatic capillaries are present in smooth muscle tissue, but this type is not as vascular as either skeletal or cardiac muscle.

Smooth muscles have two types of motor innervation: **parasympathetic** and **sympathetic.** Both types of nerves are part of the autonomic nervous system, and thus the work of the smooth muscles is not under voluntary control. Generally one type of nerve produces contraction of the smooth muscle fibers, while the other produces a relaxation of smooth muscles that are already contracting. (The specific effects vary, depending on the organ involved.) Smooth muscle fibers are able to contract independently of stimulation from the brain, whereas skeletal muscles cannot contract unless they receive an appropriate message from the brain or spinal cord. In smooth muscles, the motor nerves regulate the activity of the muscles, increasing or decreasing it to meet the changing needs of the body. Sensory nerves may also be present; these are generally stretch receptors, which inform the brain of unusual stretching of the muscles—for example, the sensation of "gas pains"

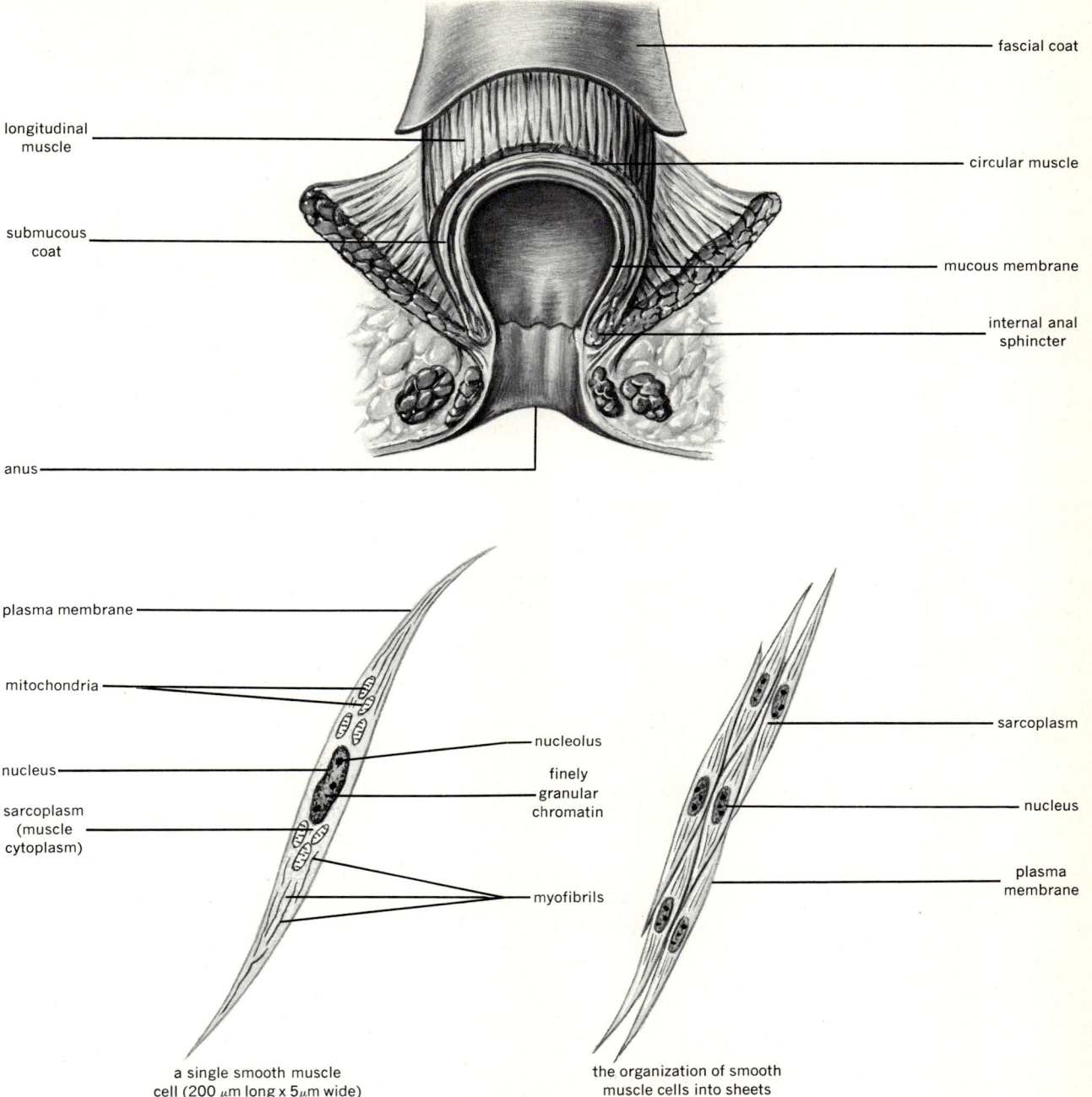

FIGURE 10-6 **Smooth muscle. Above: alternating layers of longitudinal and circular smooth muscle in the rectum. Below: a single smooth muscle cell and the arrangement of smooth muscle cells in sheets.**

when a bubble of gas accumulates in the intestines.

Cardiac Muscle

The muscle of the heart is shaped into a four-chambered organ that looks something like two ice-cream cones, fused together. The two upper chambers, the **atria,** are receiving chambers for blood, while the vigorous contractions of the thick-walled lower chambers, the **ventricles,** send the blood coursing out

through arteries. The cardiac muscle fibers are arranged in thin layers, wrapped in a connective-tissue perimysium to form fascicles. The muscle layers are arranged in a wide spiral, stretching from the base to the apex of the heart (Figure 10-7).

The branching interconnections of the cardiac muscle fibers link the muscle of the ventricles into a continuous protoplasmic sheet. The muscle fibers of the atria are similarly interlinked. This arrangement

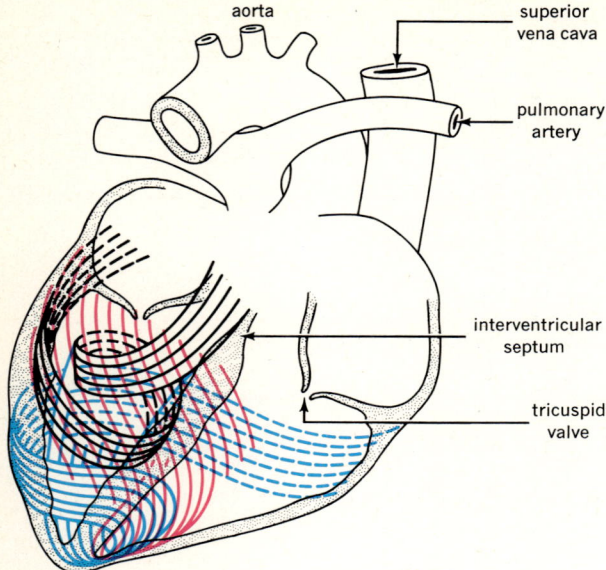

FIGURE 10-7 Orientation of the major bundles of cardiac muscle in the heart.

has an important functional significance: stimulation of one muscle fiber is transmitted to all the others with which it is interconnected, and the entire muscle contracts as a unit.

The **myocardium** (heart muscle) contains a small amount of loose connective tissue, which increases with age.

The hard-working heart has a voracious appetite for oxygen. The blood supply of cardiac muscle tissue is the richest of all—twice as great as that of the skeletal muscle. Blood capillaries form a dense network through the slitlike spaces between cardiac muscle cells. Lymphatic capillaries are also fairly abundant and are found in the endomysium in addition to the perimysium and epimysium.

Unlike skeletal and smooth muscles, cardiac muscle can contract spontaneously, independent of messages carried by the nervous system. However, temporary speedups or slowdowns of heart contraction are produced by impulses carried over sympathetic or parasympathetic nerve fibers to cardiac muscle cells and to the specialized conducting cells in the nodes. Sensory nerves carry information from the heart to the brain, mainly relating to the amount of oxygen supplied to the heart. **Angina** is a warning pain, signalling that the heart muscle is not receiving enough oxygen.

THE INDIVIDUAL SKELETAL MUSCLES

One of the topics frequently brought up in discussions of the women's liberation movement is the existence of laws restricting the employment of women in certain occupations on the basis that women are inher-

ently not as strong as men. Does such a physical difference actually exist? There are great individual variations, of course, and there are undoubtedly many individual women who are stronger than particular individual men. However, on the basis of total amount of muscle, there is a valid distinction: in women the skeletal muscles comprise about 36 percent of the total body weight, while in men the skeletal muscles average about 42 percent of the total weight. Since men are larger than women, on the average, the actual discrepancy is even greater.

Sex differences aside, the amount of muscle in the body is rather impressive. One usually tends to think of bones as being heavy, but actually the combined weight of your muscles is about three times as great as that of your bones—and more than that of any other type of tissue in your body. A 150-pound man is carrying 63 pounds of skeletal muscles around with him.

Parts and Attachments of a Skeletal Muscle

The skeletal muscle that most people think of first when the word "muscle" is mentioned is the biceps brachii—the bulging muscle of the upper arm that young men show off at the beach. If you successively contract and relax your biceps, feeling along the length of the muscle with the fingers of your other hand as you do so, you will notice that the biceps has three main parts: a bulging middle portion and two tapering ends, each of which is firmly anchored to a bone (Figure 10-8). In the case of the biceps, one end is attached to the scapula,* or shoulder bone, while the other end is attached to the radius, a bone of the forearm. When the biceps contracts, the scapula remains relatively unmoved, but the radius is pulled upward, toward the scapula.

Although there are many individual differences among the skeletal muscles, the biceps illustrates some general features of their structure. A skeletal muscle typically is made up of a middle portion, referred to as the **belly** or **body,** and two ends, each of which is attached to something. Belying their name, skeletal muscles need not necessarily be attached to bones: some are attached to other muscles, to condensations of connective tissue, to soft tissue, or to skin. But generally, each muscle has at least two attachments, and its contractions bring the body parts to which it is attached closer together.

Often, as in the biceps, one of the attachments is to a bone or other part that remains relatively immovable, while the part to which the other end of the muscle is attached is movable. In such a case, the attachment to an immovable part is called the **origin**

---

* The upper end of the biceps is actually divided into two tapering "heads," both of which are attached to the scapula.

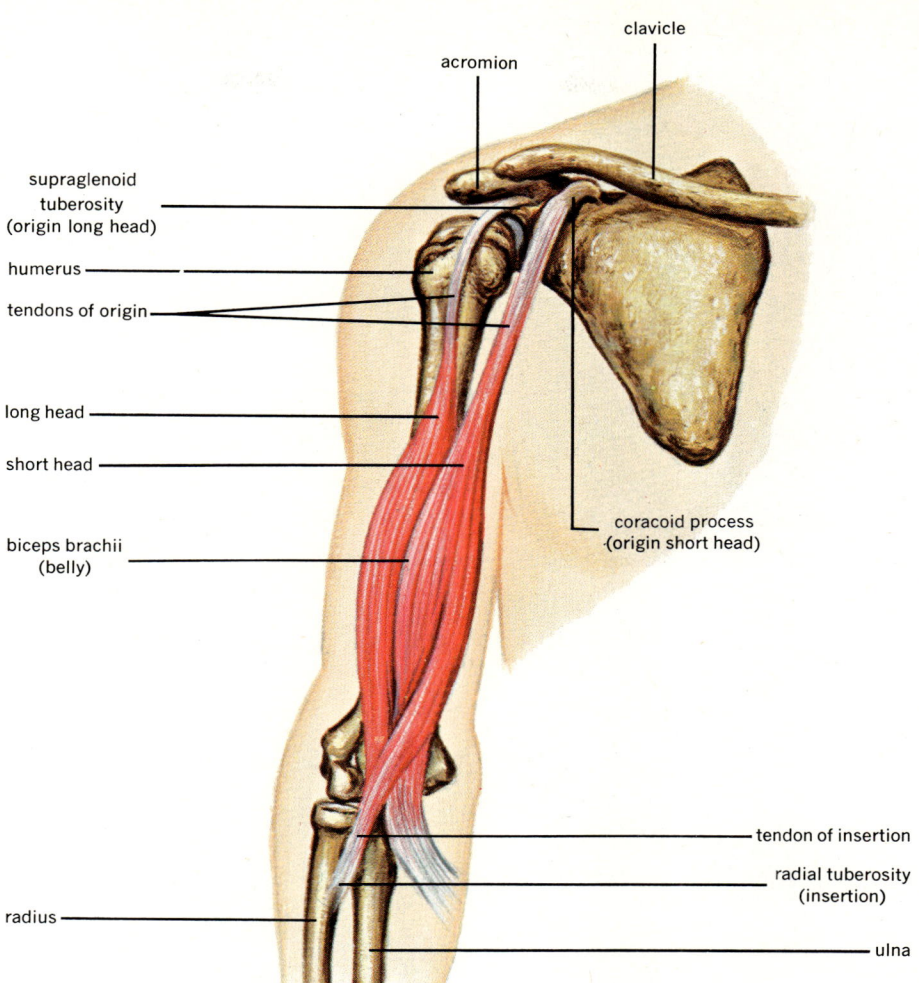

FIGURE 10-8 The biceps brachii muscle and its attachments.

clavicle

acromion

supraglenoid tuberosity (origin long head)

humerus

tendons of origin

long head

short head

biceps brachii (belly)

coracoid process (origin short head)

tendon of insertion

radial tuberosity (insertion)

radius

ulna

of the muscle, while the attachment to a movable part is called the **insertion.** In some cases, contraction of a muscle can produce movement of either or both of the parts to which it is attached—that is, the origin and insertion are interchangeable.

In general, muscles are not attached directly to bones or other body parts. Instead, the connective tissue sheaths of the bundles of muscle fibers are continuous with tendons or aponeuroses, strong cords or sheets of tough fibrous connective tissue, which bind the muscles firmly (Figure 10-9).

Some Basic Principles of Muscle Action

A book lies on the table in front of you. You can reach out your hand and either push the book away from you or pull it toward you. Both of these actions are accomplished through the work of muscles in your hand and arm. But *muscles themselves cannot push—they can only pull.* In its relaxed state, a muscle is extended; when it contracts, it shortens, and pulls on the bones to which it is attached, producing movement.

Since the muscles of the body can only pull on bones and not push them, it might seem at first thought that the numerous variations of movements of which the body parts are capable should be impossible. This would indeed be the case if each skeletal muscle worked alone. Instead, *skeletal muscles generally work in coordinated groups,* with certain muscles in the group contracting to various degrees while others relax. The muscle contracting to produce a particular movement is called the **prime mover.** Muscles in the group that work in concert with the prime mover and aid it in performing its action are called **synergists.** (Sometimes synergists stabilize an intermediate joint while the prime mover works on a distal part.) Muscles that act oppositely to the prime mover (i.e., relax while it is contracting or contract to produce an opposite effect) are called **antagonists.**

The biceps brachii muscle has an antagonist, the triceps brachii, which has its origins in the scapula and humerus and inserts in the ulna (Figure 10-10). When the biceps contracts, the triceps relaxes, and the forearm is pulled upward. When the triceps con-

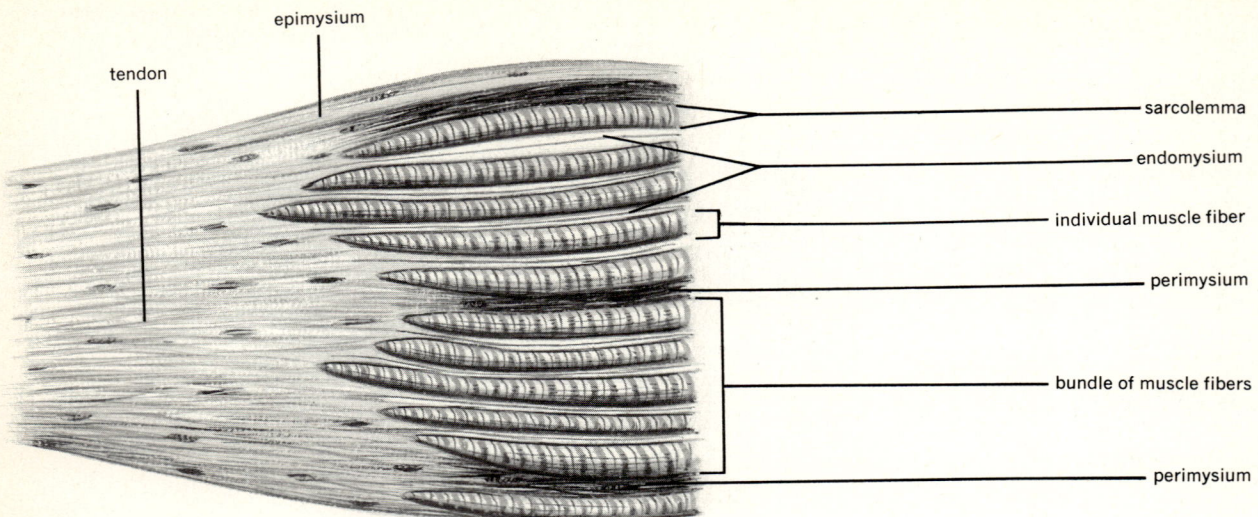

FIGURE 10-9 Longitudinal section of a muscle. Note that the sarcolemma, endomysium, perimysium, and epimysium are continuous with the connective tissue of the tendon.

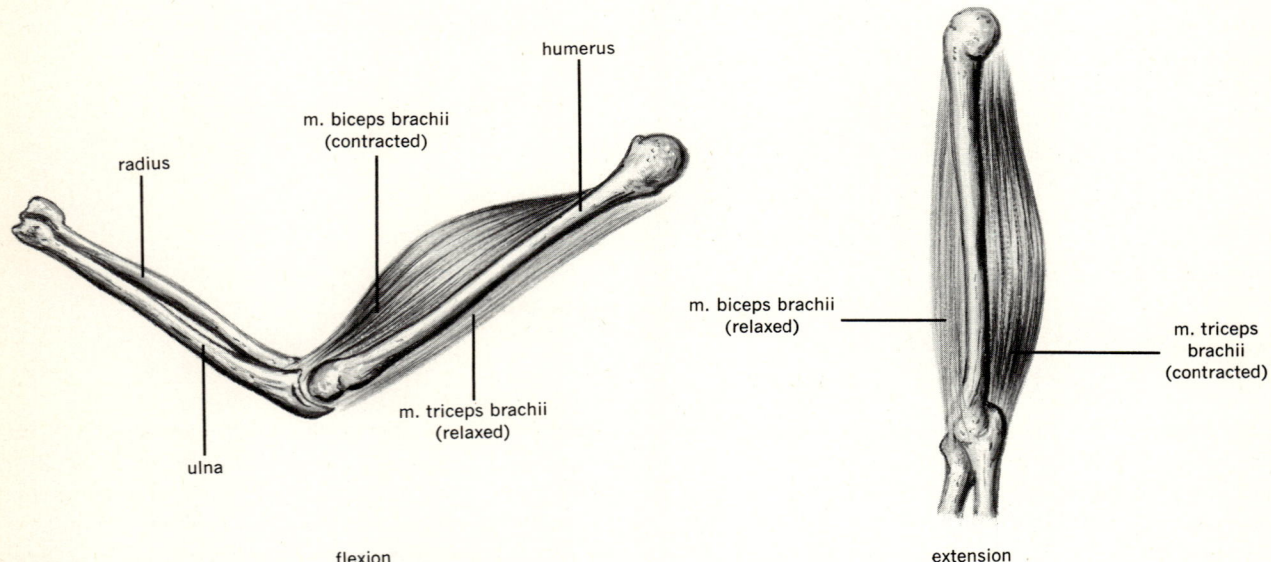

FIGURE 10-10 The biceps brachii and triceps brachii work as muscle antagonists in flexing and extending the arm.

tracts, the biceps relaxes, and the arm is straightened. (The biceps is thus a flexor muscle—producing flexion of the arm, while the triceps is an extensor muscle—producing extension of the arm.) Without the triceps working antagonistically to the biceps, you would not be able to voluntarily straighten out your arm, once you had flexed it.

A muscle's role may vary, depending on the movement being performed. For example, when you bend your arm, the biceps is the prime mover, while the triceps is an antagonist. Yet when you straighten your arm, the triceps is the prime mover and the biceps is an antagonist. If you were to do a handstand, various other muscles of the arms would work in concert with the triceps to stabilize the elbow joints in the extended position.

Names of the Skeletal Muscles

There are about 656 skeletal muscles in the human body, and each of them has a name. Moreover, as you may already have noticed from the tables and diagrams in this chapter, most of the names of the muscles are in Latin. These can be depressing thoughts for the beginning student of anatomy and physiology. Fortunately, there is some "rhyme and reason" to the naming of the skeletal muscles. Once you have learned the general principles on which muscle nomenclature is based, you will find them helpful not only in memorizing the names of some of the most important muscles, but also in using those names to suggest information about their structure and their place and role in the body.

Some muscles are named for their **location** in the body. For example, "brachii" pertains to the arm and is a part of the names of various arm muscles, including the biceps brachii and triceps brachii. The femoris muscle is found in the region of the femur, the tibialis near the tibia, and the intercostal muscles are located between the ribs.

Muscles may be named for their **points of attachment.** (The origin or origins are generally specified first, followed by the point(s) of insertion.) For example, the sternocleidomastoid muscle has origins on the sternum and clavicle ("cleido-") and inserts on the mastoid process of the temporal bone.

Another common basis of muscle nomenclature is their **shape, size,** and **structure.** The deltoid muscle is named for the Greek letter delta (Δ), which is shaped like a triangle, as is the muscle. The trapezius muscle has a four-sided, trapezoid shape. A number of muscles have names including the terms maximus (largest), minimus (smallest), longus (long), or brevis (short). Another structural feature that gives rise to muscle names is the **number of heads of origin.** Biceps, for example, literally means "two heads." (The biceps brachii has two separate origins on the scapula.) Triceps refers to a muscle with three heads, and quadriceps to four heads. The **direction of muscle fibers** provides another source of muscle names, for example: rectus (straight), transversus (crosswise), and obliquus (oblique).

Still another way of naming muscles is according to their **action** (Figure 10-11). A **flexor** is a muscle that produces the movement of flexion (bending at a joint). It is usually found in association with an antagonist, an **extensor,** which extends or straightens the limb at the same joint. An **abductor** moves a body part away from the midline, while an **adductor** moves it toward the midline. Some muscles are involved in **rotating** movements. **Supinator** muscles turn the palm of the hand upward, while **pronators** turn the palm to face the ground. In the region of the ankle, muscles of **dorsiflexion** turn the foot upward, while rotator muscles of **plantar flexion** turn the foot downward. **Levators** are muscles that raise a body part; **depressors** lower it. A **sphincter** is a ring-shaped muscle whose contractions narrow the opening of the ring.

The position and attachments of a muscle may be such that its contractions produce several different kinds of motion. A particular muscle, for example, may produce both flexion and abduction at a joint. If only a flexing movement is desired, the unwanted abduction component of the muscle's action can be cancelled out by a simultaneous contraction of one or more adductors in the same muscle group. Victims of paralysis of particular muscles are often able to regain virtually complete mobility of the affected joint by retraining the muscles that are still healthy, emphasizing certain combinations of contractions to compensate for the paralyzed muscle and promoting muscles that previously played only a secondary role to the status of prime movers.

GROUPS OF SKELETAL MUSCLES

Since the skeletal muscles work intimately with the bones, it is not surprising that they are classified in a similar manner: axial and appendicular. The axial muscles include those of the head, neck, and trunk. The appendicular group comprises the muscles of the upper and lower extremities. Figure 10-12 gives an overview of the muscles of the body.

AXIAL MUSCLES

MUSCLES OF THE HEAD AND NECK

A person can "say" a great deal without uttering a word. A nod is universally recognized as a "yes" (in our culture, at any rate), while a shake of the head means "no." A smile, a frown, a furrowed brow, a quizically raised eyebrow, a wink, a determined set of the jaw, the flaring nostrils of anger—these are subtler, sometimes unconsciously expressed signs, which still can be readily interpreted by an observer. With the great mobility of the facial features, it is not surprising that there are literally dozens of muscles concentrated in this small region of the human body (Figure 10-13). As with the bones of the skeleton, a large proportion of the muscles of the head and neck (and those of the rest of the body as well) occur in pairs, in corresponding positions on each side of the midline. In general, the muscles of the head are very thin and are attached to the skin (**cutaneous muscles**).

Muscles of the Scalp

The helmet of the cranium is entirely encased in tough, musculomembranous layer, which in turn is covered by the skin of the scalp. The bulk of the muscular portion of the covering of the top of the head is usually regarded as a single muscle, the **occipitofrontalis.** As its name implies, it extends from the occipital region of the back of the head to the front of the head, at the supraorbital ridge (just over the eyebrows). It has two separate bellies, the frontal and occipital, which are connected by an aponeurosis called the **galea aponeurotica.** When you raise your eyebrows slightly to indicate surprise, or more drastically to register horror, you are employing contractions of the frontal portion of the occipitofrontalis muscle. (Some people are able to contract the muscle to a greater degree on one side than on the other, thus raising a single brow in an ironic expression.) Years of expressing your emotional reactions in this way will gradually etch horizontal wrinkles across the skin of your forehead.

On the sides of the head, the **temporoparietalis** muscles help to tighten the scalp. Three small rudimentary muscles above each ear, the **superior, anterior,** and **posterior auricular** muscles, are all that remains in humans of the stronger muscles that permit most mammals to raise and turn their external ears, maximizing their efficiency as sound funnels. In many people, these auricular muscles are nonfunctional; some are able to control them to some degree to wiggle their ears.

Muscles of the Face

An automobile accident or a stroke may result in paralysis of some of the facial muscles (perhaps on only one side). The unfortunate victim must then cope with a difficult situation. More than we realize, we tend to respond to the people around us according to visual cues we pick up from the expressions on their faces. People who meet the paralysis victim, seeing the stiff or sagging features, may have an initial, involuntary feeling of aversion, which is only conquered later as they have an opportunity to get to know the personality within.

As you go through the material in this and the following sections, it might be helpful to have a small mirror handy. Try out the various facial expressions mentioned, such as those pictured in Figure 10-14, observe the results, and try to palpate (feel) the muscles involved wherever possible.

Muscles Around the Eyes

Each eye is surrounded by a flat, elliptical muscle forming a sphincter, the **orbicularis oculi.** This muscle consists of three parts. The **palpebral** portion closes the eyelids gently, as in sleeping or blinking. The **orbital** portion draws in the skin from surrounding areas (the brows and cheeks) and helps to protect the eye in case of emer-

gency. The **lacrimal** portion compresses the lacrimal sac, holding back the flow of tears. In strong contractions (including winking), the entire orbicularis oculi muscle is involved. Its action draws the skin at the lateral corners of the eye inward and eventually produces the wrinkles called "crow's feet."

An antagonist of the orbicularis oculi muscle is the **levator palpebrae superioris,** which raises the upper eyelids. The **corrugator** muscle, found at the medial end of the superciliary arch, draws the eyebrow downward and in a medial direction; the action of the corrugator muscles produces vertical furrows in the skin between the eyes.

Muscles Around the Nose

Anyone who has ever observed a rabbit at close quarters has noticed the animal's continual sniffing movements, wrinkling its nose rapidly as it explores its environment. Humans depend far less on their sense of smell than most animals do, but we still retain some control over the movements of the nose. Four small muscles are found in the region of the nose. The **procerus** is a muscle at the bridge of the nose, which works together with the corrugator muscles to produce transverse wrinkles in the skin between the eyebrows. A fierce scowl involves this muscle. The **nasalis** lies alongside the nose and constricts the nostril by drawing its lateral margin toward the nasal septum. While this is occurring, another muscle called the **depressor septi** depresses the septum. The antagonist of the nasalis is the **dilator nares,** adjacent to the nostril; its action is to dilate the nostril. (The flaring of the nostrils in anger may be part of the body's "fight or flight" preparations, increasing the access of air to the respiratory tract.)

If you place your fingers lightly on the sides of your upper lip and sniff like a rabbit, you will realize that another pair of muscles is involved in movements of the nose. These are two straps of muscle, running down from the sides of the bridge of the nose past the nostrils to the upper lip. Their name is the **levator labii superioris alaeque nasi,** which might seem

TABLE 10-2 **Muscles of the scalp**

MUSCLE	ORIGIN	INSERTION	ACTION
Occipitofrontalis	Occipitalis: occipital bone	Occipitalis: galea aponeurotica	Draws scalp backward
	Frontalis: galea aponeurotica	Frontalis: skin of eyebrows and root of nose	Raises eyebrows and wrinkles skin of forehead ("surprise")
Temporoparietalis	Temporal fascia above ear	Galea aponeurotica	Tightens scalp
Auricularis anterior	Superficial temporal fascia	Cartilage of ear	Draws pinna forward
Auricularis posterior	Mastoid process	Cartilage of ear	Draws pinna backward
Auricularis superior	Galea aponeurotica	Cartilage of ear	Raises pinna

A

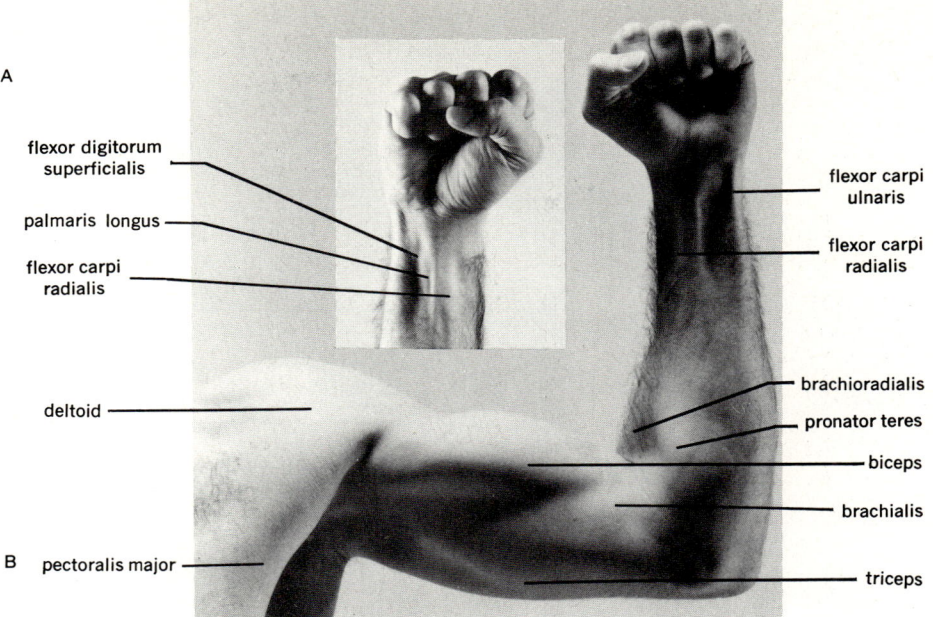

flexor digitorum superficialis

palmaris longus

flexor carpi radialis

deltoid

flexor carpi ulnaris

flexor carpi radialis

brachioradialis

pronator teres

biceps

brachialis

B

pectoralis major

triceps

C

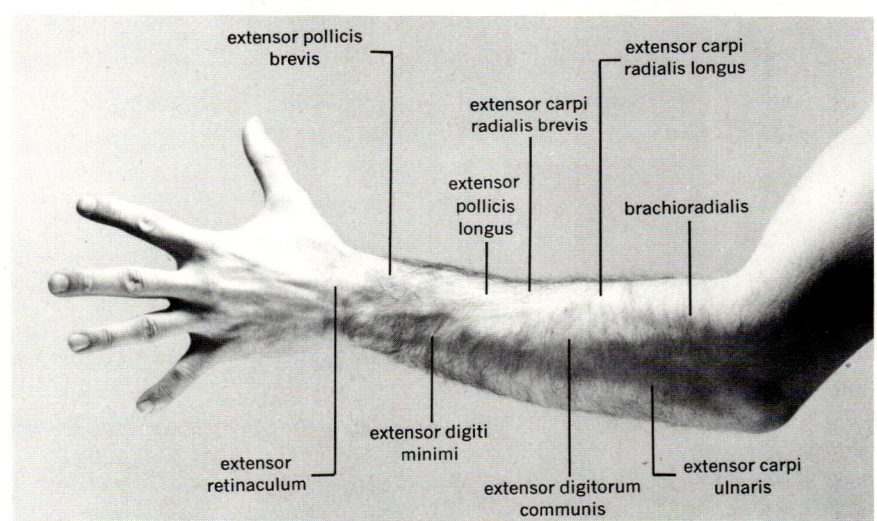

extensor pollicis brevis

extensor carpi radialis brevis

extensor carpi radialis longus

extensor pollicis longus

brachioradialis

extensor digiti minimi

extensor retinaculum

extensor digitorum communis

extensor carpi ulnaris

D

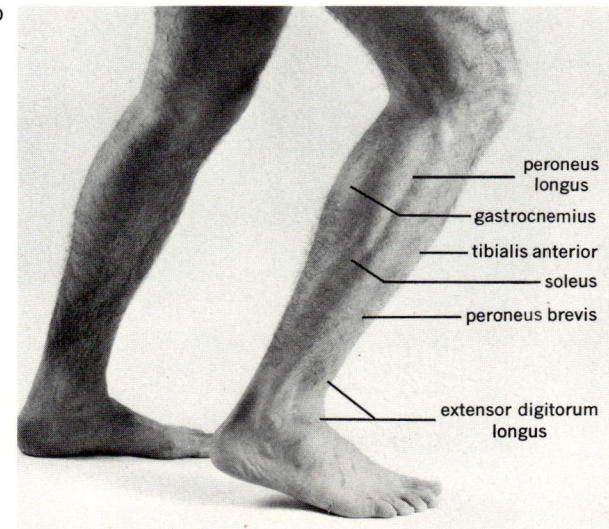

peroneus longus

gastrocnemius

tibialis anterior

soleus

peroneus brevis

extensor digitorum longus

FIGURE 10-11   Muscles move body parts. Shown here are some flexors and extensors of the forearm and arm (A,B,C) and leg (D) in action.

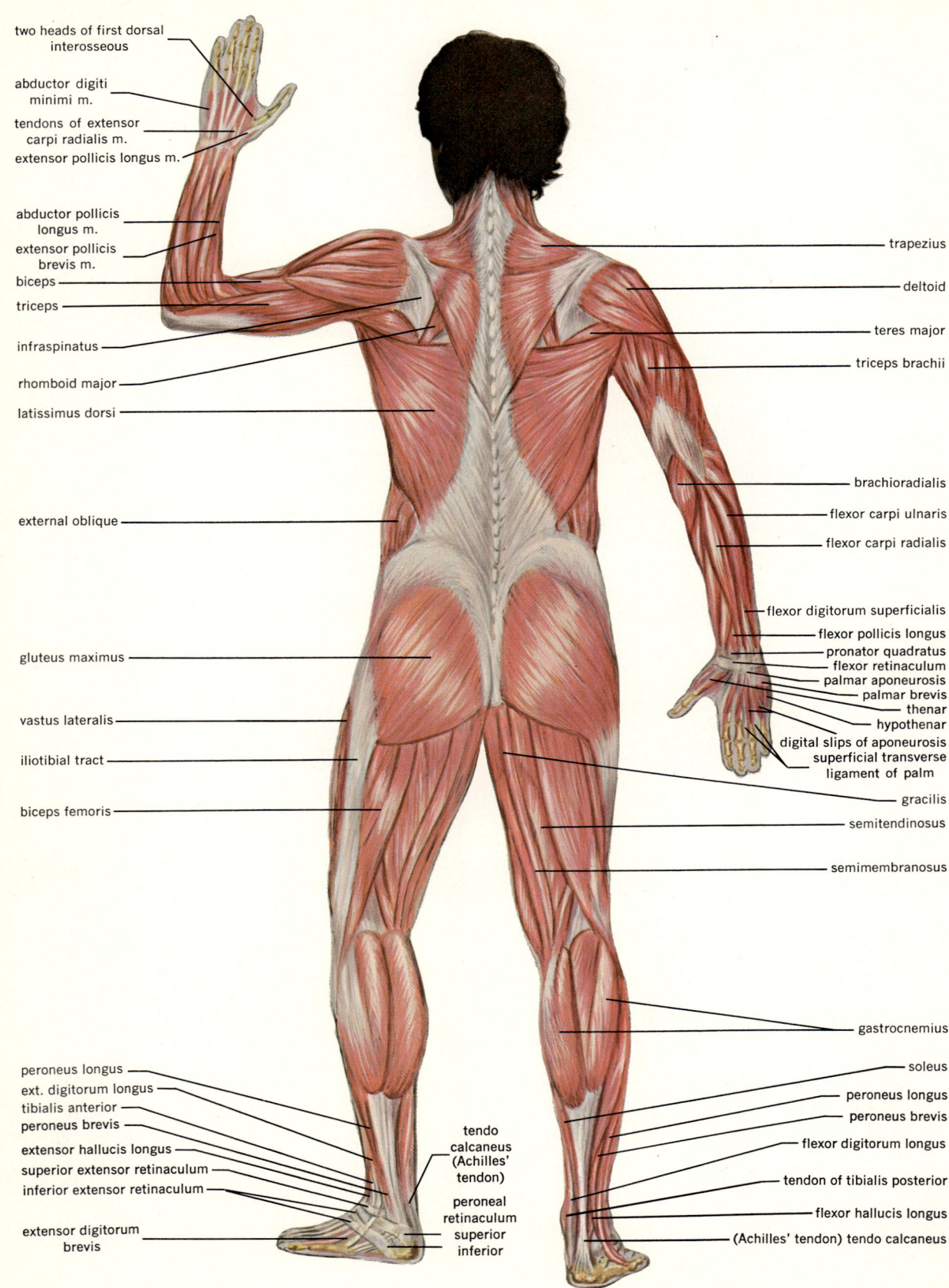

two heads of first dorsal interosseous

abductor digiti minimi m.

tendons of extensor carpi radialis m.

extensor pollicis longus m.

abductor pollicis longus m.

extensor pollicis brevis m.

biceps

triceps

infraspinatus

rhomboid major

latissimus dorsi

external oblique

gluteus maximus

vastus lateralis

iliotibial tract

biceps femoris

peroneus longus

ext. digitorum longus

tibialis anterior

peroneus brevis

extensor hallucis longus

superior extensor retinaculum

inferior extensor retinaculum

extensor digitorum brevis

tendo calcaneus (Achilles' tendon)

peroneal retinaculum
superior
inferior

trapezius

deltoid

teres major

triceps brachii

brachioradialis

flexor carpi ulnaris

flexor carpi radialis

flexor digitorum superficialis

flexor pollicis longus

pronator quadratus

flexor retinaculum

palmar aponeurosis

palmar brevis

thenar

hypothenar

digital slips of aponeurosis

superficial transverse ligament of palm

gracilis

semitendinosus

semimembranosus

gastrocnemius

soleus

peroneus longus

peroneus brevis

flexor digitorum longus

tendon of tibialis posterior

flexor hallucis longus

(Achilles' tendon) tendo calcaneus

A

FIGURE 10-12   Human skeletal musculature: anterior (A) and posterior (B) views.

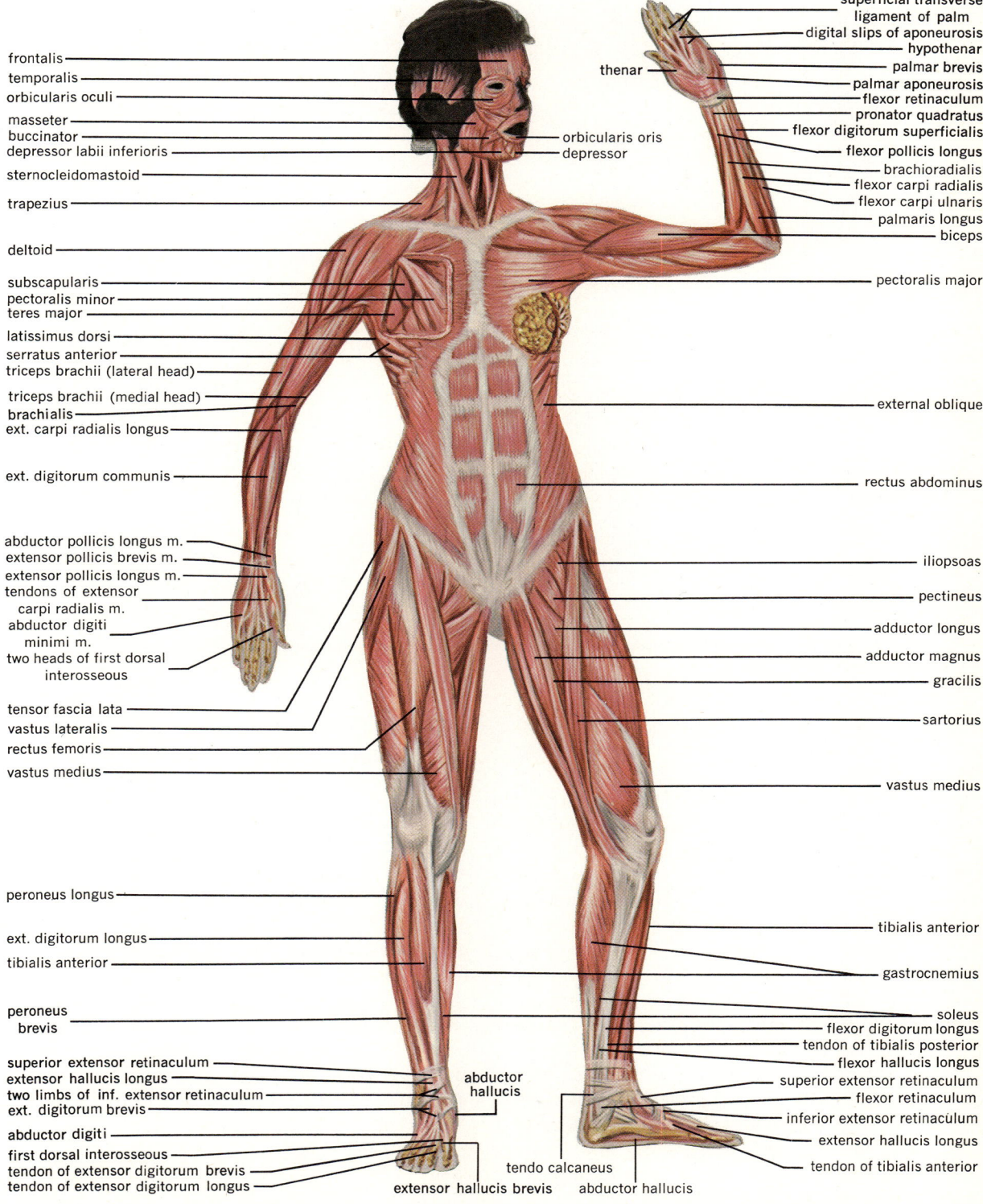

frontalis

temporalis

orbicularis oculi

masseter

buccinator

depressor labii inferioris

sternocleidomastoid

trapezius

deltoid

subscapularis

pectoralis minor

teres major

latissimus dorsi

serratus anterior

triceps brachii (lateral head)

triceps brachii (medial head)

brachialis

ext. carpi radialis longus

ext. digitorum communis

abductor pollicis longus m.

extensor pollicis brevis m.

extensor pollicis longus m.

tendons of extensor
carpi radialis m.

abductor digiti
minimi m.

two heads of first dorsal
interosseous

tensor fascia lata

vastus lateralis

rectus femoris

vastus medius

peroneus longus

ext. digitorum longus

tibialis anterior

peroneus
brevis

superior extensor retinaculum

extensor hallucis longus

two limbs of inf. extensor retinaculum

ext. digitorum brevis

abductor digiti

first dorsal interosseous

tendon of extensor digitorum brevis

tendon of extensor digitorum longus

orbicularis oris

depressor

thenar

superficial transverse
ligament of palm

digital slips of aponeurosis

hypothenar

palmar brevis

palmar aponeurosis

flexor retinaculum

pronator quadratus

flexor digitorum superficialis

flexor pollicis longus

brachioradialis

flexor carpi radialis

flexor carpi ulnaris

palmaris longus

biceps

pectoralis major

external oblique

rectus abdominus

iliopsoas

pectineus

adductor longus

adductor magnus

gracilis

sartorius

vastus medius

tibialis anterior

gastrocnemius

soleus

flexor digitorum longus

tendon of tibialis posterior

flexor hallucis longus

superior extensor retinaculum

flexor retinaculum

inferior extensor retinaculum

extensor hallucis longus

tendon of tibialis anterior

abductor
hallucis

tendo calcaneus

extensor hallucis brevis

abductor hallucis

B

A

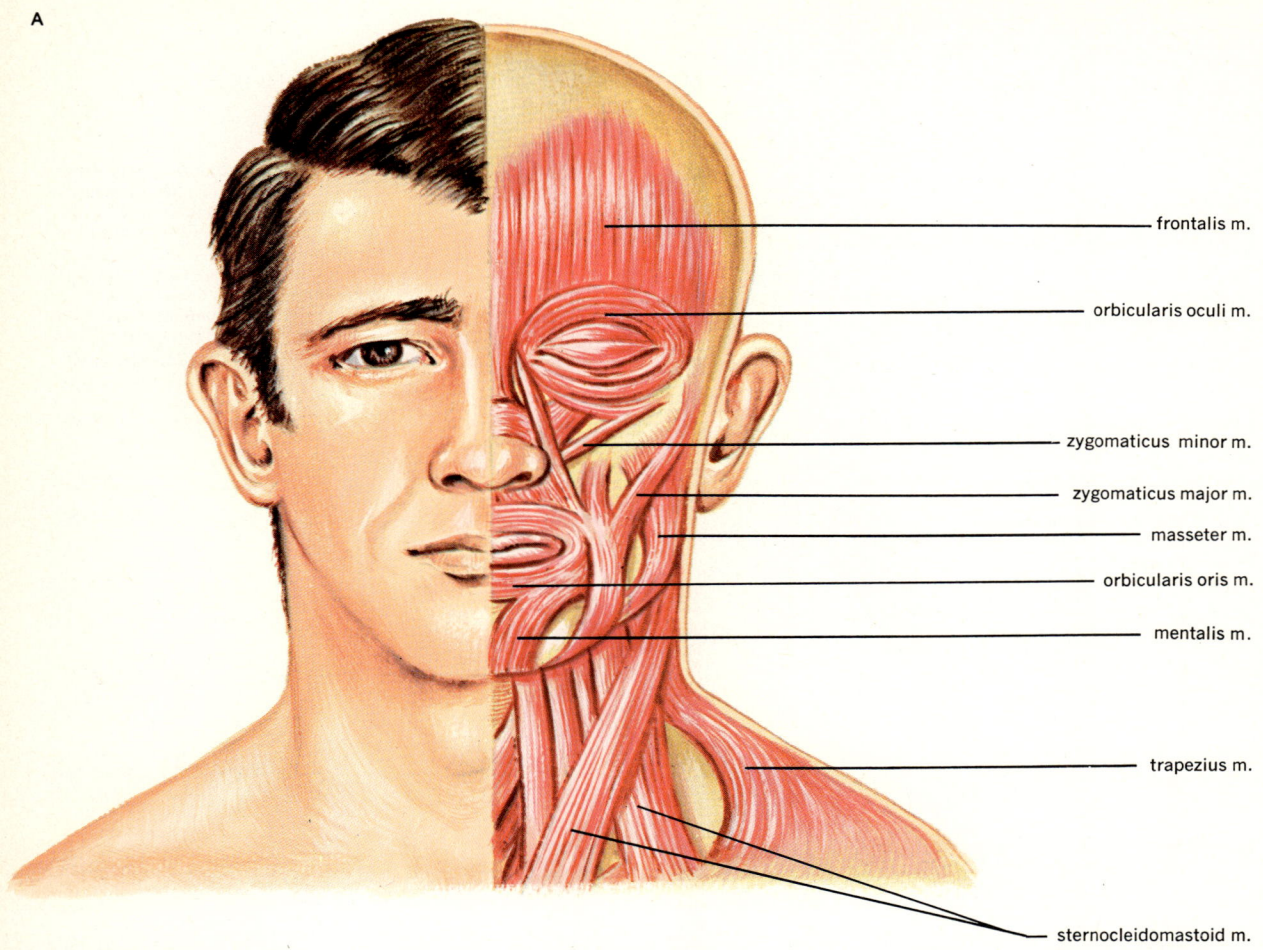

frontalis m.

orbicularis oculi m.

zygomaticus minor m.

zygomaticus major m.

masseter m.

orbicularis oris m.

mentalis m.

trapezius m.

sternocleidomastoid m.

FIGURE 10-13   Muscles of the face and neck. (A) Superficial layer of muscles of the face; (B) deep layer of facial muscles; (C) superficial muscles of the neck and muscles around the mouth.

daunting until you break it down into its parts and realize that it simply means "raiser of the upper lip and wing of the nose."

Muscles Around the Mouth   A baby's first smile is a thrill for its parents. But even before the baby has begun to smile in response to people, it has been working on little practice smiles, frowns, and lip quirkings, gaining control of the numerous muscles that help to make the region of the mouth the most mobile and expressive area of the face.

The most prominent muscle in the region of the mouth is the **orbicularis oris,** a thick sphincter muscle that makes up the bulk of the lips. It is used in protruding the lips (a kiss has been described as "the anatomical juxtaposition of two orbicularis oris muscles in a state of contraction") and also in compressing the lips over the teeth. The upper and lower halves of the orbicularis oris can be contracted separately, causing one of the lips to protrude over the other. The fibers of the orbicularis oris muscle inter-

digitate with various muscles attached to the lips.

The principle muscle support for the cheeks is provided by the **buccinator** ("trumpeter") muscles. The buccinator pulls the cheek inward when it contracts and is the main muscle involved both in sucking and in whistling and blowing a wind instrument such as a trumpet (from which it gets its name). The buccinator also aids in mastication (chewing).

The facial muscles most involved in smiling are the **zygomaticus major** and **zygomaticus minor** muscles. The greater zygomatic muscle pulls the corner of the mouth upward and backward, while the lesser zygomatic muscle draws the upper lip upward and outward. The **risorius** retracts the angle of the mouth during grinning and also in an expression of tenseness or strain. The **levator anguli oris** raises the corner of the mouth, while the **depressor anguli oris** draws the corner of the mouth downward to give a sad expression.

The **levator labii superioris** contracts to raise the upper lip. (This is not the same muscle as the levator

B

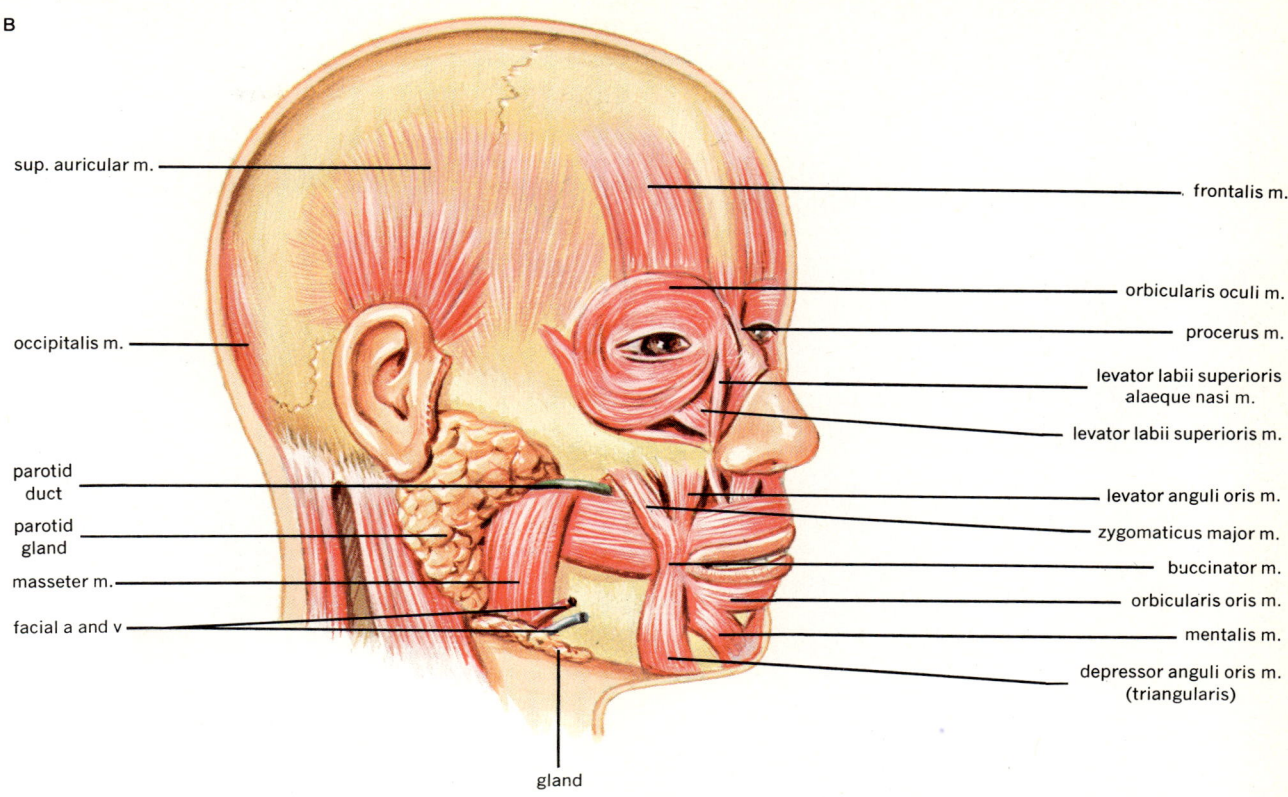

sup. auricular m.

occipitalis m.

parotid duct

parotid gland

masseter m.

facial a and v

gland

frontalis m.

orbicularis oculi m.

procerus m.

levator labii superioris alaeque nasi m.

levator labii superioris m.

levator anguli oris m.

zygomaticus major m.

buccinator m.

orbicularis oris m.

mentalis m.

depressor anguli oris m. (triangularis)

C

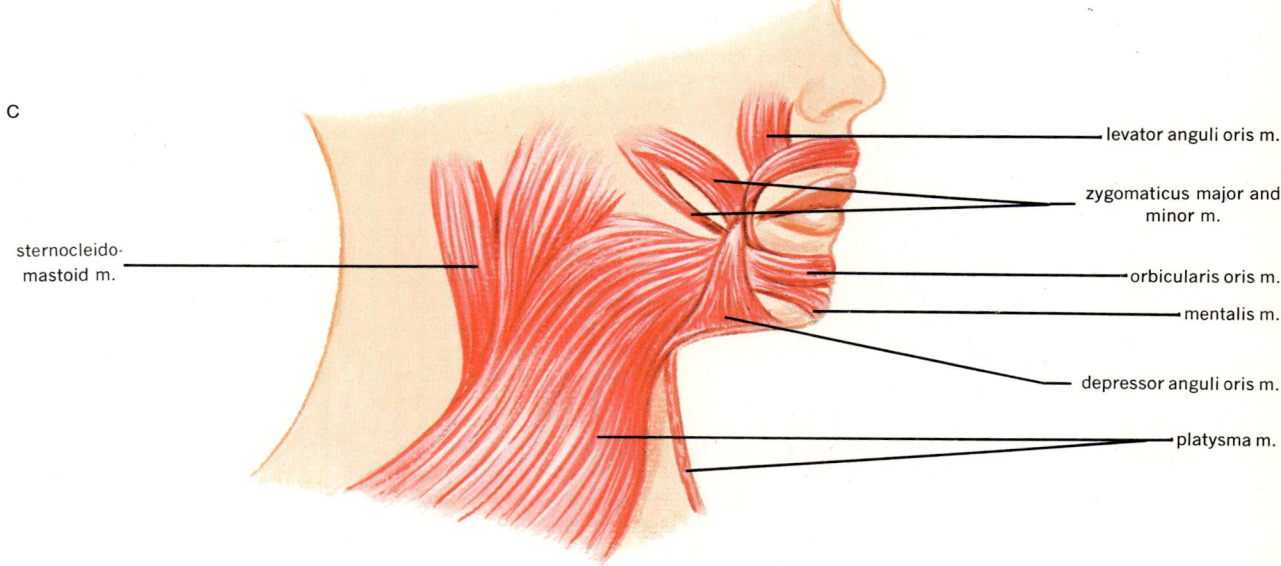

sternocleido-mastoid m.

levator anguli oris m.

zygomaticus major and minor m.

orbicularis oris m.

mentalis m.

depressor anguli oris m.

platysma m.

labii superioris alaeque nasi, already discussed, which raises the upper lip and also dilates the nostrils.) The lower lip is drawn downward and everted by the **depressor labii inferioris.**

The front part of the chin is covered by a small, rather thick muscle called the **mentalis.** When it contracts, it protrudes the lower lip and wrinkles the skin of the chin. If the mentalis muscles of both sides are very well developed, a depression appears between them—a dimple.

 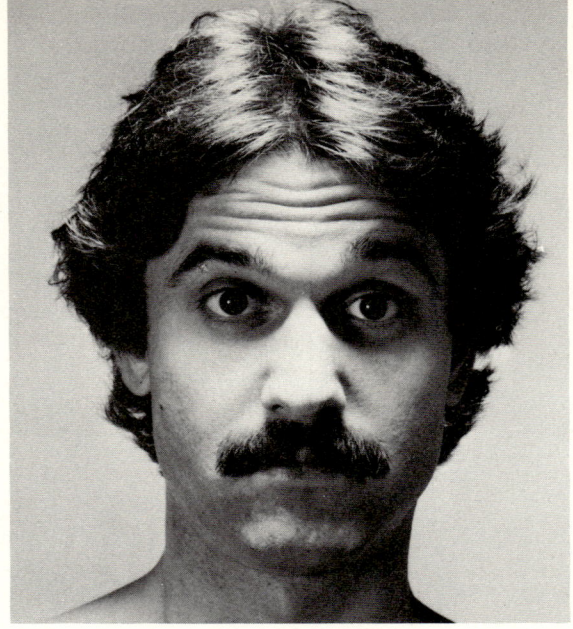

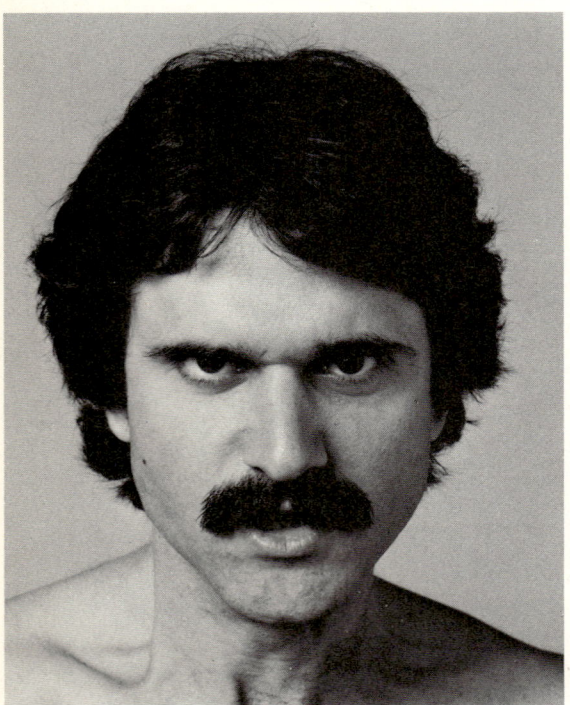 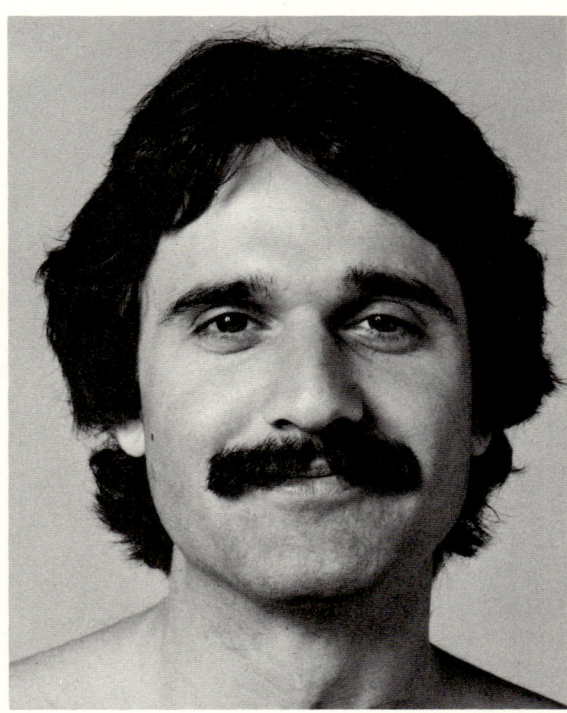

FIGURE 10-14 The facial muscles permit a great variety of expressions that convey moods and emotions.

Muscles of the Eye

One of the most continual movements of the body, of which we are usually quite aware, is that of the eyes. Your lids blink once every two to ten seconds (though if you are not consciously thinking about the matter, you have the general impression that they rarely ever blink at all),* and your eyeballs are in a constant restless vibration, jerking about from one position to another. The actual movements are so small as to be

* It has been observed that the eyes remain shut an average of 0.15 seconds during each blink, so that you actually have your eyes closed for a total of half an hour during each waking day.

TABLE 10-3 Muscles of the face

MUSCLE	ORIGIN	INSERTION	ACTION
Orbicularis oculi (palpebral, orbital, and lacrimal parts)	Medial palpebral ligament, frontal, maxillary, and zygomatic bones	Skin around eye and lids	Closes eyelids, compresses lacrimal sacs
Levator palpebrae superioris	Upper border of optic foramen	Connective tissue framework of upper eyelid	Raises upper eyelids
Corrugator supercilii	Medial end of superciliary arch	Skin of eyebrow	Draws eyebrow downward and medially
Procerus	Skin over nose	Skin of forehead	Draws down eyebrows
Nasalis	Maxilla	Side of nose and corresponding muscle of opposite side	Draws margin of nostril toward septum
Depressor septi	Maxilla	Septum and side of nose	Draws septum downward and contracts nostrils
Dilator nares	Maxilla	Margin of nostril	Dilates nostrils
Levator labii superioris alaeque nasi	Lower orbital margin	Cartilage of side of nose and upper lip	Raises upper lip and dilates nostril
Orbicularis oris	Muscles adjacent to mouth	Skin and fascia at corners of mouth and around lips and mouth	Closes and purses lips
Buccinator	Maxilla and mandible	Orbicularis oris at corner of mouth	Compresses cheek and retracts corner of mouth; accessory muscle of mastication
Zygomaticus major	Zygomatic bone	Corner of mouth	Draws corner of mouth backward and upward
Zygomaticus minor	Zygomatic bone	Orbicularis oris and levator labii superioris	Draws upper lip upward and outward
Risorius	Fascia over masseter muscle	Skin at corner of mouth	Draws corner of mouth laterally
Levator anguli oris	Maxilla at canine fossa	Orbicularis oris and skin at corner of mouth	Raises corner of mouth
Depressor anguli oris	Lower margin of mandible	Corner of mouth	Pulls down corner of mouth
Levator labii superioris	Lower orbital margin	Orbicularis oris in upper lip	Raises upper lip
Depressor labii inferioris	Mandible adjacent to mental foramen	Orbicularis oris and skin of lower lip	Draws lower lip downward
Mentalis	Incisor fossa of mandible	Skin of chin	Wrinkles skin of chin, raises and protrudes lower lip

TABLE 10-4 Muscles of the eyes

MUSCLE	ORIGIN	INSERTION	ACTION
Superior rectus	Upper border of optic foramen	Upper and central portion of eyeball	Adduction; rotates eyeball upward and medially
Inferior rectus	Circumference of optic foramen	Underside of eyeball	Adduction; rotates eyeball downward and medially
Medial rectus	Circumference of optic foramen	Medial side of eyeball	Adduction of eyeball
Lateral rectus	Lateral border of optic foramen	Lateral side of eyeball	Abduction of eyeball

TABLE 10-4 (Continued)

MUSCLE	ORIGIN	INSERTION	ACTION
Superior oblique	Lesser wing of sphenoid above optic foramen	Tendon passes through fibrous pulley, reverses direction, and inserts between superior and lateral recti of eyeball	Rotates eyeball downward and laterally
Inferior oblique	Orbital plate of maxilla	Between superior and lateral recti of eyeball	Rotates eyeball upward and laterally

barely noticeable by a close observer—only a few seconds of arc at a time. But they have a great functional importance for the eye, since the constant movement imposes a constantly changing pattern of light on the retina. If it were possible to clamp your eyeballs rigidly in place, you probably would quickly cease to see anything at all, for the continuing influx of identical signals would cause the sensory cells of the retina to fatigue.

The muscles that raise and lower the eyelids have already been discussed. In addition to those, there are six pairs of muscles that are attached to the eyeballs and move them within their bony sockets. These are the **extrinsic muscles** of the eyes (Figure 10-15). (The **intrinsic muscles** of the eyes, which modify the shape of the lens during focusing and regulate the amount of light entering the eye are smooth muscles, not skeletal muscles. Their structure and function are discussed in Chapter 17.)

Movements of the eyeballs are usually described in relation to a primary position in which the eyes are looking straight ahead. Each eyeball can be considered to move around three axes: anteroposterior (rotational movements), vertical (abduction, adduction), and transverse (elevation, depression). When the eyes are functioning properly, the two eyeballs move in coordination—for example, if one is abducted, the other is adducted, so that stereoscopic vision is maintained.

Of the six pairs of extrinsic muscles of the eyes, four are straight muscles ("rectus") and are named according to their position relative to the eyeball and the action they produce: **medial, lateral, superior,** and **inferior rectus** muscles. The remaining two, the **superior** and **inferior oblique** muscles have a slanting (oblique) arrangement. An interesting feature of the superior oblique muscle is the passage of its tendon through a small fascial pulley, the trochlea, forming an open loop between origin and insertion (see Figure 10-15).

The medial and lateral rectus muscles have a straight pull on the eyeball and produce pure adduction and abduction. The other eye muscles produce a mixed effect. Generally the extrinsic muscles of the eye act in synergistic combinations:

Adduction: medial, superior, and inferior recti
Abduction: lateral rectus, inferior and superior obliques
Elevation: superior rectus and inferior oblique
Depression: inferior rectus and superior oblique
Medial rotation: superior rectus and superior oblique
Lateral rotation: inferior rectus and inferior oblique

High wire and trapeze acts in circuses often include an especially thrilling feat: a performer grips a small bar attachment in his or her teeth and then dangles from it, suspending the entire weight of the body from this precarious grasp. Such performances dramatize

TABLE 10-5 Muscles of mastication

MUSCLE	ORIGIN	INSERTION	ACTION
Masseter	Zygomatic arch	Ramus of mandible	Raises and protracts mandible, closes jaws
Temporalis	Temporal fossa of skull and temporal fascia	Coronoid process of mandible	Raises and retracts mandible, closes mouth
Lateral pterygoid	Two heads: greater wing of sphenoid and lateral pterygoid plate	Condyle of mandible	Protrudes mandible, opens jaws, and moves mandible from side to side
Medial pterygoid	Lateral pterygoid plate and maxillary tuberosity	Ramus and angle of mandible	Closes jaws, raises and protrudes mandible

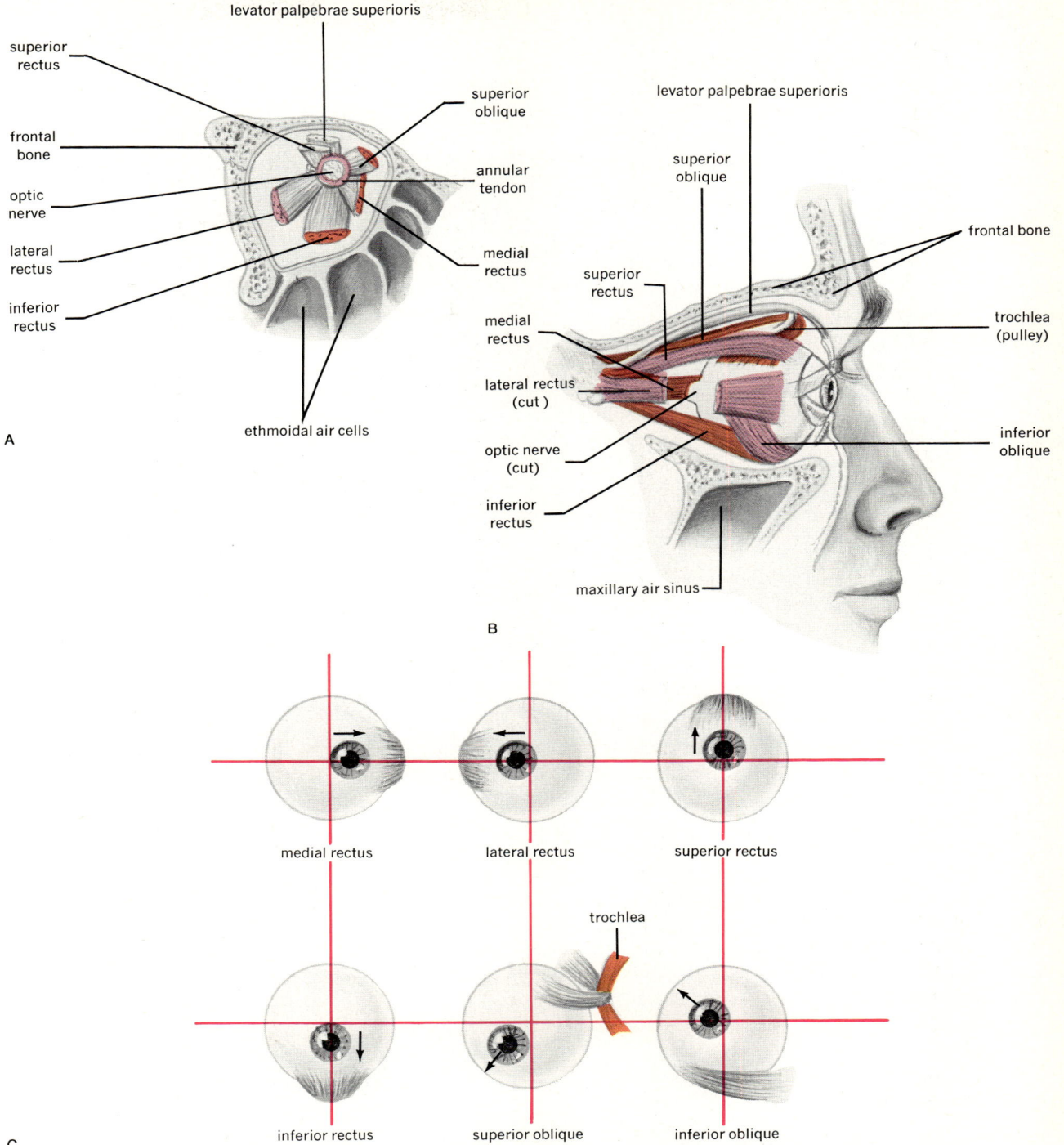

FIGURE 10-15 **Extrinsic muscles of the eyes. (A) Origin of the muscles in cross section. (B) Lateral view. (C) Action of the extrinsic eye muscles. (The direction of movement of the eyeball is indicated by the arrows.)**

the great strength of the muscles that move the lower jaw; in a healthy young adult, the jaw muscles can exert a force of 200 pounds. In normal activities, the jaw muscles are called on for much more modest tasks: they are used in speaking, in chewing food during eating, and in yawning. (A particularly wide yawn may occasionally get the better of the jaw muscles,

permitting the condyle of the mandible to slip out of the mandibular fossa of the skull and thus dislocating the jaw.)

It should be recognized that when you open your mouth the upper jaw remains stationary; the mandible is the moving part. Speaking and mastication (chewing) involve three main types of movement of the lower jaw: elevation, depression, and side-to-side or grinding movements. One pair of muscles involved in chewing movements, the buccinator, has already been discussed.

The principal elevators of the mandible, which act to close the jaw in a biting movement and clench the teeth, are two strong pairs of muscles, the **masseter** and the **temporalis** (Figure 10-16). The masseter is one of the few muscles of the face that can be easily palpated. To do so, clench your teeth tightly and feel for a lump above the angle of the jaw. You will probably also be able to feel the fan-shaped temporalis contracting in the region of the temple.

The other two major muscles of mastication are the **medial** and **lateral pterygoids.** (These are also paired, one on each side of the face.) The medial pterygoid closes the jaws and protrudes the mandible. Side-to-side grinding movements of the jaws are produced when the lateral pterygoid muscles of the two sides of the face act alternately; when they both contract simultaneously, they open and protrude the mandible.

Normally the mouth is kept closed; when the muscles of mastication are relaxed, the mandible tends to drop somewhat as a result of the pull of gravity.

Muscles of the Tongue and Palate

The tongue is one of the most flexible and dexterous structures in the body. During chewing and swallowing, the tongue deftly manipulates the food, guiding it under the teeth, rolling it into a neat ball, and then shoving it down the throat. In speech the tongue plays a pivotal role in forming sounds—so much so that at various times through human history, removal of the tongue has been used as a brutal but effective way of eliminating the victim's ability to pass on secret information. It if seems hard to believe that removal of the tongue renders intelligible speech virtually impossible, hold your own tongue down with a finger and try to say something.

The tremendous versatility of the tongue is provided for by two groups of paired muscles: **intrinsic muscles,** which lie entirely within the tongue, and **extrinsic muscles,** which have their origin outside the tongue and insert into it (Figure 10-17).

The intrinsic muscles of the tongue consist of **vertical, horizontal,** and **longitudinal** bundles, which interdigitate with the extrinsic muscles. Their contractions produce changes in the shape of the tongue.

The extrinsic muscles of the tongue include the **genioglossus,** the **styloglossus,** and the **hyoglossus.**

The genioglossus is a fan-shaped muscle, which arises from the mandible, behind the point of the chin, and spreads out to insert along the entire length of the undersurface of the tongue. The two genioglossus muscles can contract together along their whole length, drawing the tongue downward and producing a concave channel in the upper surface of the tongue, along which fluids can readily pass toward the pharynx. (When you suck a soda up through a straw, the genioglossus is contracting in this manner.) Or in-

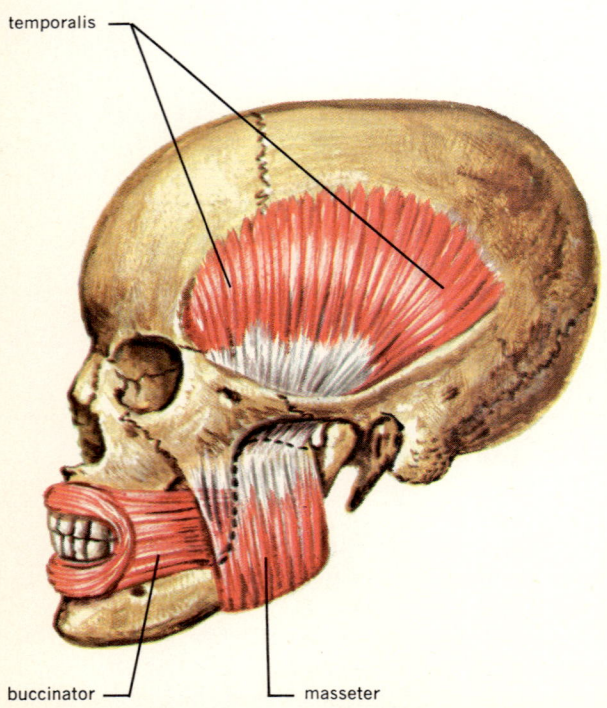
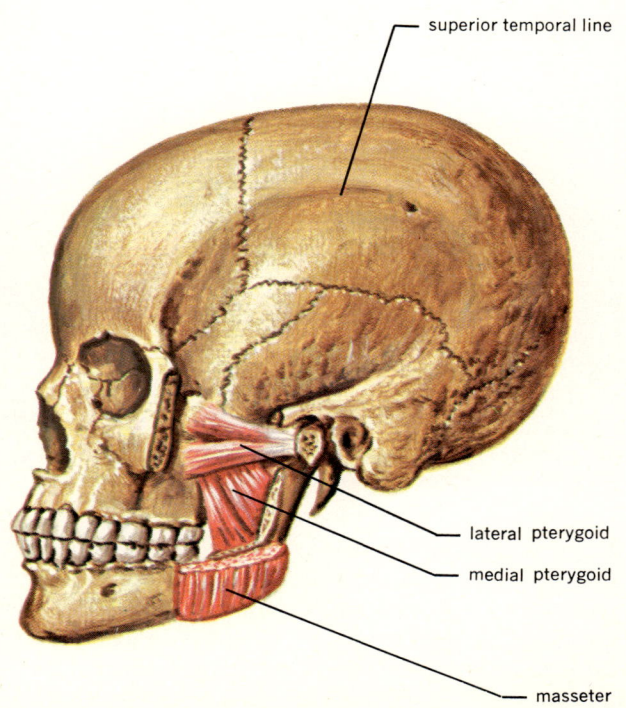

FIGURE 10-16 The muscles of mastication: superficial (A) and deep (B).

TABLE 10-6 Muscles of the tongue and palate

MUSCLE	ORIGIN	INSERTION	ACTION
Intrinsic: vertical, horizontal, longitudinal	Various parts of tongue	Various parts of tongue	Change shape of tongue during chewing and swallowing
Genioglossus	Mental spine of mandible	Undersurface of tongue; also hyoid bone	Protrudes, retracts, and depresses tongue; raises hyoid
Styloglossus	Styloid process of temporal bone	Sides and undersurface of tongue	Elevates and retracts tongue
Hyoglossus	Hyoid bone	Sides of tongue	Depresses and retracts tongue and draws its sides down
Stylohyoid	Styloid process of temporal bone	Hyoid bone	Draws hyoid and tongue upward
Mylohyoid	Mandible	Hyoid	Elevates hyoid, supports floor of mouth
Geniohyoid	Mental spine of mandible	Hyoid	Elevates and draws hyoid forward
Levator veli palatini	Temporal bone and cartilaginous auditory tube	Soft palate	Elevates palate
Tensor veli palatini	Scaphoid fossa of sphenoid and wall of auditory tube	Soft palate	Tenses palate, opens auditory tube
Uvulae	Palatine bone and palatine aponeurosis	Uvula	Raises uvula
Palatoglossus	Soft palate	Sides of tongue	Elevates tongue and constricts passageway
Palatopharyngeus	Soft palate	Thyroid cartilage and wall of pharynx	Elevates pharynx, depresses soft palate, helps close nasopharynx

stead, only part of the muscle fibers may contract. The anterior fibers of the genioglossus draw the tongue into the mouth and depress its tip; the middle fibers draw the base of the tongue forward, depress the middle part of the tongue, and protrude the tongue from the mouth. The inferior fibers of the genioglossus are connected by a thin aponeurosis to the hyoid bone, and their contractions act to raise this bone.

The styloglossus muscles, with insertions in the sides and under part of the tongue, act to retract the tongue and raise its margins. Persons who inherit an ability to "roll" the tongue (such as the one shown in Figure 10-18), apparently have a greater measure of control over the styloglossus muscles than those who cannot perform this trick.

The hyoglossus muscles, attaching the sides of the tongue to the hyoid bone, depress the tongue, retract it, and draw its sides down. Muscles inserting in the hyoid bone, such as the **stylohyoid, mylohyoid,** and **geniohyoid,** also play a role in the movements of the tongue.

The muscles of the palate play an important role in swallowing, helping to ensure that fluids and solids go "down the right pipe" rather than up into the nasopharynx. The bulk of the soft palate is formed by the **levator veli palatini,** with a contribution from the **tensor veli palatini.** (Refer back to Figure 10-18 to get an idea of the relative positions of the muscles.) If you have ever examined your throat in a mirror, you have undoubtedly noticed a fingerlike projection dangling downward from the palate in front of the opening into the pharynx. This is the uvula, which contains paired intrinsic muscles, the **uvulae.** During swallowing, the uvulae raise the soft palate and act as a trap door, blocking off the nasopharynx.

Two pairs of muscles in the lateral wall of the oral cavity, at its junction with the pharynx, mark the boundaries of the tonsils. These are the **palatoglossus,** extending from the soft palate to the tongue, and the **palatopharyngeus,** running from the soft palate to the pharynx.

Muscles of the Throat and Neck

The neck is the connecting link between the head and the body. Its muscles must support the head steadily and move it when necessary, and must also cater to the needs of the various structures that run through

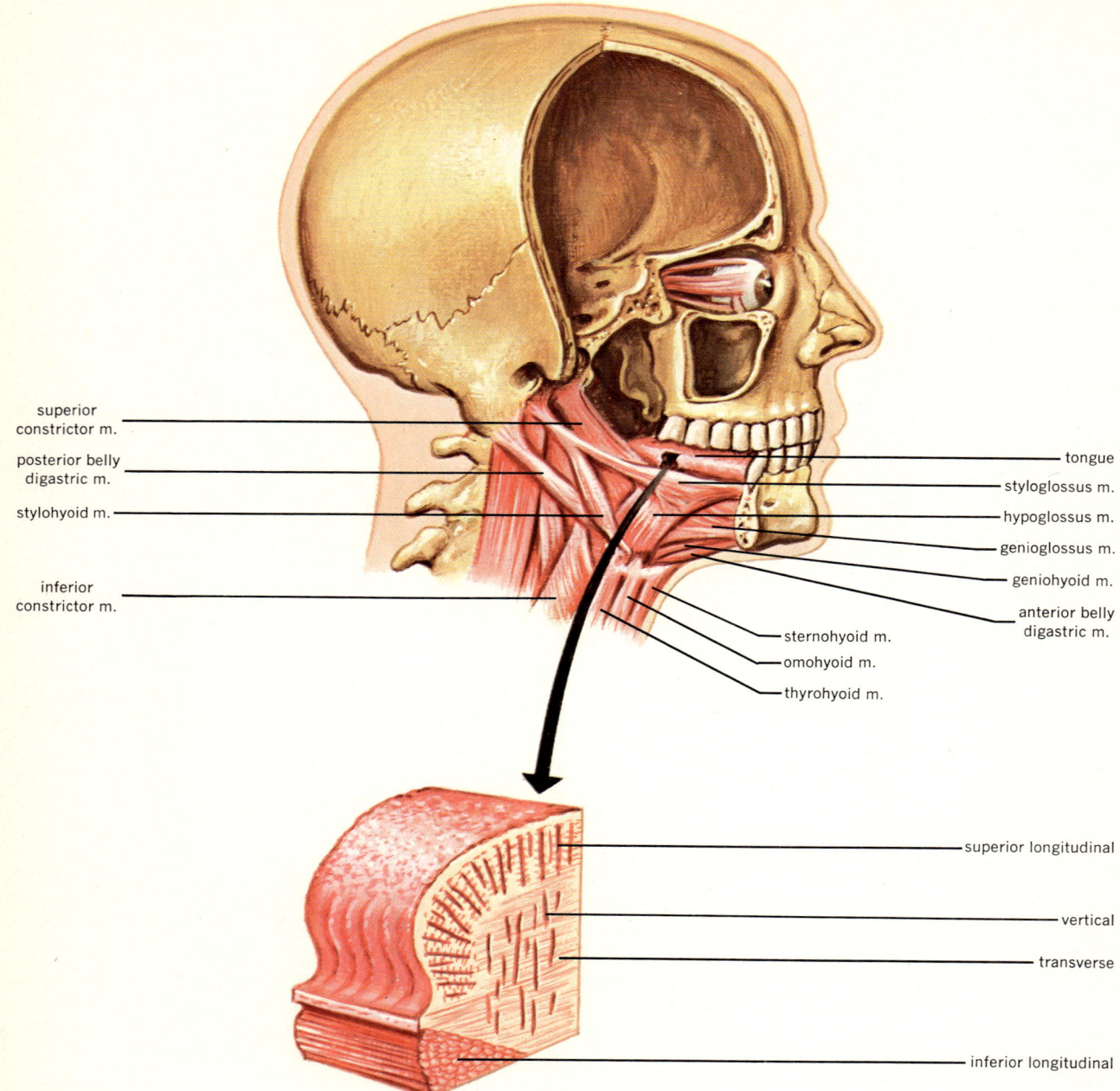

superior
constrictor m.

posterior belly
digastric m.

stylohyoid m.

inferior
constrictor m.

tongue

styloglossus m.

hypoglossus m.

genioglossus m.

geniohyoid m.

anterior belly
digastric m.

sternohyoid m.

omohyoid m.

thyrohyoid m.

superior longitudinal

vertical

transverse

inferior longitudinal

FIGURE 10-17   Muscles of the tongue and throat. (A) Extrinsic muscles; (B) intrinsic muscles of the tongue.

the neck. All the major supply lines of the body pass through this connecting link: the spinal cord, a central part of the body's communication and control system; major feedlines for air and foods; and important arteries and veins. An assortment of superficial and deep muscles attend to all the necessary functions.

The entire anterior half of the neck is covered by a thin sheet of muscle, the **platysma.** This muscle is attached at its upper end not only to the mandible, but also to the skin of the chin, corners of the mouth, and cheeks; thus, it plays a role in forming facial expres-

sions. When you grimace, ridges produced in the neck by the contractions of the platysma stand out prominently (Figure 10-19).

The main rotators of the head are the straplike **sternocleidomastoid** muscles (Figure 10-20), when they are contracting singly. (A spasm of one of the sternocleidomastoids produces the painful condition called wryneck.) When this pair of muscles act together, they pull the head forward and elevate the chin. The **obliquus capitis inferior** muscles rotate the atlas on the dens of the axis, to produce the effect of a "no" movement of the head.

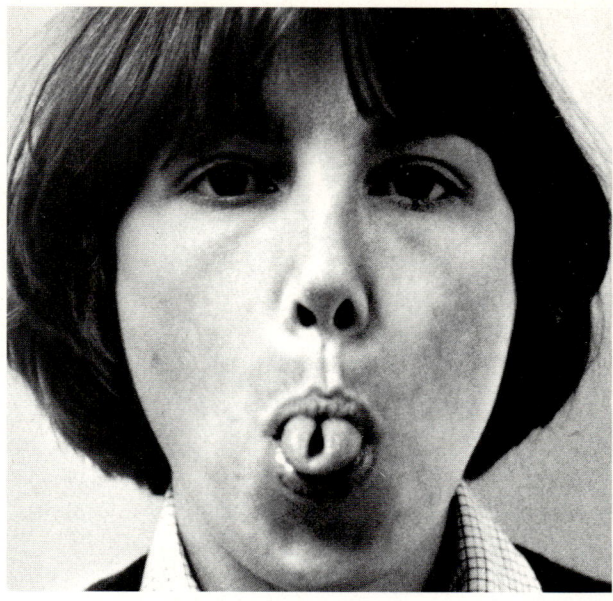

FIGURE 10-18 The ability to use tongue muscles to roll the tongue is determined by heredity.

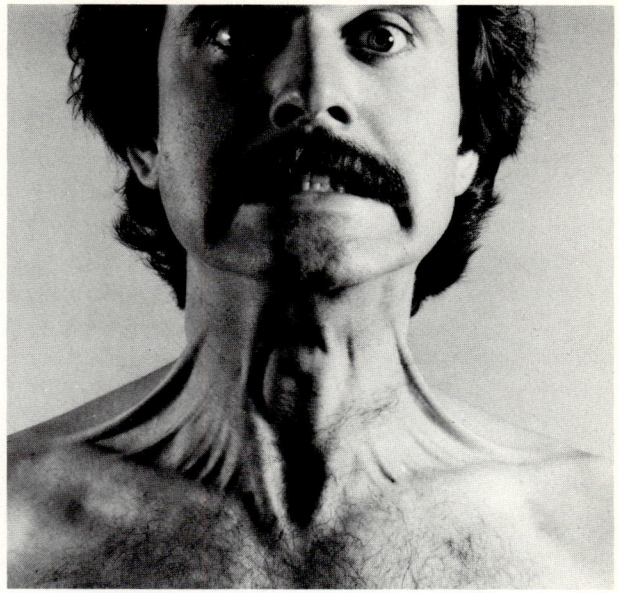

FIGURE 10-19 The contracted platysma stands out prominently in a grimace.

TABLE 10-7 Muscles of the neck and throat

MUSCLE	ORIGIN	INSERTION	ACTION
Platysma	Fascia of neck	Mandible and skin around the mouth	Depresses jaw and wrinkles skin of neck
Sternocleidomastoid	Sternum and clavicle	Mastoid process and occipital bone	Rotates head; flexes vertebral column and lifts chin
Obliquus capitis inferior	Spinous process of axis	Transverse process of atlas	Rotates atlas and head
Longus colli	Mid-cervical to upper thoracic vertebrae	Mid- and upper cervical vertebrae	Flexes and supports neck
Longus capitis	3rd to 6th cervical vertebrae	Basal portion of occipital bone	Flexes head
Rectus capitis anterior	Lateral part of atlas	Basal part of occipital bone	Flexes and supports head
Splenius capitis	Ligamentum nuchae on back of neck, 7th cervical and upper 3 thoracic vertebrae	Occipital bone	Extends and rotates head
Obliquus capitis superior	Transverse process of atlas	Occipital bone	Extends and moves head laterally
Rectus capitis posterior (major and minor)	Axis (major); atlas (minor)	Occipital bone	Extends head
Semispinalis capitis	Lower 4 cervical and upper 5 thoracic vertebrae	Occipital bone	Extends head
Longissimus capitis	Lower 3 or 4 cervical and upper 4 or 5 thoracic vertebrae	Mastoid process of temporal bone	Draws head backward and rotates head
Rectus capitis lateralis	Transverse process of atlas	Occipital bone	Bends head laterally
Digastric	Lower border of mandible and mastoid notch of temporal bone	Intermediate tendon on hyoid bone	Elevates hyoid bone, lowers jaw
Sternohyoid	Manubrium of sternum	Hyoid bone	Depresses hyoid bone and larynx

TABLE 10-7 (Continued)

MUSCLE	ORIGIN	INSERTION	ACTION
Sternothyroid	Manubrium of sternum	Thyroid cartilage	Depresses thyroid cartilage
Thyrohyoid	Thyroid cartilage	Hyoid bone	Raises and changes shape of larynx
Omohyoid	Superior border of scapula	Hyoid bone	Depresses hyoid bone
Constrictor pharyngis inferior	Undersurfaces of cricoid and thyroid cartilages	Median raphe (seam) of posterior wall of pharynx	Constricts pharynx
Constrictor pharyngis medius	Horns of hyoid and stylohyoid ligament	Median raphe of pharynx	Constricts pharynx
Constrictor pharyngis superior	Medial pterygoid plate, pterygomandibular ligament, mandible, and mucous membrane of floor of mouth	Median raphe of pharynx	Constricts pharynx
Salpingopharyngeus	Auditory tube near orifice	Posterior part of palatopharyngeus	Elevates pharynx, closes nasopharynx, aids in swallowing
Vocalis	Thyroid cartilage	Vocal process of arytenoid cartilage	Shortens vocal folds
Scalenus anterior	Transverse processes of 3rd to 6th cervical vertebrae	First rib	Raises first rib and bends neck to same side
Scalenus medius	Transverse processes of 2nd to 7th cervical	First rib	Raises first rib; bends neck to same side
Scalenus posterior	Transverse processes of 4th to 6th cervical vertebrae	Second rib	Raises second rib; bends neck to same side
Trapezius	Occipital bone, ligamentum nuchae, spinous processes of 7th cervical and all thoracic vertebrae	Clavicle, acromion and spine of scapula	Rotates scapula to raise shoulder, draws scapula backward

When you nod "yes," you are alternately using flexors and extensors (Figure 10-20). The principal flexors in the neck are the **longus colli,** the **longus capitis,** and the **rectus capitis anterior** muscles. The chief extensors are the **splenius capitis** muscles, assisted by others including the **obliquus capitis superior, rectus capitis posterior, semispinalis capitis,** and **longissimus capitis.** The **rectus capitis lateralis** bends the head laterally.

A number of muscles aid the functions of the internal structures of the neck. Two groups are the muscles attached to the hyoid bone: the **suprahyoid** muscles, which extend from the hyoid bone to the base of the skull, and the **infrahyoid** muscles, which extend downward from the hyoid to the clavicle and sternum. Several of the muscles of the suprahyoid group have already been discussed: the **stylohyoid, mylohyoid,** and **geniohyoid.** This group also includes the **digastric** muscle, a muscle with two bellies. The suprahyoid muscles raise the larynx, the hyoid, and the base of the tongue during swallowing. After food has passed through the pharynx, the elevation of the hyoid bone aids in preventing a backflow of food into the mouth.

The infrahyoid muscles include the **sternohyoid,** the **sternothyroid,** the **thyrohyoid,** and the **omohyoid** muscles. The muscles of this group depress the larynx and the hyoid bone after they have been drawn upward during swallowing. The sternothyroid and thyrohyoid also help to control the movements of the larynx during speech.

The bulk of the muscular wall of the pharynx is made up of three paired muscles, which fit into one another like stacked flowerpots. These are the **suprior, middle,** and **inferior constrictors.** These pharyngeal muscles initiate the mechanism of swallowing. The beginning of the act of swallowing is a voluntary action; but once the events have been set in motion, they become involuntary, as the action is taken over by smooth muscle in the lower end of the pharynx and esophagus. In other words, you can choose to swallow or not, but once you have started you cannot stop.

A small muscle in the pharyngeal wall, the **salpin-**

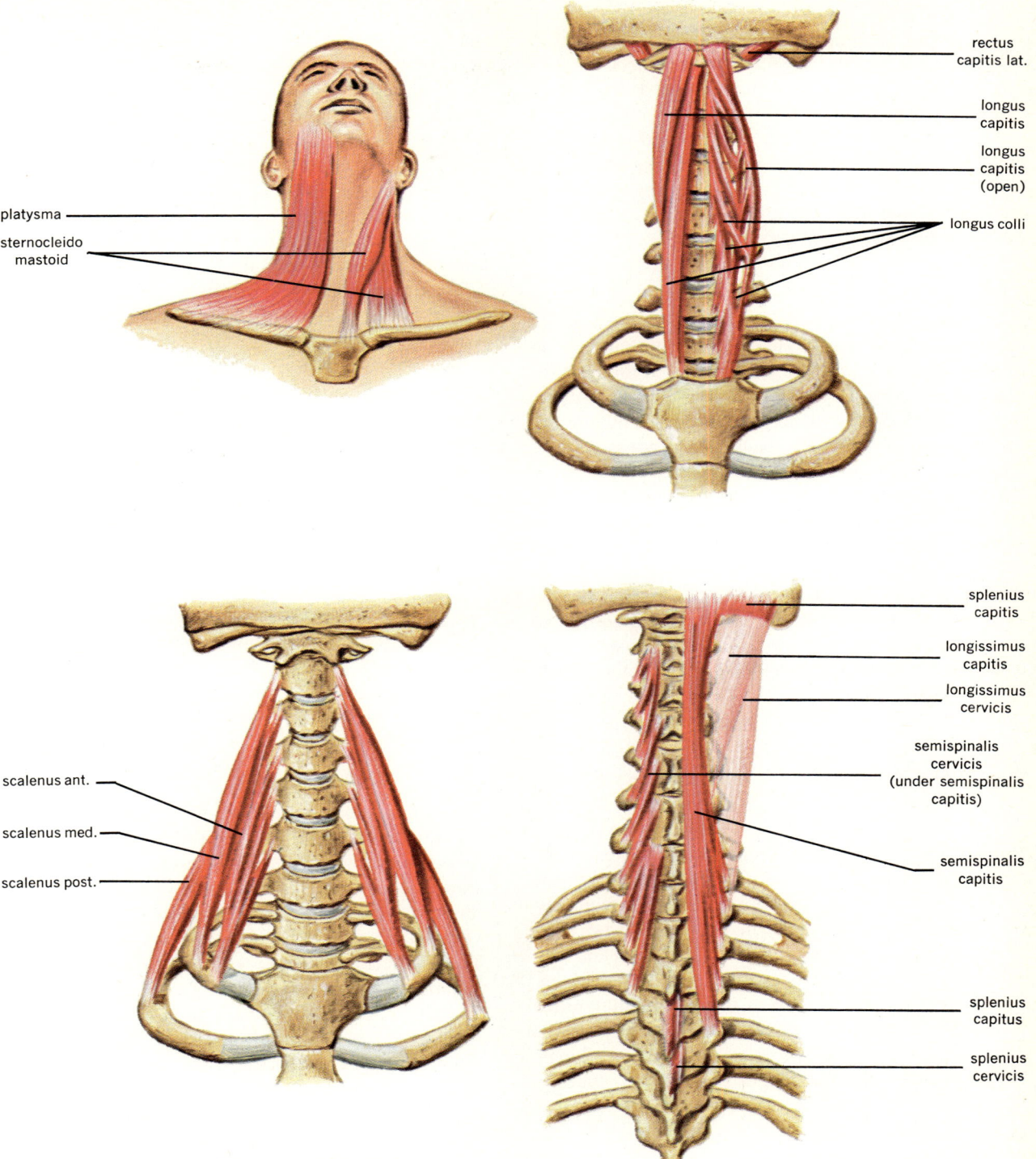

FIGURE 10-20 Muscles that support and move the head and neck.

gopharyngeus, plays a key role in swallowing. It opens the eustachian tube, helping to equalize the pressure in the middle ear cavity.

Small, sheetlike intrinsic muscles in the walls of the larynx act mainly to narrow the openings between the vocal cords. The **vocalis,** which inserts into the vocal cords, produces modulation of the voice when it contracts.

Muscles of the neck also aid in the movement of structures of the trunk. The **anterior, middle,** and **posterior scalene** muscles extend from the cervical vertebrae to the ribs. When they act from above, they aid in respiration by elevating the first and second ribs. When they act from below, they bend the vertebral column to one side or the other (contracting singly) or flex the spine slightly (when the muscles of both sides contract together).

The **trapezius** muscle extends from the occipital bone and various vertebrae to the clavicle and scapula. Its upper portions are active in raising and rotating the scapula, as in shrugging the shoulders. (This muscle is discussed in more detail later.)

MUSCLES OF THE TRUNK

A program of carefully controlled weightlifting produces a dramatic development of the musculature of the body. It is not only the arms that hold the weights that are involved. Lifting an iron bar with calibrated weights also calls for tremendous exertions by numerous muscles of the chest, back, and abdomen. The muscles that lash the vertebrae together also play an important role in maintaining the posture of the body under such stressful conditions, as well as in more everyday activities.

In addition to the obvious, superficial muscles of the trunk, there are vitally important deep muscles, such as the muscles of the chest and diaphragm, which function in breathing, and the muscles that form the abdominal wall and the floor of the pelvis.

Muscles that Move the Vertebral Column

The flexibility provided by the jointed arrangement of the vertebral column would not be effective without a complex system of muscles linking the vertebrae together and accommodating a variety of movements. With this well-coordinated bone-muscle system, people can not only maintain an upright posture (even against the additional stresses imposed by pregnancy or high-heeled shoes), but can also bend down and touch their toes, lift their heads to gaze up at the sky, and master the gyrations of the latest dance craze.

The most prominent group of muscles that move the vertebral column is the **erector spinae** (Figure 10-21). This is a long mass of muscle that extends longitudinally down the full length of the back, literally from "head to tail," and extends laterally about a hand's width on each side of the midline. It is composed of a number of individual longitudinal muscles, arranged in an overlapping manner in three main bands down each side of the spine. The most lateral segments of the erector spinae are the **iliocostalis** muscles; the muscles of the **spinalis** and **semispinalis** groups* are adjacent to the vertebral column; and the **longissimus** muscles lie in between. The name of each

* The spinalis muscles form a long band linking the spinous processes of the vertebrae; the fibers of the semispinalis muscles extend obliquely from the transverse processes of the vertebrae to the spines.

of the individual muscles carries a further designation indicating its position along the vertebral column: **capitis** (attached to the head), **cervicis** (in the neck region), **thoracis** (in the region of the thorax), and **lumborum** (in the lumbar region). We have already met some of the muscles of the erector spinae group in the discussion of the muscles of the neck—for example, the semispinalis capitis and the longissimus capitis. As the name of the group implies, the erector spinae muscles act to extend the spine and help to maintain an erect posture. This is the effect when both muscles of a pair contract simultaneously; when only the muscle on one side contracts, the effect is to flex the spine laterally.

A number of powerful flexor muscles permit a forward bending of the trunk. Flexors of the neck such as the **longus colli** and **sternocleidomastoid** have already been discussed. In the lower portions of the vertebral column, the major flexors include the **rectus abdominis, psoas major,** and **psoas minor** muscles. Lateral flexion is provided by the **quadratus lumborum.**

Minor movements between adjacent vertebrae are aided by several series of small transverse muscles, which lash the processes of adjacent vertebrae together (Figure 10-22). These transverse muscles include the **multifidus** and **rotatores** (which act in extension and rotation of the vertebral column), the **interspinales** (extension), and the **intertransversarii** (lateral bending).

Muscles of the Thoracic Wall and Diaphragm

The rise and fall of the chest during breathing is such a commonplace and universal phenomenon that we rarely notice it at all, except under special circumstances—for example, the heaving chest of an exhausted runner who has just finished a race. Spread your hands over your own rib cage for a moment. You will feel the walls of your chest cavity alternately expanding (in an upward and outward movement) and contracting (downward and inward). The rib cage of a skeleton in an anatomical demonstration looks like an actual barred cage, with an empty gap between each successive rib. But in the living rib cage, the gaps are solidly filled with layers of muscles (Figure 10-23). The thoracic wall is thus a solid wall, but it is not rigid—it can expand and contract like an accordion.

The muscles that fill the spaces between the ribs are called **intercostal** muscles, and they form two main layers. The **external intercostals** have fibers that run downward and forward, while the fibers of the **internal intercostals** course downward and backward. The effect that they produce when they contract is also quite different: the external intercostals act to lift the ribs during inspiration (breathing in), increasing the

TABLE 10-8 Muscles moving the vertebral column

MUSCLE	ORIGIN	INSERTION	ACTION
Iliocostalis	Angles of first 6 ribs	Transverse processes of 4th to 6th cervical vertebrae	Extends cervical spine
Iliocostalis thoracis	Upper border of angles of lower 6 ribs	Angles of upper 6 ribs	Keeps dorsal spine erect
Iliocostalis lumborum	Iliac crest	Angles of lower 6 or 7 ribs	Extends lumbar spine
Longissimus capitis	Articular processes of lower 3 or 4 cervical and transverse processes of upper 4 or 5 thoracic vertebrae	Mastoid process of temporal bone	Draws head backward and rotates head
Longissimus cervicis	Transverse processes of upper 4 or 5 thoracic vertebrae	Transverse processes of 2nd to 6th cervical vertebrae	Extends cervical vertebrae
Longissimus thoracis	Transverse and articular processes of lumbar vertebrae and lumbodorsal fascia	Transverse processes of all thoracic vertebrae and 9 or 10 lower ribs	Extends thoracic vertebrae
Semispinalis capitis	Transverse processes of lower 4 cervical and upper 5 or 6 thoracic vertebrae	Occipital bone	Extends head
Semispinalis cervicis	Transverse processes of upper 5 or 6 thoracic vertebrae	Spinous processes of 2nd to 5th cervical vertebrae	Extends and rotates vertebral column
Semispinalis thoracis	Transverse processes of 6th to 10th thoracic vertebrae	Spinous processes of lower 2 cervical and upper 4 thoracic vertebrae	Extends and rotates vertebral column
Spinalis capitis	Spines of lower cervical and upper thoracic vertebrae	Occipital bone	Extends head
Spinalis cervicis	Spinous processes of 5th to 7th cervical and upper 2 thoracic vertebrae	Spinous processes of axis and sometimes 2nd to 4th cervical vertebrae	Extends vertebral column
Spinalis thoracis	Spinous processes of lower 2 thoracic and upper 2 lumbar vertebrae	Spines of upper thoracic vertebrae	Extends vertebral column
Quadratus lumborum	Iliac crest; iliolumbar ligament	12th rib and transverse processes of upper 4 lumbar vertebrae	Flexes lumbar vertebrae laterally
Rectus abdominis	Pubis	Xiphoid process and cartilages of 5th to 7th ribs	Flexes lumbar vertebrae and supports abdomen
Psoas major	Transverse processes of lumbar vertebrae	Lesser trochanter of femur	Flexes trunk, flexes and rotates thigh medially
Psoas minor	Last thoracic and first lumbar vertebrae	Iliopectineal eminence	Flexes trunk on pelvis
Interspinales	Superior surface of spinous process of each vertebra	Inferior surface of spinous process of next superior vertebra	Extend vertebral column
Intertransversarii	Extend between transverse processes of adjacent vertebrae		Bend vertebral column laterally
Multifidus	Sacrum and transverse processes of lumbar, thoracic, and cervical vertebrae	Spines of next superior vertebra	Extend and rotate vertebral column
Rotatores	Transverse processes of all vertebrae below 2nd cervical	Base of spinous process of next superior vertebra	Extend vertebral column and rotate it toward opposite side

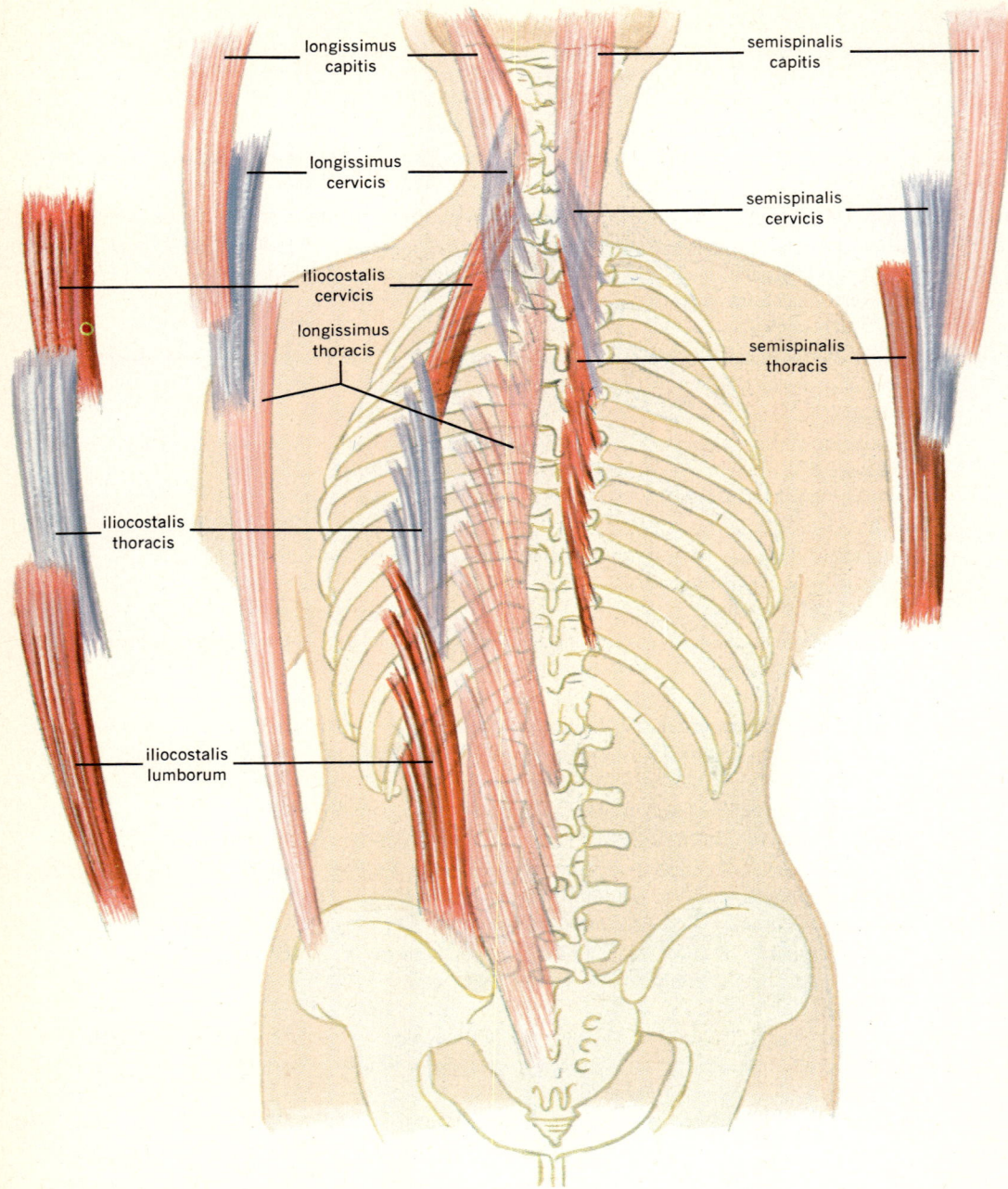

longissimus
capitis

semispinalis
capitis

longissimus
cervicis

semispinalis
cervicis

iliocostalis
cervicis

longissimus
thoracis

semispinalis
thoracis

iliocostalis
thoracis

iliocostalis
lumborum

FIGURE 10-21   **Intrinsic muscles of the back: the longitudinal muscles that move the vertebral column are arranged in overlapping layers, as indicated.**

volume of the thoracic cavity. The internal intercostals contract during expiration, drawing the adjacent ribs together and decreasing the volume of the thoracic cavity.

A third muscle layer lies on the inner surface of the rib cage. It is often considered to consist of three separate muscles: the **transverse thoracis,** in the anterior part of the rib cage; the **innermost intercostal,** in the lateral portions of the rib cage; and the **subcostalis** adjacent to the vertebral column. The subcostalis

raises the ribs during inspiration, while the innermost intercostal and transverse thoracis muscles act to constrict the chest cavity.

Several other muscles of the thoracic wall also participate in respiration, particularly in forceful inspiration, such as that following vigorous exercise. These include the **levatores costarum** ("lifters of ribs") and the **serratus posterior** muscles **(superior** and **inferior).** During forced inspiration, the **scalene** muscles already described and muscles that link the trunk with

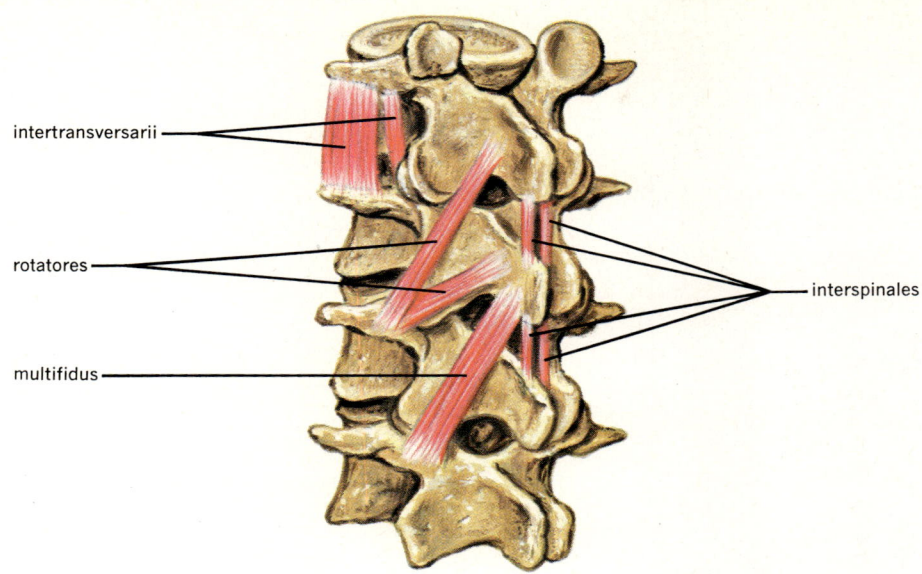

intertransversarii

rotatores

multifidus

interspinales

FIGURE 10-22 A portion of the vetebral column, showing the attachments of the transverse muscles of the back to the vertebrae.

TABLE 10-9   Muscles of the thorax

MUSCLE	ORIGIN	INSERTION	ACTION
External intercostals (11 on each side)	Inferior border of ribs	Superior border of next rib below	Draws ribs together; lifts rib cage and expands volume of thoracic cavity
Internal intercostals (11 on each side)	Inferior border of ribs	Superior border of next rib below	Draws ribs together
Transverse thoracis	Xiphoid process and lower third of sternum	Costal cartilages of 2nd to 6th ribs	Draws costal cartilages downward; narrows chest
Innermost intercostals	Inferior border of ribs	Superior border of next rib below	Draw ribs together
Subcostalis	Inner surface of ribs	Inner surface of 1st, 2nd, or 3rd rib below	Raises ribs in inspiration
Levatores costarum (12 on each side)	Transverse processes of 7th cervical and 1st to 11th thoracic vertebrae	Outer surface of rib below (medial to angle)	Raises ribs, increasing thoracic capacity
Serratus posterior superior	Ligamentum nuchae, spines of upper thoracic vertebrae	2nd to 5th ribs	Raises ribs, increasing thoracic capacity
Serratus posterior inferior	Spines of 2 lower thoracic and 2 or 3 upper lumbar vertebrae	Inferior borders of lower 4 ribs	Lowers ribs in expiration
Diaphragm	Xiphoid process, costal cartilages, lumbar vertebrae	Central tendon	Pulls central tendon downward, increasing volume of thoracic cavity; principal muscle of respiration

the upper extremities (the **trapezius** and the **pectoralis major**) also help to lift the ribs and expand the chest cavity. Expiration is normally a more passive process, following the relaxation of the inspiratory muscles, but four pairs of abdominal muscles, the **internal and external oblique** muscles, **transversus abdominis,** and

rectus abdominis also contract weakly along with the internal intercostals.

The major share of the work of respiration is performed by the **diaphragm,** the solid musculomembranous floor of the thoracic cavity (Figure 10-24). The sheetlike diaphragm is curved upward into a double

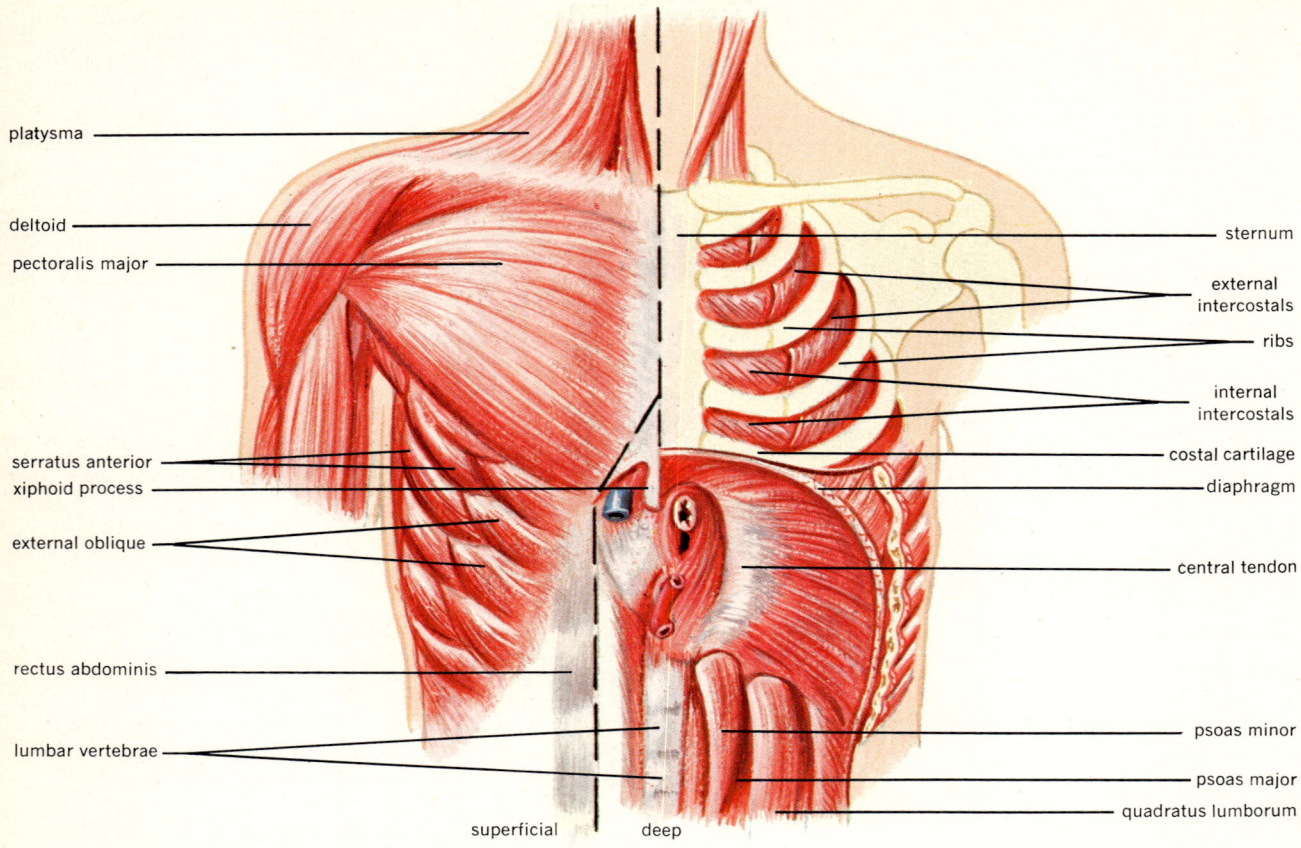

platysma

deltoid

pectoralis major

serratus anterior

xiphoid process

external oblique

rectus abdominis

lumbar vertebrae

sternum

external
intercostals

ribs

internal
intercostals

costal cartilage

diaphragm

central tendon

psoas minor

psoas major

quadratus lumborum

superficial   deep

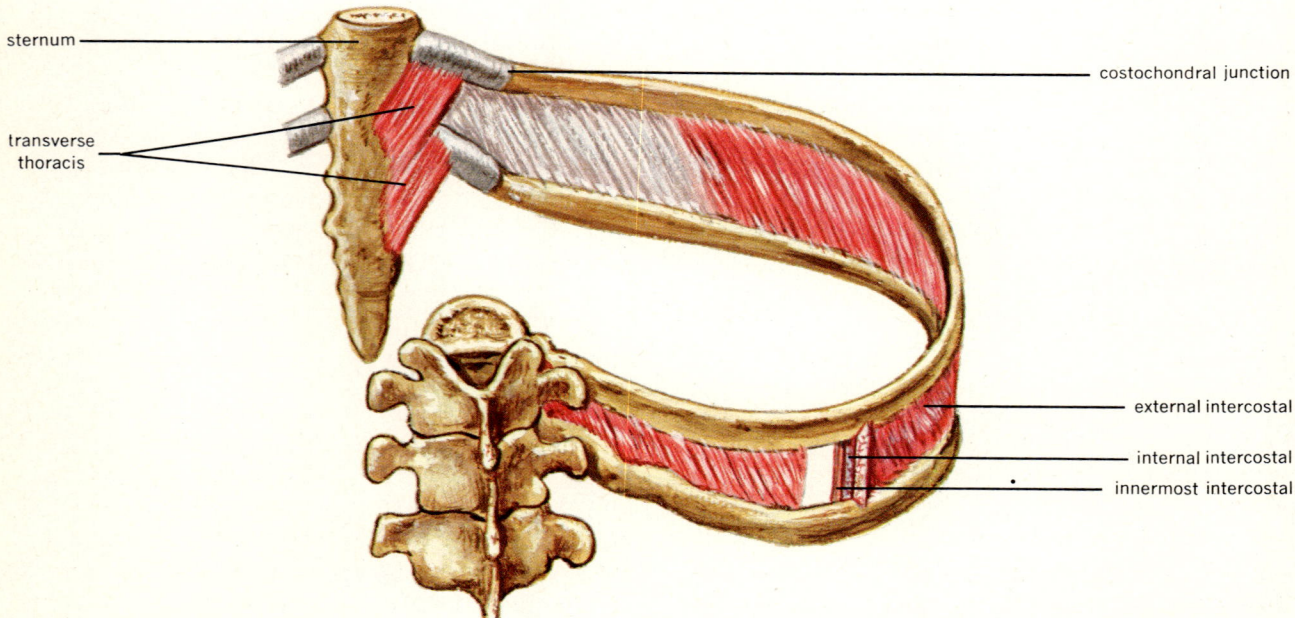

sternum

transverse
thoracis

costochondral junction

external intercostal

internal intercostal

innermost intercostal

FIGURE 10-23   Muscles of the thoracic wall and abdomen used in breathing. Details of the intercostal muscles are shown below.

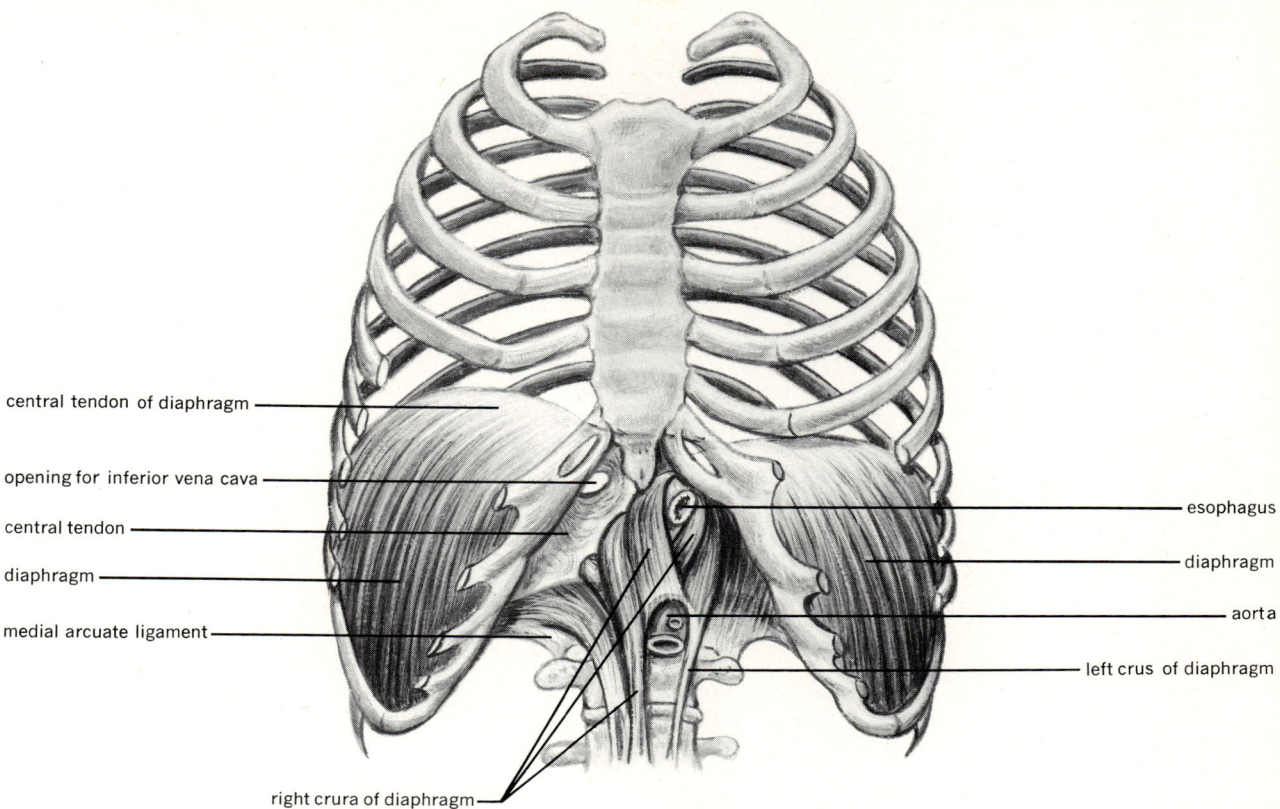

central tendon of diaphragm

opening for inferior vena cava

central tendon

diaphragm

medial arcuate ligament

esophagus

diaphragm

aorta

left crus of diaphragm

right crura of diaphragm

FIGURE 10-24   The diaphragm, seen from the front.

dome shape; the left and right domes are of powerful muscle tissue, while the central portion is composed of fibrous tissue and is called the **central tendon.** The diaphragm is simultaneously the floor of the chest cavity (the heart rests on the central tendon) and the roof of the abdominal cavity. (The liver is nestled up under the right dome, while the stomach fits snugly under the left dome.) The actual level of the diaphragm varies with the position of the body (it is higher when a person is lying down than while standing) and with the degree of distension of the stomach and intestines. If you have evern commented after a heavy meal, "I'm so stuffed, I can hardly breathe," you were noting a curtailment of the chest capacity caused by the upward displacement of the diaphragm, as well as the important function of this muscle in breathing. For the diaphragm is the principal muscle of respiration; if necessary, it could carry on the entire process of breathing unaided by other muscles. When the diaphragm contracts, its central portion is pulled downward, and the thoracic cavity expands. The pressure in the thoracic cavity is correspondingly reduced, and air is "pulled" into the lungs. Singing teachers commonly exhort their students to "Breathe with the diaphragm" and develop their chest capacity to the fullest.

Muscles of the Abdominal Wall

The abdomen is packed with soft and vulnerable organs, and unlike the organs of the thorax and head, they have no bony cage to protect them. But the muscles of the abdominal wall are capable of providing a surprising amount of protection to the viscera within. A person with a well-developed set of abdominal muscles can withstand a severe blow to the pit of the stomach without much discomfort. A misunderstanding of the implications of this fact had fateful consequences for the great magician, Harry Houdini. A college student in the audience, familiar with Houdini's boast that he could not be injured by a punch in the abdomen, hit him there suddenly, before the performer could contract his abdominal muscles. The blow ruptured Houdini's appendix, and he developed peritonitis and died.

The anterolateral portions of the abdominal wall consist of three layers of sheetlike muscles: the **external oblique,** the **internal oblique,** and the **transversus abdominis** (Figure 10-25). The structure of the muscular wall resembles that of a sheet of plywood, for the fibers of each of the three muscle layers run at an angle to those of the other layers, just as is the case in the layers of wood laminated together to form plywood. The fibers of the outermost layer, the external

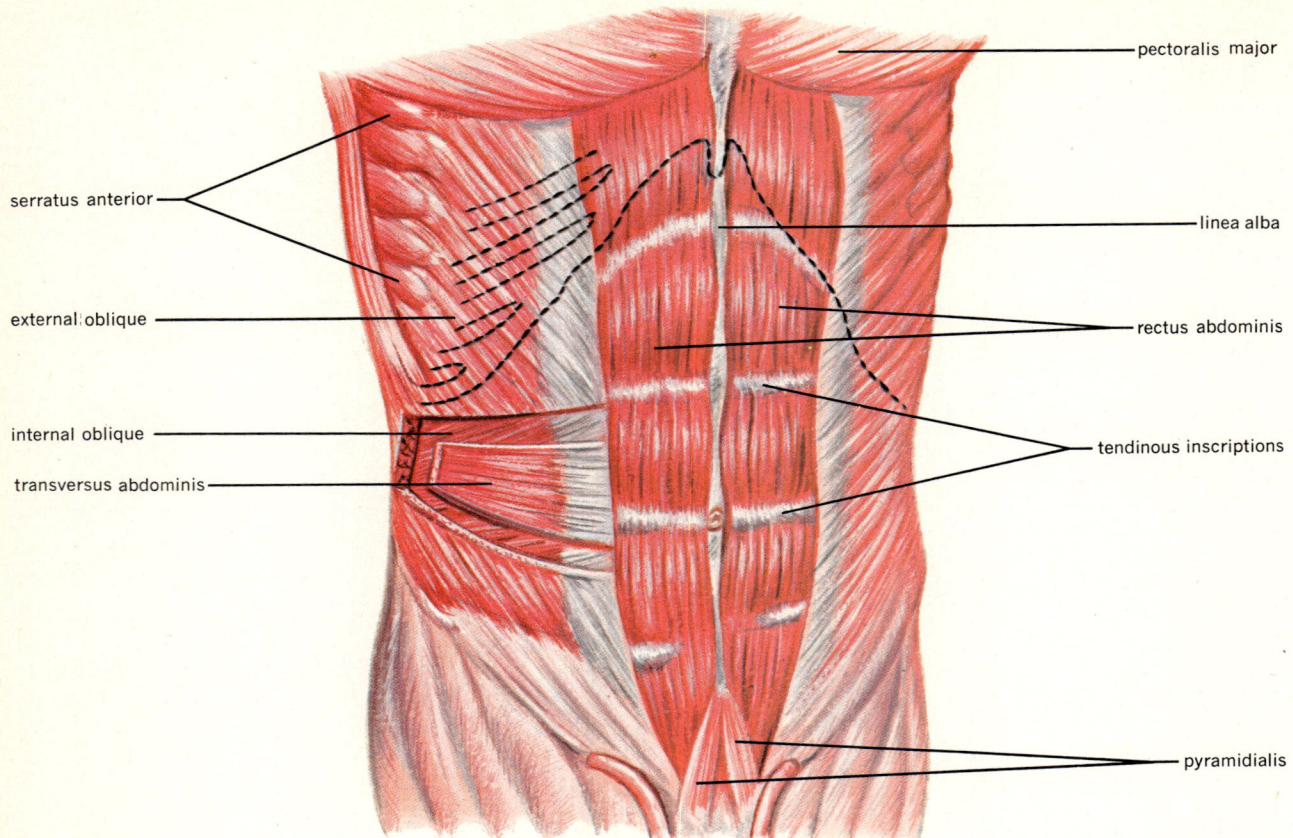

serratus anterior

external oblique

internal oblique

transversus abdominis

pectoralis major

linea alba

rectus abdominis

tendinous inscriptions

pyramidialis

FIGURE 10-25 Muscles of the anterolateral abdominal wall.

TABLE 10-10 Muscles of the abdominal wall

MUSCLE	ORIGIN	INSERTION	ACTION
External oblique	External surface of lower 8 ribs	Anterior half of iliac crest; linea alba	Flexes and rotates vertebral column; tenses abdominal wall and compresses abdominal viscera
Internal oblique	Inguinal ligament, iliac crest, lumbar aponeurosis	Lower 3 or 4 costal cartilages, linea alba	Flexes and rotates vertebral column; tenses abdominal wall and compresses abdominal viscera
Transversus abdominis	Cartilages of 6 lower ribs; lumbodorsal fascia; iliac crest; inguinal ligament	Linea alba	Supports and compresses abdominal viscera
Rectus abdominis	Pubis	Xiphoid process, cartilages of 5th to 7th ribs	Flexes lumbar vertebrae, tenses abdominal wall and supports abdomen

oblique muscles, run obliquely forward and downward; those of the next layer, the internal oblique muscles, slant forward and upward; and the fibers of the innermost layer, the transversus abdominis, run horizontally, just as their name implies.

Posteriorly, the wall of the abdominal cavity is completed by several muscles that have already been discussed, the **quadratus lumborum** and the **psoas ma-**

jor and **minor,** which course vertically.

On the anterior portion of the abdominal wall, the **rectus abdominis** forms a straplike mass of muscle about 10 cm wide, running from the pubic bone at the floor of the abdominal cavity straight up to the xiphoid process of the sternum and lower margins of the rib cage. The rectus abdominis muscle is enclosed in a tough sheath formed by the aponeuroses of the three layers of anterolateral abdominal muscles. The aponeuroses join anteriorly in a seam called the **linea alba** (literally, "white line"), which forms a depression in the rectus sheath, running down the midline of the body.

When the abdominal muscles contract, they decrease the size of the abdominal cavity and increase the pressure inside the cavity, forcing the diaphragm upward. Thus, the abdominal muscles act antagonistically to the diaphragm: when the diaphragm contracts and moves downward during inspiration, the abdominal muscles relax; when the diaphragm relaxes during expiration, the abdominal muscles contract (especially during forceful expiration). The abdominal muscles also act as antagonists to the muscles of the back in maintaining posture. In addition, they provide the compressive force needed in such activities as defecation, urination, vomiting, and childbirth.

In several places, gaps or spaces in the abdominal aponeuroses leave weak spots in the abdominal wall, where a **hernia** or rupture may occur, resulting in a protrusion of a loop or intestine or other abdominal contents out through the gap in the wall. The principal weak places are the **umbilicus,** the **inguinal canals,** and the **femoral rings** (Figure 10-26). In males the spermatic cords pass through the inguinal canals into the scrotum; in females, the round ligaments of the uterus are found here. The openings in males are larger than in females, and as a result, inguinal hernias occur more often in men than in women. The femoral rings, on the other hand, are larger in females, and femoral hernia is more prevalent in women. Usually a hernia is brought on by straining, for example, while lifting a heavy object or during a particularly difficult bowel movement. Occasionally children are born with a hernia, which may require surgical repair.

Muscles of the Pelvic Floor

Have you ever had the bottom fall out of a bag full of groceries? The human body would be in constant danger of a similar fate if it were not for the strong, muscular floor that supports the organs of the abdominal cavity.

The muscles of the pelvic floor can be divided into three main groups (Figure 10-27): (1) the **pelvic diaphragm,** formed by the **levator ani** and **coccygeus** muscles and fasciae; (2) the **urogenital diaphragm,** formed by the **superficial** and **deep transverse perineal** muscles and fasciae; and (3) the muscles of the external genitalia.

The levator ani and coccygeus are sheetlike muscles, which support the organs of the abdomen and resist the increase in pressure in the abdominal cavity that occurs when the contracting diaphragm descends during inspiration. A portion of the levator ani muscles forms a sling about the lower portion of the rectum and pulls it forward, aiding in defecation. The **external anal sphincter** is a ring of muscle around the external opening of the rectum, which provides voluntary control over defecation. (The diaper industry owes its existence to the fact that control over the sphincter muscles of elimination is learned only

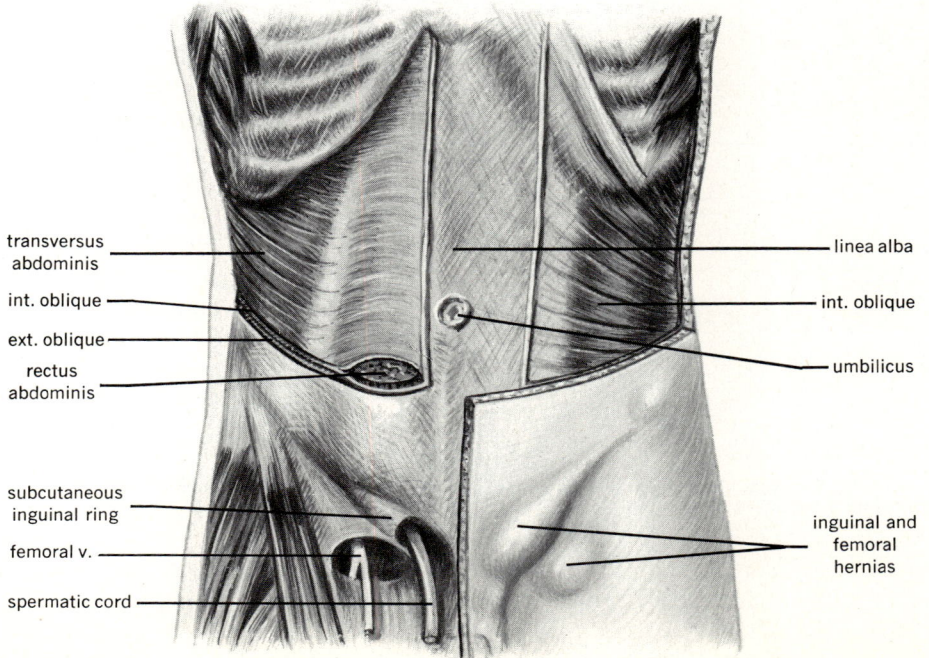

FIGURE 10-26 The structure of the muscular abdominal wall contains several weak spots, where hernias can characteristically occur. Inguinal and femoral hernias are shown; the umbilicus is another vulnerable area.

transversus abdominis

int. oblique

ext. oblique

rectus abdominis

subcutaneous inguinal ring

femoral v.

spermatic cord

linea alba

int. oblique

umbilicus

inguinal and femoral hernias

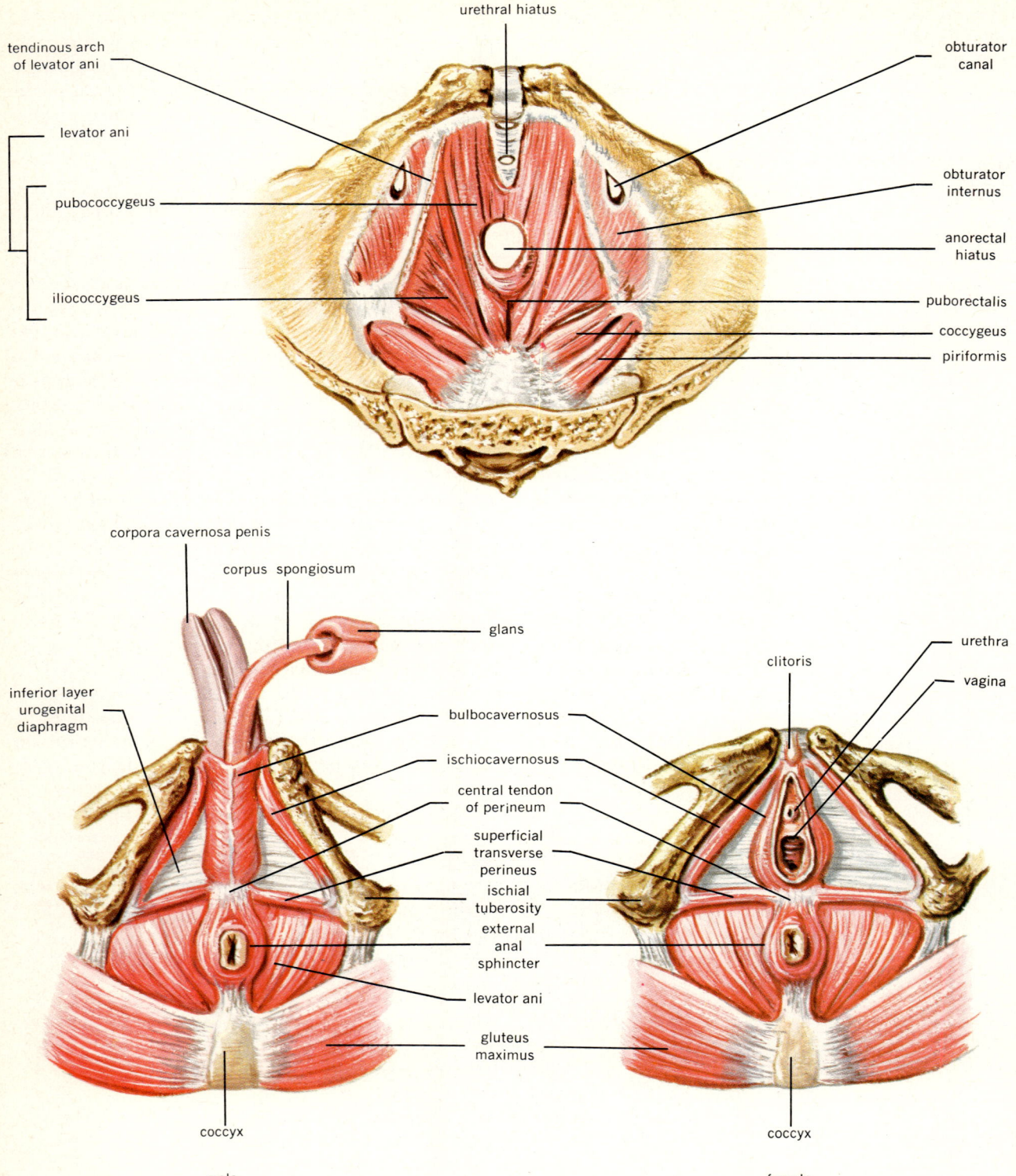

FIGURE 10-27   Muscles of the pelvic floor. (A) Pelvic diaphragm, viewed from the interior of the pelvic cavity. (B) Muscles of the perineum. Note the homologous muscles and their modifications in the male and female.

gradually, as a baby develops.) The deep portion of the external anal sphincter fuses with an internal sphincter of smooth muscle, which is not under voluntary control.

The transverse perineal muscles and the structures of the external genitalia occupy the **pelvic outlet,** the space between the tip of the coccyx, the ischial tuberosities, and the pubis. During childbirth, this area is

TABLE 10-11 Muscles of the pelvic floor

MUSCLE	ORIGIN	INSERTION	ACTION
Levator ani	Body of pubis, ischial spine, and obturator fascia	Coccyx and raphe joining coccyx to rectum	Flexes coccyx; raises anus; resists downward pressure of abdominal viscera
Coccygeus	Ischial spine	Lower sacrum, upper coccyx	Supports and raises coccyx, supports pelvic viscera
Deep transverse perineus	Inferior ramus of ischium	Median raphe of perineum	Draws back central tendon of perineum
Superficial transverse perineus	Tuberosity of ischium	Central tendon of perineum	Tenses central tendon of perineum
External anal sphincter	Tip of coccyx and surrounding fasciae	Central tendon of perineum	Closes anus
External urethral sphincter	Inferior ramus of pubis	Median raphe behind and in front of urethra	Compresses urethra
Bulbo-cavernosus	Central tendon of perineum and (in males) median raphe of bulb	Fascia of root of penis (clitoris)	Compresses bulb of penis in males; compresses vaginal orifice in females
Ischio-cavernosus	Ramus of ischium	Crus penis (crus clitoridis)	Maintains erection of penis (clitoris)

subjected to tremendous stretching forces, and some of the perineal muscles may tear. Sometimes (especially in a first birth), an incision called an episiotomy may be made instead, before any tearing has been produced; the smooth cut heals more readily then a jagged tear.

The muscles associated with the external genitalia include the **bulbocavernosus** and the **ischiocavernosus.** These muscles are found in both males and females, but they play somewhat different roles in the two sexes. In males, the bulbocavernosus muscle compresses the bulb of the penis, while in females it compresses the vaginal orifice. The ischiocavernosus maintains turgescence during sexual excitement—turgescence of the penis in males and of the clitoris in females. (The ischiocavernosus is smaller in females than in males, which is understandable in view of the size difference of the respective organs involved.) The **external urethral sphincter** compresses the urethra, providing voluntary control over the function of urination.

APPENDICULAR MUSCLES

MUSCLES OF THE UPPER EXTREMITIES

One of the most striking differences between a person and an ape is in the relative proportions of the arms and legs. The arms of a gorilla or chimpanzee are far longer and stronger than those of a human being, even adjusting for the differences in height and weight. These differences are correlated with an important difference in the functions of the upper extremities. For the anthropoid ape, the arms are im-

portant organs of locomotion: it is adept at traveling from place to place by brachiation, swinging from one tree branch to another by its arms. Even on the ground, although the ape can walk upright on two legs, it usually stoops over into a four-limbed shamble, partly supporting its weight on the knuckles of its hands. In humans, the upper extremities have been entirely freed from such a role in locomotion, and are used mainly for manipulative activities and for carrying loads. Not only the skeletal structure, but the musculature of the upper extremities reflect these modified functions in the human body.

Muscles Connecting the Upper Extremity to the Trunk

The arms of a rag doll flop limply at its sides. The movements of the arms of a human being would be just as limp and ineffective if it were not for a number of powerful muscles that bind the upper extremities to the trunk and aid in movements at the shoulder joint. If you think back to the discussion of the shoulder girdle, you should recall that the bony arrangement is actually rather precarious. The clavicles articulate with the sternum at the anterior surface of the body, and with the scapulas at the shoulder joints, from which the bones of the arms are suspended. But the scapulas are not anchored posteriorly by any bony articulations. They are held in place only by assemblies of muscles and tendons (Figure 10-28). This arrangement provides for great flexibility and versatility of movement. You would be unable to shrug your shoulders if your scapulas were firmly joined to bones of the axial skeleton, and stretching

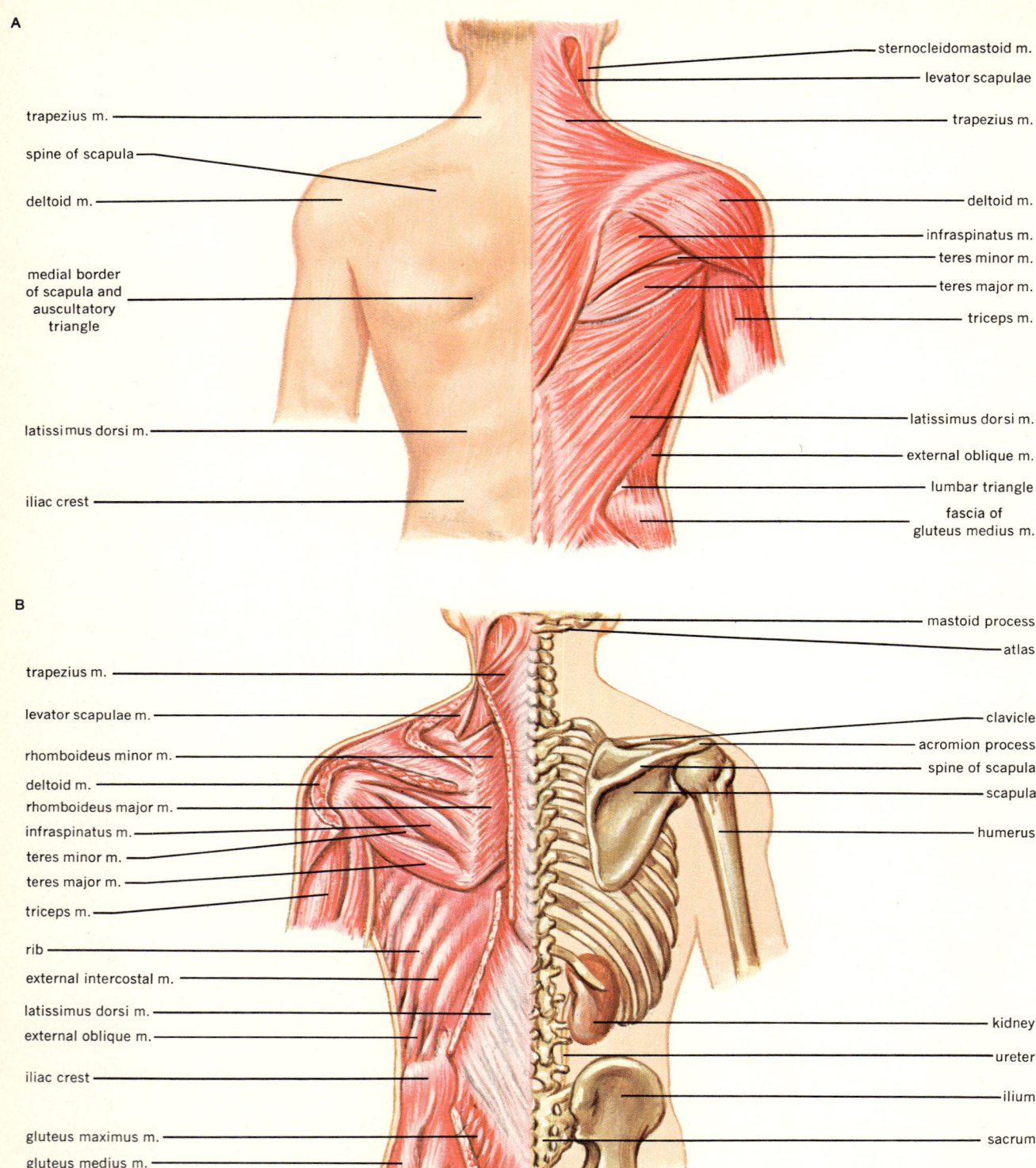

A

trapezius m.

spine of scapula

deltoid m.

medial border
of scapula and
auscultatory
triangle

latissimus dorsi m.

iliac crest

sternocleidomastoid m.

levator scapulae

trapezius m.

deltoid m.

infraspinatus m.

teres minor m.

teres major m.

triceps m.

latissimus dorsi m.

external oblique m.

lumbar triangle

fascia of
gluteus medius m.

B

trapezius m.

levator scapulae m.

rhomboideus minor m.

deltoid m.

rhomboideus major m.

infraspinatus m.

teres minor m.

teres major m.

triceps m.

rib

external intercostal m.

latissimus dorsi m.

external oblique m.

iliac crest

gluteus maximus m.

gluteus medius m.

mastoid process

atlas

clavicle

acromion process

spine of scapula

scapula

humerus

kidney

ureter

ilium

sacrum

coccyx

FIGURE 10-28   Muscles of the back: superficial (A) and deep (B).

and lifting movements of your arms would be hampered.

As you read the following discussion of the muscles that connect the upper extremities to the trunk, try performing a few actions with one arm while feeling along the surface of your chest, back, and the lateral portion of the trunk with your other hand. Stretch your arm forward, pick up a book and lift it, then slowly lower it; raise your arm over your head, touch your ear, and then the small of your back; swing your

TABLE 10-12   Muscles of the shoulder girdle and shoulder

MUSCLE	ORIGIN	INSERTION	ACTION
Trapezius	Occipital bone, ligamentum nuchae, spinous processes of 7th cervical and all thoracic vertebrae	Clavicle, acromion, spine of scapula	Rotates scapula to raise shoulder, draws scapula backward, draws head to one side
Latissimus dorsi	Spines of thoracic and lumbar vertebrae, iliac crest, lower ribs, inferior surface of scapula	Intertubercular groove of humerus	Adducts, extends, and medially rotates humerus
Levator scapulae	Transverse processes of upper 4 cervical vertebrae	Vertebral border of scapula	Raises scapula ("shrugging")
Rhomboideus major	Spines of 2nd to 5th thoracic vertebrae	Vertebral margin of scapula	Retracts and elevates scapula
Rhomboideus minor	Spines of 7th cervical to 1st thoracic vertebrae, ligamentum nuchae	Vertebral margin of scapula at root of spine	Adducts and elevates scapula and assists in adduction of arm
Pectoralis major	Clavicle, sternum, upper 6 ribs, aponeurosis of external oblique muscle of abdomen	Crest of intertubercular groove of humerus	Adducts, flexes, and medially rotates arm
Pectoralis minor	3rd to 5th ribs	Coracoid process of scapula	Draws shoulder forward and downward; raises ribs in forced inspiration when scapula is fixed
Subclavius	First rib and its cartilage	Lower surface of clavicle	Draws shoulder forward and downward
Serratus anterior	Upper 8 or 9 ribs	Vertebral border of scapula	Draws scapula forward; rotates scapula in abduction of arm
Deltoid	Clavicle, acromion, spine of scapula	Deltoid tuberosity of humerus	Abducts, flexes, and extends arm
Supraspinatus	Supraspinous fossa of scapula	Greater tubercle of humerus	Abducts humerus
Infraspinatus	Infraspinous fossa of scapula	Greater tubercle of humerus	Rotates humerus laterally
Teres major	Inferior angle of scapula	Intertubercular groove of humerus	Adducts, extends, and medially rotates arm
Teres minor	Lateral margin of scapula	Greater tubercle of humerus	Laterally rotates arm
Subscapularis	Subscapular fossa of scapula	Lesser tubercle of humerus	Rotates humerus medially; holds humerus in glenoid fossa

arm around to touch the opposite shoulder; shrug your shoulders, then bring them back as though you are standing at attention. In each activity, try to determine which muscles are contracting.

Superficial muscles of the chest and back play important roles in movements at the shoulder joints.

Dorsal Muscles   The superficial muscles of the back are in two layers. The outermost layer consists of the **trapezius** and the **latissimus dorsi.** If you look at the diagram in Figure 10-28, the trapezius might seem more triangular than trapezoidal in shape. It was so named because the two trapezius muscles (one on

each side of the body) together form a diamond-shaped trapezoid that covers most of the upper part of the back. The trapezius muscles link the occipital bone of the skull and a number of the vertebrae to both the clavicle and the scapula, helping to stabilize the entire shoulder girdle structure. The degree of contraction of the trapezius muscles determines the position of the shoulders and can play a subtle but important role in the "language of the body." Drooping shoulders may be a sign of dejection, signaling to those around you that you are feeling a little below par, physically or emotionally. The trapezius also participates in a variety of actions, including raising and shrugging the shoulders, extending the head and turning it from side to side, and bracing back the shoulders.

The latissimus dorsi is a large, flat, triangular muscle. (Its name literally means "widest of the back.") A swimmer uses the latissimus dorsi to bring the arm downward powerfully in a backward sweep, simultaneously rotating it inward. The latissimus dorsi is also the chief muscle involved in giving a downward blow with the arm. In both cases the trunk remains relatively fixed, while the arm is the moving part. The latissimus dorsi can also provide a useful effect when the arms are fixed and the trunk is moved forward, as in climbing; and it can help to raise the ribs during forceful breathing.

A deeper layer of the superficial muscles of the back, under the trapezius, consists of the **levator scapulae** and the **major and minor rhomboids.** These are all flat muscles that lash the medial (vertebral) border of the scapula to the upper part of the vertebral column. They act to elevate the scapula (as in shrugging the shoulders), rotate it, and draw it backward. In addition, all of the superficial muscles of the back help to stabilize the shoulder girdle during movements of the arms.

Ventral Muscles   The most prominent muscles of the chest are the two **pectoralis major** muscles.* In a man with a well-developed musculature, these large, fan-shaped muscles are especially powerful. In women, the breasts are attached to the fascia covering these muscles. (Part of the pectoralis major is removed in radical operations for breast cancer.) Although the pectoralis major muscles cover most of the upper, anterior part of the chest, each is inserted on the humerus of its respective side of the body (you can feel fibers of the pectoralis in the prominent fold in front of the armpit), and their action is concerned mainly with movements of the arms. The pectoralis major adducts and flexes the humerus and rotates it inward. After you raise your arm, the pectoralis major helps to bring it back to your side. It also draws the shoulder girdle forward and depresses it.

Beneath each pectoralis major is a much smaller, thin, triangular muscle, the **pectoralis minor.** It depresses the tip of the shoulder and helps to rotate the scapula downward. This muscle functions in forced respiration, as does another small, triangular muscle of the chest, the **subclavius,** which acts with the pectoral muscles to draw the ribs upward and expand the chest in forced inspiration.

The scapulae are stabilized by broad sheets of muscle that cover the sides of the chest: the **serratus ante-**

---

* In birds, the pectoralis major is the principal flight muscle. If you are fond of breast of chicken, the white meat you eat is largely pectoralis muscle.

rior muscles. These muscles pull the scapulae forward during the act of pushing, aid the trapezius muscles in supporting weights on the shoulders, and help in raising the arms above the horizontal.

Shoulder Muscles   The rounded bulge on the outer surface of the upper arms is formed by the **deltoid** muscles, powerful muscles that cover the shoulder joint like a shield. When the entire deltoid muscle contracts, it abducts the arm and raises it laterally to a horizontal position. When individual groups of muscle fibers of the deltoid contract, they assist other muscles in flexing, extending, and rotating the arm. The swelling mound of the deltoid provides an easily accessible and favored site for intramuscular injections.

The scapula is almost entirely covered by three muscles, the **supraspinatus, infraspinatus,** and **subscapularis.** The tendons of these muscles cross the shoulder joint to insert on the head of the humerus and merge with and strengthen the joint capsule. (You may recall that the ball-and-socket joint at the shoulder is a rather shallow one, easily dislocated, and thus requires strong muscle attachments.) These muscles aid in lateral rotation of the arm; in addition, the supraspinatus assists the deltoid in abduction of the arm.

The **teres major and minor** are both attached to the lateral border of the scapula, adjacent to the axilla (armpit). The fibers of the teres major form the posterior boundary of the axilla. It functions in adduction and medial rotation of the arm, while the teres minor produces lateral rotation and adduction.

The **subscapularis** fills the subscapular fossa and

A

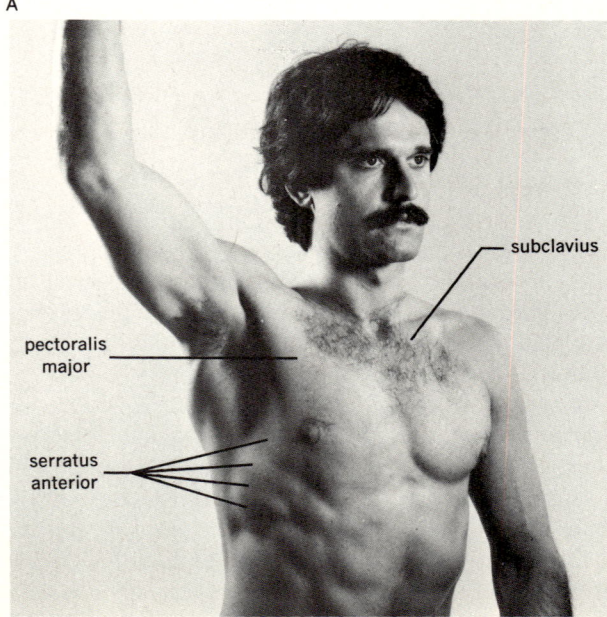

subclavius

pectoralis major

serratus anterior

helps to protect the front of the shoulder joint. It is the chief medial rotator of the arm.

The principal muscles of the shoulder and some examples of their action are shown in Figures 10-29 and 10-30.

Muscles of the Upper Arm

"I'd give my right arm for that!" is a common expression that recognizes, by implication, the great importance of the arms to a human being. We use our arms in eating, to lift things, sometimes as an aid to locomotion, and often in eloquent gestures accompanying speech. If you had to spend the next few hours with your arms tied to your sides, you would find various muscles of your arms continually tensing as you thought of customary actions involving your arms and automatically tried to carry them out.

We have already considered some of the muscles contributing to movement at the shoulder joint. Others are found mainly in the fleshy parts of the upper arm. In addition, some of the muscles of the upper arm are involved in movements of the arm at the elbow. The muscles of the upper arm are neatly divided into compartments by intermuscular septa (Figure 10-31). The anterior compartment contains flexor muscles: the **biceps brachii, brachialis,** and **coracobrachialis,** which together provide for flexion both of the arm and of the forearm. The posterior compartment contains only a single extensor muscle, the **triceps brachii,** which extends the arm and forearm.

The biceps brachii forms a large portion of the flesh of the upper arm, and it is the muscle that tends to be shown off when people are boasting of their physical strength. As its name indicates, this is a muscle with

TABLE 10-13 Muscles of the upper arm

MUSCLE	ORIGIN	INSERTION	ACTION
Biceps brachii	Long head from upper border of glenoid fossa; short head from coracoid process of scapula	Tuberosity of radius and deep fascia of forearm	Flexes arm and forearm, supinates forearm
Coracobrachialis	Coracoid process of scapula	Medial surface of middle third of humerus	Flexes and adducts arm
Brachialis	Anterior surface of humerus	Coronoid process of ulna	Flexes forearm
Triceps brachii	Long head: infraglenoid tubercle of scapula; lateral head: proximal part of humerus; medial head: distal half of humerus	Olecranon process of ulna	Extends forearm; adducts and extends arm

B

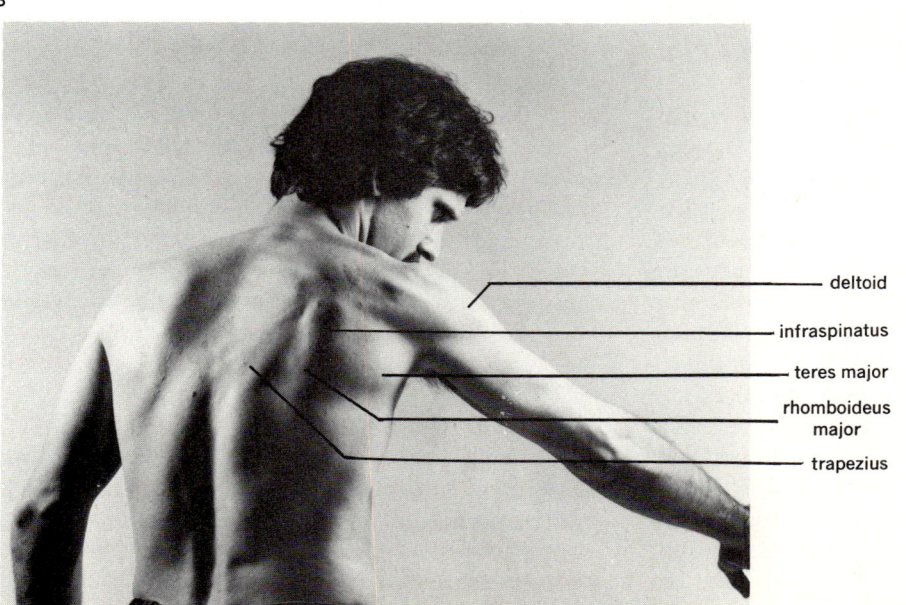

FIGURE 10-29 Muscles of the shoulder joint in action: anterior (A) and posterior (B).

— deltoid
— infraspinatus
— teres major
— rhomboideus major
— trapezius

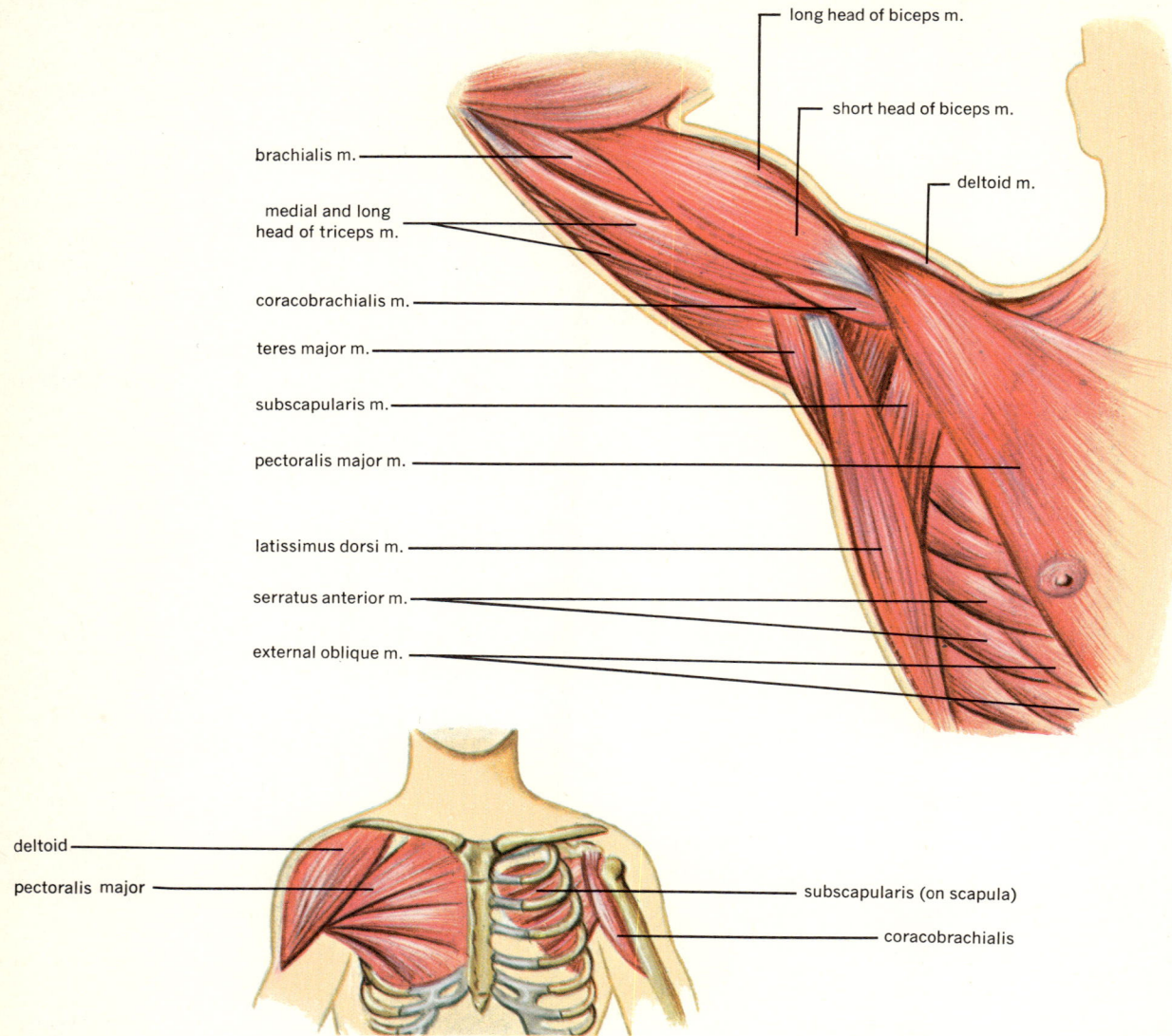

long head of biceps m.

short head of biceps m.

deltoid m.

brachialis m.

medial and long head of triceps m.

coracobrachialis m.

teres major m.

subscapularis m.

pectoralis major m.

latissimus dorsi m.

serratus anterior m.

external oblique m.

deltoid

pectoralis major

subscapularis (on scapula)

coracobrachialis

FIGURE 10-30   Muscles of the shoulder.

two heads: one arises from the glenoid fossa, and the other from the coracoid process of the scapula. The biceps brachii has just a single insertion, on the tuberosity of the radius. It thus runs from the shoulder girdle down to the forearm and produces flexion at both the shoulder and the elbow joints. This muscle also aids in supination of the hand.

The biceps brachii is assisted in its functions by two other muscles. The coracobrachialis links the coracoid process of the scapula with the middle third of the humerus and aids in flexing and adducting the arm at the shoulder. The brachialis lies deeper than the biceps and runs from the humerus down to the ulna; it aids in flexing the forearm at the elbow.

The antagonist of the biceps brachii is the triceps brachii. You can feel it contracting on the back of your arm when you extend your arm. The triceps has

three heads, arising from the margin of the glenoid fossa and two separate regions of the humerus. With a single insertion into the olecranon process of the ulna, the triceps is thus fitted to extend both the arm and the forearm, at the shoulder and elbow joints, respectively. A boxer needs well-developed triceps muscles, since these are the muscles that convert his arms into stiff rods, transmitting the force of a knockout punch.

Muscles of the Forearm

The human hand can split a block of wood with a karate chop, thread a needle, wield an ax to chop wood, repair defects inside the tiny heart of an infant, write with a pen or a typewriter, play a musical instrument, knit a sweater, hammer a nail, lift a pail of water. . . . With this tremendous diversity of activities, requiring various combinations of movements and forces, it might be expected that a large and varied assortment of muscles would control the movements of the hand and fingers. This is the case, and most of these muscles are found in the forearm. To verify this statement, grasp the middle of your right forearm with your left hand and clench your right fist, then stretch your fingers, then wiggle them. With each movement, you will feel muscles contracting in your forearm.

If you look at and feel your own forearm, you will notice that the bulk of the flesh is concentrated in two masses, just below the elbow joint: one on the radial or posterior-lateral side (remember that the thumb is on the lateral side of the hand in the standard ana-

tomical position) and the other on the ulnar or anterior-medial side (see Figure 10-31). These fleshy masses are the bellies of the muscles of the forearm: mainly extensors on the radial side and flexors on the ulnar side. The tendons of most of these muscles are inserted in the wrist and hand; some of the tendons can be distinctly felt in the region of the wrist. The muscles of these groups include both flexors and extensors of the hand and muscles that flex and extend the individual fingers and thumb.* (Some also produce adduction and abduction of the hand

* It is interesting to note that the thumb, index, and little fingers each has an individual extensor muscle of its own, while the middle and ring fingers do not, an anatomical quirk that is reflected in the relative ease of pointing with the respective fingers.

TABLE 10-14   Muscles of the forearm

MUSCLE	ORIGIN	INSERTION	ACTION
Flexor carpi radialis	Medial epicondyle of humerus	Base of 2nd metacarpal	Flexes hand and forearm, aids in pronation and abduction of hand
Flexor carpi ulnaris	Medial epicondyle of humerus, olecranon process and posterior border of ulna	Pisiform, hamate, and 5th metacarpal bones	Flexes and adducts hand
Flexor digitorum profundus	Coronoid process and shaft of ulna (proximal ¾) and interosseous membrane	Distal phalanges of fingers	Flexes hand and distal phalanges of fingers
Flexor digitorum superficialis	Medial epicondyle of humerus and coronoid process of ulna; anterior border of radius	Middle phalanges of fingers	Flexes middle phalanges, hand, and forearm
Flexor pollicis longus	Anterior surface of radius and coronoid process of ulna	Base of distal phalanx of thumb	Flexes thumb
Palmaris longus	Medial epicondyle of humerus	Transverse palmar ligament, palmar aponeurosis	Flexes hand at wrist joint
Pronator quadratus	Anterior surface and border of distal fourth of ulna	Distal fourth of shaft of radius	Pronates hand
Pronator teres	Medial epicondyle of humerus and coronoid process of ulna	Lateral surface of radius	Pronates hand
Abductor pollicis longus	Posterior surfaces of radius and ulna	Radial side of base of first metacarpal	Abducts and extends thumb
Anconeus	Back of lateral epicondyle of humerus	Olecranon and posterior surface of ulna	Extends forearm
Brachioradialis	Lateral supracondylar ridge of humerus	Styloid process of radius	Flexes forearm
Extensor carpi radialis brevis	Lateral epicondyle of humerus	Base of third metacarpal	Extends and abducts hand
Extensor carpi radialis longus	Lateral supracondylar ridge of humerus	Base of second metacarpal	Extends and abducts hand
Extensor carpi ulnaris	Lateral epicondyle of humerus; posterior border of ulna	Base of fifth metacarpal	Extends and adducts hand

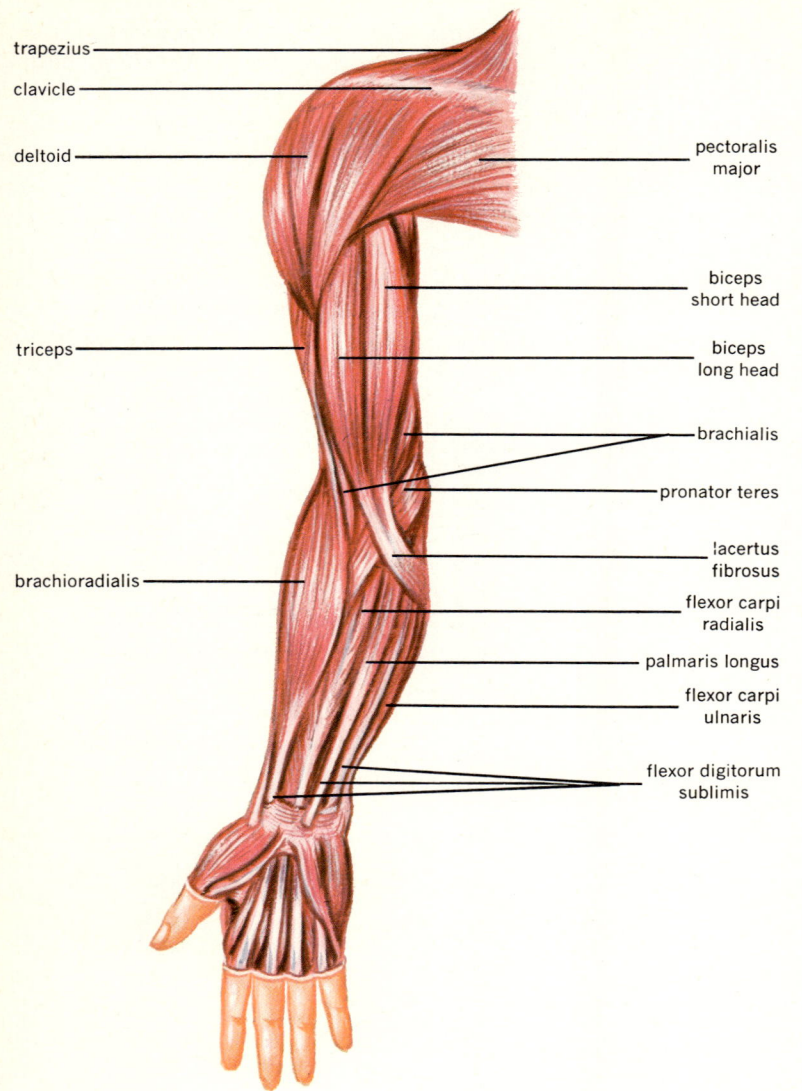

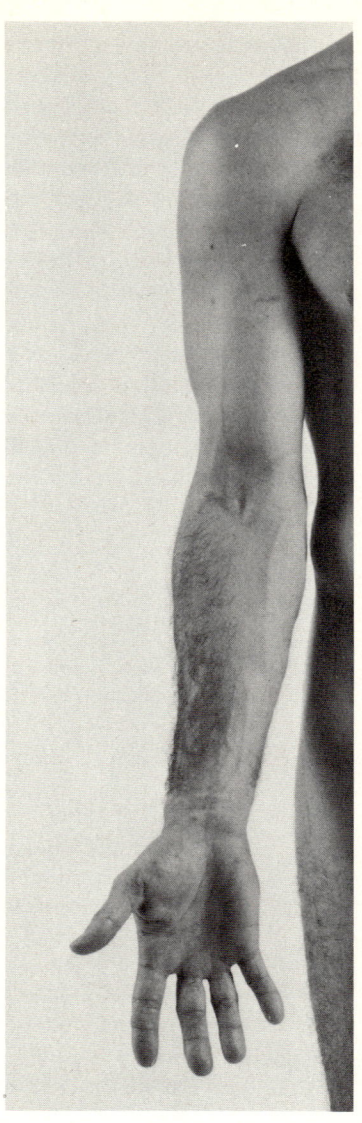

TABLE 10-14 (Continued)

MUSCLE	ORIGIN	INSERTION	ACTION
Extensor digitorum communis	Lateral epicondyle of humerus	Into middle phalanges by common extensor tendon of each finger	Extends hand and fingers
Extensor digiti minimi	Common extensor tendon of extensor digitorum communis	Phalanges of little finger	Extends little finger
Extensor indicis	Posterior surface of ulna	Common extensor tendon of index finger	Extends index finger
Extensor pollicis brevis	Middle part of posterior surface of radius	Proximal phalanx of thumb	Extends and abducts thumb
Extensor pollicis longus	Middle third of posterior surface of ulna and interosseous membrane	Distal phalanx of thumb	Extends and abducts distal phalanx of thumb
Supinator	Lateral epicondyle of humerus, ulna	Proximal third of radius	Supinates hand

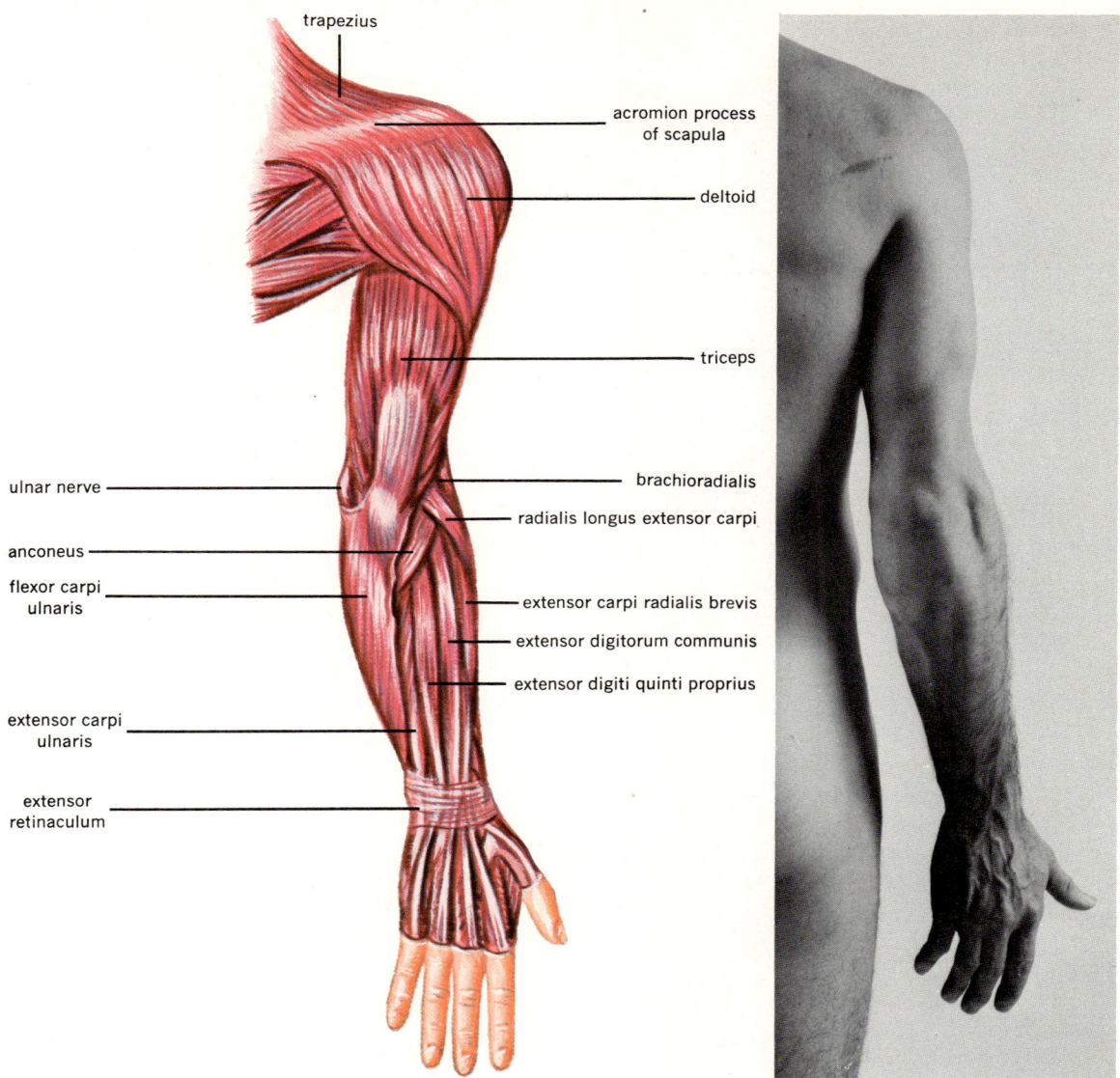

trapezius

acromion process of scapula

deltoid

triceps

brachioradialis

radialis longus extensor carpi

ulnar nerve

anconeus

flexor carpi ulnaris

extensor carpi radialis brevis

extensor digitorum communis

extensor digiti quinti proprius

extensor carpi ulnaris

extensor retinaculum

FIGURE 10-31   Muscles of the upper extremity: flexor surface (A) and extensor surface (B).

thumb.) In addition, there are muscles that pronate and supinate the hand (turn the palm down and up, respectively). The principal muscles of the forearm are summarized in Table 10-14.

Muscles of the Hand

The "hands" of lower animals often seem superficially similar to the human hand. A squirrel, for example, sits up to eat a nut or berry, gripping its food in its "fingers" much as a person would hold a sandwich. Yet a squirrel's "hands" are far less versatile than ours. (When it wants to pick up and carry something, it holds the object in its mouth, not its paws.) The key difference is in the human's opposable thumb, a feature that is shared only by our primate relatives. You can easily touch the tip of your thumb to the tips of each of your fingers in turn. Try it, and then, to contrast the grasping potentialities of your human hand with that of a squirrel, try touching the tip of your index finger to the tips of the other fingers.

Many of the muscles that move the thumb and fingers are muscles of the forearm, as we have already seen. There are also a number of muscles confined to the body of the hand, which participate in its varied actions. They fall into three main groups (Figure 10-32): muscles that act on the thumb form the **thenar eminence,** a pronounced mass on the lateral side of the palm. On the medial side of the palm, the **hypothenar eminence** consists of the muscles that move the little finger. The **midpalmar** muscles are found

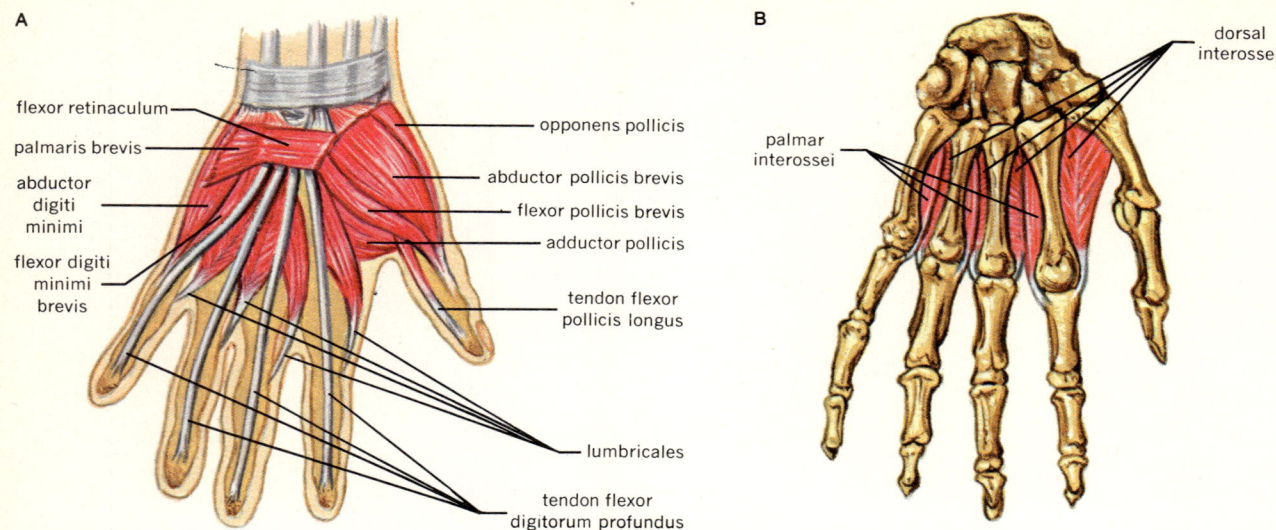

FIGURE 10-32   Muscles of the hand. (A) Superficial muscles; (B) superficial muscles have been removed to reveal the interossei.

TABLE 10-15   Muscles of the hand

MUSCLE	ORIGIN	INSERTION	ACTION
Abductor digiti minimi	Pisiform bone; tendon of flexor carpi ulnaris	Proximal phalanx of little finger	Abducts little finger
Abductor pollicis brevis	Transverse carpal ligament and lateral part of carpus (scaphoid and trapezium)	Proximal phalanx of thumb	Abducts thumb; flexes the proximal and extends the distal phalanx
Adductor pollicis	2nd and 3rd metacarpals, capitate, and ligaments	Proximal phalanx of thumb	Adducts and opposes thumb
Flexor digiti minimi brevis	Transverse carpal ligament, hook of hamate bone	Proximal phalanx of little finger	Flexes proximal phalanx of little finger
Flexor pollicis brevis	Transverse carpal ligament, ridge of trapezium	Base of proximal phalanx of thumb	Flexes and adducts thumb
Interossei volares (4)	Adjacent sides of metacarpal bones	Proximal phalanges of index, middle, and ring fingers and extensor digitorum tendon	Abduct fingers (relative to midline of hand), flex proximal and extend middle and distal phalanges
Interossei palmares (4)	Sides of 2nd, 4th, and 5th metacarpals	Proximal phalanges of index, ring, and little fingers and extensor digitorum tendon	Adduct index, ring, and little fingers (relative to midline of hand) and flex proximal and extend middle and distal phalanges
Lumbricales (4)	Tendons of flexor digitorum profundus	Tendons of extensor digitorum	Flex proximal and extend middle and distal phalanges
Opponens digiti minimi	Transverse carpal ligament and hook of hamate	5th metacarpal	Rotates and abducts little finger
Opponens pollicis	Transverse carpal ligament and ridge of trapezium	Lateral side of first metacarpal	Flexes and opposes thumb (adducts and rotates medially)
Palmaris brevis	Palmar aponeurosis	Skin of medial side of palm	Tenses palm of hand, wrinkles skin of palm

within the width of the palm, between the metacarpal bones. The muscles of the hand are summarized in Table 10-15.

MUSCLES OF THE LOWER EXTREMITIES

The picture of an executive leaning back in a chair, with feet propped up on the desk, is in sharp contrast to the normal functions of the lower extremity: support and movement. In a sitting position, the pelvis is flexed, and the weight of the body falls on the ischial tuberosities. In a standing position, the bony basin of the pelvis must support the abdominal organs, and the weight of the body is transmitted down through the bones of the legs to the feet. Walking, running, and leaping require a variety of movements at the hip joints. Flexion, extension, abduction, adduction, circumduction, and rotation are all possible at these ball-and-socket joints, but the benefits of freedom of motion are balanced against a need for stability and support. In Chapter 8 we saw some of the modifications of the bone structure of the pelvis and legs for these functions. The muscles of the lower extremities, like the bones, show many modifications for these basic functions. While similar in general plan to the muscles of the upper extremities, they are generally stronger and heavier, and in certain cases more restrictive of mobility at the joints.

A key distinction between the muscles of the upper and lower extremities is in the direction of their action: the normal function of the muscles of the arm is to transfer the hand from place to place, and their operation from a fixed insertion is the exception rather than the rule (for example, in climbing a rope); for most of the leg muscles, on the other hand, the main function is to act from their insertions to move the trunk relative to the ground. Even when a person is standing still, various groups of leg muscles must contract continually to compensate for shifts of the body's center of gravity and prevent the person from toppling over. In this reversed action of the leg muscles, their insertions are indirectly fixed through the friction between the sole of the foot and the ground. In walking, the action of the leg muscles alternates: as a foot is lifted and moved forward, the trunk is the portion of the body that is relatively fixed, and the origin and insertion of the muscles function in their normal sense. But when the foot is placed on the ground and begins to bear the body's weight, the foot is the fixed point, and each insertion can be viewed as an origin.

Muscles of the Buttocks

If your ischial tuberosities were not covered with flesh and you tried to sit for any length of time, the skin of your buttocks would quickly become a mass of bruises and sores. Fortunately for people with sedentary occupations, the buttocks contain the largest mass of muscle in the body, formed by the three **gluteal muscles** (Figure 10-33). In addition, the buttocks are padded by varying amounts of fat deposits. Among certain African tribes, fatness of the buttocks (technically referred to as **steatopygia**) is prized as an attribute of feminine beauty, and the "Hottentot bustle" sometimes reaches truly exotic proportions.

The functions of the gluteal muscles are far more important than merely serving as a seat cushion. The **gluteus maximus,** the largest muscle in the body, is a powerful extensor of the thigh, and it also rotates the lower extremity laterally. When you stand on one leg, the gluteus maximus supports your trunk on the fe-

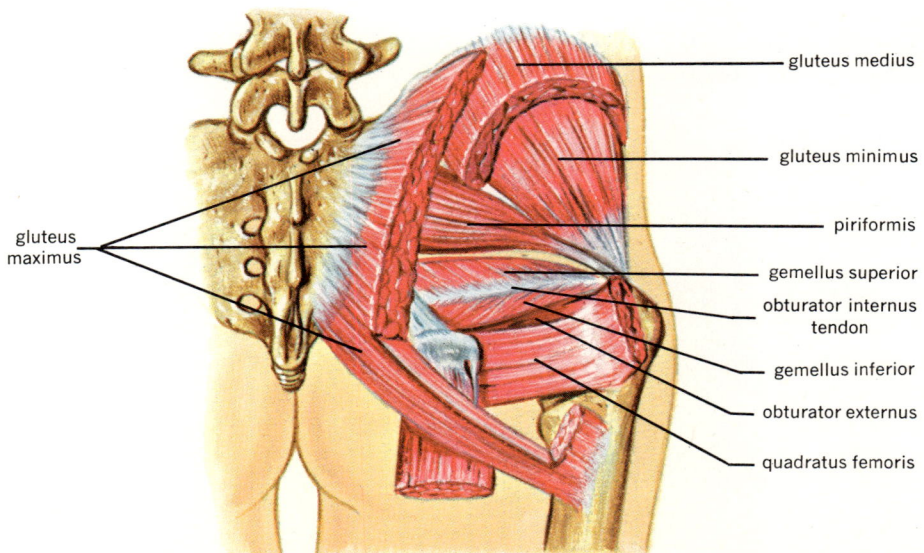

FIGURE 10-33 Muscles of the gluteal region. The gluteus maximus and gluteus medius have been cut to expose the underlying muscles.

gluteus maximus

gluteus medius

gluteus minimus

piriformis

gemellus superior

obturator internus tendon

gemellus inferior

obturator externus

quadratus femoris

mur. This muscle does a major share of the work in walking up stairs and climbing hills. It is also a favorite target for intramuscular injections. The other two gluteal muscles, the **gluteus medius** and **gluteus minimus** (whose names are an indication of their relative size), abduct the thigh when the leg is extended and also rotate the thigh medially. These and the other muscles of the gluteal region are summarized in Table 10-16.

Muscles of the Thigh

Ham and leg of lamb are cuts of meat consisting of thigh muscles. The human thigh is also a heavily muscled area, and its numerous muscles play a crucial role in supporting and moving the body. Like the muscles of the upper extremity, those of the lower extremity are covered with tough deep fascia, folds of which divide the thigh muscles into compartments. The deep fascia of the thigh are particularly tough and are referred to as the **fascia lata.** Thickened portions of the fascia lata form the **gluteal aponeuroses,** extending over a large portion of the buttocks, and the **iliotibial tract,** a band that extends downward over the thigh to the lateral condyle of the tibia.

The thigh muscles are found in three main compartments (Figure 10-34): the anterior compartment, containing extensor muscles; the medial compartment, housing adductors; and the posterior compartment, containing flexors.

The extensor muscle of the anterior compartment is the **quadriceps femoris** muscle, a four-headed structure that inserts by a common tendon into the tuberosity of the tibia and is usually described as four individual muscles: the **rectus femoris, vastus medialis, vastus lateralis,** and **vastus intermedius.** These muscles act to extend the leg at the knee joint. They do not extend the thigh; in fact, the rectus femoris acts to flex the thigh at the hip joint. The major muscle that functions in extending the thigh is the gluteus maximus, already discussed.

The long, ribbonlike **sartorius** muscle (the longest muscle in the body) crosses the anterior surface of the thigh obliquely. The sartorius is not an extensor muscle; it flexes the thigh and leg and rotates the thigh laterally. Its name comes from a Latin word meaning "tailor," for this is the muscle involved in assuming the cross-legged sitting position that old-time tailors used to use.

The medial compartment of the thigh contains a number of adductor muscles: the **adductor brevis, adductor longus, adductor magnus, gracilis, obturator externus,** and **pectineus.** These muscles act during crossing of the knees and in gripping a saddle with the thighs.

TABLE 10-16   Muscles of the buttocks

MUSCLE	ORIGIN	INSERTION	ACTION
Gemellus inferior	Tuberosity of ischium	Greater trochanter of femur (with obturator internus)	Rotates thigh laterally
Gemellus superior	Spine of ischium	Greater trochanter of femur (with obturator internus)	Rotates thigh laterally
Gluteus maximus	Lateral surface of ilium (upper portion), dorsal surface of sacrum and coccyx, and sacrotuberous ligament	Iliotibial band of fascia lata and gluteal tuberosity of femur	Extends, abducts, and rotates thigh laterally
Gluteus medius	Lateral surface of ilium (middle portion)	Greater trochanter of femur	Abducts and medially rotates thigh
Gluteus minimus	Lateral surface of ilium (middle portion)	Greater trochanter of femur	Abducts and medially rotates thigh
Obturator internus	Pelvic surface of pubis, ischium, and obturator membrane	Greater trochanter of femur	Rotates thigh laterally
Piriformis	Ilium, 2nd to 4th sacral vertebrae	Upper border of greater trochanter of femur	Rotates thigh laterally
Quadratus femoris	Ischial tuberosity	Below greater trochanter of femur	Rotates thigh laterally
Tensor fascia latae	Iliac crest	Iliotibial band of fascia lata	Tenses fascia lata (external fascia of thigh); flexes and abducts thigh

The thigh, like the upper arm, has a biceps. The **biceps femoris** is one of the flexor group, enclosed in the posterior compartment of the thigh. It acts to flex the leg and rotate it laterally, but it *extends* and adducts the thigh (for example, in arching the back). Two other muscles of this group, the **semitendinosus** and **semimembranosus,** similarly flex the leg and extend and adduct the thigh, and produce medial rotation as well.* The posterior flexor muscles are sometimes called the **hamstring muscles,** because of their

* All of the flexors of the posterior compartment of the thigh must be completely relaxed in order for you to bend over and touch your toes without bending your knees.

cordlike tendons, which can be felt at the back of the knee. (The one-time barbaric practice of crippling an enemy by cutting the tendons of his hamstring muscles survives today in a figure of speech, "to hamstring," meaning to cripple or make powerless and ineffective.)

Flexion of the thigh is produced mainly by contraction of the **iliopsoas muscle,** which is actually a combination of two muscles, the **iliacus** and the **psoas major.** It might be useful to recall here that flexion of the thigh can occur in several ways: when the leg is raised in walking or running; in sitting down; and when the legs remain fixed and the trunk is bent over at the hips, as in leaning over a table. Look back at the

TABLE 10-17   Muscles of the thigh

MUSCLE	ORIGIN	INSERTION	ACTION
Quadriceps femoris: compound muscle consisting of:			
Rectus femoris	Anterior inferior iliac spine and rim of acetabulum	Tuberosity of tibia; patella	Extends leg and flexes thigh
Vastus medialis	Medial aspect of femur	Tuberosity of tibia; patella	Extends leg
Vastus lateralis	Lateral aspect of femur and capsule of hip joint	Tuberosity of tibia; patella	Extends leg
Vastus intermedius	Anterior and lateral surfaces of femur	Tuberosity of tibia; patella	Extends leg
Sartorius	Anterior superior spine of ilium	Upper medial surface of tibia	Flexes thigh and leg and rotates thigh laterally
Adductor brevis	Inferior ramus of pubis	Upper part of linea aspera of femur	Adducts, flexes, and laterally rotates thigh
Adductor longus	Crest and symphysis of pubis	Linea aspera of femur	Adducts, flexes, and laterally rotates thigh
Adductor magnus	Rami of pubis and ischium; ischial tuberosity	Linea aspera and adductor tubercle of femur	Adducts, flexes, and laterally rotates thigh
Gracilis	Inferior ramus of pubis	Medial surface of body of tibia	Adducts thigh, flexes and medially rotates leg at knee joint
Obturator externus	Pubis, ischium, and obturator membrane	Trochanteric fossa of femur	Rotates thigh laterally, aids in adduction
Pectineus	Pectineal line of pubis	Femur between lesser trochanter and linea aspera	Flexes and adducts thigh
Biceps femoris	Ischial tuberosity (long head), linea aspera of femur (short head)	Head of fibula and lateral condyle of tibia	Flexes leg at knee, rotates leg laterally, extends thigh
Semimembranosus	Ischial tuberosity	Medial condyle of tibia	Flexes and medially rotates leg, extends thigh
Semitendinosus	Ischial tuberosity	Upper and medial surface of tibia	Flexes and medially rotates leg, extends thigh
Iliopsoas: compound muscle consisting of:			
Iliacus	Iliac fossa of ilium and base of sacrum	Lesser trochanter of femur	Flexes, adducts, and medially rotates thigh; rotates trunk on extremity
Psoas major	Transverse processes of lumbar vertebrae	Lesser trochanter of femur	Flexes trunk, flexes and medially rotates thigh

A

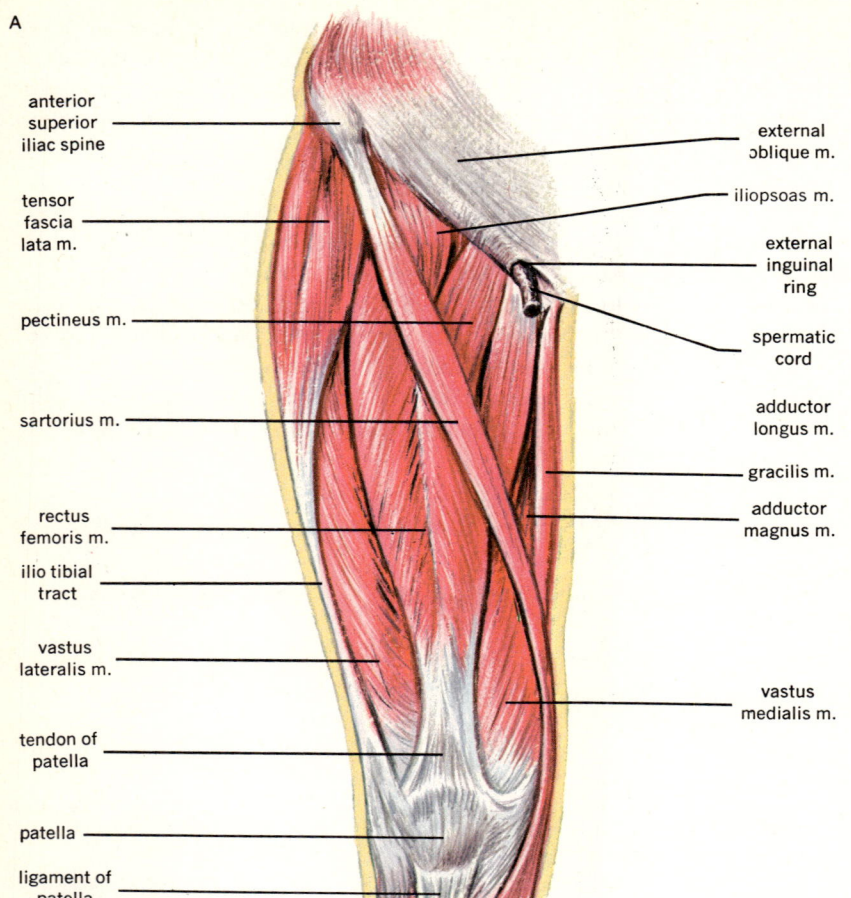

anterior
superior
iliac spine

tensor
fascia
lata m.

pectineus m.

sartorius m.

rectus
femoris m.

ilio tibial
tract

vastus
lateralis m.

tendon of
patella

patella

ligament of
patella

external
oblique m.

iliopsoas m.

external
inguinal
ring

spermatic
cord

adductor
longus m.

gracilis m.

adductor
magnus m.

vastus
medialis m.

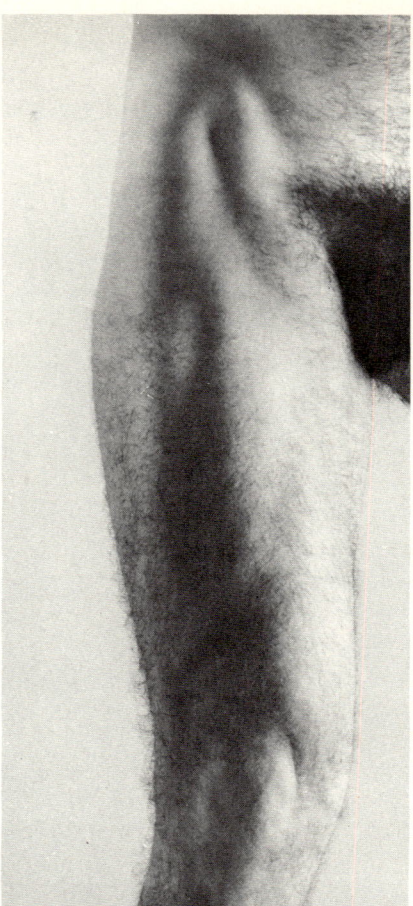

FIGURE 10-34 Superficial muscles of the right upper leg: anterior (A) and posterior (B) views.

diagrams of the thigh muscles and mentally work out the direction of their action in each case.

Muscles of the Leg

The calf muscles are among the strongest muscles of the body. They can withstand forces of more than a ton. This capacity is of more than academic interest, for jumping and leaping impose tremendous compressive forces on the lower legs, and these shocks are absorbed mainly by the calf muscles. The calf muscle and the other muscles of the lower leg help to steady the legs in a standing position and control the movements of the feet during walking, running, and other forms of locomotion.

Like the muscles of the thigh, those of the lower leg are divided into three main compartments (Figure 10-35): the anterior compartment, containing extensor muscles; the lateral or **peroneal** compartment; and the posterior compartment, containing flexors. The muscles of the lower leg produce movements at the hinge joint of the knee and at the more freely movable ankle joint.

The extensor muscles of the anterior compartment

of the leg include the **extensor digitorum longus,** the **extensor hallucis longus,** the **peroneus tertius,** and the **tibialis anterior.** All of these muscles act to extend the toes and produce **dorsiflexion** of the foot (bending at the ankle joint so that the toes are brought upward). The extensor digitorum longus is inserted by four tendons into the lateral four toes; the great toe has its own individual extensor muscle, the extensor hallucis longus. The tibialis anterior is a muscle commonly affected in poliomyelitis; paralysis of this muscle produces the typical "drop-foot" gait, as the polio victim raises the leg higher than usual in walking to keep dragging toes clear of the ground. (With the antagonist of the leg's flexor muscles out of action, the foot becomes **plantar flexed**—bent downward at the ankle joint.) When you bend your foot upward, the tendons of the extensor muscles become very prominent in the region of the ankle.

The lateral compartment contains only two muscles, the **peroneus longus** and the **peroneus brevis.** These muscles form a sling around the longitudinal arch of the foot that helps to support it.

The most prominent of the flexor muscles in the

B

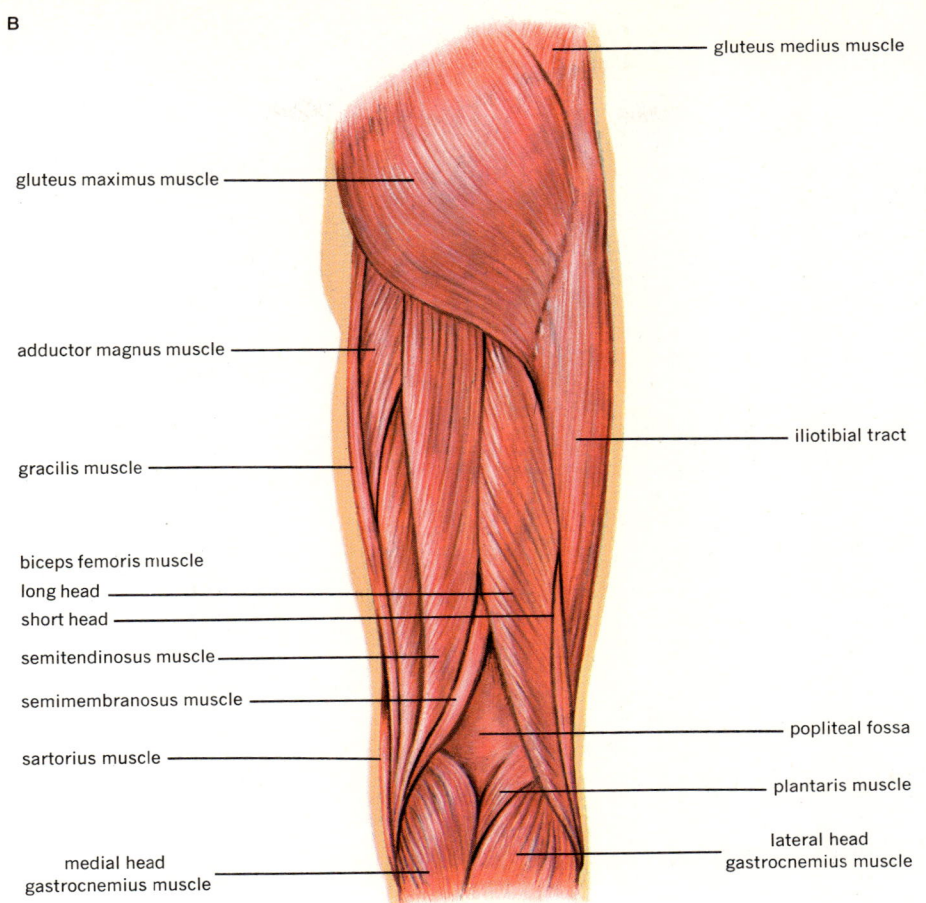

gluteus medius muscle

gluteus maximus muscle

adductor magnus muscle

gracilis muscle

iliotibial tract

biceps femoris muscle
long head
short head
semitendinosus muscle
semimembranosus muscle
sartorius muscle

popliteal fossa

plantaris muscle

lateral head
gastrocnemius muscle

medial head
gastrocnemius muscle

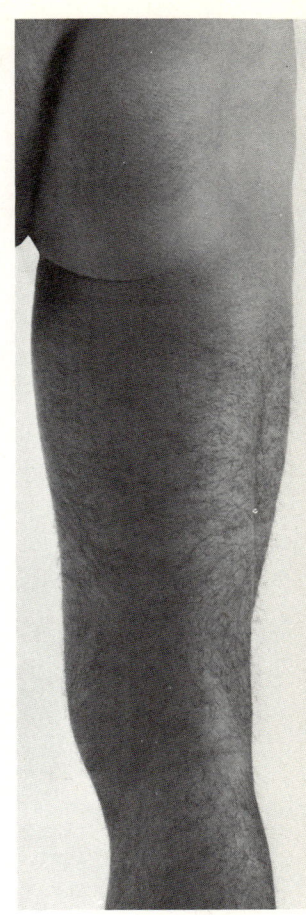

posterior compartment is the **gastrocnemius** muscle, which forms the bulging calf at the back of the leg. Together with another flexor, the **soleus,** it is inserted into the calcaneus (heel bone) by the thickest and most powerful tendon in the body, the **Achilles tendon.** The calf muscles act to lift the heel, producing plantar flexion of the foot. These are the muscles that contract when you stand on your toes. Shoes with heels produce varying degrees of plantar flexion. The "Earth shoes" that have recently been gaining in popularity are designed according to a different plan, with the fronts of the soles built up higher than the heels. Proponents of such shoes claim they promote a more natural distribution of body weight and are good for the spine; however, people who try them for the first time experience aching calf muscles for several weeks, due to the stretching of their Achilles tendons in the dorsiflexing shoes.

The **popliteus** is a thin, triangular muscle, which spans the gap between the outer condyle of the femur and the upper end of the tibia. It acts to "unlock" the extended knee joint at the beginning of flexion. The **flexor digitorum longus** and the **flexor hallucis longus,**

like the corresponding extensor muscles, are inserted by separate tendons into the four lateral toes and the great toe, respectively. The main characteristics of these and the other muscles of the lower leg are summarized in Table 10-18.

Muscles of the Foot

The feet are among the most under-appreciated structures in the body. They take thousands of steps each day, often crammed into ill-fitting or poorly designed footwear. They are capable of withstanding the crashing jar of impact after the leap of a pole vaulter, or supporting the body of a ballet dancer in graceful pirouettes. Their potentials as skilled manipulating tools are undeveloped in people who have normal arms, and the feet remain humble servants, abused and stepped on. Usually we do not even think about them except when they are aching or blistered (likely as a result of our mistreatment).

In Chapter 8 we saw the efficient engineering of the bone structure of the foot, providing for arches that enhance its strength and resiliency. Working with the bones of the foot is a complement of muscles, largely

A

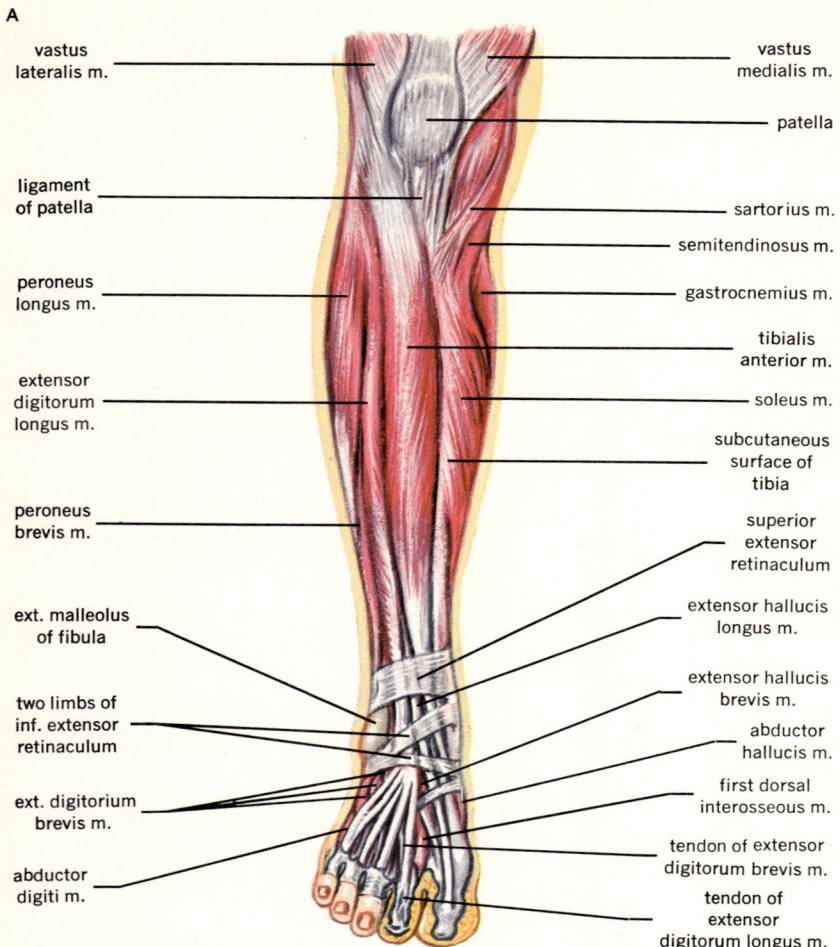

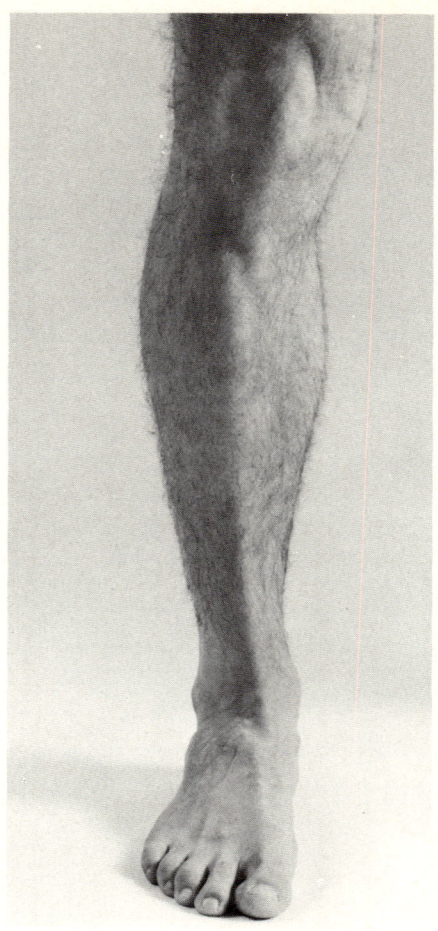

vastus lateralis m.

vastus medialis m.

patella

ligament of patella

sartorius m.

semitendinosus m.

peroneus longus m.

gastrocnemius m.

tibialis anterior m.

extensor digitorum longus m.

soleus m.

subcutaneous surface of tibia

peroneus brevis m.

superior extensor retinaculum

ext. malleolus of fibula

extensor hallucis longus m.

two limbs of inf. extensor retinaculum

extensor hallucis brevis m.

abductor hallucis m.

ext. digitorium brevis m.

first dorsal interosseous m.

tendon of extensor digitorum brevis m.

abductor digiti m.

tendon of extensor digitorum longus m.

FIGURE 10-35 Superficial muscles of the right lower leg and foot: anterior (A) and posterior (B) views.

TABLE 10-18 Muscles of the leg

MUSCLE	ORIGIN	INSERTION	ACTION
Extensor digitorum longus	Anterior surface of fibula, lateral condyle of tibia	Extensor tendons of 4 lateral toes	Extends toes
Extensor hallucis longus	Front of fibula (middle half) and interosseous membrane	Distal phalanx of great toe	Dorsiflexes ankle joint, extends great toe
Peroneus tertius	Medial surface of fibula	Fifth metatarsal	Dorsiflexes and everts foot
Tibialis anterior	Tibia, interosseous membrane	Medial cuneiform and base of first metatarsal	Dorsiflexes and inverts foot
Peroneus brevis	Lateral surface of fibula	Fifth metatarsal	Abducts, everts (turns outward) and plantar flexes foot
Peroneus longus	Lateral condyle of tibia, lateral surface of fibula	Medial cuneiform and base of first metatarsal	Abducts, everts, and plantar flexes foot; supports arch of foot
Flexor digitorum longus	Posterior surface of shaft of tibia	Distal phalanges of 4 lateral toes	Flexes toes; plantar flexes and inverts foot
Flexor hallucis longus	Posterior surface of fibula and intermuscular septum	Distal phalanx of big toe	Flexes big toe
Gastrocnemius	Condyles of femur and capsule of knee	With soleus into calcaneus via Achilles tendon	Plantar flexes ankle joint, flexes knee joint

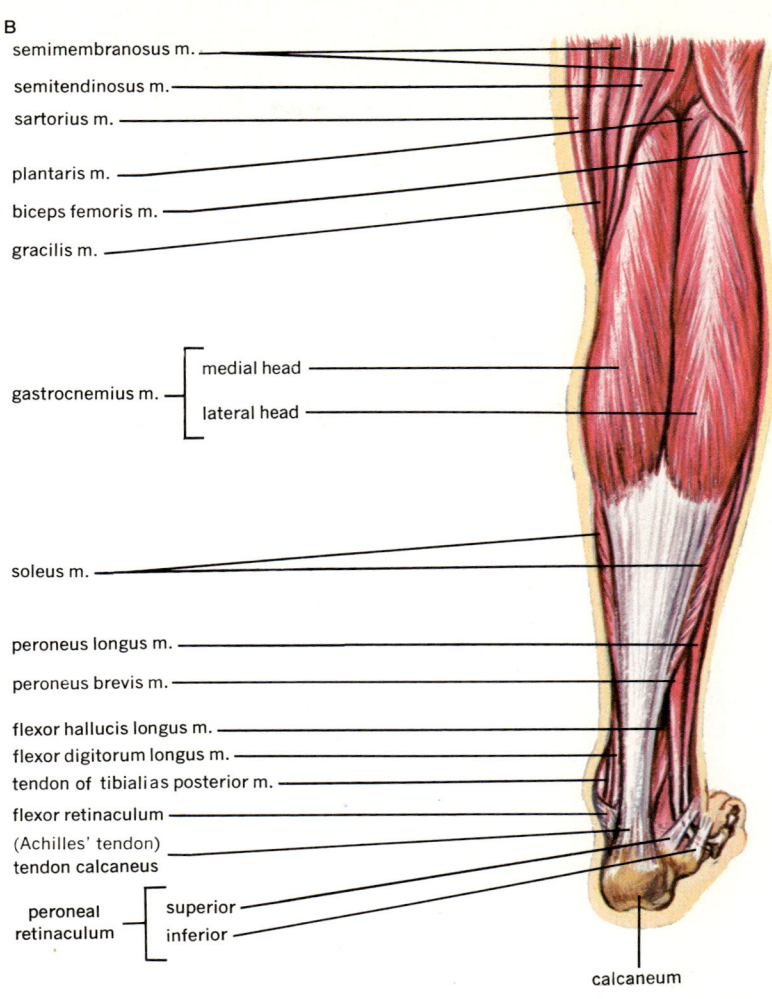

B

semimembranosus m.
semitendinosus m.
sartorius m.
plantaris m.
biceps femoris m.
gracilis m.

gastrocnemius m. — medial head / lateral head

soleus m.

peroneus longus m.
peroneus brevis m.
flexor hallucis longus m.
flexor digitorum longus m.
tendon of tibialis posterior m.
flexor retinaculum
(Achilles' tendon) tendon calcaneus

peroneal retinaculum — superior / inferior

calcaneum

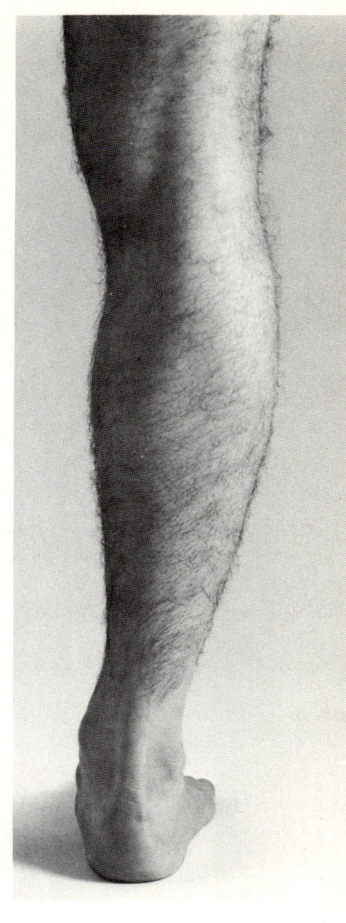

TABLE 10-18 (Continued)

MUSCLE	ORIGIN	INSERTION	ACTION
Plantaris	Lateral condyle of femur	Posterior part of calcaneus	Weakly plantar flexes foot
Popliteus	Lateral condyle of femur	Posterior surface of tibia (proximal fourth)	Flexes leg, rotates leg inward; from fixed tibia rotates femur laterally
Soleus	Fibula, popliteal fascia, tibia	With gastrocnemius into calcaneus via Achilles tendon	Plantar flexes ankle joint
Tibialis posterior	Posterior surfaces of tibia, fibula, and interosseous membrane	Navicular; cuboid; all cuneiforms; 2nd, 3rd, and 4th metatarsals	Plantar flexes and inverts foot, helps to maintain arch of foot

analogous to the muscles of the hand but modified in various respects for functions of weight bearing and locomotion.

Muscles of the leg that move the foot and toes have already been described. In addition, there are a number of intrinsic muscles of the foot. Structurally they may be viewed as lying in four successively deeper layers (Figure 10-36). Functionally, they fall into three groups: those associated with the big toe, those associated with the little toe, and those associated with the four lateral toes. The big toe is provided with individual muscles for three different types of movement: a flexor, an abductor, and an adductor. The little toe has its own individual abductor and flexor muscles. (With some practice, you may be able to learn to abduct your little toe without moving any

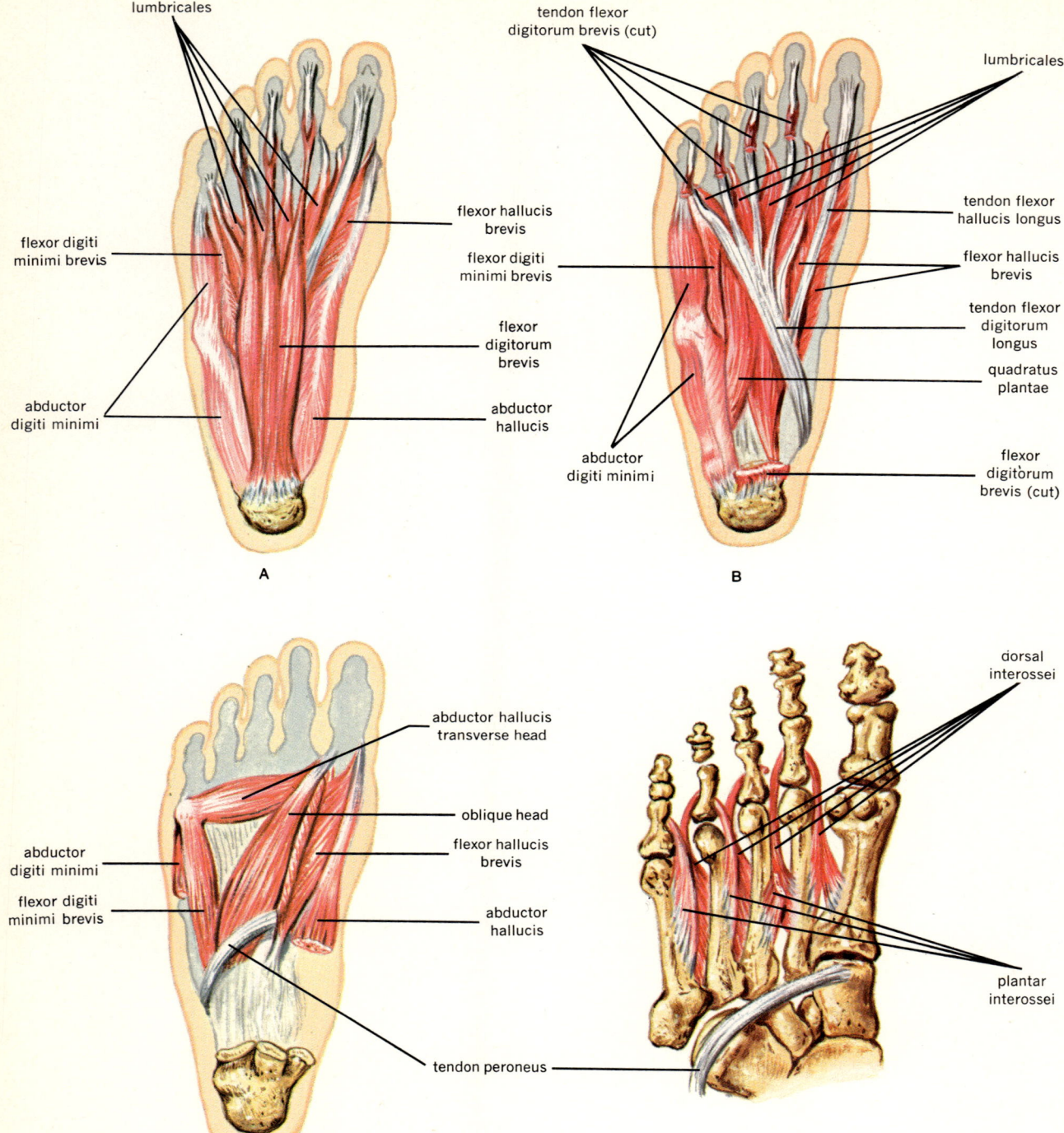

FIGURE 10-36 Intrinsic muscles of the foot. A, B, C, and D show successively deeper layers of muscles.

other part of the foot; this feat cannot be accomplished with any of the other lateral toes.) A point to recall in considering movements of the foot is that abduction and adduction are regarded as occurring relative to the second toe, whereas in the hand the middle finger is considered as the midline.

The intrinsic muscles of the foot are summarized in Table 10-19.

SUMMARY

Muscles are the machines of the body: they transform chemical energy into a directed force and generally produce movement.

Muscle cells are highly specialized for contractility. They contain the contractile proteins actin and myosin.

The three types of muscle tissue are: skeletal, smooth, and cardiac.

Skeletal muscles are usually attached to bones; they have a capacity for great power but cannot keep up contractions for long.

TABLE 10-19 Muscles of the foot

MUSCLE	ORIGIN	INSERTION	ACTION
Abductor digiti minimi pedis	Calcaneus and fascia of sole	Proximal phalanx of little toe	Abducts little toe
Abductor hallucis	Calcaneus and fascia of sole	Proximal phalanx of big toe	Abducts and flexes big toe
Adductor hallucis			
Oblique head	2nd, 3rd, and 4th metatarsals and sheath of peroneus longus	Proximal phalanx of big toe	Adducts and flexes big toe
Transverse head	Capsules of metatarsophalangeal joints of 3 lateral toes	Proximal phalanx of big toe	Adducts big toe; holds heads of metatarsal bones together and supports transverse arch
Extensor digitorum brevis	Dorsal surface of calcaneus	Extensor tendons of 1st, 2nd, 3rd, and 4th toes	Extends toes
Flexor digiti minimi brevis	5th metatarsal and fascia of sole	Proximal phalanx of little toe	Flexes little toe
Flexor digitorum brevis	Calcaneus and fascia of sole	Middle phalanges of 4 lateral toes	Flexes 4 lateral toes
Flexor hallucis brevis	Cuboid and 3rd cuneiform	Proximal phalanx of big toe	Flexes big toe
Interossei plantares (3)	Medial surface of 3rd, 4th, and 5th metatarsals	Extensor tendons of 3rd, 4th, and 5th toes	Adduct lateral 3 toes toward 2nd toe
Interossei dorsales (4)	Surfaces of adjacent metatarsals	Extensor tendons of 2nd, 3rd, and 4th toes	Abduct and flex lateral toes, moves 2nd toe from side to side
Lumbricales	Tendons of flexor digitorum longus	Extensor tendons of 4 lateral toes	Flex proximal phalanges of toes
Quadratus plantae	Calcaneus and fascia of sole	Tendons of flexor digitorum longus	Aids in flexing toes (straightens pull of tendon of flexor digitorum longus)

Smooth muscles are found in the walls of the viscera; their contractions are slow and steady and can go on indefinitely without resting.

Cardiac muscle is the muscle of the heart; it normally works steadily but can deliver high power for short periods when necessary.

Skeletal muscle tissue is also called striated muscle tissue, from the pattern of alternating dark and light bands (striations) observed on microscopic preparations.

The fine structure of striated muscle tissue includes:
   A bands
   I bands
   Z lines
   H zones
   M lines

The sarcomere is the structural and contracting unit of a muscle fiber and extends from one Z line to the next.

A skeletal muscle fiber contains myofibrils, which in turn contain myofilaments:
   Thick myofilaments are composed of myosin.
   Thin myofilaments are composed of actin, with tropomyosin and troponin.

During muscle contraction, the thick and thin myofilaments slide over one another, decreasing the overall length of the sarcomere.

Microscopic structural features of skeletal muscle cells include:
   multiple nuclei scattered over periphery of cell
   sarcolemma
   sarcoplasmic reticulum
   T-system
   myoglobin

Smooth muscle cells lack the pattern of cross-banding.
   They contain myofibrils, which are composed of myofilaments:
      Thick myofilaments (myosin)
      Intermediate-size myofilaments
      Thin myofilaments (actin)
   Other microscopic structural features of smooth muscle cells include:
      single nucleus in center of cell
      sarcolemma
      sarcoplasmic reticulum

Cardiac muscle tissue is composed of cardiac muscle fibers and specialized cells of the conducting system.
   Cardiac muscle fibers exhibit features resembling striated and smooth muscle:
      striations with A, I, and Z bands
      usually a single nucleus at center of cell
      T-system (in ventricles only)
   Special structural features of cardiac muscle tissue include:
      Joining of fibers into an interconnected network
      Intercalated discs formed by sarcolemmas of adjacent cells
      Lipofuscin ("aging pigment") deposits, increasing with age

Shapes of skeletal muscles include:
   Fusiform (tapering, with fibers parallel to long axis)
   Flat sheets (fibers parallel)
   Triangular (e.g., deltoid) (fibers converge)

Pennate (one-sided feather)

Bipennate (two-sided feather)

Ring-shaped (sphincter muscles)

Each individual skeletal muscle fiber is encased in an endomysium (connective tissue sheath); bundles of skeletal muscle cells (fasciculi) are encased in a perimysium; groups of fasciculi, wrapped in an epimysium, form a muscle.

Envelopes called septa may separate different groups of muscles.

The epimysium, perimysium, and endomysium are continuous with the tendons and aponeuroses that attach muscles to bones or other structures.

The attachment of a muscle to an immovable structure is called the origin.

The attachment of a muscle to a movable structure is called the insertion.

The fleshy expanded middle portion is called the belly or body of the muscle.

Skeletal muscle has a good blood supply.

It is supplied with afferent sensory nerves and somatic efferent nerves.

The junction between the nerve ending (motor end plate) and the muscle fiber is called a myoneural (or neuromuscular) junction.

A single neuron and the group of muscle fibers with which it is in contact is called a motor unit.

Smooth muscle tissue is arranged in cords, bundles, and sheets.

Tubular organs often contain concentric layers of circular and longitudinal smooth muscle.

Smooth muscle tissue has a fair blood supply.

Smooth muscles have parasympathetic and sympathetic innervation; their contractions are not under voluntary control.

Sensory nerves (stretch receptors) may also be present.

Cardiac muscle fibers are arranged in thin layers, forming perimysium-encased fascicles, and arranged in a wide spiral stretching from the base to the apex of the heart to form the myocardium.

The interconnections of the cardiac muscle fibers link the muscle into continuous protoplasmic sheets, the fibers of which contract as a unit.

Cardiac muscle has a rich blood supply.

Cardiac muscle contractions occur spontaneously, independent of nervous stimulation, but the rate of heart contraction may be controlled by impulses carried over sympathetic and parasympathetic nerve fibers.

Sensory nerves relay information on the heart's oxygen supply to the brain.

In women, skeletal muscles comprise 36 percent of body weight, in men 42 percent.

There are about 656 skeletal muscles in the body. Many of them are paired.

Muscles cannot push; they can only pull. Movements are produced by muscles pulling on bones. Variety of movements is achieved by muscles working in coordinated groups.

The muscle contracting to produce a particular movement is the prime mover.

Muscles that aid the prime mover are called synergists.

Muscles that act oppositely to the prime mover are called antagonists.

A particular muscle's role may vary, depending on the movement involved.

Criteria for naming muscles include:

Location in the body

Points of attachment

Shape, size, and structure

Number of heads of origin

Direction of muscle fibers

Action produced

Flexor

Extensor

Abductor

Adductor

Supinator

Pronator

Dorsiflexor

Plantar flexor

Levator

Depressor

Sphincter

Divisions of the skeletal muscles:

Axial muscles

Muscles of the head and neck

Muscles of the trunk

Appendicular muscles

Muscles of the upper extremities

Muscles of the lower extremities

Muscles of the head and neck:

Muscles of the scalp

Occipitofrontalis

Temporoparietalis

Auricularis anterior

Auricularis posterior

Auricularis superior

Muscles of the face

Orbicularis oculi

Levator palpebrae superioris

Corrugator supercilii

Procerus

Nasalis

Depressor septi

Dilator nares

Levator labii superioris alaeque nasi

Orbicularis oris

Buccinator

Zygomaticus major

Zygomaticus minor

Risorius

Levator anguli oris

Depressor anguli oris

Levator labii superioris

Depressor labii inferioris

Mentalis

Muscles of the eye

Superior rectus

Inferior rectus

Medial rectus

Lateral rectus

Superior oblique

Inferior oblique

Muscles of mastication

Masseter

Temporalis

Lateral pterygoid

Medial pterygoid

Muscles of the tongue and palate

Intrinsic: vertical, horizontal, longitudinal

Genioglossus

Styloglossus

Hyoglossus

Stylohyoid

Mylohyoid

Geniohyoid

Levator veli palatini

Tensor veli palatini

Uvulae

Palatoglossus

Palatopharyngeus
Muscles of the throat and neck
Platysma
Sternocleidomastoid
Obliquus capitis inferior
Longus colli
Longus capitis
Rectus capitis anterior
Splenius capitis
Obliquus capitis superior
Rectus capitis posterior (major and minor)
Semispinalis capitis
Longissimus capitis
Rectus capitis lateralis
Digastric
Sternohyoid
Sternothyroid
Thyrohyoid
Omohyoid
Constrictor pharyngis inferior
Constrictor pharyngis medius
Constrictor pharyngis superior
Salpingopharyngeus
Vocalis
Scalenus anterior
Scalenus medius
Scalenus posterior
Trapezius
Muscles of the trunk:
Muscles that move the vertebral column
Longus colli
Sternocleidomastoid
Iliocostalis cervicis
Iliocostalis thoracis
Iliocostalis lumborum
Longissimus capitis
Longissimus cervicis
Longissimus thoracis
Semispinalis capitis
Semispinalis cervicis
Semispinalis thoracis
Spinalis capitis
Spinalis cervicis
Spinalis thoracis
Quadratus lumborum
Rectus abdominis
Psoas major
Psoas minor
Interspinales
Intertransversarii
Multifidus
Rotatores
Muscles of the thoracic wall and diaphragm
External intercostals
Internal intercostals
Transverse thoracis
Innermost intercostals
Subcostalis
Levatores costarum
Serratus posterior superior
Serratus posterior inferior
Diaphragm
Muscles of the abdominal wall
External oblique
Internal oblique
Transversus abdominis
Rectus abdominis

Quadratus lumborum
Psoas major
Psoas minor
Muscles of the pelvic floor
Levator ani
Coccygeus
Deep transverse perineus
Superficial transverse perineus
External anal sphincter
External urethral sphincter
Bulbocavernosus
Ischiocavernosus
Muscles of the upper extremities:
Muscles connecting the upper extremity to the trunk
Back:
Trapezius
Latissimus dorsi
Levator scapulae
Rhomboideus major
Rhomboideus minor

Chest:
Pectoralis major
Subclavius
Serratus anterior

Shoulder:
Deltoid
Supraspinatus
Infraspinatus
Teres major
Teres minor
Subscapularis
Muscles of the upper arm
Biceps brachii
Coracobrachialis
Brachialis
Triceps brachii
Muscles of the forearm
Flexor carpi radialis
Flexor carpi ulnaris
Flexor digitorum profundus
Flexor digitorum superficialis
Flexor pollicis longus
Palmaris longus
Pronator quadratus
Pronator teres
Abductor pollicis longus
Anconeus
Brachioradialis
Extensor carpi radialis brevis
Extensor carpi radialis longus
Extensor carpi ulnaris
Extensor digitorum communis
Extensor digiti minimi
Extensor indicis
Extensor pollicis brevis
Extensor pollicis longus
Supinator
Muscles of the hand
Abductor digiti minimi
Abductor pollicis brevis
Adductor pollicis
Flexor digiti minimi brevis
Flexor pollicis brevis
Interossei volares
Interossei palmares
Lumbricales

Opponens digiti minimi
Opponens pollicis
Palmaris brevis
Muscles of the lower extremities
  Muscles of the buttocks
    Gemellus inferior
    Gemellus superior
    Gluteus maximus
    Gluteus medius
    Gluteus minimus
    Obturator internus
    Piriformis
    Quadratus femoris
    Tensor fascia latae
  Muscles of the thigh
    Quadriceps femoris
      Rectus femoris
      Vastus medialis
      Vastus lateralis
      Vastus intermedius
    Sartorius
    Adductor brevis
    Adductor longus
    Adductor magnus
    Gracilis
    Obturator externus
    Pectineus
    Biceps femoris
    Semimembranosus
    Semitendinosus
    Iliopsoas
      Iliacus
      Psoas major
  Muscles of the leg
    Extensor digitorum longus
    Extensor hallucis longus
    Peroneus tertius
    Tibialis anterior
    Peroneus brevis
    Peroneus longus
    Flexor digitorum longus
    Flexor hallucis longus
    Gastrocnemius
    Plantaris
    Popliteus
    Soleus
    Tibialis posterior
  Muscles of the foot
    Abductor digiti minimi pedis
    Abductor hallucis
    Adductor hallucis
    Extensor digitorum brevis
    Flexor digiti minimi brevis
    Flexor digitorum brevis
    Flexor hallucis brevis
    Interossei plantares

Interossei dorsales
Lumbricales
Quadratus plantae

Muscles of the head and neck produce movements of the head and facial expressions, move and focus the eyes, open and close the eyelids, open and close the mouth, produce chewing motions, manipulate the tongue, participate in swallowing, and produce and modulate sounds in the larynx.

Muscles of the trunk produce movements of the trunk (flexion, extension, rotation), support internal organs, maintain posture, function in breathing, and maintain turgescence in sexual excitation.

Weak places in the abdominal wall (umbilicus, inguinal canals, and femoral rings) can be sites of hernia.

Muscles of the upper extremities act chiefly to convey the hands from one place to another and control manipulations of the fingers; under certain conditions, action can also move the trunk with extremities fixed.

Muscles of the lower extremities can act either with trunk immobile and extremities movable or with foot fixed and trunk movable. They are specialized for weight bearing and locomotion.

QUESTIONS FOR REVIEW AND THOUGHT

1 Characterize and contrast skeletal, smooth, and cardiac muscles on the microscopic and macroscopic levels. What do they have in common?

2 Describe the myofilaments and their action in muscle contraction.

3 Give examples of fusiform, sheetlike, and sphincter muscles.

4 Draw a simple diagram of the biceps brachii and its attachments and indicate the origin and insertion in the actions of: (a) lifting a book; (b) climbing a ladder.

5 Which muscles act as synergists for the biceps brachii? Which muscle is its principal antagonist?

6 Where are the following muscles located: (a) biceps brachii; (b) orbicularis oculi; (c) palatopharyngeus; (d) sternocleidomastoid; (e) rectus abdominis; (f) extensor indicis; (g) gluteus maximus; (h) tibialis anterior?

7 What action does each of the following muscles perform: (a) depressor septi; (b) levator labii superioris; (c) flexor carpi radialis; (d) extensor hallucis longus; (e) abductor digiti minimi; (f) adductor pollicis; (g) corrugator supercilii?

8 What muscles are involved in: (a) smiling; (b) frowning; (c) chewing; (d) sniffing; (e) reading?

9 Discuss the action of the intercostal muscles, diaphragm, and abdominal muscles in breathing.

10 Where are the muscles that move the fingers and thumb located? Cite five examples and give origin, insertion, and action for each.

11 Compare the muscles of the upper and lower extremities with respect to size and type and amount of movement produced.

12 Discuss the effects of high heels and "Earth shoes" on specific muscles of the leg and foot.

THE
FUNCTIONS
OF THE
MUSCLES

In the last chapter it was stated that muscles are composed of cells specialized for the property of contractility, and their contractions produce movements of various kinds. Like many generalizations about the body, this seemingly simple statement holds many mysteries, which have been the subject of intensive research by generations of physiologists and still have not been entirely unraveled. The functioning of the muscles can be viewed on a number of levels, each of which generates a number of important and fascinating questions: at the level of the organ and organism—how whole muscles work and how they contribute to the functions and life of the body as a whole; at the level of muscle tissue and individual muscle cells—what stimulates a muscle cell to contract and what changes are produced in it; and at the molecular level—what are the fundamental interactions, which may hold keys to the understanding of phenomena at the micro- and macro-levels.

Physiologists study muscles in many ways. Studies of the living body can yield much information. The movements of body parts can be carefully observed, and by comparing such observations with the knowledge of muscle structure obtained by dissections, the physical principles of the action of individual muscles can be deduced. Often it is possible to feel individual muscles contracting during a particular action. Direct stimulation of specific muscles with electric current can yield further information (although inferences from such observations must be limited, since in the living body muscles normally work in groups, rather than singly). Observations of the effects of paralysis of specific muscles can also contribute to the overall picture of the functioning muscles on the macro-level (but here, too, allowances must be made for the fact that when one muscle is paralyzed, other muscles may partially compensate for its lack).

Much of our knowledge of the functioning of individual muscle cells has been obtained from muscle preparations. In the laboratory you will probably be studying frog muscles, carefully dissected out from the leg of a frog and placed in Ringer solution. Individual muscle fibers can also be studied in this way. It has been found that a number of stimuli will cause muscles and individual muscle cells to contract: electric current, heat, light, pressure, changes in pH and ionic concentrations, and various chemicals. Electric current is the most convenient stimulus for such studies, since its strength can be varied precisely, and stimulation can be stopped instantly.

Studies with conventional and scanning electron microscopes and fine chemical techniques, as well as model studies of the contractile proteins, are helping to clarify our picture of how a muscle works at the molecular level.

As might be expected, there are both similarities and differences in the functioning of skeletal, smooth, and cardiac muscles. The mechanisms of the contraction of each type and their functions in the body are discussed in this chapter.

THE CONTRACTION OF SKELETAL MUSCLES

Probably the most striking difference between a plant and an animal is in the kind of movements they can perform. Plants usually move so slowly that they often seem unable to move at all. They can turn their leaves toward a light or stretch their roots down into the ground; but these and other plant movements occur by changes in turgor (stiffness) of the cells and by differential growth, and they are normally observable only over periods of hours or days. Animals, on the other hand, can respond almost instantly with movements of body parts or the body as a whole. A frog sends its tongue out in lightning flicks to snap up an unwary fly, and you can reach up almost as quickly to catch an incoming ball or jerk your hand back from a hot pot. Such rapid actions are made possible by the fact that skeletal muscles can contract rapidly in response to a stimulus. Though a variety of stimuli have been found to affect muscles in a test tube, in the living body the skeletal muscles are normally stimulated by impulses from the nerve fibers innervating them.

Studies of muscle contraction have revealed that each contraction consists of three separate phases, following one another in rapid succession: a **latent period,** in which nothing seems to be happening; a **period of contraction,** in which the muscle fibers shorten; and a **period of relaxation,** in which the muscle fibers lengthen. The strength of the contraction of a muscle as a whole depends on how many of its individual fibers are contracting, and this in turn has been found to depend on a number of factors: the strength of the stimulus; the speed of application of the stimulus; the duration of the stimulus; the weight of the load on the muscle; and the temperature. In experiments on isolated muscles, the strength of the stimulus is regulated by the experimenter, who can adjust the strength of the electric current appropriately. In the living body, the strength of the stimulus depends on the number of impulses transmitted by motor and plates across the myoneural junctions. Stimuli of moderate duration generally produce the strongest contractions. When a muscle's contractions cause it to do work against a load, its contractions are stronger up to some optimum load, but then the strength of contraction decreases. There is also an optimum temperature for the work of skeletal muscles; for humans it is the normal body temperature, about 37° C (98.6° F). Higher temperatures lead to a loss of excitability, and the muscles become less able to function; ultimately a state of heat rigor, or permanent shortening of the muscles, may set in.

Mechanism of Skeletal Muscle Contraction

Excitation (Stimulation)
A frog gastrocnemius muscle lying in a dish of Ringer solution will just continue to lie there, limply. But if an electric current is applied to it, it will suddenly contract vigorously. In the living body, too, the skeletal muscles will not contract in the absence of a stimulus. But the individual muscle fibers possess the property of **excitability**: the ability to respond if a suitable **stimulus** is provided. For a muscle cell, the typical response to a stimulus is contraction, and the stimulus is in the form of an impulse, conducted along the nerve fibers innervating the muscle.

In the last chapter it was mentioned that the nerve endings branch and terminate in tiny buttonlike structures called motor end plates (Figure 11-1). Although each motor end plate fits into a groove in the muscle fiber, they are not actually in contact. Instead of a protoplasmic connection, there is a small gap between them, which is called the **synaptic cleft.** The nerve endings are richly supplied with mitochondria and with numerous tiny vesicles containing a neurotransmitter chemical, **acetylcholine.** When an impulse travels down a nerve fiber and reaches the nerve endings, perhaps 50 to 100 acetylcholine vesicles burst through the membrane of each motor end plate and spill out into the synaptic cleft. A movement of calcium ions from the extracellular fluid into the membranes of the nerve endings seems to be involved in this process. The acetylcholine released by the motor end plates diffuses across the synaptic cleft and comes in contact with the membrane of the muscle fiber. This contact is short-lived, for immediately an enzyme, **cholinesterase,** begins to attack the acetylcholine and breaks it down within a few milliseconds. But in this brief time, the neurotransmitter produces a powerful effect: it makes the sarcolemma very permeable to sodium ions, which rush into the muscle fiber from the extracellular fluid. The electrical potential of the membrane rises by a few millivolts, creating a potential called the **end-plate potential.** Now the muscle fiber is excited, and ready to contract.

Cholinesterase is normally plentiful in the region of the motor end plates, and it plays a key role in muscle contraction. If the acetylcholine released by the nerve endings were not broken down by cholinesterase after it had delivered its "message," it would continue to restimulate the muscle cells to contract over and over again, without any new nerve impulses, and the action of the muscles would be uncontrollable.

A knowledge of the chemical interactions at the neuromuscular junction has brought understanding of the action of a number of drugs that affect the action of muscles. Some drugs, such as nicotine, methacholine, and carbachol, act very much like acetylcholine and stimulate the muscle fiber. Muscle spasms (repeated, uncontrolled contractions of the muscles) may result, because the drugs, unlike acetylcholine, are not destroyed by cholinesterase or are destroyed very slowly. Drugs such as neostigmine produce muscle spasms in a different way, by inactivating cholinesterase. They are dangerous drugs, for spasms of the larynx can cause death by suffocation. Curare and drugs like it apparently inhibit some acetylcholine receptor on the surface of the sarcolemma and thus block the transmission of impulses at the neuromuscular junction. As a result, the muscles cannot contract. South American Indians dipped their arrow points in curare and used this drug as a death-dealing poison; but it is also a valuable tool for the modern surgeon when used in carefully controlled amounts as a muscle relaxant during delicate surgical operations, when a sudden movement of the patient's body could be damaging or even fatal.

Electrical Changes During Skeletal Muscle Contraction
In the last section, we left the muscle fiber poised on the verge of contraction. To understand the sequence of events in muscle contraction, we will first need to think about some electrical considerations. The sarcolemma, like other cell membranes, is differentially permeable to various substances, including ions. Normally, there is a higher concentration of sodium ions in the fluid outside the cells, and a higher concentration of potassium ions inside the cell. Potassium ions can diffuse out fairly readily through the membrane, while the diffusion of sodium ions is hindered; in addition, the cell possesses "pumps" for the active transport of sodium ions out and potassium ions in, against the concentration gradient. As a result of all these processes that normally occur constantly, there is a tendency for positively charged ions (such as sodium and potassium) to accumulate just outside the cell membrane. The attraction of this high concentration of positive charge results in a lineup of negative ions just inside the cell membrane (Figure 11-2). An electrical potential is thus established across the cell membrane, and it becomes a miniature capacitor. The membrane potential of a muscle cell at rest, which can be measured with microelectrodes, is about -87 millivolts; it is called the **resting potential.**

Now we are ready to pick up the train of events where we left off. Picture a resting muscle cell being

A

myofilaments

synaptic vesicles

nerve axon
terminal

mitochondria

synaptic vesicles

nerve axon
terminal

sarcolema

nucleus of muscle
cell

mitochondria

FIGURE 11-1 **(A) Electron micrograph of a motor end plate of a rat skeletal muscle, ×17,380. (B) Diagram of the neuromuscular junction at successively increasing magnifications.**

B

node of Ranvier

myelin sheath

motor nerve

myoneural
junction

nucleus of
Schwann cell

skeletal
muscle fibers

axon

myelin
sheath

glial
cell

muscle
nuclei

myofibrils

terminal nerve branches

axon terminal
in synaptic
trough

synaptic
vesicles

subneural
clefts

mitochondion

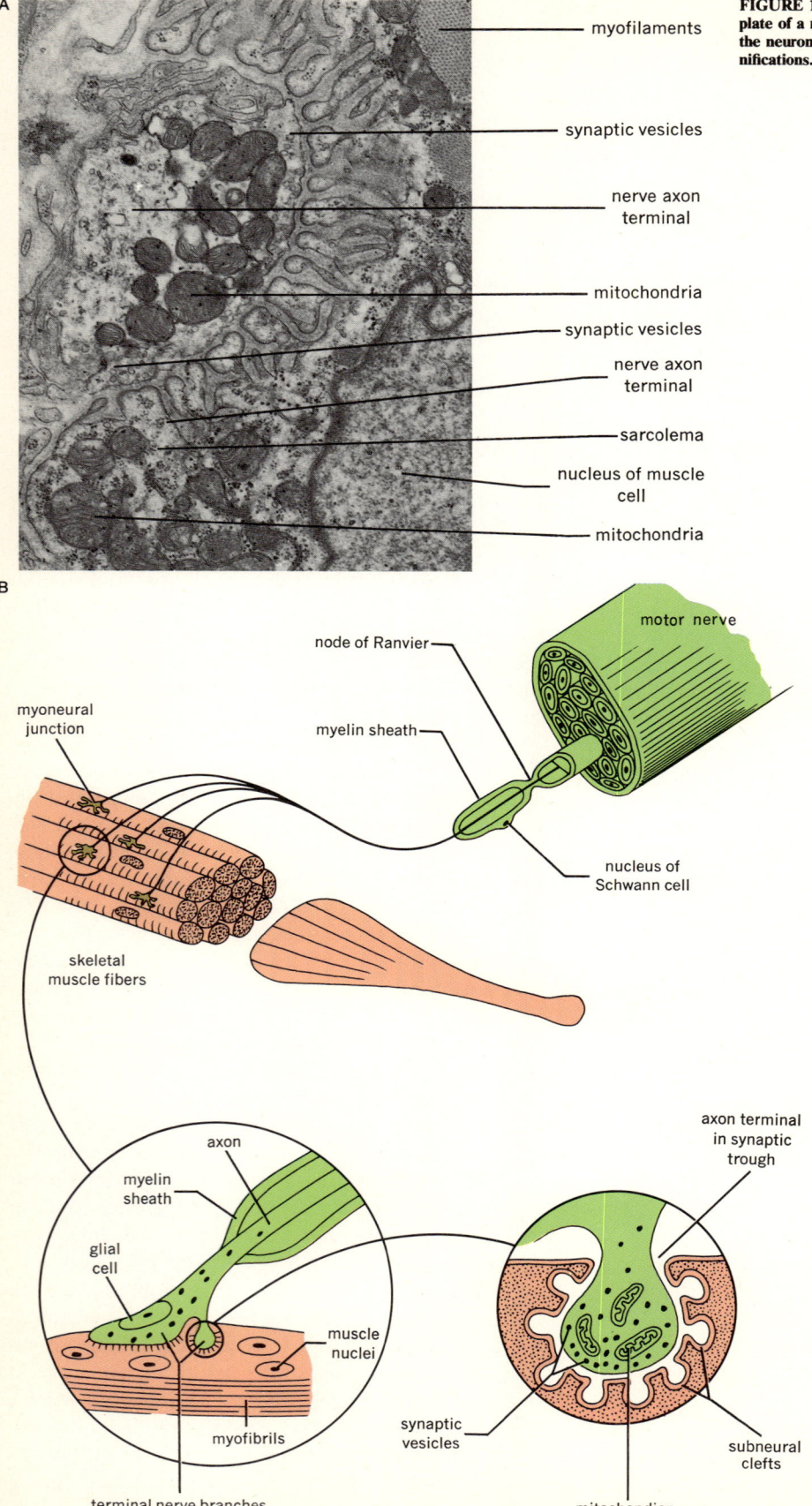

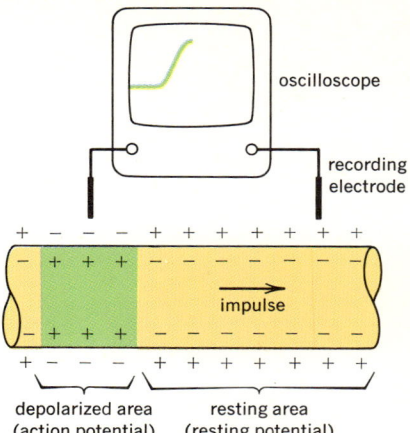

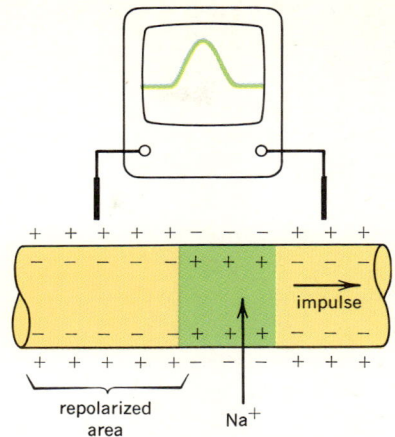

FIGURE 11-2 The action potential. The electrical changes that occur in the cell membrane during depolarization and repolarization can be recorded on an oscilloscope.

oscilloscope

recording electrode

impulse

depolarized area (action potential)

resting area (resting potential)

repolarized area

Na^+

impulse

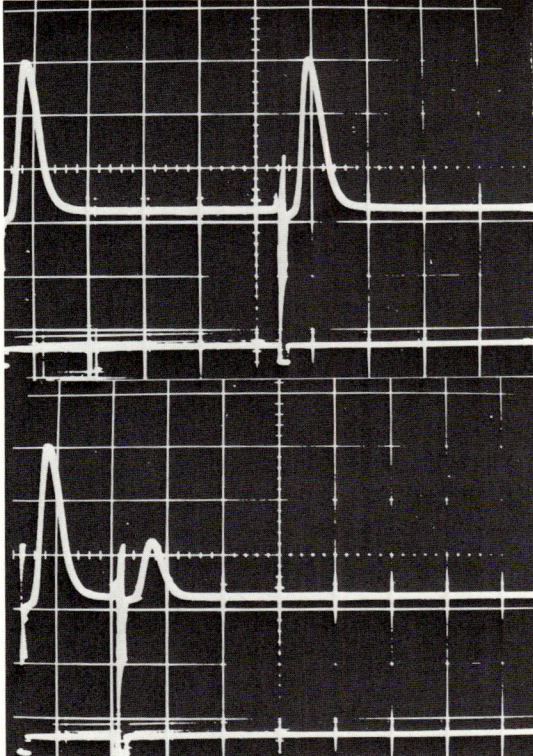

FIGURE 11-3 Oscillograms of action potentials.

stimulated by an impulse from a nerve ending. Acetylcholine abruptly changes the permeability of the sarcolemma for sodium ions, and they rush into the muscle cell from the surrounding intercellular fluid. Suddenly there is an upset in the separation of charges (**polarization**) across the membrane. Positively charged ions are flooding into the cell in such quantities that in the region of the breakthrough an opposite polarization is established: there is an excess of positive charges inside the cell, and an excess of negative charges outside. This area of the muscle fiber is now **depolarized.** But almost immediately, there is

another change in the cell membrane: it again becomes almost completely impermeable to sodium ions. Quickly the original polarization is reestablished: potassium ions diffuse out of the cell, restoring the net negative charge inside the membrane. The sodium pump operates to transport sodium ions actively out of the cell, and potassium ions diffuse back in and are pumped in as well. As a result, the fiber is restored to its original state—the normal resting potential is restored, and **repolarization** has occurred. This sequence of changes in the membrane potential is called the **action potential.** It includes both depolarization and repolarization, and it is extremely rapid, lasting a total of only a tiny fraction of a second. If the action potential is picked up with microelectrodes and displayed on an oscilloscope (Figure 11-3), a characteristic spike is observed, lasting from 5 to 10 milliseconds.

The action potential does not remain isolated to one small spot on the muscle cell membrane. It tends to excite adjacent regions of the membrane, and a wave of depolarization, followed quickly by polarization, spreads over the entire muscle fiber. During the spike potential, while the membrane is depolarized, a second stimulus, no matter how strong, could not spark a new action potential. This is the **absolute refractory period** of the muscle, during which no response to stimuli is possible. It is followed by a **relative refractory period,** while repolarization is occurring: a second stimulus can produce an action potential, but it will not be as great as the first. Finally, when the muscle fibers have been completely repolarized, they can again respond fully to stimuli.

The electrical changes that have been outlined so far are basically similar to those that occur in a nerve during the conduction of an impulse. But muscle fibers possess some unique features, associated with their function of contraction. In a skeletal muscle fiber, the action potential sparks a flow of electrical current deep into the cell by way of the tubules of the

T-system. A miniature electrical circuit is established, as the current flows through the walls of the longitudinal tubules into the sarcoplasm and back out toward the cell membrane. The flow of electric current through the walls of the longitudinal tubules causes them to release calcium ions into the surrounding sarcoplasm. Within a few ten-thousandths of a second, the calcium ions diffuse into the myofibrils and initiate the process of contraction. They remain inside the myofibrils for only a few milliseconds, for once the action potential is over, the longitudinal tubules reabsorb the calcium ions out of the sarcoplasm. After that, the muscle fiber rapidly relaxes.

Structural Changes During Skeletal Muscle Contraction

The electron microscope is one of the most powerful tools in the biomedical sciences. It has revealed new details of structure and provided new insights into the functioning of fundamental systems of the body. A prime example is the structure and contraction of the skeletal muscle fiber. Optical microscopes revealed a characteristic pattern of light and dark banding, but its fine structure was obscure until electron micrographs brought higher resolution. As described in the last chapter, the striations of skeletal muscle fibers were found to be produced by incomplete overlapping of thick and thin filaments of two contractile proteins: actin and myosin. Higher resolutions revealed further details (Figure 11-4): minute cross-bridges projecting out from the thicker myosin myofilaments.

When a muscle cell contracts, as electron micrographs show, the actin and myosin filaments seem to slide over one another, gradually closing the gaps between the ends of adjacent filaments and shortening the sarcomere (the portion of the myofibril lying between two successive Z lines). The big questions, of course, were how this sliding occurs and what causes it. The exact mechanism of muscle contraction is still incompletely understood. But some interesting working hypotheses have been constructed on the basis of comparisons of the structural events, observed in electron micrographs, with observations of fine chemical changes that occur within the contracting muscle cell.

The Chemistry of Skeletal Muscle Contraction

Many life scientists believe that the keys to an understanding of the fundamental processes in the living cell lie in a knowledge of the chemicals of life and their interactions with one another. The contraction of muscles is no exception. A close observation of structural events can take us only so far; when we begin to wonder about the why and how of such events, we find that following up chemical clues leads to the most fruitful results. Many pieces of the puzzle have already been discovered, and they are being

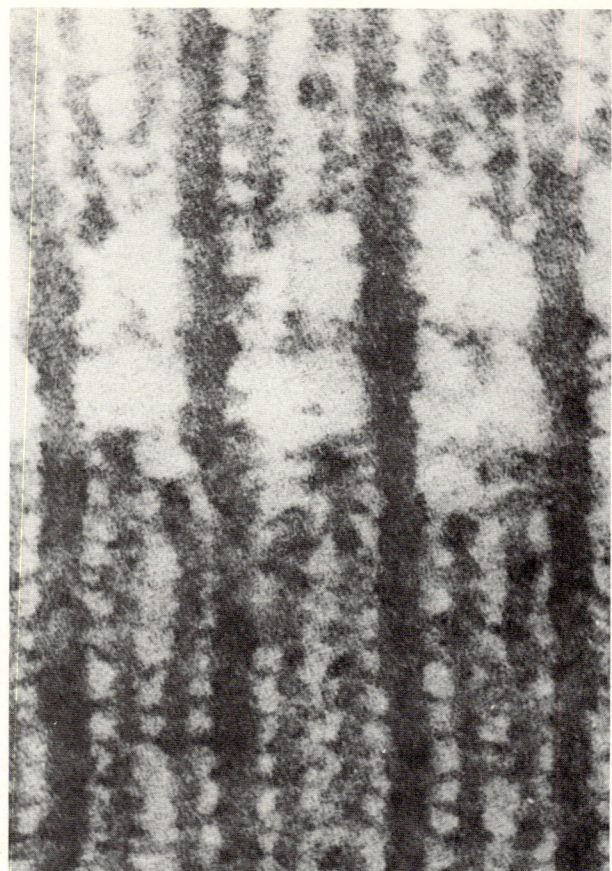

FIGURE 11-4 High-resolution micrographs have revealed cross-bridges, at 60° angles between a thick myosin filament and six thin actin filaments in the muscle myofibril. This arrangement permits the actin filaments to slide along the myosin filament toward the center of the sarcomere.

fitted together into a coherent pattern. It has been found that the actin filaments have reactive sites occurring at regular intervals along the axis, and that these reactive sites seem to have a negative charge. (Until now we have been regarding the actin and myosin as filaments, but it should be recalled that they are also chemicals—long, threadlike protein molecules.) The cross-bridges of the myosin filaments, which likewise occur at intervals along the axis of the molecule, are believed to bind ATP, in such a way that these sites also have a strong negative charge. Under resting conditions, the actin and myosin filaments, both negatively charged, would thus tend to repel one another and remain separated. But positively charged calcium ions can combine with the negatively charged sites of both the actin and myosin filaments, binding them together. (The actual calcium receptor sites on the actin filaments are believed to be found on the troponin portion of the actin-tropomyosin-troponin complex that forms the thin myofilaments.) The presence of calcium ions has another important effect, imparting an ATPase activity to the

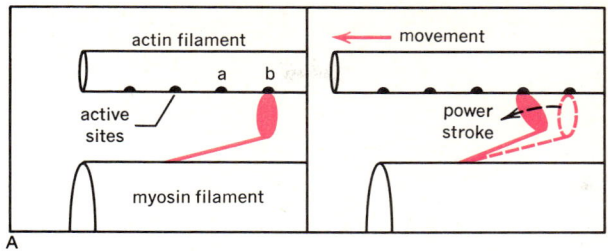

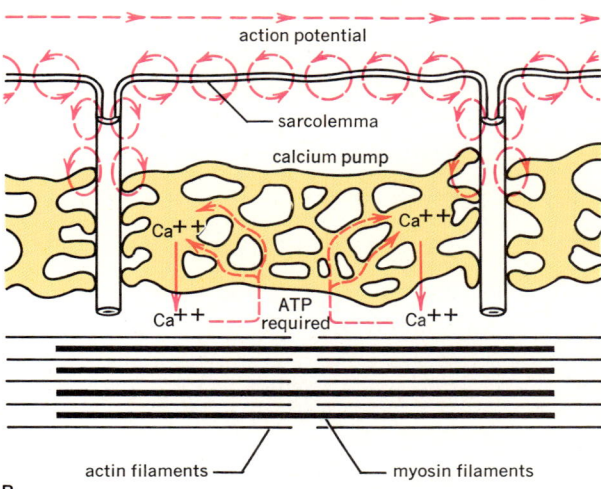

FIGURE 11-5 Mechanisms of muscle contraction: (A) actin and myosin filaments are believed to slide past each other by a ratchet mechanism; (B) the action potential causes a release of calcium ions from the sarcoplasmic reticulum, followed by uptake of Ca^{++} by a calcium pump.

myosin filaments, which can then split ATP and liberate energy.

After the sliding of the actin and myosin filaments during muscle contraction was discovered, a possible **"ratchet" mechanism** (Figure 11-5) was proposed to explain the movement of the actin filaments. This mechanism visualized the following events: calcium ions, released as a result of the action potential, diffuse into the myofibrils and bind the negatively charged reaction sites on the actin and myosin filaments together. Now that the myosin cross-bridges are no longer negatively charged, they are not repelled by the negatively charged shank of the filament, and they bend inward toward the axis of the filament. But then the ATP bound to the cross-bridges is split to ADP, and the calcium linkages are broken. Meanwhile, the actin filaments have been pulled a certain distance along the myosin filaments, and the same sequence of reactions can proceed again, pulling the filaments further along until the ends of adjacent actin filaments overlap and the muscle fiber is maximally contracted.

A more recent refinement of the mechanism of muscle contraction is the **electrostatic solenoid mecha-**nism, which postulates a similar sequence of events but suggests that the forces operating between the actin and myosin filaments are electrostatic forces, rather than actual chemical bonds. Models consisting of electrically charged metal plates have been built to illustrate this hypothesis, and they actually behave in the manner predicted, sliding over one another just as the actin and myosin filaments do in a contracting muscle fiber.

Energy Considerations One of the painful lessons a child must learn in growing up is that generally you can't get something for nothing—life's benefits usually must be paid for, in one way or another. This general rule holds true within a living organism as well. Muscle contraction, for example, is a useful process that does not come "free"; it is an energy-consuming process, and it is paid for in the "energy currency" of the cell, **adenosine triphosphate (ATP).**

The ATP needed to power muscle contraction is synthesized in the mitochondria, in the sequence of reactions of cell respiration (Figure 11-6). In these reactions, the simple sugar glucose is broken down, and energy contained in its chemical bonds is used to produce the high-energy phosphate bonds of ATP. Reserves of glucose are conveniently stored in the muscles, not in the form of free glucose molecules, but combined into a polysaccharide, glycogen ("animal starch").

The participation of ATP in muscle contraction has already been described: ATP combines with myosin filaments; an action potential provokes a release of calcium ions, which briefly bind to the ATP-myosin complexes and result in a splitting of ATP by myosin. The products of this breakdown of ATP are ADP (adenosine *di*phosphate) and inorganic phosphate, and the energy released powers the muscle contraction.

Meanwhile, whenever there is an excess of ATP in a muscle cell, it is used to generate an alternate form of energy storage, **creatine phosphate.** ATP reacts with the substance creatine, transferring a phosphate group to it and producing a high-energy phosphate bond in creatine phosphate. When ADP is formed during muscle contraction, creatine phosphate can replenish the energy supply by the reaction:

$$CP + ADP \rightarrow ATP + creatine$$

The ATP formed can then combine with myosin, readying the muscle fiber for a new contraction.

During vigorous exercise, the muscle reserves of ATP and creatine phosphate are quickly exhausted. The mitochondria work to synthesize new high-energy molecules, but if the exercise is prolonged, the bloodstream cannot deliver oxygen fast enough to

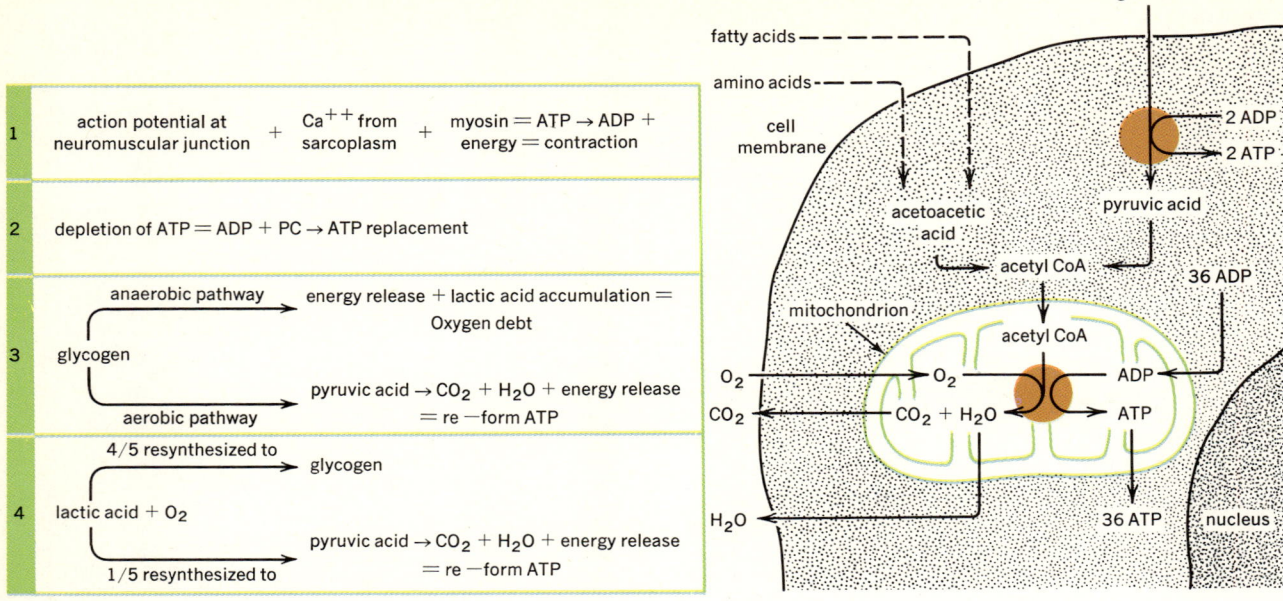

FIGURE 11-6 Cell respiration yields energy in the form of ATP. Most of the ATP is produced in the mitochondria.

keep up with the needs of the oxidative reactions of the Krebs cycle (the energy-generating reactions of cell respiration, which are discussed in Chapter 27). As a result, for a time the muscle cell relies heavily on the less efficient anaerobic (non-oxygen-requiring) reactions of glycolysis to generate energy. In this reaction sequence, a major end-product of the conversion of glucose is lactic acid. As exercise continues, ATP supplies are depleted, lactic acid accumulates and the muscles begin to show signs of **fatigue.** At first the muscle fibers become more irritable, but then, if they are continuously stimulated, the strength of the contractions progressively decreases, until the muscle fails to respond.*

If an excessive amount of lactic acid remained in the muscle cells, it would ultimately poison them. Normally, the lactic acid produced in glycolysis in muscle cells is carried by the bloodstream to the liver, where it is oxidized to pyruvic acid and then either resynthesized to glucose (later to be retransported to the muscles and stored as glycogen) or oxidized further to carbon dioxide and water. But these processes cannot take place fast enough to cope with the build-up of lactic acid during vigorous exercise. Instead, the body puts off the necessary oxidation of lactic acid until a more convenient time and runs up an **"oxygen debt."** The oxygen debt is defined as the extra oxygen

that must be used in oxidative energy processes to oxidize the lactic acid that has accumulated during vigorous muscle contraction and to reconvert the decomposed ATP and creatine phosphate to their original states. During a rest after exercise, the oxidative processes of the cells work overtime (as much as four-fifths of the extra oxygen consumption occurs *after* the vigorous muscle contraction has stopped). An exhausted runner panting after the race is over is paying off the oxygen debt (Figure 11-7).

These discussions of fatigue and oxygen debt may have given you the impression that exercise is harmful for the body, and vigorous contractions of the muscles should be avoided. This is not at all the case. Exercise, if not pushed beyond the point of exhaustion, has a very positive, toning effect for the body. It stimulates circulation and increases the size, strength, and tone of the muscle fibers.

Another aspect of energy relationships in muscle contraction is of great significance for the body. This is **heat production.** If muscle contraction occurred with 100 percent efficiency, no heat would be produced—all the energy supplied by ATP would be converted to the mechanical action of contraction. But a muscle cell is not that efficient; in fact, it is about as efficient as an automobile engine. Only about 20 to 25 percent of the energy liberated in a contracting muscle cell can be converted to useful work; the rest is given off as heat. The heat produced by the muscles is an important item of "input" that must constantly be coped with through the mechanisms of temperature regulation if homeostasis is to be maintained. The "hot and sweaty" feeling that follows vigorous exercise is a reflection of these mecha-

---

* If a fatigued muscle continues to be exerted until its supplies of ATP are completely exhausted, a state of continuous contraction referred to as **contracture** sets in. It is believed to result from the fact that ATP is needed to make the actin and myosin filaments separate; without it, the muscle cannot relax. An extreme case occurs several hours after death, when all the muscles of the body go into a state of contracture called **rigor mortis.** The dead cells cannot replace the ATP that is lost, and the muscles do not relax again until the muscle proteins are destroyed, which usually occurs as a result of bacterial putrefaction, some 15 to 25 hours later.

FIGURE 11-7 During the race, the runners build up an "oxygen debt" that must ultimately be paid off in enhanced respiration.

nisms: excess heat is being carried from the muscles into the capillary beds of the skin, where it is radiated out from the body surface and eliminated from the body by evaporation through the sweat glands. Shivering on a cold day is another aspect of homeostasis: in this case, muscle contractions are being used to produce needed heat for the body.

Mechanical Action

In the chapter thus far we have been concerned mainly with the mechanisms of skeletal muscle contraction at the micro-level. Indeed, the main focus of muscle research today has been a probing deeper and deeper into the chemical and electrical aspects of muscle contraction. But such research would not have been possible without many generations of preceding studies of the practical aspects of muscle contraction—gross effects observable on relatively simple apparatus.

Laboratory Setups for Muscle Research The **kymograph,** a device based on rather simple operating principles, is still used in many laboratories today to demonstrate muscle contraction. It is diagrammed in Figure 11-8. Originally, the paper wrapped around the revolving drum was first held over a kerosene flame to produce a coating of soot, which could be scratched away by the stylus attached to the contracting muscle to produce a visual record of the contraction. In modern versions, that combination is replaced by an ink writing mechanism. In either case, contractions of the muscle are stimulated electrically to provide a visual recording of muscle activity.

The **polygraph** is a far more modern and sophisticated apparatus, which permits the recording not only of muscle contractions, but also of minute changes in electrical potentials and other characteristics in living organisms. Several different characteristics can be recorded simultaneously on separate channels. Electrocardiograms (recordings of the electrical

FIGURE 11-8 The kymograph: a device for recording muscle contractions.

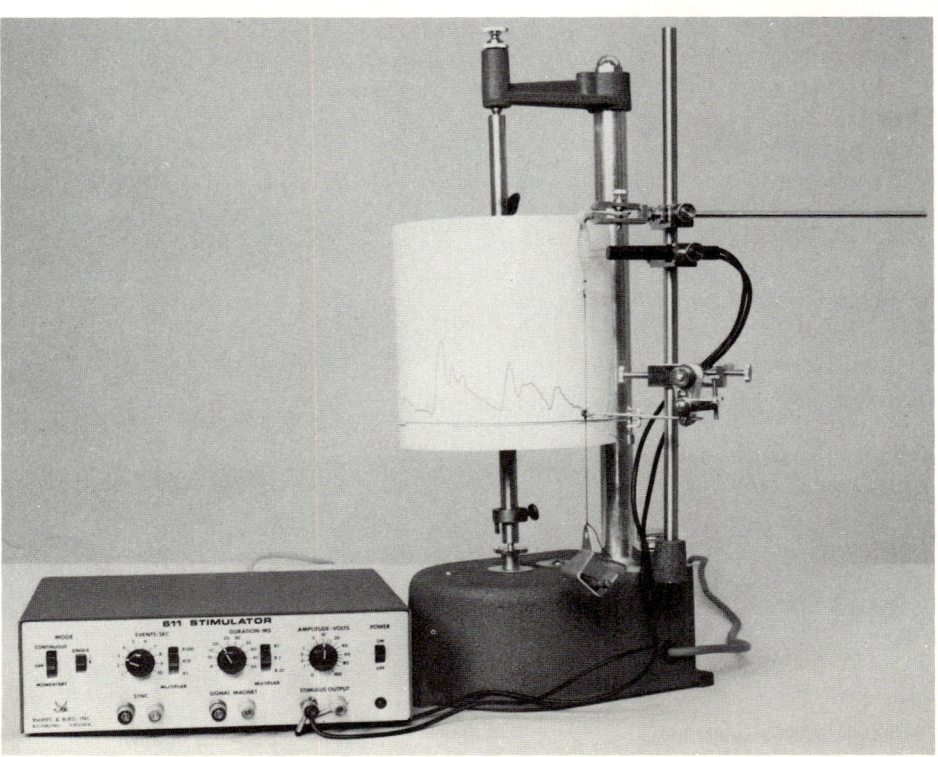

activity of the heart) and electroencephalograms (recordings of brain wave activity) are common applications; another widely publicized use of the polygraph is as a "lie detector," based on the interpretation of changes in key body indices as signs of agitation.

The Single Muscle Twitch

Sometimes very difficult problems can be solved if we can just break them down into simpler components. The contraction of a muscle is a rather complex phenomenon, involving thousands, millions, and even billions of cells. In the course of a day, a particular muscle may contract thousands of times. But much can be learned about muscle action in a simplified laboratory setup, when a single muscle, removed from the body,* is stimulated by a brief electrical stimulus, producing a single, sudden contraction lasting for a fraction of a second. Such a contraction is referred to as a single muscle twitch.

The duration of a single muscle twitch varies, depending on the muscle involved. Contractions of the muscles that move the eyes last less than 1/100 of a second; the gastrocnemius muscle of the calf has a duration of contraction of about 1/30 of a second, while the contractions of the soleus muscle are longer, about 1/10 of a second. These values are exactly what might be expected, considering the different functions of the muscles: movements of the eyes must be very rapid to maintain their fixation on specific objects; the gastrocnemius is important in running and jumping, so its contractions must also be fairly rapid; the slower soleus muscle is involved mainly in slow reactions that support the body against gravity in a standing position.

If the recording of a single muscle twitch is examined (Figure 11-9), it can be seen that, regardless of the total duration of the contraction, the mechanical response of the muscle can be broken down into three major periods. During the first, the **latent period,** nothing appears to happen: there is a time lapse (about 1 millisecond for human muscles, 4 milliseconds for frog muscles) between the application of the stimulus and the beginning of the actual muscle contraction. The second period, the **period of contraction,** extends from the beginning of the mechanical response to its peak. For frog muscles this phase lasts about 40 milliseconds; for human muscles it is generally shorter, although, as we have seen, it varies depending on the muscle. (As Figure 11-9 shows, only slow-acting muscles like the soleus have a period of contraction of the order of 40 milliseconds.) The third

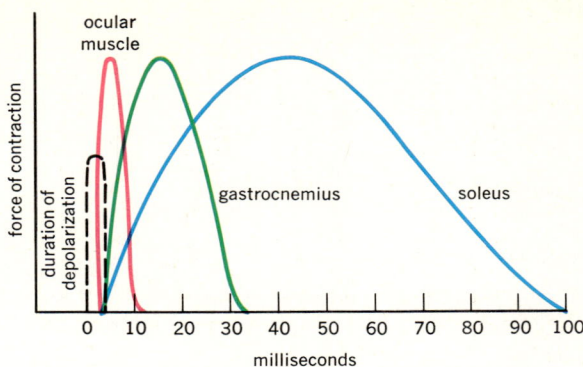

FIGURE 11-9 The single muscle twitch: isometric contractions in various types of mammalian muscles. Note the latent period between the action potential and the muscle contraction.

period is the **period of relaxation:** the time from the peak of contraction until the muscle returns to its original length. As can be seen from Figure 11-9, this period also varies according to the type of muscle and is generally somewhat longer than the period of contraction (about 500 milliseconds for frog muscles).

The All-or-Nothing Response

Everyone is familiar with the fine gradations of force that the muscles of the body can exert. The same hand that can pat a kitten and pick up an egg without cracking it can also wield a sledge hammer. It might therefore seem logical to assume that the individual muscle fibers are capable of a finely graded spectrum of contractions, depending on the strength of the nerve impulses that stimulate them. But the individual muscle fibers do not work that way at all. Instead, a muscle fiber obeys a principle that is also followed by nerve cells: the **all-or-nothing law.** According to this principle, if the exciting stimulus is strong enough, the muscle fiber will contract, and it will do so to the full extent of its ability. If the incoming stimulus is not above a certain threshold value, the muscle cell will not react at all. There are no halfway measures—its response is all or nothing. A stimulus too weak to produce a response is referred to as a **subminimal** (or **subliminal**) **stimulus.** The weakest stimulus that will produce a contraction of a muscle fiber is called the **minimal stimulus** or **threshold stimulus.**

If an individual muscle fiber contracts either completely or not at all, then how can the **graded** responses of a muscle occur? The answer is in the fact that a muscle is made up of millions of individual muscle fibers. Groups of muscle fibers are innervated by the branching nerve endings of a single neuron and make up a motor unit. When an impulse of sufficient strength travels over a particular neuron innervating a group of muscle fibers, all of the muscle fibers in that motor unit will contract simultaneously. But the fibers of neighboring motor units will not

---

* Generally a frog muscle is used, not only because it is easily dissected out intact, but also because the muscles of coldblooded animals such as amphibians are more durable than those of warm-blooded animals: their cells live longer outside the body and do not fatigue as rapidly.

contract at all, unless their neurons, too, are firing. The strength of the contractions of the muscle as a whole is determined by the total number of motor units that are being stimulated. Smoothness of action is promoted because generally the fibers innervated by a particular nerve cell are not grouped all in a bunch, but are scattered at random through a sizeable volume of muscle (up to 10 mm in diameter in the muscles of the lower leg). In general, the muscles that react rapidly and produce very fine movements have rather small motor units (10 to 15 muscle fibers per neuron in the ocular muscles, for example). The slow-acting postural muscles such as the soleus may have as many as 800 muscle fibers in each motor unit. (The average for all the muscles of the body is about 180 muscle fibers per motor unit.)

When muscle contractions are studied in the laboratory, the application of a strong electric current to the muscle can cause nearly all the fibers in the muscle to contract simultaneously. But under normal circumstances, this would very rarely happen in the living body. Even in a sustained contraction, usually the nerve cells are not all firing in synchrony; at any moment some of the muscle fibers are contracting, while others are relaxing.

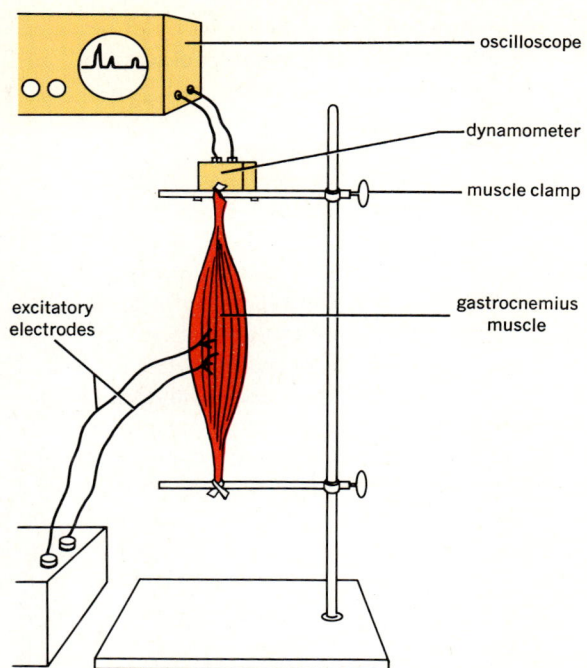

FIGURE 11-10 Laboratory setup for recording isometric contractions.

Isotonic and Isometric Contractions

In common speech, the word "contract" means to get smaller. Thus you may be surprised to learn that a muscle does not *always* shorten when it contracts. In general, there are two types of muscle contraction: isotonic and isometric. An **isotonic contraction** results in an actual decrease in the length of the muscle; if one end of the muscle is attached to a movable part, its contractions move that part. The term *isotonic* comes from "iso-," meaning "the same," and "tonic," relating to tension: while the length of the muscle is changing, its tension remains the same. In an **isometric contraction,** on the other hand, the length of the muscle remains the same (*isometric* = "same measurement"), but its tension increases. This can occur when both ends of the muscle are attached to immovable parts (Figure 11-10). For example, place your hands on the seat of your chair, straighten your arms, and then push down on the chair as hard as you can. Unless you were sitting in an extremely rickety chair, the seat did not move while you were pressing on it, yet you were certainly expending energy—muscles of your arms were contracting.

A few years ago, isometric exercises were a popular fad among people who wanted to strengthen and tone their body muscles. There is some value in such exercises, for the maximum tension a muscle can develop is actually considerably greater if it remains stretched than if it is allowed to contract. But it is now recognized that a well-rounded program of physical conditioning should include both isotonic and isometric exercises. Actually, both types of muscle contractions are used constantly in our daily activities. For example, when you take a step, isotonic contractions cause your leg to swing forward. But then you place it on the ground and put your weight on it, both flexors and extensors in the leg contract isometrically to transform it into a rigid, weight-bearing structure. Isometric contractions are especially important in maintaining posture.

There is still a third type of muscle activity that is often disregarded: muscles may also be active when they are actually lengthening. This occurs while a muscle is "paying out" under the action of its antagonists, to maintain control over the movement and protect the joint. For example, lift this book into the air and then slowly lay it down on the table, extending your arm. As the extensors in your arm contract, the flexors lengthen, but they still maintain a certain tension to produce a smooth flowing motion rather than a sudden "plop." The active lengthening of a muscle is sometimes referred to as **excentric action,** in contrast to the **concentric action** that occurs when the muscle shortens.

Repetitive Stimuli: Summation, Tetanus, and Treppe

In the laboratory it is easy to induce and study the characteristics of a single muscle twitch. But in the living body, isolated single twitches are rare; instead, each motor unit is usually subjected to repeated stimulation. You might expect that repeated stimuli would simply produce a series of identical single twitches. But muscle contraction is a prime illustration of the adage that the whole is sometimes greater than the sum of its parts.

Summation   Strong, concerted muscle movements are the result of an adding together or summation of individual muscle twitches. Such summation can occur in two different ways: by increasing the number of motor units contracting simultaneously, and by increasing the rapidity of contraction of the individual motor units. These two forms are called **multiple motor unit summation** and **wave summation.**

As might be expected, the more motor units that are contracting simultaneously, the greater the strength of contraction of the muscle as a whole.

A glance at Figure 11-11 will reveal why the second type of summation is referred to as *wave* summation. When the force of contraction is plotted against the frequency of stimulation, wavelike curves are obtained. At a frequency of about 10 per second, the first muscle twitch is not completely over when the second one starts—that is, the muscle is already in a partially contracted state when the second twitch begins. The total shortening of the muscle that results is greater than that obtained from an isolated single twitch. A third, fourth, and subsequent twitches produce even greater contraction. The actual amount of contraction produced in the second twitch is smaller than that in the first, but the overall effect is greater because the effect of the second twitch is added to the residual shortening from the first twitch. When the frequency of stimulation is increased further, the effect of summation is even greater, since the new contraction begins while more of the preceding contraction remains. The force of contraction continues to rise as the rate of contraction increases.*

As the rate of contraction is successively increased, the "scallops" on the curves in Figure 11-11 become progressively smaller. Finally, a point is reached at which individual muscle twitches cannot be distinguished, and a smooth curve is obtained. This state is called tetanus.

Tetanus   The word "tetanus" probably calls to your mind a dangerous disease that may follow a puncture wound such as that obtained by stepping on a rusty nail. If the victim has not been immunized against tetanus, the pathogenic microbes may multiply and produce a toxin that causes severe muscle spasms, with a characteristic arched back and "lockjaw," ulti-

* But recall that there is a refractory period during the spike potential, when the muscle cell membrane is depolarized and is incapable of responding to stimuli. If repetitive stimulii are delivered too rapidly, they may fall into this refractory period. Then there will be no effect of summation, and the muscle contraction will look just like a single twitch.

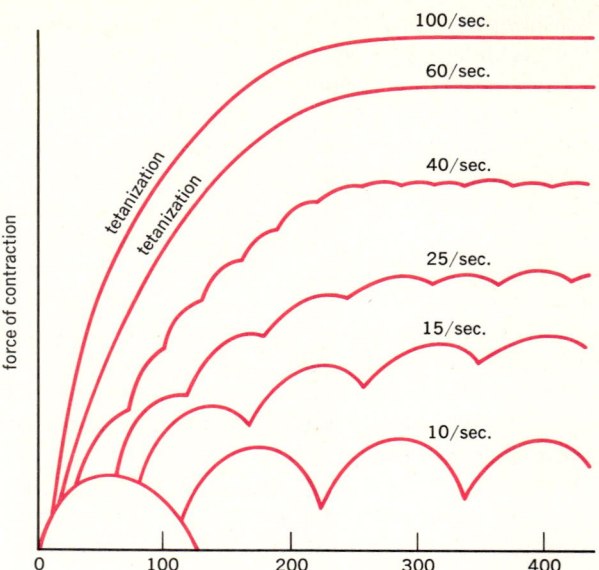

FIGURE 11-11   Wave summation and tetanization. When stimuli are repeated at frequent intervals, the degree of muscle contraction is greater than in a single muscle twitch.

mately leading to death. This disease, however, is not what a muscle physiologist is usually referring to when speaking of tetanus. In the description of muscle contraction, tetanus refers to a state in which muscle contractions follow one another so rapidly that there is not enough time for relaxation between one twitch and the next, and successive contractions cannot be distinguished from one another. (Individual action potentials, however, can be recorded.) In **complete tetanus,** a smooth and sustained contraction is observed. If the frequency of contraction permits a small degree of relaxation between successive twitches, **incomplete tetanus** is produced. Even when complete tetanus is not achieved, a smooth muscle action is provided for because the different motor units that make up a muscle fire asynchronously: at any particular moment, the muscle contains some motor units that are contracting, others that are relaxing, and as each motor unit relaxes, there are others ready to contract and take up the load.

Tetanic contractions do play a role in muscle spasms or convulsions, which are abnormal violent, involuntary and uncoordinated contractions of a skeletal muscle or group of muscles.

Treppe   Athletes know that a period of "warmup" exercises is desirable before they begin their heavy exertions in sports. As muscles are used, they seem to loosen up and reach an optimum peak of efficiency. Laboratory studies of muscle contraction have revealed a curious phenomenon that is probably the

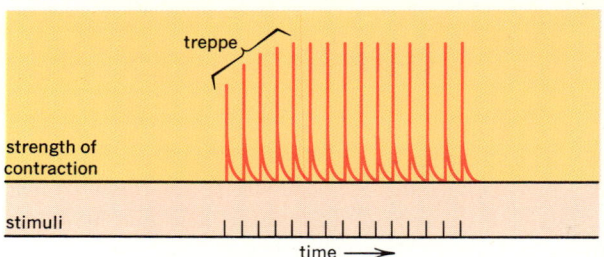

FIGURE 11-12 Treppe—the "staircase effect."

basis for the effectiveness of such warmup exercises. When a muscle first contracts after a long period of rest, its strength of contraction may be only half as great as it is 30 to 50 muscle twitches later. In other words, in a series of successive contractions (but not at a rate fast enough to produce tetanus), the strength of contraction of a muscle increases until ultimately a plateau is reached. This phenomenon is called **treppe,** or the **staircase effect.** (The rationale for the latter name should be evident from the graph in Figure 11-12.) It is thought to be caused by a progressive increase in the concentration and availability of calcium ions inside the muscle fiber. The decreased intracellular potassium and increases sodium concentrations probably also play a role, increasing the rate of liberation of calcium ions from the sarcoplasmic reticulum and allowing actin and myosin to react more readily.

It might seem that such phenomena as wave summation and treppe are violations of the all-or-nothing law. But in each case, the muscle fiber either does not contract at all (if the stimulus is below the threshold value) or it contracts completely—as much as it can, under the circumstances. Special conditions, such as having the muscle already in a state of partial contraction when the new stimulus arrives or an increase in intracellular calcium produced by previous action potentials, may increase the overall effect of the contraction; but even in summation and treppe, the strength of the muscle contraction is not determined by the strength of the incoming stimulus, as long as it is strong enough to spark a contraction at all.

Various factors affect the strength of muscle contraction. One is the **initial length** of the muscle: if a muscle is slightly stretched before contraction, the force of its contraction will be increased. Another factor is the **load** on the muscle: up to a certain limit, the greater the load, the greater the strength of contraction. If you lift a sheet of paper, for example, and then lift a heavy book, you will feel a distinct difference in the force of contraction of your arm muscles.

Muscle Tone Sitting in a chair and reading this book, you probably feel fairly relaxed (at least, physically). Yet many groups of muscle fibers are actually in a state of contraction, even if you are not actively moving any part of your body. That a residual contraction remains in your muscles even at rest would become strikingly evident if you were suddenly to faint. As you lost consciousness, your skeletal muscles would become flaccid, and you would topple out of your chair and collapse onto the floor.

The residual degree of contraction in muscles is referred to as **muscle tone** or **tonus** (literally meaning "tension"). A fraction of the muscle fibers in the muscles are in a state of complete tetanus. (No fatigue results, because the same fibers do not continue to contract indefinitely; instead, there is a system of rotation, and the cells continually "take turns.") The muscle as a whole is partially contracted; it feels firm and resists being stretched. Muscle tone is important in maintaining an erect posture and holding the head up. It also keeps the muscles in a state of readiness to respond to stimuli.

Muscle tone is maintained by a steady flow of stimuli from the nervous system. Some of these impulses are transmitted from the brain. Others arise through reflex activity via the spinal cord: specialized sense receptors in the muscles themselves, called **muscle spindles,** send signals to the spinal cord when the muscles are stretched, and such stimulation of the central nervous system results in the generation of impulses that are carried over motor nerves, back to the muscles. The level of stimulation varies. Muscle tone is at a minimum during sleep, when only a small percentage of fibers are contracting. During states of anxiety, there is a rise in the activity of the nervous system and an increase in muscle tone. If the nerves connecting the muscles with the central nervous system are damaged, by injury or by diseases such as poliomyelitis, the muscles lose their tone and become soft and flabby. Such muscles are said to be **atonic.** (If some of the nerve fibers innervating a muscle are destroyed, the remaining nerve fibers may sprout new nerve endings and innervate the paralyzed muscle fibers. Macromotor units, containing as many as ten times the usual number of muscle fibers, may be formed. When this occurs, the function of the muscle is regained, although there is no longer as fine a control over its contractions.) Muscles with less than normal tone are referred to as **flaccid,** while muscles with more than the normal tone are said to be **spastic.**

THE CONTRACTION OF SMOOTH MUSCLE

The vast majority of studies in muscle physiology have been conducted with skeletal muscle. Researchers interested in the study of smooth muscle have been hampered by the fact that smooth muscle often responds inconsistently, even when the conditions are rigidly controlled. There is much more variation in response among different types of smooth muscles than is observed in skeletal muscles, and thus it is more difficult to make generalizations about smooth muscle. Indeed, the same chemical that stimulates a contraction of the smooth muscle in one organ may cause relaxation of the smooth muscle in another organ. There are, however, several physiological characteristics that are common to most of the smooth muscles in the body. First, they are innervated by the autonomic nervous system (although certain types of smooth muscles are capable of spontaneous contractions, independent of stimulation by nerves). Like skeletal muscles, smooth muscles exhibit varying degrees of tone most of the time. The chemical reactions of contraction are basically similar to those of skeletal muscles, and actin and myosin similarly slide over one another to shorten the fiber. But smooth muscles generally contract more slowly and with less force than skeletal muscles, and smooth muscles can remain contracted for long periods of time without fatigue.

Depending on differences in response to stimuli, smooth muscles can be classified in two major categories: multi-unit muscles and visceral smooth muscle.

Multi-unit smooth muscles are found in several parts of the eye, including the iris and ciliary muscle, and in the larger blood vessels. Such muscles are well supplied with autonomic nerves, and they contract only when they are stimulated by nerve impulses.

Visceral smooth muscle, found in the hollow organs of the body, such as the uterus, the gastrointestinal tract, the ureters, and the small blood vessels, has one key distinguishing feature: it contracts spontaneously, independent of stimulation by nerves, although its activity can be modified by nerve action. Visceral smooth muscles have **pacemaker** areas, from which spontaneous contractions originate. The contractions then spread in a wave over the entire muscle mass, so that it acts as a unit. Visceral smooth muscles are characterized by rhythmical contractions. Usually we are completely unaware of the contractions of our visceral smooth muscles, but occasionally they make themselves felt painfully, as in "hunger pangs" (stomach contractions), the intestinal cramps that accompany diarrhea, the powerful contractions of the uterus during childbirth, or the milder uterine contractions that occur in dysmenorrhea (painful menstruation).

Mechanism of Smooth Muscle Contraction

Excitation of Smooth Muscle
One of the most striking differences between skeletal and smooth muscles is the fact that skeletal muscle fibers will not contract unless they are stimulated by nerve impulses, whereas visceral smooth muscle fibers can contract without nerve stimulation. This does not mean that smooth muscle can contract without being stimu-

lated, but rather that it is susceptible to a wider variety of stimuli than skeletal muscle. Smooth muscle contractions can be excited by stretching of the muscle fibers, by hypoxia (exposure to oxygen-deficient conditions), by various hormones, and other factors, in addition to nerve impulses. Contractions can also be initiated within the muscle itself: a segment of frog intestine, dissected out and placed in a dish, will continue its slow, undulating contractions.

Smooth muscles may be innervated by the **sympathetic** or the **parasympathetic nervous system,** or both. When both types of autonomic innervation are present, the impulses of one type of nerve will produce excitation or contraction of the smooth muscle, while those of the other type will cause inhibition or relaxation of the muscle. The specific effects vary from organ to organ—parasympathetic impulses may spark contractions in some organs and produce relaxation in others, while sympathetic impulses produce the opposite effects. The chemical transmitters involved in the neuromuscular transmission also differ: the vesicles in the endings of parasympathetic nerves contain **norepinephrine,** while the transmitter substance of the sympathetic nerves is **acetylcholine.** Just as in skeletal muscles, these chemical transmitters induce a local depolarization of the muscle cell membrane, and when a threshold is passed, an action potential is generated.

In addition to outside stimuli, some of the smooth muscle fibers (the pacemaker cells) are **self-excitable.** Their membranes are extremely permeable to sodium ions, which rapidly diffuse into the cell and permit an action potential to be generated. The excitation does not remain confined to the pacemaker cells, for action potentials can be readily transmitted from one visceral smooth muscle fiber to other, adjacent fibers, without the secretion of any excitatory substance. Such transmission can occur because the membranes at the sites of contact between fibers develop a highly increased permeability and permit an easy flow of current from the interior of one cell to the next. When the self-excitable cells recover from each action potential, self-excitation occurs again a few seconds later. As a result, rhythmic waves of contraction spread through the smooth muscle spontaneously, without any external stimulation.

Electrical Changes During Smooth Muscle Contraction
In most cases, recordings of the electrical activity of smooth muscles show a quite different picture from those of skeletal muscles. Indeed, there are great variations, not only among different types of smooth muscles, but also from moment to moment in the same muscle.

In the normal resting state, the membrane potential of smooth muscle is usually -50 millivolts. Inhibitory transmitters can increase the membrane potential to -70 mV or more, making the fibers inexcitable; excitatory transmitters or other influences (such as stretching) can lower the potential; at about -40 mV, an action potential usually occurs.

Sometimes smooth muscles exhibit a spike potential similar to that of skeletal muscles (Figure 11-13A). The strong contractions of uterine muscle fibers that have been exposed to large quantities of estrogen are of this type. A recording of the action potentials in smooth muscle undergoing spontaneous rhythmic contractions looks like a series of spikes (Figure 11-13B). The muscle in the pelvis of the kidney is self-excitable and transmits peristaltic waves of contractions along the ureter. Such rhythmic contractions are also characteristic of the digestive tract, the bile ducts, and various other tubular structures. One of the most common types of smooth muscle contraction is characterized by an action potential with a plateau (Figure 11-13C), which may last from 0.05 second to as long as 0.5 second, depending on the type of smooth muscle. The muscle remains contracted as long as the action potential continues.

The action potentials in smooth muscle are generated in the same way as in skeletal muscle, through a flow of ions into and out of the cell, associated with depolarization and repolarization of the cell membrane.

The Chemistry of Smooth Muscle Contraction

Viewed under a microscope, skeletal and smooth muscle fibers present a very different appearance. Yet their chemistry is quite similar. Smooth muscle cells contain the same actin and myosin contractile proteins, which are believed to slide over one another during contraction in much the same way as in skeletal muscle fibers, activated by calcium ions. The same enzyme systems are present, and the same "energy currency," ATP, provides the major source of energy for smooth muscle contraction.

An important difference in the contraction of smooth and skeletal muscles is in their timing: contractions in smooth muscle develop only one-fourth to one-twentieth as rapidly as in skeletal muscle, and relaxation is equally slow. The difference is believed to be caused by the structural differences in the two types of muscles, particularly the lack of a T-system of tubules and a well-developed sarcoplasmic reticulum in smooth muscle fibers. As a result, the release and reabsorption of calcium ions are not as rapid in smooth muscle as in skeletal muscle.

Mechanical Action

Many processes involving movement within the body go on continuously. Blood is ceaselessly pumped through the blood vessels, urine continuously trickles

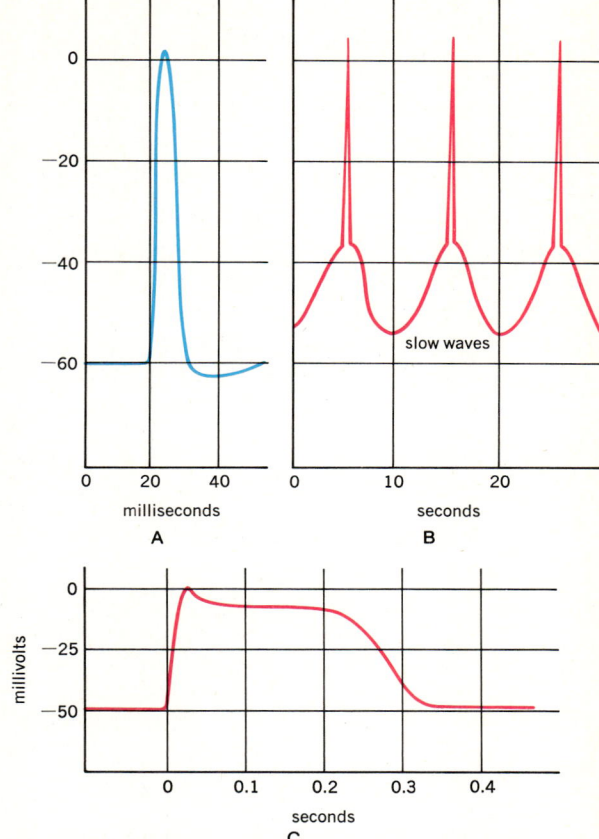

FIGURE 11-13 Smooth muscle contraction: a spike action potential (A), a series of action potentials associated with peristaltic waves in the intestine (B), and an action potential with a plateau from a smooth muscle fiber of the rat uterus (C).

from the kidneys through the ureters to the bladder, and food in various stages of digestion is propelled along the gastrointestinal tract. If the arteries, ureters, and intestines were lined with skeletal muscles, they would quickly fatigue. But the smooth muscles in these visceral organs continue their ceaseless rhythmic contractions without any undue stress.

Several distinguishing features of smooth muscle contraction have also been mentioned. Smooth muscle contracts more slowly than skeletal muscle, and it can sustain its contractions for longer periods of time, without using much energy. Although the motor units of skeletal muscles contract independently, in smooth muscles excitation spreads from one fiber to the surrounding fibers, and the entire muscle contracts as a unit.

Muscle Tone Like skeletal muscle, smooth muscle can maintain a sustained partial contraction for long periods of time. This **tonus** reflects the level of activity of the muscle at any particular moment of time, and it may affect the response of the muscle to stimuli. For example, stimulation of the vagus nerve produces

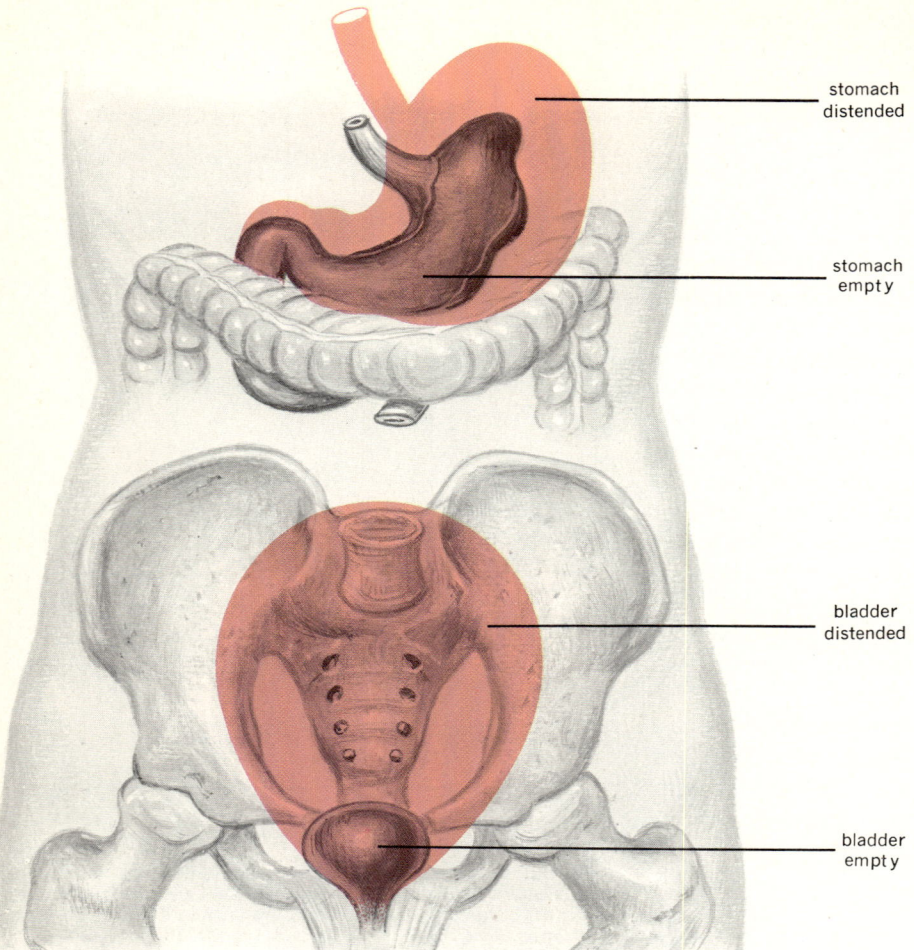

stomach distended

stomach empty

bladder distended

bladder empty

contractions of the smooth muscle in the walls of the stomach and intestines; the effect is much greater if the muscle has a low state of tonus and is relatively quiet, while if the muscle tone is high and rhythmic contractions are occurring, stimulation of the vagus nerve will inhibit contractions.

Tonic contraction in smooth muscle is believed to result from a summation of repetitive action potentials, just as it does in skeletal muscle. It may be entirely distinct from rhythmic contractions: during tonic contraction, the rhythmicity may disappear, or change in frequency, or it may become more intense.

Plasticity and Accommodation If your bladder were lined with skeletal muscle, you would spend most of the day in the bathroom. And if your stomach were lined with skeletal muscle, you would have to eat almost continuously to avoid starving to death.

The proper functioning of the stomach and urinary bladder is dependent on another important difference of smooth muscle from skeletal muscle: its ability to change its length greatly without any great change in tension. If a one-inch segment of smooth muscle is suddenly stretched to two inches, at first there will be a tremendous increase in tension between the two ends. But quickly the extra tension begins to disappear; within a few minutes it is back to its original value, even though the muscle is now twice as long. Skeletal muscle, on the other hand, increases its resistance to stretch the more it is stretched, and thus the tension in a stretched skeletal muscle remains greatly increased. The difference is probably the result of the different structural arrangement of the actin and myosin filaments: a precise, regular arrangement in skeletal muscle and a random arrangement in smooth muscle. When a smooth muscle is stretched, it is believed that the filaments rearrange their bonds and gradually allow sliding to take place, and the tension returns to its original value. This process is called **stress-relaxation,** and it permits smooth muscle to accommodate to enormous changes in size, while still retaining the ability to contract effectively. (Skeletal muscle has a useful distance of contraction of only 25 to 35 percent of its length, while smooth muscle can contract effectively from a length two times its normal length to as short as half its normal length.)

The practical consequences of the great plasticity of smooth muscle are most obvious in the stomach and bladder. When relatively empty, these organs can contract to a compact size; yet they can be distended to a far greater size, serving as reservoirs (Figure 11-14). The bladder, for example, can accommodate 100 ml or 1000 ml or urine without any significant change in internal pressure. There is a limit to the degree of stretching that smooth muscle can sustain without an increase in tension; overstretching may cause pain as a result of stimulation of afferent nerves (e.g., the "bellyache" that may result from overeating), and the increase in tension may provoke the muscle to contract forcefully, expelling the contents of the organ. But before the bladder, for example, reached the degree of distension outlined in Figure 11-14, a feeling of fullness would probably prompt its emptying (involving a voluntary relaxation of the skeletal muscle sphincter that guards its outlet). Catheterization may be necessary to empty the bladder of an unconscious person, to prevent abnormal distension of the bladder.

THE CONTRACTION OF CARDIAC MUSCLE

An accident fracturing the cervical vertebrae can have tragic effects. If the spinal cord is severely damaged, the victim may be almost totally paralyzed, unable to move arms or legs or body. But the beating of the heart is unaffected, for heart muscle has an inherent ability to contract rhythmically, independent of outside stimuli. Indeed, in dramatic heart transplant operations (Figure 11-15), a heart can be removed from the body of someone who has just died, sutured into the body of a heart disease victim, started with a shock of electricity, and then carry on, beating normally.

Mechanism of Cardiac Muscle Contraction

In its spontaneous, rhythmic contractions, cardiac muscle is very similar to smooth muscle. The contractions are initiated by specialized excitatory cells, but the heartbeat rate may also be influenced by nerve impulses, hormones, and other factors. Yet the internal structure of cardiac muscle fibers is rather similar to skeletal muscle: there are the same kinds of actin and myosin filaments, in a regular arrangement, forming the characteristic striations, and there is a T-system of tubules promoting a flow of electric current into the cell during depolarization. Contraction involves the same chemical reactions and the same kind of sliding of the actin and myosin filaments over one another as in skeletal muscle. Unlike skeletal muscle, however, cardiac muscle fibers do not contract indepently. Excitation spreads rapidly from one cell to another. You may recall that the cardiac muscle fibers are rather short and are connected end-to-end by

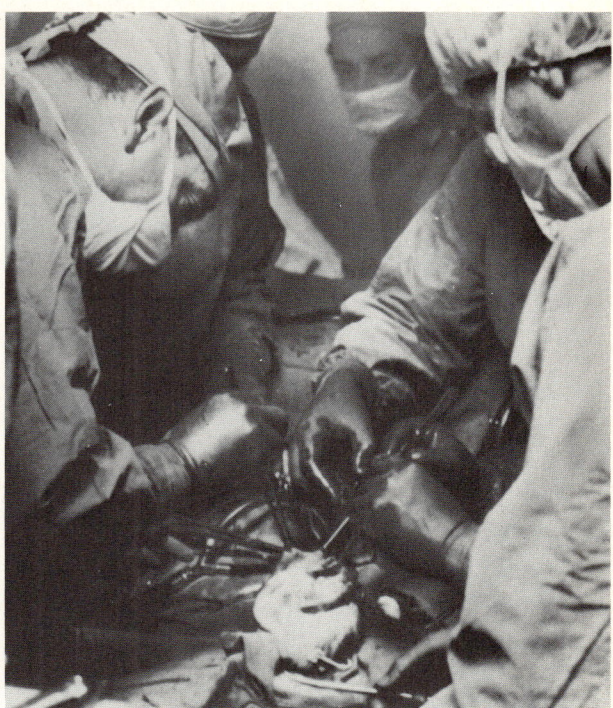

FIGURE 11-15   The heart of a traffic accident victim is being prepared for a transplant.

intercalated discs and joined into a branching and anastomosing network. The intercalated discs are formed by portions of the cell membrane, but they possess an electrical resistance about 400 times less than that of the remainder of the sarcolemma. Once an action potential starts, depolarization spreads rapidly through the entire heart muscle, which contracts as a unit. In skeletal muscle, the individual motor units obey an all-or-nothing rule, but the muscle as a whole exhibits graded contractions. In cardiac muscle, the entire muscle shows an all-or-nothing response.

The resting potential of cardiac muscle is about -80 to -85 millivolts. Its action potential is somewhat different from that of skeletal muscle (Figure 11-16). After an initial spike, the membrane remains depolarized for some time, from 0.15 to 0.3 second, showing a plateau. Then an abrupt repolarization follows. During the action potential, which lasts twenty to fifty times as long as in skeletal muscle, the cardiac muscle remains contracted, and it will not respond to a new stimulus. This is its refractory period, which normally lasts about 0.25 second in the ventricles and 0.15 second in the atria. Because of the long refractory period, summation and complete tetanus cannot be produced in cardiac muscle—if they could, the heart would be useless in its function of pumping blood. Normally the heart contractions follow one another in a regular rhythm of about 72 per minute.

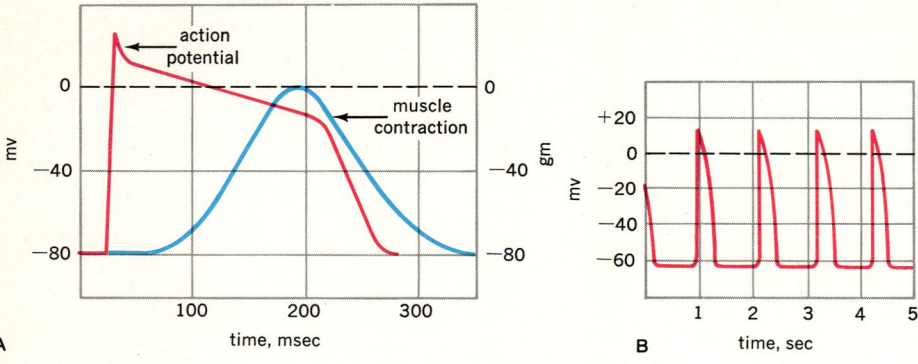

FIGURE 11-16 Cardiac muscle contraction. Comparison of the action potential with the actual muscle contraction (A) and rhythmic action potentials from the ventricle of the frog heart (B).

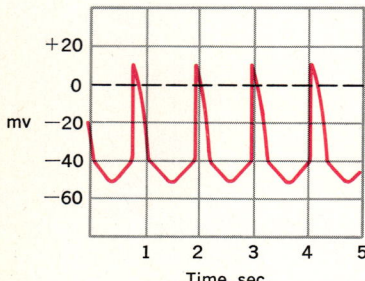

FIGURE 11-17 Action potentials from the pacemaker area (sinus venosus) of the frog heart. Note the prepotentials, which do not occur in the action potentials from the ventricle.

Action potentials recorded from the pacemaker area of the heart show a somewhat different picture (Figure 11-17). In these self-excitable cells, the membrane is somewhat permeable to sodium, which diffuses into the cells and gives rise to prepotentials, small depolarizations occurring before the actual spike.

Mechanical Action

In ancient times it was said that "all roads lead to Rome." In the body, all roads—or rather the "waterways" of the circulatory system—ultimately lead to or from the heart. This organ is not only the central intersection of all the blood flows of the body, but it also provides the motive force that propels the blood on its way. With its ceaseless, rhythmic contractions, it alternately fills with incoming blood and then pumps it out into the arteries.

The working of the heart is discussed in detail in Chapter 21. Here we shall take up only a few points relating to its functioning as a muscle. As you have undoubtedly learned long ago, the human heart is a four-chambered pump, with two upper chambers called **atria** and two cone-shaped lower chambers called **ventricles** (Figure 11-18). The atria are receiving chambers, as the name (literally meaning an "anteroom") implies; the thicker-walled ventricles are the hard-working pumps. Each atrium communicates

with its respective ventricle through an opening that can be closed by a one-way valve.

The period from the end of one heart contraction to the end of the next contraction is called the **cardiac cycle.** Each cycle is initiated by the spontaneous generation of an action potential in an excitable region called the **sinoatrial node.** The action potential travels first through both atria and then is transmitted (with a time lag of about a tenth of a second) to the ventricles. Thus, the atria contract first, pumping blood into the ventricles, which then contract to force the blood out through arteries. This arrangement is extremely effective for several reasons. Not only does it permit a maximum outflow of blood from the heart with each contraction, but it utilizes a characteristic property of the heart muscle. Like skeletal muscle, cardiac muscle shows an increase in the force of contraction when it is slightly stretched. (As in skeletal muscle, this increase in force of contraction with increasing initial length of the muscle occurs only up to a certain optimum point, after which the force of contraction drops with further stretching.) When the atria pump blood into the ventricles, their muscular walls are slightly distended. As a result, the contractions of the ventricles are more forceful than they would be if they contained a smaller volume of blood. This relationship was first described many years ago and is known as **Starling's law of the heart.**

In certain abnormal situations, such as after a coronary infarct, the normal rhythm of the heart contractions may be disturbed, and the atria or ventricles may begin to contract at a very high rate (hundreds of times a minute), with a loss of the normal coordination of the contractions. Such rapid and uncoordinated contraction of individual cardiac muscle fibers is called **fibrillation.** The heart is able to function despite atrial fibrillation, although with reduced efficiency (remember Starling's law). But if the ventricles begin to fibrillate, no blood can be pumped. This is an extreme medical emergency: unless a heart is **defibrillated** within one minute, it is usually too weak to be revived. But hand pumping the heart by powerful

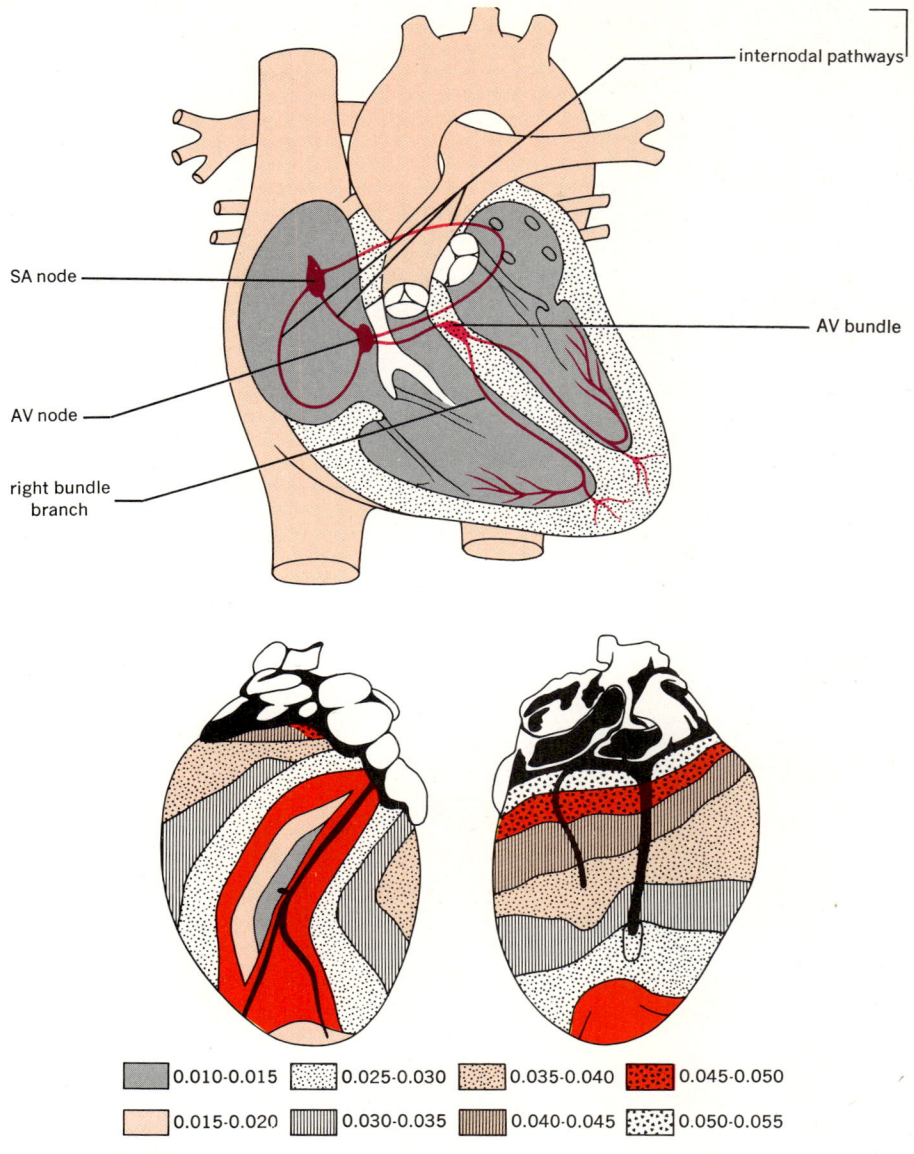

internodal pathways

SA node

AV node

right bundle branch

AV bundle

FIGURE 11-18 The conducting system of the heart (top) and sequence of activation of the anterior and posterior surfaces of the heart as the cardiac impulse spreads from the conducting system through the ventricular muscle fibers (bottom), from Sodi-Pallares and Calder: *New Bases of Electrocardiography,* C.V. Mosby Co.

0.010-0.015   0.025-0.030   0.035-0.040   0.045-0.050

0.015-0.020   0.030-0.035   0.040-0.045   0.050-0.055

0.020-0.025

thrusts on the chest wall can renew the coronary blood supply, so that the heart can eventually be restarted. Defibrillation may be accomplished by passing a strong electric current through the ventricles. The brief pulse of current makes all of the cardiac muscle fibers simultaneously become refractory. The heart remains quiet for a few seconds, then spontaneously resumes beating.

BODY MOVEMENTS AND POSTURE

How many times has a parent or teacher reminded you to "stand up straight," or not to slump over your desk? Such well-meaning reminders can be annoying at times; yet the development and maintenance of good posture is an important key to feeling well and

keeping your body ready to respond effectively to all the demands of your daily activities.

All animals that hold themselves up on legs and move about are engaged in a constant struggle against gravity. A measure of support is provided by the firm and rigid skeleton. Yet if the limbs and body were completely firm and rigid, mobility would be impossible. The design of animal bodies provides an effective compromise by introducing movable joints between adjacent bones. Yet each joint is an inherent weak spot, which must be bolstered by an elaborate arrangement of muscles, which mutually supplement, enhance, and counteract each other. Muscles and bones work together to provide for support and movement of the body and its parts.

Muscles and the Bony Levers

We live in a technological society, surrounded by a bewildering array of complicated machines. Yet all of them are elaborations of a few simple principles, and one of the most ubiquitous of these is the lever. Stripped to its essence, the **lever** is a simple machine consisting of a rigid rod resting on a pivot called a **fulcrum;** a force is applied to one part of the rod, and a weight on another part of the rod is lifted. Depending on the arrangement of the force applied, the weight, and the fulcrum, the lever may provide a **mechanical advantage;** the greater the distance from the fulcrum to the point of application of the force, the smaller the force required to overcome the resistance.

The invention of the lever, some time back in long-forgotten prehistory, was an important stage in the development of technology. But nature invented the lever long before humans discovered its principle. The bones of the body are essentially levers, which are acted on by the forces exerted by the muscles at the points of their insertion. The resistance to be overcome may be a part of the body to be moved, or an object to be lifted, or both. The skeletal muscles expend energy and perform work, which may be defined as the movement of some resisting force or object through a distance. The amount of work performed can be simply calculated by multiplying the weight lifted (or the resisting force opposed) by the distance through which it is lifted. The amount of work that muscles perform may vary greatly: considerably more work is performed in lifting a bucket of water than in winking an eye, but work is performed in each case.

Three different arrangements of the lever are possible (Figure 11-19), and all three types are found in the human body. Physicists refer to the typical "seesaw" arrangement, with the force exerted at one end, the resistance at the other, and the fulcrum somewhere in between, as a first-class lever. An example of this arrangement in the body is the semispinalis capitis muscle, which extends the head. In a second-class lever, the fulcrum is at one end, the force is exerted at the other end, and the resistance is found between them. An example of this type is the action of the calf muscle, when you stand up on your toes. A third-class lever has its fulcrum at one end, with the resistance at the opposite end, and the force exerted between them. The biceps brachii and brachialis muscles pull up on the bones of the forearm in this way. Note that the mechanical advantage is determined by the distance from the insertion of the muscle to the fulcrum (at the elbow), and not by the entire length of the muscle. A large biceps muscle can exert a maximum force of contraction of about 250 pounds; but since its insertion is found at a distance from the fulcrum only about one-seventh of the total length of the forearm lever, its effective lifting power at the hand is only about 36 pounds (250/7). A greater mechanical advantage would be obtained if its insertion were farther from the fulcrum (and, indeed, some people do have a long insertion of the biceps brachii), but having the insertion of a muscle fairly close to the joint helps to prevent it from getting in the way of movement. Generally, the arrangement of the muscles represents a compromise: an insertion close to the fulcrum allows for speed at a sacrifice of power, while a more distant insertion allows for greater force. Also as a general rule, the force exerted by a muscle is a minimum when its line of pull is nearly parallel to the long axis of the bone to which it is attached and a maximum when the line of pull is at right angles to the bone. The biceps brachii, for example, exerts a greater force when the arm is flexed than when it is extended.

Posture

The dynamic nature of the constant muscular adjustments that are necessary for maintaining an upright posture is most evident when you watch a lecturer. Even if he intends to remain quite straight and rigid (and may believe he is doing so), he actually tends to sway slightly. His body continually moves in one direction or another, and then is brought back to a central position by the postural muscles.

An important key to the understanding of both posture and locomotion is the concept of **center of gravity.** From the standpoint of physics, any irregular shaped object (for example, your body) behaves as though all of its weight were concentrated at a single point. This point is its center of gravity. For a sphere, the center of gravity would be exactly in the center of the object, but for objects of other shapes, the center of gravity does not necessarily coincide with the center of the object (Figure 11-20). When the center of gravity is well supported, the forces acting upward (in the human body, the contractions of the muscles) effectively counteract the downward pull of gravity. But if the center of gravity is shifted, the object tends to topple over. Thus, wearing high heels (Figure 11-21) shifts the center of gravity forward, and there is a tendency to lean backward with the upper part of the trunk to compensate.

A six-legged insect or a four-legged animal is relatively stable, for its center of gravity is approximately centered between a number of widely spaced legs. Even in walking, it usually has three legs on the ground at any time, forming a firm tripod. But humans, in assuming an upright posture, are really doing things the hard way. Continual tonic contractions of various groups of muscles (particularly those of the legs and back) are necessary to keep the center of gravity in a stable position. The postural muscles

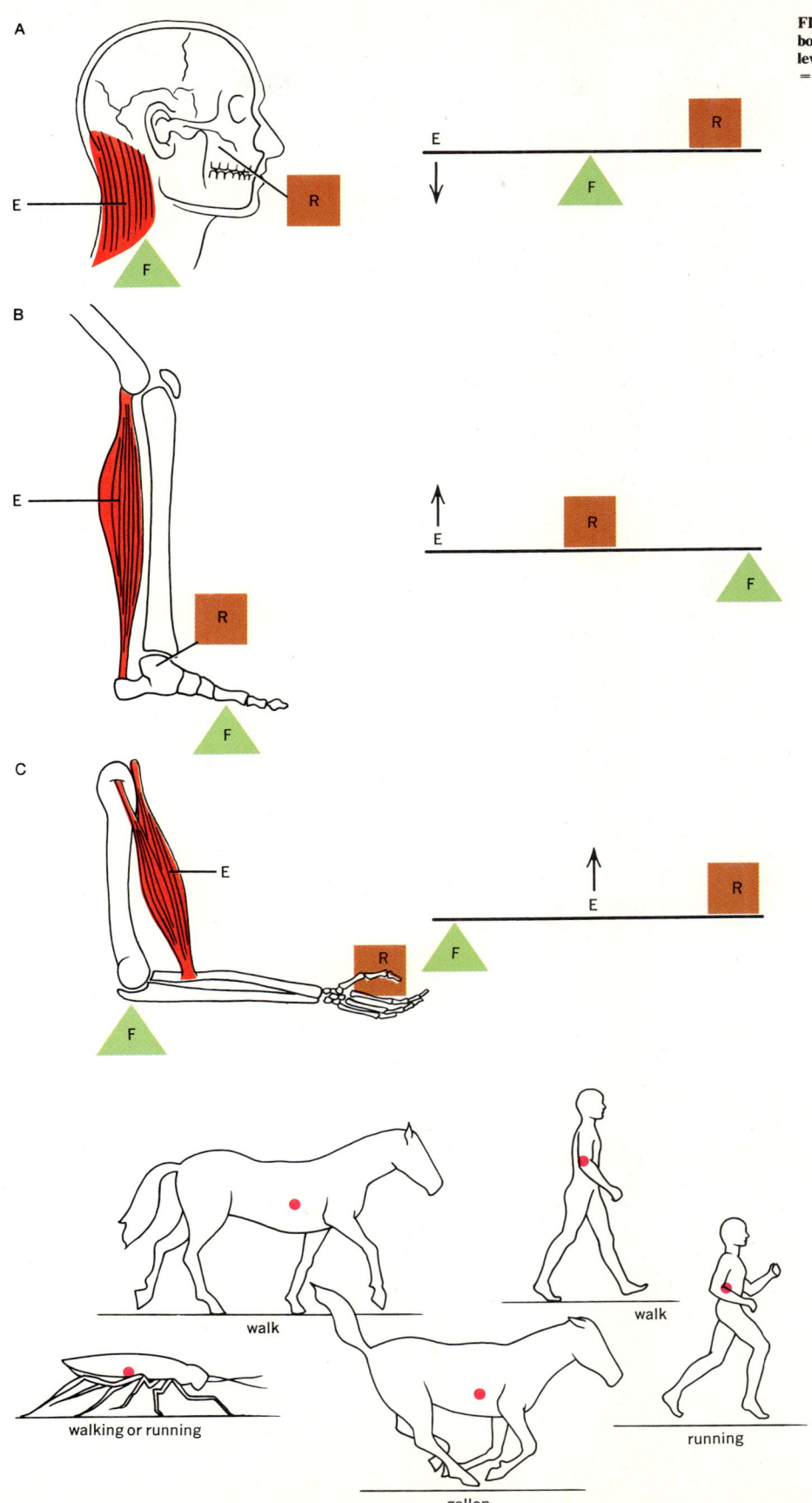

FIGURE 11-19   Classes of levers in the body: (A) first-class lever; (B) second-class lever; (C) third-class lever. (E = effort, R = resistance, F = fulcrum)

FIGURE 11-20   Hexapod and quadruped locomotion provide great inherent stability; the human biped locomotion requires continual coordinated muscular adjustments to maintain balance. The dot indicates the center of gravity in each case.

walk

walk

walking or running

gallop

running

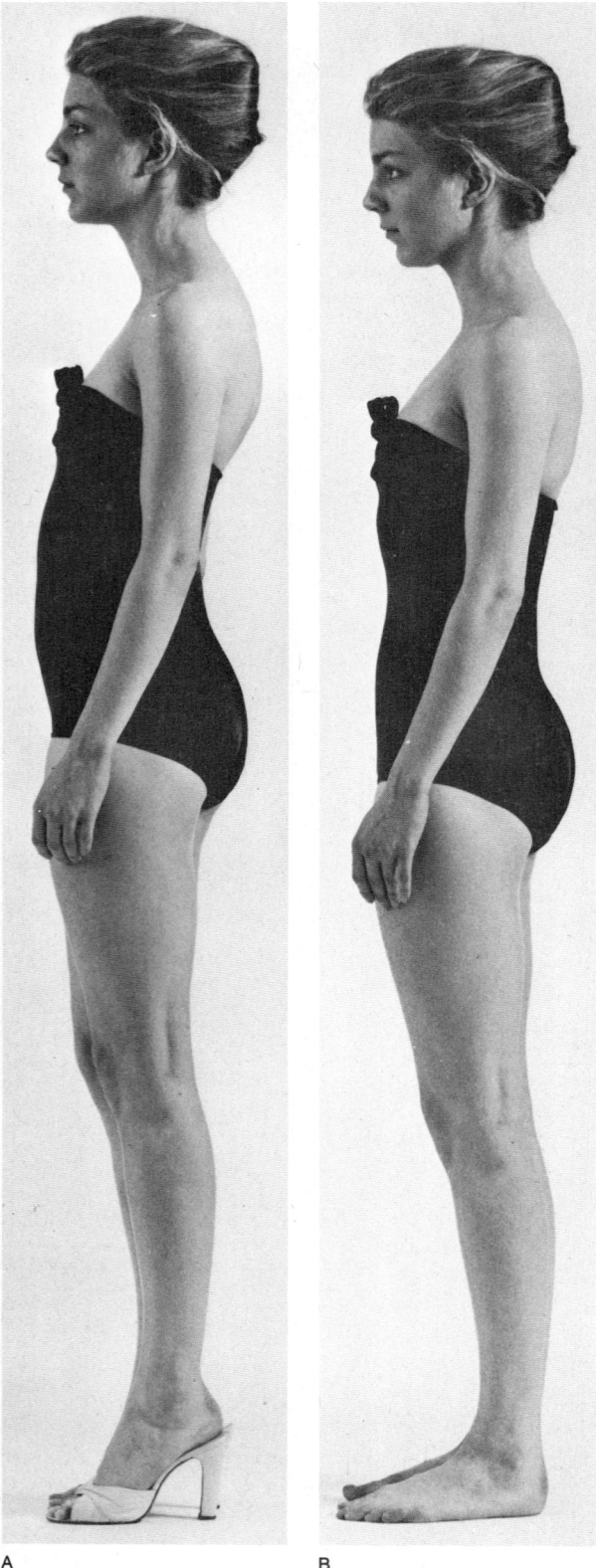

A   B

FIGURE 11-21 High heels may be stylish, but note how they shift the body's center of gravity forward and produce a deepening of the spinal curvature as the postural muscles compensate.

have strong **stretch reflexes:** when a postural muscle with an intact nerve supply is stimulated, it responds with a rapidly developed steady contraction that may last for long periods. (Stretching of a muscle that is not involved in maintaining posture typically produces only a brief contraction.) The neck muscles also play an important role in posture, since they determine the relationship between the head and the trunk. Even turning the head to one side alters the tone in the leg muscles. Information from the stretch receptors in the postural muscles, as well as from receptors in the joint capsules, the soles of the feet, the eyes, and the semicircular canals of the inner ears, is interpreted in the brain, particularly in the cerebellum, which is the coordinator of the body tone and balance.

In "correct" standing posture, the head is held high and balanced easily on the neck, the abdomen is held in, and the chest is allowed to expand freely. The shoulders are not allowed to sag forward, and the arms hang freely. Good posture is *not* a stiff military "standing to attention," but instead a relaxed position that will readily merge into any desired movement. Correct sitting posture is similar to correct standing posture, except that the leg muscles play a minor role. Deviations from "correct" posture are common—often you may be able to recognize someone from the way he or she stands or walks—but if the deviations are too great, they may result in inefficient body movements, such ailments as backaches, and even the development of deformity. Good posture is developed gradually: a small child tends to stand with abdomen thrust forward, while the upper body leans backward to compensate.

The upright posture has brought great benefits to humans, in freeing the hands for manipulation. The adaptations necessary for such posture involve far more than the skeleton. Intricate neuromuscular reflexes have been developed to maintain support for the body. The tendency of blood to pool in the lower regions of the body under the force of gravity, while the most oxygen-hungry part of the body, the brain, is situated above the heart, has necessitated a complicated system of regional vasomotor control. An upright posture also requires greater muscular effort for breathing. The widespread prevalence of such ailments as backaches, flat feet, and varicose veins is evidence that the body's design is still far from perfect.

A recumbent posture (lying down horizontally) is the easiest to maintain, since the body is supported in many places. As a result, this is the posture usually assumed for resting and sleeping. (It is possible to fall asleep sitting up, but often one wakes with a stiff neck or other signs of muscular strain.) Yet modern physicians have discovered that too much bed rest has its drawbacks, even for a patient recuperating from a major operation. Long confinement to a recumbent position can lead to pooling of bronchial secretions in the lungs, which may result in pneumonia; to an inefficient flow of venous blood, which may lead to clot formation and pulmonary embolism; to a reduced capability of the heart, an impairment of coordination (due to lack of practice), and an atrophy of the muscles and bones. (A fracture will knit better if the patient is ambulatory than if he or she is confined to bed and the minerals are gradually leached out of the bones; the excreted calcium, in addition, may contribute to the formation of stones in the urinary tract.)

Locomotion

You would hardly expect to see a plant walking down the street. With a few partial exceptions, such as tumbleweed, plants do not possess the ability to move from place to place, as most animals do. And even tumbleweed lacks another key characteristic of **locomotion,** the movement of the entire body from place to place *under its own power.* (Tumbleweeds are blown about by the wind.) The animals of the earth use a variety of modes of locomotion: swimming in the water (by paddling, kicking, undulation, or even jet propulsion); flying and gliding through the air; and creeping, walking, running, and leaping on land. Hu-

mans can swim in the water, and, using machines, can fly through the air; on land they are fairly good leapers, though not nearly as efficient as the kangaroo or the flea; they can creep and crawl as well, but the principal modes of human locomotion are walking and running.

The key factors in any kind of locomotion, as in the maintenance of posture, are support and balance. During bipedal (two-legged) locomotion, the problems brought about by our upright position are multiplied. In a standing postion, at least both feet are on the ground and provide some measure of stability. But in walking, the legs are alternately raised and swung forward, which means that for a substantial fraction of the time only one foot is on the ground, supporting the entire weight of the body. During running the alternation of the legs is speeded up, and frequently both legs are off the ground at the same time. The continual shifts of the body's center of gravity, depicted in Figure 11-22, must be constantly compensated for through body movements coordinated by the cerebellum and effected by contractions of the muscles.

As might be expected, the muscles most active in walking and running are those of the legs. As a step is taken, strong contractions of the rectus femoris, tensor fascia latae, and pectineus muscles swing one of

A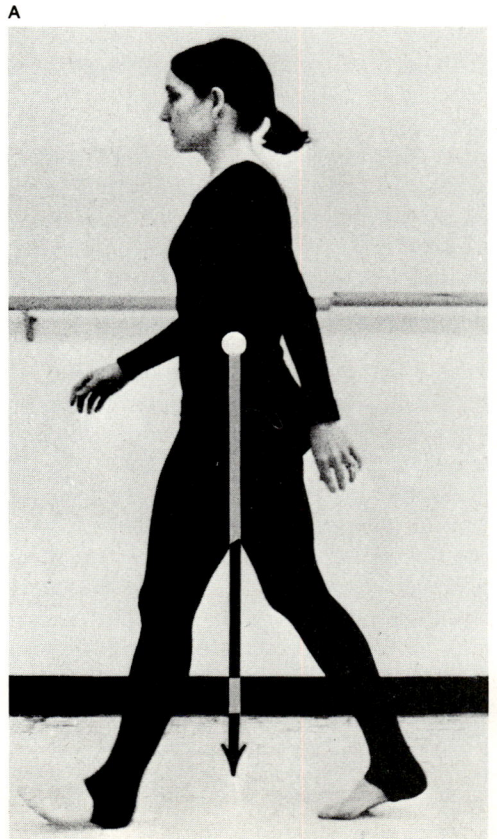

B

FIGURE 11-22 Two-legged locomotion: walking (A) and running (B). Note the shift of center of gravity, making balancing more complicated in running.

the legs forward. The extensor muscles of the lower leg maintain a certain degree of contraction, enough to prepare the foot for contact with the ground. Gravity and momentum help to complete the swing. Meanwhile, in the leg that has remained on the ground supporting the body, contractions of the gastrocnemius and soleus raise the body on tiptoe and give it a shove. The foot that has swung forward is placed on the ground, and the body weight is shifted to that leg, in which contractions of the extensors of the thigh, such as the gluteus maximus and hamstring muscles, help to support the weight. Now the leg that has just relinquished the load is swung forward in turn, with a similar sequence of muscular contractions. In walking, there is a period of overlap, when both feet are on the ground and both legs are bearing a portion of the body weight. This period is shortened as the pace is quickened, until, in running, the back foot is actually off the ground and swinging forward before the front foot has touched the ground.

The complicated sequence of movements involved in human locomotion, requiring a delicate coordination and fine balance, becomes so automatic that you rarely have to give the process any conscious thought. Yet as a baby you perfected your locomotive skills through long and laborious practice, first creeping on your belly like a reptile, then crawling on hands and knees, then finally pulling yourself up to an upright position, with much tottering and unexpected tumbles.

Although the muscles of the legs provide the major propulsive force for walking and running, the arms are not entirely inactive. Forward momentum can be augmented, particularly in running, by swinging the arms forward alternately, in synchronization with the leg movements.

In swimming, locomotion in the water, the upper extremities play a far more active role. Water, as a medium, presents some important differences from the air-land interface on which walking and running are performed. The buoyancy of water provides a considerable degree of support for the body, against the downward pull of gravity. The muscles do not have to work as hard just to keep the body up as they do on land. However, water offers considerable resistance to body movements—far more than air, but not as much as solid ground, against which the feet push in walking and running. In a typical crawl stroke, the arms are moved alternately: first the arm is flexed and abducted at the shoulder and flexed at the elbow, then straightened; then, in the downstroke that provides the main propulsive force, the arm is held rigid at the elbow and pulled downward, backward, and medially, working like the blade of a paddle to pull the body through the water. By the time one arm has completed its backward stroke, the other arm is al-

ready extended forward. Meanwhile, the legs are alternately flexed and extended (kicking) to provide additional propulsive force. Examine the diagrams in Figure 11-23 and then, referring back to the last chapter, try to work out the sequence of muscle contractions involved in swimming.

DISEASES AND DISORDERS OF THE MUSCULAR SYSTEM

For many years, one of the most dreaded diseases of childhood was polio. This disease sometimes killed, but more often left its young victims crippled for life, with paralyzed limbs and withered muscles (Figure 11-24). The development of effective vaccines against the poliomyelitis virus nearly wiped out this disease. But at this writing, public health officials are fearful that ignorance and apathy among parents, a growing proportion of whom are not bothering to have their children immunized against polio, may be setting the scene for new major outbreaks of the disease.

The effects of the poliomyelitis virus illustrate a concept of key importance for an understanding of disorders of the muscular system. The functioning unit of a muscle is not the individual muscle cell, but rather the motor unit—the combination of a motor nerve and the muscle fibers that it innervates. Anything that damages either the muscles or the nerves may result in a loss of muscle function. The poliomyelitis virus, for example, causes **paralysis** (a loss of voluntary movement) and **atrophy** (wasting) of the muscles, yet it does not attack the muscles directly; polio is a disease of the nervous system, in which virus infection can destroy the neurons. The muscle atrophy that often follows the disease is a result of disuse of the muscles innervated by damaged neurons or controlled by a damaged center in the brain stem. The treatment of polio victims and other paralysis patients includes regular exercising of the affected muscles to prevent atrophy. If not all the motor units are damaged (as is often the case), the patient can be trained to regain some control over the muscles. In addition, the healthy nerves of adjacent motor units may sprout new nerve endings and innervate the paralyzed muscle fibers, restoring their function.

When skeletal muscles themselves are damaged, for example, in an accident, they have an ability to regenerate, forming new muscle fibers. If the damage is too extensive, however, the damaged muscle is replaced by scar tissue. Smooth muscle and cardiac muscle lack the ability to regenerate when damaged, forming scar tissue instead. A coronary occlusion, or blockage of the arteries supplying the heart muscle, results in the death of the area of muscle supplied by the blocked blood vessels and scarring of the heart. The scar tissue does not contribute to the heart's contractions; if the scarred area is too extensive, the muscle

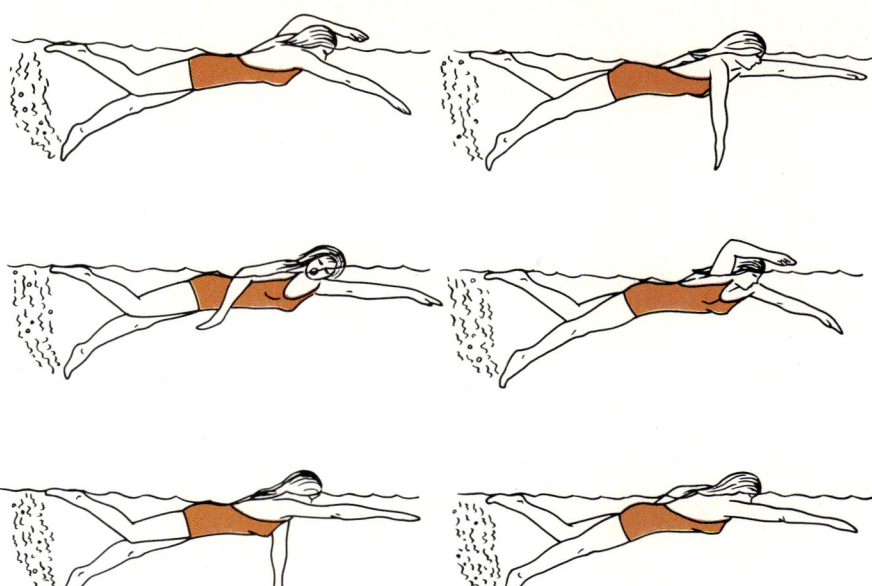

FIGURE 11-23 **Basic movements of the crawl stroke in swimming.**

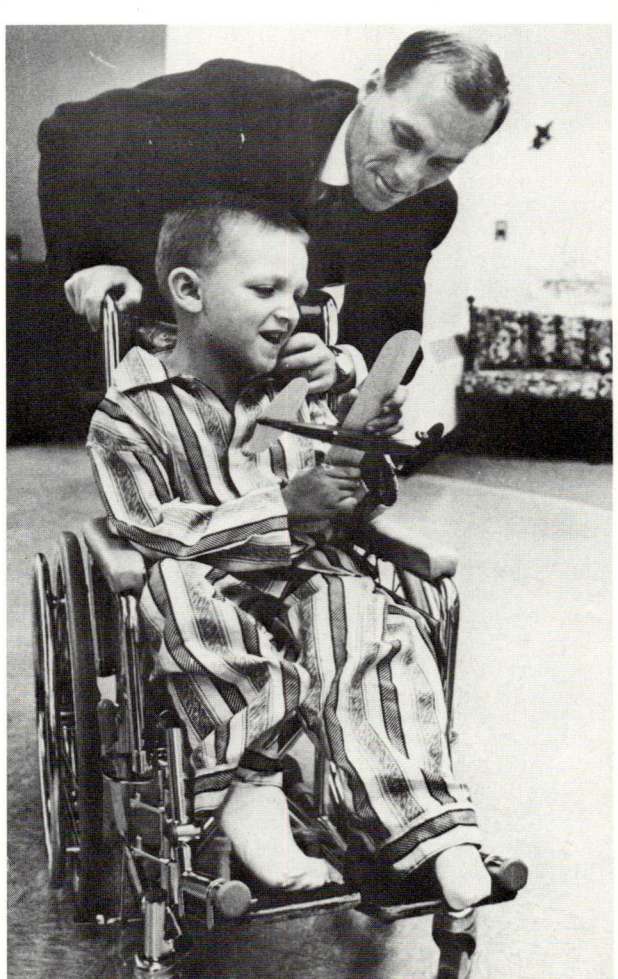

FIGURE 11-24 Effective vaccines have greatly decreased the occurrence of polio. Note the typical plantar flexion of the feet of this young polio victim, who was flown from Yugoslavia to the United States for rehabilitation therapy.

tissue remaining may no longer be able to pump blood effectively enough to keep the body adequately supplied with oxygen and nutrients.

The commonest disorders of the muscular system are **spasms:** sudden, involuntary, and painful muscle contractions. Backaches in the lower back are spasms of the long, ropelike muscles in the lumbar region, which follow stress or strain. **Torticollis,** or wryneck, involves spasms of the sternocleidomastoid and other neck muscles, on one side, and results in a turning of the head to one side. When a spasm is prolonged, it is called a **tonic spasm** or **cramp.** An intermittent spasm, characterized by alternate contractions and relaxation, is referred to as a **clonic spasm.** Spasms may occur not only in skeletal muscles, but in smooth muscles as well; in the latter case, a transitory constriction of a duct or orifice is often produced.

Contracture is a painful condition in which the muscle fibers are shortened in the resting state. It may result from strenuous exercise (muscle fatigue), or from long periods of inactivity, when the muscles do not receive sufficient exercise. Bed rest, for example, may cause the muscle fibers to adjust themselves to a shorter length, corresponding to a flexed limb, and then the muscles must be painfully exercised and relengthened. Such exercise may be either active (by the person affected) or passive (by someone else).

Spasms, cramps, and contracture are painful conditions. Physiologists often use a special term to refer to muscle pain, regardless of its cause: **myalgia. Myopathy** is the general category of diseases of the muscles. The term **myositis** refers to an inflammation of muscular tissue; **fibrositis** is an inflammation of the connective tissue in a muscle, usually near a joint. A combination of the two, **fibromyositis,** often occurs and is commonly called **rheumatism** or **lumbago.**

Paralysis may occur in a variety of diseases and disorders of the muscles and nervous system. Two types are observed: **flaccid** (limp) **paralysis,** in which there is a loss of firmness or tone of the muscles (atonia); and **spastic** (stiff) **paralysis,** in which the muscles show too much tone. Spastic paralysis in the young may result from birth injury. Spastic children may have no impairment of intelligence, and they can be taught to gain some control over their muscles. In the elderly, spastic paralysis is frequently the result of a stroke, or hemorrhage in the brain.

Muscles tend to **atrophy** (waste away) with disuse—either in paralysis, or due to extreme inactivity. When muscles are regularly subjected to vigorous contractions, the opposite occurs: they **hypertrophy,** or grow larger. In skeletal muscles, hypertrophy is not a disorder, but on the contrary is a positive change, making the muscle stronger and more effective. The key to body building is to progressively increase the load placed on the muscles; regular exercise will not produce hypertrophy if less than maximum contractions are involved. In the heart muscle, hypertrophy can be a pathological condition: the heart tends to enlarge when it is overworked, for example, in compensating for a faulty valve or for arteries clogged with fatty deposits. The resulting increased force of contraction may cause great discomfort. (The enlarged heart of an athlete in top condition is not pathological, but rather a part of a general increase in the effectiveness of the cardiovascular system.)

Two rather mysterious diseases of the muscular system have been much in the news lately. These are muscular dystrophy and myasthenia gravis. Recent evidence indicates that these may be autoimmune diseases, in which the body's defenses are turned upon its own cells.

Muscular dystrophy is most often seen in children. It is a tragic disease, in which an apparently normal child suddenly becomes clumsy, falls frequently, and then progressively loses the use of muscles until he or she is entirely helpless. The muscles are enlarged, but it is not a true hypertrophy, for the enlargement is due to large fat deposits. The actual muscle fibers atrophy, and the contractile function of the muscles becomes progressively less effective. It is thought that there may be a hereditary factor in the disease.

In **myasthenia gravis,** the skeletal muscles are extremely weak and very easily fatigued. The muscles of the face are affected first—typically, the eyelids droop, and the patient may have double vision. The condition spreads to other muscles of the body, until the patient is incapacitated. Respiratory infections are particularly dangerous for a myasthenia gravis patient, whose muscles are so weak that he or she cannot cough. The mechanism of myasthenia gravis seems to involve some sort of blockage at the neuromuscular junction. Some success in treating the disease has been achieved with neostigmine and other drugs that inhibit cholinesterase, thus leaving more acetylcholine available to transmit impulses across the neuromuscular junction. Recent studies have revealed the presence of autoantibodies in the blood of myasthenia gravis patients, and the removal of these autoantibodies by plasmapheresis (replacement of the blood plasma) has brought dramatic relief of the symptoms in some cases.

SUMMARY

Skeletal muscle contractions consist of three phases: latent period, period of contraction, and period of relaxation.

Skeletal muscles are characterized by excitability and will not contract in the absence of a stimulus.

Impulses are transmitted from motor neurons to muscle fibers across the synaptic cleft by the neurotransmitter chemical acetylcholine, which is quickly broken down by cholinesterase.

Drugs that affect muscle action may mimic acetylcholine, inactivate cholinesterase, or inhibit acetylcholine receptors on the surface of the sarcolemma.

Acetylcholine makes the sarcolemma permeable to sodium ions, which diffuse into the cell, raising the electrical potential of the membrane from the resting potential to the end-plate potential.

Local depolarization of a muscle fiber makes the sarcolemma impermeable to sodium ions, and repolarization occurs; the sequence of events is called the action potential.

The action potential spreads over the entire muscle fiber.

During the spike potential (depolarization), the muscle cell is completely unresponsive to stimuli (absolute refractory period); while repolarization is occurring, a second stimulus would produce a weaker response (relative refractory period).

The flow of electric current into the cell by way of the T-tubules and longitudinal tubules of the sarcoplasmic reticulum sparks a release of calcium ions and initiates contraction.

Interactions between actin and myosin filaments, initiated by calcium ions and involving a splitting of ATP and release of energy, cause the two types of filaments to slide over one another, shortening the overall length of the muscle fiber.

"Ratchet" and electrostatic solenoid mechanisms have been proposed to explain muscle contraction.

Energy sources utilized in muscle contraction are ATP (adenosine triphosphate) and creatine phosphate.

Vigorous exercise exhausts muscle reserves of ATP and creatine phosphate; in prolonged exercise, the mitochondria do not receive enough oxygen for the reactions of the Krebs cycle and rely on anaerobic glycolysis.

The end-product of glycolysis is lactic acid, the buildup of which causes muscle fatigue.

The delay of the further oxidation of lactic acid to a more convenient time produces an "oxygen debt," which is paid off in a period of heavy breathing after vigorous exercise.

Muscle contraction occurs with about 20 to 25 percent efficiency and generates heat.

A single muscle twitch, including latent period, period of contraction, and period of relaxation, varies in duration depending on the type of muscle.

An individual skeletal muscle fiber contracts according to the all-or-nothing principle: a subminimal (subliminal) stimulus will evoke no response, but when the threshold of stimulation is reached the muscle fiber will contract fully, regardless of the strength of the stimulus.

A skeletal muscle as a whole exhibits graded responses, rather than an all-or-nothing response; the strength of its contractions is determined by the number of motor units contracting.

Muscles that react rapidly and produce fine movements have small motor units, while slow-acting muscles have motor units containing hundreds of fibers.

Usually the contractions of the different motor units in a muscle are not synchronized, even in a sustained contraction.

Isotonic contraction results in a decrease in the length of the muscle, while its tension remains constant; in isometric contraction the length of the muscle remains constant while its tension increases.

Summation of individual muscle twitches, initiated by repetitive stimuli, can occur by increasing the number of motor units contracting simultaneously (multiple motor unit summation) and by increasing the rapidity of contraction of individual motor units (wave summation).

Repeated stimulation occurring when the muscle is already in a partially contracted state produces a total shortening of the muscle greater than that of a single muscle twitch.

The force of contraction rises as the rate of contraction increases.

Complete tetanus is a state in which muscle contractions follow one another so rapidly that relaxation does not occur and successive contractions cannot be distinguished from one another.

Treppe, or the staircase effect, is a phenomenon in which, in a series of contractions, the strength of contraction of a muscle increases progressively and reaches a plateau.

Factors affecting the strength of muscle contraction include the number of motor units being stimulated, the rate of stimulation, the initial length of the muscle, and the load on the muscle.

Muscle tone or tonus is the residual degree of contraction in muscles, resulting from a state of complete tetanus in a small fraction of the muscle fibers and imparting a firmness and resistance to stretching.

Muscle tone is important in maintaining an erect posture and keeps the muscles in a state of readiness to respond to stimuli.

Muscle spindles, stretch receptors in the muscles, are linked with the spinal cord in a reflexive flow of stimulation that maintains muscle tone.

Atonia is a lack of muscle tone; hypertonia is excessive muscle tone.

Muscles with less than normal tone are flaccid; hypertonic muscles are spastic.

Smooth muscle shows great variation and inconsistency of response.

Smooth muscles are innervated by the autonomic nervous system, exhibit varying degrees of tone, contain actin and myosin fibers, and contract through the same chemical reactions as skeletal muscles; smooth muscles generally contract more slowly and less forcefully than skeletal muscles and can remain contracted for long periods without fatigue.

Multi-unit smooth muscles contract only when stimulated by autonomic nerves.

Visceral smooth muscle contracts spontaneously, independent of nervous stimulation, but its activity can be modified by nerve action.

Spontaneous contractions originate in self-excitable pacemaker areas.

Contractions spread in a wave over the entire smooth-muscle mass, so that it acts as a unit.

Visceral smooth muscles are characterized by rhythmic contractions.

Stimulation by parasympathetic and sympathetic nerves may produce either excitation or inhibition, depending on the organ innervated.

Norepinephrine is the neurotransmitter substance of parasympathetic nerves; acetylcholine is the transmitter substance of sympathetic nerves.

Smooth muscles may exhibit a spike potential, a series of rhythmically repeated spike potentials, or an action potential with a plateau.

Smooth muscle can change its length greatly without any great change in tension; it can accommodate to changes in size while still retaining the ability to contract effectively.

Cardiac muscle is characterized by spontaneous rhythmic contractions.

Its contractions are initiated by specialized excitatory cells, but may be influenced by nerve impulses and hormones.

Cardiac muscle is structurally similar to skeletal muscle, and its contractions occur by the same mechanism, but cardiac muscles do not contract independently: cardiac muscle acts as a functional syncytium, and the entire muscle shows an all-or-nothing response.

The action potential of cardiac muscle shows an initial spike and a long plateau of depolarization, followed by repolarization; tetanus cannot be produced, which maintains the rhythmic pumping action.

The cardiac cycle is initiated by the spontaneous generation of an action potential in the sinoatrial node.

The action potential travels first through both atria, and then through the ventricles.

The atria thus act as primer pumps, while the ventricles provide the main pumping action propelling blood through the body.

Starling's law of the heart states that the contractions of the ventricles are more forceful when they are slightly distended (i.e., the muscle fibers are slightly stretched).

Fibrillation is a rapid and uncoordinated contraction of individual cardiac muscle fibers and can lead to death. (A heart with fibrillating ventricles cannot pump blood.)

Skeletal muscles and bones act according to the principle of the lever.

The mechanical advantage of a lever is determined by the relative distances of the force and resistance from the fulcrum.

Constant muscular adjustments are necessary to maintain an upright posture, counteracting the force of gravity acting from the body's center of gravity.

The postural muscles have strong stretch reflexes.

In correct standing posture, the head is held high and balanced easily on the neck, the abdomen is held in, shoulders back, and the chest is allowed to expand freely.

Locomotion is the movement of the entire body from place to place under its own power.

Human forms of locomotion include walking, running, leaping, and swimming.

Support and balance are important factors in locomotion; muscles help to provide support and maintain balance and also furnish propulsive force.

Disorders of the muscles can be produced by damage either to the muscles themselves or to motor nerves.

Paralysis, a loss of voluntary movement, may be flaccid (limp) or spastic (stiff).

Damaged nerves and skeletal muscles have some ability to regenerate; smooth muscle and cardiac muscle cannot regenerate and are replaced by ineffective scar tissue.

Atrophy is a wasting away of muscles, which may result from disuse due to paralysis or extreme inactivity.

Hypertrophy is an enlargement of muscles; in skeletal muscles it may be desirable, but in the heart it is often pathological.

Spasms are sudden, involuntary, and painful muscle contractions.

A prolonged spasm is called a tonic spasm or cramp.

An intermittent spasm is a clonic spasm.

Contracture is a shortening of muscle fibers in the resting state.

Myalgia is muscle pain.

Myopathy refers to diseases of the muscles.

Myositis is an inflammation of muscular tissue; fibrositis is an inflammation of the connective tissue in a muscle; fibromyositis is a combination of myositis and fibrositis and is often called rheumatism or lumbago.

Muscular dystrophy is a disease mainly of children, characterized by a fatty enlargement of the muscles and a progressive loss of their contractile function.

Myasthenia gravis is a disease in which the skeletal muscles are weak and easily fatigued. Its mechanism involves a blockage at the neuromuscular junction.

QUESTIONS FOR REVIEW AND THOUGHT

1 Describe the sequences of events in muscle contraction with regard to: (a) electrical changes; (b) chemical changes; (c) structural changes; (d) mechanical action of the muscle.

2 Discuss the all-or-nothing principle, graded contractions of muscles, and how the two concepts can be compatible.

3 Why is a muscle fiber unresponsive to stimuli during the refractory period?

4 What is an "oxygen debt," and how is it paid off?

5 Distinguish among contraction, contracture, cramp, and tetanus.

6 Distinguish between isotonic and isometric contractions.

7 Discuss the effectiveness of warmup exercises.

8 Define muscle tone and discuss its maintenance and role.

9 Discuss similarities and differences in the action of skeletal, smooth, and cardiac muscle.

10 Draw simple diagrams of the biceps brachii and the bones on which it acts and label force, resistance, and fulcrum in the following actions: (a) lifting a book with the hand; (b) chinning oneself on a horizontal bar.

11 Name 10 muscles whose contractions are involved in maintaining posture in a standing position.

12 Distinguish between: tonic and clonic spasms; flaccid and spastic paralysis; atrophy and hypertrophy of muscles.

OVERALL ORGANIZATION OF THE NERVOUS SYSTEM

12

Some scientists are calling the study of the nervous system the "last frontier" in biomedical research. It is a frontier that is being eagerly probed by a growing number of researchers with a wide variety of backgrounds. Nobel Prize winners from such disciplines as physics, chemistry, genetics, and plant biochemistry are now lending their efforts to the work of opening up this frontier. They believe, as do many others, that vital keys to the basic essence of humanity lie here.

The nervous system coordinates and controls the work of the other systems of the body, and through them, the activities of the body as a whole. Your every thought and movement and your perception of the world around you are all mediated by the nervous system. Without functioning nerves you would be unable to use your muscles—unable to move your hands, to blink your eyes, to sit or stand, to swallow, even to breathe. The nervous system is a crucial link in the homeostatic mechanisms of the body, such as the regulation of body temperature and the maintenance of the salt and water balances. Many of the activities of the nervous system are carried on entirely without our conscious awareness or control; we are acutely conscious of other functions, and indeed, the brain, perhaps the most important part of the nervous system, is the seat of all consciousness.

PARTS OF THE NERVOUS SYSTEM

The human nervous system has been compared to a complex telephone system, with central switchboards that interconnect, control, and coordinate a vast branching network of telephone wires, carrying a dizzying number of incoming and outgoing messages. The central switchboards of the nervous system are the brain and spinal cord, while the "wires" are the thin, threadlike nerves that stretch out through all parts of the body (Figure 12-1). The intricate interconnections of the nervous system permit an incredible versatility of functioning. Stimuli in one region of the body may produce a flow of incoming messages that affect the actions of entirely different body parts, mediated through the action of nerves innervating muscles. In addition to the momentary picture of the world transmitted through sense receptors and nerves, the vast background of past experience stored in the brain as memories may also have a profound effect on present actions.

The structural arrangement of the nervous system is the basis for an obvious division of it into the **central nervous system** (the brain and spinal cord) and the **peripheral nervous system** (the nerves that carry messages to and from the brain and spinal cord). Functional relationships are the basis for the differentiation of another division, the **autonomic nervous system.**

The Central Nervous System

In discussing the axial skeletal system, it was emphasized that the cranium and spinal column not only provide a central axis of support for the body structures, but also serve an equally important function: they provide protection for the vital yet vulnerable structures of the central nervous system, the brain and spinal cord. These structures themselves actually merge smoothly into one another, without any obvious demarcation. The foramen magnum, the large opening in the base of the skull, is generally taken as a convenient dividing line: the portion of the central nervous system above the foramen magnum is considered as the brain, while the portion below it is the spinal cord.

The brain itself includes a number of more or less distinct formations: the two hemispheres of the **forebrain,** which fill most of the cranial cavity; the **midbrain,** which extends caudally from the forebrain (the forebrain and midbrain together make up the **cerebrum**); and the **hindbrain,** which lies between the midbrain and spinal cord and is composed of the **cerebellum,** the **pons,** and the **medulla.** In ancient times, the seat of the emotions was thought to lie in the heart, the liver, or various other parts of the body, but now it is known that the major role in the formation and expression of the emotions is played by the brain. This critical organ is also the site of all conscious thought, memories, and decision-making. Though data are gathered by external receptors in various parts of the body, it is actually with the brain that we see, hear, taste, smell, and feel. The brain directs all conscious movements of the muscles, and a number of unconscious, involuntary actions as well. It is intimately associated with the pituitary and other glands of the endocrine system and helps to coordinate its work also.

The spinal cord appears far less complex than the brain—a shining rope of nerve cells, running along the channel formed by the vertebral column. Its functions, too, are less complicated, though of vital importance to the body. The spinal cord serves mainly as a relay station, receiving messages from sense receptors and working in the activation of reflex arcs that produce appropriate responses in the muscles of the body. Messages are also relayed along the spinal cord to the brain, which digests the incoming information and may initiate new nerve impulses to supplement or override the reflex actions mediated by the spinal cord.

The central location of the brain and spinal cord is ideally situated for receiving and sending messages from and to all parts of the body. Numerous nerves branch off from both the brain and the spinal cord, generally in pairs. Twelve pairs of cranial nerves enter

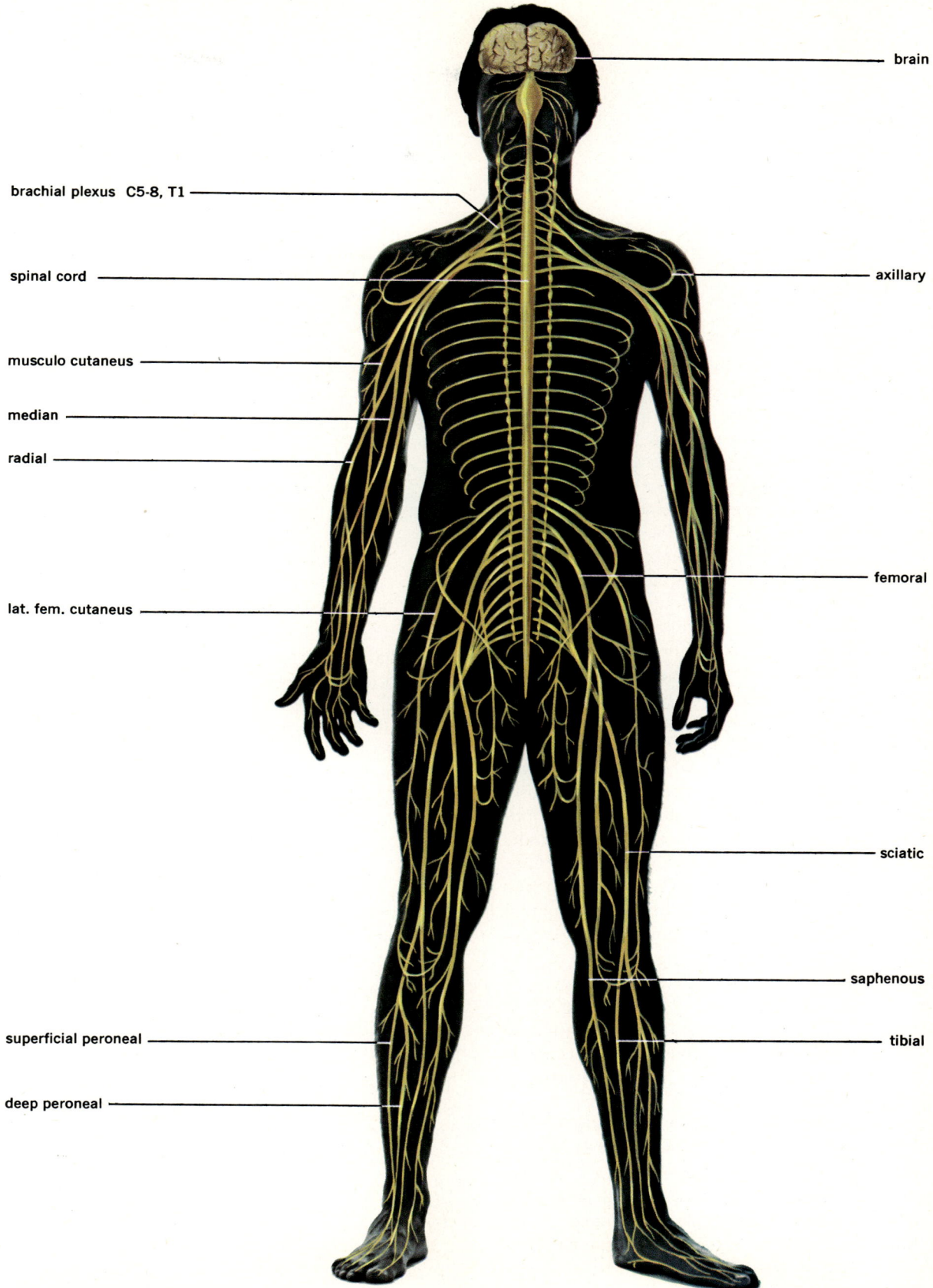

brain

brachial plexus C5-8, T1

spinal cord

musculo cutaneus

median

radial

lat. fem. cutaneus

superficial peroneal

deep peroneal

axillary

femoral

sciatic

saphenous

tibial

FIGURE 12-1   The human nervous system.

or leave the brain through appropriately placed openings in the cranial bones. The intervertebral foramina accommodate the 31 pairs of spinal nerves that enter or leave the vertebral canal. Connections between the incoming and outgoing nerves are established only within the central nervous system.

The Peripheral Nervous System

The brain is the one organ in the whole body that makes a person truly human, capable of thinking, remembering, learning, planning, dreaming. Yet if suddenly all of your nervous system except the brain and spinal cord ceased to function, you would be subjected to an excruciating torture of frustration. You would be blind, deaf, and dumb. You would be unable to walk, sit, stand, or even to turn over in bed. You would be unable to breathe unless you were placed in an iron lung; you would have to be fed through intravenous tubes, for you would be unable to eat; you would not even be able to urinate and defecate by yourself. Inside your mind, you would be aware of your existence and conscious of memories of the past; yet after awhile you might begin to doubt the reality of your situation, for there would be no incoming stimuli at all.

The peripheral nervous system consists of the numerous nerves that branch out from the brain and spinal cord. They include the cranial and spinal nerves, which carry messages to and from the central nervous system, as well as the autonomic nerves, which carry messages only from the CNS. There are hundreds of peripheral nerves, which branch and rebranch after leaving the brain or spinal cord, to form an intricate network. Scattered through the peripheral nervous system are numerous **ganglia,** knotlike masses consisting of groups of nerve cell bodies, which provide for some intercommunication among the nerve fibers. In some regions, fibers of peripheral nerves intermix in apparent confusion, forming an intricate network called a **plexus** (Figure 12-2).

Functionally, the nerves of the peripheral nervous system may be classified as: (1) **somatic afferent nerves,*** which carry incoming messages from the sense organs and from receptors in the skin, skeletal muscles, tendons, and joints; (2) **visceral afferent nerves,** which carry impulses from the viscera to the central nervous system; (3) **somatic efferent nerves,** which carry impulses from the central nervous system to skeletal muscles; and (4) **visceral efferent nerves,** which carry messages from the central nervous system to the smooth muscle, cardiac muscle, and glands. The visceral efferent nerves comprise a special

* The prefix ad- (af-) means "to," while ex- (ef-) means "from."

subdivision of the peripheral nervous system, the autonomic nervous system.

The Autonomic Nervous System

Some of the most vital activities of the body: breathing, the beating of the heart, the digestion of food, and the formation of urine, for example, are normally carried on automatically, without our giving them much conscious thought. The activities of the internal organs are the province of a special division of the nervous system, the autonomic nervous system. It consists of efferent nerve fibers, which spread throughout the body, innervating the smooth muscles of the blood vessels and viscera, the glands, and the heart. The action of the autonomic nervous system generally is not under voluntary control (some intriguing recent research in the area of biofeedback, a technique that permits some degree of control over "involuntary" functions to be mastered, is discussed in Chapter 15). The autonomic fibers are linked with and controlled by the **hypothalamus,** a part of the midbrain.

There are two main divisions of the autonomic nervous system: the **parasympathetic** or **craniosacral** division, and the **sympathetic** or **thoracolumbar** division. All of the parasympathetic fibers arise either as part of the cranial nerves or from the sacral segments of the spinal cord. The sympathetic fibers, on the other hand, originate in the spinal cord between the first thoracic and the second lumbar segments. The viscera generally receive a double innervation, with both sympathetic and parasympathetic fibers; the action of the two types of fibers is antagonistic: sympathetic impulses might cause a particular type of smooth muscle to contract, while parasympathetic impulses would cause it to relax. The particular effect depends on the organ involved. In general, the parasympathetic system exerts its influence during times of rest and helps to maintain a constant internal environment; the sympathetic system prepares the body for emergency conditions and aids in the mobilization of body resources and energy production.

NERVE TISSUE

Generations of mystery story readers have acquired an impression of the structure of brain tissue from the exclamations of Agatha Christie's fictional detective, Hercule Poirot, "Let us exercise our little gray cells!" When sections of the central nervous system are examined, portions actually do look gray, while other parts are a shining white (Figure 12-3A). **Gray matter** is found in the outer layers of the cortex and other parts of the brain and in the core of the spinal cord, as well as in peripheral nerves. It consists mainly of cell bodies of neurons, along with some nerve cell

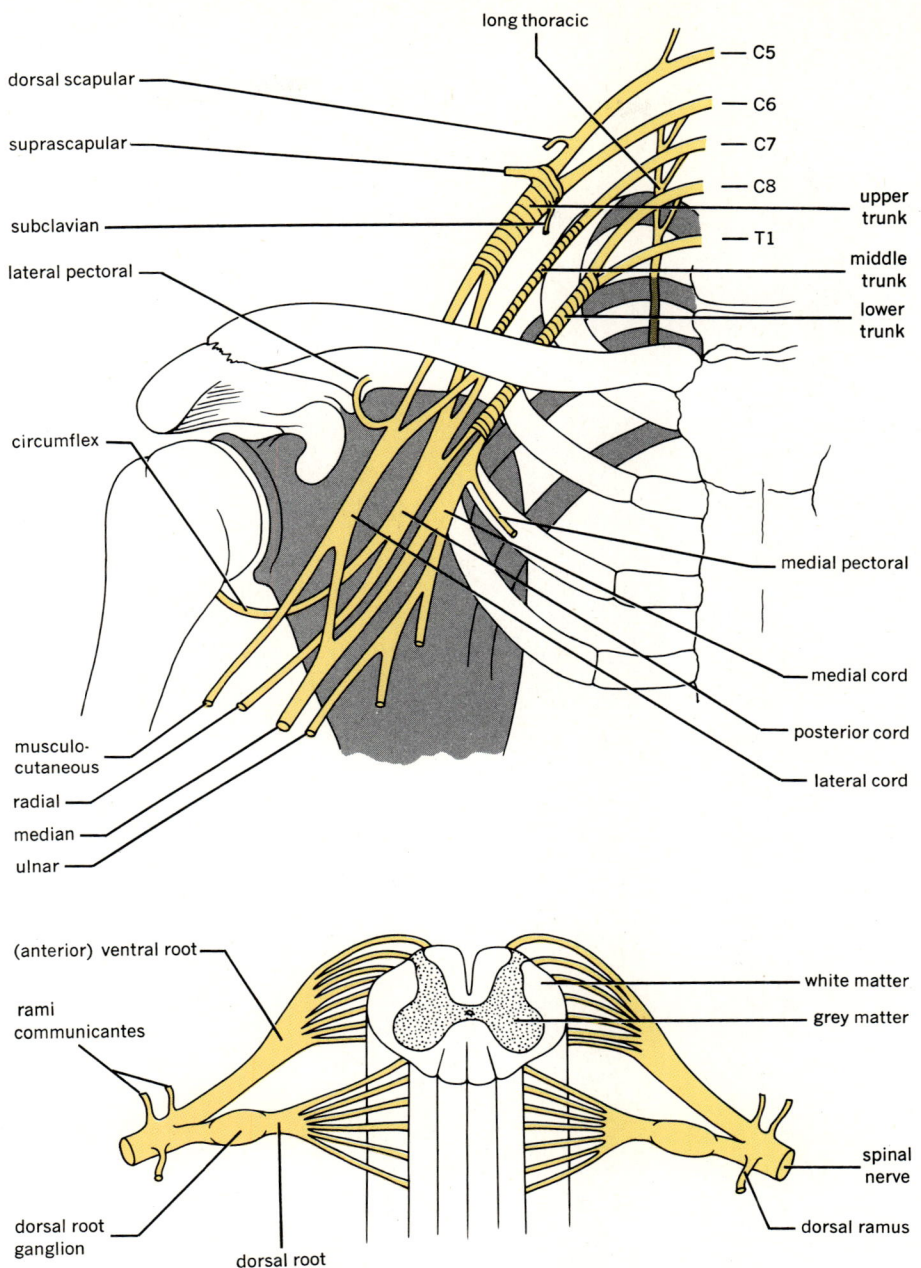

FIGURE 12-2 (A) The brachial plexus;
(B) dorsal root ganglia of spinal nerves.

processes. The **white matter,** found in the brain, spinal cord, and nerves, consists largely of the axons of neurons. In addition to the **neurons,** the active conducting elements, nerve tissue contains supporting cells, the **neuroglia** (Figure 12-3B).

The nerve fibers that branch out from the central nervous system and spread out through the body become grouped together into bundles called **nerves.**

Neuroglia

The neurons of the brain are outnumbered ten to one by the cells of the neuroglia. In addition to generally holding the nerve tissue together (*glia* literally means "glue"), these specialized connective tissue cells provide support and nourishment for the nerve cells and attend to the necessary "housecleaning" tasks.

The cells of the neuroglia are of several different structural types (Figure 12-4). **Astrocytes,** the largest of the glial cells, are named for their star-shaped bodies with numerous processes radiating outward. Many of the processes of astrocytes end on small blood vessels, which interlace the nerve tissue. **Oligodendroglia** are somewhat smaller glial cells, with fewer and shorter processes. They are thought to function in the

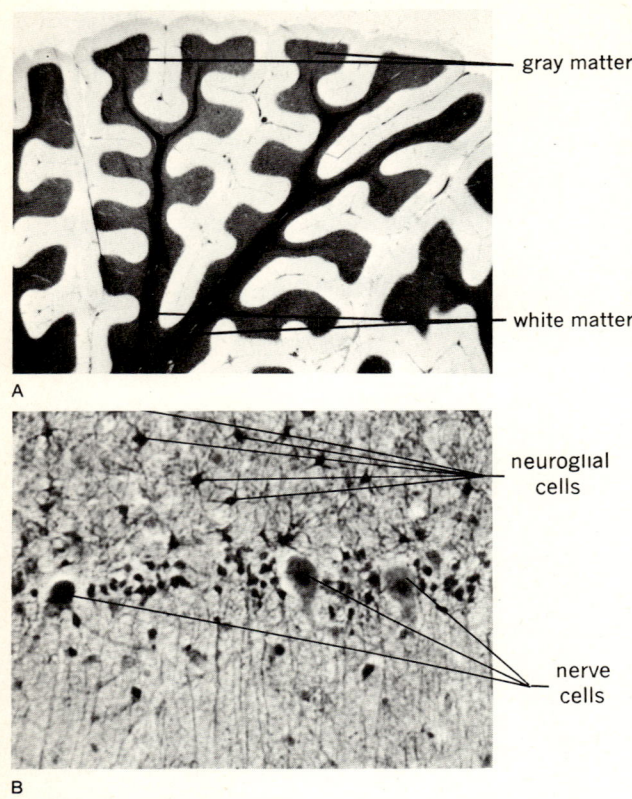

gray matter

white matter

A

neuroglial cells

nerve cells

B

FIGURE 12-3   (A) Horizontal section of the cerebellum showing gray matter and white matter. (Staining, by the Weigert method, makes myelinated nerve processes look black.) (B) Electron micrograph (×242) of the cerebellar cortex showing nerve cells and neuroglial cells.

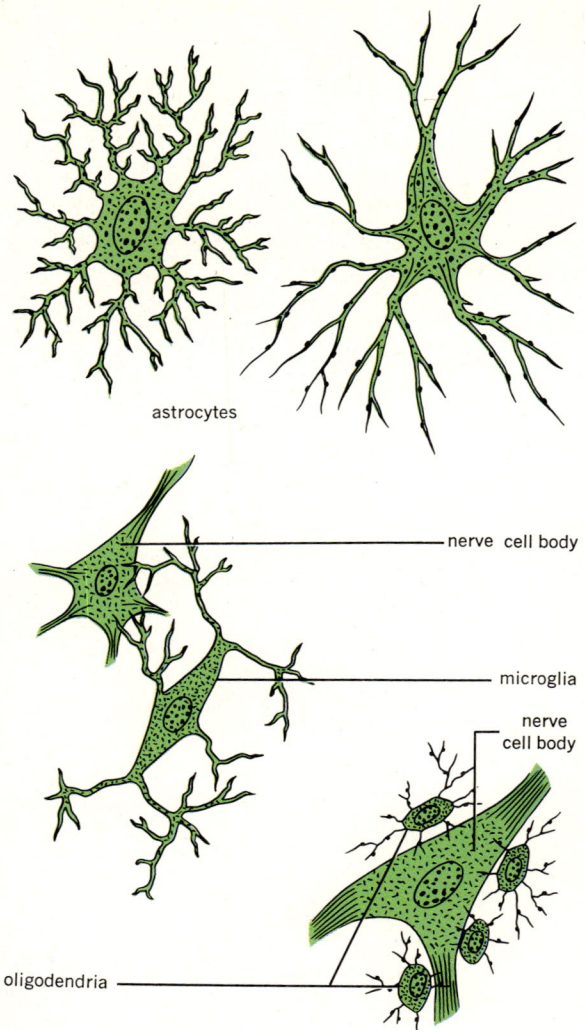

astrocytes

nerve cell body

microglia

nerve cell body

oligodendria

FIGURE 12-4   Types of neuroglial cells: astrocytes, microglia, and oligodendroglia.

formation of myelin, which sheaths certain nerve cells. The **microglia** are small, roving interstitial cells, which act as the "clean-up squad" for the nerve tissue of the central nervous system. They function as phagocytes, scavenging the waste products of the nerve tissue. The **ependyma** cells are a specialized type of neuroglia without processes, which are found lining the ventricles of the brain and the central canal of the spinal cord.

Neurons

The neuron represents a contradiction. Like nearly all the cells of the body it is microscopic; yet some of the neurons of the body are as much as three feet long!

A typical neuron (Figure 12-5) consists of a cell body and two types of protoplasmic extensions or processes: **dendrites** and **axons.** (Each neuron has only a single axon.) There is a one-way flow of messages along a neuron: impulses flow toward the cell body along the dendrites, which are also called **afferent processes;** and impulses flow away from the cell body along the axons, the **efferent processes.**

Classification of Neurons
All neurons perform essentially the same task: they conduct impulses.

However, there are enough differences in structure and function to warrant grouping the neurons of the body into several classes.

One type of classification is structural, on the basis of the number of processes that branch out from the cell body (Figure 12-6). The simplest kind of neuron is a **bipolar** neuron, which contains two processes and looks rather like a string with a knot in the middle. (Usually the ends of the "string" are frayed—that is, the processes have a number of terminal branches.) Impulses are conducted from the end of the single dendrite to the cell body and from there along the single axon to its end. Bipolar neurons are found in the retina of the eye, in the inner ear, and in the olfactory mucous membrane. A **unipolar** neuron seems at first thought to be a functional impossibility: it has just one process, a single axon. But shortly after leaving the cell body, the axon branches into two parts, which spread out in opposite directions, so that

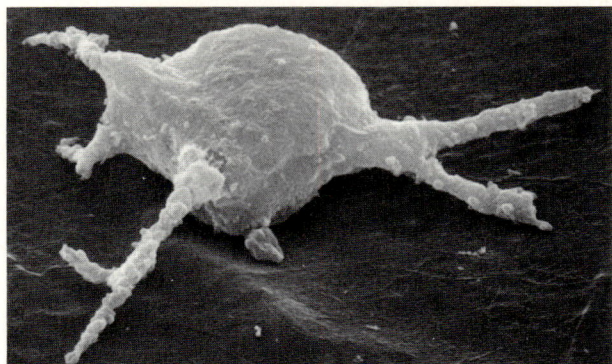

FIGURE 12-5   SEM of a rat brain neuron, × 2250.

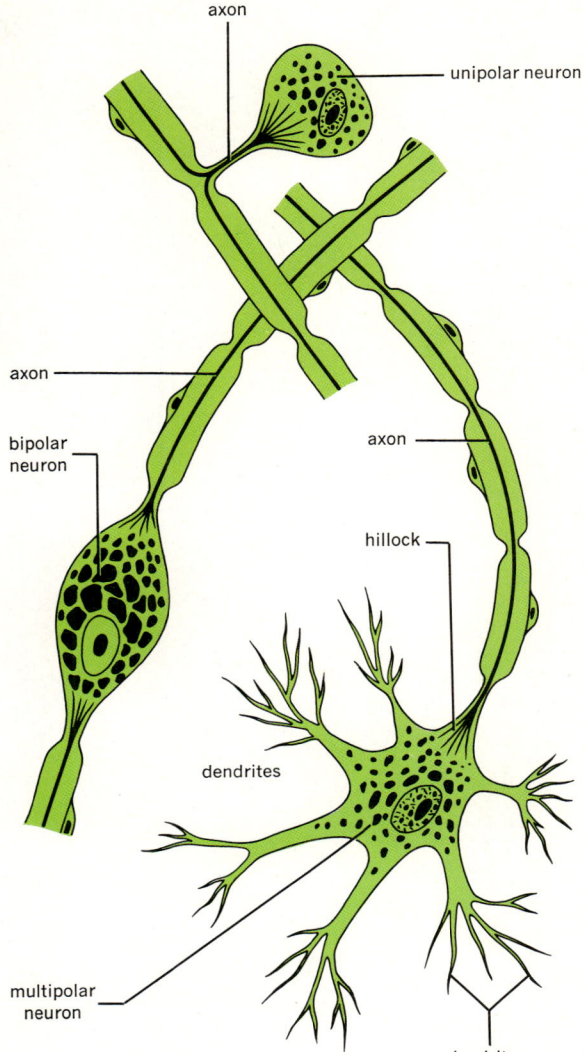

FIGURE 12-6   Unipolar, bipolar, and multipolar neurons.

one branch acts as a functional dendrite, while the other functions as an axon. Impulses are conducted straight along the dendrite-axon, bypassing the dangling cell body. (Sensory neurons are usually of this type.) The most common type of neuron is the **multipolar** neuron, which possesses numerous dendrites and a single axon. Often the dendrites are relatively short, and the axon may be extremely long. (Most of the length of the three-foot-long motor neurons that extend from the spinal cord to the feet is made up of axon; the sensory neurons from the feet, on the contrary, have a long dendrite and a short axon.)

Neurons differ just as greatly in function as they do in structure. A flood of information is constantly reported to the brain and spinal cord from the far reaches of the body. An equally heavy flow of outgoing messages continually adjusts the muscles and attends to the workings of the internal organs. Within the central nervous system itself, a great deal of switching and intercommunication is also necessary as the flow of incoming and outgoing information is processed, correlated, evaluated, and used as the basis for decisions on further actions. Each neuron conducts impulses in only one direction; thus, two separate sets of neurons are required for the two-way traffic of messages in the peripheral nervous system—one for incoming, the other for outgoing messages—and additional neurons are needed for the intercommunications within the brain and spinal cord.

Thus, a functional classification of neurons also yields three main groups (Figure 12-7). **Sensory** or **afferent** neurons, which transmit impulses from the periphery of the body to the central nervous system, have the distal end of the dendrite specialized to receive stimuli. **Motor** or **efferent** neurons transmit messages from the central nervous system to a muscle, gland, or some other effector and produce an action. (In some cases the impulse is transmitted along a chain of motor neurons, each relaying the messages from its axon to the dendrites of the next neuron in line.) The specific action produced depends on the

particular effector involved and on the particular nerve-cell route over which the message travels. Impulses carried over somatic efferent neurons stimulate the contraction of skeletal muscles. Secretory neurons produce secretion by glands. The action of effectors can be modified by impulses carried along other efferent neurons: augmentor neurons strengthen the force of contraction, accelerator neurons speed up the rate of contraction, and inhibitory neurons can decrease the force and rate of contraction of smooth muscle and cardiac muscle. The third major functional class of neurons is variously referred to as **connector** neurons, **association** neurons, **internuncial** neurons, or simply **interneurons.** These neurons are restricted to the central nervous system and, as their names imply, they act as bridges between sensory and motor neurons or relay impulses to various functional centers in the brain or spinal cord.

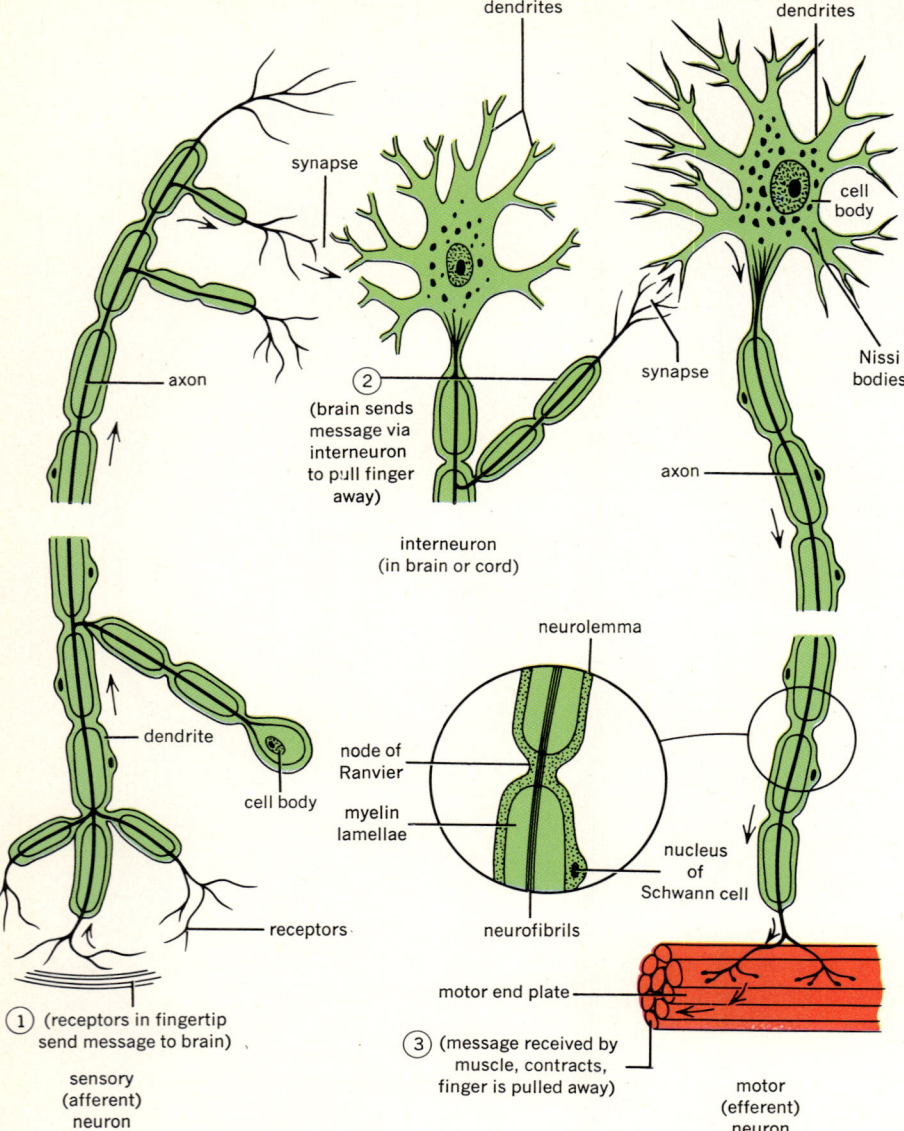

dendrites

dendrites

FIGURE 12-7 Sensory (afferent), motor (efferent), and association (connector) neurons.

synapse

cell body

axon

Nissl bodies

② (brain sends message via interneuron to pull finger away)

synapse

axon

interneuron (in brain or cord)

neurolemma

dendrite

node of Ranvier

myelin lamellae

cell body

nucleus of Schwann cell

neurofibrils

receptors

motor end plate

① (receptors in fingertip send message to brain)

③ (message received by muscle, contracts, finger is pulled away)

sensory (afferent) neuron

motor (efferent) neuron

Structure of the Neuron A nerve cell is often compared to a telephone wire, since both carry messages. Yet this comparison is a somewhat misleading oversimplification. A telephone wire carries messages via modulated electrical impulses, while a neuron, like a muscle cell, transmits its impulses by means of a complex sequence of electrochemical reactions. Moreover, the structure of a nerve cell is far more than a simple wire (Figure 12-8).

The part of a neuron that most resembles other types of cells is the cell body. It contains a nucleus and cytoplasm, like any other cell, and is surrounded by the usual cell membrane. The nucleus generally contains a single, prominent nucleolus, and the chromatin material is in the form of long, uncoiled threads. Typical organelles and inclusions of a nerve cell include: **neurofibrils,** long thin fibrils that are

found both in the cell body and in the processes; **Nissl bodies,** granules of a dark-staining substance; an abundance of ribosomes, reflecting the active protein synthesis in neurons, which contain more RNA than any other human cells; mitochondria; a well-developed Golgi network; and inclusions of fat droplets and pigment granules (a yellow pigment, lipochrome, appears in cells of the ganglia and central nervous system and increases with age; melanin is also found in some neurons). The cell body of a neuron is vital to its existence: if the cell body is irreparably damaged by mechanical injury or disease, the processes also die and are unable to conduct impulses. Nerve cells are incapable of dividing by mitosis, and when a nerve cell dies it is not replaced. All of the nerve cells in your body today were already present when you were born; they have grown since then,

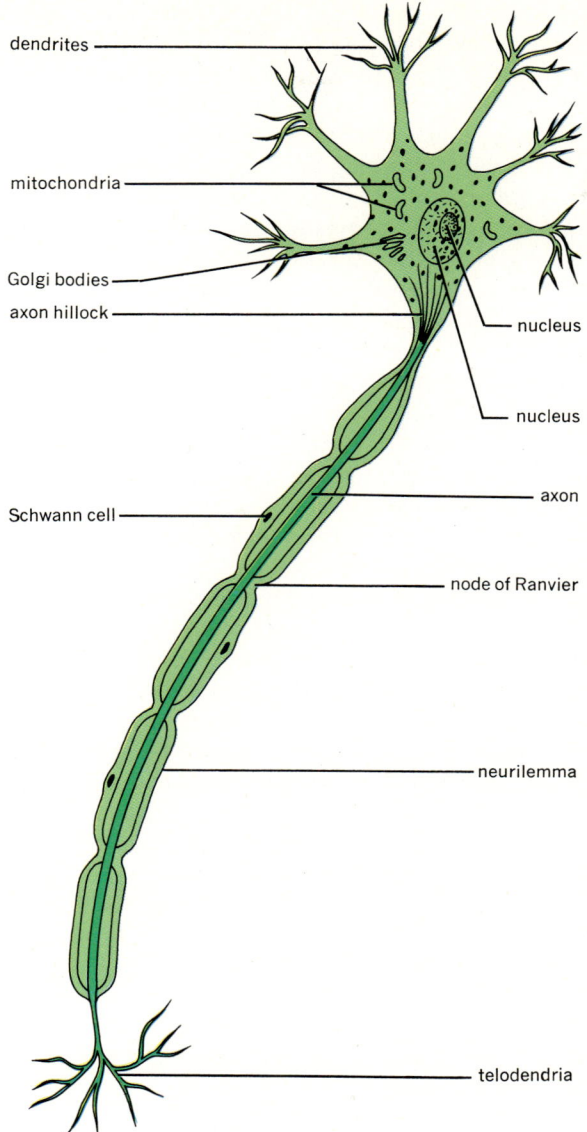

dendrites

mitochondria

Golgi bodies

axon hillock

nucleus

nucleus

axon

Schwann cell

node of Ranvier

neurilemma

telodendria

FIGURE 12-8   The structure of a neuron.

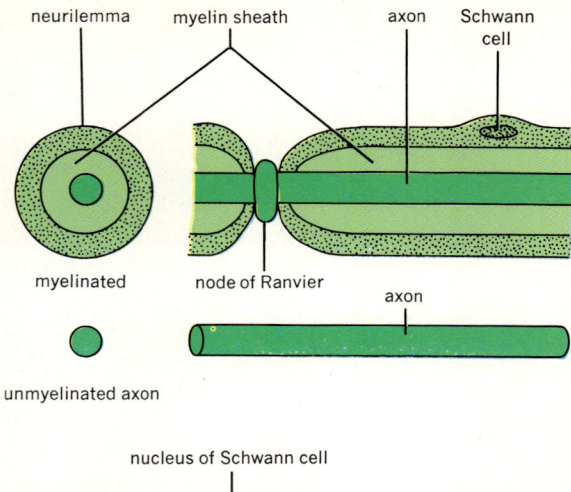

neurilemma   myelin sheath   axon   Schwann cell

myelinated   node of Ranvier   axon

unmyelinated axon

nucleus of Schwann cell

cytoplasm — axon   myelin lamellae

FIGURE 12-9   Myelinated and unmyelinated nerve fibers are shown at the top. The diagrams at the bottom indicate the formation of the myelin sheath as a Schwann cell wraps itself around the axon in "jelly-roll" fashion.

but no new ones have been added, and indeed you have already lost a considerable number of your original complement.

The specialized portions of the neuron are its threadlike processes. They are extensions of the cell body and contain cytoplasm and neurofibrils. The **dendrites** of a typical neuron look rather like tree branches, and their name literally means "treelike." The dendrites of different neurons vary considerably: some are rather long and branch only at the end, while others are short and profusely branched. This branching greatly increases the receptive surface of the neuron.

The single **axon** of a neuron emerges from the cell body at a special area, free of Nissl granules, called the **axon hillock.** The axon itself also lacks Nissl sub-

stance, but does contain neurofibrils. Some neurons in the spinal cord have axons of microscopic length; the neurons that innervate the foot muscles may be a meter long or more. Throughout its entire length, the axon has a constant diameter, but the axons of different neurons vary in thickness also, from less than a micron to several microns. Occasional branches may diverge at right angles from the midportion of the axon, but most branching occurs at the end, in the region of the effector innervated by the neuron.

The general term **axis cylinder** is sometimes used to refer to a nerve cell process, either a dendrite or an axon. In some neurons the axis cylinders are sheathed in a fatty substance called **myelin.** The myelin sheath is thought to act as a sort of insulator, permitting a particular neuron to carry impulses without transmitting the excitation to neighboring neurons. But the myelin sheath is not continuous (see Figures 12-8 and 12-9); it is interrupted at intervals by constrictions called **nodes of Ranvier.** The length of the intervals varies depending on the thickness of the axis cylinder; for a 10 micron fiber the nodes are about 2 millimeters apart. The thickness of the myelin sheath also varies: thicker nerve fibers are encased in a thicker sheath. It is the myelin sheath that imparts the shiny white appearance to certain neurons; the neurons in the "gray matter" of the brain and spinal cord are unmyelinated, as are many of the peripheral nerves.

Within the central nervous system, the myelin sheath is produced by oligodendrocytes (cells of the oligodendroglia). In the peripheral nervous system, the processes of both myelinated and unmyelinated nerve cells are ensheathed in an additional covering composed of living cells, called **Schwann cells,** which are wrapped around the nerve fiber like a jelly roll (Figure 12-9). This outer sheath is referred to as the **sheath of Schwann,** or the **neurilemma.** In myelinated nerve fibers, the space between each node of Ranvier is occupied by a single Schwann cell, which formed that portion of the myelin sheath. The edges of successive Schwann cells are interlocked, so that there are no gaps in the neurilemma, which lies close to the cell membrane of the nerve fiber at the nodes of Ranvier.

Physiology of the Neuron   Specialists in the field of bionics, in which principles learned from the study of structure and processes in living organisms are applied to the construction of machines, have built artificial analogs of the neuron. These "neuristors," "neuromimes," and other devices do not look at all like a neuron. They are generally small plates on which an array of condensors, resistors, transistors, and neatly soldered interconnecting wires is mounted. They are "artificial neurons" only in a functional sense: they have been designed to act like a neuron. A number of aspects of neuronal function have been taken into account. First of all, a neuron "fires" or transmits an impulse along its entire length when it receives a suitable stimulus. The stimulus must be of sufficient strength for the neuron to fire; if it is below a certain threshold, the impulse will not be transmitted. After a neuron has fired, it requires a certain time, perhaps a split second, to recover; until it has recovered it cannot fire again, even if a new stimulus is applied. And some stimuli work to inhibit a neuron, to keep it from firing. With suitably arranged electronic components it has been possible to mimic all these aspects of neuronal functioning, though not as compactly and efficiently as in an actual neuron in the living body. Artificial neurons have even been linked into complicated networks to provide models of living systems, such as the frog's eye and its links to the brain. The insights gained in such studies are contributing both to practical applications (such as the development of electronic guidance systems for aircraft control centers) and to greater knowledge of the workings of the living systems on which they are modeled.

The neuron is the structural and functional unit of the nervous system. An understanding of its functioning at the cellular level is basic to an understanding of the workings of the nerves and nerve tracts that comprise the central and peripheral nervous systems.

Nerve cells share many common properties with the other cells of the body. But the neurons are highly specialized in two key areas of function: **excitability,** a sensitivity to changes in the environment; and **conductivity,** the ability to carry impulses via a sequence of electrochemical reactions. The afferent nerve endings or receptors, which are concentrated in specialized sense organs and scattered throughout the body, help to protect the body and preserve homeostasis by detecting changes in the external and internal environments; their information is conveyed through nerves to the brain, which in turn initiates actions in the body's effectors by means of messages carried along efferent nerves.

THE TRANSMISSION OF IMPULSES

The conduction of impulses along a neuron is often likened to the conduction of electricity along a wire. Yet this analogy does not hold in several important respects. A nerve impulse is *not* a simple electric current. Indeed, neurons are poor conductors of electricity, and when an actual electric current is passed through a neuron, the strength of the current decreases with the distance traveled. A nerve impulse, on the other hand, retains its strength no matter how far it must travel, for it is continually being renewed as it passes along. The speed of nerve transmission is also quite different from the speed of conduction of electricity: an electric current is transmitted at a speed of 186,000 miles per second, while the fastest nerve impulses are propagated at a rate of only about 390 feet per second.

Like muscle contractions, nerve impulses can be initiated by a variety of stimuli. In the body, specialized nerve endings respond to light, mechanical pressure, and specific chemical stimuli; nerve impulses may also be sparked by impulses transmitted by other neurons. In the laboratory, nerve preparations can be stimulated by shaking or pinching them, by placing them in solutions of acids, salts, or other chemicals; the most commonly used stimulus is electrical current, for it can be precisely controlled and regulated and turned on and off instantly at will.

In many respects the transmission of impulses in neurons is very similar to the contraction of muscle cells, discussed in Chapter 11. It does not occur at all unless the stimulus is strong enough. A stimulus that is too weak to spark a nerve impulse is referred to as a **subminimal** (subliminal) or **subthreshold** stimulus. The smallest stimulus capable of exciting a nerve cell is called a **minimal** (liminal) or **threshold** stimulus. Once a stimulus is above the threshold value, no matter how strong it is, there will be no corresponding increase in the strength of the impulse transmitted by the nerve cell—that is, neurons, like muscle cells, obey an **all or nothing law.** But as the intensity of the stimulus is increased, the frequency of the nerve impulses does increase, up to a maximum. In addition, different neurons in the same nerve have different thresholds of excitation, so that stimuli of different strengths will provoke different numbers of neurons to "fire." Thus, though the individual neurons exhibit an all-or-nothing response, the nerves they comprise show a graded response to stimuli.

In the living body, the terminal branches of an axon of a particular neuron are often associated with dendrites of a number of other neurons, and the dendrites of each particular neuron, in turn, may be linked with the axons of a number of other neurons. A nerve impulse thus may be transmitted over an intricate network of converging and diverging pathways rather than along a simple 1-1-1 sequence (Figure 12-10). A neuron may receive stimuli from a number of other neurons, virtually simultaneously. In this case, a nerve impulse may be initiated even if none of the individual stimuli alone are up to the minimal strength. The subthreshold impulses that arrive initially may build up a local excitatory state in the re-

cipient neuron, **facilitating** its firing when it receives additional stimuli that would have been too weak to excite an impulse alone. There is thus a **summation** of the effects of the subthreshold stimuli. This type of summation can be referred to as **spatial summation,** since it is produced by the convergence of stimuli from different places. Another type of summation can also occur in the action of neurons: **temporal summation.** If a sequence of subthreshold stimuli is applied to a neuron rapidly enough, a local excitatory state is built up, and the neuron fires.

Transmission of Impulses along the Neuron

The electric eel of the Amazon River is an amazing living storage battery. It can deliver shocks of up to 800 volts—more than enough to kill an unwary swimmer. (The normal electric house current is only 120 volts.) Each nerve cell in your body is also a living storage battery, but its charge of electricity is far more modest. In a resting nerve cell (one that is not conducting an impulse), the potential difference across its membrane is normally between -70 and -90 millivolts. As in muscle cells, this **resting potential** is the result of differential permeability of the cell membrane to ions. Potassium ions are able to diffuse into the cell relatively freely, whereas the membrane of the resting cell is rather impermeable to sodium ions. There is a high concentration of negatively charged organic ions in the region of the membrane, to which the positively charged sodium ions in the surrounding intercellular fluid are attached. They tend to congregate just outside the cell membrane, producing an effective **polarization** or separation of charges at the membrane (Figure 12-11).

Heat, cold, electrical stimulation, mechanical damage, and various chemicals are all stimuli that can

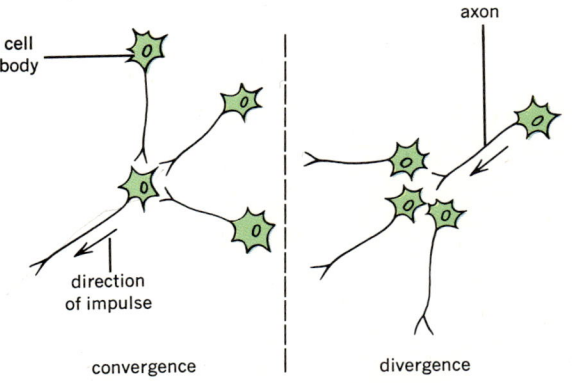

FIGURE 12-10 Converging and diverging neuron sequences.

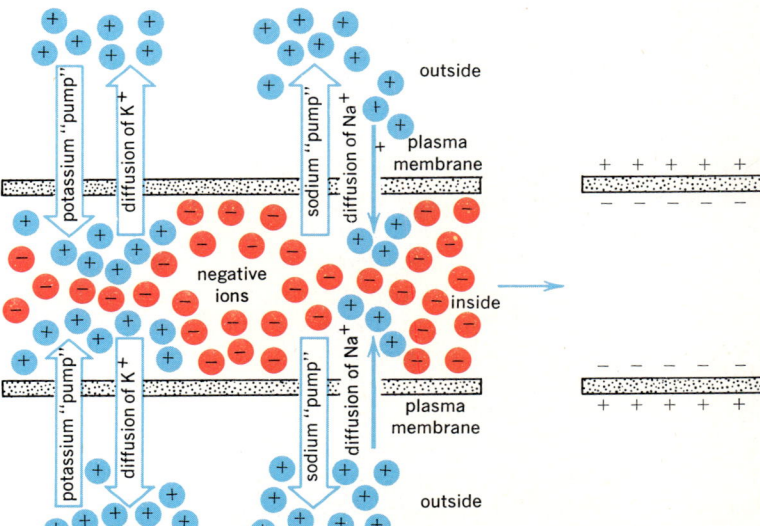

FIGURE 12-11 Polarization of the nerve cell membrane is produced by the movement of ions. A simplified view of the polarized membrane is shown at the right.

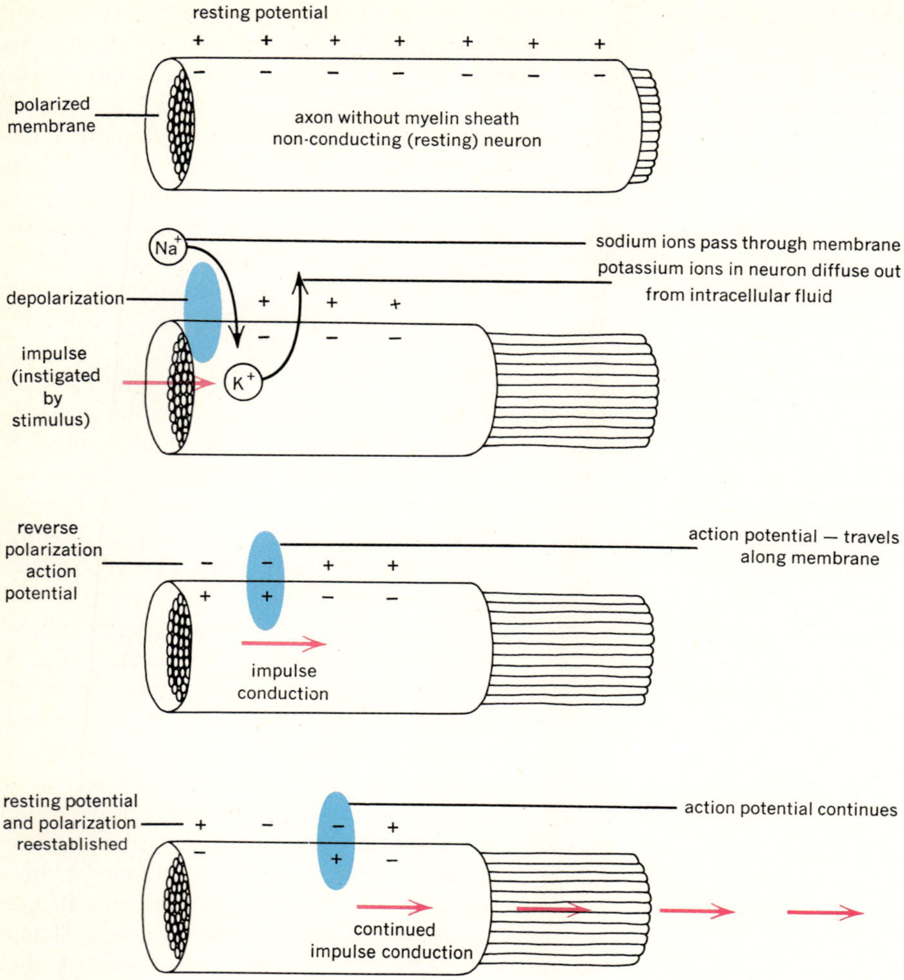

resting potential

+ + + + + + +

− − − − − − −

polarized membrane

axon without myelin sheath
non-conducting (resting) neuron

Na⁺

depolarization

sodium ions pass through membrane
potassium ions in neuron diffuse out
from intracellular fluid

+ + +

− − −

impulse (instigated by stimulus)

K⁺

reverse polarization action potential

− − + +

+ + − −

action potential — travels along membrane

impulse conduction

resting potential and polarization reestablished

+ − − +

− − + −

action potential continues

continued impulse conduction

FIGURE 12-12   Generation and propagation of an action potential along an unmyelinated neuron.

alter the permeability of the cell membrane to sodium ions, precipitating a rapid sequence of events. Sodium ions rush into the cell at the site of the stimulus, momentarily reversing the polarization that prevailed in the resting cell (Figure 12-12). This is the stage of **depolarization,** and the resting potential is replaced by an **action potential.** Immediately, the excited spot on the membrane becomes almost totally impermeable to sodium ions again, potassium ions diffuse out of the cell, and the resting potential is reestablished at that spot as sodium ions are pumped out and potassium ions return. But meanwhile, the regions of the membrane just adjacent to the excited site become excited in turn and undergo a similar influx of sodium ions. A wave of depolarization spreads out from the initial site of excitation (quickly followed by a wave of repolarization), and thus an impulse is propagated along the neuron. Generally, the impulse begins at the dendrite or cell body and is propagated throughout the length of the axon.

In myelinated neurons, the mechanism of impulse conduction is a bit different. Ions cannot pass freely through the thick myelin sheath, but they can flow with ease through the nodes of Ranvier. (Indeed, the cell membrane at these points is 500 times as permeable as the membrane of some unmyelinated nerve fibers.) In myelinated fibers, a nerve impulse is propagated from node to node, rather than continuously along the fiber: an electrical current flows through the surrounding extracellular fluids, exciting each successive node in turn (Figure 12-13). The impulse thus seems to jump along the fiber, and this type of nerve impulse conduction is termed **saltatory** propagation. (Saltatory means "leaping.") Saltatory propagation is much faster than step-by-step depolarization along the entire length of the nerve fiber, and it is also economical from the energy standpoint, since there is a need for active transport of ions only at the nodes of Ranvier. (The energy for nerve impulse transmission, like that for muscle contraction, is derived from glucose catabolism, with the high-energy bonds of ATP as the ultimate energy source.) In general, myelinated nerve fibers conduct nerve impulses much more rapidly than unmyelinated fibers. The speed of conduc-

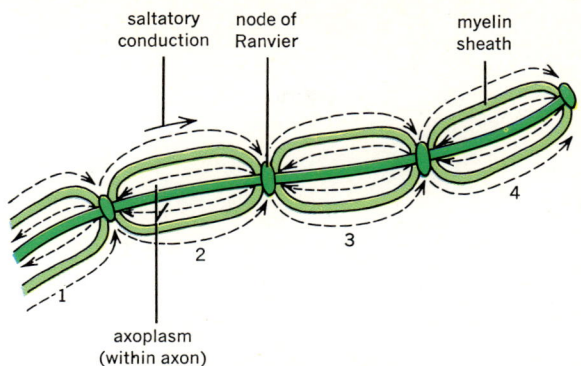

saltatory conduction · node of Ranvier · myelin sheath

axoplasm (within axon)

FIGURE 12-13 Saltatory conduction along a myelinated nerve fiber. The impulse "jumps" from node to node.

tion also varies with the diameter of the nerve fiber, ranging from 0.5 meter per second in very small fibers of the autonomic nervous system up to 130 m/sec in the very large fibers of the spinocerebellar tract.

As in muscle contraction, after a neuron has "fired" there is a brief interval during which it is incapable of being stimulated again. This **refractory period** is from about 0.0005 to 0.002 sec. Sensitive physiological measurements show that the refractory period of a neuron is divided into the initial **absolute refractory period,** during which no new impulse can be transmitted, and a subsequent **relative refractory period,** during which the neuron is recovering and will transmit an impulse if the exciting stimulus is particularly strong. In general, small nerve fibers have longer refractory periods than large ones, and thus the maximum frequency of response is lower in small fibers than in large ones.

When a stimulus of sufficient strength is applied to a receptor, nerve impulses are generated. The number of impulses sparked by a particular stimulus depends both on the nature of the stimulus (its strength and duration) and on the nature of the receptor itself. Some receptors produce action potentials as long as the stimulus continues. Other receptors exhibit an **adaptation** to the stimulus: they discharge only at the time the stimulus is first applied and soon cease discharging, even if the stimulus continues unabated. Such **rapidly adapting receptors** report to the central nervous system mainly about *changes* in conditions. The receptors at the base of hairs, for example, discharge only at the moment the hair moves and cease discharging even if the hair remains in its new position. (If this were not the case, drawing the hair up into a "ponytail" would initiate a maddening continuous flow of signals to the brain.) **Slowly adapting receptors,** on the other hand (those that continue to respond to a continuing stimulus) provide information about steady-state conditions and play a useful role in the body. The muscle spindles, for example, provide a continuous report on the static length of the muscles, as well as on changes in their length.

The Synapse

Picture a line of railroad tracks, snaking across the countryside. The tracks reach a riverbank and stop abruptly, resuming on the other side of the river. A train chugs along the tracks to the edge of the river, where it boards a ferryboat tied up at the terminal. The ferry transfers the train to the other side of the river, where it is aligned on the tracks and rolls on its way.

This analogy provides some insight into the transmission of impulses in the nervous system. For the mechanisms of nerve impulse transmission by waves of depolarization and repolarization cover the propagation of the impulse only along the neuron itself. The successive neurons in a nerve tract are not directly connected. The terminal branches of an axon are separated from the dendrites or cell body of the next neuron in the sequence by a gap called the synapse (Figure 12-14). This gap is quite small—usually only 200 to 300 Å or less. For a nerve impulse to be transmitted from one neuron to the next in the sequence, the excitation must somehow be transmitted across the synapse. The electrical reactions of membrane depolarization that conduct an impulse along a neuron cannot operate here, where there is no protoplasm. Instead, chemical transmitters carry the excitation across the synapse.

Each terminal branch of an axon ends in a knoblike structure, called a **synaptic knob** or **terminal button.** The terminal buttons are richly supplied with mitochondria and replete with vesicles. Depolarization of a neuron results in a movement of calcium ions into the terminal buttons of the axon, initiating a sequence of events in which numerous vesicles fuse with the axon membrane, open, and spill their chemical contents out into the synapse. Several transmitter chemicals function in various parts of the nervous system; they all belong to the general class of **biogenic amines.** The most common is **acetylcholine.** When this chemical is released by the terminal buttons of the axon, it diffuses through the extracellular fluid in the synapse until it reaches the surface of the postsynaptic neuron (Figure 12-15). There it is promptly bound to specific receptor sites, called cholinoreceptors. In some way that is not yet entirely understood, the binding of acetylcholine to the cholinoreceptors produces an increase in the permeability of the membrane to sodium ions, which rush into the cell and spark a spreading wave of depolarization—an action potential—in the postsynaptic neuron. Thus the impulse is transmitted from one neuron to another; but transmission across the synapse is a far slower process

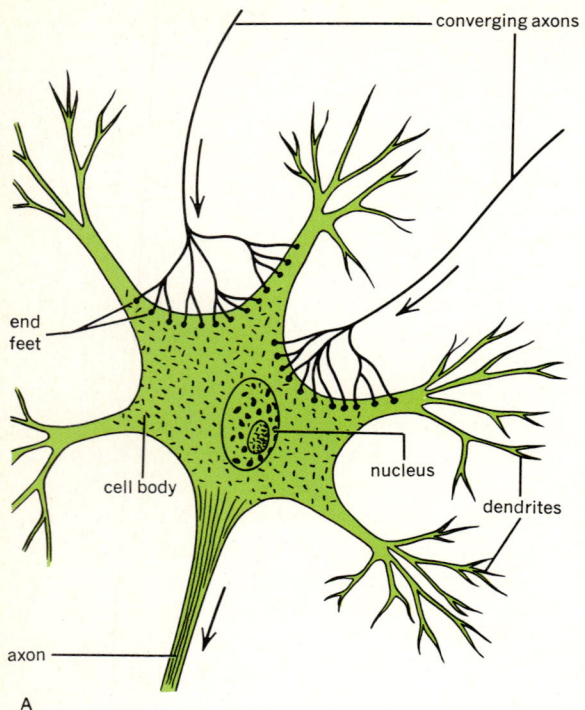

converging axons

end feet

cell body

nucleus

dendrites

axon

A

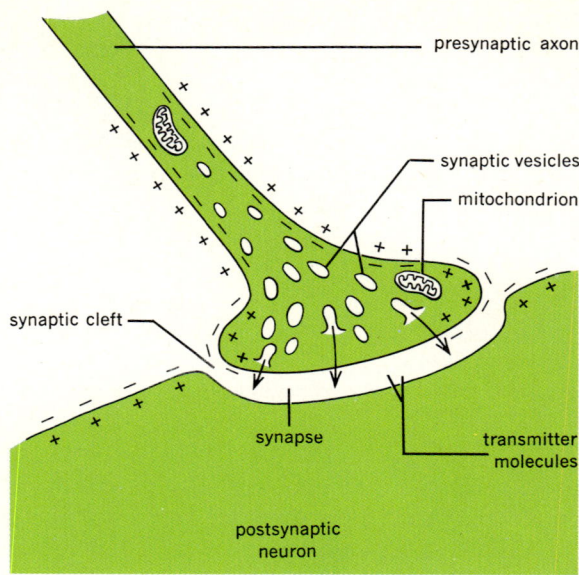

presynaptic axon

synaptic vesicles

mitochondrion

synaptic cleft

synapse

transmitter molecules

postsynaptic neuron

FIGURE 12-15 A schematic view of the synapse. Vesicles in the end feet of the presynaptic neuron release acetylcholine into the synaptic cleft. The neurotransmitter diffuses across to the membrane of the postsynaptic neuron, inducing depolarization, and then is promptly decomposed by acetyl-cholinesterase.

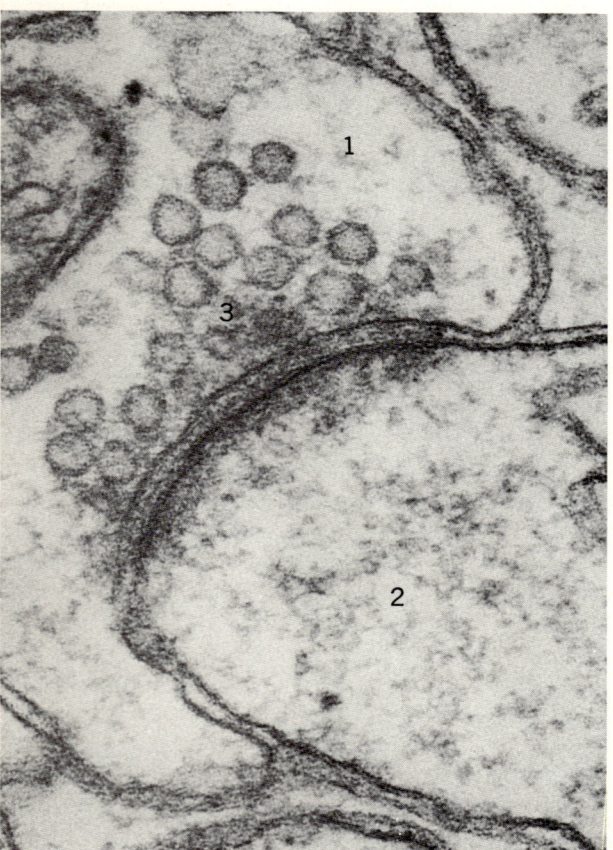

1

3

2

B

FIGURE 12-14 Synapsis: In the diagram the axons of two presynaptic neurons are shown converging on a single postsynaptic neuron. In the electron micrograph ($\times$172,000), (1) is the axon terminal, (2) the dendrite; synaptic vesicles (3) release neurotransmitters.

than the conduction of an impulse along a single neuron, and takes about a half a millisecond.

If acetylcholine remained bound to the cholinoreceptors, it would continue to restimulate the postsynaptic neuron, producing wave after wave of discharges even in the absence of any new stimulation from the presynaptic neuron. This does not occur, for the acetylcholine is neatly disposed of as soon as it has done its work. The region of the synapse is particularly rich in an enzyme, **cholinesterase,** which rapidly inactivates acetylcholine. This enzymatic reaction is one of the fastest in the body—acetylcholine is inactivated within just 1/500 of a second of its release!

This discussion of the synapse and the chemical events that occur at it may sound rather familiar—and indeed it should. It is basically similar to the **neuromuscular junction,** which links the terminal branches of a motor neuron with its effector, the muscle cell.

Other neurotransmitter chemicals, whose mode of action is basically similar to that of acetylcholine, are **norepinephrine, dopamine,** and **serotonin** (5-hydroxytryptamine). As already mentioned in the discussion of neuromuscular junctions, various drugs and poisons interfere with the normal processes of nerve impulse conduction by mimicking the natural neurotransmitters, by blocking their release, or by blocking the action of cholinesterase. When you drink coffee to "pick you up," the caffeine that it contains acts at the synapse, increasing the rate of transmission. Strych-

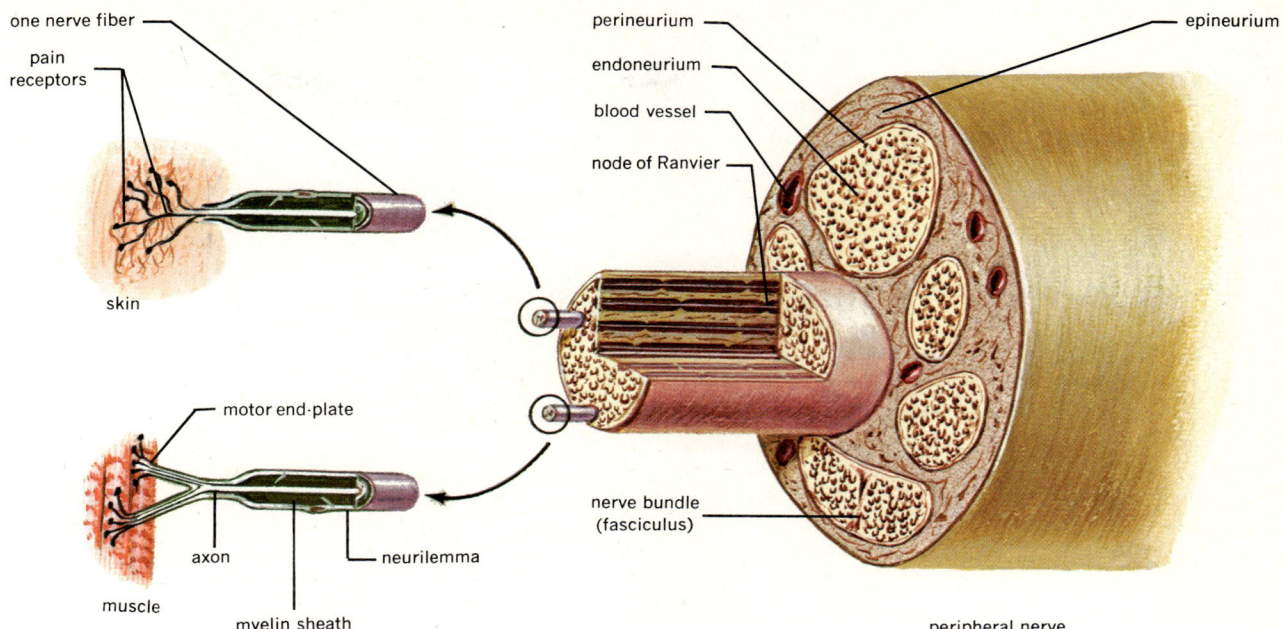

one nerve fiber

pain receptors

skin

motor end-plate

axon

muscle

myelin sheath

neurilemma

perineurium

endoneurium

blood vessel

node of Ranvier

epineurium

nerve bundle (fasciculus)

peripheral nerve

FIGURE 12-16   Structure of a nerve.

nine, a drug that can paralyze the breathing center, also acts at the synapse, reducing the transmission of impulses from one neuron to another.

The "one-way traffic" of messages along the nerve tracts is preserved by the synapse. Theoretically, the wave of depolarization in a neuron could spread in either direction (though in the actual living body, neurons are generally stimulated at the dendrite end and conduct the impulse down the axon). But the message can be transmitted across the synapse in only one direction: only the terminal buttons of the axon contain the vesicles capable of releasing neurotransmitter chemicals, and only the dendrites and cell body contain the specific binding sites for them.

Some neurons act to inhibit the neurons with which they synapse: rather than exciting them to fire in turn, they act to prevent the excitation of the postsynaptic neurons. Such **inhibitory neurons** also release neurotransmitter chemicals into the synapse, but they are of a different type. The exact nature of the inhibitory transmitters is not yet known, but it has been suggested that gamma-aminobutyric acid or glycine may play this role.

THE NERVE

Although each neuron functions essentially independently of those around it, it is their collective action that results in our sensations, our movements, our thoughts and dreams, affecting virtually everything that goes on in the body.

Like a muscle, a peripheral nerve is a bundle of bundles (Figure 12-16). Each individual nerve fiber is enclosed in a connective tissue sheath called the **endo-neurium.** A bundle of nerve fibers is wrapped in a sheath called the **perineurium.** These bundles, in turn, are grouped into a larger bundle, ensheathed in the **epineurium,** which is laced with blood vessels and often contains fat cells. Actually, less than a quarter of a nerve consists of nerve cells per se; more than half is connective tissue and blood vessels, and a quarter is myelin. Each nerve fiber runs the full length of the nerve and retains its own distinct identity, although it may branch and rebranch in its terminal region.

A **motor nerve** is one that contains only motor nerve fibers, transmitting muscles from the central nervous system to the periphery. A **sensory nerve** is one that contains only sensory nerve fibers, transmitting messages from peripheral receptors to the central nervous system. Most of the nerves in the body are **mixed nerves,** containing both motor and sensory fibers.

In the central nervous system there is also some grouping of nerve fibers: fibers transmitting impulses associated with a specific type of information, for example, pain sensations, lie together in a common pathway called a **tract.** But the fibers of a tract in the central nervous system are not enclosed in a perineurium or epineurium.

The question of nerve **regeneration** has taken on great importance in modern medicine, in attempts to rehabilitate victims of paralysis. If the cell body of a neuron is damaged, the entire cell dies and cannot be regenerated. But if the axon of a neuron is severed, leaving the cell body intact, the severed process first degenerates, and then a new axon may be regenerated. (This regeneration has been shown to occur at a rate of about 2.5 mm a day.) At one time it was thought that the presence of a neurilemma is essential for axon regeneration, which would seem to limit nerve regeneration to peripheral nerves. However, recent studies have shown some promising results in the regeneration of a severed spinal cord, stimulated by using enzymes such as trypsin and hyaluronidase to dissolve the scar tissue that forms at the break and permit the axons to grow through the gap. Ingenious surgical techniques have also been devised to take advantage of the properties of peripheral nerve regeneration. For example, the regenerating end of one nerve can be cross-sutured with the degenerated segment of another, forcing the nerve to grow into a new area and innervate muscles that it had not innervated before.

SUMMARY

Divisions of the nervous system are:
    Central nervous system
    Peripheral nervous system
    Autonomic nervous system
The central nervous system consists of the brain (including forebrain, midbrain, and hindbrain) and spinal cord.
    It houses the centers of control and coordination of body activities.
The peripheral nervous system consists of the nerves outside the central nervous system and includes:
    Somatic afferent nerves
    Visceral afferent nerves
    Somatic efferent nerves
    Visceral efferent nerves
    A ganglion is a knotlike mass of nerve cell bodies; a plexus is an intermingled network of peripheral nerves.
The autonomic nervous system controls "involuntary" functions of the body.
    It consists of:
        Parasympathetic or craniosacral division
        Sympathetic or thoracolumbar division
    The viscera receive both sympathetic and parasympathetic innervation; the two types of nerve fibers act antagonistically.
Nerve tissue consists of neurons (conducting cells) and neuroglia (supporting cells).
    Types of neuroglia include:
        Astrocytes
        Oligodendroglia
        Microglia
        Ependyma
    Gray matter consists mainly of cell bodies of neurons, along with unmyelinated nerve cell processes; white matter consists largely of axons of myelinated neurons.
    The neuron is the structural and functional unit of the nervous system.
    A typical neuron consists of cell body, dendrites, and axon.
    Impulses are transmitted in one direction, from dendrites to axon.
    Neurons may be classified according to:
        Number of processes (unipolar; bipolar; multipolar)
        Function (sensory or afferent; motor or efferent; connector, association, or internuncial)
    Characteristic organelles of neurons include neurofibrils and Nissl bodies.

The insulating myelin sheath that encloses the axis cylinders of certain neurons is interrupted at intervals by nodes of Ranvier.
Processes of peripheral nerves are ensheathed in a neurilemma, composed of Schwann cells.
Neurons are specialized in excitability and conductivity.
The conduction of an impulse in a neuron is initiated by a minimal or threshold stimulus.
    Impulse conduction in an individual neuron obeys an all or nothing law, but the action of nerves shows a graded response to stimuli.
    The firing of a neuron may be facilitated by (1) a sequence of subliminal stimuli arriving in rapid succession (temporal summation) or (2) a number of subliminal stimuli applied in different places (spatial summation).
    The resting potential across a neuron membrane is normally between -70 and -90 millivolts.
    Stimulation of the nerve cell membrane results in a local influx of sodium ions, producing depolarization; the action potential spreads throughout the neuron.
    In unmyelinated neurons, the nerve impulse is propagated by a wave of depolarization that spreads continuously through the fiber; in myelinated neurons, impulse conduction proceeds by saltatory propagation, skipping from node to node.
    The firing of a neuron is followed by a brief refractory period.
    Some receptors rapidly adapt to a stimulus, ceasing to respond to it.
Nerve impulses are transmitted from the axon of one neuron to the dendrites or cell body of another by the diffusion of chemical transmitters across a gap called the synapse.
    The terminal buttons (synaptic knobs) of an axon contain vesicles that can discharge excitatory or inhibitory neurotransmitters.
    The most common excitatory neurotransmitter is acetylcholine, which is rapidly inactivated by cholinesterase.
A peripheral nerve contains numerous nerve fibers, grouped into bundles.
    Each individual nerve fiber is ensheathed in an endoneurium.
    Bundles of nerve fibers are ensheathed in a perineurium.
    The nerve is ensheathed in an epineurium.
    A motor nerve contains only motor nerve fibers; a mixed nerve contains both types of fibers.
In the central nervous system nerve fibers are grouped into tracts but are not enclosed in a perineurium.
Nerve cells do not divide by mitosis but can regenerate an axon.

QUESTIONS FOR REVIEW AND THOUGHT

1 Briefly summarize the functions of the brain, spinal cord, and peripheral nerves (afferent and efferent).

2 Distinguish, structurally and functionally, between sensory and motor nerves.

3 Where are myelinated neurons found? Nonmyelinated neurons?

4 Why do neurons conduct impulses in one direction only? What advantages are there to one-way traffic in the nervous system?

5 How does the conduction of an impulse along a chain of neurons differ from the transmission of speech along a telephone wire?

6 A neuron cannot "fire" unless it receives a threshold stimulus. Discuss exceptions to this principle in the living body.

7 Contrast the modes of propagation of an impulse along myelinated and nonmyelinated nerve fibers.

8 Discuss adaptation of nerve cell receptors.

9 Describe the sequence of events in the transmission of a nerve impulse across a synapse. Are there any advantages to having successive neurons separated by synapses rather than joined directly into a continuous network? Discuss.

THE CENTRAL NERVOUS SYSTEM

13

More than 10 billion neurons comprise the human nervous system. Through this intricate network run impulses that are the foundations of hopes, dreams, desires, creative thoughts, and innumerable bits of data that continually flood the body's sensory organs. These data pass from the sense receptors along the peripheral nervous system to the brain and spinal cord, which together comprise the central nervous system (Figure 13-1). It is the central nervous system that screens and evaluates the incoming impulses, storing important data for future retrieval and constantly formulating decisions and initiating actions via impulses sent along peripheral nerves to the body's effectors.

The delicate central nervous system is well protected from the continual jarring that is an inevitable result of normal body movements. The brain is enclosed in a hard bony helmet, formed by the cranial bones, while the spinal cord is enclosed in the flexible vertebral column. In addition, three separate fibrous membranes, the **meninges,** provide added protection. Lymphlike **cerebrospinal fluid,** bathing the meninges and filling the chambers of the brain and the channel within the spinal cord, furnishes a cushioning effect.

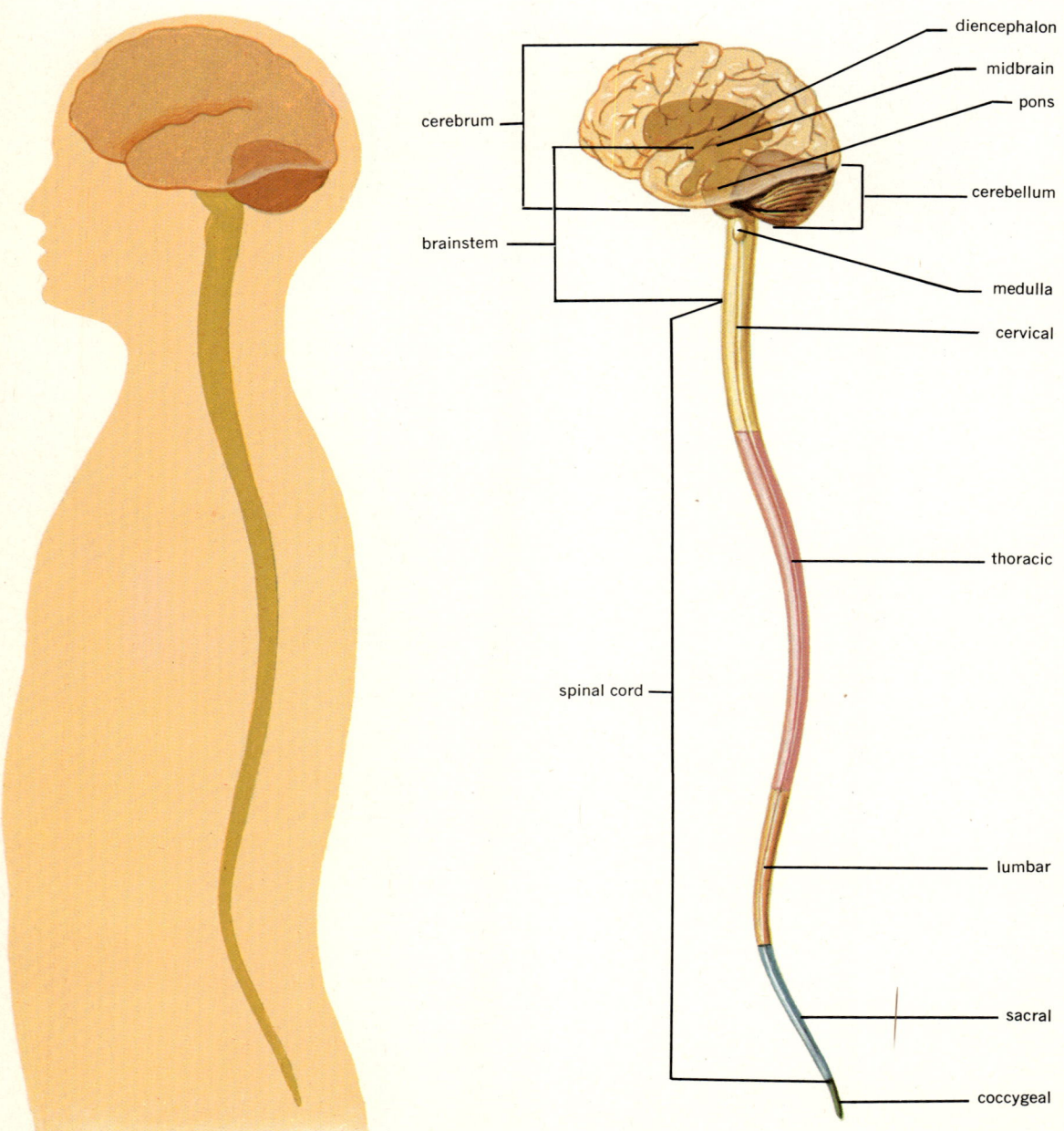

FIGURE 13-1 The central nervous system (lateral view).

As mentioned in the last chapter, the brain and spinal cord are grossly divided into masses of gray matter (nerve cell bodies and nonmyelinated fibers) and white matter (chiefly myelinated nerve fibers). A mass of gray matter in the central nervous system is often referred to as a **nucleus.** (The term ganglion is usually reserved for a similar cluster of nerve cells in the peripheral nervous system.)

Although the neurons of the central nervous system are not ensheathed in discrete bundles, like the nerves of the peripheral nervous system, there are definite functional groupings here too. Nerve fibers of the brain and spinal cord with a common origin and a common destination constitute a **tract.** The nerve tracts of the CNS follow a definite path, but are not as clearly defined as the peripheral nerves—not only because of the lack of a sheathing membrane, but also because there is some intermingling of the fibers of neighboring tracts. Some of the most distinct and characteristic bundles of fibers in the brain are given special names, such as **fasciculus, brachium, penduncle, column,** and **lemniscus.** The CNS contains both ascending tracts, which carry messages to the brain, and descending tracts, which carry impulses from the brain. The brain, like the body as a whole, is bilateral, composed of two mirror-image halves. A band of fibers joining the corresponding opposite parts of the brain or spinal cord is referred to as a **commissure.**

THE BRAIN

A science fiction story written a generation ago detailed the trials and tribulations of a rich but accident-prone man in the not-too-distant future, who successively had one body part after another replaced by prostheses, until only his brain remained of his original flesh-and-blood. In time he suffered a massive stroke. But fortunately he had already taken the precaution of having all his memories duplicated and stored in an artificial brain, which was ready to take over his vital functions. This artificial brain was so complex that it took up the whole of a huge skyscraper. The story was written in the era of the vacuum tube. Since then electronics technology has gone through not one but several generations, with the advent first of the transistor, then of integrated circuits, LSI's, and so on. The space needed for the hypothetical artificial brain rapidly shrank from a whole building to a single room, a large cabinet, a medium-sized box. Yet even now, a living brain is a far more compact, yet complex and efficient structure than the best artificial analog modern technology could devise.

Looking at a brain, it seems hard to believe that this is the major clearing center that integrates, regulates, and controls the body activities—the seat of consciousness, memories, personality, of love and rage, pleasure and fear—the center of awareness of the world around us—the source of intellect and creativity. A human brain is a jellylike structure, covered with an intricate pattern of surface grooves and folds, and in an adult weighs just about three pounds. The adult brain is usually somewhat larger in the male than in the female, averaging 1380 to 1250 grams, respectively—a difference that is not believed to indicate any inherent difference in intelligence between the sexes. The brain cells you have now were already in existence when you were a baby: mitotic division of the brain neurons ceases after the first few months of postnatal life. (Malnutrition during prenatal life or early infancy has been reported to interfere with this process, resulting in the formation of fewer brain cells.) The brain grows rapidly during the first five years or so, by an expansion of the size of the nerve cells and an increase in neuroglia, rather than an increase in the number of neurons; growth continues to some extent up to about 18 to 20 years, when the brains reaches its full size. During old age, the weight of the brain decreases.

The brain (Figure 13-2) has three major divisions: the **forebrain,** the **midbrain,** and the **hindbrain.** Each of these is further subdivided.

The most prominent portion of the forebrain, which constitutes the bulk of the brain, is the **telencephalon** or **cerebrum,** which is divided down the midline of the body into two distinct hemispheres. The cerebral hemispheres contain the highest centers of the brain—centers of sensory perception and motor control, memory, association, thought, personality. This is the part of the brain that contributes most to our "humanness," our essential "self." It is significant that the cerebrum in the human brain is proportionately the largest and most highly developed in the entire animal kingdom (with the possible exception of dolphins), and only among the dolphins and our closest relative, the primates, is there a convolution of the brain surface approaching the complex wrinking and folding of the surface of the human cerebrum.

At the base of the cerebral hemispheres, buried deep within the brain, is the **diencephalon,** which contains several important structures including the **thalamus** and the **hypothalamus.** The thalamus is the central relay station in the complex networks of interconnections between the cerebral cortex (the outer layer of the cerebrum) and the spinal cord. The hypothalamus contains a variety of control centers, regulating such body activities as temperature control, water metabolism, maintenance of blood sugar level, and reproductive cycles, as well as such drives as hunger and thirst, and such emotions as anger and pleasure. The diencephalon shares a common embryonic origin with the telencephalon (the "higher

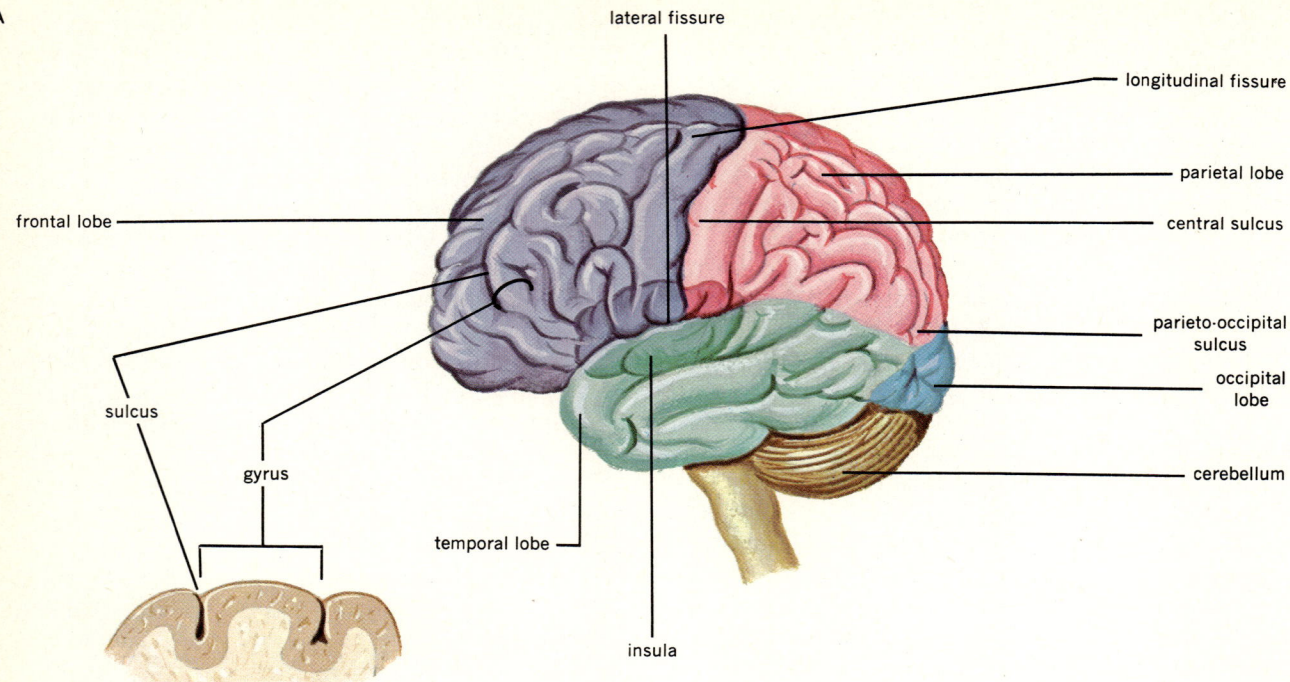

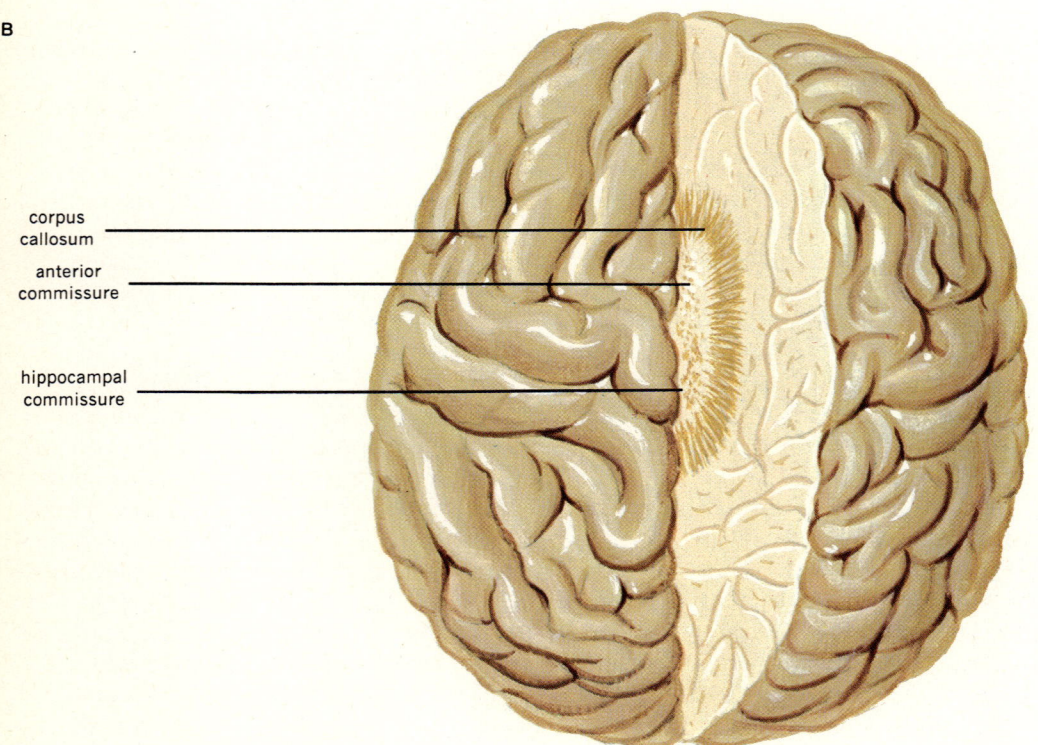

FIGURE 13-2 **The brain. Prominent fissures serve as landmarks demarcating the lobes (A). Convolutions greatly expand the surface area (inset).
In (B), the cerebral hemispheres are pulled apart somewhat to show the
corpus callosum and commissures. Midsagittal section (C) and lateral view
(D).**

C

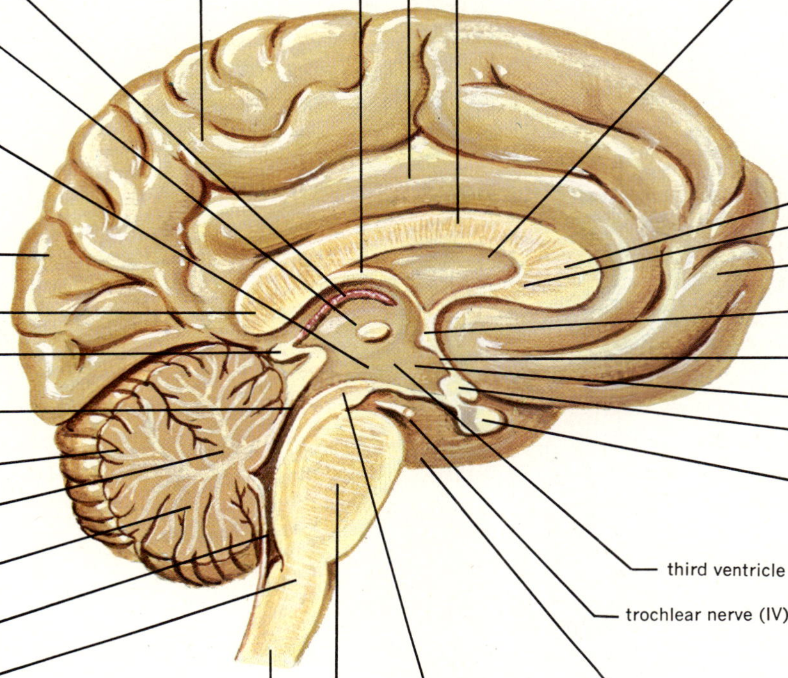

tela choroides

interthalamic
adhesion
(massa
intermedia)

thalamus

occipital
lobe

splenium

pineal
body

cerebral
aqueduct
(Sylvius)

cerebellar
cortex

medulla

cerebellum

fourth ventricle

medulla oblongata

parietal
lobe

cerebrum

fornix

corpus
callosum

septum
pellucidum (lucidum)

genu

rostrum

frontal
lobe

anterior
commissure

lamina
terminalis

hypothalmus

optic chiasm

hypophysis (pituitary)

third ventricle

trochlear nerve (IV)

spinal
cord

pons

midbrain

temporal lobe

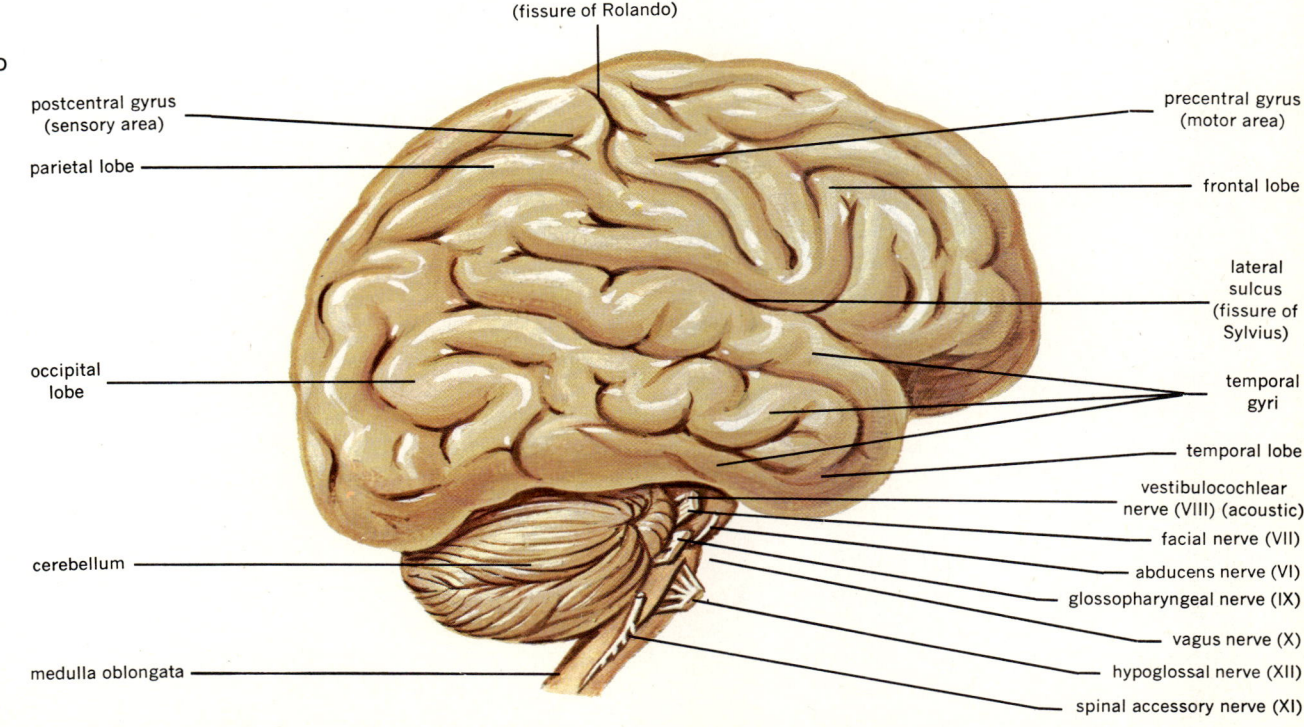

central sulcus
(fissure of Rolando)

D

postcentral gyrus
(sensory area)

parietal lobe

occipital
lobe

cerebellum

medulla oblongata

precentral gyrus
(motor area)

frontal lobe

lateral
sulcus
(fissure of
Sylvius)

temporal
gyri

temporal lobe

vestibulocochlear
nerve (VIII) (acoustic)

facial nerve (VII)

abducens nerve (VI)

glossopharyngeal nerve (IX)

vagus nerve (X)

hypoglossal nerve (XII)

spinal accessory nerve (XI)

brain"), but functionally it seems to be more suitably classed with the structures of the "lower brain."

The midbrain (**mesencephalon**) is a small region connecting the forebrain with the hindbrain. It contains numerous nuclei for the control of ocular reflexes, eye movement, and higher postural reflex actions. (The midbrain is far more prominent in lower animals such as the fish, in which it is the major region for receiving and processing incoming optical data.)

The hindbrain includes the **pons,** the **medulla,** and the **cerebellum.** The pons is an enlarged region just below the midbrain, which acts as a relay station from the lower centers to the higher ones and contains the nuclei of the fifth to eighth pairs of cranial nerves. The medulla follows the pons and merges smoothly into the spinal cord. It contains the nuclei of many cranial nerves, sensory relays, and control centers for such vital functions as breathing, the regulation of the heart rate, swallowing, and vomiting. The midbrain, pons, and medulla together are called the **brainstem,** from their resemblance to the stem of a fruit. Running up through the medulla and pons and into the thalamus and hypothalamus is a cone-shaped network of neurons called the **reticular formation,** which helps to maintain muscle tone and acts as a central clearing house for the information flooding the brain.

The other major division of the hindbrain, the cerebellum, is situated posterior to the brainstem, nestled under the overhang of the cerebrum. Convoluted and divided into two hemispheres, the cerebellum looks rather like a smaller version of the cerebrum. This is the center for coordination and balance.

THE CEREBRUM

Humans of the distant future are sometimes depicted with an exaggerated "egghead," with a greatly enlarged forebrain. Such a picture might be considered a reasonable projection of evolutionary trends—just as modern humans have far more highly developed cerebrums than their vertebrate ancestors, the beyond-man (superman?) might be expected to show even greater development of this vital thinking part of the brain. As it is, the cerebrum makes up a substantial part of the present-day human brain—about seven-eighths of its total weight—and entirely fills the upper part of the skull.

The cerebrum is composed of a mixture of gray and white matter, quite nonuniformly arranged. A section through the brain tissue reveals that the outer layer or **cortex** of the cerebrum consists entirely of gray matter, varying from 1.5 to 4 mm thick. Within this gray outer coat, most of the brain is white matter, but isolated masses of gray matter—**basal ganglia**—are scattered through it. The bulk of the white matter is composed of small fibers running in three main directions: from above downward, linking the cortex with various parts of the brain and spinal cord (the **projection fibers**); from the front backward, connecting areas of the cerebral cortex on the same side of the brain (**association fibers**); and from side to side, connecting the right and left sides of the brain (**commissural fibers**).

Cerebral Fissures and Convolutions

The outside of a bald head presents a rather plain, featureless appearance—which is not at all typical of the brain housed within the skull. Externally, the most striking features of the cerebrum are the numerous wrinkles and folds, as well as prominent grooves and deep indentations. In general, the extensive wrinklings and foldings of the surface of the cerebrum are referred to as **convolutions.** The protruding ridges are called **gyri** (singular **gyrus**); the grooves between them are called **sulci** (singular **sulcus**). Particularly deep grooves or clefts are referred to as **fissures.** A single deep cleft, the **longitudinal fissure,** running from front to back along the midline of the body, seems to separate the cerebrum entirely into two identical hemispheres. Actually, however, the left and right halves of the cerebrum are not completely separated: deep inside the brain, a thick bank of nerve fibers, called the **corpus callosum,** as well as three smaller bands or **commissures** (the **fornix** and **anterior** and **posterior commissures**) interlink the two halves of the cerebrum (see Figure 13-2) and provide for an interchange of information between them.

In addition to the longitudinal fissure, other less drastic clefts form prominent landmarks on the cerebral hemispheres (Figure 13-2).

The **central sulcus** or **fissure of Rolando** runs from the midpoint of the superior border laterally and downward along each cerebral hemisphere, demarcating the front portion of the brain.

Viewed from the side, the cerebrum looks something like a large mitten, with the wrist at the back and the fingers at the front of the head. The "thumb" of the mitten is separated from the remainder by another prominent groove, the **lateral fissure** or **fissure of Sylvius.**

At the rear of the cerebrum, another major landmark is the **parieto-occipital sulcus.**

Lobes of the Cerebrum and Cerebral Functions

Anatomists use the major fissures and sulci of the cerebrum as convenient boundaries, roughly dividing each hemisphere into four major regions, referred to as **lobes.** Each lobe fits into a depression or fossa in the skull and is named for the corresponding cranial bone that lies over it.

The front region, demarcated by the longitudinal fissure and the central fissure, is the **frontal lobe.** The **parietal lobe** lies posterior to the central fissure on the superior surface of the brain, bounded also by the longitudinal fissure, the lateral fissure, and the parieto-occipital fissure. The rear of the cerebrum is the **occipital lobe.** And the lateral region, below the lateral fissure, is the **temporal lobe.**

The boundary lines of the lobes are quite arbitrary, but these regions, as well as the characteristic sulci and fissures, are a convenience in mapping and studying the localization of specific functions of the brain.

An anatomist can observe a living brain through flaps cut into the skull, or dissect an ample supply of brain specimens. But how can a physiologist determine how the brain thinks and remembers, and what parts of it are involved in specific components of the complex activities that make up the abstraction we call "mind"? A wealth of information about precisely these aspects of brain activity has been obtained by a number of different approaches.

First of all, observations can be made of the effects of lesions in specific regions of the brain. Such lesions may be produced in animals for experimental purposes; in humans, tumors, cerebral hemorrhages, and traumatic injuries provide an abundant supply of subjects for study. About a century ago, a man named Phineas Gage made medical history by having a 13 pound iron bar blasted into the frontal lobes of his brain—and by surviving, without any gross ill effects. There were, however, some significant personality changes after the accident: from a quiet, conscientious worker, he was transformed into a drunkard, who was argumentative and unreliable and lost one job after another. The frontal lobes of the brain still remain the least understood of all, but they seem to contain seats of personality and decision-making, as well as a well-mapped strip along the central sulcus that controls voluntary movements of various parts of the body. (Because the nerves are connected to the brain in a cross-over manner, the left hemisphere controls the movements and receives sensations from the right half of the body, and the right hemisphere is responsible for the left half of the body.)

Brain surgery has also yielded a wealth of information about functions of specific regions of the brain. Curiously, the brain—perhaps the most vital and vulnerable structure in the entire body—is insensitive to pain. A surgeon can cut a tumor out of a patient's brain while the patient is wide awake and conversing with the doctor, feeling no pain at all. During brain surgery, the surgeon may stimulate specific points on the surface of the brain—for example, with a minute electric current delivered by fine wire electrodes—and observe the effects. (Such observations may be made not out of intellectual curiosity, but as an integral part of the operation—to determine what vital functions have not been impaired, or in the case of epileptics to try to reproduce the sensations that immediately precede a seizure in order to locate the damaged focus that precipitates "electrical storms" in the brain.) Stimulation of a particular region of the cortex may cause the patient to clench a fist suddenly, or kick out with a foot. When a different area is stimulated, he or she may suddenly see colors, or smell a flower scent, or hear the voice of a childhood friend speaking in an extraordinarily vivid hallucination. In addition to the "motor strip" in the frontal lobe, a "sensory strip" on the other side of the central sulcus (in the parietal lobe) and a variety of regions associated with vision, hearing, speech, word association, and so forth, have been mapped in such studies. More recently, further light on the localization of brain functions has been cast by studies of the action potentials from various regions of the brain, recorded as **electroencephalograms** or **EEG's** (Figure 13-3). Minute electrodes may actually be embedded in the brain, or the "brain waves" may be picked up by metal discs, pasted to the forehead or scalp.

Several types of characteristic wavelike patterns can be observed in brain wave tracings taken from different parts of the brain. **Alpha waves,** which occur at frequencies of 8 to 13 per second and voltages of about 50 microvolts (μV), typically are observed when the subject is awake but relaxed, with the eyes closed; these waves are most easily obtained from the frontal and occipital regions of the brain. "Biofeedback" techniques have been used to train people to produce alpha waves at will, and various beneficial effects have been claimed for this relaxation technique. **Beta waves,** with frequencies of 15 to 60 per second and voltages of 5 to 10 μV, are recorded from the frontal and parietal regions when the brain is in an attentive or stimulated state. **Delta waves,** slow waves with frequencies of 1 to 5 per second and volages of 20 to 200 μV, occur during deep sleep and in severe brain damage or injury, as well as in normal infants. They characterize the unconscious brain and can be recorded from all regions of the cortex. **Theta waves** (5 to 8 per second, 10 μV) are recorded from the temporal lobes in children and at times of emotional stress. In addition to these continuous forms of electrical activity, the brain exhibits bursts of **evoked activity,** called forth by sensory stimulations, such as a light shining in the eye, a bell ringing, or a pin prick.

The Cerebral Cortex

It is hard to believe that the essence of each of us—our memories, hopes, plans, our attitudes and personality—is all stored within a thin outer layer of the brain, less than a quarter of an inch deep. This is the cerebral cortex, the brain's outer layer of gray matter

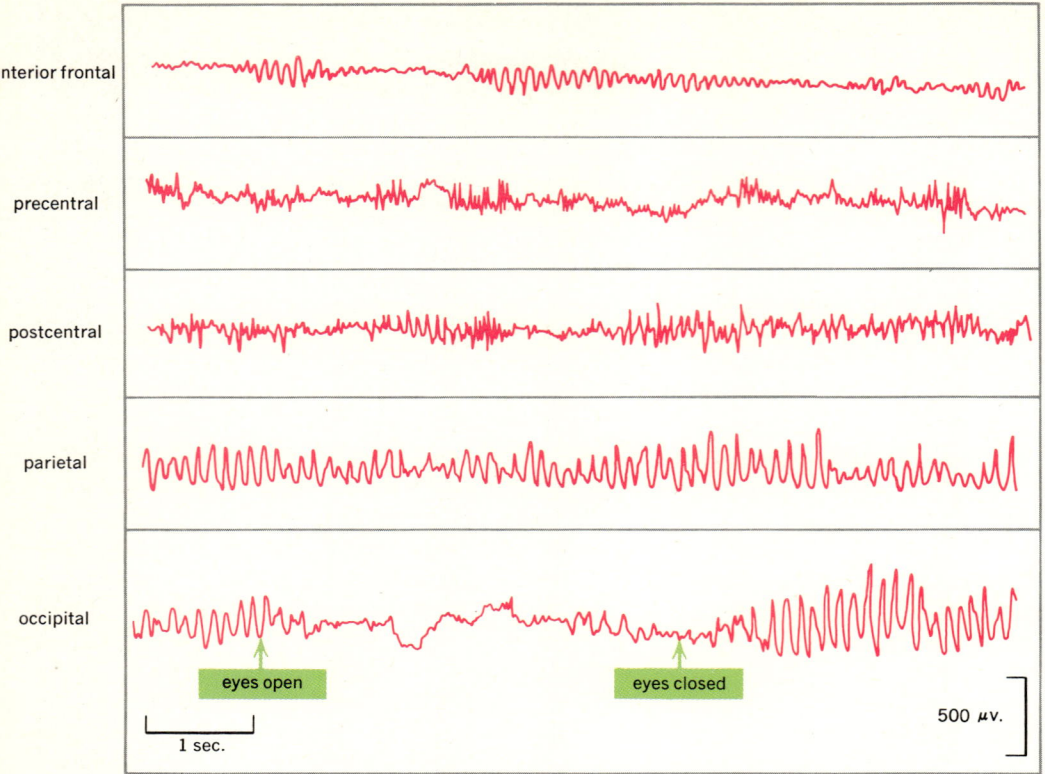

anterior frontal

precentral

postcentral

parietal

occipital

eyes open

eyes closed

500 μv.

1 sec.

FIGURE 13-3 Normal EEG patterns from different regions of the cerebral cortex.

that covers it like the rind of an orange. Its capacity is actually far more impressive than it might seem at first thought. The intricate convolutions of the brain's surface produce a tremendous increase in surface area. (Picture a sheet of newsprint spread out flat, then crumpled so that it easily fits into a teacup. Not one letter of print or picture detail has been lost, but the same amount of information has been stored in a much smaller space, just as it is in the convoluted cerebral cortex.) It has been estimated that the human cerebral cortex contains from 10 to 14 billion neurons. Every thought, every voluntary action involves some of these neurons of the cerebral cortex.

Studies of the brain have yielded elaborate functional maps of the cerebral cortex, such as that depicted in Figure 13-4. The areas with which specific functions have been linked look rather like islands, floating in seas of unmarked regions sometimes referred to as "silent" cortex, for stimulation or destruction of these areas does not seem to produce any direct or obvious effects. These areas are far from nonfunctional, however; they contain intricate meshes of neurons that interlink the sensory and motor areas of the cortex and serve as a repository for memories, thoughts, and the subtler aspects of the complex of brain activity that we class as cerebration.

The gyri immediately anterior and posterior to the central sulcus contain the motor and sensory areas,

respectively. These areas are sometimes referred to as **projection areas,** for they contain the terminals of sensory and motor nerve pathways linking the cortex with all parts of the body. The vast remainder of the cerebral cortex contains the **association areas,** responsible for the integrative activities of the brain.

Voluntary actions of all parts of the body are initiated by impulses from the **motor strip,** on the precentral gyrus. Muscle groups rather than individual muscles are controlled by the motor strip; its impulses travel down into the spinal cord and are transmitted through peripheral nerves to the appropriate individual muscles, causing them to contract and effect the intended action. It was mentioned earlier that the two halves of the brain control the body parts in a crisscross fashion: the left hemisphere controls the right half of the body, and the right hemisphere controls the left half of the body. In addition, the various parts of the body are represented on the motor strip in an upside-down arrangement: impulses governing the movements of the feet come from the top of the motor strip; then, proceeding downward along the strip, come the areas for the legs, body, hands, head and face, and mouth. As can ben seen from Figure 13-4B, the representation of different body regions seems quite disproportionate, with a far greater area allotted to the face and hands than their size would warrant. Considered from a functional standpoint, however,

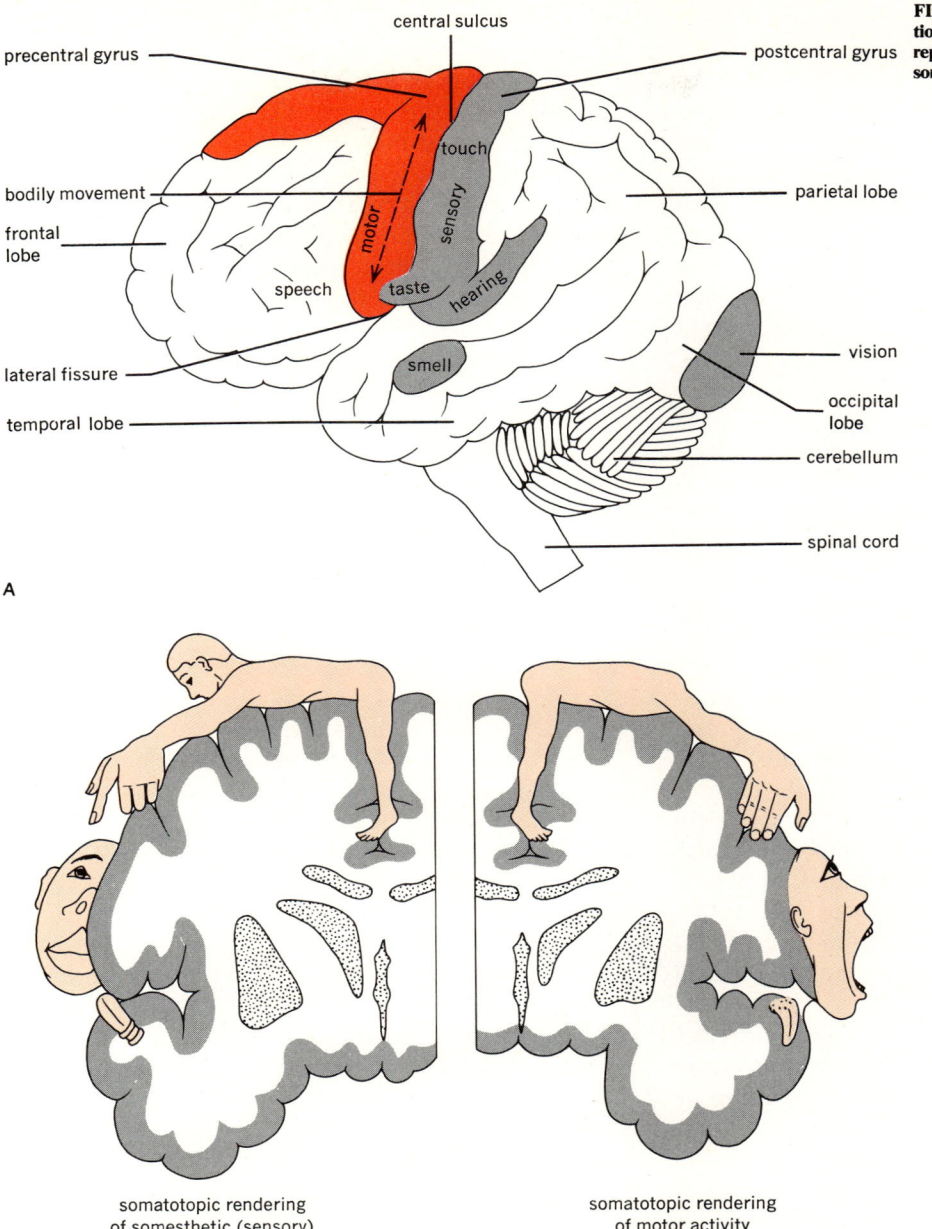

FIGURE 13-4   Maps of the brain: projection areas of the cerebral cortex (A) and representation of body parts along the sensory and motor strips (B).

precentral gyrus

central sulcus

postcentral gyrus

touch

bodily movement

sensory

parietal lobe

motor

frontal lobe

speech

taste

hearing

lateral fissure

smell

temporal lobe

vision

occipital lobe

cerebellum

spinal cord

A

somatotopic rendering of somesthetic (sensory) activity

somatotopic rendering of motor activity

B

the apparent disproportion vanishes—the face and hands have a far greater number and variety of things to do than the body and feet.

The **premotor cortex,** an area between 1 and 3 cm anterior to the motor strips, seems to be a motor association area, controlling complex coordinated movements of groups of muscles.

Sensory neurons relaying information on such general sensations as heat, cold, touch, pressure, pain, and proprioception ("muscle sense") terminate in the postcentral gyri, just behind the central sulcus in each hemisphere of the brain. The map of the **sensory strips** looks very much like that of the motor strips,

with the same apparently disproportionate representation of the head region and the same sort of inverted, criss-cross connection with the parts of the body. The point-to-point representation of all areas of the body on the sensory cortex makes it possible to localize a point of stimulation even without seeing the body part. For example, if a mosquito alighted on your arm, you would automatically slap at it without looking.

The **parietal areas,** behind the sensory strips, are association areas concerned with the interpretation of size, shape, texture, temperature, and other properties of objects conveyed by the senses of touch.

The specialized sense organs of the body—eyes, ears, nose, and taste buds—have their own functional areas on the cortex. If you have ever "seen stars" after receiving a sharp blow to the back of the head, you have firsthand knowledge of the location of a major **visual area** in the occipital lobe. Stimulation of this area can evoke a sensation of vision even if the eyes are closed; if this part of the brain is destroyed, the victim will be unable to see anything, even if his or her eyes are perfectly normally and functionally unimpaired. Further corroboration of the functioning of the occipital region of the brain in vision is provided by experiments with animals. In animals that have lost their eyesight through damage to the eyes, the occipital visual cortex gradually becomes thinner than normal, atrophying from disuse; in animals that are subjected to an unusually large number of varied visual experiences, on the other hand, the visual cortex grows thicker than usual.

The **auditory area** of the cortex is found in the superior part of the temporal lobe, just below the lateral sulcus. Just as for the eyes and the visual cortex, hearing involves more than the reception of vibrations by the ear; the vibrations are meaningless until impulses are transmitted to the auditory area of the cortex and interpreted into meaningful sounds.

The **temporal association areas** are concerned with learning and the memory of things seen and heard.

A specialized area for the reception and interpretation of **taste** sensations has been found deep in the lateral fissure, while the area involved in the interpretation of the sense of **smell** is located on the medial aspect of the temporal lobe.

The human characteristic that perhaps more than any other sets us apart from the animals is the acquisition of speech. The ability to communicate precisely with others of our species has made it possible to pass on a wealth of accumulated experience from generation to generation; without speech, the development of civilization as we know it would have been impossible. Several different regions of the cortex have been found to be associated with speech. The **motor speech area** in the motor cortex is involved in the actual physical movements associated with speech. A speech region in the **temporal** area is believed to be concerned with the choice of thoughts to be expressed, and a speech area in the **parietal** lobe with the choice of words to be used. A portion of the premotor cortex called **Broca's area** is involved in word formation: a person whose brain is damaged in this region can still speak but can utter only simple words like "yes" and "no." Damage to one of the speech areas in the brain can produce various types of **aphasia,** the inability to speak (or to speak intelligibly); **agraphia,** the inability to write; **word deafness,** the inability to understand spoken words; or **word blindness,** the inability to understand written words. Such conditions are a common aftermath of a stroke and can be maddeningly frustrating for the victims. Their minds may be keen and logical, and they may know exactly what they want to say, but when they open their mouths only nonsense syllables come out; or they may be able to hear people speaking perfectly well, but be unable to make any sense out of what they are saying.

It has been found that in early childhood, usually around the age of three or so, the speech centers in one of the hemispheres of the brain (generally the left hemisphere) become far more developed than those in the other hemisphere. Since this is about the time that "handedness"—a clear dominance of one side of the body over the other in motor ability—is generally established, it was assumed that the dominance of one cerebral hemisphere (the left, in the majority of people) is somehow associated with the development of the speech centers. Parents were cautioned not to try to change their children's handedness, despite the disadvantages left-handers face in our right-handed world, for fear of causing shuttering and other speech difficulties. But as more evidence was accumulated (e.g., by observations of victims of unilateral strokes), it was found that the relationship is not quite so simple. Although right-handed people, with a dominant left hemisphere, have their speech controlled mainly by left-hemisphere centers, so do many left-handers (whose right hemisphere is dominant).

Further light on the subject has been shed by some fascinating experiments with people whose corpus callosum has been cut surgically. (This technique is sometimes used in epilepsy: it has been found that severing the connections between the hemispheres of the brain helps to stop the spread of the aberrant electrical discharges that produce epileptic seizures.) A split-brain person literally has two independent brains in one skull. Normally, there are no obvious outward signs of this extraordinary situation, for various sensory cues usually keep both halves of the brain equally informed. Yet in test situations, the normal interchange of information can be eliminated and the capacities of the two halves of the brain tested independently. For example, a split-brain person, groping in a bag of objects with the left hand, cannot verbally identify the object that was grasped—the left brain, in charge of verbalization, had no data to go on. (Remember that sensory data from various parts of the body are relayed to the *opposite* side of the brain.) In studies such as these, as well as even more ingenious setups in which different pictures are simultaneously flashed on the two sides of a split screen watched by the split-brain volunteer, a general picture of the abilities of the two hemispheres has been developed. The left brain is the verbal half, which reads, writes, and speaks fluently and does difficult arithmetic. The right brain seems rather stupid in comparison, but can read common words, do simple arithmetic, and understand simple verbal instructions. When nonverbal responses are possible—for example, by pointing with the left hand—the right brain does fairly well, and it has a keener sense of shape, form, and texture, as well as a flair for musical rhythm and melody. It is not known what causes the early specialization of the two hemispheres of the brain. It is not an inherent difference in capacity, for when one side of the brain is massively damaged, the other hemisphere can gradually be retrained to take over all of its functions. (The adjustment is most complete if the damage occurs in childhood, but even in an adult considerable rehabilitation is possible.)

Memory and Learning

While taking exams, you probably have often wished for a photographic memory, the ability to recall all the details of your textbook or lecture notes vividly and accurately after just a single quick reading. Some people do have such a memory; indeed, there have been cases recorded of an almost eidetic memory—a total recall of every detail of past experience. But most of us remember far less easily and more selectively, retaining only the few most noteworthy details of the bewildering blizzard of information that continually bombards our brain. Even so, our brains record more information than we usually realize, as evidenced by the flood of memories that may be evoked by a chance association or dredged up under hypnosis.

The nature of memory and learning has long been an object of intensive study and heated controversy. Some basic principles do seem clear. For example, there seem to be two basic kinds of memory: **temporary memory** and **fixed, long-term memory.** Let us say you look up a telephone number, then turn away to make the call. You can retain the number without much difficulty for the short time it takes to pick up the phone and dial. But if the number is not one you expect to make use of in the future, and you make no particular effort to memorize it, it will quickly vanish from your mind—especially if something happens to distract you. (If you happen to reach a wrong number, by the time you have apologized to the person on the line, hung up, and begun to redial, you will probably discover you have to look the number up all over again.) In general, fixing a new bit of information in your long-term memory usually involves elements of **motivation** (particular interest, or pleasure, or the hope of a reward—such as an "A" in an exam—or the fear of a punishment), **repetition,** and **association.**

The most firmly retained and readily retrievable memories are those that utilize the brain's intricate cross-indexing system of associations. Indeed, elaborate systems of mnemonics (memory-aiding "tags") have been built on the basis of associations to aid people who have difficulty in remembering names, numbers, or other information.

Yet what is happening in the brain during learning, and how are memories stored and retrieved? Is there a molecular basis of memory and learning? This field of study is one of the most intriguing, exciting, and bitterly contested in modern biomedical science.

There have been numerous attempts to locate specific memory sites in the brain. These efforts have been so uniformly unsuccessful that the currently accepted view is that each memory is multiply repeated and stored in redundant fashion on many different parts of the brain. Memory storage in the brain has been compared to a hologram, a form of photographic recording that produces a vivid three-dimensional image (Figure 13-5). Information is encoded in scrambled form on all parts of a hologram. If a piece of the hologram is broken off, then unscrambled, the whole picture is still reproduced, although the detail is not as sharp as in the complete hologram. The smaller the fragment, the fuzzier the details. Quite similar results are observed when parts of the brain are damaged—some memory details are lost, but the whole is basically unchanged.

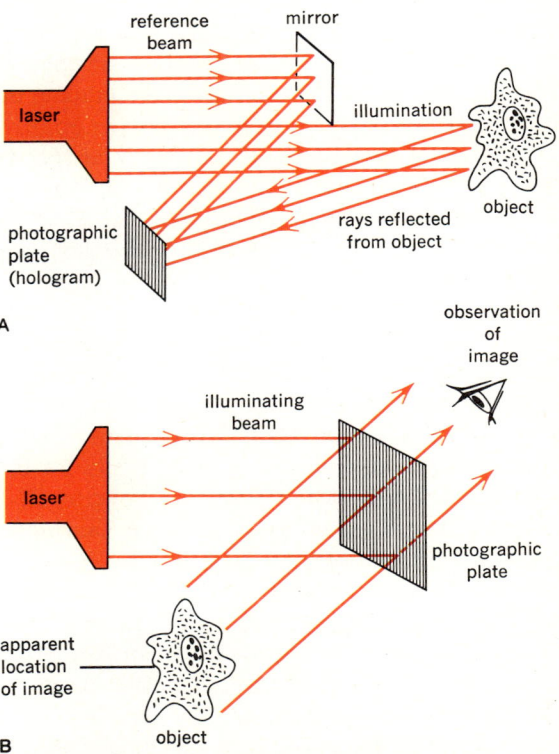

FIGURE 13-5 Recording (A) and reconstructing (B) a hologram.

Many of the landmark studies on memory and learning have been conducted with animals. For example, studies of young rats have shown that when they are raised in an "enriched" environment, in the company of other young rats, with plenty of toys to play with and interesting places to explore, the cerebral cortex is more developed and there is an increased production of the neurotransmitter chemical acetylcholine, in comparison with young rats raised in isolation in an unfurnished cage.

Experiments with the lowly flatworm raised a storm of controversy. Equipped with only the most rudimentary of brains, these tiny worms can nonetheless be trained to solve a simple T-maze, disobeying their normal inclinations to crawl toward a light to receive a food reward or escape an electric-shock punishment. Not only did experiments with flatworms indicate that their learning was linked with RNA production, but when the trained worms were minced and fed to untrained flatworms, the "memory" of the maze was somehow transmitted to the untrained cannibals. There were initial difficulties in repeating the flatworm experiments, and accusations and counteraccusations of sloppy technique, closedmindedness, and so on echoed in the pages of scientific publications for a number of years. Before the flatworm controversy was entirely resolved, a flood of corroboration came from other sources. Injections of RNA from the brains of trained hamsters seemed to transmit knowledge to untrained rats; increases in both RNA and protein synthesis were observed in various animals during active learning; injections of yeast RNA and of drugs that stimulate the body's own RNA production were found to improve the memories of senile humans; and several specific "memory chemicals" were actually isolated. (The first of these was **scotophobin,** a polypeptide that transmits a dark-avoidance response to rats, mice, and goldfish.)

Yet the neurons of the brain work by transmitting electrical impulses, carried across the synapses by special neurotransmitter chemicals and propagated along the nerve fibers by waves of depolarization and repolarization. What do RNA and proteins have to do with the fixation of memories? Gradually the bits of experimental information have been fitted together to form a coherent hypothesis on the mechanisms of memory and learning (Figure 13-6).

Temporary memories seem to be maintained by a sort of **reverberating circuit.** It has been found experimentally that if a tetanizing electrical stimulus is applied directly to the surface of the cerebral cortex for a second or more and then removed, the local area excited by the stimulus continues to emit rhythmic action potentials for minutes or even longer. Any fac-

tor that causes a general disturbance of brain function (for example, a sudden concussion of the brain) stops the reverberations and instantly erases the temporary memories—hence the partial amnesia that usually follows a concussion.

The reverberating circuit induced in the brain by a new experience consists of a sequence of neurons, linked and interlinked by synapses into a complex network that may ultimately involve millions of individual brain neurons. Once a neuron in the brain has been tetanically stimulated for a few seconds, its excitability is increased. If a new stimulation follows, it will respond more vigorously. If the particular experience is repeated or associated with other memory patterns already stored in the brain, it is believed that the neurons along the same sequences are stimulated to fire again and again, and a series of changes is set off. RNA is produced, and it in turn forms specific proteins. These may work to strengthen the connections of certain synapses along the pathway, or they may even stimulate the growth of new synapses. Gradually a particular pattern of firing neurons is fixed; this pattern is referred to as a **memory trace** or **engram.** Each of the neurons in a particular engram may be interconnected with numerous other memory traces. And from these interconnections the brain builds up its intricate "filing systems," full of "cross-references" that help in retrieving particular memories.

The growth understanding of the molecular basis of memory and learning has encouraged brain researchers in their quest for ways of correcting abnormalities of mental development and even of improving the mental capacity of normal people. The search for chemical "mental stimulators" is being avidly pursued. The potential impact of such studies on our society is enormous. Most of the major discoveries throughout history have been made by a surprisingly small segment of the population. If this base of "genius" could be significantly broadened, the fruits of the resultant quantum jump in human activity would be beyond the power of our imagination.

Basal Ganglia

In the early brain mapping studies, the main attention was focused on the more readily accessible cerebral cortex. But increasingly sophisticated techniques—it is now possible to stimulate, electrically or chemically, extremely minute areas in the brain, and even to record the electrical potentials from individual neurons!—have made it possible to probe deeper. In recent years, studies of the basal ganglia (masses of gray matter buried deep within the cerebral hemispheres), as well as the diencephalon and structures of the brainstem, have been yielding intriguing results.

The basal ganglia (Figure 13-7) include the **caudate**

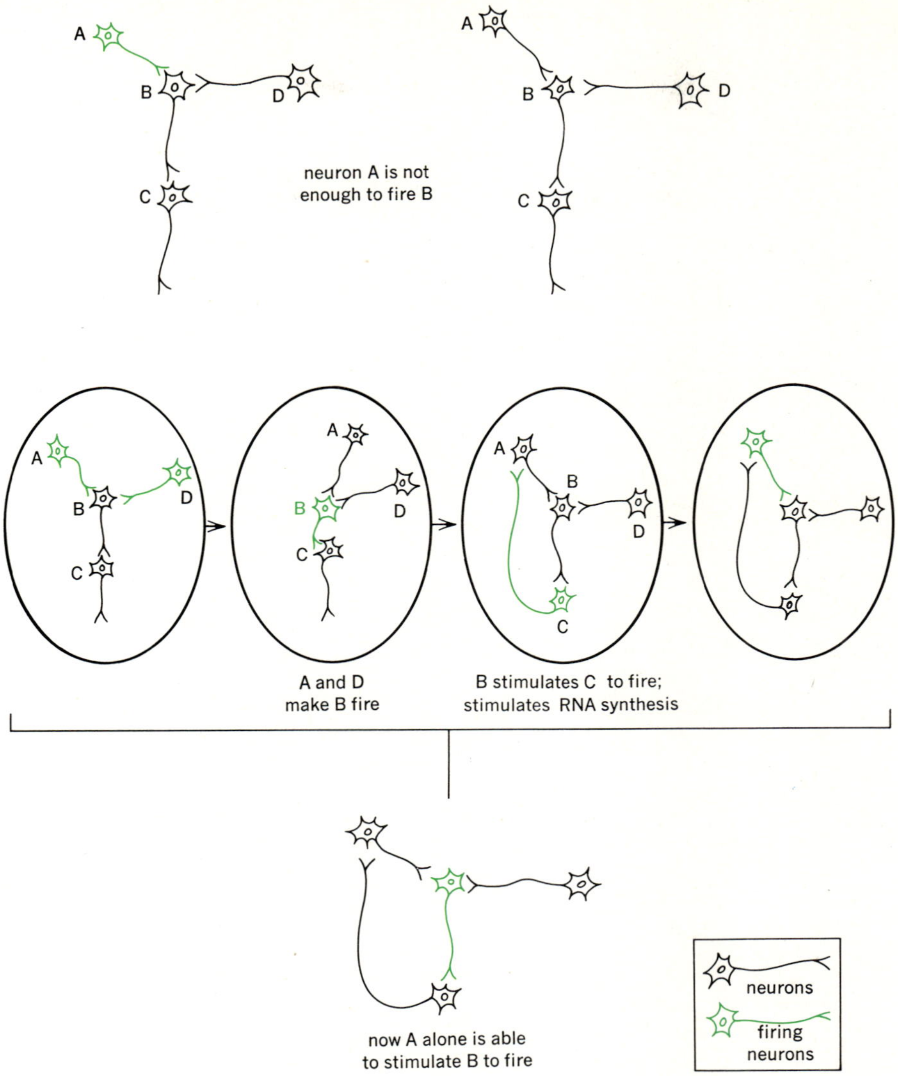

FIGURE 13-6 A theoretical mechanism for the formation of an engram or memory trace.

neuron A is not enough to fire B

A and D make B fire

B stimulates C to fire; stimulates RNA synthesis

now A alone is able to stimulate B to fire

neurons

firing neurons

and **lenticular nuclei,** the **amygdala,** and the **claustrum.** They are important way stations in the motor pathways of the central nervous system.

The caudate nucleus is shaped rather like a comma, with an anterior head and a posterior tail that curves down and forward. It has nerve connections upward through the thalamus and lenticular nucleus into the cerebral cortex, and downward into the spinal cord, and regulates gross body movements that are performed unconsciously. (The motor cortex controls conscious fine movements.)

The lenticular nucleus is a lens-shaped structure, made up of two separate groups of nuclei, the **putamen** and the **globus pallidum.** The putamen, together with the caudate nucleus, is associated with the control of gross, unconscious movements, while the globus pallidum is involved in regulating the muscle tone needed for specific, intentional body movements and can also excite the cortex. Closely associated with

these basal ganglia is a broad band of nerve fibers running from the spinal cord and brainstem to the cortex, together with fibers radiating from the cortex to lower centers. This band of nerve fibers is called the **internal capsule,** and together with the caudate and lenticular nuclei it forms a **corpus striatum** ("striped body") on each side of the brain.

The claustrum is a thin plate of gray matter just beneath the cortex.

The amygdala is one of the most ambiguous and intriguing of the brain centers. It forms a knoblike tip at the end of the tail of the caudate nucleus. When different parts of the amygdala are stimulated, a great variety of effects are produced, ranging from movements of the face and jaw to visceral effects including pupillary changes, piloerection (raising of the body hairs), changes in temperature and blood pressure, an increase in the motility of the gastrointestinal tract, salivation, defecation, changes in respiration, and a

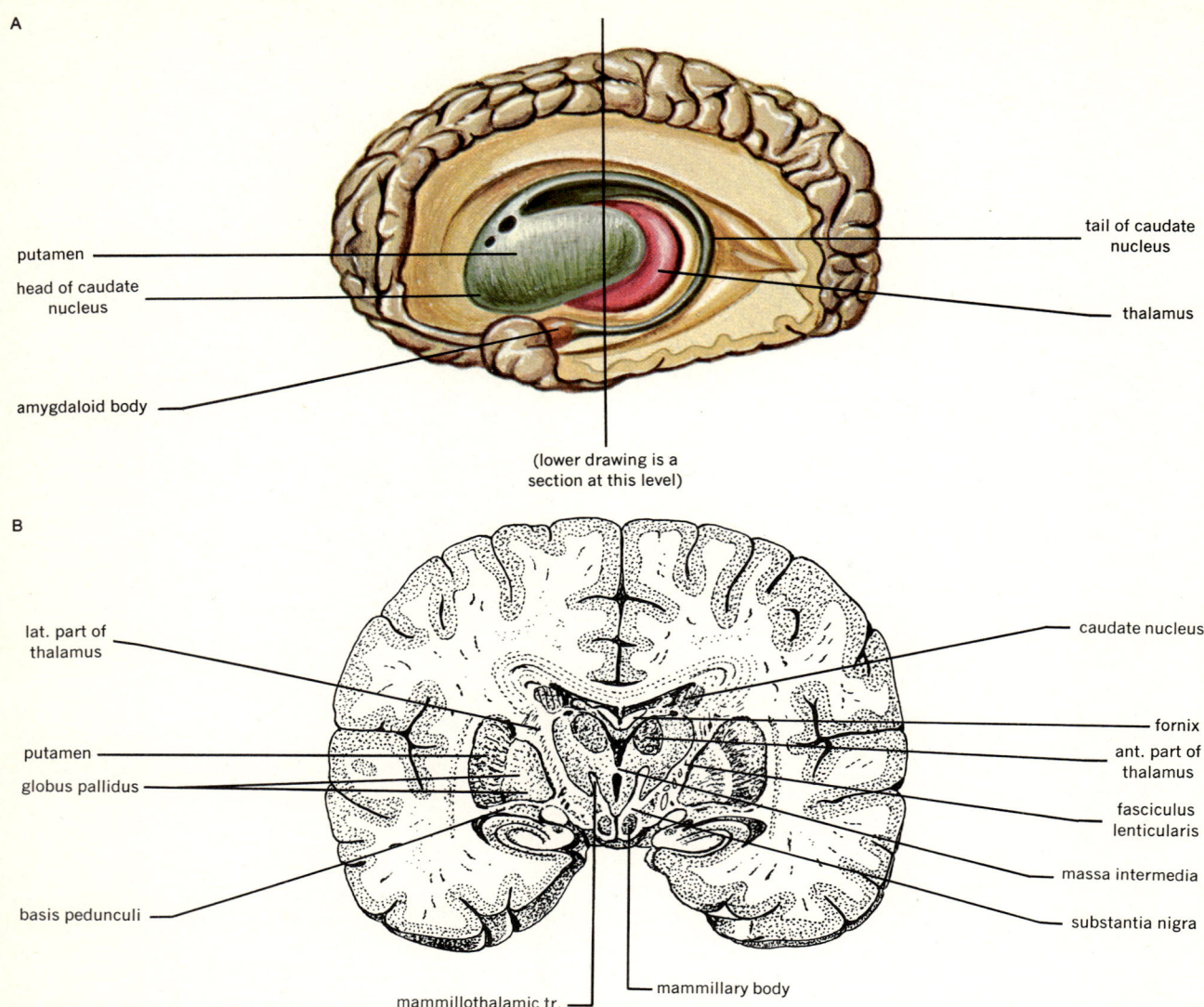

A

putamen

head of caudate
nucleus

amygdaloid body

tail of caudate
nucleus

thalamus

(lower drawing is a
section at this level)

B

lat. part of
thalamus

putamen

globus pallidus

basis pedunculi

caudate nucleus

fornix

ant. part of
thalamus

fasciculus
lenticularis

massa intermedia

substantia nigra

mammillothalamic tr.

mammillary body

FIGURE 13-7   The basal ganglia. A projection of several major ganglia on the cerebral hemisphere is shown above; below is a frontal section of the cerebrum.

gagging response. The amygdala also seems to play a role in emotional responses: its stimulation can produce reactions of fear or rage. When the amygdaloid nuclei in both hemispheres of the brain are destroyed, the effects are striking: drowsiness, indifference to surroundings, blindness (even though the eyes and the vision center of the cortex are unimpaired), and loss of appetite. It has been suggested that the amygdala helps to keep an individual awake and aware of the surroundings, reinforcing the activity of the cortex; and indeed, the neuronal firing of the amygdala increases sharply when something new or unexpected is encountered.

THE DIENCEPHALON

As we leave the cerebral hemispheres, the realm of the "thinking brain," and move inward to the structures that lie within, we are in a sense travelling backward in time. The evolution of the vertebrates has

been characterized by a progressive development of the forebrain, and the great burgeoning of the cerebrum has been essentially a mammalian invention. In more primitive vertebrates—including present-day reptiles—information about the world is perceived chiefly in the more primitive part of the forebrain, the **diencephalon.** This "tweenbrain" is a collection of structures nestled between the underside of the cerebral hemispheres and the mesencephalon (the midbrain). The structures of the diencephalon include the **thalamus,** the **hypothalamus,** the **epithalamus** or **pineal gland,** the **subthalamus,** and the **metathalamus** or **geniculate bodies** (Figure 13-8). The most important of these structures are the thalamus and hypothalamus.

The Thalamus

The thalamus has been compared to a complex telephone integrating and switching center. This pair of egg-shaped masses of gray matter is the central relay

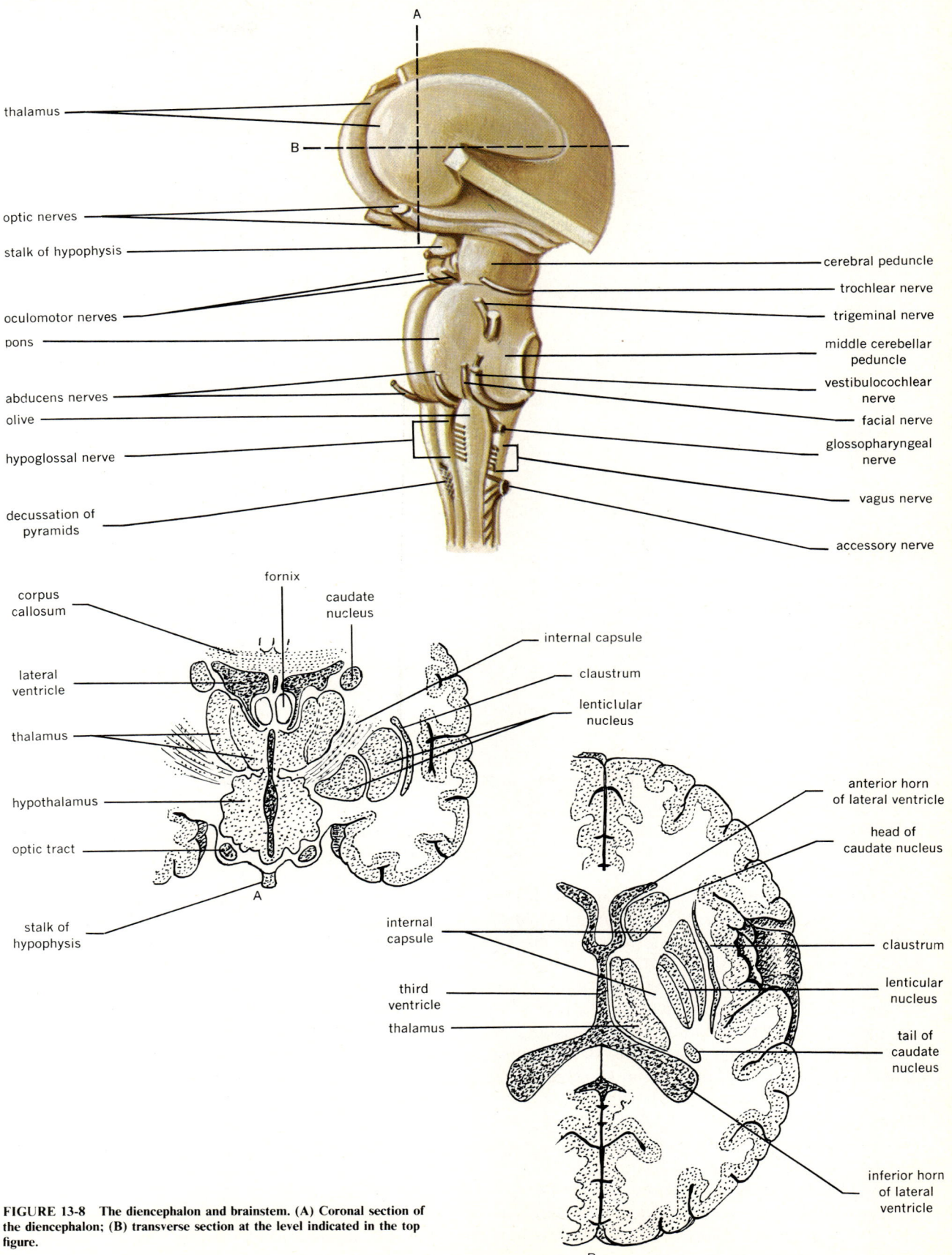

thalamus

optic nerves

stalk of hypophysis

oculomotor nerves

pons

abducens nerves

olive

hypoglossal nerve

decussation of
pyramids

cerebral peduncle

trochlear nerve

trigeminal nerve

middle cerebellar
peduncle

vestibulocochlear
nerve

facial nerve

glossopharyngeal
nerve

vagus nerve

accessory nerve

corpus
callosum

lateral
ventricle

thalamus

hypothalamus

optic tract

stalk of
hypophysis

fornix

caudate
nucleus

internal capsule

claustrum

lenticlular
nucleus

A

internal
capsule

third
ventricle

thalamus

anterior horn
of lateral ventricle

head of
caudate nucleus

claustrum

lenticular
nucleus

tail of
caudate
nucleus

inferior horn
of lateral
ventricle

B

**FIGURE 13-8   The diencephalon and brainstem. (A) Coronal section of
the diencephalon; (B) transverse section at the level indicated in the top
figure.**

station of the brain, involved in a complex network of interconnections between the cerebral cortex and the spinal cord. Messages from all the sense receptors except those of smell are filtered through the thalamus, where the sensory input is analyzed before being relayed to the appropriate areas of the cortex. The nerve connections run both ways: impulses from the motor cortex are relayed through the thalamus to the spinal cord. Many reflexes, particularly visual and auditory reflexes, are mediated by the thalamus and the geniculate bodies.

In lower vertebrates, the thalamus is the center that provides for awareness of the surroundings. In man this part of the brain retains this function to some degree, but it provides only a crude sort of awareness. Finer details are filled in by the cerebral cortex. Electrical stimulation of the thalamus provokes exaggerated sensations of pleasure or pain. (Even if the cerebral cortex is destroyed, perception of pain is still possible through the thalamus.)

The Pineal Gland

In the developing embryo, the pineal gland starts out as a third eye, which degenerates before it is completely formed. The remains of this structure, buried deep in the brain, form a small oval mass of nerve cells in the dorsomedial portion of the thalamus. The pineal gland has long been a storm center of scientific controversy. Various hormonal functions have been claimed and disputed; the problem is compounded because this structure often becomes completely calcified in adults, without any noticeable effect. It produces a hormone, melatonin, which causes the pigment granules in the skin of amphibians to clump together, lightening the overall skin color. But the hormone does not have this effect in mammals, and it is speculated that in humans it may act as a neurotransmitter. (The pineal gland also contains large quantities of the neurotransmitter serotonin.)

It has been established that the pineal gland is sensitive to changes in light, receiving its information about light from the eyes. This structure is now believed to be the body's biological clock, which synchronizes the body rhythms with the cycles of day and night. It also seems to be involved in sexual cycles, apparently aiding the pituitary in controlling the functions of the gonads. These roles of the pineal gland are discussed in more detail in Chapter 32.

The Hypothalamus

The hypothalamus is a structure of the diencephalon whose importance seems quite out of proportion to its size. Although the hypothalamus constitutes only about 1/300 of the total mass of the brain, it is a vital link in the physical and emotional life of the body.

The hypothalamus is a mass of gray matter below each thalamus, forming the floor and part of the wall of the third ventricle of the brain. (Its name literally means "under the thalamus.") Sensory nerve fibers bring messages to the hypothalamus from the cerebral cortex, the thalamus, and the brainstem, while motor fibers link the hypothalamus to the thalamus, brainstem, and spinal cord. The hypothalamus acts as a central monitoring and control station in an incredible variety of the body's activities. A wealth of information on its functions has been obtained by observing the effects of two types of experimental intervention: selectively stimulating various portions of the hypothalamus with implanted electrodes, both in animals and in human volunteers, and selectively destroying specific portions of the hypothalamus in animal experiments. A number of specialized control centers have been found.

Autonomic Nervous Control   The activities of both the parasympathetic and the sympathetic nervous systems, which are discussed in Chapter 15, are coordinated and controlled in the hypothalamus. In general, the anterior and medial portions of the hypothalamus are associated with the parasympathetic system, while the sympathetic system is regulated by the posterior and lateral portions.

Cardiovascular Regulation   The automatic regulation of the heart rate and blood pressure is an important facet of autonomic nervous activity. The hypothalamus has been found to be intimately associated in these processes. Stimulation of the posterior hypothalamus produces a rise in the blood pressure and speedup of the heart rate. Stimulation of the preoptic area has the opposite effect. The hypothalamus produces its effects on the heart and blood vessels indirectly, by impulses relayed to the cardiovascular centers of the medulla.

Body Temperature Regulation   Some of the body's complex and interrelated mechanisms for getting rid of excess heat or producing and conserving extra heat when needed were discussed in Chapter 7. A very fine coordination of all these mechanisms is needed to keep the body temperature at an even 37° C (98.6° F) despite the fiery heat of a blast furnace, the icy gusts of an Arctic winter, and other extremes of the external environment. This coordination occurs in the temperature regulation center in the anterior hypothalamus. Afferent impulses from the thermoreceptors in the skin and monitoring stations in the hypothalamus itself that assess the temperature of the blood perfusing it both contribute a continual flow of information on the body's current temperature state. If there is excess heat, impulses from the hypothalamus through the autonomic system initiate a dilation of the blood vessels in the skin (increasing the heat loss by radiation from the body surface) and sweating. If the body is colder than it should be, hypothalamic impulses trigger responses of shivering (producing heat by muscle action) and constriction of the cutaneous blood vessels, minimizing radiation heat loss. There is some evidence that the action of the body's "thermostat" in the hypothalamus is dependent on the balance of sodium and calcium ions in the hypothalamus: if the sodium ion concentration is increased, the body temperature rises, while an increase in the calcium ion concentration produces a drop in the body temperature. During fever produced by a bacterial infection, lowered calcium levels and elevated sodium levels have been observed. This relationship can also be used to advantage by the physician: in certain types of surgery it is desirable to lower the body temperature to minimize tissue damage; this can be accomplished by cooling the body with cold water or ice, or alternatively by perfusing the brain with a solution high in calcium ions.

Regulation of Food Intake and Gastrointestinal Activity

The problem of obesity is a major concern in the United States today. Each year new diet fads are announced and eagerly embraced by the hopeful fat. Often the "crash diets" seem to work, and an overweight person may lose dozens of unwanted pounds—but all too often, within months the pounds have been gained back and the unfortunate person is looking for another way to lose weight. Studies of the eating habits of people of normal weight and those with a tendency toward overweight have yielded an interesting finding: in experiments in which the volunteers were supplied with as much as they wanted to eat of bland, unappetizing foods, the normal people tended to eat just about enough to maintain their weight; the "fatties," on the other hand, ate little of the unappetizing fare. But when attractive foods were offered, while the normal people again ate just about the right amount, the overweight volunteers gorged themselves, stuffing in another chocolate eclair or bag of potato chips even when they were not particularly hungry. For the overweight, the associations of the food seemed to provide the major motivation to eat or not to eat, while the normal people were guided by sensations of hunger or satiation.

The control centers that work in normal people to regulate food intake are located in the hypothalamus. Experiments on animals have revealed that there are two separate centers: a **hunger center** in the lateral hypothalamus and a **satiety center** in the medial region. When the hunger center in an animal's hypo-

thalamus is stimulated, the animal eats and eats, until it nearly bursts. Stimulation of the satiety center causes an animal to ignore food, even if it has been starved beforehand. Destruction of the satiety center results in a voracious appetite, which cannot be satisfied, for there is nothing to moderate the activity of the hunger center. In the normally functioning hypothalamus, the hunger center is stimulated by a fall of the level of glucose in the circulating blood. The levels of blood amino acids and fatty acids also play a role, although less pronounced. After a meal, the satiety center comes into play. Recent reports indicate that a hormone, arenterin, is secreted by the intestines and carried to the hypothalamus to signal satiety. (Rats with a gastric fistula, preventing the stomach contents from flowing into the intestines, continued to eat with no signs of satiation.)

The dorsomedial nucleus of the hypothalamus stimulates peristalsis (the rhythmic contractions of the digestive tract) and increased secretion of the gastric and intestinal glands. If this control center is too active, a hypersecretion of acid gastric juice can lead to ulceration of the stomach.

Regulation of Water Balance

Specialized "osmoreceptors" in the hypothalamus continuously monitor the osmotic pressure of the blood. If there is an increase in osmotic pressure due to a water lack, two separate mechanisms go into effect. A hormone, **ADH (antidiuretic hormone),** is produced, travels along the nerve fiber that links the hypothalamus with the posterior pituitary gland, and is secreted from the latter into the bloodstream. The effect of this hormone is to cause the cells in the kidney tubules to conserve water, and a more concentrated urine is excreted. Meanwhile, a **thirst center** situated near the satiety center produces feelings of thirst, which stimulate a search for water and the action of drinking.

Sleeping and Wakefulness

The upper portions of the reticular activating system, which are discussed later in the chapter, pass through the hypothalamus. Stimulation of certain regions of the hypothalamus provokes wakefulness, alertness, and excitement. But stimulation of other regions of the hypothalamus produces sleepiness or even actual sleep. Thus it seems that the hypothalamus houses both sleep and wakefulness areas.

Sexual Activity

Stimulation of a sex site in the dorsal part of the hypothalamus produces sexual stimulation, to the point of orgasm. If an electrode implanted in the sex site of a rat's hypothalamus is connected to a lever mechanism, so that the rat can stimulate itself by pressing the lever, it will continue to do so until it collapses from exhaustion.

Emotions   A cat in a cage arches its back and hisses as electrical impulses from an implanted electrode stimulate one region of its hypothalamus. The stimulation is switched to another electrode, and the cat suddenly cringes in apparent terror as a small mouse scurries across the floor of the cage. Still another stimulation, and the cat lounges in the cage, purring ecstatically. A number of centers associated with emotional responses have been found in the hypothalamus, both in animals and in humans. Stimulation of an **anger center** provokes uncontrolled rage, in which the pupils dilate, the heart pounds rapidly, the blood pressure rises, the hair stands on end, and salivation increases. Stimulation of the **fear center** produces reactions of fear, even if there is no objective basis for alarm. One region of the hypothalamus seems to be a **pain center;** another produces sensations of pure pleasure. Rats taught to press a lever to stimulate their own **pleasure center** through an implanted electrode do so again and again until they collapse. In their singleminded pursuit of self-stimulation, these rats ignore food, water, and members of the opposite sex. A human volunteer with an experimental electrode implanted in the pleasure center of his hypothalamus pressed a button to stimulate this center three thousand times in ninety minutes before the circuit was disconnected by observing physicians. Experiments such as these have evoked lively speculations. A future world in which people seek stimulation and enjoyment by pressing buttons to stimulate implanted electrodes instead of with drinks or drugs has been postulated. Some find the potentials for abuse alarming, imagining a world populated by robotized humans with electrodes implanted in their pleasure and pain centers, enslaved by unscrupulous dictators who send out radio signals to "reward" or "punish" them and thus control their actions.

Control of Endocrine Functions   The pituitary gland is often regarded as the "master gland" of the endocrine system, since its secretions control and regulate the activity of the other endocrine glands. But it has been discovered that the pituitary in turn is controlled to a large degree by the hypothalamus. The two structures are closely situated and intimately associated, connected by a rich vascular plexus. **Releasing factors** secreted by the hypothalamus are carried by its blood portal system to the adenohypophysis (the anterior lobe of the pituitary) and trigger its secretion of such hormones as adrenocorticotropic hormone (ACTH), follicle-stimulating (FSH), luteinizing (LH), thyrotropic (TSH), and lactogenic (LTH) hormones. (This control of the anterior pituitary secretions is in addition to the functioning of the hypothalamus as an endocrine gland in its own right: the

hypothalamus secretes the hormones ADH, which has already been mentioned, and oxytocin; these hormones travel down the hypothalamo-hypophyseal nerve stalk to the posterior pituitary or neurohypophysis, which stores them and releases them into the bloodstream.)

With its key role in the regulation of the visceral functions of the body, its involvement in emotional responses, and its intimate association with the endocrine system, it is not surprising that the hypothalamus has been implicated as a major factor in **psychosomatic illness,** a dysfunction of the somatic organs of the body resulting from an abnormal functioning of the central nervous system. Peptic ulcers, insomnia, palpitations of the heart, esophageal spasms, constipation or diarrhea—these and other physical symptoms can result from emotional rather than physical causes.

THE LIMBIC SYSTEM

Some people pride themselves on their "objectivity" and make an effort to guide their actions by purely rational considerations. But no human being is truly objective; the thoughts and actions of all of us are colored to one degree or another by emotions. Love and hate, envy, revenge, selfishness, and altruism—all these play a part in our actions and the way we view the world.

The portions of the brain mainly concerned with emotions lie in an integrated network called the **limbic system,** which includes the thalamus, the hypothalamus, the septal area, the hippocampus, the amygdala, parts of the reticular formation in the brainstem, and the limbic region of the cerebral cortex (Figure 13-9). It is the limbic system that colors our thoughts with emotions. Its function might be thought of as the maintenance of a sort of emotional homeostasis—it recognizes disturbances of equilibrium—resulting from hunger or a sex drive, a danger or threat, or a less tangible worry or disappointment. The emotional "tag" that the limbic system places on such upsets helps the higher brain to recognize the problems and take steps to restore equilibrium.

The human limbic system is largely a development of the ancient structures of the **rhinencephalon,** or "smell brain." A vestige of this older function remains in that odors typically elicit a distinct emotional reaction.

In animals, the limbic system provides a set of instincts, automatic reactions to the information gathered by their senses. In humans, reasoning and learning, functions of the higher brain, are given a greater weight. Sometimes the emotional promptings of the limbic system may clash with rational decisions, made in the higher brain. Often we can deny or bury

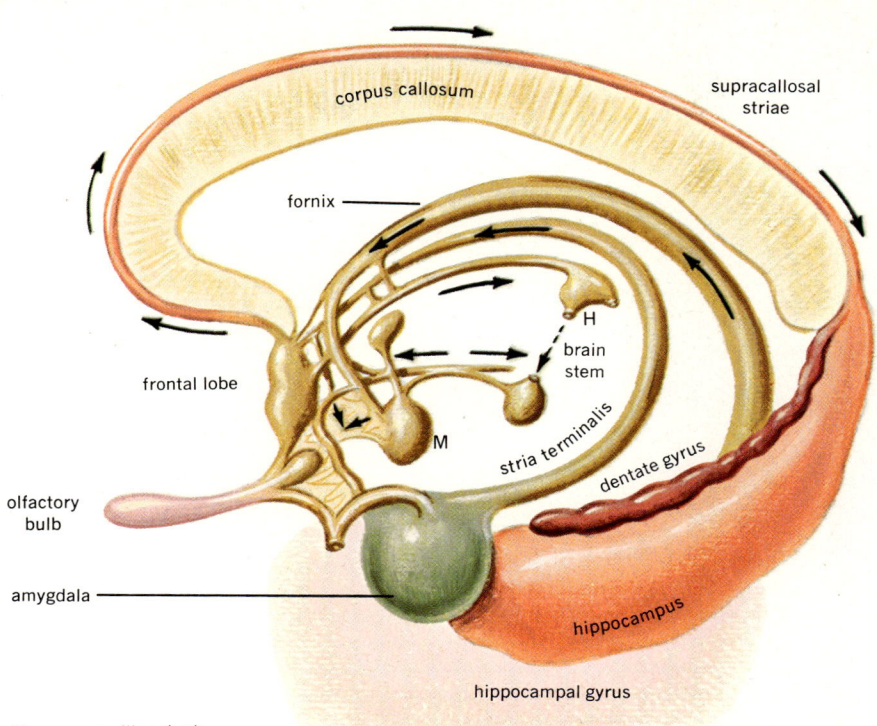

FIGURE 13-9 The limbic system. Arrows indicate the flow of impulses.

M — mammillary body
H — habenula

our feelings. For example, an "instinctive" fear of high places or of large animals can gradually be overcome. But sometimes the struggle between the limbic system and the higher brain can cause conflicts that are finally expressed in psychosomatic ailments, such as ulcers, skin rashes, and chronic fatigue.

The Hippocampus

People who have had their hippocampus destroyed by disease live in a world of the immediate present. They cannot remember anything that has happened for more than a few minutes. They can read the same newspaper article over and over again, displaying new interest in it each time. Yet they can recall quite clearly everything that happened before the brain lesion developed.

The hippocampus is a part of the cerebral cortex, a band on each side shaped roughly like a bean pod (or, viewed more fancifully, like a seahorse, from which its name was derived). It is closely interconnected with the temporal cortex and with the amygdala (see Figure 13-11), as well as with the hypothalamus and other structures of the limbic system. Indeed, it is one of the major courses of input for the hypothalamus.

An "arousal" effect of the hippocampus has been observed experimentally; it is elicited by a variety of sensory stimuli—olfactory, auditory, or somesthetic. This brain structure is extremely excitable by electrical stimuli: a weak electrical stimulus can produce local epileptic seizures in the hippocampus, accompanied by extraordinarily vivid visual, auditory, olfactory, or tactile hallucinations. Various involuntary muscular movements and emotional reactions such as rage have also been observed after stimulation of the hippocampus. But its main function seems to be in the long-term fixation of memories. It has been suggested that the hippocampus helps to evaluate new events in terms of past experiences. It may give the information from the sense organs an emotional coloring and then transmit this information to the pleasure or pain centers, thus incorporating an element of reward or punishment. In this way the hippocampus can help control which bits of information a person will learn.

THE MIDBRAIN

It was long believed that the adjustment of the opening of the pupils was a simple reflex, dependent on the amount of light striking the eyes. But then a researcher happened to notice that he did not need as much light as usual to read by if he was reading a particularly interesting book. This chance observation launched a series of experiments, in which volunteers were shown varied series of photographs. A correlation was consistently observed between the degree of interest of the volunteers in what was being viewed and the opening of the pupils. Men exhibited a widening of the pupils when they looked at an attractive

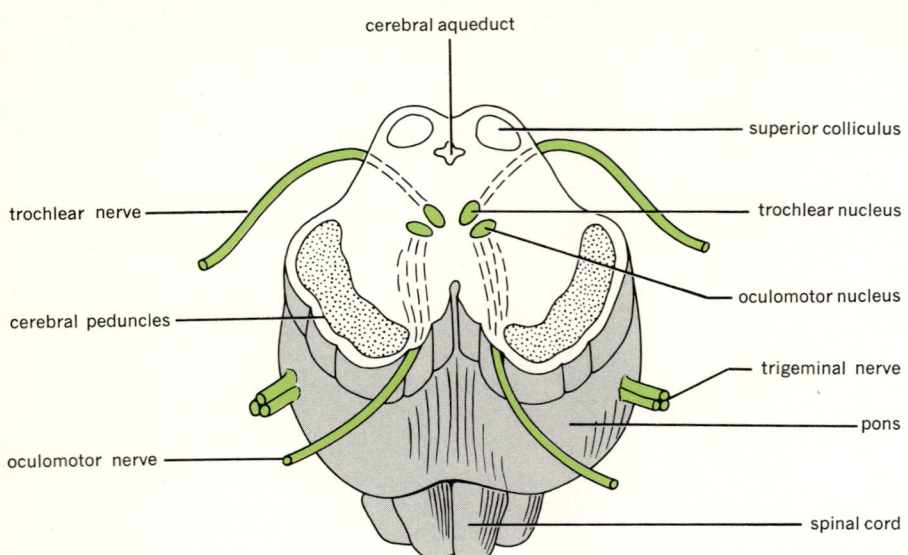

cerebral aqueduct

superior colliculus

trochlear nerve

trochlear nucleus

oculomotor nucleus

cerebral peduncles

trigeminal nerve

pons

oculomotor nerve

spinal cord

FIGURE 13-10   Structures of the midbrain in cross section.

pin-up; women's pupils widened most when they were looking at a picture of a baby. In all the subjects, a photo of something gruesome, such as mangled bodies in an automobile crash, provoked an initial widening, then a quick narrowing of the pupils.

The pupillary reflexes are controlled by the **superior colliculi,** two rounded prominences at the top of the brainstem, in the region called the **mesencephalon** or **midbrain.** The major structures of the midbrain (Figure 13-10) include the superior colliculi and the **inferior colliculi** (two smaller rounded prominences), which together are referred to as the **corpora quadrigemina** ("Quadruplet bodies"), along with the **cerebral peduncles** (two large, ropelike bundles of fibers), the **cerebral aqueduct** or **aqueduct of Sylvius** (a narrow channel connecting the third ventricle of the diencephalon and the fourth ventricle of the medulla and pons), and a distinctive oval, pigmented structure called the **red nucleus.**

In fish and reptiles, the midbrain is highly developed, containing the systems processing incoming information from the organs of sight and hearing. In humans, these functions have largely been taken over by the cerebral cortex; only small vestiges of the optic lobes and sound analyzing system of lower vertebrates remain as the corpora quadrigemina. The colliculi in humans still retain their ancestral links—the superior colliculi with the eyes and the inferior colliculi with the ears—but they function only as a sort of early warning system. The superior colliculi control optic reflexes, such as blinking, the opening of the pupil, and the focus of the lens of the eye.

The inferior colliculi are relay stations in the auditory pathway; they adjust the ear to the amount of sound coming in and are concerned in the startle reflex in response to a sudden loud noise.

The cerebral peduncles, on the ventral surface of the midbrain, are mainly projection fibers, connecting the cerebral cortex with other levels of the central nervous system. Their ventral portion contains the **substantia nigra** ("black substance"), the large cells of which store a catecholamine, probably dopamine.

The red nucleus, which contains deposits of a reddish pigment and appears pinkish yellow in fresh specimens, is a part of the reticular formation of the brainstem and gives rise to the rubrospinal tract of the extrapyramidal system. It is a key link in the postural reflexes, which help to keep the body upright.

THE HINDBRAIN

Continuing our backward journey through space and time, we reach the hindbrain, the most primitive part of the human brain, much of which has been transmitted to us little changed from our earliest vertebrate ancestors. The brainstem is a smooth continuation of the spinal cord; its principal structures are the **pons** and the **medulla oblongata,** as well as the **reticular formation** that runs through the entire brainstem from the hindbrain up into the midbrain and diencephalon. The **cerebellum** is like an appendage at the back of the brainstem, nestled under the overhang of the cerebrum.

The Cerebellum

A tightrope walker displays a finely developed coordination and balance. A drunk, lurching and staggering, shows the results of alcohol's depressant effect on the central nervous system. The cerebral cortex plays a key role in the control of muscular contractions that move body parts. But the part of the brain that coordinates body movements and makes sure that each muscle contracts not too much or too little but just

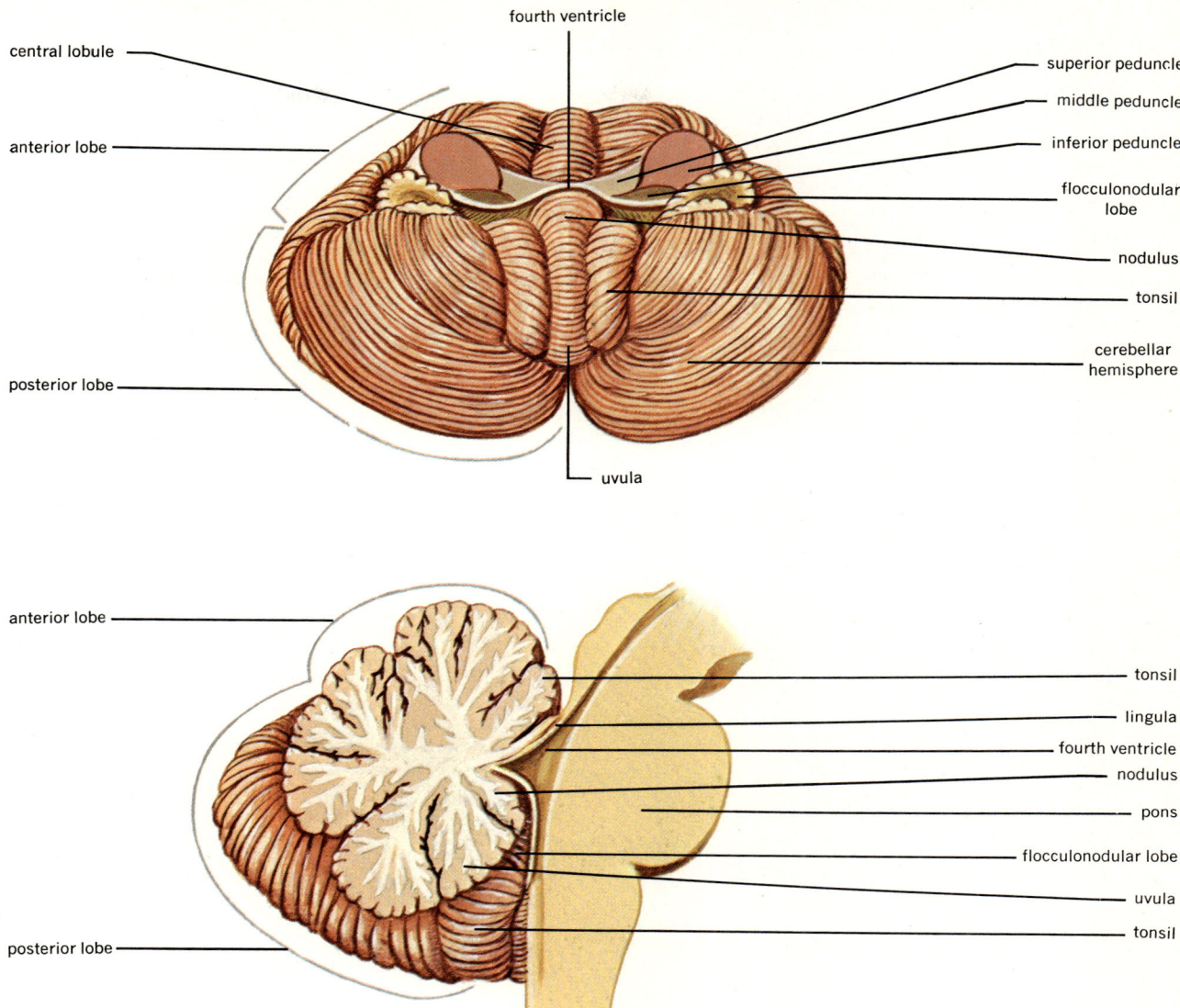

central lobule

fourth ventricle

anterior lobe

superior peduncle

middle peduncle

inferior peduncle

flocculonodular lobe

nodulus

tonsil

cerebellar hemisphere

posterior lobe

uvula

anterior lobe

tonsil

lingula

fourth ventricle

nodulus

pons

flocculonodular lobe

uvula

tonsil

posterior lobe

FIGURE 13-11 The cerebellum. The anterior aspect shown at the top is normally hidden behind the brainstem. A sagittal section is shown below.

enough to carry out the cerebrum's intentions is the cerebellum.

The ending *-ellum* is a diminutive ending, so the cerebellum is literally a "little brain." And indeed, this portion of the hindbrain looks very much like a smaller version of the cerebrum (Figure 13-11). Like the cerebrum, it has a convoluted surface, although the gyri and sulci of the cerebellum are rather narrow and somewhat straighter than those of the cerebrum. Like the cerebrum, the cerebellum is a mixture of gray and white matter, with the gray matter concentrated in the outer layer (the cerebellar cortex, which is thinner than the cerebral cortex) and internally in aggregations of cell bodies, the cerebellar nuclei.

Again like the cerebrum, the cerebellum is divided into two hemispheres, which are connected by a narrow wormlike lobe, the **vermis.**

The cerebellum is found at the back of the cranial cavity, just under the occipital lobes of the cerebrum. It is connected with various parts of the central nervous system by bundles of nerve fibers: the **superior, middle,** and **inferior cerebellar peduncles** (Figure 13-12). The superior peduncle transmits afferent impulses from the spinal cord to the cerebellar cortex and efferent impulses from cerebellar nuclei to the spinal cord by way of the red nucleus and reticular formation and to the cerebral cortex by way of the red nucleus and thalamus. The middle peduncle,

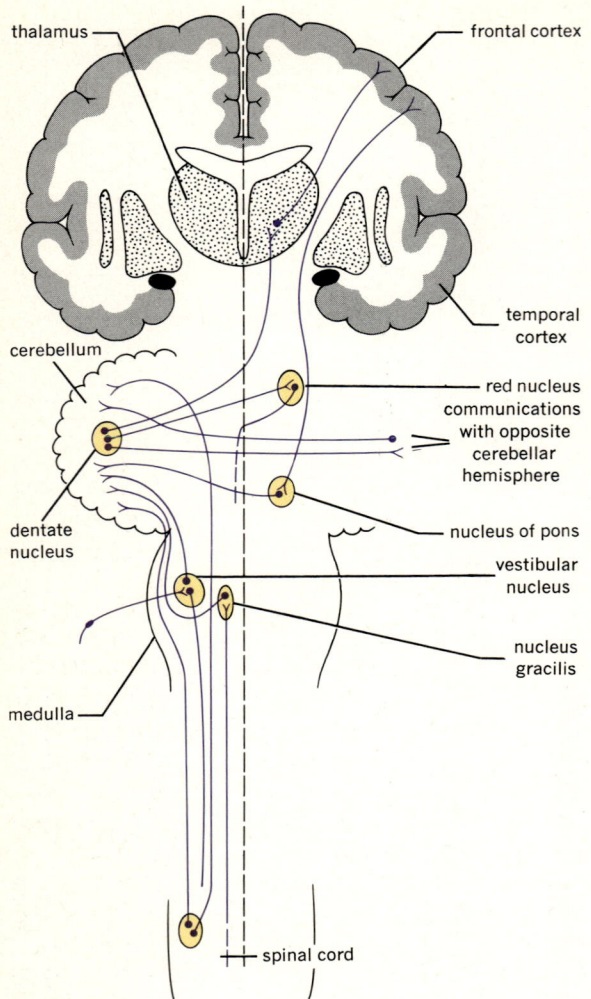

thalamus

frontal cortex

temporal cortex

cerebellum

red nucleus communicates with opposite cerebellar hemisphere

dentate nucleus

nucleus of pons

vestibular nucleus

nucleus gracilis

medulla

spinal cord

FIGURE 13-12 Afferent and efferent connections of the cerebellum with the spinal cord and cerebrum.

which is the largest of the three, transmits impulses from the cerebral cortex to the cerebellar cortex by way of the pons. The inferior peduncle transmits afferent impulses from the spinal cord, the medulla, and some of the cranial nerves to the cerebellar cortex, as well as efferent impulses from the cerebellar nuclei to the vestibular nuclei in the medulla. Thus, the cerebellum is well supplied with information from a variety of key areas in the central nervous system, as well as means of transmitting its own messages to the body's effectors.

Whenever the motor cortex directs the contraction of muscles somewhere in the body, by means of impulses transmitted by the corticospinal tract, a duplicate set of instructions is simultaneously relayed through the pons to the cerebellum. As soon as the muscles contract, the muscle spindles, joint receptors, and other peripheral receptors transmit a steady flow of information to the same area of the cerebellum, informing it exactly where each body part is at each

moment, whether it is moving, and, if so, in what direction and how fast. Like the control system of an automatic pilot, the cerebellum continually compares the higher brain's "intention" with the body's actual performance, and sends its own messages immediately to initiate appropriate corrective measures if necessary. For example, if the cerebrum has directed the arm to move to a certain point, but the muscle has contracted too forcefully and the arm has begun to move too rapidly and seems destined to overshoot, the cerebellum initiates "braking impulses," which inhibit the agonist muscle, excite its antagonist, and stop the arm precisely where the cerebrum intended. Such automatic corrections occur far more rapidly than would be possible by conscious analysis and voluntary actions initiated by the cerebrum.

If the cerebellum is destroyed by injury or disease, the person's movements become jerky and uncoordinated. Characteristically, the victim tends to "overshoot," having lost the ability to predict how far a particular movement will go and to initiate "midcourse corrections." Temporarily "losing track" of a body part when it is moving rapidly is also typical. A decrease in muscle tone that results from injury to the cerebellum is usually compensated for after a few months by an increased activity of the motor cortex. Damage to the cerebellum also results in a loss of equilibrium, similar to the effect of destruction of the semicircular canals in the ears.

The Pons
Pons means "bridge," and it is a fitting name for this brain structure. It lies in the brainstem, in the rounded bulging portion between the midbrain and the medulla, in front of the cerebellum. It is a bridge-like structure, consisting mainly of white matter and serving as a relay station linking the medulla with the higher cortical centers. Scattered groups of cell bodies near the ventral surface of the pons are part of the reticular formation. A **pneumotaxic center** in the pons provides a means of inhibiting the respiratory center in the medulla to permit exhaling.

The Medulla Oblongata
A karate chop on the back of the neck can result in an instant choking sensation, unconsciousness, and even death. The vulnerable area is the medulla oblongata, the portion of the brainstem just above the end of the spinal cord. It presents a rather exacting target for the karate expert, for it is only about an inch long. It merges continuously with the spinal cord below and the pons above. Externally it rather resembles the spinal cord, although it is somewhat enlarged. Within the medulla, the central canal of the spinal cord greatly expands to form the fourth ventricle (Figure 13-13). Pyramid-shaped nerve tracts, the

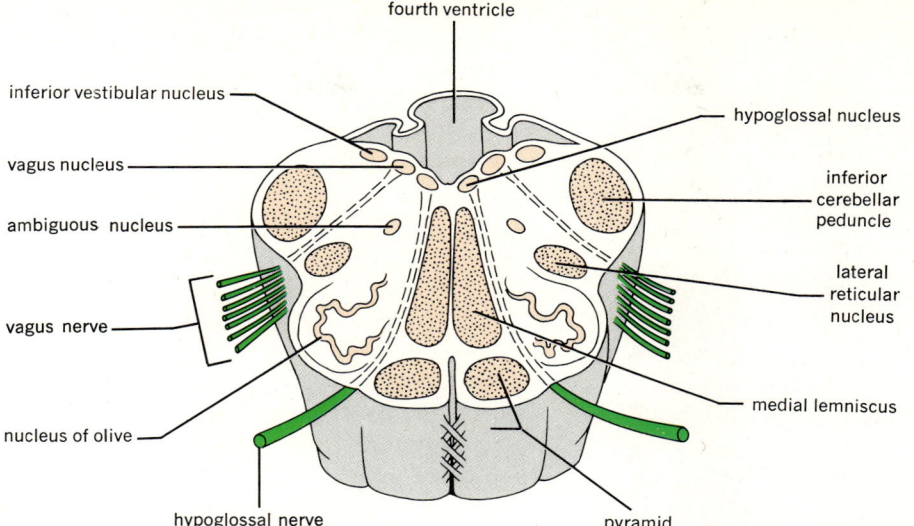

FIGURE 13-13 Cross section of the medulla oblongata.

Figure labels: fourth ventricle; inferior vestibular nucleus; vagus nucleus; ambiguous nucleus; vagus nerve; nucleus of olive; hypoglossal nerve; pyramid; hypoglossal nucleus; inferior cerebellar peduncle; lateral reticular nucleus; medial lemniscus

pyramids, lie on the ventral surface of the medulla and cross at the lower end of the medulla.

Inside the medulla, nerve cells are grouped into nuclei. Some of them, such as the **nucleus ambiguus** and the **hypoglossal nucleus,** are centers from which the cranial nerves arise. Others, such as the **nucleus gracilis** and the **nucleus cuneatus,** are relay stations in sensory tracts to the brain. Still others are centers for the control of key body functions. The most important of these are the **cardiac, vasoconstrictor,** and **respiratory centers.**

You may recall that cardiac muscle is capable of self-initiated contractions. A turtle heart, cut out of the body and placed in a dish of Ringer solution, will continue to beat long after the turtle has died, and the human heart, too, may go on beating for some time after brain death has occurred. But in the living body, a number of nervous and endocrine influences work to regulate the rate of the heartbeat. An important link in this regulatory system is the **cardiac inhibitory center** in the medulla. It consists of two groups of nerve cells, the **vagus nuclei,** one in each half of the medulla adjacent to the fourth ventricle (see Figure 13-13). These nuclei give rise to the vagus nerves, which join with the cardiac branches from the thoracolumbar nerves to form the cardiac plexus and thence innervate the heart with **inhibitory fibers.** The impulses that constantly travel along these fibers from the medulla act to slow down the heartbeat rate. They act antagonistically to the impulses from the cardiac sympathetic nerves, which speed up the heartbeat rate and therefore are called **accelerator fibers.**

The vasoconstrictor center, another bilateral group of cells in the medulla, sends impulses via spinal neurons to the smooth muscle of the arteriole walls, causing them to contract, constrict the arterioles, and raise the arterial pressure. If the brainstem is cut just below

the medulla, the arterial pressure drops to about half the normal value. The cardiovascular control centers of the medulla can be controlled in turn by impulses from higher centers, particularly those of the hypothalamus.

The medullary respiratory center, a bilateral group of cells, has an inherent rhythmic activity and controls the rate and depth of respiration. A major factor affecting its activity is the carbon dioxide concentration in the blood, reported to the respiratory center by impulses from specialized chemoreceptors in the large arteries of the thorax and neck. If the carbon dioxide concentration rises too high, the rate and depth of respiration are increased, producing a greater intake of oxygen and removal of carbon dioxide with the exhaled air. The medullary respiratory center is also very sensitive to sensory input from the cranial and spinal nerves and to messages from higher regions of the brain. Physical exercise, for example, provokes an immediate increase in the rate and depth of respiration, far more than could be accounted for by the increase in carbon dioxide concentration. Emotions such as fear also tend to increase pulmonary ventilation (presumably as part of the body's automatic preparations for "flight or fight").

In addition to the respiratory and cardiovascular control centers, the medulla contains control centers for such reflex actions as hiccupping, coughing, vomiting, sneezing, and swallowing. Swallowing may be initiated voluntarily, but once it has reached a certain point it becomes involuntary, and the action cannot be stopped.

The Reticular Formation

Stop reading for a moment, and look at and listen to your surroundings. Perhaps you are in a busy lunchroom, with people continually getting up or sitting

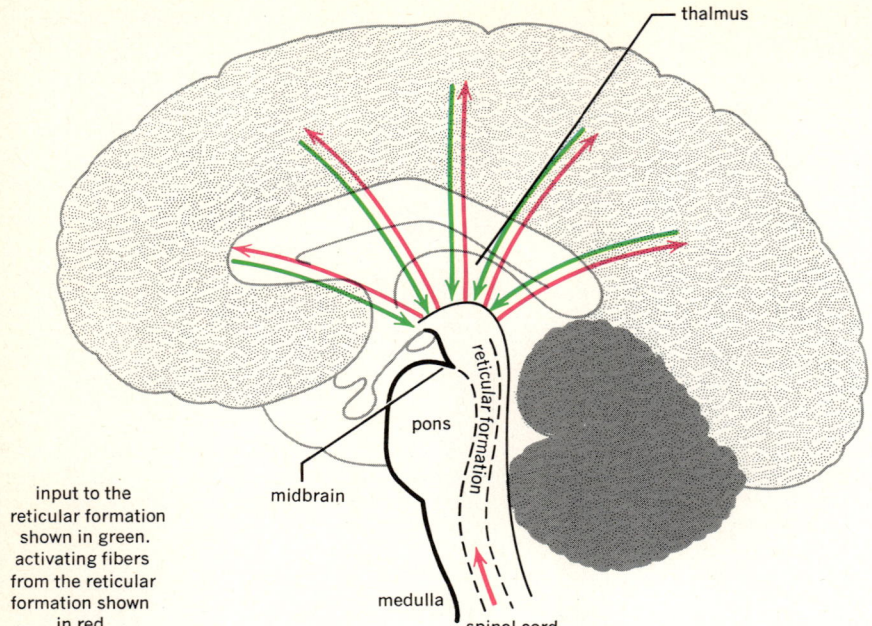

thalmus

reticular formation

pons

midbrain

medulla

spinal cord

input to the reticular formation shown in green. activating fibers from the reticular formation shown in red

FIGURE 13-14 Schematic view of the nerve pathways of the reticular activating system (RAS). Messages are continually exchanged between the reticular formation of the brainstem and the cerebral cortex.

down, eating, talking, and clanking dishes on trays. Or perhaps you are in a quiet room at home, with nothing to hear but the humming of an electric clock at your bedside and nothing to catch your eye but the flutter of leaves on a tree outside your window. Now that you are consciously thinking about your surroundings, everything around you—even the quiet humming of a clock—seems distracting. Yet while you were reading, you were barely conscious of your surroundings. You were able to "tune out" everything but the words you were concentrating on. Yet the sounds and sights about you were continuously impinging on your senses. Obviously some sort of "filter" in your brain must have been operating to select the information to be brought to your conscious attention.

The brain's efficient filter is the **reticular activating system (RAS).** It is housed in the reticular formation, an intricate cone-shaped network of nerve cells that runs through the medulla, pons, midbrain, and up into parts of the thalamus and hypothalamus (Figure 13-14). It receives afferent impulses from the spinal cord, as well as from the cerebellum and cerebral cortex, and it sends efferent fibers to all these areas. The neurons of the reticular formation tend to send out a continuous flow of impulses unless they are inhibited by signals from other parts of the brain. One effect of these impulses from the reticular formation is to maintain muscle tone. Another is to keep the higher brain in a state of alert wakefulness (hence the name reticular *activating* system). But more than this, the RAS acts as a sort of central clearing house for the flood of sense information that bombards the brain. It

filters out stimuli that are weak or form familiar patterns, letting only the particularly strong or novel signals pass up to the higher brain for conscious perception. This action of the RAS permits one to concentrate on a particular thought or activity, disregarding the background noises and other potential distractions.

In addition to the continuous flow of impulses emanating from the RAS, there is a continual flow of signals down from the cerebral cortex to the reticular formation. This continual dialogue works to keep the higher brain awake and alert. (Damage to the reticular formation by injury or disease can result in permanent unconsciousness.) At night, when you compose yourself for sleep and the influx of information into the RAS is at a minimum, this activating system shuts down the conscious mind and permits you to sleep. But an annoying noise or a distracting worry may keep the exchange of signals flowing between the RAS and cerebrum and keep you tossing and turning far into the night.

SLEEP

You will spend about one third of your life asleep. Yet from the time you close your eyes at night until you open them in the morning, you are not really consciously aware that anything is happening. You may recall a dream you had—but most likely it is only a confused wisp of a memory, and the rest of the night is a total blank.

It is only in the last few decades, with the aid of refined techniques of measuring the state of body functions, particularly electroencephalography (the study of the minute electric pulses from the cerebral cortex), that researchers have begun to explore the mysterious condition of sleep. Both animal experiments (cats have been particularly valuable subjects) and studies of human volunteers have yielded a wealth of information.

The subject of a modern sleep experiment lies down to sleep in a bed in a darkened laboratory room, festooned with a surrealistic array of taped-on electrodes, thermistors to measure body temperature, and various other sensors (Figure 13-15). It seems astonishing that a person can get to sleep at all under such conditions, but generally, after a day or two to become familiar with the laboratory surroundings, the subject is sleeping quite normally. (Indeed, studies of insomnia have been hampered by the fact that insomniac volunteers often sleep quite well in the sleep lab.) As the sleeper sleeps, a sleep researcher in an adjoining room fights his or her own fatigue while monitoring the electronic equipment that ultimately produces thousands of feet of EEG tracings in a single night's observations. Such experiments have yielded a general picture of normal sleep, as well as various significant patterns of abnormality that are already proving valuable in medical diagnosis.

During sleep there is reduced activity in a number of areas of the body. The muscles are relaxed and the breathing is slower and more regular. The heart rate and blood pressure are significantly lower, although during periods of dreaming both may increase dramatically. The body temperature during sleep is usually somewhat lower than normal (by about 1° F); the eyes are usually rolled up or unfocused, and the pupils are constricted.

Although there is considerable variation among individuals, a general pattern of sleep is usually observed when the subject is allowed to sleep for a normal span of time (Figure 13-16). After a gradual process of relaxation, an extremely deep sleep is usually attained between the first and second hour. This deep sleep seems to be essential to well-being; if a person is deprived of it for several days in a row (by

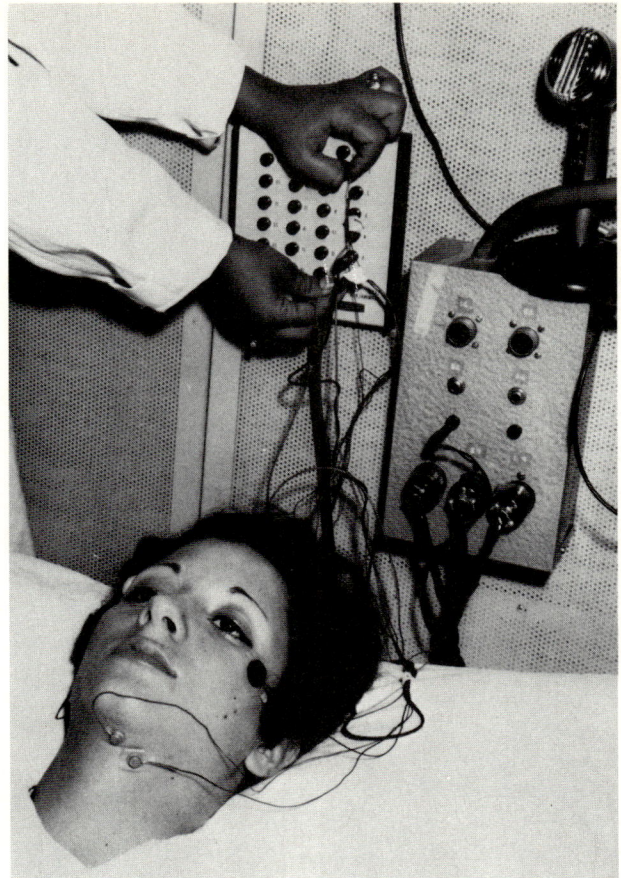

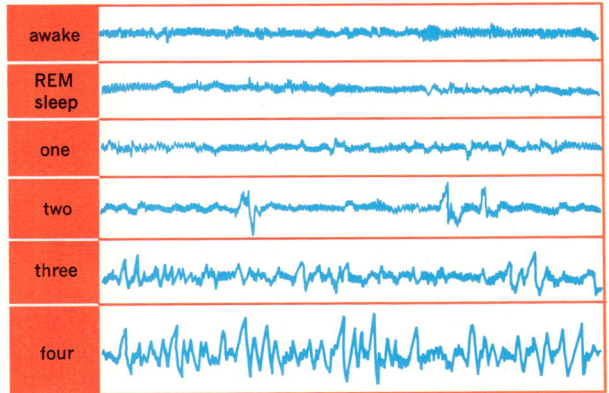

FIGURE 13-15 With electrodes pasted on, a sleep research volunteer settles down for a night's sleep. Typical EEG tracings during the waking state and various stages of sleep are shown below.

FIGURE 13-16 Graph of a night's sleep. The sleeper shuttles back and forth from one stage to another. As the night progresses, increasing time is spent in REM (dreaming) sleep and decreasing time in stage 4 (deep) sleep.

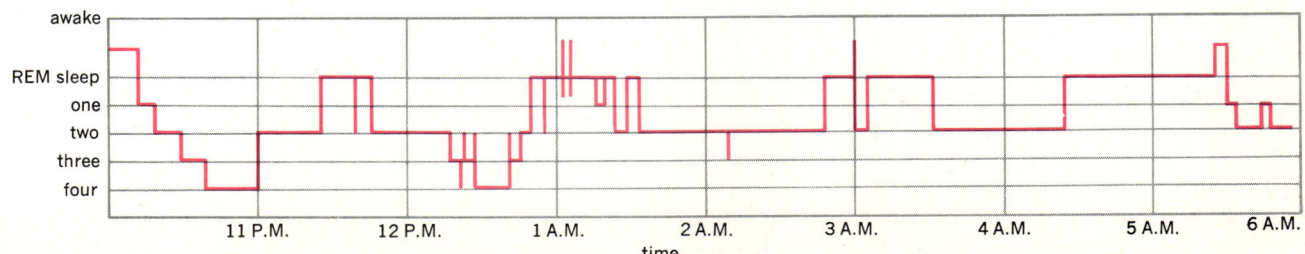

time

being disturbed slightly—not enough to be wakened entirely—each time he or she passes into the deep-sleep state) and then is allowed to sleep undisturbed on the following night, he or she will spend more time in deep sleep than usual, as though making up for lost time.

Usually after about an hour and a half, the sleeper is observed to pass into a markedly different state, the most distinctive feature of which is that, under the closed lids, the eyes can be seen to move rapidly back and forth as though watching a movie. In a way the person is, for if the sleeper is awakened during one of these REM episodes (the name comes from the "rapid eye movements"), he or she will invariably relate a dream that has been occurring. (Dream reports, by contrast, are very rare in the other stages of sleep.) After perhaps ten minutes, the sleeper again passes successively down into deeper stages of sleep, only to rise again into REM sleep in another hour and a half or so. He or she shuttles back and forth from one stage of sleep to another in cycles of roughly an hour and a half all through the night. But as the night wears on, the sleep becomes progressively shallower (virtually all of the deepest, stage 4 sleep occurs during the first half of the night) and the dreaming episodes become longer. Dreams can last from several minutes up to an hour. Contrary to popular belief, they occur in real time; that is, they unfold at the same rate at which events would normally occur in the real world.

REM sleep—that is, dreaming—has been found to be essential to mental health. If people are prevented from dreaming by awakening them at the first sign of rapid eye movements, they become fretful, irritable, and prone to hallucinations. This occurs even if the person receives a full eight hours of sleep each night. Sleep studies show that all people dream every night, even those who claim that they do not dream at all. Apparently people differ widely in their ability to recall their dreams. The vividness of recall also depends on the phase of sleep in which the person awakens and the suddenness of awakening. (Dreams are recalled most vividly when a person is awakened very rapidly right in the middle of an REM episode.) It has been suggested that dreaming may provide an opportunity for a release of psychic energy, and/or that it is a mechanism for consolidation of learning—that is, during dreaming the brain sorts out the various impressions of the day and selects and files away the ones that are important enough to remember.

The mechanisms of sleep—how people fall asleep, and why they do so periodically, even if they may wish to stay awake—are still a giant puzzle, the pieces of which are only beginning to be fitted together. It is known that the reticular activating system plays a key role in maintaining wakefulness. (You yourself have undoubtedly noticed that it is easier to stay up past your normal bedtime if you have something interesting to do—that is, plenty of external stimuli to keep the "dialogue" between the RAS and the cerebral cortex flowing.) The neurotransmitter **norepinephrine (noradrenaline)** also seems to act as a natural "pep drug," helping to keep the brain stimulated. But what causes the RAS to shut down for the night? It has been suggested that a "sleep hormone" is produced and accumulates during the waking hours, or that accumulating metabolic waste products attack the central nervous system and bring on a state of sleep. And indeed, it is during sleep that the various organs and systems of the body have a chance to rest and rejuvenate themselves, preparing for the wear and tear of another waking day. A sleep center is thought by some to lie in the hypothalamus, near the parasympathetic center. The **raphe system,** lying along the axis of the brainstem, behind the RAS, has been found to be essential for normal sleep: if it is destroyed, a person cannot sleep at all, no matter how tired he or she may become. The neurotransmitter **serotonin** is found to be prominent in the sleeping brain. A structure on the floor of the fourth ventricle, the **locus ceruleus,** seems to operate during dreaming, suppressing muscle tone and keeping the body from acting out its fantasies. If the locus ceruleus of a cat is destroyed, it will be observed to leap about, catching imaginary mice in its sleep.

Sleep deprivation can have serious consequences. Volunteers who have spent prolonged periods up to a week or more without sleep have shown a gradual and then accelerating deterioration of awareness and alertness, losses of memory, progressive inability to perform various mental and physical tasks, instability, impairment of judgment, and ultimately vivid hallucinations and even schizophrenic manifestations. In most cases these alarming manifestations clear up spontaneously after a long session of restful sleep. Enforced sleeplessness has been used as a form of "brainwashing" in police and military interrogations; when deprived of normal sleep for prolonged periods, a person tends to become highly suggestible and shows a breakdown of will. Studies of sleep deprivation have important implications in a number of areas of modern life in which persons are placed under stress for prolonged periods. A sleep-deprived soldier may disastrously misinterpret an order; a groggy intern on night duty may make an error of judgment that costs the life of a patient. Indeed, some studies indicate that mortality among hospital patients after heart attacks and operations may be correlated to a large extent with inability to sleep for long periods due to the unfamiliar surroundings, anxiety, and rigid hospital routine, which may be poorly timed to the patient's normal body rhythms.

VASCULAR SUPPLY TO THE BRAIN

The development of effective techniques of cardiopulmonary resuscitation—restarting a heart and respiration that have stopped—has raised a new moral dilemma for emergency medical workers. If the heart can be restarted within a few minutes, the victim may be literally brought back from the dead, may recover fully, and go on to live a normal life for many years. But during the time that the heart is stopped, blood is not circulated through the blood vessels of the body, and the body cells do not receive their continual resupply of oxygen and nutrients. As the oxygen lack (anoxia) continues, actively metabolizing body cells become damaged and begin to die off. The most vulnerable cells are those of the brain. Under normal conditions, after about four minutes of circulatory arrest, brain damage sets in; if resuscitation is delayed much beyond this time, there is an increasing probability that the victim will be snatched from the jaws of death only to live the life of a helpless, mindless vegetable.

The brain is so active metabolically that it receives about 17 percent of the cardiac output and about 20 percent of the oxygen consumed, even though it is only 2 percent of the body weight. This prodigious blood supply is provided for by an extensive network of blood vessels (Figure 13-17). The **internal carotid arteries** and the **basilar artery** (formed by the union of the two vertebral arteries) branch to form a circle, the **circle of Willis,** from which smaller branches enter the substance of the brain. As in other parts of the body, the actual exchange of materials with the brain cells occurs in networks of capillaries; these are more abundant in the gray matter than in the white matter. The blood drains into cerebral veins, which unite to form the **cranial venous sinuses,** passing ultimately into the **internal jugular veins.** Communication between the intracranial and extracranial venous channels is provided by the **diploic** and **emissary veins.** No lymphatics are present in the brain.

Stroke is one of the leading causes of death and disablement in the United States today. It is a sudden lesion of a blood vessel in the brain, which may be caused by hemorrhage, thrombosis, or embolism (i.e., bleeding from a cerebral blood vessel or its plugging by a blood clot or some other obstruction). An **aneurism**—a ballooning out of the walls of an artery or brain—may be formed at any time in life, from infancy onward. A sudden surge in blood pressure may rupture the aneurism, producing hemorrhage; the escaping blood pools in the enclosed area within the skull, compresses delicate brain structures, and may result in coma, followed by paralysis (if the victim survives), depending on the location of the lesion. Occlusion of a cerebral blood vessel (cutting off the blood supply to a particular region of the brain) can

have similar effects. The attack may come without warning, or may be preceded by symptoms such as dizziness or disturbance of speech. Stroke usually occurs in middle or old age; through a long and painstaking process of rehabilitation, the stroke victim can often regain his or her lost abilities, as alternate regions of the brain take over for those that have been irreparably damaged.

THE MENINGES

The brain is the most carefully protected structure in the body. Not only is it encased in a rigid helmet of bone, the skull, but within the skull it is wrapped in a series of three separate membranes, the **meninges.** Cavities inside the brain, the **ventricles,** are filled with cerebrospinal fluid, as are the spaces between the brain and its covering membranes; this fluid provides a cushioning effect, further protecting the irreplaceable brain tissues from injury by shocks and jars. The three membranes that cover the brain are (from the outside inward) the **dura mater,** the **arachnoid membrane,** and the **pia mater** (Figure 13-18). Extensions of these three membranes similarly encase and protect the spinal cord.

The Dura Mater

The name *dura mater* literally means "hard mother." This outermost membrane of the brain is a tough two-layered covering, composed of dense white fibrous connective tissue. The outer, **endosteal layer** adheres to the inner surface of the cranial bones, forming their periosteum. (At the foramen magnum, this layer terminates, and the periosteal lining of the vertebral canal takes its place.) The inner, **meningeal layer** covers the brain and sends projections inward, which serve as partitions between parts of the brain. One of these, the **falx cerebri,** penetrates deep into the longitudinal fissure that separates the left and right hemispheres of the cerebrum. Another, the **falx cerebelli,** occupies a similar position in the cleft between the two hemispheres of the cerebellum. Still another extension of the dura mater, the **tentorium cerebelli,** extends between the occipital lobes of the cerebrum and the cerebellum. The **diaphragma sellae** is an extension of the dura mater forming a roof over the bony sella turcica, in which the pituitary gland is found. (The stalk of the pituitary passes through an aperture in the diaphragma sellae to anchor on the hypothalamus.) Projections of the dura mater also form venous sinuses and sheaths for nerves that pass out of the skull.

The spinal dura mater consists of just a single layer, the continuation of the meningeal layer of the cranial dura mater. It forms a loose sheath around the spinal cord, extending from the foramen magnum to the sec-

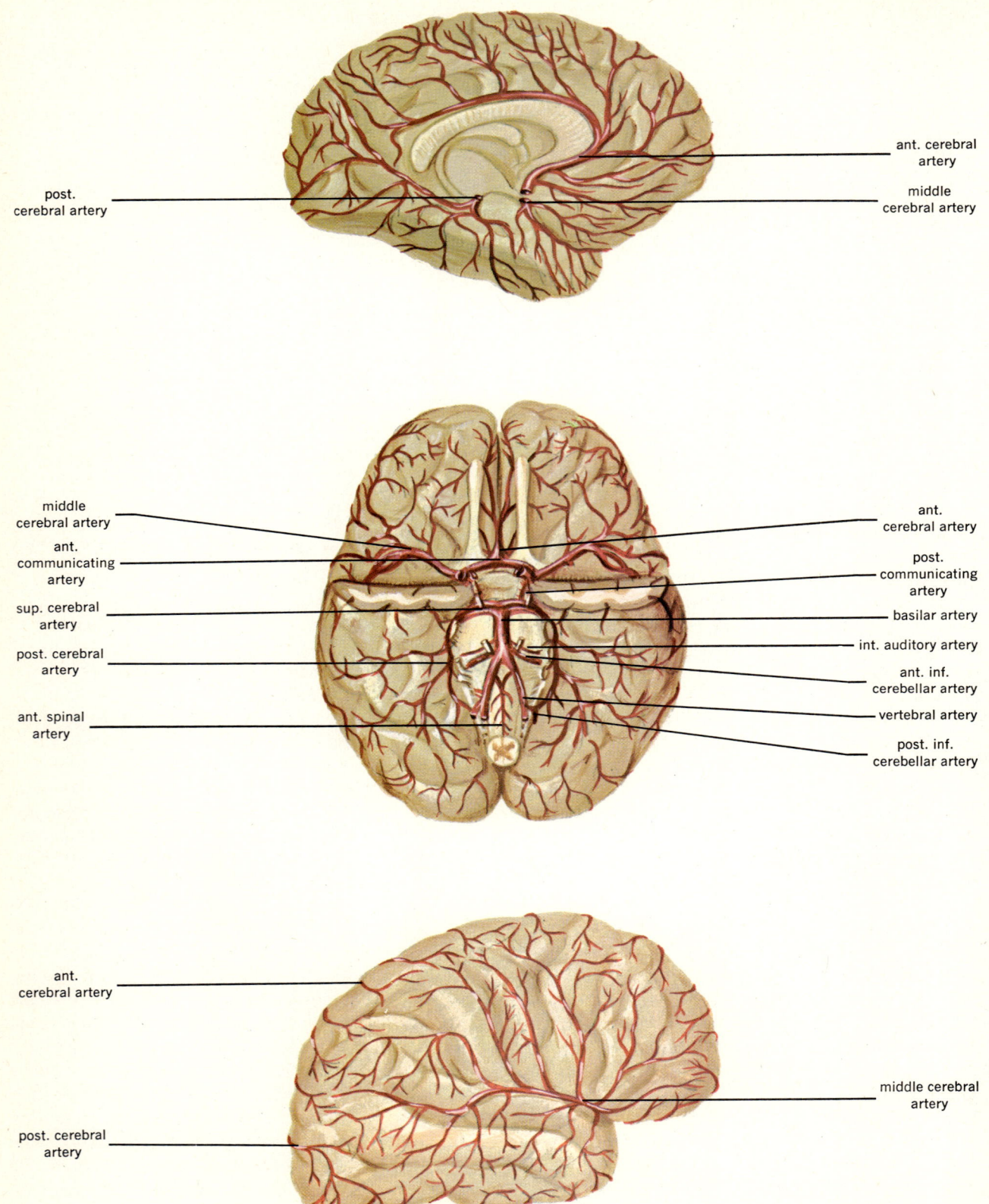

ant. cerebral
artery

middle
cerebral artery

post.
cerebral artery

middle
cerebral artery

ant.
communicating
artery

sup. cerebral
artery

post. cerebral
artery

ant. spinal
artery

ant.
cerebral artery

post.
communicating
artery

basilar artery

int. auditory artery

ant. inf.
cerebellar artery

vertebral artery

post. inf.
cerebellar artery

ant.
cerebral artery

post. cerebral
artery

middle cerebral
artery

A

**FIGURE 13-17   Arteries of the brain (A) and veins and sinuses that drain
the head and neck (B).**

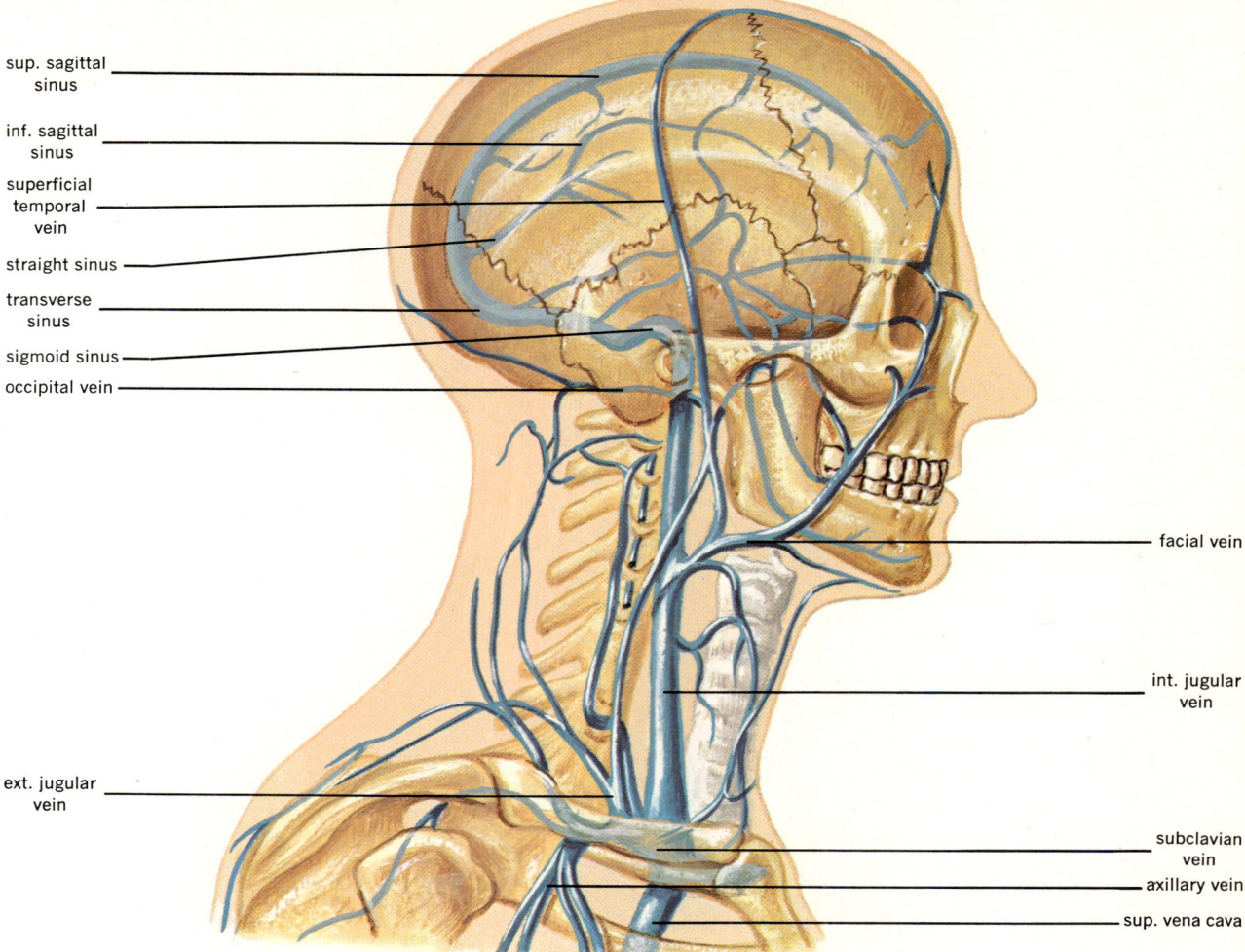

sup. sagittal sinus

inf. sagittal sinus

superficial temporal vein

straight sinus

transverse sinus

sigmoid sinus

occipital vein

facial vein

int. jugular vein

ext. jugular vein

subclavian vein

axillary vein

sup. vena cava

B

ond or third sacral vertebra (beyond the end of the cord), ending in a blind sac anchored to the coccyx by a threadlike strand of pia mater called the **filum terminale.** The fact that the meninges continue down beyond the end of the spinal cord (at L2-L3) is very convenient from the clinical standpoint: it permits specimens of cerebrospinal fluid to be withdrawn without any danger of damaging the spinal cord, by inserting a needle between the third and fourth or fourth and fifth lumbar vertebrae.

Between the dura mater and the middle membrane (the arachnoid) there is a potential cavity, which normally contains only enough fluid to moisten their contiguous surfaces.

The Arachnoid Membrane

The arachnids are spiders and their closest relatives; the name of the arachnoid membrane comes from the fact that its structure is very similar to a spider web. Unlike the tough dura mater, the arachnoid membrane is a delicate, filamentous covering. It covers the brain and spinal cord loosely. It follows the general outlines of the brain, and except in the longitudinal fissure does not dip down into the various convolutions and sulci; the spinal portion is tubular. Numerous strutlike trabeculae of delicate connective tissue extend through the subarachnoid space and attach to the pia mater; the intercommunicating channels of the subarachnoid cavity formed are filled with cerebrospinal fluid. In places the subarachnoid spaces enlarge into **cisternae;** the largest, the cisterna magna, communicates with the fourth ventricle.

At various points, small fingerlike outpouchings of the arachnoid membrane called **arachnoid villi** protrude through the dura mater into the superior sagittal and longitudinal venous sinuses; at these points cerebrospinal fluid enters the bloodstream.

The Pia Mater

The pia mater ("tender mother") is the innermost covering of the brain. It is delicate and extremely vascular, particularly in the cranial portion. It adheres

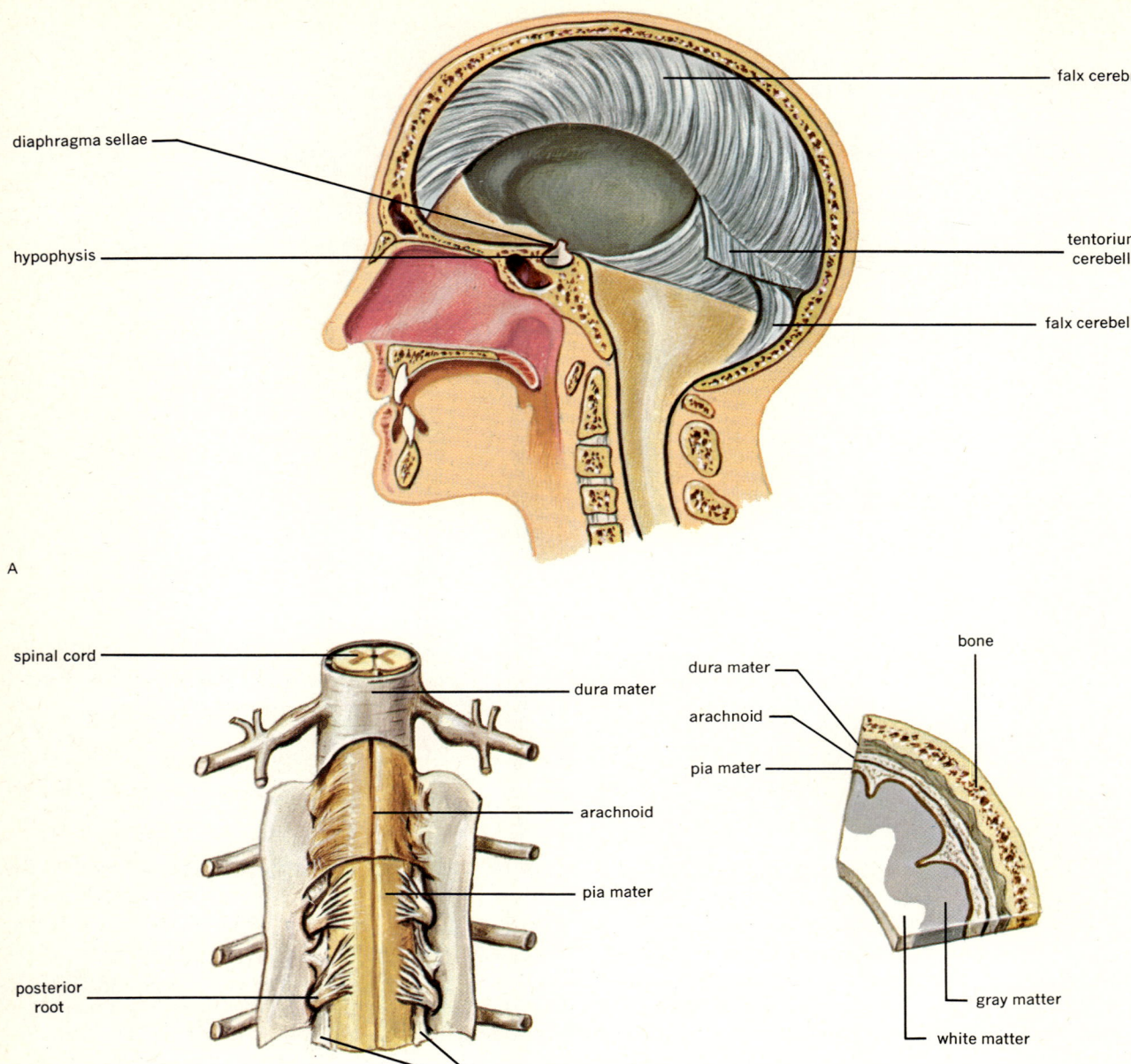

spinal cord

dura mater

bone

dura mater

arachnoid

arachnoid

pia mater

pia mater

posterior root

gray matter

white matter

dentate ligaments

B

FIGURE 13-18   The meninges: extensions of the dura mater inside the cranial cavity (A); meninges of the spinal cord (B: note that the dura mater and arachnoid sheath the origins of the spinal nerves); section through the cranium, meninges, and cerebral cortex (C).

closely to the brain and spinal cord, following their contour precisely, so that it cannot be dissected away from them without damaging them.

VENTRICLES OF THE BRAIN

In the developing embryo, the nervous system starts out as a hollow tube. Dramatic changes occur as this simple tube is transformed into a brain, spinal cord, and intricate network of threadlike nerves. But the original cavity persists and is transformed into four cavities within the brain (the ventricles), their com-

municating channels, and the central canal of the spinal cord.

The ventricles of the brain are known by numbers rather than names. The numbering goes from the top downward (Figure 13-19). The **first** and **second ventricles** (also known as the **lateral ventricles**) are the largest, and are found in the cerebral hemispheres, extending into all four lobes. The **third ventricle** is a narrow cleft that lies between the right and left thalamus. It communicates with each lateral ventricle by way of a small channel, the **interventricular foramen**

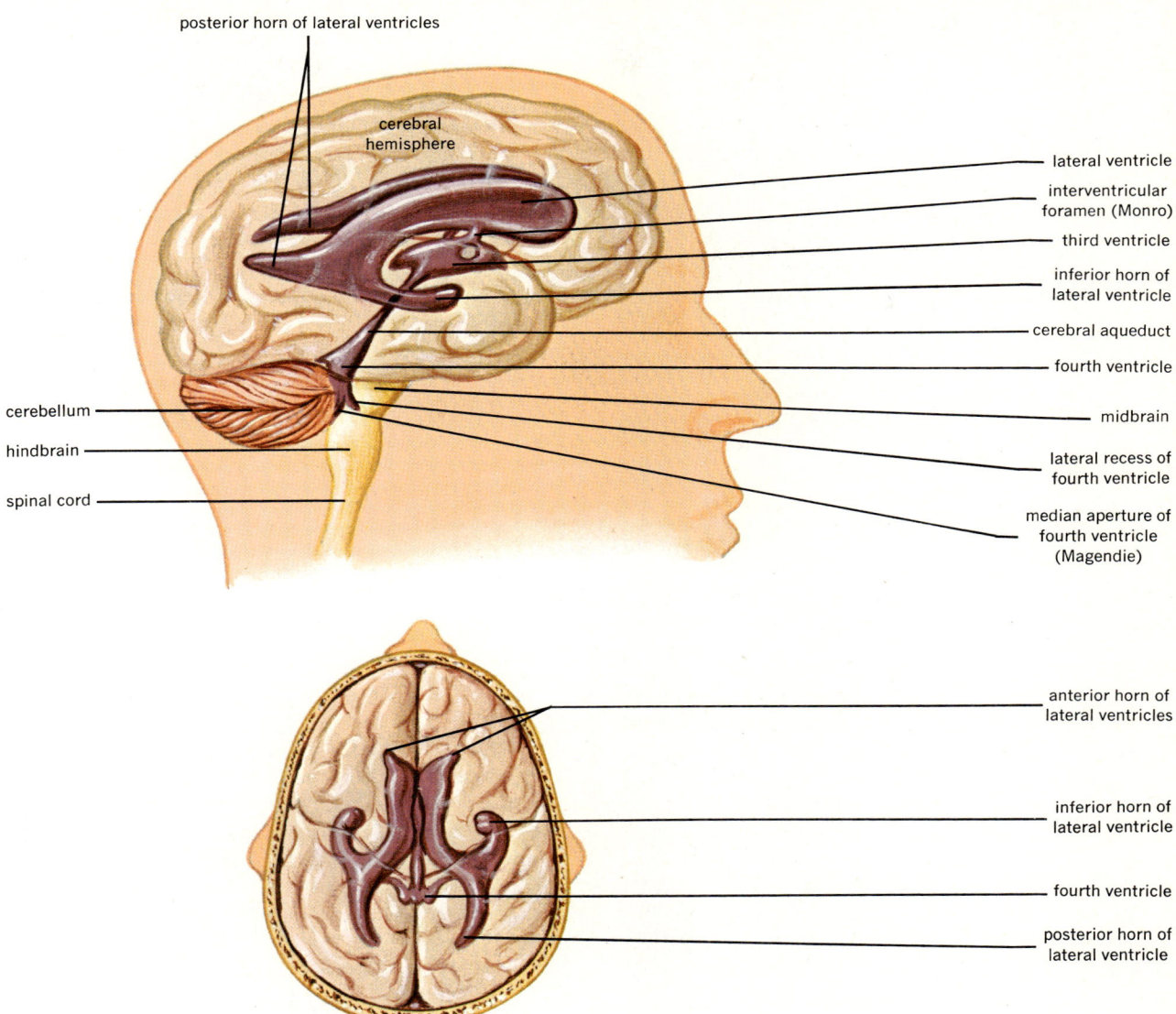

posterior horn of lateral ventricles

cerebral hemisphere

lateral ventricle

interventricular foramen (Monro)

third ventricle

inferior horn of lateral ventricle

cerebral aqueduct

fourth ventricle

cerebellum

hindbrain

spinal cord

midbrain

lateral recess of fourth ventricle

median aperture of fourth ventricle (Magendie)

anterior horn of lateral ventricles

inferior horn of lateral ventricle

fourth ventricle

posterior horn of lateral ventricle

FIGURE 13-19   The ventricles of the brain in lateral and superior views.

(of Monro), and is connected to the fourth ventricle by means of the **cerebral aqueduct** (the aqueduct of Sylvius). The **fourth ventricle** is a flattened, pyramidal cavity, bounded by the pons, medulla, and cerebellum. The fourth ventricle communicates with the central canal of the spinal canal and also has three openings into the cranial subarachnoid space: the **foramina of Luschka** (lateral openings) and the **foramen of Magendie** (medial opening).

The ventricles of the brain are all filled with cerebrospinal fluid, which acts as a shock absorber and helps to cushion the brain against injury. The cerebrospinal fluid is actually produced in the ventricles: a delicate capillary network, the **choroid plexus,** protrudes into each of the ventricles and continually exudes cerebrospinal fluid into the ventricles.

CEREBROSPINAL FLUID

The head of an infant seems large in proportion to its body, and many years of growth must pass before it reaches the adult proportions. But occasionally a child is born whose skull is far larger than even the infant norm. This is an ominous sign; not only does it make for a difficult birth, but the condition, if unchecked, can result in severe brain damage and ultimate death. The condition is known as **hydrocephalus** ("water on the brain"), and it is caused by an excess of cerebrospinal fluid inside the cranial cavity. It may result from an overactivity of the choroid plexus, or by a blockage of one of the communicating channels between ventricles (usually the aqueduct of Sylvius). Since liquids are rather incompressible, the accumulating fluid increases the volume of the ventricles

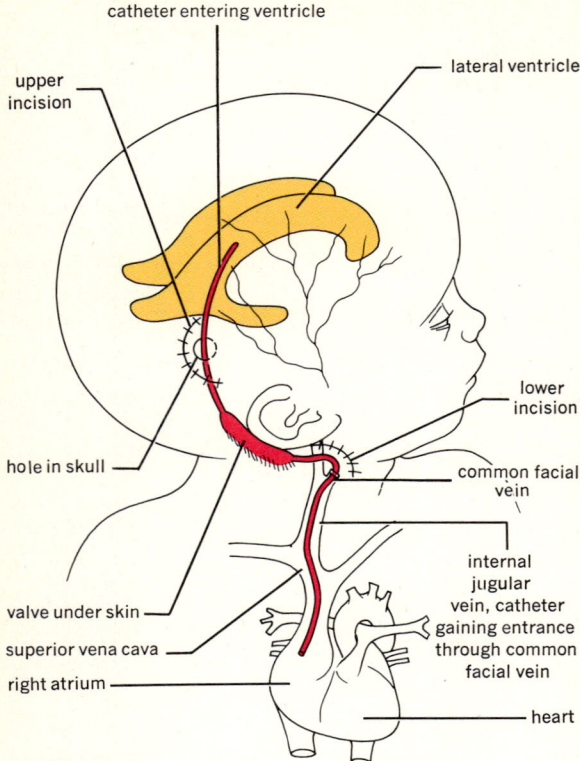

upper incision

catheter entering ventricle

lateral ventricle

lower incision

hole in skull

common facial vein

internal jugular vein, catheter gaining entrance through common facial vein

valve under skin

superior vena cava

right atrium

heart

FIGURE 13-20 An operative procedure for treatment of hydrocephalus. A catheter drains the ventricles of the brain into the right atrium of the heart.

greatly and flattens the brain into a thin shell against the skull. The soft cranial bones and open sutures of a newborn infant permit the entire head to balloon out (Figure 13-20); if hydrocephalus occurs in an older person, whose skull cannot expand, there is a tremendous increase in intracranial pressure.

Cerebrospinal fluid is a clear, colorless, watery fluid, with a composition similar to that of blood plasma. Its volume is rather variable, usually from 80 to 200 ml. (Only 15 ml of this is found in the ventricles; the remainder is in the subarachnoid spaces.) It is formed continuously, both by secretion by the choroid plexuses and by filtration through the walls of the capillaries that supply the brain tissue. Nearly all the cerebrospinal fluid that is formed each day is reabsorbed into the blood through the arachnoid villi.

All the chambers that contain cerebrospinal fluid—the ventricles, cisterns, and subarachnoid space—communicate with one another, and thus the pressure of the fluid is maintained at a constant level. In a person lying in a horizontal position, the cerebrospinal fluid pressure averages 130 mm of water (10 mm Hg); the normal range is from 70 to 180 mm of water. A large brain tumor may raise the pressure by hampering the absorption of cerebrospinal fluid, as well as

perhaps obstructing its drainage or producing inflammation of the meninges, which then exude additional fluid. Hemorrhage or infection within the cranial cavity causes large numbers of cells to appear in the cerebrospinal fluid, which can block absorption through the arachnoid villi. In such cases, the cerebrospinal fluid pressure may rise to 500 mm of water or even higher. Determinations of the pressure and examination of specimens of cerebrospinal fluid can be extremely valuable diagnostic aids.

The only known function of the cerebrospinal fluid is protection from mechanical injury. No evidence has been found that it participates in the metabolic activities of the brain. One still somewhat mysterious characteristic of the cerebrospinal fluid and the interstitial fluid of the brain is of great importance: many large molecules that pass readily from the blood into the interstitial fluids of the body will not pass into the cerebrospinal fluid or the interstitial fluid of the brain. Physiologists speak of **blood-cerebrospinal** and **blood-brain barriers,** which exist in the choroid plexus and in essentially all areas of the brain except the hypothalamus. (Recall that the hypothalamus contains numerous monitoring stations and is extremely sensitive to changes in the constituents of the extracellular fluid.) Water, carbon dioxide, and oxygen pass readily through the barriers; they are slightly permeable to electrolytes such as sodium, potassium, and chloride, and almost totally impermeable to substances such as arsenic, sulfur, and gold.

Several factors contribute to the blood-brain barrier. Cerebral capillaries seem to be relatively impermeable, in contrast to the rather porous capillaries in other parts of the body. Their endothelial cells have overlapping ends sealed by tight junctions, and the entire circumference of the cerebral capillaries is surrounded by a continuous basement membrane. To add to the barrier, about 85 percent of the outer surface of each cerebral capillary is covered with glial cells, which further restrict the passage of solutes.

The blood-cerebrospinal and blood-brain barriers are a valuable protective mechanism, but they can be a stumbling block to the physician, since it is impossible to achieve effective concentrations of drugs in the fluids of the brain by an injection into the bloodstream.

THE SPINAL CORD

Damage to the spinal cord can mean paralysis. And yet this delicate structure is bent, turned, and twisted hundreds of times a day. It is well protected, as we have seen, by the bony tube of the vertebral column, whose multiple joints provide flexibility, by three separate meninges, and by cushions of cerebrospinal fluid, mainly in the subarachnoid space. The cord itself is suspended rather loosely in the vertebral canal, which permits it to move freely without danger of damage.

The spinal cord extends from the foramen magnum (where it merges smoothly with the medulla) down to the level of the second lumbar vertebra (Figure 13-21). Its lower portion is somewhat tapered and finally ends in the threadlike filum terminale, an extension of the pia mater that is actually nonnervous tissue, incapable of conducting impulses. Although the spinal cord has a basically oval cylindrical shape, it exhibits two pronounced enlargements: one at the level of the fourth cervical to second thoracic vertebrae (cervical enlargement) and the other at roughly the tenth to twelfth thoracic vertebrae (the lumbar enlargement). Nerves supplying the arms and legs, respectively, arise from these enlargements of the spinal cord.

In cross section, the spinal cord is distinctly wider from side to side than it is from front to back. It is nearly cut in half by two grooves along the midline, one very deep one, the **anterior median fissure,** and a less distinct cleavage, the **posterior median sulcus.** Two other, rather indistinct grooves, are found lateral to the midline in each half of the posterior part of the cord; they demarcate a nerve tract, the fasciculus gracilis.

From the outside, the spinal cord looks white; but like the brain, it contains both gray and white matter. The gray matter of the cord is concentrated on the inside, surrounding the **central canal,** and arranged so that in cross section it forms the shape of a letter H (see Figure 13-23). (In some regions it looks more like a butterfly shape.) The gray matter is mainly nerve cell bodies, while the white matter consists of nerve fiber **tracts** that carry impulses up and down the cord. Some of them reach various parts of the brain; others do not.

Thirty-one pairs of spinal nerves emerge from the spinal cord at regular intervals, beginning as dorsal and ventral roots (Figures 13-21 and 13-22). There are eight pairs of cervical nerves, twelve pairs of thoracic nerves, five pairs of lumbar nerves, five pairs of sacral nerves, and one pair of coccygeal nerves. During the early development of the body, the spinal cord segments and the vertebrae are lined up correspondingly; but the vertebral column grows more rapidly than the spinal cord, and the lower levels of the vertebrae are soon displaced downward. The spinal nerves emerge from the vertebral column at the appropriate place, but the lower nerves must travel downward within the vertebral canal for some distance before emerging. The vertebral column continues beyond the point where the actual nervous tissue of the spinal cord ends. The canal is not empty at this point, however; in addition to the glistening thread of the filum

terminale, the lower spinal nerves hang down from the end of the spinal cord looking much like a horse's tail. Early anatomists, struck by this resemblance, named them the **cauda equina** ("horse's tail").

The spinal cord serves two functions: it provides **conduction pathways** to and from the brain, relaying sensory and motor impulses; and it contains numerous **reflex centers,** which function in the generation of immediate, automatic responses to certain incoming stimuli. A reflex center is quite literally the center of a reflex arc, the point where incoming sensory impulses are transformed into outgoing motor impulses. It may contain direct synapses between sensory and motor neurons, or interneurons may be interposed between them.

Conduction Pathways of the Spinal Cord

If someone steps on your toes, you don't feel the pain until the impulses set off by that crunching foot reach your brain. Before the message can reach the brain, it must travel up the spinal cord. Your reaction to this intrusion may be varied. But whatever your brain decides to do about it, the impulses implementing this decision must go back down the spinal cord before they reach your limbs.

Impulses of various kinds travel up and down the spinal cord along specific **conduction pathways** or **tracts,** which are functionally associated bundles of nerve fibers. It is easy to trace the pathway and delimit the components of a peripheral nerve; it is not so easy to delimit the nerve fibers of a particular tract in the spinal cord, for the white matter of the cord looks essentially homogeneous. The major tracts of the spinal cord have been mapped, however (Figure 13-23), in a manner similar to the mapping of the brain: by animal experiments and by observations of the effects of disease, injury, and surgery in humans. The tracts carry impulses either upward or downward along the spinal cord, relaying sensory or motor information. Some tracts run only from one level of the cord to another and are a link in reflex arcs in which the brain centers are not involved. Others convey impulses from peripheral sensory nerves up the spinal cord to various parts of the brain (**ascending tracts**) or down from the brain to peripheral motor nerves (**descending tracts**). Many of the names of tracts of the spinal cord reflect the origin and termination of their constituent fibers—for example, the dorsal spinocerebellar and ventral corticospinal tracts. All of the tracts are paired, with a corresponding structure in each half of the spinal cord.

Ascending Tracts   The pain of a pin prick, the heat from a pot handle, the soft feel of a rose petal—these are all obvious sensory messages transmitted

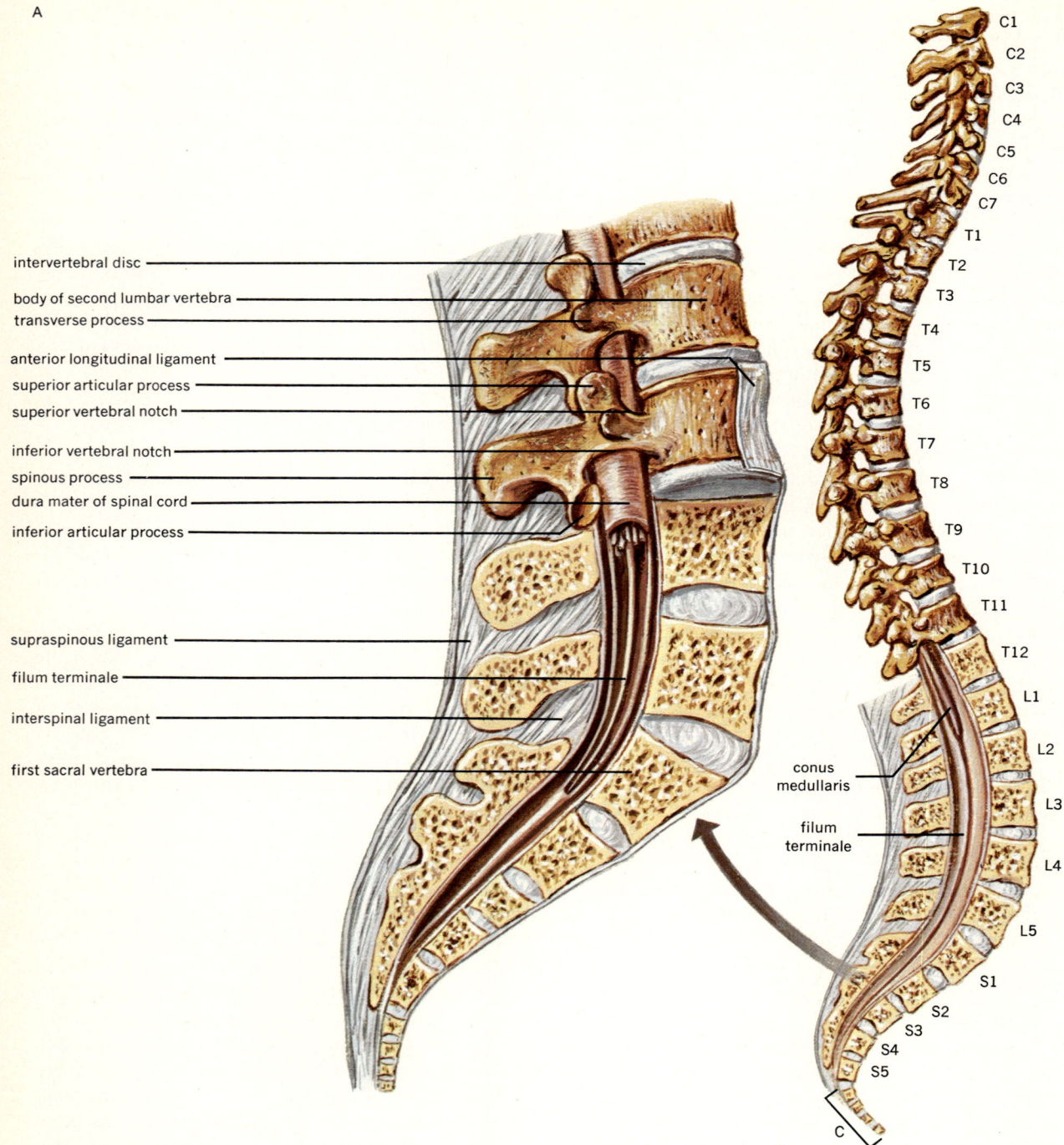

A

intervertebral disc

body of second lumbar vertebra

transverse process

anterior longitudinal ligament

superior articular process

superior vertebral notch

inferior vertebral notch

spinous process

dura mater of spinal cord

inferior articular process

supraspinous ligament

filum terminale

interspinal ligament

first sacral vertebra

conus
medullaris

filum
terminale

C1
C2
C3
C4
C5
C6
C7
T1
T2
T3
T4
T5
T6
T7
T8
T9
T10
T11
T12
L1
L2
L3
L4
L5
S1
S2
S3
S4
S5
C

FIGURE 13-21   The spinal cord is protected within the flexible channel formed by the vertebral column (A). Sections show the relation of the spinal cord and nerves to the vertebrae (B) and the internal structure of the cord, its covering membranes, and the formation of spinal nerves (C).

from peripheral nerves up the spinal cord to the brain and consciously perceived. But in addition to these messages, the brain receives a constant flow of information from the body's inner senses—the position and movements of body parts, fullness of the bladder, and various visceral sensations. Seven major ascending tracts relay information to the brain.

The **posterior funiculi**—the **fasciculus gracilis** and **fasciculus cuneatus**—arise in the spinal root ganglia and ascend without crossing to the medulla, where their impulses are relayed first to the thalamus (crossing to the opposite side in the process) and then to the cerebral cortex. The messages carried along these tracts come mainly from receptors in the extremities

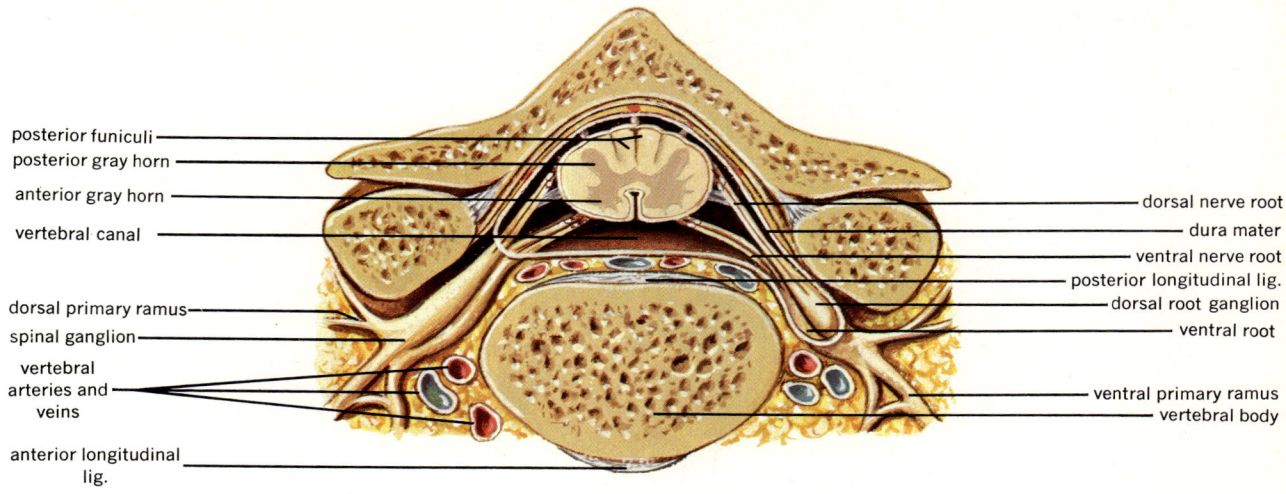

posterior funiculi
posterior gray horn
anterior gray horn
vertebral canal

dorsal primary ramus
spinal ganglion
vertebral arteries and veins

anterior longitudinal lig.

dorsal nerve root
dura mater
ventral nerve root
posterior longitudinal lig.
dorsal root ganglion
ventral root

ventral primary ramus
vertebral body

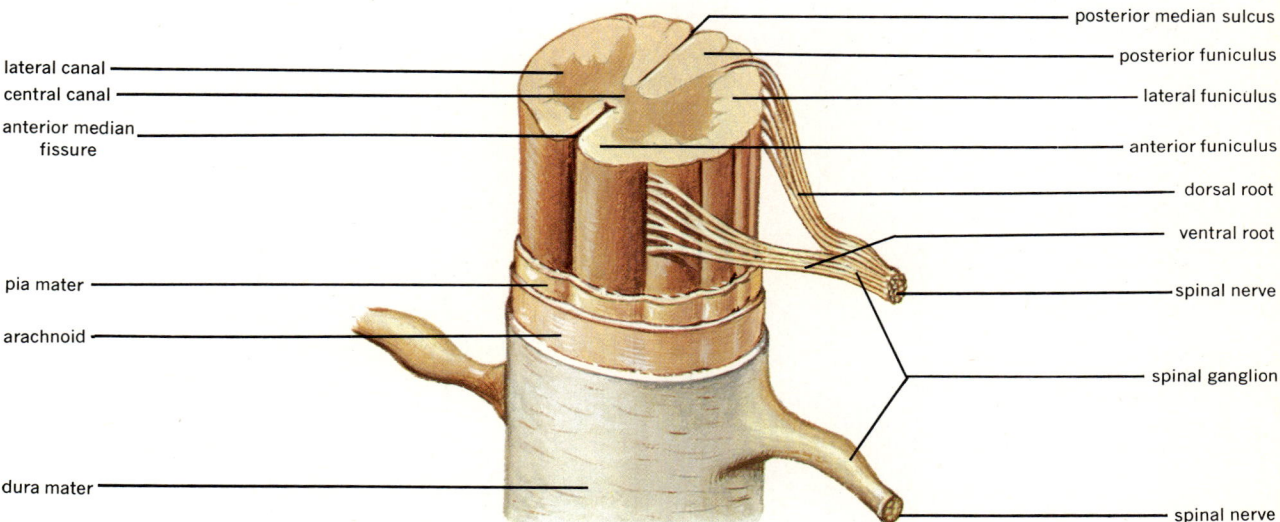

lateral canal
central canal
anterior median fissure

pia mater

arachnoid

dura mater

posterior median sulcus
posterior funiculus
lateral funiculus

anterior funiculus

dorsal root

ventral root

spinal nerve

spinal ganglion

spinal nerve

and are concerned with sensations of movement, position, touch, and pressure. They are key links in our conscious awareness of the whereabouts of body parts and in the maintenance of balance, as well as in the localization of tactile stimulation, two-point discrimination, and the perception of vibrations.

The **spinothalamic tracts** relay a wealth of sensory information. The **anterior** (or **ventral**) **spinothalamic tract** crosses in the anterior portion of the cord and ascends to the thalamus, transmitting impulses concerned with touch and pressure. The **lateral spinothalamic tract** also crosses before ascending to the thalamus and carries messages relating to pain and temperature (sensations of warmth and cold). This tract is also thought to be the pathway for sensations of tickle and itch, and muscular fatigue, as well as impulses from sense receptors in the internal organs. Sensations of the need to urinate, pain in the viscera,

and feelings of sexual arousal, are all believed to be transmitted along the lateral spinothalamic tract.

The **spinocerebellar** tracts, as deduced from their name, extend up to the cerebellum and relay the kinesthetic information needed in the maintenance of posture, coordination, and balance. The **posterior** (or **dorsal**) **spinocerebellar tract** carries impulses from the muscles and tendons mainly of the legs and trunk. The axons of this tract arise in the gray matter of the cord and ascend along the same side. Most of the nerve fibers of the **anterior** (or **ventral**) **spinocerebellar tract** cross in the cord and transmit proprioceptive impulses from all parts of the body to the cerebellum by way of the medulla and pons.

The fibers of the **spinotectal tract**, terminating in the corpora quadrigemina, carry impulses involved in sensations of touch, pain, and temperature and in auditory, visual, and other reflexes.

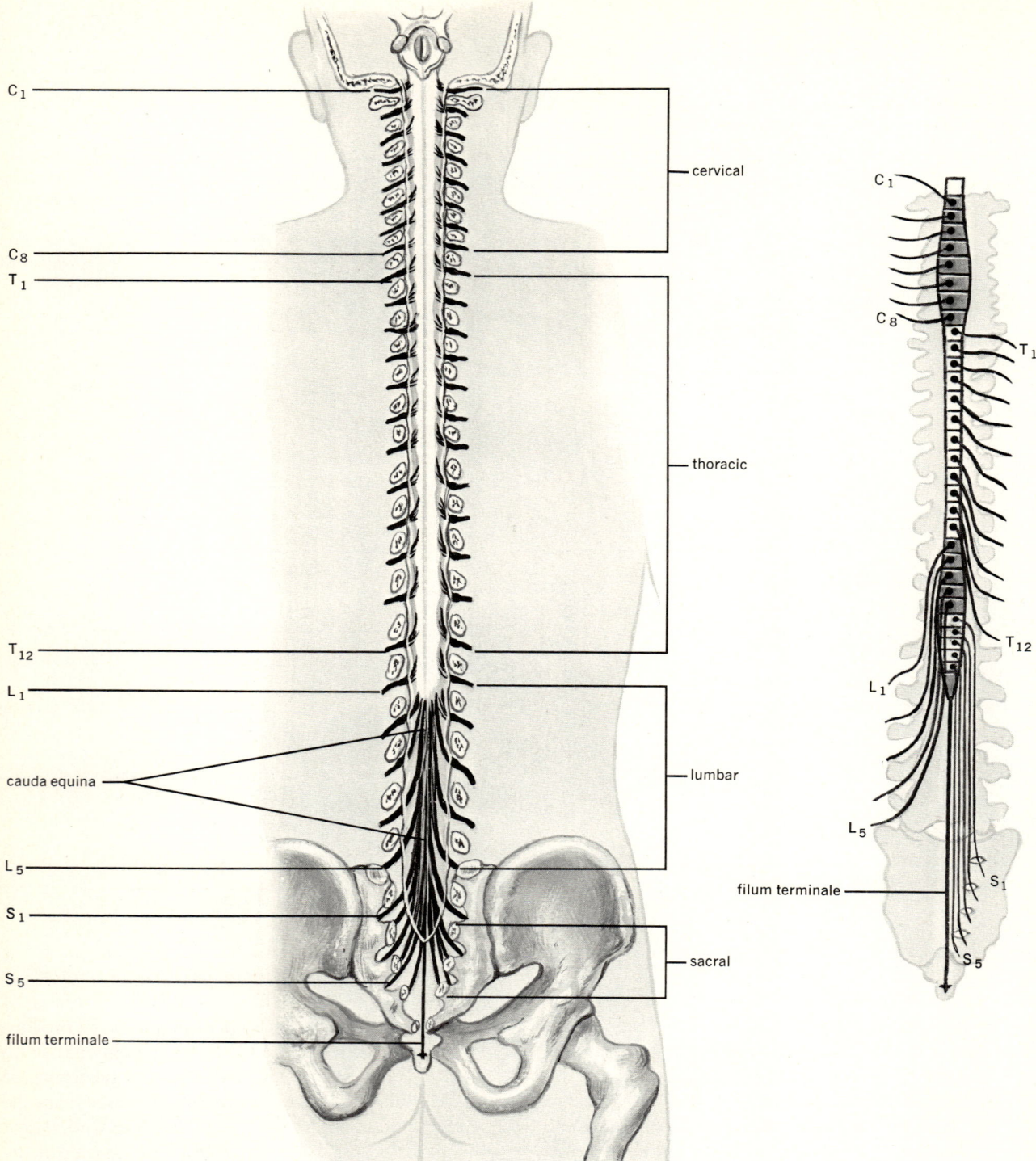

FIGURE 13-22   Longitudinal section of the spinal cord and vertebral column showing the origins and emergence of the spinal nerves.

Descending Tracts   Impulses delivered via the ascending tracts supply the brain with the information about changes in the outside world necessary to make decisions about changes in the outside world necessary to make decisions about how to adjust to these changes. Once these decisions are made in the brain, many of them are carried out through messages that pass down the descending tracts of the spinal cord. Only a few of the many descending tracts are discussed here.

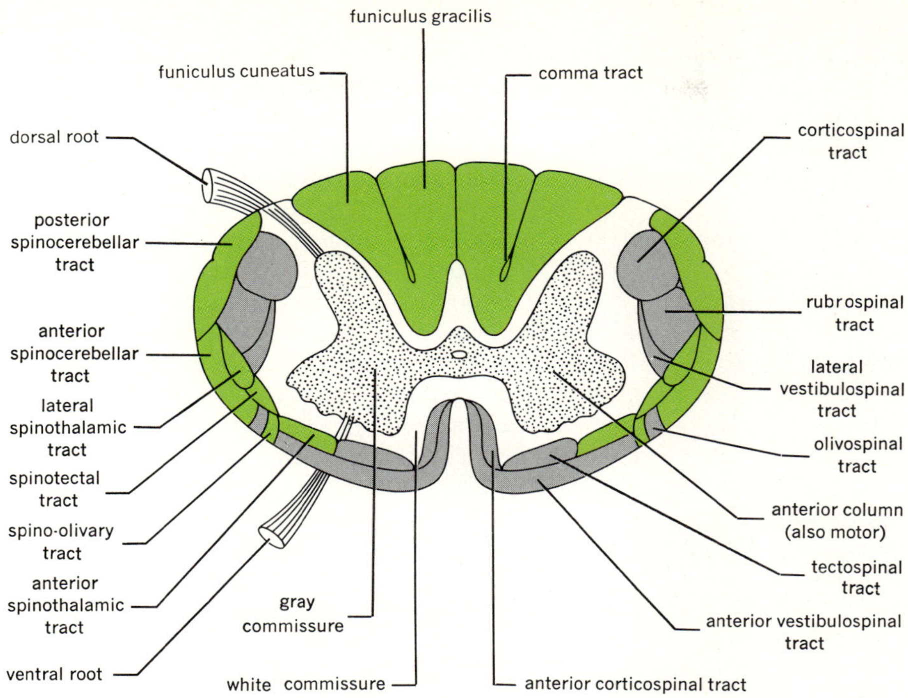

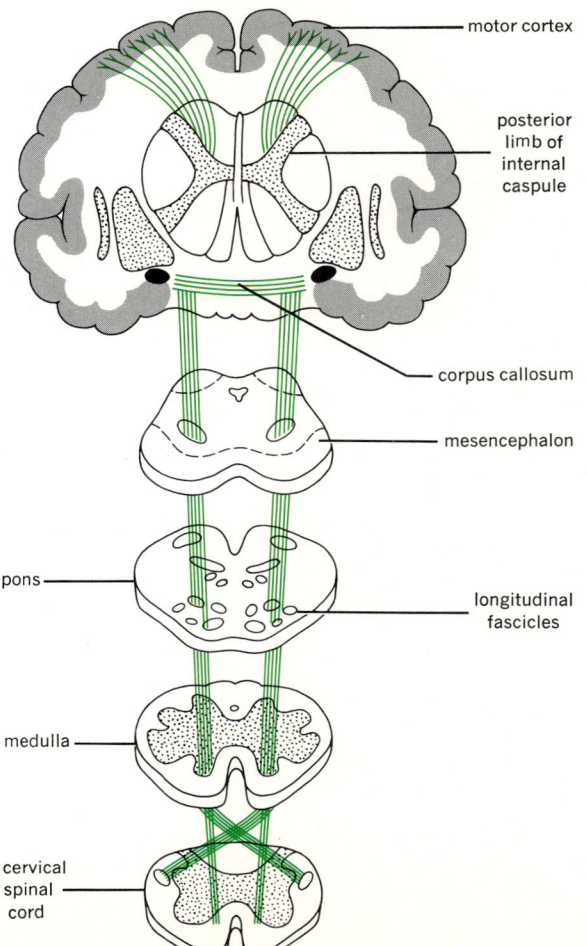

FIGURE 13-23 Cross section of the spinal cord, showing the major tracts. Sensory or ascending tracts are shown in shades of red, motor or descending tracts in tones of black.

funiculus gracilis

funiculus cuneatus — comma tract

dorsal root

corticospinal tract

posterior spinocerebellar tract

anterior spinocerebellar tract

rubrospinal tract

lateral spinothalamic tract

lateral vestibulospinal tract

spinotectal tract

olivospinal tract

spino-olivary tract

anterior column (also motor)

anterior spinothalamic tract

gray commissure

tectospinal tract

ventral root

anterior vestibulospinal tract

white commissure — anterior corticospinal tract

FIGURE 13-24 The pyramidal tract. Note that some pathways are direct, others crossed.

motor cortex

posterior limb of internal capsule

corpus callosum

mesencephalon

pons

longitudinal fascicles

medulla

cervical spinal cord

The **corticospinal,** or **pyramidal tracts** are the main motor pathway down the spinal cord, originating in the cerebral cortex and including about one million nerve fibers on each side of the spinal cord (Figure 13-24). The fibers of the pyramidal tract pass through the internal capsule, cerebral peduncle, and pons to the medulla, where most of them cross to the opposite side, continuing downward as the **lateral** or **crossed corticospinal tract** to terminate in the gray matter of the spinal cord. The fibers that do not cross in the pyramids of the medulla compose the **anterior** (or **ventral) corticospinal tract.** Some of them cross at each segment, and all have crossed by the time they terminate in the gray matter of the cord. The impulses carried along the pyramidal tracts are concerned mainly with skilled voluntary movements involving small numbers of muscle groups. Because of the crossing of the nerve fibers, the skeletal muscles on the right side of the body are controlled by the left side of the brain, and vice versa.

The **extrapyramidal tracts** consist of chains of neurons originating in such places as the caudate nucleus, lentiform nucleus, basal ganglia, or reticular formation. They include: the **rubrospinal tract,** which originates in the red nucleus of the midbrain and relays incoming impulses from the cerebellum down to the motor neurons of the anterior column; the **tectospinal** tract, which originates in the superior colliculus and mediates optic and auditory reflexes; and the **vestibulospinal tract,** arising from the vestibular nucleus of the medulla and conveying impulses from the middle ear and cerebellum that exert a tonic influence on the muscles of the extremities and trunk, helping to maintain balance and posture.

The **descending autonomic tracts** permit the forebrain to dominate the lower centers, exerting excitatory or inhibitory influences on the spinal reflex arcs. The **lateral and medial reticulospinal tracts** arise in the reticular formation and transmit impulses that facilitate or inhibit the motor neurons to the skeletal muscles.

Reflex Actions

If you accidentally touch a hot stove, your reaction is immediate: without thinking about it, your hand comes flying away from the stove. By the time you are aware of the heat and pain, your hand is already out of danger. Many of our everyday actions—blinking, swallowing, even breathing—go on without much conscious thought. The body's automatic reactions to specific situations or stimuli include not only simple actions such as jerking a hand away from a hot surface, but also more complicated, learned responses such as jamming down the brake pedal of a car when a child dashes out onto the road or the operations involved in tying a shoe. (The next time you have occasion to tie a bow, look carefully at it and make an effort to think consciously about each part of the procedure. Your sudden fumbling ineptitude will emphasize just how automatic this rather complicated series of actions had become.)

Actions performed automatically in response to a stimulus, without conscious decision or thought, are called **reflex actions.** Many simple reflex actions are handled by the spinal cord, without involvement of the brain. Jerking your hand away from a hot stove is one of them. Another is the "knee jerk reflex," a standard test in the doctor's office. When the doctor taps your knee with a rubber mallet, your foot automatically kicks outward, without any conscious effort on your part. (If you are prepared beforehand, your brain can intervene in this response, and you can consciously suppress or enhance the knee jerk reflex.) Often, while the spinal cord is handling a reflex action, collateral impulses may simultaneously be sent to the brain, informing it both of the original stimulus and of the action that has been taken. For example, in the hot stove situation, when your brain is eventually informed of the circumstances, you feel the heat and pain and perhaps exclaim "Ouch!" and wave the injured part in the air or stick it in your mouth. As the conscious brain has a chance to evaluate the situation

further, you may carefully examine your burned fingers and take appropriate first aid measures such as holding them under cold water if necessary.

Some simple reflexes, such as the adjustment of the pupil size in response to a change in the amount of light available and the continual adjustments of the heartbeat rate, blood vessel diameters, and breathing rate, are mediated by reflex centers in various parts of the lower brain.

More complicated reflex actions, involving a learned association of a specific response with a particular stimulus, involve the higher brain and are referred to as **conditioned reflexes.** The pioneer work on conditioned reflexes was done by the Russian physiologist, I. P. Pavlov. His classic experiments were on dogs, using the response of salivation. You may have noticed that your mouth begins to fill with saliva when an appetizing ("mouth-watering") dish is placed before you—or when you smell or even think about something particularly good to eat. Pavlov repeatedly presented dogs with a piece of meat and simultaneously rang a bell; then, when the sound of the bell was associated in the dogs' minds with the sight and smell of food, he tried ringing the bell only, without presenting the meat. The dogs salivated on cue. With such conditioned associations, fine distinctions are possible—for example, between bells of two different tones—and conditioned reflex experiments have proven quite valuable in revealing subtle changes in neurological functioning under the influence of drugs and various environmental factors. Conditioned reflexes play varied and important roles in our daily lives as well. Two examples have already been mentioned: salivating at the *thought* of food and jamming down the brake pedal of a car when a dangerous situation looms up. The sequence of operations involved in tying a shoe is a complicated series of conditioned reflexes, each of which serves as a stimulus for the next (e.g., "this loop now in bow position, swing other end around it").

The Reflex Arc

Each reflex action involves a definite sequence of impulses transmitted over a well-defined pathway of nerve fibers. Such an interconnected nerve pathway, the functional unit of the nervous system, is called a **reflex arc.** It generally consists of five components (Figure 13-25): (1) a sensory receptor, which is stimulated; (2) a sensory neuron, which conveys the nerve impulse to the central nervous system; (3) a connector or internuncial neuron in the gray matter of the CNS, which transmits the impulse to one or more motor neurons; (4) a motor neuron, which transmits a message from the CNS to an effector; and (5) an effector, such as a gland or muscle, whose action is stimulated

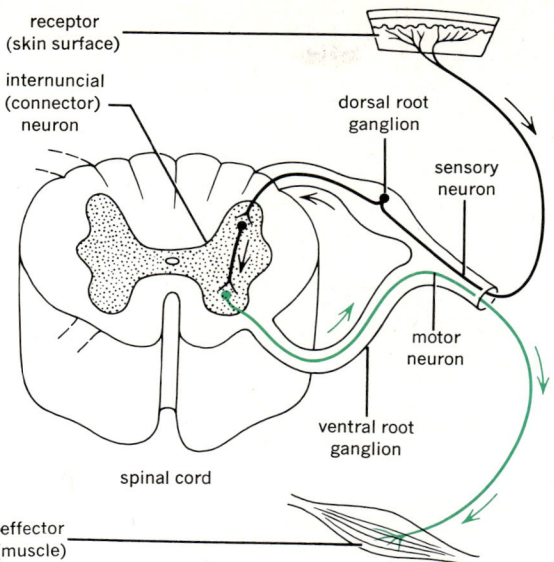

receptor
(skin surface)

internuncial
(connector)
neuron

dorsal root
ganglion

sensory
neuron

motor
neuron

ventral root
ganglion

spinal cord

effector
(muscle)

FIGURE 13-25 A simple reflex arc.

by the nerve impulse. The sensory receptor may be stimulated by something in the outside environment—for example, light or sound—or by a condition within the body—for example, distension of the bladder, or a change in the pH of the blood. The effector involved in the reflex arc may be located in the same general area of the body as the sensory receptor, or it may be somewhere else in the body.

Reflexes

Normally reflexes are quite predictable: the same stimulus always elicits the same involuntary response. But disease or injury affecting the nervous system can produce great changes in the body's normal reflexes. If any portion of a reflex arc is damaged, the reflex will be weakened or may disappear entirely. Lesion of higher brain centers that normally facilitate or inhibit particular reflexes may result in a diminution or exaggeration of the reflex. Thus, the study of certain characteristic reflexes is often of great clinical value, aiding in the diagnosis of pathological states.

Clinically, reflexes are classified in four main categories: **superficial,** involving the skin, cornea, and mucous membranes; **deep,** depending on proprioceptive impulses from muscles and tendons; **visceral,** concerned with such activities as regulation of the pupil size and heart rate, emptying of the bladder and rectum; and **pathological,** consisting of the reflexes observed only when disease or injury has damaged one of the higher CNS centers that normally modifies the expression of reflex arcs. The reflexes mediated by the spinal cord generally fall in the classifications of **flexion reflexes:** those concerned with withdrawal

from harmful stimuli; **extensor** or **stretch reflexes,** such as the knee jerk or patellar reflex; and **scratch reflexes,** which are responses to local irritation.

The familiar knee jerk reflex can provide information about two types of lesions. Injury to the spinal cord may eliminate this reflex entirely; lesions of higher centers, on the other hand, increase its intensity. This is an example of a deep reflex. Another is the Achilles reflex, which is tested by tapping the Achilles tendon while the patient is kneeling on a chair with feet hanging over, toes pointing downward. The normal response is for the gastrocnemius to contract, causing the foot to plantar flex or extend.

A clinically useful superficial reflex is the **plantar reflex.** When the lateral border of the sole of the foot is lightly stroked, the toes normally curl under, and the foot is flexed. Since this reflex is facilitated by impulses travelling down the corticospinal tract from the cerebral cortex, a normal plantar reflex indicates that all the elements of this tract are functioning properly. An abnormal response is the Babinski reflex, in which the big toe extends and the other toes tend to fan out. This response is observed in very young children (under a year and a half), in whom the nervous system is not yet completely developed. When it is observed at older ages, it is an indication of lesion of the corticospinal tract.

DISORDERS OF THE CNS

A crowd gathers at a busy street corner around a man who lies on the pavement, his body jerking and thrashing in the throes of an epileptic seizure. An autistic child sits mute in a corner while his mother tries desperately to break through the invisible barriers to communication that he has erected around himself. A young woman lies in a hospital bed, unmoving; she has been in a coma ever since she was injured in an automobile crash. A business executive walks up eight flights of stairs to his office each day because he has a morbid fear of elevators. An elderly woman suffering from Parkinsonism is treated with a new drug and is able to walk unaided for the first time in years.

Diseases and disorders of the central nervous system probably account for more human disability than any other cause. Think for a moment of all the body functions that are controlled or mediated by the brain and spinal cord, and imagine the effects of damage to some part of the CNS. Such damage may occur by **traumatic injury**—a fracture of the skull, for example, may drive bone splinters into the brain or depress a portion of the cranium so that it presses on the cerebrum; crushing of vertebrae may pinch or sever the spinal cord, disrupting the functioning of all its segments below the point of damage. **Disease pathogens,** such as the poliomyelitis virus, may attack CNS tissue. **Brain tumors,** malignant or nonmalignant neoplastic (new) growths that may occur within the cranial vault, may press on delicate nervous structures or invade and destroy them. **Hemorrhages** into the cranial cavity can produce similar devastation. The effects of such injuries vary depending on the region of damage. Lesion of the cerebral cortex can produce such varied effects as **paralysis** (a complete loss of motor function), **anesthesia** (a loss of sensation), and impairment of vision, hearing, speech, or various mental abilities. Damage to such a key structure as the hypothalamus may produce **diabetes insipidus** (a disturbance of the water balance in which extremely large amounts of very dilute urine are produced), or a disturbance of the body temperature regulation, or a pathological sleep that may last for months or even years. Damage to the spinal cord may produce a weakening or disappearance of some spinal reflexes, or an enhancement of others, or the appearance of pathological reflexes, as well as paralysis and/or anesthesia. Types of paralysis include **monoplegia,** paralysis of a single extremity; **hemiplegia,** paralysis of half of the body with the corresponding limbs; **paraplegia,** paralysis of both lower extremities; and **quadriplegia,** paralysis of all four extremities. Paralysis may be **spastic,** resulting from damage to the extrapyramidal pathways and characterized by increased muscle tone due to the removal of the controlling influence of higher brain centers. Or it may be **flaccid,** with a loss of muscle tone and deep tendon reflexes, resulting from damage to the pyramids or to the lower motor neurons.

Hydrocephalus and stroke have already been discussed. The following are some other common disorders of the central nervous system.

Cerebral Palsy

This is a condition due to lesions of the brain resulting from a birth injury or developmental defect. It is characterized by spastic paralysis, muscular incoordination, and often a severe speech impediment. Yet though the child with cerebral palsy may appear mentally retarded, this disorder generally affects the motor areas of the brain, and the intelligence is usually normal or even above normal.

Chorea

The name of this CNS disorder comes from a Greek word meaning "dance," and it is characterized by involuntary, irregular, jerky movements of the body. The type called **St. Vitus's Dance** commonly follows a disease such as rheumatic fever. **Huntington's chorea** is a hereditary mental disorder characterized by irregular movements, speech disturbances, and progressive mental deterioration. It is inherited through a dominant allele and usually appears late in life.

Coma

Coma is a state of unconsciousness or stupor in which the person is totally unable to respond to auditory, visual, tactile, thermal, pain, or other stimuli. It may result from head injury, disease, poison, or some chemical imbalance in the body. Coma may last for only a few minutes, or for days or longer. After recovering from a coma, the person may exhibit **amnesia,** a loss of memory.

Concussion

This is a bruising of the brain caused by a violent blow on the head, usually resulting in a brief period of unconsciousness. Reversible damage to the brainstem centers may be involved, and the regaining of consciousness may be followed by a temporary amnesia.

Encephalitis

This is an inflammation of the brain, caused by a virus of the genus *Erro* and characterized by lethargy, apathy, and drowsiness. It is one form of "sleeping sickness."

Epilepsy

This disorder, resulting from a brain lesion (due to traumatic injury, disease, or of unknown origin), is characterized by recurrent convulsive seizures and loss of consciousness, as an uncontrolled wave of electrical discharges sweeps through the brain (Figure 13-26). A typical **grand mal** seizure proceeds through a tonic phase of boardlike rigidity, followed by a clonic phase of uncontrolled jerking of the body. After regaining consciousness, the person may have no memory of the seizure. In a milder form, **petit mal,** the person has brief recurrent "blank spells," of which he or she may have no awareness or recollection. The majority of epileptics are now able to live normal lives through the use of seizure-controlling drugs.

Fainting

This is a brief loss of consciousness, which lasts only a few seconds or minutes. It may result from a blow on the head, or from a pooling of blood in the lower extremities, or it may be a symptom of disease.

Headache

This is the most common of all CNS disorders. The next time you are suffering through the misery of an aching head, you might reflect that it is actually not your brain that is hurting (since the nerve cells of the brain are insensitive to pain). Most headaches are due to swollen blood vessels in the head or stretching or irritation of the meninges. Headaches can occur in the absence of any definite pathology, or may be a symptom of a serious disorder such as a brain tumor. A toothache, a bad cold that blocks up the sinuses, eyestrain, fatigue, constipation, or a poison such as alcohol, which irritates the meninges, can cause a headache. Most headaches are transitory, but

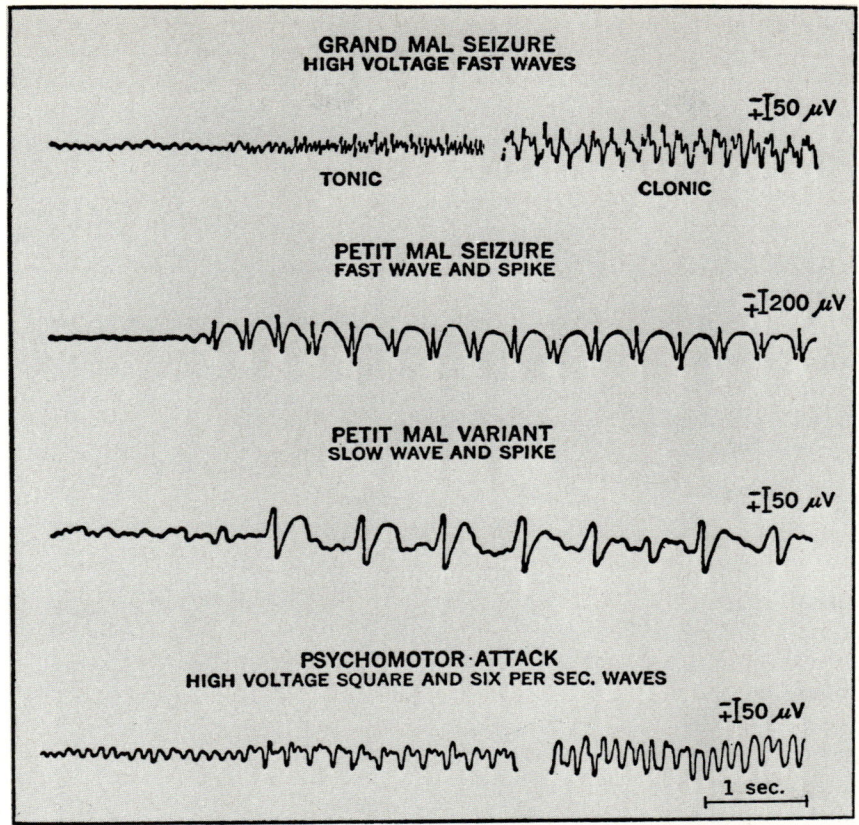

GRAND MAL SEIZURE
HIGH VOLTAGE FAST WAVES

∓[50 µV

TONIC   CLONIC

PETIT MAL SEIZURE
FAST WAVE AND SPIKE

∓[200 µV

PETIT MAL VARIANT
SLOW WAVE AND SPIKE

∓[50 µV

PSYCHOMOTOR ATTACK
HIGH VOLTAGE SQUARE AND SIX PER SEC. WAVES

∓[50 µV

1 sec.

FIGURE 13-26 Typical EEG tracings in several types of epileptic seizures. Compare these with the normal EEG patterns in the waking (Fig. 13-3) and sleeping (Fig. 13-15) states.

some may be chronic, lasting or recurring over a period of months or years. Headaches may also have psychological causes; when they are associated with emotional tension, the pain often starts in the occipital region and spreads over the entire head. One of the most effective drugs for the relief of heacache pain is **aspirin.** According to recent studies, it seems to work by blocking natural pain chemicals, **kinins,** which are released when tissues are irritated, and it inhibits the production of **prostaglandins,** hormones that can cause fever and headaches.

A common and especially painful type of headache is the **migraine,** which is commonly preceded or accompanied by visual effects, such as spots before the eyes and an extreme sensitivity to light, and by gastrointestinal upset. It occurs in five to ten percent of the population, more commonly in women, and may be triggered by an allergy or an emotional stress. The pain is often restricted to one side of the head. Caffeine (which constricts the superficial blood vessels) and ergot derivatives have proved helpful in the treatment of migraine.

Meningitis This is an inflammation of the meninges (cranial, spinal, or both). It can be caused by infection by bacteria, viruses, or fungi, and is often characterized by fever, pain in the back and extremities, and paralysis.

Mental Illness It is far more common than most people realize or are willing to admit. Two categories of mental disorders are usually distinguished: **neurosis,** in which the person can function reasonably well in society but has one or more personality "quirks," such as an irrational fear (phobia) or an obsessive emphasis on neatness; and **psychosis,** a more serious condition typified by a withdrawal from reality and behavior that is socially unacceptable. Psychosis may take a number of forms. In **schizophrenia,** a person may withdraw into a world of fantasy, eventually losing contact with the real world outside. The schizophrenic may sink into a state of almost complete inactivity or explode into a sudden outbreak of violent rage. It is now believed that the disordered thoughts and hallucinations of the schizophrenic may involve some disorder in the norepinephrine and dopamine systems, which excite the brain with more stimuli than it can cope with. The **paranoid** form of schizophrenia is a variation marked by delusions and irrational suspicions. In another type of severe mental illness, the patient's moods swing widely, from great elation to the deepest despair. This is a **manic-depressive psychosis.** In some people, only the depressive phase is observed. (Everyone gets depressed now and then, but when the depression is persistent and has no objective cause, it is a form of mental illness and can lead to an inability to function or ultimately to suicide.) Depression is sometimes successfully treated with electroshock therapy (the passage of an electric current through the brain) and with drugs such as lithium carbonate. Great progress in the treatment of mental illness has been made in recent years, since a shift of attitude has focused on a search for causes and cures in the biochemistry of the brain.

Multiple Sclerosis

This is a disease of the CNS characterized by hardening of patches of connective tissue in the brain and spinal cord. It occurs mainly in the 20 to 40 age group and gets progressively worse, with such symptoms as general weakness, muscular incoordination, blurring of vision, speech impediment, and incontinence. There may be periods of absence of symptoms lasting months or years, but ultimately death results; at present the disease is incurable.

Parkinsonism

Also called "shaking palsy," this is a disease affecting the elderly. Typical symptoms include masklike rigidity of the facial features, a monotonous voice, muscle weakness, a shuffling gait, tremor, and excessive sweating and "hot flashes." The condition has been found to be associated with lower-than-normal levels of dopamine and is now treated with a dopamine derivative, L-dopa, which is capable of crossing the blood-brain barrier and is converted to dopamine in the brain.

Poliomyelitis

The development of the Salk and Sabin polio vaccines was greeted by tremendous enthusiasm and still stands out in the minds of the public as one of the great medical achievements of this century. Yet poliomyelitis never was one of the major killers. In a way, its effects were even worse: this disease could leave its victims paralyzed and crippled for life. Poliomyelitis is a viral disease, which attacks the CNS and produces fever, sore throat, headache, vomiting, and stiffness of the neck and back. If the cell bodies of motor neurons in the anterior gray horns of the spinal cord are affected, flaccid paralysis of the lower limbs may result; involvement of nerve cells in the medulla results in paralysis of the respiratory muscles. At one time it was a scourge of the young (an alternate name was "infantile paralysis"); now public health officials fear that public complacency and a tendency not to bother about immunizations may be preparing the ground for new serious epidemics.

Syringomyelia

This is a condition characterized by abnormal liquid-filled cavities within the gray substance of the spinal cord, resulting in wasting of the muscles and a loss of the senses of temperature and pain.

Tabes Dorsalis

This is a progressive degeneration of the dorsal gray columns of the spinal cord and sensory nerve roots, caused by syphilis. It is accompanied by acute pain, loss of reflexes and muscular coordination, muscle weakness, and often incontinence and impotence.

SUMMARY

The central nervous system consists of the brain and spinal cord.
  It is protected by the skull and vertebral column, by the meninges, and by cerebrospinal fluid.
  Both the brain and spinal cord contain gray and white matter.
  A tract is a group of CNS nerve fibers with a common origin and common destination.
The brain is divided into:
  Forebrain
    Telencephalon (cerebrum)
    Diencephalon (thalamus, hypothalamus, pineal gland, etc.)
  Midbrain (mesencephalon)
    Corpora quadrigemina (superior and inferior colliculi)
    Cerebral peduncles
    Aqueduct of Sylvius
  Hindbrain
    Pons
    Medulla oblongata
    Cerebellum
The brainstem consists of the midbrain, pons, and medulla.
The cerebrum contains:
  Gray matter (cortex and basal ganglia)
  White matter (projection fibers, association fibers, and commissural fibers)
The extensive wrinkles and folds of the cerebral surface are called convolutions and consist of gyri (ridges) and sulci (grooves), with several deeper fissures.
The lobes of the cerebrum are:
  Frontal
  Parietal
  Occipital
  Temporal
An electroencephalograph records action potentials ("brain waves") from the brain.
Mapped areas of the cerebral cortex include:
  Motor strip
  Sensory strip
  Visual area
  Auditory area
  Taste area
  Smell area
  Speech areas
Dominance of one cerebral hemisphere over the other is responsible for "handedness"; each hemisphere controls and receives sensory information from the opposite side of the body; interchange of information is provided by the corpus callosum.
Memory is of two types: temporary and fixed (long-term) memory.
  Each memory is stored redundantly in the cerebral cortex.
  The storage and retrieval of memories seems to involve both electrical and chemical phenomena, including the formation of an engram (memory trace).
The basal ganglia include:
  Caudate nucleus
  Lenticular nucleus (putamen and globus pallidum)
  Amygdala
  Claustrum

The thalamus is a central relay station in the pathways interconnecting the cerebral cortex and spinal cord.

The pineal gland is believed to be the body's biological clock.

The hypothalamus contains numerous control centers, including:

Cardiovascular regulation

Body temperature regulation

Regulation of food intake (both hunger and satiety centers)

Regulation of gastrointestinal activity

Regulation of water balance (via ADH and thirst center)

Sleeping and wakefulness

Sexual activity

Emotions (anger, fear, and pleasure centers)

It also secretes releasing factors that regulate the activity of the pituitary gland, thus controlling endocrine functions.

The limbic system includes the thalamus, hypothalamus, septal area, hippocampus, amygdala, parts of the reticular formation, and the limbic region of the cerebral cortex.

It places emotional "tags" on disturbances of equilibrium for recognition by the cerebral cortex, and may produce psychosomatic illness.

The hippocampus gives sensory information an emotional coloring and functions in the long-term fixation of memories.

The superior colliculi control optic reflexes (blinking, adjustment of pupil).

The inferior colliculi are relay stations in the auditory pathway and control auditory reflexes.

The cerebellum is connected with the cerebral cortex and spinal cord and coordinates body movements, adjusting muscle contractions to carry out the cerebrum's intentions, and maintaining equilibrium.

The pons is a relay station linking the medulla with higher cortical centers and containing cell bodies of the reticular formation.

The medulla oblongata contains the origins of cranial nerves, relay stations in sensory tracts, and control centers:

Cardiac

Vasoconstrictor

Respiratory

Swallowing

Coughing

Vomiting

Sneezing

Hiccupping

The reticular formation is a network of nerve cells running through the medulla, pons, midbrain, and into parts of the thalamus and hypothalamus.

It maintains muscle tone, keeps the higher brain in a state of alert wakefulness (reticular activating system), and filters incoming stimuli.

During sleep there is a reduced activity of many body functions (breathing, heart rate, blood pressure, body temperature, etc.).

A night's sleep normally consists of repetitive cycles including phases of shallow and deep sleep and dreaming (REM) sleep, all of which show characteristic patterns on EEG tracings.

Deprivation of sleep, or of its individual phases, produces harmful effects.

The brain is extremely active metabolically and receives a disproportionate share of the cardiac output and oxygen consumed.

The internal carotid arteries and basical artery, via the circle of Willis, supply the brain; blood is drained via cranial venous sinuses into the internal jugular veins.

Stroke is a sudden lesion of a blood vessel in the brain, caused by hemorrhage, thrombosis, or embolism.

The three meninges are:

Dura mater (outer layer)

Arachnoid membrane (middle layer)

Pia mater (inner layer)

The four ventricles of the brain are:

Lateral ventricles (first and second)

Third ventricle

Fourth ventricle

The ventricles of the brain, subarachnoid space, and central canal of the spinal cord are filled with cerebrospinal fluid, which cushions the brain and spinal cord.

Hydrocephalus is caused by an excess of cerebrospinal fluid inside the cranial cavity.

Blood-cerebrospinal and blood-brain barriers prevent the passage of various chemicals and drugs into the fluids of the brain.

The spinal cord extends from the foramen magnum down to the level of the second lumbar vertebra.

It consists of outer white matter (ascending and descending nerve fiber tracts) and inner gray matter (nerve cell bodies).

Thirty-one pairs of spinal nerves emerge from the spinal cord as dorsal and ventral roots and innervate the neck, trunk, and extremities.

The spinal cord provides conduction pathways to and from the brain and contains reflex centers.

Ascending tracts of the spinal cord include:

Posterior funiculi (fasciculus gracilis and fasciculus cuneatus)—movement, position, touch, and pressure

Spinothalamic tracts (anterior and lateral)—touch, pressure, pain, temperature

Spinocerebellar tracts (posterior and anterior)—kinesthetic information

Spinotectal tract—touch, pain, temperature; auditory and visual reflexes

Descending tracts of the spinal cord include:

Corticospinal or pyramidal tracts—main motor pathway

Extrapyramidal tracts

Rubrospinal—relay from cerebellum

Tectospinal—optic and auditory reflexes

Vestibulospinal—maintenance of balance and posture

Descending autonomic tracts

Lateral and medial reticulospinal—facilitation or inhibition of motor neurons

A reflex action is performed automatically in response to a stimulus, without conscious thought or decision. Reflexes are normally consistent and predictable.

They can be consciously enhanced or inhibited, but with difficulty.

A conditioned reflex involves a learned association of a specific response with a particular stimulus and involves the higher brain.

A reflex arc is an interconnected nerve pathway including:

A sensory receptor

A sensory neuron

A connector (internuncial) neuron

A motor neuron

An effector

Reflexes studied clinically are classified as:

Superficial (e.g., plantar reflex)

Deep (e.g., knee jerk reflex)

Visceral (e.g., regulation of pupil size)

Pathological (e.g., Babinski reflex)

CNS lesions can result from traumatic injury, disease, tumors, hemorrhages.

Effects of CNS lesions include paralysis (flaccid or spastic), anesthesia, impairment of body functions controlled by the brain or spinal cord, and convulsive seizures.

Disorders of the CNS include:

Cerebral palsy

Chorea

Coma

Concussion
Encephalitis
Epilepsy (grand mal, petit mal)
Fainting
Headache (including migraine)
Hydrocephalus
Meningitis
Mental Illness
    Neuroses (phobias, obsessions, compulsions, hysteria)
    Psychoses (schizophrenia, paranoia, manic-depressive psychosis)
Multiple sclerosis
Parkinsonism
Poliomyelitis
Stroke
Syringomyelia
Tabes dorsalis

QUESTIONS FOR REVIEW AND THOUGHT

1 The cerebral cortex distinguishes *Homo sapiens* from the lower animals. Discuss.

2 List the principal divisions of the brain and their main functions.

3 Distinguish between gyrus and sulcus; forebrain and hindbrain; projection areas and association areas; sensory and motor strips; thalamus and hypothalamus.

4 If an anesthetic is injected into the left internal carotid artery while a person is singing a song, the person will suddenly forget the lyrics; a similar injection into the right internal carotid artery will make the person suddenly unable to carry a tune. Discuss in terms of cerebral blood circulation and cerebral hemisphere specialization.

5 Trace the sequence of events involved in memorizing a list of anatomical structures. (Include the formation of memory traces in the brain.) In view of what is known about the formation and retrieval of memories, what techniques can be used to make the learning process most effective? Would it be more effective to study at night before sleeping or first thing in the morning?

6 Discuss the functions of the hypothalamus.

7 Describe the structures and functions of the limbic system.

8 Describe the structures and functions of the reticular activating system.

9 Some people claim they never dream. Could this be true? If not, why might people believe they do not dream?

10 A mosquito bites your leg, and you automatically slap at it. Trace the sequence of events in this reflex action. What nervous system structures are involved? Is this a simple reflex?

11 Discuss factors that can damage the CNS and give an example of each.

THE PERIPHERAL NERVOUS SYSTEM

14

A favorite science fiction theme is the "cyborg," a living human brain removed from its original body and encased in an artificial housing, bathed with nutrients, and supplied with a variety of electrically transmitted sensory inputs and outputs to effectors. The essence of human personality is preserved in such a cyborg, for the brain is intact. But the entire peripheral nervous system, which keeps a person in touch with his or her surroundings, has been stripped away and replaced with artificial analogs. Probably attempts to create cyborgs will be undertaken at some future time, for such people/machine hybrids would offer some unique advantages. Direct linkages to powerful computers would provide an enormous increase in memory capacity and calculating speed; artificial effectors could be equipped with superhuman strength or the ability to survive in environments inhospitable to an unprotected human—even in space. But it might be wondered how long a cyborg would remain truly "human" in personality and outlook. Without the peripheral nervous system one was born with, a person's daily experiences would be unimaginably different and would tend to subtly reshape one's view of the self and the universe.

The human brain may well be the most complex entity in the universe. Yet without its links to the outside world, it would be essentially useless, unable to receive information or put its desires and decisions into effect. These links are provided by the peripheral nerves, which penetrate virtually every part of the body. Peripheral nerves branch out from the brain and spinal cord and run as slender threads through the head, trunk, and extremities.

For convenience, peripheral nerves are generally classified as **cranial nerves** and **spinal nerves,** depending on whether they depart from the brain or spinal cord. A functional distinction is between **sensory nerves,** which carry messages to the CNS, and **motor nerves,** which carry impulses away from the CNS. **Mixed nerves** contain both sensory and motor fibers. The major cranial and spinal nerves are shown in Figure 14-1.

THE CRANIAL NERVES

Generations of medical students have used a brief jingle to help them remember the cranial nerves in the order in which they emerge from the brain:

> On old Olympus' towering tops,
> A Finn and German viewed some hops.

This rhyme may not make very good poetry (or much sense), but the initial letters of the words provide memory tags for the olfactory, optic, oculomotor, trochlear, trigeminal, abducens, facial, acoustic, glossopharyngeal, vagus, (spinal) accessory, and hypo-

glossal nerves. These cranial nerves are traditionally numbered, using Roman numerals, according to their site of emergence from the brain, in the direction from most anterior (olfactory) to posterior. Often the numbers are used as convenient synonyms for the names of the cranial nerves.

A glance at Table 14-1, which summarizes the distribution and functions of these nerves, will emphasize that the cranial nerves are a heterogeneous group, with little in common other than their origin in the brain. They emerge on the underside of the brain, near the pons, medulla, and diencephalon (these **superficial origins** are shown in Figure 14-2A); their **deep origins** (the sites of the cell bodies of their neurons) are indicated in Figure 14-2B. The cranial nerves are arranged symmetrically and are usually described as 12 pairs. Actually, however, the olfactory nerves are not really a "pair," comprising about 15 or 20 on each side.

Considering the concentration of special sense organs in the head, it is not surprising that a number of the cranial nerves (the first, second, third, fourth, sixth, and eighth pairs) are expressly devoted to the sensory and motor supply of these special sense organs. Some of the cranial nerves are exclusively sensory (I, II, VIII), others motor (III, IV, VI, XI, XII), and still others mixed (V, VII, IX, X). Their distribution (Figure 14-3) also varies widely, from the extensively branching vagus nerve to the narrowly specific trochlear and abducens nerves, each of which innervates just one striated muscle. The cranial nerves supply mainly the head and neck; the vagus nerve innervates various structures of the trunk.

Olfactory Nerve (I)

If just a few molecules of butyl mercaptan (the odorous ingredient in a skunk's spray) chance to strike the specialized olfactory cells in the lining of your nose, you will promptly become conscious of a highly disagreeable odor. As with the other senses, smells are perceived only after information has been transmitted from the specialized sense receptors to the appropriate analyzing areas of the brain. The olfactory nerves provide the afferent pathways for small sensations.

The neurons of the first pair of cranial nerves have their origin in the mucous membrane lining the nasal cavities. The dendrites of the cell bodies are specialized to respond to the particular configurations of the molecules of odoriferous substances. When they are excited, impulses are transmitted along the axons, which combine to form about 40 minute nerve filaments, which pass through the cribriform plate of the ethmoid bone to join with the olfactory bulbs under the frontal lobes of the brain (see Figure 14-4). There they synapse with other neurons, whose axons form

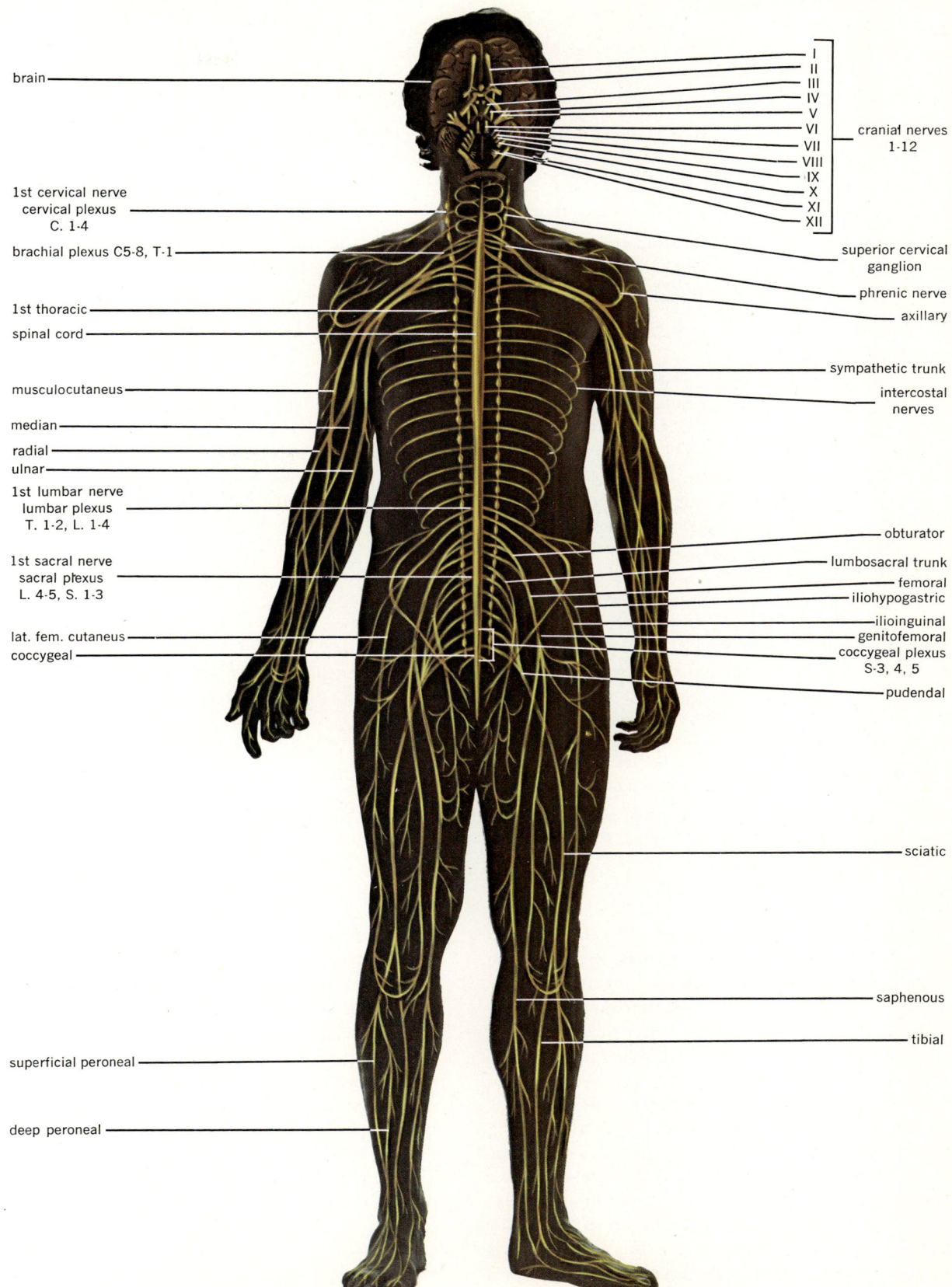

brain

I
II
III
IV
V
VI
VII
VIII
IX
X
XI
XII

cranial nerves
1-12

1st cervical nerve
cervical plexus
C. 1-4

brachial plexus C5-8, T-1

1st thoracic

spinal cord

musculocutaneus

median

radial

ulnar

1st lumbar nerve
lumbar plexus
T. 1-2, L. 1-4

1st sacral nerve
sacral plexus
L. 4-5, S. 1-3

lat. fem. cutaneus

coccygeal

superficial peroneal

deep peroneal

superior cervical
ganglion

phrenic nerve

axillary

sympathetic trunk

intercostal
nerves

obturator

lumbosacral trunk

femoral

iliohypogastric

ilioinguinal

genitofemoral

coccygeal plexus
S-3, 4, 5

pudendal

sciatic

saphenous

tibial

FIGURE 14-1 Major cranial and spinal nerves.

TABLE 14-1   The Cranial Nerves

NUMBER AND NAME		DISTRIBUTION	FUNCTION
I	Olfactory	Mucous membrane of nose	Sensory (smell)
II	Optic	Retina of eye	Sensory (vision)
III	Oculomotor	Muscles of eye (superior, medial, inferior recti; inferior oblique; levator palpebrae superioris; ciliary; iris)	Motor (eye movements, regulation of size of pupil, accommodation)
IV	Trochlear	Superior oblique muscle of eye	Motor (eye movements)
V	Trigeminal	Face and underlying structures (sensory); muscles of mastication (motor)	Mixed (sensations of head and face; chewing movements)
VI	Abducens	Lateral rectus muscle of eye	Motor (abduction of eye)
VII	Facial	Superficial muscles of face and scalp	Mixed, mainly motor (facial expressions; secretion of saliva; taste from front of tongue)
VIII	Acoustic	Vestibular branch: semicircular canals, utricle, and saccule; cochlear branch: organ of Corti	Sensory (vestibular: sense of movement of body through space, position of head; cochlear: hearing)
IX	Glossopharyngeal	Pharynx; taste buds of posterior third of tongue; carotid sinus and carotid body; stylopharyngeus muscle	Mixed (taste from back of tongue; swallowing movements; secretion of saliva; pain, touch, heat, and cold in pharynx; afferent in reflex control of blood pressure and respiration)
X	Vagus	Pharynx, larynx, thoracic and abdominal viscera	Mixed, mainly motor (parasympathetic to organs of thorax and abdomen—e.g., slows heart, increases peristalsis; contracts muscles for voice production; important in respiratory, cardiac, and circulatory reflexes)
XI	Spinal accessory	Muscles of soft palate, pharynx, larynx, and thoracic and abdominal viscera; trapezius and sternocleidomastoid muscles	Motor (shoulder movements, turning of head; movements of viscera; voice production)
XII	Hypoglossal	Muscles of tongue	Motor (tongue movements in speech, mastication, and deglutition)

the olfactory tracts of the brain and relay the impulses to the cerebral cortex. Strictly speaking, the olfactory nerves themselves can be regarded not as true peripheral nerves, but rather as tracts or extensions of the brain.

Optic Nerve (II)

More than a third of all the cranial nerve fibers are contained in the optic nerve, and a corresponding wealth of information constantly passes along these fibers. Unlike most of our mammalian relatives, we humans have been committed by evolution to an extreme degree of reliance on the organ of vision for most of our sensory input. Yet if the optic nerve is cut, a person will be blinded, even though the eyes may be perfectly undamaged. Impulses from the light-sensitive receptors in the retina of the eye are transmitted along the optic nerve to the brain, and only when they have been relayed to the visual cortex are images actually perceived.

Like the olfactory nerves, the optic nerves should be viewed as extensions of the central nervous system, rather than true peripheral nerves. (The fibers of the optic nerve lack a Schwann sheath.) Each optic nerve is composed of about 1.25 million individual nerve fibers, whose cell bodies are situated in the retina. The optic nerves enter the cranial cavity through the optic foramina, and shortly thereafter the two nerves meet at the floor of the diencephalon and appear to cross, forming an X-shaped structure called the **optic chiasma** (see Figure 14-4). The fibers from the medial portion of each retina actually do cross and enter the

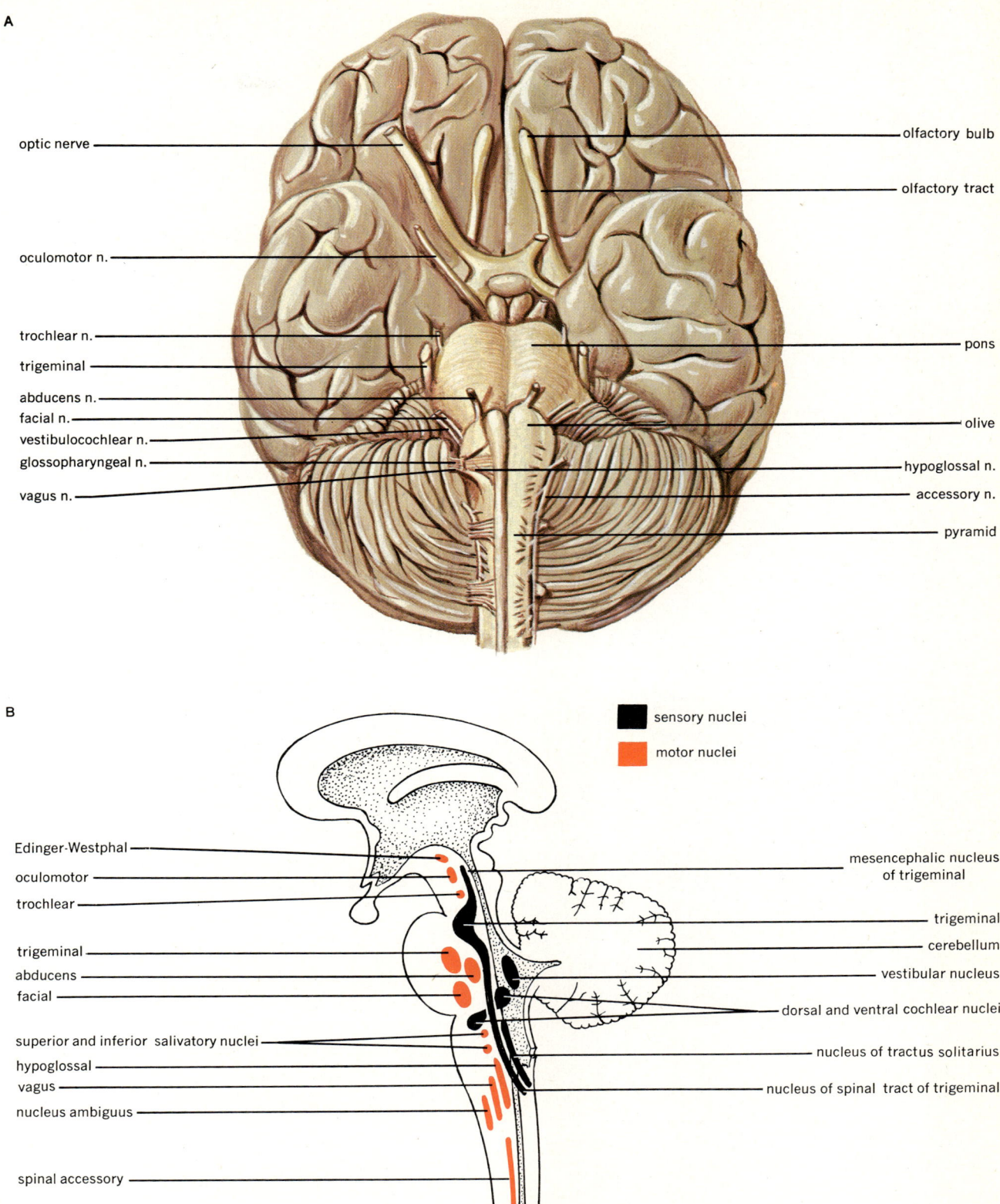

A

optic nerve

olfactory bulb

olfactory tract

oculomotor n.

trochlear n.

trigeminal

abducens n.

facial n.

vestibulocochlear n.

glossopharyngeal n.

vagus n.

pons

olive

hypoglossal n.

accessory n.

pyramid

B

sensory nuclei

motor nuclei

Edinger-Westphal

oculomotor

trochlear

trigeminal

abducens

facial

superior and inferior salivatory nuclei

hypoglossal

vagus

nucleus ambiguus

spinal accessory

mesencephalic nucleus
of trigeminal

trigeminal

cerebellum

vestibular nucleus

dorsal and ventral cochlear nuclei

nucleus of tractus solitarius

nucleus of spinal tract of trigeminal

FIGURE 14-2   The cranial nerves: view from the underside of the brain
showing their superficial origins (A) and lateral projection showing their
deep origins (B).

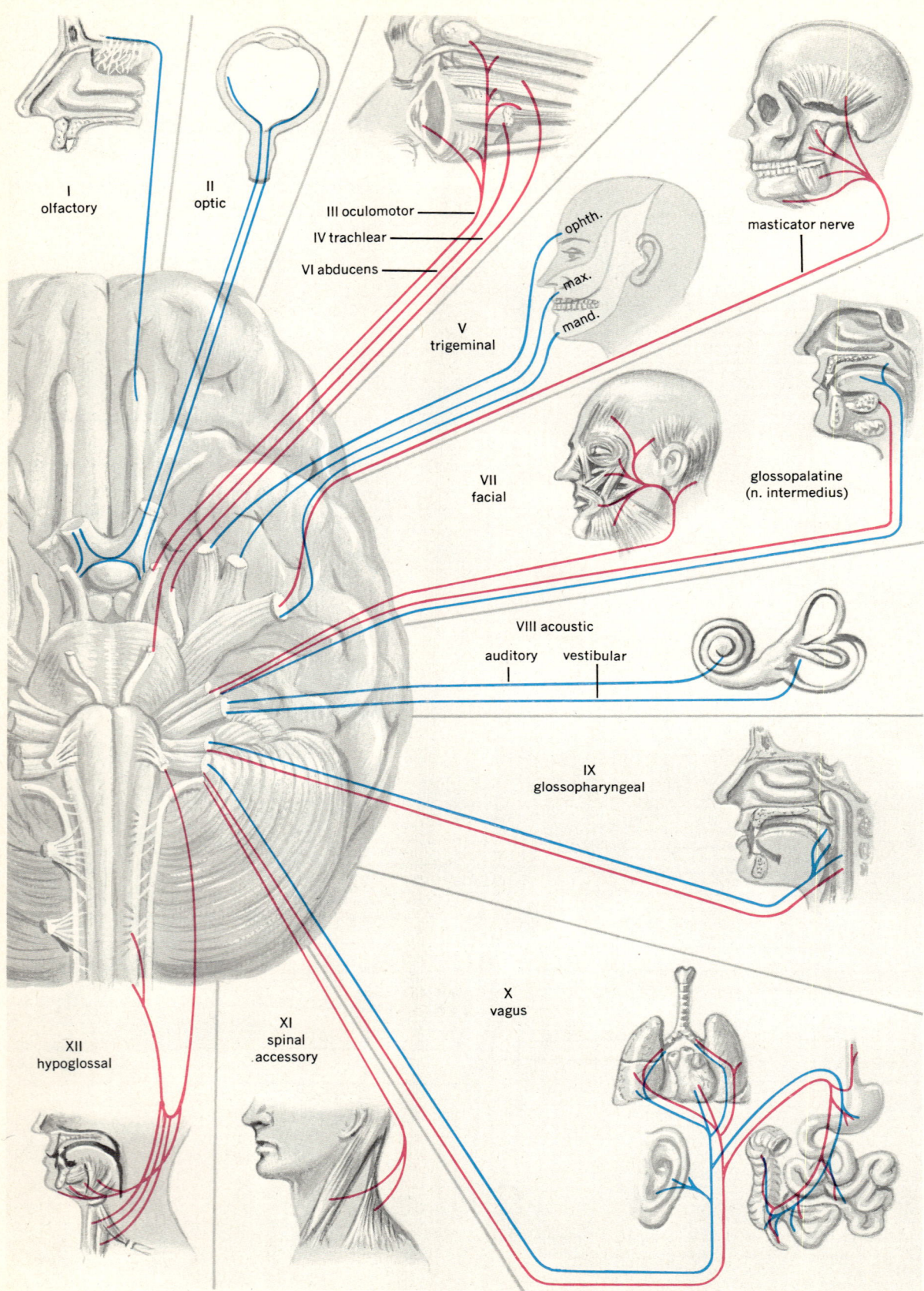

FIGURE 14-3 Distribution of the cranial nerves. Sensory nerves in blue, motor nerves in red.

hemisphere of the brain on the opposite side. Other fibers merely bend and remain on the same side of the brain. (Thus each half of the brain normally receives some information from both eyes.) The groups of nerve fibers beyond the optic chiasma are known as the **optic tracts.** The neurons of the optic tracts synapse in the thalamus with neurons leading to the visual cortex in the occipital lobe, in the superior colliculus with neurons involved in visual reflexes, and with neurons in the nucleus of the oculomotor nerve, involved in pupillary reflexes.

Oculomotor Nerve (III)

When a person complains that things look blurred or doubled, a doctor may suspect damage to the oculomotor nerve. As its name implies, the third cranial nerve is involved in eye movements. It is a mixed nerve, containing fibers that transmit impulses from the eye muscles to the brain and other fibers that carry impulses from the brain to the eye muscles (see Figure 14-4). The oculomotor nerve is thus an integral part of the feedback circuit by which the eyes are continually moved about and focused. It supplies nerve fibers to four of the six external eye muscles that move the eye, as well as the ciliary and iris muscles, involved in adjusting the size of the pupil. The oculomotor nerve also innervates the levator palpebrae superioris muscle, which raises the eyelid.

Trochlear Nerve (IV)

The fourth cranial nerve is the smallest of all. Each trochlear nerve innervates just a single muscle—the superior oblique muscle of the eye on its own side of the head—supplying it with both sensory and motor fibers. Its function is mainly motor, moving the eyeball up and out, but it also carries proprioceptive impulses, conveying muscle sense from the superior oblique muscle.

Trigeminal Nerve (V)

Neuralgia of the trigeminal nerve, known as **tic douloureux,** is an excruciatingly painful condition. Relief can be obtained by a drastic measure: removal of the **gasserian ganglion,** a large swelling at the posterior root of the nerve. After the operation, the unfortunate patient is relieved of pain, but loses sensation in face, scalp, teeth, and conjunctiva on the treated side. For the rest of his life, he must take special precautions, wearing protective goggles and irrigating the eye frequently. He will never have a toothache on that side again, which may seem like a blessing, but is actually a loss of an important warning signal.

The trigeminal nerve is the largest of all the cranial nerves. It has three sensory branches, the **ophthalmic, maxillary,** and **mandibular nerves** (see Figure 14-4), which carry afferent impulses from the skin and mu-

cosa of the head and from the teeth, via the gasserian ganglion to the main sensory nucleus of the trigeminal nerve, situated in the pons. Sensations of pain, touch, and temperature are transmitted by these sensory branches. (If you have a sudden cold sensation from a tooth while eating ice cream, it was transmitted along your fifth cranial nerve.) A smaller motor branch runs from the trigeminal motor nucleus in the pons to the muscles of mastication, via the mandibular nerve, and stimulates contraction of the muscles of mastication. Through connections with the facial, glossopharyngeal, and vagus nerves, the trigeminal nerves are involved in the mediation of a variety of reflexes: corneal, lacrimal (tears), sneezing, vomiting, salivary, and oculocardiac reflexes.

Abducens Nerve (VI)

The stereotyped "shifty-eyed criminal" tends to overuse the lateral rectus muscles of his eyes, which are innervated by the sixth cranial nerve (See Figure 14-4). The abducens nerve is a small mixed nerve, whose afferent impulses carry proprioceptive messages to the brain, while the efferent impulses stimulate contraction of the muscles that move the eyeball laterally. The cell bodies of the efferent fibers of the abducens lie in a nucleus of the pons.

Facial Nerve (VII)

A wink, a frown, a grin, a lip-pursing whistle—all these facial expressions are controlled by impulses transmitted over the seventh pair of cranial nerves. Emerging from the cranial cavity through the internal auditory meatus, each facial nerve branches repeatedly, sending fibers to the stylohyoid muscle, the posterior belly of the digastric muscle, and the superficial muscles of the face and scalp (see Figure 14-4). Motor fibers are also supplied to the submaxillary and sublingual glands. Though the facial nerve is mainly motor, it does contain sensory fibers as well. Sensory fibers run from the taste buds in the anterior two-thirds of the tongue to cell bodies in the **geniculate ganglion,** a small swelling near the cochlea of the inner ear; fibers extend from the ganglion to a nucleus in the medulla.

Damage to the motor fibers of the facial nerve on one side produces paralysis of the facial muscles on that side. The paralyzed side is flat and expressionless, and the face has a one-sided appearance. Damage to the afferent fibers of the facial nerve results in a loss of the sense of taste from the anterior two-thirds of the tongue.

Acoustic Nerve (VIII)

The human ear is two separate organs in one. It is the organ of hearing, but it is also the organ of balance, informing the brain of movements of the body and

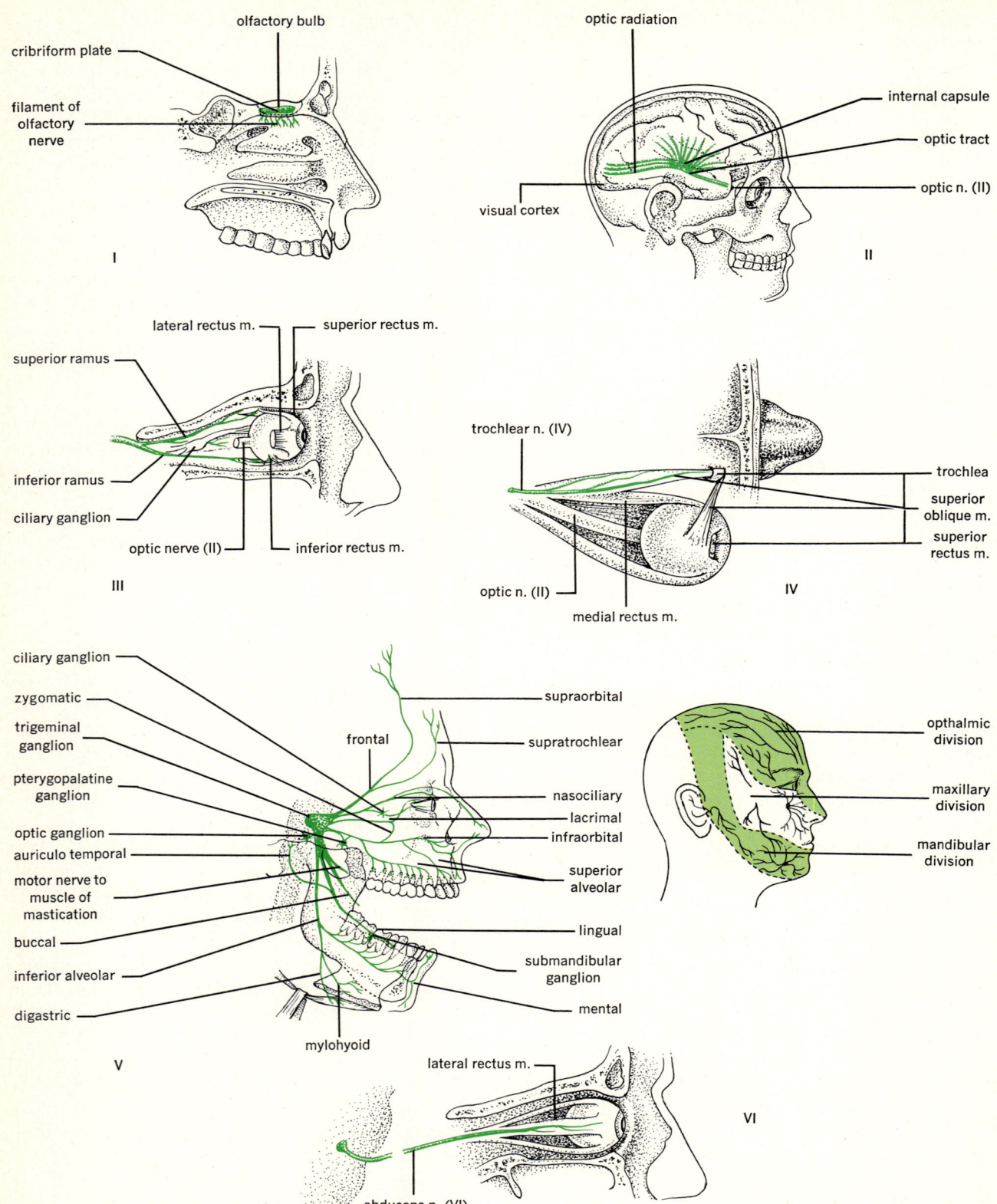

FIGURE 14-4   The cranial nerves: I. Olfactory. II. Optic. III. Oculomotor. IV. Trochlear. V. Trigeminal. VI. Abducens. VII. Facial. VIII. Acoustic. IX. Glossopharyngeal. X. Vagus. XI. Accessory. XII. Hypoglossal.

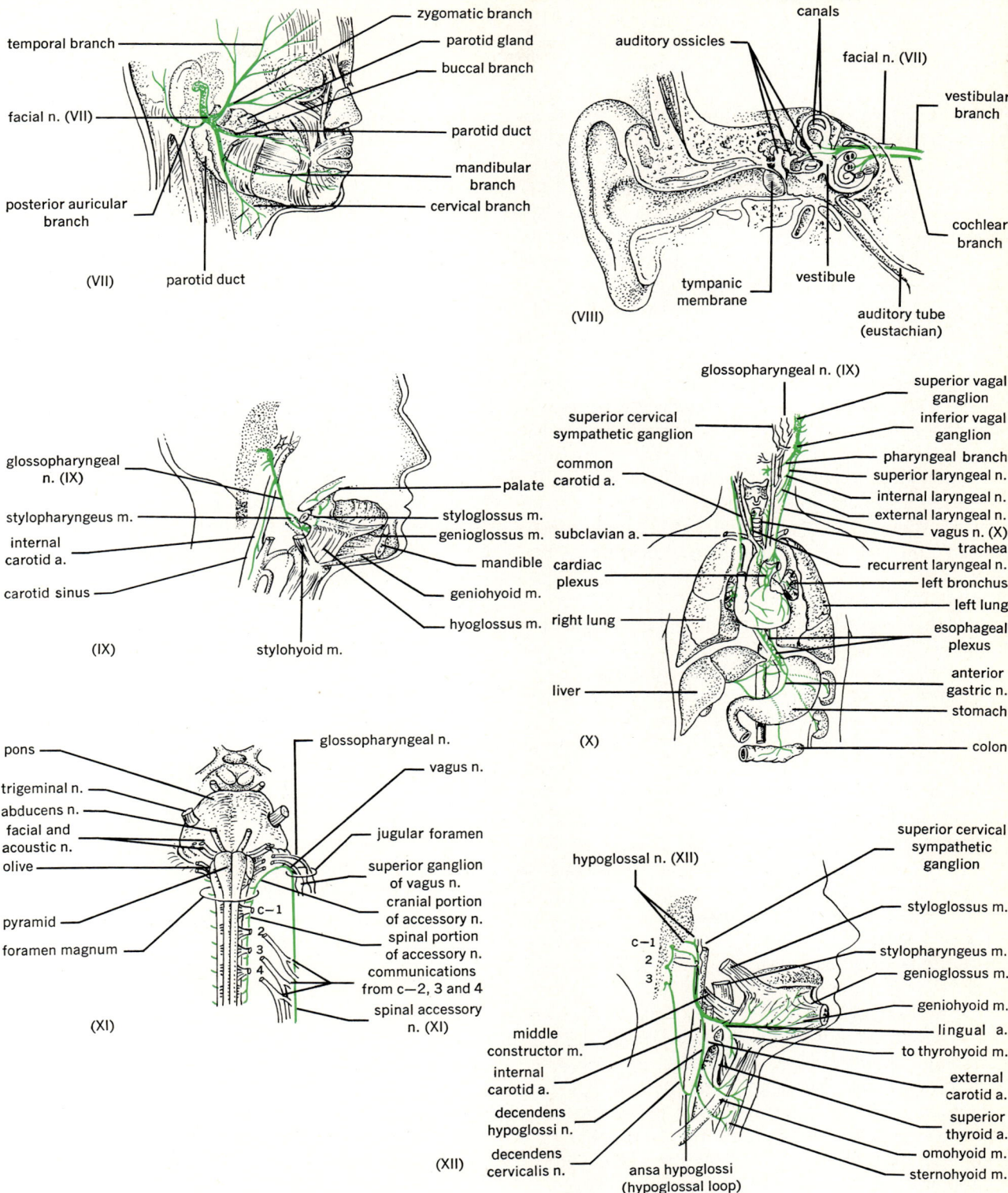

(VII)

temporal branch

facial n. (VII)

posterior auricular branch

parotid duct

zygomatic branch

parotid gland

buccal branch

parotid duct

mandibular branch

cervical branch

(VIII)

auditory ossicles

semicircular canals

facial n. (VII)

vestibular branch

cochlear branch

tympanic membrane

vestibule

auditory tube (eustachian)

(IX)

glossopharyngeal n. (IX)

stylopharyngeus m.

internal carotid a.

carotid sinus

stylohyoid m.

palate

styloglossus m.

genioglossus m.

mandible

geniohyoid m.

hyoglossus m.

(X)

glossopharyngeal n. (IX)

superior cervical sympathetic ganglion

common carotid a.

subclavian a.

cardiac plexus

right lung

liver

superior vagal ganglion

inferior vagal ganglion

pharyngeal branch

superior laryngeal n.

internal laryngeal n.

external laryngeal n.

vagus n. (X)

trachea

recurrent laryngeal n.

left bronchus

left lung

esophageal plexus

anterior gastric n.

stomach

colon

(XI)

pons

trigeminal n.

abducens n.

facial and acoustic n.

olive

pyramid

foramen magnum

glossopharyngeal n.

vagus n.

jugular foramen

superior ganglion of vagus n.

cranial portion of accessory n.

spinal portion of accessory n.

communications from c—2, 3 and 4

spinal accessory n. (XI)

c—1
2
3
4

(XII)

hypoglossal n. (XII)

c—1
2
3

middle constructor m.

internal carotid a.

decendens hypoglossi n.

decendens cervicalis n.

ansa hypoglossi (hypoglossal loop)

superior cervical sympathetic ganglion

styloglossus m.

stylopharyngeus m.

genioglossus m.

geniohyoid m.

lingual a.

to thyrohyoid m.

external carotid a.

superior thyroid a.

omohyoid m.

sternohyoid m.

head and of changes in their relative positions. The cranial nerves that supply the ear reflect this duality of function. The acoustic nerve is composed of two separate sets of sensory fibers, the **vestibular** and **cochlear** divisions (See Figure 14-4), which have different peripheral endings, central connections, and functions. The vestibular fibers run from the semicircular canals to the vestibular ganglion, situated in the internal auditory meatus, and thence to the vestibular nuclei in the pons and medulla. These are the fibers that report on movements in space and changes of position, and they play a key role in the maintenance of balance. The cochlear fibers arise from cell bodies in the spiral ganglion in the cochlea and extend from the organ of Corti to the cochlear nuclei between the medulla and pons.

Damage to the cochlear portion of the acoustic nerve results in a hearing loss. Damage to the vestibular fibers produces such symptoms as vertigo, a sensation of whirling movement, and nystagmus, rapid involuntary eye movements. The dual functions of the acoustic nerve are reflected in a newer name for the nerve, now gaining acceptance: the **statoacoustic nerve**—the nerve of equilibrium and hearing.

Glossopharyngeal Nerve (IX)

In many cases of accidental poisoning, an effective emergency first aid measure is first to dilute the poison in the stomach by having the victim drink quantities of warm salt water or milk, and then to induce vomiting, by tickling the back of the throat with a finger. The gag reflex that results in vomiting when the back of the tongue and pharynx are irritated is mediated through the glossopharyngeal nerve. As its name implies, this cranial nerve supplies mainly the tongue and pharynx (Figure 14-4). It is a mixed nerve. Sensory fibers convey information on general sensation from the posterior portion of the tongue, the tonsil, and the auditory tube to the brain. Other sensory fibers carry impulses concerned with taste sensations from the posterior third of the tongue. (This region is sensitive mainly to bitter tastes.) Another sensory branch of the ninth cranial nerve transmits sensations of touch, pain, and temperature from the skin back of the ear; still another group of afferent fibers carries messages from chemoreceptors in the carotid body and baroreceptors in the carotid sinus, playing a role in the reflex regulation of respiration and blood pressure. Efferent fibers of the glossopharyngeal nerve innervate the superior pharyngeal constrictor and stylopharyngeus muscles, which function in swallowing (and gagging); other efferent fibers, belonging to the autonomic nervous system, transmit impulses from a nucleus in the medulla to the parotid glands, the large salivary glands behind the ears.

Vagus Nerve (X)

The term *vagus* literally means "wanderer," and the nerve merits its name. After emerging from the side of the medulla, it ranges far and wide through the body, branching and rebranching to innervate such varied organs and structures as the pharynx, larynx, palate, trachea, bronchi, lungs, heart, esophagus, stomach, small intestine, liver, gall bladder, spleen, kidneys, and pancreas (See Figure 14-4). The functions of the vagus nerve are just as varied as the organs to which it is distributed. It is involved in the regulation of the circulation, heart rate, respiration, and digestion. Vagus nerve fibers are also involved in the reflexes of swallowing, coughing, and vomiting, as well as the function of phonation (the production of sounds). Afferent fibers carry impulses from scattered taste buds in the pharynx and larynx.

Vagotomy is occasionally used in the treatment of severe peptic ulcers. The vagus nerves are cut either as they pass downward over the surface of the esophagus in the thorax, or as they pass through the diaphragm to the surface of the stomach. Stomach secretions are blocked temporarily, and the ulcer usually heals within a week; but later the stomach secretions are restored, the ulcer may recur, and the motility of the stomach may be reduced to such an extent that it does not empty. Lesion of the vagus nerves at a higher level can have even more drastic effects: bilateral destruction is fatal, since it produces a complete laryngeal paralysis, resulting in death by asphyxia.

Accessory Nerve (XI)

The accessory nerve actually has two roots, one in the brainstem and the other in the upper segments of the spinal cord (See Figure 14-4). The spinal root passes upward alongside the spinal cord and emerges to join briefly with the cranial root. Then the two sets of fibers diverge again. The cranial portion travels with the vagus nerve, supplying motor fibers to the larynx and to the thoracic and abdominal viscera. The spinal portion innervates the trapezius and sternocleidomastoid muscles and is involved in movements of the head and shoulders. If this nerve is injured on one side, the head tends to turn toward the side of the injury.

Hypoglossal Nerve (XII)

By telling a patient, "Stick out your tongue and say 'Ah,'" a doctor can effectively test the functioning of two pairs of cranial nerves. The vagus nerve is involved in the production of the sound, and if it is normal the soft palate and uvula will be pulled up in the midline during phonation. (A drooping of one side indicates injury to the vagus nerve on that side.) The actual sticking out of the tongue is controlled via the motor fibers of the twelfth pair of cranial nerves.

If there is an injury to the hypoglossal nerve, the tongue will deviate toward the side of the injury.

The hypoglossal nerve fibers arise in the medulla and innervate both the extrinsic and the intrinsic muscles of the tongue (See Figure 14-4). These fibers are mainly efferent, involved in the varied movements of the tongue that are necessary for such activities as food manipulation, swallowing, and speech. But it is thought that afferent fibers are also present, carrying proprioceptive impulses from the muscle spindles in the tongue muscles to the central nervous system.

THE SPINAL NERVES

Walking, running, sitting down, writing, eating—all these common activities require a whole repertoire of finely coordinated movements of body parts. Each movement is produced by contractions of muscles, and the muscle contractions in turn are stimulated by impulses carried along nerves. In addition to the flow of motor impulses, there is a continual flow of sensory messages converging on the CNS from all parts of the body. Sensory nerves relay such information as the positions of the various body parts, the temperature of the outside environment, and the presence of an ant crawling up your leg. Most of the peripheral nerves that supply the trunk and extremities arise from the spinal cord and are referred to as spinal nerves.

Thirty-one pairs of spinal nerves, each containing thousands of nerve fibers, branch out from the spinal cord and emerge from the intervertebral foramina between adjacent vertebrae (Figure 14-5). The spinal nerves do not have special names, as the cranial nerves do. Instead, they are numbered and referred to according to the section of the vertebral column from which they emerge. Thus, there are 8 pairs of **cervical nerves,** 12 pairs of **thoracic nerves,** 5 pairs of **lumbar nerves,** 5 pairs of **sacral nerves,** and one pair of **coccygeal nerves.** In general, the spinal nerves are numbered according to the vertebra superior to the inter-

TABLE 14-2 The Spinal Nerves

SPINAL NERVES		PLEXUSES FORMED	SOME MAIN NERVES	PARTS SUPPLIED
Cervical	1 2 3 4	Cervical plexus	Branches from plexus Phrenic nerve	Sensory to back of head, front of neck, upper part of shoulder; motor to neck muscles and diaphragm
Cervical Thoracic	5 6 7 8 1	Brachial plexus	Musculocutaneous Ulnar Median Radial Axillary	Superficial muscles of scapula Pectoralis major and minor Skin and muscles of shoulder, arm, forearm, and hand
Thoracic	2–11	No plexus formed	Intercostal	Intercostal muscles, skin of thorax, back muscles
Thoracic Lumbar	12 1 2 3 4	Lumbar plexus	Iliohypogastric Ilioinguinal Genitofemoral Lateral femoral cutaneous Femoral Saphenous Obturator	Anterolateral abdominal wall, external genitalia Thigh, leg, medial side of foot
Lumbar Sacral	4 5 1 2 3	Sacral plexus	Gluteal Sciatic Tibial Peroneal Sural	Buttocks, thigh, leg, foot
Sacral	2 3 4	Pudendal plexus	Pudendal	Levator ani muscle, skin of perineum, muscles of external genitalia
Sacral Coccygeal	5 1	Coccygeal plexus	Coccygeal	Skin and ligaments in coccyx region; tail in animals

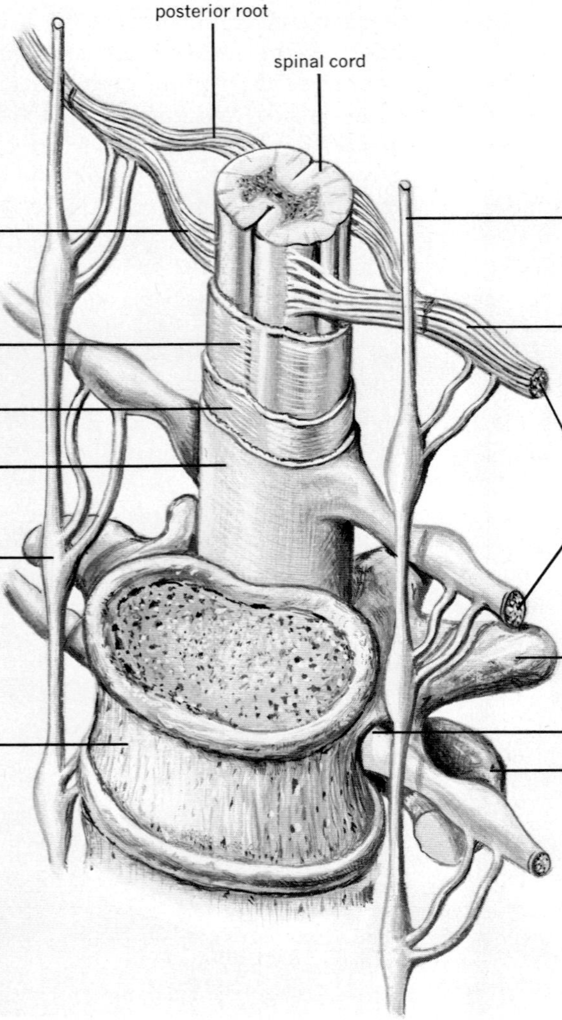

posterior root

spinal cord

anterior root

pia mater

arachnoid

dura mater

sympathetic
ganglion

body of vertebra

sympathetic
trunk

spinal ganglion

spinal nerves

transverse
process

vertebral canal

spinous process

FIGURE 14-5 The spinal cord and its
relationship to spinal nerves, a vertebra,
and the sympathetic trunk and ganglia.

vertebral foramina at which they emerge—for example, the second pair of lumbar nerves emerges just below the second lumbar vertebra. But the cervical nerves deviate from this general pattern. There are eight cervical nerves and only seven cervical vertebrae. The first pair of cervical nerves emerges between the first cervical vertebra and the skull, and each of the following six pairs of cervical nerves is also superior to the correspondingly numbered vertebra, until the eighth pair emerges between the seventh cervical vertebra and the first thoracic vertebra.

You may recall that the spinal cord does not extend down the full length of the vertebral column. As a result, the segments of the spinal cord (arbitrary divisions corresponding to the regions between the origins of adjacent pairs of spinal nerves) are not all lined up adjacent to the corresponding vertebrae. The displacement increases progressively down the vertebral column. The cervical nerves are nearly opposite the corresponding foramina. But lower down, the

nerve roots must travel downward within the spinal canal for progressively longer distances before they reach the appropriate foramina. The roots of the sacral nerves form a long bundle, the **cauda equina** ("horse's tail").

Each spinal nerve is a mixed nerve, containing both sensory and motor fibers. Each nerve emerges from the spinal cord as two separate roots (see Figure 14-5): a **dorsal root,** which contains only sensory fibers, and a **ventral root,** which contains only motor fibers. These two roots join in the intervertebral foramen to form a single mixed nerve. On the way to this junction, the dorsal nerve root develops a swelling, called a **dorsal root ganglion,** which contains the cell bodies of the sensory nerve fibers. Only a single process arises from the cell body of such a neuron, but it soon divides in two, one branch functioning as a dendrite and the other as an axon. (Such sensory neurons are called unipolar or T-shaped neurons.) The cell bodies of the motor fibers of the ventral roots lie in the spinal cord, and these roots do not form ganglia.

Shortly after the spinal nerve leaves the intervertebral foramen, it divides into four branches: a **meningeal ramus,** a **visceral** or **communicating ramus,** a **dorsal** (or posterior) **ramus,** and a **ventral** (or anterior) **ramus.** The meningeal ramus is a small branch, which turns back into the vertebral canal to supply the meninges. The visceral ramus is composed of two portions, a **white ramus** (myelinated nerve fibers) and a **gray ramus** (unmyelinated nerve fibers), and is part of the autonomic nervous system. The dorsal and ventral rami eventually split into medial and lateral branches, which branch and rebranch in turn to supply various parts of the body. The branches of the dorsal ramus supply the tissues of the back. The ventral rami are usually larger and more important; they serve the tissues of the front and sides of the body and all four extremities. An important point to remember is that the dorsal and ventral *rami* of the spinal nerves are mixed nerves, containing both afferent and efferent fibers, in contrast to the dorsal and ventral *roots,* which contain only sensory or only motor fibers, respectively.

Many of the major branches given off by spinal nerves travel together with important arteries and are given the same name as the artery they accompany; others are named for the body part they supply. The radial nerve, for example, passes down the radial side of the forearm, together with the radial artery. The intercostal nerves run around the trunk between the ribs. The sciatic nerves (their name translates as "pertaining to the ischium") run down from the sacral plexus (a network formed by the sacral nerves) through the buttocks and thighs to the popliteal region, then down into the legs and feet. The spinal nerves and their major branches are summarized in Table 14-2.

A characteristic feature of the spinal nerves is the fact that they communicate with one another, forming networks of nerve fibers called **plexuses.** These include the **cervical, brachial, lumbar, sacral,** and **pudendal** plexuses (Figure 14-6). The plexuses provide for a general redistribution of nerve fibers—that is, each branch of the plexus contains fibers derived from several different nerve roots, while the fibers from any one particular nerve root are carried to the periphery along several different pathways. The group of muscles innervated by a single ventral nerve root is called a **myotome.** There is considerable overlap between myotomes, so that any given muscle usually has a nerve supply from at least two spinal segments. It has been found that the sensory fibers are supplied to the skin in a consistent segmental pattern (Figure 14-7). The strip of skin supplied by a given dorsal nerve root is called a **dermatome.** There is extensive overlap between adjacent dermatomes, so that if a particular spinal nerve is injured, there may not necessarily be a complete loss of sensation in the region of the skin that it supplies.

Cervical Plexus

If you have a "pain in the neck"—literally rather than figuratively—it is likely that nerves of the cervical plexus are involved, for cutaneous branches from this plexus supply skin and muscles of the head, neck, and shoulder. The cervical plexus is formed by an intermingling of the anterior rami of the first four cervical spinal nerves. Motor fibers from the cervical plexus supply the trapezius and sternocleidomastoid muscles.

One of the most important branches from the cervical plexus, the **phrenic nerve,** is a motor nerve supplying the diaphragm. Irritation of the phrenic nerves leads to hiccups, spasmodic contractions of the diaphragm that result in inspiration, followed by an abrupt closing of the glottis (the opening between the vocal cords). If both phrenic nerves are cut or injured, as might occur in an automobile accident, in hanging, or in poliomyelitis, the diaphragm is paralyzed, breathing stops, and death will result. (An iron lung, which moves the diaphragm mechanically, can prolong the life of a polio victim.)

Brachial Plexus

The decidedly unfunny tingling that ensues when you hit your "funny bone" is the result of a mechanical stimulation of the **ulnar nerve,** one of the major branches from the brachial plexus. The plexus is formed by the anterior rami of the last four cervical and first thoracic spinal nerves, and it provides the nerve supply for the upper extremity. The brachial plexus is found in the shoulder region, from the neck to the armpit. Its main branches are the **musculocutaneous nerve,** which innervates the biceps brachii and provides sensory fibers for the skin on the outside of the forearm; the **radial nerve,** which is the largest branch and carries motor impulses to the triceps brachii and sensory messages from the posterior aspect of the forearm and hand; the **median nerve,** which supplies motor fibers to muscles on the anterior portion of the forearm and sensory fibers to the radial half of the palm; and the **ulnar nerve,** which supplies motor fibers to muscles of the anterior portion of the forearm and hand and sensory fibers to the ulnar portion of the hand. Injury to the ulnar nerve produces a sensation of "pins and needles" in the area where its sensory fibers are distributed.

Occasionally the brachial plexus may be stretched or torn during birth, causing numbness and paralysis

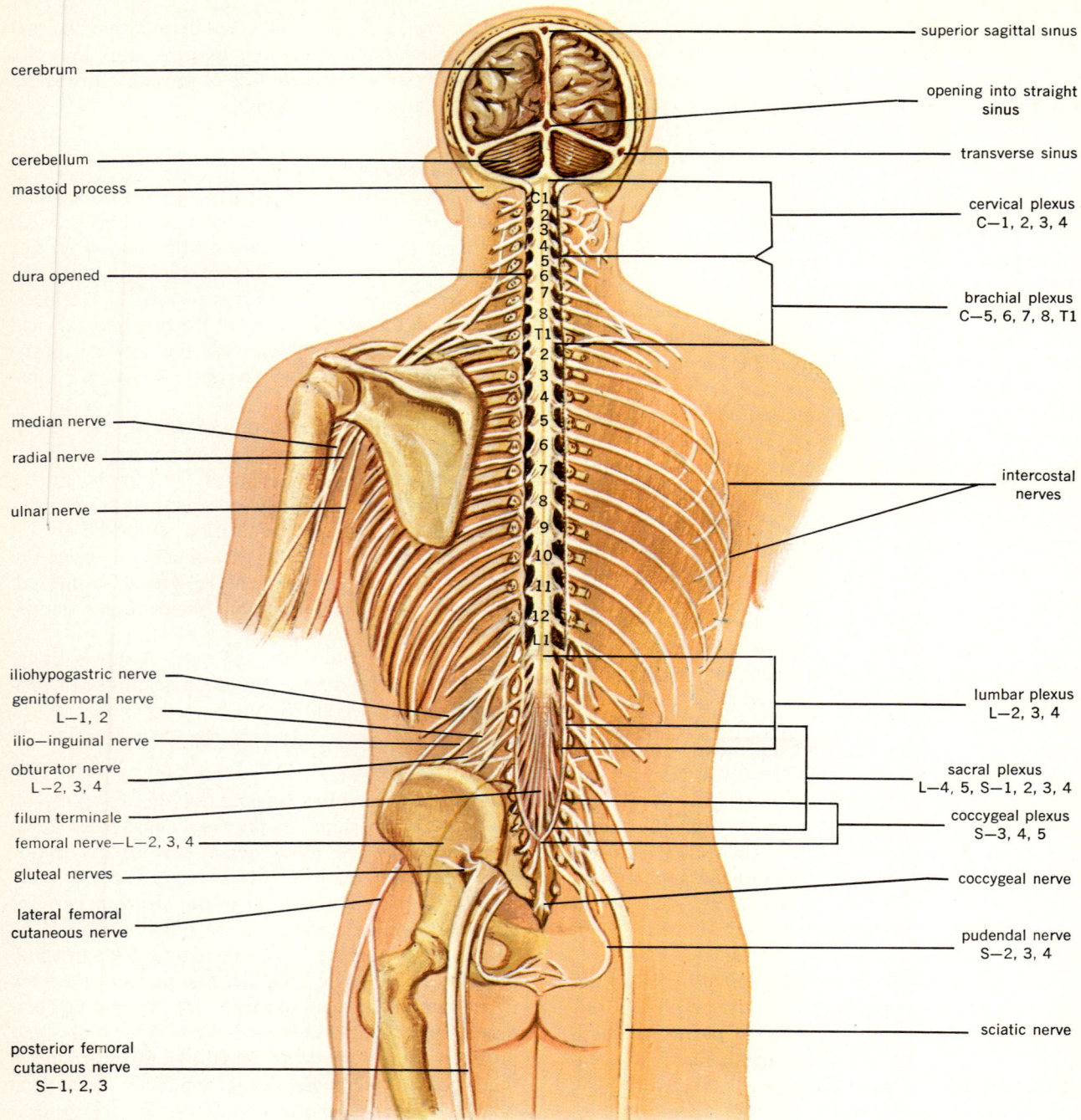

cerebrum

cerebellum

mastoid process

dura opened

median nerve

radial nerve

ulnar nerve

iliohypogastric nerve
genitofemoral nerve
L—1, 2
ilio—inguinal nerve

obturator nerve
L—2, 3, 4

filum terminale
femoral nerve—L—2, 3, 4

gluteal nerves

lateral femoral
cutaneous nerve

posterior femoral
cutaneous nerve
S—1, 2, 3

superior sagittal sinus

opening into straight
sinus

transverse sinus

cervical plexus
C—1, 2, 3, 4

brachial plexus
C—5, 6, 7, 8, T1

intercostal
nerves

lumbar plexus
L—2, 3, 4

sacral plexus
L—4, 5, S—1, 2, 3, 4

coccygeal plexus
S—3, 4, 5

coccygeal nerve

pudendal nerve
S—2, 3, 4

sciatic nerve

C1
2
3
4
5
6
7
8
T1
2
3
4
5
6
7
8
9
10
11
12
L1

FIGURE 14-6 The spinal nerves form a number of networks called plexuses.

of the baby's arm. If this condition is not treated, a withered arm will result.

Lumbar Plexus

Backaches are among the most common ailments that plague humans; they are due in large measure to our imperfect adaptation to an upright posture. Many typical backaches involve a major nerve plexus, the lumbar plexus, located in the lumbar region of the back in the psoas muscle. This plexus is formed by

the intermingling of the fibers of the first four lumbar nerves. A major branch emerging from the plexus is the **femoral nerve,** which branches repeatedly to supply the thigh and leg. A long sensory branch of the femoral nerve is the **saphenous nerve.** The **obturator nerve** is another large nerve, which supplies the adductor muscles of the thigh with motor and sensory fibers. The **iliohypogastric** and **ilioinguinal nerves** supply the pubic region, the external genitalia, and the muscles of the abdominal wall. The **genitofemoral**

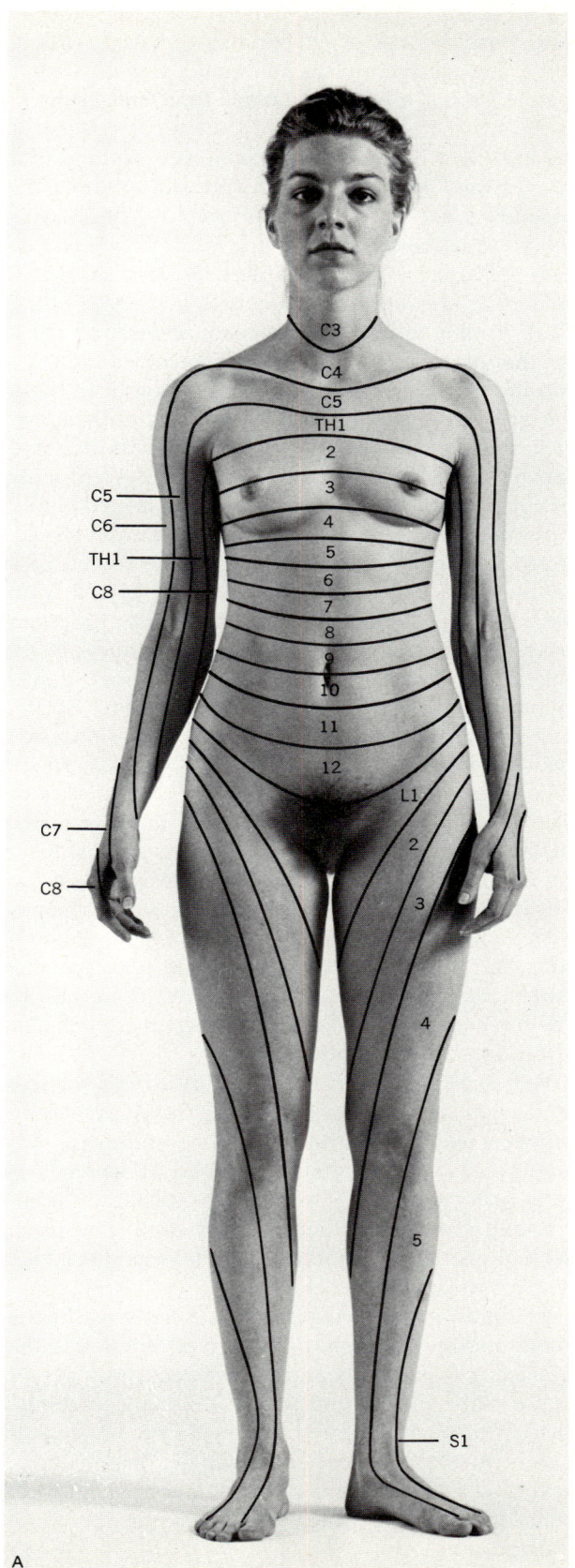

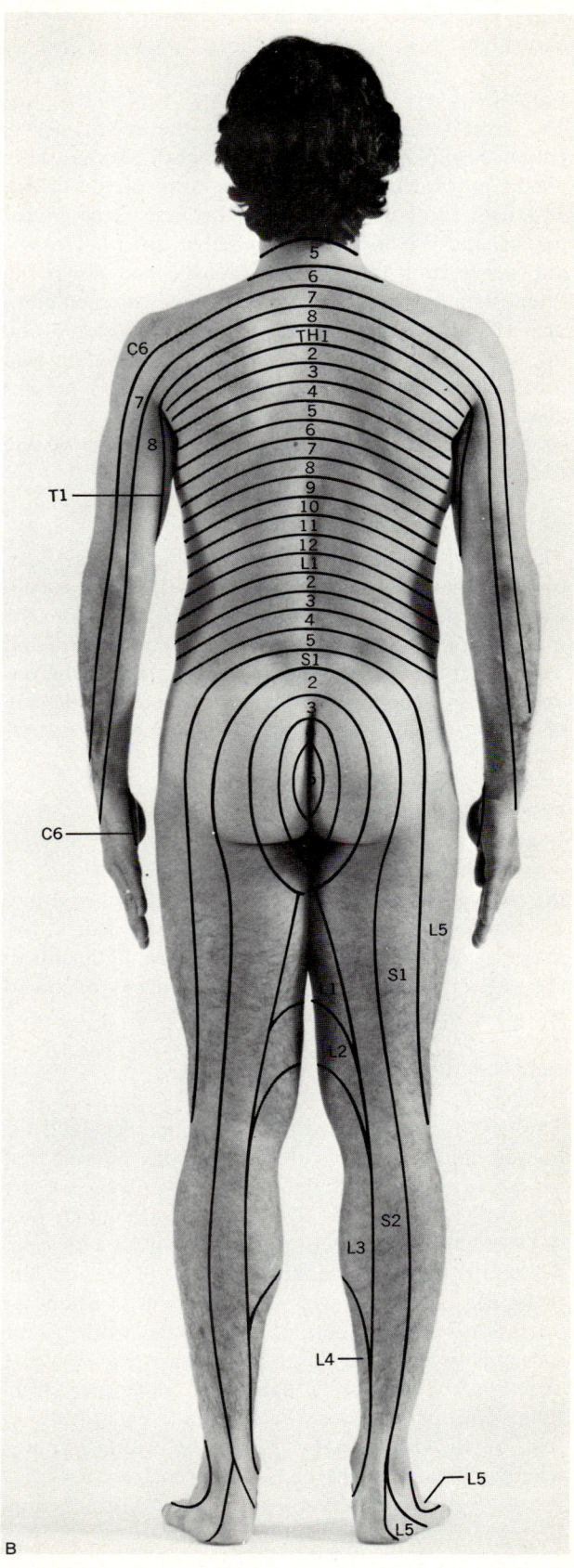

FIGURE 14-7   Dermatomes (areas innervated by spinal nerves).

nerve contributes to the innervation of the buttock and thigh.

Sacral Plexus

The largest nerve in the body is the **sciatic nerve,** which branches off from the sacral plexus. This plexus is formed by the anterior rami of the fourth and fifth lumbar nerves and the first three sacral nerves, and it is located in the pelvic cavity. The sciatic nerve runs through the buttock and down the thigh; its many branches (including the **common peroneal** and **tibial nerves**) supply nearly all the skin of the leg, as well as the posterior thigh muscles and leg and foot muscles. A common and excruciatingly painful condition is sciatica, neuralgia of the sciatic nerve resulting from pressure on the nerve, which may be due to poor posture or to a herniated disc.

Pudendal Plexus

The anal sphincter, the object of the great American obsession with laxatives, is innervated by the **pudendal nerve,** which is the major nerve resulting from the mingling of the anterior rami of the second, third, and fourth sacral nerves in the pudendal plexus. The pudendal nerve supplies the levator ani muscle, the skin of the perineum, and portions of the external genitalia.

Coccygeal Plexus

If you still had a functional tail, as most of your mammalian relatives do, it would be innervated by the **coccygeal** nerve, formed from the anterior rami of the fifth sacral and the coccygeal nerves. But in humans, aside from supplying the skin and ligaments in the region of the coccyx, the coccygeal plexus is mainly a vestige of our evolutionary past.

DISORDERS OF THE PERIPHERAL NERVOUS SYSTEM

The versatile and varied manipulations of which the human hand is capable are an everyday miracle that we usually tend to underappreciate—unless we are unfortunate enough to lose the use of a hand, partially or entirely. From time to time there is a newspaper report of the successful rejoining of an accidentally amputated hand to the stump. Such an operation requires hours of painstaking work by the surgeons, who must carefully match up and suture dozens of blood vessels, ligaments, and other structures. The operation may be a dramatic technical success, but it will be many months before it is known whether the use of the hand has been truly restored. For the peripheral nerves leading down into the hand have been cut, and unless they regenerate successfully the replaced hand will be flaccid and without sensation.

Less drastic injuries than amputation can cause serious nerve damage. A pitcher may damage his radial nerve through the violent contractions of his triceps muscle, and as a result be unable to extend his hand at the wrist. Karate chops with the ulnar portion of the hand can damage the ulnar nerve, resulting in a "claw hand" with difficulty in spreading the fingers. Alcoholics are particularly subject to "drunkard's palsy," which results from falling into a drunken sleep with the arm hanging over the back of a chair and failing to rouse (because of alcohol's depression of the CNS) in time to rescue the median nerve from damage that paralyzes the normal movements of the wrist and thumb. Deep cuts and crushing blows can damage nerves, as can infections with microorganisms, such as the poliomyelitis virus. The results of nerve damage are a loss of sensation or a paralysis of muscles, depending on the type of nerve damaged.

Fortunately nerve damage is sometimes reversible. When a peripheral nerve is cut, the nerve cell processes (whether axons or dendrites) are cut off from the parent cell bodies. For a short time the processes distal to the cut remain capable of conducting impulses, but then they rapidly begin to break down, following a pattern that was first described by the neurologist Waller in 1852 (Figure 14-8). The axis cylinder degenerates into granular fragments, which look under a microscope like the dots and dashes of the Morse code, and simultaneously the myelin coalesces into droplets of unsaturated fatty acids. Roving connective tissue cells move in to scavenge the debris and clean up the mess, and soon only the empty framework of the Schwann tubes remains. A similar process of **Wallerian degeneration** occurs in the proximal stump of the nerve, but extends only up to the first node of Ranvier of each fiber; the remainder of the axis cylinder does not die.

Within 24 hours after the injury, little buds begin to appear at the end of the intact axis cylinders, lengthen out into fibers, and branch and grow at a rate of one to three millimeters per day. The regenerating fibers enter the Schwann tubes distal to the injury and grow down them steadily until they reach the end organs. (The journey may take as much as a year or two to complete.)

The most rapid to regenerate are the sympathetic fibers, and the first sign of a return of function to the affected part is usually an improvement in skin color as a result of the restoration of vasomotor activity. Sensory fibers are restored next, with a return of sensitivity first to pressure or pinching, then to pain, heat, and cold, and finally to joint movements and touch localization. Motor function is the last to be restored.

But the recovery is usually imperfect to some degree. The regenerating nerve fibers often find their

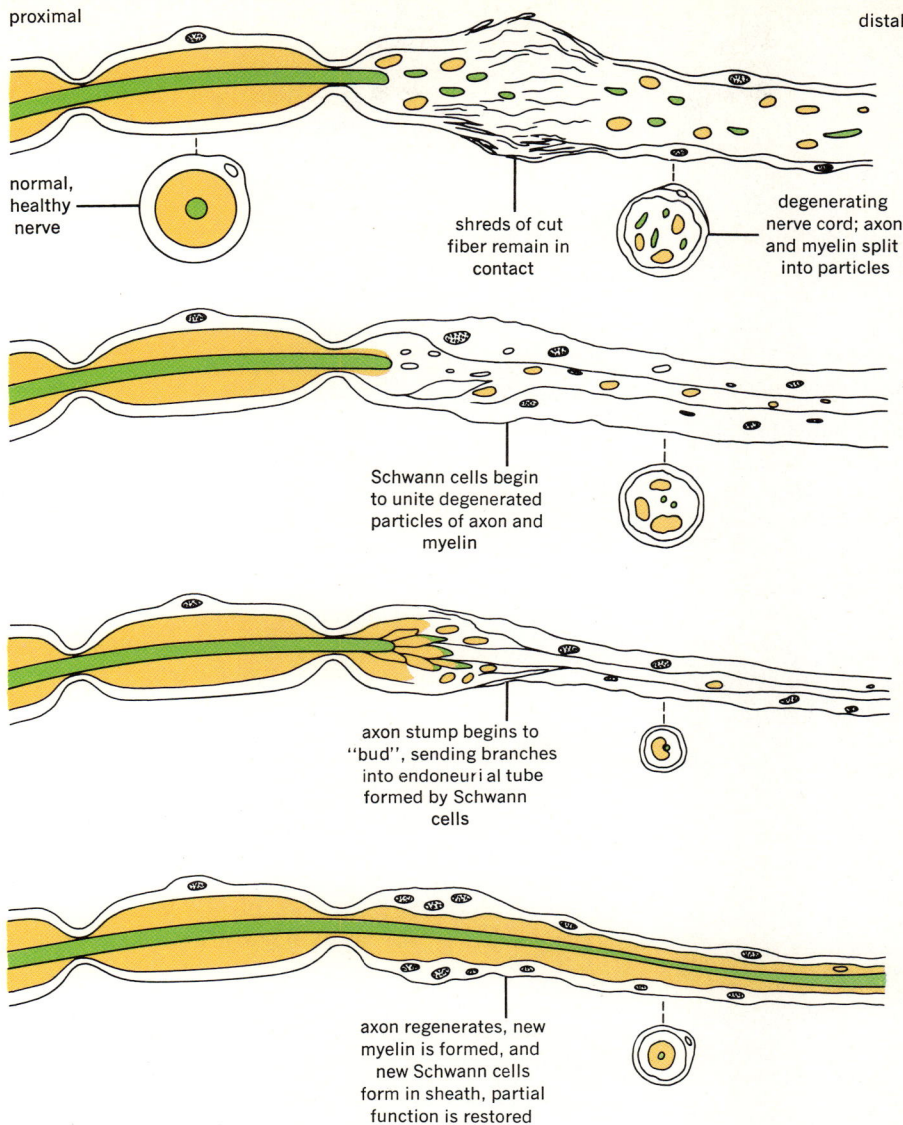

proximal

distal

normal, healthy nerve

shreds of cut fiber remain in contact

degenerating nerve cord; axon and myelin split into particles

Schwann cells begin to unite degenerated particles of axon and myelin

axon stump begins to "bud", sending branches into endoneurial tube formed by Schwann cells

axon regenerates, new myelin is formed, and new Schwann cells form in sheath, partial function is restored to nerve.

FIGURE 14-8 Regeneration of a peripheral nerve. (Modified from Ham and Leeson.)

way down the wrong Schwann tube, and if a motor fiber grows down to a sensory ending, or a sensory fiber to a motor end-plate, it may degenerate again. Even an appropriate type of tube may lead to some wrong turnings, if there has been any twisting of the stumps relative to one another. A motor fiber, for example, that had formerly controlled the flexor muscle of the little finger might wind up innervating the adductor of the thumb after regeneration. Sensory messages might be similarly mixed up in the restored nerves, all of which is highly disconcerting to the brain, which relies on a lifetime of past experience in determining which impulses belong to which parts of the body. New impulse patterns can be relearned, but this is a long, tedious process, and is more successful the younger the patient is at the time of the injury.

Some typical results of damage to particular peripheral nerves are summarized in Table 14-3.

Temporary interruptions of the passage of impulses along a nerve trunk can be produced in a variety of ways and are clinically quite useful in bringing about insensibility to pain. A **nerve block** can be produced by applying ice to the skin in a place where the nerve passes near the surface. (This method has been known for at least a thousand years to Arab physicians, who immersed the affected limb in snow.) Pressing on a nerve for a period of twenty minutes or more produces anesthesia of the body part it innervates. This method was used in wartime surgery before the introduction of chemical anesthetics, and it is also the mechanism involved when your arm "goes to sleep" after you have been lying on it in bed. If the pressure is continued too long, the paralysis becomes irreversible. A variety of chemicals act as **local anesthetics** when injected into the area around the nerve trunk. The first local anesthetic used was cocaine;

TABLE 14-3 Some Results of Damage to Peripheral Nerves

NERVE	RESULTS OF INJURY
Cranial Nerves	
Olfactory	Loss of sense of smell
Optic	Partial or total blindness depending on the site and extent of injury
Oculomotor	External strabismus (eye turned outward), ptosis (drooping of lid), mydriasis (dilation of pupil), loss of pupillary reaction to light, inability to focus and accommodate
Trochlear	Abnormal position of eyeball
Trigeminal	Loss of sensation of scalp, face. Loss of corneal reflex. Loss of sneeze reflex. Paralysis of muscles of mastication. Tic douloureux (facial neuralgia)
Abducens	Internal strabismus (eye turned inward)
Facial	Paralysis of muscles of facial expression. Bell's palsy. Inability to wrinkle forehead, frown, whistle, or close eyelids tightly. Loss of sensation on anterior two-thirds of tongue
Acoustic	Deafness (cochlear branch). Vertigo, nausea and vomiting; sweating and vasomotor changes; falling; past-pointing; nystagmus (to and fro movements of eyeballs) (vestibular branch)
Glossopharyngeal	Loss of gag reflex and carotid sinus and carotid body reflexes; loss of taste in posterior third of tongue
Vagus	Death due to asphyxia if injury is bilateral; paralysis of esophagus and stomach, loss of respiratory reflexes, dyspnea, and cardiac acceleration. If unilateral, partial paralysis of soft palate, pharynx, larynx; hoarseness; dyspnea; loss of cough reflex
Accessory	Deviation of head to the side of the injury, weakness of trapezius muscle (raising shoulder)
Hypoglossal	Loss of movements and tone of tongue, deviation toward the side of the injury; difficulty in speaking, chewing, and swallowing
Spinal Nerves	
Phrenic	Hiccups; paralysis of diaphragm
Brachial plexus	Paralysis, numbness, and withering of arm
Median	Inability to pronate forearm, or flex

TABLE 14-3 (Continued)

NERVE	RESULTS OF INJURY
	wrist; inability to flex and abduct thumb and appose it to the fingers; inability to flex middle phalanges of middle and index fingers
Ulnar	Difficulty in spreading fingers; impairment of ability to flex and adduct wrist
Radial	Inability to extend the hand at the wrist
Axillary	Loss of roundness of shoulder due to atrophy of deltoid muscle
Femoral	Inability to flex thigh or extend leg; loss of sensation in thigh, along anterior and inner surfaces of leg, inner border of foot, and ball of big toe
Sciatic	Inability to flex knee; sciatica (intense pain with tenderness, numbness, and tingling of thigh and leg, wasting of muscles)
Peroneal	Foot drop, loss of arch of foot
Tibial	Inability to plantar flex foot at ankle joint and toes

today a variety of more effective and nonaddictive local anesthetics, such as novocaine, are available. They seem to work by penetrating to the axis cylinder at the nodes of Ranvier, where they interfere with the ionizing mechanism. Local anesthetics can also be used to block the spinal nerve roots inside the vertebral canal. In an **extradural block,** the injection is made outside the protective coverings of the spinal cord; in a **spinal block,** the drug is injected inside the dural membranes.

Recovery from a nerve block produced by pressure is accompanied by a typical feeling of "pins and needles," apparently due to a chemical stimulation of the part of the nerve distal to the block. The sensation is felt not in the nerve itself, but as though it originated in the skin—it is **referred** to the normal sensory endings of the nerve. The brain does not differentiate between a direct stimulation of a nerve trunk and stimulation of its endings. The "phantom limbs" experienced by amputees are due to the same phenomenon of referred sensation: irritation of the cut ends of nerves in the healing stump by infection or developing scar tissue is perceived as sensations or movements in the arm or leg that is no longer there. (Usually as time passes, the "phantom limb" subjectively seems to shorten and finally disappears.)

FIGURE 14-9 Local anesthesia in dental work blocks transmission from pain nerve endings.

SUMMARY

Peripheral nerves are classified as:
- Cranial and spinal
- Sensory, motor, and mixed

The 12 pairs of cranial nerves are:
- Olfactory (I)
- Optic (II)
- Oculomotor (III)
- Trochlear (IV)
- Trigeminal (V)
- Abducens (VI)
- Facial (VII)
- Acoustic (VIII)
- Glossopharyngeal (IX)
- Vagus (X)
- Accessory (XI)
- Hypoglossal (XII)

The olfactory nerve is a sensory nerve (smell) distributed to the nasal membranes.

The optic nerve is a sensory nerve (sight) carrying impulses from the retina; some fibers of the two optic nerves cross at the optic chiasma; the optic tracts lead to the thalamus, from which impulses are relayed to the visual cortex in the occipital lobe.

The oculomotor nerve is a motor nerve involved with eye movements, regulation of the size of the pupil, and accommodation.

The trochlear nerve is a mixed nerve innervating the superior oblique muscle of the eye.

The trigeminal nerve is a mixed nerve supplying the head and face and the muscles of mastication.

Sensory branches are the ophthalmic, maxillary, and mandibular.

The abducens nerve is a mixed nerve innervating the lateral rectus muscle of the eye.

The facial nerve (mixed) supplies the muscles of facial expression in the face and scalp; also the submaxillary and sublingual salivary glands and taste buds of the front of the tongue.

The acoustic nerve has two sensory branches:

The cochlear branch supplies the organ of Corti (hearing).

The vestibular branch supplies the semicircular canals (balance).

The glossopharyngeal nerve (mixed) supplies the tongue and pharynx and is involved in taste perception from the back of the tongue, swallowing, and reflex control of blood pressure and respiration.

The vagus nerve (mixed) has a widespread distribution to the organs of the thorax and abdomen; it has parasympathetic effects, is important in respiratory, cardiac, and circulatory reflexes, and contracts the muscles of the pharynx and larynx for phonation.

The accessory nerve has two roots, in the brainstem and in the spinal cord; it is a motor nerve traveling with the vagus nerve.

The hypoglossal nerve is a motor nerve innervating the muscles of the tongue.

There are 31 pairs of spinal nerves, numbered and named for the vertebrae between which they emerge:
- Cervical (8 pairs)
- Thoracic (5 pairs)
- Lumbar (5 pairs)
- Sacral (5 pairs)
- Coccygeal (1 pair)

Spinal nerves emerge from the intervertebral foramina and arise from the spinal cord via dorsal (sensory) and ventral (motor) roots. They form mixed nerves, which divide into four branches: meningeal ramus, visceral ramus, dorsal or posterior ramus, and ventral or anterior ramus.

Spinal nerves intercommunicate and form plexuses:
- Cervical plexus (C-1,2,3,4)
- Brachial plexus (C-5,6,7,8, T-1)
- Lumbar plexus (T-12, L-1,2,3,4)
- Sacral plexus (L-4,5, S-1,2,3)
- Pudendal plexus (S-2,3,4)
- Coccygeal plexus (S-5, coccygeal)

Nerves of the cervical plexus supply the back of the head, neck, and shoulders.

The phrenic nerve supplies the diaphragm.

Nerves of the brachial plexus supply the skin and muscles of the shoulder, arm, forearm, and hand.

Branches include the musculocutaneous, ulnar, median, radial, and axillary.

Thoracic spinal nerves 2 to 11 do not form plexuses and supply the intercostal muscles, skin of the thorax, and back muscles.

Nerves of the lumbar plexus supply the abdominal wall, external genitalia, thigh, leg, and medial side of the foot.

Branches include the iliohypogastric, ilioinguinal, genitofemoral, lateral femoral cutaneous, femoral, saphenous, and obturator.

Nerves of the sacral plexus supply the buttocks, thigh, leg, and foot.

Branches include the gluteal, sciatic, tibial, peroneal, and sural.

Nerves of the pudendal plexus supply the anal sphincters, perineum, and external genitalia.

The coccygeal nerve supplies the coccyx region and innervates the tail in animals.

A damaged peripheral nerve undergoes Wallerian degeneration distal to the injury, then regenerates from the proximal stump. Restoration of function is usually imperfect.

Damage to peripheral nerves results in muscular paralysis and/or loss of sensation in the region supplied by the nerve.

A nerve block can be produced by cooling, pressure, and drugs (local anesthetics) such as novocaine.

QUESTIONS FOR REVIEW AND THOUGHT

1 Distinguish between cranial and spinal nerves; sensory, motor, and mixed nerves; dorsal and ventral roots of spinal nerves; dorsal and ventral rami.

2 List the 12 pairs of cranial nerves and their principal functions.

3 Which cranial nerves have functions relating to the eyes?

4 Which cranial nerve is the most extensive and has the most varied functions?

5 Describe the structure of the neurons in the dorsal and ventral roots of spinal nerves.

6 Define: plexus; myotome; dermatome. What are the advantages of a plexus organization of spinal nerves?

7 Which areas of the body are served by the cervical plexus? the brachial plexus? the lumbar plexus? the sacral plexus? the pudendal plexus? the coccygeal plexus?

8 Name a major nerve from each spinal nerve plexus and describe its function.

9 Describe Wallerian degeneration and regeneration of nerve cells. Why must a long time elapse before the success of an operation rejoining an amputated hand is known?

10 Discuss the phenomena of nerve block, "pins and needles" sensation, and "phantom limbs."

THE AUTONOMIC NERVOUS SYSTEM

15

Unless something goes wrong, we usually have little conscious awareness of the inner workings of our bodies. The heart and blood vessels, the lungs, the organs of the digestive system, glands of secretion—all these body parts must be as finely coordinated as the musicians of a symphony orchestra. The "orchestration" of the body's organs is accomplished through intricate sequences of feedback circuits, with interacting nervous and endocrine controls. Signals reporting the current status of the body's systems and present and potential effects of the outer environment are continually fed to the central nervous system via afferent pathways of the peripheral nervous system; only a small minority of these reports are ever brought to our conscious attention. Appropriate actions are taken equally automatically and independently of the conscious brain: the blood vessel diameters are continually adjusted to shunt the blood flow to the most needed areas, the heart and respiration rates are speeded or slowed, as are the movements and secretions of the stomach and intestines, the output of urine, and a variety of other physiological processes.

The efferent nerves involved in the control and coordination of visceral functions form a division of the peripheral nervous system called the **autonomic nervous system,** or **visceral motor system.** The term "autonomic" literally means self-controlled and independent of outside influences. The nerves of the autonomic nervous system actually are not quite as independent as their name implies, and are closely integrated with the other components of the nervous system; many of their axons and cell bodies are in close association with neurons of the somatic division of the peripheral nervous system (which was the subject of the last chapter), and the autonomic reflexes are under the influence of higher centers in the brain, particularly those of the hypothalamus. Setting the nerves of the autonomic nervous system aside as a separate division is more for convenience of observation and study than an indication of an actual anatomical distinction.

Although the workings of the autonomic nervous system are rarely brought to our conscious attention, they are closely interrelated with our emotional state. The common phrases, "a sinking feeling in the stomach," "pale with fury," "broke out in a cold sweat," "warm and contented," and so on are reflections of autonomic effects that accompany particular emotional states.

ANATOMY OF THE AUTONOMIC NERVOUS SYSTEM

When we are angry or happy, frightened or elated, it is a diffuse feeling. Many sensations—pain or touch or the reception of light rays—can be localized quite

specifically. But emotions seem to well up from the viscera and pervade virtually our whole being. The diffuseness and pervasiveness of autonomic effects is due in large part to the unique anatomical features of the ANS.

Autonomic nerves are efferent nerves, whose fibers carry involuntary impulses to smooth muscle, cardiac muscle, and glands. Feedback circuits are completed by associations with afferent fibers of the PNS and control centers of the CNS, but the actual autonomic nerves are motor nerves. They differ from the typical efferent nerves of the somatic division of the peripheral nervous system in that autonomic impulses are characteristically transmitted along two-neuron chains, in contrast to the one-neuron PNS innervation of the skeletal muscles. The first neuron in the chain arises from a cell body in the central nervous system (usually the spinal cord or medulla); its axon travels for a time with a cranial or spinal nerve, then leaves it to end at a **ganglion** (Figure 15-1), at which it synapses with the cell bodies and dendrites of other neurons. The neuron extending from the CNS to the ganglion is referred to as a **preganglionic neuron,** while the neurons that synapse with it are called **postganglionic neurons.** There are as many as thirty postganglionic neurons for each preganglionic neuron, which means that a single message transmitted from the CNS diverges outward from the autonomic ganglion and may be conveyed to a number of effectors.

The preganglionic fibers are small myelinated nerve fibers. Unlike the somatic efferent fibers of the PNS, they are limited to three main outflows from the central nervous system: the **cranial** outflow, accompanying the oculomotor, facial, glossopharyngeal, and vagus nerves; the **thoracolumbar** outflow, forming part of the ventral roots of the spinal nerves from the eighth cervical to the second or third lumbar segments of the spinal cord; and the **sacral** outflow, in the ventral roots of the second, third, and fourth sacral nerves.

The postganglionic fibers are unmyelinated and end in the effectors: smooth or cardiac muscle or glands of secretion. (Some of them are quite short, and lie within the wall of the organ supplied.) In smooth muscle the autonomic nerve endings may be simple branches, terminals from extensive plexuses, loops, or series of terminal swellings in contact with the smooth muscle fibers. In cardiac muscle, thin nerve fibers permeate the myocardium and end near the surface of the muscle fibers. In glands, the autonomic nerve endings arise from plexuses surrounding the tubules or acini and terminate in contact with the membranes of the secretory cells.

There are three main groups of autonomic ganglia: **lateral** or **vertebral, collateral,** and **terminal.** The lateral ganglia are arranged in two vertical chains, on

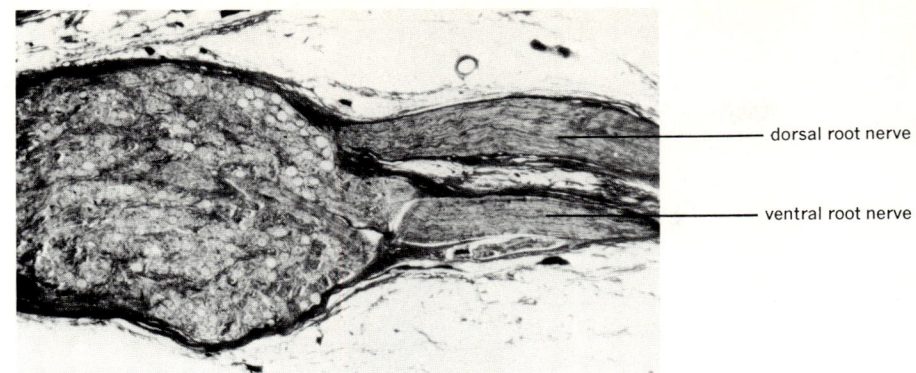

FIGURE 15-1 (A) Human dorsal root ganglion (×17) with dorsal root nerve and ventral root nerve. The diagram (B) shows the contrast between the two-neuron chain characteristic of the autonomic nervous system and the one-neuron pathway found in the somatic division of the peripheral nervous system.

dorsal root nerve

ventral root nerve

A

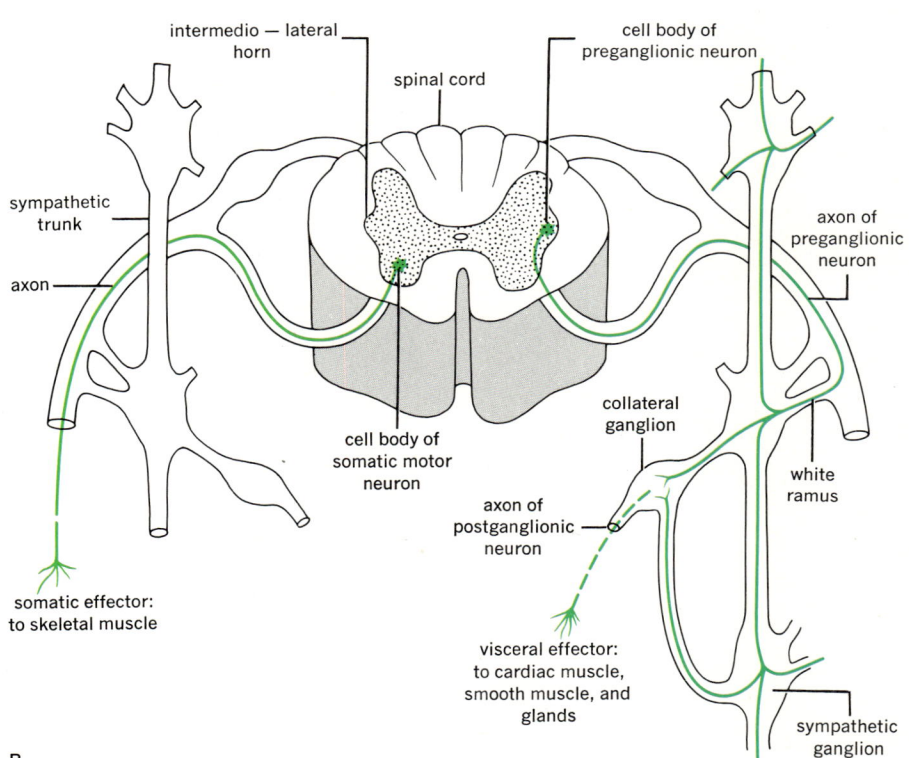

intermedio — lateral horn

spinal cord

cell body of preganglionic neuron

sympathetic trunk

axon

axon of preganglionic neuron

cell body of somatic motor neuron

axon of postganglionic neuron

collateral ganglion

white ramus

somatic effector: to skeletal muscle

visceral effector: to cardiac muscle, smooth muscle, and glands

sympathetic ganglion

B

either side of the vertebral column (Figure 15-2), which are referred to as **sympathetic trunks.** There are 22 ganglia in each chain: 3 cervical, 11 thoracic, 4 lumbar, and 4 sacral. Collateral ganglia are found in the thoracic and abdominopelvic cavities, close to the aorta and its main branches. They are named for the arteries they accompany; the most important are the **celiac, superior mesenteric,** and **inferior mesenteric ganglia.** The terminal ganglia are found at the ends of the long preganglionic fibers arising from the cranial and sacral regions of the CNS, and lie close to the structures innervated by the short postganglionic fibers. The terminal ganglia of the head region include the **ciliary, pterygopalatine, submandibular,** and **otic ganglia.** Other terminal ganglia are found in the walls of the stomach, liver, intestines, pancreas, kidney, bladder, and external genitalia.

In certain parts of the body, nerve fibers extending from the autonomic ganglia are interlaced into branching network called **plexuses.** One of the most famous is the **solar plexus,** the fibers of which surround the celiac artery and its branches. The dramatic effects on the heart, lungs, and arteries produced by a hard punch to the region of the solar plexus emphasize the vital and varied functions of the autonomic nerves. Other major plexuses include the **pulmonary, cardiac,** and **esophageal plexuses,** derived from the thoracolumbar outflows. In the neck region, fibers from the cervical sympathetic ganglia form the **carotid plexus** around the carotid arteries and their branches and provide a pathway for fibers innervating structures of the face and head. Numerous subsidiary plexuses supply structures of the abdominal and pelvic cavities.

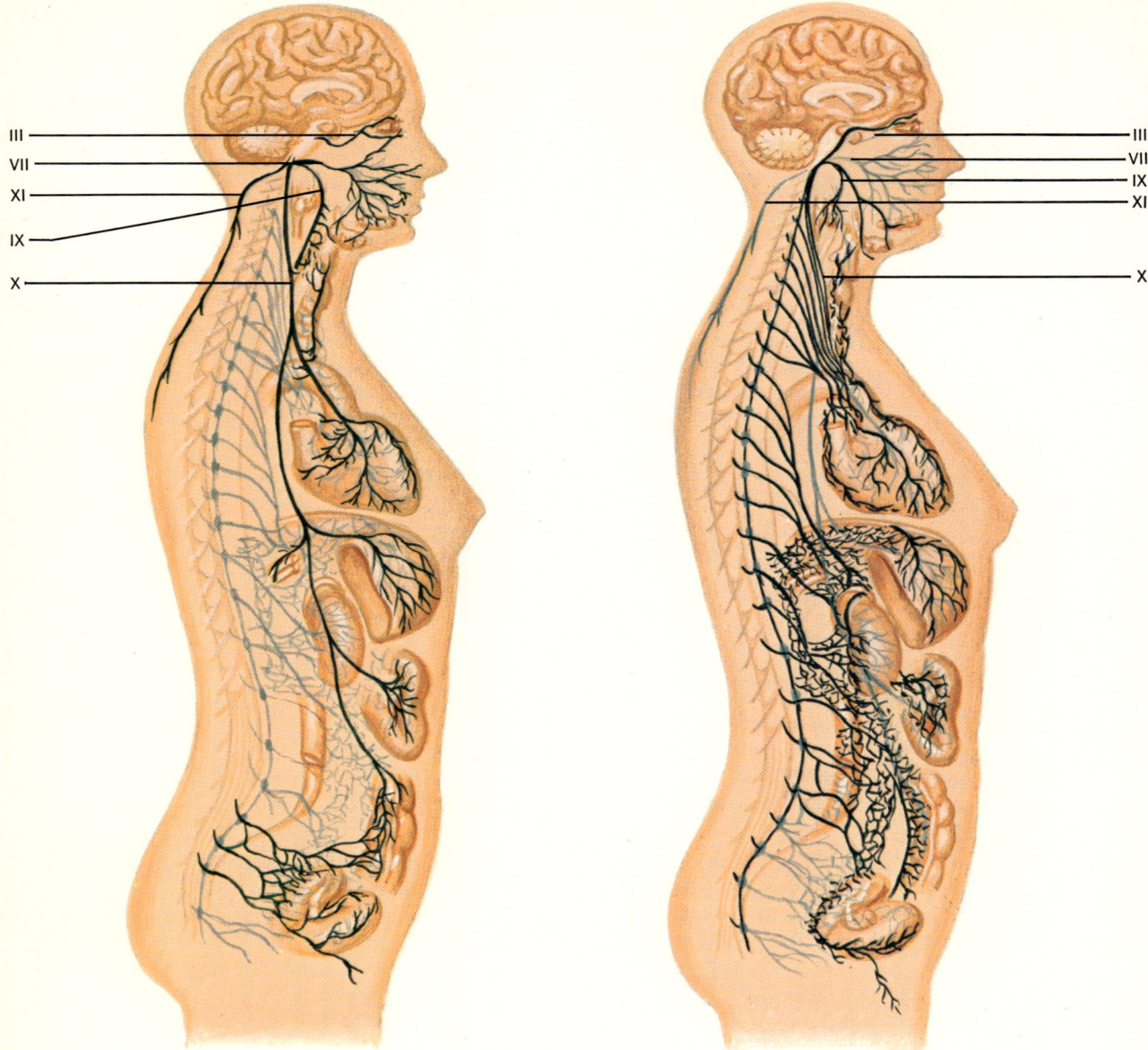

FIGURE 15-2 **The autonomic nervous system: parasympathetic (left) and sympathetic (right) pathways.**

DIVISIONS OF THE AUTONOMIC NERVOUS SYSTEM

High up in the air, the pilot of a plane was suddenly informed in tense tones by the copilot, "There's a lion in the cockpit!" A crate had broken open in the cargo area, and several lions that were being transported to a zoo in London had wandered up to explore the front of the plane. The pilot's hair stood up on end. His heart pounded, and his face was pale. Sweat soaked his shirt as he worked frantically to bring the plane down in an emergency landing, while the copilot swung an axe, keeping the lions at bay. At last the plane landed, and the two fliers dived out the emergency exit.

An important part of the functioning of the autonomic nervous system is concerned with keeping the body systems running smoothly, day in and day out. But sometimes emergency situations arise, in which there is a need for something extra—additional reserves for the body to call on to prepare for effective "flight or fight." Two separate divisions of the ANS, the **parasympathetic** and **sympathetic divisions** (Figure 15-3), provide for these two types of functions.

The parasympathetic division is concerned with conserving and restoring body resources. It protects the heart from overexerting itself, promotes a harmonious course of the digestive processes, and protects the eyes by causing the pupils to constrict in bright

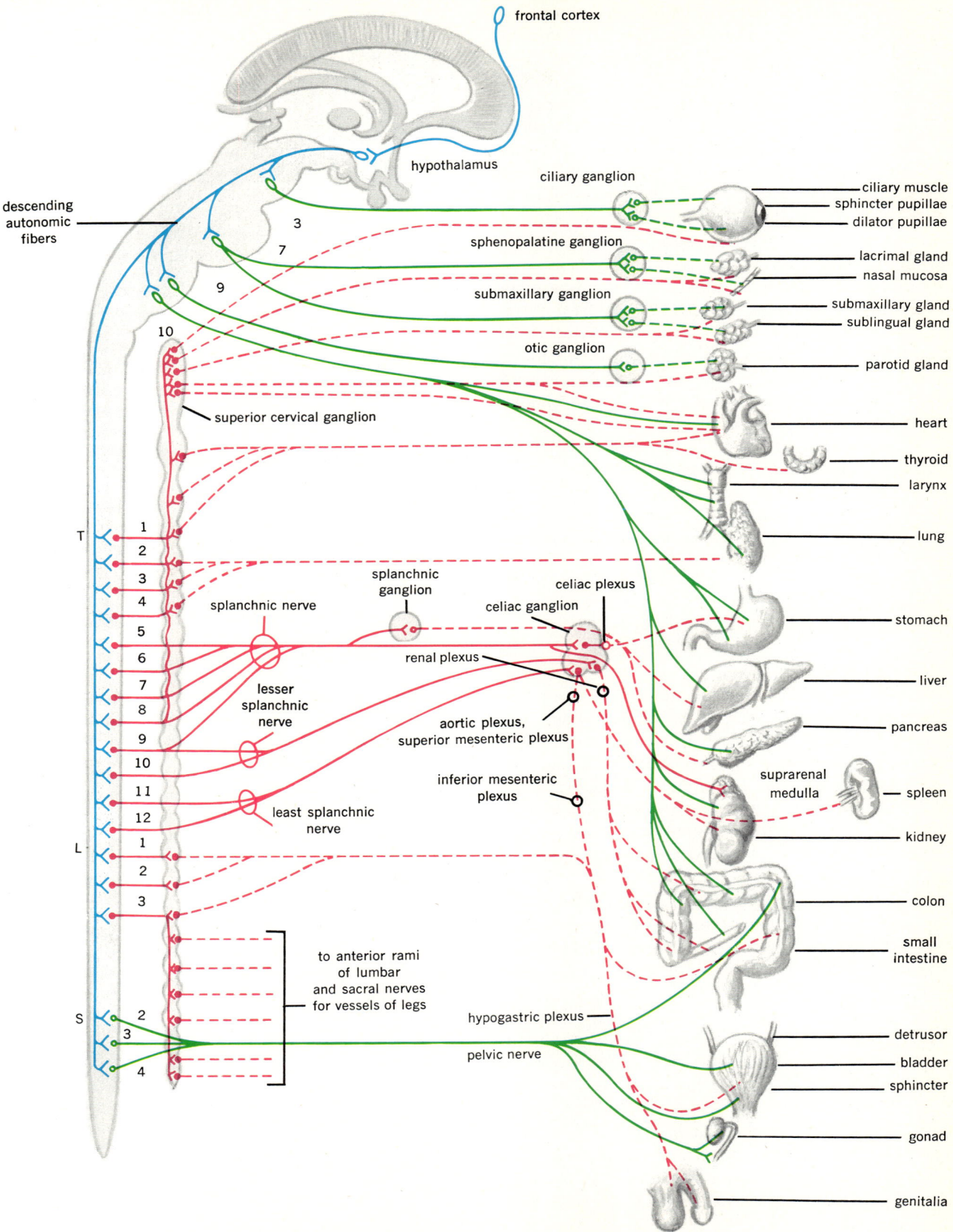

FIGURE 15-3   The autonomic system. Solid lines indicate preganglionic fibers, broken lines postganglionic fibers. *Blue:* **central conduction paths;** *red:* **sympathetic;** *green:* **parasympathetic.**

lights. The nerves of the parasympathetic division are derived from the cranial and the sacral outflows, and thus it is sometimes referred to as the **craniosacral division** of the ANS. It is concerned with "repose and repair," and it is the more structurally and functionally advanced of the two divisions, acting mainly on smooth muscles and glands and in the digestive tract.

The sympathetic division is in charge of emergency preparations for "flight or fight." It is more primitive than the parasympathetic division, and its main action is to constrict blood vessels. The action of the sympathetic division mobilizes the body's resources for emergency action, shunting the circulating blood away from vegetative structures such as the digestive organs to the heart and skeletal muscles, increasing heart and lung functions, dilating the pupils of the eyes, and moistening the skin with sweat. Anatomically, the sympathetic division is the **thoracolumbar division** of the ANS.

A glance at Figure 15-3 and at Table 15-1 will emphasize an important point: most visceral structures are innervated both by parasympathetic and by sympathetic fibers. In general, their actions are antagonistic—for example, sympathetic nerves dilate the pupils, while parasympathetic fibers produce a contraction; sympathetic fibers dilate the bronchi, while parasympathetic impulses narrow them; sympathetic impulses produce a contraction of the sphincters of the alimentary tract and urinary bladder, while parasympathetic impulses relax the sphincters; the sympathetic nerves act to speed up and strengthen the heart beat, while the parasympathetic nerves slow down the heart. In some cases their action is complementary. For example, both the parasympathetic and the sympathetic divisions of the ANS are involved in the completion of a sex act in the male: parasympathetic impulses produce an erection of the penis, and sympathetic fibers spark the actual ejaculation.

Recently there has been considerable speculation on the role of personality types in the development of heart disease. Two characteristic types, A and B, have been distinguished. A Type A personality is a typical hard-driving type, who seems to have a compulsion to work constantly, under high pressure (often self-imposed), striving for perfection and readily getting upset about problems that arise. A Type B personality is much more relaxed, less readily upset, less ambitious and striving. It might be thought that a Type A person is ruled by his sympathetic system, constantly gearing up his body for new emergencies that a Type B person would be more inclined to take in stride, leaving his parasympathetic system in gear. As might be expected, it is the Type A personality who is far more likely to develop heart disease, ulcers, and other conditions resulting from continual stress.

Sympathetic Division

When an emergency arises, whether it is a lion breathing down the back of your neck, an exam to be taken, a speech to be given, or any of life's challenges, the sympathetic division of the ANS switches the body into high gear. It has several main types of functions.

Motor or Augmentor Functions In certain structures, sympathetic impulses cause muscles to contract, or to contract more rapidly or strongly than before. Sympathetic nerve fibers produce contraction of the radial muscle of the iris, which dilates the eye; of the pilomotor muscles around the hair shafts, which make the hairs stand on end and produce "gooseflesh"; of the sphincters of the gastrointestinal tract and urinary bladder; and of the muscles in the walls of blood vessels in the skin and viscera, a **vasoconstrictive effect** that shunts blood away from the periphery of the body (producing pallor) and away from the digestive organs to provide a greater supply to the structures that may be directly involved in copying with the emergency—the heart and skeletal muscles. Sympathetic impulses have an augmentor effect on the heart, causing it to beat faster and more forcefully. (Recall that the contractions of cardiac muscle are self-initiated, so that neural influences do not initiate, but only alter the rate of the heart contractions.)

Inhibitory Functions In certain structures, impulses transmitted along sympathetic fibers cause smooth muscle to relax. This effect occurs in the blood vessels of the skeletal muscles and the coronary arteries, which supply the heart, dilating these vessels and thus increasing the blood supply to key organs. Sympathetic impulses also inhibit the smooth muscle in the walls of the gastrointestinal tract and urinary bladder, stopping their contractions and effectively postponing the functions of digestion and elimination to a later time when the body will have leisure to indulge them. An inhibitory effect on the smooth muscle in the walls of the bronchioles dilates the air passages and makes it easier for air to enter and leave the lungs.

Secretory Functions Sympathetic impulses stimulate the secretion of the sweat glands, the adrenal gland (producing epinephrine and norepinephrine, "fight or flight" hormones that produce much the same effects as the sympathetic fibers), the lacrimal glands, and the salivary glands. (The saliva produced is thick and viscid, causing a feeling of dryness in the mouth.)

Glycogenolytic Function The sympathetic division helps provide for the mobilized body's need for quick energy by stimulating the liver to break down

TABLE 15-1 Functions of the Autonomic Nervous System

STRUCTURE	EFFECT OF SYMPATHETIC STIMULATION	EFFECT OF PARASYMPATHETIC STIMULATION
Eye		
Pupil	Dilation (produced by contraction of radial muscle of iris)	Constriction (produced by contraction of sphincter muscle of iris)
Ciliary muscle		Contraction (accommodation of lens)
Glands		
Lacrimal	Vasoconstriction	Secretion
Salivary	Vasoconstriction; stimulates slight secretion (viscid)	Thin, copious secretion
Gastric	Inhibition	Secretion
Pancreas	Diminished secretion	Increased secretion of digestive juices and hormone insulin
Sweat	Copious sweating	None
Adrenal medulla	Secretion of epinephrine and norepinephrine	Little or no effect
Heart muscle	Increased rate and force of beat	Slowed rate and decreased force of atrial beat
Blood vessels		
Coronary arteries	Dilation	Constriction
In skeletal muscles	Dilation	No effect
In skin	Constriction	Dilation
In abdominal viscera	Constriction	Dilation
Pulmonary	Mild constriction	No effect
Blood clotting	Accelerated	No effect
Blood sugar	Increased	No effect
Respiratory system		
Bronchi	Dilation	Constriction
Secretions in air passages	Inhibited	Increased
Gastrointestinal tract		
Stomach wall	Decreased motility	Increased motility
Intestines	Decreased motility	Increased motility
Sphincters	Contraction	Relaxation
Liver	Release of glucose	No effect
Gall bladder	Inhibition of bile flow	Stimulation of bile flow
Kidney	Vasoconstriction; decreased urine output	No effect
Ureter	Inhibition	Excitation
Urinary bladder		
Wall	Relaxation	Contraction
Sphincter	Constricted	Relaxed
Sex organs		
Penis	Ejaculation	Vasodilation and erection
Uterus	Contraction	No effect
Piloerector muscles of hairs	Contraction ("goose bumps")	No effect
Mental activity	Increased	No effect
Basal metabolism	Increased	No effect

glycogen into glucose, which is then released into the bloodstream and raises the blood sugar level.

These functions of the sympathetic division are switched on not only in times of great emotional excitement, but also in physical emergencies, such as hemorrhage, exposure to extreme heat or cold, and strenuous exercise, working to maintain homeostasis in the face of threats to survival.

Parasympathetic Division

It is very difficult to change fundamental personality characteristics that have been a part of you for decades, but many physicians are now trying to reeducate their "Type A" patients to a more relaxed lifestyle. It is largely a matter of changing one's view of events, of learning not to regard each trivial problem as a crisis, and thus avoiding a continual unnecessary stimulation of the sympathetic nervous system so that the parasympathetic division can continue to control the body's workings. The parasympathetic division has several main types of functions.

Motor or Augmentor Functions   Parasympathetic impulses produce contraction of the sphincter muscle of the iris (constricting the pupil), the ciliary muscle of the eye (accommodating the lens for vision at different distances), the smooth muscle of the bronchioles (constricting the air passages), and the smooth muscle of the walls of the gastrointestinal tract and urinary bladder, increasing their activity.

Inhibitory Functions   In some structures, parasympathetic impulses cause relaxation of smooth muscle or decrease the activity of an organ. Such is the case for the smooth muscle in the walls of the blood vessels of the salivary glands, the lacrimal glands, the mucous membrane of the mouth, and the external genitalia. (As a result, these blood vessels dilate.) Autonomic fibers in the vagus nerves cause the heart to beat more slowly and weakly. Parasympathetic impulses also relax the sphincters of the gastrointestinal tract and the urinary bladder.

Secretory Functions   Parasympathetic impulses stimulate the glands of the mucous membrane in the respiratory passages to increase their activity. The salivary glands produce a thin, watery saliva, which keeps the mouth moistened. Secretory activity of the lacrimal glands is also increased.

The functions of the parasympathetic division are far more selective than those of the sympathetic division, acting separately on each structure innervated, according to its own particular needs at the time. (By contrast, the sympathetic nerves produce a general mobilization, acting on the whole gamut of systems of the body simultaneously.)

PHYSIOLOGY OF THE AUTONOMIC NERVOUS SYSTEM

It seems strange that impulses from the sympathetic nerves may cause a particular organ to contract, while impulses to the same organ transmitted along parasympathetic nerves produce relaxation; or that the same division of the ANS can produce such varied effects on different organs and structures of the body. Part of the explanation has been found to lie in a difference in the neurotransmitter chemicals released by the nerve endings of parasympathetic and sympathetic neurons.

It has been found that the preganglionic fibers of both parasympathetic and sympathetic neurons secrete the neurotransmitter **acetylcholine** at their synapses. Acetylcholine is also released at the nerve endings of the parasympathetic postganglionic fibers. But most of the postganglionic fibers of the sympathetic division secrete a different neurotransmitter: **norepinephrine,** which acts in a similar manner on the effectors but produces somewhat different effects. There are two main exceptions to this general rule: the sympathetic postganglionic fibers to the sweat glands and those that produce vasodilation in skeletal muscles liberate acetylcholine. The fibers that release acetylcholine are classed as **cholinergic fibers;** those that produce norepinephrine are called **adrenergic fibers** (named for the alternate name for norepinephrine, **noradrenaline**).

Like acetylcholine, the norepinephrine secreted by the endings of sympathetic fibers is deactivated very quickly after its release into the synapse. But the body also has another major source of norepinephrine: this hormone is produced by the adrenal medulla, the secretion of which is stimulated by the sympathetic division of the ANS. (The secretion of the adrenal medulla is about 25 percent norepinephrine and 75 percent epinephrine, a structurally similar hormone with mostly similar effects.) These hormones are secreted into the blood, and removed from it rather slowly, so that their effects last about 10 times as long as those of the norepinephrine directly released by the sympathetic nerve endings. The hormones of the adrenal medulla thus serve as a sort of back-up system for the sympathetic nervous system, and the two can even substitute for one another. If the sympathetic innervation to a particular organ is cut, the organ will still be observed to respond in much the usual manner during a period of sympathetic stimulation, since secretions of the adrenal medulla will provide circulating norepinephrine to act on the organ. Similarly, total loss of the two adrenal medullae has little effect if the direct pathways of the sympathetic nervous system are still intact.

An important physiological difference between the autonomic nervous system and the somatic division of the peripheral nervous system is that the autonomic effectors can be fully activated by much lower frequencies of stimulation. A normal sympathetic or parasympathetic effect can usually be maintained by only one impulse every few seconds, and full activation occurs when the nerve fibers discharge 10 to 15 times per second. In the somatic division of the PNS, on the other hand, full activation sets in at about 75 to 200 impulses per second.

The parasympathetic and sympathetic nerve fibers are continually active to some degree, maintaining a basal parasympathetic tone or sympathetic tone. This tone permits a single division to control the function of certain organs completely. For example, sympathetic tone keeps the blood vessels of the skin and viscera constricted to about half their maximum diameter. If the activity along the sympathetic fibers increases, the blood vessels are constricted; if the sympathetic activity decreases, the blood vessels dilate. Opposite effects are thus produced without the need for an antagonist system. Parasympathetic tone produces a similar regulation of activity in the gastrointestinal tract. In other organs, such as the pancreas and the respiratory tract, both parasympathetic and sympathetic fibers act as antagonists in controlling function.

A number of drugs act by mimicking the effect of one of the neurotransmitters or by inhibiting the action of one type of fiber. Nicotine and muscarine stimulate the cholinergic fibers, while these nerve cells are inhibited by atropine, scopolamine, and belladonna. Adrenergic fibers are stimulated by epinephrine, ephedrine, and amphetamines and inhibited by such drugs as ergotamine, phentolamine, benzodioxane, and phenoxybenzamine.

Autonomic nerves are intimately involved in numerous important visceral reflexes that control body functions, such as the regulation of the blood pressure, the evacuation of the bladder and bowels, and the sexual reflexes. Like other reflexes, these reflex arcs involve both afferent nerves (visceral afferent nerves of the PNS and in some cases afferent nerves from the special sense organs) and efferent nerves to the effectors (parasympathetic or sympathetic nerves, sometimes in conjunction with efferent nerves of the PNS), as well as connector neurons and control centers in the CNS.

CONTROL OF AUTONOMIC FUNCTION

For a long time it was believed that the functions of the autonomic nervous system were entirely inaccessible to voluntary control (it was even called, alternatively, the "involuntary nervous system"). It seems rather odd that this premise was considered so axiomatic, since various religious mystics had long claimed to be able to perform such seemingly miraculous feats as to control their heartbeat and respiration rate at will, cut off bleeding from peripheral blood vessels,

and so on. Such claimants were usually dismissed as charlatans, and it was not until the late 1950s that controlled scientific investigations of such phenomena were undertaken. The results of such studies were startling. In one experiment in India (Figure 15-4), for example, a yogi was sealed into an airtight box. Electrodes and other pickups attached to his body made a continuous record of his heart rate, breathing rate, body temperature, and brain waves. Samples of air were taken from the box from time to time to determine oxygen consumption and carbon dioxide production. As the observing scientists monitored the yogi, his heartbeats and breathing rate gradually slowed, and his oxygen consumption fell to one-quarter of the minimum that had been calculated as necessary to sustain life. Yet when the door of the sealed box was opened several hours later, the yogi was alive and well.

Experiments on dogs and rats have similarly shown a previously unsuspected potential for control of the visceral functions. Dogs were trained to control the amount of saliva that flowed into their mouths when they are offered a drink of water. Rats were trained to control their heart rate, blood pressure, the contrac-

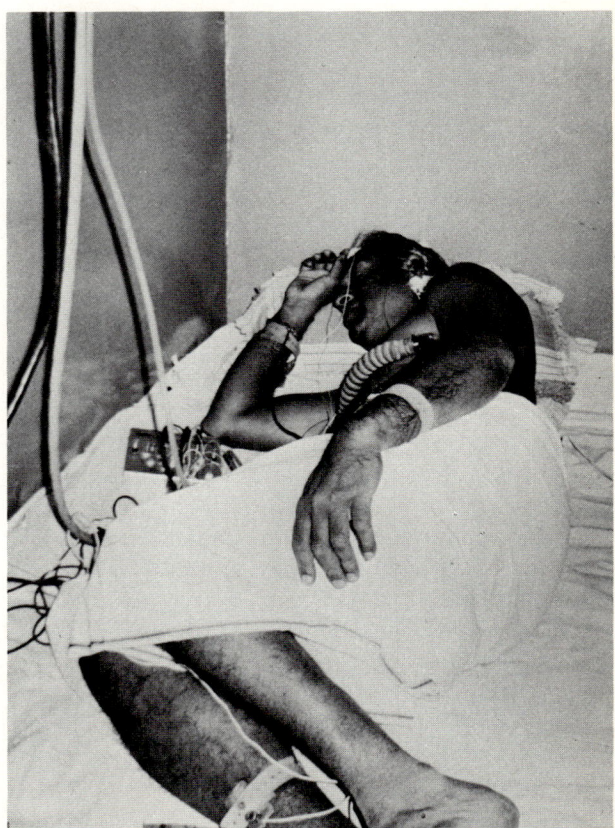

FIGURE 15-4 In a controlled experiment in New Delhi in 1970, Ramanand Yogi entered a trance in an airtight box.

tions of their intestines, and the rate of formation of urine. Highly specific control was possible: a rat learning to change its heart rate did not change its rate of bowel contraction, and vice versa. (Rats have even been trained to dilate the blood vessels in one ear and not the other, producing a one-sided "blush.")

The major center for the regulation and integration of the sympathetic and parasympathetic activity is the hypothalamus. This key center of the brain is linked both with the cerebral cortex (indirectly through the thalamus) and with centers in the spinal cord, and thus probably plays a major role in the learned control of autonomic functions that is being intensively researched at present. In a typical experiment, a subject's body indices are monitored, and a bell, a pleasing pattern of lights, or some other signal indicates when a particular visceral function has been altered in the desired direction. Gradually, the subject gains the ability to recognize the effect and ultimately to produce it at will. The applications of such control are obvious and are beginning to be exploited, as heart patients are being trained through biofeedback techniques to slow down their heart rate and lower their blood pressure, thus reducing the risk of a disabling or fatal heart attack.

DISORDERS OF THE AUTONOMIC NERVOUS SYSTEM

The autonomic nervous system is involved in just about every important process that goes on inside the body. Thus, it is not surprising that damage to autonomic nerves, through injury or disease, can have far-reaching and pervasive effects on body functions. Following are a few of the pathological conditions involving the autonomic nervous system.

A bladder disorder known as **atonic bladder** is the result of an interruption of afferent impulses of the autonomic reflex controlling the urinary bladder. The smooth muscle in the bladder wall loses its tone, and there is no sense of bladder fullness. Voluntary muscle contractions can produce a partial emptying of the bladder, but there is usually incontinence and dribbling. The condition called **automatic bladder** follows a severing of the spinal cord in the thoracic region. Autonomic reflexes in the sacral region of the spinal cord remain intact, and the bladder is emptied involuntarily.

Both the sympathetic and the parasympathetic divisions of the ANS are concerned in the regulation of **heart rate,** and damage to the nerves of either division will produce a change in the heart rate. If the parasympathetic fibers to the heart (in the vagus nerve) are damaged, the heart speeds up. If the sympathetic supply (through the cardiac nerves) is interrupted, the heart slows down.

Hirschsprung's disease is a congenital disorder in which some of the parasympathetic ganglia are missing. The condition results in a massive enlargement of the colon and persistent constipation.

A variety of **vasomotor and secretory disorders** result from injuries to the autonomic nerves supplying blood vessels and glands. Glands may cease to secrete or may secrete too copiously when deprived of their autonomic control; the appropriate regulation of the dilation and constriction of blood vessels may be impaired. **Raynaud's disease,** a condition in which there are intermittent attacks of pallor or cyanosis of the extremities, brought on by cold or emotion, is commonly treated by **sympathectomy,** the cutting of the sympathetic nerve trunks to the affected limb. With the sympathetic innervation interrupted, the blood vessels that were constricting too much dilate passively and provide a better blood supply, preventing disability and the potential development of gangrene.

SUMMARY

The autonomic nervous system or visceral motor system consists of efferent nerves involved in the control and coordination of visceral functions.

Autonomic impulses are transmitted along two-neuron chains: myelinated preganglionic fibers leading from the CNS synapse at ganglia with unmyelinated postganglionic fibers, which end in the effectors (smooth or cardiac muscle or glands).

Three main groups of autonomic ganglia are lateral (vertebral), collateral, and terminal.

In certain regions, autonomic fibers form networks called plexuses.

The two main divisions of the autonomic nervous system are the sympathetic (thoracolumbar) and parasympathetic (craniosacral).

The parasympathetic division provides for normal maintenance and repair of visceral functions.

The sympathetic division mobilizes the body's resources for extra exertions ("fight or flight") in emergency situations.

Most visceral structures are innervated by both parasympathetic and sympathetic fibers, whose actions are antagonistic.

Effects of autonomic stimulation include contraction or relaxation of muscle, stimulation or inhibition of gland secretion, and release of glucose by the liver (sympathetic); specific effects depend on the type of fiber and the structure innervated.

Autonomic nerves are involved in the regulation of the heart rate, blood pressure, breathing rate; secretion of salivary, sweat, digestive, and endocrine glands; digestive function; urine formation and elimination; regulation of pupil size; and excitation and function of the sex organs.

The neurotransmitter acetylcholine is secreted by cholinergic fibers: all preganglionic fibers, parasympathetic postganglionic fibers, and the sympathetic postganglionic fibers to the sweat glands and those producing vasodilation in the skeletal muscles.

The neurotransmitter norepinephrine is secreted by adrenergic fibers: most of the sympathetic postganglionic fibers.

Sympathetic stimulation causes secretion by the adrenal medulla of the hormones epinephrine and norepinephrine, which reinforce its effects on other organs and systems of the body.

Autonomic nerve fibers maintain a basal tone, which permits a single division to control the function of a particular organ.

The hypothalamus of the brain plays a central role in the control and integration of autonomic activity and permits some degree of learned control over autonomic functions.

Damage to autonomic nerves can result in a loss or pathological exaggeration of visceral functions (e.g., heart rate, bladder control, vasoconstriction).

QUESTIONS FOR REVIEW AND THOUGHT

1 Is the autonomic nervous system appropriately named? Discuss.

2 Describe the structure of the autonomic nervous system in contrast to the somatic division of the PNS.

3 Discuss the structural and functional differences of the parasympathetic and sympathetic nervous systems.

4 Discuss the neurotransmitters that act in the divisions of the autonomic nervous system.

5 Discuss the relationship between the sympathetic division of the ANS and the adrenal medulla.

6 Discuss the role of the hypothalamus in ANS function and suggest a mechanism by which visceral functions can be brought under conscious control through biofeedback techniques.

THE SENSE ORGANS: CUTANEOUS, VISCERAL, AND CHEMICAL

16

All that you "know" of the world around you is largely subjective, for it is filtered, analyzed, and reconstructed in your brain. Yet without a continual flow of information from specialized sense receptors, the brain would be cut off, not only from the outside world, but also from an awareness of the body's internal environment. The continual physiological juggling acts of the body systems that maintain homeostasis would be impossible without constantly updated data on what the actual conditions are, and what factors in the internal and external environment might tend to change them. A variety of information is potentially useful: radiations striking the body, the chemical composition of fluid and gas media, the temperature of the environment, the presence of impinging solid objects and their characteristics (hard or yielding, sticky, etc.)

The human body is not perfectly designed to make use of *all* the information our environment can yield—we are "blind" to ultraviolet and X rays, for example, and "deaf" to radio waves. But we are equipped with a versatile assortment of receptors providing for considerably more than the traditional "five senses." Our eyes allow us not only to detect the presence, color, and intensity of light rays, but to analyze the way they are bent or reflected by various objects to obtain information about the properties of objects in the external environment. Our ears permit us to perform similar feats with sound vibrations, and in conjunction with the analyzing centers of the brain, to distinguish the variations of pitch and modulation that make it possible to use sounds as a form of meaningful communication. The nose and mouth contain receptors for the chemical sense of smell and taste, which can warn of danger or attract us to nourishing foods. The entire body surface is endowed with a variety of cutaneous receptors, which produce sensations not only of touch, but also of pressure and pain, warmth and cold. The "inner senses" of the body, such as muscle sense, enable us to know at all times where the various body parts are and keep the central nervous system informed of the current state of the viscera and other body systems. In addition to the sense receptors with which the body is naturally endowed, humans have devised a variety of instruments—extensions of sense receptors, as it were—to detect additional types of environmental information and transform them into kinds accessible to our senses. A radio, for example, transforms radio waves into sound vibrations that we can hear, and an X-ray camera transforms "invisible" radiations into a picture visible to our eyes.

SENSATIONS

An injection of novocaine by the dentist makes us acutely aware of what it is like to lack sensation in a

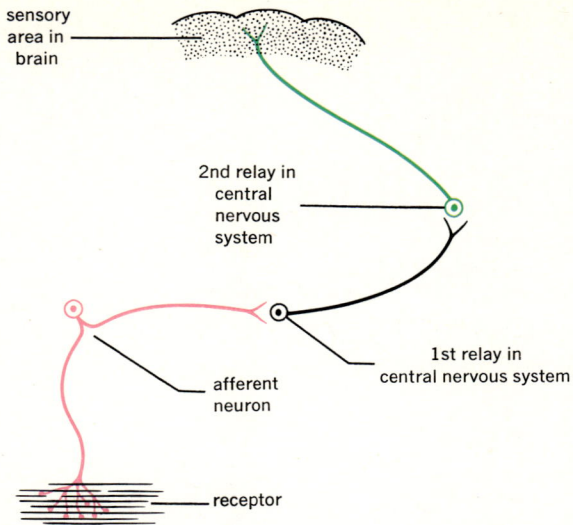

FIGURE 16-1   A sensory nerve pathway: a stimulus is relayed from the receptor to the appropriate sensory area of the brain.

part of the body. Sensations are the conscious results of a sequence of structures and processes (Figure 16-1). A sensation will be felt if the following elements are present.

1 A **stimulus,** a physical event involving a change in the external or internal environment

2 A **receptor,** a specialized sensitive cell that is depolarized by the stimulus, setting off a chain of nerve impulses

3 A **conducting pathway,** or sequence of afferent neurons, leading from the receptor to the appropriate region of the brain

4 A specialized **sensory area in the brain,** which analyzes the signals transmitted from the receptors and integrates them into meaningful information.

The **generator potential** or **receptor potential** that is established by the depolarization of the sensitive nerve ending is graded according to the strength of the stimulus and is stationary; it in turn sets up an **action potential,** which is transmitted along the conducting pathway on a self-propagated, all-or-none principle.

With the exception of olfactory (smell) impulses, all the sensory impulses are relayed to the appropriate sensory areas of the cerebral cortex through the thalamus (Figure 16-2). This central relay station sends messages on not only to the specific sensory areas, but also to diffuse cortical areas to permit the integration of sensory and motor activities and to regions of the hypothalamus, which provoke appropriate autonomic responses. When, as usual, the brain is receiving multiple sensory inputs, the thalamic relays permit a focusing of attention on those that seem most interesting or important. Thus, a person can focus on a conversation in the midst of a noisy cocktail party, or read a book while jackhammers dig up the street out-

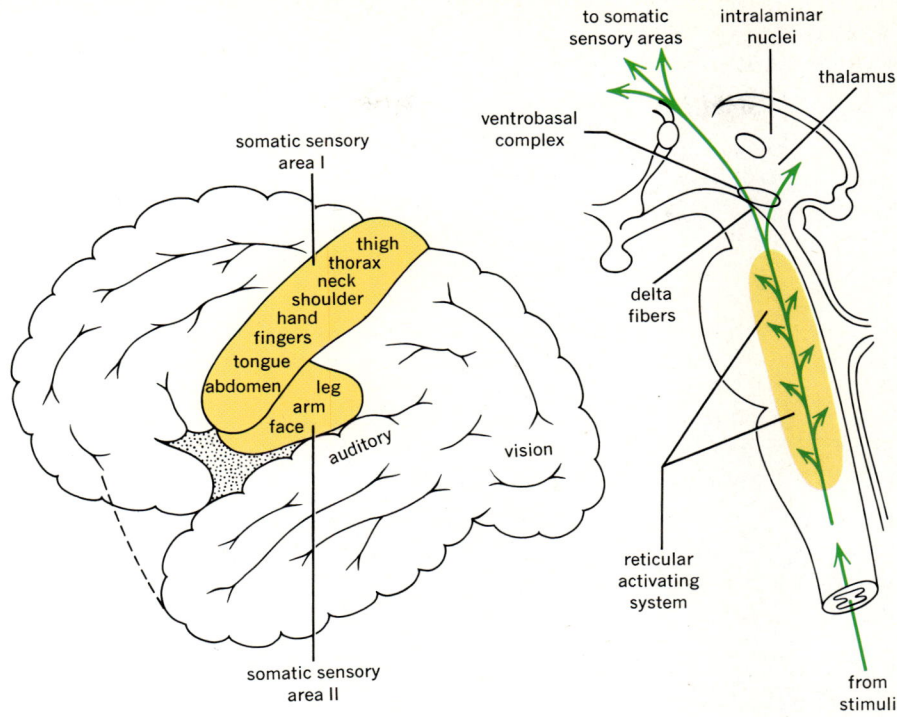

FIGURE 16-2 Major sensory areas of the central cortex (A) and some relay pathways leading to them through the spinal cord and lower brain (B).

side, or be distracted from pain by vigorously engaging in some activity; yet in the still of night, when there are few competing stimuli, the rumble of trucks on a distant highway or the ticking of a clock may seem maddeningly intrusive.

SENSE RECEPTORS

It is said that when one sense is lost, others are heightened. Many blind people are able to estimate the positions of objects by a kind of sonar, analyzing the patterns of bouncing sound waves. Helen Keller, who was both blind and deaf, gained a mental picture of people and things through her sense of touch; she even learned to speak with the aid of touch and muscle sense, feeling the lips, cheeks, and throat of her teacher and then her own, substituting tactile comparisons for the auditory feedback that children who are not handicapped use in learning to speak.

The body's sense receptors are the peripheral endings of functional dendrites of afferent neurons. Some, such as the receptors of tactile senses, are diffusely distributed over most of the body; others are concentrated in specialized sense organs, such as the eyes, ears, nose, and the taste buds of the tongue. The body's sense receptors are specialized to respond to particular types of stimuli; there are five main categories.

1 Mechanoreceptors detect mechanical deformation of the receptor or cells adjacent to it (these include not only the tactile sense of touch, pressure, and mechanical vibration,

but also the senses of hearing and equilibrium).
2 Thermoreceptors detect changes in temperature (some are sensitive to cold, while others respond to warmth).
3 Electromagnetic receptors, or **photoreceptors** detect light.
4 Chemoreceptors are sensitive to specific chemical substances (e.g., taste receptors in the mouth, smell receptors in the nose, and receptors sensitive to the oxygen level in the arterial blood, the pH, the osmolality of the body fluids, and the carbon dioxide concentration).
5 Nociceptors detect damage to the tissues (either physical or chemical damage).

In most cases, the specialization of the receptors is quite precise—the rods and cones of the eyes, for example, while highly responsive to light, are almost completely insensitive to heat, cold, pressure on the eyeballs, and chemical changes in the blood; pain receptors in the skin are not stimulated by the usual touch or pressure stimuli, but respond actively when tactile stimuli become severe enough to damage the tissues.

Structurally, sense receptors differ greatly. Some are simply bare nerve endings; others are encapsulated; whil still others are organized into highly specialized sense organs, such as the eyes and ears. Some characteristic types of sensory nerve endings are shown in Figure 16-3.

Another classification of sense receptors that is often useful is according to their location. **Exteroceptors** are surface receptors, concerned with touch, cutaneous pain, pressure, warmth, cold, smell, taste, vision,

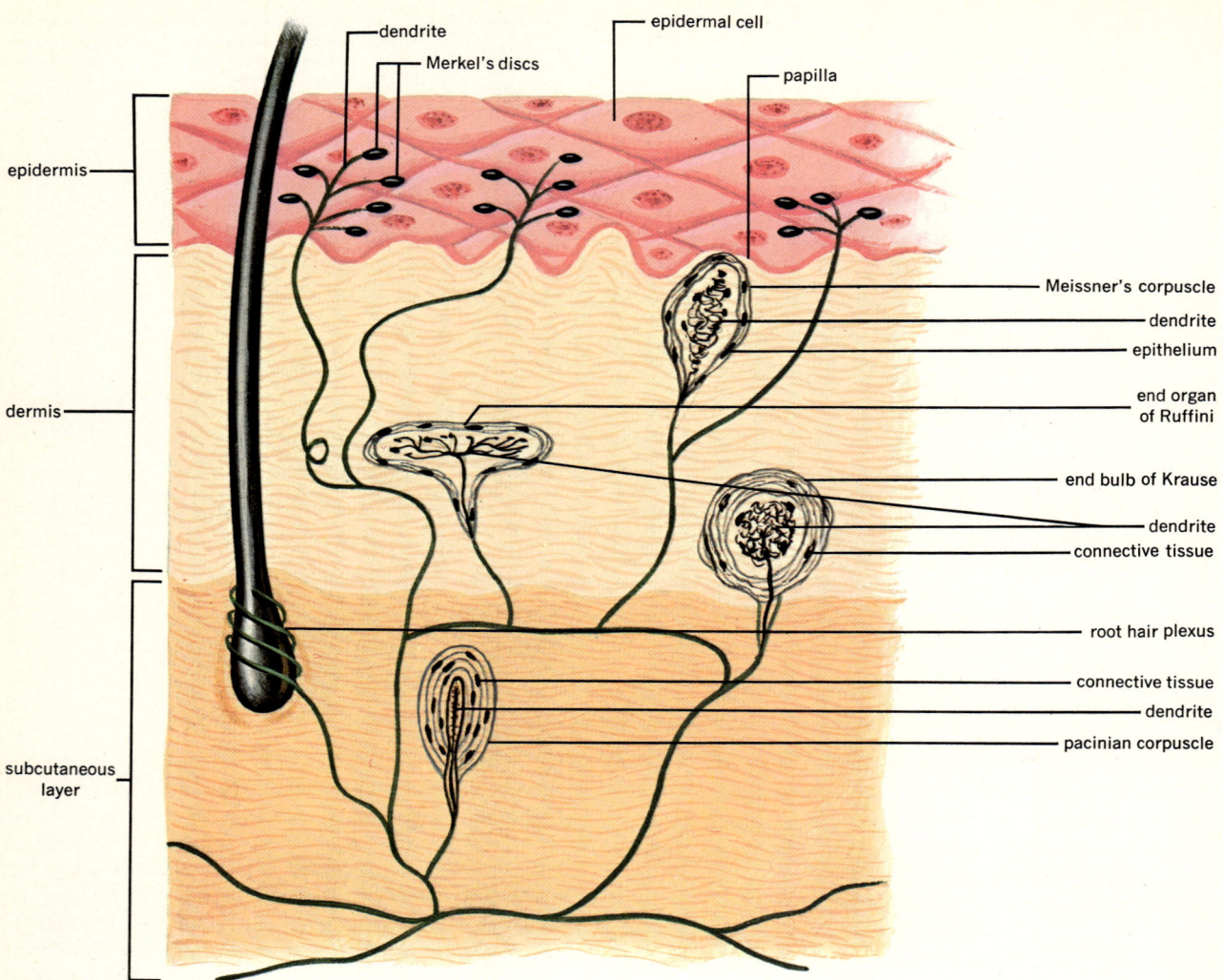

FIGURE 16-3 Major types of cutaneous receptors.

and hearing—in other words, the senses we normally think of when we speak of our "five senses." **Proprioceptors** are the receptors of muscle sense, sense of position and of movement of the body in space. They respond to changes in the skeletal muscles, tendons, joints, and the semicircular canals and utricle of the inner ear. **Interoceptors** are found in the viscera and are concerned with such internal sensations as hunger, thirst, fullness, and visceral pain.

CHARACTERISTICS OF SENSATIONS

Just how accurate is the picture of the world transmitted by our senses? Are things really what they seem? Often our impression of things and events is somewhat distorted because of quirks in the fundamental nature of sensations.

Modality of Sensation and Projection
Each of the principal types of sensation—sight, sound, touch, pain, and so on—is referred to as a modality of sensa-

tion. Yet all these modalities of sensation are produced by nerve fibers that transmit impulses. How is it that we perceive the impulses transmitted by some nerve fibers as sounds, others as cold, still others as tastes? The answer lies in the specific pathways leading from the sense receptors to the brain. Touch fibers are connected by nerve pathways to specific touch areas in the brain, fibers from the ear terminate in the auditory areas of the brain, fibers from the retina of the eye terminate in the vision areas of the brain, and so forth.

Thus, we actually perceive all sensations not in the sense organs themselves, but in the brain. But it *seems* as though a particular sensation is localized at the site of the receptor. The brain projects sensations to the receptors. This ability is gradually learned with experience, as can be observed by watching an infant's delight as it successively "discovers" hands, feet, and other parts of its body. The protection of sensation permits a fine localization of many sensations to specific sites of stimulation on the body: you can slap a mosquito that has alighted on your arm without having to check its position with your eyes. An interesting aspect of projection is the fact that stimulation of an afferent nerve anywhere along its course is perceived by the brain as arising at the nerve ending (receptor). If your arm "goes to sleep" because you have been cradling your head on your upper arm, the "pins and needles" sensation you experience as the compressed nerves recover seems to come from your hand, at the end of the nerve pathway, rather than at the site of the actual stimulation. In the sensory nerves to the viscera, a combination of tangled nerve pathways and the brain's inexperience in localizing internal stimuli can lead to some bizarre **referred pains,** such as the pain felt in the left shoulder and arm in angina pectoris (a serious heart condition).

Intensity   A kiss on the cheek and a punch in the jaw feel quite different, even though both are perceived via cutaneous receptors. The intensity of a sensation depends on the number of receptors stimulated and on the number of impulses transmitted by each afferent fiber per second. These factors in turn are directly dependent on the strength of the stimulus. Human sense receptors operate effectively over a wide range of intensities. For example, we can detect a barely audible whisper, yet can also distinguish the words and tones of a rock and roll tune blaring out of a loudspeaker at a dance; we can clearly distinguish objects in bright sunlight and in dim twilight.

Contrast   A sensation is affected by events that have just preceded it (successive contrast) or accompany it (simultaneous contrast). An interesting effect is observed when people are asked to select a weight exactly twice as heavy as another. Usually the person selects a weight that is only 50 percent heavier, having underestimated the weak stimulus and overestimated the heavy one.

After-Images   Sensations tend to persist in consciousness after the stimulus has ceased. Movies and television take advantage of this peculiarity of perception: a series of discrete images flashed on the screen is perceived as a continuous moving picture because the after-image of one frame persists until the next one takes its place.

Adaptation   When a stimulus of constant intensity continues to act on a receptor, the magnitude of the receptor potential and the frequency of the response decrease: the receptor adapts to the stimulus. When you first dive into a swimming pool, the water may seem icy cold, but soon it will feel quite confortable. Similarly, after a while a hot bath is perceived as

merely warm, and then you tend to forget about its temperature entirely. In order for a receptor to be activated, the rate of change in the environment must be faster than the rate of adaptation of the receptor. Different types of receptors differ in their rates of adaptation; touch and temperature receptors adapt very rapidly, while pain receptors and proprioceptors adapt very slowly.

CUTANEOUS SENSES

Cultures vary in the amount of physical touching considered appropriate among people in various relationships. But to some degree there seems to be a correlation between emotional stability and the amount of tactile stimulation a person has received, especially in the crucial early years of development. A baby gains comfort from the touch and warmth of its mother's body as she holds it, feeds it, and cares for it.

The cutaneous sense of truth, pressure, heat, cold, and pain are provided by a variety of specialized sense receptors, which are rather nonuniformly distributed over the surface of the body. You may recall that the area of skin supplied by a single dorsal nerve root is called a dermatome. The actual nerve endings have a point distribution, and the regions of skin between points lack sensitivity to that particular type of stimulus. The distribution of different types of cutaneous receptors over the body surface has been mapped, using a variety of pin points, heated and chilled probes, and so forth. The sensory map of the forearm shown in Figure 16-4 illustrates the nonuniformity of the distribution of the sense receptors; in this case pain receptors are the most numerous, while heat receptors are the most sparsely represented. The tongue has been found to be the most highly sensitive area of the body surface. Other regions that are richly supplied with sense receptors are the lips (that is one reason why kissing is such a pleasant activity) and fingertips; the skin of the back is sparsely supplied and relatively insensitive.

Touch and Pressure

We normally rely so much on our eyes that we tend to underestimate the amount of information the sense of touch can convey. If you close your eyes and have

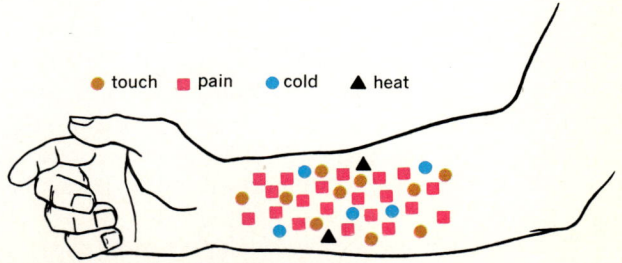

FIGURE 16-4   Sensory map of the forearm.

someone hand you an object, you will very likely be able to identify it by touch alone. Your fingers will tell you whether it is rough or smooth, hard or soft, wet or dry or sticky, as well as its size and general contours. The sense of touch is also quite accurately localized: if you are blindfolded and someone touches some spot on your skin, you will be able to put your finger on the exact spot.

The tactile sensations—touch, pressure, and vibration—are often classified as separate sensations, but all are detected by the same types of receptors. Touch sensations usually result from stimulation of tactile receptors in the skin or in the tissues immediately beneath the skin. Pressure sensations result from the deformation of deeper tissues, while the sensation of vibration results from rapidly repetitive sensory signals, detected by the same types of receptors as touch and pressure.

There are at least six different types of tactile receptors (See Figure 16-3). **Free nerve endings,** which are found everywhere in the skin and in many other tissues, are sensitive to touch and pressure. They adapt rather slowly, as evidenced by the persistent irritation produced by a particle in the eye. (The cornea is supplied only with free nerve endings.) **Meissner's corpuscles,** encapsulated nerve endings, are especially abundant in the fingertips, lips, nipples, and external genitalia—areas where the sense of touch is highly developed; they are not found in hairy regions of the skin. Meissner's corpuscles adapt within a second or so, which makes them particularly sensitive to the movement of very light objects over the surface of the skin. **Merkel's discs** are expanded discs at the end of nerve fibers. They transmit long-continuing signals and permit the detection of continuous touch of objects against the skin. They are found on the borders of the tongue and (sparsely) in hairy parts of the body. A slight movement of a hair stimulates the **hair-end-organ,** a nerve fiber twining around its base. This touch receptor adapts rapidly and detects mainly movements of objects on the body surface. **Ruffini's end-organs** are multibranched nerve endings found in the deeper layers of the skin and in deeper tissues of the body. They do not adapt rapidly and are sensitive to pressure and heavy continuous touch stimuli. **Pacinian corpuscles** are encapsulated receptors widely distributed in the skin, in the connective tissue near tendons and joints, in the mammary glands and external genitalia, and in various deep tissues of the body. They are sensitive to pressure and, because they adapt within a fraction of a second, are the sense receptors for movements of tissues and vibrations. (Pacinian corpuscles can detect vibrations up to 700 cycles per second.)

If it were not for the rapid adaptation of many of the touch receptors, we would be unable to wear

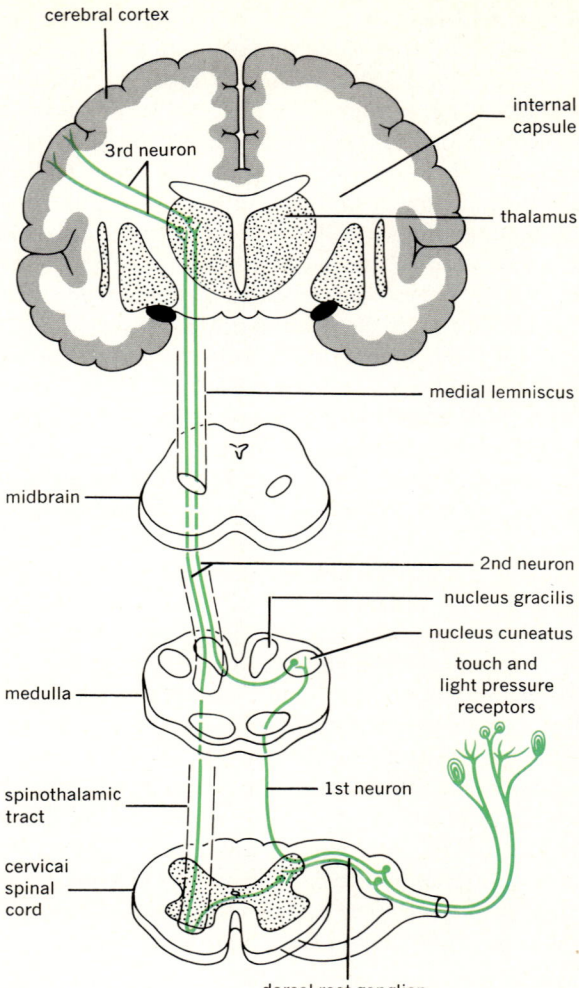

FIGURE 16-5 Afferent pathways for the perception of touch and light pressure. Some fibers cross in the spinal cord, others in the medulla.

clothes, and even the touch of our own hair against the skin would be maddening. But though we readily get used to the feel of our clothes and cease to notice them, the continuous pressure of a heavy weight continues to impinge on our attention, since it stimulates more slowly adapting pressure receptors.

Like other sensations, touch and pressure signals are not appreciated until they reach the appropriate area of the cerebral cortex (in this case, in the parietal lobe, just posterior to the central sulcus), to which they are routed via sensory nerves and through the relay-station of the thalamus (Figure 16-5).

The sense of touch plays a greater role in our lives than we normally realize. A recent attempt by Japanese merchandisers to cut down on operating costs and shoplifting by building a giant "automat-type" department store has been less successful than expected because shoppers are frustrated in their desire to handle and feel items before purchasing them.

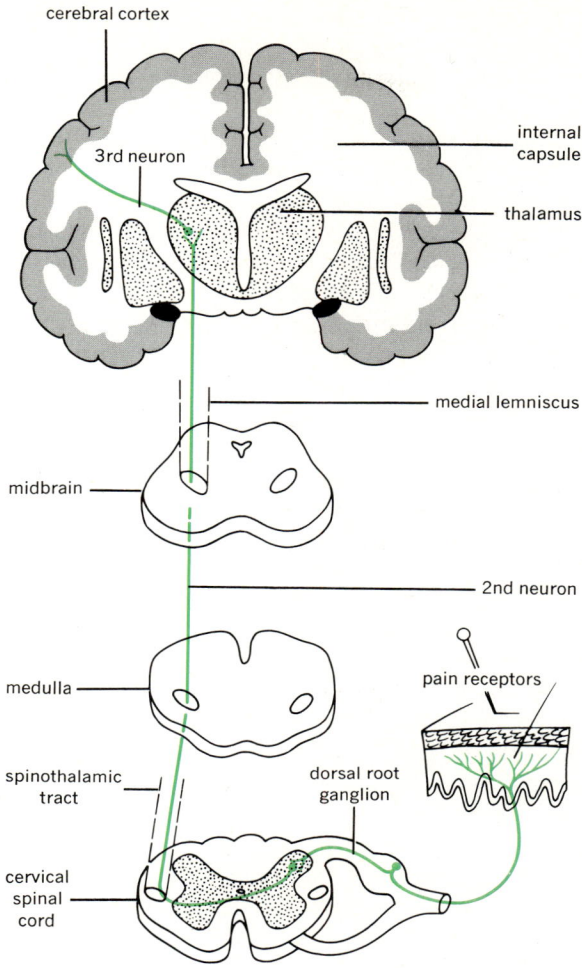

FIGURE 16-6 Afferent pathway for pain sensations.

if tissue damage is produced. Tissue ischemia, caused by a blockage of the blood supply to an area, and muscle spasms are frequent causes of pain. It has been found that extracts from damaged tissues, injected under normal skin, produce intense pain; **bradykinin** and **histamine,** substances formed in damaged tissues, have been implicated in the stimulation of the pain receptors.

Pain can be classified as **superficial,** or cutaneous **pain; deep pain** from muscles, joints, and tendons; and **visceral pain,** from internal organs. Another type of classification distinguishes among **pricking pain,** felt when a needle is stuck into the skin or the skin is cut with a knife; **burning pain,** resulting from diffuse stimulation of all the pain receptors in an area, as when the skin is burned; and **aching pain,** a deep pain with varying degrees of intensity, which may be either diffuse or localized. The intensity of the pain depends on the number of fibers stimulated. Deep pain is often associated with nausea and a drop in blood pressure, whereas superficial pain can quicken the pulse and raise blood pressure.

Pain impulses travel over small afferent nerve fibers to the CNS; they are transmitted to the thalamus via the lateral spinothalamic tract (Figure 16-6). Awareness of pain occurs in the thalamus, but impulses are additionally relayed to the cerebral cortex, where localization and recognition of the kind and intensity take place. There is little or no adaptation of the pain receptors, which is normally beneficial, making it difficult to ignore the body's persistent warning signals. (For example, sitting too long in one position produces ischemia of the tissues of the buttocks, and the resultant pain signal causes the person to automatically shift position, relieving the pressure. A patient with a damaged spinal cord, unable to receive such warning signals, is in continual danger of developing ulcers.) But in cases of severe and intractable pain, such as that caused by rapidly spreading cancer, the pain itself does indeed become a bane, often aggravating the patient's condition by making him or her unable to eat and sleep. There has been a continuing controversy about the justification of using effective but addictive narcotics such as heroin to ease the pain of terminally ill patients; another approach is to surgically cut the pain-transmitting nerve pathways at various points.

Experiments have shown that all people have just about the same threshold for pain (i.e., all become aware of pain sensations at about the same stimulus intensity), but people differ greatly in their reaction to pain. Pain elicits both motor reflexes (such as the automatic withdrawal of the hand from a hot stove) and psychic reactions such as anguish, anxiety, depression, or excitability. Such responses vary greatly from one person to another following comparable stimuli

"Worry beads" and other objects that appeal to the tactile senses provide an outlet for tension. And the popularity of hand holding, caressing, and kissing is an indication of the tremendous emotional impact that the tactile senses can convey.

Pain

We tend to think of pain as a bane, a curse, a sensation we could well do without, and yet it can be extremely valuable. Pain is the body's warning signal that something is wrong—tissues are being damaged—and some sort of corrective action should be taken immediately.

The pain receptors are all free nerve endings, an estimated several million of them. Pain receptors are particularly widespread in the superficial layers of the skin, as well as in such internal tissues as the periosteum, the arterial walls, and the joint surfaces. Most of the deep tissues are only diffusely supplied with pain receptors, but any widespread tissue damage can summate to produce an aching pain.

Any intense stimulus, such as pressure or extreme heat or cold, can stimulate pain receptors, especially

and are influenced by such factors as one's personality and emotional state, ethnic and cultural background, and childhood experiences.

The discovery of a new class of hormones is producing a revolution in research on pain and its alleviation. In 1973, researchers at Johns Hopkins University found that morphine and other opiates relieve pain by binding to specific chemical receptors on the surface of nerve cells in the brain and spinal cord. It did not seem logical that body cells would have evolved chemical sites precisely tailored to fit foreign chemicals. John Hughes and Hans Kosterlitz at the University of Aberdeen in Scotland launched a search for some natural body chemicals that would fit the morphine receptor sites. They found two natural pain killers, which they named **enkephalins** ("in the brain"). Subsequently other natural morphine-like substances, the **endorphins** ("endogenous morphines") were discovered. All of these natural pain killers are peptides and eventually turned out to be fragments of a pituitary hormone, β-lipotropin (one of the enkephalins has a substitution of one amino acid at the end of its five-amino-acid chain). The enkephalins are believed to be formed by specialized nerve cells and act as neurotransmitters that inhibit the transmission of pain impulses. Researchers theorize that people with a greater tolerance for pain may produce larger amounts of enkephalins, while those with low pain tolerance may be deficient in either enkephalins or their receptor sites.

The discovery of enkephalins and endorphins suggests explanations for some of the puzzles of pain relief. Naloxone, a drug that blocks the action of morphine by binding to the opiate receptors, provides researchers with a probe for testing the effects of the natural pain killers as well. Studies have shown that acupuncture raises the threshold of pain perception; the hypothesis that enkephalin production is involved is confirmed by the finding that this effect is blocked by naloxone. Enkephalins and endorphins are also involved in the **placebo effect,** in which about one-third of patients who *think* they are receiving a potent drug but actually receive an inactive sugar pill report a reduction of pain. Studies of dental patients who had a tooth extracted showed a prompt disappearance of the placebo effect when naloxone was injected.

Insights into the action of enkephalins and endorphins have also suggested an explanation for narcotic addiction. If a drug such as morphine is occupying opiate receptor sites on the nerve cells, the body's normal feedback mechanisms would tend to shut off the production of the natural pain killers. Then more morphine will be needed to fill the receptors that would have been occupied by enkephalins. If the narcotic is withheld, the receptors will be unfilled until the feedback mechanisms of the body have had time to resume normal enkephalin production—hence the typical painful withdrawal symptoms of drug addiction.

The phenomena of tickling and itch have been thought to be caused by very mild stimulation of the pain nerve endings. Recent studies have revealed the existence of some very sensitive free nerve endings, which respond to extremely light touch. They are believed to carry the tickle and itch sensations, and their impulses are transmitted over the same type of nerve fibers as those that carry the sensations of the burning type of pain.

Temperature

A bath that feels perfectly comfortable to the hands is often too hot for the body. An ice cube may feel "burning hot" to the touch. If you place your left hand in a basin of hot water and your right in a basin of cold water, then transfer both hands to a basin of lukewarm water, the same water will feel cold to your left hand and hot to your right one. All these curious phenomena are results of the nature and distribution of the body's temperature receptors.

A human being can perceive various gradations of cold and heat, from cold to cool to indifferent to warm to hot. Most people can perceive and discriminate temperatures from 12° C to 50° C, and some can even perceive freezing cold and burning hot. Three different types of receptors are responsible for detecting these varying gradations of temperature: **cold receptors, warm receptors,** and **pain receptors.** (The pain receptors are stimulated by extreme degrees of both heat and cold.) Free nerve endings, such as those in the cornea, can detect cold or warmth. Specialized receptors are the **Krause end bulbs** and the **corpuscles of Ruffini** (See Figure 16-3 on page 352). The Krause end bulbs consist of a multiply branched afferent nerve fiber in a capsule of connective tissue and are sensitive to cold. They are stimulated by steady-state skin temperatures between 12°C and 35°C and—surprisingly—at 50°C, and also when the skin is rapidly cooled from any temperature. Ruffini corpuscles lie deeper in the skin, are more sparsely distributed, and consist of a network of nerve endings embedded in granular material. These are the receptors for warmth, which discharge at skin temperatures between 25° and 45°C; when the skin is being warmed, they increase their firing rate. An examination of Figure 16-7, which summarizes the regions of activity of the different types of temperature receptors, leads to some surprising conclusions and explains some of the paradoxical aspects of the temperature sense. At the lowest temperatures the pain fibers are stimulated; at 12°, with a small region of overlap, the cold receptors take over; from 25° to 35°C both cold and warm

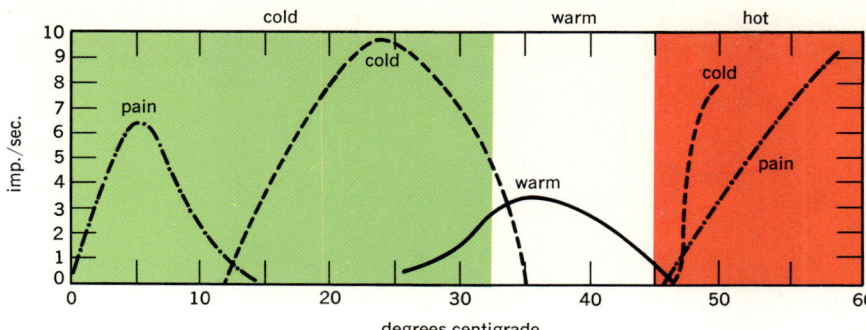

FIGURE 16-7 Responses of cold, warm, and pain receptors combine to produce sensations of cold, warm, and hot temperatures. (Modified from Zotterman: Ann. Rev. Physiol., *15*: 357, 1953.)

receptors are stimulated; and beginning at about 45°C the warm receptors are no longer stimulated, but both cold and pain receptors are. (Very cold and very hot temperatures are thus indistinguishable in sensory input.)

Because the thermal receptors respond strongly to changes in temperature, in addition to steady states of temperature, a person feels much colder when the temperature of the skin is actively falling than when the temperature remains constant, and feels hotter when the temperature is rising than when it is steady. The thermal receptors adapt readily, so that a too-hot bath or too-cold swimming pool quickly becomes bearable; but they do not adapt all the way, so that some sensation of warmth or coolness still persists, although at a lower intensity than at the initial exposure. After-images of warmth or cold persist for long periods.

The thermal receptors are distributed rather nonuniformly over the body. The skin of the face and hands is less sensitive to temperature changes than that of other parts of the body. The lips and the mucous membranes of the mouth and rectum are highly temperature sensitive (one often feels a person's forehead for fever with the lips), but other mucous membranes of the body are insensitive to temperature. People who have the habit of rapidly gulping hot coffee or other hot drinks feel no discomfort after the hot liquid leaves the mouth but may severely burn the mucous membranes of the esophagus and stomach.

VISCERAL RECEPTORS

Most of the body's sense receptors are directed outward, and bring in information about the external environment. But the brain needs a continual flow of information about what is happening inside the body as well, and the internal organs are also supplied with sense receptors. Many of the messages transmitted to the CNS from the visceral receptors are concerned with the reflex control of such vital functions as the beating of the heart, the adjustment of the size of the blood vessels, and respiration. Such sensory messages form a continuous flow, and the conditions they report are attended to automatically, usually without

being brought to conscious attention. Indeed, as a general rule, if we feel our insides, something is the matter. The problem signalled by a visceral sensation may be mild and readily remedied, such as hunger pangs calling for an intake of food, or a feeling of fullness in the bowels or bladder, calling for elimination. **Visceral pain** may be a signal of widespread tissue damage, or merely a temporary malfunction of some internal organ, such as menstrual cramps or an intestinal spasm produced by excess gas (flatulence).

Stimuli that excite visceral receptors include **ischemia** (tissue starvation due to a cutoff of the normal blood supply); **chemical stimuli,** for example, gastric juice leaking through a perforated ulcer; **spasm,** or strong contractions, of a hollow viscus, such as the gut, gallbladder, uterus, or ureter; and **distension** of a hollow viscus, which may stretch tissues and collapse blood vessels. Pain from a spastic viscus often occurs in the form of **cramps,** in which the pain increases in intensity and then subsides in rhythmic cycles.

The afferent fibers over which visceral sensations are relayed to the central nervous system travel in company with various autonomic nerves, but are quite independent of them. Visceral pain impulses are relayed through the thalamus to the cortex, but the higher brain has some difficulties in localizing the source of the sensation. The brain has no first-hand knowledge of the locations of particular internal organs, and in addition, many of the afferent nerve fibers that transmit sensations from the viscera converge with the afferent fibers from cutaneous areas and share common pathways in the second-order neurons that relay the messages up to the brain. It is small wonder that the brain becomes confused in interpreting such messages and tends to refer visceral pains to the cutaneous areas supplied by sensory nerves that enter the spinal cord at the same place as the fibers from the visceral receptors. These cutaneous areas of referred pain are quite consistent (Figure 16-8) and can serve as a valuable diagnostic aid. For example, in angina pectoris, pain from the heart receptors is characteristically referred to the left shoulder and down the left arm; in pneumonia, pain is often projected to the abdomen.

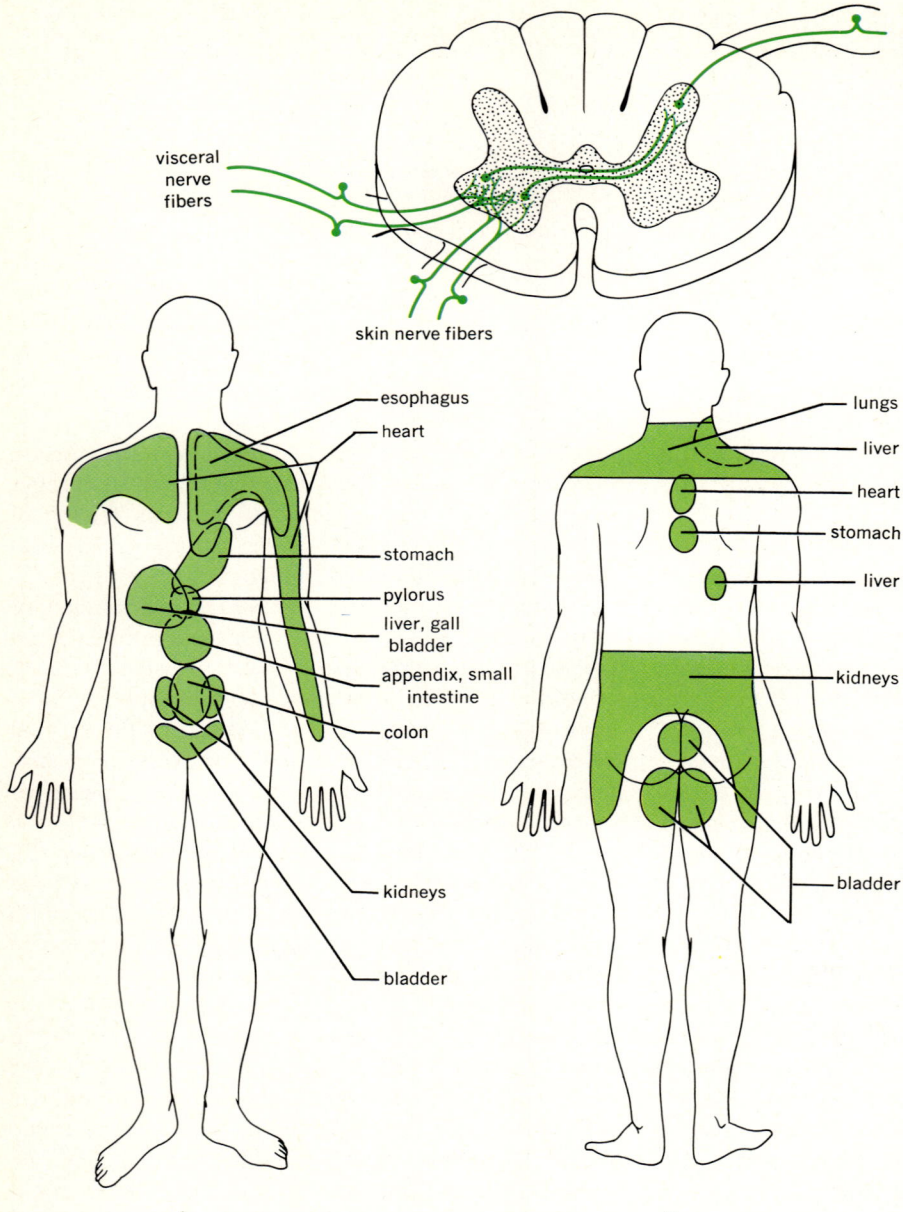

FIGURE 16-8   Referred pain: neuronal wiring complexities result in the perception of visceral pains as though localized in specific cutaneous areas.

Afferent fibers traveling with the craniosacral nerves of the parasympathetic system transmit impulses concerned with the so-called organic sensations of hunger, thirst, nausea, distension of the bladder and bowel, and feelings of sexual stimulation.

Hunger

Each day more than ten thousand people, mostly young people, die of starvation or are so weakened by it that they succumb to various diseases. For each one who actually dies of starvation, there are many who are able to subsist at a minimum level but know a continual hunger.

Hunger is a miserably unpleasant sensation. It is associated with the powerful rhythmic contractions of the empty stomach, which stimulate receptors in the mucous membrane or spindles in the stomach muscles. If food is not taken, the hunger pangs increase in intensity and may be accompanied by headache, weakness, nausea, and irritability. After a time the hunger pangs disappear, only to return again if food still has not been taken. People who have fasted for long periods say that after a few days the hunger pangs diminish and may disappear altogether. Illness may reduce the muscle tone in the stomach and prevent the occurrence of hunger pangs, even if little or no food is being taken. Food intake is normally regulated by control centers (hunger and satiety) in the hypothalamus.

Appetite and hunger are not the same thing. Hunger is a purely physiological phenomenon, related to contractions of the stomach, whereas appetite is more a state of mind, involving a desire for food. The senses of taste and smell, emotional status, and various cultural and social factors influence appetite. When you are hungry, nearly any food will satisfy you; appetite is more specific, and you may find you have an excellent appetite for dessert at the end of a meal, when your stomach is actually quite full and you are not a bit hungry.

Thirst

The scene is familiar to watchers of the Late, Late Show. A prospector, stranded out on the desert, has drained the last drop from his canteen and is searching desperately for a water hole. As the hot sun beats down on him, he becomes increasingly dehydrated and is tormented by an agonizing sensation of thirst. Hour by hour his anguish grows, and he begins to hallucinate, imagining a lush oasis just ahead.

The body's water balance is a dynamic equilibrium. Sweat and urine continually flush out body wastes, but eliminate precious water, which must be regularly replaced; otherwise the volumes of extra- and intracellular fluid drop, and if dehydration becomes too extreme, the body systems can no longer function, and death results. The body's water balance is continuously monitored in the hypothalamus, which receives reports from osmoreceptors in the nearby area on the current osmolality of the blood. If the tissues become dehydrated and the blood osmolality rises, impulses from the thirst center in the hypothalamus produce a sensation of thirst, projected to the pharynx, and the hypothalamus secretes a hormone (ADH) that causes the kidneys to produce a more concentrated urine, conserving water for the body.

Thirst can be defined as a conscious desire for water. It is usually accompanied by sensations of dryness in the mouth and throat, but these sensations and actual thirst can on occasion be independent—if dryness of the mouth is caused by decreased secretion of the salivary glands, it can be alleviated by merely moistening the mouth with water, rather than actually drinking. Experiments on people with an esophageal fistula have revealed a curious phenomenon: the sensation of thirst seems to be satisfied by the very act of drinking, even if no water actually passes into the gastrointestinal tract. (This thirst quenching, however, is only temporary, for thirst due to tissue dehydration returns again about fifteen minutes after the "sham drinking.") If the water actually does reach the stomach, the distension of the stomach walls produces a further temporary relief of thirst. (The effect can even be simulated by inflating a balloon in the stomach of the thirsty person.) It is theorized that the immediate satisfaction of thirst by the act of drinking is a protective mechanism. It takes as long as half an hour to an hour for water drunk to rehydrate the body's parched tissues and eliminate the original cause of the thirst sensation. If there were no immediate thirst-quenching effect, a person would tend to go on drinking and drinking, producing an actual overhydration, almost to the bursting point.

Nausea

Anyone who has ever been seasick is convinced that nausea is one of the most abjectly miserable sensations that the body can produce. Nausea is a conscious recognition of subconscious stimulation of the vomiting center in the medulla, and it is often quickly followed by actual vomiting. It can be caused by irritative impulses from the gastrointestinal tract, or stimulated by impulses from the organs of sight, taste, or smell. (The common phrase, "That's sickening!" may be meant literally.) The disorienting messages from the semicircular canals of the ears during a ride on a rocking, swaying boat can give rise to the nausea associated with motion sickness. A common cause of nausea is distension or irritation of the small intestine, which contracts forcefully, spewing its contents back into the stomach, as a prelude to subsequent vomiting. Many drugs can produce nausea as a side effect, as do the female sex hormones secreted during early pregnancy ("morning sickness") and used in birth control pills. For as yet unexplained reasons, some people seem to be more susceptible to nausea then others.

PROPRIOCEPTORS: THE KINESTHETIC SENSE

A tightrope walker is capable of breathtaking feats of balance. Without a downward glance, he or she can walk boldly across a slender wire, raise one leg, do handstands, headstands, ride a bicycle across the wire, and even hold up a pyramid of other perfectly balanced performers. Accomplishments such as these require years of practice; but when you stop to think of it, the feats of which your own body is capable are nearly as amazing. You are aware at all times exactly where every part of your body is and what it is doing, without the need to look over and check. You can readily learn to type on a typewriter without looking at the keys, or to play a musical instrument "by feel." A person can knit or crochet while watching television, giving only occasional and cursory supervision to what the busy hands are fashioning.

The term **kinesthesia** is used to denote the conscious recognition of the orientation of the different parts of the body relative to each other, and the rates of movement of the different parts of the body. This "position sense" is provided by specialized **proprio-**

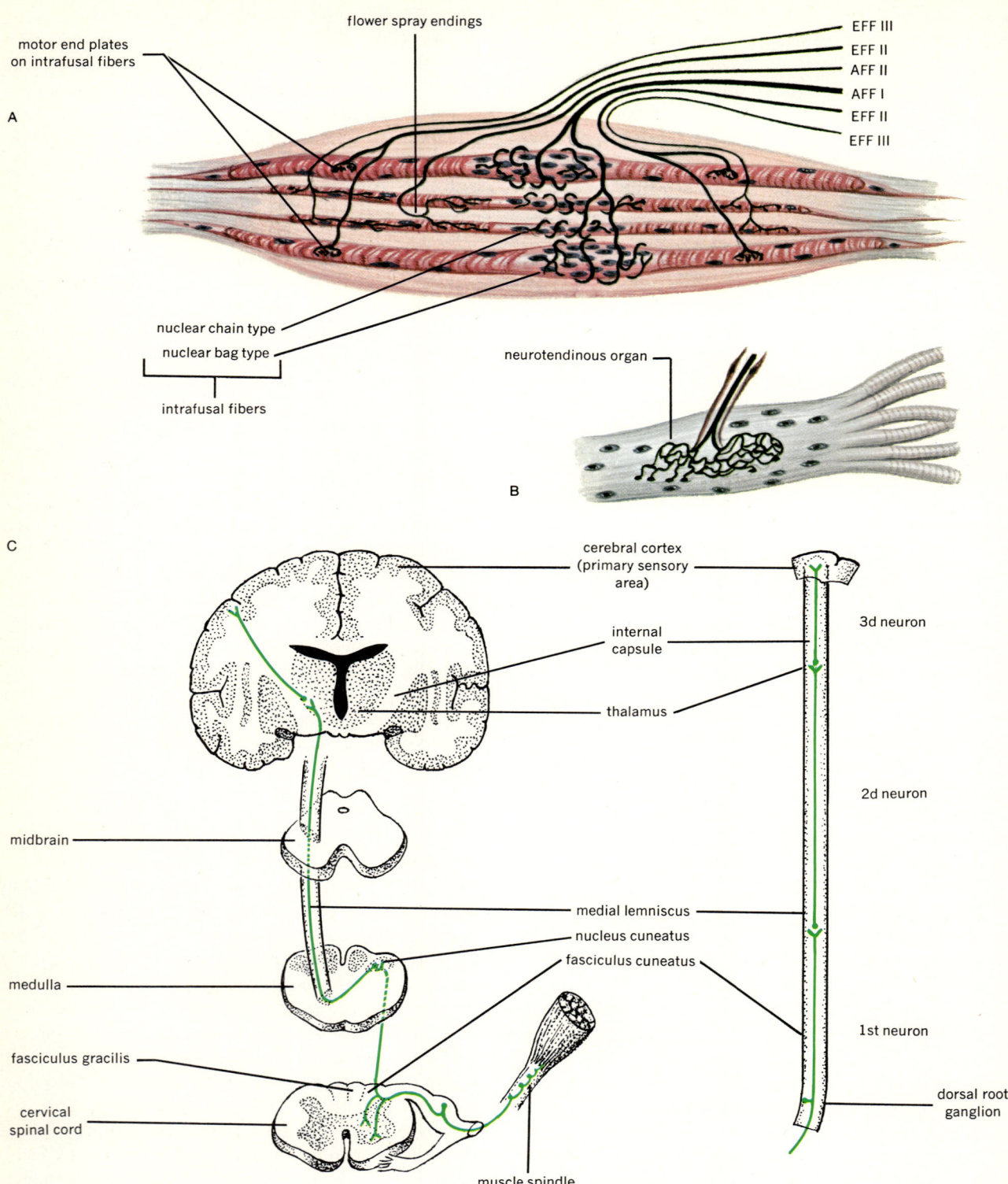

FIGURE 16-9 Proprioception: muscle spindles (A), Golgi tendon receptors (B), and the central pathway for proprioception (C).

ceptors (the prefix *proprio*-literally means "self"), located mainly in the joint capsules and ligaments.

Three main types of proprioceptors have been described (Figure 16-9). **Ruffini's end-organs** are the most abundant in the joint capsules and ligaments.

They are stimulated strongly when the joint is suddenly moved; they quickly adapt slightly, but then transmit a steady signal. The **Golgi endings** in joint capsules and the ligaments around joints respond similarly. A few **pacinian corpuscles** also found in the tissues around joints adapt extremely rapidly and apparently help to detect rate of movement at the joint.

In addition to the receptors in the joints, special receptors in the muscles and tendons report on the degree of muscle stretch and tension. **Muscle spindles** are encapsulated structures, which act as microscopic strain gauges. They are readily excited and cease discharging during active contraction of the muscle. **Golgi tendon organs** have a similar structure and are found in the tendons of muscles. They react to a pull on the tendon, produced by muscle contraction or passive pull; thus, they fire at an accelerated rate during muscle contraction, and their threshold of excitation is high. Impulses from the receptors in muscles and tendons are involved in reflex adjustments of the muscles; they are transmitted to the cerebellum rather than the cerebral cortex, and thus do not produce a conscious sensation.

The afferent pathways of the proprioceptors lead over large myelinated nerve fibers in cranial and spinal nerves. Impulses destined for conscious awareness are transmitted in ascending tracts to the thalamus, from which they are relayed to the cerebral cortex; impulses involved in reflex adjustments travel over spinocerebellar tracts to the cerebellum. An important characteristic of the transmission of kinesthetic signals is their high speed of transmission. When a body part is moving rapidly, it is essential for the central nervous system to have a continuous, almost instantaneous feedback on the exact location of the different parts of the body, so that further movements can be controlled.

SMELL

When a mouse or a dog is placed in new surroundings, it will begin to explore, sniffing about curiously. Most mammals rely to a high degree on the sense of smell for sensory input, and the olfactory region of their brains is correspondingly well developed. In comparison, the human sense of smell is almost rudimentary; and yet even the human nose can detect lower concentrations of certain volatile substances than are detectable by the most sensitive gas chromatographs yet devised. The odorous substance methyl mercaptan, for example, can be smelled in a concentration of only 1/25,000,000,000 milligram per milliliter of air. This chemical is added to odorless natural gas to make gas leaks detectable, and it can be used effectively in such minute amounts that a single cubic yard of the substance would be sufficient to treat enough gas to provide for the cooking needs of all the families in New York City for an entire year.

Smell serves a number of functions. The aroma of appetizing food attracts us and starts a flow of saliva, producing a general toning of the digestive organs in preparation for the meal. The sense of smell can warn of danger, such as the toxins lurking in spoiled food. Another possible function of smell is still speculative, at least as it pertains to humans. It has been found that animals produce a number of hormone-like substances, called **pheromones,** which are excreted from various body orifices and used as media of communication with others of their species. A dog urinating on a fireplug is leaving a sort of "Kilroy was here" message, to be "read" by the noses of other dogs passing by. Bears scent-mark trees around the boundary of their home territory with urine, laying down chemical *No Trespassing* signs; rabbits and gerbils perform a similar function on rocks and other objects with sebaceous secretions from special scent glands. An important class of pheromes, the **sex attractants,** is associated with mating signals, indicating to the males in the neighborhood that a female is receptive, or announcing to the females of the area that there is an eligible male in residence. Since the discovery of pheromones in animals, researchers have been speculating on the possibility that volatile chemicals produced by humans have a similar message content. (Perhaps women or men buying the latest "come hither" perfume or spicy colognes would be better off with their own natural body odors!) Certainly there is no dearth of substances to study: the apocrine sweat glands produce a variety of smelly secretions, the elimination or masking of which is the basis of the profitable deodorant industry. An interesting finding has been reported by French researchers, who discovered a chemical similar to the sex attractants of animals that can be smelled by adult women but is entirely odorless to men and to young girls.

Olfactory Receptors

During a cold, when the nasal passages are swollen and blocked by copious mucous secretions, our sense of smell is virtually nonexistent. For the sensation of smell requires an actual contact of molecules of odor-producing substances with the receptors in the lining of the nasal cavity.

The olfactory receptors are the least specialized of all the special senses. They occupy a total area about the size of a postage stamp in the mucosal epithelium lining the uppermost portion of the nasal cavity (Figure 16-10). The **olfactory epithelium** is very similar to the pseudostratified ciliated columnar epithelium that lines the air passages. Scattered among supporting cells and basal cells are about 100 million small bipolar receptor neurons. The hairlike peripheral processes of these neurons project outward from the epithelium and respond to various odoriferous substances, which enter the nostrils with the inhaled air and dissolve in the moist mucus secretions that cover the epithelium. The central processes of the

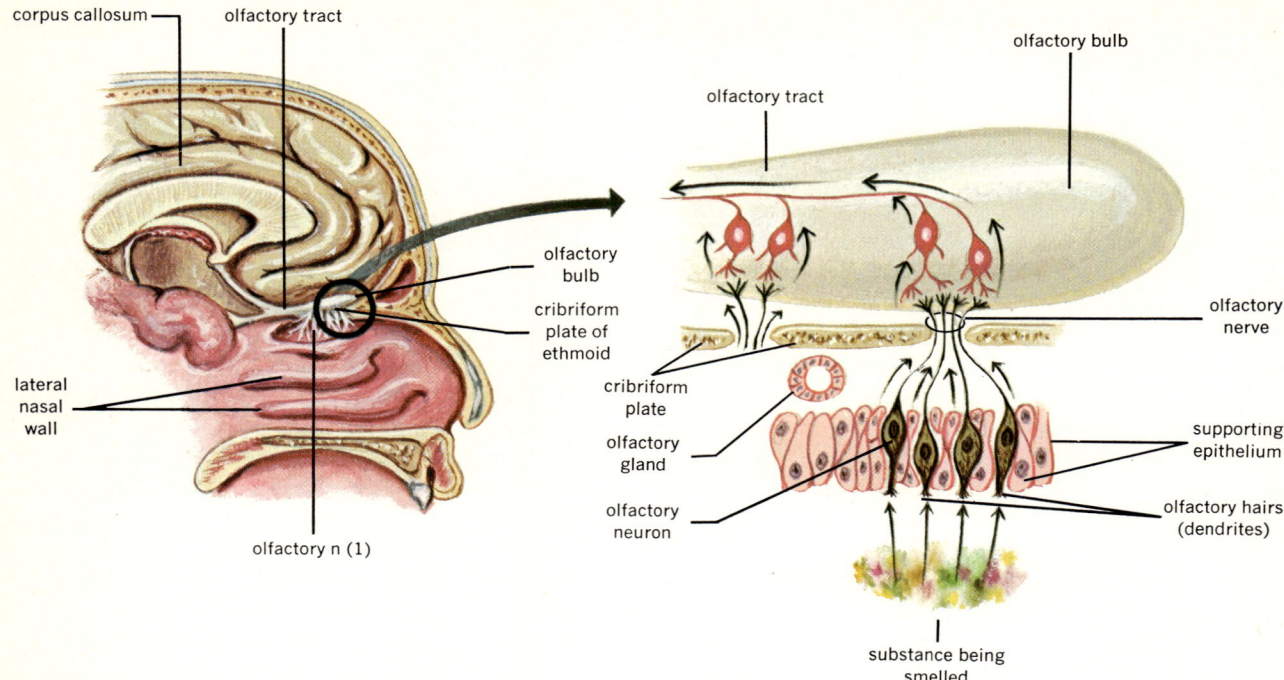

FIGURE 16-10 Olfactory receptors in the nasal cavity.

neurons coalesce to form the **olfactory nerve,** 15 to 20 filaments on each side, which pass upward through the cribriform plate of the ethmoid bone and synapse with second-order neurons in the **olfactory bulb.** Processes of these neurons, leading to the brain, form the **olfactory tract,** which travels posteriorly along the inferior surface of the frontal lobe of the brain, spreads out into the **olfactory trigone** near the optic chiasma, and ultimately leads into the olfactory area in the cortex of the temporal lobe. Secondary olfactory tracts relay impulses to other regions of the brain, including the hypothalamus, thalamus, hippocampus, and brain stem nuclei, as well as the prefrontal cortex.

Physiology of Smell

A person rarely realizes that he has bad breath or offensive body odor. It is not that he is incapable of detecting the odors, but rather that the olfactory receptors adapt very rapidly. If the same odor persists, you soon cease to notice it, even though a new odor would be detected immediately. Such adaptation, referred to as **olfactory fatigue,** can occur even with strong and pungent odors. A famous chemist tells the story of how he and a colleague were thrown off a bus they tried to board, returning home from work in the laboratory with some volatile capric esters. Their clothes had become permeated with the chemicals, and since their olfactory receptors had quickly adapted, they were quite unaware that they smelled like billy goats.

In order to stimulate the olfactory receptors, a sub-stance must possess certain physical properties. First of all, it must be **volatile,** so that it can be sniffed into the nostrils. Second, it must be at least slightly **water soluble,** so that it can dissolve in the mucous coating of the olfactory membrane. Third, it must also be **lipid soluble,** to dissolve in the membrane of the nerve fiber, where it presumably depolarizes the membrane and initiates a nerve impulse.

There appears to be some correlation between the three-dimensional configuration of a molecule and its capacity to evoke the sensation of a particular odor. Two substances that are quite different chemically may smell alike if they have the same overall spatial configuration. It has been hypothesized that there are a number of basic types of receptors, each of which responds to a specific type of odor, the chemical fitting into the receptor like a key into a lock. Seven **primary classes of odor** have been postulated: camphoraceous, musky, floral, pepperminty, ether-like, pungent, and putrid. The multitude of distinct odors that can be recognized presumably represent various combinations of primary odors.

When two or more odors are present, they may compete, with first one then the other being perceived; or the two odors may blend to produce a different odor sensation. In the manufacture of perfumes and aromatic additives for prepared foods, disparate fragrances are blended in precise amounts to produce the desired effect. "Deodorizers" used in households and hospitals utilize odoriferous substances that either overwhelm undesirable odors or combine with them to produce a new, desirable sensation.

Odors are remembered very keenly, even after they have been smelled only once. People who have eaten food that has disagreed with them may be nauseated by smelling the same type of food again. A particular perfume, or the smell of baking cookies remembered from childhood, can unlock a whole scene or incident from the "filing cabinet" of the brain and bring back the memory vividly.

Some physicians and nurses claim that the body secretions of patients with specific diseases, such as diabetes or pneumonia, produce a characteristic odor that can be detected on walking into the patient's room. Such claims are being studied; ultimately automated diagnosing machines might be devised, which would tell what is wrong with a patient by chemically "sniffing" the air around him and analyzing the odors that his body produces.

TASTE

Have you ever noticed that when you have a head cold, food seems tasteless? For all you can appreciate it, the juiciest steak might as well be wet cardboard, and even your favorite dessert seems to have lost its tempting flavor. Much of what we normally think of as the taste of foods is actually the effect of stimulation of olfactory receptors in the nasal cavities; when the nasal passages are blocked, many of the distinctive tastes that set one food off from another seem to be lost. Foods seem so bland an unappetizing, that it is an effort to eat enough to maintain your strength and regain your health.

Though olfactory stimuli are an important component of taste, there are specialized taste receptors, concentrated mainly on the surface of the tongue. Taste, like smell, is a chemical sense: the stimuli to which the taste receptors respond are chemical substances, dissolved in the fluid medium of the saliva. All the varied tastes that humans can distinguish seem to be combinations of only four **primary tastes: sweet, sour, salt,** and **bitter.** Like the four-letter "alphabet" of nucleic bases that can generate an almost infinite variety of DNA sequences, combinations of the four primary tastes provide ample scope for human creativity in the subtle blendings of the culinary art.

Gustatory Receptors

The tongue is a most versatile organ: its manipulative dexterity permits it to function in speech, mastication (chewing), deglutition (swallowing), and sucking, while its highly developed tactile and chemical senses permit it to examine foods for wholesomeness, leaving the body with the option of rejecting unsatisfactory materials before the final commitment of swallowing is made.

Cursory examination of a tongue reveals that it is covered with mucous membrane, and its upper surface has a pebbly, rather than a smooth appearance: it is studded with **papillae** (projections of connective tissue). Microscopic examination of the upper surface of the tongue (Figure 16-11) reveals that all the papillae contain **taste buds,** the specialized gustatory receptors.

A taste bud is a much more complicated structure than the olfactory receptors of the nasal cavity. Each one is about 1/30 of a millimeter in diameter and is composed of about twenty modified epithelial cells, called taste cells. (These cells are continually being replaced and have a lifespan of only about a week.) The outer tips of the taste cells are arranged around a tiny taste pore, through which microvilli or taste hairs protrude from the tips of the cells out into the mouth cavity. These microvilli apparently serve as the receptors for the specific chemicals that stimulate taste sensations. Impulses are excited in a branching network of taste nerve fibers interwoven among the taste cells, transmitted along cranial nerves (the glossopharyngeal, facial, and vagus nerves carry taste sensations from different parts of the tongue (to the medulla, and from there to the thalamus and ultimately to the cerebral cortex. The taste center in the cortex is the same area that receives other sensory impulses from the mouth, at the inferior end of the central sulcus.

Not all the taste buds are found on the tongue: a few are scattered over the soft palate, fauces, and epiglottis. Adults have a total of about 10,000 taste buds; with age, taste buds begin to degenerate progressively, and the gustatory sense gradually becomes less acute.

Most taste buds are particularly responsive to just one of the primary tastes, although they may also respond to others to some degree. The different types of taste buds are distributed quite nonuniformly over the surface of the tongue (Figure 16-11). Sweet tastes are perceived almost exclusively at the front of the tongue, salty tastes at the front and sides; taste buds responding to sour tastes are distributed along the sides of the tongue, and those sensitive to bitter tastes are found at the back of the tongue.

Physiology of Taste

If you carefully wipe your tongue dry and then sprinkle a little powdered sugar on its surface, you will be unable to taste anything at all. Chemicals that stimulate the taste receptors must be in solution to have an effect. The saliva that normally coats the surface of the tongue provides a watery solvent for taste-producing substances.

Some general patterns have been discovered among the substances that produce characteristic tastes. The sour taste is produced by acids, and the stronger the

epiglottis

foramen cecum

bitter

vallate papillae

sour

fungiform papillae

filiform papillae

sweet and salt

FIGURE 16-11 Distribution of taste buds over the surface of the tongue and their microscopic structure. The SEM shows a taste bud surrounded by filiform papillae.

taste pore

dendrite

taste bud

epithelium

taste buds

supporting cell

gustatory cell

cranial nerve fiber

connective tissue

supporting cell

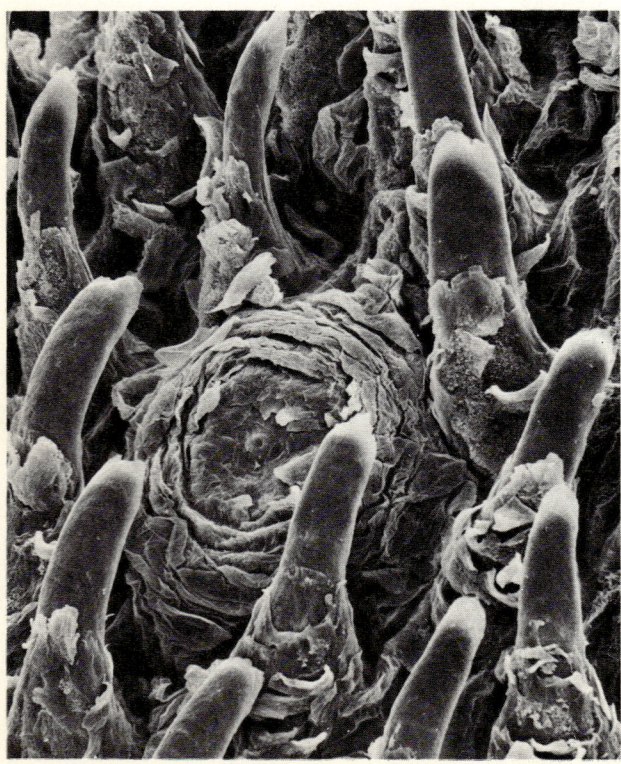

acid, the stronger the sensation. Salty tastes are elicited by ionized salts. It is possible to distinguish among the tastes of different salts, since each apparently elicits other taste sensations as well. A variety of chemicals elicit a sweet taste, including sugars, glycols, alcohols, aldehydes, ketones, amides, esters, amino acids, sulfonic acids, halogenated acids, and salts of lead and beryllium; nearly all of these are organic substances. The bitter taste is produced by a variety of substances, particularly long-chain organic substances and alkaloids. (The latter class includes many drugs, such as quinine, caffeine, nicotine, and strychnine.)

Taste sensations have a strong affective component, carrying attributes of pleasantness or unpleasantness. Sweet tastes are usually found to be unpleasant at very low concentrations, but extremely pleasant at high concentrations. For the other tastes, the responses are the reverse—they are likely to be pleasant at low concentrations, and unpleasant at high concentrations. This is especially true of the bitter taste, to which, moreover, the taste receptors are particularly sensitive. The automatic rejection of bitter-tasting substances is an important protective mechanism, since many of the deadly toxins found in poisonous plants are bitter-tasting alkaloids.

Some substances stimulate more than one type of taste receptor. One of the major drawbacks of the artificial sweetener saccharin, for example, is the fact that it has a bitter aftertaste, even though it is 675 times as sweet as sucrose (table sugar). As saccharin is being ingested, it stimulates first the sweet receptors at the front of the tongue, and then the bitter receptors at the back of the tongue.

The foods we eat contain blendings of numerous taste-stimulating substances. When sugar is sprinkled on a grapefruit, a different taste is produced, and the addition of salt produces still another taste change.

It seems strange that some foods, such as liver, eggs, and olives, are hated by some people and are particular favorites of others. To some degree this disparity is due to individual psychological reactions to particular tastes, conditioned by past experiences and cultural norms. But there is experimental evidence to indicate that there is considerable individual variation in the way tastes are perceived. Some people report that phenylhydrazine tastes bitter, others claim that it tastes sweet, while still others cannot taste anything at all. A widely used testing compound is **phenylthiocarbamide (PTC).** To the majority of the population this is a bitter-tasting chemical, but between 15 and 30 percent are unable to taste it. The tendency to be a PTC "taster" or "nontaster" is hereditary.

A loss or perversion of the sense of taste or smell may accompany such conditions as hypothyroidism, or follow a stroke or a bout with an infectious disease such as encephalitis or influenza. A loss of the sense of taste is called **hypogeusia;** in the condition of **dysgeusia,** things taste wrong or even offensive. Some studies, still rather controversial, seem to indicate that the trace metal zinc is involved in the proper functioning of the taste buds, and successes in the therapy of some forms of hypogeusia and dysgeusia with high doses of zinc have been reported (Figure 16-12).

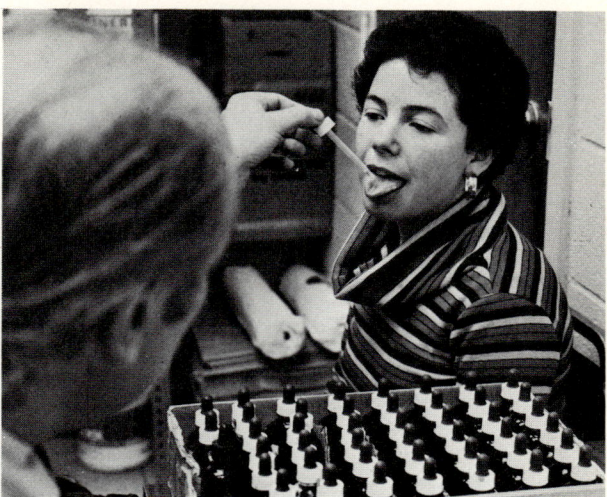

FIGURE 16-12 Testing for taste ability at the NIH taste clinic.

SUMMARY

Human senses include:
Sight
Hearing
Smell
Taste
Cutaneous senses (touch, pressure, pain, warmth, cold)
Visceral senses
Kinesthetic sense

Sensations are the conscious results of the sequence: stimulus, receptor, conducting pathway, and sensory area in the brain. The thalamus is a relay station in the brain for all sensory impulses except the olfactory.

Sense receptors include:
Mechanoreceptors (touch, pressure, hearing, equilibrium)
Thermoreceptors (warmth, cold)
Electromagnetic receptors (photoreceptors)
Chemoreceptors (taste, smell, various interoceptors)
Nociceptors (pain)
Exteroceptors (surface receptors)
Proprioceptors (muscle sense, position sense)
Interoceptors (visceral receptors)

Modalities of sensation (sight, sound, touch, pain, etc.) are appreciated in the brain and projected to the receptors.

The intensity of a sensation depends on the number of receptors stimulated and on the frequency of transmission of impulses by each afferent fiber.

A sensation is affected by events that have just preceded it or accompany it.

An after-image is the persistence of a sensation in consciousness after the stimulus has ceased.

Most sense receptors exhibit adaptation: when a stimulus of constant intensity continues to act on a receptor, the magnitude of the receptor potential and frequency of the response decrease.

Cutaneous sense receptors (touch, pressure, warmth, cold, pain) are nonuniformly distributed over the body surface.

Tactile sense receptors include:
Free nerve endings
Meissner's corpuscles
Merkel's discs
Hair end-organs
Ruffini's end-organs
Pacinian corpuscles

Touch sensations result from stimulation of superficial tactile receptors, pressure sensations from deformation of deeper tissues, and vibration sensations from rapidly repetitive stimuli.

The tactile sense conveys information on the size, shape, texture, and localization of objects.

Pain is a protective mechanism, warning that tissues are being injured or in danger of injury.

Any intense stimulus (e.g., pressure, extreme heat or cold) can stimulate pain receptors (free nerve endings).
Tissue ischemia and muscle spasms are frequent causes of pain.
Bradykinin and histamine, released by damaged tissues, produce pain.

Pain can be classified as:
Superficial
Deep
Visceral
Pricking

Burning

Aching

Pain elicits motor reflexes and psychic reactions (anguish, anxiety, depression, excitability), which vary with the individual.

The pain threshold is relatively constant among individuals.

Tickling and itch may be caused by mild stimulation of pain nerve endings or structurally similar receptors.

Gradations of temperature are detected by three types of receptors: cold, warm, and pain, alone or in combination.

Specialized receptors are Krause end bulbs (cold) and corpuscles of Ruffini (warm).

Thermal receptors respond to steady temperature states, and to changes in temperature.

Adaptation is rapid but incomplete.

Visceral receptors report on the status of the internal organs; some sensory impulses are part of reflex arcs and are not brought to conscious attention.

Visceral sensations include visceral pain, hunger, thirst, nausea, distension of bladder and bowel, and sexual stimulation.

Visceral pain may be stimulated by:

Ischemia

Chemical stimuli

Spasm

Distension

Many visceral pains are referred to characteristic cutaneous areas.

Hunger is associated with rhythmic contractions of the empty stomach.

Thirst is a conscious desire for water, produced by dehydration of body tissues and usually accompanied by a sensation of dryness of the mouth and throat.

Temporary thirst quenching is produced by the act of drinking, before the tissues are rehydrated.

Nausea is a conscious recognition of stimulation of the vomiting center in the medulla. It can be caused by irritation of the gastrointestinal tract; impulses from the organs of sight, taste, or smell; or impulses from the organs of equilibrium and balance.

Kinesthesia is the conscious recognition of the orientation of the different parts of the body relative to each other, and the rates of movement of the different parts of the body.

Proprioceptors, mainly in the joint capsules and ligaments, provide the position sense:

Ruffini's end-organs

Golgi endings

Pacinian corpuscles

Muscle spindles and Golgi tendon organs report on muscle stretch and tension, as part of reflex arcs.

The human sense of smell functions in attraction to food, warning of danger, and (possibly) sex attraction.

Olfactory receptors are relatively unspecialized sensory neurons in the olfactory epithelium of the nasal cavity.

Odoriferous substances must be volatile, water soluble, and lipid soluble.

Molecular configuration seems to be correlated with specific type of odor.

Seven primary classes of odor have been postulated: camphoraceous, musky, floral, pepperminty, ether-like, pungent, and putrid.

Olfactory receptors adapt readily.

Taste receptors (taste buds) respond to chemical substances, dissolved in saliva on the surface of the tongue.

The four primary tastes are sweet, sour, salt, and bitter; each taste bud responds mainly to one particular taste.

Taste buds of the four main types have characteristic localizations on the tongue: sweet—front, sour—sides, salt—front and sides; bitter—back.

Individual variations of tasting ability and psychological reactions to specific tastes are observed.

Hypogeusia is a loss of the sense of taste; dysgeusia is a perversion of the sense of taste.

QUESTIONS FOR REVIEW AND THOUGHT

1 Discuss the roles of the thalamus and cerebral cortex in the perception of sensations.

2 Describe five types of sense receptors and their functions.

3 Discuss the phenomenon of projection of sensations and its role in referred pain; give the cutaneous localization of several types of referred pains.

4 Give examples of adaptation relating to the senses of touch, temperature, and smell. Why is the very slow adaptation of pain receptors desirable for the body?

5 In the light of the anatomy and physiology of temperature perception, explain why a bath that feels comfortable to the hands may be too hot for the body; why an ice cube may feel "burning hot"; and why the air of the same room may feel hot after coming indoors on a cold winter day but cold after getting out of a hot shower.

6 Why do hunger pangs disappear after awhile even if food has not been taken? (Give at least two possible contributing factors.)

7 What do the receptors of smell and taste have in common?

8 List the primary classes of odor; those of taste.

9 A new type of room deodorizer recently developed actually blocks the smell receptors, so that smells are not perceived. Why would it be undesirable to use this kind of deodorizer in the dining room?

10 Discuss the structure and specialization of taste receptors and their contribution to the survival of the organism.

THE SENSE ORGANS: SIGHT

It is probably no coincidence that the two main groups of vertebrates who rely mainly on the organ of vision for sensory input are the birds and the primates. Our primate ancestors are believed to have lived in trees, as many present-day primates still do. When a friend or enemy is perched on a leafy bough across the way, or down on the ground far below, a keen sense of smell does not contribute much useful information. And when your life literally depends on your agility in negotiating a leap across the empty space between branches, you need a very precise view of exactly where you are going. (Bats, faced with a similar problem, evolved into a different alternative, specializing their sense of hearing to a highly sophisticated, "computerized" sonar system.)

"Seeing is believing," as they say, and it is true that humans depend to an exceptional degree on the sense of vision, sometimes to the neglect of the other senses. A large fraction of the continual stream of incoming sensory impulses that floods the central nervous system consists of messages from the eyes, the organs of vision. Highly specialized receptors in the human eye are capable not only of detecting light, but of distinguishing between different degrees of light and dark, and between different colors and shades of colors. Messages from these receptors are analyzed and integrated in the brain to put together a picture of the outside environment.

EXTERNAL STRUCTURE OF THE EYE

When you look in the mirror, you can see only about one-sixth of each of your eyes. The human eye, a roughly spherical fluid-filled structure, is rather vulnerable, and yet its function requires that it be exposed to the outside world. A compromise is achieved by the recessed position of the eyeball, nearly enclosed within a protective bony socket (Figure 17-1). Further protection is provided by movable fleshy

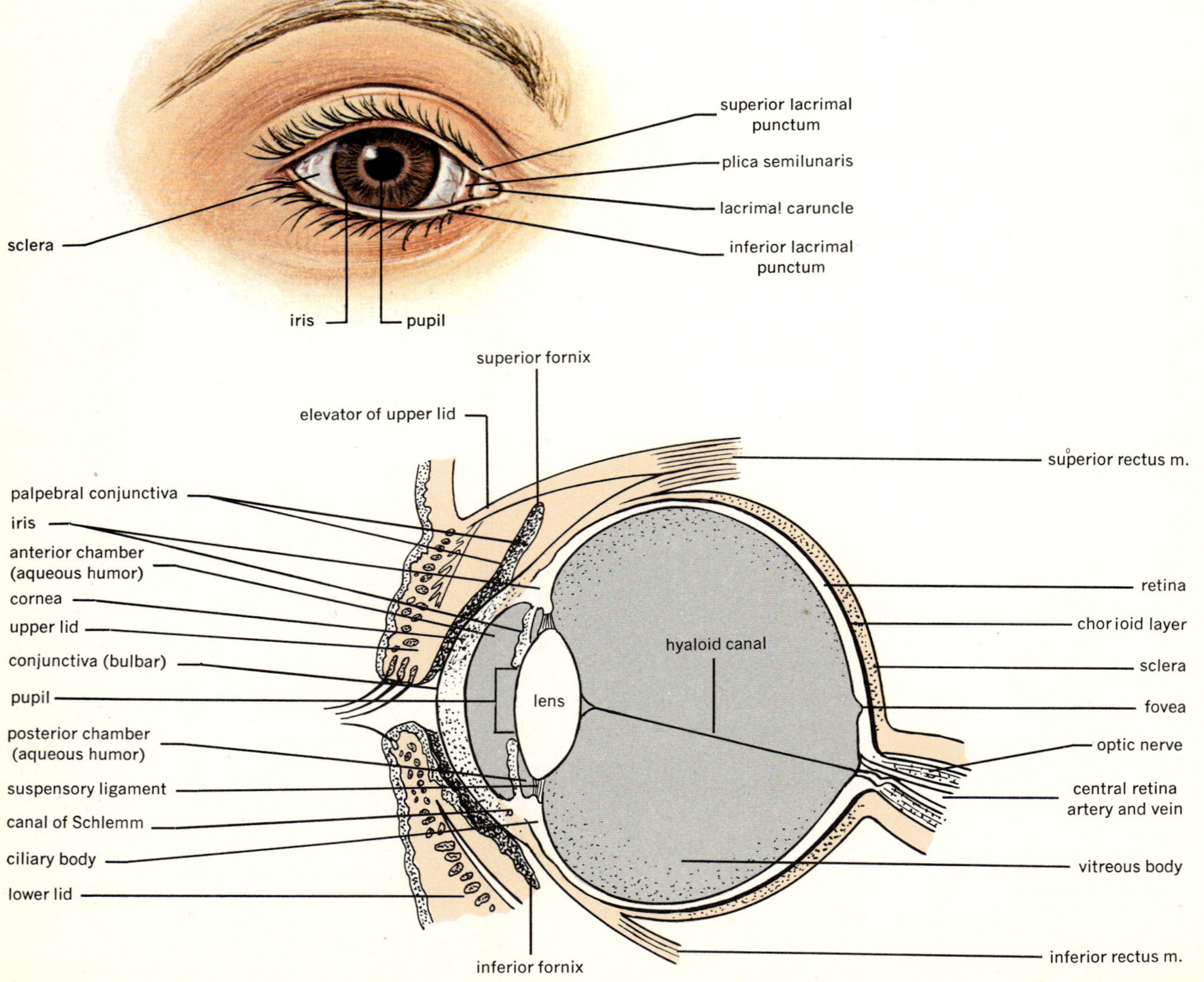

FIGURE 17-1 The eye: external structure and in section.

flaps, the eyelids, which can whisk together to shield the eyes from an incoming projectile or too bright a light and cover them during sleep. A fringe of stiff hairs, the eyelashes, along the margin of each eyelid, helps to screen out dust particles, small flying insects, and other potential irritants; the eyebrows that decorate the bony prominences above the eyes serve to shade the eyes and to catch drops of sweat rolling down the brow. A versatile assortment of extrinsic muscles permits a wide range of movements of the eyeballs. Tears secreted by the lacrimal apparatus cleanse and lubricate the eyeballs and the conjunctiva that lines the eyelids.

The Orbital Cavity

The sunken, empty eye sockets of a skull poignantly emphasize its lifelessness. In a living person, the orbital cavities are filled, and only the bony prominences around their circumference can be seen jutting out under the skin.

The orbital cavity is a bony portion in the front of the skull, shaped rather like a funnel. The large portion, directed outward and forward, is lined with a cushion of fatty tissue, in which the eyeball rests, suspended in a sling of muscles. (The eyeball itself occupies only about one-fifth of the orbital cavity. During starvation, the fat pad cushioning the eyeball is diminished, and the eyes sink into their sockets.) The small part of the funnel, directed backward and inward, is pierced by an opening, the optic foramen, through which the optic nerve and the ophthalmic artery pass. Another opening, the superior orbital fissure, provides a passageway for the arteries and nerves that supply the eye muscles.

A number of cranial bones contribute to the formation of the orbital cavity: the frontal, maxilla, zygomatic, sphenoid, ethmoid, lacrimal, and palatine. The walls of the orbit are rather thin and easily fractured.

The Eyeball

"Eyes are windows on the soul." An exaggeration, perhaps, but in addition to receiving sense impressions from the surrounding world, eyes can be extremely expressive of moods and emotions. Certainly a disproportionate emphasis is placed on the color, shape, expression, and general appearance of eyes in human encounters. The portion of the eye that attention usually focuses on is the eyeball, or more accurately, the small anterior portion of the eyeball that is visible between the two lids.

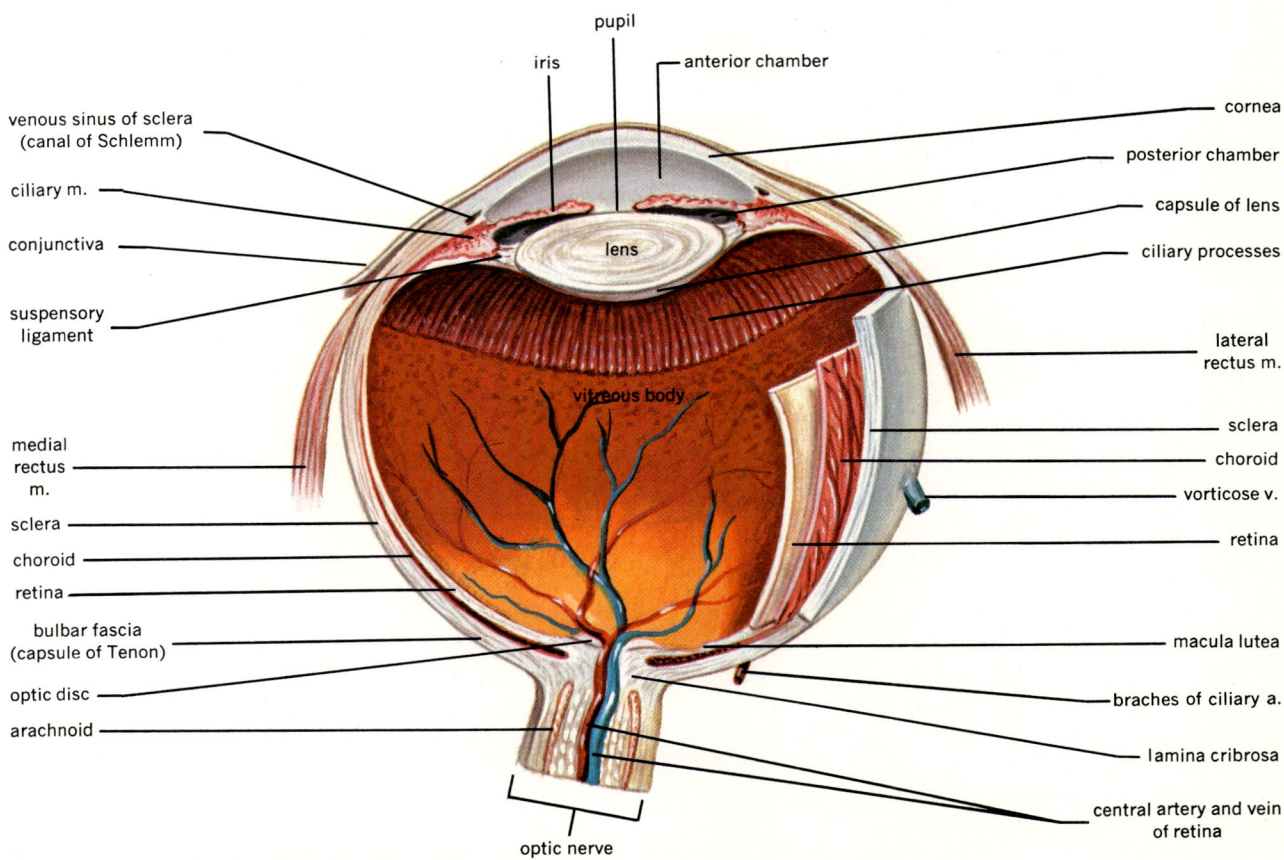

FIGURE 17-2   Structure of the eyeball (mid-sagittal section).

The eyeball is about 2.5 cm in diameter. It is not quite a perfect sphere: it is a little longer than it is wide, with a distinct anterior bulge. The wall of the eyeball is composed of three layers, or coats (Figure 17-2). The outermost, **fibrous layer** consists of the **sclera** (the "white of the eye"), the tough collagenous covering of the posterior five-sixths of the eyeball, and the **cornea,** a transparent window over the anterior one-sixth. The middle, **vascular layer,** consists of three structures. The highly vascular **choroid,** at the back, nourishes the eyeball; the **ciliary body,** near the front, includes the ciliary muscle, which changes the shape of the lens; at the front, the **iris** is suspended across the eye. This is the pigmented portion of the eyeball that gives color to the eyes; an adjustable hole in its center, the **pupil,** admits light rays to the interior of the eyeball. The inner layer of the wall of the eyeball, the **retina,** is the part of the eye on which an image is formed. It is functionally a **nervous layer,** containing specialized photo-receptor cells and attached to the optic nerve.

Light rays entering the eyeball pass successively through four **refracting media:** the **cornea;** the **aqueous humor,** which fills the anterior and posterior chambers of the front part of the eyeball; the **lens,** a transparent biconvex disc of fibrous protein; and the **vitreous body,** filling the posterior portion of the eyeball.

Extrinsic Muscles of the Eye

The eye muscles are tiny in comparison with the large skeletal muscles such as the biceps, triceps, and gastrocnemius. But they are hard working, moving the eyes about to follow a moving object, making them dance and jiggle as they cover the visual field, and supporting them in a fixed stare.

The six extrinsic, or external muscles that connect the eyeball to the orbital cavity and provide for movement and support were described in Chapter 10. They include four straight muscles (**superior, inferior, lateral,** and **medial rectus** muscles) and two oblique muscles (**superior** and **inferior oblique**). Their contractions are controlled by nuclei in the midbrain and pons.

The Eyelids

How many times do you think you have blinked in the last ten minutes? If you observe someone unawares, you will be surprised at how frequently a person blinks, usually without any conscious realization. In each blink, the upper and lower lids meet, like movable curtains, covering the eyeball and spreading lubricating secretions.

The eyelids, or **palpebrae,** are fleshy folds, covered externally with skin and internally with a mucous membrane, the **conjunctiva.** The upper and lower lids meet at the "corners" of the eye, the **medial** (inner)

canthus and the **lateral** (outer) **canthus.** Looking at your own eyes in a mirror, you will notice a small additional fold at the medial canthus. This is a vestigial structure, nonfunctional in humans, which is a remant of the **nictitating membrane** or "third eyelid" of lower animals. In birds, for example, this is a semitransparent membrane, which can be extended laterally to cover the entire eyeball—a useful device to have while flying through dusty air.

The eyelids are given substance and shape by the **tarsus,** a plate of condensed fibrous tissue, located at the free edge of each eyelid. The margins of the eyelids are studded with stiff hairs, the eyelashes. Sebaceous glands associated with the tarsus open onto the lid margin and secrete an oily substance that lubricates the edges of the lid and keeps them from adhering. Sebaceous glands also open into the follicles of the eyelashes; infection of one of these glands results in a sty.

The upper eyelid has a special elevator muscle, the **levator palpebrae superioris;** a sphincter around the lids, the **orbicularis oculi** muscle, closes the eyelids.

In persons of the Mongoloid races, a fold of skin from the upper eyelid continues vertically downward to cover the inner canthus. Such **epicanthic folds,** together with a narrower and more slanting eye slit than in Caucasoid races, are a prominent racial distinction (Figure 17-3). Epicanthic folds are also observed in some congenital disorders, such as Down's syndrome.

The Conjunctiva

Bloodshot eyes are commonly considered a sign of dissipation. They tend to follow a sleepless night, a drinking bout, or an eye irritation, caused by a foreign particle or a pollen allergy. The reddened appearance of "bloodshot" eyes is produced by dilation of the minute blood vessels in the conjunctiva, the

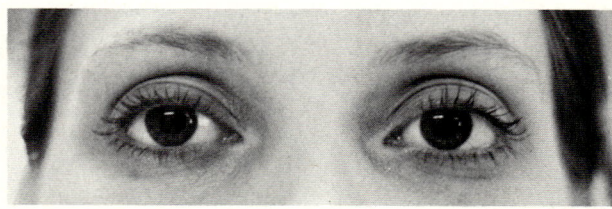

A

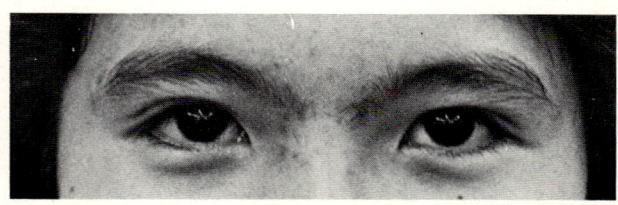

B

FIGURE 17-3 Eye shape and color are governed by heredity. Here are typical Caucasoid (A) and Mongoloid (B) eyes. Note the epicanthic folds of the Mongoloid.

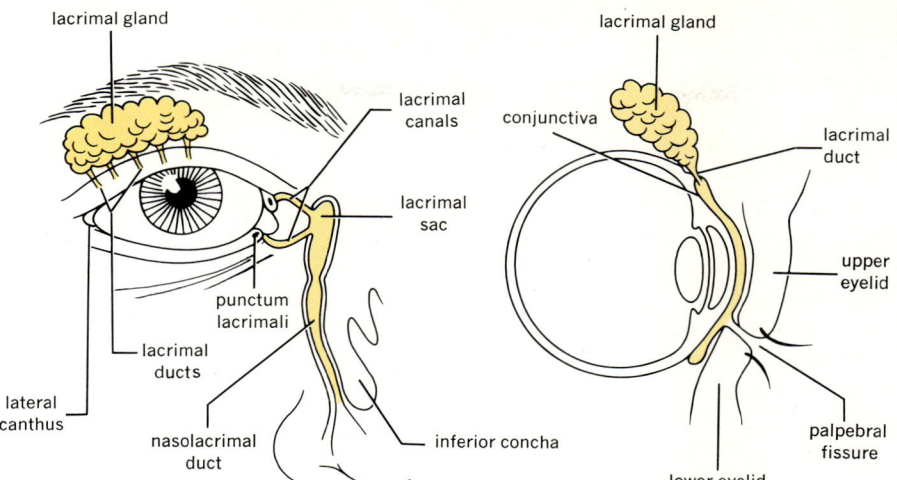

FIGURE 17-4 The lacrimal apparatus: front view (A) and sagittal section (B).

thin, transparent mucous membrane that lines the eyelids (palpebral portion) and continues over the anterior part of the eyeball (bulbar or ocular portion).

When the conjunctiva becomes infected, the condition is called **conjunctivitis,** or pinkeye. In the infant, this delicate membrane is vulnerable to infection by the venereal disease pathogen, *Neisseria gonorrhoeae,* during passage through the birth canal of an infected mother; the infection can produce blindness. Since gonorrhea is often a "silent" disease through much of its course in women, a mother might be unaware that she is harboring the pathogen. As a result, it has been a routine procedure to place a drop of silver nitrate or other antigonorrheic agent such as aqueous ampicillin in the eyes of newborn babies to forestall the possibility of infection.

The Lacrimal Apparatus

In ancient Greece, men cried freely and unashamedly. In our culture, however, tears are commonly considered signs of weakness, immaturity, or femininity. As a result of this prevailing climate of opinion, men tend to develop a difficulty in expressing emotions, which is believed to be taking a severe toll in emotional problems and strained relationships.

The emotional aspect of tears is actually a secondary effect. The main function of the watery secretions of the lacrimal apparatus of the eyes is to keep the surface of the eyes moist and to help wash away microorganisms and dust perticles.

The lacrimal apparatus consists of the lacrimal gland and its ducts and passages (Figure 17-4). The **lacrimal gland** is an almond-shaped structure, lodged in a depression of the frontal bone at the upper, outer corner of the eye. The gland secretes tears, a sterile, watery fluid containing various salts, mucin, and the bactericidal enzyme lysozyme. Normally about 0.02 ounce of this secretion is produced each day; it drains down from the gland through about a dozen short

ducts, the **lacrimal canals,** into the lacrimal sac at the inner corner of the eye. The **lacrimal sac** is the expanded upper end of the **nasolacrimal duct,** a passage that drains down into the inferior meatus of the nose.

Blinking usually occurs once every two to ten seconds and lasts 0.3 to 0.4 second at a time. During each blink, muscles associated with the blinking reflex compress the lacrimal sac. When the muscles relax, the sac expands, and fluid is pulled from the edges of the lids along the lacrimal canals into the lacrimal sacs, producing a continuous irrigation of the eyes. The sebaceous secretion at the margin of the lids keeps the tears from overflowing, unless an irritant such as a foreign object or cold wind stimulates the production of an excess of tears, which overflow the dam and stream out of the eyes in visible drops. Laughing, yawning, coughing, and vomiting also cause an excess production of tears. The **psychogenic** production of tears (i.e., prompted by emotions) is unique to humans and is not observed in a young baby until the age of a month or more.

INTERNAL STRUCTURE OF THE EYE

Dissecting an ox's eye in the laboratory carries the same hazard as eating a grapefruit: an unwary thrust may send a jet of fluid squirting into your eye. Chambers of the eyeball are filled with watery and semisolid fluids. But the eyeball is far more than just a bag of water; it is a complexly organized structure, providing for the admission of measured amounts of light rays and their passage through a precisely engineered sequence of adjustable refracting media to impinge on specialized, discriminating receptors.

Outer Coat: the Sclera

"Don't shoot until you see the whites of their eyes." Actually, when the eyes are looking straight ahead, not much white is visible, since the anterior sixth of the eyeball is colored.

Neither of the delicate inner two layers of the eyeball would be strong enough to maintain the shape of this fluid-filled structure. The functions of protection and support of the eyeball are performed by the **sclera,** a tough, unyielding, fibrous membrane. Over the posterior five-sixths of the eyeball, the sclera is opaque, white, and smooth externally—this is the **white of the eye.** Bundles of collagenous fibers with flattened fibroblasts between them, along with a few elastic fibers, provide strength to the membrane.

The anterior one-sixth of the outer layer is modified into a transparent "window," the **cornea.** The cornea is composed of dense fibrous tissue, but it has no color and permits the passage of light rays. It provides for a preliminary coarse focusing; the crystalline lens of the eye sharpens the focus.

The opaque sclera is supplied with a few blood vessels, but the cornea lacks blood vessels and is dependent on lymph for nourishment. Its epithelium is abundantly supplied with free nerve endings, which give rise to the sensation of pain when stimulated. Injury to the cornea causes scarring and an impairment of vision.

Middle Coat: the Choroid

Popular folklore has long equated the color of eyes with various traits of character and personality—for example, "blue-eyed" innocence, the "green-eyed monster" of jealousy. A recent controversial psychological hypothesis asserts that both in humans and in animals, light eyes are correlated with a patient, self-paced personality and way of life (e.g., a cat waiting at a mouse-hole, or a football quarterback), while dark eyes are correlated with excellence in reactive tasks (e.g., a watchdog, or a baseball hitter).

The pigment of eyes, which shows through the cornea, is found in the **iris,** a modified portion of the middle, vascular layer of the eyeball, the **choroid.** The choroid is a thin, highly vascular and darkly pigmented membrane, lining the inner surface of the posterior five-sixths of the sclera. (The pigmentation prevents internal reflection of light rays within the eyeball.)

Anterior to the choroid is the **ciliary body,** much of which consists of the **ciliary muscle,** which has its origin on the sclera near the cornea and its insertion on the choroid. When this muscle contracts, it allows the ligament that suspends the lens to relax and permits the elastic lens to take on a more convex shape.

The iris is a circular, pigmented disc, composed of connective tissue containing numerous blood vessels and nerves. The number of pigment-bearing cells in the iris determines the color of the eyes: if there is very little of the dark pigment, melanin, the eyes are blue; increasing amounts of melanin produce gray, brown, or black eyes. (In albinism, characterized by a hereditary lack of pigment, the eyes appear pink because of the abundant blood vessels in the iris.) The iris is attached at its circumference to the ciliary body, and it is also connected to the sclera and cornea at the point where they merge. But the rest of the iris is freely suspended in the fluid in the interior of the eyeball.

The iris functions as a diaphragm. It has a round opening at the center, known as the **pupil,** which can be dilated or constricted by two sets of muscle fibers present in the iris: radiating muscle fibers (the dilator muscle) and an encircling sphincter muscle, respectively. The opening and closing of the pupil regulates the amount of light entering the interior of the eye, and it normally operates automatically, by reflex action. In strong light and near vision, the sphincter muscle contracts the pupil, while in dim light and far vision the radiating fibers dilate the pupil. A particularly interesting sight also tends to produce dilation of the pupils, while an emotionally distressing sight can spark a constriction. The pigmented epithelium that covers the posterior surface of the iris prevents the passage of light rays, so that the only light admitted to the eye enters through the pupil.

Inner Coat: the Retina

A tiny image of this page is now being projected onto a specialized, light-sensitive lining at the back of each of your eyeballs. The innermost coat of the eyeball is the **retina,** the nervous layer of the eye that translates light waves into neural impulses, which are then relayed to the brain. The retina extends forward almost to the posterior part of the ciliary body, where it terminates in a jagged margin called the **ora serrata.**

The microscopic structure of the retina is rather complicated, including ten distinct layers (Figure 17-5). The outermost layer, adjacent to the choroid, is a layer of pigmented epithelium, which absorbs excess light that might be reflected and interfere with the formation of an image on the retina. Next comes a layer of specialized photoreceptor cells. There are two types, **rods** and **cones.** As might be expected from their names, rods are narrow and cylindrical, while cones are shorter, blunt, and cone-shaped. It takes only a little light, of almost any wavelength in the visible spectrum, to stimulate the rods, and thus they are particularly important for vision in dim light. The rods permit light and dark discrimination and the perception of form and movement, but they do not produce any sensation of color and provide poor visual acuity. The cones are the receptors that permit color vision in bright illumination, and they are responsible for visual acuity. The human eye contains about 125 million rods and 5.5 million cones.

The following layers of the retina, in the direction toward the interior of the eyeball, include limiting membranes, networks of supporting cells (neuroglia), and regions in which the rods and cones synapse with bipolar neurons, these in turn synapse with large multipolar ganglionic cells, and the axons of the latter converge toward the center of the retina, then turn and leave the retina together as the optic nerve. Entering light rays must pass successively through nearly all the layers of the retina before reaching the light-sensitive rods and cones.

Looking into the interior of the eyeball at the retina, two important landmarks are visible. Near the center of the retina there is a small, oval, yellowish spot called the **macula lutea.** The center of this spot is depressed and the retina is thinner in this region, which is called the **fovea centralis.** Only cones are present in the fovea, and it is the area of the highest visual acuity. (Indeed, in this region each cone synapses with its own private nerve fiber; elsewhere in the retina groups of receptor cells synapse with a single nerve fiber, and the total number of rods and cones far exceeds the total number of fibers in the optic nerve.) During reading, the eyes move continually to bring the rays of light from each successive word into the fovea.

About two millimeters to the nasal side of the macula lutea lies the other important landmark on the retina, the **optic disc.** This is the point at which the optic nerve pierces the eyeball, and it contains no receptor cells at all. As a result, it forms a natural "blind spot" on the retina. Normally you are quite unconscious of your blind spot, since the eyes compensate for it by continually moving about, constantly shifting their focus slightly even when you think you are staring fixedly. The overlapping afterimages fill in a continuous picture, without any blank corresponding to the blind spot on the retina; the overlap provided by the slightly different vantagepoints of the two eyes also helps to cover any gaps. The diagram in Figure 17-6 can be used to demonstrate the existence of the blind spot.

The Optic Nerve

The optic nerve is a godsend to writers of melodramatic fiction. With just a small stretch of the imagination, a poignant situation is created: a bullet, lodged in the brain, presses on the optic nerve, and the tragic heroine, whose eyes are perfectly normal and functionally adequate, is totally blind. Then a blow on the head dislodges the bullet and precipitates the stirring denouement, in which her sight is miraculously restored.

After leaving the eyeball at the optic disc, the **optic nerve** passes into the cranial cavity through the optic foramen, converges with its counterpart from the other eye at the **optic chiasma,** and then after a partial crisscrossing of fibers, the two separate again and continue posteriorly as the **optic tracts,** leading to the brain. The optic nerve is actually an extension of the brain, rather than a peripheral nerve. As such it is unmyelinated and is surrounded throughout its course in the orbital cavity by fluid-filled meninges. At the point where the optic nerve is attached to the eyeball, the dura mater fuses to the sclera.

The afferent pathways of the optic nerves lead ultimately to the vision center, in the occipital lobes of the cerebral cortex.

Refracting Media of the Eye

Light rays entering the eye pass successively through four separate media, each of which bends or refracts the rays and contributes to their focusing into an image. The four refracting media of the eye are, in order, the **cornea,** the **aqueous humor,** the **crystalline lens,** and the **vitreous body.**

After passing through the transparent cornea, which covers the anterior surface of the eyeball, the light rays enter a watery fluid, the aqueous humor, which fills the anterior compartment of the eye. This fluid-filled chamber is bounded in front by the cornea, and behind by the lens, the suspensory ligament, and the ciliary body. This space is partly divided by the iris into an anterior and a posterior chamber.

The main function of the aqueous humor is to nourish the internal structures of the eye that do not possess a blood supply of their own. It is a clear, dilute solution of salts (mainly sodium chloride), which diffuses out of the capillaries in the ciliary body, circulates through the pupil into the anterior chamber, and is drained out into the venous canal of Schlemm. Increased blood pressure in the larger blood vessels of the eye, altered osmotic conditions of the blood and eye fluids, rigidity of the eyeball, or improper functioning of the intrinsic muscles of the eye can result in **glaucoma,** a condition in which the intraocular pressure increases, interfering with the proper distribution of blood to the inner tissues of the eye, and ultimately causing blindness due to irreversible damage to the visual cells.

The crystalline lens, which lies immediately posterior to the iris, is a transparent semisolid body with convex anterior and posterior surfaces, enclosed in a thin, transparent, elastic capsule. It is supported by the suspensory ligaments, which bind the periphery of the lens to the ciliary processes. The tension of the suspensory ligaments adjusts the shape of the lens to keep objects focused on the retina: for distant vision, the tension is increased, and the lens thins, while for near vision the tension is decreased and the lens thickens.

The lens is formed by the epithelium and must last a lifetime, for it is not repaired or replaced. In infants the lens is almost spherical; in old age it becomes progressively flattened, loses water, and becomes

A

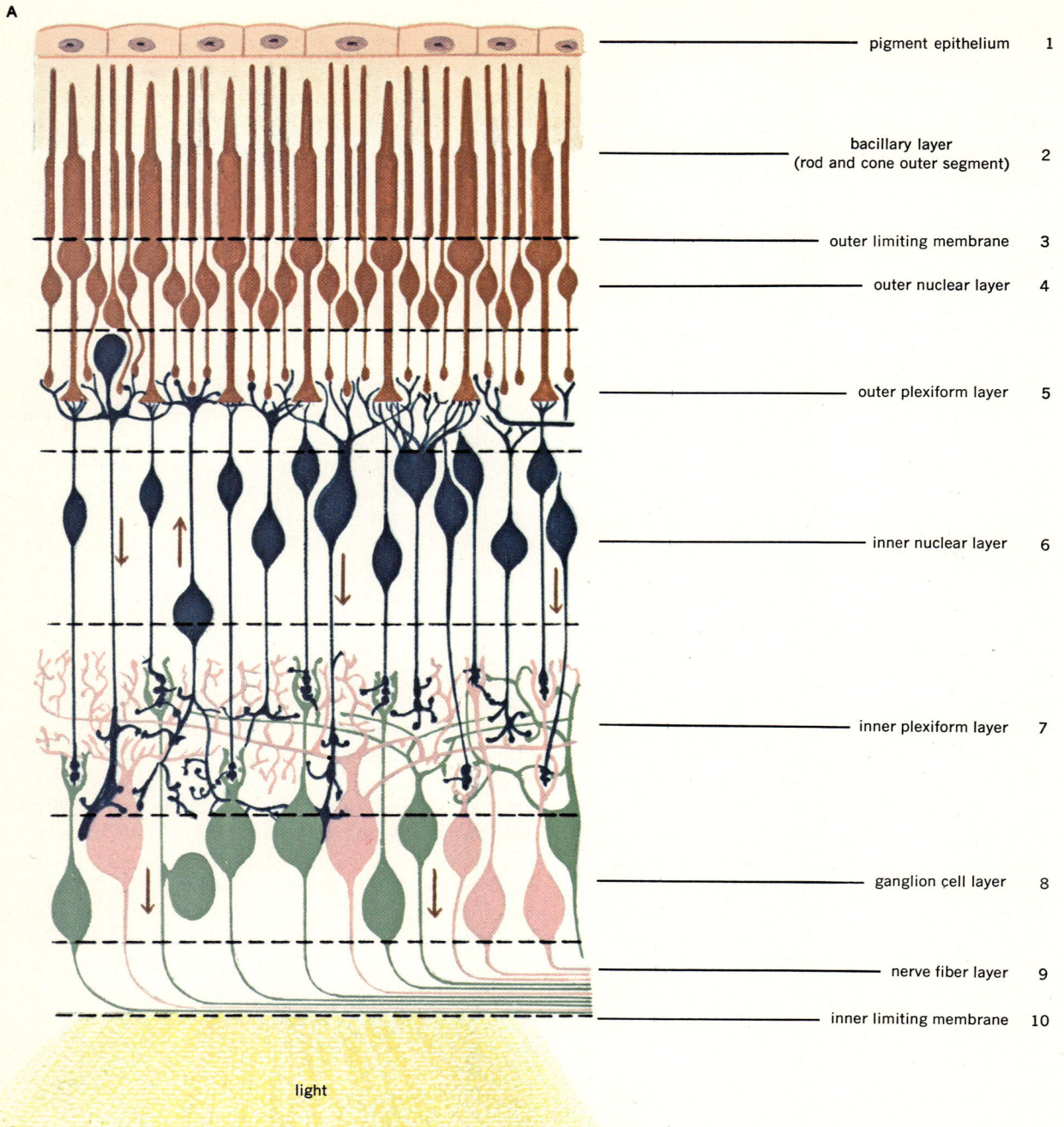

pigment epithelium	1
bacillary layer (rod and cone outer segment)	2
outer limiting membrane	3
outer nuclear layer	4
outer plexiform layer	5
inner nuclear layer	6
inner plexiform layer	7
ganglion cell layer	8
nerve fiber layer	9
inner limiting membrane	10

light

denser and less elastic. As a result, it is less able to bend light rays, and the near vision tends to deteriorate. (Older people who have had perfect vision in their youth often find they need glasses for reading and close work, while their far vision is still satisfactory.) In **cataract** the lens or its capsule loses its transparency and blocks the passage of light rays, resulting in a loss of vision. Cataracts are treated by removing the opaque lens and compensating with glasses (i.e., artificial lenses).

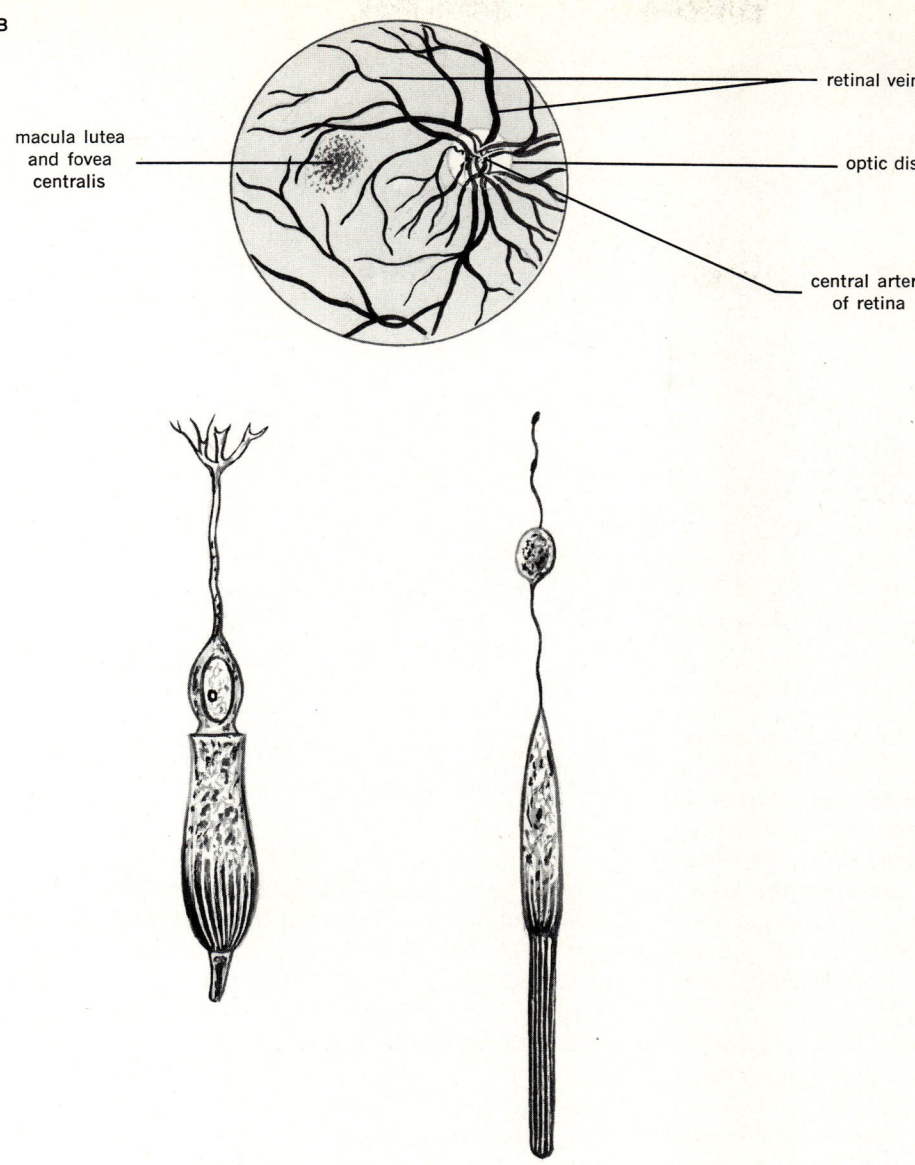

B

macula lutea
and fovea
centralis

retinal veins

optic disc

central artery
of retina

FIGURE 17-5 Anatomy of the retina: (A) schematic section through the ten layers; (B) the retina as seen with an ophthalmoscope; (C) cone and (D) rod cells.

C

D

The posterior cavity of the eyeball (i.e., the space behind the lens) is filled with a jellylike albuminous material, the vitreous humor (or vitreous body). *Vitreous* means "glassy," and refers to the fact that the molecules in the semisolid vitreous body are less regularly arranged than the fibers in the crystalline lens. The vitreous body is enclosed in a thin membrane, the hyaloid membrane, and fills the posterior four-fifths of the eyeball. It supports and nourishes the retina and helps to maintain the spheroidal shape of the eyeball. If the eyeball is wounded and vitreous humor leaks out, it is not reformed, and blindness can result as the retina collapses inward.

The Eye as a Camera

The human eye has many features in common with the best of the automatic cameras available today (Figure 17-7). Each has a lens, which focuses light rays and produces an image of external objects. The admission of light to the lens of a camera is controlled by a shutter (comparable to the eyelids) and determined by an aperture (pupil of the eye), the size of which is regulated by an adjustable diaphragm (the iris). In a camera the image is focused onto a film coated with an emulsion of light-sensitive chemicals;

FIGURE 17-6 Test for the "blind spot": cover the left eye and focus with the right on the cross. Then move the page closer and farther until the dot seems to disappear. At that point its image is falling on the optic disk, which lacks rods and cones.

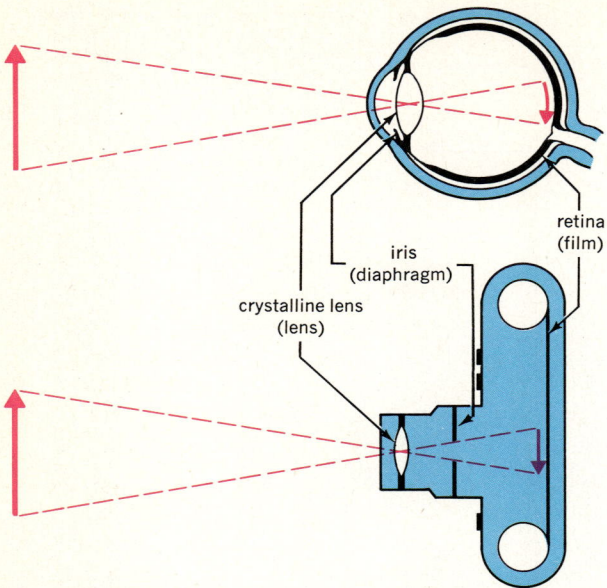

FIGURE 17-7 The construction of a camera has a number of similarities to the human eye.

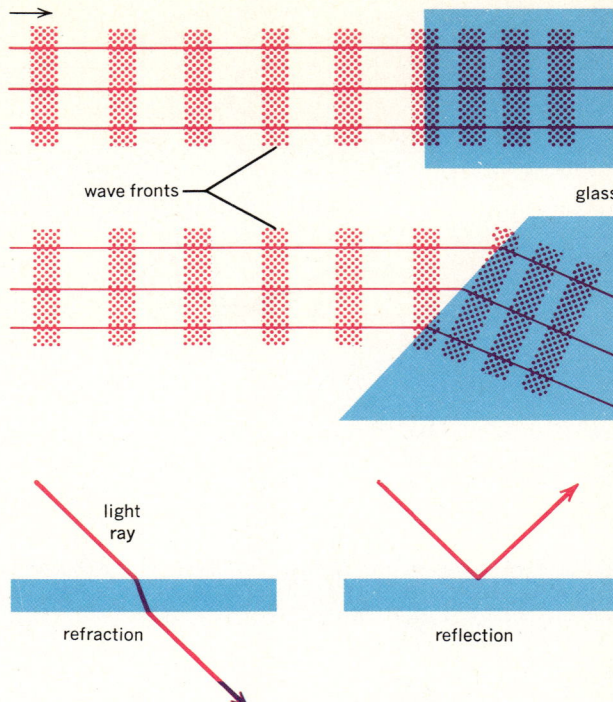

FIGURE 17-8 Some basic optics. Note that the distance between wave fronts is shortened when light rays enter glass. At a boundary between two media, light rays may be reflected and/or refracted.

the resultant photochemical reactions produce areas of varying shades, depending on the relative intensities of the light rays. In the eye the image is focused onto the light-sensitive retina, producing photochemical reactions in the rods and cones, which generate impulses that are relayed to the brain via the optic nerve. The image produced both on the photographic film and on the retina is inverted; the visual area of the brain compensates for this phenomenon and yields a right-side-up mental image.

The eye is more versatile than a camera, for camera film can be used only once and requires lengthy and laborious operations for developing and printing pictures, while the retina registers a continuous procession of images, which the brain analyzes and synthesizes almost instantly into a smooth-flowing "moving picture."

THE OPTICS OF VISION

The discoveries of the twentieth century have forced physicists to stretch their minds and accept a number of paradoxical and contradictory phenomena. One important paradox concerns the nature of light. Sometimes light rays behave like tiny, discrete particles, flying through space. Other aspects of the behavior of light (and other forms of electromagnetic radiation) can best be understood if light is pictured as consisting of immaterial waves, spreading out through space. Leaving the theoretical physicists to wrestle with the philosophical puzzle of how something can be both a particle and a wave at the same time, we will adopt the usual compromise and think of electromagnetic radiations as consisting either of

waves or of particles, depending on which is most convenient for the problem at hand. **Visible light** is a form of electromagnetic radiation with wavelengths in the range from about 3850 to 7200 Å.

Figure 17-8 illustrates some simple principles and definitions of **optics**, the science of light and vision. Light can be viewed as advancing in **wave fronts;** a light **ray** is a line constructed along the line of travel of the waves, perpendicular to the wave fronts. When light rays strike a surface of a different medium, they may be **reflected** (i.e., bounced back) from the interface, or they may be transmitted through the new medium. If the light rays enter the new medium at right angles, they continue to follow the same straight path. But light rays striking the surface obliquely may be bent or **refracted** by the new medium. Refraction occurs when the speed of light changes from one medium to another. Air, water, glass, and other common media differ in their refractive properties. In general, light rays travel through a vacuum at a velocity of approximately 300,000 kilometers per second, and nearly as fast in air and other gases. But light travels more slowly through liquids and solids. The **refractive index** of a transparent substance (one that transmits light) is the ratio of the velocity of light in air to that in the substance. Air itself, of course, has a refractive index of 1.00; for glass it is about 1.50. The refractive indices of the refracting media of the eye are: cornea

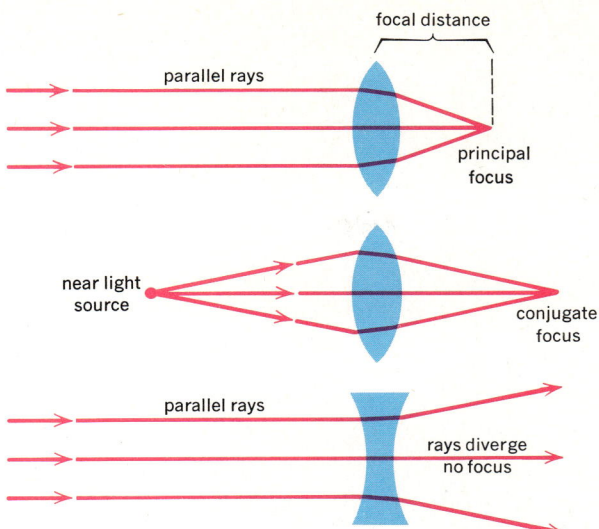

FIGURE 17-9 Lenses work by refraction; depending on their structure, they converge or diverge light rays.

1.38, aqueous humor 1.33, lens 1.40, and vitreous humor 1.34. Thus, light rays traveling through air to the eye are bent as they pass through the medium of the cornea, and then successively bent again by the other refractive media.

Lenses

Whenever a solar eclipse is predicted, the articles in the press about the coming phenomenon are liberally sprinkled with warnings to use dark glasses or other suitable devices in viewing the eclipse. If the sun is viewed directly with the unprotected eyes, light rays may be focused by the lens of the eye to form so intense a beam that it burns a portion of the retina, producing partial or total blindness. (An analogous phenomenon occurs when a child playing with a magnifying lens uses it to focus sun rays to set fire to a piece of paper.)

A **lens** is a transparent object that bends light rays and causes them to converge or diverge. Artificial lenses are usually made of ground and polished glass. The sixteenth-century Dutch microscopist Anton van Leeuwenhoek was such a skillful lensmaker that, using simple magnifying glasses, he was able to discover a variety of protozoa and bacteria, many of which were not to be seen again until a century or more later, when compound microscopes were perfected.

The lens of the eye is of the **biconvex** variety, that is, both the anterior and the posterior surfaces curve outward. But other variations of lenses are possible, for examples, **biconcave** (both surfaces curving inward), **concave-convex, planoconvex** (one surface flat, the other curving outward), **planoconcave,** and so on. As seen in Figure 17-9, the effects that these types of lenses produce on incident light rays differ greatly.

Light rays coming from a distant source can be considered as parallel. Those that strike the central portion of the cornea are perpendicular to its surface (and farther along the path, perpendicular to the surface of the lens as well), and so they are transmitted with an unchanged path. Light rays that strike the sides of the cornea form an oblique angle with its surface, and thus are refracted in the eye. The convex shape of the cornea and the biconvex construction of the lens result in convergence of the entire beam of parallel rays to a single point, which is referred to as the **focus** or **focal point.** The distance from the lens to the focal point is called the **focal length,** and the **refractive power** of a lens is measured in **diopters,** a unit equal to one meter divided by the focal length of the lens. In the human eye, the system of the cornea plus the lens has a focal length of 16.7 mm, approximately the length of the normal adult eyeball (i.e., images are focused upon the retina), and the refractive power ranges from about 60 to 75 diopters.

Light rays coming from a close source diverge, and thus they must be bent more to be focused onto the retina. The adjustable shape of the lens allows for the focusing both of nearby objects and of far-off vistas.

Formation of an Image on the Retina

Experiments in which volunteers continuously wore inverting spectacles for periods of several weeks yielded some intriguing results. At first everything seemed upside-down. But after a few days the brain learned to compensate for the changed sensory input, and the subjects began to see everything right-side-up again. When they were allowed to remove the spectacles, and view the world with their own unaided eyes, everything seemed turned upside-down again, returning to normal only after another adjustment period.

You are already wearing a pair of "inverting spectacles"—the lenses of your own eyes. As you can see from the diagram in Figure 17-10, a biconvex lens typically produces an **inverted image.** The brain, drawing on its experience, translates the image appropriately, so that you don't go around with the impression that people are walking on the ceiling. The image produced on the retina is also greatly **reduced**—obviously you would not have room to project a six-foot image of a six-foot man onto the inside of your eyeballs. The size of the image depends on the distance from the object to your eyes: more distant objects appear smaller than closer ones of the same actual size. This apparent size difference, determined by distance, is known as **perspective.** It is used by artists to give an illusion of depth in a flat, two-dimensional drawing (Figure 17-11). The brain also uses perspective as an important cue in estimating relative distances.

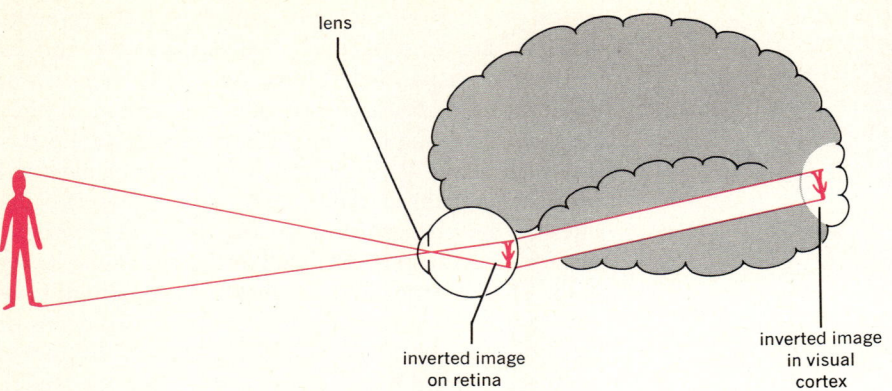

lens

inverted image
on retina

inverted image
in visual
cortex

FIGURE 17-10 Light rays focused by
the lens of the eye produce a reduced, inverted image on the retina, which is transmitted to the visual cortex of the brain.

FIGURE 17-11 The artist uses perspective to give an illusion of distance.

PHYSIOLOGY OF VISION

In a simple box camera, the shutter speed, size of the
aperture, and distance of the lens from the film are all
fixed, and the results obtained with such a camera
reflect its lack of versatility. Objects within a certain
distance from the camera come out clear and sharp in
the photographs, but distant vistas are rather indistinct, and closeups are just a blur. If the light is too
dim, the pictures will be underexposed, while too
bright a light can produce a washed-out, overexposed
effect. More expensive cameras provide a variety of
options—a range of adjustments of the shutter speed
and aperture (plus a light meter to determine which
settings will be optimum for the prevailing conditions), and a lens mounted on a movable framework,
so that its distance from the film can be changed to
bring a larger range of distances into sharp focus. The
human visual apparatus is even more versatile and
efficient—comparable not to a camera, but to an expensive camera hooked up to a computer, which continuously assesses the light conditions and automatically adjusts the apertures and lens system of the eyes
to admit the optimum amount of light and bring
items of interest into focus. The computer is the
brain, linked to the eyes by feedback circuits via sensory and motor cranial nerves.

The Nervous Pathway for Vision

Seated in a laboratory, a woman gazes at a rather
curious picture, flashed on a screen. It is a composite
photograph, the left half of which shows half of the
face of a man wearing glasses; the right half shows
half of the face of a child. Next to the woman an
array of complete photographs is spread out on the
table. She is asked to point to the picture she saw on
the screen and unhesitatingly picks out the man with

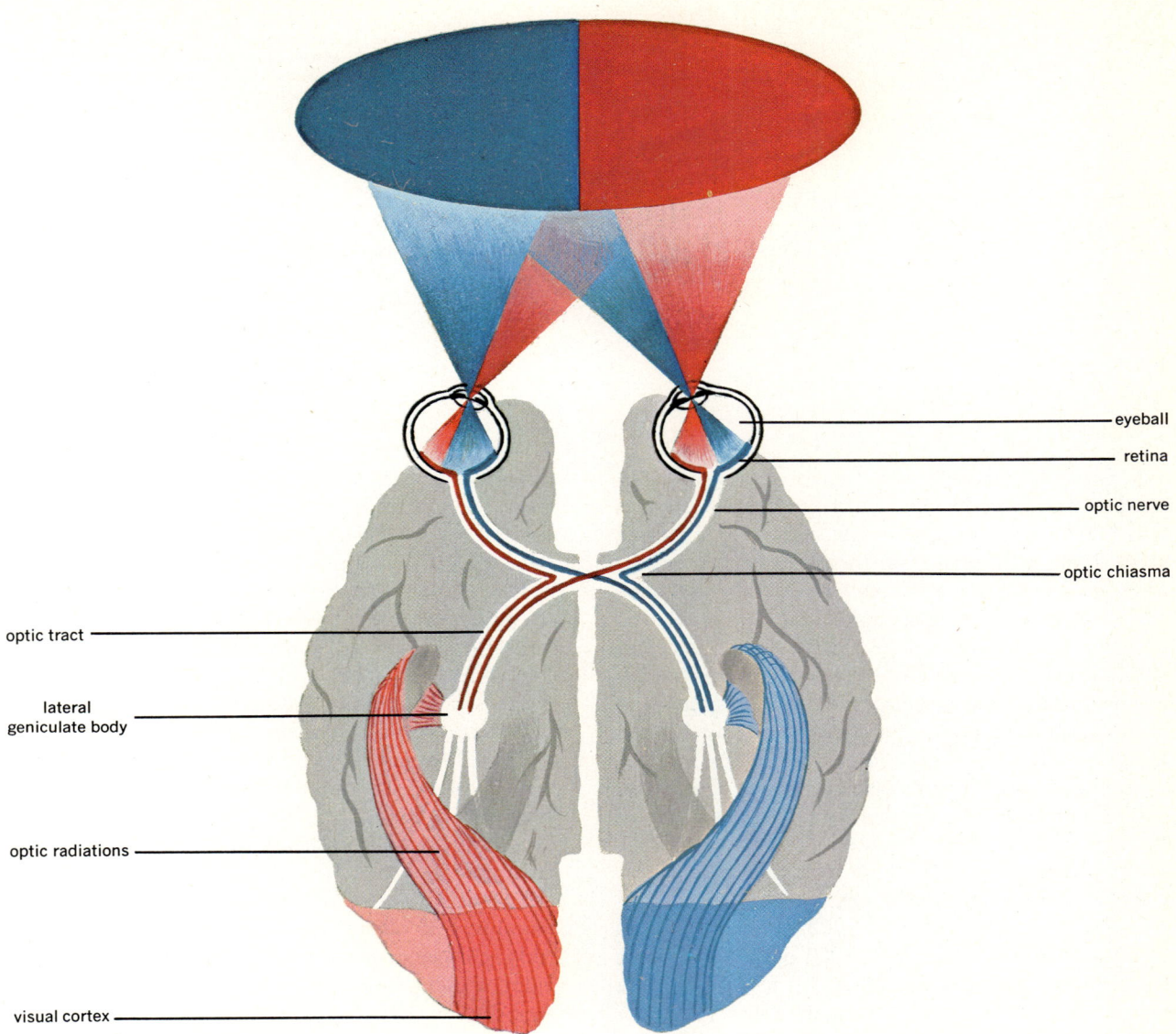

eyeball

retina

optic nerve

optic chiasma

optic tract

lateral geniculate body

optic radiations

visual cortex

FIGURE 17-12 **The visual pathways. Note the partial crossing of nerve fibers from the retina. Fibers from both eyes go to each half of the brain, but the left half of the visual field is perceived in the right half of the brain, and vice versa.**

glasses. Next a composite of a movie star and an old man with a beard is flashed onto the screen. The woman is asked to describe what she saw; she talks about the old man with the beard and denies that there was anything unusual about the picture.

The subject of the experiment had been treated for severe epilepsy by a surgical operation, which severed the corpus callosum, the connection between the hemispheres of the brain. Her replies to the experimenters' questions were the result of two aspects of human physiology: the arrangement of nerve pathways from the eyes to the brain and the split between the articulate left hemisphere, which houses the speech centers, and the "silent" right brain. As mentioned in an earlier chapter, the fibers from the me-

dial half of the retina cross over at the optic chiasma and enter the opposite hemisphere of the brain (Figure 17-12); the fibers from the outer half of each retina continue along the same side. As a result, the images from the left half of the visual field are transmitted entirely to the right hemisphere of the brain, while those from the right half of the visual field all go to the left hemisphere. In the normal brain, there is a continual interchange of information between the two hemispheres, so that a whole image is perceived, rather than two halves. But if the corpus callosum is cut, the left half of the brain literally does not know what the right half is seeing, and vice versa.

The following stages are involved in the nervous pathway for vision. Impulses are generated by the

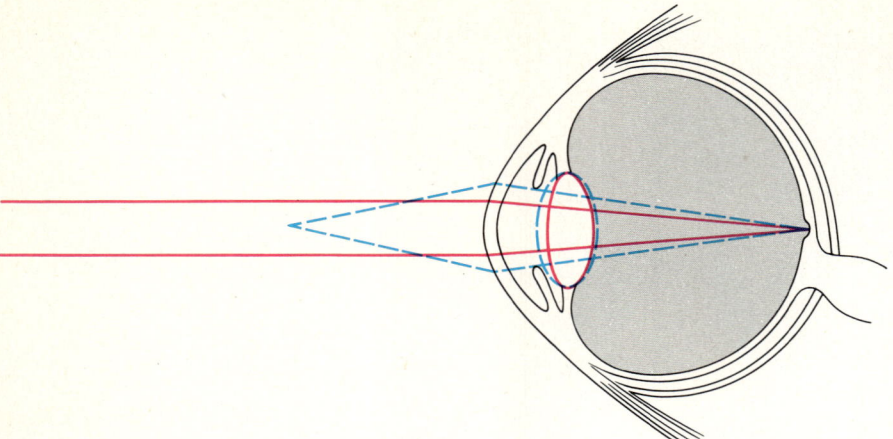

FIGURE 17-13 Accommodation: the lens can change its shape to focus light rays from distant or nearby objects onto the retina. Note that the lens is flatter in viewing distant objects.

rods and cones, pass through synapses into the bipolar cells, and then through synapses into the ganglion cells. The axons of the ganglion cells form the optic nerve, leaving the eyeball at the optic disc, through a sieve-like structure, the **lamina cribrosa.** The two optic nerves meet at the **optic chiasma,** then diverge and continue as the **optic tract** on each side of the midbrain. The fibers of the optic tract synapse in the **lateral geniculate body** with fibers that relay the impulses to the visual cortex in the occipital lobe. In addition, visual fibers pass from the lateral geniculate body to the thalamus, the superior colliculi (which control pupillary and protective eye reflexes), and the pretectal nuclei of the brainstem; from the optic tracts directly to the superior colliculi; and from the optic tracts directly into the pretectal nuclei.

Each retina contains about 125 million rods and 5.5 million cones, yet only 900,000 optic nerve fibers lead from the retina to the brain. In the region of the fovea, which contains only cones, the ratio of receptor cells to nerve fibers is almost one-to-one, which explains the high visual acuity in this area of the retina. The center of the retina is the area for detailed vision. In the periphery of the retina, where rods predominate, as many as 600 rods converge on a single optic nerve fiber. This arrangement accounts for the great sensitivity of the periphery of the retina to dim light, for the signals from large numbers of rods are summated to give a more intense stimulation of the peripheral ganglion cells. Moving objects, which stimulate large numbers of receptor cells in rapid succession, register particularly in this peripheral area of the retina; thus, you often have the sensation of catching sight of a movement "out of the corner of your eye."

Accommodation

When you focus a camera, you change the distance from the lens to the film, so that the focus of the image will coincide with the light-sensitive area. The human eye uses a somewhat different mechanism, since the eyeball cannot change its shape, and the distance between lens and retina remains fixed. Instead, the shape of the lens itself is changed, so that light rays from different distances are converged upon the retina (Figure 17-13). This change in the curvature of the lens is called **accommodation.**

To view a nearby object, greater refraction is needed. This is accomplished by a contraction of the ciliary muscle, which draws the ciliary processes forward and lessens the tension on the suspensory ligaments. As a result, the tension on the capsule of the crystalline lens is reduced, and the elastic lens bulges, becoming more convex, with a greater refracting power.

Two other mechanisms also come into play in looking at a close object. The sphincter muscle of the iris contracts, constricting the pupil and cutting down the amount of light entering the eye, and the two eyes turn slightly toward one another, or **converge.**

Accommodation for near vision is a reflex action, triggered by the stimulus of a defocused image and by convergence of the eyes. It is mediated by the parasympathetic division of the autonomic nervous system.

In viewing a distant object, the ciliary muscles are relaxed, which makes the suspensory ligaments pull tautly on the lens, flattening it and decreasing its refracting power. Recent research indicates that an active process of contraction of the radial fibers, placing greater tension on the lens, also contributes to the accommodation to distant vision and is under the control of the sympathetic nervous system.

The Chemistry of Vision

During the dissection of an ox eye in the laboratory, the retina is peeled off, and the color of the receptor cells changes gradually, from a deep purple to a pale yellowish color.

Both the rods and the cones contain chemicals that

decompose when they are exposed to light, and in the process, excite the nerve fibers leading out of the eye. The chemical in the rods has been isolated and studied; it is a pigment called **rhodopsin,** or **visual purple.** The chemical in the cones of the human eye has not yet been isolated, but there is evidence to indicate that it is similar to rhodopsin. Rhodopsin is a combination of a protein, **scotopsin,** and the carotenoid pigment **retinene.** (The folk-medicine remedy of eating carrots to improve night vision thus has some basis in fact, since carrots are rich in carotenoid pigments. Vitamin A is a precursor of rhodopsin in the body's synthesis of the pigment; a deficiency of this vitamin in the diet causes **night blindness,** a reduction of visual acuity in dim light due to a lack of sufficient photosensitive chemicals in the rods and cones.)

When light energy is absorbed by rhodopsin, a chain reaction is initiated (Figure 17-14). Rhodopsin begins to break down, yielding first an unstable intermediate product, **lumi-rhodopsin,** which breaks down in a fraction of a second to another unstable product, **meta-rhodopsin,** which decomposes in turn, splitting into retinene (visual yellow) and scotopsin. It is believed that scotopsin ionizes and generates a receptor potential in the nerve cell membrane. The retinene and scotopsin promptly recombine, reforming rhodopsin, in a reaction whose initial stage requires an input of metabolic energy. The resynthesis of the photosensitive chemical is more rapid in the cones than in the rods.

Dark and Light Adaptation

When you walk into a movie theater on a bright sunny day, for a few moments the theater seems dark, and you find it difficult to see. But after awhile, more and more details become clearly visible. A similar phenomenon occurs while driving a car at night, after your eyes have been struck by the headlight beams of inconsiderate drivers who have their "brights" on. During the Vietnam war, soldiers who were to conduct night patrols sometimes prepared for duty by shutting themselves up in a dark room during the early evening hours.

If the eyes have been exposed to bright light for a long time, a large proportion of the photochemicals in both the rods and the cones is reduced to retinene and opsins, and much of the retinene is converted to vitamin A. With this decrease in the concentration of photochemicals, the sensitivity of the retina to light is greatly reduced. This phenomenon is called **light adaptation.**

Long exposure to darkness, on the other hand, results in a conversion of nearly all the retinene and opsins in the rods and cones into light-sensitive pigments. The conversion of vitamin A to retinene is also stimulated. In time, the visual receptors become so

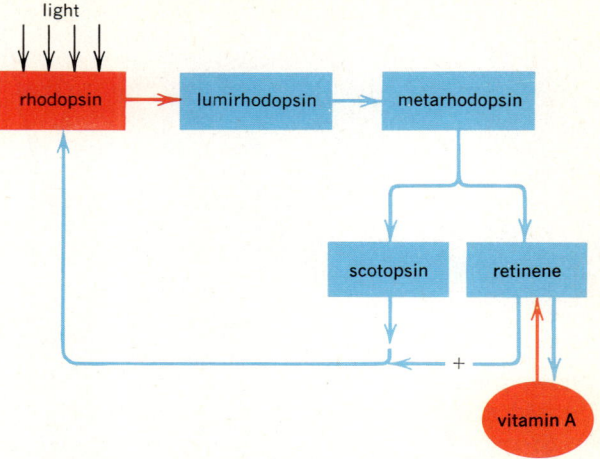

FIGURE 17-14   The rhodopsin cycle: the sequence of chemical reactions involved in rod function.

sensitive that minute amounts of light produce excitation. This is **dark adaptation.**

The range of light sensitivity of the retina is phenomenal: between the limits of maximum dark adaptation and maximum light adaptation, the retina can change its sensitivity to light as much as 500,000 to 1,000,000 times. Dark adaptation after a long exposure to bright light can take as long as several hours; light adaptation, on the other hand, takes only a few minutes.

A curious effect of light and dark adaptation is the formation of **negative after-images.** If you stare at a scene for awhile, the areas of the retina stimulated by bright portions of the scene will become less sensitive, while the areas of the retina on which dark portions of the scene are projected will become more sensitive. Then, if you move your eyes away from the scene and look at a bright white surface, you will see the same scene you had been looking at—except that each area that was dark will be bright, and each bright area will be dark—that is, the after-image will look like a photographic negative. Under favorable conditions, such a negative after-image could persist for as long as an hour.

Color Vision

Humans are among the few animals possessing the ability to see a full range of colors. Dogs, cats, and most of the other mammals see the world in shades of gray, like a black-and-white movie. Birds generally have good color vision, and so do many insects (although the range of "visible" light for them may not coincide with ours: bees, for example, can see blue and yellow, are blind to red, and can see ultraviolet light that is invisible to humans).

Sunlight can be broken up by a prism into a rainbow of colors called the **visible spectrum:** red, orange,

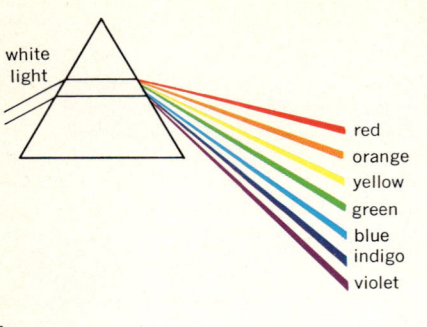

A

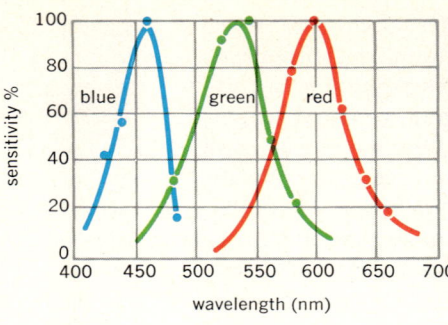

B

FIGURE 17-15 A prism refracts sunlight into the visible spectrum (A). Three different types of cones in the human eye are sensitive mainly to light waves in the red, blue, or green range, as shown by absorption curves for the three types of cones (B).

yellow, green, blue, indigo, violet (Figure 17-15A). The red rays have the longest wavelength (and the lowest energy), while the violet rays are the shortest (and have the highest energy). The human eye can distinguish not only these basic colors, but also more than seventeen thousand intermediate hues.

The currently accepted theory of color vision was originally put forward by Thomas Young in England, back in 1802, and tested experimentally by the German physicist Hermann von Helmholtz sixty years later. According to the **Young-Helmholtz theory,** we see colors by the operation of three different kinds of cones, each of which contains a different light-sensitive pigment and is sensitive mainly to a single color: **red, blue,** or **green** (Figure 17-15B). Combined stimulation of two or more types of cones produces the sensation of other colors, such as yellow.

After-images of colored objects may be either positive (in the same color as the original stimulus) or negative (in complementary colors). A common positive after-image occurs when you stare at a light bulb for a few seconds, then close your eyes. To produce a negative after-image, stare at a colored object for about 20 seconds, and then look at a white surface. Reds will seem green in the after-image, yellows violet, and so on.

Everyone is colorblind when the light is weak, for the cones require a greater light intensity for stimulation than the rods. As evening falls, the ability to discriminate red is lost first, and then on to the violet end of the spectrum. In the morning, blue is the first color to become perceptible.

Binocular Vision

If you close one eye and look at an unfamiliar object in an unfamiliar environment, it may be difficult to judge its distance. Depth perception with only one eye is not impossible: in fact, we regularly employ two different techniques to judge distances that need involve only one eye. One is the use of **visual cues** to determine relative sizes. If you look at a scene and see a man apparently next to a house that is much smaller than he is, you will immediately deduce that either it is a model house, or it is considerably farther

away than the man; you can also gauge from experience just about how far away the man is according to the size of his image on your retina. Another technique for determining distance is the use of **moving parallax.** If you look at a scene with one eye and move your head to the side, nearby objects will appear to move rapidly, while distant objects will remain stationary. But useful as these techniques may be, a far more effective perception of depth is provided by binocular vision, using two eyes.

The picture that two normally functioning eyes provide is **stereoscopic,** consisting of two optical images, made from slightly different angles. In binocular vision the eyes are moved so that the images of a given object fall on corresponding points on the retinas of both eyes (Figure 17-16). The visual fields of the two eyes are slightly different, but there is a large area of overlap, and the two images are blended in consciousness to produce an impression of distance and depth. (Remember that one hemisphere of the brain receives the images of the right side of the visual field from *both* the left and right eyes, while the other hemisphere receives the left-side images from both eyes; intercommunications between the two hemispheres make it possible to put the two halves of the picture together.) Binocular vision is maintained through nervous and muscular coordination of eye

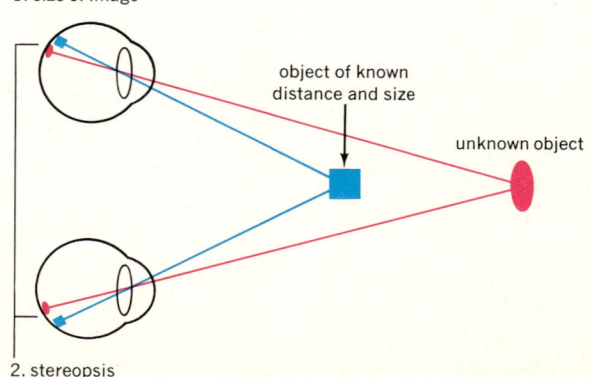

FIGURE 17-16 Binocular vision permits judgment of distance and depth.

movements, involving convergence, change in the size of the pupil, and accommodation. If the images do not fall on corresponding points in the retinas of the two eyes, **diplopia,** or double vision results.

In the merging of the stereoscopic images, one eye tends to dominate, and the resultant image is seen from its vantagepoint. To demonstrate the differences in angle of vision of your two eyes and determine whether you are right-eyed or left-eyed, look across the room and locate a spot on the wall. Then raise one finger and hold it so that it seems to cover the spot. Holding the finger steady, close first one eye, then the other. Looking through your dominant eye, your finger will continue to cover the spot; using the other eye, your finger will appear to move, uncovering the spot.

The difference in visual fields of the two eyes can be demonstrated by staring straight ahead, extending your arms backward, and then moving your hands forward until you just catch sight of them. Then close first one eye, then the other, and notice that one hand or the other disappears. You will also notice that the peripheral vision is far more sensitive to moving objects than to stationary ones.

Optical Illusions

Things are not always what they seem. Which of the horizontal lines below is longer?

If you take a ruler and measure them, you will find that they are exactly the same length, even though the right-hand line looks longer. What we "see" is the result of the brain's interpretations of input from the visual organs, on the basis of past experience. Optical illusions, false interpretations of visual sensations, are very common experiences. For example, objects appear larger on a foggy night, since their outlines are hazy and they appear to be farther away than they really are. Some typical examples of optical illusions are depicted in Figure 17-17.

ABNORMALITIES OF VISION

Eye tests are a standard part of physical examinations, both because vision is so important in our lives and because eye problems of various types are so common. Abnormalities of vision may involve either the eye itself or the nervous pathways from the eye to the brain.

Eye Infections

One of the most common types of eye infection is **conjunctivitis,** inflammation of the conjunctiva. It can be caused by bacterial or viral infection, or by irritation by dust or pollen, and it is characterized by an increased flow of tears and a pink or fiery red color of the conjunctival membrane—hence the common name for the condition: "pinkeye." A **hordeolum** or sty is an infection of a sebaceous gland associated with the follicles of the eyelashes; a **chalazion** is an infection of a sebaceous gland associated with the tarsus. Inflammation of the eyelids is referred to as **blepharitis.** A scourge of the underdeveloped countries is **trachoma,** a highly contagious viral disease of the conjunctiva and cornea, which produces pain, hypersensitivity to light, and degenerative changes in the eyes. Trachoma is estimated to afflict about 500 million people, but responds to sulfonamides and some antibiotics.

Refractive Errors

In the normal eye, accommodation permits images of either near or far objects to be focused precisely on the retina. But some people are born with eyeballs that are longer or shorter than normal (Figure 17-18). If the eyeball is too long, even with the most heroic

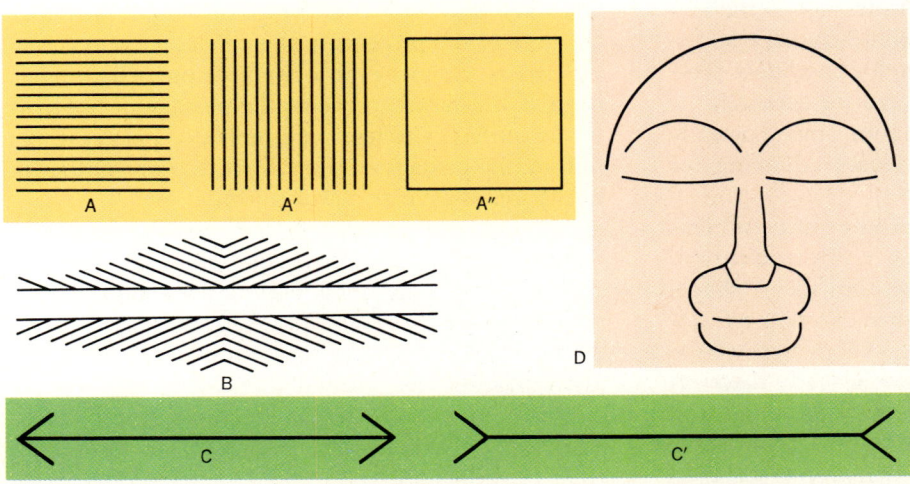

FIGURE 17-17 Optical illusions: the squares in A, A′, and A″ are all the same size and shape; the horizontal lines in B are parallel; lines C and C′ are the same length; in D the eyes see a pattern of lines that the brain attempts to make meaningful, "flipping" back and forth between an enigmatic face and a mushroom-shaped lamp.

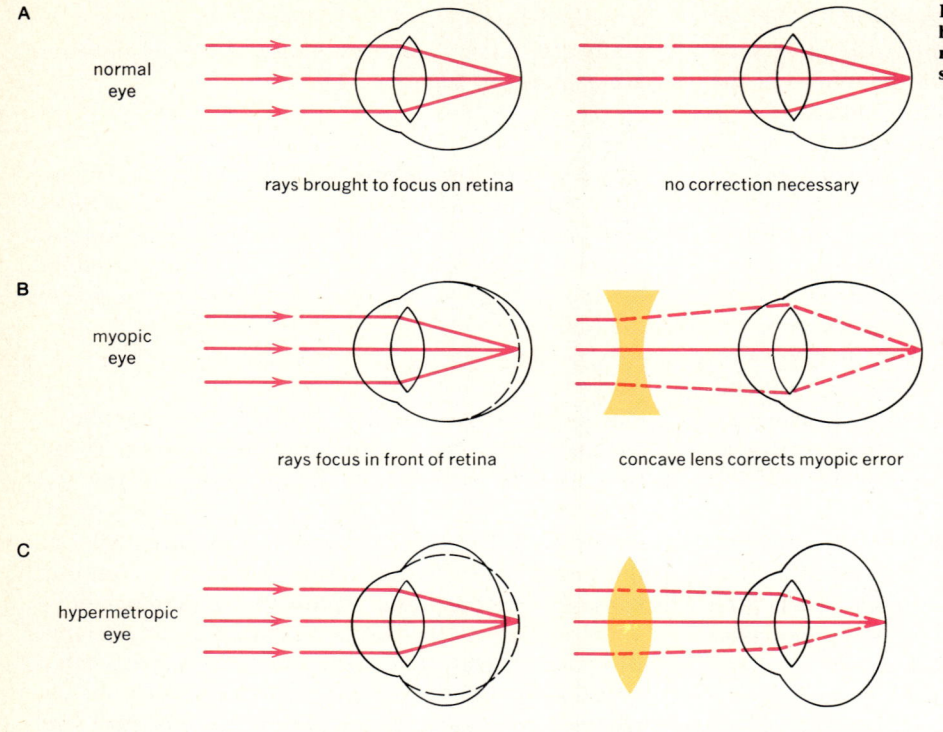

A

normal eye

rays brought to focus on retina

no correction necessary

FIGURE 17-18 Normal (A), myopic (B), and hypermetropic (C) eyes and types of lenses needed to correct nearsightedness and farsightedness.

B

myopic eye

rays focus in front of retina

concave lens corrects myopic error

C

hypermetropic eye

rays focus behind retina

convex lens corrects hypermetropic error

efforts of the eye muscles, the focus will fall somewhat short of the retina for distant objects. The condition of **myopia,** or nearsightedness, results: the person can see nearby objects clearly, but is unable to focus distant objects clearly. Myopia can be corrected with a suitable biconcave lens, as shown in Figure 17-18.

In **hypermetropia** (hyperopia), or farsightedness, the eyeball is too short, and the focal point falls behind the retina. Distant objects may be seen satisfactorily, but close objects cannot be focused clearly. Hypermetropia is corrected with a biconvex lens, which adds converging power to the eye's natural converging apparatus.

An old person holding a newspaper out at arm's length is a common sight. In advancing age, the lens tends to lose its elasticity and ultimately may be entirely unable to accommodate. In this condition, **presbyopia,** even distant objects may not be seen clearly. Presbyopia is corrected with convex lenses; usually bifocals, combinations of two lenses adjusting for near and distant vision, are used.

Few people's eyes are perfect. The cornea and lens are rarely parts of perfect spheres, but instead exhibit greater or smaller deviations from the "ideal" shape. As a result, different parts will have different refracting powers, and not all parts of an image will be perfectly focused at the same time. Usually these refracting errors are so minor that they are unnoticed and do not interfere with normal activities. But some eyes have such severe deviations (e.g., a spoon-shaped

or oblong cornea) that blurred vision, fatigue, and chronic headaches may result. This condition, **astigmatism,** is far more difficult to correct than myopia or hypermetropia; it requires a careful assessment of the irregularities of the lens or cornea, using test patterns such as the one depicted in Figure 17-19, and the prescription of specially ground lenses, usually incorporating cylindrical lenses.

Cataract

It is a depressing fact that despite major medical advances, there has been no sharp decline in cases of blindness, for more people are living to an age at which degenerative changes in the eyes are common. One such condition is a change in the physicochemical state of the proteins in the crystalline lens, resulting in its clouding or opacification. The opacity formed, a **cataract,** prevents the passage of light rays to the retina. (The lens may remain translucent, permitting the passage of some light, but preventing the formation of clear images.) Injury to the eye, overexposure to bright sunlight, X rays, or diseases such as diabetes can produce cataracts; congenital cataract may be caused by an illness of the mother during pregnancy, such as German measles at three months. Sight can be restored by removing the clouded lenses and replacing their refractive function with powerful glasses. (Small plastic lenses that are inserted into the suspensory ligament, inside the eye, are now being tried experimentally.)

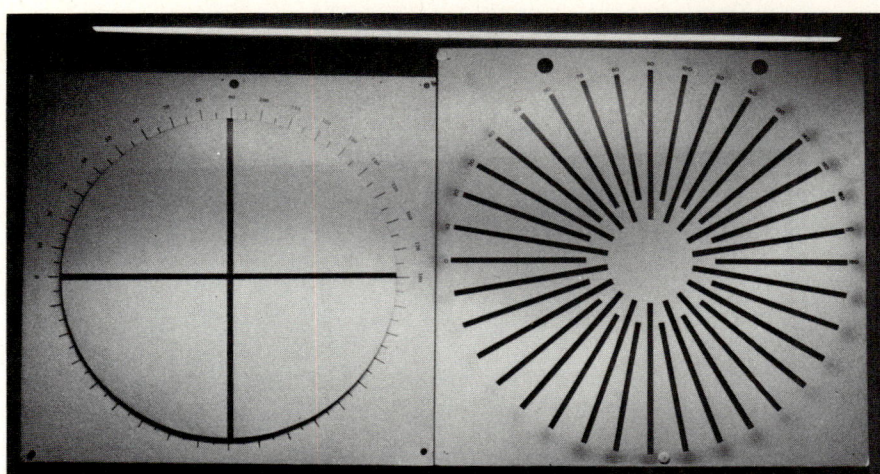

FIGURE 17-19 Tests for astigmatism.

Opacity of the cornea can result from injuries or infections and lead to blindness. This condition can be treated by a corneal transplant, which will be tolerated because the cornea of the eye lacks blood and lymph vessels.

Glaucoma

In **glaucoma,** the intraocular pressure is elevated, as a result of an imbalance between the rate of formation of aqueous humor and its drainage through the canal of Schlemm. Blindness can result, due to compression of the retinal artery, which reduces the nutrition to the retina and can lead to permanent atrophy of the retina and optic nerve. Glaucoma is commonly treated with a drug, Diamox, which reduces the intraocular pressure; if this therapy is ineffective, a small hole is made into the anterior chamber of the eyeball, permitting the aqueous humor to leak out.

Detached Retina

One of the most dramatic applications of the laser is in the treatment of **detachment of the retina,** a condition in which patches of the retina peel off from the choroid. An ultrathin, finely focused beam of coherent light is used to spot-weld the detached patches back into place.

Strabismus

An unfortunate person afflicted with **strabismus** or "squint" not only has a facial expression that tends to repel people, but suffers from faulty vision. The condition usually results from an imbalance of the extrinsic eye muscles: the internal rectus is stronger than the external rectus and pulls the eye inward toward the nose. As a result, light rays from objects fall on noncorresponding points of the two retinas, and a double image is produced. In mild cases, the muscular imbalance can be compensated for by extra effort, but a toll is taken in muscular and nervous strain. In severe cases, the person does not experience diplopia: since the deviation of the eye cannot be overcome, even by neuromuscular effort, the person learns to suppress the image from one of the eyes and gets along with monocular vision; the deviant eye becomes functionally blind. Strabismus is treated by surgical alteration of the extrinsic eye muscles or of the lenses, so that images will fall on corresponding points of the two retinas.

Color Blindness

About 8 percent of the male population and less than 0.5 percent of the female population suffer from color blindness, in which one or more of the three types of cones is absent. The most common type is red-green color blindness, in which either the red or the green cones are lacking, making the person unable to distinguish between red and green. Blue weakness, resulting from diminished or absent blue receptors, is a much rarer condition, and total color blindness, in which the person sees the world in shades of gray, is far rarer still. Color blindness does not usually create much difficulty in daily living, since the colorblind person uses differences in color intensities and a variety of positional cues to find his way around a world that others see in a full spectrum of colors. But red-green color blindness may occasionally be disastrous if an out-of-town colorblind driver happens to drive into one of the rare localities where the usual arrangement of "stop" and "go" traffic lights is reversed.

Color blindness is a hereditary, sex-linked condition, transmitted on the X chromosome. It is a recessive trait, and thus appears far more frequently in males, who lack a second X chromosome to contribute normal color vision genes.

Effect of Drugs on the Pupil

If you are going to be fitted for glasses, don't plan to drive yourself home: part of the procedure in measur-

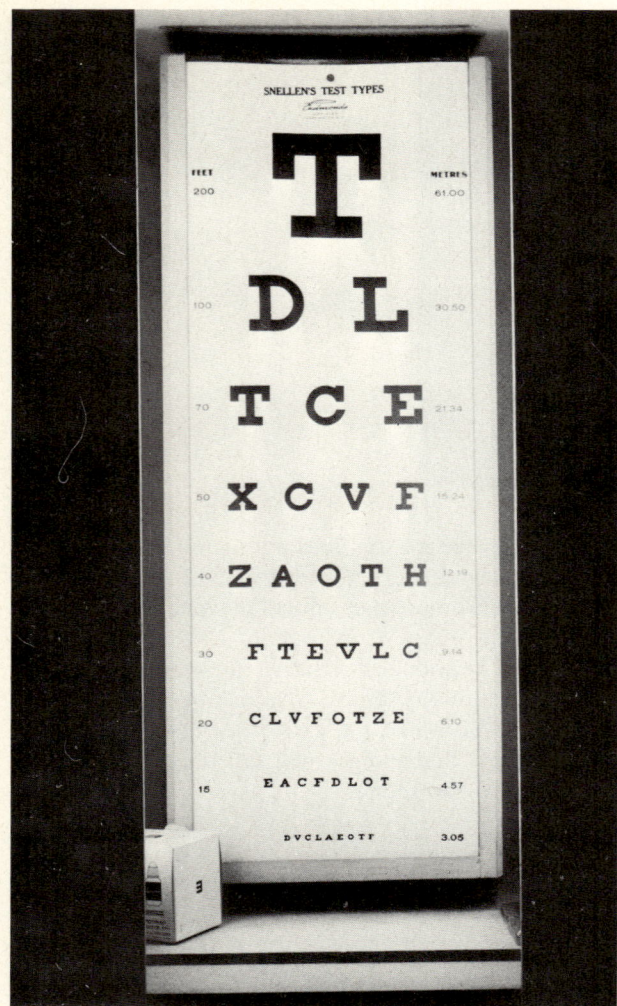

FIGURE 17-20 The Snellen eye test for visual acuity.

FIGURE 17-21 The Ishihara test for color blindness. If you have normal color vision, you will see the number 16 in this plate. A person with complete red-green color blindness would be unable to distinguish any number. Other Ishihara plates test for more subtle differences in color vision.

Visual acuity, or the sharpness of vision, is commonly tested for with a **Snellen test,** depicted in Figure 17-20. A person with normal vision is defined as one who can read standard-sized letters of the alphabet at a distance of 20 feet. Visual acuity is expressed in a fraction: 20/20 vision is normal, 20/40 vision means that a person can see at 20 feet what a person with normal vision can see at forty feet (or the person must move closer, to 10 feet, to read letters that someone with normal vision can read at 20 feet); 20/15 is better than "normal" vision.

Color vision is tested with **Ishihara charts** (Figure 17-21), which are collections of various-sized dots in which numbers are formed by dots of contrasting colors. Persons with normal color vision easily pick out the numbers from the patterns of dots, while those with one of the types of color blindness either see no numbers at all or see a different number, depending on the type of receptors lacking.

An **ophthalmoscope** is used to look into the eyeball and observe the retina by means of reflected light. Such an examination reveals the general condition of the retina (which is called the **fundus,** or **eye grounds**), as well as the condition of the blood vessels and the optic disc. Figure 17-22 shows photographs of a normal retina and a pathological retina.

A **tonometer** is used to measure the intraocular pressure. The cornea is anesthetized with a local anesthetic, and a small force is applied to the cornea, causing it to be displaced inward. The amount of displacement is recorded on the tonometer scale, which is calibrated in units of intraocular pressure.

Tests of pupillary reflexes can disclose lesions in the

ing the refracting properties of the lens involves the introduction of drops of an **atropine** solution into the eyes. This drug temporarily paralyzes the sphincter muscle of the iris and the ciliary muscle, so that the pupil dilates and the ability for accommodation is lost. For a few hours, you will be unusually sensitive to light and unable to focus clearly, especially on nearby objects. **Epinephrine** and **cocaine** also lead to dilation of the pupil, but by a different mechanism: through stimulation of the radial muscle of the iris. Drugs that dilate the pupils are called **mydriatic** drugs. **Miotic** drugs produce the opposite effect, a constriction of the pupils. Examples are **pilocarpine,** which stimulates the sphincter muscle of the iris, and **morphine,** which produces extremely constricted, "pinpoint" pupils.

Eye Examinations

A complete ophthalmological examination includes a number of tests, which can reveal a variety of conditions.

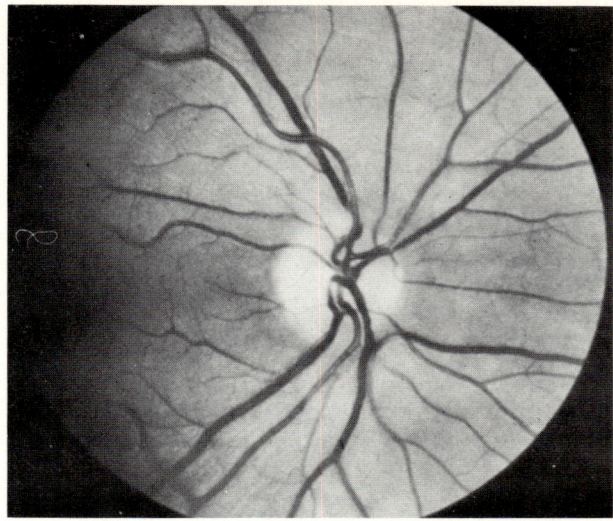

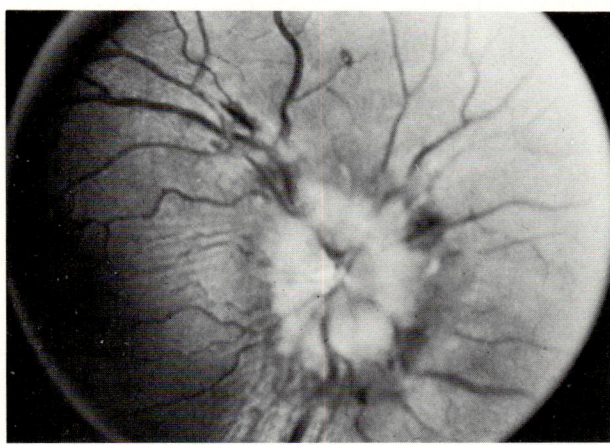

FIGURE 17-22 Eye grounds seen in retinal examination with an ophthalmoscope: normal (A) and pathological (B).

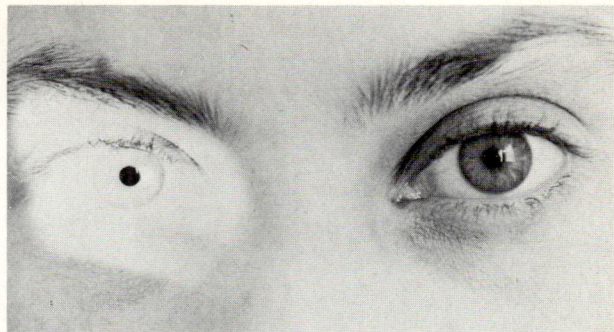

FIGURE 17-23 The pupillary light reflex: shining a light into one eye causes both pupils to constrict if the neural pathways are functioning normally.

An instrument called a **perimeter** is used to map out the visual field. Lesions of the visual cortex, or of various parts of the visual pathways, result in a loss of vision in characteristic portions of the visual field, as depicted in Figure 17-24. A condition called **tunnel vision** is characterized by a loss of the peripheral portions of the visual field, so that the patient sees the world as though looking through a long, narrow tunnel. This condition may be produced by pressure of enlarged carotid arteries on the optic nerves, or it may be a psychosomatic symptom in hysterical individuals.

SUMMARY

The eyeball rests on a cushion of fat within the bony socket of the orbital cavity.

The wall of the eyeball is composed of three layers or coats:
    Outer fibrous layer: sclera (includes cornea)
    Middle vascular layer: choroid (includes ciliary body and iris)
    Inner nervous layer: retina

Light rays entering the eye pass successively through four refracting media:
    Cornea
    Aqueous humor
    Lens
    Vitreous body

The extrinsic muscles of the eye are:
    Superior rectus
    Inferior rectus
    Lateral rectus
    Medial rectus
    Superior oblique
    Inferior oblique

The eyelids (palpebrae) cover and protect the eyeball and spread lubricating secretions.

The conjunctiva is a thin, transparent mucous membrane that lines the eyelids and continues over the anterior part of the eyeball.

The lacrimal gland secretes tears, which cleanse and lubricate the eye surface. Tears are spread by the blinking reflex and drain down into the nose via the nasolacrimal duct.

The sclera, or white of the eye, protects and supports the eyeball.

The anterior one-sixth of the sclera is modified into a transparent "window," the cornea, which preliminarily focuses entering light rays.

The vascular choroid lines the sclera and is darkly pigmented, preventing internal reflection.

visual pathway. The **light reflex** is tested by shining a light into the eye and noting whether the pupil constricts. (If the nervous pathways are normal, the pupils of *both* eyes become constricted in response to a light stimulus on one of them, as shown in the photograph in Figure 17-23. This reflex is frequently tested after head injuries.) The **accommodation reflex** is tested by having the person shift her gaze from a distant to a near object, whereupon the pupil should become smaller. In syphilis that has progressed to damage to the central nervous system, the light reflex may be lost, while the accommodation reflex is retained. This condition is called **Argyll Robertson pupil.**

In a **refraction,** a variety of techniques are used to test the refractive properties of the eye, with the muscles of accommodation temporarily paralyzed. A normal, or **emmetropic** eye will be able to focus rays from a distance of 20 feet or more to form an image on the retina.

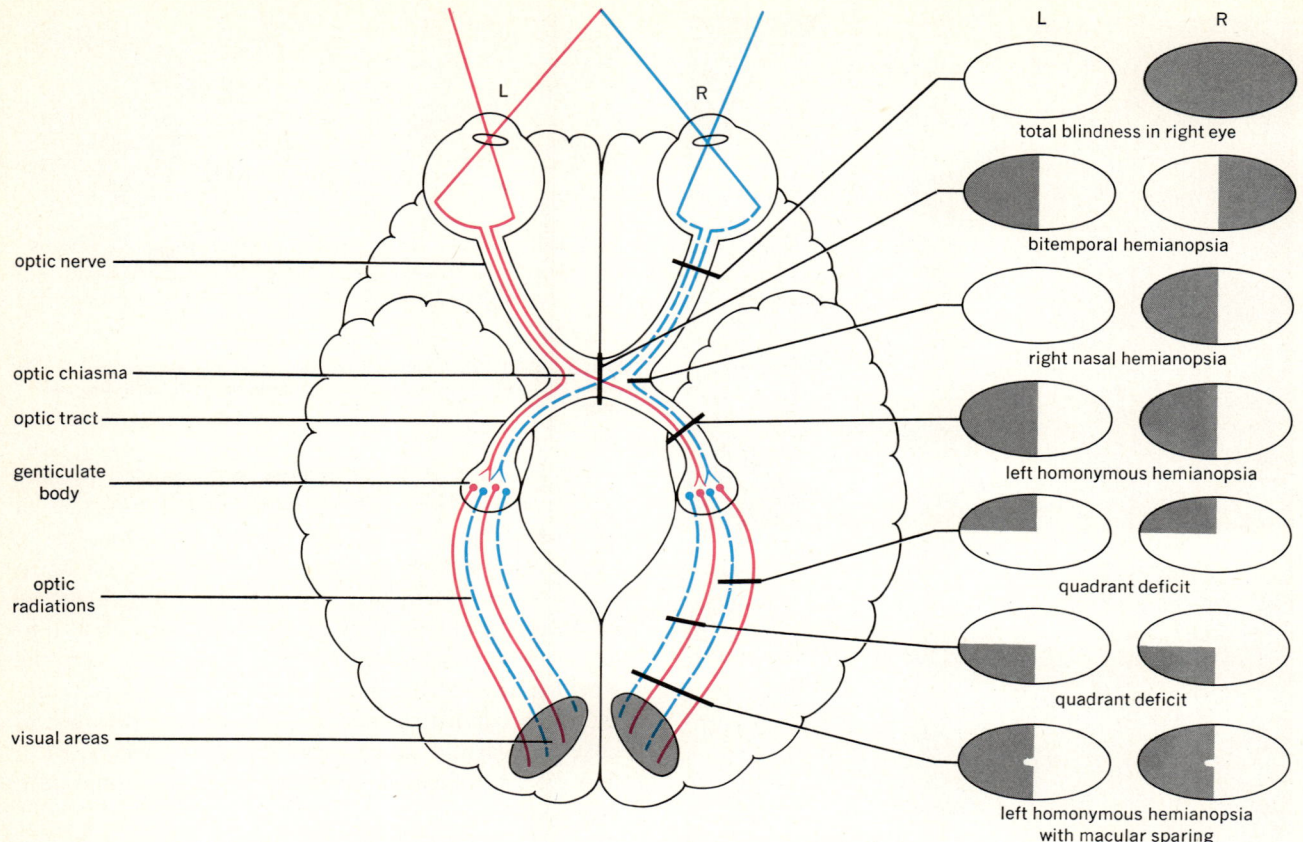

FIGURE 17-24 Lesions of various levels of the visual pathways produce characteristic vision losses, as shown in the visual fields to the right. (Modified from Langley, Telford, and Christensen, *Dynamic Anatomy and Physiology*, 4th edition, McGraw-Hill, 1974.)

Contraction of the ciliary muscle relaxes the suspensory ligament of the lens and permits the lens to take a more convex shape.

The pigmented iris acts as a diaphragm; its radiating (dilator) and encircling (sphincter) muscles open and close the central opening, the pupil, limiting the entrance of light rays.

The retina translates light rays into neural impulses, which are relayed to the brain.

The retina consists of ten layers, including light-sensitive receptors (rods and cones), bipolar neurons, and ganglionic cells.

Rods are sensitive to low light intensities and are important for vision in dim light, light and dark discrimination, and perception of form and movement.

Cones are responsible for visual acuity and are the receptors for color vision in bright illumination.

The macula lutea near the center of the retina contains the fovea centralis, the area of highest visual acuity (containing only cones).

The optic nerve leaves the eyeball at the optic disc, which is a natural "blind spot" because of lack of receptors.

The two optic nerves meet at the optic chiasma, at which fibers from the medial halves of the retinas cross over to the opposite side, then separate as the optic tracts, which lead into the brain.

The afferent pathways of the optic nerves lead ultimately to the vision center, in the occipital lobes of the cortex.

The anterior cavity of the eyeball is partly divided by the iris into the anterior and posterior chambers and contains the aqueous humor.

The aqueous humor nourishes the internal structure of the eye and is continually formed and drained.

The crystalline lens is a transparent, elastic, biconvex body, supported by suspensory ligaments.

For distant vision the tension of the ligaments is increased and the lens thins.

For near vision the tension is decreased and the lens thickens.

The vitreous body fills the posterior cavity of the eyeball and supports and nourishes the retina.

Visible light is a form of electromagnetic radiation with wavelengths from 3850 to 7200 Å.

Light rays can be reflected or refracted at an interface.

Refraction occurs when the light beams strike a surface obliquely and the speed of light changes from one medium to another.

The refractive index of a transparent substance is the ratio of the velocity of light in air to that in the substance.

A lens is a transparent object that bends light rays and causes them to converge or diverge.

Lenses may be biconvex, biconcave, concave-convex, planoconvex, or planoconcave.

The human eye has a biconvex lens.

The point to which a beam of parallel rays is converged by a lens is the focus or focal point.

The refractive power of a lens is measured in diopters.

The image produced on the retina is inverted and reduced.

In the fovea, the ratio of receptor cells to nerve fibers is almost one to one; in peripheral areas of the retina it is as much as 600 to one.

Near vision involves accommodation, convergence, and constriction of the pupil.

Accommodation is a change in the curvature of the lens produced by a reduction or increase in the tension of the suspensory ligaments.

Accommodation for near vision is a reflex action, mediated by the parasympathetic nervous system.

Accommodation for distant vision is controlled by the sympathetic nervous system.

Excitation of the receptor cells in the retina involves a series of photochemical reactions.

In the rods, rhodopsin (visual purple) breaks down to lumi-rhodopsin, then to meta-rhodopsin, which yields retinene (visual yellow) and scotopsin.

Retinene and scotopsin recombine to form rhodopsin.

Retinene is synthesized from vitamin A; a lack of the vitamin leads to night blindness.

Light adaptation is a decrease in a sensitivity of the retina to light after prolonged exposure to bright light.

Dark adaptation is an increase in the sensitivity of the retina to light after prolonged exposure to darkness.

Light and dark adaptation can result in the formation of negative after-images.

The visible spectrum includes the colors red, orange, yellow, green, blue, indigo, and violet.

The Young-Helmholtz theory states that human color vision is produced by the presence of three different kinds of cones, sensitive primarily to red, blue, and green.

Binocular vision provides a stereoscopic picture, formed by the blending of the partly overlapping visual fields of the two eyes, viewed from slightly different angles, and producing an impression of distance and depth.

The eyes are moved in unison so that images fall on corresponding points on the two retinas.

If images fall on noncorresponding points on the two retinas, diplopia (double vision) results.

Optical illusions are false interpretations of visual sensations.

Abnormalities of vision may involve the eye itself, the nervous pathways from the eye to the brain, or the visual center of the brain. They include:

Eye infections
    Conjunctivitis
    Hordeolum
    Chalazion
    Blepharitis
    Trachoma
Refractive errors
    Myopia (nearsightedness)
    Hypermetropia (farsightedness)
    Presbyopia
    Astigmatism
Cataract and corneal opacity
Glaucoma
Detached retina
Strabismus
Colorblindness (usually red-green)

Drugs can affect the pupil:
Mydriatic drugs (atropine, epinephrine, cocaine) dilate the pupils.
Miotic drugs (pilocarpine, morphine) constrict the pupils.

A complete ophthalmological examination includes:
Test for visual acuity (Snellen test)
Test for color vision (Ishihara charts)
Observation of eye grounds with opthalmoscope
Measurement of intraocular pressure with tonometer
Tests of pupillary reflexes (light and accommodation)
Refraction
Mapping of visual field with perimeter

QUESTIONS FOR REVIEW AND THOUGHT

1 Discuss structures and mechanisms that protect the eyes from injury, irritation, and dehydration.

2 List all the structures of the eye through which a light ray passes, until an image is formed.

3 Describe the nervous pathways and brain structures involved in the perception of the image.

4 Distinguish between: cornea and retina; aqueous and vitreous humors; sclera and choroid; pupil and lens; fovea and "blind spot"; rods and cones; myopia and hypermetropia.

5 Why are corneal transplants possible?

6 Discuss the nature and functions of the pigments in the: (a) iris; (b) retina.

7 Is the "eye as a camera" analogy valid? Discuss.

8 You are driving along a highway at night. Suddenly the bright headlights of an oncoming car flash into your eyes. Describe the reflex mechanisms that are triggered and other effects. Include chemical reactions in the retina.

9 Describe techniques utilized for depth perception.

10 Diagram the defects of focusing in myopia and hypermetropia and their correction with appropriate lenses.

THE SENSE ORGANS: HEARING AND EQUILIBRIUM

18

If you close your eyes and have someone drop a series of coins of different denominations onto a bare table-top, you will soon find that you are able to distinguish a dime from a nickel, a nickel from a quarter, just from the sounds they make. We tend to underappreciate our sense of hearing, since we rely so heavily on our sight; yet imagine for a moment what your life would be like in total silence. No music, no sound of the wind rustling the leaves, or the water gurgling out of the faucet, no alarm clock to wake you up in the morning, no sound of speech! In our word-oriented world, one of the worst deprivations is the inability to converse freely with others.

A normal human being inherits as a birthright a sense of hearing so keen that if it were any more sensitive we would be continually bothered by the buzz of air molecules colliding inside our ears. A native in the African bush at the age of 70 still has hearing nearly as acute as it was in his teens. Yet modern citizens of the developed countries suffer a progressive and to a large extent unnecessary deterioration of their hearing with age. Noise pollution is a serious and growing menace to our society. The noise of traffic on the streets and highways, the roar of jet planes passing overhead, the amplified music at a dance—all these are assaults on our ears and can result in a distinct and irreversible damage to the organ of hearing.

The ears are two organs in one. They are the organs of **hearing,** the perception of sounds. They also contain receptors for another body sense, the sense of **equilibrium,** the perception of changes in position and movement of the body.

PHYSICAL PROPERTIES OF SOUND

During an electrical storm, you can tell roughly how far away the lightning is striking by counting seconds from the lightning flash until the rumbling thunder is heard. (An elapsed span of five seconds is equivalent to approximately a mile of distance.) This method is based on the difference in the velocities of propagation of sound and light: in air sound waves travel at a speed of about 1100 feet per second (or 330 m/sec), while light waves travel far faster, about 300,000 km/sec. Thus, the light waves from the lightning flash reach you more rapidly than the sound of the thun-

der, even though both left their source simultaneously; the greater the distance traveled, the larger the time discrepancy will be.

Sound waves are vibratory disturbances, transmitted through air or some other elastic medium by means of alternate compressions and rarefactions (Figure 18-1). Actually, sound waves (in contrast to light waves) are transmitted more rapidly through liquids and solids than through gases such as air. (In Westerns, the Army scout may put his ear to the ground to hear if the Indians are coming; the sound of their hoofbeats would be transmitted more rapidly through the solid ground than through the air.) The excellent conduction of sounds through solids is the basis for the implanted bone conduction microphones that are standard equipment for explorers and spies in futuristic fiction. It also partly explains why your own voice sounds different to you from the most faithful tape recording of your speech: you hear your own voice both through the air and by bone conduction.

Sound has three important properties: pitch, intensity, and quality. The **pitch** is a function of the frequency of the sound waves, that is, the number of vibrations of the sound waves per second. (Frequencies are usually expressed in cycles per second (cps), or hertz (Hz) units.) The human ear can detect frequencies from 20 to 20,000 cycles per second, with the greatest sensitivity in the range from 1000 to 4000 cps. The fundamental tone of the human larynx is about 100 cps for men and 150 cps for women, but speech also employs high-pitched hisses; these are lacking in telephone transmission, making the speech less intelligible.

The **intensity** or loudness of sound varies directly with the amplitude of the sound waves. It is usually expressed in **decibels** (db), which are measures of air pressure changes. The scale of sound intensities (Figure 18-2) is a logarithmic scale: the reference level of 0 db refers to a pressure difference of 1 dyne per square centimeter between the peak of a sound compression wave and the trough of the wave; an intensity of 10 db is 10 times as great (10^1), an intensity of 20 db is 100 times as great (10^2), and so on. (The original unit of sound intensity was the *bel,* named after Alexander Graham Bell, the inventer of the tele-

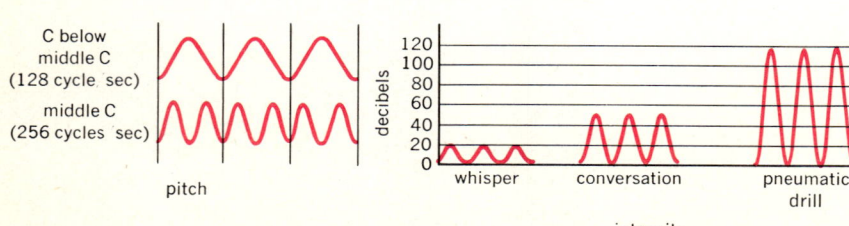

FIGURE 18-1 The pitch of a sound is determined by the number of vibrations per second. Its intensity is determined by the amplitude of the sound waves.

sound	rating decibels	
absolute silence	0	
watch ticking	20	
residential street no traffic	40	
stream	50	
automobile at 30 ft	60	
conversation at 3 ft	70	
loud radio	80	
truck at 15 ft	90	
car horn at 15 ft	100	
pneumatic hammer at 3 ft	120	
amplified rock music	130	
propeller airplane at 15 ft	140	
jet aircraft at takeoff	150+	

FIGURE 18-2   Noise: decibel ratings of some common sounds.

phone, but it proved inconveniently large to work with, and has been replaced in practice by 1/10 bel, or the decibel.) A whisper has a loudness of about 30 db, a normal conversation 60 or 70 db, heavy traffic noise 80 db; a noise of 120 db causes discomfort, 140 db is painful. A jet plane rates 160 db.

The **quality** or timbre of sound depends on **overtones,** secondary vibrations whose frequencies are multiples of the basic frequency. A piano, a flute, a violin, and a trumpet sound quite different when they play the same musical note (same frequency); the difference lies in the particular overtones they produce.

STRUCTURE OF THE EAR

The development of a variety of electronic listening devices has made the concept of privacy a burning question in the modern world. Such "bugs" are pickups of various kinds that transform sound waves into electrical impulses or radio waves, later to be retransformed into sound waves so that they can be detected by human listening devices—ears—and ultimately analyzed and evaluated by human brains.

The human ear consists of three main parts (Figure 18-3): the external ear, which acts as a sound-gather-

ing funnel; the middle ear, or tympanic cavity; and the internal ear, or labyrinth. Sound waves, directed by the external ear, pass through the external acoustic meatus, strike the tympanic membrane (eardrum), and cause it to vibrate. (The human ear can pick up sounds that deflect the tympanic membrane by only 0.00000001 mm!) The vibrations are transmitted by a series of three movable bones, the ear ossicles, which extend to the internal ear and set up waves of motion in the fluid in the labyrinth of the internal ear. The motion of the fluid excites sensory cells in the labyrinth, which transmit impulses to the acoustic and equilibrium centers in the brain.

The External Ear

The human external ear is not as efficient a sound-gatherer as the outer ear of a horse or rabbit, which can be raised, lowered, and swiveled about like a radar antenna. (If you are one of the minority who can wiggle their ears, you retain better-than-average use of the vestigial ear-moving muscles possessed by many of our mammal relatives.)

The external ear has two main parts: the ear flap, called the **auricle** or **pinna;** and the tubular passage leading into the temporal bone, called the **external acoustic meatus** or **external auditory canal.**

Looking at your family members and acquaintances, you will notice numerous variations of ear shape (Figure 18-4), which are faithfully copied from generation to generation as inherited characteristics. This apparent diversity, however, is merely a minor variation on the basic design. The framework of the pinna is made of cartilage (except for the earlobe, which is all soft tissue). The cartilage is elastic, which gives the external ear resiliency and maintains its basic shape. If the cartilage is ruptured, it heals by an overgrowth of tissue, as in the typical boxer's "cauliflower ear."

The external acoustic meatus is an S-shaped tube about 2.5 cm long, which leads inward, forward, and downward. (In applying ear drops, the canal should be straightened by pulling the ear up and back.) Its external portion is molded from cartilage, while the inner portion is hollowed out of the temporal bone. The external acoustic meatus is lined with a continuation of the skin of the pinna, which is thick and rather insensitive in the outer half and thin and highly sensitive in the inner half. A sprinkling of hairs near the opening helps to screen out foreign particles; numerous exocrine glands secrete a yellow, waxy substance, **cerumen** (earwax), which lubricates and protects the ear canal. The external acoustic meatus transmits sound waves to the tympanic membrane, which stretches across the end of the canal.

The tympanic membrane, or eardrum, is a thin layer of fibrous tissue, covered on its outer surface with

temporalis m.

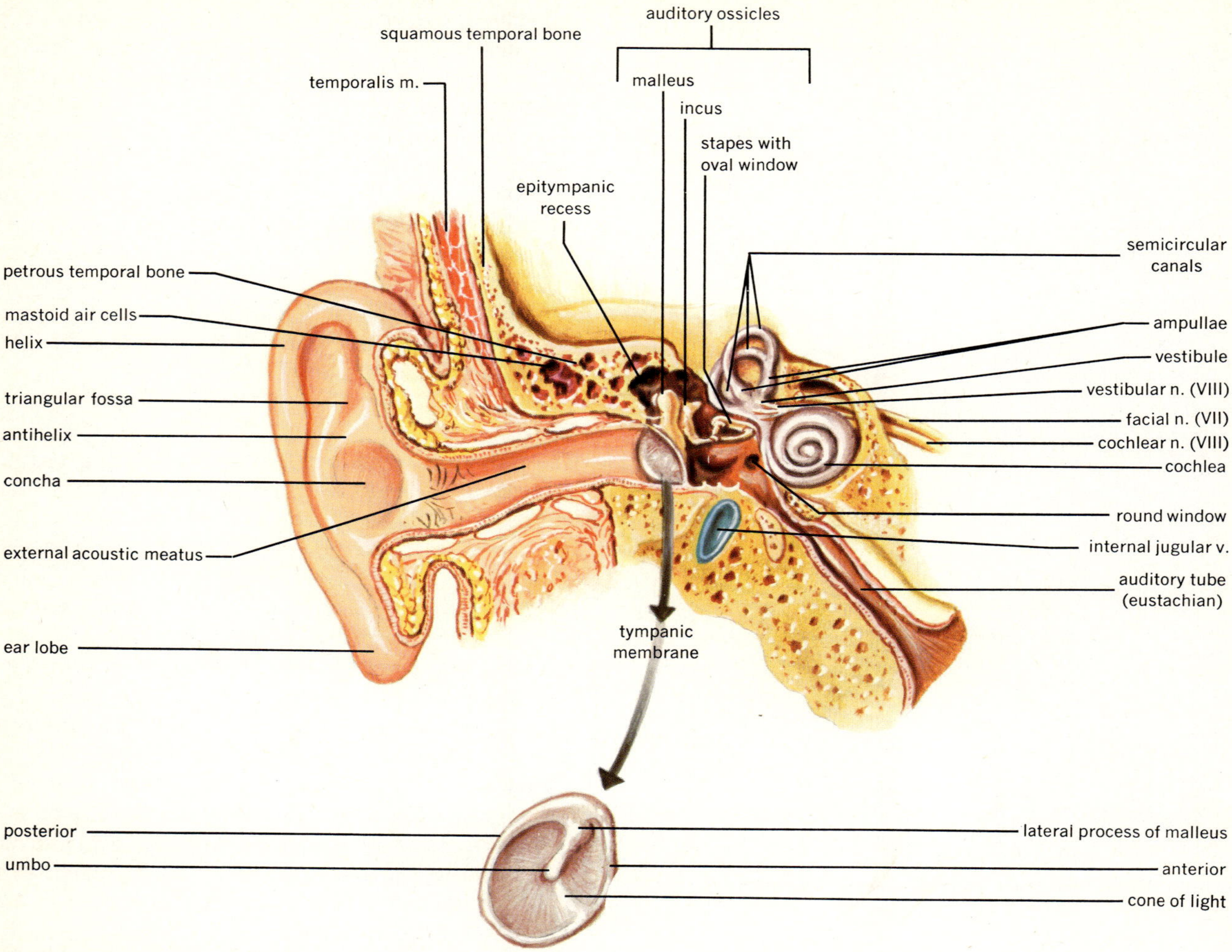

squamous temporal bone

auditory ossicles

malleus

incus

stapes with oval window

epitympanic recess

petrous temporal bone

mastoid air cells

helix

triangular fossa

antihelix

concha

external acoustic meatus

ear lobe

semicircular canals

ampullae

vestibule

vestibular n. (VIII)

facial n. (VII)

cochlear n. (VIII)

cochlea

round window

internal jugular v.

auditory tube (eustachian)

tympanic membrane

posterior

umbo

lateral process of malleus

anterior

cone of light

FIGURE 18-3   Structure of the ear: frontal section through the outer, middle, and inner ear.

FIGURE 18-4   Ear shape varies considerably and is governed by heredity.

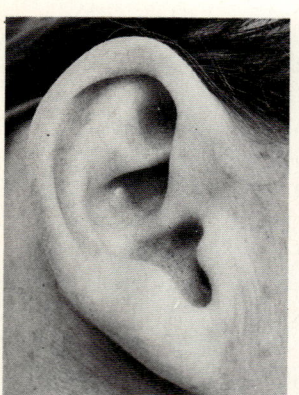
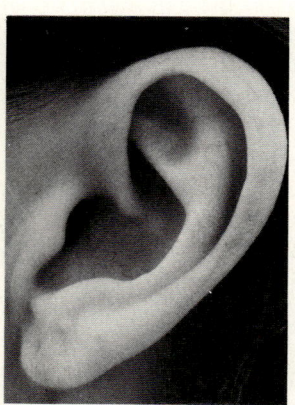
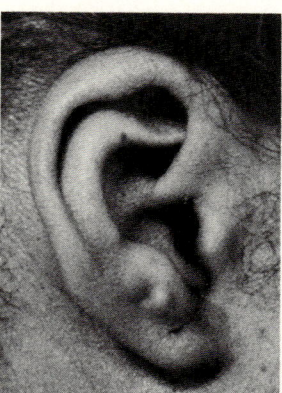

skin and lined internally with mucous membrane. The eardrum separates the auditory canal of the outer ear from the tympanic cavity of the middle ear, and it is attached so as to be able to vibrate freely when sound waves impinge on it.

The Middle Ear

Seasoned travelers know that it is wise to chew gum during an airplane flight, and they avoid flying (if possible) when they are suffering from a head cold. Normally the air within the middle ear is at the same

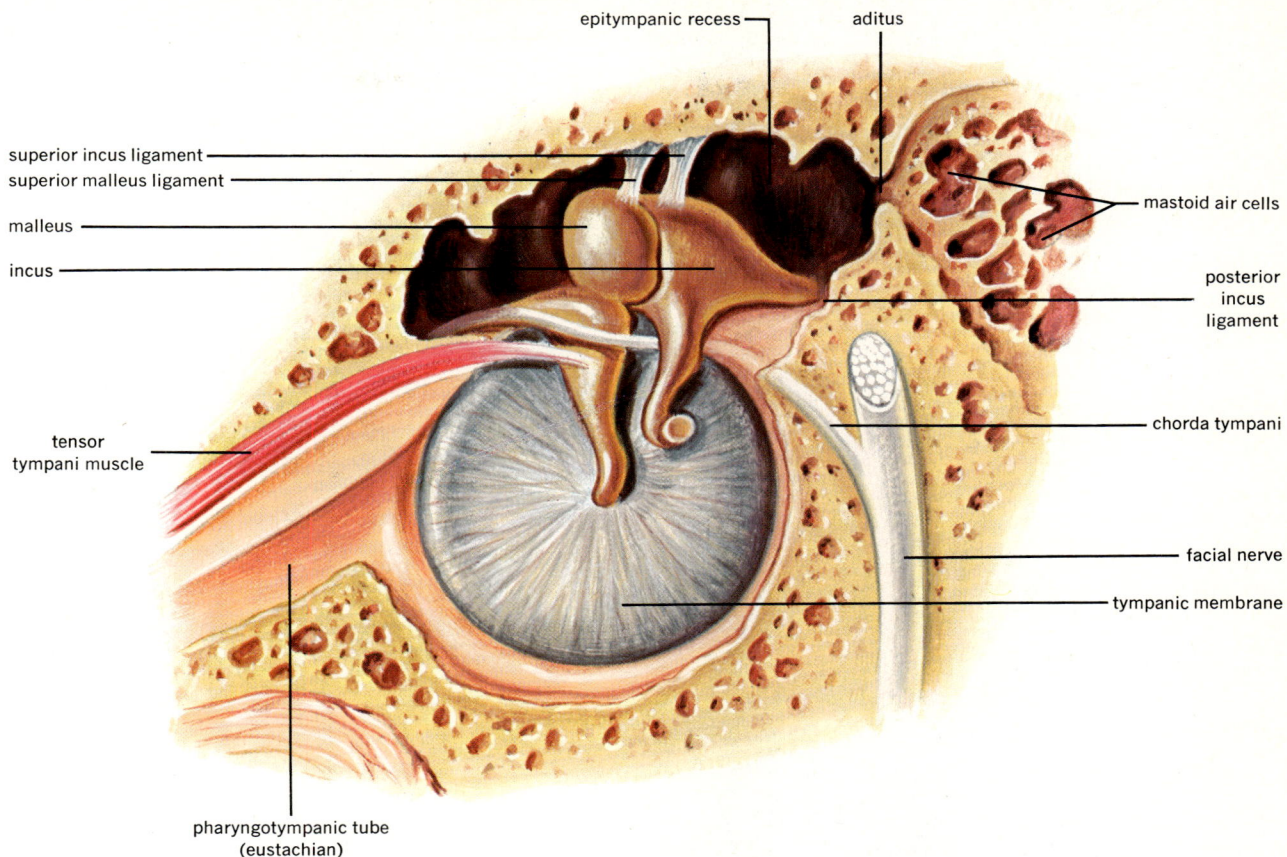

epitympanic recess

aditus

superior incus ligament

superior malleus ligament

malleus

incus

mastoid air cells

posterior incus ligament

tensor tympani muscle

chorda tympani

facial nerve

tympanic membrane

pharyngotympanic tube (eustachian)

FIGURE 18-5 The middle ear: lateral wall, viewed from inside. (The stapes is omitted; it articulates with the incus.)

pressure as the external atmosphere. Equalization of the air pressure on both sides of the tympanic membrane is accomplished automatically by way of the **eustachian tube,** which connects the middle ear cavity to the nasopharynx (Figure 18-5). When a plane (or an elevator) changes altitude rapidly, the atmospheric pressure outside the eardrum changes too rapidly for the normal equalizing mechanism to keep up with it. The pressure difference that builds up stretches the eardrums taut and can produce temporary deafness; if it continues, the tympanic membranes may rupture. Chewing gum or yawning spreads air rapidly through the eustachian tubes and helps to equalize the pressure. But the mucous secretions that accompany a head cold block the nasopharynx and prevent the equalization of air pressure.

The tympanic cavity or middle ear is a small bony cavity—so small that only five or six drops of water would fill it. It is filled with air, lined with mucous membrane, and contains three tiny bones, the **ear ossicles.** The middle ear is separated from the external auditory canal by the tympanic membrane and from the internal ear by a very thin bony wall, pierced by two openings: the **round window** and the **oval window.**

The middle ear cavity also communicates with a number of mastoid cells in the temporal bone. This connection is of clinical importance because it provides a route for infection. Especially in children, head colds may lead to mastoid infections via the nasopharynx-eustachian tube-middle ear-mastoid route.

The three tiny ear bones stretch across the tympanic cavity, from the tympanic membrane to the oval window. Their shapes seem made to order for fanciful naming. The first ossicle is called the **malleus,** or hammer. Its handle is attached to the tympanic membrane, and its head is attached to the base of the next bone, the **incus,** or anvil. The incus in turn is attached by its long process to the third ossicle, the **stapes,** or stirrup. The foot-plate of the stapes fits nearly into the oval window. The three ossicles are lashed together and held in position by minute ligaments and muscles. The linkage is not rigid, so that the slightest vibration of the tympanic membrane sets the ossicles into jiggling motion, transmitting the sound waves across the middle ear cavity to the inner ear. In the process, the amplitude of the sound waves is decreased, thus protecting the inner ear from shock in

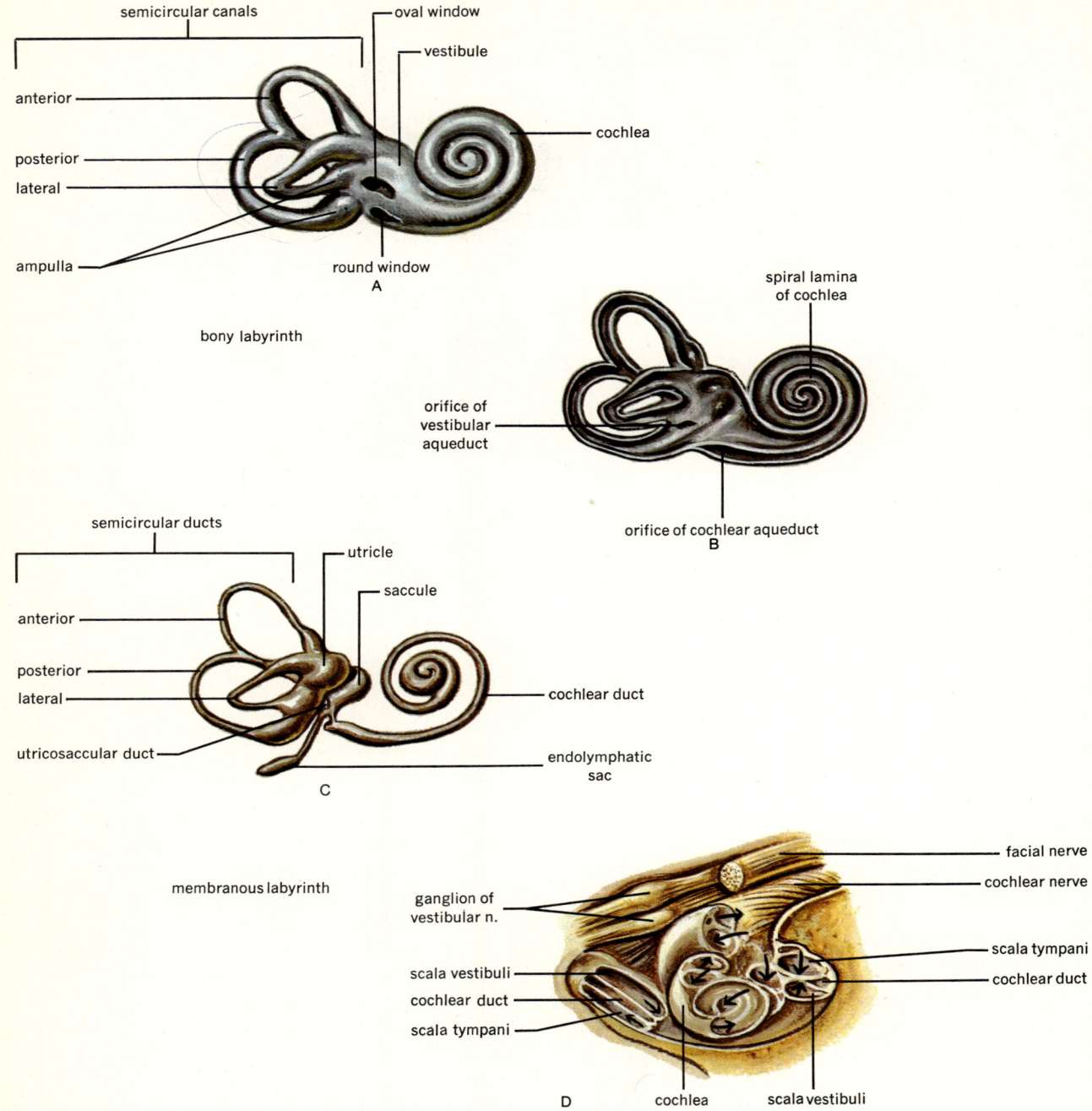

FIGURE 18-6 Labyrinths of the inner ear: bony labyrinth whole (A) and in section (B); membranous labyrinth whole (C) and in section (D).

the case of high-amplitude low-frequency sounds. But the articulated lever system of the ossicles increases the force of the sound waves: the pressure exerted at the foot-plate of the stapes is 22 times as great as that exerted at the tympanic membrane.

The Inner Ear

In ancient Crete, it was said, a monster called the Minotaur was imprisoned within a labyrinth, a winding, branching maze of corridors so confusing that only those specially trained could find their way through it. The **labyrinth** of the inner ear (Figure 18-6) is a complicated network of intercommunicating tubes, which houses not a monster but three different kinds of sense receptors: those for hearing, in the cochlea; those for static equilibrium, in the utricle; and those for dynamic equilibrium, in the semicircular canals.

The bony labyrinth, hollowed out inside the temporal bone, consists of three main parts: the vestibule, the cochlea, and the semicircular canals. It is filled with a fluid, **perilymph,** in which is suspended a membranous labyrinth, attached to the bone by fibrous bands. The membranous labyrinth has the same general shape as the bony labyrinth but is considerably smaller. The membranous labyrinth is also filled with a fluid, **endolymph.** Its principal divisions are the utricle and saccule, inside the vestibule; the cochlear duct inside the cochlea, and the membranous semicircular canals inside the bony ones.

The **vestibule** is the central cavity of the bony labyrinth, behind the cochlea and in front of the semicircular canals. Both the oval and round windows open into it from the tympanic cavity. The foot-plate of the stapes moves in and out in the oval window as it transmits sound vibrations. But liquids, unlike gases, are relatively incompressible. The membrane-covered round window acts as a safety valve, providing a place for the liquid to go. When the stapes presses inward on the oval window, the membrane of the round window bulges outward; when the stapes moves outward, the membrane of the round window moves inward, thus maintaining a constant volume within the inner ear chamber.

Two small membranous sacs, the **saccule** and the **utricle,** lie within the bony vestibule. The inner walls of these sacs are lined with modified columnar epithelium, forming a gelatinous membrane. Some of the modified cells are **hair cells (maculae),** specialized nerve cells provided with delicate hairs that project into the fluid-filled cavity. Tiny crystals of calcium carbonate, called **otoliths** ("ear stones") pull and push on the hairs, generating sensory impulses. A change in the position of the head changes the pattern of stimulation of the hair cells by the otoliths and thus provides a sense of the position of the head and a sensation of a change in the pull of gravity.

The three **semicircular canals,** arranged at right angles to one another, permit the detection of rotational movements of the head.

The **cochlea** (Figure 18-7) looks like a snail shell. (Its name means "snail.") It is a tube coiled for about two and a half turns into a spiral, around a central axis of bone. Membranes divide the space within the bony canal of the cochlea into three canals: an upper passage, the **scala vestibuli,** which is filled with perilymph and ends at the oval window; a lower passage, the **scala tympani,** which is also filled with perilymph and ends at the round window; and the middle passage, the **scala media** or **cochlear duct,** which is a continuation of the membranous labyrinth and is filled with endolymph. The floor of the cochlear duct is formed by the **basilar membrane,** and its roof is formed by the **vestibular membrane.** Movement of the foot-plate of the stapes sets the perilymph of the scala vestibuli in motion. The distal ends of the scala vestibuli and scala tympani communicate with one another through a small opening, the **helicotrema.** If the stapes moves inward very slowly, fluid from the scala vestibuli is pushed through the helicotrema into the scala tympani, causing the round window to bulge. But if the stapes moves in and out rapidly, the fluid does not have time to travel that far between successive vibrations. Instead, the fluid wave takes a short-cut, by causing the basilar membrane to bulge back and forth with each sound vibration.

The sound receptors of the ear are found within a complex structure, the **organ of Corti** (see Figure 18-7), which lies within the cochlear duct, resting on the basilar membrane. It is a ridge of epithelium, which extends spirally through the entire length of the cochlear duct and consists of two types of cells: supporting cells and about 15,000 hair cells (like the hair cells in the saccule and utricle). The bases of the hair cells are anchored in the basilar membrane; their tips are embedded in a gelatinous mass, the **tectorial membrane,** which forms a canopylike covering over them.

More than 20,000 stiff, hairlike fibers run across the basilar membrane, projecting from the bony center of the cochlea toward the outer wall. These **basilar fibers** can vibrate like the reeds of a harmonica. Their lengths increase progressively, from about 0.04 mm at the base of the cochlea to 0.5 mm at the helicotrema. The shorter fibers vibrate at a high frequency, the longer ones at a low frequency. As transmitted sound waves set different portions of the basilar fibers vibrating, different hair cells of the organ of Corti are stimulated and relay their impulses along the auditory nerve to the brain.

THE PHYSIOLOGY OF HEARING

If you have ever heard a mouse squeak, you have heard only part of the squeak. Mice can produce sounds too high-pitched for human ears to hear. The auditory range of mice extends up to higher frequencies than the human range, and thus mice can communicate with sounds that are inaudible to us. Cats are also equipped with the ability to hear extremely high-pitched sounds and tune in on the mouse "conversations," using the squeaks to help them locate their prey.

Parts of the mechanism by which sound waves are detected by the ears and perceived in the brain have already been described. The following brief summary describes the sequence of events involved in hearing (see Figure 18-8).

Sound waves travel through air as alternate compressions and rarefactions of the air molecules. They enter the external auditory canal (probably without much sound-gathering help from the pinna) and strike the tympanic membrane, setting it vibrating. The vibrations are transmitted from the eardrum to

A

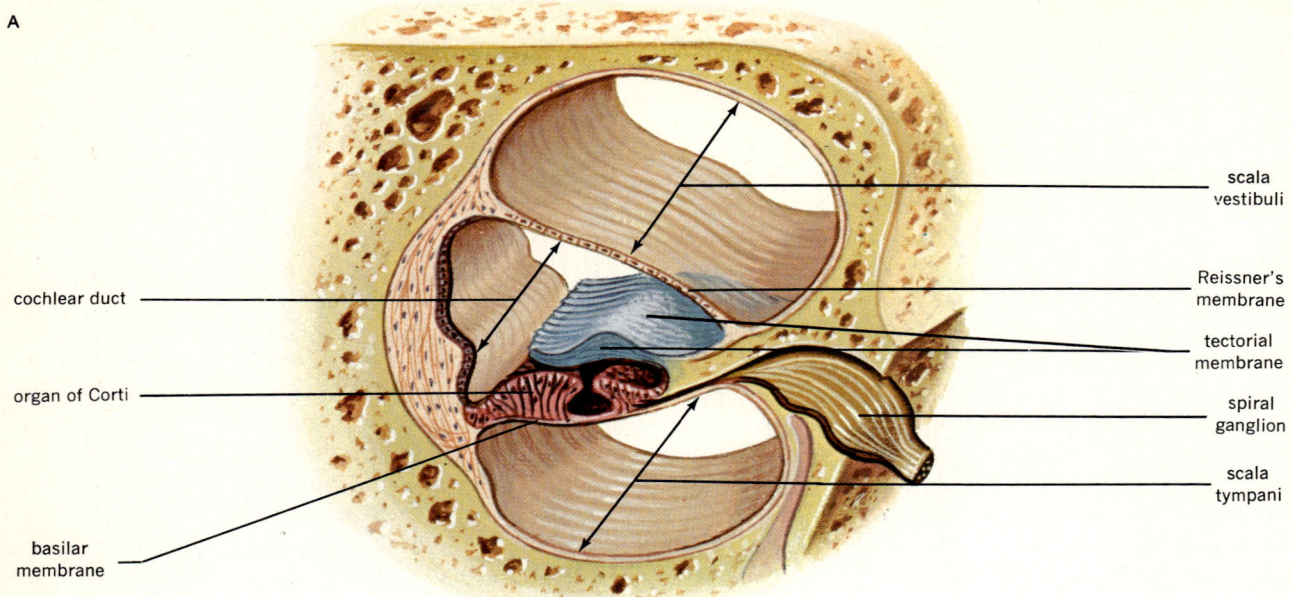

scala
vestibuli

Reissner's
membrane

tectorial
membrane

spiral
ganglion

scala
tympani

cochlear duct

organ of Corti

basilar
membrane

B

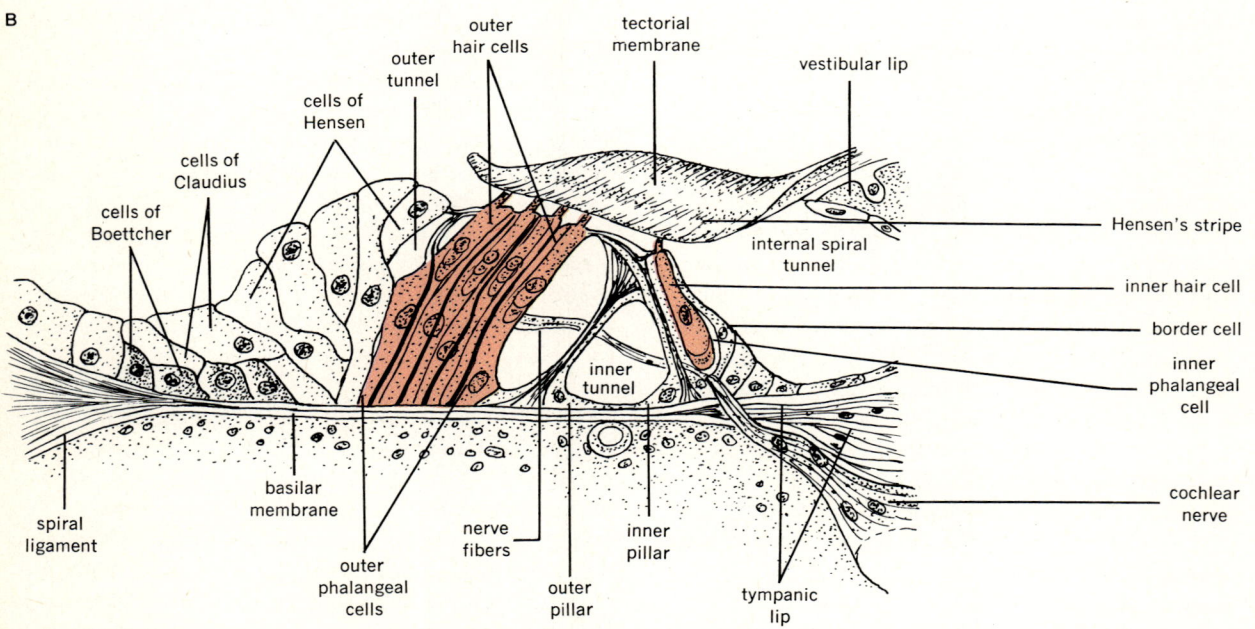

outer
hair cells

tectorial
membrane

outer
tunnel

vestibular lip

cells of
Hensen

cells of
Claudius

Hensen's stripe

cells of
Boettcher

internal spiral
tunnel

inner hair cell

border cell

inner
phalangeal
cell

inner
tunnel

spiral
ligament

basilar
membrane

nerve
fibers

inner
pillar

cochlear
nerve

outer
phalangeal
cells

outer
pillar

tympanic
lip

FIGURE 18-7   The organ of hearing: section through one of the coils of the cochlea (A); details of the organ of Corti (B).

the first of the three tiny ear ossicles, the malleus, which begins to vibrate, jostling the incus, which then begins to vibrate in turn, transmitting its vibration to the stapes. The foot-plate of the stapes, moving in and out, presses against the covering membrane of the oval window, setting up pressure waves in the fluid within the scala vestibuli, which winds through the spiral coils of the cochlea. The increased pressure near the base of the cochlea causes the basilar membrane to bulge at that point. The elastic membrane

bounces back, producing a wave that travels along the basilar membrane toward the apex of the cochlea. The amplitude of the wave increases as it travels along the basilar membrane, then drops abruptly when the wave reaches the part of the membrane whose fibers have a natural resonant frequency equal to the frequency of the sound that initiated the wave.

The vibrations of the basilar membrane cause the hair cells of the organ of Corti to bend, first in one direction, then in the other. The bending of the hair

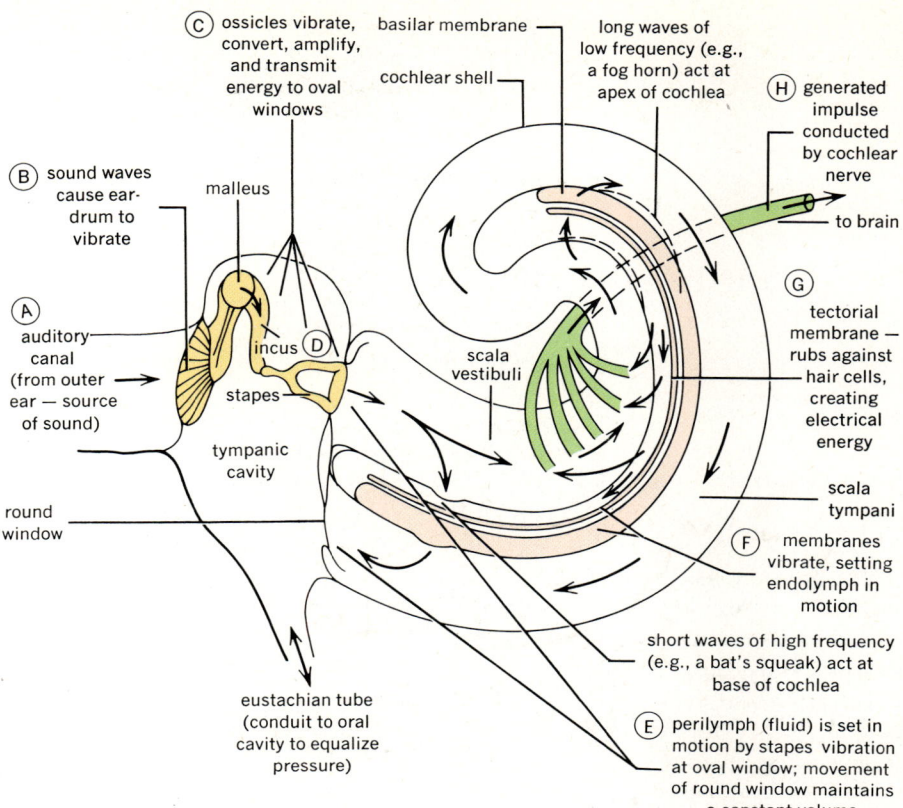

ⓒ ossicles vibrate,
convert, amplify,
and transmit
energy to oval
windows

basilar membrane

cochlear shell

long waves of
low frequency (e.g.,
a fog horn) act at
apex of cochlea

Ⓗ generated
impulse
conducted
by cochlear
nerve

to brain

Ⓑ sound waves
cause ear-
drum to
vibrate

malleus

Ⓖ

Ⓐ
auditory
canal
(from outer
ear — source
of sound)

incus Ⓓ

stapes

scala
vestibuli

tectorial
membrane —
rubs against
hair cells,
creating
electrical
energy

tympanic
cavity

scala
tympani

round
window

Ⓕ membranes
vibrate, setting
endolymph in
motion

eustachian tube
(conduit to oral
cavity to equalize
pressure)

short waves of high frequency
(e.g., a bat's squeak) act at
base of cochlea

Ⓔ perilymph (fluid) is set in
motion by stapes vibration
at oval window; movement
of round window maintains
a constant volume

FIGURE 18-8 Sound waves are transmitted through the ear and ultimately
"heard" in the brain.

cells generates a receptor potential, which activates
neurons of the cochlear nerve, whose impulses are
ultimately transmitted to the brain.

Discrimination of Pitch

The basilar membrane looks something like a long
xylophone, which gets wider as it stretches out along
the coil of the cochlea: at the helicotrema it is 12
times as wide as at the base of the cochlea, near the
oval window. Each sound sets up sympathetic vibrations in a particular place in the basilar membrane:
high-frequency sounds stimulate the short fibers at
the base of the cochlea, while low-frequency sounds
cause vibrations of the fibers at its apex, and interme-
diate-pitch sounds cause vibrations in between, at
points along the basilar membrane depending on
their frequency. The impulses transmitted to the
brain carry not only the information that receptor
cells have been stimulated, but also data on the place
on the basilar membrane at which the stimulation
occurred, and the cerebral cortex is thus able to determine the frequency of the sound. This principle of
pitch discrimination is called the **place principle** for
determination of pitch. But it apparently is not the
only principle operating. If portions of the cochlea

are destroyed, a crude discrimination of low frequencies from high frequencies is still possible. Another
mechanism provides a backup for the more accurate
place principle of discrimination. The number of impulses transmitted by the auditory neurons varies
with the frequency of the sound, up to a maximum of
about 1000 cps. Thus, for pitches below this level, the
number of impulses transmitted per unit time provides the brain with clues for pitch discrimination.
This crude back-up mechanism is called the **volley
principle.**

Determination of Loudness

The faintest whispers detectable by the human ear are
about one-trillionth as loud as the loudest audible
sounds. Within this enormous range, the ears can detect changes in sound intensity of about 1 decibel.
There are three mechanisms for the discrimination of
sound intensities (i.e., loudness). First, as a sound becomes louder, the amplitude of vibration of the basilar membrane and hair cells increases, so that the
nerve cells fire at faster rates. Second, an increase in
the amplitude of vibration causes more of the hair
cells on the fringes of the vibrating portion of the
basilar membrane to become excited, producing a

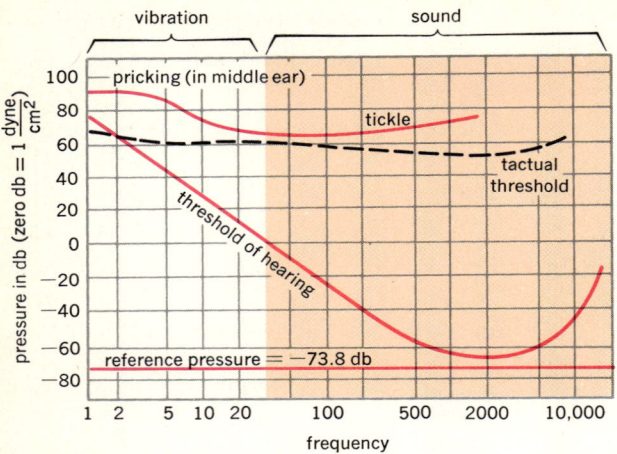

FIGURE 18-9 **The threshold of hearing varies with the frequency of sound.**

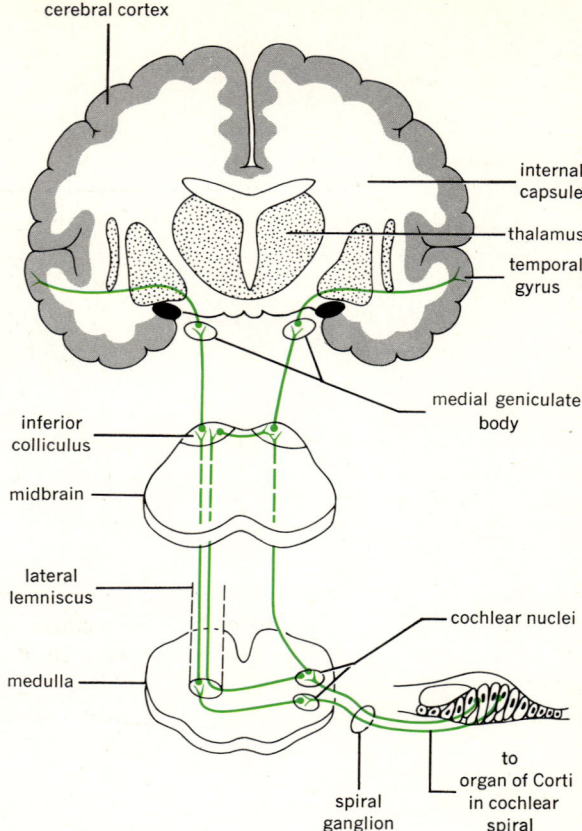

FIGURE 18-10 **The auditory pathways.**

spatial summation of impulses. Third, certain hair cells have a high threshold for stimulation: they do not fire at all unless the vibration of the basilar membrane reaches a relatively high intensity. Thus, these high-threshold cells act as signals to the brain that the sound is particularly loud.

The threshold of hearing varies depending on the frequency of the sound, as indicated in the graph of Figure 18-9. A 2000 cps sound can be heard at an intensity of only −70 decibels, while a 100 cps sound cannot be heard unless its intensity is at least −30 db. (Because of the logarithmic nature of the decibel scale, this represents a 10,000-fold difference in intensity.)

Localization of Sound

A blindfolded bat can fly through a maze of dangling wires and catch a moth on the wing in mid-air, using its sophisticated sonar system. High-pitched sounds emitted by the bat bounce off objects, and their reflection patterns are analyzed in the highly developed auditory region of the bat's brain. The human auditory equipment is far less developed than that of a bat, but we are still able to get a considerable amount of information out of the sounds our ears pick up. We can not only distinguish pitch and intensity and appreciate the overtones that contribute to sound quality, but, like the bat, we can also use sounds to localize objects, at least to some degree. Indeed, some blind people develop their sound perception to such an acute pitch that they can detect the presence of obstacles by a form of sonar, interpreting the reflections of finger snaps or other small sounds.

The key to localizing the source of sound waves lies in the use of two ears for hearing. One clue is provided by the difference in loudness of the sound, as received by the two ears. Sound intensity decreases with distance, so the sound will be louder for the ear closer to its source. In addition, there is a small time lag in traveling the distance to the farther ear. A time difference as small as 10 milliseconds can be detected. You utilize these clues automatically when you turn your head from side to side in trying to localize an impinging sound.

The Nervous Pathway for Hearing

Like the messages of the other senses, the sounds detected by the ears are not meaningful until they are analyzed and interpreted in the brain. The neurons that initiate the nerve impulses for sound have their endings scattered among the **hair cells** of the organ of Corti (Figure 18-10). The axons of these neurons extend from the **spiral ganglion** of the cochlea to form the cochlear division of the **auditory nerve** (the eighth cranial nerve). They travel to the **dorsal** and **ventral cochlear nuclei,** located in the upper part of the medulla. There they synapse with second-order neurons, some of which pass up the same side of the brain stem, to the **inferior colliculus** in the midbrain; other second-order nerve fibers cross over to the opposite side of the brain stem and end in the **superior olivary nucleus** or continue up to the inferior colliculus on the opposite side. Thus, each ear sends impulses to both sides of the brain, and even a total destruction of the hearing center in one hemisphere would not interfere with hearing.

Auditory reflexes such as adjusting the sensitivity of the ears to the intensity of the impinging sound are controlled by the inferior colliculi. Collateral pathways from these brainstem centers into the cerebellum are part of the reflex arcs that make you automatically start when you hear a sudden loud noise. But the main pathways lead upward, to the **medial geniculate body** and then to the cerebral cortex in the upper part of the **temporal lobe.** Here sounds are perceived and interpreted, and tonal patterns are discriminated.

The **reticular activating system** plays a major role in filtering out sounds that do not seem novel or significant enough to merit attention by the cerebral cortex. The husband immersed in his newspaper who automatically mutters, "Yes, dear," at appropriate intervals while not hearing a word of his wife's conversation and the child who can respond to the bell of an ice cream truck three blocks away but fails to hear a parent's request to do a chore are selectively tuning out nonsignificant items, even though the sounds are impinging on their eardrums. During sleep the ears continue to receive incoming sound stimuli; these are processed in the lower brain and screened for items important enough to rouse the cortex via the RAS. A parent may wake instantly to the sound of a baby's cry, yet sleep placidly through the rumble of trucks, the wail of sirens, and other sounds that disturb the night.

EQUILIBRIUM AND ORIENTATION

A number of receptor systems contribute to our awareness of "which way is up." The messages of the eyes are one important source of information. But if you try to walk through a room in the dark, although you may feel a trifle unsteady and disoriented, you will not stagger and lurch like a drunkard. Proprioceptors in the joints and muscles and in the soles of the feet are still sending in a flow of information on relative body positions and the pull of gravity. Still more information is provided by the **vestibular apparatus** of the ears, the body's main organ of balance (Figure 18-11).

The **saccule** and **utricle** are the organs of **static equilibrium,** which provide information on the orientation of the head relative to the pull of gravity. (If the pilot of an airplane flying through a cloud had damaged saccules and utricles, he might emerge from the cloud flying upside-down.) Both the saccule and utricle contain sensory hairs with small calcium carbonate particles **(otoliths)** on the ends, embedded in a gelatinous layer. Any movement of the head produces a movement of the otoliths, which in turn stimulates the hairs and sparks neural impulses, which are transmitted to the brain.

The three **semicircular canals** are the organs of **dynamic equilibrium.** They are arranged so as to be mutually perpendicular, two vertical and one horizontal, and are filled with endolymph. A swelling at the base of each semicircular canal, called the **ampulla,** contains hair cells, each of which has from 40 to 60 nonmotile cilia on its free surface. A movement of the head in any direction will set the fluid in at least one of the semicircular canals in motion, stimulating the hair cells in its ampulla and initiating impulses that are relayed to the brain.

Impulses from the vestibular apparatus of the ear are transmitted over the vestibular division of the eighth cranial nerve to the vestibular nuclei at the junction of the medulla and the pons. From there the impulses are relayed mainly to the cerebellum, where corrective reflexes are initiated to maintain the body's equilibrium. Impulses from the utricle and saccule initiate the vestibular **righting reflex,** which works to return the body to an upright position. The messages from the semicircular canals are especially important in permitting corrections to be made ahead of time, when the body is *about* to fall off balance.

When a person is being rapidly rotated (as on a merry-go-round), or subjected to the combination of rocking, swaying, and up-and-down motion of a boat on the ocean, impulses from the semicircular canals, together with the confusing sensations from the eyes, may produce a feeling of **vertigo,** or dizziness. This may be accompanied by nausea and vomiting and by various visceral reflexes, including a fall in blood pressure, a change in the heart rate, and pallor of the skin.

EAR DISORDERS

It is estimated that three million Americans suffer from hearing loss. Although the sense of hearing has been relegated to a minor role in the survival of modern humans, a person suffering from partial or complete deafness is to a large extent cut off from normal communication. For children born deaf or afflicted with severe hearing loss at a very early age, learning to speak is extremely difficult and requires specially adapted teaching methods. (Before such methods were developed, it was generally believed that deaf children could not be taught to speak, and functional deaf-mutes were common.)

Any portion of the auditory apparatus can be damaged by disease or injury, leading to hearing loss. The main links are the eardrum, the ossicles in the middle ear, the labyrinth, and the nerve pathways to the

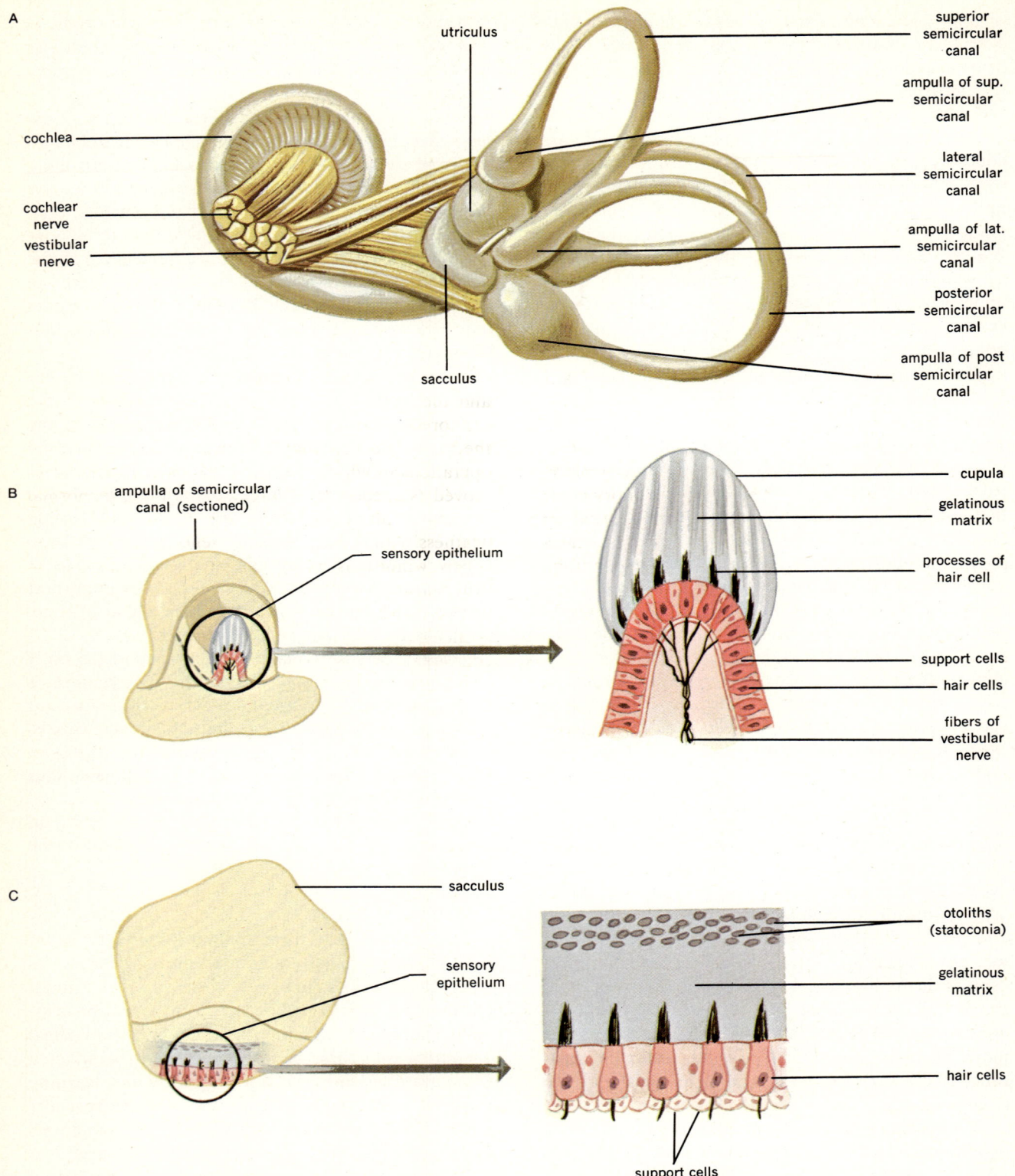

A

cochlea

cochlear nerve

vestibular nerve

utriculus

sacculus

superior semicircular canal

ampulla of sup. semicircular canal

lateral semicircular canal

ampulla of lat. semicircular canal

posterior semicircular canal

ampulla of post semicircular canal

B

ampulla of semicircular canal (sectioned)

sensory epithelium

cupula

gelatinous matrix

processes of hair cell

support cells

hair cells

fibers of vestibular nerve

C

sacculus

sensory epithelium

otoliths (statoconia)

gelatinous matrix

hair cells

support cells

FIGURE 18-11   The structures of balance: semicircular canals (A) with details of the internal structure of the ampulla (B); macula of the saccule or utricle (C).

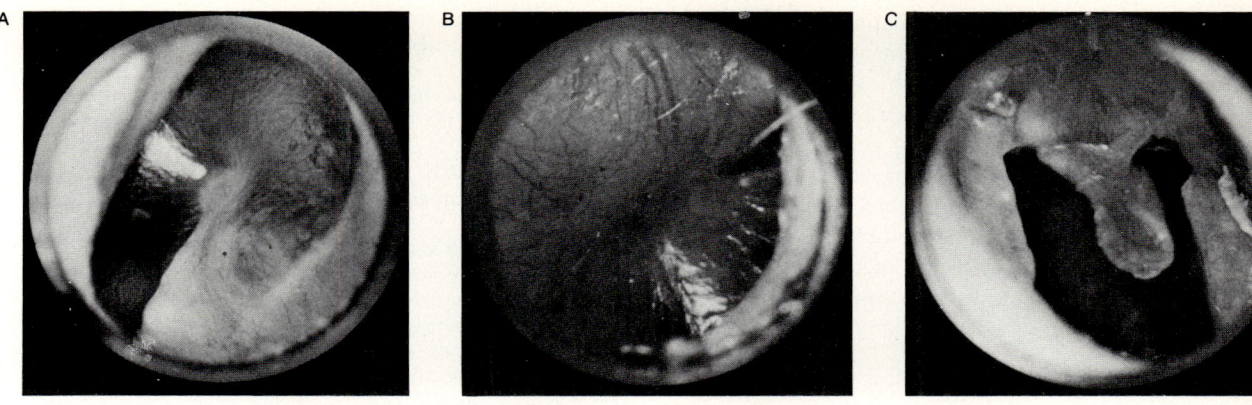

FIGURE 18-12 Normal (A), inflamed (B), and perforated (C) eardrums.

brain, as well as the auditory centers in the brain.

Deafness

Several types of deafness are distinguished. **Conduction deafness** may result from damage to the tympanic membrane, blockage of the external auditory canal by hardened wax, inflammation of the middle ear, or degenerative changes in the ossicles. **Nerve deafness** results from damage to the cochlea or to the auditory nerve. **Central deafness,** involving the hearing centers of the brain, may be a manifestation of aphasia; it may be due to an actual brain lesion or may be psychogenic.

The tympanic membrane (Figure 18-12) is vulnerable to inflammation and rupture due to infections of various kinds. Bacterial respiratory infections may invade the middle ear via the eustachian tubes; infections of the outer ear, often caused by crude attempts to relieve itching or remove ear wax, can spread to the eardrum. (Excessive accumulations of ear wax may be removed by gently syringing the canal with warm water.) Rupture of the eardrum can also be caused by exposure to an extremely loud noise or explosion, such as a cannon blast. Usually a tear in the eardrum eventually heals spontaneously, but the scar may be a weak point for subsequent rupture, and scar tissue lessens the sensitivity of the eardrum. Perforation of the tympanic membrane does not lead to total deafness, since sound vibrations can also be conducted to the inner ear (though less effectively) by way of the bones of the skull.

Otitis media, an inflammation of the middle ear, can result from infection or allergy. The resultant buildup of fluids in the middle ear produces a partial or complete loss of hearing (conduction deafness) that is especially common in young children. Fortunately, the hearing is usually restored when the inflammation is successfully treated.

In another type of "middle ear deafness," bony overgrowths reduce the mobility of the three ossicles,

so that they cannot conduct vibrations effectively, and the foot-plate of the stapes may become firmly anchored to the oval window. (This kind of fusion of the bones is called **ankylosis** of the ossicles.) Surgical operations in which the foot-plate of the stapes is removed (stapedectomy) have restored nearly normal hearing to many victims of this form of conduction deafness. Another approach is fenestration, in which a new window is made and covered with a flap of skin. Various types of hearing aids are also helpful for people with forms of conduction deafness.

In nerve deafness, the ability to hear both by air conduction and by bone conduction is lost. If the damage is to a portion of the cochlea, only certain frequencies may be affected. In most older persons, for example, degenerative changes result in a loss of the ability to hear high frequencies; this progressive hearing loss in old age is called **presbycusis.** Antibiot-

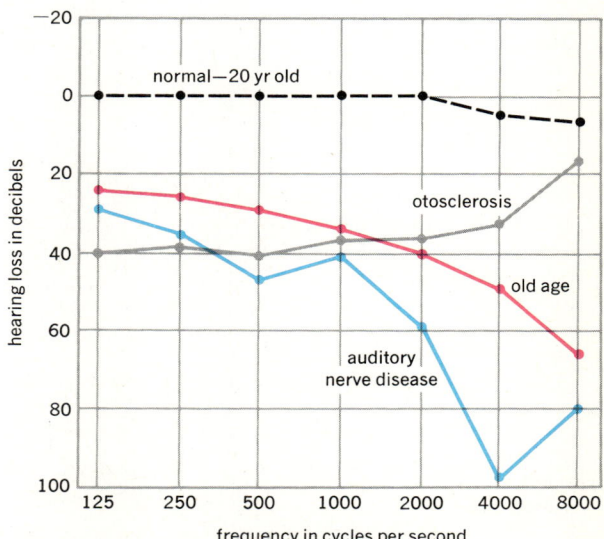

FIGURE 18-13 Audiograms showing normal hearing and several types of hearing loss.

ics of the streptomycin group can cause degeneration of the hair cells, leading to nerve deafness. Damage to the cochlea is frequently signaled by **tinnitus,** a ringing or roaring in the ears without any external stimulus. Tinnitus can also be caused by accumulations of ear wax, perforation of the eardrum, fluid in the middle ear, hardening of the blood vessels in the ear, or disturbances of the auditory nerve or brain. Hearing aids are not very helpful in cases of nerve deafness, since a more selective amplification of sounds is needed.

Ménière's Syndrome

Disorders of the labyrinth may result not only in hearing loss, but also in an upsetting disorientation of the equilibrium. Victims of Ménière's syndrome experience sudden attacks of **vertigo,** in which it seems that objects about them are whirling, along with tinnitus and rapid, uneven movements of the eyeballs called **nystagmus.** Nausea, vomiting, and extreme discomfort in the head may accompany the attacks, which may last for up to several days and recur at intervals of days, weeks, or months. Antinausea drugs or sedatives may help to control the vertigo; in some cases the diseased portion of the labyrinth is selectively destroyed, or the vestibular branch of the auditory nerve is cut. Draining of the saccule may provide relief, and one theory holds that the condition is due to an imbalance of pressure between the perilymph and the endolymph. Many patients recover spontaneously.

SUMMARY

The ears are the organs of hearing and contain receptors for equilibrium.
Sound waves are vibratory disturbances transmitted through an elastic medium by means of alternate compressions and rarefactions.
  The speed of propagation in air is about 330 m/sec.
  Conduction of sound in liquids and solids (e.g., bone) is more rapid than in gases.
Properties of sound are:
  Pitch (a function of the frequency of sound waves)
  Intensity or loudness (a function of the amplitude of sound waves)
  Quality (dependent on overtones)
Sound intensity is measured in decibels, a logarithmic scale.
The human ear consists of:
  External ear (sound-gathering funnel)
  Middle ear (from tympanic membrane to oval and round windows)
  Internal ear (labyrinth, containing hearing and equilibrium receptors)
The external ear consists of:
  Auricle or pinna
  External acoustic meatus (tubular passage ending at tympanic membrane)
The eustachian tube connects the middle ear cavity to the nasopharynx and permits equalization of air pressure.

The middle ear contains the ear ossicles: malleus (hammer), incus (anvil), and stapes (stirrup), stretching from the eardrum to the oval window.
The middle ear communicates with mastoid cells in the temporal bone and with the inner ear via membrane-covered oval and round windows.
The bony labyrinth of the inner ear consists of the vestibule (containing the saccule and utricle), the cochlea, and the semicircular canals.
The bony labyrinth is filled with perilymph, and the membranous labyrinth is filled with endolymph.
The saccule and utricle contain maculae (hair cells) and otoliths (calcium carbonate crystals).
The three semicircular canals are mutually perpendicular (two vertical, one horizontal).
The cochlea is shaped like a snail shell, a tube coiled into a spiral.
  The basilar membrane and vestibular membrane divide the cochlea into three canals: the scala tympani, scala media (cochlear duct), and scala vestibuli.
  The distal ends of the scala vestibuli and scala tympani communicate through the helicotrema.
  The sound receptors are found in the organ of Corti, inside the cochlear duct, which contains hair cells.
Sound waves enter the external auditory canal, cause the tympanic membrane to vibrate, and are transmitted by vibrations of the three ossicles to the oval window, setting up pressure waves in the scala vestibuli, which in turn produce sympathetic vibrations in certain fibers of the basilar membrane; the corresponding hair cells of the organ of Corti are stimulated, and neural impulses are transmitted along the cochlear branch of the auditory nerve through the inferior colliculi to the cerebral cortex in the temporal lobe.
Pitch is discriminated by the place principle and the volley principle.
Loudness is discriminated by the rate of firing of nerve cells, the number of nerve cells firing, and the firing of high-threshold neurons.
Sounds are localized by comparison of intensity and time difference of reception in the two ears.
Information on equilibrium and orientation is provided by:
  The eyes
  Proprioceptors in the muscles and joints
  The vestibular apparatus:
    Saccule and utricle (organs of static equilibrium)
    Semicircular canals (organs of dynamic equilibrium)
Movements of the head shift otoliths in the saccule and utricle, stimulating hair cells.
Movements of the head set the fluid in at least one of the semicircular canals in motion, stimulating hair cells in its ampulla.
Impulses from the vestibular apparatus are transmitted via the vestibular division of the auditory nerve through the vestibular nuclei in the brainstem, mainly to the cerebellum.
  Impulses from the utricle and saccule initiate the vestibular righting reflex.
  Impulses from the semicircular canals permit corrections of balance to be made ahead of time.
Rapid rotation, rocking, swaying, and so on can produce sensations of vertigo and nausea.
Types of deafness include:
  Conduction deafness (damage to tympanic membrane, blockage of canal, otitis media, ankylosis of ossicles)
  Nerve deafness (damage to cochlea or auditory nerve)
  Central deafness (brain damage or psychogenic)
Presbycusis is the progressive hearing loss in old age.
Tinnitus is a ringing in the ears.
Ménière's syndrome affects both hearing (hearing loss, tinnitus) and equilibrium (vertigo, nystagmus).

QUESTIONS FOR REVIEW AND THOUGHT

1 What structures of the ear would you expect to be most vulnerable to damage by the "noise pollution" that accompanies modern life?

2 Define pitch, intensity, and quality of sounds and discuss the physiological mechanisms for distinguishing them.

3 How many times louder is the sound of a jet plane (160 db) than a normal conversation (60 db)?

4 What happens in the middle ear during a ride on an express elevator, and what can you do to relieve the uncomfortable sensation?

5 Many pediatricians and family doctors now routinely test children's hearing when they have throat or ear infections and urge the prompt use of decongestants in infections and allergies. Discuss.

6 Describe the structures of the external, middle, and inner ear and their functions.

7 Describe the action of the structures of the vestibular apparatus during a somersault.

8 A person embarking from a ship after a long voyage feels as though the solid ground is heaving and rolling and may have difficulty walking normally at first. Discuss this condition in terms of the vestibular apparatus and the other systems involved in equilibrium and balance.

9 How does the presence of fluid in the middle ear in otitis media produce temporary or permanent hearing loss?

THE BLOOD

19

The flowing waters of a river and the tiny streams into which it branches make the lands of the earth bloom and help to nourish the animals and plants that inhabit them. In the microcosm of the body the blood that courses through arteries, veins, and capillaries nourishes the body cells and keeps them alive and vigorous.

The waterways of the bloodstream are the major transportation systems of the body. Through the delicate capillaries that interlace the tissues and organs, there is a constant flow of blood past nearly every body cell. Water and other small molecules continually filter out through the thin capillary walls into the tissue fluid that bathes these cells. Fluids diffuse back into the bloodstream through the capillary walls and are returned to the blood circulation by the lymphatic system. A ceaseless exchange of gases occurs between the blood and the body cells. Thus, the blood is ever changing. And yet, overall, its composition remains surprisingly constant. The maintenance of this constancy is part of the body mechanisms of **homeostasis,** a dynamic maintenance of relatively constant conditions in the internal environment.

CHARACTERISTICS OF BLOOD

With the first cut finger, a child learns what blood is like. It is a red-colored fluid, with a salty taste and a characteristic odor. The common saying "blood is thicker than water" is accurate. The specific gravity of blood (the ratio of its weight to the weight of an equal volume of pure water) is about 1.055. Blood is not as free-flowing as water; its viscosity is about five times as high—for blood is a mixture of water and suspended particles and cells.

Viewed with the naked eye, blood presents a uniform, opaque appearance. But place a drop of blood on a slide, smear it out into a thin film, and look at it under a microscope, and a whole microworld springs into view (Figure 19-1). Flattened biconcave discs—the red blood cells—float lazily in the fluid matrix. Among them, an occasional colorless, irregularly shaped white blood cell creeps and oozes along the slide. Smaller platelets are scattered about, and too small to see even in the best optical microscopes are proteins, salts, and other chemicals dissolved and suspended in the watery fluid.

The volume of blood in a human body varies with the size of the person. An average-sized adult man has about 5 liters of blood flowing through his blood vessels—about 7 percent of the total weight of his body. The total volume of blood varies with age. Infants have a greater blood volume in proportion to their body weight than adults. The blood volume also varies with sex (the average woman has about 4.5 liters of blood), and other conditions such as the de-

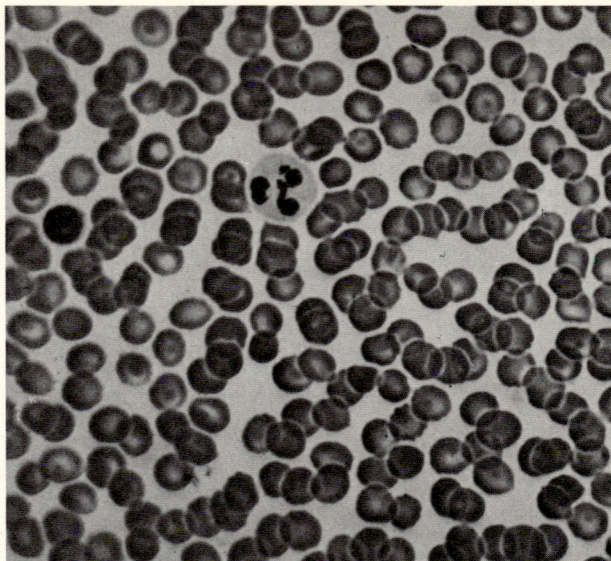

FIGURE 19-1 A normal human blood smear. (Carolina Biological Supply Company)

gree of muscular development and adiposity, the condition of the heart and blood vessels, and the state of hydration of the body in general. Activity or inactivity also influences the blood volume—prolonged bed rest, for example, produces a drop of 300 to 500 ml in blood volume as fluid leaks out into the interstitial spaces.

FUNCTIONS OF BLOOD

For a hundred years, researchers have been trying to duplicate human blood. But they have failed to find a wholly satisfactory substitute. Some blood replacements can perform one or a few of the functions of blood, but none even comes near to performing all. At best, the blood substitutes devised so far can only help to tide a patient over after severe blood loss, until his or her own body is able to fill the gap by producing more blood.

The main functions of the blood are in the area of transport—carrying anything and everything that needs to be shipped from one part of the body to another. Oxygen from the air that is breathed into the lungs is carried in the blood to all the body cells. Carbon dioxide, a potentially poisonous product of the cells' metabolism, is carried away in the blood to the lungs, where the excess is eliminated from the body in the exhaled air. Food substances, absorbed from the intestines, are distributed by the blood to the hungry cells, and their waste products are carried by the blood to the kidneys and other sites for excretion. Hormones, chemical messengers that regulate and coordinate the activities of the body, are carried by the blood from the glands that manufacture them to the target cells on which they act. The blood provides a continual supply of water for the needs of the body cells. Even heat, produced by the contractions of muscles, is distributed through the body by the blood, which thus is an important link in the body's system of temperature regulation.

The blood is also the heart of the body's system of defenses against invading bacteria and other potentially harmful intruders. It contains the white blood cells, roving "policemen" that go after foreign particles, immobilize them, and ultimately literally eat them.

The buffering action of proteins and other substances dissolved in the blood helps to maintain the acid–base balance of the body media within a sensitively adjusted optimum range for the functioning of various reaction systems. Indeed, all the functions of the blood help to maintain a dynamic equilibrium in the internal media of the body. The various chemical changes that accompany the action of the body systems—the contractions of muscles, the transmission of nerve impulses, the secretions of the glands, and the metabolic reactions of the individual cells—might gradually shift this equilibrium and ultimately result in drastic changes that could lead to death if it were not for the unceasing homeostatic activities of the blood and its components.

COMPOSITION OF THE BLOOD

A single drop of blood contains more than 250 *million* blood cells, suspended in a clear fluid. The seemingly homogeneous fluid teems with countless numbers of molecules of proteins and other substances, of thousands of different kinds, each with its own specific job or jobs to do.

The solid particles of the blood—the red and white blood cells and the smaller, delicate platelets—are commonly referred to as the **formed elements.** They can be separated from the liquid matrix by centrifuging. In the centrifuge tube, after the blood specimen is spun down, the formed elements can be seen as a red mass at the bottom, topped by a thin, whitish layer, the "buffy coat." Above it is a clear, straw-colored fluid, the blood **plasma.** Often a graduated centrifuge tube is used, which permits a direct reading of the volume of the formed elements in the total volume of the blood sample (Figure 19-2). The red mass consists of packed red cells, and its percentage in the total blood volume is called the **hematocrit.** It varies somewhat, but in normal humans it generally ranges from 42 to 47 percent (about 45 percent in men, 42 percent in women). The buffy coat contains white blood cells and platelets. Thus, the blood, which superficially seems like a homogeneous, watery fluid, is actually only about 55 percent fluid (plasma) and contains

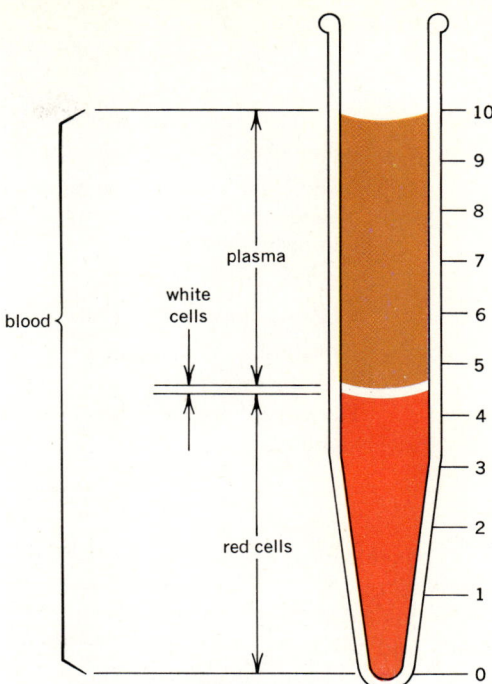

FIGURE 19-2   Determination of hematocrit. Whole blood is centrifuged; the hematocrit (volume of red cells per 100 ml of blood) is found by multiplying the reading at the top of the column of packed red cells by 10.

about 45 percent solid matter (formed elements).

PLASMA

It is believed that the first life forms on earth evolved in the oceans that cover more than two-thirds of our planet. Gradually, over long eons of time, animals and plants developed. Some of them migrated to the land areas of earth and colonized them. But they carried with them a memento of their past life, in their body fluids that once were at equilibrium with the sea waters that bathed them. Thus, it should not be surprising that the salt concentrations in blood plasma resemble a sort of dilute sea water.

But blood plasma is not merely a solution of salts. Indeed, this clear, rather sticky fluid is a far more complex mixture—perhaps one of the most complex mixtures in the universe. In addition to salts, it contains proteins, sugar, lipids, dissolved gases, hormones, vitamins, amino acids, and metabolic waste products such as urea and lactic acid. The various solutes and colloids together constitute 8 to 10 percent of the volume of plasma, the remaining 90 to 92 percent being water.

Some of the major constituents of plasma are summarized in Table 19-1.

Plasma Proteins

If you had a dollar bill for each kind of protein found in your blood, you would have enough money to

TABLE 19-1   Constituents of Plasma

COMPONENT	EXAMPLES
Water (90-92%)	
Proteins (7%)	Albumin, globulins, fibrinogen
Minerals	Sodium, potassium, calcium, magnesium, chloride, phosphate, fluoride, iodide
Gases	Oxygen, carbon dioxide
Nutrients	Glucose, lipids, amino acids
Metabolic products	Urea, uric acid, creatinine, lactic acid
Other substances	Hormones, antibodies, enzymes, vitamins

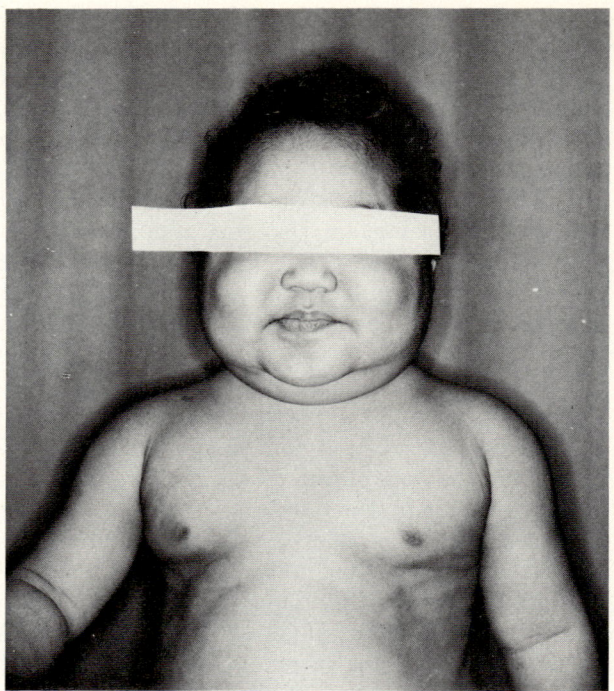

FIGURE 19-3   A decrease in plasma proteins can result in edema.

complete your college education. Yet with all this variety, the plasma proteins are usually separated into three basic fractions, according to their solubilities in various solvents and solutions of electrolytes. These three basic groups are called **albumin, globulin,** and **fibrinogen.**

The albumin fraction is the largest of the plasma protein fractions, usually about 4.2 g per 100 ml (4.2 g%) of plasma. Albumin is not a pure substance; more than one type of albumin is found in blood plasma. Albumin molecules are the smallest of all the plasma proteins, but they still are not small enough to pass readily through the capillary walls. Albumin, formed in the liver, provides the primary source of **osmotic pressure** in the blood. This osmotic pressure tends to draw water into the bloodstream, counteracting the opposing hydrostatic pressure of the blood within the capillaries, which tends to force water out of the capillaries into the tissue fluid. Albumin is thus a key factor in regulating the volume of the plasma and maintaining the balance of fluids between the blood system and the tissue fluids. A decrease in the plasma proteins can result in an accumulation of fluid in the tissues, a condition called **edema** (Figure 19-3). Albumin is valuable in the treatment of extensive burns, where the patient has lost large amounts of protein. An albumin solution may also be given intravenously to increase the blood volume after severe hemorrhage, if whole blood or plasma is not available.

The plasma globulins are a particularly complex mixture, together comprising about 2.5 g per 100 ml of plasma. Three important fractions are the alpha, beta, and gamma globulins. Alpha and beta globulins are formed mainly in the liver. They aid in the transport of lipids and other substances through the blood, by combining with them to form temporary complexes. Gamma globulins are the main source of circulating antibodies. They are produced by plasma cells and are key factors in the body's disease-fighting system, which is discussed in Chapter 37.

The third fraction of the plasma proteins, fibrinogen, represents only a small percentage of the total, only 0.3 g per 100 ml of plasma. But this protein, produced in the liver, is an important link in the chain of chemical reactions that yield blood clots, thus helping to prevent excessive blood loss if the blood vessel walls are breached. In circulating blood, fibrinogen is in a liquid, "sol" form. But when a clot is formed, it is converted to a solid "gel" form, called **fibrin** and separates from the plasma in the form of fine strands. If fibrin is removed from plasma, the liquid remaining is called **serum;** that is, blood serum is plasma minus its fibrinogen.

In addition to their specific functions, the plasma proteins serve as an important dynamic pool, which can be drawn on for raw materials whenever any tissue of the body needs amino acids. All the plasma proteins contribute to some degree to the osmotic pressure of the blood, and they also aid in maintaining the acid–base balance in the blood.

Other Plasma Constituents

Human beings can adapt to a great variety of conditions in the external environment—variations of temperature, of pressure, and of composition of the gas atmosphere. This adaptability is made possible by the finely regulated balance of the internal environment of the body, which maintains constancy of the internal conditions within extremely narrow tolerances. It is fortunate that the body possesses such mechanisms. Deviations in the pH of the internal media, or in the concentrations of sugar or salts, can lead to illness and even death.

Human blood is normally slightly alkaline, with a pH of 7.35 to 7.45. Its hydrogen ion concentration is maintained within this narrow range in spite of great fluctuations in the amounts of acids and bases that are taken in with food or produced in the metabolic activities of the body cells. The blood pH is regulated automatically by a number of natural buffer systems found in the plasma. The plasma proteins can act as buffers by accepting excess hydrogen ions or hydroxyl ions present in the blood. So can some of the inorganic electrolytes of the plasma, such as the bicarbonate system.

When carbon dioxide dissolves in water, it can associate with a water molecule to form carbonic acid, H_2CO_3. This is a weak acid, which can ionize to form H^+ and HCO_3^-. The latter can ionize further to produce H^+ and $CO_3^=$. But since carbonic acid is a rather weak acid, not all the molecules undergo ionization, and a series of equilibria is established, with all possible varieties present in solution in various amounts:

$$CO_2 + H_2O \rightleftharpoons H_2CO_3 \rightleftharpoons H^+ + HCO_3^- \rightleftharpoons 2H^+ + CO_3^=$$

If excess acid (H^+) is added to the system, it reacts with some of the bicarbonate ions present:

$$H^+ + HCO_3^- \rightarrow H_2CO_3$$

The excess acid is thus effectively removed from circulation, and a constant plasma pH is maintained. The addition of a base (hydroxyl ions, OH^-) can be taken care of just as readily:

$$OH^- + HCO_3^- \rightarrow H_2O + CO_3^=$$

or

$$OH^- + H_2CO_3 \rightarrow H_2O + HCO_3^-$$

This buffer system, together with the many others in the body fluids, plays an important role in maintaining homeostasis.

Inorganic ions in blood plasma have a number of other important functions in the body. They help to maintain the osmotic pressure of the plasma. A proper balance of calcium, magnesium, sodium, and potassium ions in the body fluids is essential to the integrity of the cell membranes. Inorganic ions also act as cofactors for enzymes, work in the functioning of nerves and muscles, and are also vital to the activities of various glands. The hard tissues of the body, bones, and teeth draw upon the plasma salts for their raw materials.

Salts are generally present in the plasma in ionized forms. But some other plasma constituents—nonelectrolytes—cannot dissociate into ions. The plasma nonelectrolytes include the sugar glucose, lipids, and various metabolic wastes.

The **blood sugar level** normally ranges from 80 to 120 mg per 100 ml of blood. Temporary increases in the glucose level occur after a meal. But a dynamic interaction with the nervous system and the hormones of the pancreas quickly brings the blood sugar down to normal levels and maintains it there. Excess plasma glucose is converted to glycogen and stored in the liver. The stored glycogen is reconverted to glucose and supplied to the circulating blood as it is needed.

In the disease diabetes mellitus, caused by a deficiency of the pancreatic hormone insulin, the blood sugar level rises far above the normal values. Without treatment, coma and death can result. However, an appropriately adjusted dosage of insulin (or drugs in certain cases) can permit a diabetic to lead a relatively normal life.

Fasting can cause a drop in the blood sugar level below the normal values. A low blood sugar level, or hypoglycemia, can also result, paradoxically, from the ingestion of carbohydrates in cases of a tumor of the pancreas or other conditions in which the pancreas is stimulated to overreact to a rise in the blood sugar level by producing excessive amounts of insulin. Hypoglycemia can result in fainting, fatigue, irritability, and a variety of other symptoms, as the brain and other key organs of the body are starved of nutrients.

The blood lipids include fats (triglycerides), phospholipids, and cholesterol. The fats occur in the plasma in the form of small particles (about 1 μ in diameter) called **chylomicrons.** The main source of plasma fats is the food absorbed from the intestines. They are not actually functioning in the blood but are merely being transported to their sites of storage or use. Plasma phospholipids, which function in the transport and utilization of fats, are formed in the liver, which is also the principal organ of cholesterol synthesis in the body.

The roles of cholesterol in the body and its possible implication in heart disease are still a center of controversy. Plasma cholesterol normally ranges from 160 to 280 mg per 100 ml of blood. Excess cholesterol (whether from the diet or produced in the body) is normally excreted, but sometimes the cholesterol level rises, and this lipid may be deposited in the connective tissue of the artery walls. The resulting condition, called **atherosclerosis,** narrows the blood vessels and roughens their inner surface; it can lead to clotting and heart attacks or strokes. The condition evidently results from a change in cholesterol metabolism. The blood cholesterol level of heart patients is commonly monitored periodically, and if the level is above normal, the patient is advised to reduce the consumption of eggs and other cholesterol-rich foods. Recent evidence indicates that a determining factor in heart attack risk is the form in which cholesterol is traveling in the blood, rather than its total level. Plasma cholesterol is complexed with lipoproteins. One form of these transport molecules, **low-density lipoprotein** (LDL), transports cholesterol from its site of synthesis in the liver to the various body cells. Excess LDL-transported cholesterol is deposited in the artery walls. Another type of cholesterol transporter, **high-density lipoprotein** (HDL), is believed to remove cholesterol from artery walls and prevent its deposition.

Another category of plasma constituents that can provide an index of health is the **nonprotein nitrogen** (NPN). The total normal NPN is about 30 mg per 100 ml of plasma. Its major constituent is urea; it also includes amino acids, uric acid, creatine, and creatinine. Urea is the end product of protein catabolism, and in humans it is the form in which nitrogenous substances are excreted. Amino acids, the building blocks of proteins, are formed when food proteins are digested. Thus, the NPN level provides a good index of the body's protein balance. Normally, protein ingestion, formation, and breakdown are nicely balanced, so that the plasma NPN remains relatively constant. But in kidney diseases a decrease in the rate of excretion produces a rise in the NPN. Infections, fevers, and hyperthyroidism can also produce a rise in the NPN by increasing protein catabolism.

Hormones, vitamins, and various other substances in the plasma are generally on their way to the sites of their action, like commuters riding the subway to work. The concentrations of the various plasma constituents are continually monitored by various control centers of the body, such as the hypothalamus in the brain and the kidneys. If the level of any key substance deviates from its optimum value, a chain of reactions is promptly initiated to adjust it and preserve homeostasis.

A discussion of the major constituents of the plasma would be grossly incomplete without at least a brief highlighting of the largest fraction of all: water. In addition to serving as the fluid medium in which all the other constituents of plasma (and the formed elements) are transported through the body, water acts as a "universal solvent" that brings together an intricate variety of chemical substances and helps them to react.

FORMED ELEMENTS

Most of the cells of the body are pretty much confined to the areas of their birth. But the formed elements of the blood are rovers. Not only do they migrate from their place of origin to a different organ system, but they are constantly on the move from the moment of their release into the blood to the moment of their death.

As we have seen, the solid formed elements, suspended in the fluid plasma, make up 45 percent of the total volume of the blood. They include three main types: red blood cells or erythrocytes, white blood cells or leukocytes, and platelets or thrombocytes.

ERYTHROCYTES

When you look at a smear of fresh human blood under a microscope, it might occur to you that the red blood cells seem to be misnamed. Their common name emphasizes their red color. Even their technical name, erythrocytes, comes from Greek words meaning "red" and "cell." Yet an individual red cell does not look red under magnification. It is more yellowish or straw-colored. It does contain a red pigment, hemoglobin, but the erythrocyte is so tiny and thin that the full intensity of the pigment cannot be appreciated. It is only the huge masses of red cells, hundreds of millions in each drop of blood, that together give blood its rich red color.

Appearance and Structure of RBC

The red cells of human blood are unique among all the cells of the body. All the other cells have a nucleus, containing the hereditary blueprints for structure and function and controlling and coordinating the cell's activities. But the erythrocytes that circulate in the blood of humans and other mammals are different. They are small flattened biconcave discs, about 7 to 8 μ in diameter and 2.2 μ thick. Though they are covered with a cell membrane like other body cells, mature red cells have no nucleus at all.

The shape and structure of the red blood cell represent an extreme of adaptation for its function. The erythrocyte is the gas carrier for the body. Like tankers, plying the rivers and canals of the circulatory system, erythrocytes pick up cargoes of the oxygen that diffuses through the thin walls of the capillaries in the lungs and deliver them to the body cells. Unloading the oxygen, they may pick up a cargo of waste carbon dioxide for the return voyage.

A spherical shape would provide the ultimate in carrying capacity. But the shape of the red blood cell is a compromise. As a biconcave disc, thicker at the

FIGURE 19-4 Human red blood cells showing rouleaux formation (SEM, ×2600).

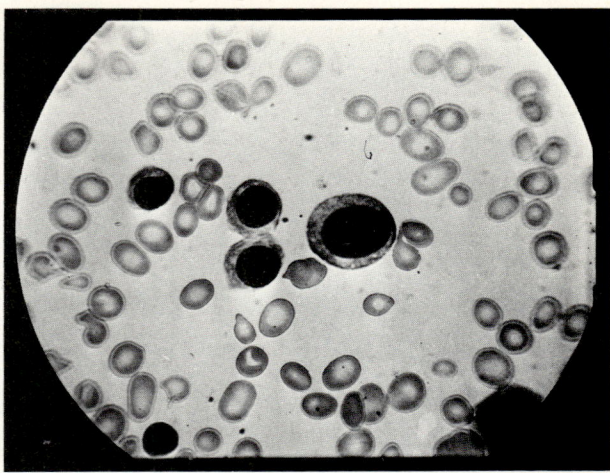

FIGURE 19-5 Blood smear in pernicious anemia showing anisocytosis.

edges and thinner in the center, it combines a high carrying capacity with a maximized surface area for the diffusion of gases in and out of the cell.

Within its bounding membrane, the erythrocyte has a filmy, elastic inner framework of lipids and proteins, called the **stroma.** Hemoglobin molecules, the working parts of the red cell, are held in the stroma. The red cell membrane contains blood group factors, such as A, B, and Rh.

Erythrocytes are small—if they were lined up side by side, more than 3000 of them would be needed to measure an inch. Yet, they are still larger than the diameters of the smallest capillaries. Fortunately, these cells are soft and flexible, so that they can bend and twist as they are carried single file through the capillary networks of the body.

On a slide, red blood cells are frequently seen in groups with their flattened edges sticking together, so that they resemble a stack of coins (Figure 19-4). Such a formation is called a rouleau formation, from a French word meaning "roll."

In a smear of normal blood, all the red blood cells are the same size and perfectly round. In some diseases, there may be a change in the size or shape of the erythrocytes. In pernicious anemia, for example, the red cells vary in shape and are much larger than those of a normal person (Figure 19-5). The condition in which there is a great variation in the size of the red blood cells is called **anisocytosis,** which means "a condition of varied cells."

Most other mammals have erythrocytes that are smaller than human red cells. But they generally make up in numbers for their smaller size. Goats, for example, have about 18 million red cells per cubic millimeter, compared with the human 5 million. But the individual goat erythrocytes are so much smaller

that the hematocrit of goats, at 30 percent, is not too different from the human value of 45 percent.

Formation of RBC

With each tick of the clock, three million of your red blood cells die. Their delicate membranes rupture, and the cell contents spill out. Yet with each tick of the clock an equal number of new red cells are born, replacing those that have died.

The formation of red blood cells is called **erythropoiesis.** In the embryo, erythropoiesis occurs in the liver and spleen, as well as in the yolk sac and bone marrow. But at some time before birth, the liver and spleen shut down their red cell production, and the erythropoietic function is taken over entirely by the bone marrow. In an adult, the marrow of the ends of the long bones, such as the humerus and femur, and that of the ribs, vertebrae, sternum, pelvis, and portions of the skull is interlaced with a network of small blood sinuses lined with endothelial cells, which give it a deep red color. Normally the shafts of the long bones contain yellow bone marrow, indicating their inactivity in blood cell production. But in times of need, after severe hemorrhage or in certain diseases, the yellow bone marrow can temporarily take up an auxiliary erythropoietic function; even the liver and spleen may be reenlisted in this task until the lost cells are restored.

A bone marrow section taken from an active portion of the red bone marrow shows a variety of stages of blood cell formation. The sequence of stages in erythropoiesis has been worked out in detail (Figure 19-6).

When the red blood cell begins its life, it has a nucleus, just like the other cells of the body. In fact, both red and white cells develop from undifferenti-

genesis of RBC

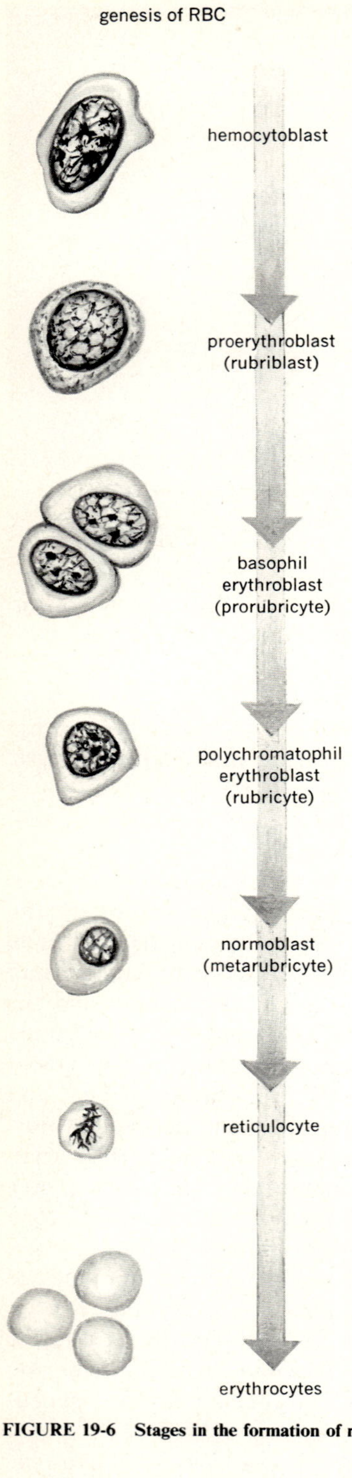

hemocytoblast

proerythroblast
(rubriblast)

basophil
erythroblast
(prorubricyte)

polychromatophil
erythroblast
(rubricyte)

normoblast
(metarubricyte)

reticulocyte

erythrocytes

FIGURE 19-6 Stages in the formation of red blood cells.

as they develop into erythrocytes. The first step along the way is a large cell called a **proerythroblast,** or **rubriblast,** in which an increase in the number of ribosomes signals a step-up of internal activity. This increase is observed in the light microscope as an increase in the basophilia of the cells, that is, their affinity for basic dyes (which stain the cells blue). The size of the cell decreases slightly and the basophilia increases as the developing blood cells reach the next stage, the **basophil erythroblast** or **prorubricyte.**

The basophil erythroblast soon divides to form smaller cells, each of which begins to produce hemoglobin. Now the developing red cell is a **polychromatophil erythroblast** or **rubricyte.** When stained, it shows various shades of blue, combined with tinges of pink due to its hemoglobin. At this stage, the developing red cell is about half the size of the original hemocytoblast, but it still has a prominent nucleus, and it divides frequently.

The polychromatophil erythroblasts continue to divide, decrease in size, and produce increasing amounts of hemoglobin. They become increasingly acidophilic (stain readily with acid dyes). Now they have reached the **normoblast** or **metarubricyte** stage.

When the cytoplasm of the normoblast is about 34 percent filled with hemoglobin, it loses its nucleus. Now it is an immature erythrocyte, called a **reticulocyte** because a network of basophilic material is spread through its interior. (The term "reticulum" means "network.") The network is probably the remains of the endoplasmic reticulum that manufactures hemoglobin in the early stages. Hemoglobin continues to be produced in the immature erythrocyte as long as the reticulum remains, about two to three days.

The mature erythrocytes travel out of the sinuses and squeeze into the blood capillaries through the pores in their walls. Occasionally reticulocytes enter the circulating blood. However, their numbers normally do not exceed 0.5 to 1.5 percent of the total number of red blood cells. An increase in the **reticulocyte count** is an early indication that the production of red cells has been speeded up, usually to meet some increased need by the body tissues. But the presence of normoblasts in the circulating blood alerts the clinician to the fact that something distinctly abnormal is going on in the body: the need for red blood cells is so acute that they are being released from the marrow before they have had time to fully mature.

The body is alerted to a need for new formation of red blood cells and is stimulated to respond to the alert through the action of the kidneys. The blood flowing through the kidneys is constantly monitored for its concentrations of a multitude of key substances. If the oxygen content of the blood passing

ated **stem cells,** called **hemocytoblasts.** (The term "blast" is used for an immature stage in cell development.) The direction of their differentiation, into erythrocytes or leukocytes, depends on the needs of the body.

Hemocytoblasts in the endothelial lining of the bone marrow sinuses pass through a series of changes

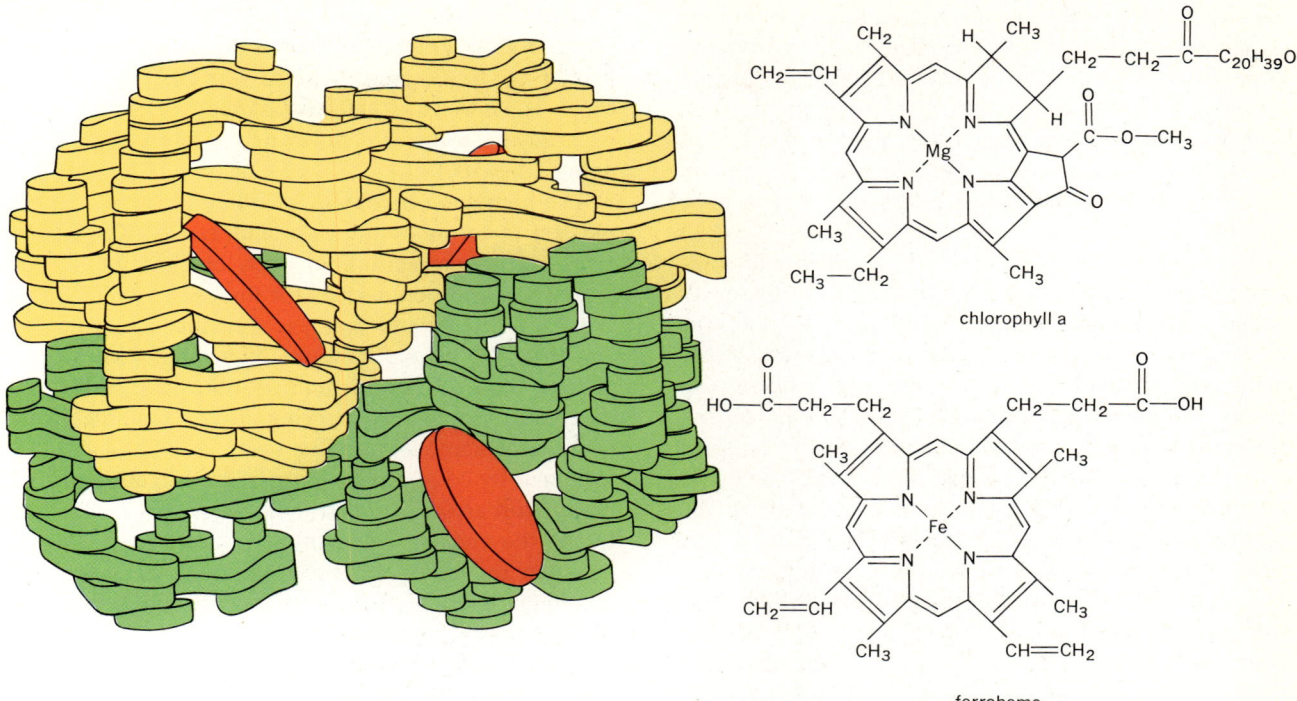

chlorophyll a

ferroheme

FIGURE 19-7   Structure of the hemoglobin molecule, as deduced from X-ray diffraction studies (A). Two identical alpha chains (lighter blocks) and two identical beta chains (darker blocks) each enfold a heme group (colored disks). The chemical structure of heme (B) shows a striking similarity to the chlorophyll molecule. (Part A from "The Hemoglobin Molecule" by M. F. Perutz. Copyright © November 1964 by *Scientific American*, Inc. All rights reserved.)

through the kidneys is below the optimum value, the kidneys secrete an enzyme that acts on a plasma protein to produce a hormone, **erythropoietin;** this hormone controls the production and release of red cells from the bone marrow. The triggering drop in oxygen content of the blood may be caused by a variety of factors, including severe blood loss (fewer erythrocytes available to carry oxygen), anemia (a reduction in the number of red cells due to disease or dietary deficiency), and a reduction of the oxygen content in the atmospheric air (moving to a high-altitude region produces an increase in a person's red cell count).

Hemoglobin

If the iron in the hemoglobin of all the red blood cells in your body could be isolated and formed into a coin, it would be about the size of a dime. Yet this small amount—only about three grams—is literally priceless to you—you could not live without it.

Hemoglobin is a metal-containing protein. It is a complex of an iron-containing pigment called **heme** (about 4 percent of the molecule) and a protein called **globin** that has been found to consist of four chains, two identical alpha chains and two identical beta chains, each about 140 amino acids long. The three-dimensional structure of the hemoglobin molecule is pictured in Figure 19-7, together with a closeup of the

heme portion of the molecule. Each protein chain of globin enfolds a heme group, in which a single atom of iron in the center is bound to four nitrogen atoms, included in a system of interconnected rings. The ring system is called a **porphyrin.** Other porphyrins found in nature include the green pigment chlorophyll, contained in plants. Chlorophyll plays an important role in plant metabolism: it acts as an energy trap, permitting plants to utilize the energy of sunlight to manufacture carbohydrates from simple raw materials. Its central metal atom, however, is magnesium rather than iron; and chlorophyll does not possess the ability to combine with oxygen.

A single hemoglobin molecule, which contains four heme-coordinated iron atoms, can combine loosely with four molecules of oxygen. Since there are about 280 million hemoglobin molecules packed into each red blood cell, and about 5 million red blood cells in each cubic millimeter of blood, it is easy to understand the enormous oxygen-carrying capacity of blood. Pure water can carry only 1/60 as much oxygen as an equal amount of whole blood.

As blood flows through the capillaries of the lungs, oxygen diffuses into the blood and through the cell membranes of the red blood cells. Within these cells it is picked up by the hemoglobin molecules. The oxidized form of hemoglobin is called **oxyhemoglobin.** It is a much brighter, crimson red than hemoglobin that is not combined with oxygen. The reaction between hemoglobin and oxygen is readily reversible. As the blood flows on through the body, reaching regions where the oxygen pressure is low, oxygen is released from its combination with hemoglobin and diffuses out through the capillary walls into the oxygen-poor tissues.

Meanwhile, the hemoglobin is also capable of combining with carbon dioxide, to form a compound called **carbaminohemoglobin.** (Different parts of the hemoglobin molecule react with the two gases, so that a hemoglobin molecule can carry both oxygen and carbon dioxide at the same time.) About 30 percent of the carbon dioxide carried in the blood is in the form of carbaminohemoglobin. Another 60 to 65 percent is contained in the water of the red blood cells in the form of potassium bicarbonate; the remaining 7 percent or so is dissolved in the blood plasma. Hemoglobin participates indirectly in this form of carbon dioxide transport. The gas initially dissolves and associates with a water molecule to form carbonic acid (H_2CO_3), which promptly dissociates to some degree into hydrogen and bicarbonate ions (H^+ and HCO_3^-). Hemoglobin has a much greater affinity for hydrogen ions than do bicarbonate ions; the hemoglobin ties up the hydrogen ions produced and permits large amounts of carbon dioxide to be carried in the blood in this way without disturbing the acid-base balance.

In addition to oxygen and carbon dioxide, hemoglobin has an ability to combine with other gases, including hydrogen sulfide, nitric oxide, and carbon monoxide. Carbon monoxide is a product of incomplete combustion and is present in the fumes from leaking furnaces and automobile exhausts. Colorless, odorless, and imperceptible, it is a particularly insidious and dangerous poison. For hemoglobin will combine with carbon monoxide in preference to oxygen, and this reaction is *not* readily reversible. Thus, hemoglobin molecules that have combined with carbon monoxide to form the bright-red compound **carboxyhemoglobin** are just as effectively removed from their oxygen-carrying function as though the red blood cells containing them had been lost from the body by hemorrhage. A victim of carbon monoxide poisoning may gradually succumb to the effects of oxygen lack without realizing anything is wrong. It is believed that the impairment of judgment caused in drivers by the effects of carbon monoxide in the air of congested streets and highways may be a major cause of highway accidents.

The oxygen-carrying function of hemoglobin is so vital to the body that the content of hemoglobin in the blood is an important index of health. In a normal adult human male, the hemoglobin content ranges from 14 to 18 grams per 100 ml of blood, or an average of 16 g/100 ml. In adult females, the normal range is 12 to 16 g/100 ml (average 14), while children have a somewhat lower hemoglobin level, averaging 12 g/100 ml.

The hemoglobin content of blood may also be expressed in terms of the **color index,** the ratio of the amount of hemoglobin in each erythrocyte to the amount considered normal for the cell. A color index less than 1.0 means that each erythrocyte contains less than the normal amount of hemoglobin. Values greater than 1.0 are sometimes observed, indicating that each red cell is carrying more than the usual amount of hemoglobin. The color index is easily determined by comparing a drop of fresh blood on filter paper with a standard series of colors. It is a valuable test in the analysis of anemias.

When red blood cells die, some of the iron from their hemoglobin is retrieved and reprocessed by the body into new hemoglobin molecules. But part of it is excreted. Thus, a continual intake of iron in the diet is essential to provide for the formation of new red blood cells. Normally the adult body produces about 6.25 g of hemoglobin each day; for this and other uses in the body, a minimum of 5 to 15 mg of iron must be consumed in the daily food. Women require a higher iron intake than men to replace the blood lost periodically in the menstrual flow.

Hemolysis

When a hematologist talks about ghosts, he is not speaking about diaphanous apparitions that frighten people in the dead of night. He is referring to the crumpled membranous overcoats that remain when red blood cells lose their hemoglobin.

This loss of hemoglobin, called **hemolysis** or **laking,** occurs when blood is diluted with distilled water. The cell membrane of a red blood cell, like the membranes of other body cells, is semipermeable: it permits small molecules, such as gases and water, to pass readily through it, while retaining larger molecules, such as proteins. When blood is diluted, an unstable situation is set up. Within the cells, there is a high concentration of proteins and salts; in the fluid outside the cells, the added water has created a greatly lowered concentration of solutes, while the water concentration is greatly increased. Diffusion tends to equalize the concentrations within and outside the cell membrane. But because the membrane is permeable to water molecules and not to the proteins and certain cations within the blood cells, a one-way traffic effectively develops. Water molecules diffuse into the red cells from the hypotonic medium and continue to enter the cells until, swollen to the bursting point, they literally explode, spilling out their pigment and other cell contents. The colorless "ghosts" remain, becoming visible only after they are stained.

The hemoglobin that is released into the plasma in hemolysis dissolves in it and colors it. The blood, normally opaque, becomes transparent. Such blood is referred to as **laked blood.**

Hemolysis can be produced in a test tube with a variety of hemolytic agents in addition to hypotonic solutions. These include ether or chloroform, salts or fatty acids, amyl alcohol or saponin, and ammonia or other alkalis. Hemolysis can also be induced by alternate freezing and thawing. Within the body, hemolysis can be induced by the action of foreign blood serums, snake venom, bacterial toxins, products of defective metabolism, or immune reactions. It is a potentially dangerous condition, for erythrocytes that have lost their hemoglobin can no longer serve as oxygen carriers.

Lifespan of the RBC

A red blood cell lives only about 120 days, and yet in that short time it makes more than 300,000 trips around the body, travelling more than 700 miles, carries more than 3 quadrillion molecules of oxygen to the tissues of the body, and performs other vital services.

All those trips around the body, bending and squeezing through the capillaries, are very hard on a red blood cell, and it does not have a nucleus to initiate and direct processes of repair. Gradually its membrane becomes increasingly fragile and may eventually rupture, causing the cell to break apart in the capillaries. Worn-out red blood cells are also removed from circulation by roving macrophages (a type of white blood cell) in the "blood cell graveyards" of the liver and spleen. Their hemoglobin is broken down to an iron-containing pigment, hemosiderin, and the bile pigments bilirubin and biliverdin. Most of the iron is transported to the bone marrow and is reutilized. The greenish-yellow bilirubin gives bile its color. In cases of liver damage and certain other pathological conditions, bilirubin production greatly exceeds its excretion, and it accumulates in the body, producing the characteristic yellow color of jaundice.

How could researchers possibly determine the lifespan of an erythrocyte, when one red blood cell looks just like any other? This feat was accomplished by "tagging" some of the red cells with isotopes. For example, if a person consumes a small amount of radioactive iron, the radioactive isotope is incorporated into some of the hemoglobin molecules in immature red cells that are being formed in the bone marrow. Once formed, the hemoglobin stays inside its red blood cell until the cell dies. Thus, by collecting blood specimens periodically, and measuring their radioactivity, the lifespan of the RBC can be simply determined.

Number of RBC

If all the red blood cells of a single human being were spread out in a layer one cell thick, they could carpet four tennis courts! Each individual red blood cell is tiny—only 7 to 8 μ in diameter, far too small to be seen with the naked eye. But blood teems with enormous numbers of them. An average adult man has an average of 5.4 million erythrocytes per cubic millimeter of blood, while an average adult woman has a red cell count of 4.6 million per mm³. Thus, an adult human has about 25 *trillion* (25,000,000,000,000) red blood cells circulating through his or her body.

There is some variation in the number of red blood cells in healthy humans. The red cell count varies not only with sex (men usually have more than women), but also with age (the fetus and newborn child have the highest numbers of RBC). Temporary rises and drops in the number of erythrocytes may occur during the day, and depending on special circumstances; there is normally a drop after meals, while a temporarily increased count follows a session of strenuous exercise. Such temporary changes reflect expansion or contraction of the spleen, rather than any change in the rate of blood cell production or destruction. A move to a higher altitude, however, soon results in an increased production of erythrocytes, which may rise to 8 million per mm³ after a few weeks' stay at an altitude of 14,000 feet. After full acclimatization to high altitudes, which takes many months, the hematocrit rises from the normal average of 45 to a value of 60 to 65, with an average increase in hemoglobin from the normal 15 g% to about 22 g%. A rise in the red blood cell count above normal levels is called **polycythemia.**

The rise in the number of red blood cells in response to the drop in atmospheric oxygen at high altitudes is an example of one of the important homeostatic mechanisms of the body. It operates on a **feedback principle:** the reaction sequence is controlled and regulated by its own product. A drop in the oxygen content in the atmosphere results in a drop in the amount of oxygen carried by the blood to the tissues of the body. When the body's oxygen demands exceed the supply, the kidneys, and to some extent the liver also, respond by promoting a step-up of erythropoietin production. This hormone is carried to the bone marrow, where it stimulates an increased production of erythrocytes. As additional red blood cells enter the circulating blood, the amount of oxygen carried to the tissues rises. Oxygen supply again equals demand, the production of erythropoietin ceases, and the extra red blood cell production slows down. A feedback mechanism such as this, in which the product of a reaction sequence slows or stops the reaction, is referred to as **negative feedback.***

Increased red cell production results from a variety of conditions causing a drop in the oxygen carried by the blood. These include a loss of red blood cells due to hemorrhage, various disease-produced red blood cell deficiencies, or a clogging of blood vessels, which reduces the blood flow and thus cuts the amount of oxygen delivered to the tissues per unit time.

A malignant condition of the bone marrow may produce a rise in the hematocrit far out of proportion to the body's oxygen needs. This condition, called **polycythemia vera,** is characterized by red cell counts up to 11 million per mm^3, and the hematocrit may reach 70 to 80 percent. Paradoxically, the tissues of a person with polycythemia vera may be starved for oxygen. The high level of blood cells makes the blood so viscous that it moves sluggishly through the blood vessels. As a result, the red cells contain abnormally high levels of nonoxygenated hemoglobin, which give the person's skin a bluish, **cyanotic** tinge.

A different type of blood cell abnormality, **anemia,** is characterized by a deficiency of hemoglobin, due either to a decreased number of red cells or to an insufficient amount of hemoglobin per cell; it can be caused by a variety of factors.

Anemia

"Are you missing out on the joys of life?" goes a typical commercial, "Perhaps you are suffering from tired blood." The ailment that many patent "tonics" have purported to cure is anemia, a red blood cell deficiency condition that is often characterized by chronic fatigue.

The average red blood cell lives only about 120 days. Thus, in any four-month period throughout a person's whole life, an entire new supply of functioning erythrocytes, each with the appropriate cargo of hemoglobin, must be produced. If anything goes wrong in the sequence of red cell formation, if insufficient raw materials are available, or if blood cells are lost faster than new ones can be produced, anemia can result.

A variety of raw materials is needed for the production of red blood cells. The need for amino acids to build into proteins, and iron for the formation of hemoglobin, is obvious. But it has been found that

other minerals and vitamins—in particular the cobalt-containing vitamin B$_{12}$ and another B vitamin, folic acid—are essential for erythropoiesis. Vitamin B$_{12}$ is supplied by a well-balanced diet. But it cannot be absorbed into the body in significant amounts without the aid of a special protein produced by the stomach lining. This substance is called **intrinsic factor,** so named because it is supplied within the body. (By contrast, vitamin B$_{12}$ is sometimes called "extrinsic factor," for it must be taken in from outside.)

Vitamin B$_{12}$ is a key compound in processes of DNA formation, and is essential in the maturation of the red blood cells. If it is lacking in the diet, or if a deficiency of intrinsic factor prevents its absorption, abnormally large, misshapen erythrocytes called macrocytes are formed. Their membranes are thin and fragile, and they rupture after only a few weeks. A sharp drop in the number of effective red blood cells—anemia—results. When this condition is due to a deficiency of intrinsic factor, it is called **pernicious anemia,** which at one time was always fatal. Now that more is known about the mechanisms of red cell formation, pernicious anemia can be successfully treated either with liver or liver extract (which contains both intrinsic factor and vitamin B$_{12}$, as well as iron and other nutrients) or with doses of intrinsic factor together with vitamin and mineral supplements.

Another type of anemia, **aplastic anemia,** results from a sharp reduction in blood cell production. Radiations, certain industrial chemicals, and certain drugs may damage the bone marrow and prevent it from forming new red blood cells.

Other anemias may result from an increased loss of erythrocytes, too rapid to be made up by new red cell formation. An obvious cause is hemorrhage. After a single, rapid hemorrhage, a normal red cell count can be restored within three to four weeks. But chronic hemorrhage, as occurs in stomach ulcers, may lead to a loss of more iron than can be absorbed from food in the intestines. As a result, the red blood cells produced are small, with less than the normal amount of hemoglobin, and their oxygen-transporting ability is correspondingly reduced.

A number of hereditary conditions result in the formation of extremely fragile red blood cells, which rupture easily and produce **hemolytic anemia.** One of the most widespread forms is **sickle cell anemia,** which occurs mainly among people of African and Mediterranean descent. It has been found that sickle cell anemia patients have a variant form of hemoglobin, hemoglobin S. The change is astonishingly small: only one of nearly 300 amino acids is different.** But

---

* The opposite type, **positive feedback,** in which the products of a reaction stimulate the reaction to continue or increase, pouring out still more products, is far less common in the healthy body. In certain disease states, positive feedback mechanisms can produce a runaway process known as a **vicious cycle.** The vicious cycle in sickle cell anemia is described in the next section. An example of positive feedback in normal body functioning is discussed later in this chapter, in the section on platelet functions.

** The protein portion of the hemoglobin molecule is constructed from two pairs of identical chains; the four chains together contain a total of 574 amino acids.

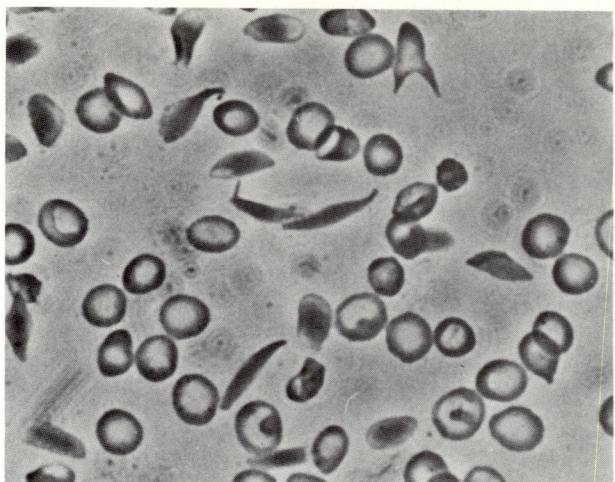

FIGURE 19-8   Blood smear in sickle cell anemia.

this small change is enough to make the molecules of hemoglobin S less soluble than those of the normal variant. As a result, they tend to form crystals inside the red blood cells. The cells become elongated, producing the characteristic "sickle" shape (Figure 19-8). The sickle cells tend to form clumps and block the small blood vessels, impairing the blood circulation and producing pain. The hemoglobin crystals also damage the cell membrane, and the sickle cells rupture easily, resulting in anemia.

Cells containing hemoglobin S assume the sickle shape most readily when the oxygen content of the blood is low. Thus, the sickling leads to a vicious cycle: by impairing circulation and producing anemia, it reduces the oxygen carried in the blood and thus leads to further sickling. Crippling and death may result.

Sickle cell anemia has been found to be inherited as a recessive trait: each parent must contribute a sickle cell gene for the condition to be expressed. In people who have inherited only one sickle cell gene, about 45 percent of the hemoglobin is of the variant type, and the cells normally do not sickle, unless they are exposed to extremely oxygen-deficient conditions. A simple test, requiring only a drop of blood, can be used to determine whether a person is carrying the sickle cell trait. Two people who wish to marry and suspect that they may be carrying the trait can thus determine the potential risk to their future children. Curiously, in regions where malaria is endemic, sickle cell trait seems to confer some protection against this disease when it is carried in the heterozygous state, with a sickle cell gene balanced by a normal gene. This advantage, counterbalancing the hazards of sickle cell anemia, is undoubtedly a factor in its widespread occurrence in persons of African and Mediterranean descent.

LEUKOCYTES

The human body is like an ancient walled city. The skin and mucous membranes that cover the body surfaces are the walls, the first line of defense. They protect us from the armies of microbes that swarm constantly, ready to take advantage of the slightest breach in the outer defenses. But let bacteria or other "foreign invaders" slip in through a cut or other gap in the wall, and the second-line defenders are ready to fight—to the death if need be. These are the white blood cells, the soldiers of the body.

The name of the white blood cells is descriptive of one of their most striking properties; unlike the red blood cells, colored by the red pigment hemoglobin, leukocytes do not contain a pigment and are essentially colorless. (Their technical name literally means "white cells.") They differ from the erythrocytes in other ways, too. White blood cells are generally larger than red blood cells, and each has a prominent nucleus, which it keeps throughout its entire lifetime. Like the microscopic amoebas that live in ponds, a leukocyte can change its shape, oozing and flowing, and sometimes sending out armlike **pseudopods.** Unlike red blood cells, which are carried passively along in the blood flow, white blood cells move actively. They can travel through the bloodstream (even against the current), creeping along in a characteristically **amoeboid movement.** A portion of the cell bulges out into a pseudopod, and the cell contents literally flow into it.

Leukocytes do not confine their travels to the bloodstream. Indeed, they use the bloodstream more as a commuter uses a highway to drive to work. The main functions of most of the white blood cells are performed outside the actual blood, in the neighboring tissues. A white cell leaves the bloodstream by oozing through a pore in a capillary wall, a process known as **diapedesis** (Figure 19-9).

The white cell soldiers of the body are called to battle by chemical messengers, released by damaged cells at sites of inflammation or cell destruction. Their response to these chemical messengers is another of their characteristic properties, referred to as **chemotaxis.**

In any normal blood specimen, the leukocytes can be seen to be greatly outnumbered by the erythrocytes—by about 700 to 1. Unlike the erythrocytes, white blood cells are not uniform in size, shape, and appearance. Studies of stained preparations have revealed a number of different types, which can be grouped into about five main categories.

Classification of WBC

White blood cells are classified on the basis of a number of characteristics: their structure (particularly that of the nucleus), the presence of granules in the

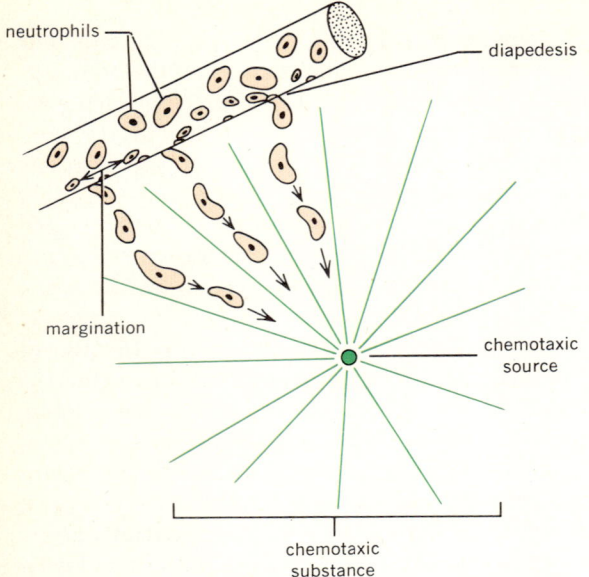

FIGURE 19-9 Summoned by chemical messengers to a site of tissue damage, leukocytes can actually squeeze through the pores of blood vessel walls by a process called diapedesis and roam through the tissues.

cytoplasm, and their reactions to the dyes used in specific stains (Figure 19-10).

One main division is between the **granulocytes,** which have a granular cytoplasm, and the **agranulocytes,** which are nongranular.

The granulocytes, produced in the bone marrow or myeloid tissue, are the most numerous, averaging about 70 percent of all the white blood cells. Three types of granulocytes can be distinguished, depending on their responses to stains: **eosinophils,** which take up the acid dye eosin; **basophils,** which are stained by

basic dyes; and **neutrophils,** which are stained by both acid and basic dyes (i.e., they are "neutral" in their staining preference). Their nuclei are generally divided into a variable number of lobes or segments, connected by thin strands of nuclear substance. Because of this nuclear variation, the granulocytes are sometimes referred to as **polymorphonuclear leukocytes,** or simply "polys."

Agranulocytes, derived from lymphoid tissue, make up the other 30 percent or so of leukocytes. They can in turn be classified as **lymphocytes** (large or small) and **monocytes** (the largest of the leukocytes). The nuclei of monocytes may be indented to a kidney shape, but they are never actually divided into lobes.

Functions of the WBC

We live in a potentially hostile environment. Invisible enemies lurk everywhere. Microorganisms swarm in uncountable numbers on "clean" skin. Microbes and molecules of possibly harmful chemicals are drawn into the lungs with every breath, swallowed with every bite of food. Pitched battles rage constantly between the invaders and the body's defenders.

The white blood cells are an important part of the widespread system of organs, tissues, and cells that protect the human body against disease and chemical assaults. Unravelling the secrets of the body's defenses and discovering ways to help them to work even more effectively are among the most actively researched fields in the biomedical sciences today. The body's defenses are discussed in greater detail in Chapter 37. Here we will have a brief acquaintance with part of the cast of characters: the white blood cells.

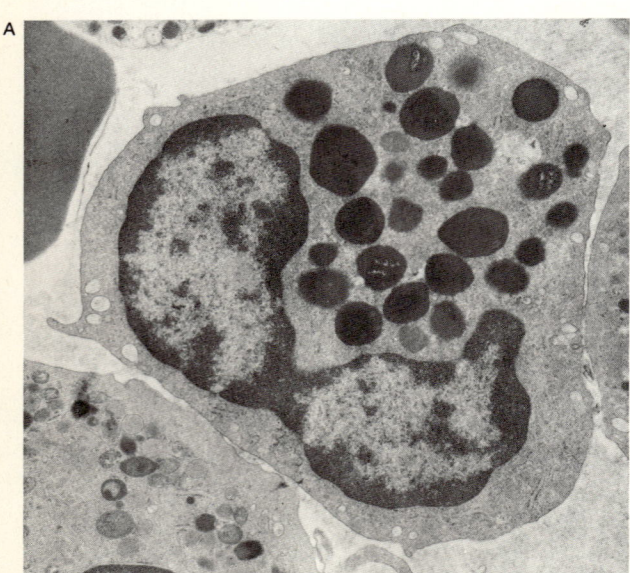

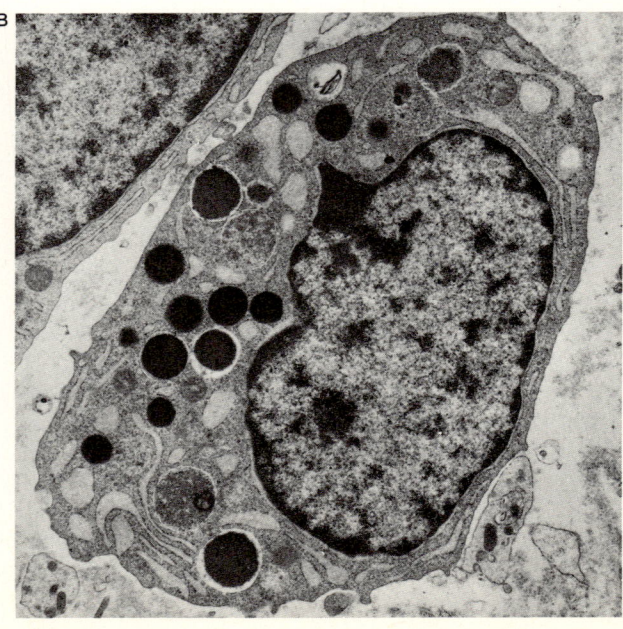

FIGURE 19-10 Some typical leukocytes: eosinophil (A), basophil (B), neutrophil (C), and lymphocyte (D).

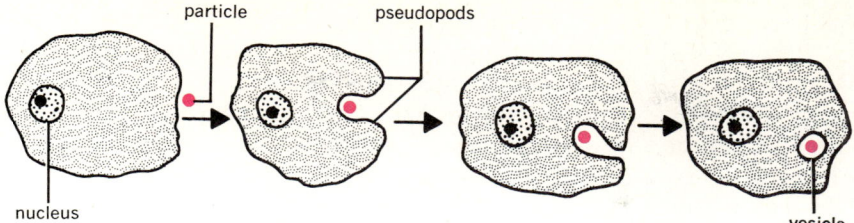

particle   pseudopods

nucleus

vesicle

FIGURE 19-11 White blood cells engulf foreign particles by phagocytosis, shown here in schematic form. For a photographic sequence of the process, see Figure 6-5.

Neutrophils

Neutrophils are the most numerous of all the white blood cells, about 60 to 70 percent of the total. Since they take up both acid and basic dyes, they stain a lilac color. Neutrophils are usually about 9 to 12 μ in diameter. The nucleus characteristically has two to five lobes; the cytoplasm is filled with fine granules. Neutrophils are particularly active cells, which serve as the spearhead of the body's mobile defense force. When tissues are damaged, they are the first on the scene. They are particularly effective in phagocytosis, the engulfing of bacteria or other foreign particles (Figure 19-11). Their pseudopods flow around the invader and enclose it in the cell, where it is literally digested. But their efforts take a heavy toll. Each bacterium ingested by a leukocyte carries a small portion of poison; ultimately the accumulation of toxins from the ingested bacteria, together with the powerful digestive enzymes released from the white cell's lysosomes, kills the battling leukocyte. (From 5 to 25 ingested bacteria is generally a neutrophil's quota before it succumbs.) Pus, which forms at the site of an infection, is made up chiefly of living and dead neutrophils, together with bits of cell debris. After the disease is under control, neutrophils may remain on the scene, aiding in the healing of tissues.

In the case of a heavy invasion of bacteria, the numbers of neutrophils in the circulating blood may be greatly increased. If the need is great enough, immature forms may be released from the bone marrow to aid in the fight. Such cells are called band or stab neutrophils, because their nuclei are horseshoe-shaped.

Eosinophils

Far less numerous than the neutrophils, the eosinophils generally account for 2 to 4 percent of the leukocytes. They are fairly large, about 10 to 14 μ in diameter. The nucleus usually has two lobes, and the cytoplasm is filled with large, uniform granules, which are stained a shiny red or red-orange by the acid dye eosin. Eosinophils are slow-moving, and they are poor at phagocytosis, but they contain many enzymes, including peroxidases, oxidases, trypsin, and phosphatases. These enzymes may enable them to detoxify foreign proteins and other substances. Eosinophils are mobilized particularly in certain allergic conditions, such as asthma, and in the presence of various bronchial and skin infections and parasites. They are also indicators of adrenal function; administration of ACTH produces a drop in the number of circulating eosinophils. It seems likely that

C
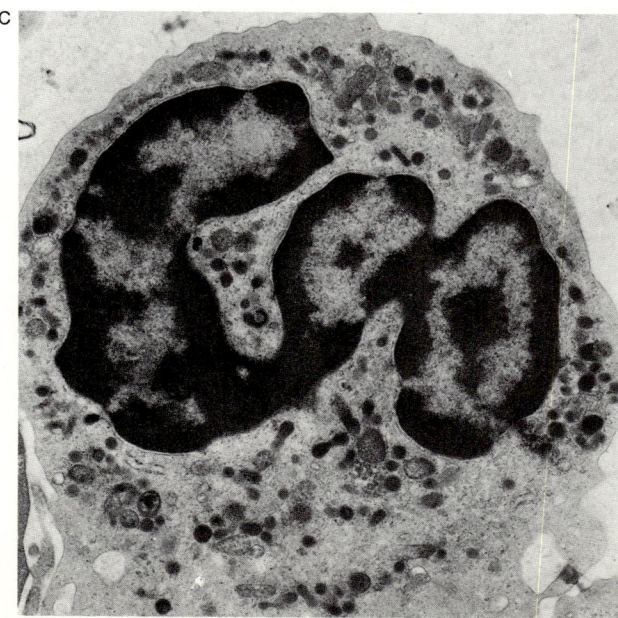

D
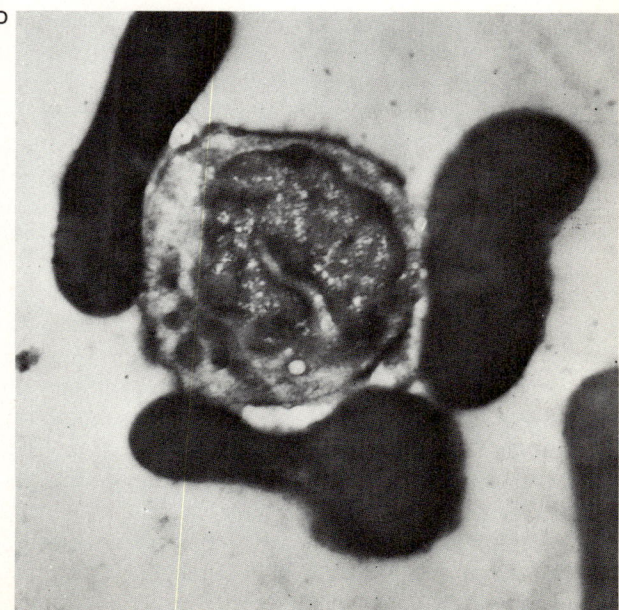

these granular leukocytes are a key link in the body's defenses against chemical invaders.

Basophils

The basophils are the rarest of the leukocytes, averaging only about 0.4 percent of all the white blood cells. As their name implies, their granules are stained a dull blue-purple by basic dyes. Their cytoplasm is packed with irregular basophilic granules, which partially obscure the S-shaped nucleus. They are very similar to the large **mast cells** found just outside the walls of the capillaries. Like the mast cells, basophils contain large amounts of **heparin** (an anticoagulant), **histamine** (a vasodilator), and **serotonin** (a vasoconstrictor). Their number increases during the healing of an inflammation and during chronic inflammatory processes. They thus may help to counteract the tendency for clumping of the red blood cells that arises during prolonged inflammation. Basophils may also be the source of the mast cells—simply an earlier phase of development, in transit before settling down.

Lymphocytes

As the most numerous of the agranulocytes, lymphocytes make up about 20 to 25 percent of the circulating white blood cells. Lymphocytes come in two sizes: large (about 12 μ) and small (about 8 μ). It was once thought that they were a relatively homogeneous group, except for the size difference. But now it is known that the lymphocytes include a number of different kinds of cells, all with the same staining properties. Lymphocytes have a very large, round nucleus, surrounded by a thin layer of clear blue cytoplasm. They are active cells and good phagocytes. Usually the second type of cells on the scene of a tissue injury, they accumulate in great numbers during the late stages of inflammation and also collect around cancerous lesions and other degenerative tissue. Because they are particularly rich in globulins, the lymphocytes are an important means of specific defense against disease microbes and may offer hope for an ultimate weapon against cancer. The role of the lymphocytes in the body's immunological defenses is discussed in greater detail in Chapter 37.

Monocytes

Monocytes are the largest of all the white blood cells, up to about 20 μ in diameter. The large nucleus may be oval or kidney-bean-shaped, and there is more cytoplasm than in a lymphocyte. Monocytes, making up about 3 to 8 percent of the white blood cells, wander back and forth from the blood to the tissues and persist for a long time in areas of infection. After a few hours in the tissue spaces, monocytes can swell to become **macrophages,** which are far more powerful phagocytes than the neutrophils. They can engulf more particles (up to 100 bacteria) and much larger particles. Macrophages are particularly effective in cleaning up large particles of cell debris and can even phagocytize whole worn-out red blood cells and malarial parasites. In chronic inflammations, the number of monocytes in the blood may rise sharply, up to 30 to 50 percent of all the leukocytes.

Formation of WBC

The life of a white blood cell is an even harder one than that of a red blood cell. Slipping in and out of the capillaries, patrolling the blood and tissues, and battling foreign invaders, it is likely to meet an untimely death in the service of the body. Yet the body's white cell "troops" must constantly be kept at full strength if good health is to be maintained. Thus, a continual production of new leukocytes is essential.

The red bone marrow, the birthplace of the erythrocytes, is also the site of the formation of many of the leukocytes. Indeed, both red and white blood cells are formed by differentiation of the same type of primitive stem cells. But the stem cells that differentiate into white blood cells retain their nucleus and never produce hemoglobin.

A bone marrow cell passes through a series of recognizable stages on the way to becoming a leukocyte (Figure 19-12): **myeloblast, promyelocyte, myelocyte, metamyelocyte,** and mature leukocyte. In the case of the granulocytes, the characteristically staining cytoplasmic granules are acquired at an early stage of development (the myelocyte).

Some of the agranular leukocytes are also produced in the bone marrow. But most seem to be produced in the various lymphoid organs, including the lymph nodes, the spleen, the thymus, and the tonsils.

Good nutrition is just as important for leukocyte formation as it is for erythropoiesis. In particular, the vitamin folic acid is necessary for the formation of white blood cells. Both malnutrition and extreme debilitation can interfere with leukocyte production and thus lower the body's resistance to disease.

Lifespan of WBC

Most of the body cells "wear out" in a harmoniously programmed sequence and are replaced in due course by fresh new cells. But the life of the white blood cells is a far more uncertain one, and death, when it comes, is often violent. Thus, the lifespan of the leukocytes is extremely variable. It may be only a few hours; or, with luck and a period of comparative peace in the body, it may be measured in months.

Unlike the red blood cells, the time spent by leukocytes in the blood is not their whole lifespan. They merely cruise the bloodstream until they are needed elsewhere. Granulocytes have been found to average about a 12 hour stay in the blood—less if there is a serious infection somewhere in the tissues, or up to a

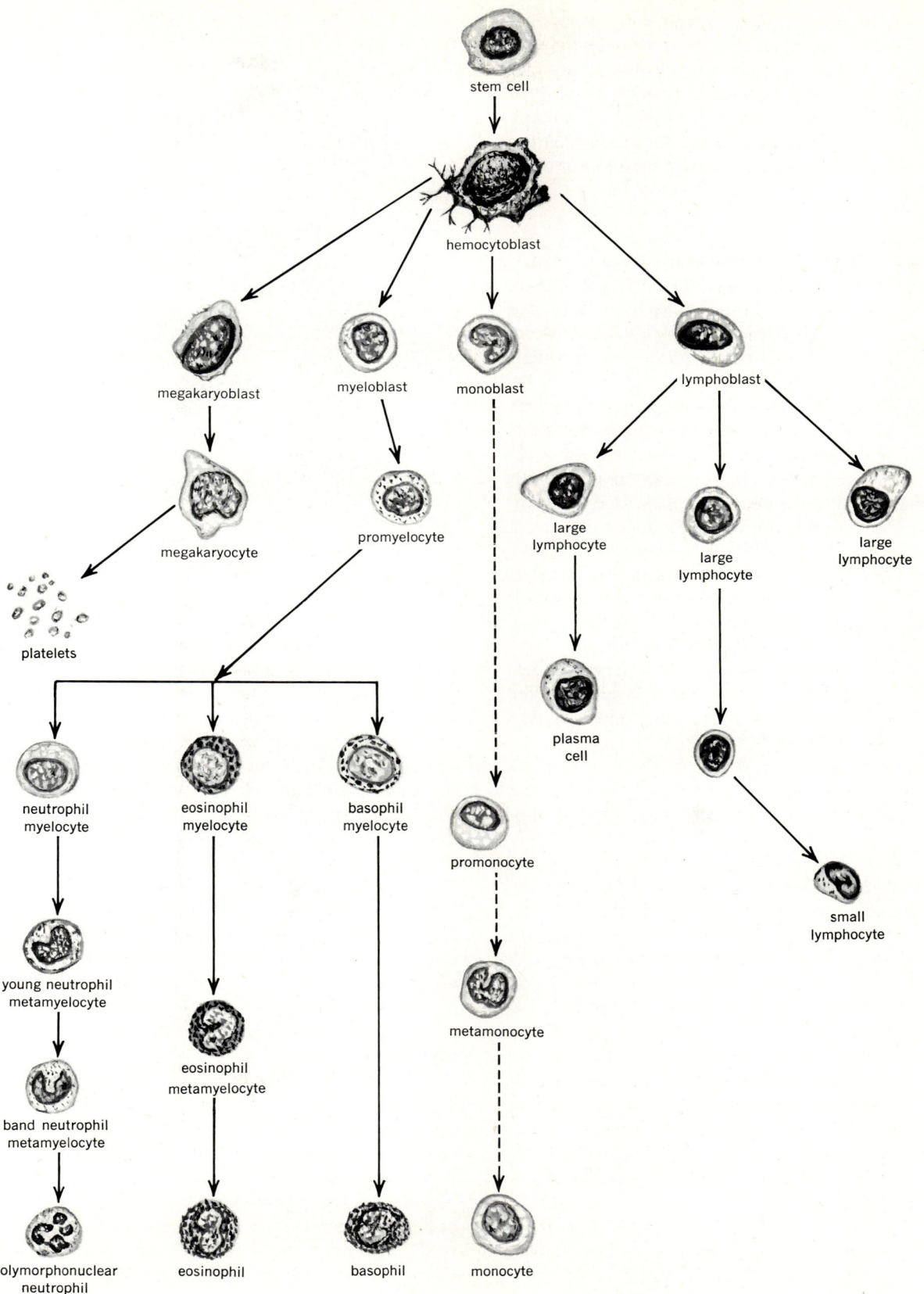

FIGURE 19-12 Stages in the formation of white blood cells and platelets.

few days if things are quiet. Lymphocytes commonly spend only a few hours in the blood. But experiments with lymphocytes tagged with radioactive isotopes have shown that they continually pass back and forth from the blood to the tissues, reenter the lymph nodes, and enter the blood again. Depending on the body's needs, lymphocytes can have lifespans of up to 300 days.

Number of WBC

Burning with fever, breathing with difficulty, the patient lies on the hospital bed. Doctors and nurses watch tensely, waiting for word from the lab—the differential white cell count that may give them a crucial clue to the nature of the infection that threatens the patient's life.

Perhaps no other part of the body can reveal as much about the body's health as the white blood cells. A rise in the total count suggests that an infection is raging somewhere. A drop below normal levels can signal a dangerous depletion of the body's defensive resources. And counts of the individual types of white blood cells—a **differential count**—can provide hints of what type of invader is causing the trouble.

A normal adult has an average of 5,000 to 10,000 leukocytes per cubic millimeter of circulating blood, or about one leukocyte to 700 erythrocytes. The number may vary within these limits from person to person and even in the same person according to the time of day (it is lowest in the early morning and highest in the afternoon).

An increase in the number of leukocytes in the blood above 10,000 per mm³ is referred to as **leukocytosis**; a decrease below 5,000 per mm³ is called **leukopenia**.

Leukocytosis Temporary increases in the number of leukocytes in the blood may occur after exercise, after cold baths, during digestion, and in conditions such as pregnancy. Such physiological leukocytosis is believed to be the result of changes in circulation rather than an actual stimulation of new white blood cell formation.

Persistent leukocytosis is usually an indication of pathology. Acute infections such as pneumonia and appendicitis are characterized by elevated white blood cell counts. (In appendicitis, both the total white cell count and the percentage of neutrophils are elevated. Thus a differential count may be the deciding factor for surgery.)

Leukemia Extraordinarily high white cell counts, up to 500,000 per mm³, with the presence of many immature white cells in the bloodstream, are characteristic of leukemia (Figure 19-13). This disease is a form of cancer, in which white cells proliferate wildly

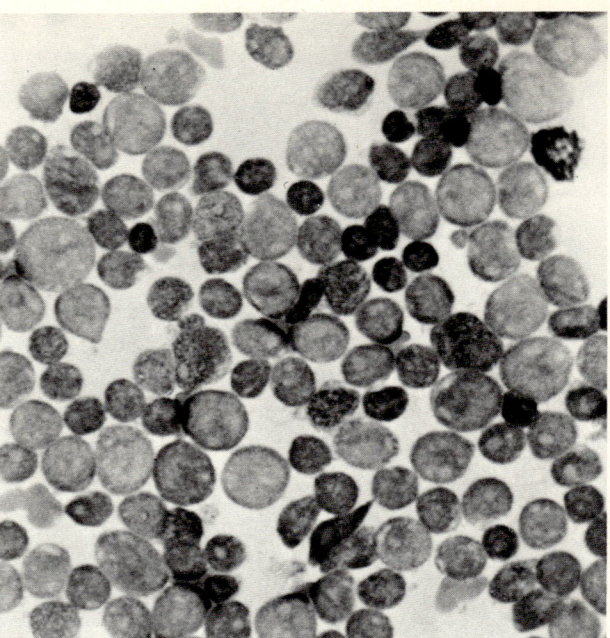

FIGURE 19-13 Blood smear from an acute lymphocytic leukemia patient.

in the bone marrow, literally starving out the immature red cells and producing anemia. The white blood cells formed in leukemia are usually abnormal and poorly equipped for their task of disease fighting. A vicious cycle is set up, in which more and more leukemic cells are churned out in the body's vain efforts to meet its needs for phagocytes. Meanwhile, the masses of circulating white cells plug up key blood vessels in the brain, heart, lungs, and kidneys. They invade bones, lymph nodes, spleen, liver, and other organs, interfering with their function and destroying tissues. These factors, the lowered resistance to infectious diseases, the debilitating anemia, and the tremendous drain of energy and materials to produce the leukemic cells all contribute to make untreated leukemia a virulent and ultimately fatal disease. However, promising strides have been made in recent years toward the control and cure of leukemia, as discussed in Chapter 37.

Infectious Mononucleosis Mononucleosis is an acute infectious disease believed to be caused by a virus. It commonly affects young adults and is sometimes called "the kissing disease," referring to its supposed mode of transmission. Characteristic symptoms of infectious mononucleosis are fever, sore throat, and swollen cervical lymph nodes. A differential count is important in establishing the diagnosis: with an elevated total white cell count, there is a decrease in the percentage of polymorphonuclear cells and an increase in the mononuclear cells (agranulocytes).

Leukopenia

Leukopenia may be brought about by poor nutrition, chronic diseases such as tuberculosis, and certain drugs. Mild cases of leukopenia are often associated with viral diseases, such as influenza, measles, mumps, chickenpox, and poliomyelitis. Severe leukopenia, leaving the body dangerously defenseless against infectious diseases, may be produced by radiations or poisons that damage the bone marrow. Extreme leukopenia, down to a zero white cell count, has been observed in victims of atomic bomb explosions. Radiation therapy of cancer may lead to leukopenia; however, if part of the bone marrow is carefully shielded, stem cells from the protected marrow migrate through the body and repopulate the irradiated bone marrow, restoring its normal hemopoietic functions.

PLATELETS

The blood platelets, the smallest of the formed elements, are also called **thrombocytes,** literally "clotting cells." But they are actually misnamed. For they are not really cells, but rather fragments of cells. They are small discs, 2 to 4 μ in diameter, which contain granules but lack a nucleus. They are formed in the bone marrow, by the breakdown of giant cells called **megakaryocytes** (see Figure 19-12).

The blood of a normal human adult contains from 250,000 to 400,000 platelets per mm³. Thus, these formed elements are more numerous than the leukocytes, but less numerous than the erythrocytes. A sharp drop in the number of blood platelets is called **thrombocytopenia;** a marked increase is referred to as **thrombocytosis.**

Platelets are short-lived bodies. They normally live in the blood for about five to eight days, after which they are destroyed in the spleen and other organs of the reticuloendothelial system by patrolling macrophages. But the life of the platelets may be cut even shorter if there is damage to a blood vessel. For blood platelets are a key link in the body's mechanisms of **hemostasis,** the prevention of blood loss.

Functions of Platelets

A blood platelet can perform its special service for the body only once in its life, for it is destroyed in the act. Yet this self-sacrifice may be vital to the safety of the body. Platelets go into action under emergency conditions, when a blood vessel is cut or pierced and precious blood is being lost.

When a blood vessel is cut, the damaged edges become rough and lose their nonwetting properties. Within a few seconds, platelets are sticking to the roughened edges. The platelets swell, take on an irregular shape, and secrete ADP, which activates nearby platelets. These, too, become sticky and begin to clump together. As this positive feedback mechanism involves growing numbers of platelets, a **platelet plug** is formed, and if the hole in the blood vessel is small enough, it can close it entirely. This mechanism effectively takes care of the minute ruptures that normally occur in the capillaries hundreds of times each day.

If, however, the hole in the blood vessel is too large to be closed by a platelet plug, or if the vessel is severed entirely, the platelets participate in a further sequence of events. They are extremely fragile structures, and exposure to air or to rough surfaces causes them to break up. When a platelet disintegrates, a variety of substances spill out into the blood. Powerful vasoconstrictors, such as serotonin, help to control bleeding. A substance called **platelet factor** initiates a chain of chemical reactions leading to the formation of a fibrous protein structure. Platelets and red and white blood cells from the passing blood are caught up in the crisscrossing protein fibers and form a **clot,** which effectively plugs the hole. Then, once the clot has formed, platelets cause it to shrink or **retract,** pressing out most of the fluid serum. In the process, the clot is transformed from a soft mass into a firm one, which further helps to stop bleeding.

BLOOD COAGULATION

A fresh sample of blood, collected from a patient or volunteer, is a red, rather free-flowing liquid. But if it is allowed to stand in an open test tube, it quickly coagulates into a jellylike mass. Leave the specimen undisturbed, and further changes occur. A pale, straw-colored liquid begins to appear on the surface as the mass of the clot settles and contracts. Finally there is a distinct separation, between the firm, solid clot and a thin liquid called blood serum.

More can be learned about the process of blood coagulation or clotting by observing a drop of blood on a slide under a microscope. Then it can be seen that the clot is formed by a fine network of threadlike structures, which entrap red and white blood cells (Figure 19-14). As the clot shrinks or retracts, the red cells are held even more firmly in place, although some of the white cells are able to ooze out, amoeba-fashion, and slip away into the serum.

The fibers that form the network structure of a clot are made of a protein called fibrin. But where do they come from? They must not be present in any significant amounts in the blood flowing through the blood vessels, for they would quickly block the vessels and hopelessly impede circulation. Yet under emergency conditions, when there is a gaping hole in a blood vessel and blood is spilling out, the mechanism of fibrin formation must operate rapidly and reliably.

Mechanisms of Blood Clotting

Few areas of research have been as intensively studied as the mechanisms of blood clotting. Yet few

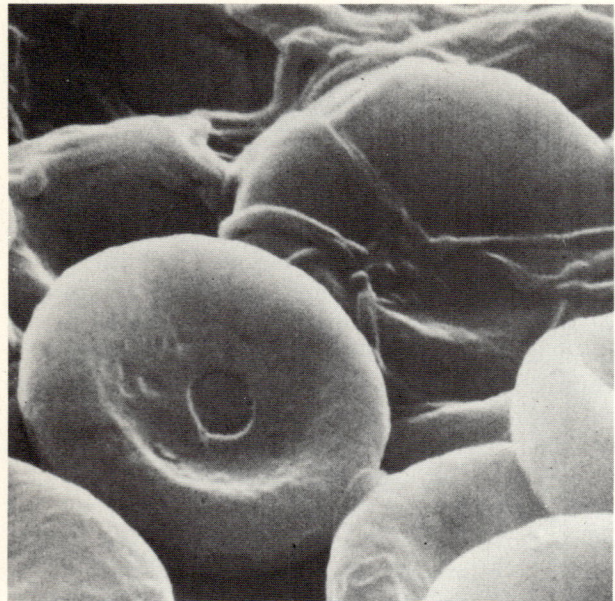

FIGURE 19-14 A blood clot: this scanning electron micrograph shows red blood cells caught in a fibrin mesh. (SEM courtesy of Thomas L. Hayes and Lawrence-Berkeley Laboratory, U. of Calif.)

chain of consecutive and interlinked chemical reactions. Thirteen separate factors involved in blood clotting have already been isolated (see Table 19-2), and it is likely that further research will continue to cast light on the intricacies of their interactions. Here we shall give only a basic outline of the sequence of events that begins with the emergency state of blood vessel damage and ends with the production of a firm clot, as diagramed in Figure 19-15.

Platelets, coming in contact with the roughened edges of the torn blood vessel, disintegrate and release a substance called **platelet factor,** a phospholipid that takes part in the formation of the enzyme **thromboplastin.** Thromboplastin is also released into the blood by the traumatized tissues at the site of the wound. Interacting with some of the plasma proteins, thromboplastin is activated. It can then interact with the plasma protein **prothrombin,** with the aid of **calcium ions** and other accessory factors, converting the prothrombin to **thrombin.** Thrombin in turn acts as an enzyme that catalyzes the conversion of the plasma protein **fibrinogen** to the solid, fibrous form, **fibrin.** Networks of fibrin form the framework of the clot.

areas of research have been marked by such a confusing array of conflicting reports. This confusion is due, in part, to the extreme complexity of the process. Blood clotting is not a single reaction, but rather a

Abnormalities of Blood Clotting

The organs and systems of a healthy body are intri-

FIGURE 19-15 Formation of a blood clot following injury.

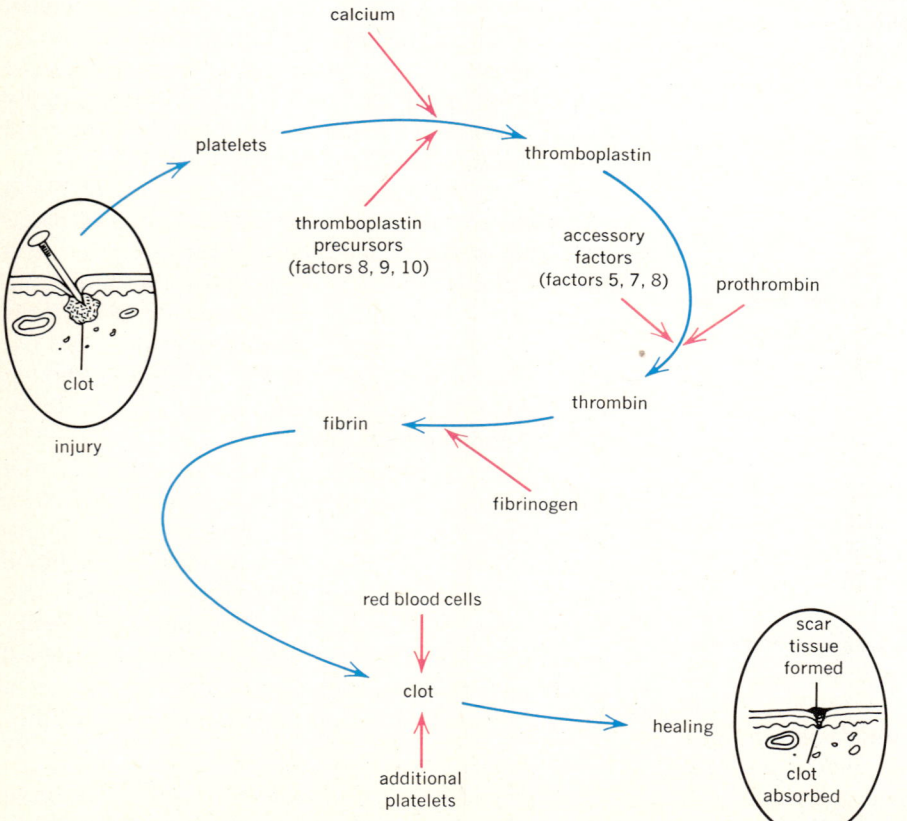

cately interrelated into a smoothly functioning whole. But a disorder in one body part, due perhaps to an inborn defect or to conditions of the external environment, can have far-reaching and sometimes unexpected effects on other organs and systems of the body. Thus, abnormalities of blood clotting can be caused by defects or damage to a variety of organs.

The liver, for example, is a key organ of vital importance for normal blood clotting. Plasma fibrinogen, prothrombin, and various other clotting factors are produced in the liver. Thus, liver disease may give rise to clotting abnormalities that may result in severe or even fatal blood loss.

Nutrition is also of great importance. In addition to an adequate supply of amino acids and other nutrients, vitamin K is essential for the formation of prothrombin. This vitamin may be obtained in the diet; it is also synthesized by the bacteria that live in the intestines. A heavy course of antibiotic therapy, wiping out the normal intestinal flora in addition to pathogenic organisms, might therefore cause a vita-

min K deficiency if combined with improper nutrition. Another possible cause of vitamin K deficiency is an inability to absorb it through the intestinal wall. The absorption of vitamin K, a fat-soluble vitamin, requires bile salts. If they are lacking (again, through some liver defect), vitamin K becomes unavailable to the body, and clotting failure results.

Bone marrow damage, causing thrombocytopenia, also produces a failure of the normal clotting mechanisms.

Thrombocytopenia   When the number of blood platelets falls below about 70,000 per mm³ of blood, excessive bleeding occurs. Each time a tiny capillary ruptures, blood escapes from the blood vessels out into the tissues. As a result, the skin of such a person shows many small purplish patches, giving the disease the name **thrombocytopenia purpura.** Damage to the bone marrow by drugs or irradiation and pernicious anemia can cause thrombocytopenia. Many cases seem to be the result of development of immunity to

TABLE 19-2   Blood-clotting Factors

INTERNATIONAL NOMENCLATURE	SYNONYMS	FUNCTION
Platelet Factor	Cephalin (a phospholipid)	Participates in thromboplastin formation
Factor I	Fibrinogen (a plasma protein)	Converted to fibrin
Factor II	Prothrombin (a plasma protein)	Converted to thrombin (vitamin K is required for prothrombin synthesis in the liver)
Factor III	Thromboplastin (an enzyme)	Produced in the blood or released by injured cells; promotes conversion of prothrombin to thrombin
Factor IV	Calcium (Ca^{++} ions in plasma)	Catalyzes or participates in several stages of coagulation
Factor V	Labile factor; accelerator globulin (a plasma protein)	Accelerates conversion of prothrombin to thrombin
Factor VI	(Apparently identical to Factor V; no longer recognized as a separate entity)	
Factor VII	Serum prothrombin conversion accelerator (SPCA)	Accelerates conversion of prothrombin to thrombin in presence of tissue thromboplastin; not needed with intrinsic thromboplastin (produced in plasma)
Factor VIII	Antihemophilic factor (AHF); antihemophilic globulin (AHG)	Aids in thromboplastin production; deficiency results in hemophilia
Factor IX	Plasma thromboplastin component (PTC); Christmas factor	Influences amount of thromboplastin formed; deficiency results in hemophilia
Factor X	Stuart-Prower factor	Necessary for full activation of both intrinsic and tissue thromboplastin
Factor XI	Plasma thromboplastin antecedent (PTA)	Necessary for early stages of formation of prothrombin activator
Factor XII	Hageman factor; contact factor	Initiates clotting reaction
Factor XIII	Fibrin stabilizing factor; Laki-Lorand factor	Makes fibrin insoluble in urea and stabilizes clot

the person's own platelets. Somehow the body's immune system has become sensitized to some substance in the platelets and has begun to manufacture antibodies against them. Thus, although normal numbers of platelets are produced, they are destroyed by the reaction with antibodies in the plasma. Such patients can sometimes be helped by removal of the spleen, which is normally responsible for the destruction of large numbers of platelets. Cortisone, which suppresses immune reactions, may be beneficial. Whole blood transfusions can give temporary relief from bleeding.

Hemophilia A parent whose child has hemophilia lives in constant terror. At any moment the child might fall and be injured. For normal children, a bruise or cut is a minor incident, quickly healed and forgotten. But a hemophilic child with a "minor" cut could literally bleed to death.

Hemophilia, the "bleeder's disease," is characterized by a deficiency of one or more of the blood clotting factors, particularly the **antihemophilic factor (AHF),** which operates in the first phase of blood clotting. It is a hereditary disease, and it has been found to be sex-linked—that is, it is transmitted by a recessive gene on the female sex chromosome (the X-chromosome). As a result, hemophilia occurs far more often in males than in females. A male has only one X-chromosome. A single hemophilia gene can thus be expressed in a male, even though it is normally recessive, because there is no corresponding normal gene to counterbalance its effects. A female, with two X-chromosomes, on the other hand, can be hemophilic only if she has inherited a defective gene from each of her parents (Figure 19-16).

The most famous series of hemophilia cases occurred in the royal families of Europe during the late nineteenth and early twentieth centuries. From the "royal hemophilia pedigree" that was eventually compiled, the defect apparently originated through a mutation in one of Queen Victoria's X-chromosomes. The mutant gene, passed down through her children and grandchildren, resulted in a number of "bleeder" sons who suffered an early death and "carrier" daughters who married and spread the disease through the royal houses of Europe. (The present ruling family of England does not carry the gene.) This disease probably had a major effect on the course of world history, for the preoccupation of the Russian Czar and Czarina with their hemophilic only son set in motion a chain of events that led to the Russian revolution.

In addition to difficult-to-control hemorrhaging from cuts and wounds, hemophilics often experience spontaneous bleeding in the skin, muscles, or joints, which can be painful and dangerous.

After the causes of hemophilia were discovered, the disease was at first treated by transfusions of normal blood. But now AHF is routinely extracted from stored blood that is too old to use for transfusions. Prophylactic treatments with AHF and self-injection at home can in many cases permit hemophilia patients to lead a relatively normal life.

Thrombosis and Embolism Heart attacks kill more Americans than any other condition or disease. The majority of these victims die because a blood clot lodges in the vessels of the heart, blocking the flow of blood and causing irreparable damage to the heart muscle.

Ideally, the blood clotting mechanisms would operate only when a blood vessel is damaged, effectively closing off the hole and stopping the loss of blood. But actually clots sometimes form inside an undamaged blood vessel, blocking it off and impeding circulation. The formation of a blood clot inside a blood vessel, partially or completely closing it, is called **thrombosis** (Figure 19-17). The clot itself is called a **thrombus.** Sometimes a thrombus or a portion of it breaks away and begins to travel through the circulatory system, carried by the flowing blood. Such a traveling thrombus is referred to as an **embolus.** Ultimately, if the embolus reaches a blood vessel that is too narrow to permit it to pass, it may come to rest, plugging the vessel. Tissues beyond the plug will no longer receive the nourishing blood flow that the blood vessel normally supplied. The amount of damage caused by an embolus depends on the region in which it lodges. A pulmonary embolus, plugging an artery leading to a lung, can interfere with the vital gas exchange. A coronary embolus can cut off the supply of oxygen to the heart and cause a myocardial infarction (heart attack). An embolus carried to the blood vessels of the brain may result in a stroke, causing a loss of part of the mental functions or death.

What causes a clot to form inside a blood vessel? An injury crushing a blood vessel might stimulate clot formation. Deposits of fat inside the blood vessel walls **(atherosclerosis)** can roughen their inner surface, causing platelets to adhere, disintegrate, and initiate the clotting mechanism. The introduction of some foreign substance into the bloodstream—even a large air bubble introduced during the improper administration of an injection—might provide a center for platelet congregation and result in thrombosis. Periods of sluggish blood flow can also promote clot formation, for small quantities of thrombin and other clotting factors are constantly being formed in the blood. Normally the blood flows rapidly enough to disperse these clotting factors before they can react to any significant degree. But the partial blocking or occlusion of the blood vessels that is produced by ath-

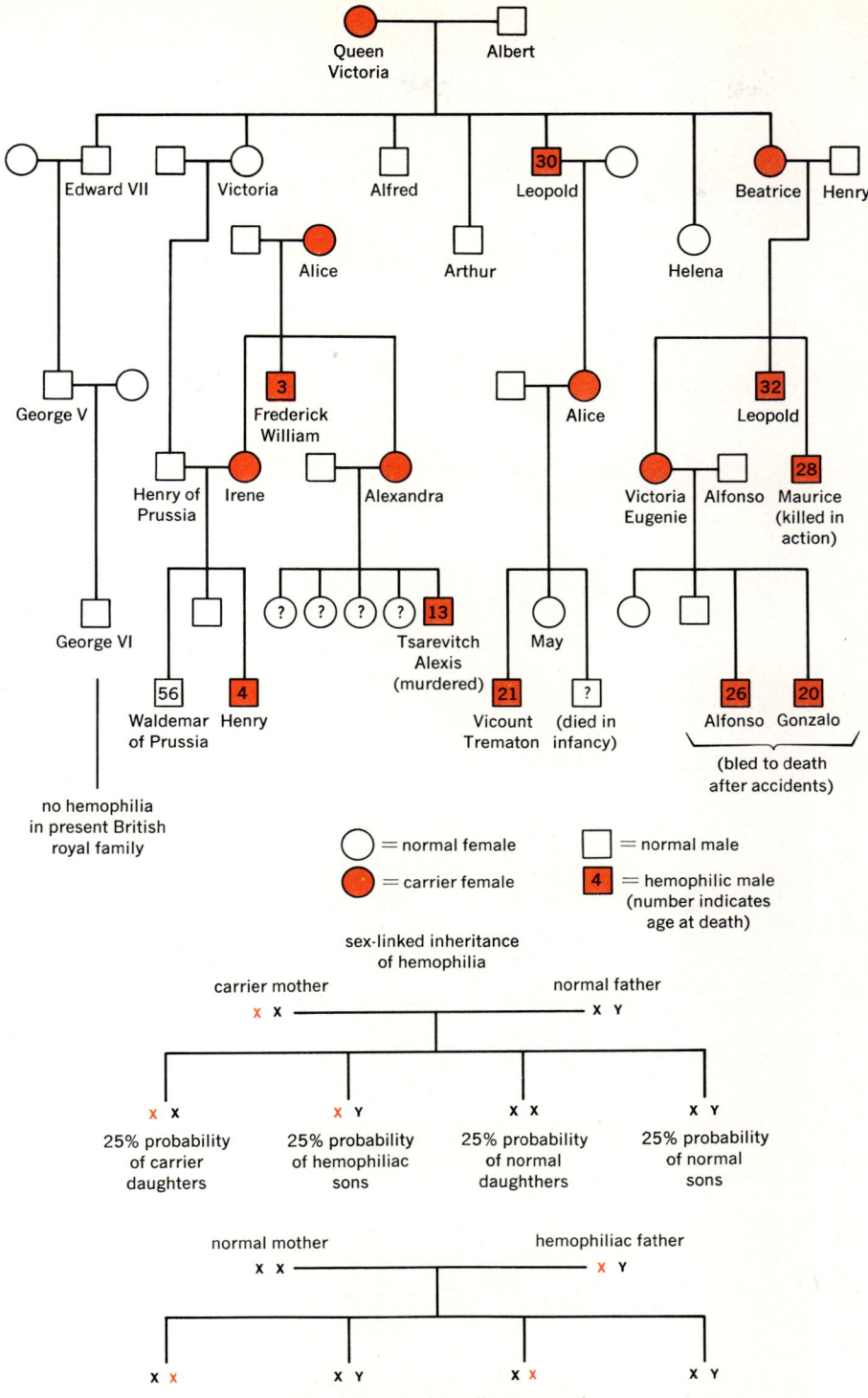

FIGURE 19-16 The royal hemophilia pedigree among the descendants of Queen Victoria (A) and a schematic depiction of the sex-linked inheritance of hemophilia (B).

erosclerosis can slow down circulation sufficiently to permit clot formation to begin. Prolonged bed rest, in which there is a pooling or stasis of blood in the vessels of the extremities, can also result in clot formation. When the person does get out of bed, the contractions of the leg muscles may cause the clots to break loose and be carried to the pulmonary arteries.

Thus, pulmonary embolism is a possible complication in operations and illnesses unless early ambulation is possible.

Factors Affecting Clotting

Theoretically, at any moment—perhaps at the very moment you read these words—a clot might form

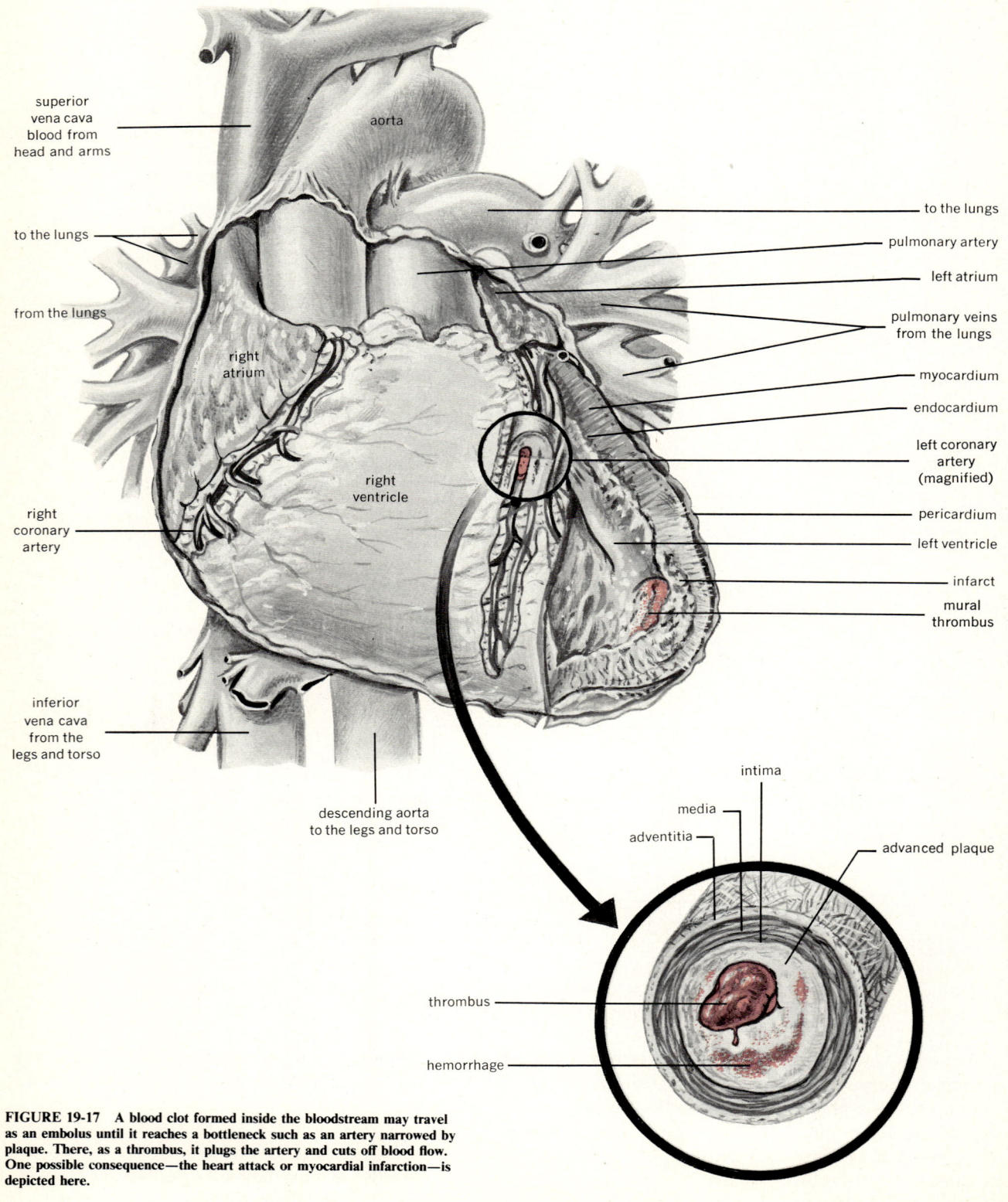

superior
vena cava
blood from
head and arms

aorta

to the lungs

pulmonary artery

left atrium

pulmonary veins
from the lungs

to the lungs

from the lungs

right
atrium

myocardium

endocardium

left coronary
artery
(magnified)

right
ventricle

pericardium

left ventricle

right
coronary
artery

infarct

mural
thrombus

inferior
vena cava
from the
legs and torso

descending aorta
to the legs and torso

intima

media

adventitia

advanced plaque

thrombus

hemorrhage

FIGURE 19-17 A blood clot formed inside the bloodstream may travel
as an embolus until it reaches a bottleneck such as an artery narrowed by
plaque. There, as a thrombus, it plugs the artery and cuts off blood flow.
One possible consequence—the heart attack or myocardial infarction—is
depicted here.

cross section of coronary artery

inside one of your blood vessels, and, once formed, be swept on to plug a vital artery in heart, lungs, or brain. Fortunately, the normal, healthy body has an assortment of natural mechanisms for coping with the danger of thrombosis.

First of all, the extremely smooth surface of the endothelium lining the blood vessels helps to prevent the initiation of clotting. In addition, the inner surface of the vessels is coated with a very thin film of a negatively charged protein substance, which repels the clotting factors and the platelets. Both the smoothness and the negative electric charge are lost when a blood vessel wall is damaged. But even when a clot has begun to form, the fibrin threads themselves tend to adsorb most of the thrombin that is being formed, keeping the clot from spreading too far into the surrounding blood.

An alpha globulin called **antithrombin,** normally present in the blood, also acts to remove thrombin from the blood and this inhibits clotting.

Heparin, a powerful anticoagulant, is secreted into the blood by the basophilic mast cells found in the connective tissue around the capillaries. (The basophils of the circulating blood also produce heparin, but their numbers are so small that they are not believed to have any significant effect on blood clotting.) The tissues surrounding the capillaries of the lungs and the liver are especially richly supplied with mast cells. Heparin prevents clotting in several ways: it blocks the formation of thromboplastin, inhibits the formation of thrombin, inhibits the action of thrombin on fibrinogen, aids in the deactivation of thrombin by antithrombin, and increases the amount of thrombin adsorbed by fibrin.

Some substances not normally found in the body can also have a powerful anticoagulant action. Leeches secrete a substance called **hirudin,** which inhibits clotting and keeps the blood of their victims flowing freely. Mosquitoes and other blood-sucking insects also inject a small dose of anticoagulant with their saliva when they bite.

Dicumarol, which is now administered prophylactically to heart patients to reduce the risk of thromboembolism, was discovered when a bleeding disease was observed in cattle fed on spoiled sweet clover. (A synthetic form is now used as a drug, rather than the natural product.) Dicumarol acts by blocking the action of vitamin K and thus interfering with the formation of prothrombin and the other clotting factors in the liver. Frequent tests of prothrombin activity are usually prescribed, so that the dose of the anticoagulant can be carefully adjusted.

Sometimes it is necessary to promote blood clotting. This is the case in some forms of surgery, in making skin grafts adhere, and in treating patients with a defective blood clotting system. Commercial preparations of thrombin and fibrinogen can be used. In addition, the clotting of a wound may be hastened by the application of gauze (contact with the rough surface causes platelet disintegration) and hot sponges or towels (a temperature above 46° C accelerates the chemical reactions of clotting).

Clotting in Blood Samples Within minutes after a fresh sample of blood is drawn, it solidifies into a jellied mass. In this form it would be useless for most blood tests, as well as for transfusions. Therefore, means have been devised to control and prevent the clotting of blood specimens.

Mechanical means of inhibiting clotting include drawing the blood very carefully into a syringe coated with paraffin. In this case, the smooth coating minimizes platelet damage, and clotting may not occur. Though agitation tends to foster clotting, vigorous stirring with a glass rod may keep a blood sample clot-free. The stirring promotes fibrin formation, but the fibrin formed sticks to the rod and can be removed. The blood remaining is referred to as **defibrinated blood.**

Low temperature can inhibit clotting; in blood kept at 0°C, clotting is delayed for days.

Anticoagulant chemicals are most frequently used to prevent clotting of blood samples. **Oxalates, citrates,** and **EDTA (ethylenediaminetetraacetate)** prevent clotting by precipitating calcium, thus stopping it from participating in a key step of the clotting sequence. Heparin, dicumarol, or hirudin may also be used.

Dissolution of Clots If an accident blocks an important roadway, the traffic may build up for miles. This, at worst, may be an inconvenience to drivers. But if an important blood vessel of the body is blocked, the obstruction deprives body tissues of vital supplies of oxygen and nutrients. Poisonous waste products build up in the starved tissues, and if they are part of a key organ, the damage that results may lead to death. Thus, clearing a clot may literally be a race against death.

To some extent, clot formation and dissolution go on continuously in the normal body. One of the plasma proteins is a substance called **plasminogen** or **profibrinolysin.** When it is activated, it is changed into a form called **plasmin** or **fibrinolysin.** This substance resembles the digestive enzyme trypsin. It literally digests a blood clot, dissolving it away. (The process is called **fibrinolysis.**)

Fibrinolysis also works to clear away clots that form when blood leaks out into the tissues.

In view of the great hazard a thrombus or embolus

may pose to the life of a patient, the mechanisms of fibrinolysis have been a focus of active research. An activator called **urokinase** has been discovered in urine. It is believed to play a role in the body's natural clot-clearing mechanism, and it has also shown promise as a drug for dissolving pulmonary embolisms.

Another activator enzyme under study is **streptokinase,** a substance produced by streptococci. The bacteria use this substance to dissolve clotted tissue fluids and spread through the tissues. It acts on plasminogen to produce plasmin.

Blood Clotting Tests

Tests that assess the effectiveness of a person's blood clotting system may be of great value in a number of clinical situations: a hemophilia victim being treated with a blood-clotting factor, a heart patient taking an anticoagulant prophylactically, a patient being prepared for major surgery, a woman about to give birth to a child. The procedures most often used measure the clotting time, the bleeding time, the prothrombin blood level, the platelet count, and clot retraction.

Clotting Time
The method most widely used to determine blood clotting time is to collect blood in a clean glass test tube. The tube is then immersed in a water bath at 37°C (normal body temperature) and tipped back and forth every 30 seconds, checking for signs of clotting. The time it takes for a clot to adhere to the wall of the tube is taken as the endpoint. Measured in this way, the normal clotting time ranges from five to eight minutes.

Bleeding Time
Bleeding time is usually determined by piercing the tip of the finger or the earlobe with a sharp knife. The wound is touched gently with a clean filter paper every 30 seconds. The time when the paper is no longer stained is recorded as the bleeding time. Normal values range from three to six minutes, but they are so variable that the test is of only limited value.

Prothrombin Time
In the determination of prothrombin time, the blood drawn from the patient is immediately oxalated, so that none of the prothrombin has a chance to be converted to thrombin. Then an excess of thromboplastin and calcium ions is suddenly mixed with the blood. The calcium nullifies the effect of oxalate, while thromboplastin activates the conversion of prothrombin to thrombin. The time required for clotting to occur is noted. This is the prothrombin time, and it is directly related to the amount of prothrombin in the blood if the other clotting factors are normal. (A calibration curve is drawn to relate prothrombin times to actual prothrombin contents, so that the results of any particular test can be quickly evaluated.) The normal prothrombin time is 12 to 20 seconds.

Platelet Determinations
Platelets can be counted directly on blood smears. An indirect indication of the platelet count is given by a determination of clot retraction. Once a clot has formed in a test tube, retraction normally occurs within 30 to 60 minutes. If clot retraction does not occur, the platelet level may be greatly reduced.

HEMORRHAGE

Many people feel a bit squeamish at the sight of blood; indeed, strong men, volunteering as blood donors, have been known to faint at the first glimpse of their blood flowing out. There is perhaps some justification for the upsetting emotional effect that the sight of blood has on many, since uncontrolled bleeding can pose a serious threat to life.

Hemorrhage is the escape of blood from the vessels in which it is normally contained. As a first-aid measure, excessive bleeding is most effectively controlled by direct pressure at the site of the injury. (The pressure stimulates reflex vascular spasms, which help to close the gap in the blood vessel and stop the blood loss.) During surgery, hemorrhage may be controlled with hemostats (surgical clamps) or ligatures (ties). Gauze applied over the bleeding surface can aid in stopping hemorrhage by promoting the breakdown of platelets, initiating the reactions of clotting.

The body has an assortment of mechanisms for compensating for a moderate blood loss, such as the 500 cc of a typical blood donation. Vasoconstriction decreases the total capacity of the circulatory system. The liver and spleen contract to send their blood reserves into the veins. Tissue fluids diffuse into the blood vessels, and a blood donor is thus enabled to regain the plasma volume within a few hours. Plasma proteins are restored more slowly. Although the production of blood cells is speeded up, the replacement of the formed elements may take a month or more.

A healthy person can recover fairly easily from a moderate loss of blood. But in more severe hemorrhage, symptoms of shock may develop: the pulse rapid and weak, the skin pale, clammy, and cold; the victim exhibits listlessness and oxygen hunger (with the reduced blood flow, the needs of the tissues for oxygen are not being met). If more than 30 to 35 percent of the total blood volume is lost, the body cannot compensate rapidly enough. Unless a blood transfusion is administered quickly, the person may die.

BLOOD TRANSFUSIONS

Blood transfusions have saved the lives of more Americans than have been killed in all the wars in the history of this country. Now more than 6.5 million pints of blood are used each year to replace blood lost in accidents and surgery and to treat people with blood diseases.

Attempts to replace blood lost by hemorrhage date back to the 1600s. But, despite an occasional success, these early attempts almost uniformly led to serious illness or sudden death of the patients. No one knew why, until in 1900 Karl Landsteiner discovered that red blood cells of certain humans contain substances that can react with proteins in the plasma of certain other humans, causing the red cells to clump together when the bloods are mixed. It was this type of **agglutination** reaction that was killing the early transfusion patients. Once it was realized that there are several different types of human blood, and rapid tests were devised to determine blood types, careful crossmatching of the blood for transfusions could avoid the possibility of dangerous reactions. The foundations for successful routine transfusions had been laid.

The early blood transfusions were accomplished directly, by permitting the blood to flow from the vein of one person (the **donor**) through a needle and tubing into the vein of the patient (the **recipient**). But direct transfusions are rare today. Instead, donor blood is collected in bottles, mixed with citrate to prevent it from clotting, and stored in a blood bank until it is needed.

The blood of a prospective donor is subjected to a number of tests. It is typed, so that the blood can later be correlated with an appropriate recipient. It is tested for hemoglobin, for serum isohemolysins that could hemolyze red cells, and for syphilis with Wassermann and VDRL tests. Another test that is becoming increasingly widespread reveals the presence of **serum hepatitis** virus. Serum hepatitis, which can cause serious or even fatal liver damage, has been the major hazard in blood transfusions in modern times. The problem has been aggravated by the fact that commercial blood banks have often accepted blood from drug addicts (who may have acquired the disease by using contaminated needles) and people living in crowded and unsanitary conditions, where hepatitis is endemic. Many hospitals have restricted their blood collections to unpaid volunteer donors. But there are difficulties in attracting sufficient volunteers, and blood bank shortages are a chronic problem in many areas.

During a blood transfusion, care must be taken to introduce the blood into the recipient's veins at the proper temperature and rate. If the blood is trans-

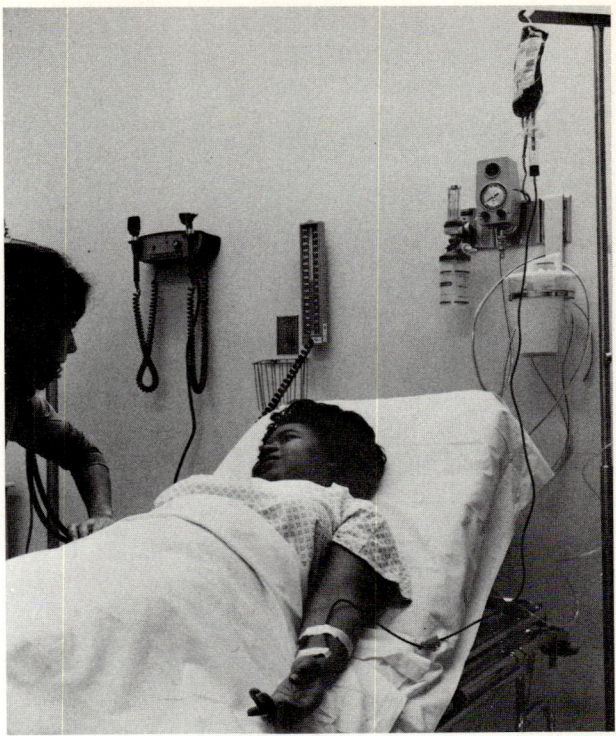

FIGURE 19-18 Blood transfusion.

fused too rapidly, the heart may be overloaded.

Preserving Blood   According to some estimates, as much as a third of the blood that is collected from donors is wasted. For whole blood, even when stored at a temperature of 4 to 6°C, has a "shelf life" of only three weeks. After that, the red cells degenerate and will no longer survive. Thus, conventionally stored blood more than 21 days old is considered "spoiled."

With the chronic shortages of blood that already exist and the growing need for blood, researchers have been actively seeking means of keeping donor blood usable longer. Additions of the nucleic acid base adenine have been found to extend the useful life of whole blood to 35 to 42 days. By separating the red cells from the plasma and then suspending the cells in purified albumin, they can be kept viable for as much as three months.

Techniques of frozen storage currently offer the best hope of extending the life of donor blood. The red cells are separated from the plasma and placed in a solution of glycerol, which protects them from the damaging effects of freezing. Frozen and stored at −85°C, the red cells can be kept indefinitely. Before use in transfusions, however, the glycerol must be washed out with a sugar-salt mixture. This freezing technique offers an added bonus: it has been found to kill any hepatitis virus that might be lurking in the blood, and it also destroys white cells that could provoke a potentially dangerous antibody reaction in the recipient.

Blood Substitutes

In many emergency situations—at the battlefront, or in an ambulance rushing to the scene of a highway disaster, for example—it would be difficult or impossible to have adequate supplies of carefully typed and crossmatched whole blood ready for transfusions. Yet immediate action may be necessary to save a victim whose life is literally bleeding away. The search for safe and effective blood substitutes has therefore been a major focus of attention among blood researchers for many years.

One obvious possibility for a blood substitute is plasma, or plasma fractions. During the second World War, wounded soldiers at the front were given transfusions of dried plasma, dissolved in sterile water. Such transfusions, however, cannot replace the oxygen-carrying function of the red cells in the lost blood and therefore are of limited value in cases of severe hemorrhage. Transfusions of saline or sugar solutions, too, work only to restore lost blood volume, and their effect may be only temporary as water rapidly leaks out into the tissues.

Researchers are now working on a completely synthetic blood substitute, composed of fluorocarbons and polyols in a solution containing salt and sugar. The fluorocarbons are chemicals with an enormous capacity for adsorbing dissolved gases, and thus they take the place of the erythrocytes. The polyols emulsify the fluorocarbons so that they can be carried readily through the bloodstream and bind water, preventing it from leaking out into the tissues. Although the mixture has not yet been used on humans, rats have been subjected to a complete exchange transfusion, in which all their blood has been replaced by the synthetic blood substitute. They have survived and regenerated their normal blood components in about a week. In addition to its potential value in transfusions, such a blood substitute could also perfuse organs that are to be used in transplants.

BLOOD GROUPS

One of the arguments raised in support of nationwide computerized data banks, containing information on all citizens, is that they would provide a rapidly retrievable source of medical information that could prove invaluable in emergency situations. If such data banks were ever established, one of the items that would certainly be listed would be each person's blood type. If a transfusion were needed, a call to the data bank would quickly indicate the type of blood needed to avoid the possibility of a dangerous agglutination reaction.

Agglutination, or clumping of red blood cells, occurs because of a reaction of a substance in the red cells with another substance in the plasma. The substance in the red cells is called an **antigen** or **agglutinogen**. The substance in the plasma is referred to as an **antibody** or **agglutinin**. Clumping does not occur in a person's own blood because it normally does not contain both of any particular agglutinogen–agglutinin pair. But if blood containing the appropriate antigen is introduced in a transfusion, the antibodies in the person's blood will respond immediately to the invasion of the "foreign" proteins. In the "transfusion reaction" that ensues, the transfused red cells are clumped, followed by hemolysis—rupture of the red cell membranes permitting the hemoglobin they contain to escape into the blood. The hemoglobin may accumulate in masses in the kidney tubules, blocking them and preventing them from functioning normally.

The system of agglutinogens and agglutinins that Landsteiner originally discovered is called the ABO system. Other blood group factors have since been discovered, including the Rh factor (named for the rhesus monkeys in which it was first found) and the M and N factors. Each set of blood group factors is inherited independently, giving a person a characteristic "blood type."

The ABO Blood Groups

A crowd of onlookers presses in closer around the scene of the crash. In a space at the center, a doctor bends over the body of a man, dragged clear of the blood-spattered wrecks. "Hemorrhaging under control now," he thinks, "but he's lost a lot of blood." He looks up and calls out to the crowd, "Is anyone here type O?"

In a modern hospital, the blood for transfusions is carefully typed and crossmatched, so that the donor blood is as close to identical with the blood of the recipient as possible. But in emergency situations, occasionally a transfusion must be given when the blood type of the victim is not known, or an exact match cannot be obtained. Then the medical worker seeks someone with type O blood, the "universal donor." In type O, as seen from Table 19-3, the red blood cells contain no agglutinogens of the A–B group at all; type O blood can thus be given to recipients of any blood type without the danger of stimulating a transfusion reaction.

A careful examination of the table reveals that type O blood does contain agglutinins in the plasma, corresponding to both the A and B agglutinogens. Why, then, you may be wondering, would a transfusion of type O blood into a type A recipient, for example, not stimulate clumping of the recipient's blood cells? The explanation is that if the transfusion is conducted

TABLE 19-3   The Human Blood Groups

BLOOD GROUP	AGGLUTIN- OGEN IN ERYTHRO- CYTES	AGGLU- TININ IN PLASMA	CAN GIVE BLOOD TO:	CAN RECEIVE BLOOD FROM:
O	None	a and b	O,A,B,AB	O
A	A	b	A,AB	O,A
B	B	a	B,AB	O,B
AB	A and B	None	AB	O,A,B,AB

TABLE 19-4   Relative Frequency of Blood Types Among Caucasians[a]

GENOTYPES	BLOOD GROUPS	PERCENTAGE
OO	O	40–45
AO, AA	A	40
BO, BB	B	10–15
AB	AB	5

[a] Blood type frequencies vary in different races and population groups, and comparative studies of them are useful in tracing historical relationships among peoples.

slowly enough, the inflowing type O plasma will be greatly diluted in the blood of the recipient. Thus, though some agglutination does occur, the donor agglutinogens will not be present in sufficient concentration to significantly affect the recipient's erythrocytes.

Note that type A blood contains A agglutinogens in the red cells and anti-B or b agglutinins in the plasma (see Figure 19-19). Type B blood contains B agglutinogens in the red cells and anti-A or a agglutinins in the plasma. Type AB blood is characterized by both A and B agglutinogens in the erythrocytes and hence no agglutinins at all in the plasma. (Actually, this is somewhat of a simplification; observations subsequent to Landsteiner's original discovery revealed that there are two slightly different variations of A agglutinogens, A_1 and A_2, with the corresponding two variant anti-A agglutinins.) Because type AB plasma does not agglutinate any red blood cells, type AB blood is sometimes referred to as the "universal recipient."

The blood group factors are inherited through combinations of three different genes, all alleles of the same gene pair. The A and B genes are dominant, while the O gene is recessive to both of them.

Thus, a person may have any of the following pos-

sible genotypes of the ABO blood group:

AO, AA, BO, BB, AB, OO

With either one or two A genes, a person will have A antigens in his or her red blood cells. Either one or two B genes will result in the presence of B antigens. If both A and B genes are present, both will be expressed. But the only way a person can have type O blood is to inherit two O genes. Yet type O is the commonest type of blood among the population, as seen from Table 19-4.

Blood typing

The method of determining A–B–O blood types is simple and rapid, and requires only a few drops of blood. A drop of a known type A blood serum is placed on one part of a glass slide, and a drop of known type B serum on another part. Then a drop of the unknown blood is added to each drop of standard serum. Unless the unknown blood belongs to type O, clumping will occur in one or both of the drops, usually within a few minutes. If the drops are large enough, clumping can be seen with the naked eye:

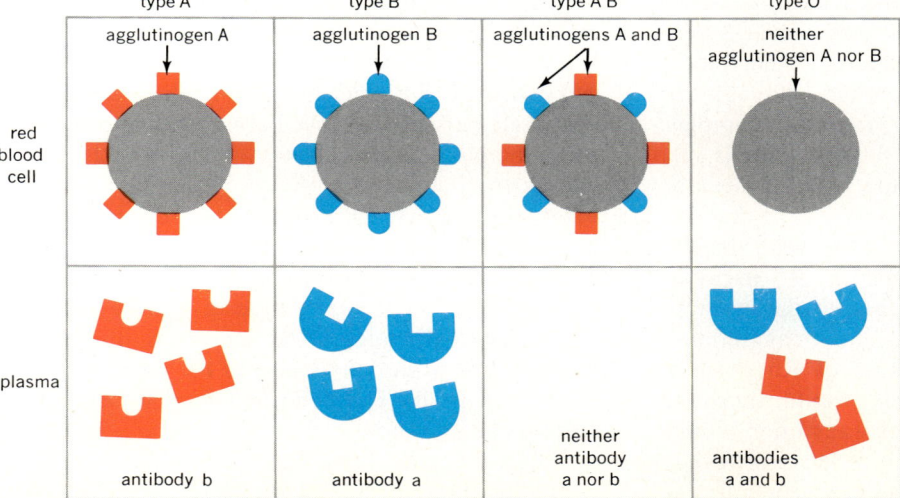

FIGURE 19-19   The ABO blood groups.

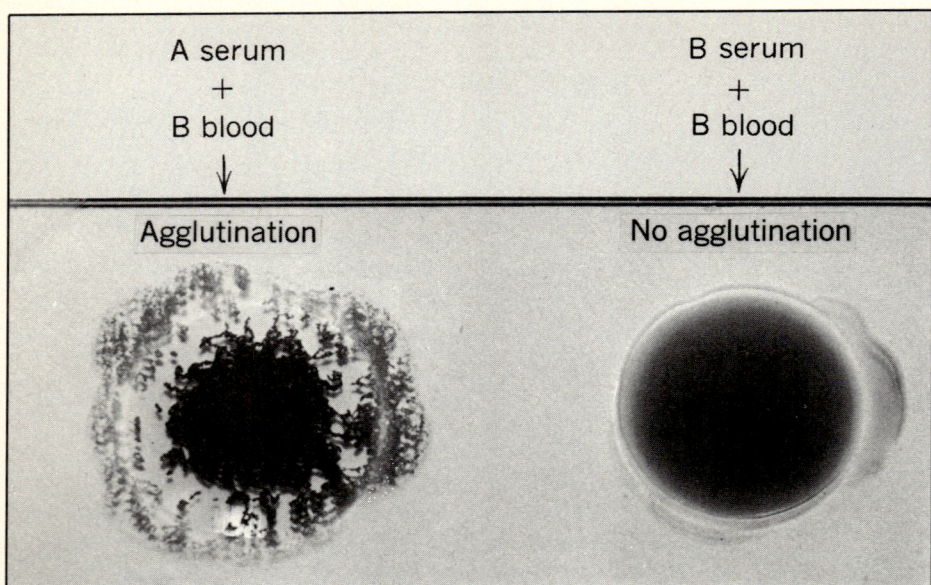

A serum + B blood ↓	B serum + B blood ↓
Agglutination	No agglutination

FIGURE 19-20 Blood typing. The unknown blood is mixed with sera of known blood types. Agglutination only with A serum showed that this unknown specimen was type B.

otherwise it can be observed with the aid of a magnifying glass.

Figure 19-20 shows the results obtained in a typical blood-typing test.

Rh Factor

Karl Landsteiner's discovery of the A-B-O blood groups was a major landmark in the history of medical research, so important that it was ultimately rewarded with a Nobel Prize. But Landsteiner did not rest on his laurels after this discovery. He continued his studies, particularly in the field of blood research. In 1927 he discovered the M and N blood factors. Then in 1940, when he was already 72 years old, he found a whole new class of blood group factors. The agglutinogens were originally found in the blood of rhesus monkeys and were therefore named Rh factor.

The Rh factor is found in the erythrocytes of a majority of humans: about 85 percent of Caucasians are Rh positive, 95 percent of Negroes, and 98 percent of Japanese and Chinese. Like the other blood group factors, the Rh factor is inherited, although the pattern of its inheritance is somewhat more complex than that of the A-B-O or M-N factors; there is still some uncertainty as to exactly how many genes are involved.

There is an important distinction between the Rh factor and the other blood groups: an Rh negative person, lacking the Rh agglutinogen in the erythrocytes, does not normally have any anti-Rh agglutinins in the plasma. Thus, a transfusion of Rh positive blood into an Rh negative recipient would not cause clumping. But such a mismatched transfusion would stimulate the recipient's body to produce antibodies to the foreign antigen. If the person subsequently received *another* exposure to Rh positive blood, immediate agglutination would result.

To avoid the possibility of Rh sensitization through transfusions, the Rh factor is now routinely determined as a part of the blood typing procedure. A standard serum containing anti-Rh agglutinin is used for this test, and the blood type is commonly listed as O+, B−, and so on.

But an Rh negative woman faces one potential danger of sensitization that cannot be avoided by careful blood typing—unless she is willing to change her marriage plans if necessary, on the basis of her blood type. If such a woman marries an Rh positive man, there is a high likelihood that her children will be Rh positive (the Rh factor is dominant). The blood of such children will contain the foreign agglutinogen. If it should come in contact with her blood during pregnancy, it would stimulate the formation of anti-Rh agglutinins (Figure 19-21). Normally the fetal and maternal circulations are entirely separate, and there is no mixing of blood. But occasionally there may be leaks through the placenta. The likelihood of this is increased particularly just before and during birth, when the placenta breaks away from its anchorage in the uterus.

Usually the first Rh positive child of an Rh negative mother is born without any difficulties. But if her blood becomes sensitized to the Rh agglutinogen during the birth, her second Rh positive child will be in danger. Anti-Rh agglutinins may pass through the placenta and attack the blood of the fetus, clumping its red blood cells. This condition is known as **erythroblastosis fetalis,** and it may result in severe damage or death of the fetus. It has been estimated that in the United States, one child in ten is an Rh positive child

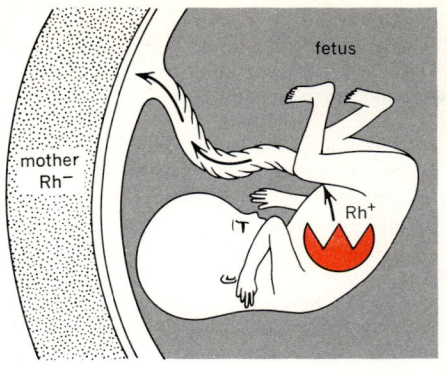
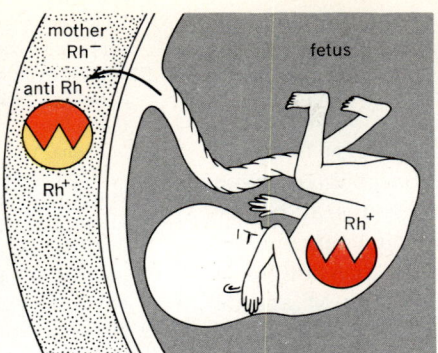
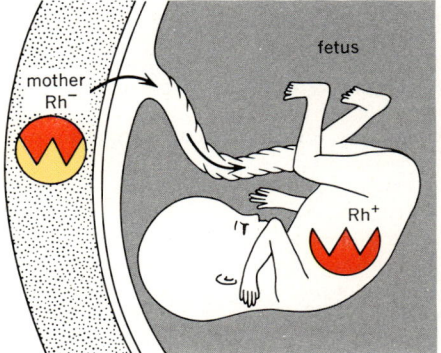
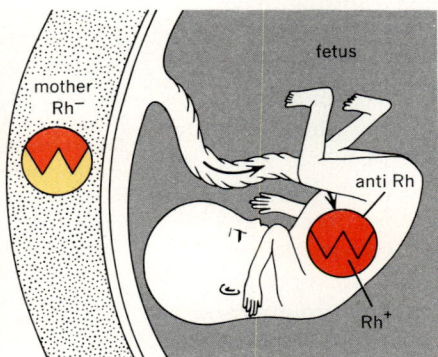

FIGURE 19-21 Rh conflict. If an Rh⁻ mother's blood is sensitized to produce anti-Rh antibodies, clumping of red blood cells in subsequent Rh⁺ offspring may result.

clumping of red blood cells

of an Rh negative mother, but only about one in 500 is likely to develop erythroblastosis fetalis. Still, considering the more than 200 million population, this is an enormous number of potential victims. As a result, much research has been done in the area of treating and preventing the Rh disease. First, tests were devised to monitor the blood of a pregnant Rh negative woman for the presence of Rh antibodies. If such antibodies were found, the hospital would be alerted to institute an immediate exchange transfusion as soon as the baby was born, replacing all of its damaged blood with fresh whole blood. Later, techniques were developed to perform exchange transfusions before birth, while the fetus was still in the uterus.

But in the early 1970s, a new treatment for Rh conflicts became widespread, and may ultimately make the whole problem of erythroblastosis fetalis obsolete. This treatment is a vaccine, called Rho-GAM, which is administered to an Rh negative mother within 72 hours after the birth of an Rh positive child. At this time, her body may have become sensitized to the Rh antigen and may be starting to manufacture antibodies against it. Paradoxically, the RhoGAM vaccine *contains* anti-Rh agglutinins. Flooding the mother's system with the antibodies relieves her own immunity system of the stimulus to manufacture antibodies of its own. The injected antibodies disappear from her body after awhile. But by that time, the Rh antigens are no longer present, and

her blood remains unsensitized. (Unfortunately, the vaccine cannot help a woman whose blood has already become sensitized to the Rh antigen.)

Cross Matching

People can make mistakes, and even computerized records can be in error. So as a routine procedure, donor blood of the appropriate type is carefully cross matched with a sample of the patient's blood before it is used in a transfusion.

The cross matching procedure consists of mixing a suspension of red blood cells from the donor with a small amount of defibrinated serum from the recipient. Then the reverse is often done: a suspension of the recipient's red cells is mixed with donor serum. If no agglutination occurs in either case, the blood of the donor and that of the recipient are considered to be compatible, and the donor blood can be used for the transfusion. Cross matching can also be used in emergency situations to determine the compatibility of donor and recipient blood without going through a complete blood-typing procedure.

Legal Aspects of Blood Groups

One of the hazards of being a famous man is the danger of paternity suits. Blood tests can often aid in resolving the question of whether a particular man is indeed the father of the disputed child.

A child inherits one blood group gene of a particular type from each of his parents. A type O man, for example, could not possibly be the father of a child with AB blood, for he does not possess either an A or a B gene to pass on to a child. A type B man, however, could be the father of a child with type O blood, for the man might have the heterozygous genotype BO. The Rh factor, M and N blood groups, and other less important blood factors can introduce further refinements that may help to resolve the question when the A-B-O results are ambiguous. (The M and N agglutinogens are inherited in the same way as A and B—both genes are dominant—but there is no recessive gene in the group. Thus, the only possible types are M, N, and MN.)

As an example, let us suppose that a woman with A, Rh−, M blood is unsure which of two men is the father of her child. The child has A, Rh−, MN blood. One of the men has A, Rh−, M blood, while tests reveal the other's blood type to be A, Rh+, N. Neither the A type nor the Rh factor can cast any light on the paternity question. (The Rh positive man might be heterozygous, carrying genes for both the positive and the negative types.) The MN group provides the final evidence—of the two men, only the second could have provided an N gene.

One important point should be remembered when blood tests are used to resolve paternity questions: the blood type can tell only whether a particular man *could be* the father of the child, not whether he *is* the father. In the example cited, the mother might not have been telling all—it is entirely conceivable that a different man, perhaps with O, Rh−, N blood, was really the father of the child.

Blood tests and comparable tests of tissue fragments can also be used in some criminal cases—for example, to establish the possible presence of the suspect at the scene of the crime or to establish that the blood on the suspect's clothes was indeed that of the victim. But again, a positive answer indicates only a possibility, and only a negative answer is certain.

SUMMARY

Blood is a suspension of formed elements (red and white blood cells and platelets) in a fluid matrix (plasma) in which proteins, salts, sugars, hormones, and other chemicals are dissolved.
It has a specific gravity of 1.055 and a viscosity five times as high as water.
The hematocrit is the volume percentage of formed elements (normally 42 to 47 percent).
An average adult man has about 5 liters of blood, and the average woman 4.5 liters.
The main functions of blood help to maintain homeostasis:
Transport of oxygen, carbon dioxide, food substances, cell waste products, hormones, water, and heat.
Disease-fighting functions.
Buffering action (pH 7.35 to 7.45).
The basic groups of plasma proteins are:
Albumins (provide osmotic pressure, regulate fluid balance).
Globulins:
Alpha, beta: aid in transport of lipids.
Gamma: main source of circulating antibodies.
Fibrinogen (blood clotting).
Other plasma constituents are:
Inorganic ions
Glucose (normal blood sugar level 80 to 120 mg/ml)
Lipids (triglycerides, phospholipids, cholesterol)
Nonprotein nitrogen (urea, amino acids, uric acid, creatine, creatinine)
Hormones
Vitamins
Water
Erythrocytes (red blood cells) are nonnucleated flattened biconcave discs, combining high carrying capacity and maximized surface area for diffusion.
The stroma, an elastic inner framework, holds hemoglobin molecules and blood group factors.
In anisocytosis the erythrocytes are varied in size.
The normal red cell count is about 5.4 million per mm^3 of blood (adult males) or 4.6 million/mm^3 (adult females).
Polycythemia is an elevated red blood cell count.
Anemia is a deficiency of red blood cells. Forms include:
Pernicious anemia
Aplastic anemia
Hemolytic anemia
Sickle cell anemia
Erythropoiesis occurs in the red bone marrow and follows the sequence:
Hemocytoblast (stem cell) → basophil erythroblast → polychromatophil erythroblast → normoblast → reticulocyte → mature erythrocyte.
Erythropoiesis is stimulated by the kidney hormone erythropoietin.
Iron, amino acids, and vitamins (vitamin B$_{12}$ and folic acid) are required.
The RBC has an average lifespan of 120 days.
Hemoglobin is a metal-containing protein (heme + globin).
A hemoglobin molecule can combine reversibly with four molecules of oxygen, producing oxyhemoglobin.
Carbaminohemoglobin is a combination of hemoglobin with carbon dioxide.
Carboxyhemoglobin is a combination of hemoglobin with carbon monoxide.
The normal adult hemoglobin content is 14 to 18 g/100 ml (males), 12 to 16 g/100 ml (females).
The color index is the ratio of the amount of hemoglobin in each erythrocyte to the amount considered normal.
Hemolysis or laking is a bursting of red blood cells that occurs in a hypotonic medium.
Leukocytes (white blood cells) are nucleated amoeboid cells, which travel through the bloodstream and surrounding tissues and function in the body's defense against disease.
Diapedesis is the movement of a white blood cell through a capillary pore.
Chemotaxis is the attraction of white blood cells by chemicals released at sites of inflammation or tissue damage.
Types of leukocytes are:
Granulocytes
Eosinophils
Basophils

Neutrophils
Agranulocytes
Lymphocytes
Monocytes

Neutrophils are the most numerous WBC and function in phagocytosis.

Eosinophils contain enzymes (peroxidases, oxidases, trypsin, phosphatases).

Basophils are the least numerous WBC and contain heparin, histamine, and serotonin; they may be precursors of mast cells.

Lymphocytes are a heterogeneous group; they contain globulins and function in phagocytosis.

Monocytes are the largest WBC and function in phagocytosis; they can swell up into macrophages in the tissue spaces.

WBC formation occurs in the red bone marrow and follows the sequence: Hemocytoblast (stem cell) → myeloblast → promyelocyte → myelocyte → metamyelocyte → mature leukocyte.

The lifespan of the WBC varies from a few hours to 300 days.

The normal leukocyte level is 5,000 to 10,000 per mm³ of blood. Leukocytosis is an elevated WBC level above 10,000/mm³. Leukopenia is a WBC level below 5,000/mm³.

A differential white cell count can provide clues to the type of infection.

Leukemia is a form of bone marrow cancer characterized by extremely high levels of functionally inadequate leukocytes and anemia.

Platelets (thrombocytes) are cell fragments formed from megakaryocytes and function in blood clotting.

The normal platelet level is 250,000 to 400,000/mm³.

Thrombocytopenia is a lowered level of platelets.

Thrombocytosis is an elevated level of platelets.

The average lifetime of platelets is 5 to 8 days.

Platelets function in hemostasis by clumping at a site of damage to the vessel wall and disintegrate, releasing vasoconstrictors (such as serotonin) and platelet factor, which initiates the chain of reactions of clot formation.

A blood clot is formed by a network of fibrin with entrapped blood cells.

Blood clotting is a complicated chain of chemical reactions, involving at least 13 separate factors.

Platelet factor promotes formation of thromboplastin, which is activated by interaction with plasma proteins and converts prothrombin to thrombin with the aid of calcium ions; thrombin catalyzes the conversion of fibrinogen to fibrin.

Hemophilia is a hereditary disease characterized by a deficiency of one or more of the blood clotting factors, especially antihemophilic factor (AHF).

A thrombus is a clot formed inside a blood vessel, partially or completely closing it; an embolus is a traveling thrombus. Embolism can result in a myocardial infarction or a stroke. Atherosclerosis contributes to thrombosis and embolism.

Anticoagulants include antithrombin, heparin, hirudin, dicumarol, oxalates, citrates, and EDTA.

Blood clots can be dissolved by fibrinolysis (plasminogen is converted to plasmin and digests the clot); activators are urokinase and streptokinase.

Hemorrhage is the escape of blood from blood vessels; severe hemorrhage can result in shock.

Blood transfusion replaces blood lost in hemorrhage.

Potential complications are agglutination reactions and serum hepatitis.

Plasma, saline solutions, and glucose solutions replace only lost blood volume, not oxygen-carrying capacity of RBC.

Agglutination (clumping) of RBC is produced by the reaction of an antigen (agglutinogen) in the RBC with an antibody (agglutinin) in the plasma. In a transfusion reaction, transfused antigen-containing RBC are clumped and hemolyzed.

Blood groups include ABO, Rh, and MN.

For ABO blood groups:

Blood type	Genotype	Agglutinogen in erythrocytes	Agglutinin in plasma
O	OO	None	a and b
A	AA, AO	A	b
B	BB, BO	B	a
AB	AB	A and B	None

The Rh blood factor may be important when an Rh negative woman marries an Rh positive man; if her blood becomes sensitized and produces anti-Rh agglutinins, an Rh positive baby may be born with erythroblastosis fetalis.

Blood for transfusions is routinely typed and cross matched.

Blood types sometimes permit the resolution of disputed paternity cases and identification in criminal cases.

QUESTIONS FOR REVIEW AND THOUGHT

1 List the basic constituents of: blood; plasma; serum; formed elements.

2 Compare and contrast the structure of erythrocytes, leukocytes, and thrombocytes.

3 Compare the processes of formation of red blood cells and white blood cells.

4 List five types of blood tests and the information they provide.

5 Define: anemia, polycythemia, leukemia, hemophilia, and erythroblastosis fetalis.

6 Discuss the interactions of hemoglobin with oxygen, carbon dioxide, and carbon monoxide.

7 How does compensatory polycythemia make the body better able to function at high altitudes? Do you agree with the complaint that athletes from sea-level countries who were not permitted a prolonged period of high-altitude conditioning were placed at an unfair disadvantage when the Olympics were held in Mexico City (elevation 7439 feet)?

8 Describe the action of positive and negative feedback mechanisms involving the blood.

9 Describe the structure and functions of the major types of leukocytes.

10 Outline the mechanisms of blood clotting. What mechanisms normally operate to keep the blood vessels from becoming plugged by internal clots? Define thrombus, embolus, and atherosclerosis.

11 Some regard the concept of type O blood as a "universal donor" as a dangerous myth. Discuss in the light of agglutinogen-agglutinin systems in the blood.

12 In a recent novel, a crucial plot twist hung on the result of a blood typing. A young boy with rare type AB blood was dying of leukemia and needed an emergency transfusion. No suitable donor blood was available, but the hero of the book, a doctor with type O blood, set up a direct transfusion from his veins to the child's. Thinking about the situation, he suddenly realized that the blood types proved he was the child's father. (The mother was type B.) What was wrong with the author's medical facts? If the hero had a blood type compatible with paternity in the case, could he have given the child a direct transfusion without danger of an agglutination reaction?

THE
HEART
AND
BLOOD
VESSELS

20

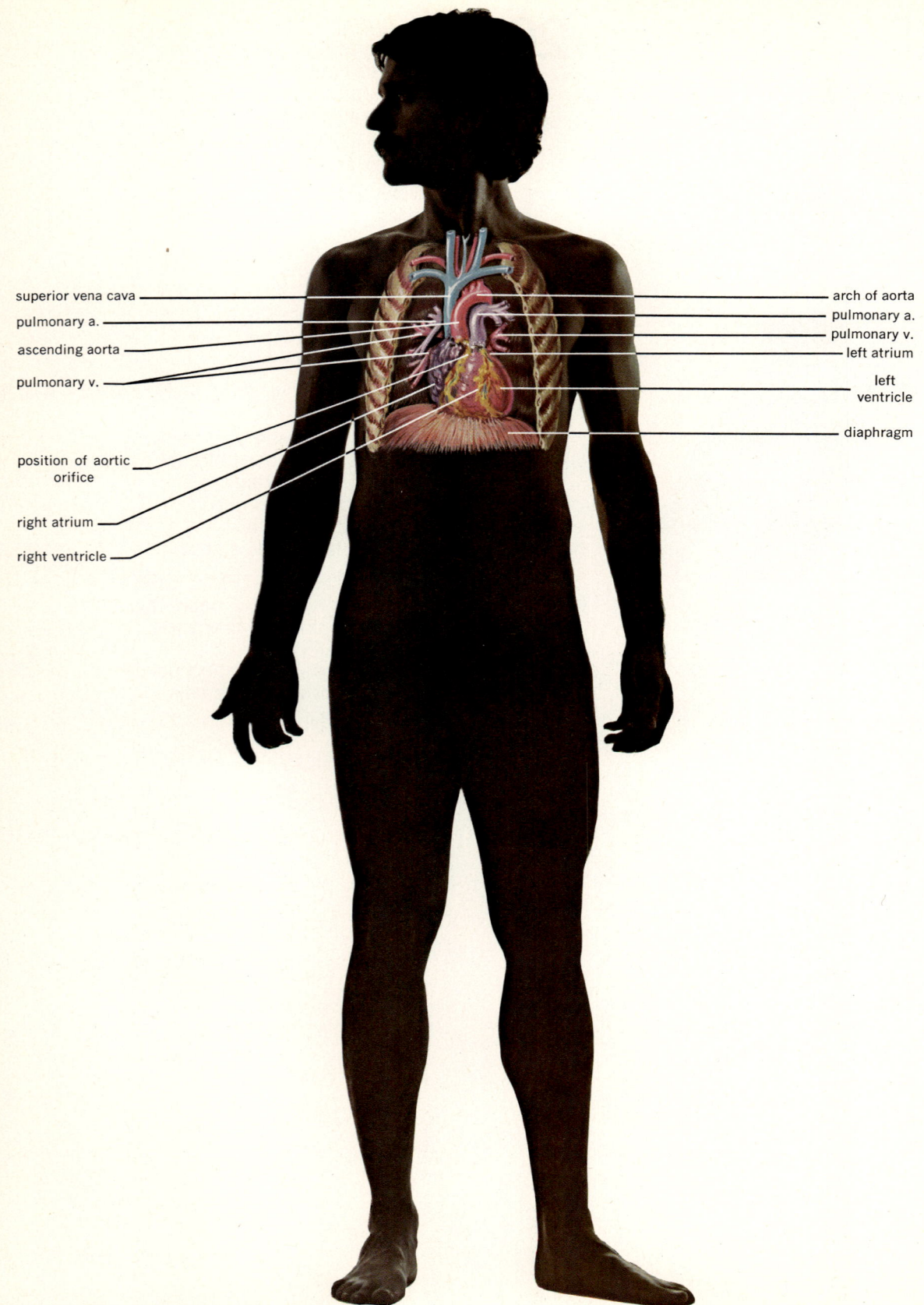

superior vena cava

pulmonary a.

ascending aorta

pulmonary v.

position of aortic
orifice

right atrium

right ventricle

arch of aorta

pulmonary a.

pulmonary v.

left atrium

left
ventricle

diaphragm

FIGURE 20-1 **The heart in situ in the thoracic cavity.**

No city could function without an intricate system of streets and roads linking houses, offices, stores, factories, hospitals, and other key places. The individual cells of the human body need a continual supply of nutrients and oxygen and a continual removal of wastes; the roving disease-fighters need channels of easy access to the various tissues and organs, and chemical messengers, too, need a transporting medium to distribute them through the body. The circulatory system, with its intricately branching and interconnecting tubes, is like the intricate system of streets and highways of a modern city, providing for the transport of necessary goods and services.

Unlike the cars, trucks, and buses that ply a city's streets, most of the cells and chemicals that travel the waterways of the circulatory system are not self-propelled. They are carried passively along in the flow of moving blood. The propulsive force that keeps the blood moving is the steady beating of a powerful pump, the heart. The contractions of this hard-working muscle propel blood into arteries, which add their contractions to help maintain the flow. The arteries branch and rebranch, into smaller and smaller tubes, ultimately leading into the tiny capillaries that permeate the tissues. Here gases are exchanged with the body cells, and dissolved chemicals pass in and out through the delicate capillary walls. In time, the blood begins the return trip, draining into successively larger blood vessels and ultimately into the large veins that empty into the heart.

THE HEART

Your heart first began to beat about a month after you were conceived and has continued to beat steadily ever since. If you live an average lifetime, your heart will contract about two and a half *billion* times, pumping a total volume of some 50 million gallons of blood. This prodigious pump is about the size of a man's closed fist, weighs less than a pound (about 300 grams), and is shaped like a blunt cone. It is nestled in a space in the thoracic cavity called the **mediastinum,** between the two pleural cavities, bounded anteriorly by the sternum and posteriorly by the vertebral column (Figure 20-1). The pointed end, or **apex** of the heart points downward, forward, and to the left, and rests on the diaphragm. The broader end, or **base,** is at the top of the heart, turned upward, backward, and to the right. (Its upper margin lies just below the second rib.) The tipped arrangement of the heart means that about two-thirds of its mass is to the left of the midline, and the impact of its beating is felt a little below the left nipple, where the apex comes in contact with the chest wall.

The heart is a hollow muscular organ (Figure 20-2), which is divided by a septum into left and right halves. Each half is divided in turn into two chambers, an upper **atrium** and a lower **ventricle.** The atria, as their name implies, are receiving chambers, while the ventricles are the heavy-duty pumps. The heart is thus two pumps in one: one sends blood coursing out through the body via the many blood vessels of the **systemic circulatory system;** the other sends blood through the **pulmonary circulation,** a circuit that leads to the lungs and back again.

Covering of the Heart

Any machine with moving parts will develop friction unless it is well lubricated. The heart is no exception. It is saved from potential irritation by its loose-fitting covering, the **pericardium** (Figure 20-3). This is a two-layered sac, which is attached to the large blood vessels that enter or leave the heart and to the diaphragm and sternum. The outer layer is made of tough white fibrous tissue and is not actually attached to the heart. It is lined with smooth, moist serous membrane, the **parietal pericardium.** The same kind of serous membrane covers the entire outer surface of the heart and is called the **visceral pericardium,** or **epicardium.** The space between the parietal and visceral layers contains a small amount of lubricating fluid **(pericardial fluid)** secreted by the serous membrane. **Pericarditis** is an inflammation of the pericardium that may result from bacterial or viral infection or a metastatic malignant neoplasm. Fluid or pus accumulates in the space between the visceral and parietal layers, and they may stick together, hampering the work of the heart.

The Heart Wall

The working part of the heart is its muscular wall. It is made up of three distinct layers: the outer **epicardium,** the middle **myocardium,** and the inner **endocardium** (Figure 20-4).

The epicardium, already described, is a serous membrane that is considered part of the pericardium although it adheres closely to the outer surface of the heart. It is a connective tissue structure with an outer mesothelial layer and a subserous layer containing a network of elastic fibers, blood vessels, and nerves; it is frequently infiltrated with fat.

The myocardium forms the bulk of the heart wall and does the actual work of contracting. It is cardiac muscle, in which the individual striated muscle fibers are intricately branched and joined into a three-dimensional network. Bundles of muscle fibers are attached to deep-lying collections of fibrous tissue, which forms the "skeleton" of the heart, separating the atria from the ventricles, dividing the heart into left and right halves, and surrounding the atrioventricular, aortic, and pulmonary orifices. The myocar-

A

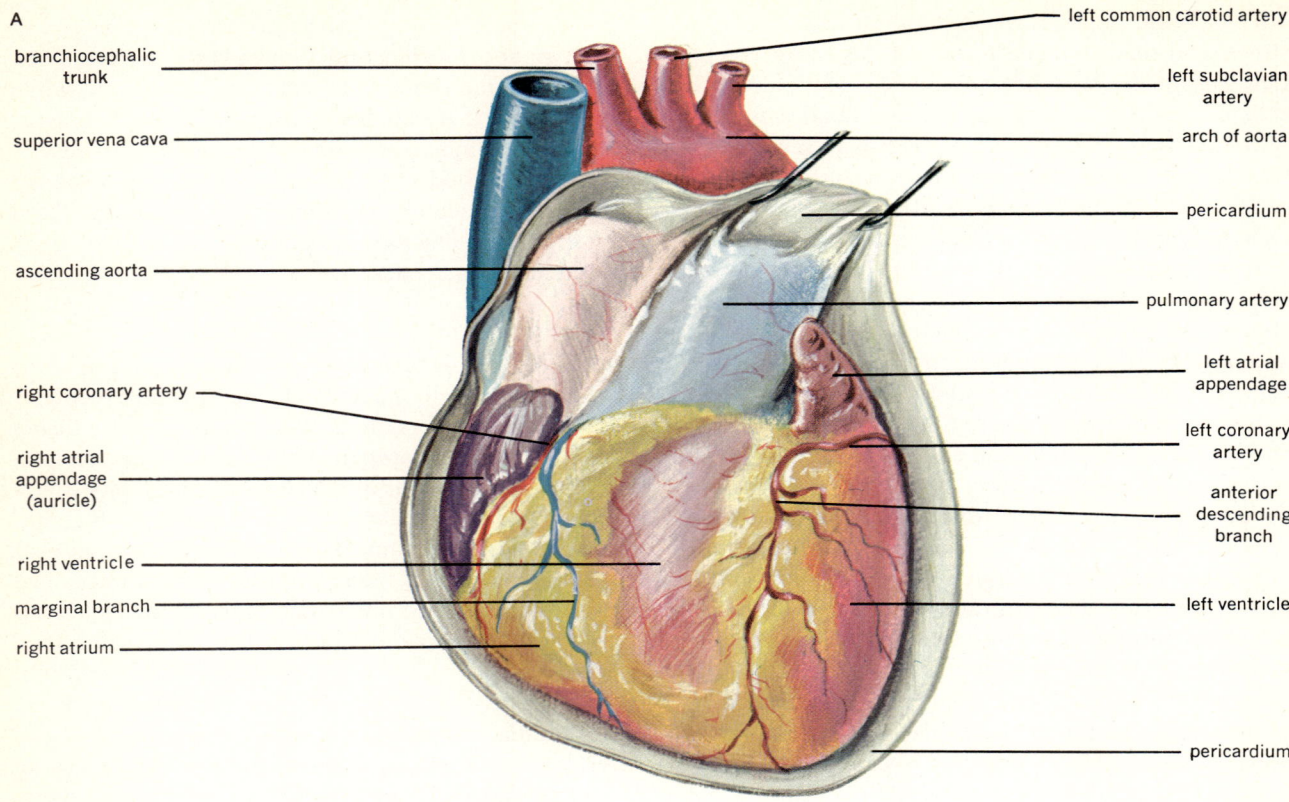

branchiocephalic trunk

superior vena cava

ascending aorta

right coronary artery

right atrial appendage (auricle)

right ventricle

marginal branch

right atrium

left common carotid artery

left subclavian artery

arch of aorta

pericardium

pulmonary artery

left atrial appendage

left coronary artery

anterior descending branch

left ventricle

pericardium

B

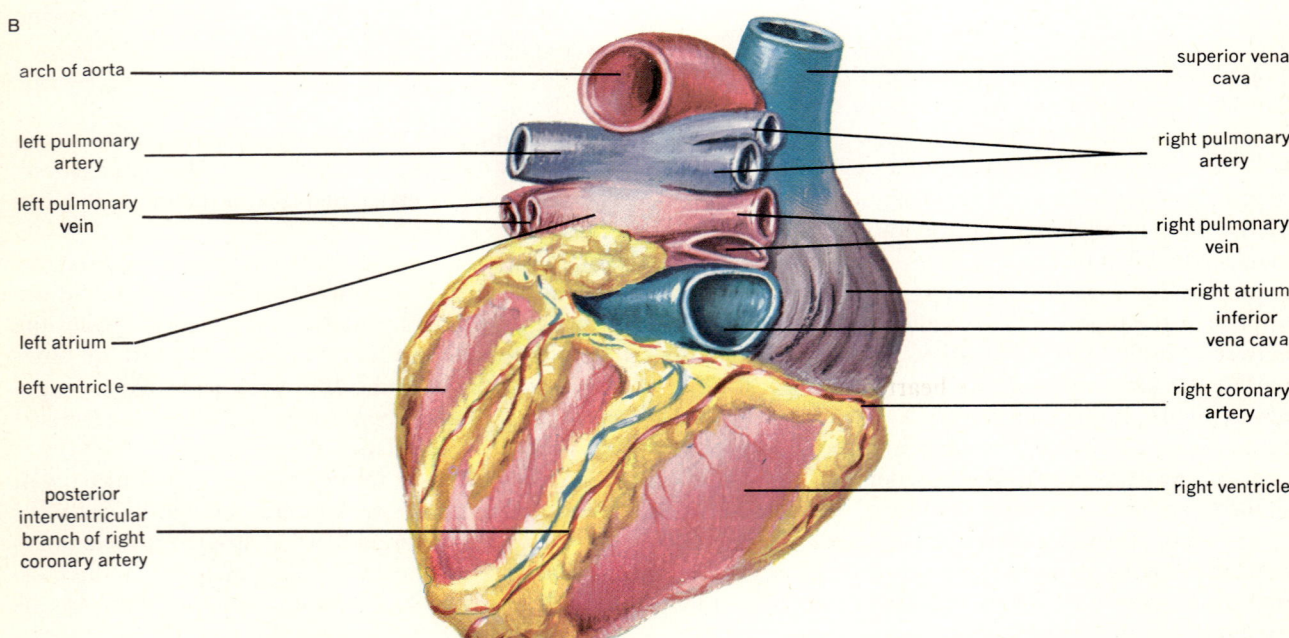

arch of aorta

left pulmonary artery

left pulmonary vein

left atrium

left ventricle

posterior interventricular branch of right coronary artery

superior vena cava

right pulmonary artery

right pulmonary vein

right atrium

inferior vena cava

right coronary artery

right ventricle

FIGURE 20-2   The heart: anterior view (A), posterior view (B), and frontal section (C). Arrows indicate the direction of blood flow (red arrows represent oxygenated blood and blue arrows represent deoxygenated blood).

c

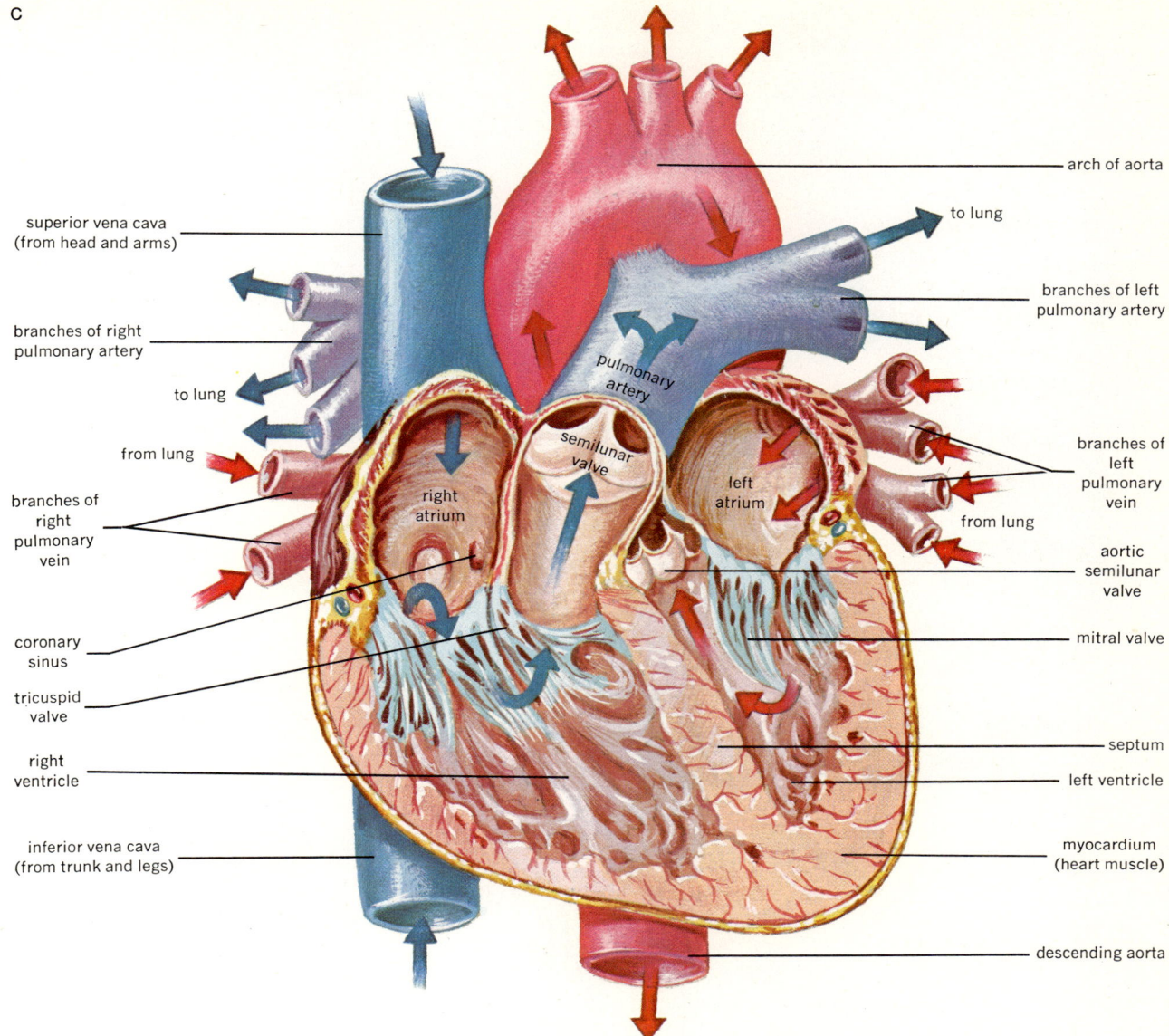

superior vena cava
(from head and arms)

branches of right
pulmonary artery

to lung

from lung

branches of
right
pulmonary
vein

coronary
sinus

tricuspid
valve

right
ventricle

inferior vena cava
(from trunk and legs)

arch of aorta

to lung

branches of left
pulmonary artery

pulmonary
artery

semilunar
valve

right
atrium

left
atrium

branches of
left
pulmonary
vein

from lung

aortic
semilunar
valve

mitral valve

septum

left ventricle

myocardium
(heart muscle)

descending aorta

dium is much thicker in the ventricles, where it is reinforced by interlaced muscular ridges, the **trabeculae carnae,** which project into the lumen of the ventricles. Inflammation of the heart muscle is called **myocarditis;** obstruction of the coronary blood vessels, cutting off the supply of blood to the myocardium, may cause a **myocardial infarction** ("heart attack").

The endocardium, which lines the inner surface of the heart cavities, is a thin, delicate membrane composed of endothelial cells. It covers the valves, surrounds the chordae tendinae ("heart strings"), and is continuous with the lining membrane of the large blood vessels. Inflammation of the endocardium is called **endocarditis.**

Chambers of the Heart

Is the division of the human heart into two separate pumps necessary? Could we get along just as well with a single pump? The amphibian heart has just such a structure. Deoxygenated blood, laden with waste products from the body cells, enters one atrium, while freshly oxygenated blood from the lungs enters another; the two blood flows mix in a single ventricle, the contractions of which send the mixed blood spurting out into arteries leading to the lungs and to the systemic circulation. But this is a very inefficient system. The blood sent to the lungs is already partly oxygenated, so that a maximum gas exchange cannot be achieved; the blood carried around the body is partly deoxygenated, so that the body cells do not

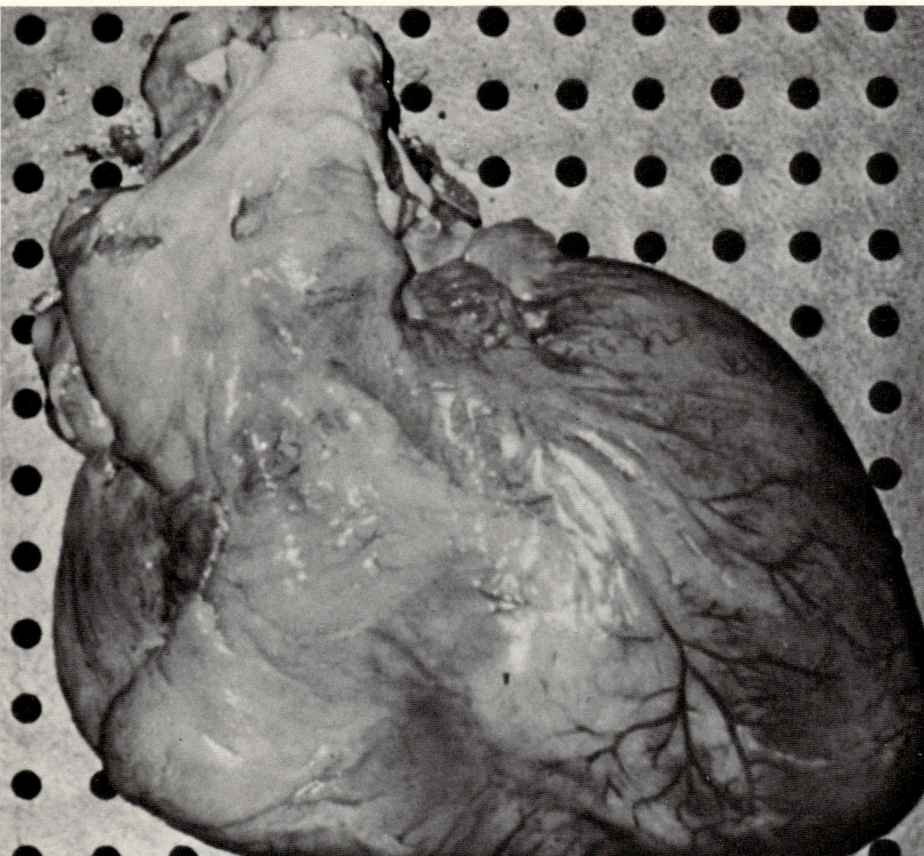

FIGURE 20-3 The heart is wrapped in the pericardium.

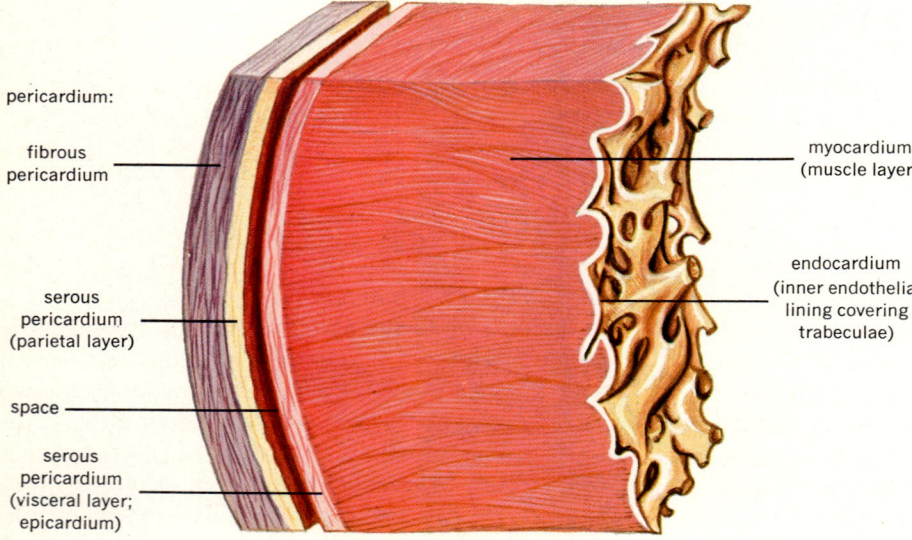

pericardium:

fibrous
pericardium

serous
pericardium
(parietal layer)

space

serous
pericardium
(visceral layer;
epicardium)

myocardium
(muscle layer)

endocardium
(inner endothelial
lining covering
trabeculae)

FIGURE 20-4 Section through the heart wall, showing its layered structure.

receive as much oxygen as they could. A frog manages to get by with its inefficient circulatory system, but in a larger, more complex, and warm-blooded human, a mixing of oxygenated and deoxygenated blood in the heart means trouble. Occasionally an infant is born with a large hole in the septum that separates the two sides of the heart, permitting mix-

ing of the oxygenated and deoxygenated blood. Such a child is called a "blue baby," because of the cyanotic tinge of its skin. If the defect is not repaired surgically, the child will be sickly, easily fatigued, with a heart grossly enlarged in the vain attempt to pump enough blood to get more oxygen to the body cells.

After birth, the normal heart is separated into right

and left halves, which have no communication with each other. Each half is subdivided into an upper chamber, the **atrium,** and a lower chamber, the **ventricle.** The two ventricles are separated by a muscular partition, the **interventricular septum;** the **interatrial septum** that divides the two atria is much less substantial. The septum that separates each atrium from its ventricle is pierced by a **valve,** which can open, permitting blood to flow down from the atrium to the ventricle, or close, making the separation of the upper and lower chambers complete. Thus, oxygenated blood from the lungs is delivered only to the left atrium and pumped out by the left ventricle to the body without ever mixing with the deoxygenated blood that is delivered to the right atrium and pumped out by the right ventricle to the lungs.

Two grooves can be seen on the anterior surface of the heart. The atrioventricular groove marks the division between the right atrium and ventricle, while the anterior interventricular sulcus marks the position of the interventricular septum that separates the right and left ventricles. The coronary blood vessels lie in these grooves.

Right Atrium

Waste-laden blood from the entire body drains into the right atrium through three major blood vessels: the **superior vena cava,** which carries blood from the upper portion of the body; the **inferior vena cava,** which brings blood from the lower portion of the body; and the **coronary sinus,** which drains blood from the heart muscle itself. The right atrium is larger than the left, and its walls are very thin. It opens into the right ventricle through the **tricuspid valve,** which closes when the ventricle contracts, preventing blood from flowing back up into the atrium.

Left Atrium

The left atrium is the receiving chamber for blood from the lungs, which is carried to it by four **pulmonary veins.** Considering the smaller source of supply, it is not surprising that the left atrium is smaller than the right, but its walls are thicker. The left atrium opens into the left ventricle through the **bicuspid valve,** which operates like the tricuspid valve to shut off the atrium when the ventricle contracts.

Right Ventricle

The right ventricle is a pump, which sends blood coursing out through the **pulmonary trunk,** on the way to the lungs. As befits its harder work, its walls are much thicker than the walls of the atria, but they are only one-third as thick as the walls of the left ventricle, which pumps blood around the much longer circuit of the systemic circulation. The outlet from the right ventricle is guarded by the semilunar valve, which prevents a backflow of blood from the pulmonary trunk when the ventricle relaxes. A latticework of muscular columns, the **trabeculae carnae,** can be seen projecting from the inner surface of the ventricle. Thin fibrous strands stretch out from the apexes of some of these muscles, extending upward to attach to the edges of the tricuspid valve. These are the **chordae tendinae** ("heart strings"), which keep the cusps of the valve from turning inside out when pressure builds up inside the ventricle.

Left Ventricle

The blood flowing through your head, that in your hands, your feet, your stomach—all has been propelled on its way by contractions of the left ventricle. This heavy-duty pump is particularly thick-walled, and its inner surface looks much like that of the right ventricle, with trabeculae carnae and chordae tendinae. It pumps blood out into the largest blood vessel in the body, the **aorta,** the entrance to which is guarded by the **aortic semilunar valve.** Both the left and right ventricles contract simultaneously, sending blood coursing out into their respective arteries.

Valves of the Heart

Sometimes a multimillion-dollar space shot fails because of the malfunction of a simple valve worth less than a dollar. The human heart is also equipped with valves, which regulate the blood flow, and their malfunction can be equally disastrous. Fortunately, effective prostheses for the heart valves have been devised, and their insertion has become a relatively routine operation. Thousands of people living today have artificial valves in their hearts.

Two types of valves are found in the heart: the **atrioventricular valves** that can close off the openings between the atria and the corresponding ventricles; and the **semilunar valves** at the entrances to the aorta and pulmonary artery (Figure 20-5).

The atrioventricular valves consist of fibrous rings, to which thin, leaflike cusps (or flaps) are attached. The **right atrioventricular valve** has three cusps, and an alternate name for it is the **tricuspid valve.** When it is fully open, it is large enough to admit three or four fingertips. The **left atrioventricular valve** is smaller—only large enough for two fingertips—and it has only two cusps, leading to the name **bicuspid valve.** This valve also has a third alternate name, the **mitral valve,** from a fancied resemblance to the shape of a bishop's miter. It is stronger and thicker than the tricuspid valve, able to withstand the more forceful pumping of the left ventricle.

The pointed ends of the cusps of both atrioventricular valves project down into the ventricle and are attached by chordae tendinae to a type of trabeculae carnae called **papillary muscles.** Blood flows down freely through the valve from the atrium to the ventricle. But when the ventricle contracts, the backward flow of blood forces the flaps upward until they meet

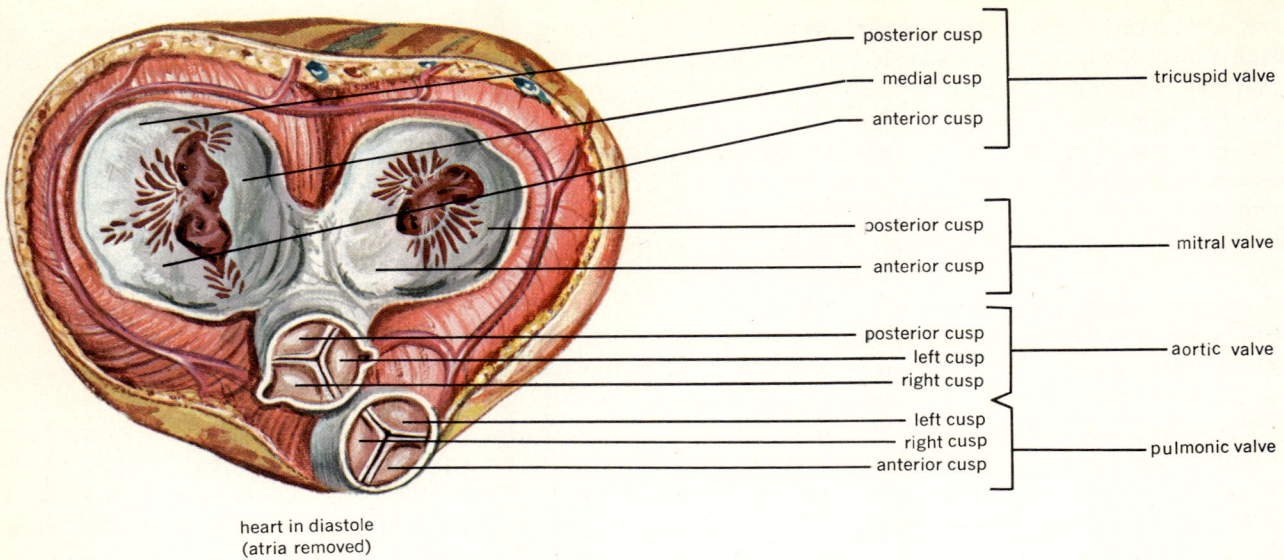

posterior cusp ⎤
medial cusp ⎬ tricuspid valve
anterior cusp ⎦

posterior cusp ⎤ mitral valve
anterior cusp ⎦

posterior cusp ⎤
left cusp ⎬ aortic valve
right cusp ⎦

left cusp ⎤
right cusp ⎬ pulmonic valve
anterior cusp ⎦

heart in diastole
(atria removed)

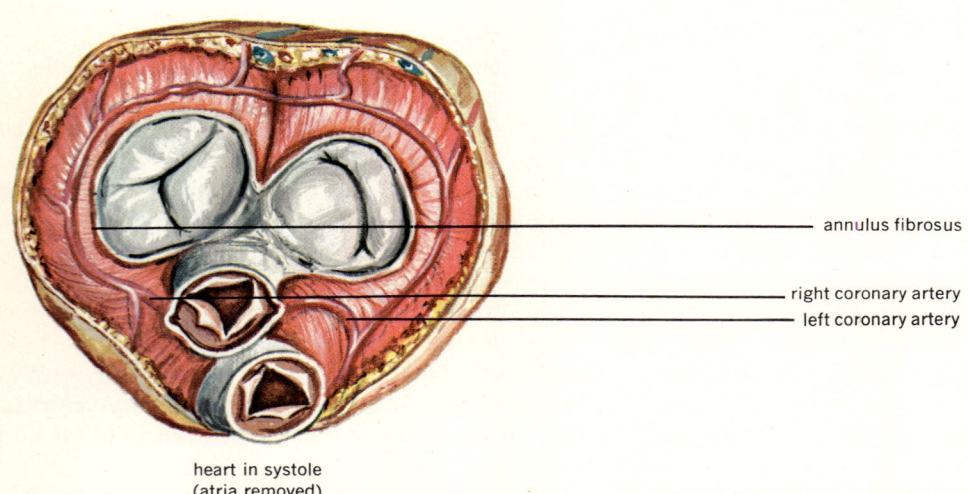

annulus fibrosus

right coronary artery
left coronary artery

heart in systole
(atria removed)

FIGURE 20-5   Valves of the heart, viewed with the atria removed. In diastole the atrioventricular (tricuspid and mitral) valves open, permitting blood to pass into the ventricles. In systole the semilunar (aortic and pulmonic) valves open, permitting blood to be pumped into the aorta and pulmonary trunk. The X rays show implanted artificial heart valves: aortic (A), mitral (M), and tricuspid (T).

at their edges and close off the atrioventricular partition entirely. The chordae tendinae check the upward movement of the valves and prevent them from flapping up into the atrium.

The semilunar valves guard the orifices of the aorta and pulmonary artery. Their name comes from the half-moon shape of the three cusps that form each valve. The **aortic valve** is larger and stronger than the **pulmonary valve.** When the ventricles contract, blood pushes up the cusps of the semilunar valves and flows freely through the openings that they provide. But when the ventricles relax, the backflow of blood in the arteries fills the bowl-like cusps, forcing them down-

ward so that their edges meet and shut off the opening.

When you listen to the heartbeat with a stethoscope, two distinct sounds are heard, a sort of "lubb-dup." The "lubb" is a mixture of sounds, produced by vibrations set up in the valves and in the walls of the heart and major blood vessels as the ventricles contract and then the atrioventricular valves slam shut. The second sound ("dup") is produced when the semilunar valves slam shut after the pulse of blood has spurted past them.

If any of the heart valves loses its ability to close tightly (a condition called **valvular insufficiency**), a

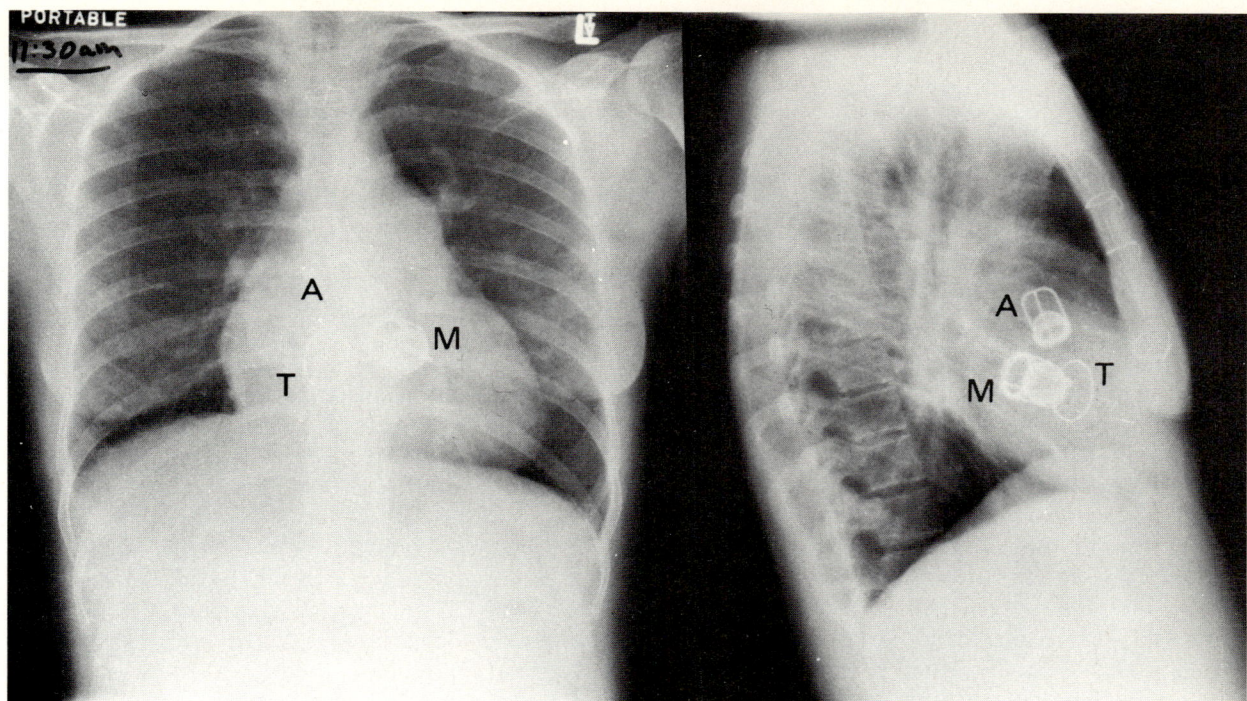

leakage of blood results, and the heart's pumping efficiency is reduced. In **mitral stenosis,** the left atrioventricular orifice is narrowed by the formation of scar tissue as a result of disease. The flow of blood from the left atrium into the left ventricle slows down to a trickle, and the heart is unable to pump out enough blood for the body's needs. The techniques of open-heart surgery and the installation of artificial valves now permit many types of valvular defects to be repaired.

The Conducting System of the Heart

While you are at rest, your heart beats steadily along at a relatively constant pace—probably about 72 contractions per minute. But if you are running for a bus, your body needs a speeded-up circulation of blood to provide for the extra muscular exertion, and your heartbeat rate may rise to double its usual level. The contractions of the heart are synchronized and their rate controlled by specially modified muscular tissue, the conducting system of the heart. This system consists of four structures: the sinoatrial node, the atrioventricular node, the atrioventricular bundle, and the Purkinje fibers. The small muscle fibers that compose these structures are specialized for conduction, in contrast to the extreme specialization of the usual muscle fibers for contraction.

The **sinoatrial node,** also known as the **SA node** or **pacemaker,** is found in the right atrial wall near the opening of the superior vena cava. It consists of hundreds of cells with a built-in time keeper. Without any

stimulation by nerve impulses, these cells continually contract at a constant rate. Impulses from the cells of the SA node spread through the cardiac muscle and initiate contractions. This node thus sets the basic pace of the heart contractions and is fittingly called the pacemaker. Its pace can be changed, though, by impulses from sympathetic and parasympathetic nerves and by hormones circulating in the blood, particularly epinephrine and thyroid hormone. The dash for the bus brings the sympathetic nervous system into action, backed up by an increased secretion of epinephrine by the adrenal glands, and both these influences act to speed up the heartbeat rate. (One major drawback of the artificial pacemakers that have saved many thousands of lives is that they cannot respond to nervous and hormonal influences and speed up the heart rate for strenuous physical activity—they just keep on setting a steady pace.)

The **atrioventricular node,** or **AV node,** is found in the right atrium, in the lower part of the interatrial septum. It gives rise to a bundle of specialized cardiac muscle fibers, the **atrioventricular bundle** (or **bundle of His**), which divides into two branches and extends down the two sides of the interventricular septum. From there the fibers continue as **Purkinje fibers,** which extend out to the papillary muscles and the lateral walls of the ventricles.

Impulses that start at the sinoatrial node spread through the atrial muscle fibers in all directions, producing atrial contractions. When the impulses reach the atrioventricular node, they are relayed to the ventricles via the bundle of His and the Purkinje fibers, producing synchronized contractions of the ventricles. The minute electrical currents that are generated by the conducting system of the heart spread through the surrounding tissues to the surface of the body. There they can be picked up and amplified with suitable recording instruments, producing the **electrocardiogram,** a visible record of heart conduction.

The nerve signals that can change the rate of heart contraction reach the heart's conducting system via an abundant supply of nerve fibers. Both the sympathetic and the parasympathetic nervous systems send efferent fibers to the heart. The sympathetic fibers, contained in the **middle, superior,** and **inferior cardiac nerves,** combine with the parasympathetic fibers, in branches of the **vagus nerve,** to form **cardiac plexuses** close to the arch of the aorta. Fibers from the cardiac plexuses travel with the left and right coronary arteries and enter the heart. Most terminate in the sinoatrial node, but some of the nerve fibers end in the atrioventricular node and in the atrial myocardium. The sympathetic nerves to the heart act as **accelerator nerves,** speeding up the heartbeat rate. In a strenuous exertion, the heart can boost its output nearly fivefold, providing for the body's increased needs in a "fight or flight" situation. Impulses from the parasympathetic fibers slow down and weaken the heartbeat; these fibers thus serve as **inhibitory** or **depressor nerves.**

The heart is also supplied with afferent nerve fibers, which travel in the sheath of the vagus nerve to the cardiac center in the medulla. Impulses transmitted via **depressor fibers** from the aortic arch bring about reflex inhibition of the heart. Impulses carried by **pressor fibers** from the right side of the heart stimulate a reflex acceleration of the heart. Visceral afferent fibers carry impulses producing a sensation of pain when the heart is deprived of oxygen.

Coronary Circulation

The heart, which supplies blood to the entire body, is also one of the body's major blood consumers, receiving about ten percent of the heart output. This hardworking muscle requires a continual supply of oxygen and nutrients to provide for its energy metabolism. If one of the major arteries supplying the heart is plugged, for example, by a blood clot in coronary thrombosis or embolism, a substantial section of the heart muscle becomes ischemic. That is, deprived of oxygen, the muscle cells cannot produce enough energy. **Myocardial infarction,** the death of the ischemic heart muscle cells, soon results, and the heart loses some of its contracting power. If too large a portion of the heart muscle dies, the heart will be unable to pump enough blood to maintain the life of the body as a whole. Coronary disease claims the lives of over

half a million Americans each year, and it is estimated that several million more heart disease victims are incapacitated to one degree or another.

Blood is supplied to the heart by the **right and left coronary arteries,** the first branches from the aorta (Figure 20-6). Branches of these two arteries encircle the heart and supply all parts of the myocardium. Both ventricles receive blood from both the right and left coronary arteries; each atrium is supplied only by a small branch from the coronary artery on its own side.

A severe anterior chest pain called **angina pectoris** is a sign of an inadequate oxygen supply to the heart, usually due to a partial occlusion of the coronary blood vessels by fat deposits in their walls. This pain may radiate into the left shoulder and arm, neck, or epigastrium, but usually lasts only three to five minutes. It is often brought on by physical exertion or emotional upset and can be relieved by resting or by the administration of nitrites. The pain of myocardial infarction is longer lasting. A key to recovery from a myocardial infarction is the presence of **anastomoses** (cross-connections between blood vessels), which provide alternate routes for blood to reach the ischemic areas, bypassing the occluded vessel. A supervised program of exercise can aid in developing such **collateral circulation** to ischemic areas; surgical operations grafting blood vessels into the coronary circulation have been tried, but their effectiveness is controversial.

The circuit of coronary circulation is completed by a system of veins, which collect deoxygenated blood from the heart muscle. The **cardiac veins** begin at the apex of the heart and ascend, picking up side branches from various parts of the myocardium. Most of these veins empty into the **coronary sinus,** which discharges into the right atrium. (A few of the veins of the heart, such as the anterior cardiac vein, empty directly into the right atrium.)

The heart is also abundantly supplied with **lymph capillaries,** which form a continuous network from the endocardium through the myocardium to the epicardium. The lymph capillaries form larger vessels, which travel with the coronary blood vessels and empty into the thoracic duct.

It might seem strange that the heart has to have an organized system of arteries, veins, and capillaries to provide for blood circulation. After all, all four chambers of the heart are continually being filled with blood, more than once every second. However, the blood that fills the atria and ventricles comes in contact only with the endocardium, not with the myocardium.

BLOOD VESSELS

There are more than 60,000 miles of blood vessels in a

A

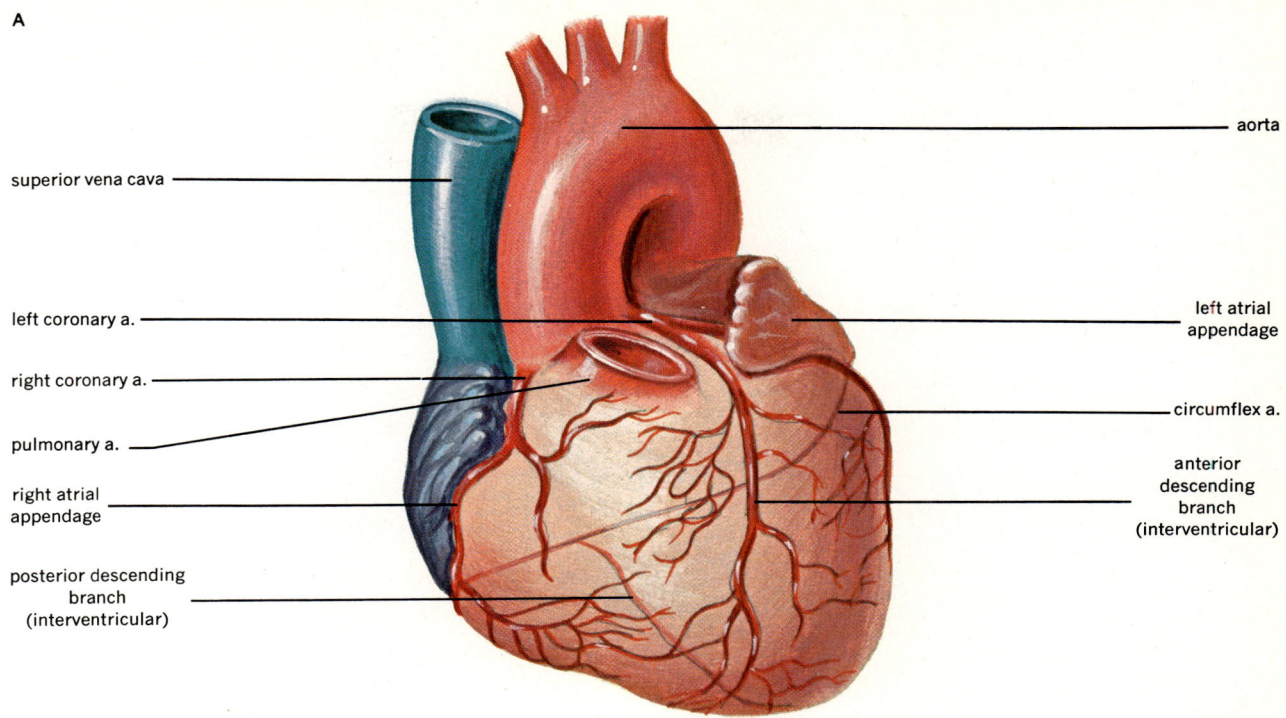

superior vena cava

aorta

left coronary a.

left atrial appendage

right coronary a.

circumflex a.

pulmonary a.

anterior descending branch (interventricular)

right atrial appendage

posterior descending branch (interventricular)

coronary arteries supplying the heart

B

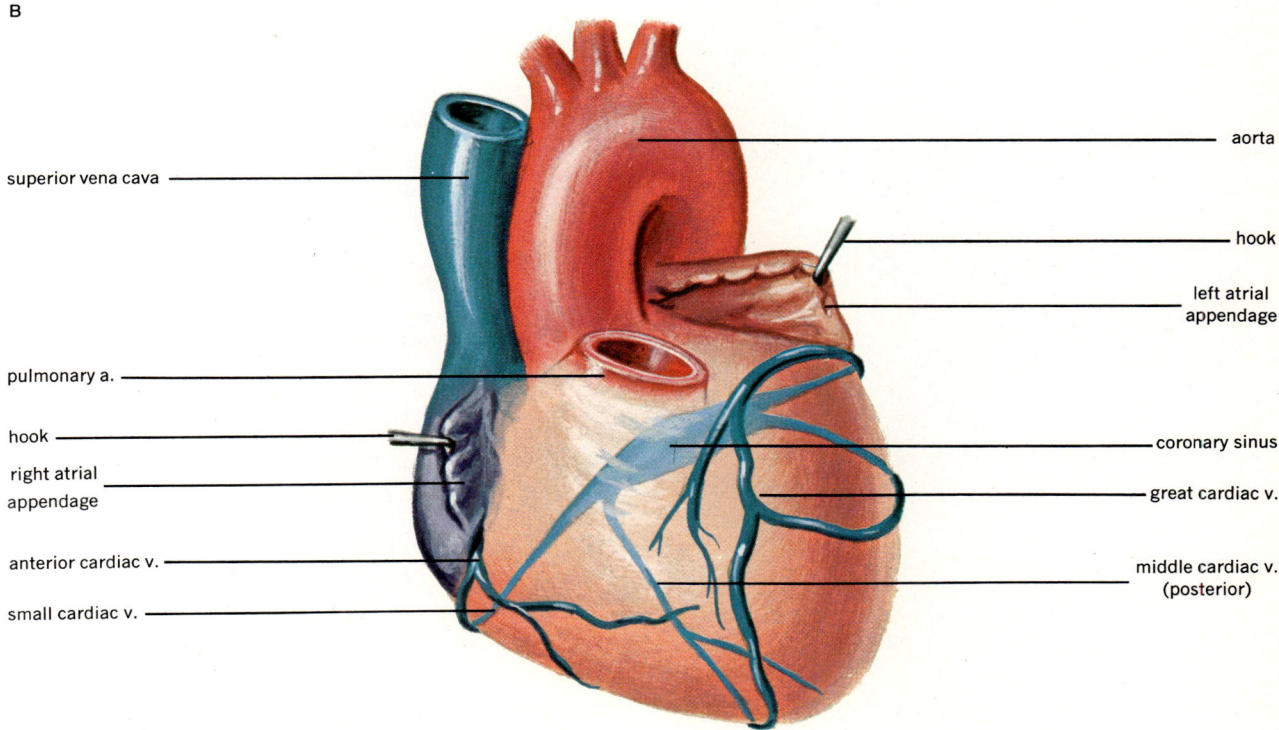

superior vena cava

aorta

hook

left atrial appendage

pulmonary a.

hook

coronary sinus

right atrial appendage

great cardiac v.

anterior cardiac v.

middle cardiac v. (posterior)

small cardiac v.

venous drainage of the heart

FIGURE 20-6 The coronary circulation: arteries (A) and veins and sinuses (B).

single human adult—enough to stretch around the earth's equator nearly two and a half times. Of course, in a living body the blood vessels are not stretched out into a single 60,000-mile-long tube; instead, they are multitudinous branches of blood vessels of various sizes, forming a complex interconnect-

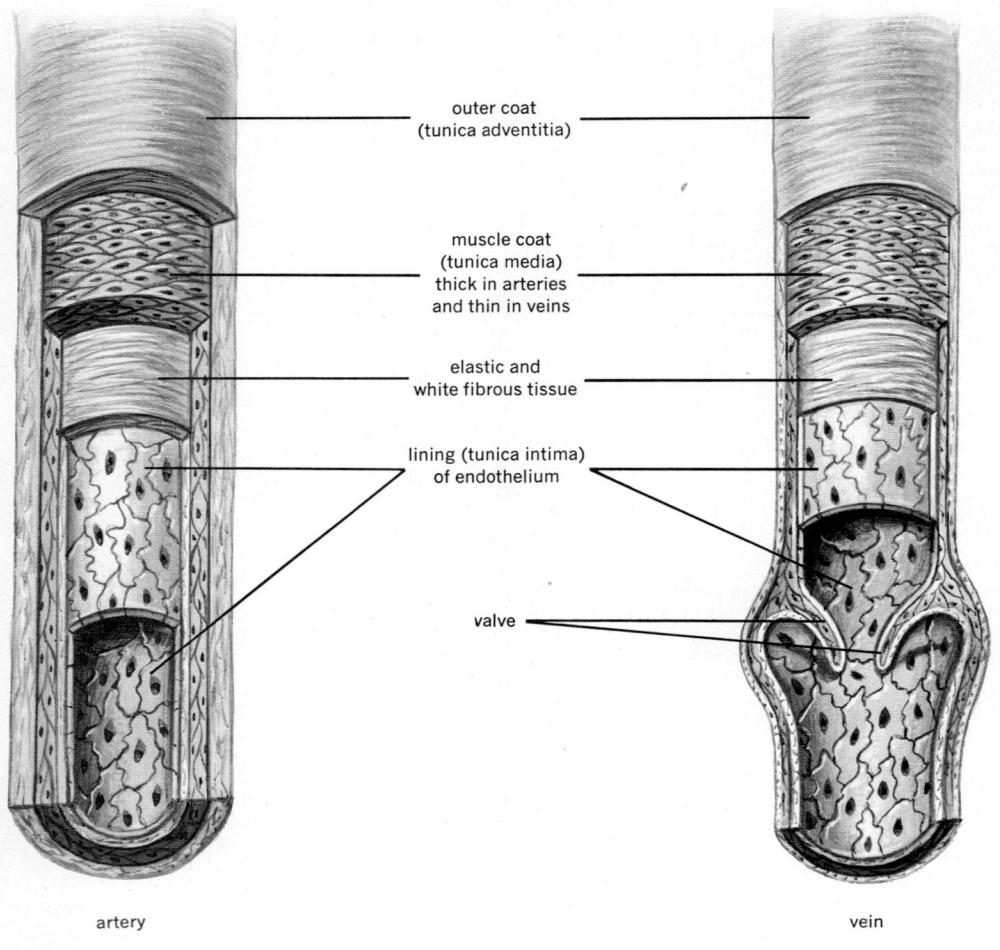

FIGURE 20-7 Structure of arteries, veins, and capillaries. The drawings of artery and vein segments show the relative thicknesses of the three coats. The capillary, the walls of which consist of only a single layer of endothelial cells, is not drawn to the same scale.

outer coat
(tunica adventitia)

muscle coat
(tunica media)
thick in arteries
and thin in veins

elastic and
white fibrous tissue

lining (tunica intima)
of endothelium

valve

artery

vein

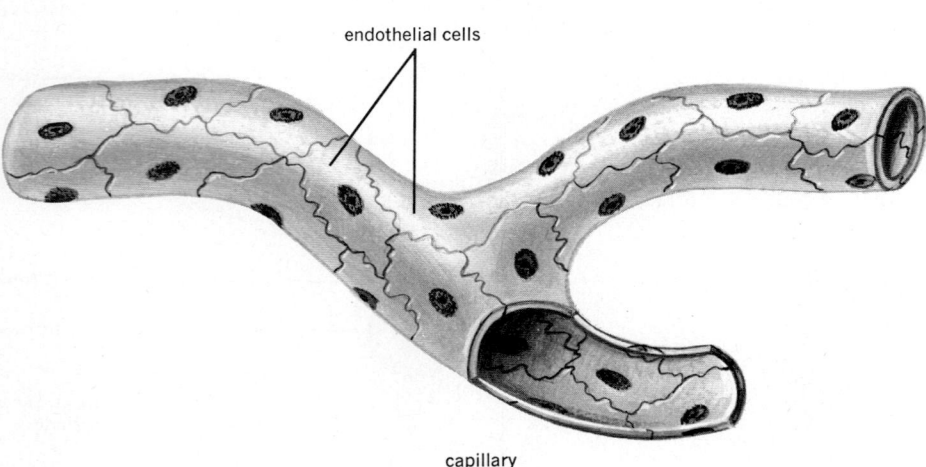

endothelial cells

capillary

ed network that reaches practically every cell in the body.

There are three main types of blood vessels: arteries, veins, and capillaries (Figure 20-7). **Arteries** are large, muscular-walled blood vessels that carry blood *away from* the heart. They branch and rebranch, forming progressively smaller arteries; the smallest varieties are referred to as **arterioles.** The arterioles lead into a vast network of very fine blood vessels, the **capillaries.** These are the blood vessels that permeate the tissues and service the body cells directly. They are too small to be seen without a microscope—so small, in fact, that the red blood cells must pass through them in single file. The capillary networks eventually connect up with slightly larger blood vessels, **venules,** which merge into larger and larger

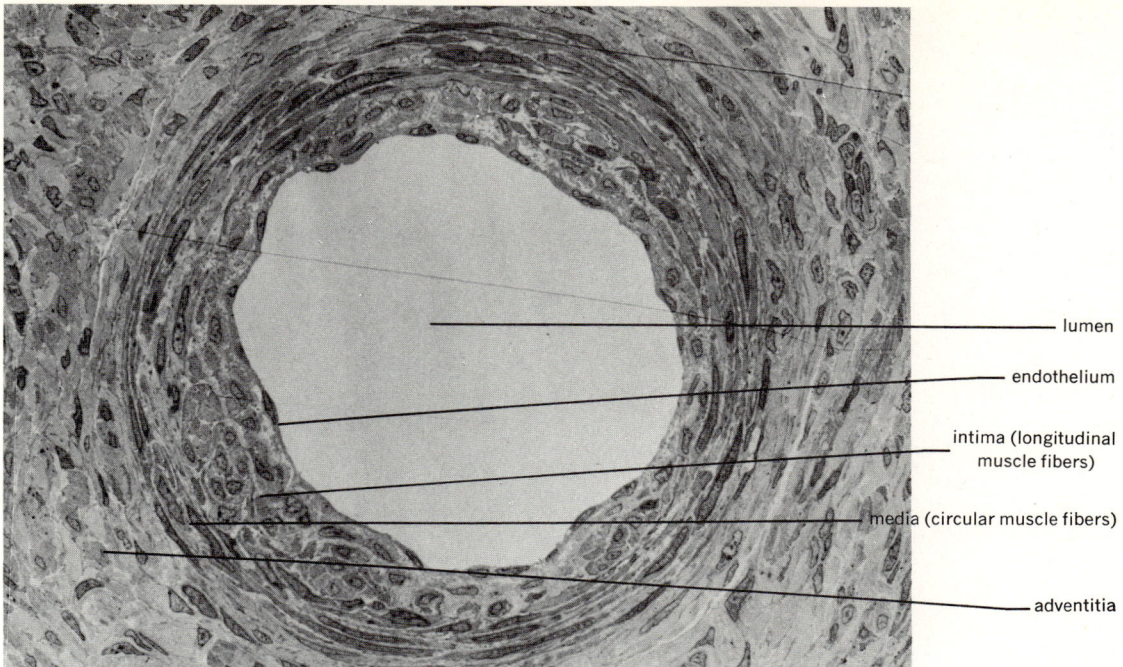

lumen

endothelium

intima (longitudinal muscle fibers)

media (circular muscle fibers)

adventitia

FIGURE 20-8 A small artery in cross section (×560), showing its three-layered wall.

veins. Veins are blood vessels that carry blood *toward* the heart. Their walls are considerably thinner and less muscular than those of the arteries. The cross section of a single capillary is much smaller than that of a single vein or artery. But there are so many capillaries that the sum of all their diameters is considerably larger than the sum of the diameters of all the arteries. As the blood flows from the heart toward the capillaries, it flows in a constantly widening bed.

The blood vessels are often pictured as the "plumbing" of the body. But the analogy is limited. The pipes that circulate water in a house are static, whereas blood vessels are dynamic—they pulsate, dilate, contract, with the rhythmic blood flows and the changing needs of the body.

Another statement that is frequently made about blood vessels is that arteries carry oxygenated blood, while veins carry deoxygenated blood. This generalization is true only of the systemic circulation; in the pulmonary circulation the situation is exactly the reverse.

Arteries

"You are as old as your arteries." This medical truism was long unquestioned. It seems logical that strong, healthy arteries, free of internal obstructions, provide a vigorous blood supply that does much to promote good health and well-being. Disease and deterioration of the arteries can lead to a variety of illnesses and to varying degrees of invalidism, senility, and ultimate death. Indeed, people who retain clear minds

and vigorous bodies in extreme old age are found to have "the arteries of a young person." Imagine the shock that reverberated through the medical community in the 1950s, when autopsies of Korean War victims revealed that many apparently healthy nineteen-year-old G.I.'s had arteries showing advanced stages of atherosclerosis, with substantial buildups of fat deposits embedded in the artery walls. This finding sparked a massive reevaluation of medical thought that is still going on about the circulatory system and various aspects of the American diet and way of life.

The arteries of the body vary in cross section from the 2.5-cm-thick aorta down to arterioles less than 0.5 mm in diameter. They have a thick-walled construction, consisting of three concentric layers enclosing a central tubular space of **lumen** (Figure 20-8). The outer coat, or **tunica adventitia,** is made up mostly of loose collagenous fibers. The thick middle coat, the **tunica media,** is composed of smooth muscle fibers encircling the tube. In the large arteries, numerous elastic fibers are scattered among them. The inner coat, the **tunica intima,** consists of epithelium resting on an elastic membrane.

The powerful contractions of the ventricles expel blood from the heart under pressure. The arteries periodically distend and constrict with the passage of each pulse of blood. Their thick walls permit them to retain their shape without collapsing when the pressure is low. The blood flow is helped along by rhythmic contractions in the muscular artery walls. (When you take a pulse at the wrist, you are feeling the con-

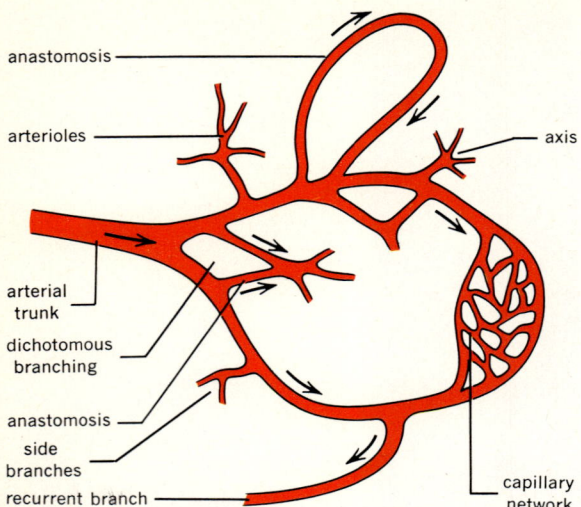

FIGURE 20-9 Branching and anastomosis of arteries promote a free movement of blood.

Labels on figure: anastomosis, arterioles, axis, arterial trunk, dichotomous branching, anastomosis, side branches, recurrent branch, capillary network

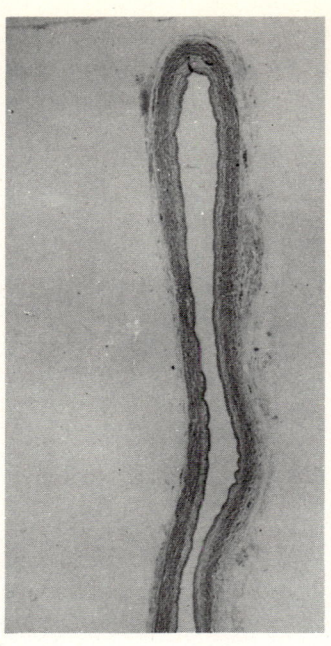

FIGURE 20-10   Cross section of human vena cava, ×5. Note the collapsed lumen.

tractions of arteries, not of the heart.)

The large arteries have their own blood supply, provided by minute vessels called **vasa vasorum.** They are also supplied with fibers chiefly from the sympathetic division of the autonomic nervous system: **vasoconstrictors,** which stimulate muscle contraction and produce a narrowing of the lumen, and **vasodilators,** which cause the smooth muscle in the artery walls to relax and dilate the lumen. During heavy exertion or emotional arousal, when the sympathetic nervous system dominates, blood is shunted away from the digestive organs and from the periphery of the body (a vasoconstrictive effect), but at the same time the blood vessels supplying the heart and skeletal muscles are dilated.

An artery may give off several branches in succession while still continuing as a recognizable main trunk (e.g., the aorta); or it may divide at one point into two or more branches of about equal size (e.g., the celiac artery). In addition to branching, the distal ends of arteries frequently unite, forming **anastomoses** (Figure 20-9). These interconnections are of great importance, since they provide alternate routes for blood flow and permit the bypassing of damaged or occluded areas without disrupting the blood supply to the organs and tissues. Anastomoses also help to equalize distribution and pressure. Anastomoses are plentiful around the joints of limbs and in organs requiring active circulation (e.g., the brain and abdominal organs). In some regions there are no anastomoses; the arteries in these areas are called **end arteries.** If the blood flow through these arteries is interrupted, **gangrene** (death of tissue) results, since there is no alternate blood supply.

Veins

When blood specimens are collected for tests, or a pint of blood is withdrawn from a donor, the needle of the syringe is not inserted into an artery. The arteries of the body are generally embedded deep in the muscles, close to bones, where they are protected from all but severe injuries. For when an artery is cut, blood comes gushing out in spurts, and large quantities of blood may be lost rapidly. It is thus much simpler and safer to collect blood specimens from one of the superficial veins, usually from the inner surface of the elbow joint. The blood flow from a cut vein is much slower and steadier; it has slowed down during its passage through the capillary beds, and the veins, unlike the arteries, do not contract rhythmically to propel the blood along.

Veins have the same three-layered structure as arteries (Figure 20-10), but their walls are thinner and less elastic. The tunica media, containing circular smooth muscle, is not as well developed as in the arteries. The tunica adventitia is thicker than the tunica media, and in some veins it contains longitudinal smooth muscle fibers in addition to the loose connective tissue. The walls of the veins are so much thinner and less muscular than those of the arteries that the veins tend to collapse when the blood pressure drops.

Veins carry blood back to the heart, and in the large vessels of the legs it is literally an uphill battle, with the blood flowing against gravity. Without a propulsive force in the venous flow, the pull of gravity tends to create a backflow. The veins of the limbs, as well as a number of others, are equipped with valves, which counteract this effect (Figure 20-11). They are bicuspid valves, which freely permit the flow of blood

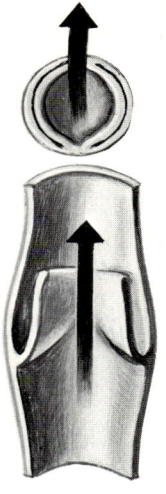 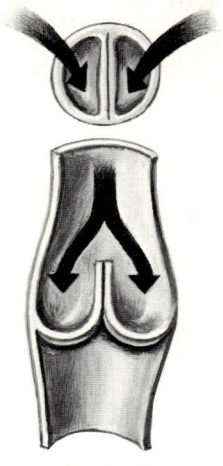 

valve open   valve closed   valve in
                                       varicose vein

FIGURE 20-11   Bicuspid valves in the veins normally permit only a one-way flow of blood.

in the direction toward the heart but are closed by a backflow. Some people inherit weak valves in their veins, which are not able to withstand the back pressure. During long periods of standing, blood pools in the lower extremities, overloading the veins and bulging their walls outward. Eventually the walls lose their elasticity and become permanently flabby, like a stretched-out rubber band. Such damaged veins are called **varicose veins.** Blood tends to accumulate in the flabby areas of the veins, causing them to bulge out and promoting seepage of excess fluid into the surrounding tissues, producing edema. The surface veins of the legs are particularly susceptible to varicosities (the deeper veins are protected from overstretching by the surrounding muscles). Another frequent site of varicosities is the wall of the rectum; varicose veins in this area are called **hemorrhoids,** and they can be extremely painful. (It is said that one of the factors contributing to the outcome of the Battle of Waterloo was the fact that Napoleon, forced to remain in the saddle for hours on end, was suffering from a tormenting case of hemorrhoids.)

Like the arteries, veins are supplied with their own tiny blood vessels (vasa vasorum) and with autonomic nerves.

Capillaries

The idea that blood circulates, that is, is carried from the heart through the body and back again through an unbroken network of blood vessels, was not formulated until the early seventeenth century by the English physician William Harvey. Harvey's hypothesis was greeted with derision—the prevailing view at that time was that the movement of blood in the body was like the ebb and flow of the tides. In a way the

disbelief of Harvey's contemporaries is understandable, for there did not seem to be any connecting link between the arteries and the veins. It was not until microscopes were better developed that the "missing links"—the capillaries—were finally revealed.

Capillaries are about 7 to 9 μ in diameter (comparable with the red blood cells) and are so tiny that it would take about 25 of them, laid end to end, to stretch an inch. Yet there are so many capillaries in the body (about ten billion) that their total length is about 62,000 miles, more than 99 percent of the entire length of the circulatory system. The capillaries might be thought of as the most important part of the circulatory system. The heart and the large blood vessels merely serve to deliver blood to and from the capillaries. But it is in these minute blood vessels that the actual exchange of materials with the trillions of body cells takes place. Oxygen passes out through the thin capillary walls and diffuses into the body cells, while their waste carbon dioxide travels an opposite route. Food materials and hormones, transported in the blood, are transferred to the cells in the capillary beds, while toxic wastes, substances produced "for export," and other cell products diffuse out of the cells and into the blood. This exchange takes place in a surprisingly short time: each given unit of blood spends only one to three seconds in a particular capillary.

The structure of the capillaries is ideally suited to their role in the body (Figure 20-12). They have very thin walls, consisting of an endothelium usually only one cell thick. They are linked into intricate networks, connecting arterioles and venules. (They arise as ramifications of the arterioles and merge to form venules.) Actually, it is often rather hard to make the

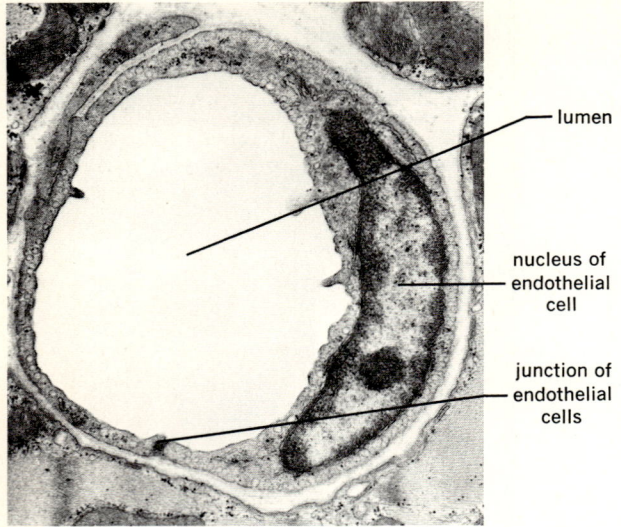

lumen

nucleus of endothelial cell

junction of endothelial cells

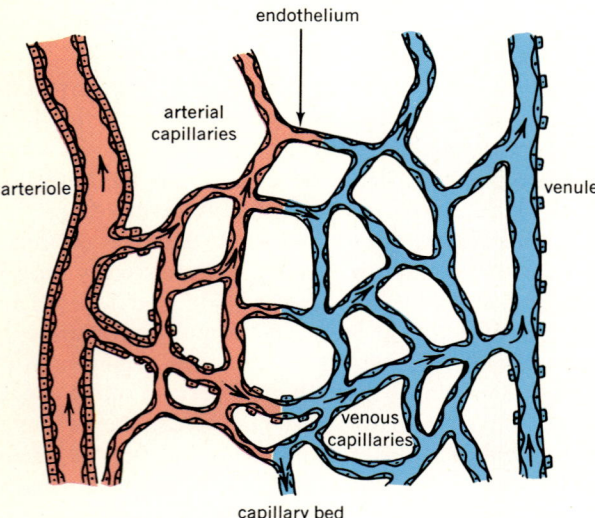

endothelium

arterial capillaries

arteriole

venule

arteriole

venous capillaries

capillary bed

FIGURE 20-12   Capillary in cross section (× 14,250). The diagram shows a capillary bed linking an arteriole and a venule.

distinction between types of small blood vessels; the venules only gradually acquire their three coats as they leave the capillary networks, and the arterioles merge equally imperceptibly into the capillaries.

In certain areas, there are direct communications between the arterioles and venules, bypassing the capillary networks. These **arteriovenous anastomoses** are common in muscles and in the gastrointestinal tract and permit a shunting of the blood flow to accommodate the needs of the body. During great exertion, for example, the muscles receive 88 percent of the heart's output, while at rest they receive only 20 percent. The abdominal organs, on the other hand, normally get 24 percent of the heart output, and during exertion their share of the blood supply is cut to a mere 1 percent.

Sinusoids

If the liver or spleen is cut open, an unusual amount of bleeding occurs. Not only are these organs copiously supplied with blood vessels, but they also contain numerous chambers filled with blood. These are **sinusoids** or **sinuses,** broad irregular vascular channels that act as a reservoir for blood. Sinusoids are characterized by wide lumens, a sluggish blood flow, freely joining channels, and thin walls that contain reticular fibers but no muscle. They can be distended greatly when filled with blood, or collapse when they are empty. In some areas the cells of the walls of the sinusoids are phagocytic and are counted as part of the reticuloendothelial system.

The role of the veins and sinusoids as blood reservoirs is often underestimated. About 79 percent of the entire blood volume is contained in the systemic circulation, and of this 59 percent is found in the veins and sinuses, 15 percent in the arteries, and only 5 percent in the capillaries.

DIVISIONS OF THE CIRCULATORY SYSTEM

The major arteries and veins of the body, pictured in Figure 20-13, may at first seem like confusing masses of branches and crisscrosses. But with closer examination, a number of basic principles emerge. First of all, blood is distributed to and drained from all the major organs and areas of the body. For each major artery carrying blood to an area there is usually a corresponding vein draining blood from it. Often the artery and vein have the same name, which corresponds either to the organ supplied or to the bones along which the blood vessels pass. Not shown on the figure are the small arteries and veins, as well as the arterioles, venules, and capillaries that complete the circuit.

We commonly speak of the circulatory system, but actually the human body has two separate circulatory systems, each containing its own complement of arteries, veins, and capillaries. These are the pulmonary and systemic circulations (Figure 20-14). The **pulmonary circulation** is the "short loop," from the heart to the lungs and back again. The **systemic circulation** consists of the many ramifying vessels that supply all parts of the body except for the lungs. Both circuits begin and end in the heart, but there is no mixing between them: the pulmonary circulation is routed from the right ventricle through the lungs to the left atrium, while the systemic circulation goes from the left ventricle around the body to the right atrium. The functions of the two circulations are also distinct. Arteries of the pulmonary circulation carry deoxygenated blood to the lungs, where an exchange of gases occurs in the capillary beds around the air sacs; veins carry oxygenated blood back to the heart. Arteries of

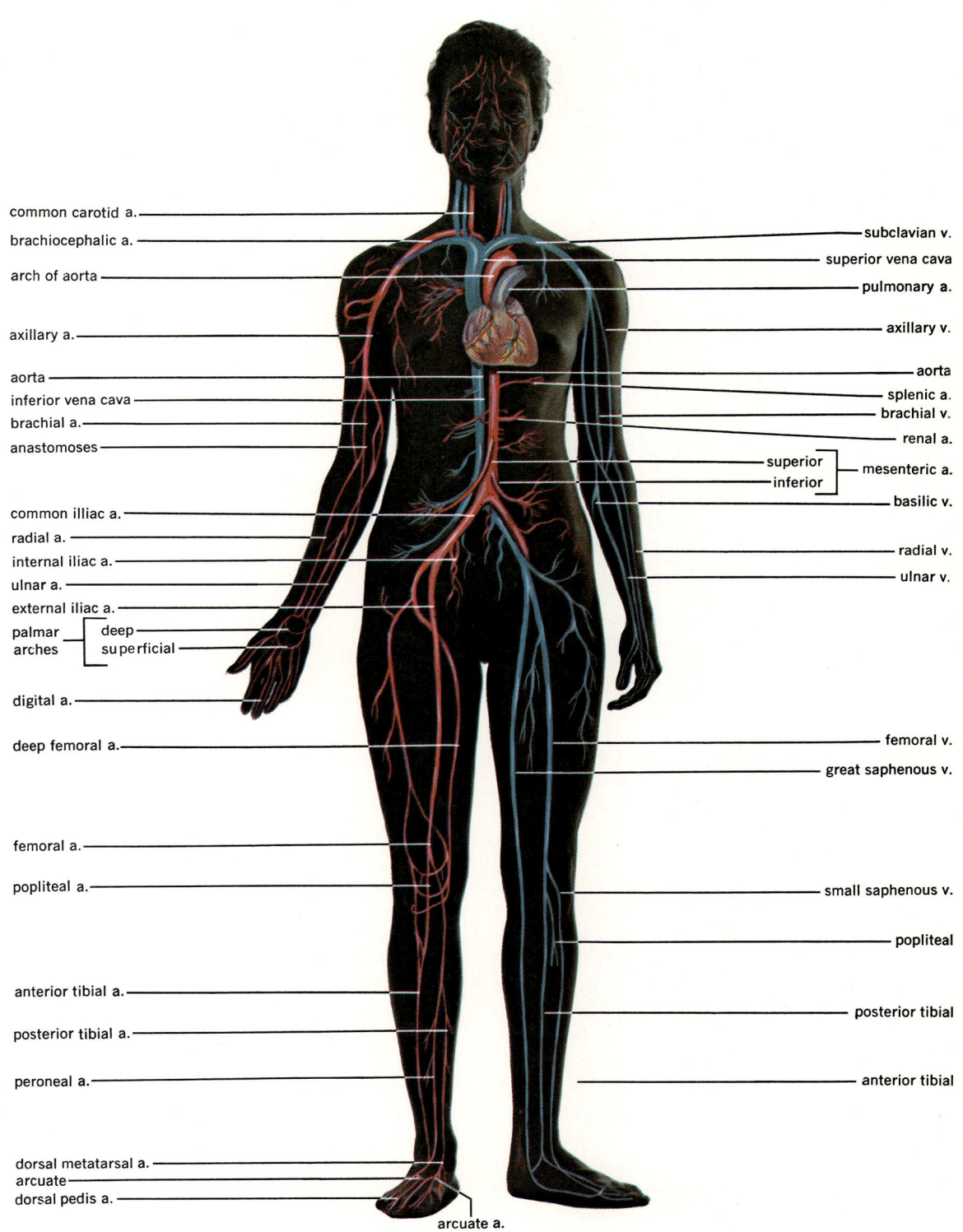

common carotid a.

brachiocephalic a.

arch of aorta

axillary a.

aorta

inferior vena cava

brachial a.

anastomoses

common illiac a.

radial a.

internal iliac a.

ulnar a.

external iliac a.

palmar arches — deep / superficial

digital a.

deep femoral a.

femoral a.

popliteal a.

anterior tibial a.

posterior tibial a.

peroneal a.

dorsal metatarsal a.

arcuate

dorsal pedis a.

arcuate a.

subclavian v.

superior vena cava

pulmonary a.

axillary v.

aorta

splenic a.

brachial v.

renal a.

superior / inferior — mesenteric a.

basilic v.

radial v.

ulnar v.

femoral v.

great saphenous v.

small saphenous v.

popliteal

posterior tibial

anterior tibial

FIGURE 20-13   The vascular system: major arteries and veins of the body.

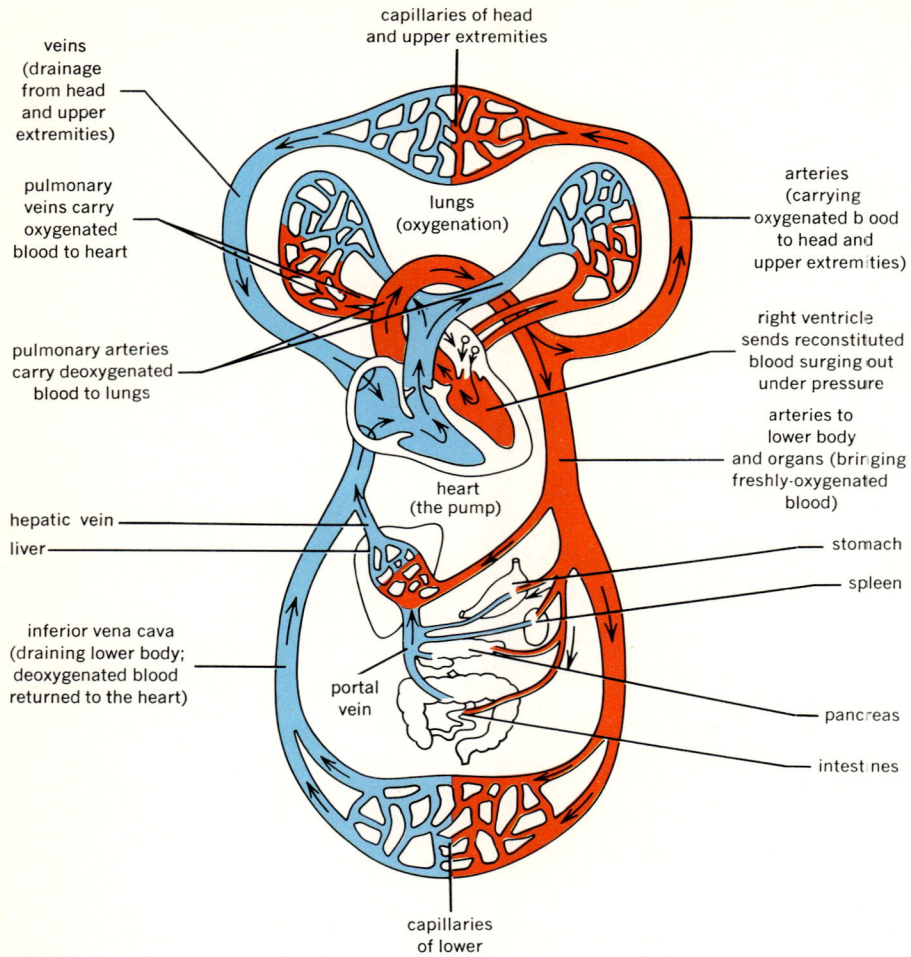

FIGURE 20-14 The pulmonary and systemic circulations.

capillaries of head
and upper extremities

veins
(drainage
from head
and upper
extremities)

pulmonary
veins carry
oxygenated
blood to heart

pulmonary arteries
carry deoxygenated
blood to lungs

hepatic vein

liver

inferior vena cava
(draining lower body;
deoxygenated blood
returned to the heart)

lungs
(oxygenation)

heart
(the pump)

portal
vein

capillaries
of lower
extremities

arteries
(carrying
oxygenated blood
to head and
upper extremities)

right ventricle
sends reconstituted
blood surging out
under pressure

arteries to
lower body
and organs (bringing
freshly-oxygenated
blood)

stomach

spleen

pancreas

intestines

the systemic circulation carry freshly oxygenated blood from the heart to the cells of the body, and veins of the systemic system return deoxygenated blood to the heart.

Pulmonary Circulation

The operation the day before was a success, and now the patient is doing well, propped up in bed and chatting with a visiting family member. Suddenly the bedside monitor registers some abupt changes in the patient's vital signs. Warning signals flash at the nurse's station outside, and medical personnel come dashing into the room. The patient is unconscious, pale and clammy, heart racing. Undetected until now, a blood clot has been working its way around the circulatory system and has finally lodged in a major branch of one of the pulmonary arteries. Pulmonary embolism is an important postoperative complication. If the major pulmonary artery is obstructed, death often results.

The arterial branch of the pulmonary circulation begins at the right ventricle, which pumps blood into the large **pulmonary trunk** (Figure 20-15). This major artery lies in front of the aorta and ascends diagonally toward the left about 8 cm before dividing into two equal-sized branches, the **right and left pulmonary arteries.** These arteries travel to the respective lungs. There the right pulmonary artery divides into three **lobar branches,** one of which supplies each lobe of the right lung; the left pulmonary artery gives rise to only two branches, which supply the two lobes of the left lung. (The left lung is somewhat smaller than the right one, to accommodate the greater mass of the heart on the left side of the body.) Each lobar branch divides and subdivides further, ramifying into arterioles and ultimately into intricate capillary plexuses in the walls of the alveoli (air sacs). It is there that the gas exchange takes place: carbon dioxide carried in the blood from the heart diffuses through the thin walls of the capillaries and alveoli and into the air spaces, eventually to be exhaled; inhaled oxygen diffuses into the capillaries and is carried along in the blood. The capillaries merge into venules, which coalesce into veins; each lung sends two **pulmonary veins** to the left atrium of the heart, completing the circuit.

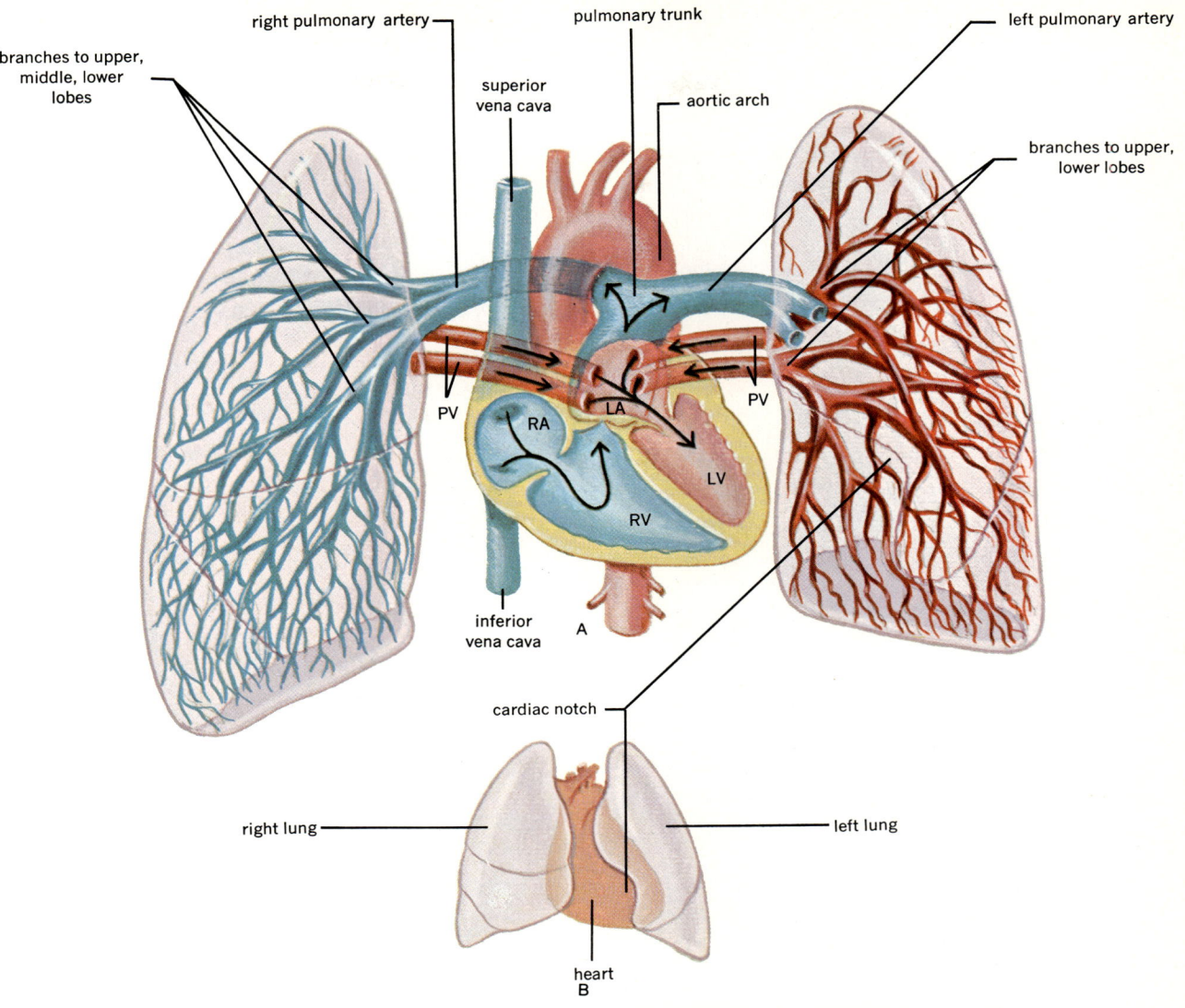

right pulmonary artery

pulmonary trunk

left pulmonary artery

branches to upper, middle, lower lobes

superior vena cava

aortic arch

branches to upper, lower lobes

PV

RA

LA

PV

LV

RV

inferior vena cava

A

cardiac notch

right lung

left lung

heart
B

FIGURE 20-15 The pulmonary circulation. Note that the pulmonary arteries (shown in blue) carry deoxygenated blood and the pulmonary veins (shown in red) carry freshly oxygenated blood—the reverse of the systemic circulation. In the view (A) the lungs are pulled outward to expose the heart; the small view (B) shows the actual arrangement of heart and lungs.

Systemic Circulation

In the science fiction movie "Fantastic Voyage," the life of a dying scientist was saved by miniaturizing a crew of medical specialists and injecting them into his bloodstream. Braving such hazards as closing valves and attacking phagocytes, the intrepid crew sailed the waterways of the body to the site of damage and repaired it.

Any particular drop of blood (or miniaturized science fiction submarine) can take a variety of routes around the systemic circulation. Starting from the left ventricle of the heart, it will be propelled out through the aorta, the largest blood vessel of the body. The aorta at first passes upward **(ascending aorta),** then loops over to the left **(aortic arch)** and curves downward **(descending aorta),** sending off branches as it goes. The coronary artery, supplying the heart mus-

cle, branches off from the ascending aorta. Branches from the aortic arch service the head and neck, the upper thorax, and the upper extremities. The descending aorta travels through the thorax, giving off branches that supply the thoracic organs and structures, passes through the diaphragm into the abdomen, supplying the abdominal organs via numerous branches, and terminates at the level of the fourth lumbar vertebra, dividing into the two **common iliac arteries,** which supply the pelvis and lower extremities.

The arteries ramify into arterioles and capillaries (a single arteriole can give rise to from ten to one hundred capillaries). The capillaries merge into venules, which join to form veins, returning the blood to the heart. Usually the total diameter of veins returning blood from an organ is at least twice the total diameter of the arteries supplying blood to the organ. Yet the total volume of blood entering the organ is the same as that leaving it: the far more sluggish flow in the veins requires the greater carrying capacity to maintain the balance.

All the veins of the systemic circulatory system (except for the cardiac veins) empty into either the **superior** or the **inferior vena cava,** which drains into the right atrium.

No particular blood cell visits all parts of the body in a single circuit. It may be carried up a branch leading to the head, then returned to the heart via veins that drain into the superior vena cava. Or it may travel to one of the extremities, or to an abdominal organ, or even around the very short circuit via the coronary arteries to the heart and back through the coronary sinus. An average trip around a loop of the systemic circulation takes less than a minute!

The major blood vessels of the systemic circulation are summarized in Table 20-1.

TABLE 20-1   Blood Vessels of the Systemic Circulation

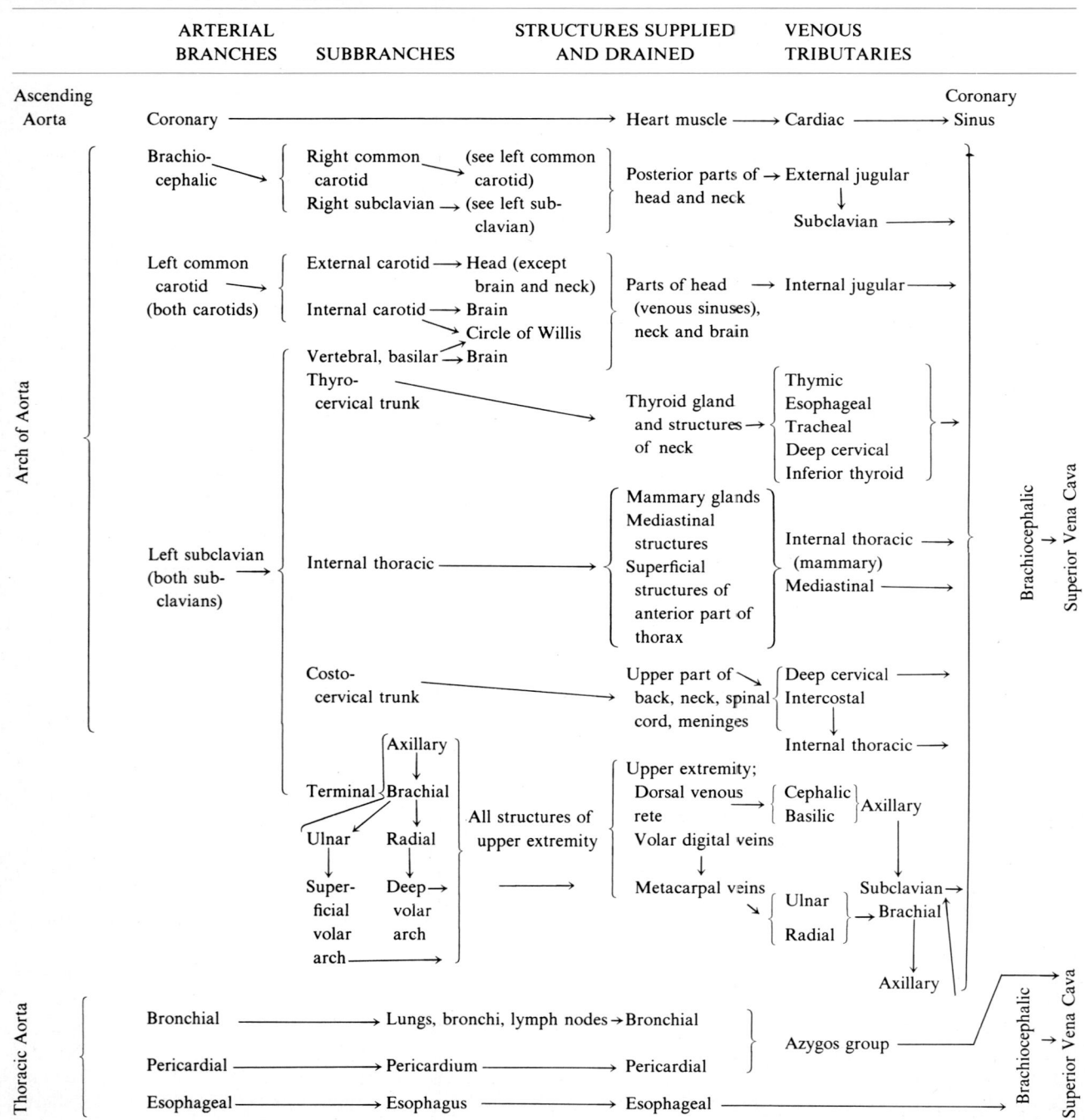

TABLE 20-1 (Continued)

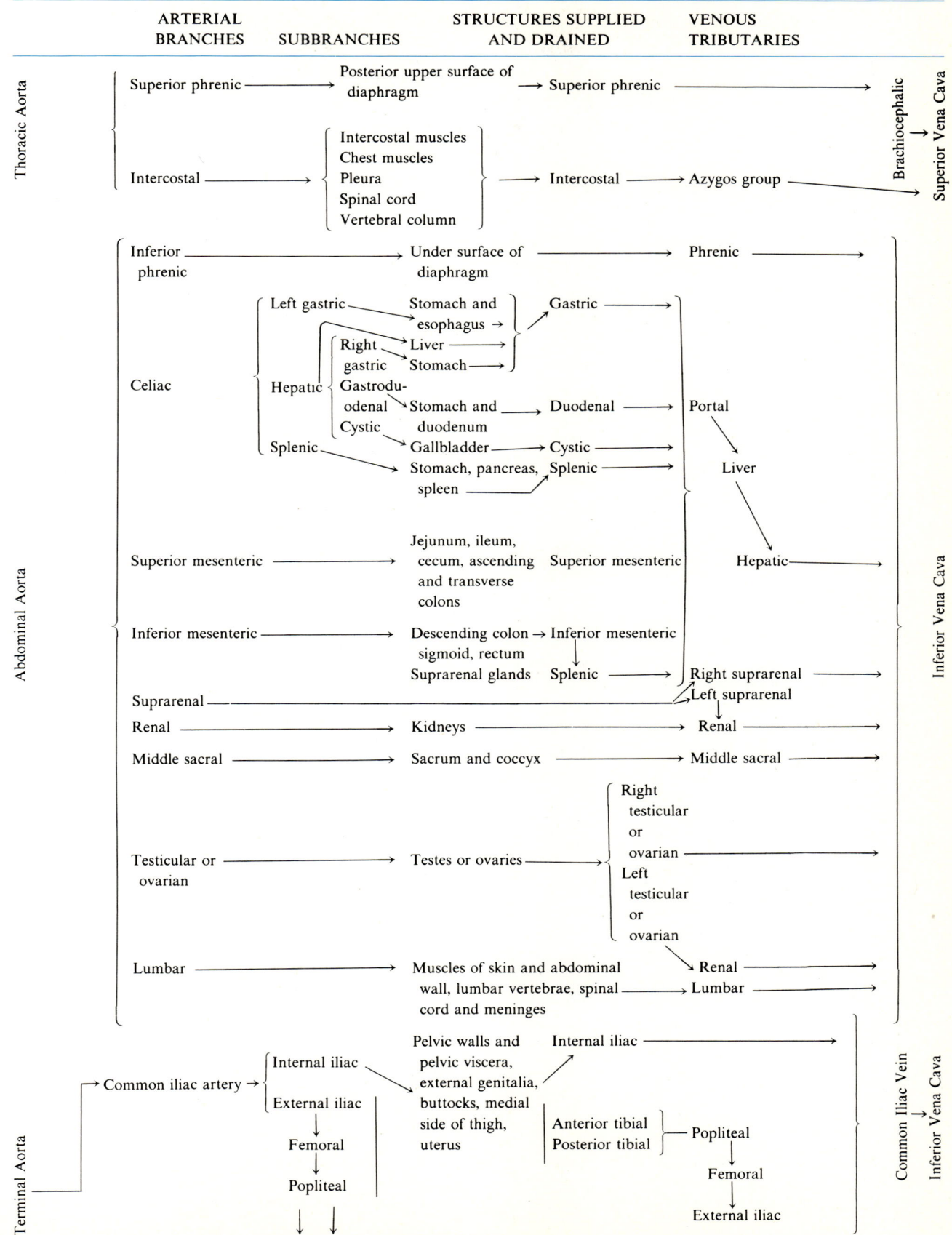

TABLE 20-1   (Continued)

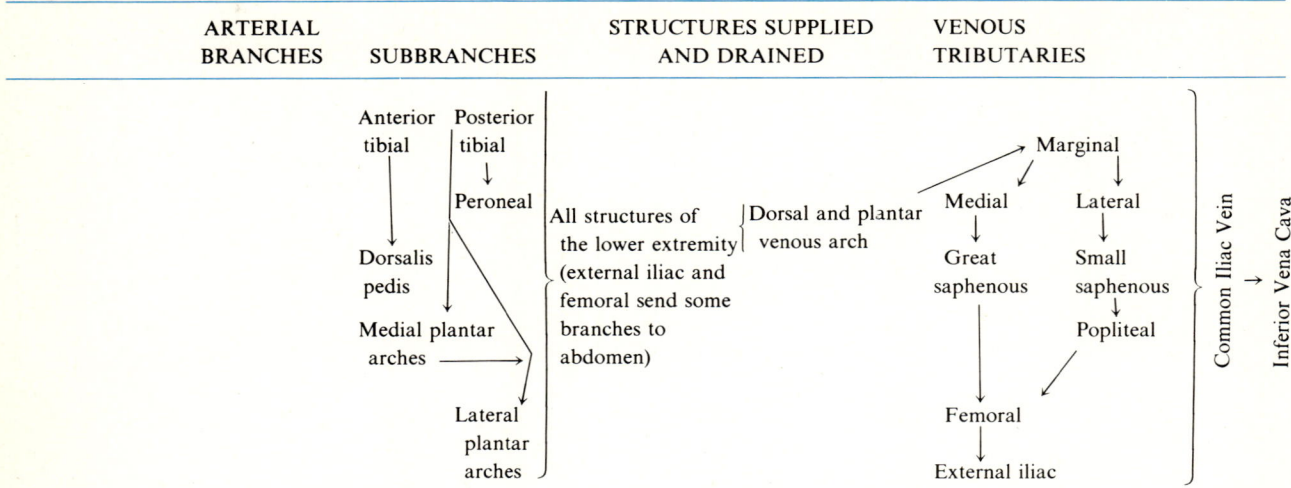

| ARTERIAL BRANCHES | SUBBRANCHES | STRUCTURES SUPPLIED AND DRAINED | VENOUS TRIBUTARIES |

ARTERIES OF THE SYSTEMIC CIRCULATION

The major arteries of the body are shown in Figure 20-16.

The Aorta

If a "popularity contest" were held among the blood vessels of the body, the aorta would doubtless win. For this massive artery supplies blood to virtually all parts of the body.

About an inch in diameter at the point where it arises from the left ventricle of the heart, the aorta follows a looping course, up and then down again, gradually decreasing in diameter and sending out branches as it goes. The different portions of the aorta are given individual names: the ascending aorta, the aortic arch, and the descending aorta, which is divided in turn into the thoracic aorta (the portion above the diaphragm) and the abdominal aorta (Figure 20-17).

Ascending Aorta   This is a short segment, about 5 cm (2 inches) long, which courses upward from the left ventricle. The junction of the aorta with the heart is guarded by the aortic semilunar valve, which prevents backflow when the ventricle relaxes. (Rhythmic contractions of the muscular wall of the aorta also help to speed the blood along.) Just above the valve, the right and left **coronary arteries** branch off from the aorta and encircle the heart, branching and rebranching to supply the myocardium. These are the only branches from the ascending portion of the aorta.

Aortic Arch   After its short upward course, the aorta curves to the left and backward, then bends downward, forming the aortic arch. This portion is generally considered to extend down to the fourth thoracic vertebra. Three large arteries branch off from the aortic arch: the brachiocephalic (or innominate), the left common carotid, and the left subclavian arteries.

The first and largest of the branches from the aortic arch, the **brachiocephalic artery,** arises from the right upper surface of the arch and passes upward and to the right until, at the level of the upper margin of the clavicle, it divides into the **right common carotid** and **right subclavian arteries,** which supply parts of the head and neck.

The **left common carotid artery** is the middle branch arising from the aortic arch. Both common carotid arteries (left and right) pass upward along the side of the trachea and larynx and divide into the **external and internal carotid arteries** at the upper border of the thyroid cartilage. When the throat is cut, blood spurts from the common carotid arteries.

The **left subclavian artery** is the third branch from the aortic arch. Like its counterpart, the right subclavian artery, it divides into a number of branches that supply various structures in the neck, upper thorax, and upper extremity. Note that both the left common carotid artery and the left subclavian artery arise directly from the aorta, whereas the corresponding arteries that supply the right side of the body arise from the brachiocephalic artery.

Descending Aorta   As the aorta descends through thorax, it gradually moves closer to the midline and roughly parallels the vertebral column. The **thoracic aorta** is considered to extend to the level of the twelfth thoracic vertebra, where the aorta passes through the diaphragm; the aorta continues as the **abdominal aorta** down to the level of the sacral promontory,

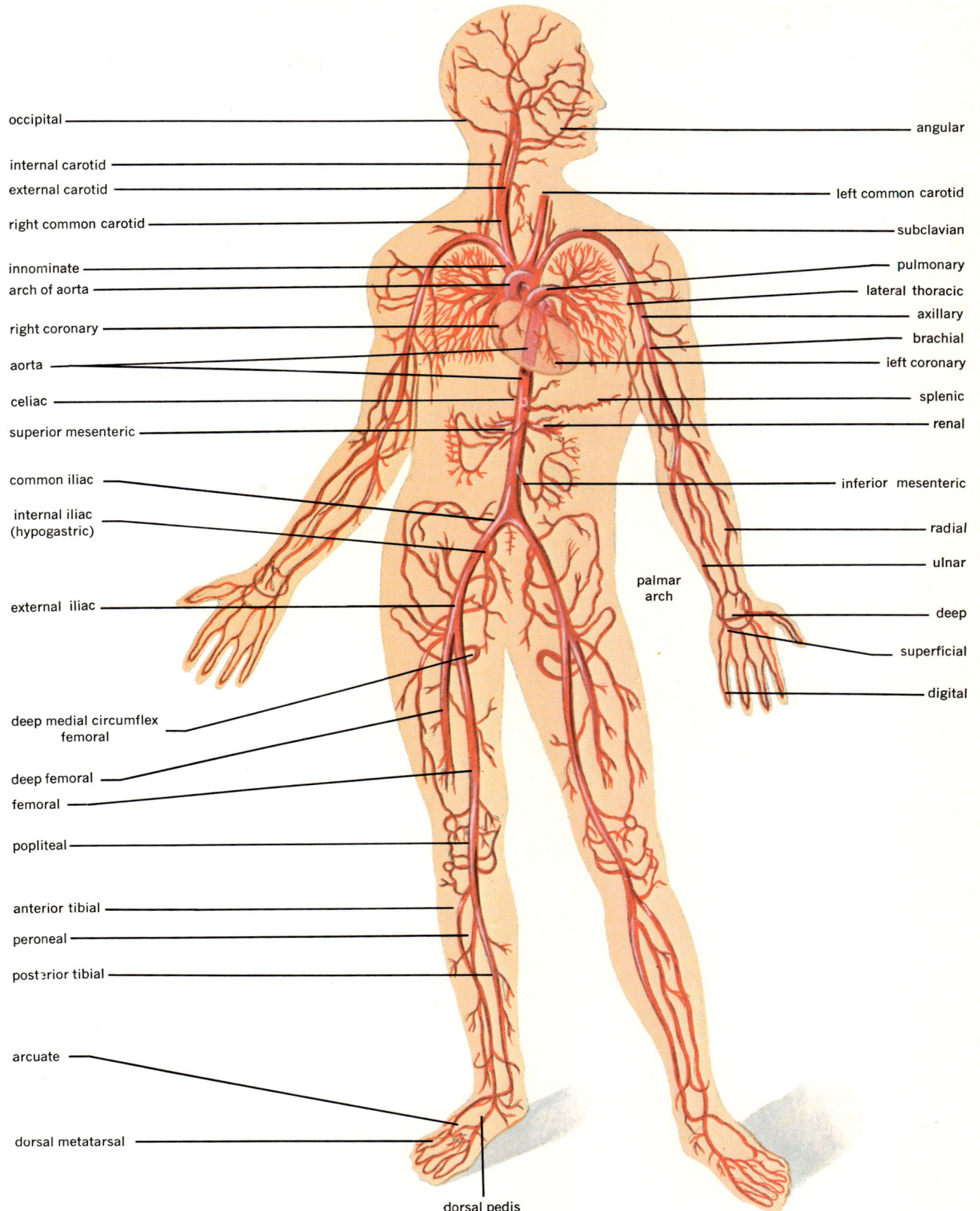

occipital

internal carotid

external carotid

right common carotid

innominate

arch of aorta

right coronary

aorta

celiac

superior mesenteric

common iliac

internal iliac
(hypogastric)

external iliac

deep medial circumflex
femoral

deep femoral

femoral

popliteal

anterior tibial

peroneal

posterior tibial

arcuate

dorsal metatarsal

angular

left common carotid

subclavian

pulmonary

lateral thoracic

axillary

brachial

ieft coronary

splenic

renal

inferior mesenteric

radial

ulnar

palmar
arch

deep

superficial

digital

dorsal pedis

FIGURE 20-16   The major arteries of the body.

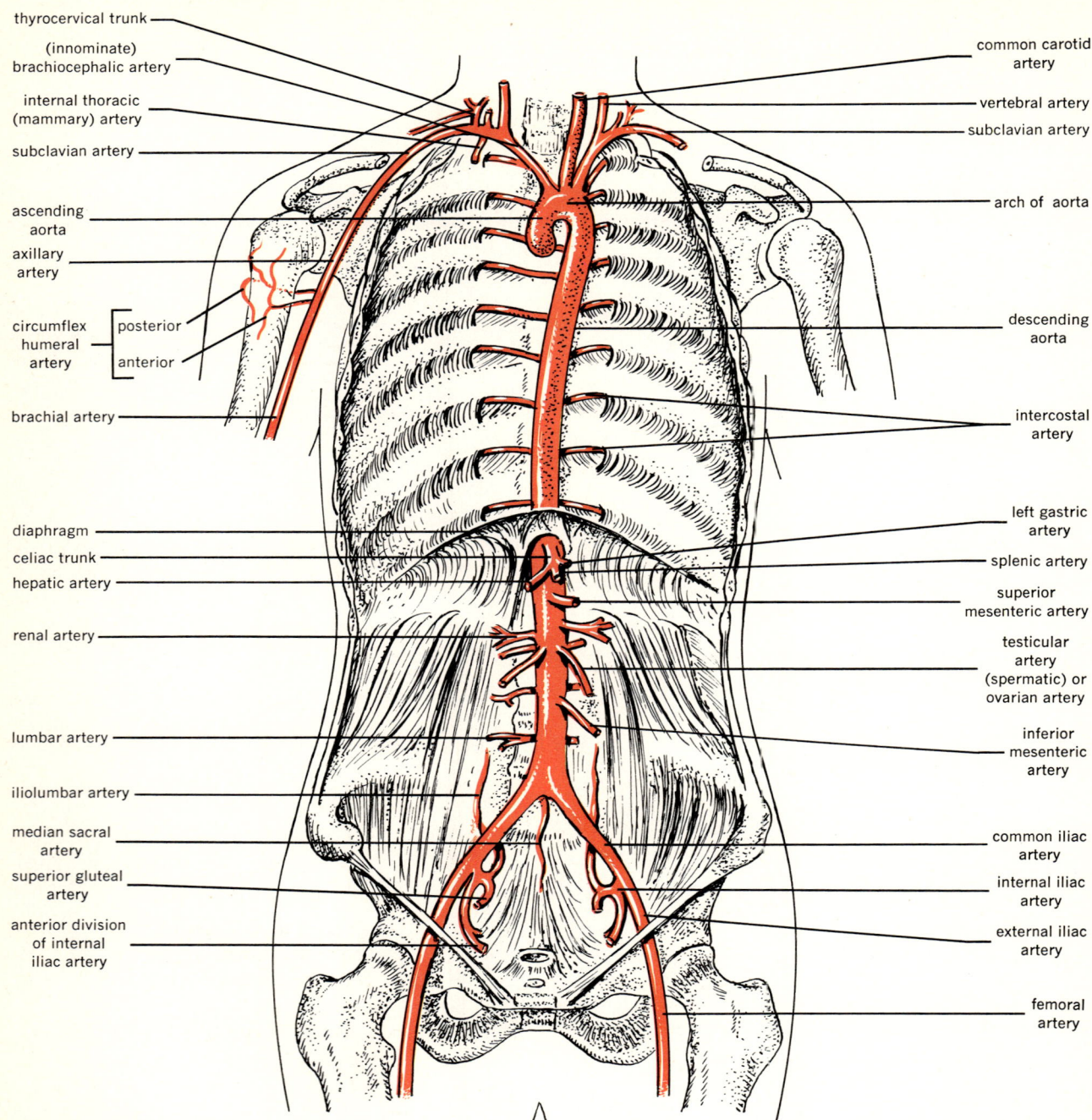

thyrocervical trunk

(innominate)
brachiocephalic artery

internal thoracic
(mammary) artery

subclavian artery

ascending
aorta

axillary
artery

circumflex
humeral
artery

posterior

anterior

brachial artery

diaphragm

celiac trunk

hepatic artery

renal artery

lumbar artery

iliolumbar artery

median sacral
artery

superior gluteal
artery

anterior division
of internal
iliac artery

common carotid
artery

vertebral artery

subclavian artery

arch of aorta

descending
aorta

intercostal
artery

left gastric
artery

splenic artery

superior
mesenteric artery

testicular
artery
(spermatic) or
ovarian artery

inferior
mesenteric
artery

common iliac
artery

internal iliac
artery

external iliac
artery

femoral
artery

FIGURE 20-17   The aorta and its major branches.

where it divides into two large arteries, the right and
left common iliac arteries. (The site of the bifurcation
corresponds to a spot on the front of the abdomen a
little below and to the left of the umbilicus.)

The thoracic aorta gives off **visceral branches**,
which supply the organs of the chest cavity (including
nutrient arteries to the lungs), and **parietal branches**,
which supply the intercostal muscles and other muscles of the thoracic wall, the pleurae, spinal cord, ver-

tebral column, and the posterior part of the diaphragm.

Branches from the abdominal aorta supply the
body wall of the abdominal cavity and its viscera.
The two common iliac arteries are the major blood
vessels carrying blood to the lower extremities.

Arteries of the Head and Neck
If you press gently with your fingertips along the sides

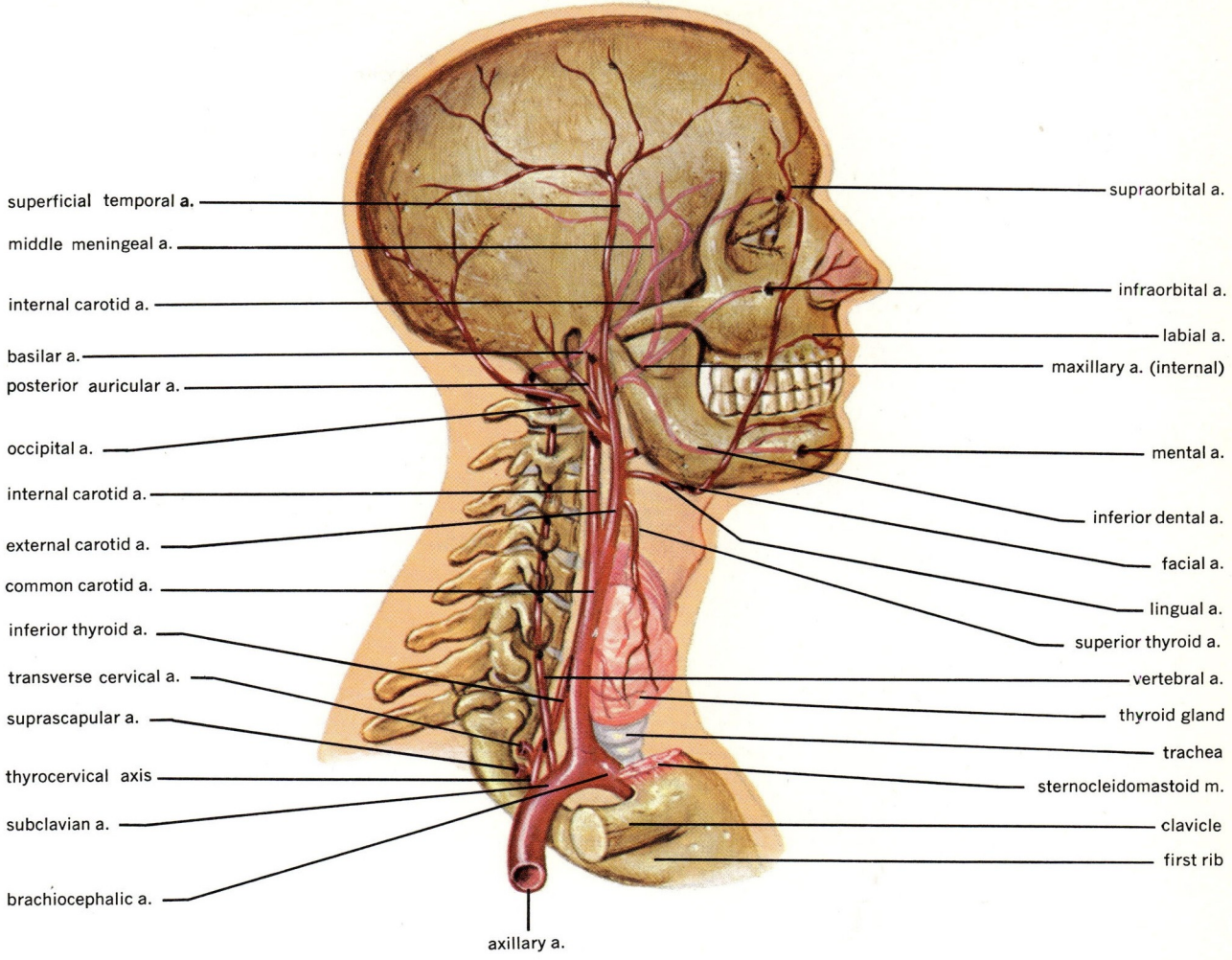

superficial temporal **a.**

middle meningeal a.

internal carotid a.

basilar a.

posterior auricular a.

occipital a.

internal carotid a.

external carotid a.

common carotid a.

inferior thyroid a.

transverse cervical a.

suprascapular a.

thyrocervical axis

subclavian a.

brachiocephalic a.

axillary a.

supraorbital a.

infraorbital a.

labial a.

maxillary a. (internal)

mental a.

inferior dental a.

facial a.

lingual a.

superior thyroid a.

vertebral a.

thyroid gland

trachea

sternocleidomastoid m.

clavicle

first rib

FIGURE 20-18 Arteries of the head and neck.

of the trachea, you will feel the pulsations of the common carotid arteries. In cases of severe bleeding from a head wound, pressure on the carotid artery on the side of the injury is sometimes recommended as an emergency first aid measure, since the common carotid arteries provide the entire blood supply to the head. But this "pressure point" should be used with caution: cutting off the carotid blood flow can lead to unconsciousness by restricting the flow of blood to the brain. (The brain is a voracious consumer of oxygen and nutrients, receiving 15 percent of the resting heart output.)

Each of the common carotid arteries divides at the upper border of the larynx to form two branches, the internal and external carotids (Figure 20-18). At the site of the division, there is a dilation of the internal carotid, forming the **carotid sinus.** A small bundle of nerve tissue, the **carotid body,** is embedded in the wall of the sinus. Pressoreceptors associated with the carotid sinus and chemoreceptors of the carotid body

send afferent impulses to the medulla via the ninth and tenth cranial nerves, forming part of the reflex arcs concerned with the control of blood pressure and heartbeat.

The **external carotid artery** runs upward to the level of the neck of the mandible, where it divides into the **superficial temporal** and **maxillary arteries.** During its upward course, it gives off a number of branches, which supply various structures of the head and neck. One of the major branches is the **facial artery,** which runs through the notch in the lower margin of the mandible (another "pressure point," used to control bleeding from the face) and then upward, beyond the orbits. The superficial temporal artery travels up past the temples to the scalp. As its name implies, this artery runs rather close to the surface, and a pulse can easily be felt in the region of the temples. The maxillary artery gives off branches to the teeth, the muscles of mastication, and the dura mater.

The **internal carotid artery** runs deeper than the ex-

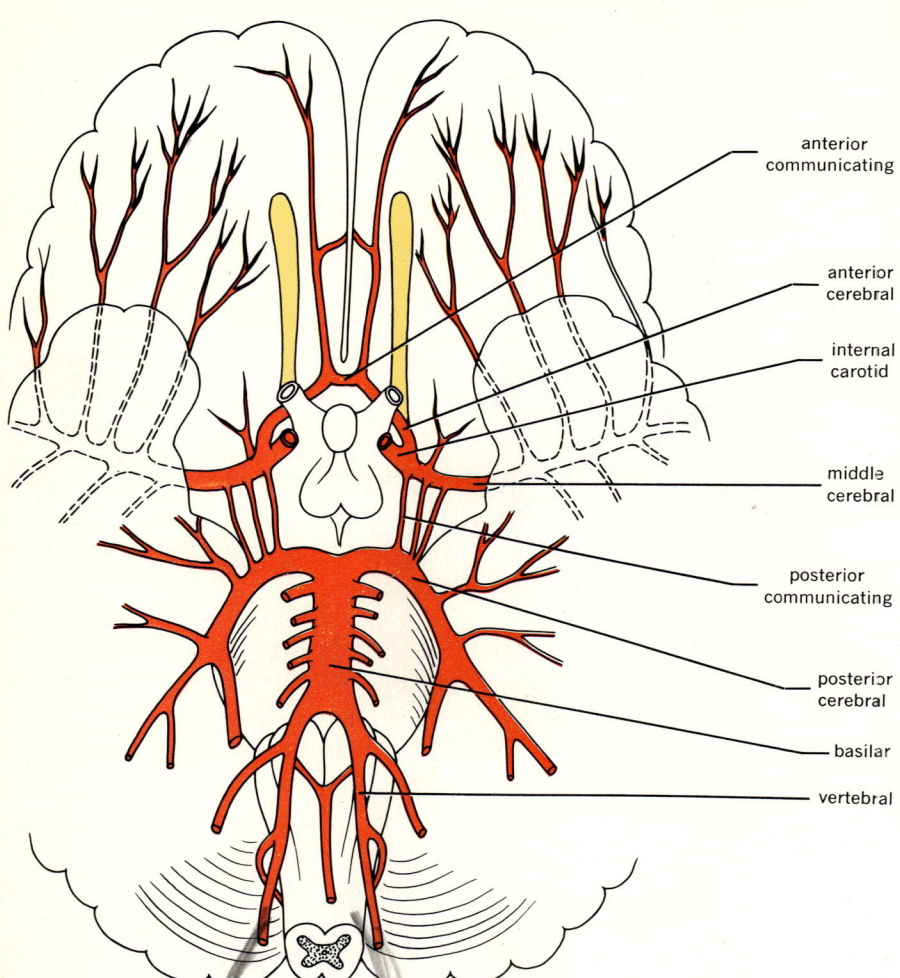

anterior
communicating

anterior
cerebral

internal
carotid

middle
cerebral

posterior
communicating

posterior
cerebral

basilar

vertebral

ternal branch. It supplies the eye and associated structures (via a branch, the **ophthalmic artery**) and parts of the brain via the **anterior and middle cerebral arteries.** Other branches go to the forehead and nose.

The **subclavian arteries** also contribute to the blood supply of the head and neck. The **vertebral arteries** arise from the subclavians in the root of the neck. They ascend through the foramina in the transverse processes of the cervical vertebrae, supplying the deep neck structures and then entering the cranial cavity through the foramen magnum. **Anterior and posterior spinal arteries** branch off and course downward along the length of the spinal cord, supplying the cord and its meninges. The vertebral arteries continue upward and join, forming the **basilar artery,** which ascends along the ventral surface of the brainstem and supplies the cerebellum, brainstem, and the inner ear. Finally it divides to form the two **posterior cerebral arteries,** which supply the posterior portion of the cerebrum.

Circle of Willis   The entire flood of blood entering the cerebrum must first pass through the circle of Willis (Figure 20-19). This is an arterial anastomosis at the base of the brain, consisting of the proximal portions of the posterior cerebral arteries, the posterior communicating arteries, the internal carotid arteries, the proximal portions of the anterior cerebral arteries, and the anterior communicating artery. The circle formed by the connections of these arteries permits the two internal carotids to communicate with each other and with the vertebral arteries.

Two types of branches are given off from the circle of Willis. **Central branches** pass into the brain substance and are terminal arteries. (That is, they do not provide interconnected alternate pathways of blood supply; if one of them is blocked, the supply to the region of the brain that it services will be cut off, potentially resulting in death of brain cells.) **Cortical branches** enter the pia mater and form superficial plexuses, which give rise to short branches that supply the cerebral cortex and long branches that supply white matter beneath it.

Arteries of the Upper Extremities

The pulse is traditionally taken by applying gentle pressure to the inner surface of the wrist, at a point where the radial artery passes close to the surface. But pulsations of the major artery supplying the upper extremity can also be felt in several other sites: on the inner surface of the elbow joint, on the inner surface of the upper arm just under the swelling biceps muscle, and inside the outward curve of the clavicle (Figure 20-20). (The latter site is sometimes used as a "pressure point" to stop bleeding from the arm that cannot be controlled by direct pressure on the wound.)

A main branch from the aortic arch is the **brachiocephalic artery,** whose name indicates that it services the arm and head. This major artery branches in turn into the **right common carotid,** which ascends to supply the neck and head, and the **right subclavian artery,** which courses laterally and downward into the right upper arm. The portion passing through the armpit is referred to as the **axillary artery;** in the upper arm proper it is called the **brachial artery.** The **left subclavian artery** arises directly from the aortic arch; its subsequent course is similar to that of the right subclavian, and it supplies the left arm.

The **superior thoracic, lateral thoracic,** and **thoracodorsal** branches of the subclavian artery supply tissues of the thorax. Branches that supply the shoulder and axillary regions are the **thoracoacromial, subscapular,** and **anterior and posterior humeral circumflex arteries.** In the upper arm the **deep brachial artery** is a branch off the main trunk that curves posteriorly around the humerus, traveling with the radial nerve, to supply the triceps muscle. Other branches supply the flexor muscles in the arm and contribute to the anastomosis around the elbow joint.

About 1 cm below the elbow joint, the brachial artery ends by dividing into two major branches, the radial and ulnar arteries. The **radial artery** sends a branch back to the elbow joint (the **radial recurrent artery**), then travels down the radial side of the forearm, giving off branches to supply the superficial extensor muscles on the back of the forearm. At the wrist it is adjacent to the radius; this is the site used to take the pulse. At the metacarpals the radial artery passes forward into the palmar surface of the hand, gives off branches that anastomose with branches from the ulnar artery, and supplies the principal arteries of the thumb **(princeps pollicis)** and index finger **(radialis indicis proprius).** (The other fingers are supplied by branches from the arches of the anastomosis.)

The **ulnar artery** is the larger terminal branch of the brachial artery. It travels down the ulnar side of the forearm (after sending a recurrent branch back to the elbow joint) and gives off branches supplying the deep flexor and deep extensor muscles of the forearm. At the wrist the ulnar artery ends, anastomosing with branches from the radial artery to form the **deep and superficial palmar arches.** The latter supplies most of the blood to the hand.

Arteries of the Thorax

The thorax contains two of the most vital organs in the body: the heart, the pump that keeps blood moving through the circulatory system, and the lungs, in which the body's oxygen supply is continually renewed and through which the metabolic waste product carbon dioxide is disposed of. Superficially, the thorax is supplied with mammary glands, which in the female function to feed the young (though the trend in recent decades has been to relegate that function to cows and retain the breasts as sex symbols), and with powerful muscles that come into play in lifting heavy objects. All of these organs and structures need a blood supply, which is provided by branches from the aortic arch and thoracic aorta (Figure 20-21).

A major artery supplying the thorax is the **internal thoracic artery,** which arises from the subclavian artery and sends branches to the mediastinum (region between the two lungs), the mammary glands, the superficial structures of the anterior chest wall, and the diaphragm. It extends down to the level of the sixth intercostal space, where it divides into the **musculophrenic** and **superior epigastric arteries,** which supply the lower intercostal spaces and the rectus abdominis muscle, respectively.

Another branch from the subclavian artery, the **costocervical trunk,** gives off two **posterior intercostal arteries,** which follow the inferior borders of the ribs and supply the intercostal muscles of the upper two intercostal spaces. Nine more posterior intercostal arteries branch off from the thoracic aorta and supply the next lower intercostal spaces.

The **bronchial arteries,** which supply the lungs, the **esophageal arteries,** which form a chain of anastomoses along the esophagus, and the **superior phrenic arteries** to the upper surface of the diaphragm are all small branches from the anterior surface of the thoracic aorta.

Arteries of the Abdomen

You have probably been warned numerous times by your parents not to swim or engage in strenuous exercise right after a heavy meal. There is a good physiological basis for these warnings. When you take in a

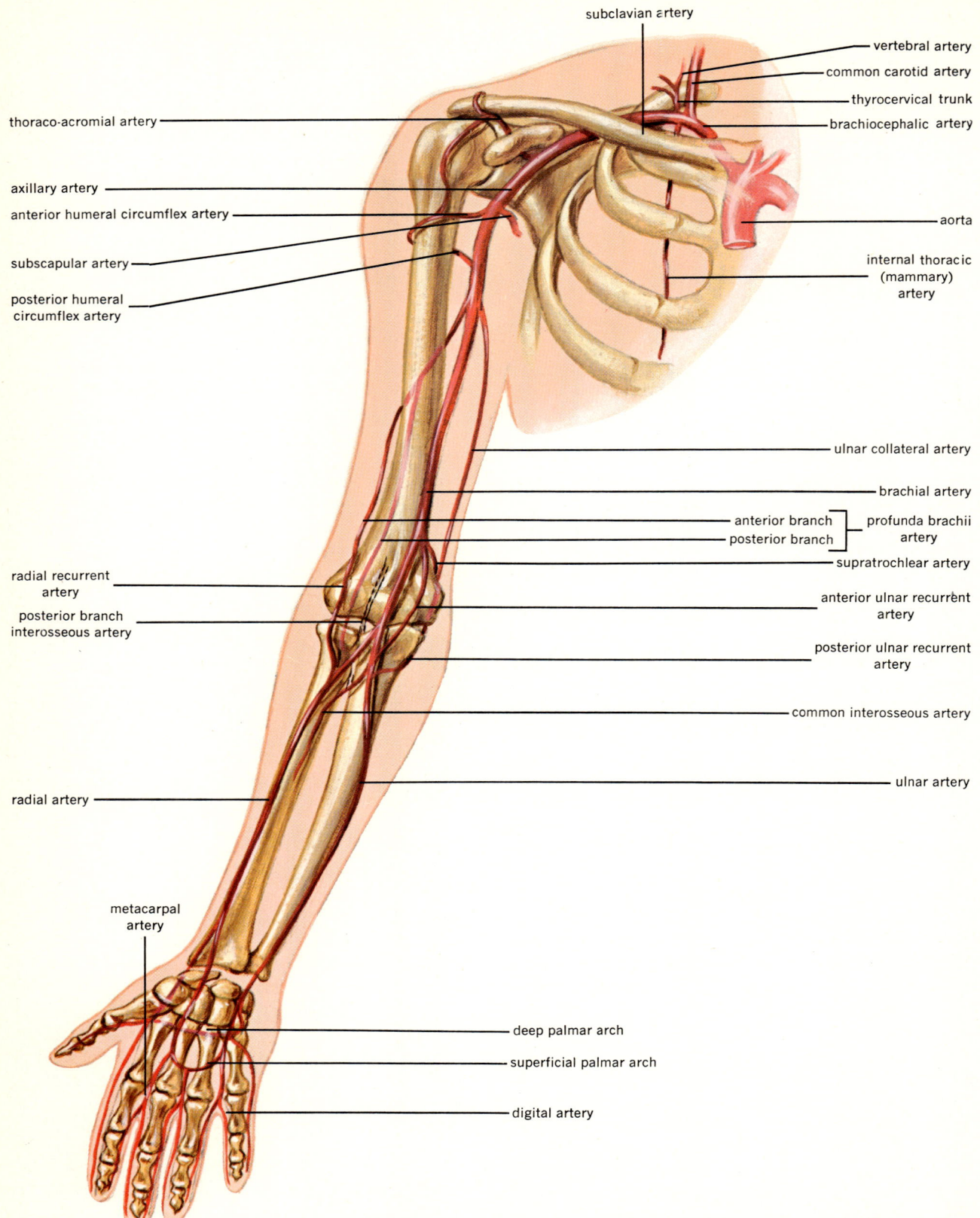

subclavian artery

vertebral artery

common carotid artery

thyrocervical trunk

brachiocephalic artery

thoraco-acromial artery

axillary artery

anterior humeral circumflex artery

subscapular artery

posterior humeral
circumflex artery

aorta

internal thoracic
(mammary)
artery

ulnar collateral artery

brachial artery

anterior branch | profunda brachii
posterior branch | artery

supratrochlear artery

anterior ulnar recurrent
artery

posterior ulnar recurrent
artery

common interosseous artery

ulnar artery

radial recurrent
artery

posterior branch
interosseous artery

radial artery

metacarpal
artery

deep palmar arch

superficial palmar arch

digital artery

FIGURE 20-20 Arteries of the upper extremity.

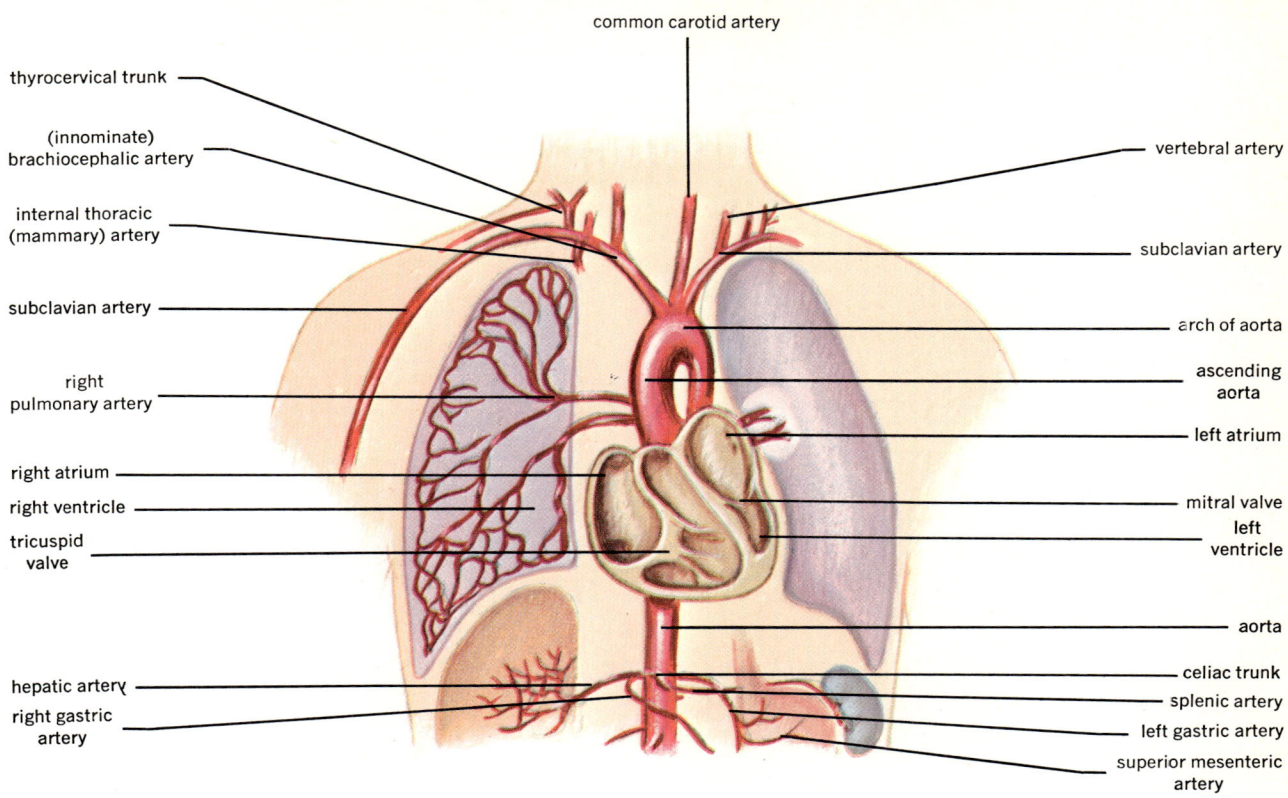

FIGURE 20-21 Arteries of the thorax.

large amount of food, your efficient body shunts the maximum possible amount of blood to the digestive organs in the abdomen, at the expense of the circulation to the peripheral regions of the body—especially the skeletal muscles and skin. If you engage in heavy physical exertion right after a meal, you will either be overworking a set of half-starved muscles, running the risk of precipitating painful muscle cramps, or will trigger a reallocation of the blood volume to the muscles at the expense of the abdominal organs, risking an attack of indigestion. (You may also notice that your hands and feet feel somewhat cooler than usual while you are digesting a heavy dinner, again because of a shunting of the available blood from the periphery to the abdominal organs.)

Under normal resting conditions, the abdomen receives about 24 percent of the total heart output. This blood is supplied by branches of the abdominal aorta (Figure 20-22). The **visceral branches** are three single arteries, the celiac, the superior mesenteric, and the inferior mesenteric, and three pairs of arteries, the middle suprarenal, the renal, and the testicular or ovarian arteries. **Parietal branches** of the abdominal aorta are the inferior phrenic, lumbar, and middle sacral arteries.

The **celiac artery** branches off from the anterior surface of the aorta just after it emerges from the

underside of the diaphragm; after a short course, it divides in turn into the left gastric, splenic, and hepatic arteries. The left gastric artery sends branches to the esophagus and stomach; branches of the splenic artery carry blood to the pancreas, stomach, and spleen. The hepatic artery sends branches to the stomach, pancreas, and duodenum, terminating as the right and left hepatic arteries, which supply the lobes of the liver.

The **superior mesenteric artery** branches off from the aorta about 2.5 cm below the origin of the celiac trunk and sends numerous branches to various parts of the small and large intestines.

The **inferior mesenteric artery** arises farther down on the anterior surface of the abdominal aorta and supplies the lower part of the large intestine.

The **middle suprarenal arteries** travel to the adrenal glands, where they anastomose with other branches. The **renal arteries** supply the kidneys. The **testicular arteries** (in the male; or **ovarian arteries** in the female) branch off from the abdominal aorta just below the origin of the renal arteries and supply the testes (ovaries).

The **inferior phrenic arteries** supply the adrenal glands and the undersurface of the diaphragm. The four pairs of **lumbar arteries** supply the muscles of the abdominal wall, the skin of the abdomen, the lumbar

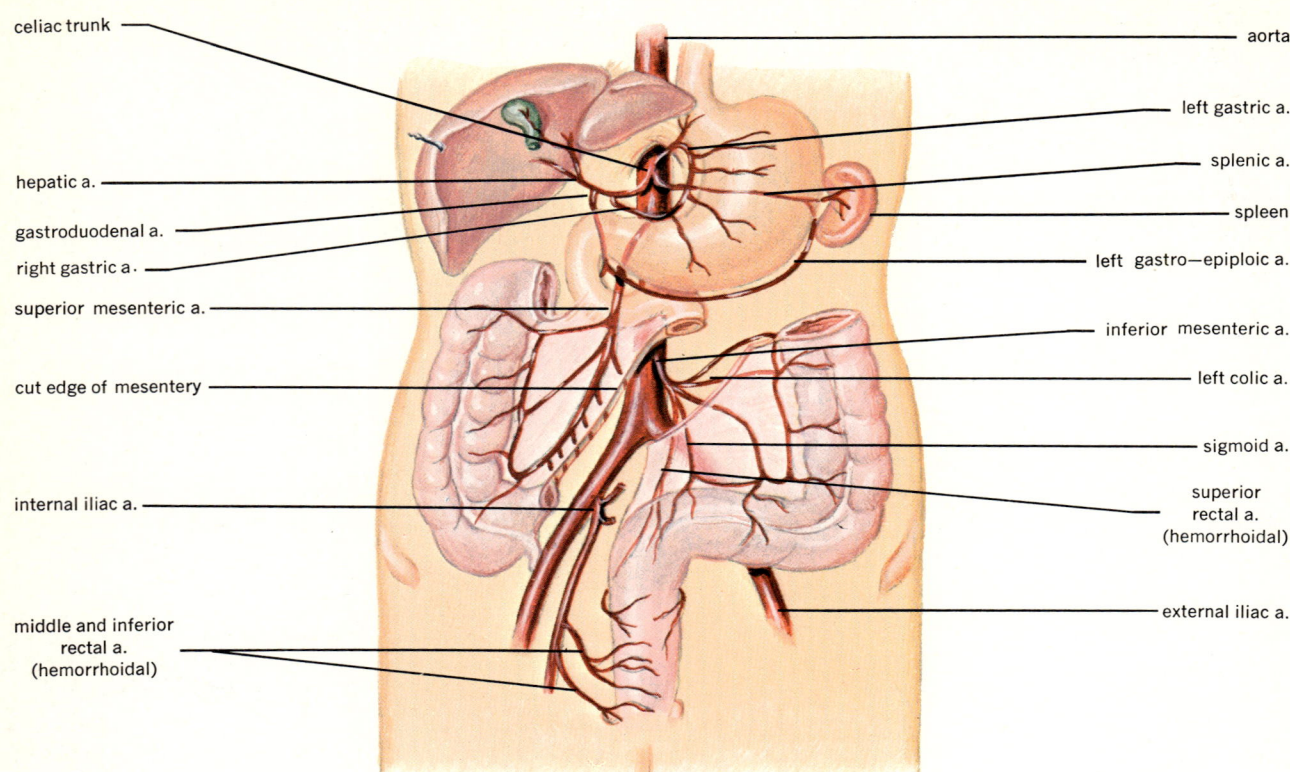

celiac trunk

aorta

left gastric a.

splenic a.

hepatic a.

spleen

gastroduodenal a.

left gastro—epiploic a.

right gastric a.

superior mesenteric a.

inferior mesenteric a.

left colic a.

cut edge of mesentery

sigmoid a.

superior rectal a. (hemorrhoidal)

internal iliac a.

external iliac a.

middle and inferior rectal a. (hemorrhoidal)

FIGURE 20-22   Arteries that supply the abdominal viscera.

vertebrae, the spinal cord and meninges, and the renal capsule. The unpaired **middle sacral artery** supplies the sacrum and coccyx, gluteus maximus, and the rectum.

Arteries of the Pelvis

The circulatory system plays an important role in sexual activity, for the erection of the penis and corresponding excitation of the external genitalia in the female are due to engorgement of blood vessels, mediated by the autonomic nervous system. The blood supply to the organs of the pelvis and perineum is carried mainly by the **internal iliac arteries** (Figure 20-23).

The abdominal aorta terminates by bifurcating into the two common iliac arteries, and each common iliac in turn divides into an external iliac and an internal iliac artery. The external iliacs descend to supply the muscles of the lower extremities. The internal iliacs send branches to the pelvic walls (**iliolumbar** and **lateral sacral arteries**), the pelvic viscera (**uterine, vaginal, middle rectal,** and the **superior, middle,** and **inferor vesicals** to the bladder), external genitalia (**internal pudendal artery**), buttocks (**superior and inferior gluteal arteries**), and the medial side of each thigh (**obturator artery**).

Arteries of the Lower Extremities

An accident in which one of the major arteries to the leg is severed presents a terrible dilemma. If nothing is done, the victim's life blood will literally spurt away from the severed trunk. The application of pressure on the "pressure point" in the groin will slow the flow, but probably will not stop it entirely. If medical aid is not immediately available, the only alternative may be to shut off the blood flow to the leg by applying a tourniquet. Yet a cut-off blood supply to a body part means ischemia, with resultant tissue damage and ultimately tissue death. By the time the victim reaches a hospital or medical aid station, such extensive irreversible damage may have set in that the leg must be amputated.*

Blood is supplied to the lower extremities by the **external iliac arteries** (Figure 20-24), which are branches from the common iliacs, the terminal branches of the aorta. Each external iliac artery ex-

---

* At one time it was recommended that a tourniquet should be loosened every 20 minutes. However, it was found that this practice enhances the risk of dislodging blood clots, producing potentially dangerous embolism, and also releases toxic tissue-destruction products into the general circulation, causing a further deterioration of the victim's general condition. The currently accepted first aid practice is to apply a tourniquet only when absolutely necessary to prevent bleeding to death and leave it in place until skilled medical aid is available.

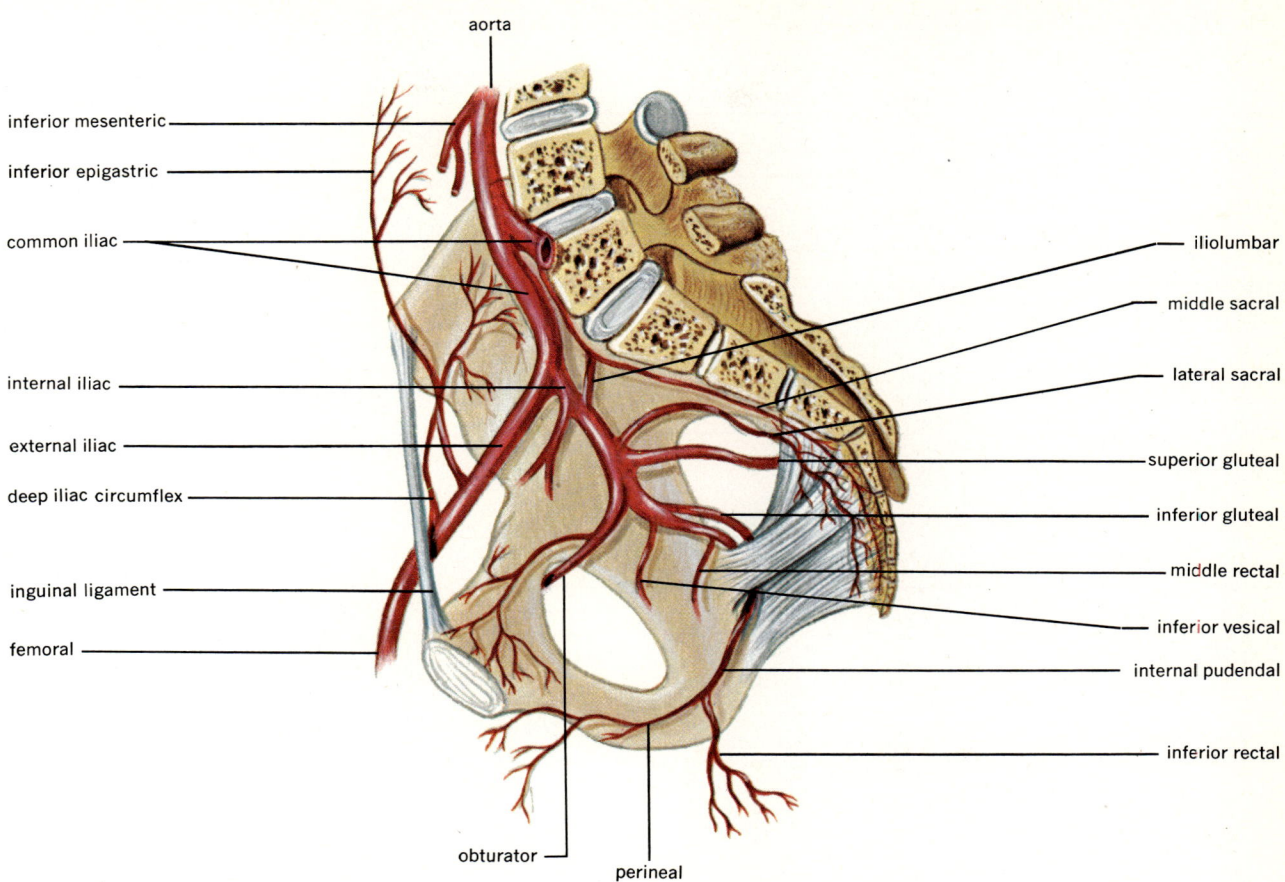

inferior mesenteric

inferior epigastric

common iliac

internal iliac

external iliac

deep iliac circumflex

inguinal ligament

femoral

aorta

iliolumbar

middle sacral

lateral sacral

superior gluteal

inferior gluteal

middle rectal

inferior vesical

internal pudendal

inferior rectal

obturator

perineal

FIGURE 20-23   Arteries of the pelvis.

tends to a point beneath the inguinal ligament, midway between the anterior superior spine of the ilium and the symphysis pubis. At that point it becomes the **femoral artery,** which travels down into the leg. Branches from the external iliac artery supply the psoas major muscle and the inguinal lymph nodes. The **inferior epigastric artery** branches off from the external iliac and passes upward to supply the skin and muscles of the anterior abdominal wall. The **deep circumflex iliac artery** is a branch that travels laterally and supplies structures in the iliac fossa.

The femoral artery passes downward through the thigh. Small branches supply the skin in the region of the groin. The **lateral and medial femoral circumflex arteries** are two large branches that encircle the upper end of the femur and supply the muscles in this area, anastomosing with the gluteal branches of the internal iliac artery. The **deep femoral artery** is a branch that parallels the main trunk and sends **perforating branches** to supply the muscles in the flexor compartment of the thigh. The femoral artery travels down the thigh in the adductor canal and sends branches to the extensor muscles. After passing through the adductor hiatus, it continues as the **popliteal artery** until

the lower border of the popliteus muscle, where it divides into two branches, the **anterior and posterior tibial arteries.** Branches from the popliteal artery supply structures in the lower thigh, the knee, and the upper leg and anastomose in the region of the knee.

The anterior tibial artery passes down the anterior compartment of the leg, supplying the extensor muscles of this compartment. At the ankle joint it becomes the **dorsalis pedis,** which supplies the ankle and the dorsum of the foot and contributes to the formation of the **plantar arch** of the foot. Palpation of the dorsalis pedis artery can give information on the circulation in the foot and the condition of the arteries of the body.

The posterior tibial artery travels down through the posterior compartment of the leg, supplying the flexor muscles. A large branch, the **peroneal artery,** parallels the fibula and sends perforating branches into the lateral compartment to supply the peroneal muscles. The nutrient artery to the tibia is also a branch of the posterior tibial artery. At the ankle the posterior tibial divides into the **lateral and medial plantar arteries,** which travel along the sole of the foot and supply branches to the ankle and the foot muscles. The lat-

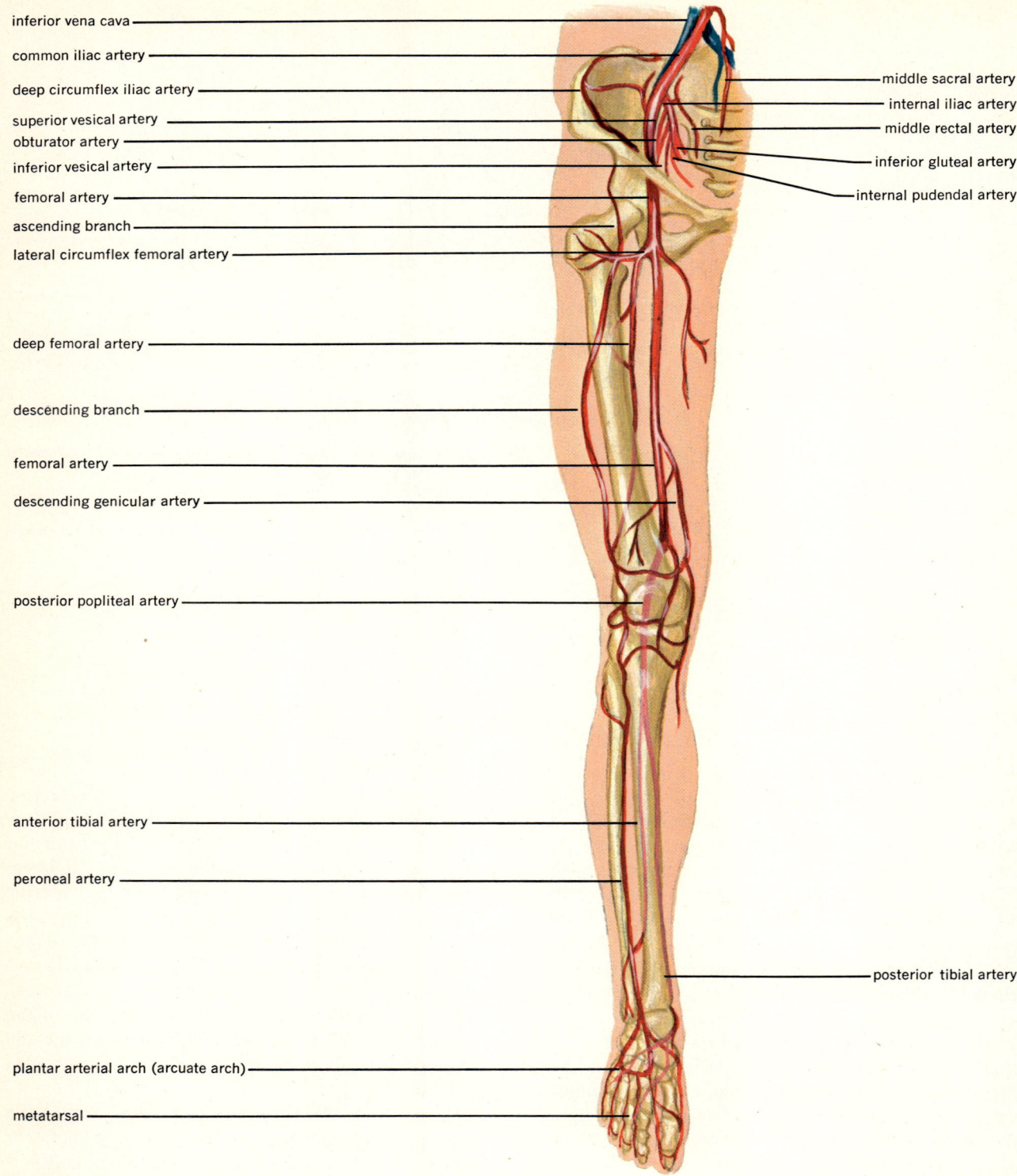

inferior vena cava

common iliac artery

deep circumflex iliac artery

superior vesical artery

obturator artery

inferior vesical artery

femoral artery

ascending branch

lateral circumflex femoral artery

deep femoral artery

descending branch

femoral artery

descending genicular artery

posterior popliteal artery

anterior tibial artery

peroneal artery

plantar arterial arch (arcuate arch)

metatarsal

middle sacral artery

internal iliac artery

middle rectal artery

inferior gluteal artery

internal pudendal artery

posterior tibial artery

FIGURE 20-24   Arteries of the lower extremity.

eral plantar artery joins with a branch of the dorsalis pedis to form the plantar arch, which is analogous to the superficial palmar arch in the hand and sends branches into the toes.

VEINS OF THE SYSTEMIC CIRCULATION

The very name of the *circulatory* system implies that whatever blood goes out from the heart has to come back, completing the circuit. Blood is returned from

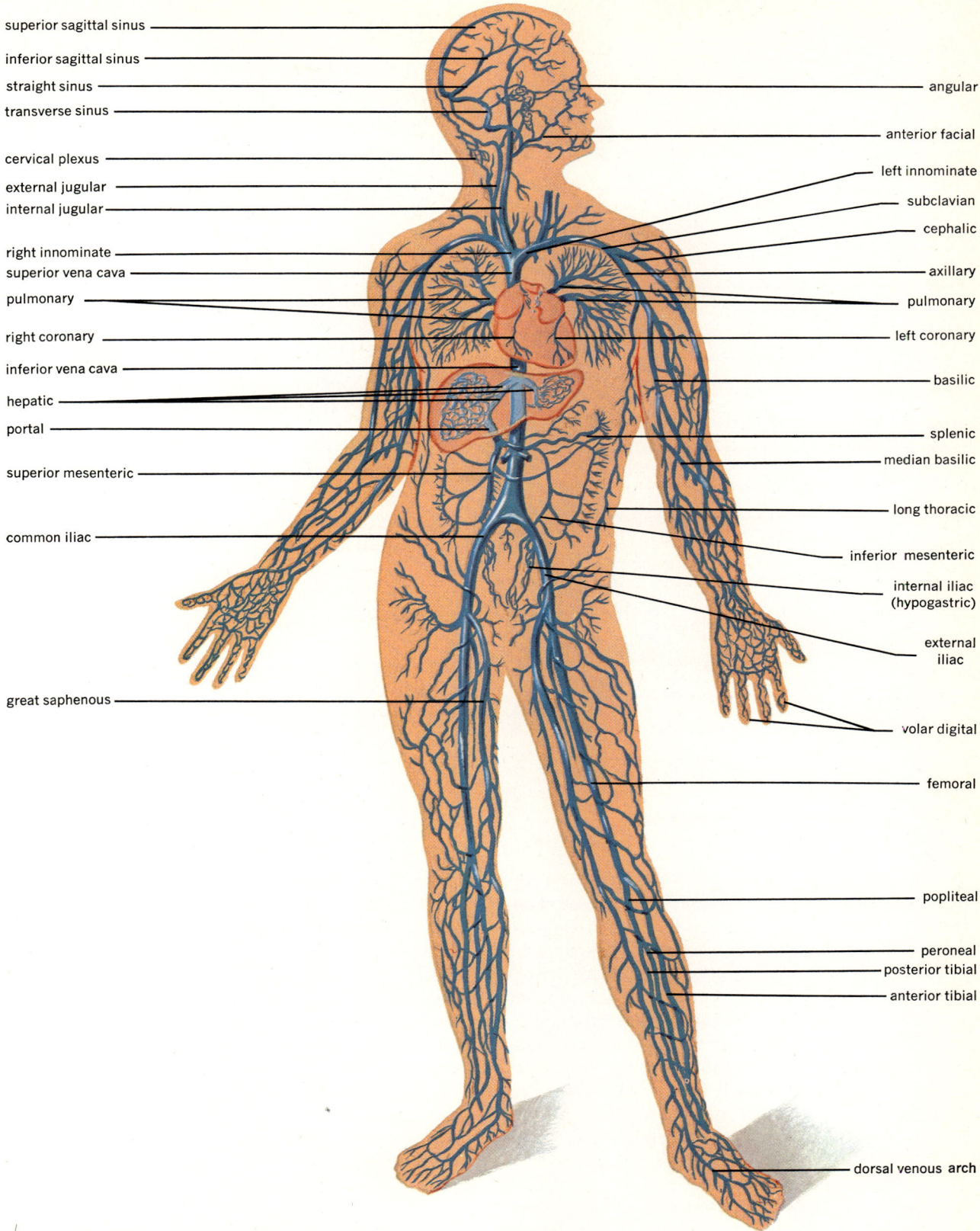

superior sagittal sinus

inferior sagittal sinus

straight sinus

transverse sinus

cervical plexus

external jugular

internal jugular

right innominate

superior vena cava

pulmonary

right coronary

inferior vena cava

hepatic

portal

superior mesenteric

common iliac

great saphenous

angular

anterior facial

left innominate

subclavian

cephalic

axillary

pulmonary

left coronary

basilic

splenic

median basilic

long thoracic

inferior mesenteric

internal iliac
(hypogastric)

external
iliac

volar digital

femoral

popliteal

peroneal

posterior tibial

anterior tibial

dorsal venous arch

FIGURE 20-25   Major veins of the body.

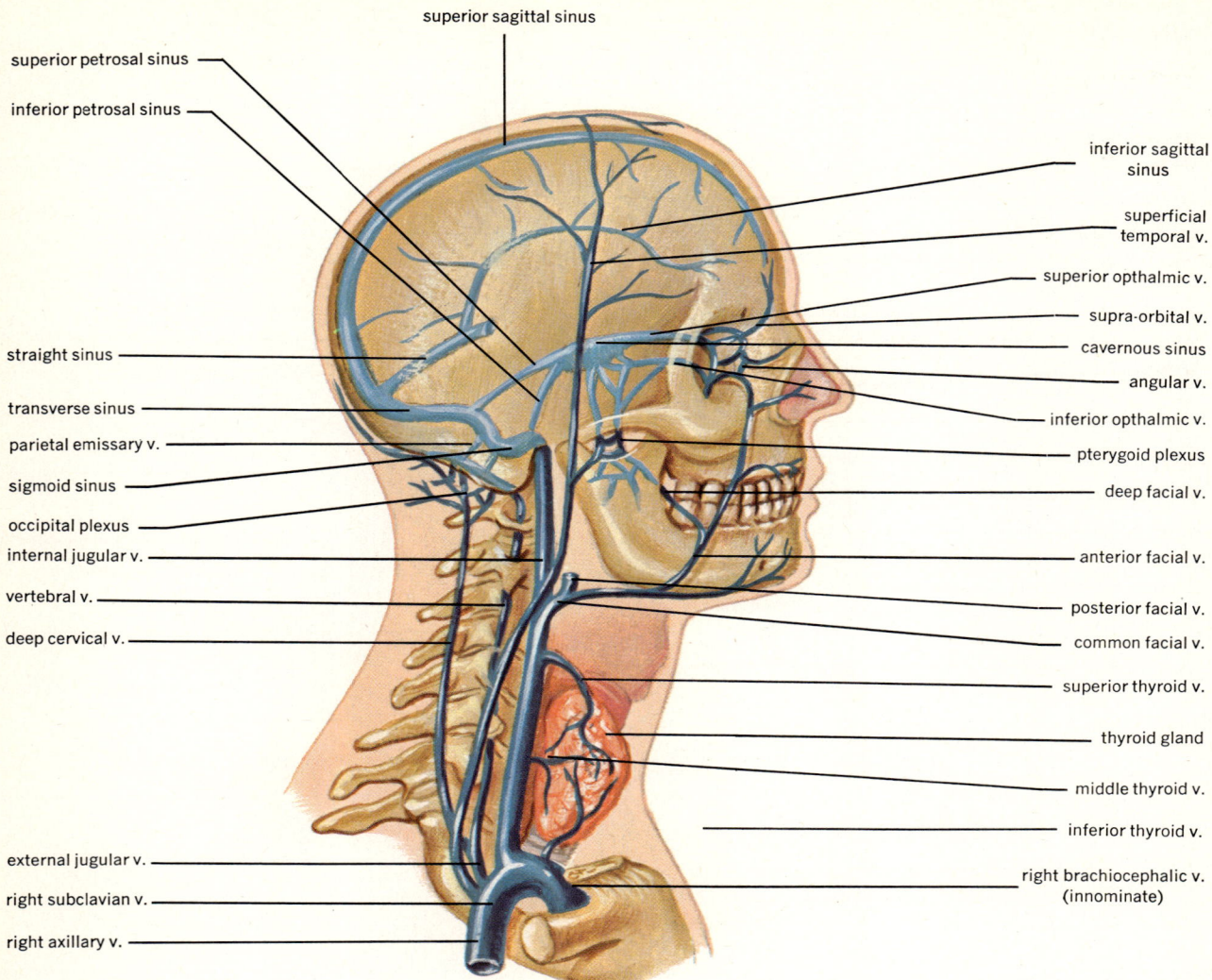

superior sagittal sinus

superior petrosal sinus

inferior petrosal sinus

inferior sagittal sinus

superficial temporal v.

superior opthalmic v.

supra-orbital v.

cavernous sinus

angular v.

inferior opthalmic v.

pterygoid plexus

deep facial v.

anterior facial v.

posterior facial v.

common facial v.

superior thyroid v.

thyroid gland

middle thyroid v.

inferior thyroid v.

right brachiocephalic v. (innominate)

straight sinus

transverse sinus

parietal emissary v.

sigmoid sinus

occipital plexus

internal jugular v.

vertebral v.

deep cervical v.

external jugular v.

right subclavian v.

right axillary v.

FIGURE 20-26   Veins and sinuses of the head and neck.

most of the body parts through veins that are companions of the corresponding arteries, the **venae comitantes.** Often there are two veins for each artery, and the veins that drain the area are given the same name as the artery that supplies blood to it. There are exceptions to this general rule, including the superior and inferior venae cavae, the jugular veins, the azygos veins, the hepatic portal system, and certain superficial veins, such as those of the face, neck, and upper and lower extremities. Nearly all the veins of the systemic system empty either into the heart or into the superior or inferior vena cava (Figure 20-25).

Veins of the Head and Neck

In a fight to the death, an animal instinctively goes for the jugular vein of its adversary; a slashing bite in just the right place to sever this major vein of the neck will quickly kill.

The copious capillary beds that supply the brain are drained by veins that form plexuses in the pia mater and empty into channels in the subarachnoid space (the space between the layers of the dura mater) called **venous sinuses** (Figure 20-26). The cranial venous sinuses also receive blood from the **meningeal, diploic,** and **extracranial veins.**

Blood from the venous sinuses and from the veins of the face drains into the largest veins of the neck, the **internal jugular veins.** Each is a continuation of the sigmoid sinus and the inferior petrosal sinus of the corresponding side; the arbitrary dividing line is at the level of the jugular foramen. The internal jugular veins pass down through the neck, receiving additional branches from the thyroid gland and neck tissues. At the level of the sternoclavicular joints, each joins with the **subclavian vein** of that side to form the **brachiocephalic vein.**

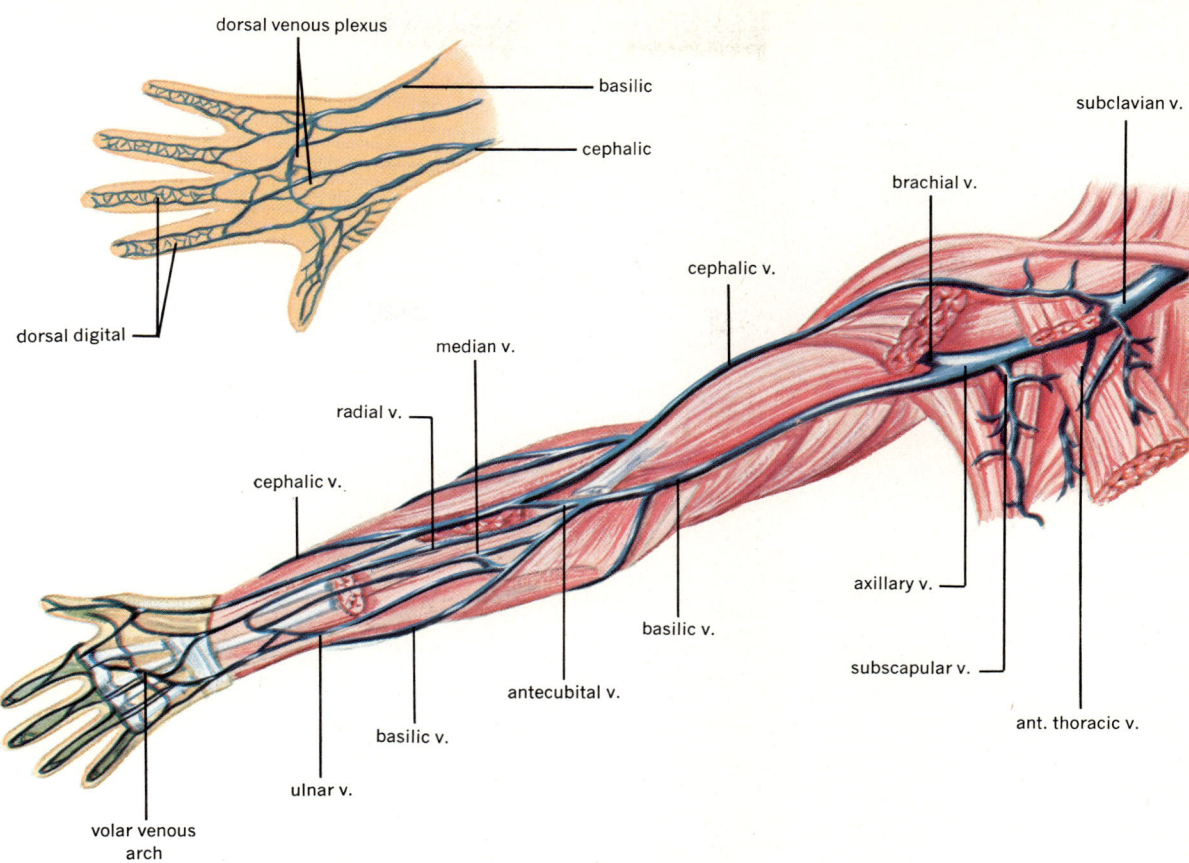

FIGURE 20-27 Veins of the upper extremity.

Smaller veins passing down through the neck to drain into the subclavian veins are the **external jugular veins,** carrying blood from the superficial regions of the side of the head, drained via the **superficial temporal veins;** the **deep cervical veins,** which travel down from a plexus in the suboccipital region in company with the deep cervical arteries; and the **vertebral veins,** which arise from the same venous plexus and thread their way down through the foramina of the transverse processes of the upper six cervical vertebrae, together with the vertebral arteries.

Sometimes pulsations can be seen in the external jugular vein, just above the clavicle. This may seem strange, since the walls of veins are not very muscular, and they do not contract rhythmically, as arteries do. The explanation for these pulsations (referred to as the central venous pulse) lies in the nearness to the heart: pressure changes are transmitted upward from the right atrium through the superior vena cava, since there are no valves at its entrance into the heart.

Veins of the Upper Extremities

The arms of a heroin addict are pockmarked with the telltale scars of needle punctures. The addict's first choice, like that of a lab technician drawing a blood specimen or making an intravenous injection, is the median cubital vein at the bend of the elbow. But repeated "fixes," often with unsterilized hypodermics, produce so much tissue damage that the addict is soon forced to seek other veins for "mainlining." The veins of the arms are convenient for injections because many of them run quite close to the surface (as you can verify by looking at the bluish traceries on your own arms and hands). In addition to these **superficial veins** (Figure 20-27), the upper extremity is also provided with a set of **deep veins,** which are the venae comitantes of the hand, forearm, and arm and are called by the same names as the corresponding arteries. The superficial veins, however, are larger and return more blood.

The **venous plexuses** on the dorsal and palmar surfaces of the hand drain into two major superficial veins of the forearm, the **cephalic** and **basilic veins.** These two veins continue into the upper arm and are joined at the bend of the elbow by the **median cubital vein** (the favored injection site). The cephalic vein remains superficial throughout most of its course, eventually joining the **subclavian vein** in the shoulder

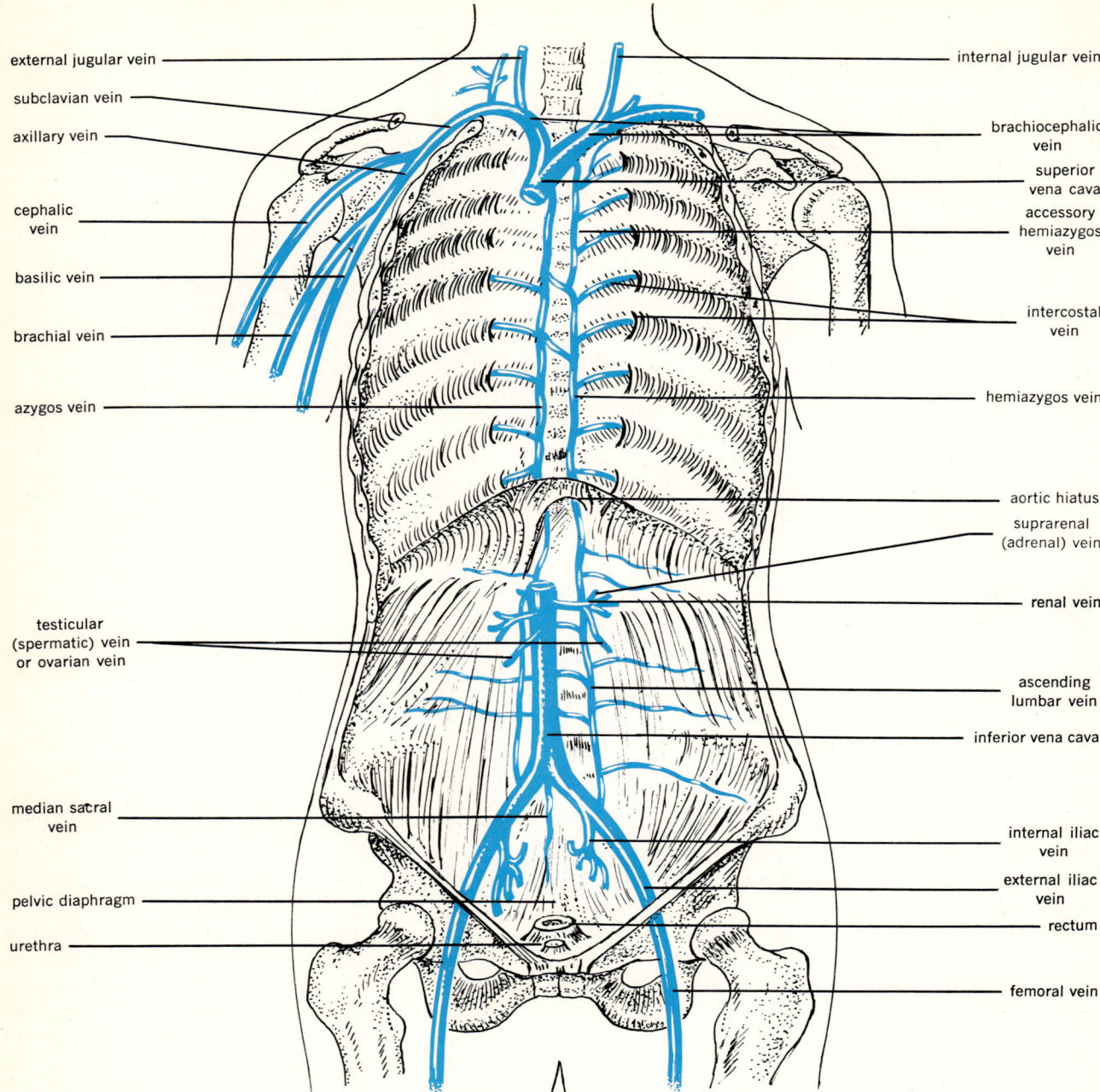

external jugular vein

subclavian vein

axillary vein

cephalic vein

basilic vein

brachial vein

azygos vein

testicular (spermatic) vein or ovarian vein

median sacral vein

pelvic diaphragm

urethra

internal jugular vein

brachiocephalic vein

superior vena cava

accessory hemiazygos vein

intercostal vein

hemiazygos vein

aortic hiatus

suprarenal (adrenal) vein

renal vein

ascending lumbar vein

inferior vena cava

internal iliac vein

external iliac vein

rectum

femoral vein

FIGURE 20-28   The vena cava and its tributaries.

region. The basilic vein turns inward about halfway up the brachium (upper arm) and follows a deep course until it merges into the **axillary vein.**

In addition to the major superficial veins mentioned, there are numerous smaller branches returning blood from the tissues of the arm and forming intricate anastomosing networks, as can be seen from Figure 20-27.

Veins of the Thorax

The pulmonary veins, which drain into the left atrium, are the only veins in the body that carry oxy-

genated blood. However, these veins are not part of the systemic circulation. The systemic veins that are found in the thorax all carry deoxygenated blood and are tributaries of the **superior vena cava,** which empties into the right atrium (Figure 20-28).

The superior vena cava is formed by the union of the **right and left brachiocephalic veins.** It returns the blood from the head, neck, upper extremity, and thorax to the right atrium.

In addition to the brachiocephalic flows, the superior vena cava receives blood from the **azygos group** of veins, which provide a connecting link between the

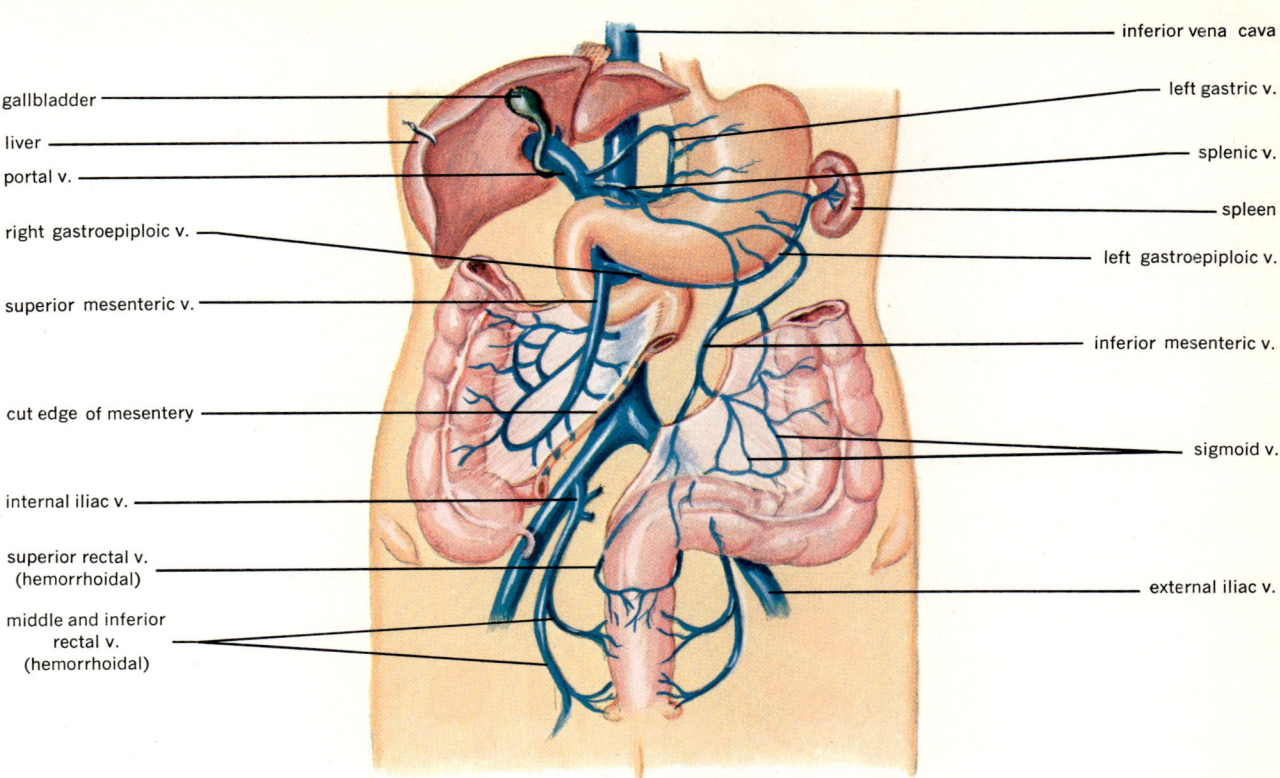

gallbladder

liver

portal v.

right gastroepiploic v.

superior mesenteric v.

cut edge of mesentery

internal iliac v.

superior rectal v.
(hemorrhoidal)

middle and inferior
rectal v.
(hemorrhoidal)

inferior vena cava

left gastric v.

splenic v.

spleen

left gastroepiploic v.

inferior mesenteric v.

sigmoid v.

external iliac v.

FIGURE 20-29 Veins of the abdomen and pelvis.

superior and inferior vena caval systems. (If the inferior vena cava is blocked, the azygos veins serve as a back-up system for drainage of the lower body, providing collateral circulation for the venous blood.) Three main veins make up the azygos group. The **azygos vein** begins just below the diaphragm as a continuation of the right ascending lumbar vein and ascends along the right side of the vertebral column, receiving **intercostal veins** from the right side. The **hemiazygos vein** has a corresponding origin on the left side but ascends only to the level of the ninth thoracic vertebra, crossing over the midline to connect with the azygos vein. The **accessory hemiazygos vein** runs down along the left side of the vertebral column in the upper part of the thoracic space and opens into either the azygos or the hemiazygos. The hemiazygos and accessory hemiazygos veins receive intercostal veins from the left side and together cover an area corresponding to the single azygos vein on the right.

Veins of the Abdomen and Pelvis

The abdomen resembles a three-dimensional puzzle, in which a number of different-shaped parts are carefully arranged and interlocked, each fitting precisely into its own niche. The stomach, liver, gallbladder, pancreas, spleen, kidneys, a couple of dozen feet of tubular intestines coiled like spaghetti, and the reproductive organs are all crammed inside this cavity, roofed by the diaphragm and floored by the pelvis.

All these organs, as well as the muscles and superficial tissues of the abdominal wall, require a copious blood supply, provided by extensive arterial and venous systems. The major arteries and veins of the abdomen are also linked with the blood vessels that supply and drain the lower extremities.

The blood of the lower part of the body all drains ultimately into the **inferior vena cava** (Figure 20-29), which empties into the right atrium. This massive trunk is analogous to the abdominal aorta; it arises from the union of the two **common iliac veins** at the level of the fifth lumbar vertebra and ascends on the right on the aorta.

Other notable veins of the abdomen and pelvis include:

The **phrenic vein**, which drains the undersurface of the diaphragm and also receives blood from the adrenal gland. Four pairs of **lumbar veins**, which arise in the muscles of the abdominal wall and receive tributaries that return blood from the skin and muscles of the dorsal part of the trunk, the spinal cord, and the meninges.
The **renal veins**, each formed by the union of three to five tributaries, which drain the kidney.
The **suprarenal veins**, which drain the middle portion of the adrenal glands.
The **testicular and ovarian veins**, which receive blood from the male and female reproductive organs.
The **hepatic portal system**, including the veins that drain the digestive tract, pancreas, spleen, and gallbladder; tributar-

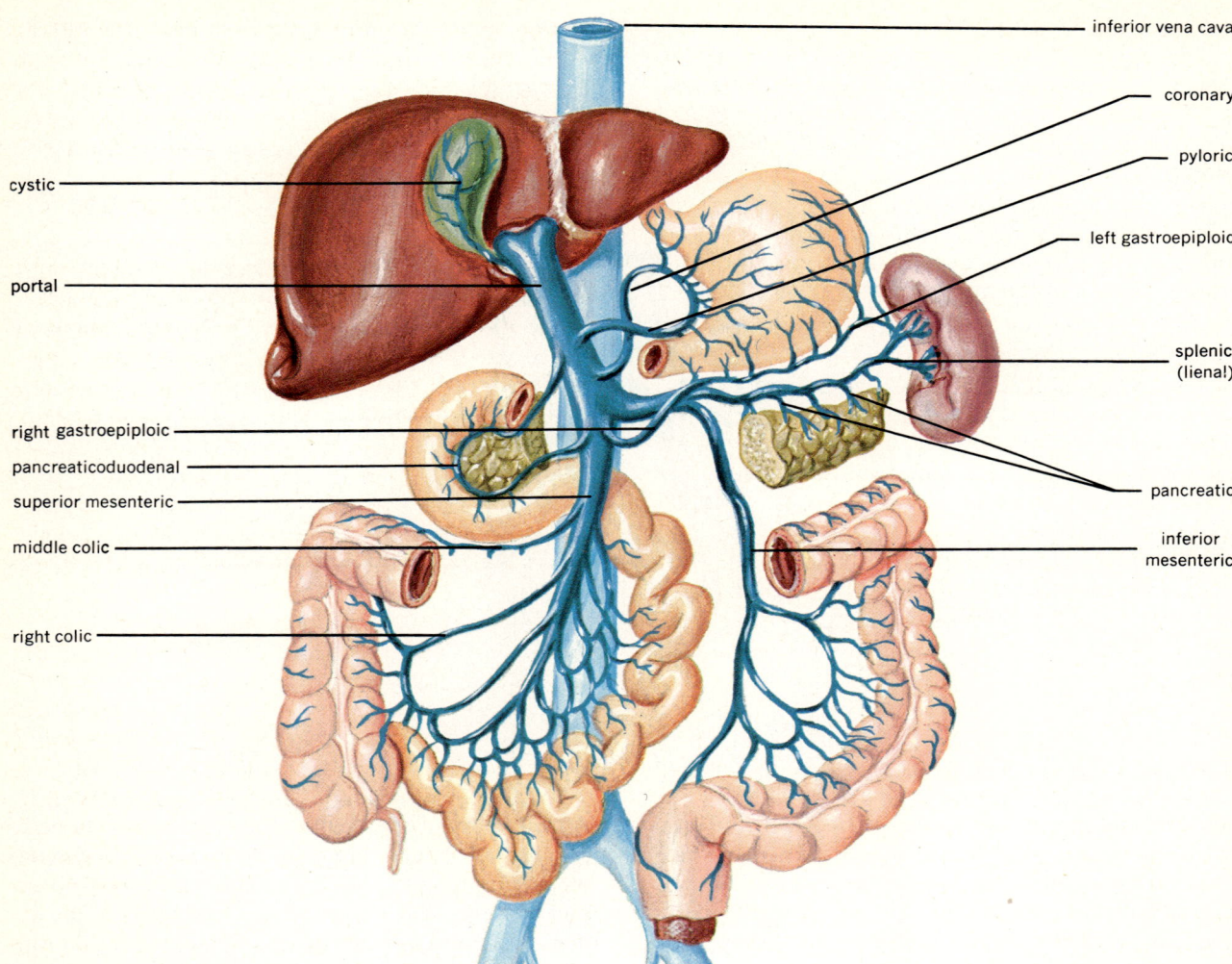

cystic

portal

right gastroepiploic

pancreaticoduodenal

superior mesenteric

middle colic

right colic

inferior vena cava

coronary

pyloric

left gastroepiploic

splenic
(liena!)

pancreatic

inferior
mesenteric

FIGURE 20-30   The hepatic portal system.

ies of the **hepatic portal vein** are the **superior mesenteric vein** (receiving blood from the stomach, small intestine, part of the large intestine, and the pancreas) and the **splenic vein** (receiving blood from the spleen, stomach, pancreas, and lower part of the large intestine); the **hepatic veins** carry blood from the liver to the inferior vena cava.

Nearly all the circulatory pathways of the systemic circulation follow the sequence: heart → arteries → capillaries → veins → heart. But in the hepatic portal system (Figure 20-30), the blood from the digestive tract and accessory organs follows a special pathway, which contains an extra loop—from capillaries to veins to capillaries. This unique arrangement permits the special talents of the liver to be utilized. The liver is the chemical factory of the body. It receives blood from the spleen, stomach, pancreas, and intestine, via the hepatic portal vein (about 80 percent of its total blood influx), as well as oxygenated blood from the heart, via the hepatic artery (about 20 percent). The liver removes glucose from the blood delivered from the abdominal viscera and stores it as glycogen. It

extracts toxic substances—either toxins ingested in food or toxic metabolic products—and detoxifies them. Agents such as fibrinogen and prothrombin are added to the blood as it passes through the liver. Finally, the "processed" blood is drained into the right and left hepatic veins, which empty into the inferior vena cava.

Veins of the Lower Extremities

Typists and others who must sit for long periods of time at work sometimes suffer from swelling of the feet and ankles. The veins of the lower extremities have hard going at any time to return the blood against the pull of gravity, and the difficulty is aggravated by the pressure of the chair seat against the backs of the legs, compressing the tissues and partially collapsing the veins. As a result of the hindered flow, fluid oozes out through the blood vessel pores into the tissues, producing edema. Salespeople and others who must stand for long periods face a similar problem (while standing, the entire length of the legs

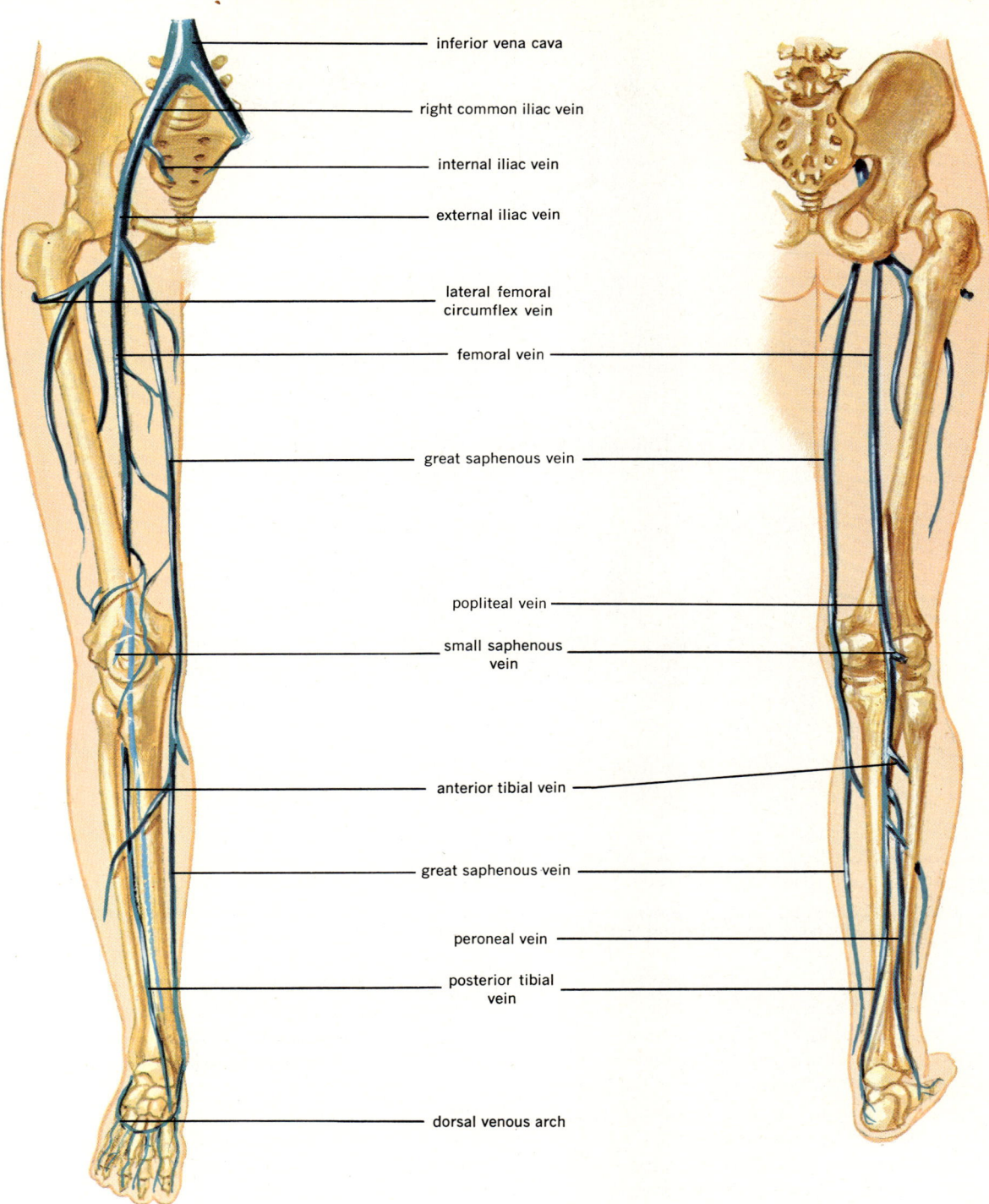

inferior vena cava

right common iliac vein

internal iliac vein

external iliac vein

lateral femoral circumflex vein

femoral vein

great saphenous vein

popliteal vein

small saphenous vein

anterior tibial vein

great saphenous vein

peroneal vein

posterior tibial vein

dorsal venous arch

FIGURE 20-31   Veins of the lower extremity.

is "uphill"), and may become faint if the pooling of blood in the lower extremities draws too much blood out of the general circulation, leaving the brain undersupplied. This problem can be alleviated by inconspicuously moving about or tensing and untensing the leg muscles, which exert a "milking" action on the leg veins and help to pump the blood upward. (The swaying movement typical of many public speakers is an unconscious protective mechanism that achieves this end.)

Like the upper extremities, the lower extremities are provided with both deep and superficial veins. The deep veins are venae comitantes for the arteries that carry the same names. The major veins of the lower extremity are illustrated in Figure 20-31.

The **small saphenous vein** is a superficial vein,

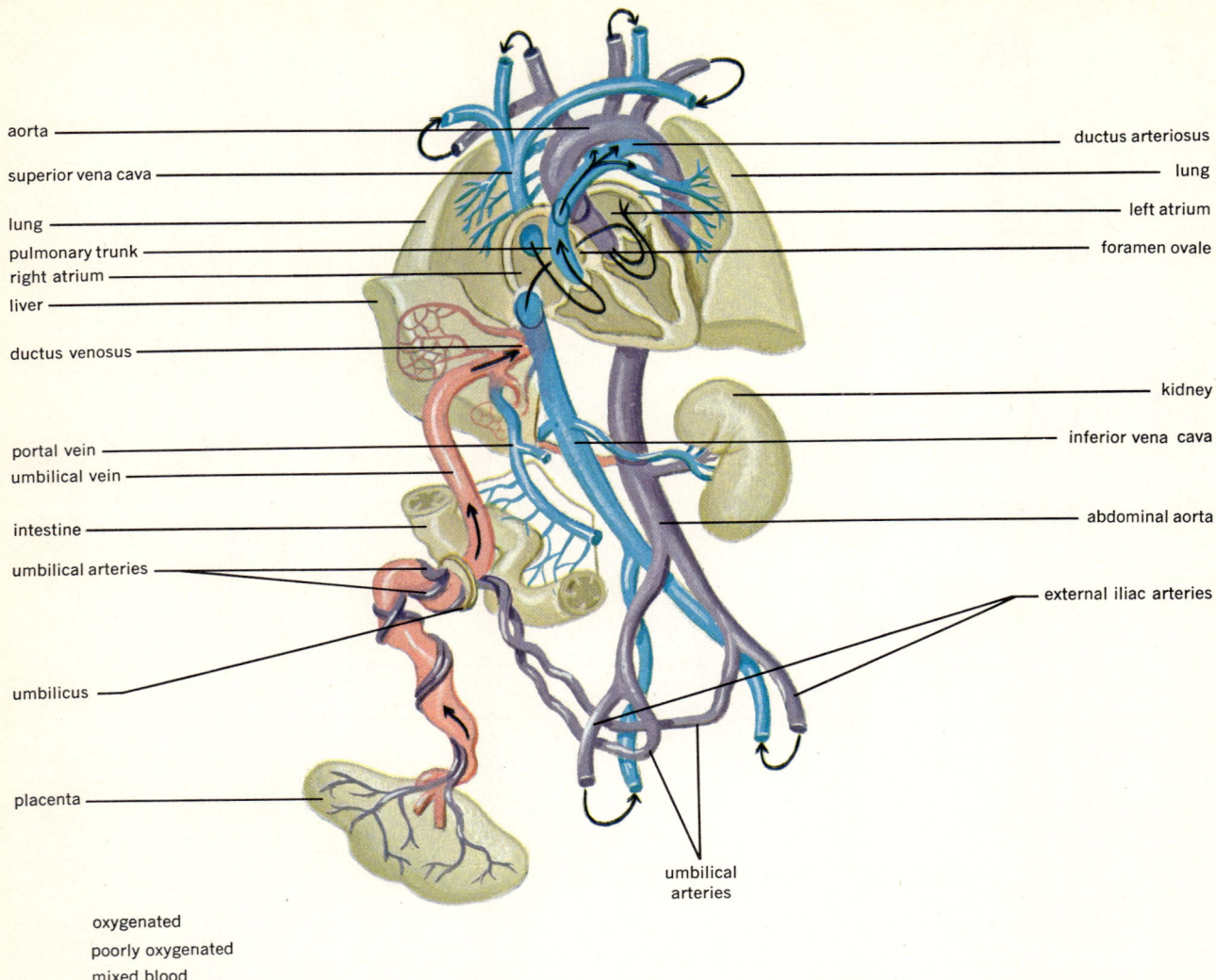

aorta

superior vena cava

lung

pulmonary trunk

right atrium

liver

ductus venosus

portal vein

umbilical vein

intestine

umbilical arteries

umbilicus

placenta

ductus arteriosus

lung

left atrium

foramen ovale

kidney

inferior vena cava

abdominal aorta

external iliac arteries

umbilical arteries

oxygenated

poorly oxygenated

mixed blood

FIGURE 20-32 Fetal circulation. Direction of blood flow is indicated by arrows. Oxygenated, unoxygenated, and mixed blood are indicated in pink, blue, and lavendar, respectively. Note that oxygenation occurs in the placenta, rather than the lungs.

which begins behind the lateral malleolus (the "knob" on the outside of the ankle) and ascends the back surface of the leg to the knee joint, where it empties into the **popliteal vein** (a deep vein). The popliteal vein is formed from the union of the **peroneal** and **posterior tibial veins** of the lower leg.

The **great saphenous vein** is the longest vein in the body. It extends from the dorsum of the foot to just below the inguinal ligament, where it empties into the **femoral vein,** a large deep vein that is the direct continuation of the popliteal vein and becomes the **external iliac vein** at the level of the inguinal ligament.

FETAL CIRCULATION

Your birth was one of the most difficult crises your body will ever face. For nine months you lived as an aquatic creature, sheltered in a lukewarm bath of amniotic fluid, never taking a single breath of air. You

never had to eat or drink, for all the needed nutrients and oxygen were carried into your body through the "lifeline" that linked your abdomen with the placenta in the wall of your mother's uterus. You did not have to urinate or defecate, for waste products were carried out of your body along this same umbilical cord. Then suddenly you were plunged into a totally different world. For the first time you had to inflate your lungs and breathe air. It was cold out there, and gradually your body had to develop an efficient system of temperature control. With the cutting of the umbilical cord, your source of effortless nourishment was cut off; from then on you had to either eat or starve. Kidneys and bowels took on the full task of elimination of wastes. Dramatic changes occurred in your circulatory system, some within minutes, others in days, and still others not completed for several months after birth.

Several major features distinguish the fetal circulation from the circulatory system after birth (Figure 20-32).

The **placenta** provides an *indirect* connection between the mother's body and that of her unborn child. It is a mass of richly vascular tissue, in which branching networks of arteries and veins belonging to the fetus and to the mother intermingle but *do not join.* Oxygen, nutrients, and waste products diffuse across freely, providing an interchange of substances between the two blood-vessel systems. The tubular umbilical cord links the placenta with the abdomen of the fetus. It contains a thick **umbilical vein,** which carries *oxygenated* blood from the placenta to the fetus, and coiled around it, two slender **umbilical arteries,** which carry *deoxygenated* blood from the fetus to the placenta. (Thus, the umbilical blood vessels are functionally analogous to the pulmonary circulatory system in the postnatal circulation.)

Inside the body of the fetus, the umbilical vein travels to the liver, passes through it as the **ductus venosus,** and discharges into the **inferior vena cava,** through which blood is carried to the right atrium. The blood carried by the inferior vena cava is mixed, for veins of the systemic circulation also discharge into it.

The layout of the fetal heart is quite different from that after birth. A gaping hole, the **foramen ovale,** connects the two atria, and the blood that flows in from the inferior vena cava passes from the right atrium into the left atrium, down into the left ventricle, and out the **aorta,** which distributes blood through the body. Blood from the head and upper extremities is returned via the **superior vena cava** to the right atrium, where it is deflected mainly into the right ventricle (in contrast to the flow from the inferior vena cava, which is deflected mainly into the left atrium). The right ventricle pumps blood out into the **pulmonary artery.** But most of the blood does not go to the lungs, which in the fetus are mostly collapsed. Instead, a blood vessel called the **ductus arteriosus** links the pulmonary artery and the aorta, and much of the blood flows through it into the general circulation.

The umbilical arteries branch off from the external iliac arteries and continue out through the umbilicus along the cord to the placenta, carrying waste-laden blood out of the fetus's body.

As can be seen from the above description and from the shading in Figure 20-32, the blood that is carried to practically all of the fetus's body does not have a very high oxygen content, because of the extensive mixing of oxygenated and deoxygenated blood in the inferior vena cava and heart. This inherent inefficiency is compensated for to some extent by the presence of a special variety of hemoglobin, **fetal hemoglobin,** which combines with oxygen at a much lower oxygen tension than does adult hemoglobin, greatly improving the oxygen-carrying capacity of the fetal blood.

When an infant takes its first gasping breath, its lungs inflate, and its pulmonary blood vessels become fully functional. At the same time, the blood flow through the placenta is cut off, and the pressure in the aorta, left ventricle, and left atrium increases greatly. Blood now tends to flow from the left atrium back into the right atrium, which causes the small valve covering the foramen ovale to close. In most people, within a few months the valve grows together, providing a permanent closure. Meanwhile, the ductus arteriosus gradually constricts, closing off the connection between the aorta and the pulmonary artery. (During the second month of life, this closure becomes permanent, as the ductus arteriosus is occluded by a growth of fibrous tissue into its lumen.) Over a period of several days, the stump of the umbilical cord shrivels up and finally drops off, leaving the umbilicus as a permanent memento. Inside the body, the umbilical arteries atrophy, becoming the lateral umbilical ligaments. The umbilical vein is converted to the round ligament of the liver (the ligamentum teres). The ductus venosus is converted to a fibrous cord (the ligamentum venosum) embedded in the wall of the liver.

CONGENITAL HEART DEFECTS

Before the invention of the heart-lung machine, surgeons could do very little to save the lives of people with heart defects. A blood-filled, constantly moving, beating heart could not be operated on; yet if all the major vessels leading to the heart were clamped, circulation would stop, and the patient would die long before the operation was over. Now, however, the heart can be literally taken out of circulation without depriving the body of its continuous flow of nourishing fluid (Figure 20-33). The repair of congenital heart defects, as well as those caused by rheumatic fever, has become standard surgical practice. The most common types of congenital heart defects are depicted in Figure 20-34.

A **patent ductus arteriosus** is a condition in which the fetal blood vessel linking the aorta and pulmonary artery has failed to close. As a result, there is a mixing of oxygenated and deoxygenated blood, and the circulatory system is not efficient enough for a healthy postnatal life. Recently it has been discovered that early treatment with the drug indomethacin induces a patent ductus arteriosus to close in most cases, and thus surgery can be avoided.

Septal defects are holes in the septa separating the left and right sides of the heart. One type is produced by a failure of the foramen ovale to close, leaving the left and right atria connected. Holes may also exist in

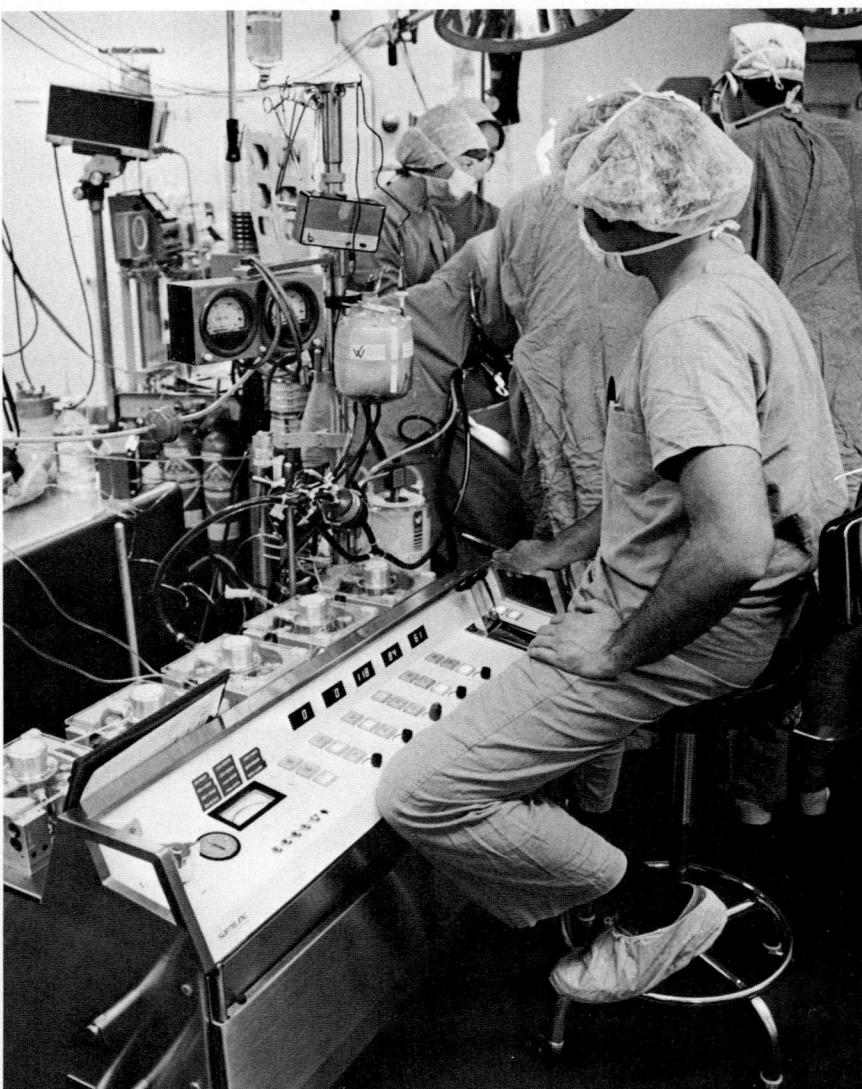

FIGURE 20-33 During heart operations, a heart-lung machine takes over the functions of heart and lungs.

the septum between the ventricles. As a result of such defects, part of the blood tends to flow directly from the left heart back to the right heart, bypassing the systemic circulation. Compensatory effects occur in the circulatory system to make up for the extra blood flow through the shunt; for example, the cardiac output may be correspondingly increased. But this puts an extra load on the heart and usually causes it to fail at an early age.

Stenosis refers to a narrowing of a channel in the heart or one of the major blood vessels attached to the heart, cutting down the blood flow. One type is **coarctation of the aorta,** a drastic narrowing of the aorta. If it is severe, collateral circulation develops, bypassing the bottleneck. The left ventricle may hypertrophy tremendously. The condition can be corrected surgically by removing the constricted portion and either stitching the cut ends of the aorta together

or inserting a plastic section to replace the removed portion.

The **tetralogy of Fallot** is a combination of four different defects: (1) the aorta originates from the right ventricle instead of the left, or straddles the septum; (2) the pulmonary artery is stenosed, so that blood passes into the aorta instead of being carried to the lungs; (3) a septal defect between the ventricles permits blood to flow from the left ventricle into the right ventricle and then into the aorta; (4) under the increased load, the right ventricle becomes hypertrophied. The combination of defects in the tetralogy of Fallot is a major cause of cyanosis in babies ("blue babies"), for a large fraction of the blood flows directly from the right ventricle into the aorta without being oxygenated.

What causes congenital heart defects? A common cause is a virus disease such as German measles, suf-

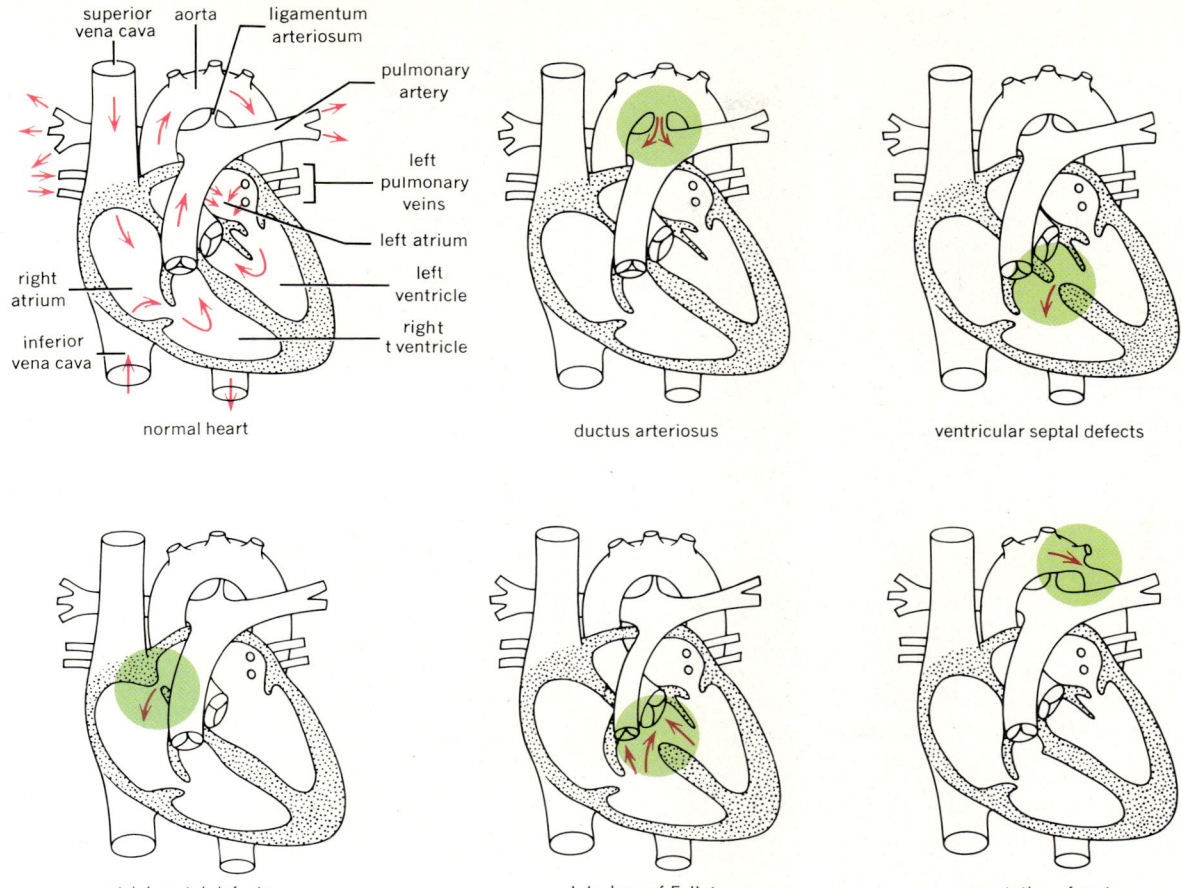

FIGURE 20-34 Congenital heart defects.

fered by the mother during the first trimester of pregnancy, when the fetal heart is being formed. Drugs such as Thalidomide, taken by the mother during this crucial early period of pregnancy, can also result in congenital heart defects. Some congenital heart anomalies seem to be hereditary, since the same defect has been observed in both of identical twins, or in succeeding generations.

SUMMARY

The circulatory system consists of:
   The heart (a pump)
   Arteries (carry blood away from the heart)
   Arterioles (small arteries)
   Capillaries (tiny blood vessels that permeate the tissues)
   Venules (small veins)
   Veins (carry blood toward the heart)
The heart is located in the mediastinum, tipped, with two-thirds of its mass to the left of the midline.
   The pointed apex of the heart is at the bottom and the broader base at the top.
   The heart is divided by a muscular septum into right and left halves, which are divided in turn into atria (upper chambers) and ventricles (lower chambers).

The atria are receiving chambers, and the ventricles pump blood out into the body.
The covering of the heart is the pericardium, consisting of the parietal pericardium and visceral pericardium (epicardium), with lubricating pericardial fluid between the layers.
The muscular heart wall is made up of three layers:
   Epicardium (outer)
   Myocardium (middle; the muscular layer)
   Endocardium (inner)
The right atrium receives deoxygenated blood from the superior vena cava, inferior vena cava, and coronary sinus.
The left atrium receives oxygenated blood from the pulmonary veins.
The right ventricle pumps deoxygenated blood into the pulmonary artery.
The left ventricle pumps oxygenated blood into the aorta.
Valves open and close openings in the heart:
   Tricuspid or right atrioventricular valve (between right atrium and right ventricle)
   Bicuspid or left atrioventricular valve (between left atrium and left ventricle)
   Aortic semilunar valve (at junction of aorta and left ventricle)
   Pulmonary semilunar valve (at junction of pulmonary artery and right ventricle)
Chordae tendinae, attached to papillary muscles (type of trabeculae carnae) keep the bicuspid and tricuspid valves from opening upward when pressure builds up in the ventricle.

The conducting system of the heart synchronizes the heart contractions and controls their rate. It includes:
Sinoatrial node (pacemaker)
Atrioventricular node
Atrioventricular bundle (bundle of His)
Purkinje fibers
The heartbeat rate can be changed by:
Autonomic accelerator nerves (sympathetic) and inhibitory or depressor nerves (parasympathetic)
Endocrine hormones such as epinephrine
The coronary circulation consists of:
Right and left coronary arteries
Cardiac veins
Coronary sinus
Blood and lymph capillaries
Myocardial infarction is the death of ischemic heart muscle cells; angina pectoris is a pain indicating inadequate oxygen supply to the heart.
Arteries have thick muscular three-layered walls enclosing a central tubular lumen. The layers are:
Tunica adventitia (outer)
Tunica media (middle)
Tunica intima (inner)
Arteries are supplied with blood vessels (vasa vasorum) and autonomic nerves (vasoconstrictors and vasodilators).
Arteries branch and anastomose, providing collateral circulation.
End arteries are those in areas with no anastomoses.
Arteries contract to propel blood along in spurts.
Veins have a three-layered structure but are thinner-walled and less muscular than arteries.
Blood flow in a vein is steady, and veins collapse when pressure is low.
Veins of the limbs and certain other areas are equipped with valves to prevent backflow.
Varicose veins have become stretched and flabby due to repeated pooling of blood as a result of weak valves.
Veins are supplied with vasa vasorum and autonomic nerves.
Capillaries are tiny blood vessels that connect arteries and veins.
Diffusion of gases and nutrients occurs through the thin capillary walls (usually only one cell thick), permitting an exchange of materials with body cells.
In certain areas arteriovenous anastomoses bypass capillary networks, permitting a shunting of blood to areas of greatest need.
Sinusoids, found in the liver, spleen, and brain, are characterized by:
Wide lumens
Sluggish blood flow
Freely joining channels
Thin, nonmuscular, distensible walls.
They serve as blood reservoirs.
The body has two circulatory systems: pulmonary and systemic.
The pulmonary circulation is a loop from the right ventricle of the heart to the lungs via the pulmonary trunk and two pulmonary arteries, and back to the left atrium of the heart via the four pulmonary veins. It permits oxygenation of blood in the lungs.
The systemic circulation consists of blood vessel systems leading from the left ventricle of the heart via the aorta to various parts of the body and back to the right atrium via the superior and inferior venae cavae.
The aorta is the largest blood vessel in the body (2.5 cm thick). It consists of three portions: ascending aorta, aortic arch, and descending aorta. Major branches from the aorta are:
Ascending aorta: coronary arteries
Aortic arch: brachiocephalic, left common carotid, and left subclavian arteries
Descending aorta: visceral and parietal branches of thoracic aorta; visceral and parietal branches of abdominal aorta; common iliac arteries
Major arteries of the head and neck include:
Common carotid
External carotid
Superficial temporal
Maxillary
Facial
Internal carotid
Ophthalmic
Anterior and middle cerebral
Subclavian
Vertebral
Anterior and posterior spinal
Basilar
Posterior cerebral
Circle of Willis
Central branches
Cortical branches
Major arteries of the upper extremities include:
Brachiocephalic
Right common carotid
Right subclavian and left subclavian
Superior thoracic
Lateral thoracic
Thoracodorsal
Thoracoacromial
Subscapular
Anterior and posterior humeral
Axillary
Brachial
Deep brachial
Radial
Radial recurrent
Princeps pollicis
Radialis indicis proprius
Ulnar
Deep and superficial palmar arches
Major arteries of the thorax include:
Internal thoracic
Musculophrenic
Superior epigastric
Costocervical trunk
Posterior intercostal
Bronchial
Esophageal
Superior phrenic
Major arteries of the abdomen include:
Celiac
Left gastric
Splenic
Hepatic
Superior mesenteric
Inferior mesenteric
Middle suprarenal
Renal
Testicular (or ovarian)
Inferior phrenic
Lumbar (four pairs)
Middle sacral
Major arteries of the pelvis include:
Internal iliac
Iliolumbar

Lateral sacral
Uterine
Vaginal
Middle rectal
Superior, middle, and inferior vesicals
Internal pudendal
Superior and inferior gluteal
Obturator
Major arteries of the lower extremities include:
External iliac
Inferior epigastric
Deep circumflex iliac
Femoral
Lateral and medial femoral circumflex
Deep femoral
Popliteal
Anterior tibial
Dorsalis pedis
Posterior tibial
Peroneal
Lateral and medial plantar
Plantar arch
Arteries that supply blood to an area are usually accompanied by veins that drain blood from the area (venae comitantes), which bear the same name as the artery.
The superior and inferior venae cavae, jugular veins, azygos veins, hepatic portal system, and certain superficial veins are not venae comitantes.
Major veins of the head and neck include:
Venous sinuses in the subarachnoid space
Superior and inferior sagittal
Straight
Transverse
Sigmoid
Superior and inferior petrosal
Cavernous
Meningeal
Diploid
Extracranial
Internal jugular
Subclavian
Brachiocephalic
External jugular
Superficial temporal
Deep cervical
Vertebral
Major veins of the upper extremities include:
Deep veins (venae comitantes)
Superficial veins
Venous plexuses on dorsal and palmar surfaces of hand
Cephalic
Basilic
Median cubital
Subclavian
Major veins of the thorax include:
Pulmonary
Superior vena cava
Right and left brachiocephalic
Azygos group
Azygos
Right ascending lumbar
Intercostal
Hemiazygos
Accessory hemiazygos
Major veins of the abdomen and pelvis include:
Inferior vena cava

Common iliac
Phrenic
Lumbar
Renal
Suprarenal
Testicular (or ovarian)
Hepatic portal system
Superior mesenteric
Splenic
Hepatic
The hepatic portal system shunts blood from the abdominal viscera to the liver via capillary-vein-capillary pathways.
Major veins of the lower extremities include:
Small saphenous
Popliteal
Peroneal
Posterior tibial
Great saphenous
Femoral
External iliac
Fetal circulation exhibits a number of differences from postnatal circulation:
Lungs are collapsed and pulmonary vessels virtually inoperative.
Blood is oxygenated in the placenta, which is connected to the body of the fetus by the umbilical cord, containing the umbilical vein and two umbilical arteries.
Oxygenated blood is carried to the fetal heart by the route: umbilical vein → ductus venosus → inferior vena cava → right atrium.
In the fetal heart the foramen ovale connects the two atria, so that blood delivered by the inferior vena cava flows into the left atrium and out the aorta, which distributes it through the body.
Blood delivered by the superior vena cava from the head and upper extremities flows down into the right ventricle and is pumped out the pulmonary artery.
The ductus arteriosus connecting the pulmonary artery and aorta permits much of the blood carried by the pulmonary artery to flow out into the general circulation.
Deoxygenated blood is carried via the external iliac arteries and umbilical arteries out to the placenta.
Fetal hemoglobin permits the blood in the inefficient fetal circulatory system to carry sufficient oxygen.
At birth and shortly thereafter, changes occur in the circulatory system:
The lungs inflate and pulmonary circulation is established.
The flow through the umbilical cord is cut off.
The foramen ovale closes.
The ductus arteriosus constricts and then is occluded.
Congenital heart defects may be caused by a virus infection of the mother during the first trimester of pregnancy or by hereditary factors.
Major types include:
Patent ductus arteriosus
Septal defects (e.g., patent foramen ovale)
Stenosis of a major vessel (e.g., coarctation of the aorta).
The tetralogy of Fallot

QUESTIONS FOR REVIEW AND THOUGHT

1 Ancient warriors traditionally carried their shields on the left side. Modern scholars have theorized that this practice provided better protection for the heart. Is there any anatomical basis for this conclusion?

2 Discuss the structure and functions of the pericardium.

3 Trace the path of a single drop of blood on a route through the systemic circulatory system and then through the pulmonary circulatory system. Specify blood vessels and chambers of the heart passed through, in sequence.

4 Describe the operation of all the heart valves.

5 Trace the spread of excitation through the conducting system of the heart.

6 True or false: arteries are blood vessels that carry oxygenated blood; veins are blood vessels that carry deoxygenated blood. Discuss your answer.

7 Cite examples of arterial and arteriovenous anastomoses and their importance to the body.

8 Describe the mechanisms preventing backflow of blood in (a) arteries and (b) veins.

9 Discuss the functions of capillaries. How do their structural distinctions from arteries and veins promote efficient function?

10 List the major arteries that branch off from the aorta and the structures or body regions they supply.

11 List the major veins that empty into the superior and inferior venae cavae and the structures or body regions they drain.

12 What is the unusual structural feature of the hepatic portal system, and what function does it serve?

13 Outline the distinctions between fetal and postnatal circulation.

THE PHYSIOLOGY OF CIRCULATION

21

The heart and blood vessels never have a chance to take a "day off." For about eight months before birth, and throughout the entire life after birth, the heart beats on ceaselessly, day and night, more than once every second, and the blood flows on in its never-ending journey through the blood-vessel networks of the body. The body cells are absolutely dependent on this steady stream of blood for their supply of oxygen and nutrients and the removal of their wastes. If the heart stops and circulation does not resume quickly, body cells are starved and begin to die. After only four minutes irreversible brain damage sets in, and after that, one by one the other major organs succumb.

It seems amazing that an organ can continue to work so hard and so ceaselessly as the heart. Most machines are ready for the scrap heap after ten or twenty years. Yet most hearts come with a "warranty" for sixty or seventy years, and some are still going after a century. Of course, even a strong, healthy heart does show signs of wear and tear in time. And just as the organs and systems of the body are dependent on the heart to keep them supplied with the vital substances they need to go on functioning, the heart is dependent on the proper functioning of the body systems—particularly the blood vessels that keep it supplied.

In the last two chapters we have gained some familiarity with the nature and functions of blood and the structures through which it flows (the **cardiovascular system**). This chapter describes how these structures work, what can go wrong with them, and ways that modern medicine is fighting the diseases of the heart and blood vessels that claim the lives of more Americans than all other causes of death together.

THE CIRCULATION OF BLOOD

The body is dynamic and ever changing in its needs. When you are lounging in an easy chair after a big meal, your body's focus is on the organs of the abdomen, which are busy digesting and absorbing the food. If you are dashing to get to class before the bell rings, your skeletal muscles have the greatest need for oxygen and nutrients. In hot weather your body needs to be cooled, and enhanced circulation of blood through the peripheral vessels makes a major contribution to heat removal; in cold weather, the need is for heat conservation, which can be achieved by constriction of the peripheral blood flow. The changing needs of the body cells and systems are met promptly by adjustments of the heart rate and the volume of blood flowing through blood vessels in particular areas of the body, controlled by nervous and endocrine influences.

As we have seen, the circulatory system is a complex assembly of tubular blood vessels of various lengths, diameters, and capacities, linked into interconnecting circuits. In ancient times it was said that "all roads lead to Rome." In the circulatory system, all roads lead to the heart, the primary pump that provides the initial motive force propelling the blood on its way. The heart is like a busy intersection—or perhaps more like a modern highway cloverleaf, since the different flows of blood entering and leaving the heart do not actually cross or mix. Blood is propelled by the right ventricle into the short circuit leading to the lungs and back to the left atrium. From that receiving chamber it passes down into the left ventricle, which pumps it out into the longer systemic circulation, which eventually carries it back to the right atrium, to repeat the loop again and again. A variety of alternate pathways by which blood can flow from the major arteries to the veins permits drastic alterations of pressure and volume in one part of the body without necessarily changing the blood pressure and volume elsewhere.

THE HEART AS A PUMP

When it is suspected that someone may be dead, the first thing usually checked is the presence or absence of a heartbeat. The rhythmic contractions of the heart can be felt at the anterior wall of the chest, a little below the left nipple.

When the muscular walls of the heart contract, the capacity of the chambers they enclose is decreased, and the pressure of the fluid they contain is raised. The heart contractions thus force the blood first from the atria into the ventricles and then out of the ventricles into the arteries.

The physiology of cardiac muscle contraction was discussed in detail in Chapter 11. Here we shall briefly review some major principles.

The cardiac muscle fibers are functionally linked into a **syncytium:** once a contraction has begun, it spreads throughout the entire cardiac muscle, and the entire muscle shows an **all-or-none response.** Cardiac muscle contraction is **self-initiated,** requiring no nervous or chemical stimulation, and it has an inherent **rhythmicity.** Cardiac muscle has a relatively long **refractory period,** which protects it from tetanus that would nullify the heart's value as a pump.

The heartbeat has been found to begin in the right atrium, in the **sinoatrial node** or **pacemaker** (Figure 21-1). The SA node sets the rhythm of contraction for the entire heart: once an impulse is initiated in it, a wave of excitation spreads over fibers radiating outward from the SA node, causing the two atria to contract. When the wave of excitation reaches the **atrioventricular node,** it spreads downward into the ventricles via the **bundle of His,** radiating through the

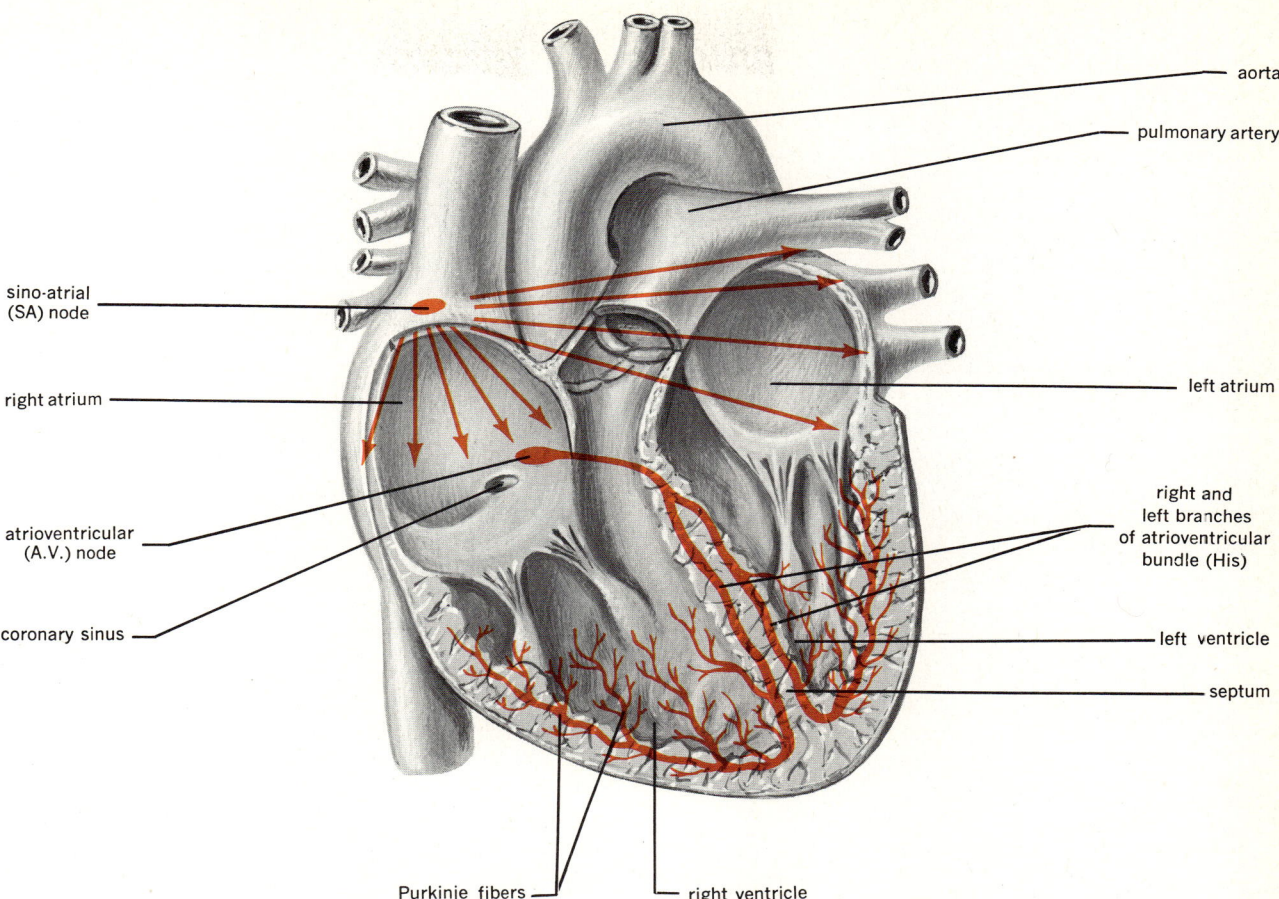

FIGURE 21-1 The conducting system of the heart.

The Cardiac Cycle

ramifying fibers of the **Purkinje system** in the ventricle walls. Thus, quickly after the atria have contracted, the ventricles follow suit.

A full cardiac cycle takes less than a second. Yet during that brief time a complicated sequence of events takes place (Figures 21-2 and 21-3). A wave of excitation begins at the SA node, and the two atria contract. The pressure of the blood they contain is raised, and blood is pumped down through the atrioventricular valves into the respective ventricles. Then the ventricles contract. The bicuspid and tricuspid valves prevent blood from flowing back into the atria, but the blood pressure inside the ventricles has been raised by the contraction, and the blood must flow somewhere. Out it spurts into the pulmonary trunk and aorta. Now the ventricles relax, and the ventricular pressure abruptly drops. The semilunar valves at the entrance to the aorta and pulmonary trunk close, and the atrioventricular valves open. Blood flows passively into the atria and down into the ventricles.

The phase of ventricular contraction is referred to as **systole;** the phase of relaxation is called **diastole.** The actual pumping of blood occurs during systole, while diastole is a phase of passive filling. The atrial systole slightly precedes the ventricular systole. Although the contraction of the atria produces some increase in the pressure in the chambers of the heart, the bulk of the filling of the ventricles occurs early in diastole.

At the normal heart rate of about 70 to 72 beats per minute, diastole is considerably longer than systole: 0.49 and 0.36 second, respectively. But when the heart speeds up, as during heavy physical exertion, the phase of relaxation is shortened proportionately more than that of contraction. At a heart rate of 170 beats per minute, systole lasts 0.23 second, while diastole is only 0.12 second.

Figure 21-3 depicts the sequence of events in the cardiac cycle only for the aorta and the left side of the heart. But it should be emphasized that with every heartbeat *both* atria and *both* ventricles contract, sending blood out into the pulmonary and systemic circuits; then both sides of the heart relax, and receive blood returned from both circulatory routes.

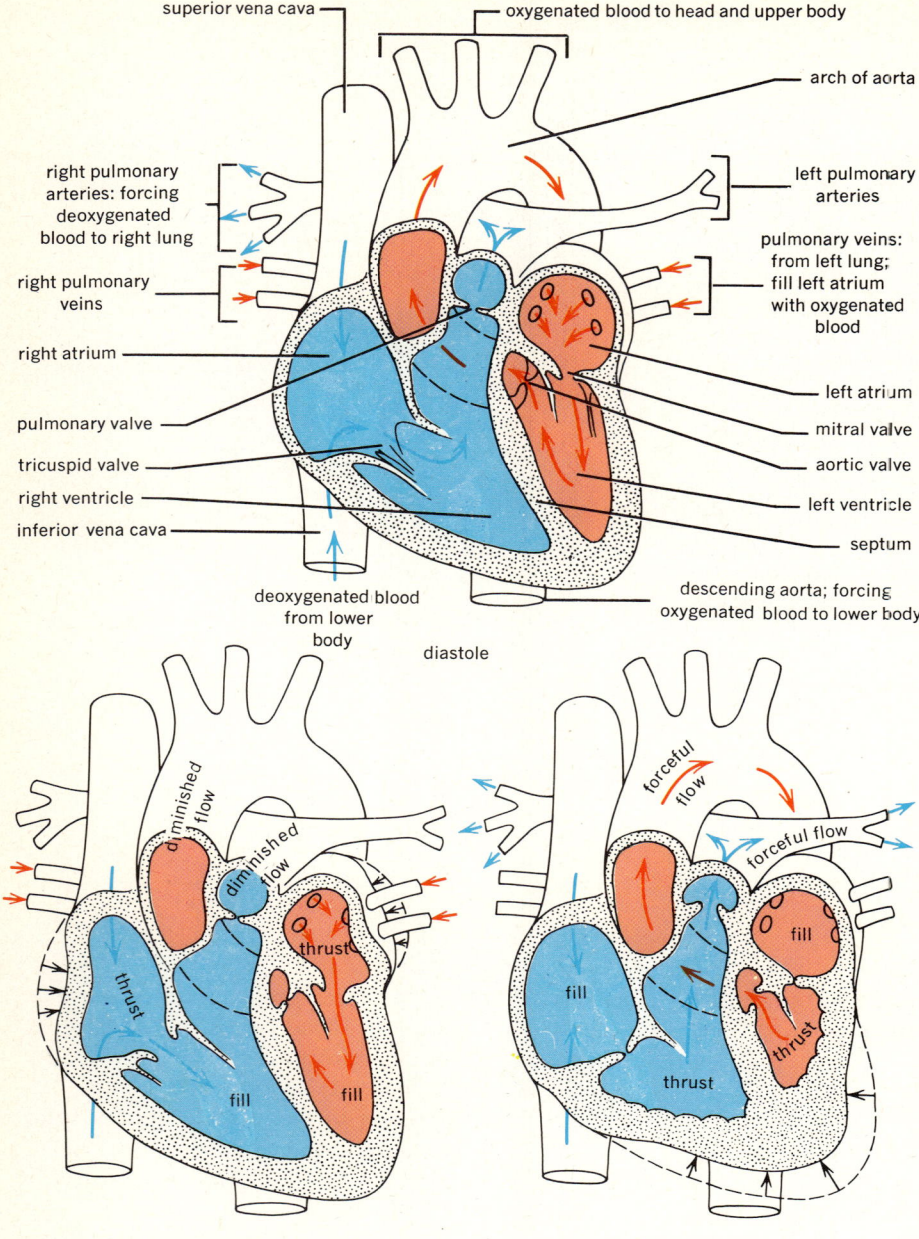

superior vena cava

oxygenated blood to head and upper body

FIGURE 21-2 The cardiac cycle: sequence of events in diastole and systole.

arch of aorta

right pulmonary arteries: forcing deoxygenated blood to right lung

left pulmonary arteries

right pulmonary veins

pulmonary veins: from left lung; fill left atrium with oxygenated blood

right atrium

left atrium

pulmonary valve

mitral valve

tricuspid valve

aortic valve

right ventricle

left ventricle

inferior vena cava

septum

deoxygenated blood from lower body

descending aorta; forcing oxygenated blood to lower body

diastole

diminished flow

diminished flow

thrust

thrust

fill

fill

fill

atrial systolic phase

forceful flow

forceful flow

fill

thrust

thrust

fill

ventricular systolic phase

Heart Sounds

If you place your ear against someone's chest, you will hear rhythmically repeating sounds. First there is a long, booming sound, which sounds something like *lubb*. Then comes a shorter, softer, snapping sound, *dup*. Then there is a pause, and the sounds are repeated, always in the same order. These sounds are produced by the turbulent flow of blood in the heart.

The **first heart sound** (*lubb*) is produced during the vigorous contraction of the ventricles. Blood surges up toward the atrioventricular valves, and they slam shut. A fraction of a second later, the surge of blood snaps the semilunar valves open, so that the blood

rushes out into the aorta and pulmonary trunk. The turbulence produced in the surging blood by these events sets up vibrations, which are transmitted through the chest. At the body surface they can be heard as sounds either directly with the ear or amplified through a stethoscope. The sound is louder, the stronger the contraction of the ventricles.

The **second heart sound** (*dup*) is heard toward the end of systole. The ventricular and atrial pressures fall, and blood rushes back toward the ventricles along the aorta and pulmonary trunk. But the semilunar valves snap shut, setting up new turbulence and producing a distinct sound.

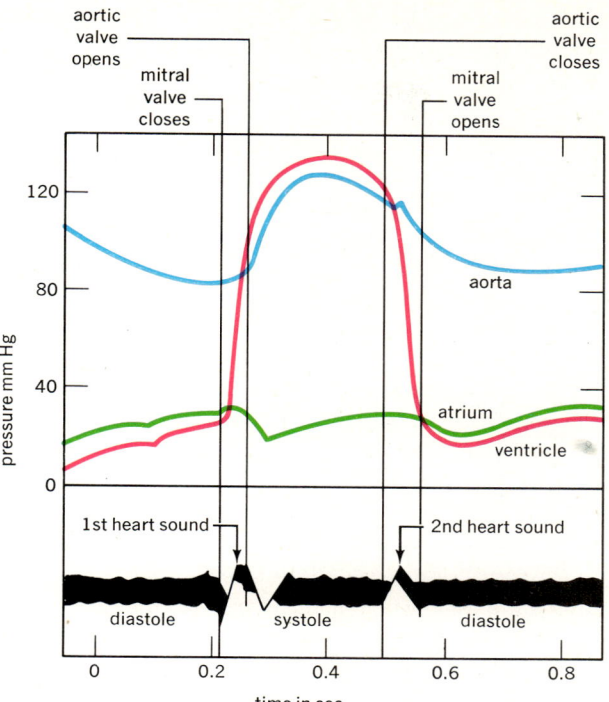

FIGURE 21-3   The cardiac cycle: blood pressure, blood volume, and heart sounds.

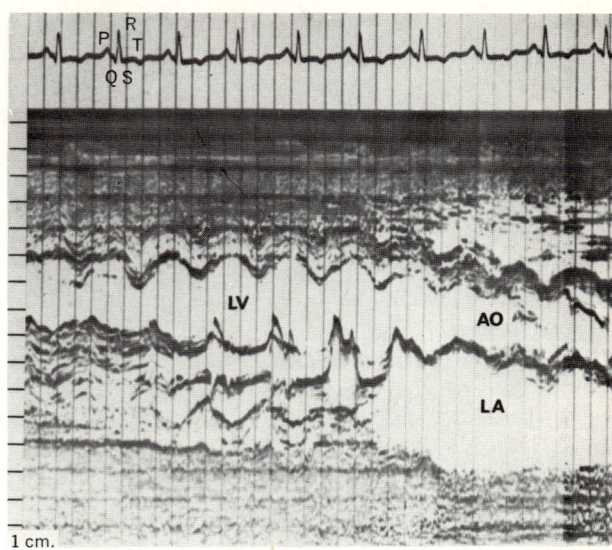

FIGURE 21-4   A typical electrocardiogram (ECG) is shown at the top. Below is an echogram, which provides additional information about the state of the heart in the patterns of high-frequency ultrasonic waves bounced off heart structures.

A third heart sound can be heard in some people while the ventricles are filling, just after the second heart sound. But it is usually too faint to be heard without electronic amplification. A very low-pitched fourth heart sound, entirely inaudible to the human ear, is produced by the contraction of the atria. The third and fourth heart sounds can be recorded by placing a microphone against the chest and displaying the sound waves, converted to electrical impulses, on an oscillograph or recording device. The instrument used to record heart sounds is a **phonocardiograph.**

The four heart sounds are all normal sounds. But if the heart valves are damaged, additional turbulence will be set up, producing a soft hissing sound. This sound is called a heart **murmur;** it will be heard at different phases of the cardiac cycle, depending on where the damage is, and thus provides valuable diagnostic clues. Occasionally, murmurs may be heard in sound, healthy hearts. This effect is most often produced during especially heavy exercise, when the blood flow through the heart valves is so fast that it produces turbulence.

The Electrocardiogram

Few machines in the doctor's office are regarded with as much apprehension by the patient as the **electrocardiograph.** For the tracings recorded by this device may indicate that a heart attack has occurred.

When a wave of excitation spreads through the conducting system of the heart, minute electrical currents are generated and can be detected at the body surface. During contraction, electrical changes constantly take place in the heart muscle. Each portion of the cardiac cycle produces a different electrical impulse. To record these characteristic electrical changes, electrodes are attached to the patient's wrists, ankles, and chest. Each placement of two electrodes is referred to as a lead, and each of the standard leads produces its own characteristic tracing. A typical **electrocardiogram (ECG)** is illustrated in Figure 21-4. It shows characteristic waves and spikes, which have been arbitrarily named the **P wave, QRS complex,** and **T wave.** The P wave represents depolarization of the atria; the QRS complex represents the spread of the electrical impulse through the ventricles. And the dome-shaped T wave corresponds to ventricular repolarization as the ventricles relax.

An electrocardiogram can show up abnormalities in the heart's conducting system and is valuable in the diagnosis of such abnormal cardiac rhythms as heart block, atrial flutter, atrial fibrillation, ventricular fibrillation, and abnormalities of the ventricular wall. It can also be used to detect the presence of fetal life and to determine multiple pregnancies.

Cardiac Output

In the space of just a minute, a volume equivalent to all the blood in your body passes through your heart.

Under resting conditions, with each systole about 70 ml of blood is pumped by the left ventricle into the aorta, and a similar volume is forced from the right ventricle into the pulmonary artery. The volume of blood pumped by the left ventricle with each beat of the heart is called the **stroke volume.** The **cardiac output** is defined as the product of the stroke volume times the heart rate. Assuming an average heart rate of 70 to 72 beats per minute, the resting cardiac output is thus approximately 5 liters of blood. (The average man has a total blood volume of five to six liters.) Another term commonly used for the cardiac output is the **minute volume**—it represents the amount of blood pumped by the left ventricle in a minute.

The cardiac output does not remain constant, but is continually adjusted to meet the varying needs of the body. During strenuous exercise or emotional stress, the body's needs for oxygen and glucose increase drastically, and the heart is capable of increasing its output by five-fold or more. From the definition:

$$\text{Cardiac output } = \text{ Heart rate } \times \text{ Stroke volume}$$

you can guess that there are two possible ways of increasing cardiac output—by increasing the heart rate or by increasing the stroke volume—and the body utilizes both these methods. The sympathetic nervous system and its backup adrenal hormone epinephrine can act on the conducting system of the heart and speed up its rate to more than double the normal value. (Some of the modern exercise programs utilize a continual monitoring of the pulse rate as an indication of effectiveness of the exertion.) In addition, the contractions of skeletal muscles, squeezing the veins, increase venous return, filling the heart with more blood in each diastole. The increased input results in an increased output with each systole, according to a mechanism called **Starling's law of the heart:** *the force of cardiac muscle contraction is proportional to the amount of stretch placed on the muscle fibers.* That is, the more the heart is stretched by incoming blood, the more forcefully the ventricles contract, and the more blood is pumped out. This law holds as long as the total amount of blood does not rise above the physiologic limit of the heart's pumping capacity.

Starling's law of the heart operates under normal conditions. But in certain pathological situations, the stroke volume may fall dangerously. For example, if a portion of the heart muscle has been damaged by a myocardial infarction, the ventricles cannot contract strongly. Or if a large amount of blood has been lost by hemorrhage, the venous return will be below normal, the heart will be underfilled, and its contractions will be correspondingly weak. In such situations, the body attempts to compensate and maintain a safe cardiac output by speeding up the heart rate.

Variations of the Heart Rate

Your heart rate has been steadily slowing down. Before you were born, your normal heart rate was about 140 beats per minute; as a child it was about 90, and now, if you have an average heart rate, it is down to about 70 per minute. To some extent, this slowdown was correlated with your increase in size, a pattern that is observed in general throughout the animal kingdom. Small animals have a high rate of metabolism and a very rapid heart rate; the heart of a mouse, for example, may beat as much as 700 times per minute. A rabbit's heart beats about 150 times a minute, and an elephant's normal heart rate is only 25 beats per minute.

Even in adult humans there is considerable variation in the normal resting heart rate. The normal range extends from 60 to 100 beats per minute. Generally women have a faster heart rate than men. A rapid but rhythmic heartbeat—above 100 beats per minute—is referred to as **sinus tachycardia.** It may be produced by exercise or emotional stimulation or may be the result of disease. **Sinus bradycardia** is the opposite condition—a regular heartbeat with a rate of less than 60 beats per minute. In some individuals, usually well-conditioned athletes, a heart rate as low as 50 is normal.

Control of the Heart Function

Stop a moment and take your pulse to determine your resting heart rate. Then think about the most exciting or frightening experience you have ever had, reliving each detail in your imagination. If you take your pulse again, you will probably find that your heart has speeded up. It will slow down again if you now compose yourself and think about something soothing or dull.

The intrinsic heart rate is set by the sinoatrial node in the right atrium, which initiates waves of excitation at a steady pace. But the body needs mechanisms to speed up the heart when more oxygen is needed by the tissues and to slow it down (as an energy-saving measure) during periods of relative inactivity. These mechanisms are provided by reflex arcs that operate through the autonomic nervous system and control centers in the brain (Figure 21-5), and by backup endocrine controls.

Parasympathetic fibers in the **vagus nerve** innervate the sinoatrial and atrioventricular nodes of the heart. They are **inhibitory** fibers, which act to slow down the heart and decrease the force of its contractions. In diseased hearts, parasympathetic stimulation can also produce varying degrees of heart block, preventing the spread of excitation in various parts of the heart's conducting system.

Sympathetic nerve fibers follow the path of the coronary blood vessels and innervate all regions of the atria and ventricles. They act as **accelerator** nerves, speeding up the heart rate and increasing the force of heart contractions.

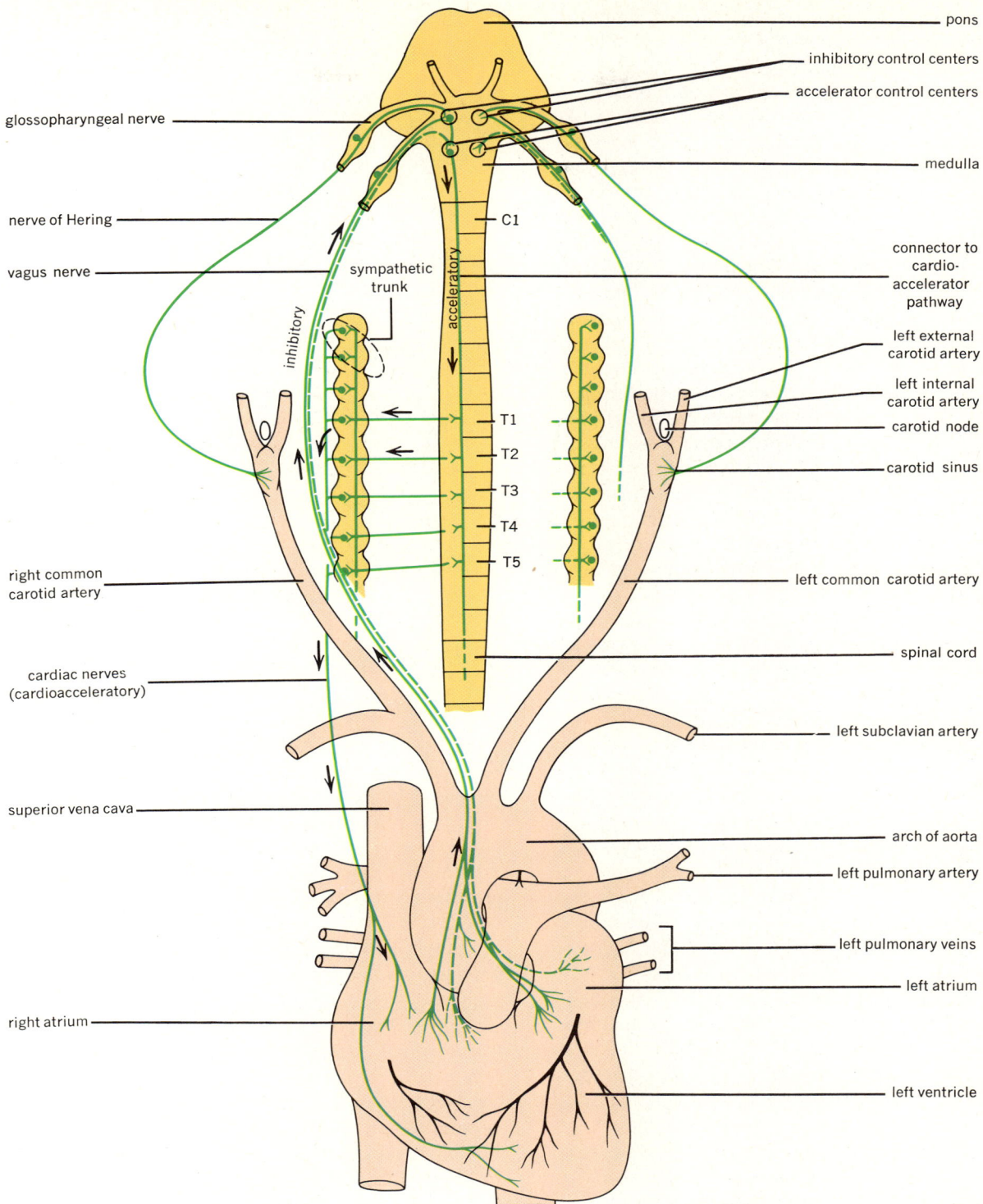

FIGURE 21-5 Reflex control of the heart includes autonomic nerve pathways and CNS accelerator and inhibitory control centers.

The nervous influences controlling the heart rate thus act as a continuous tug-of-war between the two antagonistic influences, with the parasympathetic tending to slow down the heart while the sympathetic tends to speed it up.

The nervous influences on the heart are integrated through cardiac centers in the **medulla oblongata.** The **cardioinhibitory center** and the **cardioaccelerator center** are two clusters of nerve cells linked in such a way that when one is stimulated, the other is depressed.

These centers are stimulated by afferent impulses originating in several types of receptors in various parts of the cardiovascular system.

Pressoreceptors or stretch receptors are found in a number of major blood vessels. An increase in the blood pressure in one of these vessels stretches the blood vessel walls and stimulates the pressoreceptors, which are specialized nerve cells. One important group of pressoreceptors is located in the walls of the **carotid sinus,** a small widening of the internal carotid artery just above the point where it branches off from the common carotid. Afferent pathways from these pressoreceptors lead to the cardioinhibitory and cardioaccelerator centers in the medulla. If the arterial pressure rises, the reflex arc involving the cardioinhibitory center is stimulated and produces a lowering of the heart rate, which serves to return the blood pressure to its normal level (a **depressor response**). A fall in the arterial pressure in the carotid sinus stimulates the cardioaccelerator center and sparks a reflex speedup of the heart and raising of the intraarterial pressure (a **pressor response**). The changes in the heart rate are accompanied by corresponding changes in the peripheral resistance.

Other pressoreceptors are found in the walls of the aortic arch, in the superior and inferior venae cavae, and in the right atrium. Like the carotid sinus receptors, they are involved in reflex arcs that help to regulate cardiac output.

Chemoreceptors sensitive to the oxygen and carbon dioxide concentrations of the blood are found in the carotid and aortic sinuses. These chemoreceptors play an important role in respiration, and it was thought that they also act reflexly to speed up the heart in the presence of a low blood oxygen concentration or a high carbon dioxide concentration. But there is evidence that this function is performed instead by a direct action of hypoxemia on the medullary cardiac centers.

In addition to the direct action of the sympathetic nerves on the heart, stimulation of the sympathetic system produces a secretion of catecholamine hormones, **epinephrine** and **norepinephrine,** by the adrenal medulla. These hormones act directly on the myocardium, increasing the rate and strength of contraction. But an injection of a pharmaceutical preparation of catecholamines is usually followed by an initial rise in the heart rate, and then a decrease in it. The decrease is due to a reflex response to the elevated blood pressure that these drugs produce.

Plasma ion concentrations also affect the heart function. Elevated calcium ion concentrations excite the heart, while both potassium and sodium ions have a depressing effect.

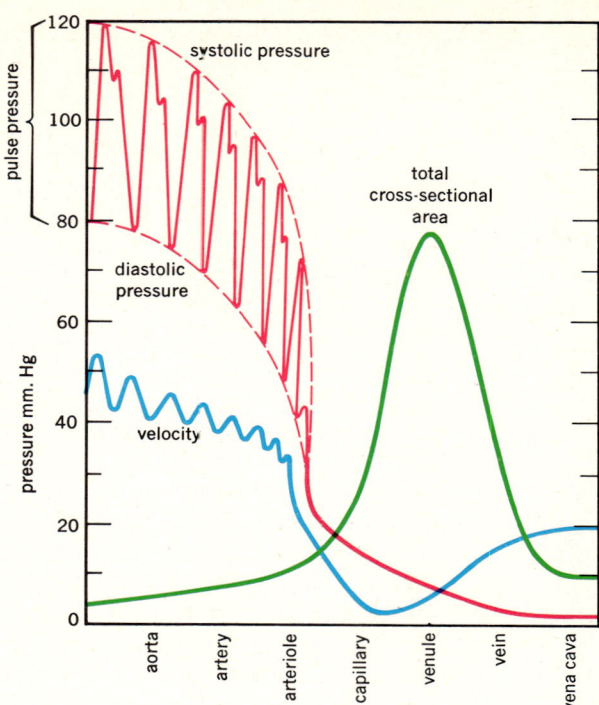

FIGURE 21-6 Blood pressure, velocity, and total cross-sectional area in various parts of the vascular system.

CIRCULATION THROUGH THE BLOOD VESSELS

Each beat of the heart sends a metered amount of blood gushing out into the arteries. The propulsive force exerted by the pumping ventricles builds up the pressure of the blood inside the closed system of the blood vessels. And, like any liquid, blood flows down the pressure gradient, that is, from regions of higher pressure to regions of lower pressure. As the blood flows around the closed circuit of arteries, arterioles, capillaries, venules, and veins, back to the heart, its pressure, volume, and speed of flow vary greatly.

Blood Pressure

Probably tens of thousands of lives could be saved each year if everyone had his or her blood pressure checked annually. It is estimated that one-sixth of the population has high blood pressure; many of these people are completely unaware of this condition, and yet they statistically stand a much higher-than-average risk of suffering heart attacks and strokes. Early detection and treatment of high blood pressure can bring it under control and greatly lower the risk of cardiovascular problems.

The blood pressure is defined as the pressure exerted by the blood against the walls of the vessels. It can pertain to the pressure in arteries, veins, or capillaries, but it is commonly measured in the large brachial artery, just above the elbow. As might be expected, the arterial blood pressure is highest during ventricular systole, when the heart is pumping a new spurt of blood into the arteries. Yet there is also a blood pressure during diastole, due mainly to the elastic rebound of the arterial wall. Blood pressure is generally indicated in the form of a fraction, for example, 120/80, in which the first number represents the systolic pressure and the second is the diastolic pressure. The normal range of the systolic pressure in a healthy young adult at rest is 100 to 120; the diastolic pressure ranges from 60 to 80. Pressures above 140/90 are classed as **hypertension** (high blood pressure) and shorten the life expectancy.

The blood pressure falls progressively in the sequence from arteries to arterioles to capillaries and on to the venules and veins (Figure 21-6). A normal systolic pressure of 120 millimeters of mercury drops to about 50 mm Hg in the arterioles, to 25 to 30 mm Hg at the entrance to the capillaries, and down to about 15 millimeters of mercury at the venous end of the capillary bed. In contrast to the high and fluctuating pressure in the arteries, the blood pressure in the veins is steady and close to zero.

Velocity of Blood Flow

The blood flow in the capillaries is nearly a thousand times slower than in the aorta. This differential is ideally suited to their functions. The aorta serves to convey blood through the body. It is like a superhighway, in which high speed of transit from place to place is a primary advantage. But when you want to look at the scenery, or stop frequently to make deliveries, you don't take a superhighway; you turn off onto the network of small local roads. The capillaries are the local supply network of the body, in which the exchange of materials with the body cells takes place. The slow blood flow in the capillaries permits a far more effective exchange than would be possible if the blood went rushing by as it does in the arteries.

What causes the drastic drop in velocity of the blood flow, from about 300 mm per second in the aorta down to a mere 0.5 mm per second in the capillaries? It is the result of a simple physical relationship: a liquid flows more slowly as the cross-sectional area of the channels through which it flows is increased. Each time an artery or arteriole branches, the total cross-sectional area of the blood vessels increases. (The individual cross-sectional area of each branch is smaller than that of the "parent" blood vessel, but the number of vessels increases so rapidly that there is an overall increase in area.) You utilize this relationship automatically when you water the gar-

den with a hose: if you adjust the nozzle to narrow the opening, the water comes out in a rapid jet; when the nozzle opening is widened, the flow slows down.

Relationship Between Pressure, Resistance, and Flow

If you roll a ball along the street, eventually it will come to a stop. The force exerted by your initial push sets the ball in motion, but as it rolls, it is acted upon by friction with the surface of the street, opposing the original force. In the contest between the initial force and friction, the energy you imparted to the ball is dissipated, and the ball stops rolling.

In the circulatory system, the initial impetus is contributed by the pumping action of the heart. But as the blood flows through the blood-vessel channels, friction between the flowing liquid and the walls of the vessels constantly drags on the liquid, offering resistance to the flow. The relationship between flow, pressure, and resistance can be expressed by the equation:

$$\text{Flow} = \frac{\text{Pressure}}{\text{Resistance}}$$

In other words, the greater the driving pressure, or the lower the resistance, the greater the flow will be. Rearranging the equation provides another way to express the relationship:

$$\text{Pressure} = \text{Flow} \times \text{Resistance}$$

The pressure in the blood vessels is directly dependent on the flow—that is, the volume of liquid flowing by a given point in a unit time, and on the resistance. An increase in the cardiac output would increase the flow and thus increase the blood pressure. The resistance is dependent on the diameter of the blood vessel: the narrower the vessel, the greater the resistance. (In a narrow blood vessel, a larger proportion of the flowing liquid comes in direct contact with the walls and thus experiences the drag of friction.)

Physical Factors in the Regulation of Blood Pressure

Chronic hypertension means a shortened life expectancy. But too *low* a blood pressure would be rapidly fatal, since insufficient supplies would reach the body cells. Fortunately, the blood pressure is normally self-regulating, and even in pathological conditions that threaten the blood circulation, compensatory mechanisms may operate. In general, five main factors function in the maintenance of arterial blood pressure: the rate and force of the heartbeat, the peripheral resistance, the volume of blood in the vascular system, the viscosity of the blood, and the elasticity of the arterial walls. The physical principles discussed in the preceding sections should help you to understand how these five factors operate.

Cardiac Output

Up to a certain point, the faster the heart beats and the greater its force of contraction, the higher the arterial pressure will be.

Peripheral Resistance

The resistance is determined by friction and thus is greater the narrower the blood vessels. The arterioles are important regulators of pressure in the vascular system. They offer resistance to flow and thus act to maintain a high pressure in the larger arteries that precede them, with a lower pressure in the capillaries that follow them. The pressure drop produced by flow through the arterioles is about 50 to 60 mm of mercury.

Blood Volume

The total amount of blood in the cardiovascular system is a determinant of blood pressure. The elastic arteries can expand to accommodate a moderate increase in blood volume without too great an increase in pressure. But if the blood volume is greatly reduced, as, for example, by hemorrhage, the blood pressure will fall. If the blood loss is not too severe, it can be compensated for by a transfer of liquid from the tissues into the blood vessels. In severe blood loss, the heart will try to compensate for the reduced volume by speeding up its rate of contraction.

Viscosity of Blood

Blood is indeed thicker than water: as a result of the presence of formed elements and plasma proteins, its viscosity is five times as great as that of water. Increased viscosity causes increased resistance to flow, and thus an increase in the blood pressure. In polycythemia vera, in which the erythrocyte count is greatly elevated, there is a rise in the blood pressure; anemia, in which the number of erythrocytes is decreased, is characterized by below-normal arterial blood pressure.

Elasticity of the Arterial Walls

The elasticity of the arterial walls helps to even out the blood pressure between the phases of active contraction and relaxation of the heart. Part of the energy of ventricular systole is expended in moving blood through the vessels (kinetic energy), while part is used to stretch the elastic artery walls (i.e., is converted to potential energy). During diastole, the artery walls spring back, converting the potential energy back to kinetic energy as the blood is propelled along. When the large arteries lose their elasticity, due to aging or disease, the

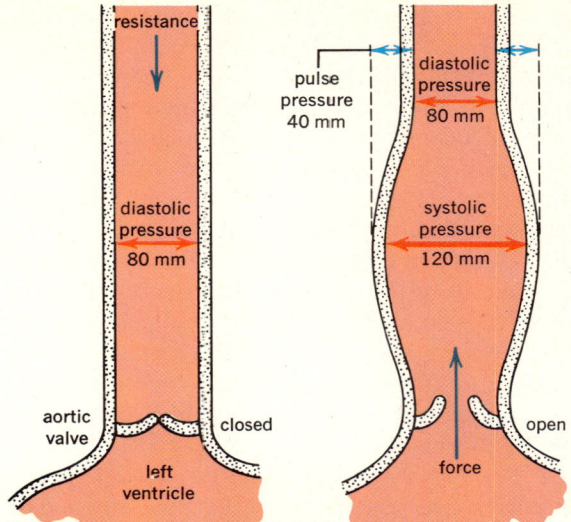

FIGURE 21-7 Force and pressure relationships in the measurement of arterial blood pressure.

systolic pressure rises unusually high, while the diastolic pressure falls quite low, increasing the differential between them (the **pulse pressure**).

Measuring Arterial Blood Pressure

In 1733 an English clergyman tied a horse to a post, inserted a small glass tube into one of its leg arteries, and connected the tube by means of a section of a goose's windpipe to a very long, vertical glass tube. The horse's blood shot up the tubes to a height of 9 feet, and then oscillated with each heartbeat. This was a direct measurement of arterial blood pressure, the first that was ever performed. Fortunately, more convenient techniques are available for clinical use today. Blood pressure is generally measured indirectly, using an instrument called a **sphygmomanometer** in conjunction with a stethoscope (Figure 21-7).

The sphygmomanometer consists of a cuff, which is wrapped snugly around the arm just above the elbow, then inflated with air from a bulb, placing pressure on the arm and compressing the brachial artery until the flow of blood to the distal portion of the arm is cut off. The cuff is connected to a mercury manometer, and as air is pumped into the cuff the mercury in the manometer rises. Then the air is slowly let out of the cuff, reducing the pressure on the arm, while listening to the sounds coming from the artery with a stethoscope. At some point a distinct tapping sound is heard, as blood begins to flow through the artery again. The value registered by the mercury at this point is the systolic pressure, for only during systole is the arterial pressure great enough to force blood through the partially compressed artery. As the deflation of the cuff continues, the tapping at first grows louder, then changes to a soft murmur, which becomes louder and then grows less intense and muffled. Finally it disappears entirely. The point at which the sounds fade is recorded as the diastolic pressure. (The reason the noise stops is that the cuff pressure is now below diastolic pressure, and blood flows throughout the cardiac cycle; as a result, there is no turbulence and hence no sound.) The sounds heard during the blood pressure measurement are known as **Korotkow's sounds,** after the man who first described them.

Variations of Arterial Blood Pressure and Heart Rate

When blood pressure is being taken for the first time, the reading is often higher than the person's normal value. For the action of the heart and the peripheral resistance of the blood vessels are controlled by nervous and endocrine mechanisms. Fear of the unfamiliar procedure and the restraint of the cuff may stimulate the patient's sympathetic nervous system and spark an outpouring of epinephrine from the adrenal glands. The resultant increase in the rate and force of the heartbeat and constriction of the arterioles produce a rise in the blood pressure.

Emotions are an important factor affecting the blood pressure. Fear, excitement, worry, and other emotions that stimulate the sympathetic nervous system produce a rise in the systolic blood pressure. Depression, loneliness, and grief, however, are often associated with a fall in blood pressure. A number of other physiological factors, as well as a variety of pathological processes, can affect the blood pressure.

Age and Sex

Unlike the heart rate, which tends to fall from prenatal life to adulthood, the blood pressure tends to rise. Systolic pressure for a newborn baby is only about 40 mm of mercury; it rises quickly to about 80 by the end of the first month, and then continues to rise more slowly—by ten years it is about 100. At puberty the adult level of 100 to 120 is reached. After the age of 25, the systolic blood pressure may creep up by about 0.5 per year, reaching an average of about 140 at age 60 and 160 at age 80. Before menopause, women usually have a blood pressure about 10 mm Hg lower than men. By the age of about 60, however, this difference is usually eliminated, and the blood pressure of postmenopausal women often exceeds that of men of the same age.

Exercise

Physical activity (even such a mild exertion as rising from a sitting to a standing position) can raise the blood pressure. The systolic pressure may rise sharply during strenuous exercise. A major contributing factor is the increase in cardiac output, involving both an increase in the heart rate and an increase in stroke volume. (In a nonathlete, the main factor is the speeded-up heart rate.)

Temperature

Cold, which constricts peripheral blood vessels, may raise the blood pressure. (Vasoconstrictor drugs have a similar effect.) Heat, which dilates blood vessels, tends to lower the blood pressure. (Vasodilator drugs such as nitroglycerin also have a pressure-lowering effect.)

Body Weight

Obesity is often associated with hypertension, especially after the age of 40. The extra work involved in carrying around the excess pounds and pumping blood through the extra miles of capillaries that supply the adipose tissue places an additional load of work on the cardiovascular system.

Arteriosclerosis

The state of the blood vessels is an important determining factor. If the arteries are easily distended, the influx of blood during systole will not produce a very large increase in pressure, since the elastic vessels can expand to accommodate the increased volume. But as a person ages, fatty deposits appear in the walls of the arteries **(atherosclerosis),** and calcium often precipitates with the lipids, producing arteriosclerosis, or "hardening of the arteries." These deposits narrow the arteries and make them more rigid, increasing the resistance to the ejected blood and thus raising the systolic pressure.

The Arterial Pulse

One of the aspects of hospital routine that seems most memorable to a patient is the frequent visits of the nurse to take one's temperature and pulse. At times these interruptions seem calculated to annoy, but the basic indices provide a valuable barometer of the patient's condition. A rise in temperature could signal a potentially dangerous infection, while the rate, strength, and regularity of the pulse are indications of how effectively the heart is working.

The pulse that can be felt in arteries lying close to the surface of the skin is an effect of the heart's contractions. With each systole, the blood spurting into the aorta impacts on its elastic walls and creates a pressure wave, which sweeps over the arterial system. This wave of expansion and recoil travels rapidly, at a rate of 6 to 9 meters per second. Indeed, the pulse wave reaches the periphery well before the blood that was pumped out of the left ventricle and initiated the wave.

The pulse is usually taken at the wrist, where the radial artery passes close to the surface. Several fingertips are placed over the artery and light pressure applied. (Never use your thumb in taking a pulse, for you have a pulse in your own thumb, in the princeps pollicis artery, and you might mistakenly count that instead of the patient's pulse.) In addition to the frequency (i.e., the number of beats per minute), the regularity and strength of the pulse and the tension or

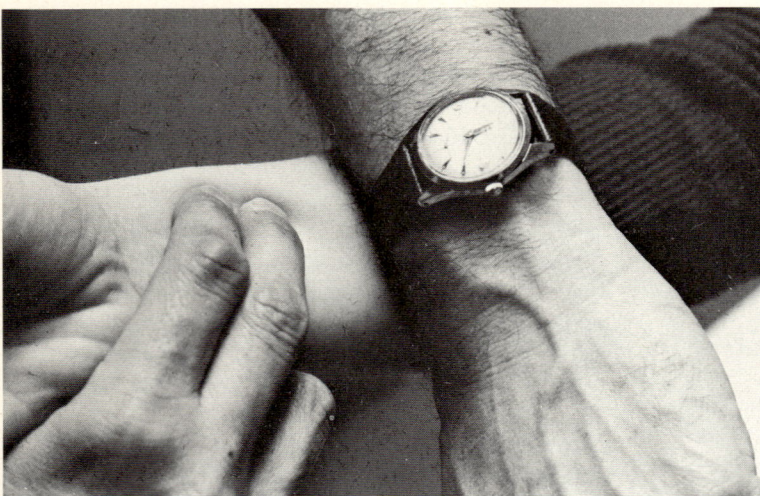

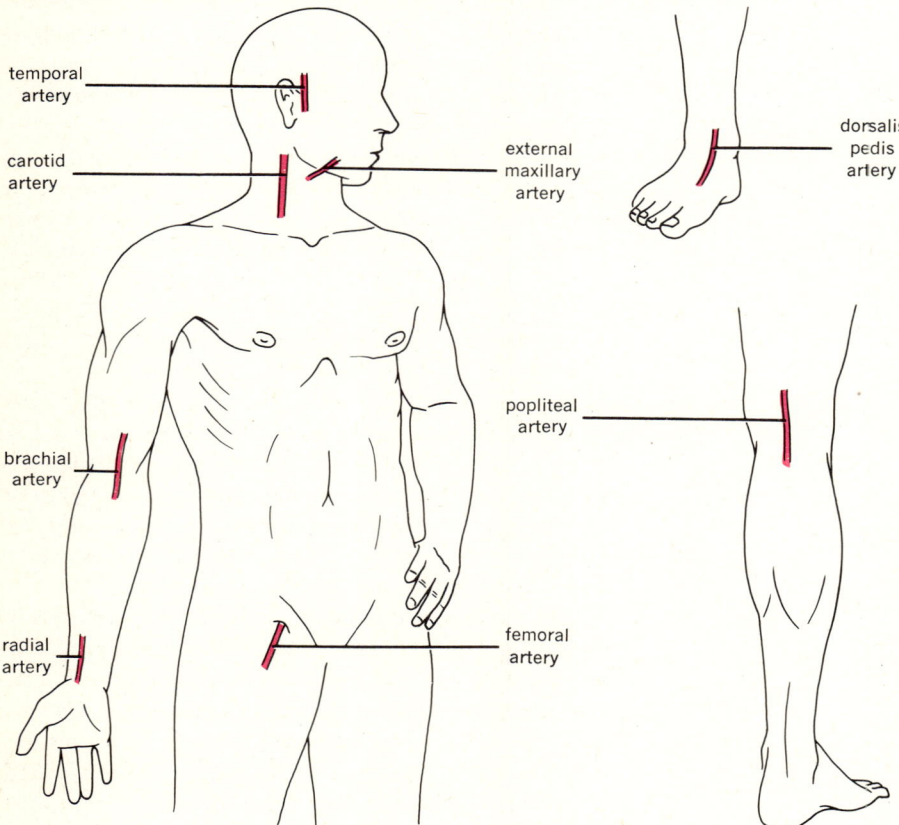

temporal artery

carotid artery

external maxillary artery

dorsalis pedis artery

popliteal artery

brachial artery

radial artery

femoral artery

resistance offered by the artery to the finger are noted. As a rule, the more rapid the pulse, the weaker it is, while a slow pulse is usually associated with a strong heart action. In high fever, the pulse is characteristically fast and feeble.

Sometimes the radial arteries may not be convenient for taking a pulse (e.g., if the patient's wrists have been injured). The pulse can also be felt at a number of other sites (Figure 21-8), including the external maxillary (facial) artery at the point where it crosses the mandible, the temporal artery at the temple, the carotid artery on the side of the neck, the brachial artery on the inner side of the biceps, the femoral artery in the groin, the popliteal artery behind the knee, and the dorsalis pedis artery over the instep of the foot. Another alternative is to count the heart rate directly with a stethoscope over the chest. (Two heart sounds correspond to each beat of the arterial pulse.)

Regulation of Arterial Blood Pressure

A fail-safe system is one in which there are alternative methods of control, so that if one fails, a backup system takes over. The body is equipped with an intricate fail-safe system for controlling the blood pressure, since a reliable supply of blood to the major organs and systems is absolutely vital to life and health. Regulation of the cardiovascular system occurs at several levels. Changes in the heart rate and venous return can alter cardiac output and thus change the blood pressure. The peripheral resistance of the blood vessels is also a dynamic factor, which is controlled by local effects on the smooth muscle in the blood-vessel walls, by nerve impulses, and by chemical influences. Vasoconstriction (narrowing of the blood vessels as a result of contraction of the smooth muscle in their walls) increases the peripheral resistance and raises the systemic blood pressure. Vasodilation (a widening of the diameter of the vessels as a result of the relaxation of the vascular smooth muscle) decreases peripheral resistance and lowers the systemic blood pressure.

Nervous Control of Peripheral Resistance

People have been taught to lower their blood pressure by techniques of biofeedback. Signals inform the subject each time he or she has achieved a small effect in the desired direction, and the person gradually becomes able to produce the effect consciously at will. The control over the blood pressure is exerted through the autonomic nervous system, which acts both on the heart action and on the muscles in the blood-vessel walls. The sympathetic division of the autonomic nervous system supplies vasoconstrictor fibers to some blood vessels and vasodilator fibers to others; parasympathetic fibers produce only a vasodilator effect. The neurotransmitter chemical released by the ends of the sympathetic vasoconstrictor fibers is **norepinephrine.** Both the sympathetic and the parasympathetic vasodilator fibers liberate **acetylcholine.**

The action of the autonomic nerves on the arterial blood vessels is mediated by the **vasomotor center** in the medulla, through reflex arcs that begin in the pressoreceptors and chemoreceptors in the carotid and aortic sinuses. If the blood pressure rises, for example, the flow of impulses from the pressoreceptors to the vasomotor center increases, inhibiting the center; the vasomotor tone decreases, vasodilation results, and the arterial pressure falls. Low oxygen, high carbon dioxide, and low pH activate the chemoreceptors in the carotid and aortic bodies, sending a stream of impulses that stimulate the vasomotor center and activating reflex arcs involving sympathetic nerve fibers, which produce vasoconstriction and a rise in arterial pressure.

Secondary constrictor centers in the spinal cord send impulses via autonomic nerves to the smooth muscles of the arterial vessels and maintain a certain degree of tone. Higher centers in the hypothalamus and cerebral cortex can also alter the arterial blood pressure and are undoubtedly involved in the changes in peripheral resistance and blood pressure that result from such emotional states as fear or excitement.

Chemical Control of Peripheral Resistance

The minute-to-minute adjustments of the cardiovascular system are mediated mainly by the nervous system. But endocrine hormones and other chemicals provide an important backup. The adrenal hormones **norepinephrine** and **epinephrine** both cause vasoconstriction. But though norepinephrine produces vasoconstriction in virtually all arterioles, epinephrine causes vasodilation in the arterioles that supply the skeletal muscles. **Angiotensin,** which is formed in the blood under the action of the kidney hormone **renin,** is a powerful vasoconstrictor and thus raises the blood pressure. **Histamine,** a substance that is released wherever tissues are damaged, has a dual action: it produces dilation of the arterioles and constriction of veins. The result is an increase in the venous return, which increases cardiac output. The combination of increased blood flow, widened arterioles, and narrowed veins produces an increase in the pressure in the capillaries, forcing fluid out through their porous walls into the tissue spaces—hence the swelling characteristic of allergies and infections.

Venous Pressure and Venous Return

When a spacecraft is taking off, the astronauts are subjected to a force considerably greater than the usual pull of gravity, and they may experience dizziness or even blackouts. The acceleration makes the venous return of blood from the lower extremities even more difficult than usual, and blood tends to pool in the legs and abdominal cavity. The removal of large quantities of blood from the general circulation leaves the brain in short supply, and oxygen lack causes the dizziness and fainting.

Even under the more ordinary circumstances of everyday life, the pull of gravity creates difficulties for the venous return of blood. Little is left of the contractile force of the ventricles by the time the blood passes through the network of arteries, arterioles, and capillaries. The residual force is enough to propel the blood into the heart when the body is in a horizontal position, especially since the diameter of the veins

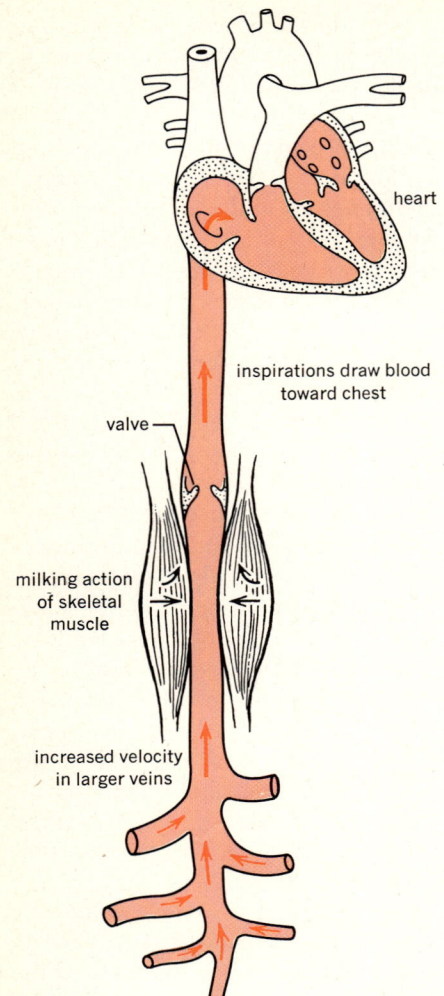

FIGURE 21-9 Mechanisms promoting venous return of blood to the heart.

heart

inspirations draw blood toward chest

valve

milking action of skeletal muscle

increased velocity in larger veins

veins, reducing their capacity and taking up the slack if the blood volume drops.

Muscular Pump The skeletal muscles that surround veins support them and keep them from bulging. Skeletal muscle contraction squeezes the veins, exerting a milking action that helps to keep the blood flowing along. If a person stands perfectly still, the venous pressures in the lower part of the leg can rise to 90 mm Hg within about 30 seconds. Inexperienced soldiers standing at attention try to keep absolutely motionless; without the massaging action of their leg muscles, the veins of the legs become distended and overfilled with blood, which leaks out into the tissue spaces. As this pooling continues, the blood flow to the brain is diminished. But the problem is self-correcting: after about 15 minutes, oxygen deprivation of the brain causes the soldier to topple over in a faint. As soon as he is in a horizontal position, the blood flows freely, and full circulation to the brain is restored.

Respiratory Pump As you breathe in and out, the pressure within your thoracic cavity changes, and the blood flow in the thin-walled veins is readily affected by the pressure change. During inspiration, subatmospheric pressure in the thorax increases the venous blood flow. Expiration is accompanied by an increased thoracic pressure, and the venous blood flow is reduced. Strenuous exercise produces much wider fluctuations of the pressure, and as a result, enhances the venous return.

The venous return is one of the most important factors determining the output of the heart. The heart responds to the demands placed on it. The more blood flowing into the heart, the more vigorously it contracts, increasing the stroke volume. In addition, stretching of the right atrium acts on the SA node to increase the heart rate by 10 to 15 percent. An increase in venous return alone can increase the cardiac output from the resting level of about 5 liters per minute to 15 liters per minute. If the venous return increases further, sympathetic nervous stimulation is needed for the heart to keep up with the inflow. In a trained athlete, vigorous exercise can produce a cardiac output of over 30 liters per minute.

A rough estimate of the venous pressure can be made by raising an arm and recording the level above the heart at which the antecubital veins in the hand suddenly collapse (Figure 21-10).

Capillary Circulation
The capillaries are the unsung heroes of the circulatory system. The arteries and veins get all the publicity, with their names carefully noted on textbook diagrams. The capillaries, however, are so tiny and

increases progressively, offering little resistance to blood flow. But in a standing position, blood from the lower extremities and abdomen must flow against gravity. (There is no problem in draining blood from the head and neck, since that flow is aided by gravity. In fact, the venous pressure in the sinuses of the brain is estimated at −10 mm Hg.) Three important mechanisms aid in the venous return: vasomotor activity, the muscular pump, and the respiratory pump (Figure 21-9).

Vasomotor Activity The veins can contract and expand in response to nervous stimulation. Constriction is produced by sympathetic impulses, while dilation results from inhibition of the sympathetic nerves. As in the arteries, the vasomotor activity of the veins is coordinated by reflex arcs including the pressoreceptors in the carotid and aortic sinuses and the control center in the medulla. Vasoconstriction induced by nerve impulses involves the entire lengths of long

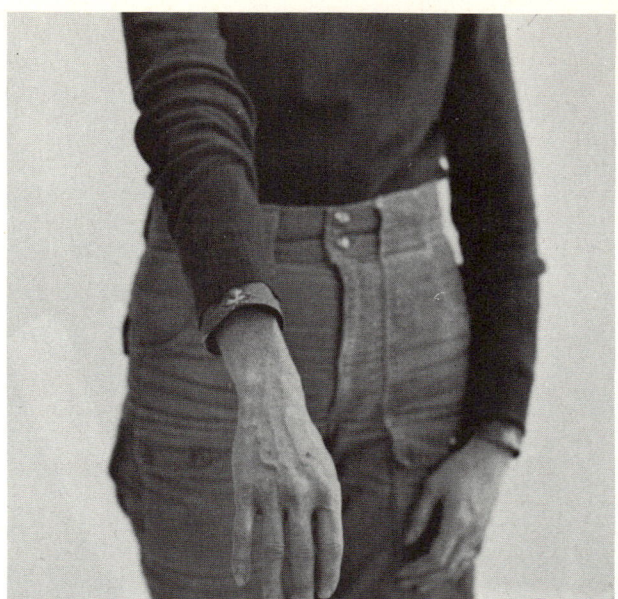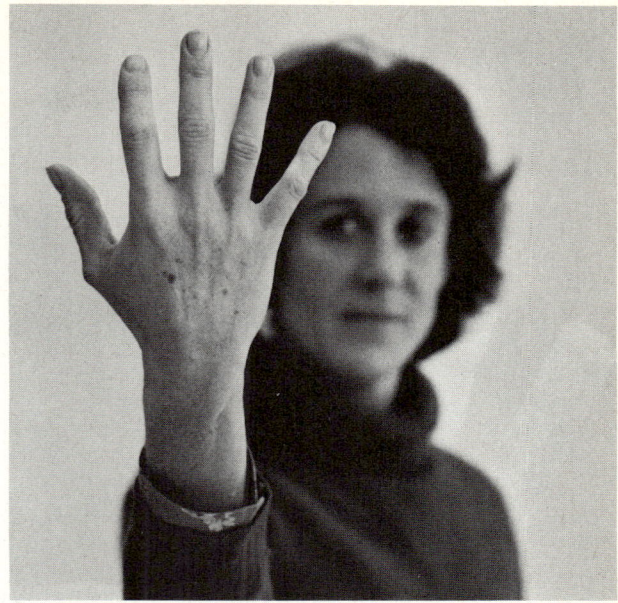

FIGURE 21-10 When the hand is raised above the level of the heart, the antecubital veins collapse.

numerous that they usually do not even appear on the diagrams. When they are indicated, they are generally anonymous. (That is probably just as well—imagine trying to memorize the names of billions of capillaries!) Yet it is in the capillaries that the actual exchange of materials with the body cells takes place.

The intricate capillary networks that ramify through the body tissues are formed by the branching of **terminal arterioles,** which feed them, and in turn merge to form **postcapillary venules,** which drain them (Figure 21-11). The total cross-sectional area of all the capillaries is greater than that of the arterioles, and as a result, the blood flow slows down as it enters the capillary networks. The total cross-sectional area of the venules is smaller than the total capillary cross-sectional area, so that the blood flow speeds up again as it passes from the capillaries into the venules. Thus, the flow is the slowest in the capillaries, an obvious advantage in enhancing the effective exchange of materials.

The flow of blood through the capillary networks is intermittent, rather than steady. At the point where arteriole merges into capillary, there is a smooth muscle sphincter, which can constrict to close off the vessel. The **precapillary sphincters** open and close rhythmically, about eight to ten times a minute. The sphincters are sensitive to oxygen demand in the tissues of the capillary bed and increase the flow when more blood is needed. The precapillary sphincters are also influenced by hormones and metabolites carried in the blood, but are not under the control of the autonomic nervous system. In some regions, arteriovenous anastomoses permit the capillary network to be bypassed entirely. (The thin-walled capillaries collapse when the blood pressure drops.)

Gases diffuse freely in and out of the thin-walled capillaries. Plasma, with the exception of the large protein molecules, can also pass out through the capillary walls into the tissue spaces, and fluid from the tissue spaces can pass into the capillaries. The movement of fluid through the capillary walls is determined by the combination of **hydrostatic pressure** (i.e., the differential between the blood pressure inside the capillaries and the pressure of the interstitial fluid, which tend to push fluid out of the respective compartments) and **osmotic pressure,** dependent on the contents of solutes in the fluids inside and outside the capillaries and tending to pull water into the respective compartments (Figure 21-12). The interaction of these two factors produces a net movement of fluid out of the capillary at the arteriolar end and movement back into the capillary at the end close to the

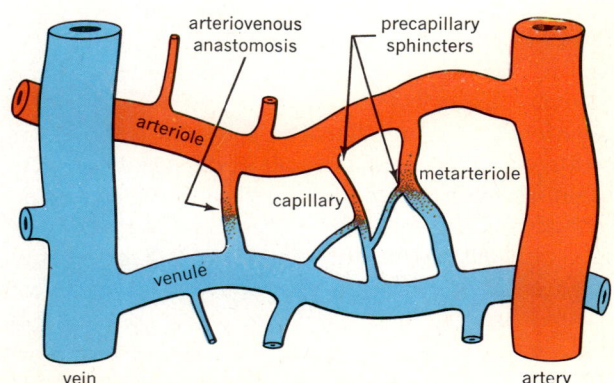

FIGURE 21-11 The terminal vascular bed.

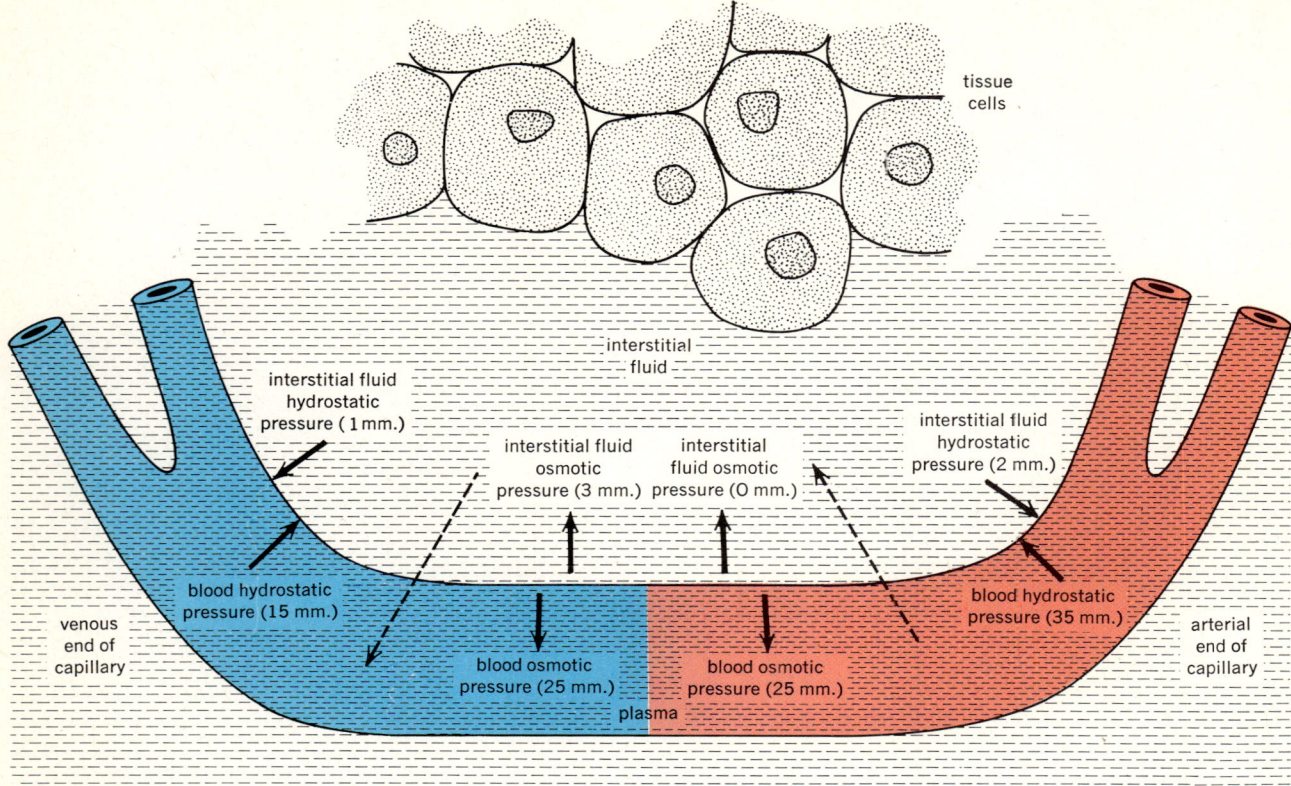

FIGURE 21-12 In the capillary beds, fluid is exchanged between the blood and interstitial fluid. (Modified from Tortora and Anagnostakos, *Principles of Anatomy and Physiology*, Canfield Press, 1975.)

venule. The amount of fluid returned to the blood capillaries at the venous end is always less than the amount that leaves the capillaries at the arteriole end. The excess augments the interstitial fluid and eventually finds its way into lymph capillaries.

PRACTICAL CONSIDERATIONS

Since 1968 the total number of deaths from cardiovascular diseases among men in the 45 to 60 age group has been decreasing each year. This encouraging trend has been due, in part, to a better understanding of the physiology of the heart and circulatory system. Yet diseases of the cardiovascular system still claim more lives of Americans than all other causes of death combined.

Arteriosclerosis

Arteriosclerosis, or "hardening of the arteries," is commonly considered a disease of old age, but it may begin in childhood and show no symptoms for many decades. It is produced by a progressive deposition of soft, fatty **plaques** in the inner layer of the arteries (Figure 21-13). The plaques usually consist of a core of lipid (mainly cholesterol), covered by a cap of fibrous tissue. At this stage the condition is referred to as atherosclerosis. Arteriosclerosis develops when the soft fatty deposits calcify. Arteriosclerotic plaques

may cause trouble in several ways. They reduce the elasticity of the blood vessels, promoting hypertension. As they grow larger, plaques may reduce or cut off the blood flow in the arteries, causing damage to

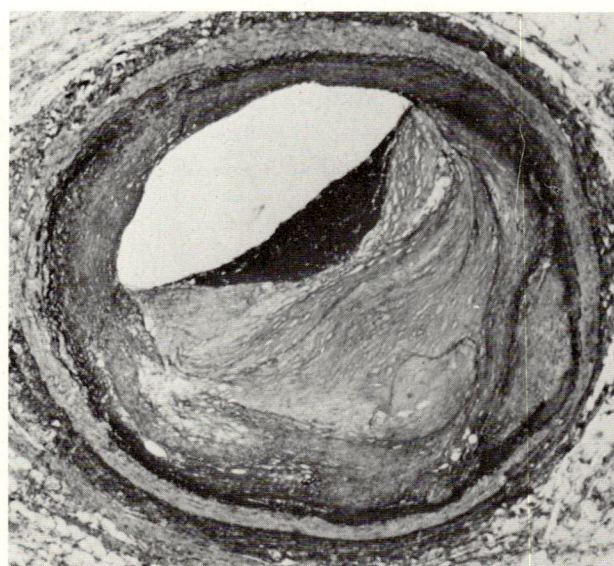

FIGURE 21-13 This cross section shows a buildup of fatty deposits gradually occluding the artery and drastically reducing the channel for blood flow.

the tissues supplied by the arteries. The roughened surfaces of the plaques may rupture the fragile platelets and produce clot formation inside the arteries; the clot may plug the artery (thrombosis) or travel as an embolus to lodge ultimately in some other part of the cardiovascular system. The lipid core of the plaques themselves may also break away and be carried through the bloodstream as an embolus.

The cause and prevention of arteriosclerosis are currently subjects of intensive research and hot debate. Hypertension promotes plaque formation, and, according to one current theory, environmental mutagens, acting on cells in the artery walls, may also play a role. There seem to be hereditary predisposing factors, but diet also seems to play a role in plaque formation. High levels of dietary saturated fats have been implicated as culprits; other researchers claim that the determining factor is a high sugar intake. The role of exercise in maintaining the health of the cardiovascular system and the possible artery-clearing action of such agents as vitamin C and chondroitin sulfate are storm centers of controversy.

Hypertension

A resting systolic blood pressure above 140 mm Hg is classified as hypertension, or high blood pressure. It is believed that as many as 22 million adult Americans may be afflicted. About 15 percent of the cases are found to be the result of specific diseases or disorders, such as arteriosclerosis, kidney disease, or adrenal hypersecretion. But in the vast majority of cases, no definite cause can be discovered. In people who suffer from this idiopathic, or **essential hypertension,** the pressoreceptors in the carotid and aortic sinuses still function to regulate the blood pressure via reflex arcs, but the controls somehow seem to have been reset at a higher level. If hypertension is uncontrolled, it can damage various important body organs. When the blood pressure is elevated, the heart must work harder to pump blood and eventually enlarges; it requires more oxygen, and if it cannot meet the demands placed on it, angina pectoris or myocardial infarction may result. Hypertension also sets up a vicious cycle involving the kidneys. The high pressure causes the walls of the arterioles to thicken, narrowing them and cutting down the blood supply to the kidneys. The kidneys respond by secreting their hormone renin, which raises the blood pressure still further and compounds the problem. If there is a weak spot in the artery walls anywhere in the body, chronic high blood pressure may cause the artery to balloon out, producing an **aneurism** (Figure 21-14). If this occurs in the cerebral blood vessels, a cerebral vascular accident or "stroke" will result, either from pressure by the ballooning artery or from the hemorrhaging that occurs if the weak spot ruptures.

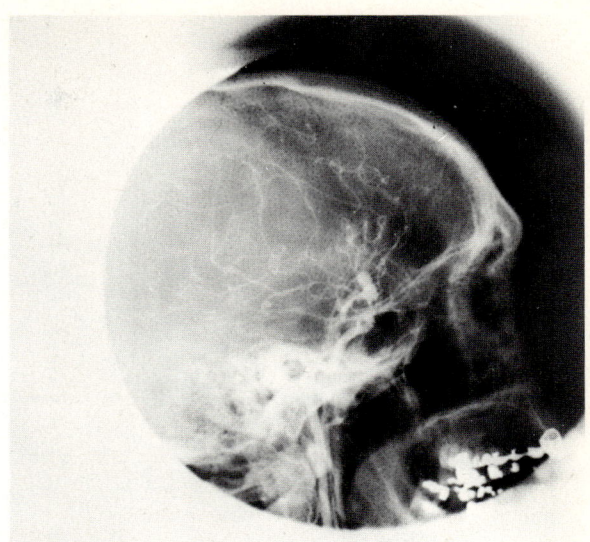

FIGURE 21-14 A ruptured aneurism.

Heart Disorders

Heart Block In a symphony orchestra the conductor sets the pace that all the musicians follow. But what would happen if a screen were placed in front of the conductor, so that the orchestra members could not see him or her. They would still have the musical score and enough innate musical sense to go on playing; but the tempo of their rendition might differ substantially from the pace set by the conductor's signals. The pacemaker of the heart, the SA node, sets the rhythm of the heartbeat. But the coordination of the heart contractions depends on the spread of excitation through the conducting system of the heart. Damage to the conduction system produces a heart block of varying degrees. A common type of heart block is the **AV block,** occurring at the atrioventricular node. In such a block, the contractions of the atria are still paced by the SA node, but the ventricles no longer receive the coordinating impulses and contract independently. Heart block may be partial or complete. In **first-degree heart block,** there is just a delay in the atrioventricular conduction, and the ventricles contract a little late on each beat. (Clinically there are no symptoms, but the electrocardiogram shows a prolonged PR interval). **Second-degree heart block** is characterized by "dropped beats"—that is, some of the ventricular contractions are missed entirely, at regular intervals, producing a slower rate of ventricular contraction that is related to the rate of atrial contraction in a definite whole-number ratio, for example, 2:1 (a ventricular rate of contraction half the atrial rate), 3:1, 4:1, and so on. In **third-degree heart block,** conduction between the atria and the ventricles is blocked completely, and the ventricles contract entirely independently of the atria, usually at a rate of 30 to 45 beats per minute. Other types of heart blocks

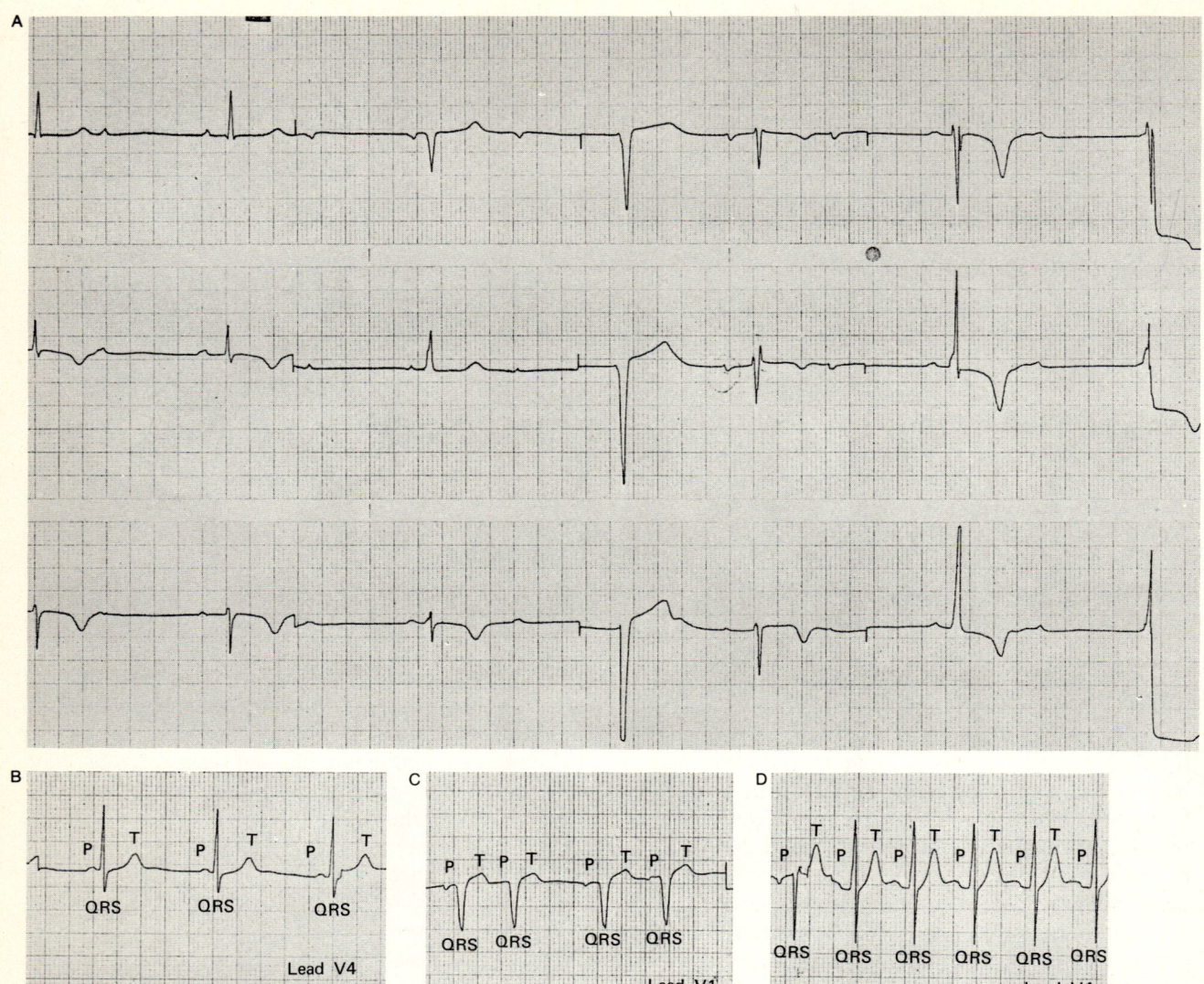

FIGURE 21-15 Abnormal electrocardiograms show damage to the heart. The complete electrocardiogram in (A) revealed advanced atrio-ventricular block some time after myocardial infarction: the QT interval is lengthened, and the ST segment and T wave show abnormalities. Segments (one-lead) of other electrocardiograms: B) normal ECG: a regular pattern of P, QRS, and T waves; C) wandering atrial pacemaker: arrhythmia and ST segment and T wave abnormalities; D) sinus tachycardia.

include **intraatrial (IA) block, interventricular (IV) block,** and **bundle branch block.** In the latter case, there is a block in one of the branches of the bundle of His, and the two ventricles contract separately because of the delay in transmission of the impulse in the blocked branch. Some abnormal electrocardiograms are shown in Figure 21-15.

Abnormal Rhythms Do you ever have the sensation that your heart is racing or has skipped a beat? Variations of the heart rhythm (arrhythmias) may be a sign of a heart disorder, but sometimes occur in healthy people. A heart rate below 60 beats per minute is called **bradycardia,** while a regular heart rate above 100 is referred to as **tachycardia.** A very rapid

and weak pulse, such as that observed in a high fever, is described as "thready." The sensation of the heart skipping a beat comes from a **premature systole,** which is followed by a compensatory pause. Premature heart contractions are caused by impulses spreading from an irritable area of cardiac muscle, which may result from the use of stimulants such as caffeine or nicotine, or from lack of sleep or anxiety. **Atrial flutter** is a very fast, regular atrial rhythm, between 240 and 360 beats per minute, while the ventricular rate is only a half, third, or quarter of the atrial rate; it is actually an atrial tachycardia combined with a second-degree AV block, and is usually an indication of severe damage to the heart muscle. After a few days or weeks, atrial flutter may develop into atrial fibrillation. **Atrial fibrillation** is characterized by rapid, irregular, uncoordinated atrial contractions. Instead of contracting together, the atria quiver individually, and the pumping action of the atria ceases. As a result of the less effective filling of the ventricles, the overall pumping effectiveness of the heart drops. Atrial flutter and atrial fibrillation may occur in myocardial infarction, rheumatic heart disease, and hyperthyroidism. **Ventricular fibrillation** is a condition characterized by asynchronous, irregular, ventricular contractions. The rate may be rapid or slow. Different parts of the ventricle contract at different times, so that the overall ventricular contractions become ineffective, and the pumping of blood ceases. If a normal heart rhythm is not quickly restored, death will result. Only rarely are fibrillating ventricles able to return to a rhythmic beat of their own accord. But fibrillation can be stopped by applying two electrodes to the chest (or directly to the heart, during an operation) and sending a strong electrical current through the ventricles for a fraction of a second. Unless the heart is defibrillated within one minute after fibrillation begins, it is usually too weak to be revived, since the circulatory failure deprives the myocardium of its coronary circulation. But techniques have been developed for hand-pumping stopped hearts, until electrical defibrillation becomes possible. At first it was thought to be necessary to cut open the chest and squeeze the heart directly; now techniques of **closed cardiac massage,** involving rhythmic thrusts of pressure on the chest wall, are being successfully used to save lives (Figure 21-16). But speed is still vital: if circulation has been stopped for more than four minutes, irreversible damage to the brain may occur.

Heart Murmurs

Every so often a wave of surprise is generated by a news report that a star athlete has been barred from further competition, or an astronaut has been dropped from active service in the space program because a routine physical examination has revealed a suspicious heart murmur. Any additions to the characteristic heart sounds are an indication of additional turbulence in the blood flow in the heart, which may be caused by a leaky valve or a narrowed orifice. In mitral insufficiency, the left atrioventricular valve fails to close tightly, and blood regurgitates into the left atrium during ventricular systole; this condition produces a **systolic murmur.** Aortic regurgitation gives a **diastolic murmur,** as blood leaks back into the left ventricle from the aorta through a faulty semilunar valve during diastole. In mitral stenosis, the opening from the left atrium into the left ventricle is narrowed, altering the flow of blood through the left heart during diastole; in this

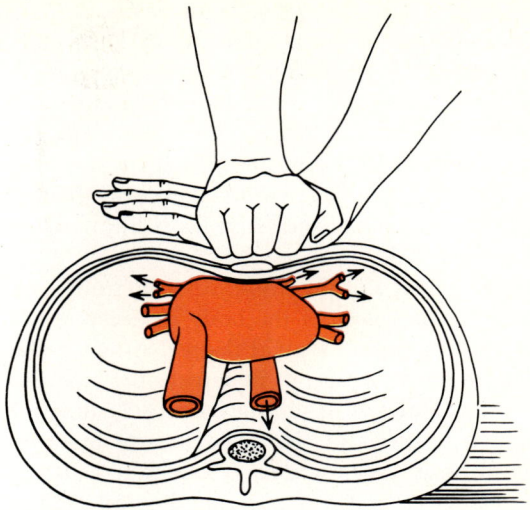

FIGURE 21-16 Closed cardiac massage.

condition, a **presystolic murmur** is heard late in ventricular diastole, at the time of atrial systole. Pathological changes in the heart valves that develop in adult life generally involve the left side of the heart. (Eventually, as blood chronically backs up in the lungs, the right ventricle is enlarged and the valves of the right side of the heart are damaged also.) Congenital defects usually involve the right side of the heart.

The Heart Attack

When a myocardial infarction strikes, time is vital. Many heart attack victims die before they reach the hospital. But if they can reach trained medical help rapidly, their chances for recovery are greatly improved. A **myocardial infarction** is a sudden damage to the heart muscle, caused by a cut-off of coronary circulation. In addition to the severe pain that is felt (often over the area of the sternum, or radiating down into the left arm), there are immediate effects on the heart function: a reduced cardiac output (since the damaged muscle cannot contribute, the effectiveness of the ventricular contractions is decreased) and an increased systemic venous pressure, as blood swells the ventricles and backs up in the veins. Generalized weakness and fainting may occur. The next events are an immediate switch-on of compensatory sympathetic reflexes, with an inhibition of the parasympathetic nerves. The heart rate is speeded up, and the force of contraction is increased in the undamaged portions of the heart muscle. Side effects of the sympathetic stimulation are cold skin, pallor, sweating, and a thready pulse. If the damage is not too severe, the combination of increased venous return and increased heart ability may be enough to compensate for the impaired function and restore adequate circulation—at least as long as the person remains quiet. If a low cardiac output persists, another level of compensatory mechanisms is switched on, as the kidneys begin to retain fluid. The venous return is enhanced, which has a positive effect on the heart function if the damage is moderate. But in severe cardiac failure, the heart cannot keep pace, the ventricles are distended, and the cardiac muscle fibers become overstretched, decreasing their effectiveness. A vicious cycle is established and leads ultimately to death.

After the damage of the myocardial infarction, the natural repair processes of the body can restore normal cardiac function to a great degree. A new collateral blood supply begins to penetrate the infarcted area, often completely restoring its muscle function. Undamaged portions of the heart muscle hypertrophy, taking over the functions of the damaged area. The degree of recovery varies, depending on the type of damage, and is usually completed within two to six months.

The various compensatory mechanisms can restore a normal resting cardiac output after acute cardiac failure, but a person with **compensated heart failure** does not have a normal circulatory system. A healthy person has strong reserves that can provide for greatly increased heart function in response to the demands of strenuous exercise or stress. But a person with compensated heart failure is already using part of his reserves just to maintain a normal output. The damage may have occurred in such mild and gradual stages that compensation kept pace, and he is quite unaware that his heart is below par. Then the sudden exertion of shoveling snow or a fast set of weekend tennis after a week of sedentary office work may overtax the heart and precipitate a massive collapse.

Hemorrhage and Shock

You can donate a pint of blood without any serious changes in your blood pressure. But if more than about 25 percent of the total blood volume is lost, the blood pressure falls precipitously; a 40 percent blood loss usually proves fatal. Hemorrhage (bleeding) may be either external, in which blood escapes from the body, or internal, in which a ruptured blood vessel discharges blood into a body cavity or tissue space. External hemorrhage can be checked by appropriate first aid measures. Internal hemorrhage is more difficult to recognize: characteristic signs are a gasping type of respiration; pale, cold, and clammy skin; restlessness; a thready pulse; and low blood pressure. As blood is lost, the volume of blood falls below the capacity of the circulatory system, the output of the heart decreases, and the blood pressure drops. Reflex responses produce prompt vasoconstriction, which helps to compensate (and may also help to cut off the bleeding), and catecholamines secreted by the adrenal

medulla reinforce the cardiovascular adjustments. Reflex stimulation of the respiratory center increases respiratory activity, which helps to enhance venous return (the respiratory pump). Fluid moves into the capillaries from the interstitial spaces, helping to raise the blood volume back to normal. Erythropoietin secretion increases, and more red blood cells are produced.

If hemorrhaging continues and no transfusion is given, a condition called **circulatory shock** sets in. The blood pressure continues to fall, and blood-starved vital organs, such as the brain, heart, kidneys, and liver, are damaged. Not only hemorrhage, but also any other condition that decreases the heart output and results in an inadequate blood supply to the tissues can produce shock: for example, the loss of plasma after severe burns, dehydration, intestinal obstruction, and massive vasodilation due to substances such as histamine acting directly on the arterioles. The latter condition occurs in **anaphylactic shock,** when a foreign protein (allergen) is taken in or injected into a person whose body has previously been sensitized to it. Collapse, sometimes leading to death, has been observed in sensitized individuals after such seemingly innocuous events as a bee sting, an injection of penicillin, or the eating of a particular food such as strawberries.

SUMMARY

Cardiac muscle fibers are functionally linked into a syncytium; the entire heart muscle shows an all-or-none response.
 Cardiac muscle contraction is self-initiated and has an inherent rhythmicity.
 Cardiac muscle has a relatively long refractory period.
 The rhythm of the heartbeat is set by the sinoatrial node (pacemaker); excitation spreads through the heart via the conducting system: atrioventricular node, bundle of His, and Purkinje fibers.
 Atrial contractions are followed by ventricular contractions.
The cardiac cycle consists of initiation of excitation; contraction of the atria, pumping blood into the ventricles; contraction of the ventricles, pumping blood into the pulmonary trunk and aorta; relaxation of the ventricles and passive filling.
 The phase of heart contraction is called systole.
 The phase of relaxation is called diastole.
Turbulence in the blood flow in the heart, caused by the closing of valves and the pumping of ventricles, produces characteristic heart sounds (lubb-dup).
 The first heart sound (lubb) corresponds to contraction of the ventricles and shutting of the atrioventricular valves.
 The second heart sound (dup) corresponds to shutting of the semilunar valves.
 Third and fourth heart sounds (filling of ventricles and contraction of atria) can be recorded electronically.
 Additional heart sounds (murmurs) may indicate valvular damage.
The electrocardiograph produces a recording of the electrical activity of the heart (electrocardiogram), normally characterized by a P wave, QRS complex, and T wave.

The stroke volume is the volume of blood pumped by the left ventricle with each beat of the heart.

The cardiac output is the amount of blood pumped by the left ventricle in one minute (i.e., stroke volume × heart rate).

Increased venous return produces increased stroke volume according to Starling's law of the heart: the force of cardiac muscle contraction is proportional to the amount of stretch placed on the muscle fibers.

The normal resting heart rate in an adult is 60 to 100 beats per minute.

The heart rate is affected by:

Age (decreases from prenatal heart rate of 140 to adult average of 70).

Sex (women have a faster heart rate than men).

Physical exercise (speeds up the heart).

Athletic conditioning (decreases resting heart rate).

Emotional excitement (speeds up the heart).

Heart function is under nervous and endocrine control.

Parasympathetic (inhibitory) fibers slow down the heart and decrease the force of its contractions.

Sympathetic (accelerator) fibers speed up the heart and increase the force of its contractions.

Cardiac centers in the medulla oblongata coordinate nervous control.

Reflex arcs include pressoreceptors (stretch receptors) and chemoreceptors (sensitive to oxygen, carbon dioxide, and pH) in the carotid and aortic sinuses.

Catecholamine hormones (epinephrine and norepinephrine) secreted by the adrenal medulla increase the rate and strength of heart contraction.

The propulsive force of the pumping ventricles builds up blood pressure inside the closed vascular system.

Blood flows down the pressure gradient.

Blood pressure, volume, and speed of flow vary greatly in the circuit of arteries, arterioles, capillaries, venules, and veins.

Blood pressure is defined as the pressure exerted by the blood against the walls of the vessels.

Arterial pressure is high and fluctuating. Normal adult resting values are: systolic 100 to 120 mm Hg, diastolic 60 to 80 mm Hg.

Blood pressure drops progressively from arteries to veins.

Blood pressure in the veins leading to the heart is steady and close to zero.

The velocity of blood flow drops from 300 mm/sec in the aorta to 0.5 mm/sec in the capillaries, as a result of the progressive increase in total cross-sectional area.

Blood flow = pressure/resistance.

Peripheral resistance is produced by friction between the flowing liquid and the vessel walls.

The narrower the blood vessels, the greater the resistance.

Pressure = flow × resistance, that is, pressure can be increased by an increase in cardiac output (flow) or an increase in resistance.

Physical factors regulating blood pressure are:

Cardiac output

Peripheral resistance

Blood volume

Viscosity of blood

Elasticity of arterial walls

Blood pressure is measured with a sphygmomanometer.

The blood pressure is affected by:

Emotions (fear and excitement raise pressure; depression and grief lower it).

Age (rises with age from 40 mm Hg in newborn baby to 160 mm Hg at age 80).

Sex (before menopause, women have a lower blood pressure than men; after age 60, women have a higher blood pressure).

Exercise (raises blood pressure).

Temperature (cold raises blood pressure; heat lowers blood pressure).

Body weight (obesity is often associated with hypertension).

Arteriosclerosis (raises systolic pressure).

The arterial pulse is a pressure wave from the heart systole transmitted over the arteries.

It can be taken at the wrist (radial artery) or at various other sites of superficial arteries.

Arterial blood pressure is under nervous and endocrine regulation.

Autonomic nerves can produce vasodilator (parasympathetic and sympathetic) and vasoconstrictor (sympathetic) effects.

Autonomic reflexes are coordinated by the vasomotor center in the medulla, through reflex arcs beginning with pressoreceptors and chemoreceptors in the carotid and aortic sinuses.

Secondary constrictor centers in the spinal cord maintain vascular tone.

Higher centers in the hypothalamus and cerebral cortex can also alter peripheral resistance.

Chemical control of peripheral resistance is exerted by:

Norepinephrine

Epinephrine

Angiotensin

Histamine

Venous return is promoted by:

Vasomotor activity (controlled by autonomic nerves).

Muscular pump ("milking" action of surrounding skeletal muscles).

Respiratory pump (fluctuations of intrathoracic pressure).

The heart responds to the demands of venous return.

Capillary networks are formed from terminal arterioles and drained by postcapillary venules.

Precapillary sphincters open and close rhythmically, making capillary blood flow intermittent.

Gases and fluids diffuse in and out of the thin capillary walls.

Fluid movement is determined by hydrostatic pressure and osmotic pressure.

Disorders of the cardiovascular system include:

Arteriosclerosis (hardening of the arteries), which can lead to thrombosis and embolism, producing myocardial infarction or occlusion of other blood vessels.

Hypertension (high blood pressure: greater than 140/90), which forces the heart to work harder and may result in angina pectoris, kidney failure, and aneurism.

Heart block: damage to the conducting system of the heart, including:

AV block (first-degree, second-degree, third-degree)

IA block

IV block

Bundle branch block

Abnormal rhythms:

Bradycardia (less than 60 beats per minute)

Tachycardia (more than 100 beats per minute)

Premature systole ("skipping a beat")

Atrial flutter (fast, regular atrial rhythm with second-degree AV block)

Atrial fibrillation (rapid, irregular, uncoordinated atrial contractions)

Ventricular fibrillation (asynchronous, irregular, ventricular contractions; circulatory failure results)

Heart murmurs:

Systolic (left atrioventricular regurgitation)

Diastolic (aortic regurgitation)

Presystolic (mitral stenosis)

Heart attack: myocardial infarction is followed by reduced cardiac output and increased systemic venous pressure.

Compensatory mechanisms include:

Sympathetic reflexes

Fluid retention by kidneys

Establishment of collateral circulation to infarcted area and hypertrophy of normal myocardium

Hemorrhage results in a drop in blood pressure; circulatory failure results from a loss of 40 percent of the total blood volume.

Severe hemorrhage can result in circulatory shock, which can also be caused by burns (loss of plasma), dehydration, intestinal obstruction, and anaphylactic reaction.

QUESTIONS FOR REVIEW AND THOUGHT

1 Trace the sequence of events in the cardiac cycle.

2 Define: stroke volume, minute volume, cardiac output, systole, diastole.

3 Discuss Starling's law of the heart and the mechanisms of venous return. How is a vicious cycle set up in severe cardiac failure?

4 Describe nervous and endocrine effects on the heart and blood vessels in the following situations: resting in bed; pitching a baseball game on a hot summer day; fleeing from an attempted mugging.

5 What factors contribute to the drop in blood flow in the capillaries in comparison with the arteries and arterioles?

6 Describe the compensatory mechanisms induced in the cardiovascular system by blood loss. What happens in the body if these mechanisms cannot compensate sufficiently?

7 Why is blood pressure usually measured with the patient in a sitting or lying position?

8 Discuss the relationship between arteriosclerosis and hypertension.

9 Distinguish between myocardial infarction and compensated heart failure; first, second, and third-degree heart block; bradycardia and tachycardia; atrial and ventricular fibrillation; systolic and diastolic murmurs.

THE LYMPHATIC SYSTEM

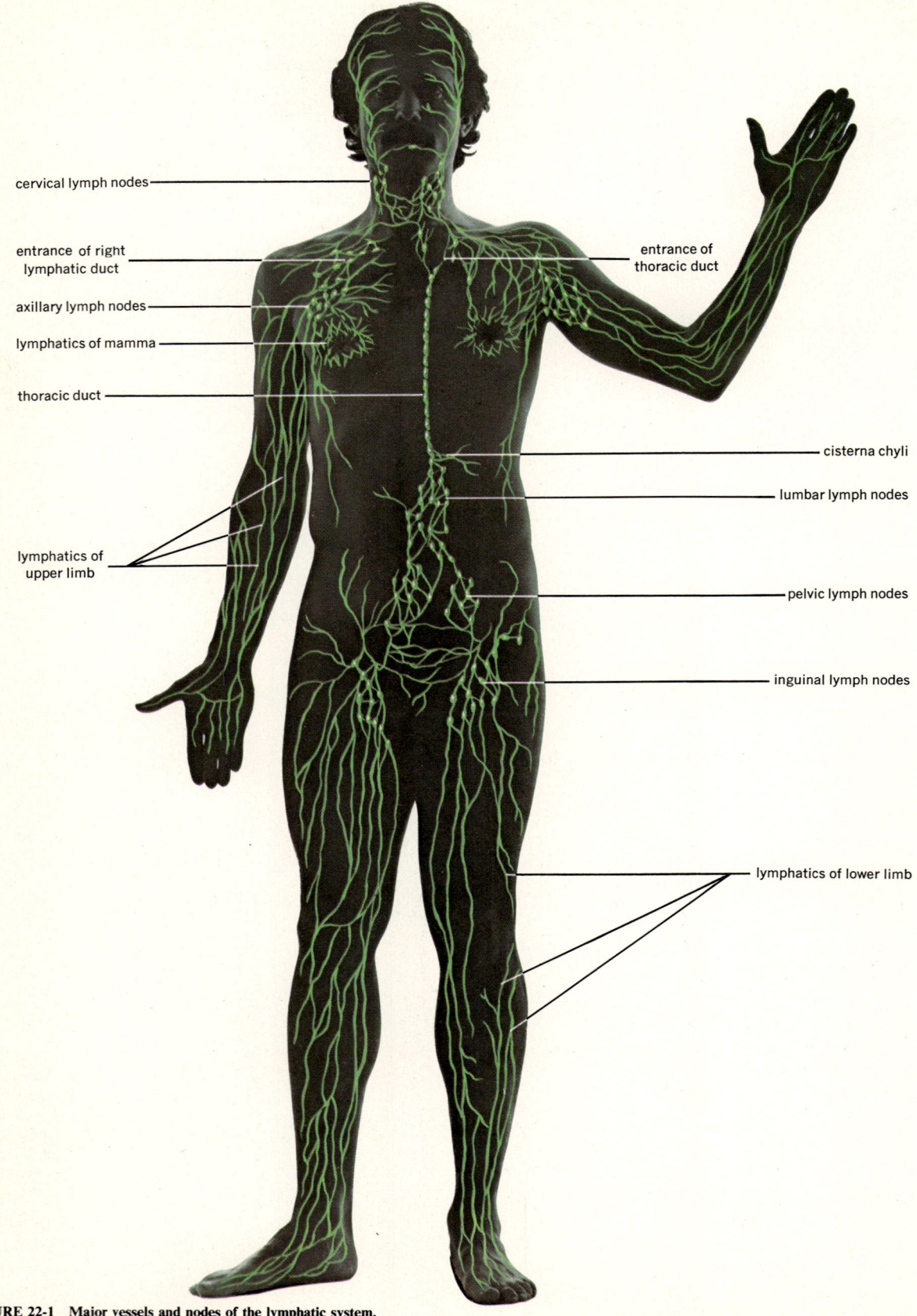

cervical lymph nodes

entrance of right
lymphatic duct

axillary lymph nodes

lymphatics of mamma

thoracic duct

lymphatics of
upper limb

entrance of
thoracic duct

cisterna chyli

lumbar lymph nodes

pelvic lymph nodes

inguinal lymph nodes

lymphatics of lower limb

FIGURE 22-1 Major vessels and nodes of the lymphatic system.

The human circulatory system is described as a closed system, and this is technically correct. But the capillaries are rather leaky. Not only is there a continual exchange of materials between the bloodstream and the body tissues, but there is also a continual net flow of fluid out through the capillary walls, adding to the tissue fluid. The problem is compounded because some protein leaks out of the capillaries. Protein in the tissue fluid adds to its osmotic pressure, further tending to draw fluid out of the capillaries. The blood vessels can reabsorb some of the lost fluid, but not all (and none of the escaped protein), and a one-way flow occurs, out into the tissues. If there were no way to return the excess fluid and escaped proteins to the circulatory system, the tissues would progressively swell, while the blood would soon become so thick that it could not circulate. The return of fluid and proteins is provided for by an elaborate system of collecting vessels, the **lymphatic system** (Figure 22-1). This system may be regarded as part of the circulatory system and consists of the fluid **lymph,** a network of transporting vessels, and lymphoid structures: the **lymph nodes, spleen, thymus,** and **tonsils.**

If the lymphatic system did nothing else but return fluid and escaped protein to the circulatory system, it would be performing a vital function for the body. But the lymphatic system also provides the "headquarters" for an important line of defenses against disease. It provides **lymphocytes,** which, when exposed to antigens, can develop into antibody-producing cells, and it also manufactures **monocytes,** which are delivered to the blood via the lymph. Foreign matter is effectively filtered out by the lymphatic system as the lymph passes through the lymph nodes.

LYMPH

What is the difference between lymph and interstitial fluid? Nothing, really; once the tissue fluid has passed into the lymphatic vessels, it is simply referred to as lymph. Lymph is a watery, plasmalike fluid. It has almost the same content of salts and various other constituents as plasma, but lymph has a much lower protein content than plasma, and high-molecular-weight proteins are generally absent. Lymph contains large numbers of white cells, mainly lymphocytes, along with a few platelets and some stray erythrocytes. In most of the body, lymph is a clear liquid, but the lymph from the intestines after a meal is milky white, as a result of the presence of minute, finely dispersed fat globules absorbed from the alimentary tract. Such fat-laden lymph is called **chyle.**

LYMPH VESSELS

Wherever you find blood vessels, you'll find lymph vessels as well. Nearly all the tissues of the body have lymphatic channels that drain excess fluid from the interstitial spaces. The few exceptions include the superficial portions of the skin, the central nervous system, and the bones; but even these tissues have minute interstitial channels through which tissue fluid can flow, and eventually this fluid flows into lymphatic vessels. (In the brain, the interstitial fluid drains into the cerebrospinal fluid.)

The organization of the lymphatic system resembles a portion of the blood vascular system. Microscopic **lymph capillaries** unite to form larger, veinlike vessels called **lymphatics,** which unite in turn to form larger and larger vessels. All the lymph vessels are directed toward the thoracic cavity and converge into two main channels, the **thoracic duct** and the **right lymphatic** duct (Figure 22-2). Both these ducts empty into the venous portion of the blood circulatory system.

Lymph Capillaries

You might logically expect the tiny terminal collecting vessels of the lymphatic system to be shaped like little funnels, open to the interstitial spaces. But in fact, the terminal lymph capillaries are blind-ended. Fluid, protein molecules, and even larger particles such as bacteria and erythrocytes can enter the lymph capillaries freely, and once substances have entered, they stay inside the lymph channels and are conducted on the route leading to the bloodstream, without leaking back out into the tissues. How this occurs was a mystery that puzzled physiologists for some time.

Like the blood capillaries, lymph capillaries are very thin-walled tubes, with walls consisting of just a single layer of endothelial cells. They are even more permeable than blood capillaries, yet it is a one-way permeability. The endothelial cells that form the walls of the terminal lymph capillaries are not attached to each other, but instead are anchored by filaments to the connective tissue between the surrounding tissue cells. Adjacent endothelial cells overlap slightly, forming tiny flap valves (Figure 22-3). Fluid, protein molecules, and larger particles can move freely into the lymph capillaries, but once they are inside the flap valves keep them from leaving.

The lymph capillaries branch and anastomose profusely, forming intricate drainage networks in various organs and tissues. Superficial and deep lymph capillary networks are connected by anastomoses. Each villus in the lining of the intestine contains a minute lymph capillary, called a **lacteal,** which absorbs digested fat.

Lymphatics

Like the veins, the lymphatics function to carry fluid toward the heart, so it is not surprising that their structure is rather similar to that of the veins. The

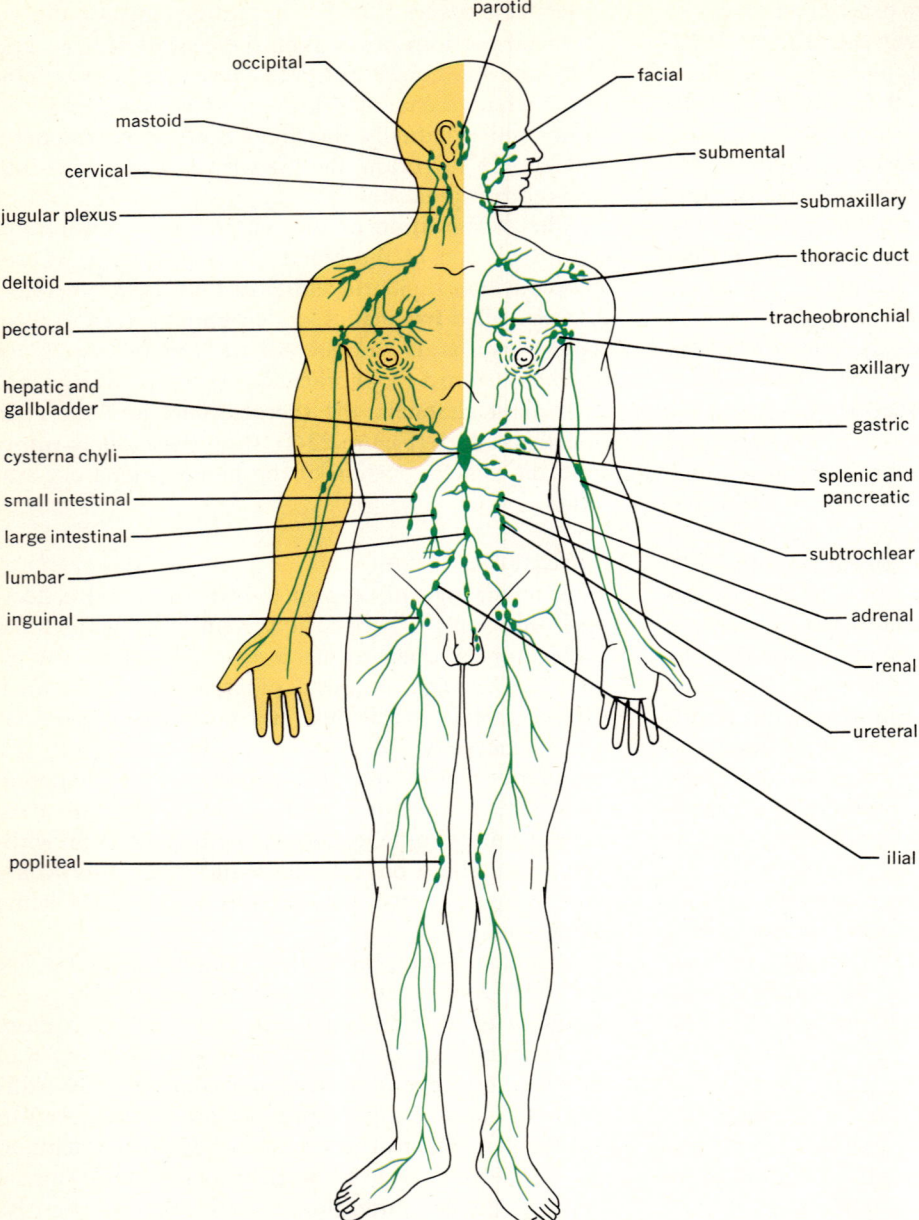

parotid
occipital
facial
mastoid
cervical
jugular plexus
deltoid
pectoral
hepatic and gallbladder
cysterna chyli
small intestinal
large intestinal
lumbar
inguinal
popliteal

submental
submaxillary
thoracic duct
tracheobronchial
axillary
gastric
splenic and pancreatic
subtrochlear
adrenal
renal
ureteral
ilial

FIGURE 22-2 Drainage of the lymphatic system. Lymph from the colored region flows into the right lymphatic duct; the thoracic duct receives the lymph flow from the much larger remainder of the body.

larger lymphatics have a veinlike three-layered wall, though their walls are thinner than those of the veins. Like veins, lymphatics contain valves (Figure 22-4), which prevent backflow of fluid. In fact, the valves in lymphatics are more numerous than those of veins; in some areas the valves are so close together that they give the vessel a beaded appearance.

A major difference of lymphatics from veins is the presence of lymph nodes at intervals along their course.

Lymphatic Ducts

All the fluid collected by the vessels of the lymphatic system eventually drains into one of two large lymph ducts, the **thoracic duct** and the **right lymphatic duct.** The thoracic duct takes the lion's share: it drains the entire left half of the body and the right half below the diaphragm; the right lymphatic duct receives fluid only from the right half above the diaphragm.

The thoracic duct begins as a dilation called the **cisterna chyli,** in the lumbar region of the abdominal cavity, which receives lymph from the large vessels that drain the lower extremities and the pelvis and abdomen. The duct ascends to the root of the neck, where it empties into the left subclavian vein at the point where it joins the left internal jugular vein. The thoracic duct is considerably larger than the other main lymph channels, but is much smaller than the

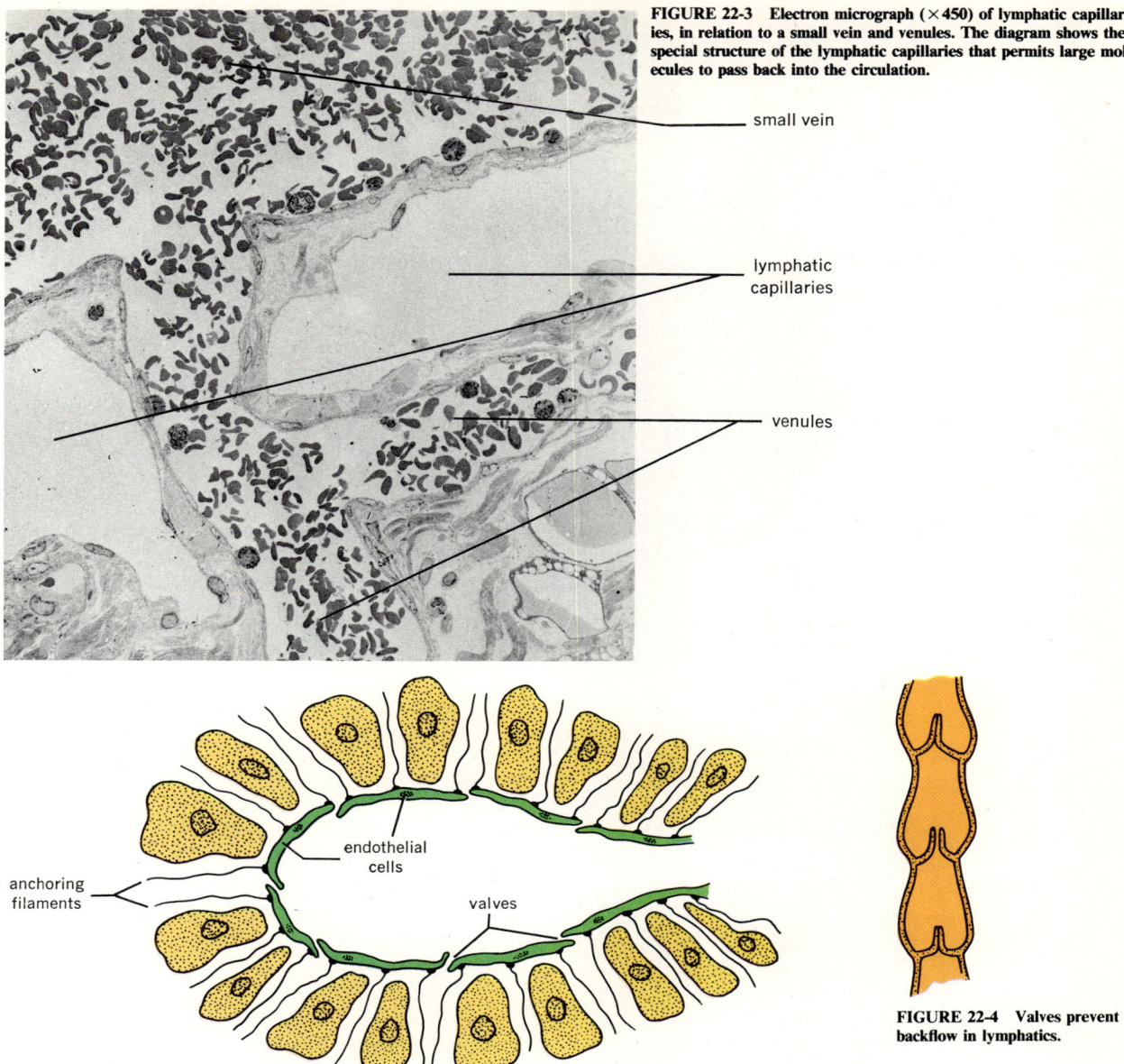

FIGURE 22-3 Electron micrograph (×450) of lymphatic capillaries, in relation to a small vein and venules. The diagram shows the special structure of the lymphatic capillaries that permits large molecules to pass back into the circulation.

small vein

lymphatic capillaries

venules

anchoring filaments

endothelial cells

valves

FIGURE 22-4 Valves prevent backflow in lymphatics.

large veins, to which it is similar in structure.

The right lymphatic duct is a short vessel, which receives lymph from the right side of the head, neck, and chest and empties into the right subclavian vein.

LYMPH FLOW

Like the veins, most of the lymphatic vessels must carry blood "uphill." And the lymphatic system has no pump at all to propel the fluid along. The mechanisms that contribute to the return of fluid through the lymphatic vessels are very similar to those that aid the return of blood to the heart via the venous system. The reduced pressure in the thorax during respiration helps to move fluid through lymph vessels as well as through veins. Contractions of skeletal muscles squeeze on lymphatic vessels, pumping the fluid along. Indeed, any movements of body parts—pulsations in the heart and arteries, peristaltic contractions of smooth muscle in the intestines, compression of tissues from outside—help to massage the lymphatic vessels and move the fluid inside them. The lymphatics are so abundantly supplied with valves that any movement can go only one way—toward the junction with the major veins of the circulatory system. As might be expected, the lymphatic "pump" is most active during exercise, and very sluggish when the body is at rest.

The continuous formation of new lymph in the terminal capillaries produces a pressure gradient that further promotes the movement of lymph from the

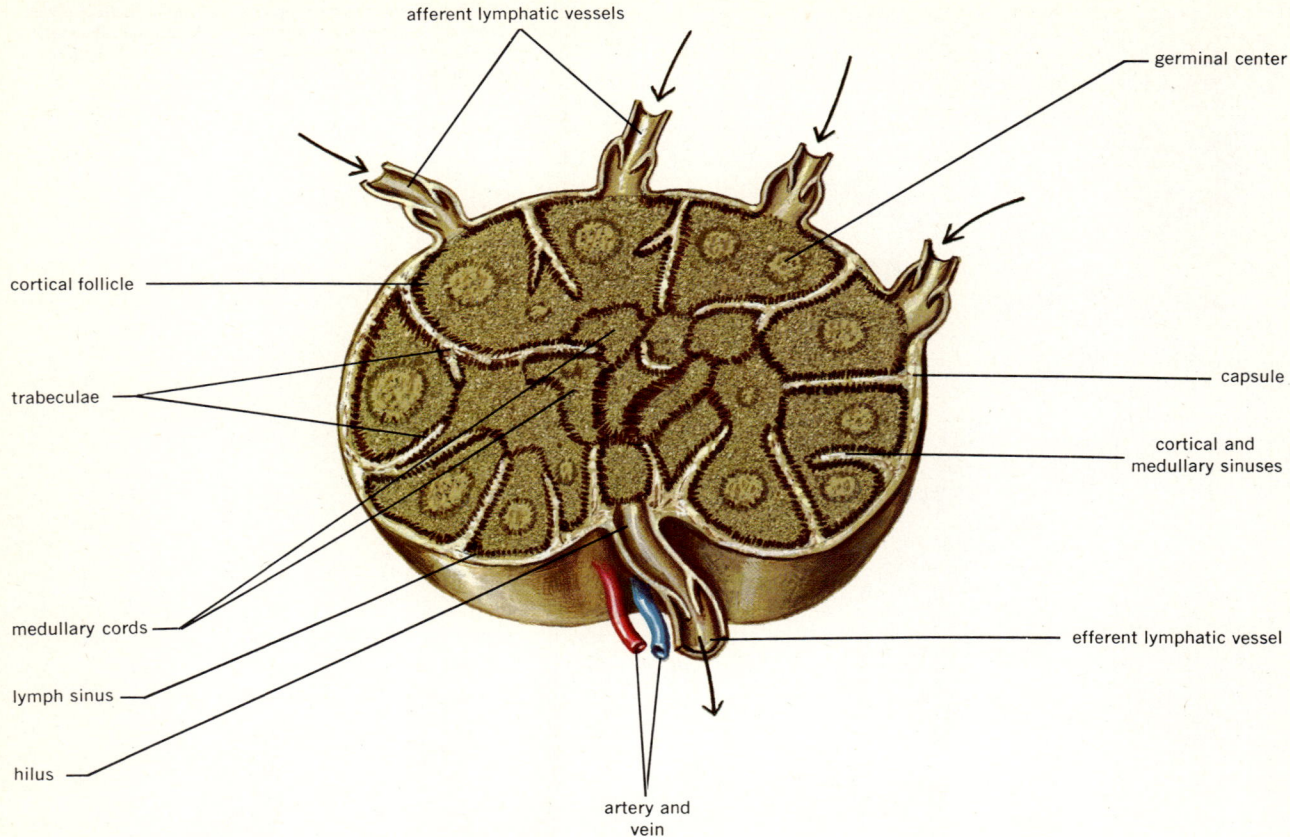

afferent lymphatic vessels

germinal center

cortical follicle

capsule

trabeculae

cortical and
medullary sinuses

medullary cords

lymph sinus

efferent lymphatic vessel

hilus

artery and
vein

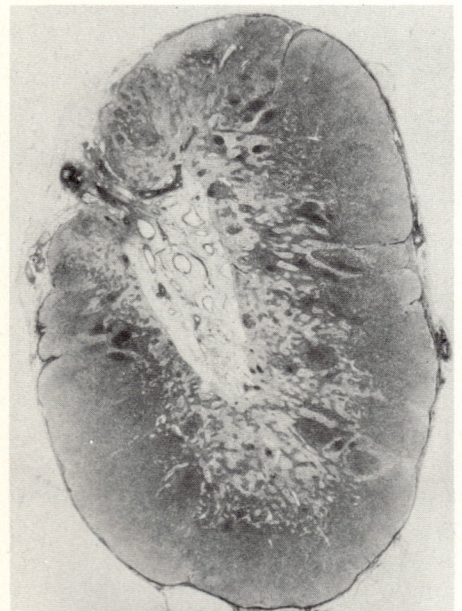

FIGURE 22-5 Structure of a lymph node. Micrograph ×9.

capillaries to larger and larger lymphatics and into the major ducts. Certain pathological changes can increase the rate of lymph flow above the normal values. For example, increased capillary permeability may result from fever, toxins, or anoxia; the increased

leakage of fluid into the tissues raises the interstitial pressure, providing a driving force for increased formation of lymph and hence a more rapid flow. Increased capillary pressure resulting from obstruction of a vein produces a similar effect.

LYMPHATIC TISSUE
In terms of weight, lymphatic tissue makes up only a tiny fraction of the body's mass, but it plays a number of very important roles. It is essentially a connective-tissue **stroma** (network), in which **lymphocytes, phagocytic leukocytes,** and antibody-producing cells called **plasma cells** are found. From this assortment, you can guess that lymphatic tissue is active in defending the body against disease germs and other "foreign invaders." It is found in the **lymph nodes, spleen, thymus, tonsils,** and small aggregates of lymphoid cells that form tiny **nodules** or merge into confluent structures called **Peyer's patches.** Lymph nodules are especially abundant under the mucous membrane of the ileum, the lower portion of the small intestine.

Lymph Nodes
A sore throat or other infection is often accompanied by painful lumps in the sides of the neck. These are commonly referred to as "swollen glands," but actu-

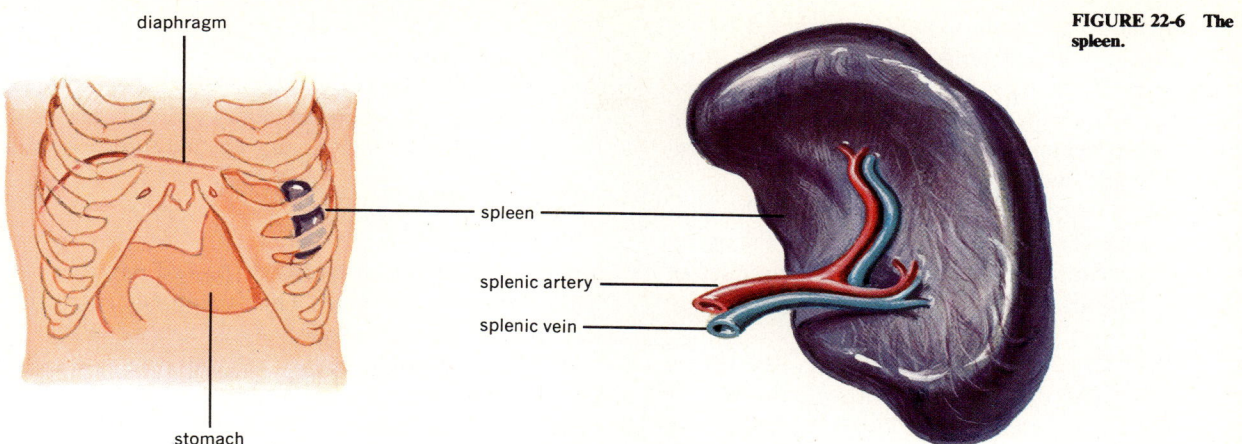

diaphragm

spleen

splenic artery

splenic vein

stomach

FIGURE 22-6 The spleen.

ally they are lymph nodes, in which a furious battle is raging between the body's defenders and the invading pathogens.

Lymph nodes are oval or bean-shaped structures, scattered through the body along the course of the lymphatic vessels. Some are only pinhead-sized, others as big as a lima bean. All have the same basic internal structure (Figure 22-5). A small depression on one side, called the **hilus,** is the site at which an artery and vein enter and leave the lymph node. One or more efferent lymphatics depart from the hilus, while afferent lymphatics carry lymph into various parts of the node. A capsule of fibrous connective tissue covers the lymph node and sends extensions called **trabeculae** into the node, dividing it into irregular spaces called **lymph sinuses,** which freely communicate with one another. The lymph sinuses contain masses of lymphoid tissue and channels through which lymph can flow.

The lymph nodes act as sentries, guarding against the spread of infection. As the lymph trickles through the sinuses, it is filtered and receives lymphocytes, globulin, and antibodies. Red blood cells and bacteria are efficiently removed by the phagocytic cells lining the sinuses, but viruses slip through the lymph node filters. Lymph nodes battling an infection are usually enlarged and tender. In very severe infections, the lymph node defenses may be overpowered, and the lymph nodes themselves become inflamed.

It is said that no lymph collected by the lymph capillaries ever reaches the bloodstream without passing through at least one lymph node. The lymph nodes occur mainly in groups or clusters, in certain areas of the body (see Figure 22-1). Some of the superficial groups of lymph nodes are the following: **cervical lymph nodes,** in the neck along the sternocleidomastoid muscles, drain lymph from the head and neck; **submaxillary lymph nodes,** in the floor of the mouth, drain the nose, lips, and teeth; **axillary lymph nodes,** in the underarm and chest, drain lymph from the arm and upper part of the thoracic wall, including the breast; **inguinal lymph nodes,** in the groin, drain lymph from the external genitalia and legs. Some groups of deep lymph nodes include the **iliac** (in the iliac fossa), **lumbar** (adjacent to the lumbar vertebrae), **thoracic** (in the root of the lungs), **mesenteric** (at the attachment of the mesentery of the small intestine), and **portal** (at the portal fissure of the liver) **lymph nodes.**

Cancer cells from malignant tumors often break away and enter lymphatics, migrating to lymph nodes and settling down there to form new growths. The resultant blockage of lymph channels can produce swelling "upstream" from the invaded lymph nodes, as fluid accumulates in the interstitial spaces. In breast cancer, the axillary lymph nodes are frequently involved, and the surgical treatment usually includes the removal both of the cancerous breast and of the axillary lymph nodes on that side.

The Spleen

It may seem strange that the spleen is classified as a lymphoid organ. If a living spleen is cut or ruptured, blood wells copiously from masses of red, spongy tissue. Yet in some respects the spleen (Figure 22-6) resembles an oversized lymph node. About 5½ inches long by 3 inches wide, it is covered by a connective-tissue capsule, from which **trabeculae** run inward, dividing the spleen into compartments. The pulp that fills these compartments has a spongy framework of reticular fibers and includes masses of typical lymphatic tissue **(white pulp)** and regions permeated by numerous venous **sinusoids (red pulp).** The roughly ovoid shape of the spleen includes a hilum at which the **splenic artery** enters and the **splenic vein** leaves. The splenic artery ramifies into many branches, which terminate into tufts of small, straight arterioles, which open freely into the red pulp. The venous sinuses are lined with macrophages, supported by reticular fibers (i.e., **reticuloendothelial** cells), and drain into the veins of the red pulp; these unite successively, ultimately forming the splenic vein, which joins with the superior mesenteric to form the portal vein, carrying blood to the liver.

The spleen is situated directly below the diaphragm, above the left kidney and behind the stomach. It is a versatile organ, performing a number of different functions.

Blood Filtration

Like the lymph nodes, the spleen acts as a filter. As blood trickles through the venous sinuses, the phagocytic cells of their lining capture and remove bacteria, debris, parasites, and other infectious agents that have penetrated into the bloodstream. Like the lymph nodes, the spleen may enlarge when it is battling an infection.

Destruction of Old Blood Cells

The spleen is often called the "graveyard" of the red blood cells. It acts as a quality control monitor for the red cells and platelets that pass through it. To reach the sinusoids, the blood cells must squeeze through narrow channels and pores in the splenic pulp. Any formed elements that are too fragile to pass this test rupture, and their remains are swept up by the macrophages. The phagocytic cells act as scavengers, breaking down the hemoglobin molecules from the destroyed red cells and salvaging the iron and globin, which are returned to the bloodstream for recycling.

Production of Blood Cells

Lymphocytes, monocytes, and plasma cells are produced in the spleen and released into the bloodstream. Before birth, the spleen also manufactures red blood cells, but in a newborn baby this function has normally been entirely taken over by the bone marrow. In the case of extraordinary demands on the hemopoietic system, for example, in hemolytic anemia, the spleen may retain or regain its ability to form red cells.

Blood Reservoir

The spongy framework of the spleen permits a tremendous variation of size as the venous sinuses distend with blood or constrict, expelling their contents into the general circulation. The stress imposed by strenuous exercise or hemorrhage causes the spleen capsule to constrict in response to sympathetic stimulation, adding about 200 ml to the circulating blood within less than a minute. The blood stored in the spleen has a high concentration of blood cells, since the very permeable capillaries in the pulp normally tend to leak fluid and retain blood cells. Thus, when the spleen enlarges, the hematocrit of the circulating blood drops slightly, and splenic contraction can increase the hematocrit of the systemic blood by as much as 3 to 4 percent.

With all these useful functions, the spleen still is not essential to the body. It can be removed (e.g., in hemolytic anemia when too many red cells are being destroyed) without producing any apparent disabilities.

The Thymus

Your thymus gland has already passed its prime and is on its way to oblivion. This lymphoid structure, a flat, pinkish-gray, two-lobed organ, located in the mediastinum and extending up into the neck, was rather a mystery to physiologists for a long time. It is large relative to the total body size during fatal life and in the first two years after birth (Figure 22-7). After that it continues to grow (though not as fast as the rest of the body) until puberty, and then begins to atrophy; in old age it may be barely recognizable. The thymus is a lymphoid organ, since it contains closely packed lymphocytes, interspersed with reticular cells. But unlike the lymph nodes, it does not have any afferent lymphatics. The mystery was: what does the thymus do?

Experiments in 1961 finally provided a key to the answer. The thymus glands of newborn mice were removed, and the mice were found to be totally defenseless against infections. Further experiments revealed that the role of the thymus is apparently played out early in life. Very shortly after birth, a baby acquires the ability to recognize foreign substances as foreign, and this ability is a vital part of the immunity mechanism; only the ability to distinguish between one's own body chemicals and foreign substances permits the body to defend itself by producing antibodies against foreign invaders. In a fetus, the reticular cells of the thymus entrap stem cells circulating in the blood. These stem cells then settle down and begin to proliferate rapidly, forming the first lymphocytes. These cells migrate into the blood and are carried through the body, seeding the lymph nodes, spleen, and other lymphatic tissue so that they too gain the ability to produce lymphocytes. Even after this seeding process, the thymus continues to exert an influence, fostering the development of immunocompetent cells, by means of a hormone.

It is theorized that during the early seeding process, the thymus manufactures lymphocytes so rapidly that many mutations occur, producing literally thousands of different types of lymphocytes, each of which is potentially capable of forming immunity against one particular type of macromolecule. Some of these lymphocytes "match" proteins, polysaccharides, or other chemicals of the body, and immediately form complexes with them. Such lymphocytes are thus inactivated or destroyed before they can seed the lymphatic organs, and henceforth the body's macromolecules

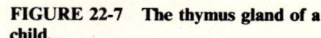

FIGURE 22-7 The thymus gland of a child.

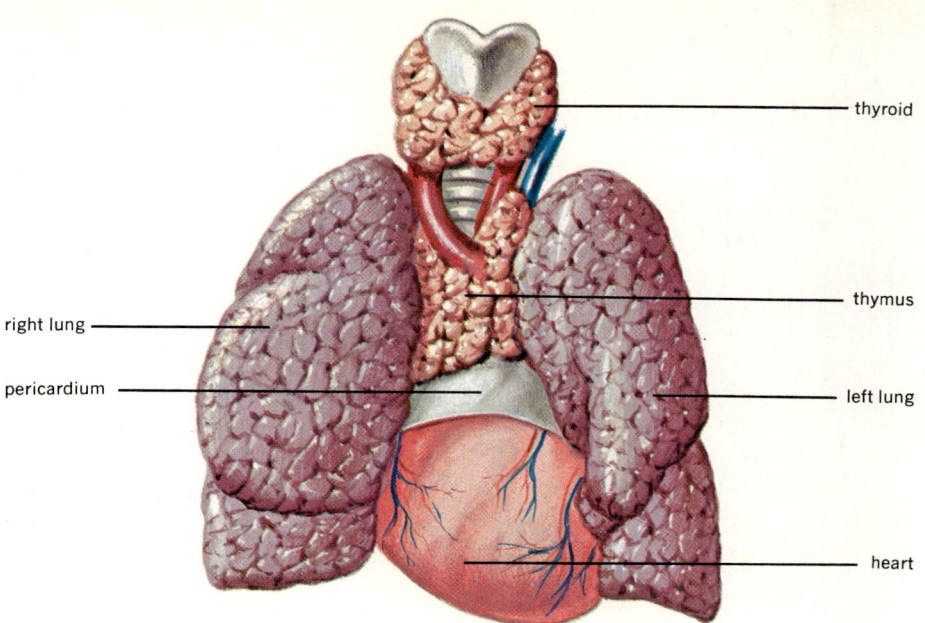

thyroid

thymus

right lung

pericardium

left lung

heart

are safe from attack by the immune system.

An intriguing correlation that has recently attracted the attention of researchers is the fact that there is a dramatic increase in autoimmune diseases (conditions in which the body attacks its own macromolecules, as a result of errors in the recognition mechanism) with increasing age—precisely at the time when the thymus is atrophying and losing its functional capacity.

Tonsils

Fads come and go, in medicine as in other areas of life. Removing the tonsils to prevent recurrent throat and ear infections was one such fad; now far fewer tonsillectomies are performed. Paradoxically, in past years tonsils frequently fell victim to the surgeon's knife precisely because they were doing their job. The respiratory tract is an open invitation to a world filled with disease germs. The tonsils guard the entranceways of the respiratory tract and serve as an early line of defense.

The tonsils located at the back of the throat are actually one of three separate pairs of lymphatic structures that provide a protective barrier for the mouth, throat, larynx, trachea, and lungs (Figure 22-8). Technically they are known as the **palatine tonsils,** two oval masses of lymphoid tissue embedded in the posterior lateral walls of the throat. The **lingual tonsils** are two masses of lymphoid tissue on the posterior portion of the tongue. The **nasopharyngeal tonsils** are located on the posterior wall of the nasopharynx, extending from the roof of the nasopharynx to the free edge of the soft palate. (The nasopharyngeal ton-

sils are often hypertrophied in children and in that condition are known as **adenoids.**)

The tonsils are copiously supplied with reticuloendothelial cells and help to filter out invading pathogens. During an infection, they may become enlarged and painful, leading to a tendency to call any sore throat in a child who still has tonsils "tonsillitis." In true infection of the tonsils, enlargement of the cervical lymph nodes is common, and the tonsils themselves may be enlarged, red, and pus-covered. A belated recognition of the value of the tonsils in guarding the respiratory tract and a suspicion that they may contribute lymphocytes and immune substances to the body's defenses has led modern physicians to treat throat infections with antibiotics and avoid removing the tonsils unless they are really prone to severe, recurrent infections, in which they swell to the extent of blocking the respiratory and digestive passages.

PRACTICAL CONSIDERATIONS

In tropical regions, the bite of a mosquito can transmit a number of serious diseases. One of the most bizarre is filariasis, produced when the larvae of parasitic filarial worms are injected under the skin by a mosquito carrying infected blood. The larvae make their way into the lymphatic system, where they mature into hairlike worms about two inches long. If there are many worms, they obstruct the lymphatics and prevent the return of fluid and escaped protein to the bloodstream. The resulting accumulation of fluid in the tissue spaces **(edema)** may become so extreme that an affected limb swells up to a gigantic size,

A

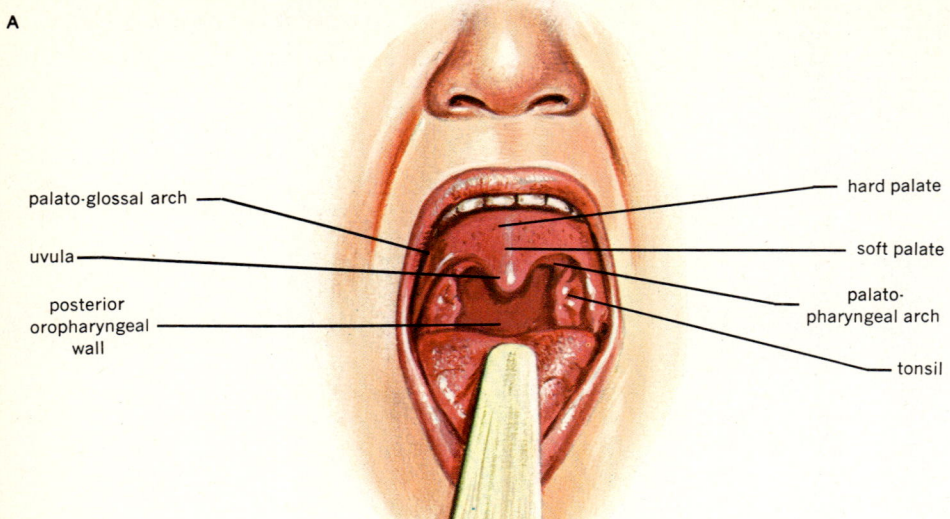

palato-glossal arch

uvula

posterior
oropharyngeal
wall

hard palate

soft palate

palato-
pharyngeal arch

tonsil

FIGURE 22-8   A view of the interior of
the oral cavity (A) reveals the prominent
palatine tonsils; the positions of the
three pairs of tonsils: nasopharyngeal,
palatine, and lingual, are shown in (B).
The photo (C) shows inflamed tonsils in
malignant lymphoma.

B

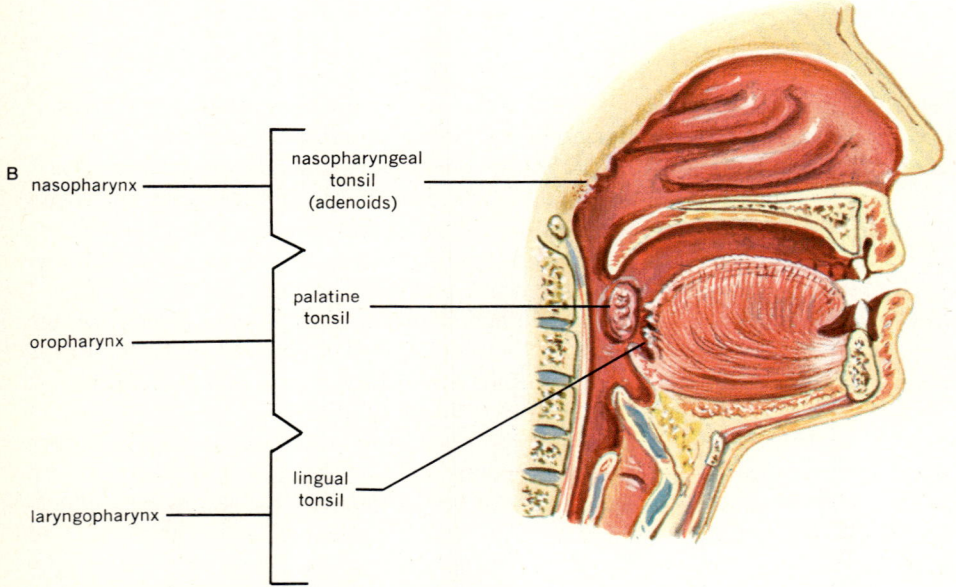

nasopharynx

oropharynx

laryngopharynx

nasopharyngeal
tonsil
(adenoids)

palatine
tonsil

lingual
tonsil

C

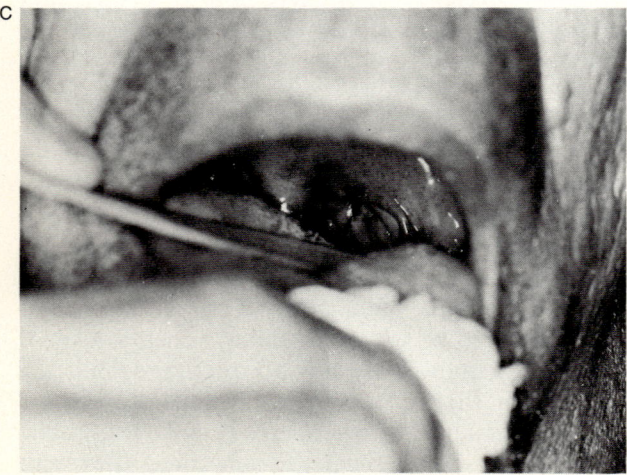

prompting the application of the term **elephantiasis** to
the condition (Figure 22-9). Edema will occur whenever the lymphatics are obstructed, whether by parasitic worms or by cancer, scar tissue, or surgical removal of the lymph nodes of the groin or armpit. The
condition superficially resembles the edema due to
congestive heart failure, but a chemical analysis of
the fluid in the swollen skin indicating abnormally
high protein concentrations is a clue to primary involvement of the lymphatic system.

An infection in almost any part of the body is generally accompanied by an enlargement and tenderness of the lymph nodes in that area. An inflammation of lymph nodes is called **lymphadenitis.** If the

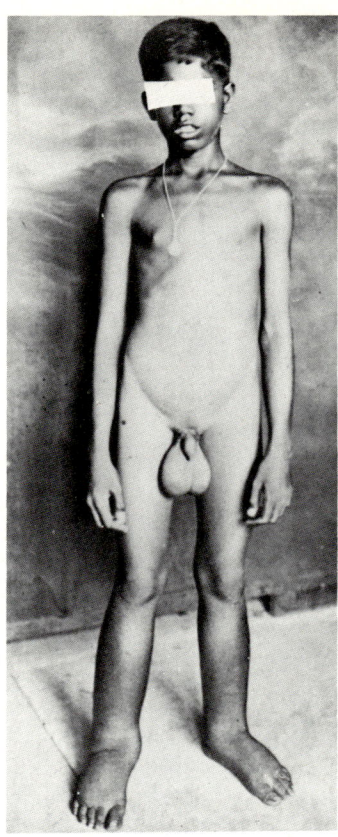

FIGURE 22-9 The edema in elephantiasis results from blockage of lymphatics by parasitic worms.

bacteria in the area drained by a node are too numerous, they may overcome the lymph node's defenses and attack the node itself, producing an **abcess** (a localized collection of pus in a cavity formed by tissue destruction).

If an infection breaks through the lymph node defenses, an inflammation of the lymphatic vessels, **lymphangitis,** may ensue. If the lymphatics are superficial vessels, narrow red streaks can be seen in the skin, extending from the area of infection to the draining group of lymph nodes. Lymphangitis is potentially dangerous, for unless the infection is stopped, the invading pathogen will eventually reach the bloodstream, producing **septicemia** (blood poisoning).

The Epstein-Barr virus is a pathogen that attacks the lymphoid organs, causing the disease **mononucleosis.** This condition, often erroneously called "kissing disease" (probably because it is most prevalent among teenagers and young adults), is a viral infection of the cervical and axillary lymph nodes and often the lingual tonsils and spleen. It is characterized by an increase in the numbers of monocytes and lymphocytes and a decrease in the polymorphonuclear white cells. The acute phase usually runs its course

within one to three weeks, but debilitating fatigue may linger on for several months.

Like other body tissues, the lymphatic tissues may undergo malignant changes. When this occurs, the lymphatic tissue is hypertrophied, and the number of lymphocytes in the blood is greatly increased. **Lymphogenous leukemia** is a malignant disease of the lymphatic tissues in which lymphocytes predominate. (In the myelogenous form of leukemia, due to bone marrow malignancy, granular polymorphonuclear leukocytes predominate.) **Lymphadenoma** or **Hodgkin's disease** is a malignant disease of the lymphatic tissues, which manifests itself first in a painless enlargement of lymph nodes, usually on one side of the neck, and then progresses to involve the spleen, liver, and other vital organs. **Lymphosarcoma** is a malignant tumor of the lymph nodes or other lymphatic tissues, with symptoms resembling those of Hodgkin's disease and leukemia.

The lymphatic system also provides a migration route for metastasizing **carcinomas** (e.g., breast cancer). Cells from the original tumor may enter lymphatic vessels and travel to lymph nodes, where they may form secondary growths. In the surgical treatment of cancer, the lymph nodes "downstream" from the tumor are routinely checked; if the malignancy has not yet spread to them, the outlook for survival is much brighter.

SUMMARY

The lymphatic system consists of lymph, lymphatics, lymph nodes, spleen, thymus, and tonsils.
The functions of the lymphatic system are:
  Return of fluid and escaped protein to the bloodstream.
  Production of lymphocytes and monocytes.
  Filtering of foreign matter.
Lymph is a watery, plasmalike fluid, with a low protein content, and contains white cells (mainly lymphocytes).
Lymph vessels include:
  Lymph capillaries
  Lymphatics
  Thoracic duct and right lymphatic duct
Lymph capillaries are thin-walled, blind-ended, porous tubes, which admit fluid and particles and convey them to larger lymph vessels.
  They form intricate networks in all tissues possessing a blood supply.
  Lymph capillaries in the villi of the intestines are called lacteals; the lymph they carry is called chyle.
Lymphatics resemble veins, with a three-layered wall and numerous valves.
The thoracic duct drains the left half of the body and the right half below the diaphragm.
The right lymphatic duct drains the right half of the body above the diaphragm.
Factors promoting the flow of lymph are:
  Skeletal muscle contraction ("milking")
  Pulsations in the heart and arteries
  Peristaltic contractions of smooth muscles in the intestines

Respiratory pump

Action of the valves, preventing backflow

Pressure gradient produced by continuous formation of lymph in the lymph capillaries

Lymphatic tissue is a connective-tissue stroma (network) in which lymphocytes, phagocytic leukocytes, and plasma cells are found. Peyer's patches are aggregates of lymph nodules.

Lymph nodes are scattered along the course of the lymphatic vessels.

They are covered by a capsule and divided by trabeculae into lymph sinuses.

They filter lymph, removing red blood cells and bacteria, and contribute lymphocytes, globulin, and antibodies.

Principal groups of lymph nodes include:

Cervical

Submaxillary

Axillary

Inguinal

Iliac

Lumbar

Thoracic

Mesenteric

Portal

The spleen contains white pulp (lymphoid tissue) and red pulp, containing venous sinusoids lined with reticuloendothelial cells.

Functions of the spleen include:

Blood filtration

Destruction of old blood cells

Production of lymphocytes, monocytes, and plasma cells (and red blood cells in the fetus)

Blood reservoir

The thymus gland is relatively largest and most active before birth and during the first two years of life; after puberty it atrophies.

It provides the first lymphocytes, which seed the lymphatic tissues, and also secretes a hormone that promotes the develop-ment of immunocompetent cells.

The tonsils protect the respiratory tract from invading microorganisms.

They include:

Palatine tonsils

Lingual tonsils

Nasopharyngeal tonsils (adenoids)

Disorders of the lymphatic system include:

Edema (accumulation of fluid in tissue spaces); elephantiasis (extreme swelling due to blockage of lymphatics)

Lymphadenitis (inflammation of lymph nodes)

Lymphangitis (inflammation of lymphatic vessels)

Mononucleosis (viral infection of lymphoid organs)

Malignancies:

Lymphogenous leukemia

Lymphadenoma (Hodgkin's disease)

Lymphosarcoma

Secondary growths of metastasized carcinomas

QUESTIONS FOR REVIEW AND THOUGHT

1 Discuss the functional relationship of the lymphatic and blood circulatory systems.

2 Compare and contrast blood, lymph, and interstitial fluid.

3 Describe the mechanisms of fluid movement: (a) into the blind-ended lymph capillaries; (b) "uphill" through lymphatics and lymphatic ducts.

4 How does the structure of lymph nodes promote their function?

5 Describe the functions of the spleen. What organs or systems do you think might take over these functions if the spleen is removed?

6 Occasionally a child is born without a functioning thymus. What do you think the probable fate of such a child would be?

7 If a child suffers from repeated tonsillitis attacks, should the tonsils be removed?

ANATOMY OF THE RESPIRATORY SYSTEM

23

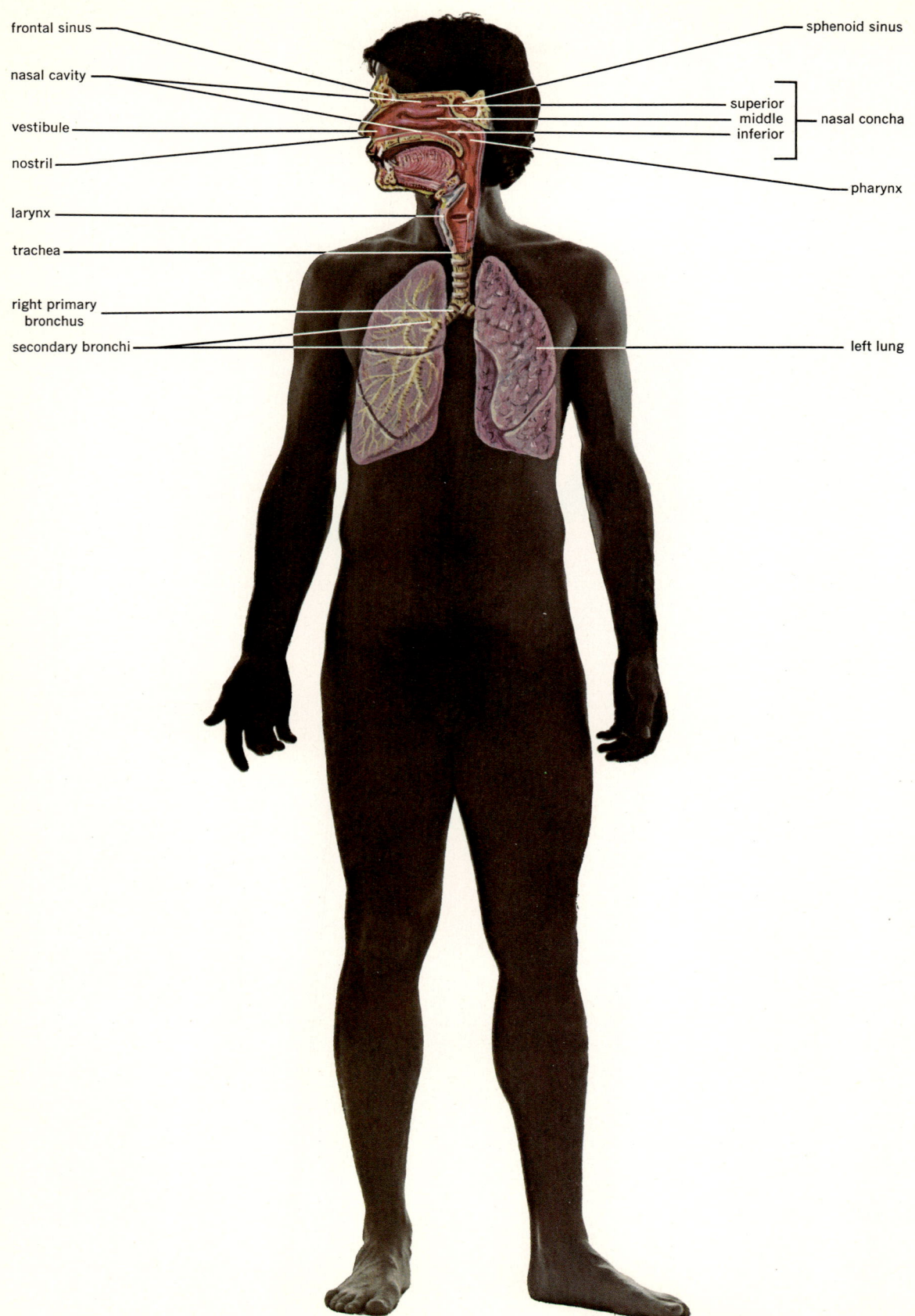

frontal sinus

nasal cavity

vestibule

nostril

larynx

trachea

right primary
bronchus

secondary bronchi

sphenoid sinus

superior
middle
inferior

nasal concha

pharynx

left lung

FIGURE 23-1 Organs of the respiratory system.

Your body needs a continual supply of certain substances from the environment. You might be able to survive for a month or so without food; without a source of water, you would die in less than a week. But if you were deprived of oxygen, you would not last more than a few minutes. Oxygen is an essential participant in many of the key chemical reactions of the body, particularly those that generate energy. Many of these reactions produce carbon dioxide as a by-product, so that in addition to a need for a continual oxygen supply, the body also needs some means of disposing of the waste carbon dioxide promptly and effectively. If you were a single-celled organism, floating in a pond or ocean, you would not need any sort of organized system for delivering oxygen and removing carbon dioxide; your needs could be satisfied readily by simple diffusion through your cell membrane, providing an exchange of dissolved gases with the surrounding medium. Even if you were a tiny multicelled creature like a flatworm, all your body cells would be close enough to the surrounding medium that their needs could be provided for by diffusion. But your body contains trillions of cells, most of which are far too deep to have any contact with the surrounding medium. Your problems are compounded by the fact that you do not live in a watery medium, but in air, so that all your outer body surfaces must be covered with a protective barrier to prevent your drying out. In order to survive, you need an organized system for periodically bringing fresh supplies of oxygen into the body and shipping out the accumulations of carbon dioxide. You also need an efficient distribution system, to deliver the oxygen to all the body cells and carry off their carbon dioxide. You have already gained a thorough acquaintance with the distribution system: the circulatory system. In this and the following chapter the anatomy and functions of the organs of the respiratory system are discussed.

THE RESPIRATORY ORGANS

Would you be tempted by an ad for an air-distributing system that automatically warms and filters the air, is self-lubricating and self-repairing, and offers such attractive "extras" as a built-in speaker and a chemical detector? You already have one—it's supplied as "standard equipment" with every normal human being.

Your respiratory system includes passageways through which air is conducted: the **nasal passages, pharynx, larynx, trachea, bronchi,** and **bronchioles,** arranged in a sequence that branches like an upsidedown tree (Figure 23-1). The conducting tubes end in tiny air sacs, the **alveoli,** in which the exchange of gases with the bloodstream takes place. The bronchi-

oles and alveoli constitute the **lungs,** the essential organ of respiration. The respiratory apparatus also includes a bellows arrangement, the **thoracic cage,** operated by muscles (especially the **diaphragm** and rib muscles) and controlled by nerves.

On the way down to the lungs and back up again, the moving air provides some secondary benefits. Inhaled air passes over specialized olfactory receptors in the nasal cavities and produces sensations of smell. The resonating chambers of the nasal cavities and the vibrating cords of the larynx contribute to the production of voiced sounds.

THE NOSE

Noses come in a wide variety of shapes and sizes, but all serve the same functions. The nose is the special organ of the sense of smell, but it also is the entranceway to the respiratory tract. It filters, warms, and moistens the incoming air, and its resonating chambers contribute to phonation. There is more to the nose than meets the eye; in addition to the external portion, which protrudes from the face, there are extensive nasal cavities, most of which actually lie above the roof of the mouth (Figure 23-2).

The external nose consists of a triangular framework of bone and cartilage, covered with skin and lined with mucous membrane. The **septal cartilage** divides the nose into two lateral halves, each of which opens to the exterior via an oval **nostrils** (the **external nares**). The **alar cartilages** partly encircle the nostrils and form a supportive framework for them. Both the bony framework of the upper portion of the nose (the **nasal bones**) and the nasal and alar cartilages that frame out the lower part of the nose provide attachments for muscles of facial expression.

The nasal cavity is separated by a septum into two wedge-shaped cavities. The septum is formed by the crest of the nasal bones and the septal cartilage anteriorly and by the perpendicular plate of the **ethmoid bone** and the **vomer** posteriorly. (The typical crooked nose of the boxer is the result of trauma to the nose, which disrupts the attachment of the cartilage to the bony parts of the septum.) Actually, the septum is normally somewhat bent to one side, which must be taken into account when inserting a tube into the nasal passageway.

The roof of the nasal cavity is formed mainly by the ethmoid bone, while the floor is formed by the palatine bones and the maxilla of the hard palate. (Occasionally, the palatine bones fail to fuse during fetal development, and the child is born with a **cleft palate,** a gap in the bony wall separating the nasal cavity from the mouth.) The lateral walls of the nasal cavities are very irregular, since three bony plates project into each passage. These are the **turbinate**

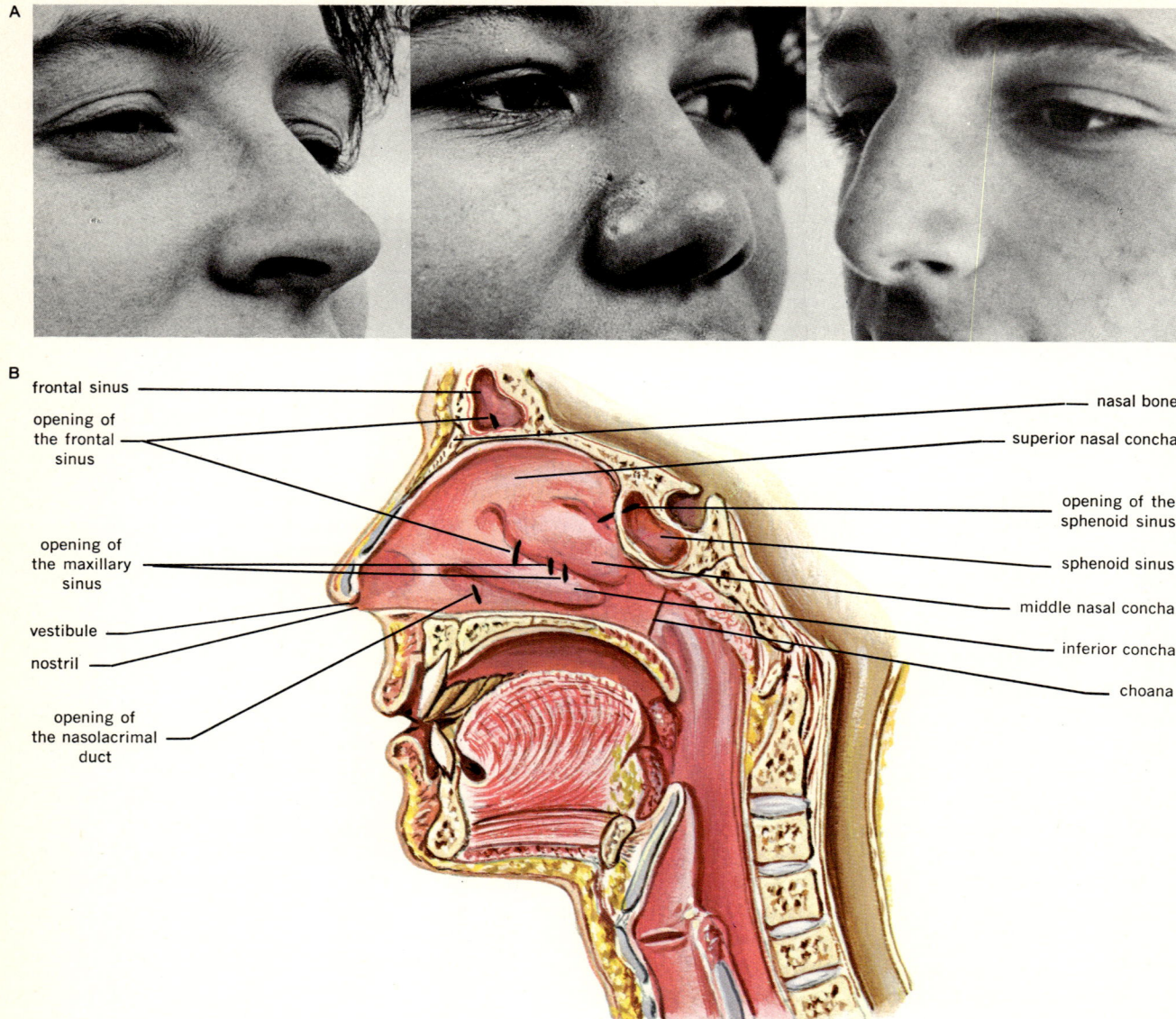

FIGURE 23-2 Noses come in many sizes and shapes (A), but all have the same basic internal structure (B) and functions.

bones or conchae: the **superior nasal concha, middle nasal concha,** and **inferior nasal concha.** These bony processes are very light and spongy, and divide the nasal cavity into three air passages: the **superior, middle,** and **inferior meatuses.** The area above the superior concha is called the **sphenoethmoid recess.**

The nostril and the area just inside, the **vestibule,** are lined with skin (a continuation of the skin of the face). A bristling picket-fence of short, stiff hairs, the **vibrissae,** projects from this skin into the lumen of the nostril. This is the first line of defense, screening insects and other large particles out of the entering air.

The interior of the nasal cavity is lined with mucous membrane, consisting of a ciliated epithelium richly supplied with goblet cells. The goblet cells se-

crete a copious supply of mucous—up to half a liter a day. Dust, powder, and other fine particles are caught in the sticky mucus and carried by currents produced by the continual waving motion of the cilia down to the pharynx, then swallowed or expectorated. (Expectoration used to be considered an acceptable form of public behavior, with spittoons conveniently provided, but with current increased standards of sanitation, one must suffer in silence and swallow or resort to an inconspicuous handkerchief.) A common cold or a pollen allergy may produce an inflammation of the nasal mucosa, or **rhinitis,** characterized by a swelling of the mucosa, which may block the nasal passages, and an increased secretion of mucus by the goblet cells.

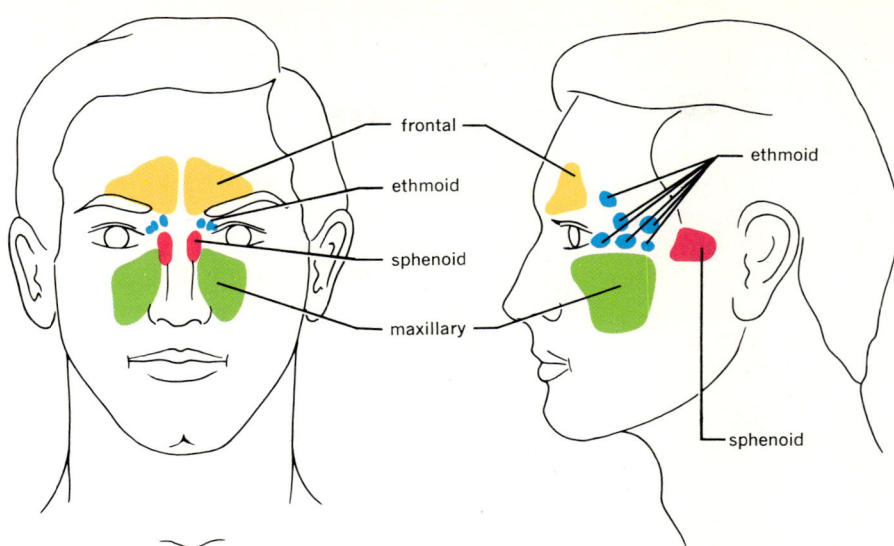

FIGURE 23-3   The paranasal sinuses.

The mucous membrane lining of the nasal cavities contains a dense **vascular plexus,** which acts as a radiator to warm the air passing through. The jutting shelves of the conchae increase the radiating surface, making the warming action more effective. They also act as baffles, breaking up the air flow and creating turbulence that aids in the precipitation of suspended particles on the nasal surfaces. The mucous membrane helps to moisten the inflowing air.

The specialized **olfactory epithelium** is found only in a small area at the top of the nasal cavity, over the uppermost portion of the nasal septum and the adjacent superior concha.

The nasal passages are not the only entrance to the respiratory tract; it is also possible to breathe through the mouth, bypassing the nose and nasopharynx. But the mouth is not supplied with the elaborate apparatus for cleaning, warming, and moistening air. When blocked nasal passages necessitate mouth breathing, the throat often becomes dry and irritated as a result.

THE PARANASAL SINUSES

When you have a head cold, your voice often sounds strange. This effect is due mainly to blockage of your paranasal sinuses—air spaces in the bones of the skull that communicate with the nasal cavity. The primary function of these sinuses is to lighten the bones of the skull. But they also contribute mucus to the nasal cavity and act as resonating chambers for the production of sound.

There are four sinuses communicating with each nasal cavity. They take their names from the bones in which they are found: **maxillary, frontal, ethmoid,** and **sphenoid sinuses** (Figure 23-3). (Although the sinuses are paired, they are often asymmetrical.)

The maxillary sinuses are the largest of the paranasal sinuses and open into the middle meatus. The sockets of the upper molar teeth project into this sinus, and a tooth abscess may cause inflammation of the sinus. The frontal sinus is located superior and medial to the eye sockets and drains into the middle meatus. The ethmoid sinuses are actually numerous irregularly shaped air cells in the ethmoid bone, which open into the superior and middle meatuses. The sphenoid sinuses drain into the superior meatus of each nasal cavity. They are located in the sphenoid bone, in close proximity to the optic nerves; infection of the sphenoid sinus can spread to the optic nerve and damage vision.

During a cold or an allergy, the sinuses may become blocked by swelling of the mucous membrane. Drainage into the nasal cavity is stopped, but the formation of mucus continues, and pressure builds up in the sinuses, causing severe headaches. Some people suffer from chronic **sinusitis,** and it may be necessary to open the wall of the sinus surgically. Such an operation is called "draining the sinuses."

THE PHARYNX

A doctor who tells you to open your mouth and say "Ahhh" is usually trying to look into your pharynx. This five-inch-long muscular tube is an important junction point for the passageways leading into the body. The nasal passages lead into the pharynx, and so does the mouth cavity; the pharynx also communicates with the middle ear cavities via the eustachian tubes. Air, food, and water all pass through the pharynx. When they leave it, they have two options: they can go down the trachea and ultimately into the lungs; or they can take the other part of the "fork" and go down the esophagus to the stomach. Usually the body's automatic mechanisms operate efficiently, and everything goes to the right place—inhaled air to the lungs and swallowed food and water to the stomach. But occasionally there is a mixup, and one swallows air or has a bit of liquid or a solid particle go "down the wrong pipe" into the trachea, a mishap that is promptly remedied by a reflex spasm of coughing and sputtering.

The pharynx extends from the base of the skull to the esophagus. It is divided into three parts: the **nasopharynx,** which lies behind the nose; the **oropharynx,** which lies behind the mouth; and the **laryngopharynx,** which lies below the hyoid bone and behind the larynx. The nasopharynx is always open. It has four openings in its walls: two leading to the nasal cavities (the **internal nares**) and two openings into the eustachian tubes. The oropharynx has just one opening, the **fauces,** leading from the mouth cavity, and bounded by the uvula, the margin of the soft palate, and the palatopharyngeal arches. The laryngopharnyx opens into the larynx and esophagus.

Masses of lymphoid tissue on the posterior wall of the nasopharynx are called the **pharyngeal tonsils.** If these tonsils become inflamed and enlarged, a condition in which they are referred to as adenoids, they obstruct the internal nares. The person develops a nasal voice quality and must breathe through the mouth. The **palatine tonsils,** commonly referred to as "the tonsils," are embedded in the wall of the oropharynx, while the **lingual tonsils** lie at the back of the tongue. The tonsils act as defenders, screening out microorganisms from the air, food, and liquids that enter the body through the nose and mouth, and attacking them with phagocytic cells of the reticuloendothelial system.

THE LARYNX

If you place your fingers over the front of your neck, in the region of the "Adam's apple," and say something, you will be able to feel distinct vibrations. These vibrations are produced by the passage of air against bands of elastic cartilage in the larynx, the portion of the respiratory tract connecting the pharynx with the trachea.

The larynx is commonly called the "voicebox," and its major function is its use in the production of sounds. But it is also important in coughing, swallowing, expectorating, breathing, and protecting the lower regions of the respiratory tract from foreign objects.

The larynx is shaped like a triangular box, with the broad part at the superior end (Figure 23-4). It consists of nine cartilages, bound together by ligaments and by extrinsic and intrinsic muscles. There are three single cartilages (the cricoid, thyroid, and epiglottis) and three paired cartilages (the arytenoid, corniculate, and cuneiform).

The **cricoid cartilage** is at the narrow lower end of the larynx, attached to the first cartilage ring of the trachea. It is shaped like a signet ring, with the band in the front and the signet at the back of the larynx.

The **thyroid cartilage** is the largest cartilage in the larynx. It is shield-shaped, formed from two broad plates that meet and fuse in the midline in front. The anterior prominence popularly called the "Adam's apple" is formed by the thyroid cartilage and is generally more pronounced in males than in females.

The **epiglottis** is a leaf-shaped cartilage, the "stem" of which is attached to the superior border of the thyroid cartilage. It acts as a hinged "trap door" at the entrance to the larynx. During swallowing the larynx is pulled up and forward, and the epiglottis closes like a lid to prevent the aspiration of liquids or solids into the trachea. The automatic mechanism occasionally fails to operate, whereupon a cough mechanism is initiated to expel the intruder.

The **arytenoid cartilages** are small pyramid-shaped cartilages above the cricoid cartilage. They provide attachments for the vocal ligaments. The apex of each arytenoid cartilage is covered by a cone-shaped elastic cartilage, the **corniculate cartilage.** The **cuneiform cartilages** are small, rod-shaped, elastic cartilages found at the base of the epiglottis, just anterior to the corniculate cartilages.

Like the other parts of the respiratory tract, the interior of the larynx is lined with mucous membrane; much of it contains cilia, which beat rhythmically to move particles upward toward the pharynx. The interior of the larynx is not a simple tube. It is divided into three parts by two pairs of horizontal folds, which project into the lumen. The upper pair is called the **vestibular,** or **false vocal folds;** the portion of the larynx above them is called the **vestibule.** The lower pair is called the **true vocal folds,** or **vocal cords.** These are the structures responsible for phonation, the formation of sounds. The slitlike opening between the folds is called the **rima glottidis** or **glottis;** this is the air passageway that the *epi*glottis guards. The shape of the opening is determined by the action of the muscles that act on the vocal folds and varies in different phases of respiration, talking, and singing.

As in many structures of the body, the larynx is supplied with both extrinsic and intrinsic muscles. The **extrinsic muscles** have their origin in structures surrounding the larynx and function to move the larynx. These are the muscles that raise the larynx during swallowing and depress it after the act of swallowing is completed.

The **intrinsic muscles** are located entirely within the

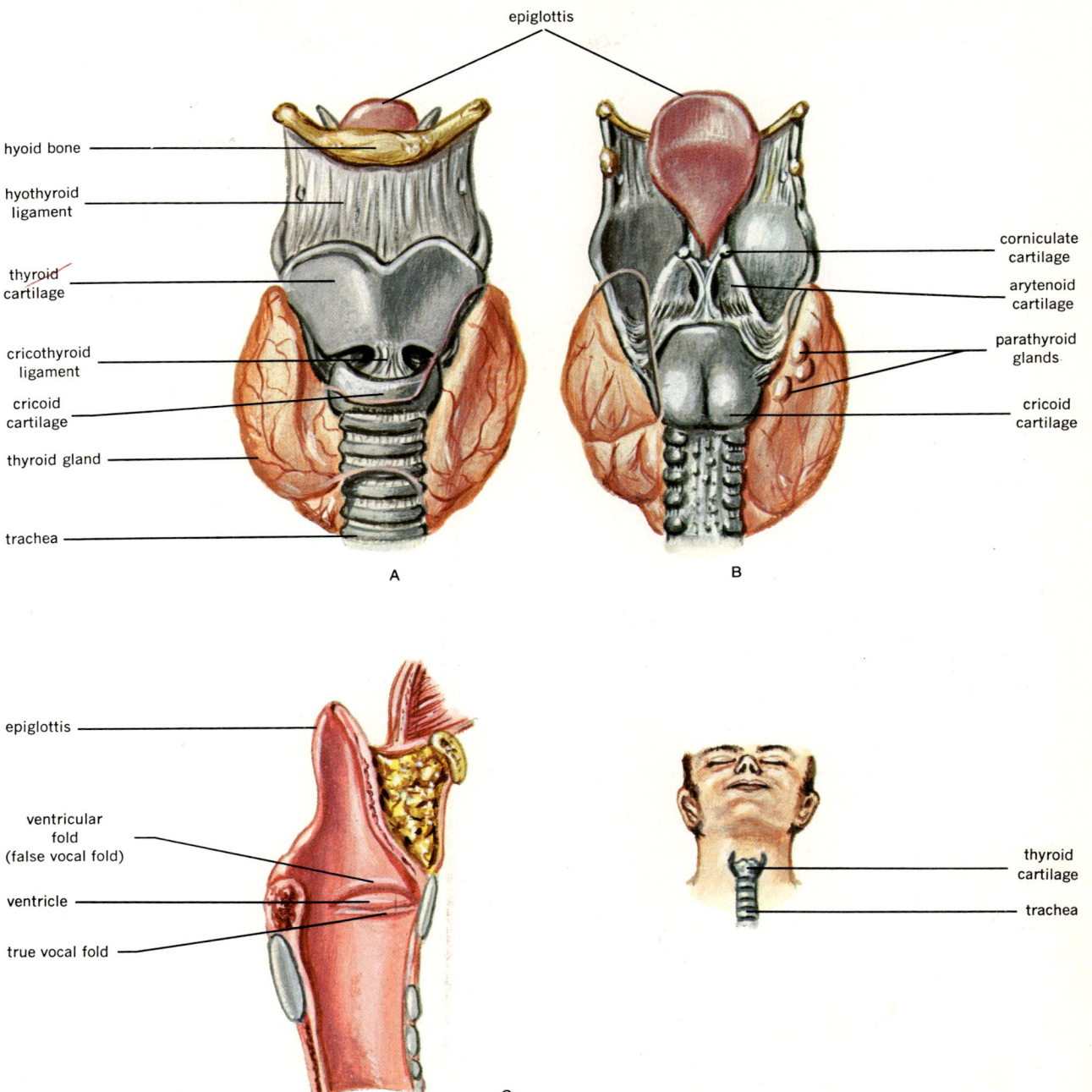

FIGURE 23-4 The larynx: anterior (A) and posterior (B) views; the vocal folds (C).

larynx. They act to modify the size of the slit between the vocal folds and the tension of the vocal cords. Thus, they ensure a free passage for air during breathing and control the exhalation of air in speech and singing.

Both the extrinsic and the intrinsic muscles of the larynx are striated muscles. They are supplied by branches of the vagus nerve. Occasionally, a respiratory ailment, an allergic reaction, or some other factor (e.g., the induction of sleep by mild electrical impulses into the brain, practiced in the Soviet Union as

a therapy for various disorders) may spark spasmodic contractions of the muscles of the larynx. Laryngeal spasm is an extremely dangerous condition, since it cuts off the flow of air into the lungs. Death due to asphyxia may occur unless the spasm is relieved promptly.

The Vocal Cords and Phonation

In the 1950s, the scientific world was excited by reports that a chimpanzee named Vicki, who had been raised like a human child by human foster parents,

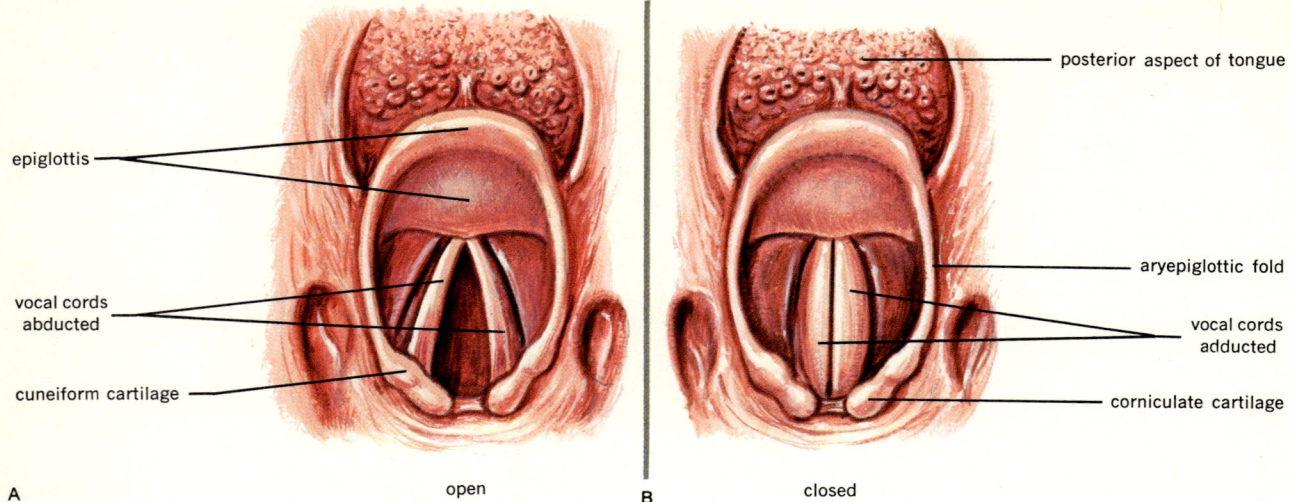

epiglottis

vocal cords
abducted

cuneiform cartilage

posterior aspect of tongue

aryepiglottic fold

vocal cords
adducted

corniculate cartilage

A   open   B   closed

FIGURE 23-5   The vocal cords (superior view). The glottis is open during quiet breathing (A) and nearly closed while singing a high note (B).

had learned to say several recognizable words, including "Mama," "Papa," and "cup," and used them in a meaningful manner. It was expected that further efforts would open up a fruitful dialogue with more of our anthropoid relatives. But it was eventually found that chimpanzees were generally unable to go beyond a vocabulary of half a dozen words or so. More recent studies, in which chimps have been taught to communicate by means of the standard sign language used by the deaf or through visual symbols generated on a display by punching appropriate keys on an electronic board, have shown that chimpanzees do have an innate capacity for language and take eagerly to opportunities to express themselves. The current feeling is that the early attempts to develop verbal speech in chimpanzees reached a dead end because chimps simply do not have sufficiently versatile vocal equipment to produce the intricate patterns of sounds that constitute human speech. In the versatility of the vocal cords, and the association areas in the brain that govern their functioning, humans are practically unique in the animal kingdom.

Fibrous and elastic ligaments are embedded in the mucous membrane at the edges of the vocal folds. They are stretched like the strings of a guitar and firmly attached at both ends to the cartilages of the larynx. Striated muscles attached to the vocal folds change the size and shape of the glottis (Figure 23-5). During quiet breathing, the muscles are relaxed, and the space between the vocal folds (the glottis) is in the shape of an elongated triangle. In heavy or rapid breathing, the opening widens. During swallowing, the muscles contract, pull the vocal cords tight, and adduct the vocal folds so that the glottis is tightly closed, blocking the entry of any particles that may

have slipped into the larynx. During the singing of a high note, the vocal folds are nearly closed. Fine adjustments of the tension of the cords are made by the **vocalis muscles,** enclosed within the vocal cords.

When air is directed against the vocal folds, they vibrate, generating sound waves in the column of air in the pharynx, nose, and mouth. The paranasal sinuses act as additional resonating chambers. The volume and force of the expelled air determine the loudness of the voice. The pitch of the sound depends on the shape and tension of the vocal cords. Long, slack cords produce low tones, while short, taut cords produce high tones. Each person can voluntarily alter the pitch of his or her voice by changing the tension on the vocal cords, but only within preset limits, determined by the size and shape of the larynx. In women the vocal cords are generally shorter, tauter, and closer together than those of men, and thus women usually have higher-pitched voices. But there is considerable individual variation within the sexes (hereditarily determined), and a particular woman might have a lower voice than a particular man. Children have a smaller larynx than adults, and hence a higher-pitched voice. There is an explosive growth of the larynx at puberty, greater in males than in females, which establishes the adult sex differences. The sometimes ludicrous breaking voice of the adolescent boy is due to his inability to control his newly acquired longer vocal folds. Chronic irritation of the vocal folds, as from smoking, may permanently deepen or hoarsen the voice.

The voice produced by the vibrations of the vocal cords would be a meaningless "Aaaahhhh," if it were not for the modifications introduced by the tongue, jaws, and lips. The activities of all the muscles

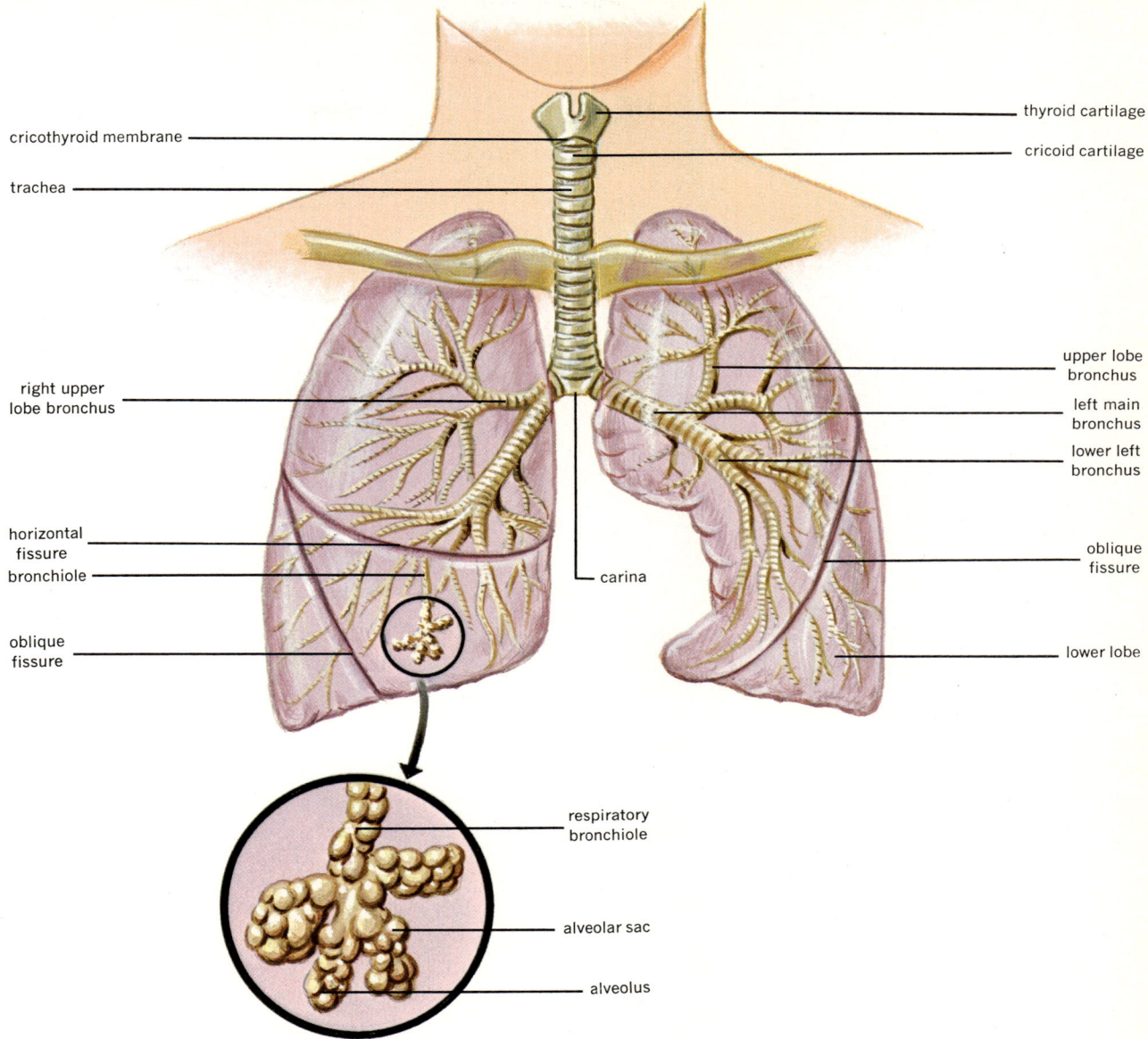

FIGURE 23-6 The bronchopulmonary tree. The inset shows enlarged detail of an alveolar cluster.

involved in the production and modification of sounds are integrated and coordinated by the speech center in the cerebral cortex—in this lies the true distinction of human speech from the voiced sounds of lower animals.

THE TRACHEA

When a person is strangled, the fatal damage is usually inflicted on the trachea. This portion of the respiratory tract, the "windpipe," is a cylindrical tube, about 11 cm long and 2 to 2.5 cm in diameter. It lies in front of the esophagus and extends from the larynx at the level of the sixth cervical vertebra down to the upper border of the fifth thoracic vertebra, where it divides into the two bronchi, one leading into each

lung (Figure 23-6). The walls of the trachea are strengthened by a series of 16 to 20 C-shaped rings of hyaline cartilage, separated by fibrous and muscular tissue. The gaps in the Cs are bridged by a connective-tissue membrane and lie at the back of the trachea, facing toward the esophagus. (You can readily feel the series of cartilage rings on your own neck.) This design provides a functional advantage: it permits the esophagus to encroach upon the trachea when it expands during the swallowing of a bolus of food. The stiffening provided by the cartilage rings holds the trachea open as a continuous passageway for air.

The trachea is lined with a mucosa of ciliated epithelium with mucus-secreting goblet cells. Inhaled

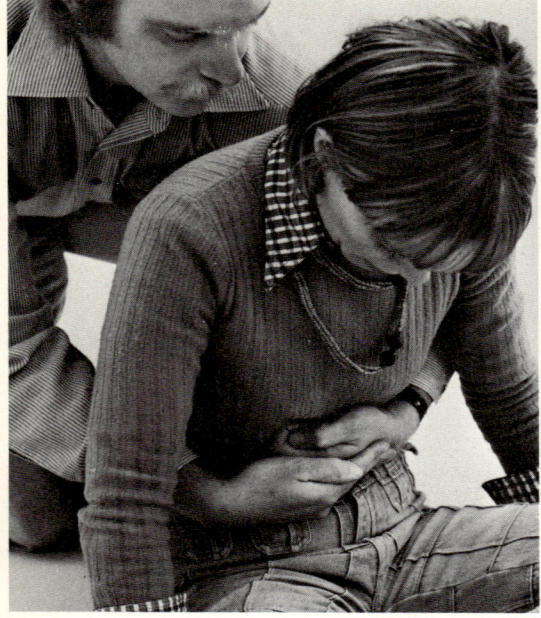
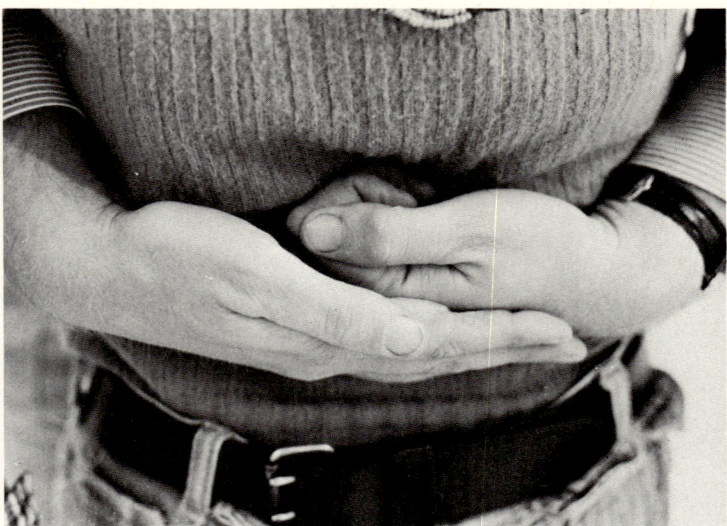

FIGURE 23-7 The Heimlich maneuver is a simple technique that can save lives. Pulling back and up against the diaphragm creates pressure in the respiratory tract and pops an obstruction out of the trachea.

particles are trapped in the mucus, and the beating of the cilia continually sweeps them upward toward the pharynx, where they can be swallowed or expectorated. Cigarette smoke paralyzes the cilia in the lining of the trachea and bronchi and stops their clearing action, so that they cannot "whisk up" the dust-laden mucus to the pharynx. If the habitual smoker stops smoking, this clearing function is reactivated within several months.

The trachea normally serves as an open passageway for air traveling to and from the lungs. But swelling of the mucosal lining, accumulated secretions, or aspiration of material into the trachea may occlude it, cutting off the air flow.

An estimated 4000 people die each year from the accidental aspiration of solid food particles. The accident typically occurs when a person is swallowing large chunks of food without chewing them properly; heavy drinking of alcoholic beverages during the meal may also contribute. The person suddenly gasps, turns blue, and cannot speak or breathe. The combination of these circumstances has prompted the popular name of "cafe coronary" for the syndrome, which is often mistaken for a heart attack. If aid is not rendered within about four minutes, the victim will die—a tragically needless death, for a very simple and effective first-aid technique called the **Heimlich maneuver** has recently been devised to save choking victims (Figure 23-7). The rescuer stands behind the victim with arms around his or her waist, grasps one fist with the other hand, and presses in on the victim's abdomen with a sharp upward thrust. The sudden pressure forces the diaphragm upward, compresses

the lungs, and expels the obstruction like a cork popping out of a bottle.

An obstruction above the level of the trachea may also cut off the flow of air through the trachea. The childhood disorder croup is characterized by a frightening difficulty in breathing and an inspiratory stridor (a harsh, high-pitched sound) due to laryngospasm. Diphtheria, a bacterial disease in which a tough false membrane forms over the upper respiratory passages, used to be one of the most dreaded childhood diseases; public health officials fear that if the present trend toward laxness in providing DPT and other recommended immunizations continues, the spectre of this disease may come to haunt parents again. When the airway is cut off, either at the level of the trachea or above, an emergency **tracheotomy** may be necessary to save the victim's life; an incision is made into the trachea to allow air to flow directly into the windpipe. (If a tube is placed in the opening to keep it open for a period of time, the operation is called a **tracheostomy.**)

THE BRONCHIAL TREE

The trachea, with its two branches the **bronchi,** and their numerous branches, the **bronchial tubes** and **bronchioles,** looks very much like an upside-down tree (see Figure 23-6). Like most real trees, the "bronchial tree" is not entirely symmetrical. The right bronchus is shorter and wider and has a more vertical course. As a result, if any foreign particle manages to penetrate as far as the bifurcation of the trachea, it is much more likely to enter the right bronchus.

The right primary bronchus divides into three sec-

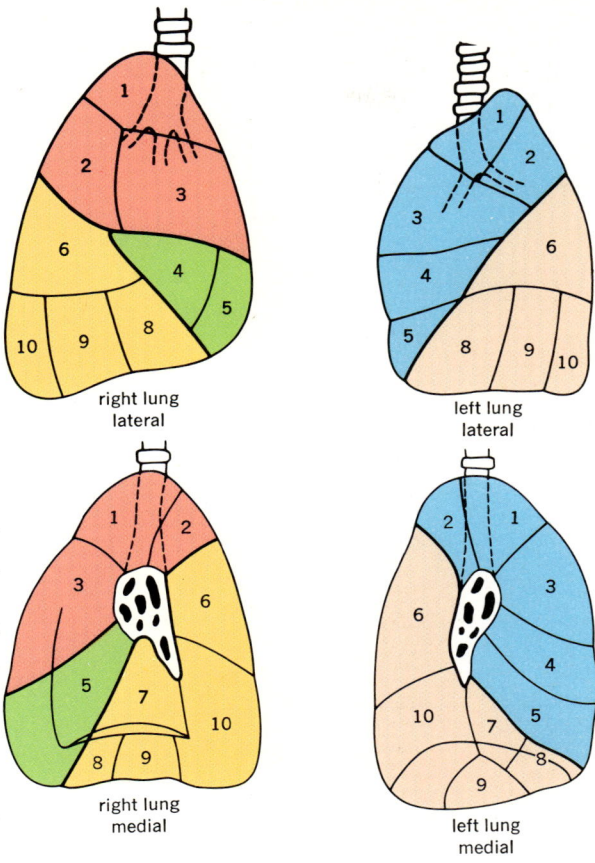

bronchopulmonary segments

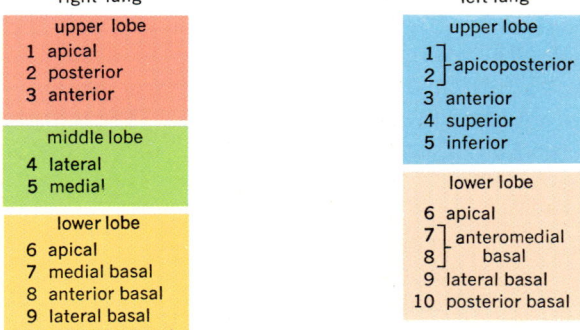

right lung		left lung
upper lobe		**upper lobe**
1 apical		1,2 apicoposterior
2 posterior		3 anterior
3 anterior		4 superior
		5 inferior
middle lobe		
4 lateral		**lower lobe**
5 medial		6 apical
		7,8 anteromedial basal
lower lobe		9 lateral basal
6 apical		10 posterior basal
7 medial basal		
8 anterior basal		
9 lateral basal		
10 posterior basal		

FIGURE 23-8   The bronchopulmonary segments.

ondary bronchi, one for each of the three lobes of the right lung. The left primary bronchus divides into only two secondary bronchi, corresponding to the two lobes of the left lung. The secondary bronchi in turn divide into tertiary bronchi, which pass to the **bronchopulmonary segments** (Figure 23-8) in each lung.

Contraction of the smooth muscle in the walls of the bronchioles is produced by parasympathetic fibers, which travel in the vagus nerve; sympathetic fibers cause relaxation of the smooth muscle and thus dilate the lumen of the bronchioles.

The structure of the bronchi is very similar to that of the trachea, with incomplete rings of cartilage reinforcing their walls. But as the bronchial tubes divide and subdivide, the cartilage rings are replaced by cartilaginous plates; with further subdivision the walls become thinner, the cartilaginous plates and fibrous tissue disappear, and the smallest bronchioles are composed of only a thin layer of muscular and elastic tissue, lined with ciliated epithelium. Each tiny bronchiole terminates in a cluster of minute air sacs, the **alveoli,** which look like a miniature bunch of grapes. Each alveolus has a lining of very thin squamous epithelium on a thin basement membrane very similar to the capillary wall. An extensive network of capillaries surrounds each alveolus; gases diffuse back and forth readily between the alveoli and capillary networks, and the actual exchange of oxygen and carbon dioxide occurs here.

THE THORACIC CAVITY

The thoracic cavity, which contains some of the most vital organs and structures in the body, changes in size with every breath. The lungs, heart, and major blood vessels are protected by the bony rib cage, but it is constructed so as to expand and contract readily as the lungs periodically inflate and deflate.

The thoracic cavity is bounded below by the diaphragm, a large sheet of muscle that assumes a dome shape at rest. The thoracic cavity is closed at the top by the scalene muscles and the fascia of the neck, and it is enclosed on the sides, front, and back by the ribs, the intercostal muscles, the vertebrae, the sternum, and the ligaments.

The major fraction of the thoracic cavity is taken up by the lungs, one on the left and one on the right (Figure 23-9). In the center between the two lungs is sandwiched a smaller space, the **mediastinum,** which contains the heart and pericardium; major blood vessels such as the thoracic aorta and its branches, the pulmonary arteries and pulmonary veins, and the venae cavae and azygos veins; the thymus, lymph nodes and lymph vessels; the trachea and esophagus; and such major nerves as the vagus nerve, cardiac and phrenic nerves.

THE PLEURA

If you puncture a balloon, it collapses. If the chest wall is punctured, piercing a lung, the lung collapses, but for a different reason.

Each lung is enclosed in a double-walled serous membrane called the **pleura** (Figure 23-10). The outer layer, the **parietal pleura,** adheres closely to the inner wall of the chest and the superior surface of the diaphragm. The inner layer, the **visceral pleura,** forms the outer covering of the lung. There is a potential

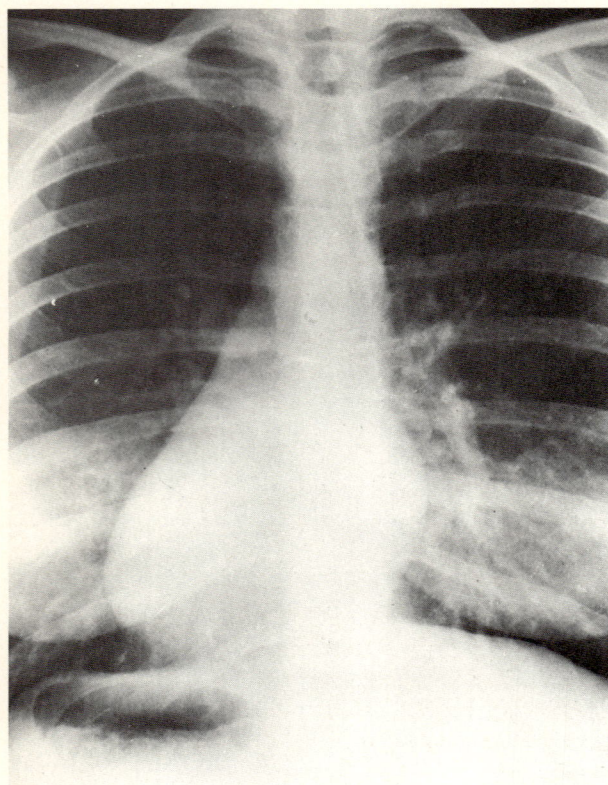

FIGURE 23-9   As seen in this chest X ray, the lungs take up most of the thoracic cavity. Note the outline of the heart, somewhat off-center between them.

space between the two layers of the pleura, but normally it contains only a small amount of serous fluid, and the layers lie close together. If the pleura is punctured, however, so that air from outside the body can enter the potential space between the two layers of the pleura, the space will balloon up and the lung will collapse, a condition called **pneumothorax.** If the puncture is closed, the air will be gradually absorbed by the body, and the lung will reinflate. Artifically induced pneumothorax, induced by injecting air into the chest cavity or surgically removing part of the chest wall, is used to treat certain types of tuberculosis.

Like the two-layered pericardium, which covers the heart, the main function of the pleura is to reduce friction on the surface of the continually moving lungs. (Try rubbing the palms of your hands together, back and forth, for a moment or two and notice how much heat is generated by the friction between moving parts that are not sufficiently lubricated.) **Pleurisy,** an inflammation of the pleural membranes, produces an increase in the fluid in the pleural cavity and may result in the layers sticking to each other. In this condition, normal respiratory movements become painful, and surgery may be required to separate the layers.

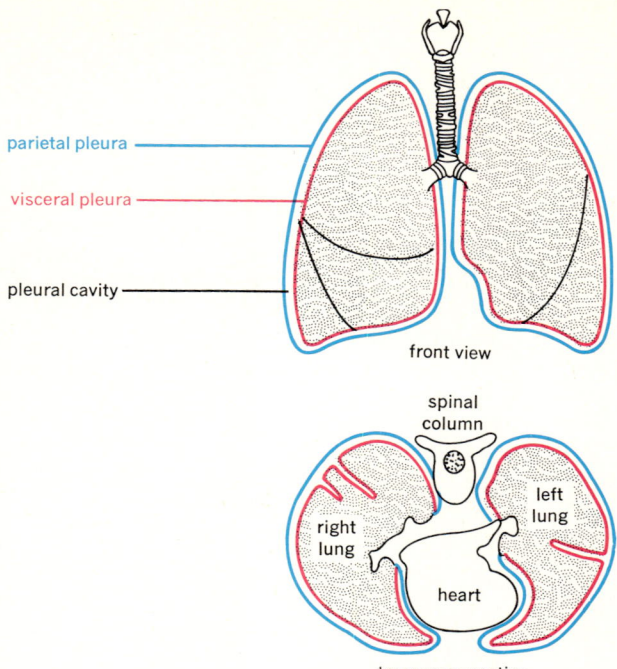

FIGURE 23-10   The pleura.

THE LUNGS

It has been estimated that a pair of human lungs contains about 300 million alveoli, which together have a total surface area of about 1000 square feet—enough to carpet a tennis court. (Such a carpeting, if feasible in some surrealistic fashion, would be exceedingly thin, for the walls of an alveolus are only 0.00004 inch thick.) The enormous surface area of the alveoli provides a tremendous functional advantage, greatly increasing the surface for gas exchange. (The total area of the outer surface of your body is only about 21 square feet.)

The two lungs are cone-shaped, with the base resting on the diaphragm and the apex extending up into the root of the neck (Figure 23-11). Each bronchus enters its respective lung at a vertical slit on its mediastinal surface, called the **hilus.** At this spot, the pulmonary artery, pulmonary vein, bronchial arteries and veins, plexuses of nerves, lymphatics, lymph nodes, and aerolar tissue, which with the bronchi form the **root** of the lung, also enter. The lungs are freely movable except at their roots.

The tilted position of the heart provides more room in the right side of the chest cavity, and this extra space is filled by the lungs; the right lung is larger and broader than the left. (But it is shorter, for the diaphragm rises higher on the right side to accommodate the liver.) The right lung is divided by deep fissures into three lobes; the smaller left lung is divided into two lobes.

The lungs are light, porous, and spongy—if they

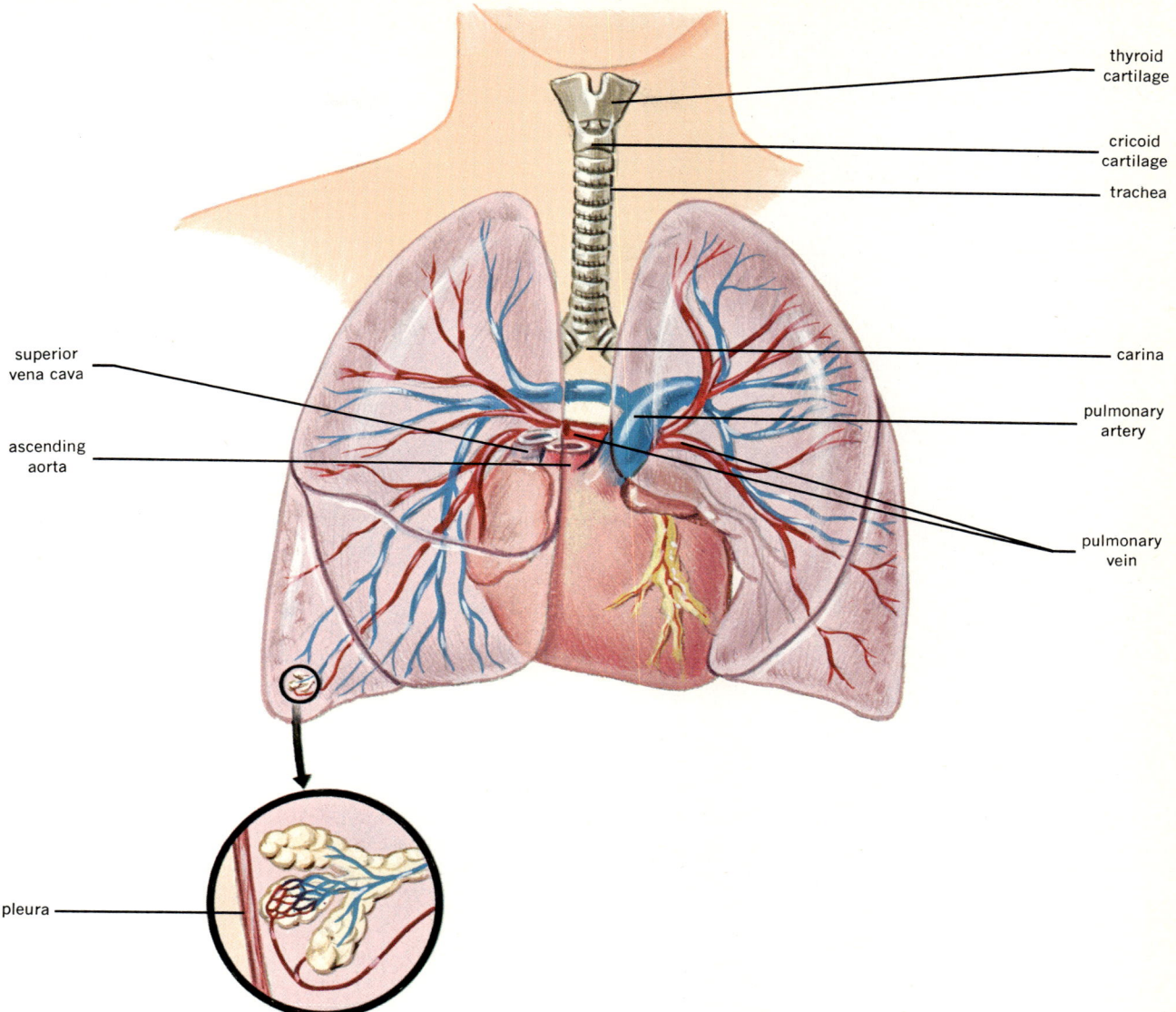

thyroid
cartilage

cricoid
cartilage

trachea

superior
vena cava

carina

ascending
aorta

pulmonary
artery

pulmonary
vein

pleura

FIGURE 23-11   The lungs and their relationship to the heart and pulmonary blood vessels.

were placed in water, they would float. Their internal structure is a mass of branching tubes and air sacs. The lobes of the lungs are divided functionally into **bronchopulmonary segments** or **lobules,** each of which encloses a tertiary bronchus, its branches, and their terminal air sacs. There are ten bronchopulmonary segments in the right lung, and eight in the left; they vary in size and are separated by incomplete fibrous septa. The tertiary bronchi branch into numerous bronchioles, which divide in turn, finally ending in a cluster of alveoli (see Figures 23-11 and 23-12). Each of the bronchopulmonary segments has its own blood supply, provided by a branch of the pulmonary artery; but pulmonary veins lie between segments and drain adjacent segments. Often pathological conditions of the lungs affect only one or two lobules; as a result, bronchopulmonary resection—the surgical re-

moval of lung segments—is usually performed instead of removing an entire diseased lung.

The **alveolus** is a roughly globular structure, about 100 microns in diameter. It has an extremely thin wall, lined with thin squamous epithelium, and is surrounded by a network of equally thin-walled capillaries. (The total surface area of the capillary networks of the lungs is estimated at about 90 square meters, about the same as the total surface area of the alveoli.) It has been found that the air spaces in the lungs are coated with a **surfactant,** a complex lipoprotein substance that lowers surface tension. The surfactant equalizes the tension in the alveoli as they expand and contract, decreases the overall pressure, and thus reduces the muscular effort required for respiration. A small percentage of babies secrete insufficient surfactant at the time of birth. They suffer great diffi-

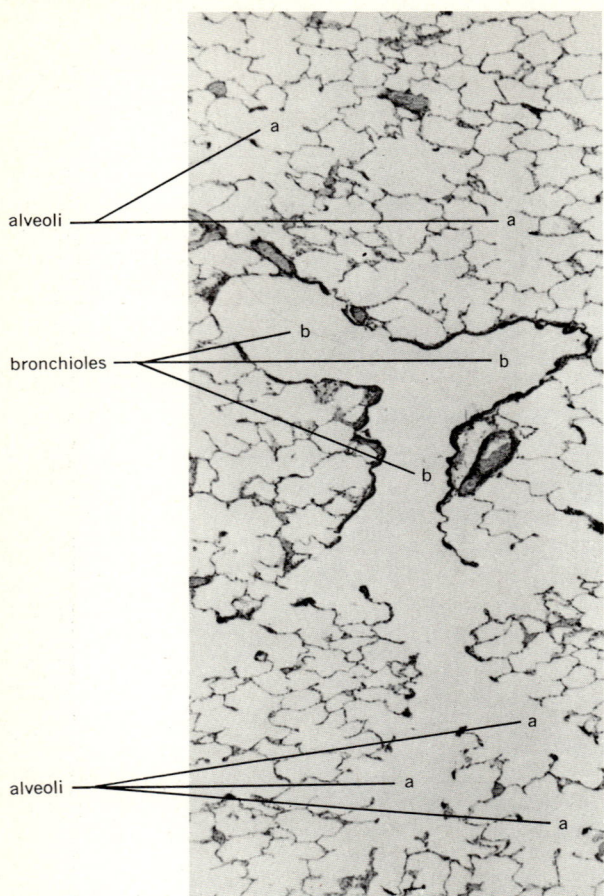

alveoli

bronchioles

alveoli

FIGURE 23-12 **Micrograph of a section of lung tissue showing alveoli and bronchioles,** ×40.

culty in breathing, and their alveoli may fill with a proteinaceous fluid, preventing gas exchange in the lungs. This condition, called **hyaline membrane disease** or **respiratory distress syndrome,** is a major cause of death in infancy. It occurs most often in premature babies. (The surfactant is not produced until the twenty-eighth week of gestation, and babies born before this time generally do not survive.)

SUMMARY

The respiratory system serves to bring oxygen into the body and eliminate carbon dioxide formed in oxidation reactions.

The respiratory system consists of:
Nasal passages
Pharynx
Larynx
Trachea
Bronchi ⎫
Bronchioles ⎬ Lungs
Alveoli ⎭
Thoracic cage
Diaphragm

The nose has a framework of bone and cartilage and is divided into two lateral halves by the septal cartilage.

The superior, middle, and inferior nasal conchae project into the nasal cavity from the lateral walls, breaking up the air flow and providing additional radiating and moistening area.

The interior of the nasal cavity is lined with ciliated epithelium containing mucus-secreting goblet cells.

Air passing through the nasal cavity is warmed, moistened, and cleaned.

Specialized olfactory epithelium is found at the top of the nasal cavity.

The paranasal sinuses are hollow chambers in cranial bones:
Maxillary
Frontal
Ethmoid
Sphenoid
They are lined with mucous membrane and open into the nasal cavities.

The pharynx leads down from the nasal passages to the trachea and esophagus.

It also communicates with the mouth cavity and auditory tubes.
The divisions of the pharnyx are:
Nasopharynx
Oropharynx
Laryngopharynx

Pharyngeal tonsils are found in the nasopharynx and palatine tonsils in the oropharynx.

The larynx or "voicebox" lies between the pharynx and trachea.
It consists of nine cartilages:
Single: cricoid, thyroid, epiglottis
Paired: arytenoid, corniculate, cuneiform

The thyroid cartilage forms the Adam's apple.

The epiglottis closes during swallowing to bar the entry of solids or liquids into the trachea.

A pair of vestibular or false vocal folds and a pair of true vocal folds or vocal cords project into the larynx.

The slitlike opening between the vocal folds is the glottis.

The vocal folds can be adducted to close off the larynx.

The vocal cords vibrate, generating sound waves in the column of air.

The shape and tension of the vocal cords, controlled by muscle action, determine the pitch of voiced sounds.

Voiced sounds are modified by the resonating chambers of the pharynx, nose, mouth, and paranasal sinuses and by movements of the tongue, jaws, and lips.

The activities of the muscles involved are coordinated by the speech center in the cerebral cortex.

The trachea or "windpipe" extends downward from the larynx and branches into two bronchi.

Its tubular walls are reinforced by C-shaped rings of cartilage.

The ciliated epithelium lining the trachea and bronchi provides a clearing action, removing inhaled particles.

The bronchi branch into secondary and tertiary bronchi, which in turn branch into bronchioles, which branch in turn and terminate in clusters of alveoli.

Each tertiary bronchus, with its branches and air sacs, forms a bronchopulmonary segment.

The thoracic cavity is bounded by the diaphragm, scalene muscles, ribs, intercostal muscles, vertebrae, and sternum.

It contains the two lungs and the organs of the mediastinum.

Each lung is enclosed in a double-layered serous membrane, the pleura: parietal pleura and visceral pleura.

The pleural membranes reduce friction on the surface of the moving lungs.

Collapse of a lung due to filling of the pleural space with air is called pneumothorax.

The lungs are cone-shaped organs containing the bronchi, bronchioles, and alveoli.

The bronchus, blood and lymphatic vessels, and nerves enter the lung at the hilus and form the root of the lung.

The right lung is larger than the left lung. It is divided into three lobes, while the left lung is divided into two lobes.

Each lobe is divided into bronchopulmonary segments of lobules, incompletely separated by fibrous septa.

The alveolus is thin-walled, surrounded by a capillary network, and coated with a surfactant that reduces the muscular effort required for respiration.

A lack of sufficient surfactant at birth can cause respiratory distress syndrome (hyaline membrane disease).

QUESTIONS FOR REVIEW AND THOUGHT

1 Describe the mechanisms for warming, moistening, and cleaning air in the upper respiratory tract.

2 What are the functions of the sinuses, and how can they become blocked during a cold or allergy?

3 Describe the divisions of the pharynx and their communications with other structures and cavities. What mechanisms usually ensure the correct routing of air and food?

4 Describe the functioning of the vocal cords during speech and singing. What factors determine the pitch and loudness of sounds produced?

5 What special structural features of the trachea contribute to its efficient functioning?

6 Describe the structural asymmetry of the lungs.

7 Distinguish between pneumothorax and pleurisy.

8 What is respiratory distress syndrome, and why is it most common among premature babies?

PHYSIOLOGY OF RESPIRATION

24

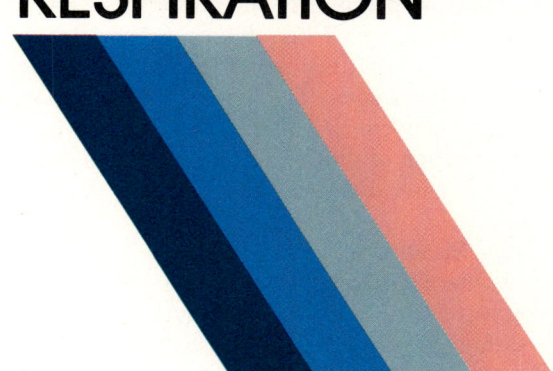

ventilation = inspiration + expiration

If the brain cells are deprived of oxygen for as little as four minutes, they begin to die. The vital oxygen is transported to the brain and other parts of the body by the circulatory system, which also removes the carbon dioxide produced in oxidation reactions. But these functions of the circulatory system would not be possible if there were no means of bringing oxygen into the body and eliminating carbon dioxide from it. These tasks are accomplished in the processes of respiration.

The aspect of respiration that the average person thinks of first is the physical act of **breathing,** in which air is drawn into the lungs and expelled from them. Normally, this is an unconscious act that goes on continually and rhythmically throughout your daily activities and even when you are asleep. In a lifetime of breathing, you will take in about 13 million cubic feet of air! The technical term for breathing is **ventilation,** and it includes two phases: **inspiration,** or breathing in, and **expiration,** or breathing out.

Another phase of respiration of interest to physiologists is **external respiration,** the passage of oxygen from the alveoli of the lungs into the blood and the passage of carbon dioxide and water vapor from the blood to the alveoli. The circulatory system distributes dissolved gases through the body, providing for still another phase of respiration, **internal respiration,** in which the body cells exchange carbon dioxide for fresh oxygen carried by the blood.

The final aspect of respiration is **cellular respiration,** which is concerned with the release of energy from food materials within the cells, by chemical reactions of oxidation. This aspect is discussed in Chapter 27. In this chapter we shall focus on the dynamics of how oxygen is brought into the body and exchanged for carbon dioxide, in the lungs and in the body tissues.

Although the main functions of respiration are to supply the body cells with oxygen and eliminate their excess carbon dioxide, respiration also helps to maintain the normal pH of the body fluids and normal body temperature and is responsible for the elimination of about 350 ml of water each day.

functions
① pH   ④ body temp.
② CO₂
③ O₂

water tidal volume ≈ 500 ml

VENTILATION (Breathing)

While you are relaxing quietly, you breathe in and out about 16 times a minute, drawing some 500 ml of air into your lungs with each breath. With strenuous physical exercise, your body's demand for oxygen will increase perhaps 15 or 20-fold, and without conscious thought or control you will quickly begin to pant, with only a second or so for each breath.

Ventilation provides a continual replenishment of the air in the lungs, drawing in fresh air and expelling waste gases. The lungs might be thought of as elastic

sacs, the interiors of which are permanently open to the atmosphere via the bronchi, trachea, larynx, pharynx, and nasal passages. Air flows into or out of the lungs for the same reason that blood flows through the vessels of the circulatory system: it moves down a pressure gradient. When the pressure inside the lungs is greater than the pressure of the atmosphere, air is expelled from the lungs. When the atmospheric pressure is greater than that inside the lungs, air flows in through the air passages. The pressure differentials are created by movements of the chest cavity, produced by the action of the diaphragm and other muscles.

Respiratory Movements

In a movie where someone has been "killed" on camera, if you watch carefully, you will invariably notice slight breathing movements, no matter how hard the actor playing the "corpse" has tried to conceal them.

There are two ways that the lungs can be expanded and contracted: by downward and upward movements of the diaphragm, lengthening or shortening the chest cavity, and by elevation and depression of the ribs produced by the external intercostal muscles and other chest muscles, increasing or decreasing the diameter of the chest cavity (Figure 24-1). **Diaphragm breathing** is slow and deep. This is the type seen during sleep, and singing teachers exhort their students to "breathe with your diaphragm!" **Costal breathing** is characteristically rapid and shallow, as in a runner at the end of a race. In normal quiet breathing, the diaphragm plays the major role. But when the body's oxygen demands increase and breathing is intensified, costal breathing can contribute more than half of the lung enlargement.

diaphragm
chest

When the chest cavity is expanded or contracted, the volume of the lungs changes right along with it. Remember that the parietal pleura adheres tightly to the inner surface of the thoracic wall, while the visceral pleura adheres just as closely to the outer surface of the lung. The surface tension of the lubricating liquid between the two layers helps them to cohere, and thus when the chest expands, it pulls the lungs along with it.

Inspiration

In a single normal breath, you inhale about enough air to fill half a milk bottle. The term physiologists use for "breathing in" is **inspiration.** The sequence of muscle contractions involved in inspiration is directed toward one goal: decreasing the gas pressure inside the lungs below atmospheric pressure so that air will flow in through the respiratory tract. This is achieved by increasing the volume of the lungs.

Why should the pressure of the gases inside the

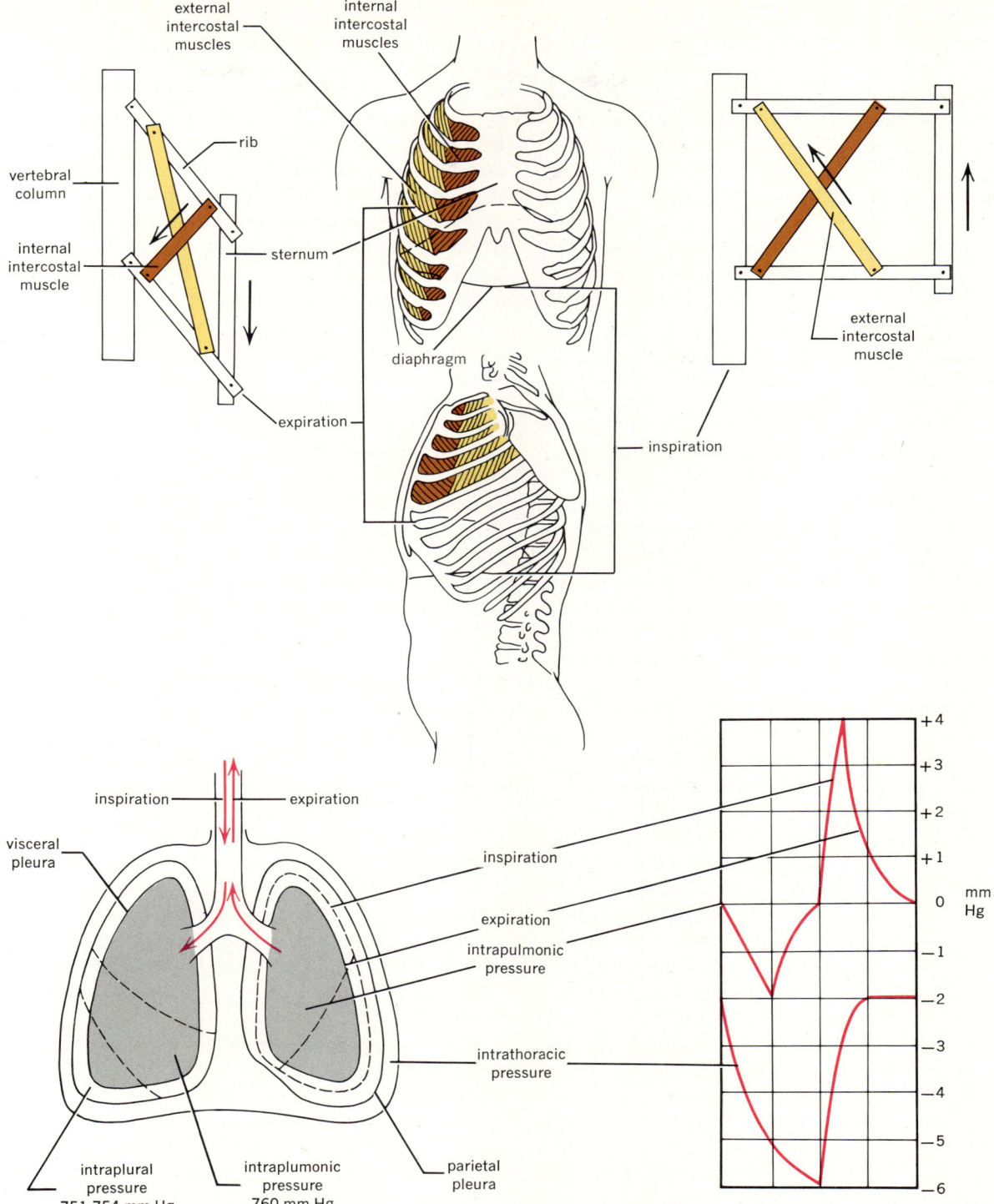

FIGURE 24-1 **The mechanics of respiration. Movements of the diaphragm and intercostal muscles expand and contract the lungs in inspiration and expiration.**

lungs automatically decrease when their volume is expanded? Let us briefly review some physical principles that will make this relationship clear. The molecules of matter are in a constant random motion. When a given amount of gas is confined in a con-

tainer, the gas molecules move about freely inside, frequently colliding with one another and bouncing off the walls of the container. The pressure that the gas exerts on the walls of the container is due to the collisions of gas molecules with the walls, and it will be greater, the more gas molecules there are in the container—that is, the higher the concentration of the gas. Now imagine the container expanding, without any change in the amount of gas inside. The gas molecules have more room to move around (their concentration is lower), and each one will collide less frequently with the walls of the container—that is, the pressure has been lowered by the increase in volume. This simple relationship has been formulated as one of the "gas laws," describing the behavior of gases. It is **Boyle's Law,** which states that *the pressure of a gas is inversely proportional to its volume, as long as the temperature is kept constant.*

One mechanism for increasing the volume of the chest cavity (and therefore the volume of the lungs) is the contraction of the **diaphragm.** This sheetlike muscle that forms the floor of the thoracic cavity has a dome shape when it is relaxed. When the diaphragm contracts, it flattens out, thus lowering the "floor" and expanding the chest cavity. The diaphragm has a surface area of about 270 cm^2. So if it descends only 1 cm, it will increase the thoracic capacity by about 270 cm^3. In quiet respiration, the diaphragm actually moves down about 1.5 cm, producing an increase in the capacity of about 400 cm^3. In forceful breathing, the diaphragm may descend as much as 7 cm, producing a far larger increase in capacity.

The circumference of the chest cavity is increased by contractions of the **external intercostal muscles,** which make the ribs swing upward and push the sternum forward. In forceful inspiration, the **scalene** and **pectoralis minor muscles** also contribute to expanding the chest cavity. But there is a limit to what all these muscles can accomplish, since they must work against the external pressure exerted by the atmosphere on the outside of the chest wall. This presents no problems at atmospheric pressure, but when a diver descends into the water or an astronaut is subjected to acceleration during takeoff, the external force may be greater than the breathing muscles can successfully oppose. It has been found that the inspiratory muscles cannot overcome a pressure greater than that produced by four feet of water. The deep-sea diver gets around that problem by breathing air (or a specially prepared oxygen mixture) from a tank of compressed gas, which provides a pressure gradient without excessive work by the inspiratory muscles.

The expansion of the chest cavity automatically inflates the lungs, because of the **surface tension** holding the moist layers of the pleura together. You may have encountered a similar phenomenon in your daily life if you have ever stacked wet beverage glasses while washing the dishes. The forces of molecular attraction between the wet surfaces hold the glasses together so tightly that it is difficult to get them apart without breaking them.

The inner surfaces of the alveoli are also moist, and you might expect them to cohere as well. But this would be disastrous, since they then would be unable to inflate and fill with the inflowing air. However, the surface tension of the alveolar walls is greatly reduced by a lipoprotein mixture that acts as a natural **surfactant.** Without sufficient surfactant, the lung, or part of it, would tend to collapse (a condition known as **atelectasis**), and powerful work of the inspiratory muscles would be necessary to counteract the surface tension in the alveoli. In premature babies born without a sufficient supply of surfactant in their lungs, the effort required to breathe is too great, and the often fatal **respiratory distress syndrome (hyaline membrane disease)** results.

Inspiration is frequently referred to as the active phase of pulmonary ventilation, since it is initiated by the contractions of the inspiratory muscles. When the chest expands, and the cohesion of the visceral and parietal pleurae causes the lungs to expand as well, the intrapulmonic pressure (the pressure inside the lungs) falls from 760 mm Hg (atmospheric pressure) to about 758 mm Hg. A pressure gradient is established, and air rushes into the lungs.

Expiration

When you breathe out, and your chest moves and air comes rushing out of your lungs, it might seem as though **expiration** is an active process. Normally, though, it is essentially passive. In quiet breathing, after inspiration the neurons innervating the inspiratory muscles are inhibited, the muscles relax, the chest capacity is decreased, and elastic recoil of the lungs causes them to contract. Now the gases they contain are compressed, raising their pressure to about 4 mm Hg above atmospheric pressure, and a new pressure gradient is established. This time air flows out of the lungs, up through the respiratory passages, and out into the atmosphere, until the pressures are equalized again.

Forced expiration, as when you blow out a candle, *is an active process.* Contractions of the **internal intercostal muscles** pull the ribs downward, while contractions of the **abdominal muscles** raise the intraabdominal pressure and force the diaphragm upward, further decreasing the thoracic capacity.

You very likely have the impression that all of the air in your lungs is expelled each time you breathe out, and the lungs are entirely filled with new air each time you breathe in. But this is not the case. Even the most forceful expiration does not expel *all* the air from the lungs, and not all of the air that is inhaled actually reaches the alveoli where the gas exchange takes place. Let us look more closely at the lung capacities and the volumes of air exchanged in respiration.

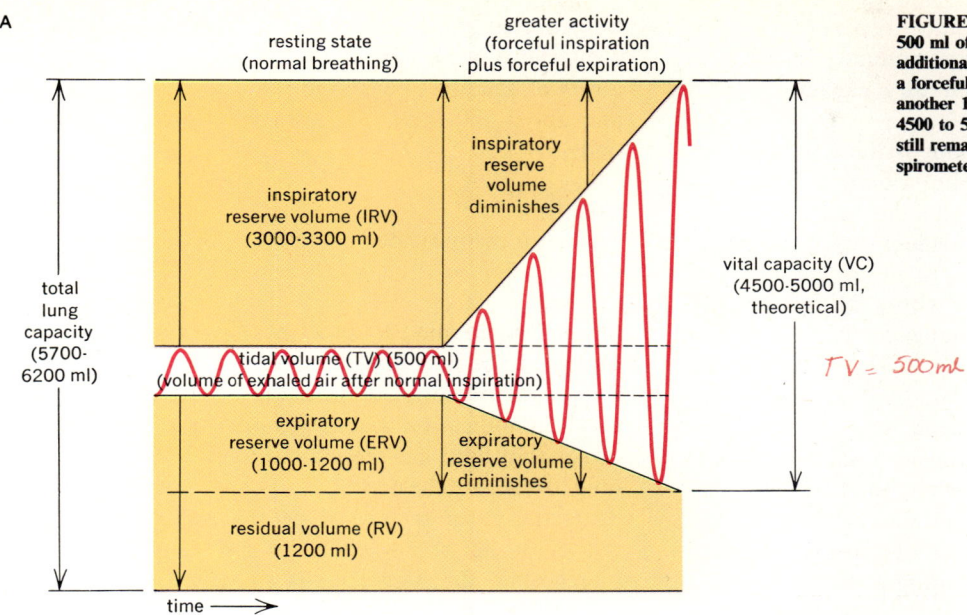

A

resting state
(normal breathing)

greater activity
(forceful inspiration
plus forceful expiration)

inspiratory
reserve
volume
diminishes

inspiratory
reserve volume (IRV)
(3000-3300 ml)

total
lung
capacity
(5700-
6200 ml)

vital capacity (VC)
(4500-5000 ml,
theoretical)

tidal volume (TV) (500 ml)
(volume of exhaled air after normal inspiration)

TV = 500ml

expiratory
reserve volume (ERV)
(1000-1200 ml)

expiratory
reserve
volume
diminishes

residual volume (RV)
(1200 ml)

time ⟶

FIGURE 24-2 (A) In quiet respiration about 500 ml of air is inhaled and exhaled (TV). An additional 3000 to 3300 ml can be inspired with a forceful effort (IRV); forceful expiration yields another 1000 ml (ERV), giving a total of about 4500 to 5000 ml (VC). But about 1200 ml of air still remains trapped in the alveoli (RV). (B) A spirometer is used to determine lung volumes.

Total lung cap. = 6 liters
residual volume = 1200

500ml out tidal volume

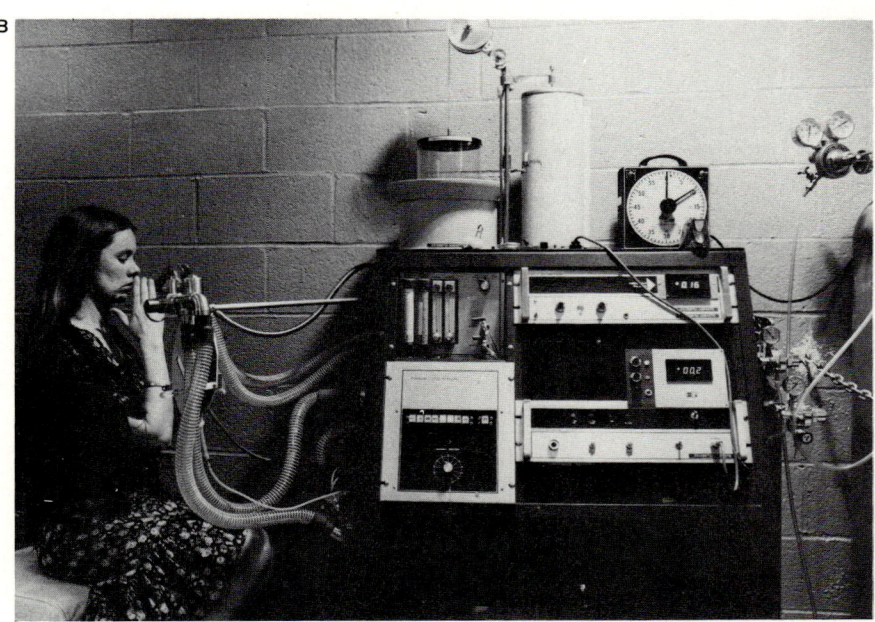

B

Air Volumes in Respiration

You normally breathe out about half a liter of air with each expiration. But when you blow up a large balloon, you can expel close to five liters in one blow (if you took a deep breath first). Even this is not all the air your lungs can hold. Respiratory volumes and capacities are measured clinically with an instrument called a **spirometer** (Figure 24-2).

The **total lung capacity** is the maximum amount of air the lungs and respiratory passages can hold, after a maximum inspiration. It is an average of about 6000 ml (6 liters).

A maximum expiration expels all but about 1200 ml of air, which remains in the lungs. This residual amount of air is called the **residual volume.**

The amount of air that a person can expel by a maximal expiration, after the deepest possible inspiration, is called the **vital capacity.** For an adult man it averages 4600 ml.

In normal quiet breathing, the **resting chest volume** is about 2.5 liters. A normal inspiration increases this amount by about 500 ml for an average adult male. The volume of air that flows into and out of the lungs with each breath in normal quiet respiration (i.e., about 500 ml) is called the **tidal volume.** Thus, there is normally some air in the lungs after expiration, and room for additional air even after normal inspiration.

The **inspiratory reserve volume** is the volume of air

that can be inspired after quiet inspiration—about 3000 ml. The inspiratory reserve volume plus the tidal volume is equal to the **inspiratory capacity**—about 3500 ml.

The **expiratory reserve volume** is the volume of air that can be expired at the end of a quiet expiration—about 1100 ml. This volume plus the residual volume is equal to the **functional residual capacity**—about 2300 ml.

The relationships among these quantities are shown in Figure 24-2. Note that each "capacity" consists of two or more "volumes." The volumes and capacities depend on the size and build of the individual (men normally have a greater lung capacity than women, for example), and can be modified to some extent by exercise. (A well-developed athlete may have a vital capacity 40 percent above normal.) They also change with body position; generally, the lung capacities are greater in a standing position than in a recumbent position.

Not all of the air drawn in with each breath (the tidal volume) is available for gas exchange in the aveoli. Part of it remains in the nasal passages, pharynx, larynx, trachea, bronchi, and bronchioles. The volume of these air passages constitutes **dead space** and is about 150 ml. Thus, of the tidal volume of 500 ml, only 350 ml represents the actual **alveolar ventilation.** If some of the alveoli become damaged and cease to function, as in emphysema, the physiological dead space is increased, sometimes to a liter or more.

It might seem rather inefficient that there is not a complete replacement of the air in the lungs with each breath. Instead, the 350 ml of the alveolar ventilation mixes with the 2500 ml or so of air that is already in the lungs. An important effect of this mixing is a buffering action: the residual air buffers the incoming new air, which is much higher in oxygen and lower in carbon dioxide, preventing large fluctuations of the partial pressures of these gases. A temperature and moisture buffering is similarly provided.

Some air remains in the lungs even after death. When the thorax is opened, the lungs collapse, and the air they contain is forced out. But before the alveoli are completely emptied, the bronchioles leading to them collapse, trapping a little air inside the alveoli. This amount is referred to as **minimal air.** It is enough to make a lung removed from the body float in water.

A spirograph measures not only volumes and capacities, but also the rate of respiration, so that the **minute volume of respiration** can be calculated by multiplying the tidal volume by the numbers of respirations per minute. For the average person this is 6000 to 7500 ml. The **maximal breathing capacity** is determined by having the person breathe as rapidly and deeply as possible for about 30 seconds. Usually

a maximum effort cannot be sustained for more than a quarter minute; a young adult male can breathe at a rate of 150 liters per minute for the first 15 seconds, and about 100 liters per minute for the next 15 seconds.

Breath Sounds

A doctor who suspects pneumonia or some other complication in the lower respiratory tract applies a stethoscope to the chest wall. Each inspiration is normally accompanied by a low rustling sound, which is thought to be produced by the dilation of the alveoli. If the sound cannot be heard in a particular region, this is an indication that air is not entering those alveoli, or that fluid has seeped out and is separating the lung from the chest wall. A louder sound, called a bronchial murmur, is produced by air passing in and out of the larynx, trachea, and bronchial tubes. In pneumonia, the lung conducts sounds more readily than usual, and the murmur can be heard in various parts of the chest, not just in the region of the air tubes. Diseased conditions can produce abnormal sounds, such as bubbling, clicking, crackling, or gurgling, in the lungs and air passages. These abnormal sounds are referred to as **rales** or **crackles.**

EXTERNAL RESPIRATION: GAS EXCHANGE IN THE LUNGS

If a mouse is placed in a closed jar with a lighted candle, the candle will soon go out. Quickly thereafter, the mouse will lose consciousness, and if not immediately rescued, it will soon die.

The air we breathe into our lungs contains about 21 percent oxygen, about 79 percent nitrogen, about 0.04 percent carbon dioxide, and small quantities of water vapor and other gases. The air we breathe out has a quite different composition: it contains about 15 percent oxygen and 5 percent carbon dioxide. An exchange of these two gases occurs in the lungs, with oxygen passing out through the thin walls of the alveoli and in through the thin walls of the capillaries that surround them, while there is a net movement of car-

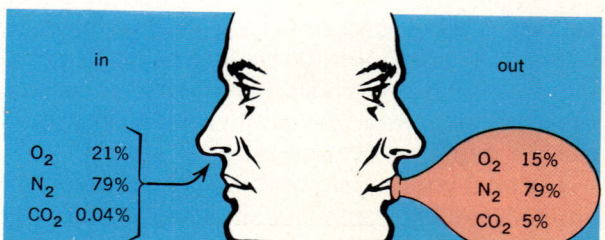

FIGURE 24-3 The gas exchange in the lungs changes the proportions of gases in air: exhaled air contains less oxygen and more carbon dioxide than inhaled air.

bon dioxide in the opposite direction. Oxygen is continually consumed in combustion reactions in the body cells, and carbon dioxide is a product of these reactions. The mouse in the jar and the candle in the illustration mentioned at the beginning of the section compete for the available oxygen, which is soon consumed (the burning of a candle is also an oxidation reaction), and both increase the concentration of carbon dioxide in the air of the jar.

To understand how the exchange of gases in the lungs occurs, we will first need to consider another of the "gas laws," **Dalton's Law of partial pressures.** This generalization of gas behavior states that *the pressure exerted by a particular gas in a mixture of gases—that is, its partial pressure—is directly related to the concentration of that gas in the mixture and to the total pressure of the mixture.* For example, in atmospheric air at the normal barometric pressure at sea level (760 mm Hg), the partial pressure of oxygen is equal to its concentration (21 percent) times the total pressure, or $pO_2 = 21 \times 760 = 159.6$ mm Hg. The term **tension** is commonly used as a synonym for partial pressure; thus, the oxygen tension is the same thing as pO_2.

When a gas is dissolved in a liquid, it still exerts a partial pressure, for molecules of the gas are constantly leaving the surface of the liquid and flying out into the gas medium above it. (Other gas molecules in the atmosphere continually reenter the liquid.) The partial pressure of a gas dissolved in a liquid is directly proportional to the concentration of the gas in the liquid, and the amount of gas dissolved is directly related to the partial pressure of the gas in the atmosphere above it.

When fresh air is drawn into the lungs, a pressure gradient is established. The atmospheric air is relatively rich in oxygen and poor in carbon dioxide. The blood flowing through the capillary network surrounding each aveolus, on the other hand, is poor in oxygen and rich in carbon dioxide, for it represents the blood returned to the heart after the circuit around the vessels of the systemic circulation. Whenever a pressure gradient exists, and there is no effective barrier to diffusion, there will be a net movement of molecules until an equalization of the partial pressures occurs. This is exactly what happens in the alveoli of the lungs. Oxygen moves down its pressure gradient, out of the alveoli and into the blood. Carbon dioxide moves down its own pressure gradient, from the blood into the alveoli. As a result of these flows and the continual replenishment of the air in the lungs, the alveolar air has a relatively constant content of 14 to 15 percent oxygen and about 5.5 percent carbon dioxide.

A number of factors determine the diffusion of respiratory gases in the lungs:

1 The area of contact for exchange, that is, the total functional surface area of the alveolar and capillary membranes
2 The pressure gradient between the alveolar air and the blood in the capillary network
3 The length of time the blood and air are in contact, which is dependent on the rate of pulmonary circulation
4 The permeability of the aveolar and capillary membranes
5 The respiratory minute volume
6 The chemical reactions in the blood.

Factors that tend to decrease pO_2 in the aveoli will reduce the alveolar-capillary oxygen pressure gradient and thus decrease the amount of oxygen entering the blood. For example, as the altitude above sea level increases, the atmosphere thins out, and its total pressure decreases. Less oxygen enters the lungs with each breath, and therefore the alveolar pO_2 decreases and less oxygen enters the blood. A decrease in the respiratory minute volume also reduces the amount of oxygen available for diffusion into the bloodstream. (Such an effect is produced by the drug morphine, which slows respiration.) Emphysema and other conditions that decrease the functional surface area in the alveoli also reduce the effectiveness of the gas exchange in the lungs. Physical exercise enhances the pulmonary gas exchange in two ways: during physical activity the volume of blood flowing through the capillaries of the lungs is increased (doubled during hard exertion), and physical activity speeds up the respiration rate.

Many factors in the structure of the lungs favor an effective gas exchange. The walls of the alveoli and of the capillaries are exceedingly thin; it is estimated that together they form a barrier of not more than 0.004 mm for the diffusing gases to cross. The surfaces for exchange are extremely large. (Imagine the number of microscopic molecules that could bounce back and forth on a tennis court!) The capillary networks accommodate a large volume of blood—about 900 ml at a time—and yet the capillaries themselves are so narrow that the blood cells have to pass through them in single file; thus, each red cell is exposed to the alveolar air.

TRANSPORT OF GASES IN THE BLOOD

Getting oxygen into the bloodstream is only part of the battle in supplying it to the body cells. It must also be efficiently transported around the body, and then it must diffuse into the body tissues. Similar processes are necessary for effective removal of waste carbon dioxide from the body cells; it must diffuse out of the tissues into the blood, be carried to the lungs, pass into the alveoli, and then be exhaled (Figure 24-4).

If blood were a simple flowing liquid, the transport of gases would not be very effective. At atmospheric

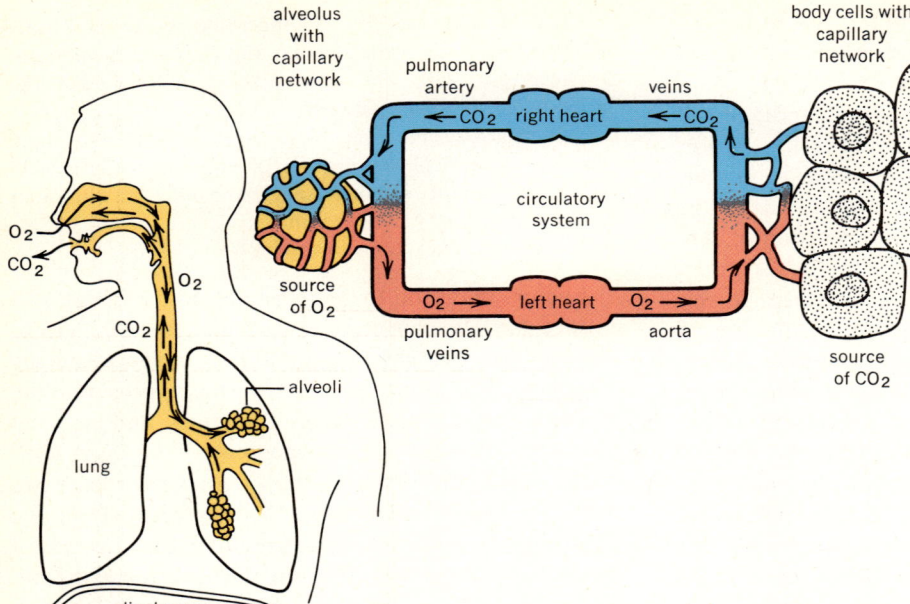

alveolus with capillary network

pulmonary artery

veins

body cells with capillary network

CO_2 right heart CO_2

circulatory system

source of O_2

O_2 left heart O_2

pulmonary veins

aorta

source of CO_2

O_2
CO_2
O_2
CO_2

alveoli

lung

diaphragm

FIGURE 24-4 Schematic summary of external and internal respiration.

pressure, gases are not usually very soluble in water. You may have noticed that if you leave a bottle of a carbonated beverage open, it soon goes "flat." The carbon dioxide that makes the drink bubbly is forced into solution under pressure. (The foam jackets that are now commonly provided around large bottles of carbonated beverages were a response to the fact that soft drink bottles have occasionally exploded under the high pressure of the gas inside them.) Extra transporting capacity in the blood is provided by the hemoglobin in the red blood cells.

Oxygen Transport

The blood leaving the lungs is a bright scarlet red. This is the color imparted to it by the oxidized form of hemoglobin, **oxyhemoglobin.** Each hemoglobin molecule can combine reversibly with four molecules of oxygen, one for each of the iron atoms. This blood flowing from the lungs contains about 20 volumes of oxygen per 100 volumes of blood. About 95 percent of this oxygen is carried in the form of oxyhemoglobin; only 5 percent is dissolved in the fluid plasma. As the blood flows to the heart and from there out into the systemic circulation, there is a continual diffusion of oxygen out of the erythrocytes into the plasma, from the plasma out through the capillary membranes into the tissue fluid, and from the tissue fluid into the cells. The flow of oxygen, as usual, occurs down the pressure gradient, from oxygen-rich regions to oxygen-poor regions.

The more hemoglobin the blood contains, the more oxygen it can transport. The fatigue that is a characteristic symptom of anemia is therefore understandable: the hemoglobin content of the blood is decreased, the blood cannot carry the normal amount of oxygen, and therefore the body tissues suffer from a chronic **hypoxia** (inadequate oxygen supply).

Carbon Dioxide Transport

The hemoglobin molecule is a versatile chemical. Not only can each of its iron atoms reversibly bind a molecule of oxygen, but an amino group can combine with carbon dioxide to form a carbamino compound. But the transport of carbon dioxide in the blood is not as much of a "one man show" as the transport of oxygen. Somewhat less than a third of the carbon dioxide transported in the blood is carried in the form of **carbaminohemoglobin.** A small amount dissolves in the plasma. And about 60 to 90 percent of the carbon dioxide transported is carried in the plasma in the form of bicarbonate ions (HCO_3^-).

As blood flows through the body tissues, carbon dioxide diffuses into the capillaries. Some of it reacts with water in the plasma to form **carbonic acid.** But this is a rather slow reaction, and most of the carbon dioxide diffuses into the erythrocytes. Here the same reaction takes place, but at a much faster rate. For carbonic acid formation in the red blood cells is catalyzed by the enzyme **carbonic anhydrase,** which speeds up the rate of the reaction many thousand-fold. Within a fraction of a second, the reaction has reached equilibrium. Then in another fraction of a second, another reaction occurs: the carbonic acid dissociates into bicarbonate and hydrogen ions. The reaction sequence in the erythrocytes is thus:

$$CO_2 + H_2O \rightarrow H_2CO_3 \rightarrow HCO_3^- + H^+$$

Most of the hydrogen ions formed in the dissociation react rapidly with hemoglobin, leaving a large quantity of bicarbonate ions dissolved in the fluid inside the red cells. Many of the bicarbonate ions diffuse out into the plasma, but now an electrical imbalance has been created—there is an excess of positive charge inside the red cells and an excess of negative charge in the plasma surrounding them. The electrical balance is quickly reestablished by a diffusion of negatively charged chloride ions (Cl^-) from the plasma into the erythrocytes. This adjustment is referred to as the **chloride shift.**

The blood flowing through the body tissues picks up about 4 volumes percent carbon dioxide and deposits about 5 volumes percent oxygen. But there is already quite a bit of carbon dioxide present in the blood (mainly in the form of bicarbonate). The blood leaving the lungs has a carbon dioxide concentration of about 48 volumes percent; this value rises to about 52 volumes percent on the trip back from the body tissues.

A rise in the carbon concentration in the blood is correlated with a decrease in the blood pH (the carbonic anhydrase reaction yields hydrogen ions) and lowers the oxygen-carrying capacity of hemoglobin, since the excess hydrogen ions are absorbed in the reaction:

$$H^+ + HbO_2^- \rightleftharpoons HHb + O_2$$

The oxygen released tends to diffuse out of the blood, and thus a rise in pCO_2 tends to produce a fall in pO_2.

Other Gases

In our discussion of the transport of gases in the blood, we have been ignoring nitrogen, which constitutes nearly four-fifths of the gas in atmospheric air. Essentially, the body ignores the nitrogen, but some of this gas does diffuse into the capillary networks in the lungs and is dissolved in the plasma. Under special circumstances, this can cause problems. When a diver descends deep into the sea and breathes a normal air mixture, more than the usual amount of nitrogen dissolves in his blood, because of the greatly increased pressure. If he then ascends to the surface too rapidly, the nitrogen rapidly bubbles out of solution, producing gas bubbles inside his blood vessels. The painful condition called **decompression sickness** or **the bends** results, and severe tissue damage (particularly to the nervous system) may occur. The most effective treatment is to place the diver under high pressure again (either by sending him back down or by placing him in a pressure chamber) and then gradually reduce the pressure, at a slow enough rate that the excess nitrogen can come out of solution gradually and be carried off by the lungs.

Another problem that may be encountered by divers breathing air under pressure is a form of **nitrogen narcosis** referred to as "rapture of the depths." The first signs are feelings of euphoria, followed by an impairment of higher nervous system functions and unconsciousness—characteristics very similar to alcohol intoxication. The narcotic effect is believed to be the result of nitrogen's dissolving freely in the membranes or other lipid structures of the nerve cells, decreasing their excitability.

Sometimes a mixture of oxygen and helium is used by deep-sea divers instead of the oxygen-nitrogen mixture of atmospheric air, to avoid possible problems.

INTERNAL RESPIRATION: GAS EXCHANGE IN THE TISSUES

The major function of the elaborate circulatory system is to deliver oxygen and nutrients to the body tissues and carry off their waste products. The gas exchange that occurs between the blood and the tissues is very similar to that in the lungs, but in this case the pressure gradients go in the opposite direction; carbon dioxide tension in the tissue fluid and in the cells (where CO_2 is produced in cell respiration) is higher than that in the capillaries, while oxygen tension is lower. Thus, carbon dioxide diffuses from the tissue fluid into the blood, and oxygen moves out from the blood into the tissue fluid, and from there into the cells. As the blood flows around the systemic circulation, the oxygen it carries is fed out gradually, as the chemical equilibria in the blood are shifted and molecules of oxygen are successively released from oxyhemoglobin. There is a similar continual flow of carbon dioxide from the tissues into the blood. But even at the end of the trip, some of the oxygen still remains in the blood.

CONTROL OF RESPIRATION

You can control your breathing voluntarily to some degree, breathing more rapidly or more slowly, more deeply or more shallowly at will. You can even stop breathing entirely for a time. But if you try to hold your breath, you will discover that after about half a minute to a minute, the impulse to breathe becomes uncontrollable. Suddenly the automatic mechanisms override your conscious controls, and, will it or not, you draw in a convulsive gasp of air. Special techniques such as **hyperventilation** (drawing in a series of very deep breaths) can prolong the period of breath-holding for up to 8 minutes or more— a trick used by underwater swimmers. But even hyperventilation cannot be continued indefinitely—after a few minutes, the person becomes giddy and weak, and may even black out; soon he or she lapses automatically into a more normal mode of breathing.

It is fortunate that respiration is under automatic control—imagine how onerous it would be to have to remember consciously to breathe, about 16 times every minute, even while you were asleep! Like other automatic functions of the body, respiration is controlled by special centers in the central nervous system through reflex arcs, in which chemical stimuli play an important role.

Nervous Control

A broken neck or a case of paralytic polio can paralyze the respiratory muscles by interrupting the flow of impulses to and from the central nervous system. (A deep coma, in which the CNS is depressed, can have a similar effect.) A mechanical respirator must then be used to aid the victim to breathe.

The control centers for breathing do not seem to be discrete, clearly delimited bodies in the brain substance. Instead, they consist of a widely dispersed group of neurons, located bilaterally in the reticular substance of the medulla and pons (Figure 24-5). The basic rhythms of respiration seem to be set in the **medullary respiratory center.** Often separate **inspiratory** and **expiratory centers** are spoken of, but actually the evidence seems to indicate that the inspiratory and expiratory neurons of the medulla are intermingled. Stimulation of the inspiratory neurons in the medullary center causes the inspiratory muscles to contract, while stimulation of the expiratory neurons causes the expiratory muscles to contract. The action of this center produces the usual respiratory rhythm of inspirations lasting about 2 seconds and expirations lasting about 3 seconds. But if the brainstem is cut just above the medullary rhythmicity areas, the breathing becomes quite abnormal—although still rhythmic, it occurs in gasps. The normal smooth pattern of respiration is produced by the action of two additional control centers in the pons, the **apneustic** and **pneumotaxic** centers.

The apneustic center continually sends stimulatory impulses to the inspiratory areas in the medulla. This center in turn sends messages over motor neurons, which stimulate the inspiratory muscles to contract. If the effects of the apneustic center were not counteracted, it would produce a forceful inspiration lasting 20 to 30 seconds, with weak expirations lasting only 2 to 3 seconds. But when the lungs are filled, automatic cutoff mechanisms shut off the inspiratory impulses and bring about expiration. One set of controls is called the **Hering–Breuer** reflex. Stretch receptors in the visceral pleura are stimulated when the lungs are inflated. Impulses from these receptors pass along the vagus nerve to the medulla, where they inhibit the inspiratory areas and excite the expiratory neurons. Relaxation of the inspiratory muscles results, and ex-

piration follows. But as the lungs are deflated, the stretch receptors are no longer stimulated, and a new cycle of inspiration and expiration begins. The Hering–Breuer reflex helps to control the depth and rhythmicity of respiration and also acts as a protective mechanism, preventing the lungs from overinflating to the bursting point.

The pneumotaxic center provides another automatic control mechanism, which helps to maintain rhythmicity of respirations. When the inspiratory center is stimulated, it sends impulses up to the pneumotaxic center in the pons, in addition to the impulses that flow down the spinal cord and out to the inspiratory muscles. After a small delay, the pneumotaxic center sends messages down to the expiratory area, which inhibits the inspiratory center.

Other regions of the central nervous system also participate in the control of breathing. The hypothalamus seems to be linked with the neurons of the medullary respiratory center. Certain neurons in the hypothalamus are extremely sensitive to the carbon dioxide tension, and stimulate increased ventilation when pCO_2 rises above a certain value. The temperature of the blood circulating through the hypothalamus is another influencing factor; a rise in temperature causes hyperventilation. Autonomic reflexes in which the hypothalamus participates can have an effect on respiration—anger or fright will stimulate the sympathetic nervous system and cause you to breathe faster and deeper. The cerebral cortex can also modify the respiratory controls. The mere anticipation of physical exercise increases ventilation long before the actual exertion sets the chemical mechanisms in motion.

The reflex arcs originating in the pressoreceptors of the **carotid and aortic sinuses** and in the chemoreceptors in the **carotid and aortic bodies** are major regulators of cardiovascular function, but they also affect the respiratory function. Stimulation of the pressoreceptors in the carotid and aortic sinuses when the blood pressure rises depresses breathing, while a fall in blood pressure (as occurs during hemorrhaging) causes hyperventilation. Stimulation of the carotid and aortic bodies increases ventilation.

A variety of sensory stimulations can produce a reflexive change in the respiratory rate. A sudden pain produces a reflex **apnea** (cessation of breathing), but prolonged painful stimuli cause faster and deeper respirations. A sudden cold stimulus applied to the skin produces apnea. Stimulation of the pharynx or larynx by touch or by irritating chemicals also causes a temporary apnea. The protective value of this choking reflex is obvious, since it can help to prevent the aspiration of food or liquid. But the utility of another respiratory reflex is more obscure—stretching of the

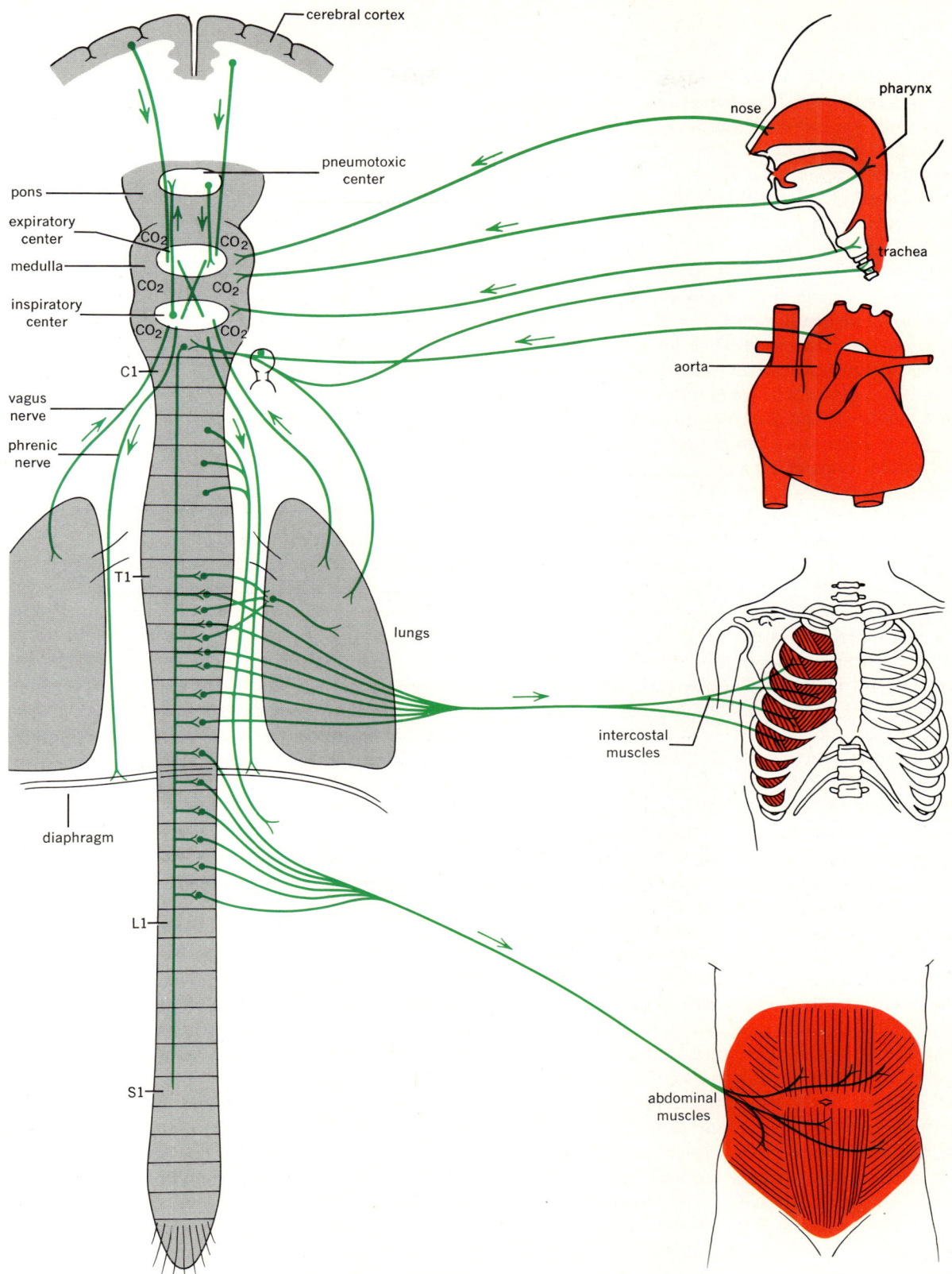

FIGURE 24-5   Nervous control of respiration.

anal sphincter increases the respiratory rate and deepens respiration. Sometimes this mechanism is used as an emergency measure to stimulate respiration. Impulses originating from the receptors in the joints when the limbs are moved initiate reflexes that speed up and deepen respiration. During exercise, these reflexes contribute to the acceleration of respiration, producing an effect greater than could be accounted for by the rise in pCO_2 alone.

Chemical Control

People commit suicide in many ways, but holding one's breath until death comes is not one of them. During apnea, no new oxygen-rich air is drawn into the lungs. But cell metabolism and the gas exchange in the tissues continue. The carbon dioxide tension in the blood builds up, and the blood pH decreases. The neurons of the inspiratory center are extremely sensitive to elevated levels of carbon dioxide in the blood flowing through the brain and step up the respiration rate in response to high pCO_2. Elevated carbon dioxide levels also stimulate the carotid and aortic chemoreceptors. There is some debate as to which effect is most important in the control of respiration, but the prevailing opinion is that the direct effect on the respiratory center predominates.

A low pH also stimulates both the medullary respiratory center and the carotid and aortic chemoreceptors. This effect is additive with the stimulation produced by pCO_2.

The effect of carbon dioxide on the respiratory system is dramatic (Figure 24-6). Even a small increase in the percentage of CO_2 in the inspired air produces a tremendous increase in ventilation. Sometimes this effect is utilized by having patients breathe into a paper bag for brief periods after surgery; rebreathing their exhaled air in this way sparks an increased ventilation that exercises the lungs and helps prevent the development of postoperative pneumonia. But extremely high carbon dioxide levels in the inspired air have a depressant effect, and a 30 percent level may be fatal.

A stoppage of breathing or an increase in the carbon dioxide content in the inspired air is not the only cause of elevation of the blood pCO_2. Far more common in everyday life is the buildup of carbon dioxide produced by an increase in the rate of metabolism of the body cells, such as occurs during physical exercise. This rise in pCO_2 is a self-correcting condition—it stimulates an increase in ventilation, and the excess carbon dioxide is rapidly eliminated from the body in the expired air.

Considering the vital importance of oxygen to the body's activities, you might expect that a low pO_2 would be the most powerful stimulating factor in the

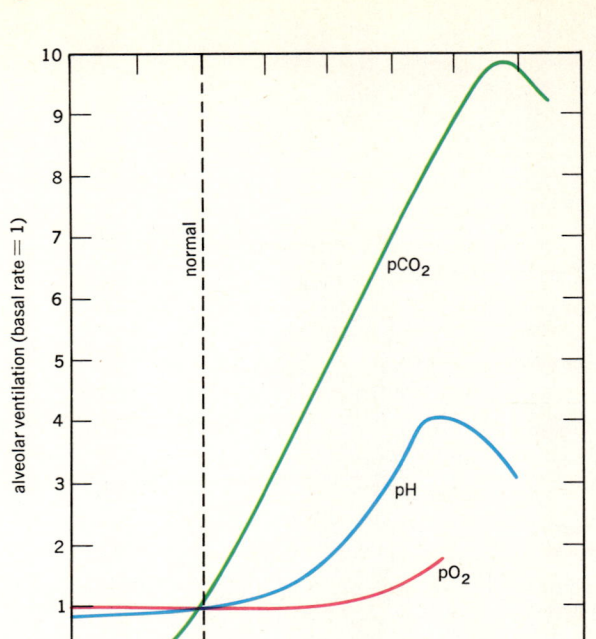

FIGURE 24-6 Effects of pCO_2, pH, and pO_2 on respiration.

control of respiration. But the oxygen-sensitive chemoreceptors are not stimulated until the oxygen level falls so low that tissue anoxia develops. As a result, the role of oxygen in respiratory control is minor. The reason for this is that wide fluctuations in the respiratory rate produce negligible changes in the oxygenation of the blood. (Remember that the exhaled air normally contains about 15 percent oxygen, which provides a considerable reserve even if there is a brief temporary cessation of breathing.)

THE RHYTHM OF BREATHING

If you try to observe the number of respiratory movements you normally make, the results are likely to be misleading because conscious control may then overwhelm the automatic control mechanisms. Have someone else observe you at a moment when you are unaware.

The average adult, at rest and not emotionally excited, breathes about 14 to 20 times a minute. Many factors cause variations from this basic level. Some of them, such as emotional stimulation, pain, temperature, and the carbon dioxide level in the atmosphere, have already been discussed. Another influencing factor is age. Like the heartbeat, the respiration rate tends to decrease from birth to adulthood. A newborn baby breathes rapidly, from 40 to 70 times a minute. By the end of the first year, the rate has settled down to 35 to 40 times a minute, by 5 years about 25 times a minute, at 10 years 20 per minute. By the late teen years, the normal adult level of 14 to 20 is reached. But then, in old age, the rate may speed up to more than 20 times per minute.

Normal quiet breathing is called **eupnea. Hypernea** refers to increased breathing, with an increased tidal volume and usually an increased rate. **Apnea** is a cessation of breathing after the phase of expiration; when breathing stops after inspiration, the cessation is called **apneusis.** The clinical term for difficult breathing of any sort is **dyspnea.** Varieties include **tachypnea** (rapid, shallow breathing); **orthopnea** (dyspnea that is relieved when the person sits upright); and **polypnea** (hyperventilation that may follow an emotional upset). Sometimes breathing abnormalities are rhythmic. **Cheyne–Stokes respirations,** which may be caused by congestive heart failure, brain injuries, or narcotics, consist of cycles in which the tidal volume gradually increases for several breaths, then gradually decreases. In **Biot's respirations,** deep gasps alternate with apnea.

Normally breathing is accomplished not only without conscious thought, but also with minimal effort. But certain pathological conditions can greatly increase the effort required for breathing. The work of breathing is determined mainly by three factors: the airway resistance, the lung compliance, and the lung elastance.

The **airway resistance** depends on the length and diameter of the tubes through which the air flows. The longer and narrower an air passage, the more gas molecules are exposed to contact with its walls and subjected to frictional drag. Thus, air flows more freely through wider tubes. Such conditions as bronchial asthma constrict the bronchial tubes and thus increase airway resistance and the work of breathing. A condition such as emphysema, in which the alveoli do not empty fully, also increases airway resistance (since the air is flowing into air sacs that are already occupied).

Lung compliance is the ability of the alveoli and lung tissue to expand on inspiration. In emphysema and in some infections, the normally elastic lung tissue is replaced by tough, fibrous tissue, and more work is required to expand the lungs in breathing.

Lung elastance is the ability of the lung tissues to recoil during expiration and force air out of the lungs. A decrease in the elasticity of lung tissue makes it harder to empty the lungs, and in turn increases the airway resistance, making it all the more laborious to breathe.

OXYGEN INSUFFICIENCY

When the Summer Olympics were held in Mexico City in 1968, many visiting athletes were at a disadvantage. The site of the games was at an altitude of 7349 feet above sea level, where the atmosphere is considerably thinner (and hence the oxygen tension lower) than at sea level. Athletes from sea-level regions were permitted to train at the high-altitude site for only four weeks. Not surprisingly, four of the five races for distances greater than 800 meters were won by natives of high-altitude regions.

The general term for an insufficiency of oxygen is **hypoxia.** Chronic hypoxia may occur in people who live at high altitudes, where the supply of oxygen in the inhaled air is below normal. Certain compensatory mechanisms develop in time and permit mountain dwellers to live and function normally. These include an enlargement of the lungs, enhancing pulmonary ventilation, and an enlargement of the right ventricle of the heart, increase in the number of capillaries, and substantial rise in the number of erythrocytes, which promote a more effective gas exchange and transport of oxygen in the bloodstream.

A lack of sufficient oxygen in the atmosphere is only one of a number of factors that can cause hypoxia. Hypoventilation due to neuromuscular disorder (e.g., polio), an obstruction of the airways, or pulmonary disease that reduces the number of functioning alveoli (e.g., emphysema) can also contribute to an oxygen insufficiency. So can disorders of the circulatory system. In heart defects producing a mixing of venous and arterial blood, the oxygen tension of the arterial blood is lowered, and the cells suffer an oxygen lack. In the presence of generalized or local circulatory deficiencies, the arterial blood contains a normal amount of oxygen, but it is not supplied to the body cells fast enough to meet their needs. Anemia or abnormal hemoglobin produces hypoxia by lowering the oxygen-carrying capacity of the blood. Tissue edema, which increases the distance through which oxygen must diffuse to supply the cells, and a poisoning of the cell enzymes (e.g., the **histotoxic hypoxia** produced by such poisons as cyanide) can starve the cells of oxygen even if normal amounts are being delivered by the respiratory and circulatory systems. Abnormal oxygen demands by the tissues, which cannot be satisfied by the normal supply routes, can also produce hypoxia. Thus, a major limiting factor on the amount of strenuous exercise that can be performed is the tissue hypoxia that develops.

If hypoxia is severe enough, it can actually kill cells. In milder degrees, it results mainly in a depressed mental activity (sometimes coma) and a reduced work capacity of the muscles.

Dyspnea, or a sensation of "air hunger," can be produced by hypoxia, or to an even greater degree by **hypercapnia** (an elevated carbon dioxide tension in the blood). Air hunger may also occur when the gas levels in the blood are perfectly normal but forceful breathing is necessary to achieve this. The forceful activity of the respiratory muscles gives the person a sensation of a need for air. Dyspnea also frequently results from mental or emotional causes. A person who is afraid of crowds may get a feeling of suffocating when he or she enters a large group of people. Even thinking about your breathing can produce a momentary deepening of your respiration because of a mild feeling of dyspnea.

In certain types of hypoxia, there is a characteristic **cyanosis,** a blueness of the skin, which results from the dark color of deoxygenated hemoglobin. (In anemia, despite the oxygen lack, there is not enough hemoglobin to give a bluish cast to the skin.) Cyanosis depends on the amount of deoxygenated hemoglobin in the blood, regardless of the percentage of deoxygenation (and thus is observed in polycythemia, in which the red cell count is elevated). It also depends on the thickness of the skin—cyanosis shows up first in regions such as the lips and fingernails, where the capillaries are very close to the surface. In carbon monoxide poisoning, while the body cells may be dying from oxygen lack because CO competes successfully for the oxygen-binding sites on hemoglobin, the skin is not cyanotic; instead it has a bright cherry red color, produced by the stable compound of carbon monoxide with hemoglobin.

Certain types of hypoxia are greatly helped by **oxygen therapy.** It can be administered by enriching the atmosphere with oxygen under a "tent," by allowing the patient to breathe pure oxygen through a mask, or by delivering oxygen directly into the nasopharynx through an intranasal tube. Hypoxia due to insufficient oxygen in the atmosphere or to hypoventilation responds dramatically to oxygen therapy. In hypoxia caused by anemia, carbon monoxide poisoning, or circulatory deficiency, oxygen therapy can be of some benefit because the increased oxygen tension in the inhaled air somewhat increases the amount of the gas that can dissolve in the blood plasma; the increase is small, but may mean the difference in saving the patient's life. Additional benefits can be gained in such cases by administering the oxygen at increased pressures (up to three atmospheres) in a **hyperbaric chamber.** (The higher the pressure, the more gas will dissolve in a liquid.) Hyperbaric oxygen therapy has also proved helpful in the treatment of patients with tetanus (an anaerobic infection in which the bacterial pathogens multiply in the absence of air) and in operations on children with heart disease.

MUSCULAR EXERCISE

Directly after a long-distance race, particularly a closely fought one, the participants may seem at the point of collapse. Muscle contraction is a highly oxygen-demanding activity. The resting body has unused reserves of oxygen (arterial blood normally carries about 20 percent oxygen, and only 5 percent passes into the body tissues), but even these are not enough to meet the drastically increased demands during strenuous physical exercise.

During exercise, there are a number of compensatory changes in the body. The efficiency of blood circulation is greatly increased; the heart beats faster and more forcefully as a result of the enhanced venous return and autonomic influences, and the blood vessels in the skeletal muscles are dilated at the expense of those in the abdominal organs. In addition, ventilation is dramatically increased: from 8 to over 100 liters per minute. Both oxygen utilization and carbon dioxide elimination rise sharply.

There has been considerable debate about the causes of the increased ventilation during exercise (Figure 24-7). The increase in pCO_2 and decrease in pO_2 in the blood, caused by the vigorous muscle activity, would tend to stimulate respiration. The rise in acidity due to the formation of **lactic acid,** a product of muscle metabolism, would have a similar effect, and so would the increase in body temperature produced by vigorous muscle contraction. Yet attempts to explain the increased respiration during exercise as the effect of these factors encounter certain difficulties—measurements have shown that the changes in gas concentrations in the blood alone are not enough to account for the dramatic hyperpnea observed; and the faster, deeper breathing begins immediately at the start of exercise, before the chemical changes in the body have had a chance to build up to significant levels. Indeed, even the thought of exercising may spark an increase in the respiration rate. The current theories hold that the major factors in exercise hyperventilation are impulses from the cerebral cortex and from proprioceptors in the contracting muscles and joints. Hypercapnia, hypoxia, lactic acid, elevated body temperature, and enhanced circulation participate as fine regulators, helping to adjust the balance between oxygen demand and supply.

Even the enormous potentials for increasing the efficiency of respiration and circulation cannot keep up with the muscle demands during very strenuous exercise. Like a bank that permits its customers to write checks for more money than they have in their accounts, the body has a mechanism for permitting its muscles to run up a temporary **oxygen debt.** Glycogen, the energy substrate, breaks down to pyruvic acid, which in normal metabolism is oxidized by oxygen to carbon dioxide and water. But in vigorous exercise, the muscles do not have enough oxygen available to accomplish these conversions. Instead, pyruvic acid is converted to lactic acid, which accu-

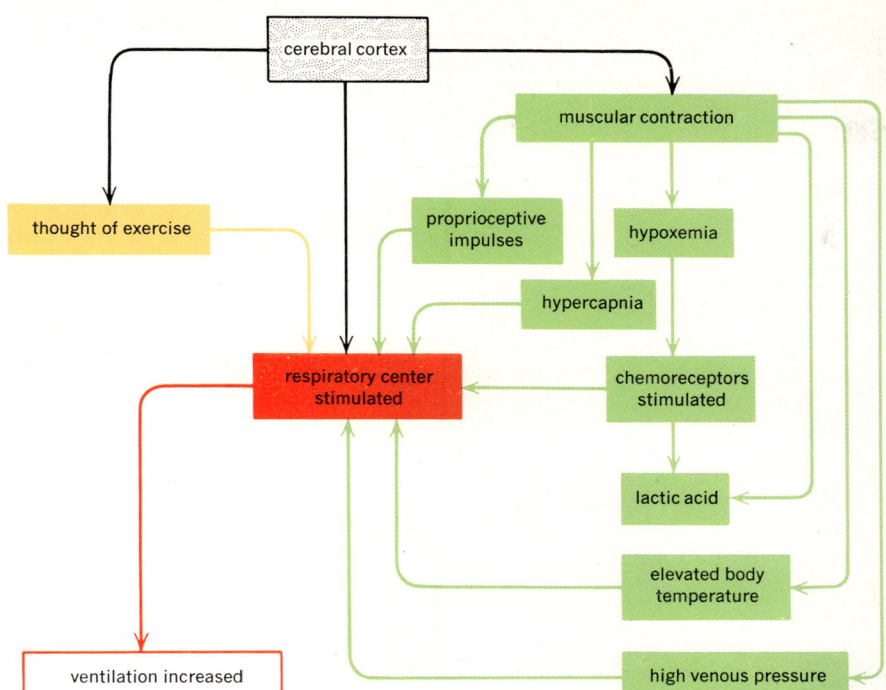

FIGURE 24-7 Regulation of respiration during exercise. The response is initiated by the cerebral cortex and augmented by the indirect effects of muscle contraction.

mulates. (During strenuous exercise, the concentration of lactic acid in the blood and urine may rise to as much as ten times the normal level.) This metabolic switch permits the body to "live beyond its means" for a short time. But the oxygen debt must be paid off as soon as possible. After the strenuous muscular efforts are over, the exhausted person pants for a while, bringing in extra oxygen to supply the reactions eliminating the excess lactic acid.

MODIFIED RESPIRATORY MOVEMENTS

Speak roughly to your little boy,
And beat him when he sneezes.
He only does it to annoy,
Because he knows it teases.

The Duchess' baby in *Alice in Wonderland* really was not trying to be annoying; he was simply sneezing because his upper respiratory passages were being irritated by the particles of pepper floating in the air. In addition to the normal actions of respiration, the respiratory passages participate in a number of reflex mechanisms and other modified movements (Figure 24-8).

Coughing. Both coughing and sneezing are protective reflex mechanisms used to clear the respiratory passages of obstructions or of inhaled or aspirated particles that have not been swept out by the ciliated epithelium. The lining of the trachea and bronchi is extremely sensitive to foreign particles and other types of irritation. Afferent impulses to the cough center in the medulla trigger an automatic sequence of events. A **cough** is preceded by a long, deep inspiration of about 2 liters of air. Then the glottis is closed, and a forceful expiratory effort is made, raising the air pressure in the chest. Suddenly the glottis is forced open, and a high-speed blast of air explodes out of the upper respiratory passages, blowing the obstruction and mucus out with it. A cough serves to clear the trachea and bronchi (i.e., the passages below the glottis). Inflammation caused by a respiratory infection or the damage produced in the respiratory passages by heavy smoking may trigger a chronic cough that can be annoying and debilitating. Some ingredients of cough medicines soothe the irritated mucous membranes; others, such as codeine compounds, depress the cough center in the medulla.

Sneezing A **sneeze** has been described as an upper respiratory cough. An irritation in the nasal passages stimulates an indrawn breath, which is expelled with explosive force. In a sneeze the glottis is open, but the mouth and nose provide momentary resistance. Thus, a sneeze serves to clear the passages of the nose and mouth.

Sighing A **sigh** is a deep, long-drawn inspiration, immediately followed by a shorter but forceful expiration, sometimes with accompanying vocalization.

Yawning Have you ever noticed that when someone in the room yawns, everyone else begins to yawn also? (In fact, just reading about yawning can bring

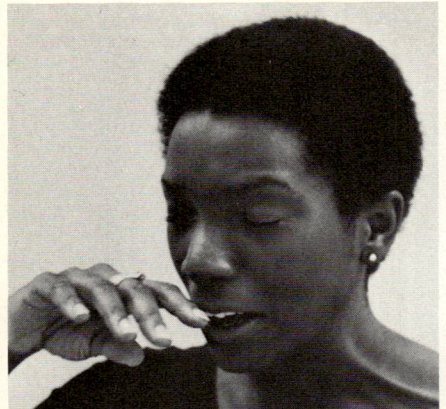

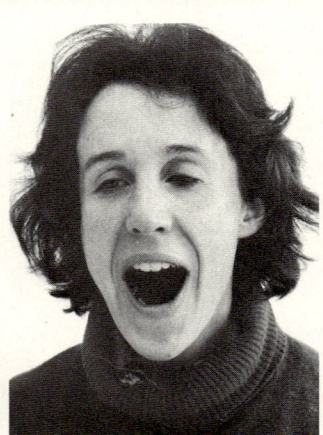

FIGURE 24-8 Sneezing, crying, laughing, and yawning all involve modified respiratory movements.

about an uncontrollable desire to yawn.) A **yawn** is a deep inspiration through a wide-open mouth. Yawning produces a more complete ventilation of the lungs than usual. In normal breathing, not all the alveoli are equally ventilated, and some actually close periodically. Blood coming in contact with poorly ventilated alveoli is incompletely oxygenated and dilutes the average oxygen content. The long, deep inspiration of a yawn opens up the collapsed alveoli and brings the oxygen tension back to normal. The yawning reflex is thought to be triggered by inadequately oxygenated arterial blood. But the frequent correlation of yawning with drowsiness, fatigue, and boredom, and the extreme suggestibility of yawning indicate that some degree of higher brain control must also be involved.

Laughing and Crying Sometimes it is difficult to tell whether a person is laughing or crying. The basic respiratory movements are practically identical: an inspiration followed by many short, convulsive expirations, while the glottis remains open and the vocal cords vibrate. The accompanying facial expressions usually differ somewhat, however, and crying is more likely to be accompanied by an active flow of tears

from the lacrimal glands. (Though sustained laughter may also be accompanied by tears.)

Hiccuping Everyone seems to have a pet remedy for stopping hiccups. A **hiccup** is a spasmodic contraction of the diaphragm, followed by a spasmodic closure of the glottis. The vocal cords vibrate during expiration, producing the characteristic sound. Hiccuping does not serve any known useful function. It is stimulated by irritation of the sensory nerve endings of the digestive tract and can often be stopped by inhalation of air containing 5 to 7 percent carbon dioxide. (This therapy is easily administered by having the person breathe in and out of a paper bag.) Swallowing a spoonful of sugar is another of the numerous remedies recommended.

PRACTICAL CONSIDERATIONS

The respiratory tract is one of the gateways into the body. Despite its formidable array of defenses, it is vulnerable to a variety of environmental influences, from the insidious onslaught of air pollution to the ever-present danger of mishaps during eating and drinking. (A surprising number of people choke to death because an insufficiently chewed piece of food is mis-swallowed and blocks the trachea.) The respiratory passages also provide a convenient avenue for introducing anesthetics and other drugs.

Disorders of the Respiratory System

Do people get sick more than they used to? The question must remain moot, especially since old-timers tend to have a view of the past that is rosier than reality. Certainly, modern immunization programs, increased standards of sanitation, and antibiotics have brought freedom from fear of many diseases that used to be scourges. Respiratory infections such as diphtheria and whooping cough, which used to kill large numbers of young children, have now become so rare that many doctors never see a single case in their practice. The incidence of tuberculosis has dropped sharply, and the pneumonia death rate has been lowered dramatically. Yet certain factors in the modern environment are promoting a rise in respiratory and other ailments that were nonexistent or only minor problems in the past. Air pollution—both the widespread type produced by the effluvia of factories and vehicles and the personal air pollution produced by smoking—has brought a rise not only in the well-publicized lung cancer, but also in emphysema. Better building techniques have eliminated drafts in houses, but have also promoted seasonal rises in respiratory infections during the cold months of the year, when people congregate in airtight, often overheated buildings, in which germs linger. Both central heating and air conditioning can dry the mucous membranes of the respiratory passages, leaving them more vulnerable to trauma and infection. And the proliferation of food additives and aerosol sprays has loosed a plague of potential allergens, which can trigger an inflammation of the respiratory passages in sensitive individuals.

Allergies   The air we breathe is filled with microscopic particles—dust particles, pollen grains, mold spores. Most people go through life both unaware of and unbothered by these substances. But for susceptible individuals, particular kinds of air-borne particles can act as **allergens,** triggering a special kind of antigen-antibody reaction that results in a localized inflammatory response. Symptoms of allergic reactions vary among individuals, but for many the respiratory organs are particular "shock organs." The respiratory membranes become swollen and inflamed, sneezing fits are common, and a watery fluid drains from the eyes and nose. Seasonal variations of allergies have names such as "hay fever" or "rose fever," and it is popularly supposed that the allergy sufferers are allergic to hay or roses; but actually the names merely correspond to types of vegetation that are prevalent at the particular allergy season. "Hay fever" sufferers are most likely allergic to ragweed pollen, individuals with "rose fever" to various grasses, and indeed, most people with seasonal pollen allergies have multiple allergies—for example, to dust, mold spores, and certain foods in addition. Because of the prominence of histamine in the inflammatory reaction, antihistamines are effective treatments for allergies. Avoidance of the allergen is a method of control that may be effective in food allergies, but, for seasonal pollen allergies, a series of desensitizing injections of minute quantities of the allergens is commonly used.

A special type of allergic reaction that can be terrifying for the patient is **asthma.** The term comes from a Greek word meaning "to pant"; the condition is characterized by edema in the bronchioles, secretion of thick mucus into their lumen, and bronchial spasm. The intermittent obstruction of the bronchi gives rise to labored breathing and wheezing. Characteristically, the outflow of air through the bronchioles is obstructed more than the inflow, and the lungs become increasingly distended. Food sensitivities are a frequent cause of asthma in children; in adults, asthmatic attacks may be caused by pollen sensitivities. A psychological component may also be present, since asthmatic attacks are often precipitated by an emotional crisis.

Asphyxia   Many restaurants are now training their personnel in emergency procedures for aiding people who have accidentally aspirated a solid chunk of food. Before several widely publicized cases focused attention on this problem, victims often went undiagnosed until it was too late. Typically, the victim is unable to speak (since the windpipe is blocked by the intruding object) and is likely to be misdiagnosed as having a heart attack. The Heimlich maneuver described in the previous chapter can usually dislodge the obstruction.

Asphyxia, or suffocation, is characterized by anoxia and hypercapnia (an increased carbon dioxide level in the blood). In addition to an obstruction of the trachea, it may be caused by drowning or by being trapped in a place with a limited amount of air—for example, a burning building, an abandoned refrigerator, or a caved-in mine. As hypercapnia builds up, the excess CO_2 stimulates respiration, and breathing becomes violent. The heart rate and blood pressure rise. But eventually breathing efforts cease, and the heart slows and stops. Prompt artificial respiration and administration of oxygen can revive the victim.

Carbon monoxide can also produce asphyxia by tying up the hemoglobin in the erythrocytes, preventing them from carrying oxygen. Oxygen therapy can raise the amount of oxygen dissolved in the plasma and ultimately displace the carbon monoxide, making the hemoglobin available for oxygen transport again.

Atelectasis

Atelectasis means a collapse of alveoli. A portion or all of the lung may deflate, not only occluding the alveoli but also greatly increasing the resistance to blood flow through the pulmonary blood vessels. Atelectasis may be caused by obstruction of an airway (e.g., due to aspiration of mucus or vomit during the administration of an anesthetic), by external compression of the lung, or by a lack of surfactant (e.g., in hyaline membrane disease).

Bronchiectasis

Bronchiectasis is a chronic dilation of the bronchi, characterized by spasms of coughing and the production of large quantities of pus-containing sputum. Dyspnea and fever are common symptoms. Fatigue, malnutrition, and exposure to cold can contribute to the onset of bronchiectasis.

Common Cold

Discussions of medical progress often elicit the comment, "How can they expect to cure cancer and heart disease when they can't even cure the common cold?" For a time it seemed that researchers were on the verge of developing a cold vaccine that would provide immunization against colds. Such vaccines have indeed been developed; unfortunately, it has been found that colds are caused not by one or two specific pathogens, but by more than 100 different viruses, and the vaccines provide protection only against a few of them. A common cold is an inflammation of the mucous membrane of the nose **(rhinitis).** Typical symptoms include an acute congestion of the mucous membrane and increased secretion. The swelling of the membrane and accumulated secretions make breathing difficult. Fever and headache may also occur.

Children up to the age of six are most susceptible to colds and often have six to twelve a year; people over the age of 45 seldom catch colds, probably as a result of accumulated immunity to cold viruses encountered over the years. Excessively dry air, which hampers the proper functioning of the mucous membranes, makes people more susceptible to colds and is a major factor in the fall and winter peak seasons.

Despite the misery they produce, colds are usually relatively mild illnesses that run their course in about a week. However, the infection may spread into the nasolacrimal duct, producing conjunctivitis, into the paranasal sinuses, producing sinusitis, or along the auditory tube, producing a middle ear infection, possibly leading to a mastoid infection. Colds also lower the body defenses and may prepare the way for secondary bacterial infections, such as bronchitis, meningitis, or pneumonia.

The use of large doses of vitamin C to prevent colds, proposed by Linus Pauling, has stirred a controversy in medical cricles. Another approach that is being pursued is the use of agents to stimulate the production of **interferon,** the body's natural virus-fighting chemical.

Emphysema

Emphysema is one of the fastest-growing diseases in the modern world. Its increased prevalence results partly from the fact that it is a disease of old age, and the average age of the population is increasing, but even more from the effects of smoking and air pollution. In emphysema, there is a pathological enlargement of the aveoli and air passages, and the walls of the alveoli are atrophied and thin. Many of the bronchioles are obstructed, and the total surface of the respiratory membrane becomes greatly reduced, sometimes to less than one quarter of the normal value. The capillary bed around the alveoli is reduced. All these changes, which contribute to a progressively increasing dyspnea, are irreversible. The chronic straining to draw breath produces a typical barrel-shaped thorax and distended lungs. The disease usually progresses slowly over many years, until the hypoxia and hypercapnia eventually cause death.

Influenza

Outbreaks of **influenza** periodically sweep through the world. Before the development of effective vaccines, such pandemics brought a high death toll—not from the influenza itself, but from pneumonia and other secondary infections that developed in the weakened influenza victims. Influenza is caused by a group of viruses and is highly contagious. Common symptoms are body aches, fever, general weakness, and inflammation of the mucous membranes of the respiratory tract. Immunity to the particular virus is acquired after an attack, but the fact that there are several types of influenza viruses (usually designated as types A, B, and C) and that they have exhibited a great tendency to mutate into new virulent forms means that there is usually a pool of susceptible individuals for the periodic outbreaks.

Lung Cancer

Every cigarette ad must carry the warning: "The Surgeon General has determined that cigarette smoking is dangerous to your health." Smoking causes a variety of ills, promoting the development of emphysema and heart disease, producing a chronic cough, and increasing the chances of prematurity for children born to a smoking mother. The result of smoking that has most captured the public imagination is the development of **carcinoma of the lung,** or lung cancer. This is a neoplastic growth, often malignant and often fatal, which is more than 20

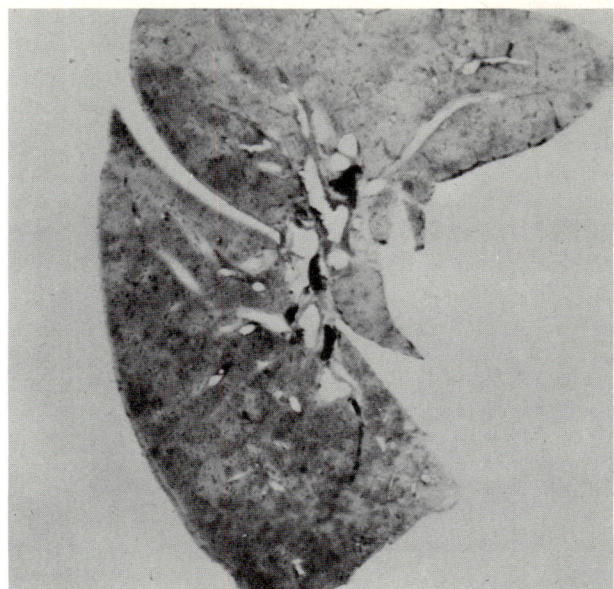

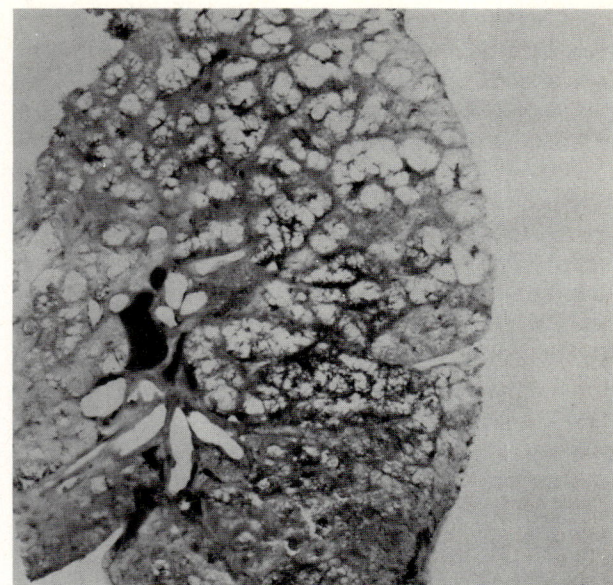

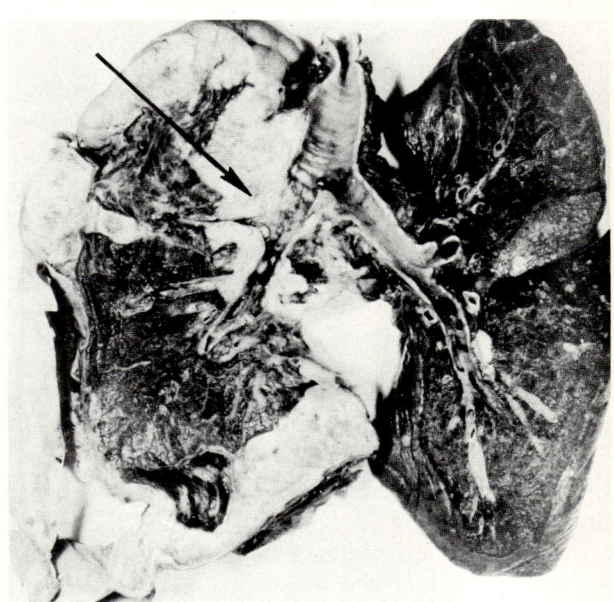

times as prevalent in heavy smokers than in non-smokers. As the malignant cells multiply, they crowd out normal cells and destroy tissue. Chemotherapy, radiation, and surgery (removal of affected segments or of the entire diseased lung) are used as treatments.

Pneumonia **Pneumonia** is much less feared now that effective antibiotics are available. It is an acute infection in which the lung tissue or the walls of the bronchi are inflamed. Pneumonia is usually caused by a bacterium, especially *Pneumococcus.* (There is also a viral pneumonia, which is similar to influenza.) Forms of pneumonia include **lobar pneumonia,** in which an entire lung is affected, **lobular pneumonia,** in which only portions of a lobe are affected, and **bronchopneumonia,** affecting the bronchi. When fluid collects in the alveoli, the condition is referred to as **consolidation.** The inflammation and generalized edema of the alveolar walls hamper the oxygenation of the blood, and dyspnea and cyanosis result. Chills, chest pain, fever, coughing, profuse sweating, and delerium are also frequent symptoms. Pneumonia occurs most often in young children and in the aged.

Pulmonary Fibrosis In pulmonary fibrosis, the normal lung tissue is replaced by fibrous tissue, reducing the elasticity of the lungs. The lung capacity is reduced, and respiration is difficult. There is a large residual air volume and a small tidal volume. Hypoxia and hypercapnia develop and stimulate deeper and faster respiration; breathing becomes labored. Chest pain, a dry cough, and fatigue after slight exertion are common symptoms. Pulmonary fibrosis may

FIGURE 24-9 Smoking is a significant factor in emphysema, lung cancer, and other respiratory pathologies, as these photos vividly show.

result from a healing tuberculosis lesion, a fungus infection, or scars from a lung injury. In about a fourth of the cases, no definite cause can be found.

Silicosis is a diffuse fibrosis of the lungs caused by many years of inhalation of dust-laden air containing silicon dioxide particles. It is an occupational disease of miners and is sometimes called "miner's asthma." Coal miners commonly suffer from a form of pulmonary fibrosis called **black lung,** named for the deposits of carbon particles in the lungs.

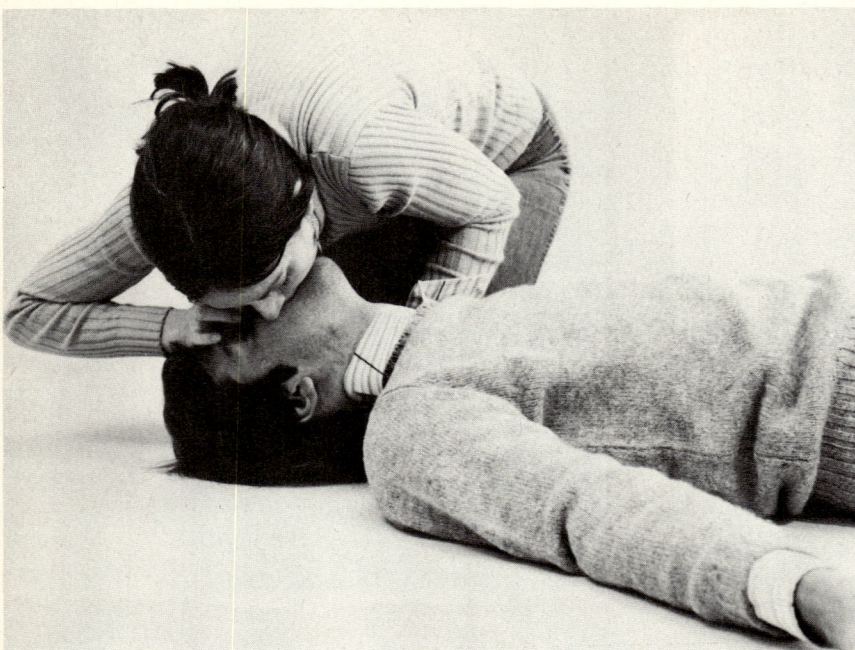

FIGURE 24-10 Mouth-to-mouth resuscitation. See text for the steps in using this life-saving technique.

Cystic fibrosis, a hereditary condition responsible for most of the serious chronic lung disease in American children, is not a type of pulmonary fibrosis. The disease was named for the secondary effect of scarring and cyst formation in the pancreas, observed in autopsies of victims. Impairment of lung function is caused by the secretion of an abnormally thick and adhesive mucus, which clogs the bronchioles and leads to emphysema, atelectasis, and repeated Staph infections, which further inflame and damage the lung tissues.

Tuberculosis Literary fashions change with the times. Today tragic heroines in books and movies die of leukemia; a few generations ago, tuberculosis was the favored disease of novelists, who euphemistically referred to it as "consumption." It is estimated that about half the population becomes infected with tuberculosis at some time or another, but when the general health is good, the body's defenses can usually contain the invading pathogens. The **tubercule bacilli** *(Mycobacterium tuberculosis)* invade the lungs, producing a local tissue reaction. The infected area becomes walled off by fibrous connective tissue, forming the characteristic "tubercle." In a small percentage of cases, the walling-off process fails, and the tubercule bacilli spread, producing fibrous tubercles in various sites. In the late stage, secondary infections by other bacteria cause massive damage of the lung tissue. The reduced vital capacity, decreased pulmonary membrane area, and increased membrane thickness make breathing progressively more difficult and less effec-

tive. Pneumothorax is often produced in the infected lung to permit it to rest and repair itself. A diseased lobe may be removed surgically (lobectomy). Effective drugs, including streptomycin, isoniazid, and para-aminosalicylic acid, are now available.

Artificial Respiration

If more people were aware of the techniques of artificial respiration, there is no doubt that many more lives could be saved. Centuries ago, a person was considered dead if breathing had stopped, and one of the methods of determining whether life still persisted was to hold a small mirror in front of the victim's nose and mouth to see if it would be clouded by breath. But now it is known that when respiration is stopped by various causes—for example, drowning, obstruction of the trachea, heart attack, brain injury, smoke inhalation, electric shock—the victim may still be saved in many cases if respiration is promptly restarted artificially.

Mouth-to-mouth resuscitation (the "kiss of life") has been found to be the most effective emergency method of artificial respiration. Figure 24-10 illustrates this technique, which consists of the following steps. The victim is placed on his back, with head tilted backward, so that airways are open. The rescuer takes a deep breath, then places his mouth over the victim's mouth, forming a tight seal, and pinches the victim's nostrils together to prevent air leakage. He blows into the victim's mouth, about twice the amount of a normal breath, then removes his mouth and allows the victim to exhale passively. This se-

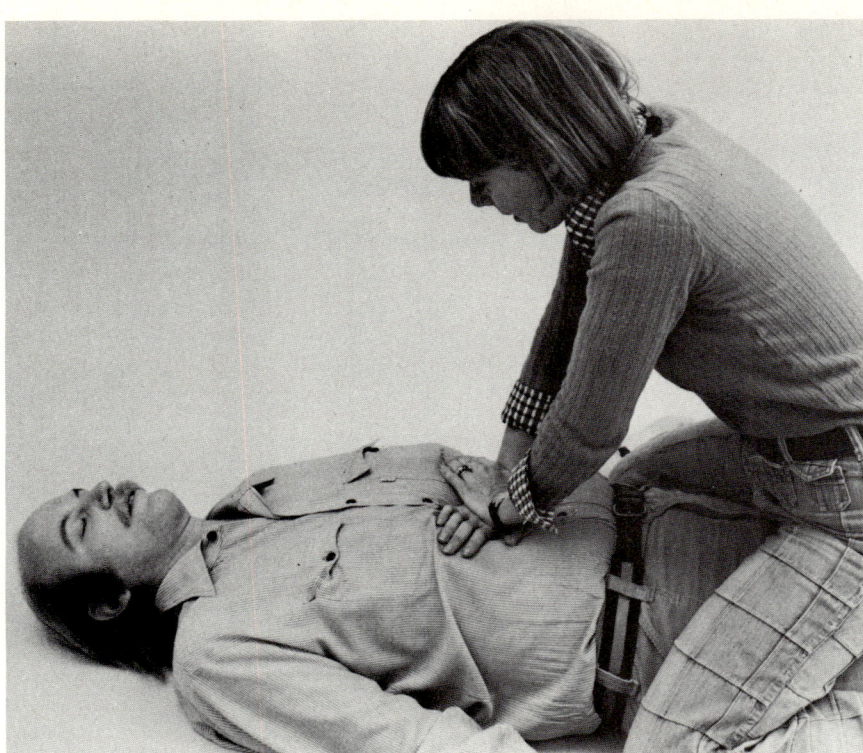

FIGURE 24-11 Cardiopulmonary resuscitation (CPR) combines mouth-to-mouth resuscitation, shown in Figure 24-10, with closed cardiac massage, shown here.

quence is repeated about 12 times a minute for an adult. (For a child, the rescuer's mouth is usually placed over the child's mouth and nose, and short puffs of air are blown in, about 20 per minute.) There are several signs the rescuer can observe to be sure he or she is performing the procedure correctly and adequate ventilation is occuring: the victim's chest rises and falls with every breath; resistance of the victim's lungs is felt as they expand; and the escape of air during exhalation can be heard or felt. If these signs are not observed, the problem may be faulty technique—the victim's head may not be tilted back far enough, or the mouth-to-mouth seal may not be tight enough. Or a foreign object may be blocking the victim's airways. If such blockage is suspected, the Heimlich maneuver should be used to dislodge the obstruction. Then artificial respiration should be resumed immediately. It should be continued until the victim either resumes breathing of his own accord or is pronounced dead, even if no signs of recovery are observed at first.

Mouth-to-mouth resuscitation is easy to carry out and moves a large volume of air. The forceful blowing of air into the victim's mouth provides a pressure gradient; the carbon dioxide in the rescuer's exhaled breath may help to stimulate the victim's respiration center. (The oxygen level is still sufficient to provide aeration of the victim's blood.)

When both respiration and heart action are stopped, mouth-to-mouth resuscitation can be combined with closed cardiac massage (Figure 24-11) in the first-aid technique of **cardiopulmonary resuscitation** (CPR), so that both pulmonary ventilation and blood circulation are continued.

A variety of mechanical respirators are available in medical centers for cases when artificial respiration must be administered over longer periods. In **intermittent positive pressure respiration,** gas is delivered to the lungs through an endotracheal tube passed into the nose or mouth or through a tracheotomy tube. A tank respirator (iron lung) may be used when the respiratory muscles are weakened or paralyzed, as after a case of polio. The patient is placed into a rigid tank, with his head protruding and an airtight seal around the neck. A bellows arrangement periodically lowers the pressure in the tank, inflating the lungs, then raises the pressure, forcing expiration.

Inhalation of Drugs and Anesthetics

A patient awaiting surgery in a modern hospital may be apprehensive as to the outcome, but at least she knows that she will not experience any actual pain during the operation. A variety of anesthetics are used to produce unconsciousness or deaden pain during surgery and childbirth. Some are injected into the bloodstream, but some of the best general anesthetics, such as **ether, halothane, cyclopropane,** and **nitrous oxide,** are administered by inhalation, through a mask placed over the nose and mouth. These anesthetic gases pass into the lungs, diffuse through the alveolar membranes into the blood, and are carried to the brain, where they depress the cerebral cortex. During the operation, the anesthetist carefully monitors the patient's condition, delivering the anesthetic gas intermittently as needed, and sometimes alternating it with oxygen.

Disorders of the respiratory tract are sometimes treated by inhalation of medication in a fine mist from a **nebulizer.** Tiny droplets of the drug are suspended in air and carried by various parts of the respiratory system, depending on their size. (The finest droplets, about 2 μ in diameter, reach the aveoli, while larger droplets, 7 to 16 μ, are carried mostly to the bronchi and bronchioles; the largest droplets, about 40 μ and larger, are deposited in the upper respiratory tract—the mouth, pharynx, trachea, and bronchi.) Drugs that relax the smooth muscle of the respiratory tract, antibiotics, and chemicals that decrease the thickness of mucus can be administered by nebulization.

As a major gateway into the body, the respiratory tract also lends itself to drug abuse. The effects the smoker gets from an ordinary cigarette are produced mainly by the alkaloid **nicotine;** the active ingredient in a marijuana cigarette, **tetrahydrocannabinol,** is also introduced into the body via the respiratory tract. Even the toxic solvents in glue preparations have been sniffed in the potentially dangerous pursuit of a "high."

SUMMARY

Respiration includes:
  Ventilation (breathing) = inspiration + expiration
  External respiration (gas exchange in the lungs)
  Internal respiration (gas exchange in the tissues)
  Cellular respiration (release of energy from food materials by oxidation reactions)
Ventilation occurs about 16 times a minute, with the creation of pressure gradients by expansion and contraction of the chest cavity.
  Contraction of the diaphragm lengthens the chest cavity; contraction of the external intercostal muscles and other chest muscles increases the diameter of the chest cavity.
  Surface tension holding the visceral and parietal pleurae together causes the lungs to inflate when the chest cavity expands.
  Boyle's Law states that the pressure of a gas is inversely proportional to its volume, when the temperature is kept constant.
  Inspiration is an active process involving muscle contraction.
    Quiet expiration is a passive process of muscle relaxation.
    Forced expiration is produced by contractions of the internal intercostal muscles and abdominal muscles.
Respiratory volumes and capacities are measured with a spirometer.
  The total lung capacity is the maximum amount of air the lungs

and respiratory passages can hold after a maximum inspiration.
  The residual volume is the air remaining in the lungs after a maximum expiration.
  The vital capacity is the amount of air that can be expelled by a maximum expiration after a maximum inspiration.
  The tidal volume is the volume of air flowing into and out of the lungs with each breath.
  The inspiratory reserve volume is the amount of air that can be inspired after quiet inspiration.
  The inspiratory capacity is the inspiratory reserve volume plus the tidal volume.
  The expiratory reserve volume is the amount of air that can be expired after a quiet expiration.
  The functional residual capacity is the expiratory reserve volume plus the residual volume.
  The tidal volume includes the alveolar ventilation plus the dead space.
  The minute volume of respiration is the product of the tidal volume by the number of respirations per minute.
Breath sounds produced by the dilation of the alveoli can be heard over healthy lung tissue.
  Abnormal breath sounds are called rales.
Inhaled air contains about 79 percent nitrogen, 21 percent oxygen, and 0.04 percent carbon dioxide.
  Exhaled air contains about 15 percent oxygen and 5.5 percent carbon dioxide.
  Dalton's Law of partial pressures states that the pressure exerted by a particular gas in a mixture of gases is directly related to the concentration of that gas in the mixture and to the total pressure of the mixture.
The diffusion of gases in the lungs is determined by:
  Functional surface area of the alveolar and capillary membranes.
  Pressure gradient between the alveolar air and the blood in the capillaries.
  Length of time blood and air are in contact.
  Permeability of alveolar and capillary membranes.
  Respiratory minute volume.
  Chemical reactions in the blood.
The alveolar gas exchange is influenced by:
  Altitude above sea level (thin atmosphere decreases pO_2).
  Respiration-depressing drugs such as morphine.
  Emphysema (reduces functional surface area of alveoli).
  Physical exercise (increases capillary circulation and respiration rate).
Oxygen is transported in the blood:
  In oxyhemoglobin in the erythrocytes (about 95 percent)
  Dissolved in plasma (about 5 percent)
Carbon dioxide is transported in the blood:
  As bicarbonate ions in the plasma (about 60 to 90 percent)
  As dissolved CO_2 in the plasma (about 7 percent)
  As carbaminohemoglobin in erythrocytes (about 10 to 30 percent)
The reaction of CO_2 with water to form carbonic acid occurs both in the plasma (slowly) and in the erythrocytes (rapidly, due to catalysis by carbonic anhydrase).
  Carbonic acid then dissociates into bicarbonate and hydrogen ions.
  Diffusion of bicarbonate ions out into the plasma produces an electrical imbalance that is corrected by the chloride shift.
Blood flowing through the body tissues picks up about 4 volumes percent carbon dioxide and deposits about 5 volumes percent oxygen.
Respiration is an automatic function, which can also be controlled

voluntarily to some degree.

Reflex arcs controlling respiration include control centers in the central nervous system and chemo- and pressoreceptors.

The medullary respiratory center (including inspiratory and expiratory neurons) sets the basic rhythms of respiration.

The apneustic and pneumotaxic centers in the pons modify the action of the medullary respiratory center, producing a smooth rhythm.

The Hering–Breuer reflex helps to control depth and rhythmicity of respiration; it includes stimulation of stretch receptors in the visceral pleura, transmission of impulses along vagus nerve fibers to the medulla, inhibition of the inspiratory areas and excitation of expiratory neurons, producing relaxation of the inspiratory muscles and expiration.

The hypothalamus and cerebral cortex participate in respiratory control.

Elevated carbon dioxide tension acts on neurons in the hypothalamus, medullary respiratory center, and carotid and aortic bodies, stimulating respiration.

A low pH (acidity) stimulates respiration.

Tissue anoxia stimulates respiration.

Terms for kinds of breathing are:

Eupnea: normal quiet breathing

Hyperpnea or hyperventilation: increased breathing

Apnea: cessation of breathing after expiration

Apneusis: cessation of breathing after inspiration

Dyspnea: difficult breathing, "air hunger"

Tachypnea: rapid, shallow breathing

Orthopnea: dyspnea relieved by sitting upright

Polypnea: hyperventilation following an emotional upset

Cheyne–Stokes respiration: rhythmic abnormal breathing pattern with alternating deep and shallow respirations

Biot's respiration: alternation of deep gasps with apnea

The work of breathing is determined by:

Airway resistance

Lung compliance

Lung elastance

Oxygen insufficiency (hypoxia) can be caused by:

Insufficient oxygen in the atmosphere (e.g., at high altitude)

Hypoventilation due to a neuromuscular disorder

Obstruction of the airways

Pulmonary disease that reduces the number of functioning alveoli (e.g., emphysema)

Circulatory disorders:

Heart defects with arteriovenous shunts

Generalized or localized circulatory deficiencies

Anemia

Tissue edema

Histotoxic hypoxia

Abnormal oxygen demands by the tissues

Hypoxia may be accompanied by:

Dyspnea

Cyanosis

Oxygen therapy is helpful in certain types of hypoxia.

Muscular exercise stimulates respiration. Mechanisms include:

Impulses from cerebral cortex

Impulses from proprioceptors in muscles and joints

Hypercapnia (elevated pCO_2)

Hypoxia

Lactic acid (lowered pH)

Elevated body temperature

Enhanced circulation

Contracting muscles can temporarily switch their energy metabolism to an anaerobic (without oxygen) pathway, producing lactic acid and running up an oxygen debt, which must eventually be paid by increased respiration.

Modified respiratory movements include:

Coughing

Sneezing

Sighing

Yawning

Laughing

Crying

Hiccuping

Disorders of the respiratory system include:

Allergies (localized inflammatory response to air-borne allergens)

Hay fever

Asthma

Asphyxia (suffocation)

Atelectasis (collapse of alveoli)

Bronchiectasis (chronic dilation of bronchi)

Common cold (virus-caused rhinitis)

Emphysema (enlargement and obliteration of alveoli)

Influenza

Lung cancer (carcinoma of the lung)

Pneumonia (bacterial or viral)

Lobar pneumonia

Lobular pneumonia

Bronchopneumonia

Pulmonary fibrosis (scarring of lung tissue)

Silicosis

Tuberculosis (infection by tubercule bacilli)

Artificial respiration can revive victims of drowning, suffocation, heart attack, brain injury, smoke inhalation, and electric shock. Techniques include:

Mouth-to-mouth resuscitation

Cardio pulmonary resuscitation

Intermittent positive pressure respiration

Tank respirator

Anesthetics administered by inhalation include ether, halothane, cyclopropane, and nitrous oxide.

Medications for the respiratory tract can be administered with a nebulizer.

Mood-changing drugs such as nicotine, tetrahydrocannabinol, and airplane glue are inhaled.

QUESTIONS FOR REVIEW AND THOUGHT

1 Distinguish between inspiration and expiration; external respiration and internal respiration.

2 Describe the mechanisms that establish a pressure gradient resulting in a flow of air into the lungs.

3 State the gas laws of Boyle and Dalton and describe their application to respiration.

4 Discuss respiratory problems of the deep-sea diver relating to: a) pressure and b) composition of inhaled gas.

5 How does the tidal volume compare with the (a) total lung capacity; (b) vital capacity; (c) resting chest volume; (d) residual volume?

6 Humans in unpressurized aircraft cannot survive above an altitude of 50,313 feet. Discuss.

7 Describe the mechanisms of oxygen and carbon dioxide transport in the blood.

8 Describe the nervous and chemical mechanisms controlling respiration.

9 Describe the effects of emphysema on respiration.

10 Distinguish between coughing and sneezing. What functions do they serve? Under what conditions can they be harmful? Why may holding the nose during a sneeze cause damage to the eardrums?

11 You are at a dinner party. In the middle of a toast, the host suddenly slumps over in his chair and turns blue. When you ask him what is wrong, he does not answer. What should you do?

ANATOMY OF THE DIGESTIVE SYSTEM

25

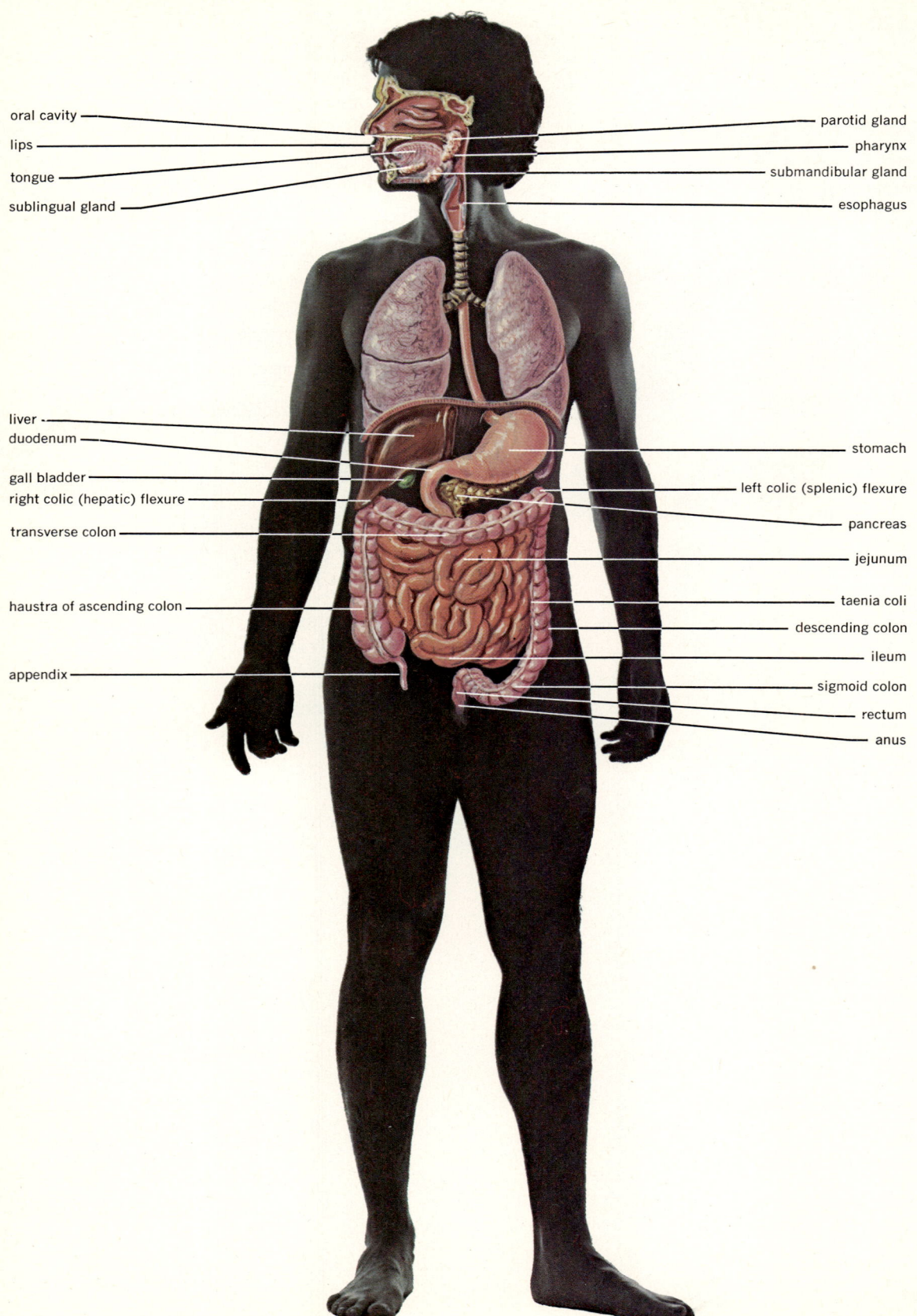

oral cavity

lips

tongue

sublingual gland

parotid gland

pharynx

submandibular gland

esophagus

liver

duodenum

gall bladder

right colic (hepatic) flexure

transverse colon

haustra of ascending colon

appendix

stomach

left colic (splenic) flexure

pancreas

jejunum

taenia coli

descending colon

ileum

sigmoid colon

rectum

anus

FIGURE 25-1   Organs of the digestive system.

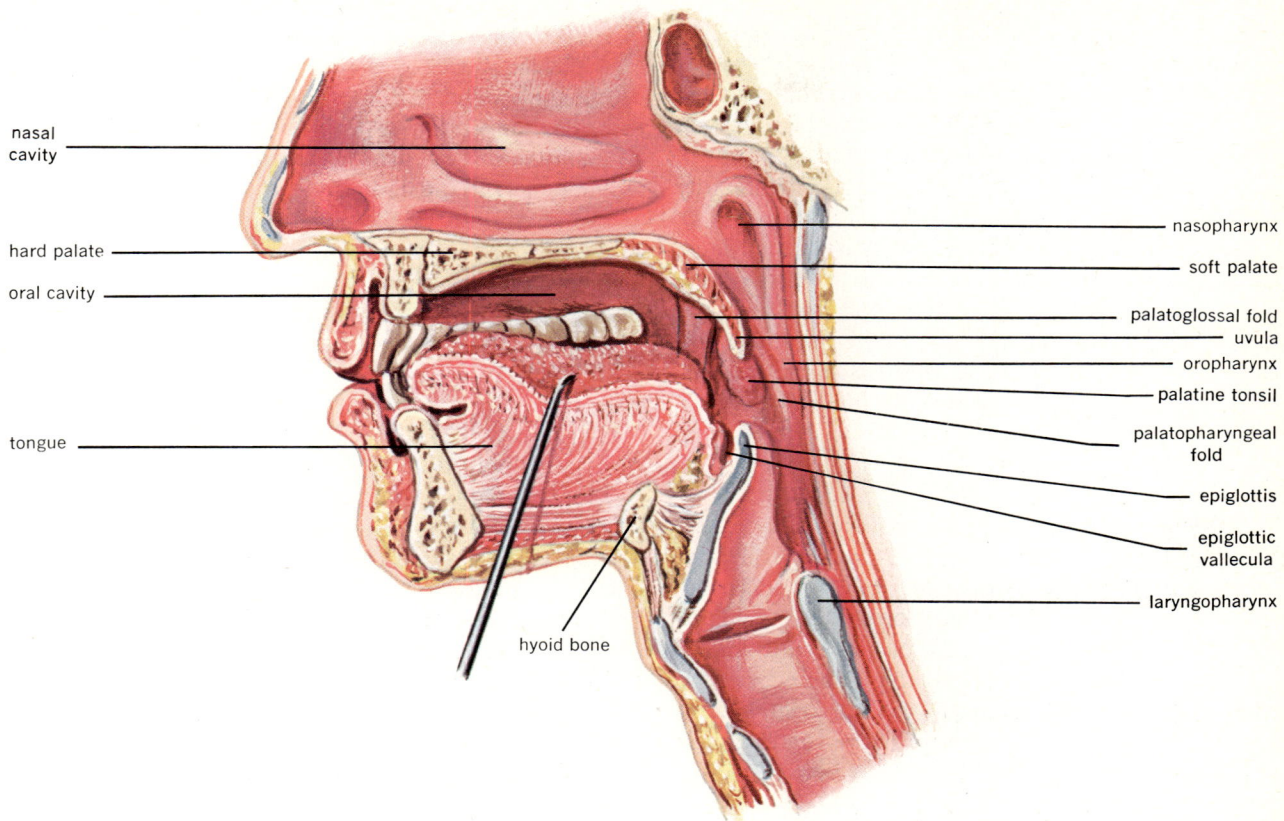

nasal cavity

hard palate

oral cavity

tongue

hyoid bone

nasopharynx

soft palate

palatoglossal fold

uvula

oropharynx

palatine tonsil

palatopharyngeal fold

epiglottis

epiglottic vallecula

laryngopharynx

FIGURE 25-2 The oral, nasal, and pharyngeal cavities (sagittal view).

If a coin is swallowed, in time it will duly emerge from the other end of the body unchanged, never encountering any significant barriers on its way. In a sense, it has never truly been inside the body, since the **alimentary tract** is like a tube, some thirty feet long, elaborately looped and coiled within the head, neck, and trunk of the body (Figure 25-1). Food materials that are ingested do not really penetrate into the body, where they can be utilized by the body cells, until they have been broken down into smaller, simpler components and have passed through the wall of the alimentary or **gastrointestinal tract.**

Food is taken into the **mouth,** passes down the tubular **esophagus,** into the baglike **stomach,** thence into the **small intestine,** which is coiled in the abdominal cavity like loops of spaghetti, and finally into the **large intestine,** which swings up, across, and down again through the abdomen, leading to the orifice called the **anus.** Various processing stations are strategically located along the way, to prepare and process the food and take up useful materials. In the mouth the food is broken into smaller morsels by chewing with teeth and by the chemical action of saliva; the stomach serves as a temporary repository, but also churns the food and subjects it to an acid enzyme bath that continues the breakdown process. A whole array of enzymes is delivered to the small intestine, working on various food components, and it is here that the absorption of nutrients mainly takes place; by the time the ingested mass reaches the large intestine, chiefly indigestible materials remain, and these are concentrated and expelled from the body.

THE ORAL CAVITY (MOUTH)

The first station on the route of the alimentary canal is the mouth. The movable lips open into a chamber (the oral or buccal cavity) that is equipped with an array of devices for starting the digestion process: grinders and cutters, lubricators and tasters, manipulators and movers.

The oral cavity extends from the lips to the oropharynx; it is bounded laterally by the cheeks, roofed by the hard and soft palate, and its floor is formed by the tongue, sublingual region, and lower jaw (Figure 25-2). It can be divided into the mouth cavity proper and the **vestibule,** the area between the teeth and the lips or cheeks. The mouth cavity is lined with mucous membrane, a wet epithelial membrane.

The Cheeks

Cheek cells are often the first human cells a beginning biology student examines in the laboratory. The superficial cells of the mucous membrane lining of the cheeks are easily rubbed off by food particles (or by a toothpick lightly stroked along the inside of the cheek in collecting a specimen of cells) and are continually replaced by new cells from below.

The main substance of the cheeks is striated muscle, chiefly the buccinators. These are accessory muscles of mastication, which prevent food from escaping the chewing action of the teeth. When the jaws are closed, the strands of fibroelastic tissue that anchor the cheek lining to the underlying muscle draw the relaxed mucous membrane into folds.

The Lips

The lips are one of the most sensitive areas of the body. Their thin, translucent outer covering is neither skin nor mucous membrane, but a sort of transition between them. Since it is not keratinized, the lips must be moistened frequently or protected with a cream to keep them from cracking. The connective tissue papillae of the dermis of the lips contain profusely ramifying capillaries, which give the lips their red color. On the inner surface of the lips, there is a transition to mucous membrane.

The substance of the lips consists of striated muscle fibers and fibroelastic connective tissue. Their main function is simply to close the mouth cavity, but the lips also are important in speech and in facial expression. Their lavish supply of sense receptors promotes an erotic function, in the act of kissing.

The Tongue

For sheer versatility, the tongue is one of the leading structures in the body. It is shaped somewhat like a boot turned upside down (the "sole" or **dorsum** is the portion you see when a person's mouth is open) and is formed mainly of interlacing bundles of muscles, which were described in Chapter 10.

The dorsum of the tongue is studded with minute projections, the papillae (Figure 25-3), which vary from slender, threadlike **filiform papillae** to larger, mushroom-shaped **fungiform papillae.** Another variety, the **vallate papillae,** are distributed in a broad V at the back of the tongue; these papillae have been described as looking like castles surrounded by moats. Both the fungiform and the vallate papillae contain taste buds, which were discussed in Chapter 16.

Though the tongue is the organ of taste, this is not its principal function. It is a master manipulator. It pushes food between the teeth, shapes masticated food into a convenient glob, or **bolus,** and then shoves it back into the oropharynx. In addition to aiding in mastication, the tongue also plays a major role in speech—so vital in fact, that in more brutal times a witness's silence was sometimes insured by cutting out the tongue.

The underside of the tongue forms a fold, the **frenulum linguae,** which extends from near the tip of the tongue to the floor of the oral cavity. Occasionally the separation of the tongue from the floor of the mouth may be incomplete, and it is bound down by membranes over nearly its whole length. In this condition, **ankyloglossia,** the tongue is not freely movable, and the "tongue-tied" person may have great difficulty in speaking clearly. (The condition can be simply corrected, by cutting the binding membrane.)

The Salivary Glands

More than a liter of fluid flows into your mouth each day, moistening the membranes and helping to moisten and digest food. This fluid is saliva, a thin, watery fluid secreted by the salivary glands.

The salivary glands are actually accessory organs of the digestive system. There are three pairs of them, all of which empty by ducts into the oral cavity (Figure 25-4).

The **parotid glands** are the largest of the salivary glands, located just under and in front of each ear. The duct of the parotid gland pierces the buccinator muscle and opens into the mouth in the inner surface of the cheek, opposite the second molar of the upper jaw. The parotid glands secrete a serous fluid.

The **submaxillary** or **submandibular glands,** on the inner surface of the mandible, discharge their secretions through ducts that open just behind the incisor teeth of the lower jaw. Their secretions are also mostly serous.

The **sublingual glands** are located deep in the floor of the mouth. Each sends a number of small ducts up to the surface, opening under the tongue. Their secretion is mostly mucous in nature.

The moistening action of saliva is particularly valuable when dry foods are being eaten. The moistened foods can be shaped into a bolus more easily, and saliva acts as a lubricant for the trip down the esophagus, protecting the inner surface of the tube from possible abrasion by incompletely pulverized food particles. Saliva also contains the enzyme ptyalin (salivary amylase), which begins the digestion of complex carbohydrates.

The Teeth

A paleontologist, looking at fossil teeth, can deduce a great deal about how the animal lived and what it ate. The human complement of teeth indicates an animal that is ready for almost any kind of food. There are cutting teeth, modified slashing teeth, and a service-

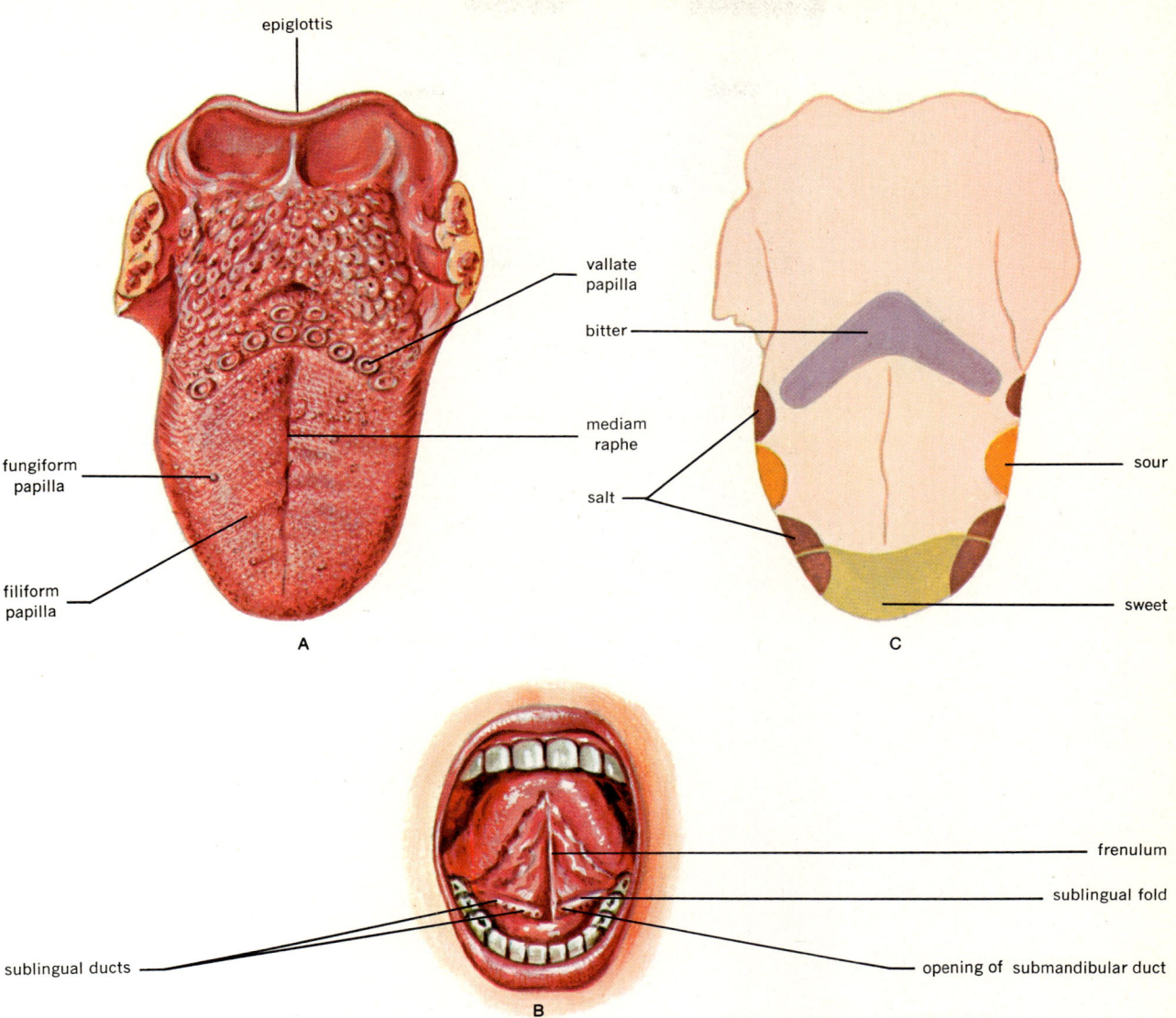

FIGURE 25-3 The tongue: dorsal view of the tongue (A) and anterior view of the oral cavity with the tongue raised (B). The diagram (C) shows the distribution of the four types of taste buds.

able set of grinding teeth. Humans are well equipped for their omnivorous eating habits.

The teeth are anchored in sockets in the **alveolar processes** of the maxillae and mandible. The processes are covered with dense connective tissue and smooth mucous membrane, forming the **gums** or **gingivae.** The gums are connected to the **periosteum** lining the tooth sockets, which serves for attachment (via **cementum,** a calcified nonvascular connective tissue) and nourishment of the teeth.

Each tooth consists of a **crown** (the portion protruding above the gum), a **neck,** and a **root** (Figure 25-5). The crown is covered with a dense layer of **enamel,** the hardest substance in the body. It contains only about 4 percent organic matter and is largely composed of calcium apatite with small amounts of

calcium phosphate. Beneath the layer of enamel is a layer of bonelike substance, **dentin.** Within the dentin is a region of soft tissue interlaced with connective tissue, blood vessels, and nerves; this is the **pulp.**

The jaws of a child would not be large enough to accommodate the full set of adult teeth. The problem is neatly solved by the fact that normal humans have two complete sets of teeth during their lifetime (Figure 25-6). The first set of 20 **milk teeth** or **deciduous teeth** begins to appear in the first year after birth, and generally is completed by the end of the second year. At about five to seven years of age, the deciduous teeth begin to fall out, and the **permanent teeth** begin to erupt. By about twelve years of age a person usually has his or her first 28 permanent teeth. The last four teeth (**wisdom teeth**) usually erupt at about eigh-

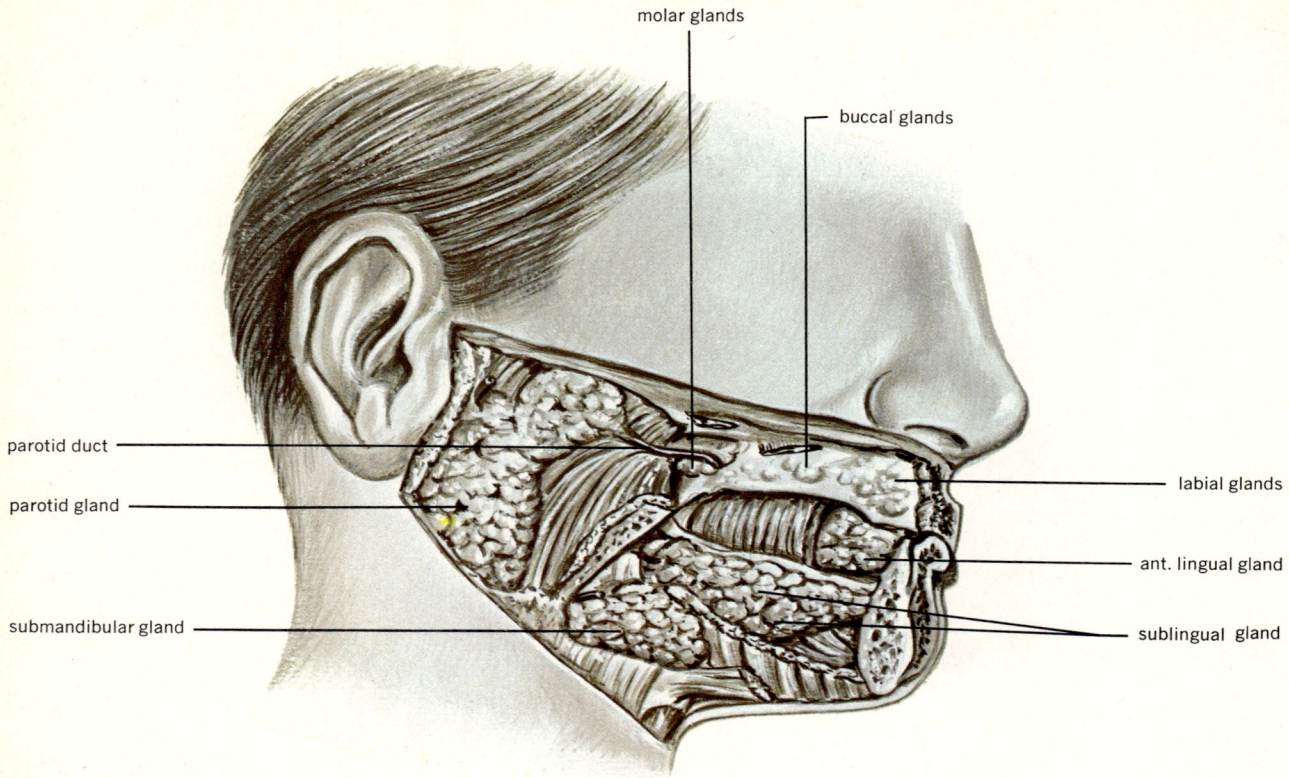

molar glands

buccal glands

parotid duct

parotid gland

submandibular gland

labial glands

ant. lingual gland

sublingual gland

FIGURE 25-4   The salivary and oral glands.

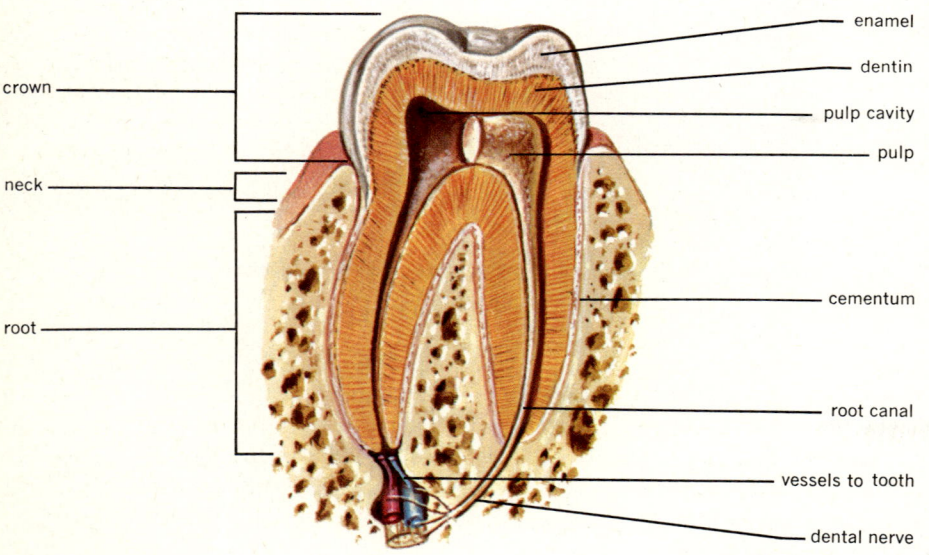

crown

neck

root

enamel

dentin

pulp cavity

pulp

cementum

root canal

vessels to tooth

dental nerve

FIGURE 25-5   Structure of a tooth: a molar in mid-sagittal section.

teen years, but in many people they are undersized and decay readily or do not erupt at all.

The complete adult set of 32 teeth includes 8 **incisors** (chisel-shaped cutting teeth), 4 **canines** (cone-shaped teeth that resemble the fangs of a dog and are used for tearing food), 8 **bicuspids** or **premolars** (used for crushing and tearing food), and 12 **molars** or **tricuspids** (large, broad teeth used for crushing and grinding food).

The formation of the teeth begins before birth, and continues through childhood; thus a diet rich in calcium and vitamin D, both for the pregnant mother and for the growing child, is important for good tooth formation. The ingestion of fluoride in drinking water or the application of a fluoride coating on children's teeth can help to strengthen the enamel still further and protect against **dental caries** (tooth decay). Regular and thorough cleaning is also important. If teeth

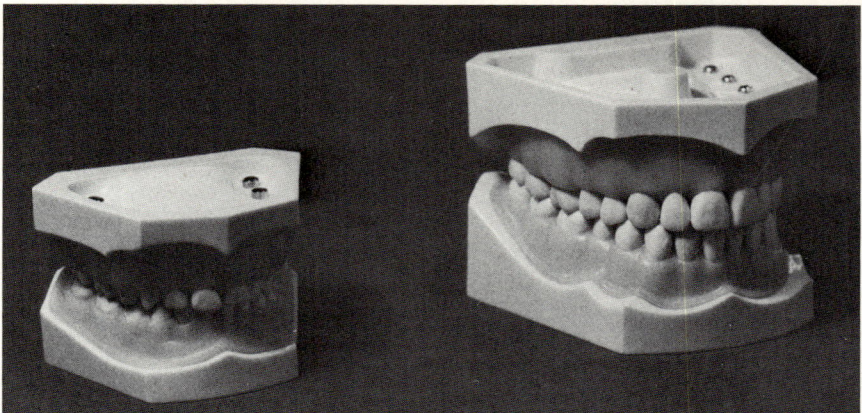

FIGURE 25-6 The two sets of human teeth. The deciduous teeth are smaller and fewer in number, to fit into the child-sized jaw. Note that the set of "baby teeth" pictured on the left actually contains the first four permanent teeth (six-year molars) in addition to the 20 deciduous teeth. The permanent teeth shown include a full set of 32. (Dental models such as those pictured are made from moldings taken from actual teeth and gums.)

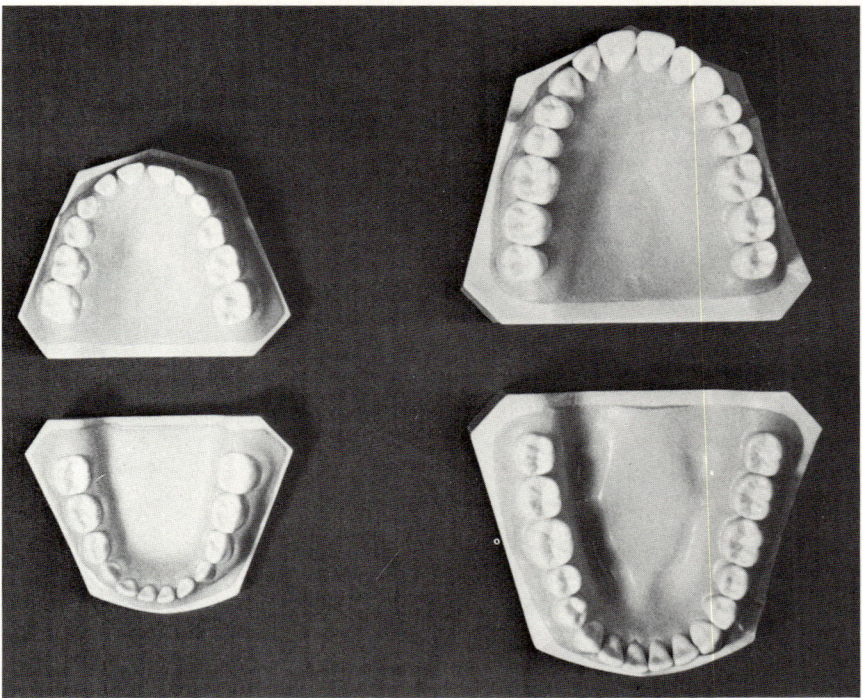

are not cleaned sufficiently, they become coated with a deposit called **plaque.** Bacteria thrive in the bits of decomposing food and tissue debris contained in plaque, particularly in the crevices between teeth. The bacteria secrete acids that can destroy tooth enamel, producing decay. A diet high in sugars promotes the growth of decay bacteria, particularly if the teeth are not cleaned after eating. Hereditary factors also appear to contribute to tooth strength. About 1 percent of the population has teeth highly resistant to decay; researchers hope ultimately to be able to isolate some bacteriostatic active ingredient from the saliva of such fortunate persons.

The Palate

If you run your tongue over the roof of your mouth you will notice that in front, the roof of the mouth is hard; toward the back, where it may be difficult to feel with the tongue, it is soft.

The anterior portion of the roof of the mouth is formed by the maxillae and palatine bones, covered with a thick periosteum and a protective epithelium. This is the **hard palate.** The posterior portion is the **soft palate,** composed of muscles and ending in a dangling projection, the **uvula.** (If you have ever opened your mouth and said "Ahh" in front of a mirror, you have undoubtedly noticed the uvula hanging down at the entrance to the throat.) The soft palate is attached to the posterior margin of the hard palate. During swallowing it is drawn up to close the nasopharynx and prevent food or liquids from entering the nasal cavity. (If you try to talk or laugh while drinking, the closing nechanism may fail to operate, and liquid will back up into your nose.)

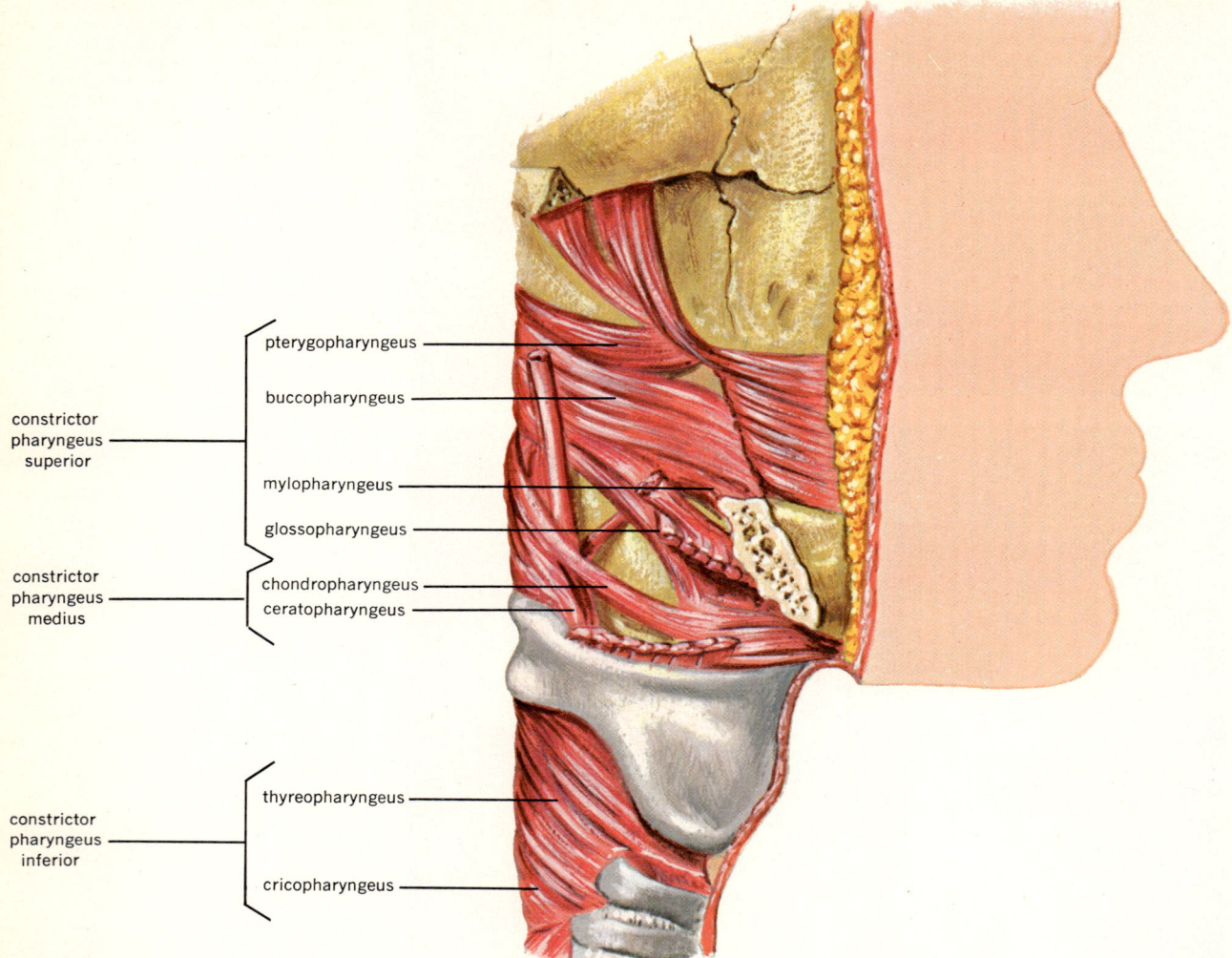

constrictor
pharyngeus
superior
{
pterygopharyngeus
buccopharyngeus
}

mylopharyngeus
glossopharyngeus

constrictor
pharyngeus
medius
{
chondropharyngeus
ceratopharyngeus
}

constrictor
pharyngeus
inferior
{
thyreopharyngeus
cricopharyngeus
}

FIGURE 25-7 Muscles of the pharynx.

THE PHARYNX

The pharynx is a double-duty passageway, leading both to the digestive tract and to the respiratory tract. It does not contain an assortment of digestive aids, as the mouth does, but it does help in swallowing. Layers of striated muscles—an inner layer of longitudinal fibers and an outer layer of circular fibers—permit the pharynx to be widened or narrowed (Figure 25-7). When a bolus of food enters the pharynx, the constrictor muscles (the circular layer) contract to grasp the bolus and move it on down to the esophagus. Other muscles raise the pharynx during swallowing, widen it by drawing the sides laterally, and help the soft palate to close the nasopharynx.

There is a small, pocketlike recess between the lateral wall of the pharynx and the upper part of the larynx. If, when swallowing a pill, you have the feeling it is "caught in your throat," it may be temporarily lodged in this **piriform recess**. (It is advisiable to

drink plenty of water while swallowing pills, particularly acid substance such as vitamin C tablets or aspirins, to avoid damage to the lining of the pharynx and esophagus.)

The entrance to the oropharynx from the mouth cavity is called the fauces. At the lower end (the laryngopharynx), the entrance to the larynx is the well-defined glottis, but the entrance to the esophagus is not so distinct—the tubes merge smoothly.

WALLS OF THE DIGESTIVE ORGANS

From the esophagus down, the digestive tract is really a continuous tube of variable thickness, from the bulging baglike stomach to the thin, spaghetti-like small intestine. All of its parts, no matter how externally dissimilar, have the same basic structure of their tubular walls. There are four basic layers: a **mucous membrane**, a **submucous coat**, a **muscular coat**, and a **fibroserous coat** (Figure 25-8).

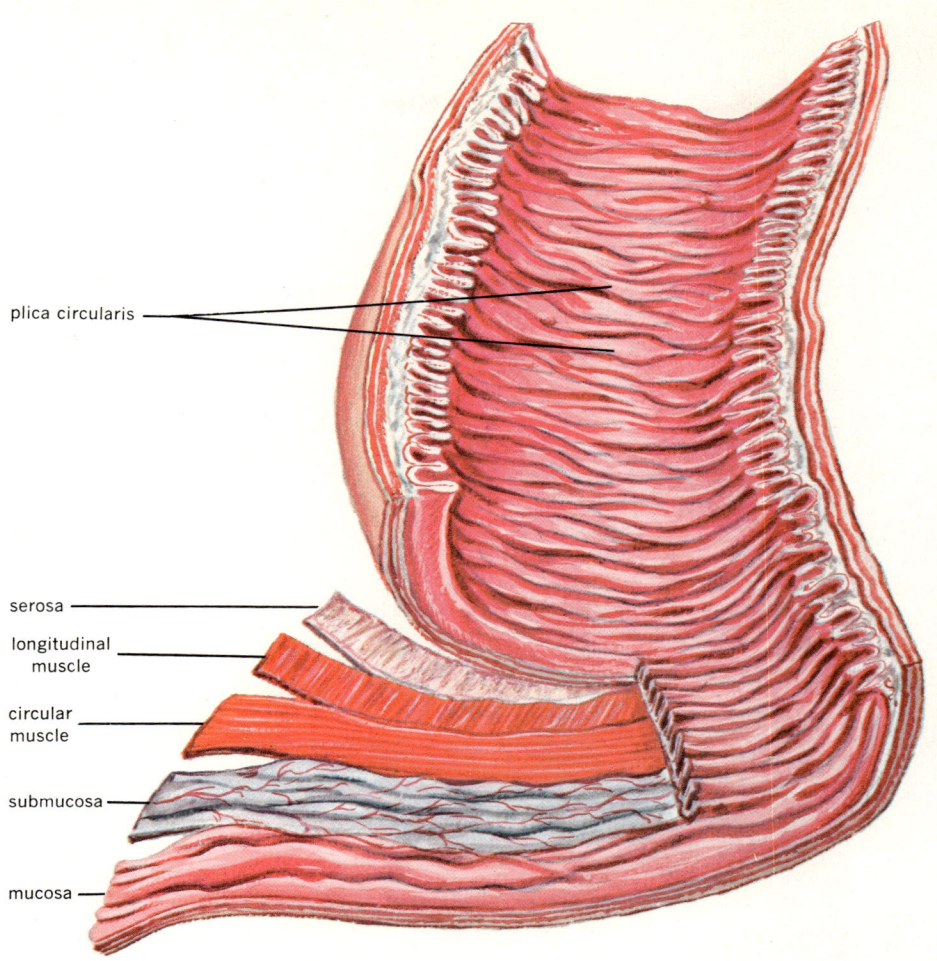

FIGURE 25-8 Section of the small intestine showing the layered structure of the wall.

plica circularis

serosa

longitudinal muscle

circular muscle

submucosa

mucosa

The mucous membrane, or **tunica mucosa,** is the innermost layer or lining of the digestive tract. It consists of an epithelium; an underlying supporting layer of connective tissue, the **lamina propria;** and a thin layer of smooth muscle fibers, the **muscularis mucosae.** Glandular cells secrete mucus and—in the stomach and small intestine—digestive juices. The supporting connective tissue contains numerous accumulations of lymphoid tissue. (Considering the unsterile nature of many of the things we swallow, the digestive tract is an especially busy arena for the body's defenders.)

The submucous layer, or **tela submucosa,** is composed of loose connective tissue, in which abundant blood vessels, lymphatics, and nerves are embedded. The nerve fibers and terminal ganglia are interwoven to form a submucous plexus, called **Meissner's plexus,** containing components of both divisions of the autonomic nervous system.

The muscular coat, or **tunica muscularis externa,** consists of two sheets of smooth muscle. The inner layer is composed of circular fibers, which contract to narrow the lumen of the tube. The fibers of the outer layer are arranged longitudinally; when they contract, the tube is shortened. Spontaneous rhythmic contractions of these muscles serve to mix the contents of the lumen and move them along. A plexus of autonomic nerve fibers and terminal ganglia, called **Auerbach's plexus,** is found between the two sheets of smooth muscle and can alter their tonus and rhythm of contraction.

The fibrious outer coat of the digestive tract is called the **tunica adventitia** or **serosa,** depending on its nature and location: a fibrous layer (tunica adventitia) above the diaphragm and a mostly serous coat (serosa) below the diaphragm. In the abdominal region the serosa is actually the **visceral peritoneum;** the corresponding **parietal peritoneum** lines the abdominal wall, and in many regions there is a **peritoneal cavity** between them (Figure 25-9). The serous fluid secreted by both the visceral and the parietal peritoneum makes their surfaces smooth and slick, so that the abdominal organs can move easily over the well-lubricated surfaces. Double folds of the parietal peri-

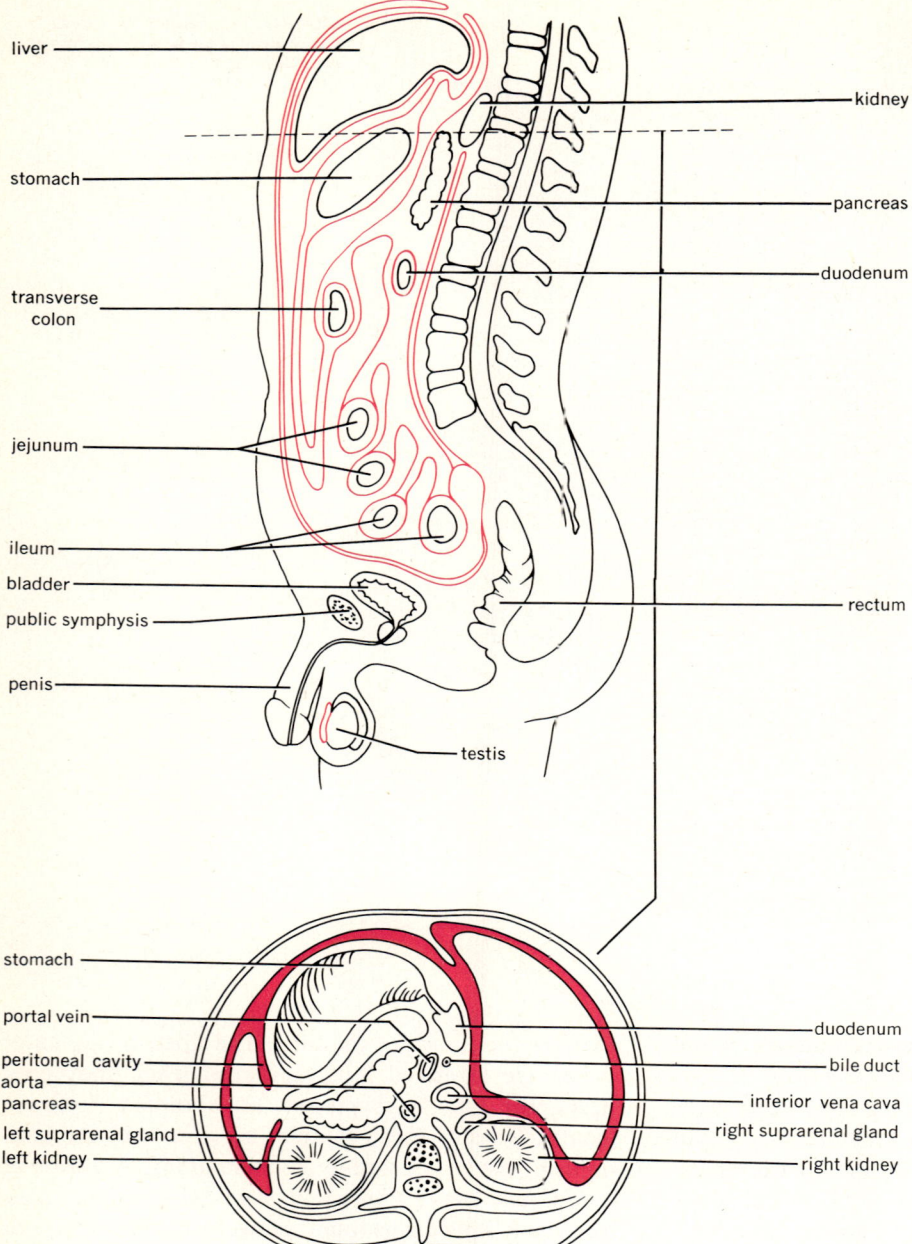

FIGURE 25-9 Mesenteries supporting the abdominal viscera in sagittal section (top) and transverse section of the abdomen showing the peritoneum (bottom).

toneum called **mesenteries, omenta,** and **ligaments** project into the abdominal cavity and support the abdominal organs. A large, fan-shaped mesentery anchors the small intestine to the posterior abdominal wall. The **greater omentum** is a fat-laden apron-shaped double fold of peritoneum that hangs down from the stomach and upper duodenum over the intestines. If there is a local infection in the abdominal cavity, such as appendicitis, the omentum envelops the inflamed area, preventing the infection from spreading into the rest of the cavity. The **lesser omentum** is a fold of peritoneum that attaches the liver to the stomach and duodenum.

THE ESOPHAGUS

Before the first manned space flights were launched, doctors were worried about whether the astronauts would be able to eat normally under conditions of weightlessness. Without the pull of gravity, when they swallowed, would the food go down the esophagus or lodge there and choke them? Fortunately, that was one worry that proved to be without foundation. Eating may present some problems in orbit—any loose bits of food have a tendency to float around the cabin and decorate the walls—but the actual swallowing posed no difficulty at all, and peristaltic waves of muscle contraction in the walls of the esophagus con-

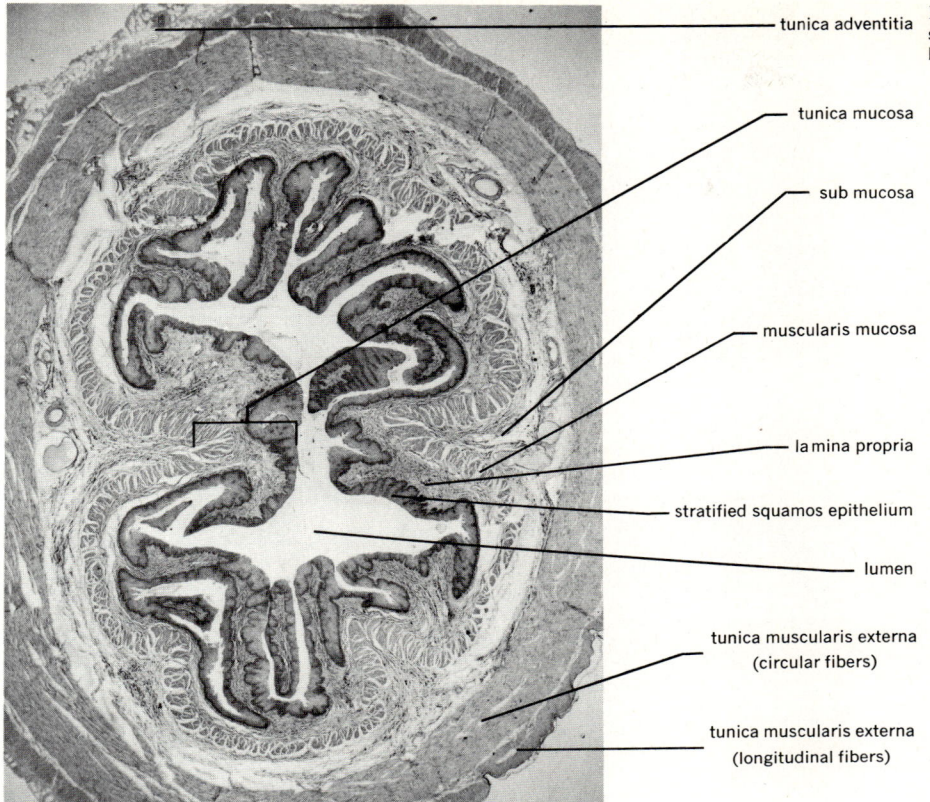

tunica adventitia

tunica mucosa

sub mucosa

muscularis mucosa

lamina propria

stratified squamos epithelium

lumen

tunica muscularis externa
(circular fibers)

tunica muscularis externa
(longitudinal fibers)

FIGURE 25-10   Cross section of mid-section of the esophagus, showing its layered structure.

ducted the food smoothly down to the stomach even when "down" had no real objective meaning.

The esophagus is a straight tube, about an inch in diameter and 10 inches long, which serves simply to conduct food from the pharynx to the stomach. It is posterior to the trachea, and unlike the windpipe the esophagus is collapsible—it lacks the reinforcing rings of cartilage that strengthen the trachea. If the mass of swallowed food is larger than the diameter of the relaxed esophagus, it can expand to accommodate it, protruding into the posterior wall of the trachea (i.e., into the gaps in the C-shaped rings of cartilage).

The esophagus has the four-layered structure of the wall typical of the organs of the digestive tract (Figure 25-10), but in one respect it is not typical. The muscles in the upper third of the esophagus are striated muscles, which in the middle third are gradually replaced by smooth muscle fibers, so that the muscle coat of the lower third is entirely smooth muscle. Even the striated muscles of the esophagus are not under voluntary control; they are supplied by autonomic fibers that travel in the vagus nerve.

The mucous membrane that lines the esophagus forms longitudinal folds, which disappear when food is passing through and the esophagus is distended. The membrane is studded with tiny papillae and con-

tains numerous irregularly spaced small glands, which secrete mucus to lubricate the membrane.

At the bottom of the esophagus, where it joins the stomach, the circular muscle fibers contract and relax like a "purse-string" valve, acting as a sphincter. Since the esophagus joins the stomach in the cardiac region, this portion of the circular muscle coat is often called the **cardiac sphincter,** although it is not a true valve and cannot be distinguished in a dissection. The sensation of heartburn occurs when the cardiac sphincter relaxes and a bit of the acid stomach contents regurgitates into the esophagus. In some babies, the cardiac sphincter frequently opens after a meal, resulting in "cheesing" or regurgitation of a mouthful of milk.

THE STOMACH

The size and shape of the stomach vary greatly, both from person to person and depending on how full the stomach is. A tall, thin person tends to have a long, narrow stomach, while a short, fat person usually has a short, fat stomach. A woman's stomach is usually smaller and slenderer than a man's. The stomach is never completely empty (it always contains at least a little gastric juice and mucin), but since it is essentially a collapsible bag, it assumes a slender J shape

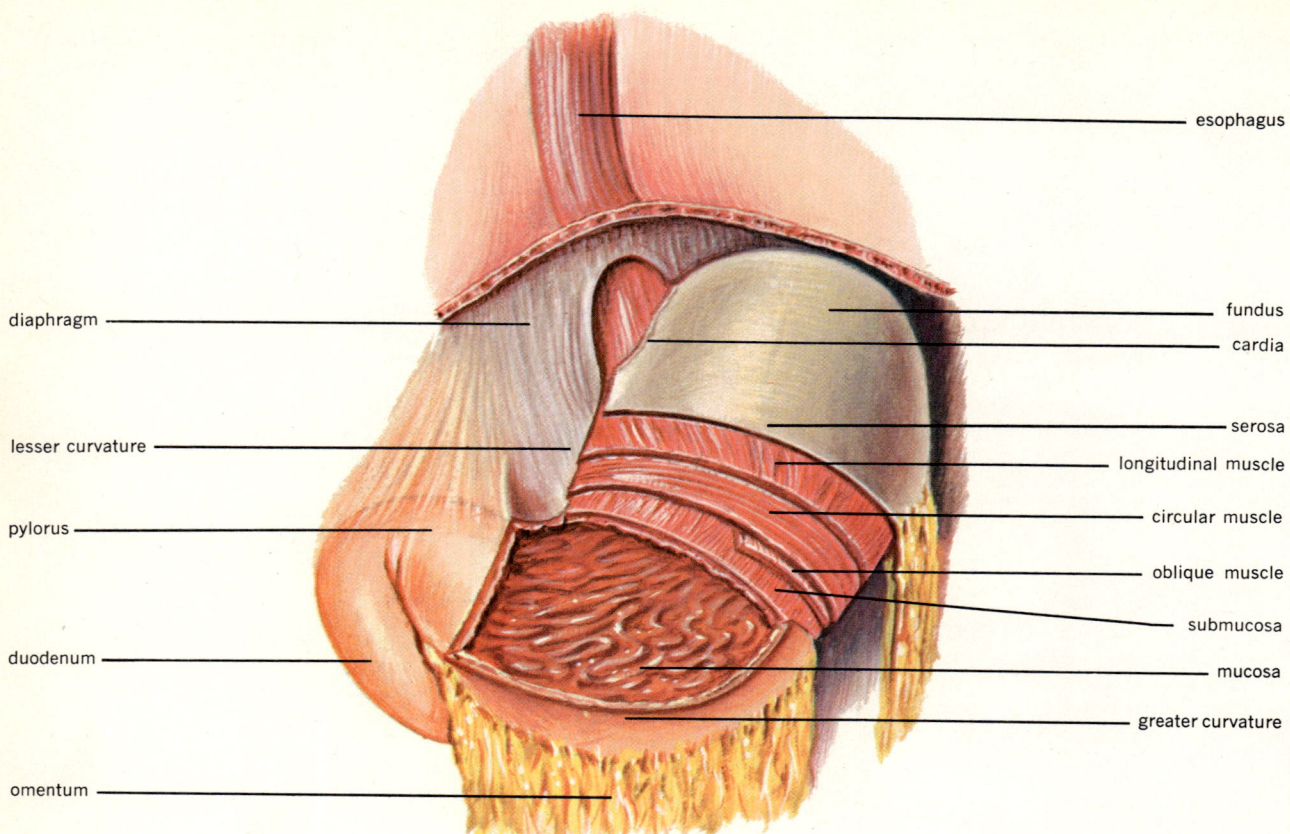

FIGURE 25-11　The stomach, partly cut away to show the interior surface and the layers of the muscular wall.

when it contains no food. After a meal, the stomach swells to accommodate the load—up to its full two-and-a-half pint capacity if necessary—and looks rather like a boxing glove.

The stomach lies in the upper part of the abdominal cavity, under the diaphragm and liver. When the diaphragm contracts with each inspiration, the stomach is pushed downward, and it rises with each expiration. (When you have overeaten, the stomach is distended and interferes with the descent of the diaphragm, giving rise to a feeling of dyspnea.)

The stomach extends from the esophagus to the duodenum (the first portion of the small intestine). As seen in Figure 25-11, the entrance from the esophagus is not at the top of the stomach. The balloonlike portion that extends above the level of the junction with the esophagus is called the **fundus;** it is commonly filled with air or gas. The middle portion of the stomach is called the **body,** and the constricted region at the terminal end, near the junction with the duodenum, is the **pylorus.** (The region near the junction with the esophagus is called the **cardiac region** of the stomach, because it is near the heart.) In the pyloric region the muscle coat of the stomach wall is thickened into the **pyloric sphincter,** which guards the en-

trance to the duodenum and prevents backflow of the intestinal contents. When a meal is being digested, peristaltic waves sweep over the stomach and down to the duodenum, periodically relaxing the pyloric sphincter and allowing a bit of semidigested food to squirt into the duodenum.

The stomach wall has the same basic structure as the other parts of the alimentary canal, with certain modifications. The inner mucous membrane is drawn up into longitudinal folds, called **rugae,** which disappear when the stomach is distended. The surface of the mucosa is pitted with numerous small openings—the site of specialized **gastric glands,** which secrete the constituents of gastric juice. The muscle coat is also somewhat atypical: in addition to the outer **longitudinal** and inner **circular muscle** sheets, there is a third coat of diagonal muscle fibers **(oblique muscle)** internal to the circular muscle, which maintain the curvature of the stomach.

The Gastric Glands

If an iron nail is left in a 0.17 N solution of hydrochloric acid, it will dissolve. Yet glands in the soft mucous membrane lining of the human stomach continually produce just such an acid solution, and nei-

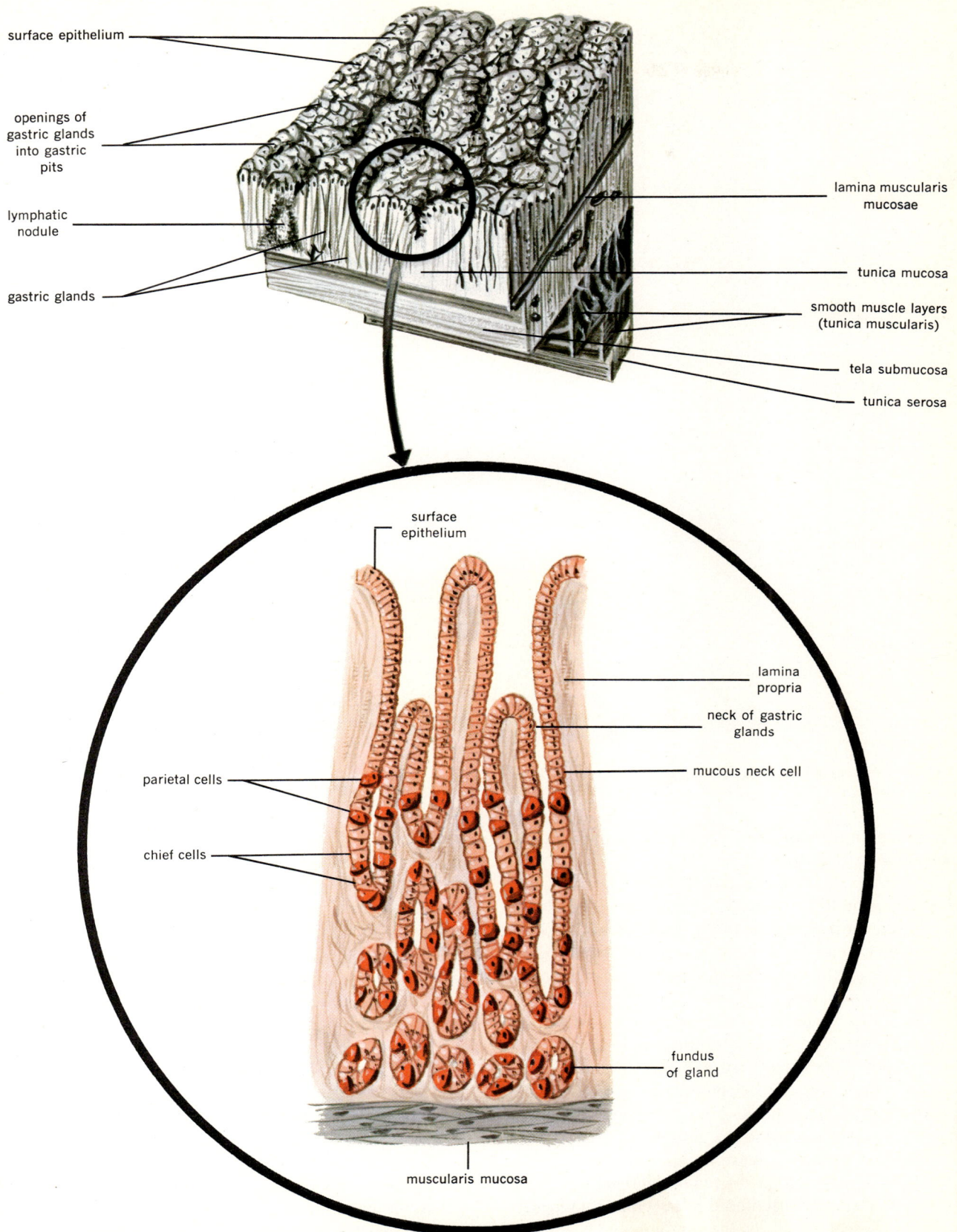

surface epithelium

openings of
gastric glands
into gastric
pits

lymphatic
nodule

gastric glands

lamina muscularis
mucosae

tunica mucosa

smooth muscle layers
(tunica muscularis)

tela submucosa

tunica serosa

surface
epithelium

lamina
propria

neck of gastric
glands

mucous neck cell

parietal cells

chief cells

fundus
of gland

muscularis mucosa

FIGURE 25-12   Structure of the stomach lining with details of the fundic glands.

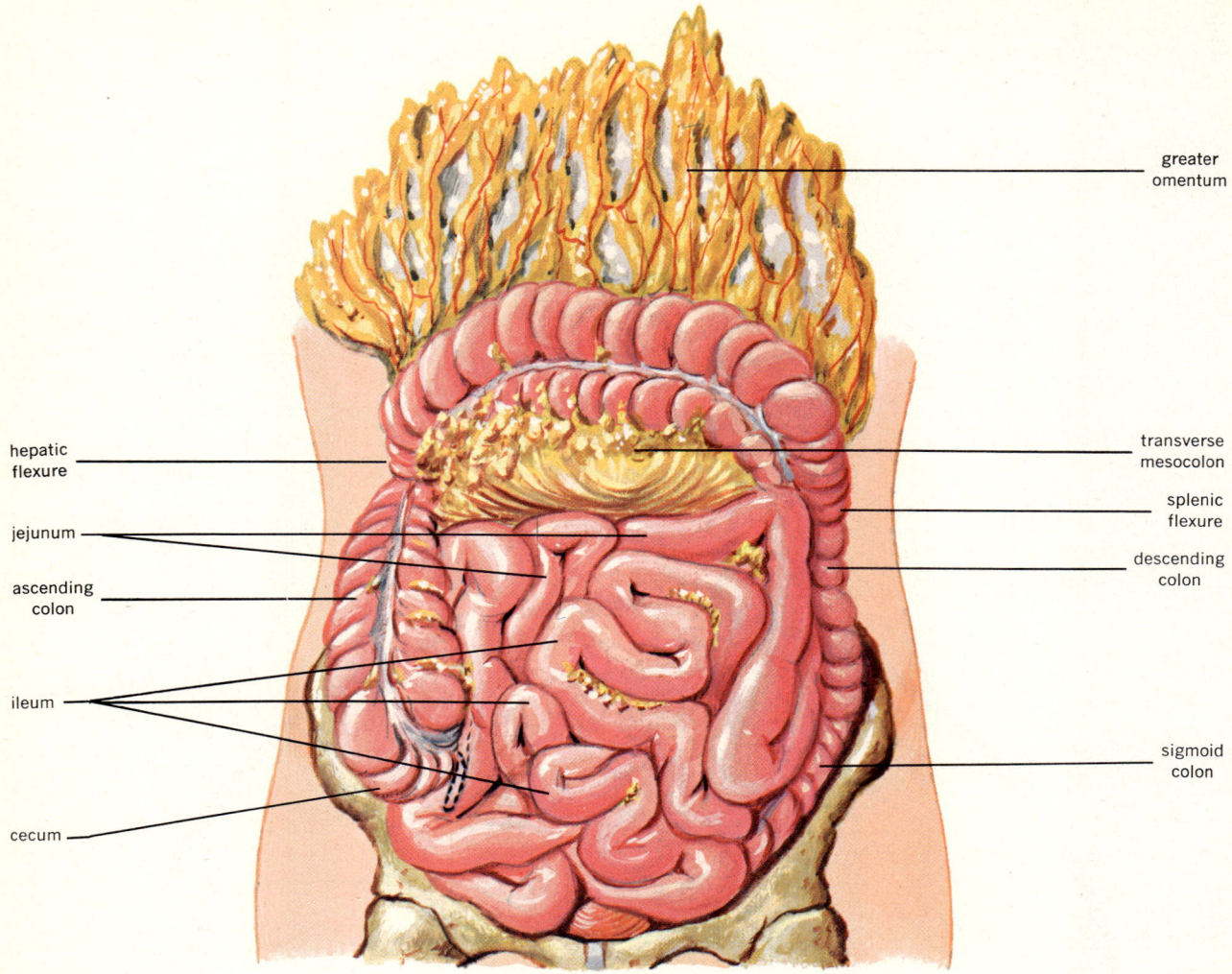

greater
omentum

transverse
mesocolon

splenic
flexure

descending
colon

sigmoid
colon

hepatic
flexure

jejunum

ascending
colon

ileum

cecum

FIGURE 25-13 The abdominal viscera, anterior view. The transverse colon and omentum are raised to show the folds of the small intestine.

ther the glands themselves nor the stomach lining are normally harmed by it.

The stomach mucosa is packed with glands, which open into small pits that dot the surface. The glands are called **cardiac, fundic,** and **pyloric glands,** depending on their location in the stomach, and they take the form of straight or coiled tubes. Several open into the bottom of each pit.

The fundic glands are the most numerous. They are simple straight tubes, containing several kinds of specialized secretory cells (Figure 25-12). **Mucous (neck) cells** surround the constricted upper portion of the gland and secret mucus. Numerous **zymogenic** or **chief cells** secrete pepsinogen, a substance that is converted to the protein-digesting enzyme pepsin in the stomach. Larger, wedge-shaped **parietal cells** produce hydrochloric acid. **Argentaffin cells,** which secrete serotonin, are scattered over the fundic glands.

The cardiac glands occupy a narrow region around the junction with the esophagus. They are simple or compound tubular glands and are lined only with mucous cells. The pyloric glands are coiled tubular glands found in the pyloric region. They, too, secrete mucus, which coats the stomach lining and protects it from being digested by its own gastric juices. Indeed, the slightest irritation of the stomach lining stimulates the mucous cells to pour out copious amounts of thick, viscid mucus.

THE SMALL INTESTINE

If a person is shot in the abdomen, the odds are that the bullet will penetrate some portion of the small intestine. This is the longest segment of the alimentary canal; about twenty feet of this flexible tubing is coiled and packed into the abdominal cavity. It is about an inch in diameter and extends from the distal end of the pyloric sphincter to the junction with the large intestine. The small intestine is divided into three regions: the duodenum, the jejunum, and the ileum (Figure 25-13).

The **duodenum** gets its name from the Latin word for "twelve," because it is about the length of twelve finger widths (i.e., about 10 inches long). It has a C-shaped course, curving over the head of the pancreas and behind the transverse portion of the large intestine. The duodenum is notorious as a site of ulcers, since it bears the brunt of the jets of acid chyme that periodically squirt into it from the stomach. Large clusters of mucus-secreting glands called **Brunner's glands** are found in the submucosa of the duodenum. In addition, this part of the small intestine receives the secretions of accessory organs: the common bile duct and the pancreatic duct open into the duodenum about three inches from the pylorus.

Although the position of the duodenum is fixed, the **jejunum** and **ileum** are somewhat movable, since they are suspended by a mesentery attached to the posterior wall of the abdominal cavity. There is no clear demarcation between the jejunum and ileum, although their membranes differ somewhat in structure. The jejunum is usually considered to constitute about two-fifths of the small intestine, and the somewhat longer ileum the remainder. The ileum ends in a right-angled T-junction with the large intestine, guarded by the **ileocecal valve.**

In much of the small intestine, particularly the jejunum, the mucosa is drawn into circular folds, **plicae circulares,** that do not disappear when the intestine is distended. These folds serve to increase the surface area of the intestinal lining. Another type of structure increases the intestinal surface area still more. The inner surface of the small intestine has a velvety appearance; under a microscope this is resolved into millions of tiny fingerlike projections called **villi,** packed about 10 to 40 per square millimeter (Figure 25-14). These are the working structures of the small intestine in its function of absorption of digested nutrients. The villi are covered with epithelium that in turn is crowned with a border of closely packed **microvilli.** The villi and microvilli increase the total surface area of the small intestine to an estimated 10 square meters—about three times the entire surface area of the body! Each villus contains a network of capillaries surrounding a single lymph vessel called a **lacteal.** Food materials pass readily through the epithelium into the vessels of the blood or lymph circulation. (Fats are absorbed into the lacteals.)

Between the villi of the small intestine, the mucous membrane is thickly covered with secretory glands and nodes. **Intestinal glands,** or **crypts of Lieberkühn** produce a variety of enzymes, such as lipase, amylase, and proteinase, apparently secreted by a type of cells called **Paneth cells** at the bottom of the crypts. The intestinal glands also produce mucus (secreted by **goblet cells**) and serotonin (produced by **argentaffin** or **enterchromaffin cells**). Solitary lymph nodules and aggregates of lymph nodules called **Peyer's patches** are found in the submucosa of the ileum.

THE LARGE INTESTINE

The difference between the large and small intestines are striking. The large intestine is much wider—about 2½ inches in diameter—but it is much shorter, only 6 feet long. Its mucosa contains no villi. Its longitudinal muscle layer is limited to three bands called **teniae coli,** which extend the length of the colon and are visible on its surface. The bands are shorter than the colon and pucker its wall to form small pouches called **haustra,** which give the colon a scalloped appearance. Small tabs of fat-filled peritoneum, called **epiploic appendages,** can be seen along the free border of the colon.

The junction of the ileum with the large intestine in the lower right portion of the abdomen forms a T (Figure 25-15). One arm of the T is a long tube, forming the major portion of the large intestine (the **colon** and **rectum**). The other arm is a short pouch called the **cecum,** which extends downward for about 5 to 7.6 cm. (In rabbits, the cecum is large and serves as a food-filled "culture flask" for colonies of bacteria that helpfully manufacture cellulose-digesting enzymes.) The ileocecal valve at the upper border of the cecum prevents liquid contents from the cecum and colon from being returned to the small intestine. A narrow wormlike outgrowth of the cecum, called the **vermiform appendix,** hangs down about 7 to 10 cm. The functions of the appendix are unknown, but it is frequently a trouble spot. It is not easily drained and its blood supply is limited, so that an obstruction by waste matter of digestion may cause an inflammation. A gangrenous condition may set in, and there is danger that an inflamed appendix may rupture, spewing out its purulent contents into the abdominal cavity and spreading the infection to the peritoneum (peritonitis). Acute appendicitis is generally treated by removing the appendix to prevent serious complications.

From the cecum the colon courses upward in the right-hand part of the abdomen, as the **ascending colon.** At the level of the liver, it makes a sharp bend to the left (the **hepatic flexure**) and then travels a sagging transverse path across the abdomen just below the stomach, as the **transverse colon.** At the spleen the tube turns abruptly downward (the **splenic flexure**) and becomes the descending colon. After an almost straight downward course for a few inches, the colon turns in an S-shaped bend (the **sigmoid colon**), crosses the brim of the pelvis, and enters the pelvic cavity,

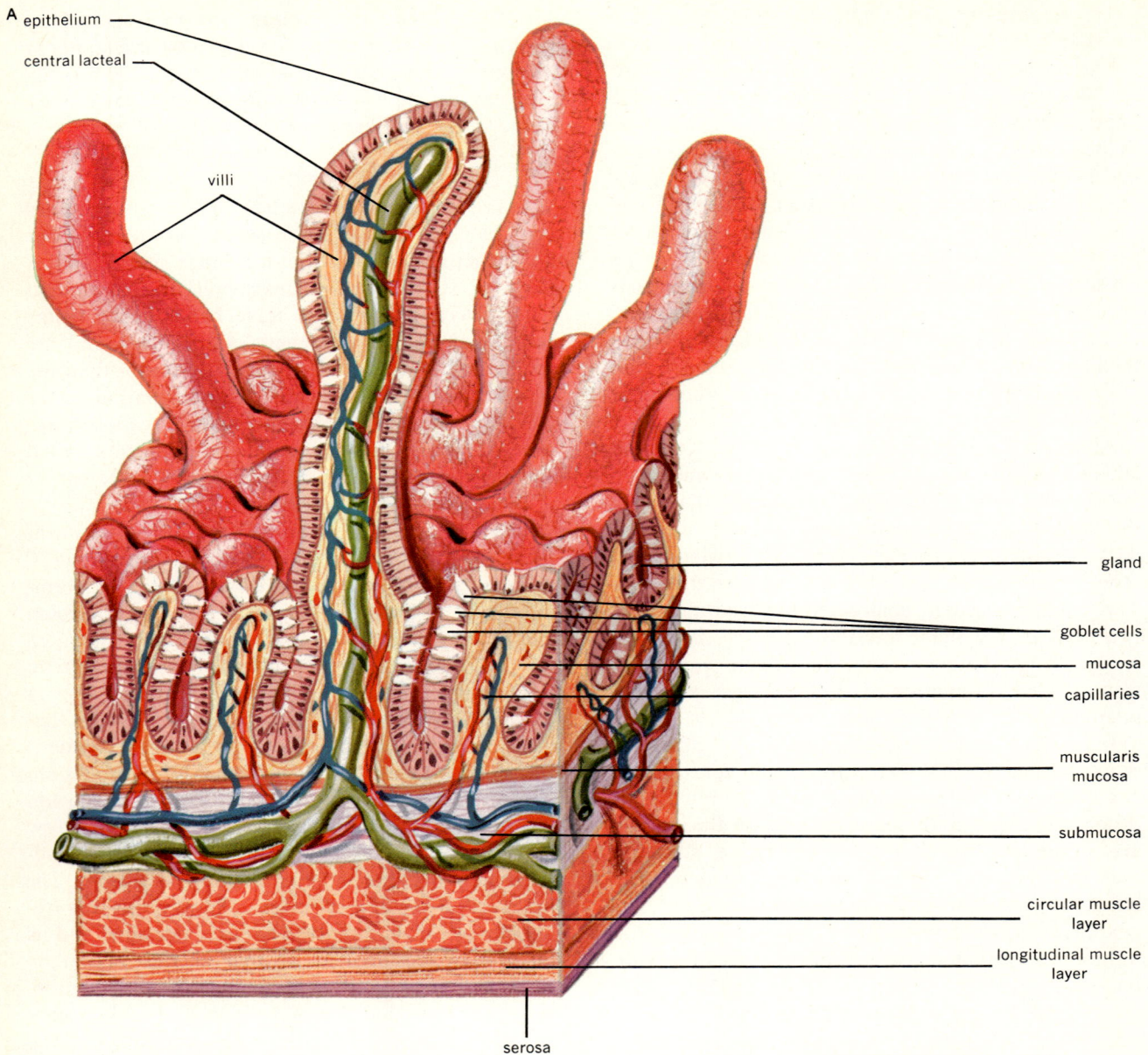

A
epithelium
central lacteal
villi
gland
goblet cells
mucosa
capillaries
muscularis mucosa
submucosa
circular muscle layer
longitudinal muscle layer
serosa

FIGURE 25-14 Working structures of the small intestine: (A) section of intestinal mucosa showing the structure of villi, lacteal, and glands. (B) Electron micrograph of a longitudinal section through a villus from the duodenum of a rat (×600). (C) EM (×6000) of the surface of an intestinal villus showing the microvilli.

where it becomes the **rectum.** The name *rectum* comes from a word meaning "straight," but it actually follows the curve of the sacrum as it travels downward for a few inches, then turning sharply backward to form the **anal canal,** leading to the external opening, the **anus.**

The rectum serves as a reservoir for semisolid feces. Three transverse folds, which appear as creases on the outer surface, form shelves in the interior, helping to support the fecal mass. The teniae coli fan out in the rectum, enclosing the tube in a uniformly thick outer longitudinal muscle layer. Five to ten vertical folds called **rectal columns** can be seen in the mucosa, each

containing an artery and a vein. Enlargement of the rectal veins, called **hemorrhoids,** may be produced by the increased intraabdominal pressure during pregnancy, or by chronic constipation, especially in persons who have inherited a weakness of the vein wall. Hemorrhoids may be either external (covered with skin) or internal (covered with mucosa) and can cause bleeding and pain.

At the anus, three sphincters guard the exit of the alimentary canal.

1 The **internal sphincter,** of circular smooth muscle, which is not under voluntary control

B

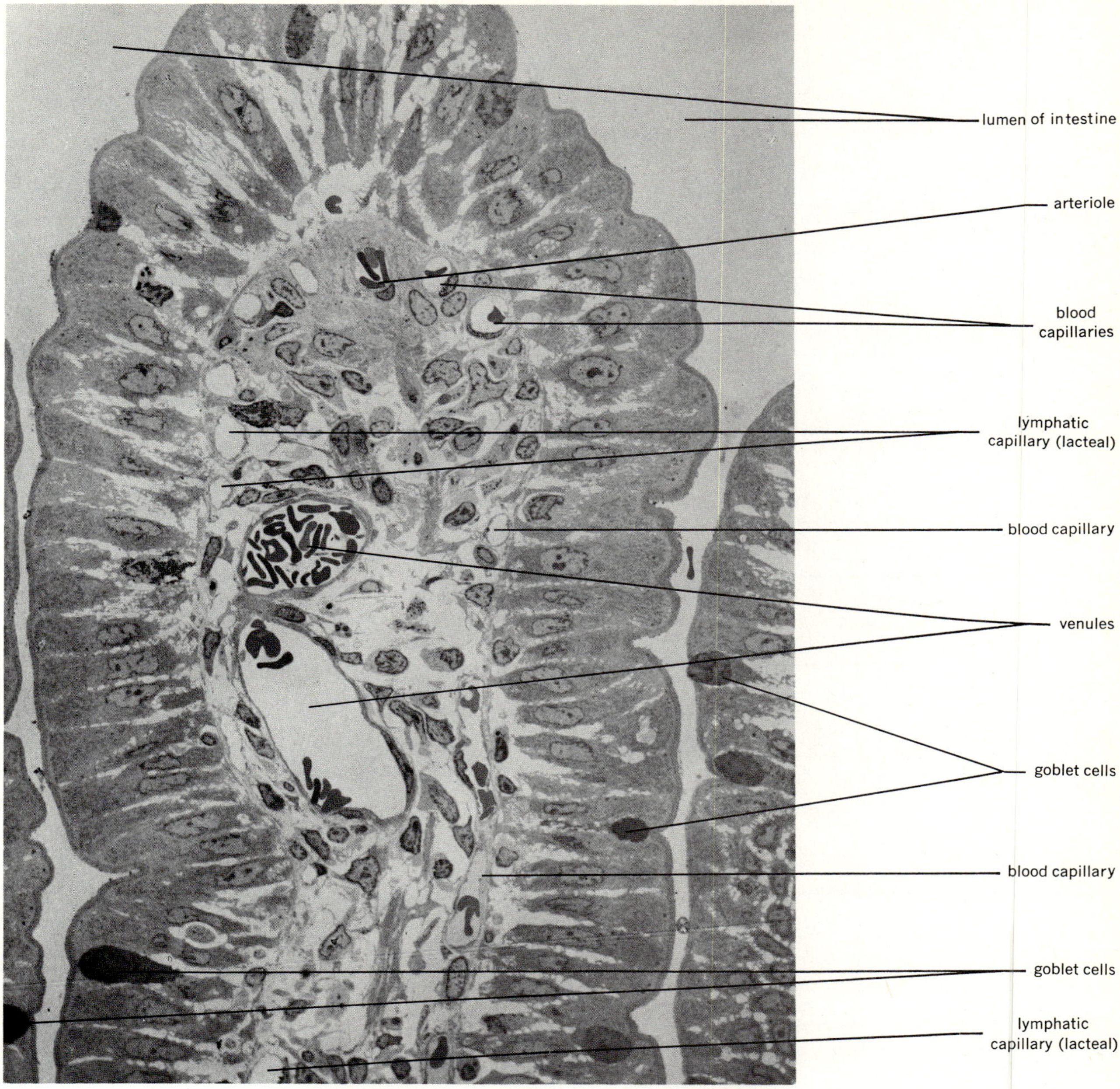

lumen of intestine

arteriole

blood
capillaries

lymphatic
capillary (lacteal)

blood capillary

venules

goblet cells

blood capillary

goblet cells

lymphatic
capillary (lacteal)

2 The **levatores ani,** skeletal muscles that exert a sphincterlike action and are under voluntary control

3 The **external sphincter,** a cylinder of skeletal muscle encircling the lower two-thirds of the anal canal and attached to the skin and to the coccyx by a tendon, also under voluntary control

Control over the anal sphincters must be learned; an infant evacuates automatically when the rectum is full.

The mucous membrane of the large intestine is smooth, without villi, but it does contain numerous intestinal glands with abundant mucus-secreting goblet cells. By the time the food residue reaches the large intestine, the basic work of digestion and ab-

C

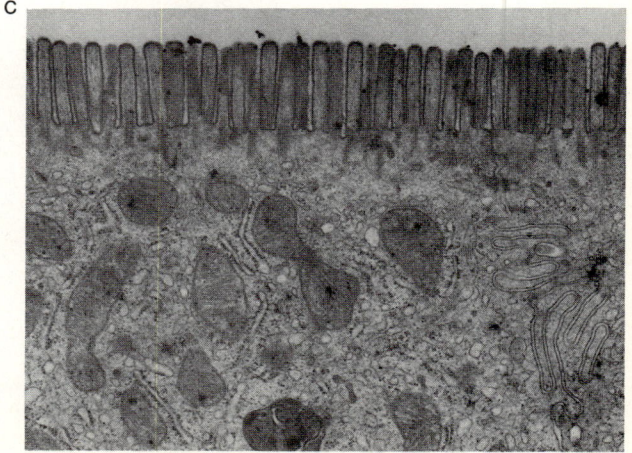

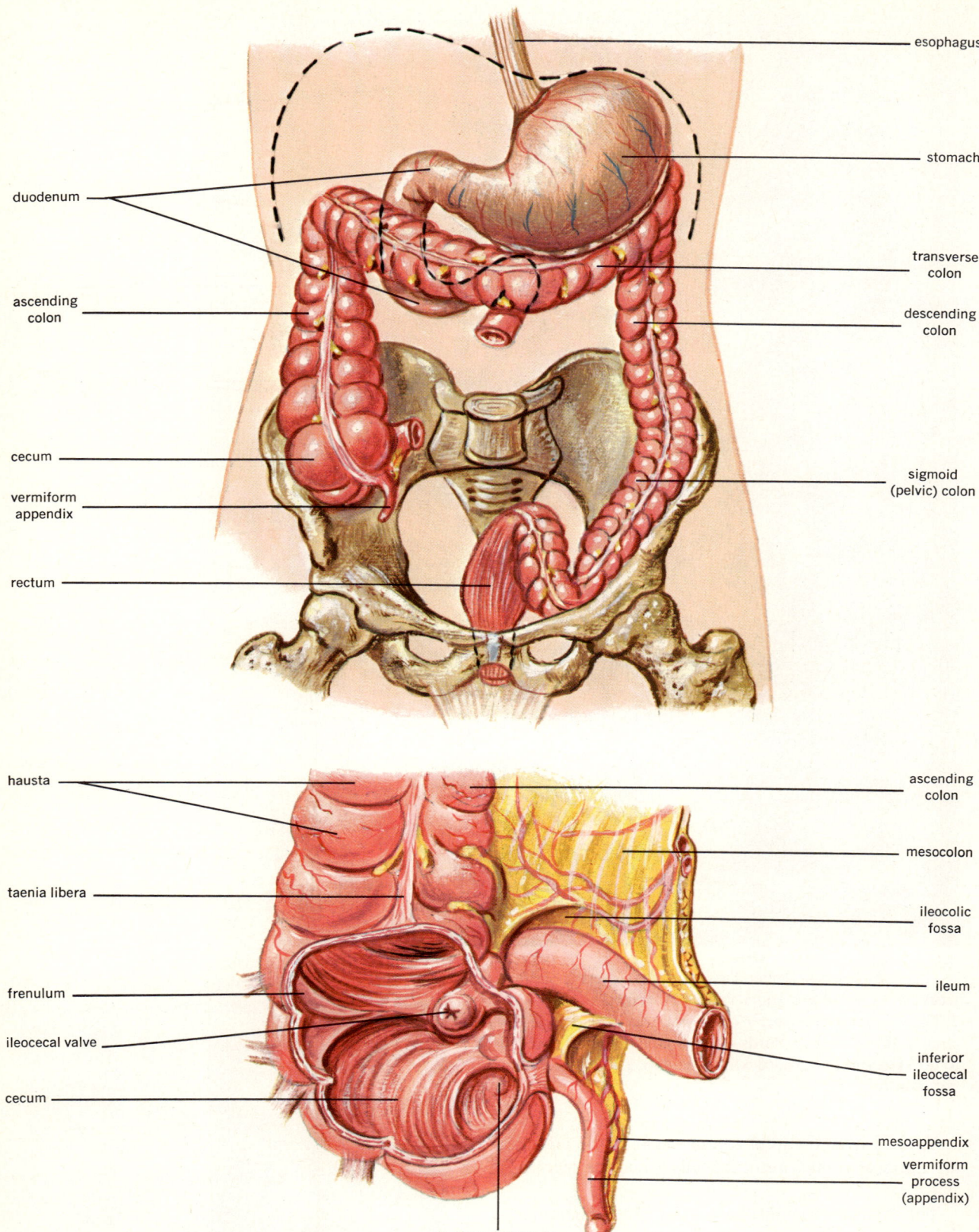

esophagus

stomach

duodenum

transverse colon

ascending colon

descending colon

cecum

vermiform appendix

sigmoid (pelvic) colon

rectum

hausta

ascending colon

mesocolon

taenia libera

ileocolic fossa

frenulum

ileum

ileocecal valve

inferior ileocecal fossa

cecum

mesoappendix

vermiform process (appendix)

opening of appendix

FIGURE 25-15 (A) Large intestine (colon and rectum) in relation to the stomach, diaphragm (dotted line), and bony pelvis; (B) ileocecal junction and vermiform appendix. (The cecum is cut open to show the ileocecal valve.)

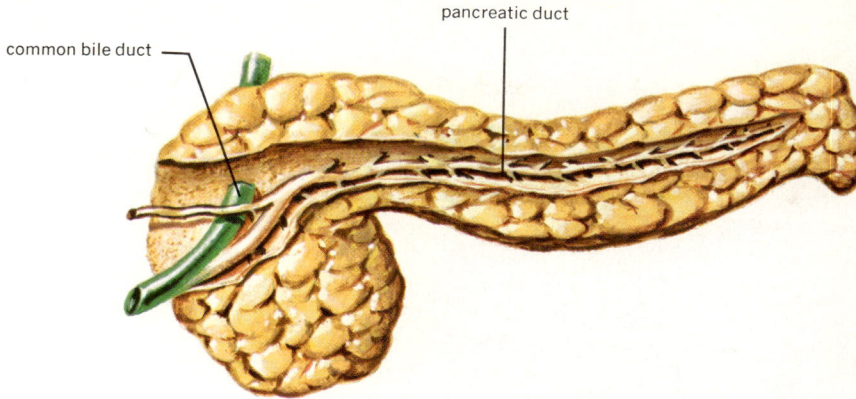

common bile duct

pancreatic duct

FIGURE 25-16 The pancreas, dissected to show the ducts. The micrograph shows a section, ×185. The acinar cells (exocrine cells) produce enzymes that are carried off through ducts. The islet cells (endocrine cells) secrete hormones into the blood of the surrounding capillaries.

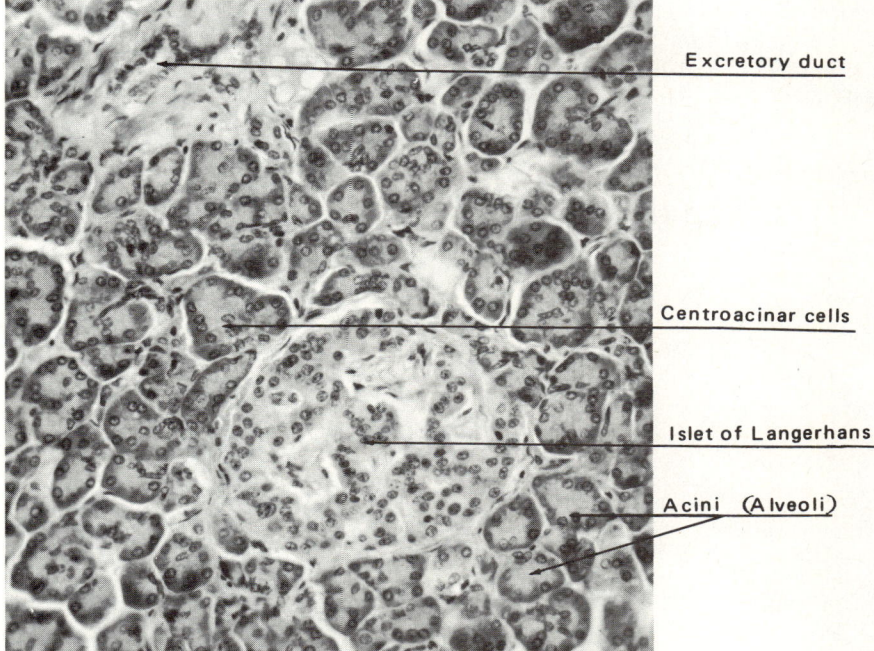

Excretory duct

Centroacinar cells

Islet of Langerhans

Acini (Alveoli)

sorption is done, and all that remains is to concentrate the semisolid feces by the absorption of water, to store them until a convenient time, and then to evacuate them. If a diseased rectum is removed surgically, the distal end of the colon is joined to an opening made in the lateral abdominal wall (a procedure called a **colostomy**). A plastic bag is attached to this artificial opening and receives the evacuations of the bowel.

ACCESSORY ORGANS OF DIGESTION

Effective digestion of foods would be virtually impossible without the aid of the accessory organs of the digestive system. These include the tongue, teeth, and salivary glands, which have already been discussed, as well as the pancreas, the liver, and the gallbladder.

The Pancreas

The name of the pancreas comes from Greek words meaning "all meat," referring to its boneless, fatless structure. The ancients who named this organ were obviously thinking gastronomically (the pancreas is eaten as "sweetbread"), but in the living body the pancreas is a versatile organ, the second largest gland in the body (the largest is the liver), and functions both as a digestive organ (exocrine gland) and as an endocrine gland.

The pancreas is an oblong, rather fish-shaped flattened gland, about 15 cm long and pink in color (Figure 25-16). It consists of a head, a body, and a tail; its head rests in the curve of the duodenum, and its tail touches the spleen. A thin layer of connective tissue, rather than a definite capsule, covers the outer surface of the pancreas, and connective tissue containing blood and lymph vessels and nerves divides its interior into lobules.

The exocrine portion of the pancreas is rather similar to the salivary glands. It consists of **acini,** which

A

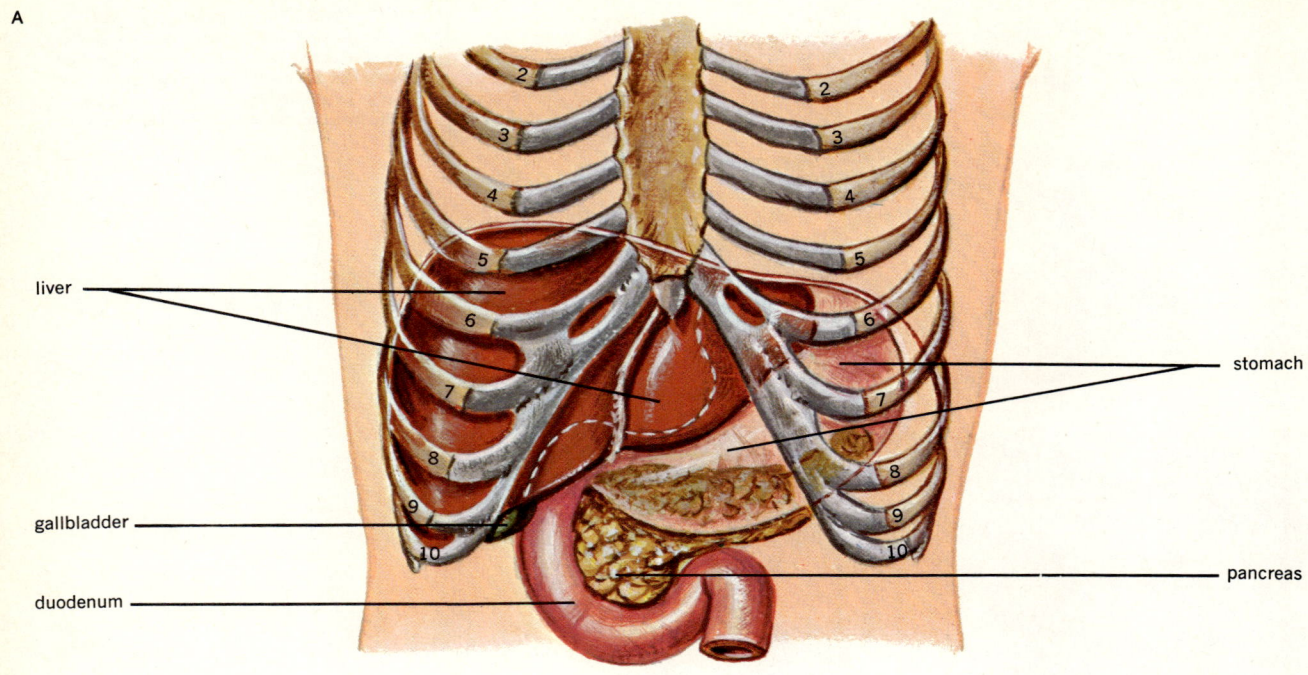

liver

stomach

gallbladder

pancreas

duodenum

B

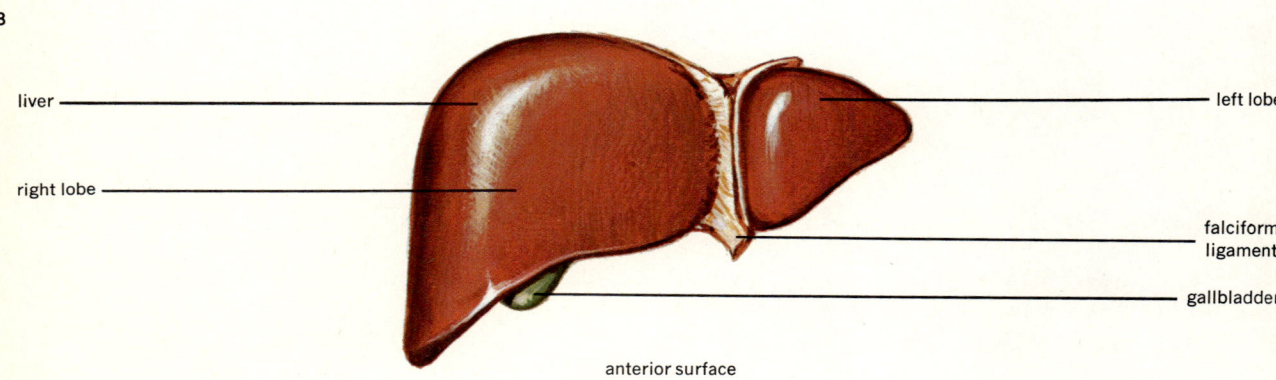

liver

right lobe

left lobe

falciform
ligament

gallbladder

anterior surface

C

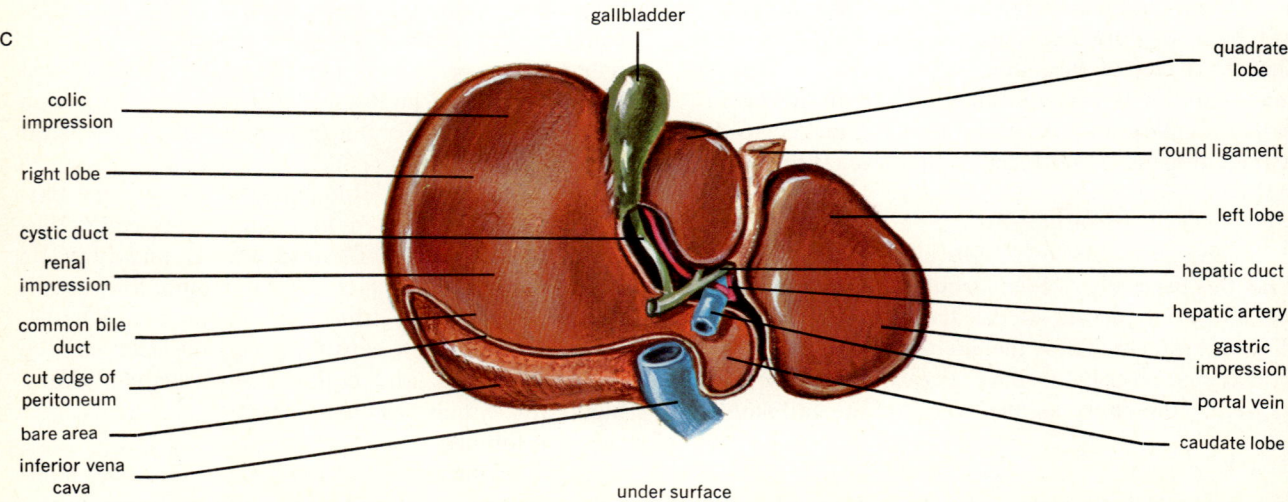

gallbladder

quadrate
lobe

colic
impression

round ligament

right lobe

left lobe

cystic duct

hepatic duct

renal
impression

hepatic artery

common bile
duct

gastric
impression

cut edge of
peritoneum

portal vein

bare area

caudate lobe

inferior vena
cava

under surface

resemble tiny grapes and contain secretory cells, which empty their secretions into microscopic ducts. These tiny ducts combine to form larger ducts, which unite in turn, ultimately joining the main **pancreatic duct,** which extends throughout the length of the pancreas, from head to tail. It empties into the duodenum at the same place as the bile duct. The exocrine portions of the pancreas produce the digestive enzymes contained in pancreatic juice: proteases such as trypsin and chymotrypsin; amylase; lipase; and carboxypeptidase. The acinar cells also produce sodium ions and bicarbonate ions, which are added to the secretions.

The endocrine portions of the pancreas are clusters of cells, scattered like isolated islands among the tubuloacinar units. These are the **islets of Langerhands,** and they contain two main types of secreting cells, alpha and beta cells, which secrete the hormones glucagon and insulin, respectively. Like other endocrine organs, the pancreas secretes its hormones directly into the bloodstream, rather than into ducts.

The Liver

The liver is an extraordinary organ in many ways. It is the largest organ of the body, weighing between three and four pounds. It is one of the most versatile and vital organs in the body. More than 500 different functions of the liver have already been discovered, including:

The secretion of about a pint of bile a day
Participation in the metabolism of proteins, fats, and carbohydrates
Detoxification of poisons and wastes, including nitrogenous wastes such as ammonia
The storage of substances such as iron, vitamins A, B₁₂, and D, and glycogen

The destruction of old erythrocytes and phagocytosis of bacteria and foreign bodies from the blood
The synthesis of prothrombin and fibrinogen, key factors in the blood clotting mechanism

No one can live long without a liver, and fortunately this essential organ has remarkable regenerative powers: if 90 percent of it is removed, the remainder will grow back, as long as the body as a whole is not overtaxed.

The liver lies in the upper part of the abdominal cavity, fitting snugly under the dome of the diaphragm and resting on the stomach and other abdominal viscera (Figure 25-17). The upper surface, in contact with the diaphragm, is smooth and convex, while the lower surface is concave and shows impressions of the abdominal viscera with which it is in contact. The blood supply of the liver is also unique; befitting its functions; it receives not only arterial blood from the aorta via the **hepatic artery,** but also a supply of venous blood from the digestive tract, laden with absorbed nutrients, delivered by the **portal vein.** Both the portal vein and the hepatic artery branch repeatedly, making the liver a highly vascular organ. At rest, a quarter of the body's blood supply is in the liver, but a pint or two are sent out into the general circulation during exercise. (Still another function of the liver is thus to act as a blood reservoir, which can be drawn on in times of need.) The hepatic artery and portal vein, together with bile ducts and lymphatic vessels, enter the liver in a region called the **porta hepatis.**

The liver is divided into four lobes (see Figure 25-17). The **right and left lobes** are demarcated by the **falciform ligament.** The right lobe, which is much larger, is subdivided into the **right lobe proper,** the **quadrate lobe,** and the **caudate lobe.** Each lobe con-

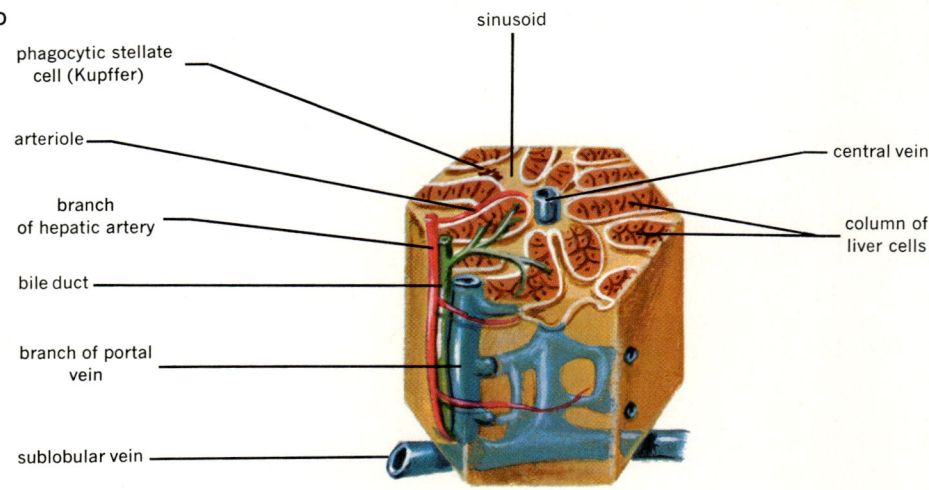

D

phagocytic stellate cell (Kupffer)

arteriole

branch of hepatic artery

bile duct

branch of portal vein

sublobular vein

sinusoid

central vein

column of liver cells

liver lobule

FIGURE 25-17 The liver: (A) in relation to the rib cage, diaphragm, and stomach; (B) anterior surface; (C) under surface; (D) structure of a liver lobule.

A

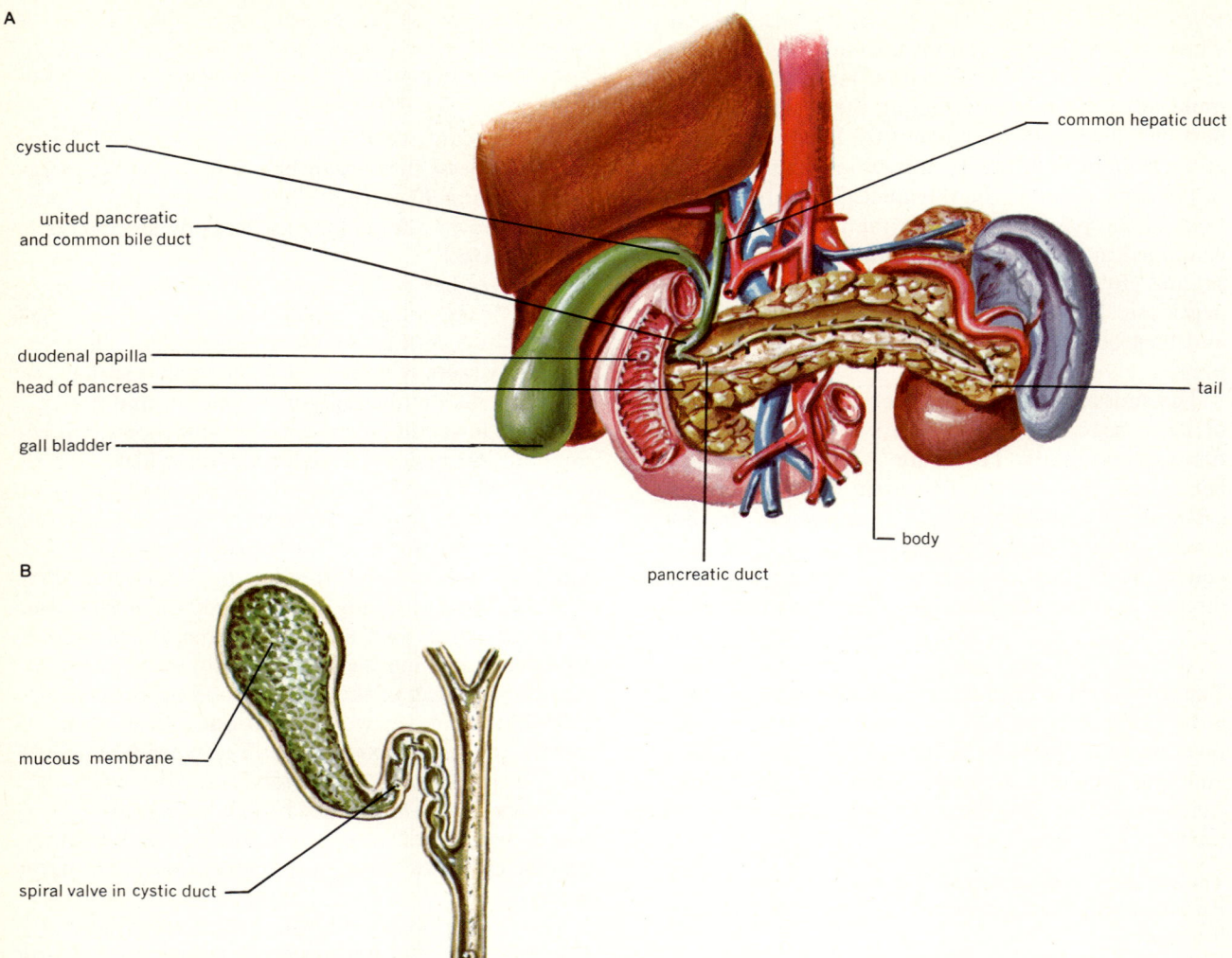

cystic duct

common hepatic duct

united pancreatic
and common bile duct

duodenal papilla

head of pancreas

tail

gall bladder

body

pancreatic duct

B

mucous membrane

spiral valve in cystic duct

FIGURE 25-18   The gall bladder, bile ducts, and pancreas (A); enlarged view of the gall bladder, sectioned to show internal structure (B).

tains numerous **lobules,** the functional units of the liver. Branching cords of epithelial cells radiate from the center to the periphery of the lobule and form the liver **parenchyma.** Branches of the hepatic artery and portal vein and a bile duct lie in the interlobular connective tissue. **Sinusoids,** lined with phagocytic **Kupffer cells,** receive the blood from the hepatic artery and portal vein; the sinusoids empty into the central vein of the lobule, which in turn discharge into the **hepatic veins** via the **intercalated** and **collecting veins.** The **hepatocytes** (liver cells) have microvilli that project toward the sinusoids, increasing the surface of contact between the hepatocytes and plasma.

The liver's main digestive function is the production of **bile,** a thick, yellow-green fluid. This secretion (an exocrine secretion, since it is discharged through ducts) does not contain enzymes; its main components are bile salts, bilirubin (a conversion product of hemoglobin from the destroyed red blood cells), and

cholesterol. Bile helps to emulsify fats, so that they can be digested and absorbed more easily.

The Gallbladder

No one can live without a liver, but many people get along quite nicely without a gallbladder. The gallbladder is a pear-shaped sac of smooth muscle, lined with mucous membrane, located on the undersurface of the liver (Figure 25-18). The wall of the gallbladder has a four-layered structure, similar to that of the other digestive organs. Its mucosal lining is arranged in folds or rugae, much like those of the stomach lining.

The function of the gallbladder is simply temporary storage of bile. The liver secretes bile continuously, but it is needed only periodically, when a meal is being digested. Ducts carry the bile to the gallbladder as the liver makes it, and it accumulates until digestion is taking place in the stomach and intestines. Then the gallbladder contracts, ejecting the concentrated bile into the duodenum. Contractions of the gallbladder are stimulated by gastric juice and fatty foods in the small intestine, as well as the hormone **cholecystokinin,** which cells of the small intestine secrete in the presence of fats.

The Bile Ducts

Clogging of the ducts that drain the liver and gallbladder leads to an accumulation of bile. The bile pigments are absorbed into the blood, producing a yellow color that gives the skin and mucosa a yellowish hue (jaundice). Meanwhile, the feces, lacking the normal amount of bile pigments, become a grayish color.

The system of bile ducts begins in the liver. Adjacent liver cells pour their bile into an intricate network of tiny ducts in grooves between the cells. These ducts are the **biliary canaliculi,** and they empty into the **interlobular bile ducts,** located in the interlobular connective tissue. The interlobular ducts unite to form progressively larger ducts. Finally, two main ducts, one from the right side of the liver and one from the left side, join in the portal fossa, forming the **hepatic duct.** The hepatic duct passes downward for about 5 cm and then joins with the slender **cystic duct** from the gallbladder to form the **common bile duct.** This tube continues downward for about 7.5 cm and then enters the duodenum in a common orifice with the pancreatic duct. The opening is very small and is guarded by a sphincter, which remains closed except during digestion. Normally bile flows down the hepatic duct and then back *up* the cystic duct, to be stored in the gallbladder until it is needed.

PRACTICAL CONSIDERATIONS

With some thirty feet of alimentary canal in the average adult, it is small wonder that disorders of the digestive tract are among the most common causes of visits to doctors and pharmacies. The following is a very brief survey of some of the things that can go wrong with various organs of the digestive system. Additional disorders, associated with the functioning of the digestive organs, are discussed in the next chapter.

The Mouth and Pharynx

Ankyloglossia (tonguetie). The tongue is bound to the floor of the mouth by a membrane and is not freely movable.

Carcinoma. Cancer may occur in the mouth, lips, tongue, or pharynx. Pipe smoking has been linked with an increased incidence of lip cancer.

Cleft palate and **harelip.** A failure of the maxillary bones to fuse during prenatal development can leave a cleft in the upper lip (harelip) or in the upper lip and palate (cleft palate).

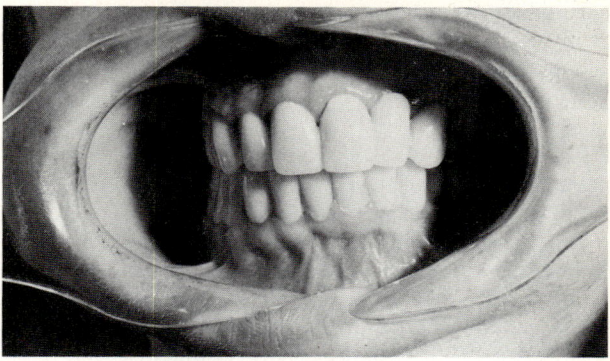

A

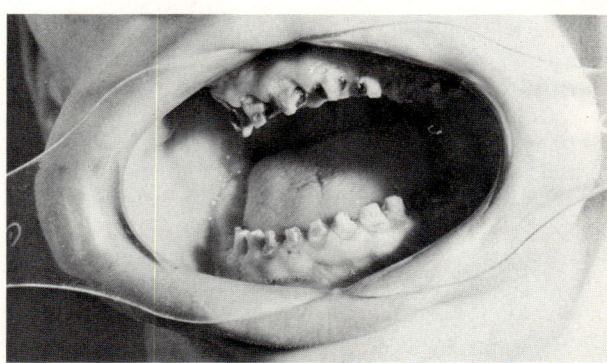

B

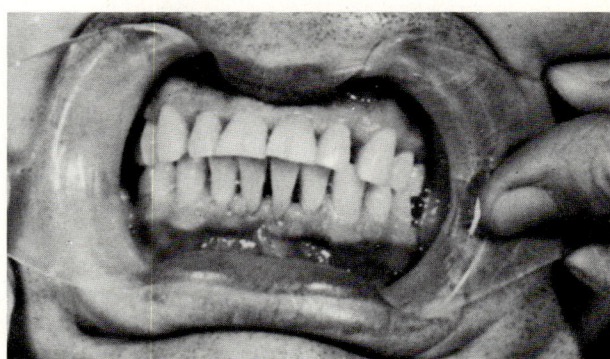

C

FIGURE 25-19 Healthy teeth (A), severe dental caries (B), and periodontal disease (C).

Dental caries. Tooth decay is a gradual disintegration of the enamel and dentin, caused by acid-producing bacteria (Figure 25-19B).

Gingivitis. Inflammation of the gums (gingiva).

Halitosis. Bad breath is perceived in the exhalations from the mouth, but may actually originate in the stomach or small intestine.

Malocclusion. Irregularities in the position and relationship of the teeth may prevent proper chewing action.

Parotitis. An inflammation of the parotid glands. A common type of parotitis is mumps, caused by a virus infection.

Periodontal disease or **pyorrhea.** An inflammatory infection or degeneration of the gums, alveolar bone, periodontal membrane, and cementum, which may lead to loosening and loss of the teeth (Figure 25-19C). Causes include poor oral hygiene, local irritants such as cigarette smoke, allergies, vitamin deficiencies, and systemic disorders.

Stomatitis. An inflammation of the soft tissues of the oral cavity, accompanied by pain, salivation, and often by fetor (offensive breath odor).

The Esophagus

Atresia of the esophagus. A congenital absence of the esophagus or its closure by disease.

Belching (eructation). The act of expelling gas from the stomach into the esophagus and mouth after a meal. (In some socieities, belching is not considered a disorder but rather a polite compliment to the cook.)

Carcinoma. Cancer of the esophagus usually occurs in the lower or midportion.

Dysphagia. Difficulty in swallowing.

Esophageal varices. The veins of the esophagus may become swollen and tortuous. Esophageal varices may rupture, causing severe internal hemorrhage.

Esophagitis. An inflammation of the esophagus, characterized by pain, a burning feeling beneath the sternum, difficulty in swallowing, and an increase in mucus secretion in the pharynx and mouth.

Heartburn. A burning sensation in the esophagus due to irritation of the mucosa by acid stomach contents regurgitated into the esophagus.

Obstruction. Blockage of the esophagus may be produced by a swallowed object, such as a toy.

Perforation, strictures, and **ulcers** of the esophagus may be produced by acute burns caused by drinking caustic liquids such as lye.

The Stomach

Carcinoma. Cancer of the stomach has been linked with carcinogens in the diet. Unhealed ulcers may develop into gastric cancers. Gastrectomy (removal of the stomach) or gastric resection (removal of part of the stomach) is a surgical treatment that is effective if performed early enough.

Dyspepsia, or indigestion, is one of the most common ailments.

Gastritis. An inflammation of the stomach lining. It may be caused by food poisoning or overeating, or by the ingestion of corrosive substances.

Hiatus hernia. A portion of the stomach may protrude upward alongside the esophagus through an opening (hiatus) in the diaphragm. Symptoms, including heartburn, indigestion, difficulty in breathing, and pain, commonly occur after a meal, when the stomach is full.

Pyloric stenosis. A persistent spasm of the pyloric sphincter, with hypertrophy of the sphincter, sometimes occurs in young male infants. The baby may seem normal for the first few days, then projectile vomiting, weight loss, and scanty production of urine set in. The condition must be corrected surgically.

Ulcers. The formation of ulcers in the gastric mucosa occurs most often on the posterior wall at the pyloric end, along the lesser curvature. It is caused by an overproduction of gastric acid, which eats a hole in the stomach lining, and is characterized by burning pain. One of the most serious complications is acute perforation through the stomach wall, which occurs suddenly and can lead to peritonitis.

The Small Intestine

Colic. Spasmodic contractions of the muscular coat of the intestine, producing a cramplike pain.

Ileitis. Inflammation of the ileum.

Inflammation of the mucous membrane of the intestine may be caused by viral infection. Acute inflammation is characterized by pain, nausea, vomiting, diarrhea or constipation, distension of the abdomen, and poor absorption of the fluid contents of the intestine. Chronic inflammation may result in obstruction due to scar tissue formation.

Intestinal obstruction may be caused by: foreign bodies; trapping of a hernial sac; structure from an ulcer, peritonitis, or tumor; volvulus (a twisting or knotting of the intestine); intussusception (telescoping of one part of the intestine into another, like turning the finger of a glove partly inside out); constricting bands arising from adhesions; paralytic ileus, which may occur after abdominal surgery.

Peritonitis. Inflammation of the peritoneum is characterized by rigidity of the muscles of the abdominal wall, tenderness over the abdomen, paralysis of the intestine, vomiting, and pain. It may be a complication of a perforated ulcer or appendicitis.

Ulcers. The region of the duodenum near the pylorus is a frequent site of ulcers.

The Large Intestine

Appendicitis. Inflammation of the appendix. Symptoms are muscular rigidity, pain, and vomiting.

Cancer can occur in any region of the colon or rectum. A cancer checkup includes an examination of the large intestine with a **sigmoidoscope** (Figure 25-20).

Colitis is inflammation of the colon. It may be accompanied by ulcers (ulcerative colitis).

Distension of the colon may be caused by the accumulation of gas, a mechanical obstruction, or nervous tension resulting in an inhibition of the normal peristaltic movements of the intestine or a spasm of the anal sphincter.

Diverticulitis. Small pockets (diverticula) may occur in the walls of the large intestine in older people, especially in the descending and sigmoid colon. Infection of diverticula (diverticulitis) produces cramplike pains and may lead to localized abscesses, perforation, or obstruction of the bowel.

Fissures, abscesses, and **fistulas of the anus** (Figure 25-21). Infection of small crypts in the tissues adjacent to the anus can lead to an ulcer of the anal canal, which appears as a crack in the skin at the anal margin and produces pain on defecation. The infection may spread through the wall of the anus, producing an abscess, which may burst through either internally or externally, forming a chronically discharging fistula.

Hemorrhoids. Varicose veins in the anal canal, which may become filled with blood clots (thrombosed), causing pain, bleeding, and protrusion.

Parasitism. A variety of parasitic worms can take up residence in the intestinal tract, including pinworms, hookworms, *Trinchinella spiralis,* and *Ascaris* (roundworms) and tapeworms and flukes (flatworms). *Entamoeba histolytica,* the protozoan parasite that causes amebic dysentery, can also live in the human intestine.

Pruritis. Itching, smarting, or burning of the anal region

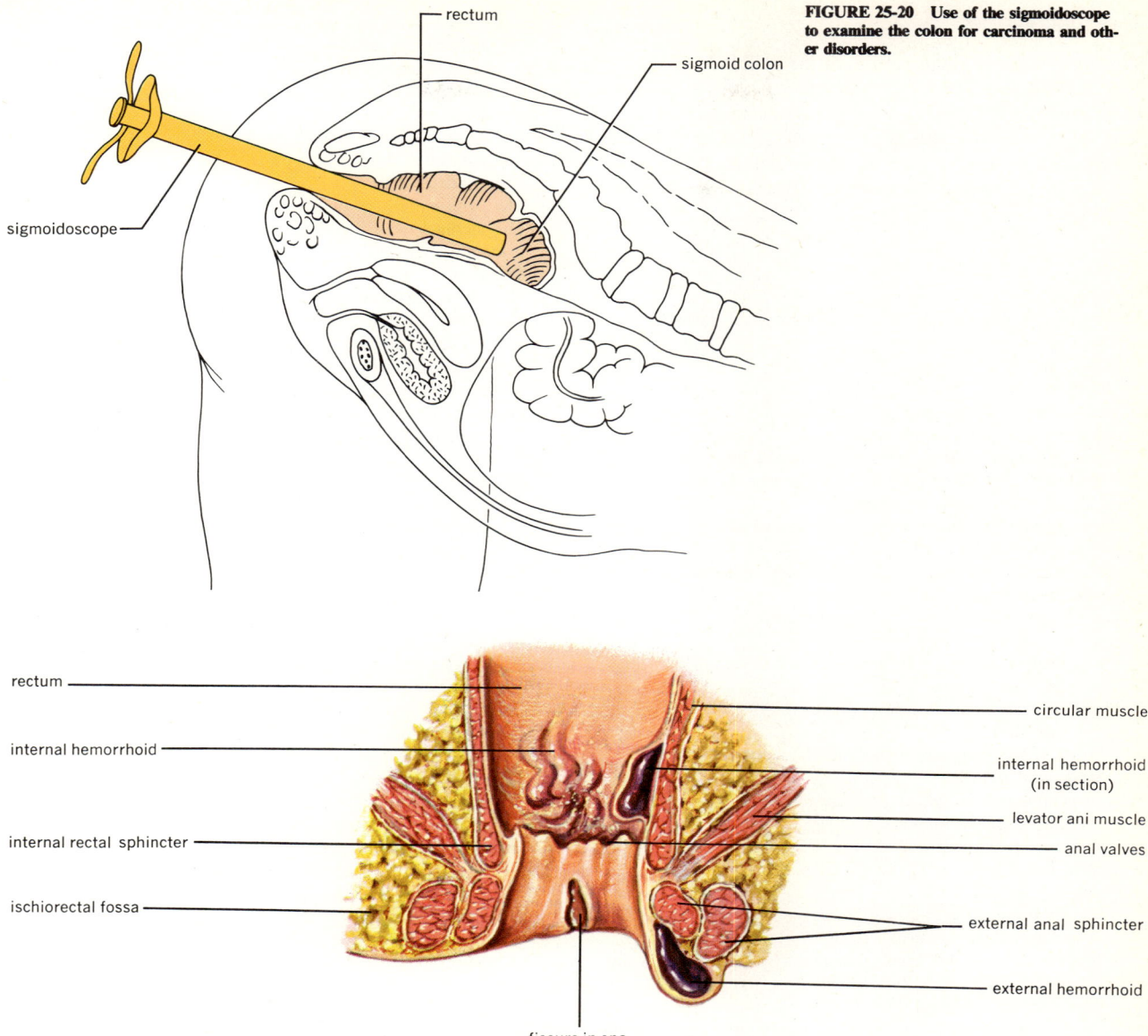

FIGURE 25-20 Use of the sigmoidoscope to examine the colon for carcinoma and other disorders.

rectum

sigmoid colon

sigmoidoscope

rectum

internal hemorrhoid

internal rectal sphincter

ischiorectal fossa

circular muscle

internal hemorrhoid (in section)

levator ani muscle

anal valves

external anal sphincter

external hemorrhoid

fissure in ano

FIGURE 25-21 Disorders of the anal canal.

(anal pruritis) may be caused by hemorrhoids or infection, may be a side effect of antibiotic drugs, or may occur without any determinable cause.

Tumors. Both benign and malignant tumors occur in the large intestine. Benign polyps of glandular or fatty tissue frequently occur in older people and may cause no symptoms unless they become ulcerated or obstruct the bowel. Surgical removal and resection of the intestine is the treatment for both benign and malignant tumors.

The Pancreas

Cancer of the pancreas sometimes occurs.

Diabetes mellitus is a condition in which the islets of Langerhans are insufficiently active, resulting in a lack of insulin.

Pancreatitis is an inflammation of the pancreas.

The Liver

Cirrhosis is a degenerative disease of the liver in which much of its parenchyma is replaced by connective tissue, progressively interfering with its function. It may be caused by chronic overconsumption of alcoholic beverages.

Hepatitis is an inflammation of the liver. Infectious hepatitis is caused by viral or bacterial infection and transmitted through contaminated food or water. Serum hepatitis is caused by the transmission of viruses from infected persons through blood transfusions. Hepatitis may be accompanied by jaundice, fever, and enlargement of the liver.

Jaundice is a yellowish coloration of the skin and mucous membranes due to the presence of bile pigments. These pigments enter the circulation instead of being eliminated through the intestine when the liver or biliary apparatus is diseased.

The Gallbladder

Cholecystitis is an inflammation of the gallbladder.
Cholelithiasis is the presence of gallstones in the gallbladder or bile ducts. The stones are solidified accretions of cholesterol and bile salts and pigments. If gallstones become lodged in the bile duct, causing severe colicky pain, **cholecystectomy** (removal of the diseased gallbladder and stones) is performed.

SUMMARY

The organs of the digestive tract (alimentary canal) include:
  Mouth
  Esophagus
  Stomach
  Small intestine (duodenum, jejunum, ileum)
  Large intestine (colon, rectum)
  Accessory organs (salivary glands, pancreas, liver, gallbladder)
The oral cavity includes the mouth cavity proper and the vestibule.
  It is lined with mucous membrane.
  The cheeks contains the buccinators and other accessory muscles of mastication.
  The lips have a thin covering transitional between skin and mucous membrane.
  The tongue functions in manipulation and is also the organ of taste.
    The dorsum of the tongue is covered with filiform, fungiform, and vallate papillae.
  There are three pairs of salivary glands:
    Parotid glands
    Submaxillary (submandibular) glands
    Sublingual glands
    They secrete saliva, which moistens food and begins the digestion of carbohydrates.
  The human set of teeth includes:
    Incisors (cutting)
    Canines (tearing)
    Bicuspids (crushing and tearing)
    Molars (crushing and grinding)
    A set of 20 deciduous teeth is replaced by a set of 32 permanent teeth.
    The teeth are anchored in sockets in the alveolar processes of the maxillae and mandible and partly submerged in the gums (gingivae).
      Each tooth consists of a crown, neck, and root.
      The tooth is composed of enamel, dentin, and pulp.
    The roof of the mouth is formed by the hard palate (maxillae and palatine bones) and soft palate (muscles), ending in the uvula.
The pharynx is a shared passageway of the digestive and respiratory tracts and aids in swallowing through muscular action.
The organs of the digestive tract usually have a four-layered wall structure:
  Mucous membrane (tunica mucosa)
    Epithelium
    Lamina propria
    Muscularis mucosae
  Submucous coat (tela submucosa)
  Muscular coat (tunica muscularis externa)
    Circular fibers
    Longitudinal fibers
  Fibroserous coat (tunica adventitia or serosa)
  Visceral peritoneum covers the abdominal viscera and parietal peritoneum lines the abdominal wall.

Double folds of parietal peritoneum called mesenteries, omenta, and ligaments project into the abdominal cavity and support abdominal organs.
The esophagus is a muscular tube connecting the pharynx with the stomach.
  The cardiac sphincter at the junction of the esophagus with the stomach acts as a "purse-string" valve.
The stomach consists of a fundus, body, and pylorus.
  The pyloric phincter guards the entrance to the duodenum.
  The stomach wall has three layers of muscle fibers: circular, longitudinal, and oblique.
  The stomach mucosa is drawn into longitudinal folds (rugae).
  Gastric glands (cardiac, fundic, and pyloric) secrete mucus, pepsinogen, hydrochloric acid, and serotonin.
The small intestine is a long, coiled and folded tube, in which digestion and absorption take place.
  It includes the duodenum, jejunum, and ileum.
  Brunner's glands in the duodenum secrete mucus.
  The common bile duct and pancreatic duct open into the duodenum.
  The mucosa of the small intestine is drawn into circular folds (plicae circulares) and covered with villi, the cells of which are bordered by microvilli, greatly increasing the absorbing surface.
  Each villus contains a capillary network surrounding a lacteal.
  Intestinal glands (crypts of Lieberkühn) produce enzymes (lipase, amylase, proteinase), mucus, and serotonin.
  The ileum ends in a right-angle junction with the large intestine, guarded by the ileocecal valve.
The large intestine consists of:
  Cecum (blind pouch with vermiform appendix)
  Colon (ascending, transverse, descending, sigmoid)
  Rectum (terminating in anus)
  The longitudinal muscle layer of the large intestine is the teniae coli (three bands running the length of the colon, then expanded into uniform layers around the rectum).
  Haustra are pouches in the wall of the colon.
  Epiploic appendages are fat-filled tabs of peritoneum along the free border of the colon.
  The anus is guarded by three sphincters:
    Internal sphincter (circular smooth muscle)
    Levatores ani (striated muscles)
    External sphincter (cylinder of striated muscle)
The pancreas functions both as an exocrine gland and as an endocrine gland.
  The exocrine portion consists of acini, which secrete digestive juices (enzymes, sodium and bicarbonate ions) into ducts.
  The endocrine portion consists of scattered islets of Langerhans, containing hormone-producing alpha cells (glucagon) and beta cells (insulin).
The liver is the largest organ in the body and has at least 500 functions.
  It secretes bile (containing cholesterol, bile pigments such as bilirubin, and bile salts), which aids in the emulsification and digestion of fats.
  The liver is divided into four lobes:
    Left lobe
    Right lobe proper
    Quadrate lobe
    Caudate lobe
  Its internal structure consists of lobules containing a parenchyma consisting of hepatocytes radiating from the center to the periphery; and sinusoids, which empty into the venous system.
  The liver receives a dual blood supply: from the hepatic artery and the portal vein.

The gallbladder is a muscular sac on the underside of the liver, used for the temporary storage of bile.

During digestion, the gallbladder contracts, discharging the stored bile through the common bile duct into the duodenum.

The biliary apparatus includes biliary canaliculi and interlobular ducts in the liver, the hepatic duct, cystic duct (from the gallbladder), and common bile duct.

Disorders of the alimentary tract include:

Mouth and pharynx:

Ankyloglossia

Carcinoma of the mouth, lips, tongue, or pharynx

Cleft palate and harelip

Dental caries

Gingivitis

Halitosis

Malocclusion

Parotitis

Periodontal disease or pyorrhea

Stomatitis

Esophagus

Atresia of the esophagus

Belching (eructation)

Carcinoma

Dysphagia

Esophageal varices

Esophagitis

Heartburn

Obstruction

Perforation

Stomach

Carcinoma

Dyspepsia (indigestion)

Gastritis

Hiatus hernia

Pyloric stenosis

Ulcers

Small intestine

Colic

Ileitis

Inflammation

Intestinal obstruction

Peritonitis

Ulcers (duodenal)

Large intestine

Appendicitis

Cancer

Colitis

Distension of the colon

Diverticulitis

Fissures, abscesses, and fistulas of the anus

Hemorrhoids

Parasitism

Pruritis (anal)

Tumors (malignant and benign polyps)

Pancreas

Cancer

Diabetes mellitus

Pancreatitis

Liver

Cirrhosis

Jaundice

Hepatitis

Gallbladder

Cholecystitis

Cholelithiasis

QUESTIONS FOR REVIEW AND THOUGHT

1 Describe the structures of the oral cavity and their roles in digestion.

2 There has been some controversy among anthropologists as to whether the prehumans that were our immediate ancestors were predatory meat-eaters or peaceful fruit-gatherers. Judging by the composition of the human set of teeth, what can you infer about the eating habits of early humans?

3 What are the advantages of having two sets of teeth—deciduous and permanent?

4 Why can the practice of gulping pills without water be harmful?

5 What do the esophagus, stomach, small and large intestines all have in common?

6 Describe the glands of the stomach lining and their secretions.

7 What structures increase the surface area of the small intestine?

8 Define: peritoneum; rugae; plicae circularis; villi; haustra.

9 What muscles guard the exit from the rectum? Which can be controlled voluntarily?

10 Would you classify the liver as an accessory organ of the digestive system or the circulatory system? Or—? Discuss.

11 What effects might be expected if the gallbladder is removed?

12 What parts of the digestive system are affected by the following conditions: ankyloglossia; gastritis; hiatus hernia; gingivitis; colic; diverticulitis; ulcers; cancer; hemorrhoids?

THE DIGESTION OF FOOD

26

Energy is the currency of life. The food we eat might be regarded as currency in foreign denominations, of a size too large to use in ordinary affairs. First we break down the large denominations into more manageable bills, then we exchange them (convert them to energy).

Each of the organs of the digestive system contributes to the basic functions of breaking down food materials into fragments small enough to pass through cell membranes, so that they can be used by the body; absorbing these more manageable fragments into the bloodstream and lymph circulation, which carry them to the tissues; and concentrating and eliminating whatever is left over—the waste products of digestion. The various organs in the approximately thirty feet of alimentary canal in a human body are like work stations along a conveyor belt in a factory.

The mouth is the first station along the way, and there the ingested food is subjected to preliminary preparations. It is mechanically pulverized into smaller pieces by mastication (chewing with the teeth), and saliva begins the chemical breakdown reactions, splitting apart some of the complex, high-polymer polysaccharide molecules in starches. At the end of its stay at this first work station, the food is roughly shaped into a ball (the bolus), held together by the moistening saliva, and shoved preemptorily along to the next station.

The esophagus functions simply as a conveyor belt, contributing mechanical movements (normally aided by gravity) to deliver the bolus of food to the next major work station, the stomach. There it is mechanically churned, soaked in an acid bath, and protein molecules are split by enzymes into simpler peptides. The end product of this stage is a soupy fluid called chyme, which is squirted in batches into the next processing station, the small intestine.

Here the serious work of digestion and absorption takes place, as a whole repertoire of enzymes and emulsifiers attack the major types of food materials: proteins (and peptides), carbohydrates, lipids, and nucleic acids. As in the esophagus, rhythmic waves of muscular contraction keep the soupy food material flowing along the intestinal conveyor belt and also help mix the food and bring it into intimate contact with the tiny absorbing units, the villi, that stud the lining of the small intestine.

By the time the food materials reach the large intestine, nearly everything of value to the body has been extracted, and the residue consists of indigestible materials and waste products. This mass of the body's "leavings" provides a rich food supply for a varied assortment of microorganisms that inhabit the colon. These microflora occasionally may cause illness or inconveniently produce gas, but for the most part they are innocuous guests, and some even contribute vitamins that they have manufactured in excess of their own needs. In the large intestine, much of the water in the waste mass is thriftily absorbed and recycled to the body's circulation, while the residue is formed into the semisolid masses called feces. When sufficient fecal matter has accumulated, further rhythmic contractions of the intestinal wall expel the feces from the body through the anal canal.

The **mechanical** actions of the digestive organs serve to move the food materials along, moisten and liquefy them, and pulverize them, increasing the surface area exposed to the action of the digestive enzymes. The **chemical** actions convert the large and complicated molecules of foodstuffs to smaller, simpler units that can pass through cell membranes and be utilized as building blocks or energy substrates. Such chemical reactions can be reproduced in the laboratory, but usually require strong acids, high temperatures, or both; the highly efficient enzymes of the digestive system accomplish the same ends under much milder conditions.

DIGESTION IN THE MOUTH

The digestive processes in the mouth begin even before a bite of food is taken. Smelling the "mouth-watering" aroma of a steak sizzling on the grill, looking at the gaudy color photos in a magazine recipe collection, even thinking about food are enough to start the flow of **saliva** into the mouth. (Indeed, the body is still another step ahead of itself, for such psychological stimuli can also start the flow of gastric juice in the stomach, in preparation for the meal.) However, the first effective action the food actually meets is the mechanical action of **mastication,** or chewing.

Mastication: Mechanical Action

From early childhood, we are cautioned to chew our food thoroughly, and this is good advice. Many doctors believe that disorders of digestion are often caused by bolting one's food, gulping it down without chewing it thoroughly. Carnivores do this habitually; they rip off pieces of meat and swallow them whole. But they are not equipped with as varied a set of teeth as we are, and the rest of their digestive tract is modified to deal with solid chunks of food. (Seals, in fact, swallow stones, which remain in the stomach and literally grind the food.)

Mastication begins with the operations of **prehension** and **division,** which are simply technical terms for grasping the food and biting off a piece. As soon as the food morsel is inside the mouth, it is repeatedly cut and ground by the action of the teeth, being

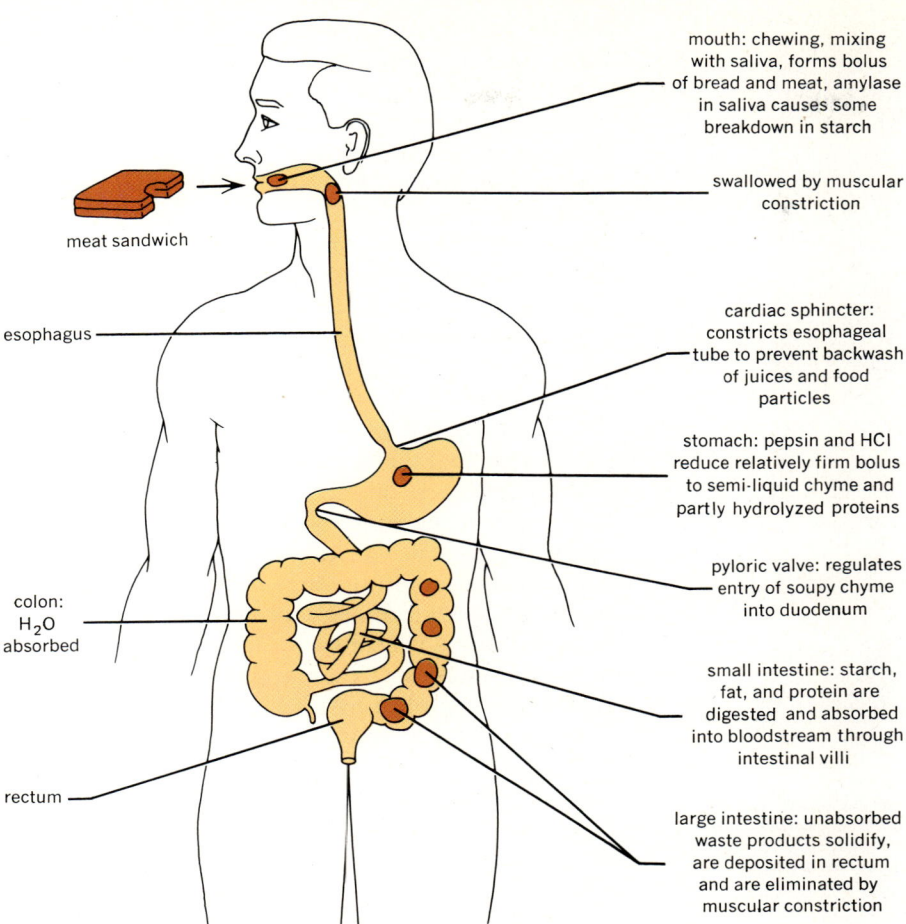

FIGURE 26-1 The digestive tract.

mouth: chewing, mixing with saliva, forms bolus of bread and meat, amylase in saliva causes some breakdown in starch

swallowed by muscular constriction

meat sandwich

esophagus

cardiac sphincter: constricts esophageal tube to prevent backwash of juices and food particles

stomach: pepsin and HCl reduce relatively firm bolus to semi-liquid chyme and partly hydrolyzed proteins

pyloric valve: regulates entry of soupy chyme into duodenum

colon: H_2O absorbed

small intestine: starch, fat, and protein are digested and absorbed into bloodstream through intestinal villi

rectum

large intestine: unabsorbed waste products solidify, are deposited in rectum and are eliminated by muscular constriction

pushed between them again and again by the action of the cheek muscles and tongue. The efficiency of mastication is determined by how well the upper and lower teeth meet and oppose one another. Missing or misaligned teeth reduce the masticatory efficiency.

During chewing, the food is mixed with saliva, which moistens it and converts it to a solid mass, which is shaped into a ball or **bolus** by the tongue.

Saliva: Chemical Action

The three pairs of salivary glands pour about a liter of saliva into the mouth each day. Saliva is a thin, watery fluid, about 99.5 percent water. Its somewhat slippery feel is produced by a protein substance, **mucin;** it also contains inorganic salts, the digestive enzyme **salivary amylase** (sometimes called ptyalin), and a bactericidal enzyme **lysozyme.** The pH of human saliva is usually fairly close to neutral, from 6.4 to 7.0. The exact composition of saliva depends on the numbers and types of cells that are secreting it: the parotid glands secrete only a serous type of saliva, rich in salivary amylase; the sublingual glands secrete mainly a mucous type of saliva, which serves to lubri-

cate the mouth lining and the food particles; and the submaxillary glands secrete both types of saliva. Autonomic nervous influences can affect the composition of saliva: impulses transmitted along parasympathetic nerves produce copious secretion of a thin, watery saliva, while sympathetic impulses cause a scanty secretion of thick, viscid saliva. Nuclei in the brain controlling the secretion of saliva are located at the junction of the medulla and pons and are excited both by taste and tactile stimuli from the mouth (even a smooth pebble in the mouth can stimulate a flow of saliva) and by impulses from higher centers of the central nervous system. (For example, more saliva flows when you are eating something you especially like than when you are eating something you dislike.)

Saliva serves several functions. First, it is a solvent, which permits the taste buds on the tongue to operate. Second, it begins the digestion of complex carbohydrates, splitting them to the disaccharide maltose in a series of hydrolytic reactions. This chemical digestive function of saliva is not very efficient. Food particles are incompletely mixed with saliva in the mouth (especially if chewing is not very thorough), and the

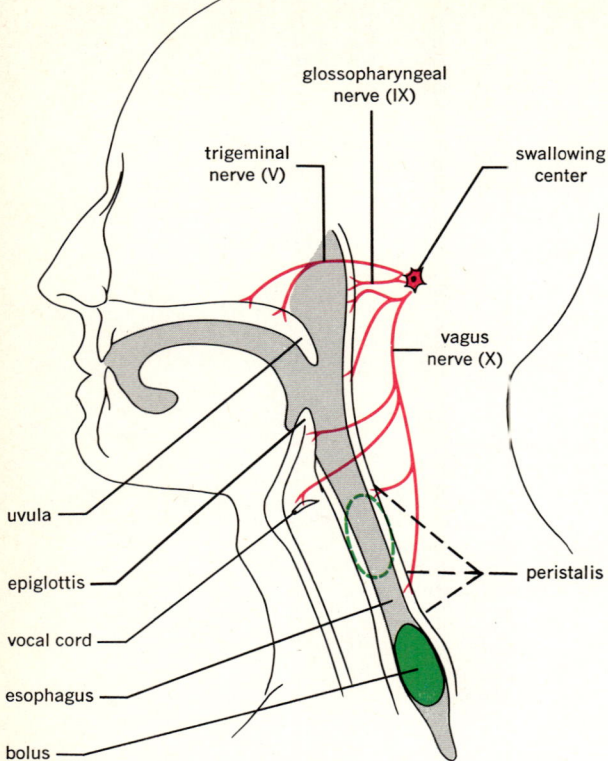

glossopharyngeal
nerve (IX)

trigeminal
nerve (V)

swallowing
center

vagus
nerve (X)

uvula

epiglottis

vocal cord

esophagus

bolus

peristalis

FIGURE 26-2 Swallowing is controlled by the nervous system. The trigeminal nerve controls the muscles of mastication; the glossopharyngeal nerve controls the stylopharyngeus muscle; and the vagus nerve controls the esophageal peristalsis that propels the bolus toward the stomach.

food is often quickly washed down with milk or some other liquid beverage; as soon as the bolus hits the stomach and the acid gastric juices penetrate it, salivary amylase is inactivated, and its action ceases, usually long before all the carbohydrates have been converted to maltose. A third function of saliva is to lubricate the food with a slippery coat of mucin, so that it can be swallowed easily. After the mouth is emptied, the continual flow of saliva keeps the delicate cells of the mouth lining moistened and helps to wash food particles away from the teeth, acting as a mild germicide in addition. The salivary glands also serve to some extent as glands of excretion, eliminating certain drugs, viruses, and metals such as lead and mercury that have penetrated into the body. When body tissues are dehydrated, salivation is decreased, and the dryness of the mucous membranes of the mouth stimulates a sensation of thirst, warning that more fluid must be taken into the body.

Swallowing

The *beginning* of swallowing is a voluntary act—but once you have started to swallow, you cannot stop. The process of swallowing, or deglutition, is a rather complex phenomenon, involving not only the tongue, pharynx, and esophagus, but also the brain and

nerves (Figure 26-2). It can be divided into three stages: buccal, pharyngeal, and esophageal.

In the **first stage,** moistened food is shaped into a bolus and directed by the tongue to the back of the mouth, then pressed against the soft palate. The levator veli palatini muscles raise the soft palate, closing the nasopharynx, and the bolus is forced into the pharynx. All these actions are voluntary, but as soon as the bolus has entered the pharynx the voluntary phase is over, and reflex mechanisms take over.

In the **second stage** of swallowing, the bolus is passed through the pharynx to the esophagus. A number of involuntary mechanisms operate to ensure that the food will go where it is supposed to. The larynx rises, and the epiglottis folds over to become a trap door shutting off the air passage. The sphincter-like action of the surrounding muscles also helps to guard the entrance to the larynx. Meanwhile, the tongue is closing off the mouth cavity, and the soft palate is blocking the entrance to the nasopharynx. The bolus has nowhere to go but the esophagus. The reflex mechanisms in the pharyngeal stage of swallowing are controlled by the deglutition center in the medulla and lower pons.

During the **third stage** of swallowing, the food passes down the esophagus to the stomach. This stage begins with the relaxation of the cricopharyngeus muscle, admitting the food to the esophagus. Alternate waves of contraction and relaxation sweep down this muscular tube, grasping and propelling the food along. These wavelike movements, both in the esophagus and in other parts of the alimentary canal, are called **peristalsis.** Peristalsis is under reflex control, involving both afferent and efferent fibers in the vagus nerve.

The propulsive force of peristalsis in the esophagus is rather weak, and it is normally aided by gravity, since people typically eat in an upright position. But if necessary, the esophagus can do the job of food moving by itself. Astronauts have demonstrated this under the weightless conditions of space, but you can do so more simply by swallowing something while hanging upside down or standing on your head.

When the pressure inside the esophagus is greater than that in the stomach, the cardiac sphincter (a portion of the muscular wall at the lower end of the esophagus) relaxes, and food enters the stomach.

DIGESTION IN THE STOMACH

The "landmark study" on the digestive functions of the stomach was made possible by a shooting accident. Back in 1822, a French-Canadian trapper named Alexis St. Martin was shot at close range by a musket that accidentally went off. A large chunk of his chest was literally blown out by the charge, parts of his ribs were destroyed, his left lung was lacerated, and his stomach was perforated. He survived the accident, but when the wound healed, a 2½ inch hole remained in both his side and the wall of his stomach. The U.S. Army surgeon who treated St. Martin, William Beaumont, tried to close the hole, but a permanent fistula or opening remained. Beaumont realized that this curious anomaly presented a unique opportunity for studying the functions of the stomach, the interior of which could actually be seen through the fistula. For eight years Beaumont doggedly followed the young French-Canadian, who quickly tired of the novelty of being a human "guinea pig"; the surgeon supported St. Martin and his family while he conducted painstaking experiments. He noted that the fasting stomach was empty and contracted, and that it became flushed with blood when St. Martin was angry. He drew off samples of gastric juice and identified hydrochloric acid as a constituent of it for the first time. Beaumont tied little samples of food into silk bags and lowered them into the stomach through the fistula, then withdrew them at hourly intervals to be observed and weighed. Beaumont's findings were summarized in "Experiments and Observations on Gastric Juice and the Physiology of Digestion," which he published in 1833. This study represented the first definitive factual data on the relationship between structure and function of the digestive system.

The stomach plays three main roles in digestion: storing food, forming chyme by mixing the food with gastric secretions, and a slow, controlled emptying, delivering the food to the duodenum at a suitable rate for the processes of digestion and absorption in the small intestine. Like the mouth, the stomach performs its functions by both mechanical and chemical actions.

Mechanical Action: Stomach Movements

If you place a stethoscope to your stomach, you may be surprised at the variety and magnitude of the sounds you hear. Try it before thoughts of a meal, while *looking* at a delicious meal, and while digesting one. (Indeed, the sounds produced by stomach movements may sometimes be embarrassingly audible even without a stethoscope!)

When food enters the stomach from the esophagus, it pushes any old food that might still be in the stomach aside, toward the walls. Thus, concentric circles are formed in the stomach contents, with the newest food closest to the cardiac sphincter and progressively older lots of food around it (Figure 26-3). Since the older food has been subjected longer to the mechanical and chemical action of the stomach, the outer layers of food have been broken down into progressively smaller and smaller particles.

Like other smooth-muscle bags, the stomach has the ability to accommodate itself to successive in-

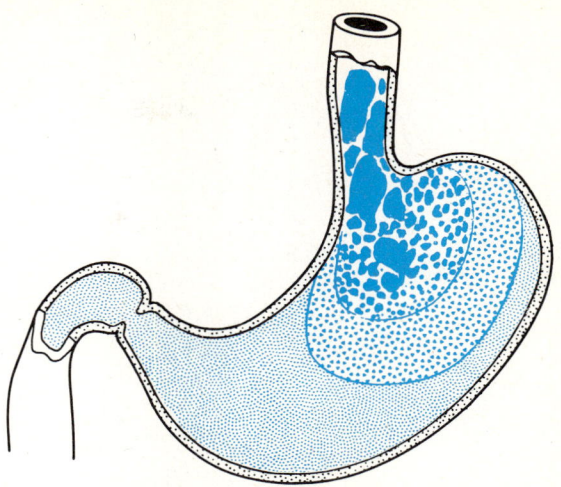

FIGURE 26-3 Food that enters the stomach is subjected to a progressive physical and chemical breakdown. The size of the dots indicates the degree of breakdown.

creases in contents without any significant increase in internal pressure—up to a certain limit, after which the pressure increases rapidly. Under normal circumstances, the limit is about a liter, but it is possible to stretch one's stomach by habitually ingesting large quantities of food or fluids at a sitting. The prodigious feats performed by the winners of eating and drinking contests are made possible by just such stretched-out stomachs. For most of us, however, overindulgence can result in considerable pain and discomfort.

Within a few minutes after food enters the stomach, mild waves of contractions begin to sweep over the stomach wall, recurring regularly about once every 20 seconds. These **mixing waves** begin near the cardiac sphincter and spread for various distances toward the pylorus. They toss, turn, and mix the stomach contents, gradually macerating the food materials, mixing them with the acid gastric juice, and converting them to the thin, semifluid mixture called **chyme.**

As digestion proceeds, more intense waves of contraction, also about every 20 seconds, begin to spread from about the middle of the stomach down to the pylorus and sometimes on into the duodenum. These **peristaltic waves** raise the pressure of the intragastric contents and propel them toward the opening into the small intestine. The pyloric sphincter is usually in a state of mild tonic contraction, which keeps the opening almost closed. As the pressure gradient between the stomach and duodenum rises, however, the sphincter is inhibited, and with each peristaltic wave a few milliliters of chyme are forced out of the stomach and into the duodenum.

The rate of emptying of the stomach is determined mainly by two factors: the fluidity of the chyme in the stomach and the receptivity of the duodenum. (A

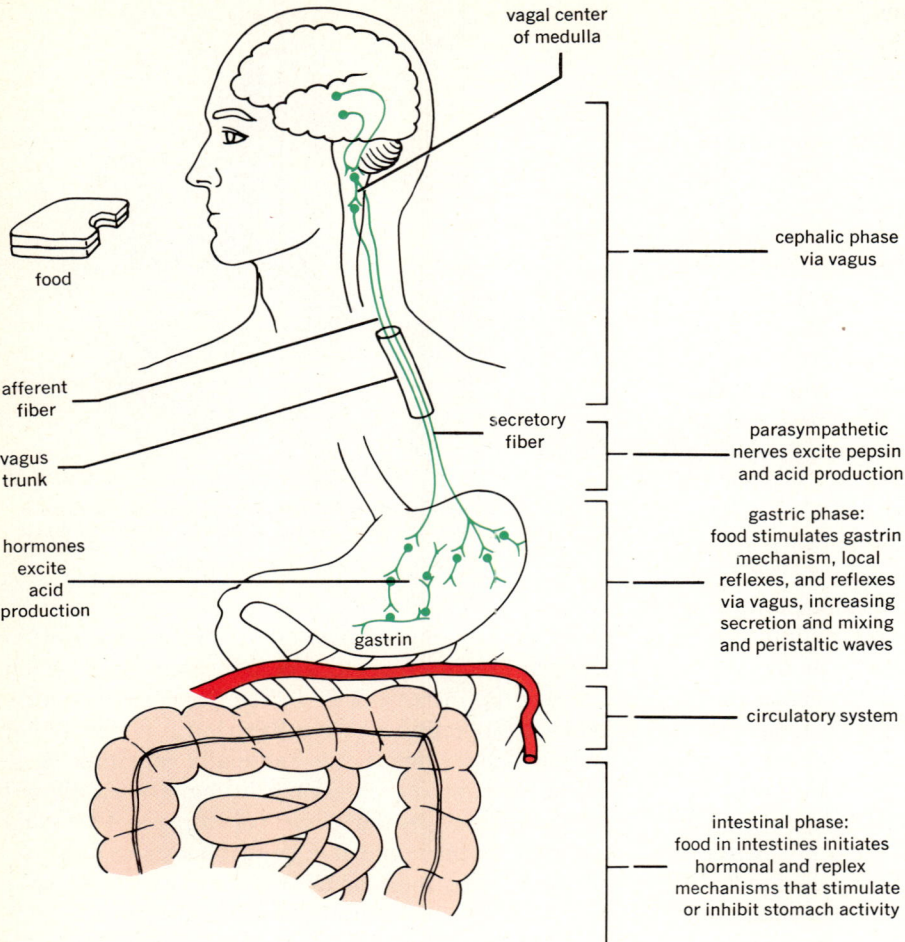

FIGURE 26-4 **Mechanisms regulating stomach motility and gastric secretions.**

vagal center
of medulla

food

cephalic phase
via vagus

afferent
fiber

vagus
trunk

secretory
fiber

parasympathetic
nerves excite pepsin
and acid production

hormones
excite
acid
production

gastric phase:
food stimulates gastrin
mechanism, local
reflexes, and reflexes
via vagus, increasing
secretion and mixing
and peristaltic waves

gastrin

circulatory system

intestinal phase:
food in intestines initiates
hormonal and replex
mechanisms that stimulate
or inhibit stomach activity

spasm of the pyloric sphincter, caused by extreme irritation of the small intestine, can also prevent emptying of the stomach, but normally the action of the sphincter plays a very minor role in controlling the rate of emptying; it acts merely to prevent regurgitation.)

The fluidity of the chyme depends on the type of food, how well it has been masticated, how long it has been subjected to the actions of the stomach, and the intensity of the mixing and peristaltic waves of the stomach. Peristalsis in the stomach, as elsewhere in the body, is regulated by impulses from the autonomic nervous system: sympathetic impulses inhibit stomach movements, while parasympathetic stimulation enhances peristalsis (Figure 26-4).

The receptivity of the duodenum is determined by the amount of chyme present in it, the acidity of the chyme, and the kind of foods the chyme contains. The condition of the duodenum affects the activity of the stomach by feedback mechanisms, and thus effectively controls the "pyloric pump." When the duodenum is full, the stretching of its walls stimulates the

enterogastric reflex, which acts to inhibit gastric peristalsis. In this way the small intestine protects itself from being overloaded by too rapid emptying of the stomach. Irritation of the duodenum, for example, by highly acid chyme, can also stimulate the enterogastric reflex, protecting the intestinal lining from damage. Gradually, the alkaline secretions of the small intestine neutralize the excess acidity, and the emptying of the stomach resumes. Fats take the longest of all foods to be digested, and a special feedback mechanism ensures more time for them in the small intestine. When the chyme is rich in fats, the mucosa of the duodenum and jejunum secretes a hormone, **enterogastrone,** which is absorbed into the blood and travels to the stomach, where it inhibits movements and slows down the rate of emptying to as little as one-third of its previous rate.

Generally, a meal is entirely emptied from the stomach into the intestine within a few hours after ingestion. But a fat-rich meal may take as long as six hours to be completely emptied; carbohydrates are digested most rapidly and leave the stomach in the shortest time. Extremely cold liquids and substances such as ice cream inhibit the action of the stomach and delay its emptying.

When the stomach is empty, it is greatly contracted, and the tone of its wall is increased. After it has been empty for a long time, intense rhythmic contractions may sweep over the body of the stomach. These **hunger contractions** often fuse together to produce a continuing tetanic contraction that may last for two to three minutes.

Chemical Action: Gastric Juice

About 35 million tiny gastric glands in the lining of the stomach contribute their secretions to the gastric juice, and they work constantly—even when the stomach is empty. During eating and throughout the time of digestion, the rate of secretion increases greatly. A total of about 2 liters of gastric juice is secreted each day.

Gastric juice contains water, mucin, hydrochloric acid, and several enzymes: pepsin (the main component) and small amounts of rennin and gastric lipase. The juice is quite acid, with a pH close to 1.

The mechanism by which a strong inorganic acid, **hydrochloric acid,** is produced by delicate living cells is still somewhat mysterious. According to one current hypothesis HCl secretion by the parietal cells in the stomach lining involves a diffusion of water and CO_2 into the cell, where H_2CO_3 is formed under the influence of carbonic anhydrase. The carbonic acid then ionizes to HCO_3^- and H^+. Bicarbonate ions diffuse out of the cell into the blood, and the hydrogen ions are actively transported into the gastric juice. Meanwhile, chloride ions are actively transported from the blood through the cells into the juice, and H^+ and Cl^- combine to form hydrochloric acid. Hydrochloric acid in the stomach causes proteins to expand and soften, and it kills or inactivates bacteria in the stomach contents.

The **mucin** secreted by the neck cells is somewhat alkaline. It serves to buffer the strong acid somewhat and to form a protective barrier between it and the delicate mucous membrane of the stomach lining.

The zymogenic, or chief cells do not actually secrete the enzyme **pepsin,** but instead an inactive form with a higher molecular weight, **pepsinogen.** When pepsinogen comes in contact with small amounts of pepsin already present in the stomach, in the presence of hydrochloric acid, it is split into smaller fragments, producing the active proteolytic enzyme pepsin. This enzyme hydrolyzes peptide bonds, breaking down proteins into simpler units, proteoses, peptones, and polypeptides.

Both **rennin** and **gastric lipase** are not very effective at an acid pH; they function better in a close to neu-

tral medium. Hence, these two enzymes are not very important components of gastric juice in the adult. However, in a child's stomach conditions are less acid, and the infant has a special need for the abilities of rennin and gastric lipase. Rennin is an enzyme that is very specific:—it acts on the casein in milk to form coagulated globs called curds. (In the adult stomach this function is taken over by hydrochloric acid.) The curdling action helps to retain milk in the stomach long enough for digestion to occur. Rennin extracted from calf stomachs is sold commercially as "rennet" for making easily digestible "junket"-type desserts. Gastric lipase starts the digestion of fats. But in the adult stomach, fat digestion is carried on almost exclusively by the intestinal lipases.

The secretion of the gastric glands is under both nervous and hormonal control. Its regulation is often divided into three phases: cephalic, gastric, and intestinal, but in practice these phases usually merge.

Cephalic Phase   Seeing, smelling, tasting, or even thinking about food will stimulate a flow of gastric juice. Afferent impulses to the cerebral cortex stimulate efferent impulses that descend via the vagus nerves to the stomach. The gastric secretion that results has been called the **appetite juice,** and it can account for up to a fifth of the gastric secretion associated with a meal.

Gastric Phase   The presence of food in the stomach evokes the second phase of gastric secretion. Food in the stomach stimulates the secretion of the hormone **gastrin** by the pylorus. This hormone is absorbed through the stomach lining into the blood and carried to the gastric glands, causing them to secrete. This hormonal mechanism is backed up by reflex loops, proceeding via local nerves in the intramural plexus of the stomach and also up to the brainstem and back via vagus nerve fibers (see Figure 26-4). The gastric phase accounts for about two-thirds of the gastric juice secreted.

Intestinal Phase   Even after the food leaves the stomach, gastric juice continues to be secreted for six to eight hours, as long as chyme remains in the small intestine. This mechanism seems to be controlled by a hormone or hormones secreted by the intestine. It accounts for only about 5 percent of the gastric juice secretion.

Gastric secretion may be inhibited by several factors. Unappetizing food may depress the cephalic phase. The accumulation of acid in the stomach inhibits gastrin formation and thus acts as a feedback mechanism, preventing too much acid from accumulating. Fatty chyme in the duodenum stimulates the secretion of enterogastrone, which not only inhibits stomach movements, but also is a potent inhibitor of gastric secretion. Stimulation of the sympathetic nervous system likewise inhibits both gastric motility and gastric secretion. Strenuous exercise after a meal will slow down the stomach action because of the diversion of circulating blood away from the abdominal viscera to the heart and skeletal muscles. If the gastric digestion is delayed too long, microorganisms may ferment sugars in the food, producing gas that may cause discomfort (cramps).

Vomiting

Vomiting is an act generally regarded with great repugnance. Yet it is a valuable protective mechanism. Rats are unable to vomit, and as a result are vulnerable to rat poisons that would merely make a person ill.

While you are vomiting, it may feel as though your stomach muscles are contracting, but this is actually not so. The stomach, esophagus, and cardiac sphincter are all relaxed during vomiting, and the propulsive force is provided by spasmodic contractions of the abdominal muscles and diaphragm, which literally squeeze out the stomach contents in spurts. After the stomach has been evacuated, the pyloric sphincter may also relax, permitting the duodenal contents to be expelled as well (hence the taste of bile after a long bout of vomiting).

Vomiting is usually preceded by a feeling of nausea. It is a reflex act, coordinated by the **vomiting center** in the medulla. It may be stimulated by mechanical irritation of the throat or by irritating substances in the stomach and duodenum (e.g., toxins in spoiled food). Pain, motion sickness, and strong emotions such as fear and revulsion can also stimulate vomiting. **Emetics** such as ipecac may be administered to induce vomiting if a person has taken poison.

DIGESTION IN THE SMALL INTESTINE

In the body cells, finely tuned mechanisms keep conditions as constant as possible. Variations of only a fraction of a pH unit, for example, could cause serious disorders. Yet in the digestive tract (which, remember, is in a sense not really *inside* the body), the normal rules of homeostasis seem to be suspended. In the sequence of organs along the alimentary canal, the pH swings widely. It is approximately neutral in the mouth cavity and highly acid in the stomach. Yet in the small intestine the pH becomes quite alkaline, close to pH 8. Since the pH scale is a logarithmic scale, the change from the pH 1 of the stomach to the pH 8 of the ileum represents a *millionfold* difference in the hydrogen ion concentration! There is a reason

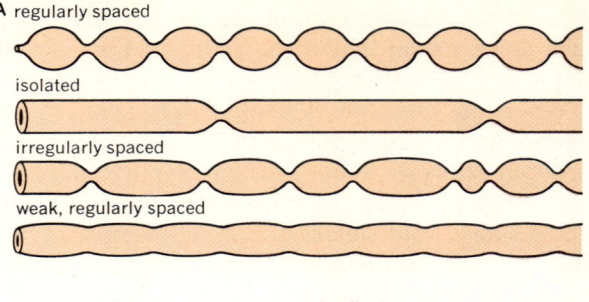

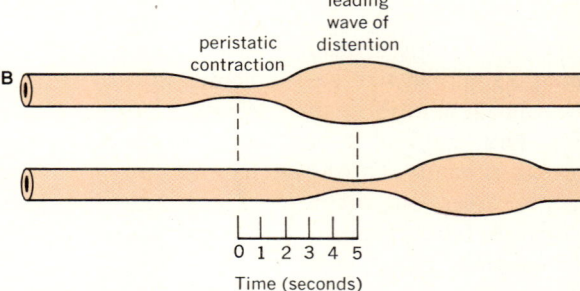

FIGURE 26-5 Movements of the small intestine: segmentation contractions (A) and peristalsis (B).

for the seemingly chaotic fluctuations of the pH in the digestive tract—each characteristic pH value represents the optimum for the action of the main enzymes found in that particular organ.

Like the stomach, the small intestine mixes and moves the food (now in the form of chyme). It is here that the main work of digestion occurs. A variety of enzymes and other substances secreted not only by the small intestine, but also by the liver and pancreas, act on the food materials in the small intestine and complete the breakdown of proteins, carbohydrates, fats, and nucleic acids into simple constituents. Here, too, the major work of absorption takes place, as nutrients are absorbed through the intestinal wall into the blood and lymph circulation.

Mechanical Action: Segmentation and Peristalsis

During the digestion of a meal, the small intestine looks very much like a chain of sausages. Instead of a long, uniform tube, it is constricted at intervals by contractions of the circular muscle fibers in its wall (Figure 26-5A). These small ringlike contractions may occur irregularly, or they may be rhythmic, occurring at a rate of 8 to 9 per minute in the duodenum and at progressively slower rates down the length of the small intestine. Successive contractions occur at different points, effectively chopping up the column of chyme into segments, which are continually broken up and rejoined. Such **segmentation contractions** ensure good mixing of the chyme and continually bring

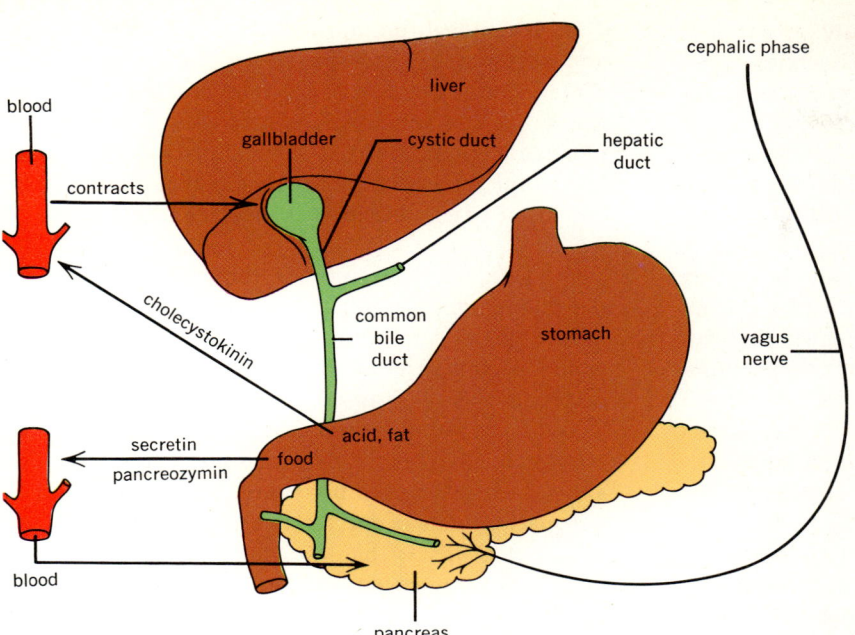

FIGURE 26-6 Regulation of pancreatic secretion. Both hormones and nerve impulses play a role.

Chemical Action

The chyme that enters the duodenum is still largely undigested. It is freed of coarse particles, and a start has been made in hydrolyzing carbohydrates and proteins, but the fats have only been liquefied and mixed with the other food materials. All this unfinished business is attended to in the small intestine, for the enzymes secreted into this part of the digestive tract are capable of digesting nearly any kind of food substance (see Figures 26–8, 9, and 10 on page 603). Proteins are broken down into polypeptides, and these, in turn, are hydrolyzed to their constituent amino acids. Starch and other complex carbohydrates are hydrolyzed to maltose and other disaccharides, which are further split to the simple sugars glucose, galactose, and fructose. Fats are hydrolyzed to free fatty acids, monoglycerides, diglycerides, triglycerides, and glycerol. And nucleic acids are split into nucleotides, which are in turn broken down to nucleosides and phosphoric acid, and further to sugars and purine and pyrimidine bases.

Pancreatic Juice The pancreas waits on call, ready to supply a powerful arsenal of digestive enzymes as soon as they are needed. It does not begin to pour its digestive juices into the duodenum until food reaches the intestine.

The pancreas actually produces two juices, an **aqueous juice** and an **enzyme juice,** the secretion of each of which is stimulated by a hormone secreted by the intestinal mucosa (Figure 26-6). The aqueous juice is a copious, watery fluid, with a high concentra-

new parts of the food mass in contact with the mucous membrane lining of the small intestine.

Pendular movements also contribute to the mixing of chyme. These are small constrictive waves that sweep up and down a few centimeters of the intestine, moving the contents back and forth.

The **villi** also contract intermittently during the digestion process, shortening and lengthening rhythmically. The contractions of the villi stir up currents in the fluid around them, bringing successive new areas of fluid continually into contact for absorption. The contractions also "milk" the villi, keeping the lymph flowing freely from the lacteals into the lymphatic system.

Chyme is moved along the intestine by **peristalsis.** This type of movement is produced by waves of contraction that sweep along the intestine analward (Figure 26-5B). Normally, peristaltic contractions are weak contractions, which move slowly at a velocity of 1 to 2 cm per second and die out after traveling only a few centimeters. But distension of the duodenum after the stomach has emptied produces an increase in the intensity of the peristaltic contractions—a **peristaltic rush**—that sweeps the food along more rapidly over greater distances.

The contractions of the small intestine are believed to be **myogenic;** that is, they originate in the muscle tissue itself rather than in the nerves.

Food moves slowly through the small intestine; normally, 3 to 10 hours are required for chyme to pass from the pylorus at the entrance to the duodenum to the ileocecal valve at the end of the ileum.

tion of bicarbonate ions and practically no enzymes. Its secretion is evoked by the hormone **secretin,** which is produced by the mucosa of the upper small intestine. The hydrochloric acid in the chyme that squirts from the stomach into the duodenum stimulates the release of secretin, which is absorbed into the blood and travels to the pancreas, where it in turn stimulates the secretion of the aqueous juice, which flows through the pancreatic duct into the duodenum. There bicarbonate ions (HCO_3^-) neutralize the hydrochloric acid in the chyme. Meanwhile, the presence of food in the upper small intestine also stimulates the production of a second hormone, **pancreozymin.** This hormone, too, is absorbed into the blood, travels to the pancreas, and stimulates the secretion of the enzyme juice, which contains a battery of digestive agents.

The **proteolytic** (protein-digesting) enzymes of the pancreas are **trypsin, chymotrypsin,** and **carboxypeptidase.** If these powerful protein-digesting enzymes accumulated in the pancreas, they would digest it. As a protective mechanism, they are secreted in an inactive form, as **trypsinogen, chymotrypsinogen,** and **procarboxypeptidase;** in addition, a special trypsin inhibitor prevents the activation of trypsin.* The inactive enzyme precursors are activated in the intestine: trypsinogen is converted to trypsin by the intestinal enzyme **enterokinase** and also to some extent by trypsin that is already there; chymotrypsinogen yields active chymotrypsin under the action of trypsin. Procarboxypeptidase is converted to carboxypeptidase in a similar manner. Trypsin and chymotrypsin hydrolyze proteins and polypeptides to peptides. Carboxypeptidase breaks the peptides down into their component amino acids.

The **amylolytic** (starch-digesting) enzyme of the pancreas, **amylase,** is similar to salivary amylase, hydrolyzing starch to maltose. It has more leisure to work on starches than the salivary amylase, the action of which is cut short when the acid gastric juice penetrates into the bolus.

The **lipolytic** (fat-digesting) enzyme of the pancreas, **lipase,** can hydrolyze fats to monoglycerides and some to glycerol and fatty acids. Lipases are also secreted by the small intestine, but the pancreatic lipase accounts for about 80 percent of fat digestion. The emulsifying action of bile prepares the fats for the action of lipase.

Nucleases, DNase and **RNase,** break down nucleic acids into their constituent units, nucleotides.

The enzymes of the pancreas thus play key roles in the digestion of all the major groups of foods.

* If the pancreatic duct is blocked, large amounts of digestive enzymes build up in the pancreas and overwhelm the trypsin inhibitor, destroying the pancreas. This condition, acute pancreatitis, can be fatal.

In addition to the hormonal regulation of pancreatic secretion, the exocrine activity of the pancreas is also regulated by nervous mechanisms. Stimulation of the vagus and splanchnic nerves causes secretion of pancreatic juice, but the hormonal control is more important in regulating its secretion. About 600 to 800 ml of pancreatic juice is produced each day.

Bile Bile, the liver secretion that is discharged into the duodenum by the gallbladder, is not really a digestive juice. Yet without it, the digestion of fats would be much less effective, and only half the ingested fat would be absorbed into the body. This lack would have serious consequences, for some of the vitamins (A, D, E, and K) are fat-soluble; if dietary fats are not absorbed, the body will also be deprived of adequate rations of the fat-soluble vitamins.

About a liter of bile is formed by the liver each day. It is secreted continuously (though at varying rates—the amount increases when the blood flow through the liver is increased) but is stored in the baglike gallbladder and released into the duodenum only when it is needed. The bile that is produced by the liver is a thick, yellowish-green fluid, with a slightly alkaline pH. It consists mainly of water, cholesterol, bile pigments, inorganic salts, and salts of bile acids. The **bile pigments,** bilirubin and biliverdin, are breakdown products of hemoglobin scavenged from worn-out red blood cells. They are responsible for the color of bile and of the feces as well. The **inorganic salts,** including considerable bicarbonate, help to neutralize and buffer the acid chyme that is delivered into the intestine from the stomach. The **bile salts,** sodium glycocholate and sodium taurocholate, facilitate the action of lipase. They lower the surface tension, permitting the fats to be emulsified and increasing the surface area of the fat particles, on which the pancreatic lipase and other enzymes can act. Bile salts also aid in the absorption of fats, "ferrying" fatty digestion products to the intestinal mucosa.

The bile salts are thriftily recycled and used again and again, stimulating their own secretion in a sort of continuous loop. About 80 to 90 percent of the bile salts that reach the intestine are reabsorbed through the intestinal wall and carried through the bloodstream to the liver. There they act as a stimulus for an increased secretion of bile, which flows through the hepatic and cystic ducts to the gallbladder and is eventually discharged into the duodenum. In the small intestine most of the bile salts are reabsorbed again, continuing the feedback mechanism. Radioisotope studies have shown that the total pool of bile salts circulates at least twice during the digestion of a single average meal. Bile secretion is also increased by the hormone secretin and nervous stimulation via vagus nerve fibers.

In the gallbladder the bile is concentrated 6 to 10 times by the absorption of water, and mucus is added to it. The contraction of the gallbladder, propelling its contents down the common bile duct into the duodenum, is stimulated by a hormone, **cholecystokinin,** which is produced by the intestinal mucosa in response to the presence of fatty chyme. When digestion is completed and the small intestine is empty, the sphincter guarding the opening of the common bile duct closes, the discharge of bile from the gallbladder ceases, and the biliary system neatly regulates itself—no more bile salts are absorbed through the intestinal wall, bile secretion slows down, and the gallbladder slowly fills, awaiting another hormonal message that its stored contents are needed.

Intestinal Secretions If samples of pure intestinal juice, free of cell debris, are collected, they are found to contain only two enzymes: **enterokinase,** which activates the pancreatic enzyme trypsin, and a rather weak **amylase.** This finding might seem to indicate that most of the work of digestion in the small intestine is done by "imported" enzymes from the pancreas, rather than by local products. However, the epithelial cells of the intestinal mucosa contain large quantities of digestive enzymes, which apparently digest food materials *while* they are being absorbed. These enzymes, which put the "finishing touches" on the digestion of foodstuffs, include: **peptidases** such as **erepsin,** which split polypeptides into amino acids; enzymes for splitting disaccharides into monosaccharides: **sucrase, maltase,** and **lactase** (which act on sucrose, maltose, and lactose, respectively); **intestinal lipase,** which splits neutral fats into glycerol and fatty acids; and **nucleotidases** and **nucleosidases,** which act on nucleic acid components.

It might seem that the presence of all these active digestive enzymes in delicate epithelial cells would be hard on the cells, and this is apparently the case. The epithelial cells deep in the crypts of Lieberkühn continually undergo mitosis, and the new cells migrate upward while the old cells are shed into the intestinal secretions. The lifetime of a typical intestinal epithelial cell is just 48 hours. This rapid growth of new cells permits rapid repair of any damage to the epithelial lining that may occur.

The major factor regulating the secretion of the intestinal enzymes seems to be the distension of the intestinal wall due to the presence of chyme. The larger the amount of chyme, the more secretions poured out. Autonomic nervous control is also important; parasympathetic stimulation enhances secretion, while sympathetic stimulation inhibits it—especially

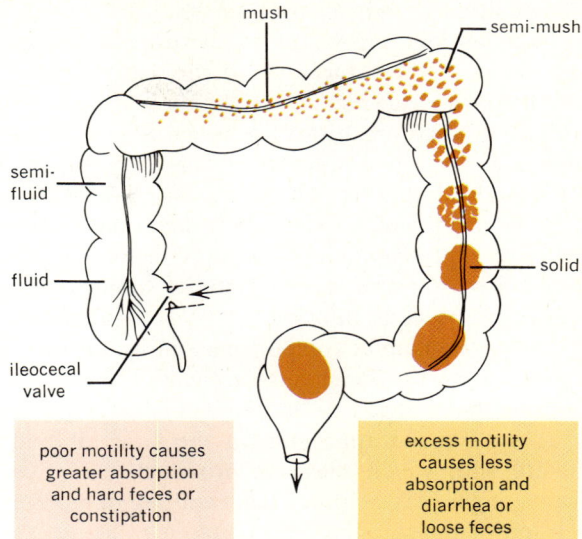

FIGURE 26-7 Formation of feces in the large intestine.

the secretion of mucus by the Brunner's glands. When sympathetic excitement is prolonged or habitual, the reduction of mucus secretion leaves the intestinal lining without adequate protection against the repeated onslaughts of acid chyme, and duodenal ulcers may form. (That is why ulcer patients are advised to slow down and adopt a more relaxed, less stressful attitude.) A hormone, **enterocrinin,** has also been extracted from the intestinal mucosa and is believed to stimulate the secretion of intestinal juice.

THE LARGE INTESTINE

The large intestine is the "garbage dump" of the body. By the time this part of the digestive tract is reached, nearly all the useful nutrients have already been digested and absorbed. What remain are fibers and other indigestible materials, salts, excretory products such as the bile pigments, and large quantities of water. (Considerable amounts of water are added to the contents of the alimentary canal as they pass through the mouth, stomach, and small intestine—the digestive juices are about 95 percent water.) Thus, the large intestine contains mainly things that the body does not need, on their way to elimination, along with valuable fluid that could be usefully recycled. The functions of the large intestine are mainly to move these materials along and out of the body, and on the way to extract most of the water from the intestinal contents. These materials are gradually shaped into firm masses called **feces** (Figure 26-7).

A garbage dump typically smells bad, as a result of the action of decay processes carried out by fermentative bacteria and other microorganisms. The feces that emerge from the large intestine likewise have a rather unpleasant odor for precisely the same reason. The food we ingest contains numerous microorganisms. Most of them succumb to the action of the strong acid and enzymes in the stomach. But some survive, and microorganisms are noted for their tremendous reproductive potential, given favorable environmental conditions. They find these favorable conditions in the colon, where they settle down and undergo an explosive multiplication, living on the undigested food residues there. Bacterial **fermentation** reactions in the large intestine break down complex substances into simpler components and usually produce various gases. Depending on the kind of microorganisms that happen to be dominant in the intestine at a particular time and on the kind of food substrate with which they are provided, excessive amounts of gas may be produced, resulting in painful distension of the intestine and **flatus** (a rather noisy ejection of intestinal gas via the rectum). The pungent odor of feces is due to **putrefaction** reactions, in which protein substances are converted to various compounds including indole, skatole, phenol, hydrogen sulfide, and ammonia.

The microorganisms inhabiting the intestinal tract are called the **microflora.** The group of species constituting the microflora is usually characteristic for a given animal species; the human microflora may include not only various bacteria, such as the **coliforms,** *Escherichia coli* and *Enterobacter aerogenes,* but also yeasts (e.g., *Candida* species) and other types. The species composition of a person's microflora and their relative proportions vary depending on the diet, state of health, and other factors. Antiobiotic therapy may wipe out the entire colony of microflora, but the intestine is soon repopulated; a danger is that undesirable forms may dominate when the new equilibrium is reached.

Bacteria that live in the human large intestine synthesize a variety of vitamins in excess of their own needs and excrete them into the intestinal contents. These vitamins include vitamin K and several vitamins of the B-complex group, which are absorbed and used by the body.

Movements of the Large Intestine

Cancer of the colon is a major health problem in the United States and other modern nations. Yet it is a minor problem in less developed countries, among various African tribes, for example. Some medical researchers believe that the cause of this difference lies in the modern diet, in which natural fibers have been largely refined out of foods. It has been found that on a diet rich in bran or other fibers, the contents of the large intestine are moved along much more rapidly and eliminated sooner than on the typical low-fiber modern diet of refined foods. It is theorized that when

the same fecal matter lies around in the large intestine for as much as several days, the intestinal lining is subjected to prolonged attack by various toxic substances, which may contribute to the high incidence of cancer and various other diseases.

Several types of movements occur in the large intestine, serving two main functions: to facilitate absorption and to propel the contents along toward the anus. **Segmenting movements** similar to those in the small intestine aid in bringing the intestinal contents in contact with the mucosal lining. These movements occur mainly in the ascending and transverse colon, where most of the absorption of water takes place. **Kneading movements** also occur, in which fairly large segments of the intestinal wall are contracted while adjacent segments relax. **Haustral churning** is produced when both circular muscles and the longitudinal fibers of the teniae coli contract, causing baglike haustra to bulge outward, then empty as another group of circular fibers constricts.

Materials are propelled along the large intestine by **mass movements,** a kind of vigorous peristalsis that occurs only a few times a day. Mass movements are most likely to occur during or shortly after meals, especially the first meal of the day; they are stimulated by the **gastrocolic reflex.** Mass movements occur most often in the transverse and descending colon; when they force a mass of feces into the rectum, the desire to defecate is felt.

Secretions of the Colon

The large intestine secretes a juice with a pH of about 8, which contains no enzymes at all. It does contain mucus, and serves to lubricate the intestinal lining and bind the fecal matter together into a mass that can be effectively propelled along the intestinal tract. The alkaline secretions of the colon also neutralize potentially irritating acids produced by the intestinal microflora.

Feces and Defecation

A child's first explorations of the forbidden delights of using dirty language usually are focused on the function and products of defecation. The child is gradually persuaded that defecation is not a suitable topic for polite conversation, but judging by the volume of laxative sales, an almost morbid preoccupation with bowel function often persists into adulthood.

About 10 to 12 hours after a meal, the residue of undigested materials, together with a mass of microorganisms that may make up close to fifty percent of the bulk of the feces, is approaching the end of the alimentary canal. Peristaltic movements in the colon force the feces along into the rectum, which becomes distended. When the intrarectal pressure reaches about 40 mm Hg, a reflex arc is excited, involving the sacral level of the spinal cord and parasympathetic nerves innervating the rectum. Vigorous peristaltic waves are initiated, and the internal anal sphincter relaxes. In an infant, this reflex results in an immediate, automatic defecation or expulsion of feces. But gradually the child learns to control the external anal sphincter voluntarily and can prevent defecation by keeping that striated muscle sphincter tightly constricted.

The defecation reflex can be initiated and aided by voluntary efforts. Contractions of the abdominal muscles increase the intraabdominal pressure, while a powerful expiratory effort made with the epiglottis closed forces the diaphragm downward. The increased pressure squeezes the rectum and aids in expelling its contents.

An urge for defecation may come at an inopportune time. If the act is delayed, by keeping the external sphincter closed, sensory adaptation occurs and the urge passes even though the rectum is full. The adaptation may persist for 24 hours. During this time the feces lose water and become hard and difficult to expel. (Normally, the feces contain about 75 percent water, a level that is maintained in the colon by either removing or adding liquid as necessary.) The pain experienced in attempting to evacuate hardened feces may result in incomplete defecation, perpetuating the vicious cycle. Habitual disregarding of the urge to defecate can give rise to chronic constipation. Eating a diet with sufficient fiber (which tends to absorb water and make the feces soft and easily expelled), drinking adequate amounts of water, sufficient exercise, and regular bowel habits can help to prevent constipation.

Not all of the residue of any particular meal is expelled at the same time. Part of the residue remains in the colon and is mixed with that of subsequent meals, so that part of the feces may contain the remains of a meal eaten several days before.

In addition to a substantial amount of water, the feces normally contain fatty acids and lecithin, mucus, bile pigments, large amounts of bacteria (largely dead), undigested cellulose, and epithelial cells that have been sloughed off from the intestinal mucosa, as well as various amounts of minerals including calcium, potassium, iron, magnesium, bismuth, and mercury. For some substances, such as iron and bismuth, the feces provide the only means of excretion.

THE DIGESTIVE PROCESSES

Mechanical actions, grinding, mixing, and churning the food, play an important role in digestion. But if we had to depend on a mere mechanical breakdown of food during the digestive process, we would doubt-less starve to death. The mechanical action of the various digestive organs prepares the way for chemical reactions that reduce the food materials to their constituents. **Hydrolysis reactions** play the primary role: in these reactions, chemical bonds are broken and the elements of water (H and OH) are added to the fragments. (In fact, hydrolysis reactions are just the reverse of the reactions in which the complex food chemicals were formed.) The chemical reactions that go on in the digestive tract can be reproduced in the laboratory, but far less rapidly and efficiently than they proceed in the body. The difference is in the action of **enzymes,** intricate protein molecules that act as catalysts, bringing the reactants together and speeding the rates of their reactions. The work of the digestive enzymes is aided by various substances, such as hydrochloric acid in the stomach and bile in the small intestine. The production of the digestive secretions is controlled by nervous reflexes and by hormones, which are produced and act in finely tuned feedback mechanisms.

The principal digestive secretions are summarized in Table 26-1. Following that is a brief summary of the processes of digestion of the main types of foods: carbohydrates, proteins, and fats. (Foods also contain vitamins, mineral salts, and water, but these substances do not have to be chemically digested in order to be absorbed.) After that we will observe the fate of a typical meal on its way through the alimentary canal.

Digestion of Carbohydrates

Starch molecules may seem very large and complicated, but they are actually made up of chains of sugars, linked together by condensation reactions, in which the elements of water were lost from the simple sugar units. The amylases of the saliva and pancreas hydrolyze polysaccharides such as starch into disaccharides (two-sugar compounds) such as maltose, which is a combination of two glucose units (Figure 26-8). Foods also contain the disaccharides sucrose (cane sugar) and lactose (milk sugar). All these disaccharides are split into simple sugars by specific enzymes in the intestinal juice: maltase, sucrase, and lactase. The simple sugars that result from the hydrolysis of the carbohydrates in food are mainly glucose, along with some fructose (from sucrose) and galactose (from lactose).

There is one abundant carbohydrate that we are not equipped to digest, even though it is formed from chains of glucose units. This is cellulose, which forms the cell walls of plants and constitutes the bulk of the natural fiber or "roughage" in the diet. Some microorganisms have appropriate enzymes for breaking down cellulose and have formed mutually beneficial partnerships with herbivorous animals such as cows

TABLE 26-1 Digestive Secretions

SECRETION	TYPE	SOURCE	ACTION
Active in mouth			
Salivary amylase	Enzyme	Salivary glands	Starch → maltose
Mucin	Carbohydrate-protein		Binds food particles together
Active in stomach			
Gastrin	Hormone		Secretion of gastric juice (HCl + enzymes)
Hydrochloric acid	Mineral acid		Pepsinogen → pepsin; curdles milk; kills bacteria
Pepsin	Enzyme	Stomach	Proteins → proteoses, peptones, and polypeptides
Rennin	Enzyme		Coagulates milk proteins (in child's stomach)
Gastric lipase	Enzyme		Fats → glycerides, fatty acids
Enterogastrone	Hormone	Small intestine	Inhibits gastric motility and secretion
Active in small intestine			
Sodium bicarbonate	Salt		Neutralizes HCl
Amylase	Enzyme		Starch → maltose
Lipase	Enzyme		Fats → fatty acids + glycerol
Trypsin	Enzyme	Pancreas	Proteins and polypeptides → small polypeptides; chymotrypsinogen → chymotrypsin
Chymotrypsin	Enzyme		Proteins and polypeptides → small polypeptides
Carboxypeptidase	Enzyme		Polypeptides → amino acids (removal of C-terminal amino acid)
Nucleases (RNase, DNase)	Enzyme		Nucleic acids → nucleotides
Bile salts	Steroids	Liver	Emulsify fats
Aminopeptidases (e.g., erepsin)	Enzyme		Peptides → amino acids (removal of N-terminal amino acid)
Enterokinase	Enzyme		Trypsinogen → trypsin
Maltase	Enzyme		Maltose → glucose
Sucrase	Enzyme		Sucrose → glucose + fructose
Lactase	Enzyme	Intestinal glands	Lactose → glucose + galactose
Nucleotidase	Enzyme		Nucleotides → nucleosides + phosphoric acid
Nucleosidase	Enzyme		Nucleosides → purines, pyrimidines, pentose
Lipase	Enzyme		Fat → glycerides, fatty acids, and glycerol
Enterocrinin	Hormone		Stimulates secretion of intestinal juice
Villikinin	Hormone		Stimulates movements of intestinal villi
Active in pancreas			
Secretin	Hormone	Duodenum	Stimulates secretion of sodium bicarbonate
Pancreozymin	Hormone		Stimulates secretion of digestive enzymes
Active in gallbladder			
Cholecystokinin	Hormone	Duodenum	Stimulates release of bile

and rabbits, living as microflora in their digestive tract. But the human microflora does not happen to include any of these useful species. Instead, cellulose passes through our alimentary canal basically unchanged, and its presence helps to stimulate intestinal peristalsis, promoting regular evacuation.

Digestion of Proteins

Proteins are very large polymers composed of chains of amino acids, linked together by peptide bonds, and then intricately coiled and folded. Like carbohydrates, proteins are digested in stages, rather than all at once (Figure 26-9). First the proteins are broken

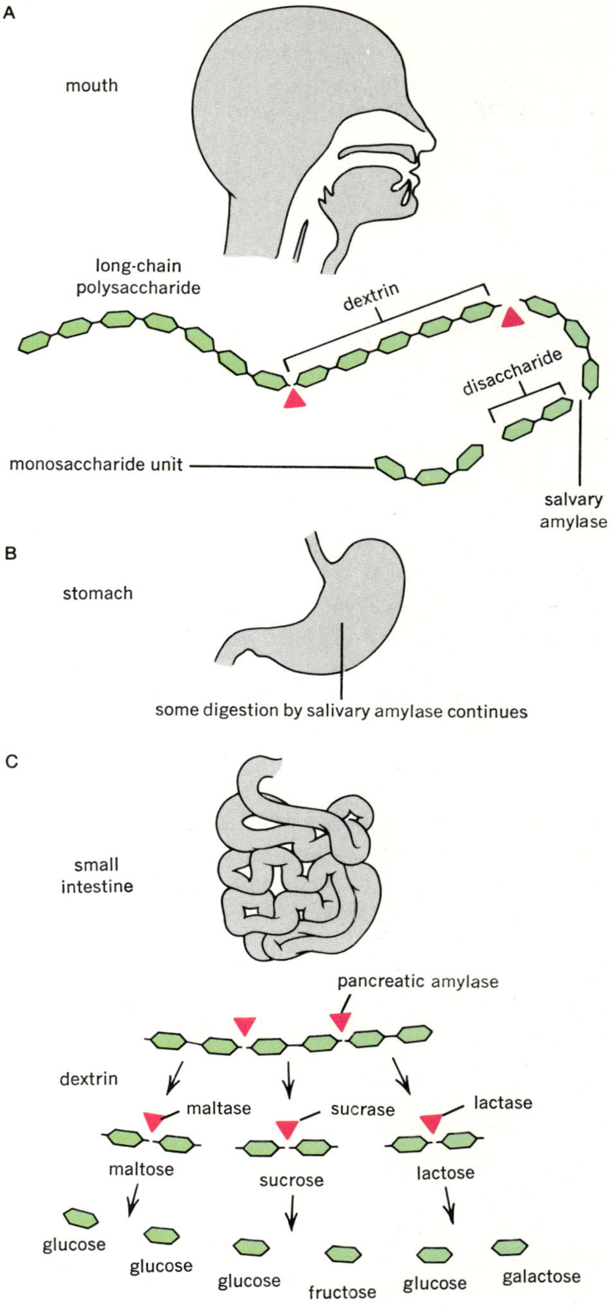

A

mouth

long-chain
polysaccharide

dextrin

disaccharide

monosaccharide unit

salvary
amylase

B

stomach

some digestion by salivary amylase continues

C

small
intestine

pancreatic amylase

dextrin

maltase   sucrase   lactase

maltose   sucrose   lactose

glucose

glucose

glucose   fructose   glucose   galactose

FIGURE 26-8   Digestion of carbohydrates.

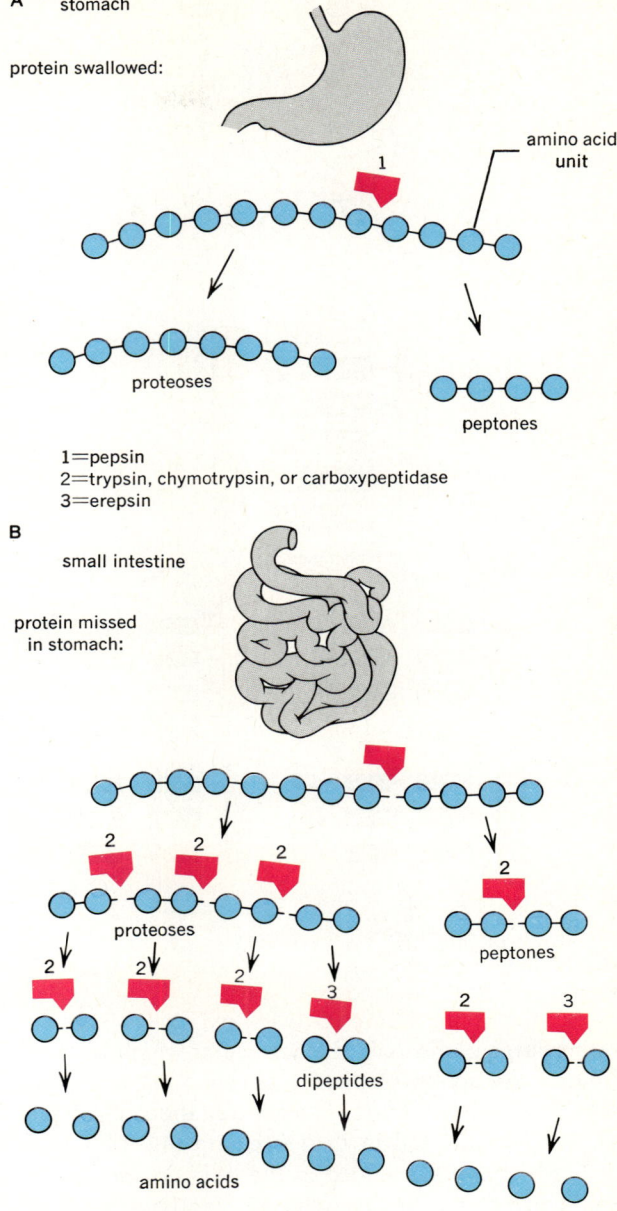

A   stomach

protein swallowed:

amino acid
unit

proteoses

peptones

1=pepsin
2=trypsin, chymotrypsin, or carboxypeptidase
3=erepsin

B

small intestine

protein missed
in stomach:

proteoses

peptones

dipeptides

amino acids

FIGURE 26-9   Digestion of proteins.

down into smaller segments—proteoses, peptones, and polypeptides—by the action of pepsin in the stomach. This is an enzyme that works best in the acid medium produced by the HCl in the gastric juice. Then, in the small intestine, additional proteolytic enzymes work on the results of pepsin digestion. The proteoses, peptones, and polypeptides are broken down into still smaller fragments (peptides) by trypsin and chymotrypsin, enzymes secreted by the pancreas. The job of protein digestion is finished up by carbox-

ypeptidase from the pancreas and peptidases secreted by the intestinal glands. These enzymes hydrolyze the peptides to their constituent amino acids.

A curious facet of protein digestion is the action of some of the proteolytic enzymes on each other. Pepsin, trypsin, chymotrypsin, and carboxypeptidase are all secreted in larger, inactive forms, which must be activated by a selective proteolysis, catalyzed by enzymes, before they can act on food materials.

Digestion of Fats

Fats are insoluble in water, and even after the churning action of the stomach, they are still in the form of

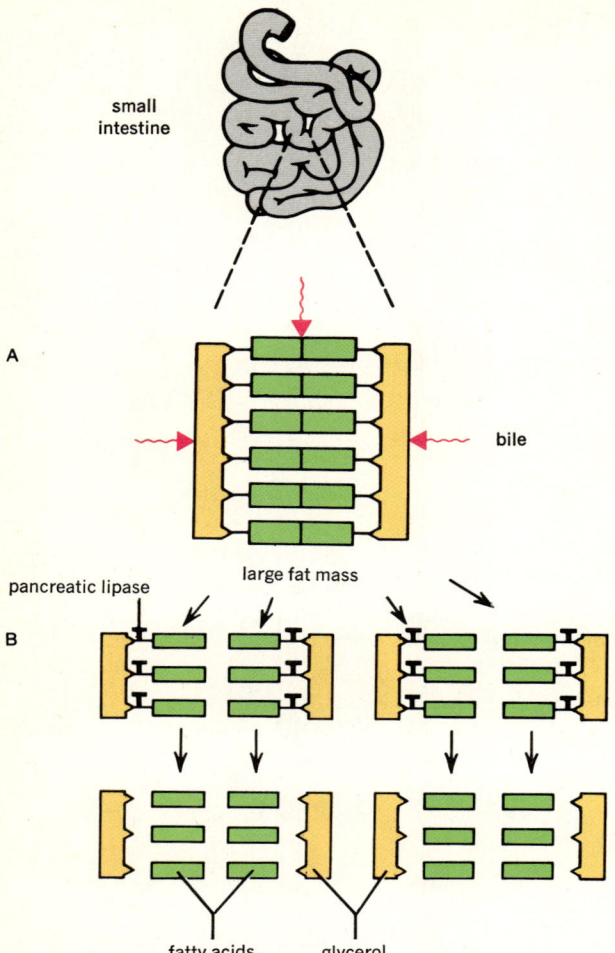

small
intestine

A

bile

pancreatic lipase

large fat mass

B

fatty acids   glycerol

FIGURE 26-10   Digestion of fats.

rather large globs, only the surface of which is accessible to the action of the fat-digesting enzymes. The bile salts secreted by the liver lower the surface tension of fats and aid in their breakup into tiny globules, which are suspended in the fluid chyme. In this emulsified form, the fat molecules can be more effectively attacked by the lipases of the pancreas and intestine.

Most of the fats in the diet consist of triglycerides (neutral fats), which are combinations of a single molecule of glycerol with three molecules of fatty acids. As in proteins and carbohydrates, the bonds that hold the constituents of fats together are formed by condensation reactions in which the elements of water are eliminated. Thus, fat digestion also consists of hydrolysis reactions, yielding fatty acids and glycerol (Figure 26-10).

A Journey through the Digestive Tract

It is lunchtime, and you are just about to sit down to a tempting meal. On the table before you is a hot

roast beef sandwich, with some crisp lettuce leaves, a juicy tomato, and a frosty glass of milk. All the major types of food are represented in the meal: carbohydrates in the bread, lettuce and tomato, and milk; proteins in the meat, bread, and milk; and fats mainly in the meat and milk. Water, vitamins, and minerals are also provided by the meal, but they will not need to be digested.

Just looking at the meal and smelling the mingled odors of the food, your mouth begins to water. As you take a bite, saliva is already pouring into your mouth, and in your stomach gastric juice is beginning to flow. Your teeth methodically pulverize the food and mix it with saliva. Salivary amylase gets a head start on breaking down the starch in the bread, but so far the proteins and fats are being subjected only to mechanical action.

Now the bite of sandwich is a soggy mass, moistened and mixed with saliva. Your tongue shapes it into a glob and shoves it backward, into the oropharynx. With a convulsive gulp, you swallow, and the bolus begins to descend the muscular tube of the esophagus. You wash it down with a sip of milk.

At the bottom of the esophagus, the bolus and milk have raised the pressure, so that the cardiac sphincter relaxes, and the food enters the stomach. For a while the salivary amylase in the interior of the bolus will continue to act on the starches, but as the stomach mixes and churns the food, acid gastric juice penetrates and inactivates the salivery enzyme. Meanwhile, the stomach secretions are working on the food. Hydrochloric acid quickly curdles the milk, so that if you happen to regurgitate some you will notice that it is lumpy rather than fluid. The pepsin and acid begin to work on the proteins of the scraps of beef and bread, hydrolyzing them into medium-sized molecular forms such as polypeptides. Under the vigorous churning movements of the stomach wall, the food is gradually broken up into smaller and smaller particles and is displaced toward the wall as new boluses descend from the mouth. In time, the food is no longer recognizable as fragments of a roast beef sandwich, salad, and milk. It is a murky, semifluid mass, making its way down to the pylorus. The valve opens, and part of the first bite squirts into the duodenum.

Now the secretions of the intestinal wall are galvanized, and in turn stimulate the pancreas and gallbladder to pour their contributions down their respective ducts into the duodenum. The acid is neutralized by bicarbonate. Trypsin and chymotrypsin, and then carboxypeptidase and the intestinal peptidases work on the polypeptides from the meat, bread, and milk, gradually reducing them to individual amino acids. Bile salts emulsify the fat globules from the meat and milk, and the pancreatic lipase splits the fat molecules into fatty acids and glycerol. Amylase continues the work of the salivary amylase and splits the remaining starch molecules to disaccharides; maltase, sucrase, and lactase work on the disaccharides and free the simple sugars.

Sugars, amino acids, fatty acids, and glycerol are all gradually absorbed into the tiny villi that project from the intestinal lining, as the muscular wall mixes and churns the chyme and propels it along. Finally, the dregs pass through the ileocecal valve and enter the large intestine.

More mixing and churning occur, as water is absorbed through the mucous membrane lining. Bacteria feed on the undigested materials, and you may feel a few faint rumbles from the gas they produce. Finally, the next morning, a wave of strong contractions sweeps over the wall of the colon, and fecal matter containing the remains of your roast beef sandwich is propelled with a rush into the rectum. You feel an urge to defecate, and in a few moments the feces are expelled.

PRACTICAL CONSIDERATIONS

Next to aspirin, antacids and laxatives are probably the most widely used over-the-counter medications. Yet in many cases, these self-administered medications are unnecessary and may even be harmful.

Indigestion, or dyspepsia, is a vague term used loosely for a variety of upsets of the digestive system. It may be caused by such conditions as spasm of the esophagus, failure of the cardiac sphincter to relax properly, inflammation of the stomach wall (**gastritis**—frequently caused by irritation of alcohol), peptic ulcer, cancer of the stomach, gallbladder disease, intestinal disorders, or emotional upset. Obviously no one treatment could be a panacea for such a diverse assortment of ills, and persistent indigestion should be a warning signal to have a comprehensive series of medical tests to rule out some of the more serious possible causes. Yet the popular idea for managing indigestion is to chew a few antacid tablets to neutralize the "excess acid." In fact, the presence of fairly strong hydrochloric acid is necessary for proper stomach function. Indeed, a hyposecretion of hydrochloric acid, due to atrophy of the gastric mucosa, is a not uncommon cause of gastritis, and some gastrointestinal disorders, including chronic diarrhea of undetermined cause, respond well to the taking of a dilute hydrochloric acid solution after meals.

Food poisoning is a common disorder of the digestive tract, caused by eating foods or drinking water contaminated with bacteria or their toxins or with other poisons. Meat, milk, and eggs, in particular, may carry *Salmonella,* and unrefrigerated sauces containing eggs or cream, salad dressings, and custards

are the most common carriers of *Staphylococcus.* (The bacteria may be introduced into the foods by food handlers who carry the germs in their nose and throat.) In the case of *Salmonella,* the bacteria themselves become established in the intestinal tract, producing various combinations of fever, nausea, vomiting, cramping, and diarrhea for several days. Staphylococcal food poisoning, which is characterized by nausea, vomiting, abdominal cramps, prostration and diarrhea, and usually lasts for 12 to 24 hours, is caused by toxins produced by the bacteria as they grow in unrefrigerated food. High standards of sanitation and proper cooking and refrigeration of foods can prevent most outbreaks of such bacteria-caused food poisoning. **Botulism** is a special type of gastritis, caused by the toxins of the bacterium *Clostridium botulinum.* This is a bacterium that grows only in the absence of air—conditions such as those found inside canned foods that have not been sufficiently heated during preparation. With rare exceptions, botulism is a problem mainly in home-canned foods. It is an extremely serious condition, producing not only nausea and vomiting, but also muscular paralysis, and may be fatal. Food poisoning may also be caused by eating shellfish infected with the protozoa *Gonyaulax catenella* (which produces a powerful toxin) or infectious hepatitis virus; by the toxins contained in certain varieties of mushrooms; by cadmium and other metals, absorbed from the coatings of ice cube trays or improperly glazed pottery; and by pesticide contaminants. Travelers to foreign countries often suffer for a few days from intestinal upset and diarrhea, a malady colloquially referred to as "turista." The problem here seems to be not so much a specific pathogen as simply the presence of an unaccustomed assortment of microorganisms in the water.

Malabsorption from the small intestine may sometimes be a problem. Nutrients may not be adequately absorbed, even though the food is well digested. In young children the condition is often called **celiac disease;** in adults it is referred to as **sprue.** In some cases the cause seems to be an inability to fully digest the protein gliadin in wheat; the glutamine-containing polypeptides that remain are toxic to the intestinal mucosa, damaging the villi and reducing the absorptive area of the intestine. The victim suffers from severe nutritional deficiency even though the diet may be perfectly adequate.

Abnormalities of defecation are an object of great preoccupation for many people. The failure to have a regular bowel movement every day is viewed with alarm and quickly dosed with laxatives, which when taken habitually can decrease the tone of the large intestine and set up a vicious cycle producing chronic **constipation.** A frequent cause of colonic stasis, or constipation, is the habit of failing to respond to an urge to defecate, putting the action off until a more convenient time. The excessive resorption of water from the feces that occurs during constipation produces large, hard fecal masses that are difficult to pass. The straining that is necessary to eliminate them may give rise to hemorrhoids and anal fissures, which in turn cause pain in later defecations, promoting further constipation. Fruits, vegetables, and whole-grain cereals, which contain a considerable amount of indigestible fiber, have a stimulating effect on the bowel. Fats may also stimulate bowel function: undigested fats have a lubricating effect, while partially digested fats are mildly irritating to the intestinal lining and stimulate peristalsis.

Diarrhea is an excessive elimination of semifluid feces. It may be the result of an infection in the gastrointestinal tract (gastroenteritis) or of excessive parasympathetic stimulation of the large intestine (neurogenic diarrhea). In the presence of infection, the irritability of the inflamed mucosal lining promotes peristalsis, sweeping the intestinal contents out of the body faster and helping to get rid of the infection. But this protective mechanism, if prolonged, may cause harm to the body by producing dehydration and decreasing the absorption of needed nutrients. The neurogenic form of diarrhea is commonly exprienced in times of stress, such as in a soldier just before going into battle or in a student during an examination.

Even with all the preoccupation with bowel habits, many people neglect a simple but valuable means of monitoring their health: observation of the appearance of the stools. Many disorders of the gastrointestinal tract show up in changes in the consistency and general appearance of the stools. A disorder of the biliary system may be reflected in clay-colored stools, for the normal color is imparted to feces by the bile pigments. Bleeding from the upper part of the gastrointestinal tract results in tarry-looking stools. Red streaks in the stools are an indication of fresh blood, which may come from hemorrhoids or from cancer of the rectum. In parasitic infections, eggs, segments, or whole worms may be present in the stools.

A variety of clinical tests are used to evaluate the state of the gastrointestinal tract and its accessory organs (Figure 26-11). A thick solution of **barium,** a substance opaque to X rays, is given by mouth, and the patient is X-rayed at intervals to observe the esophagus, stomach, and small intestine. A barium enema is given to examine the large intestine. The barium coats the lining of the gastrointestinal tract, outlining it and showing up any ulcers, masses, or other pathological processes. Liver function is tested by a dye test (determining the effectiveness of uptake

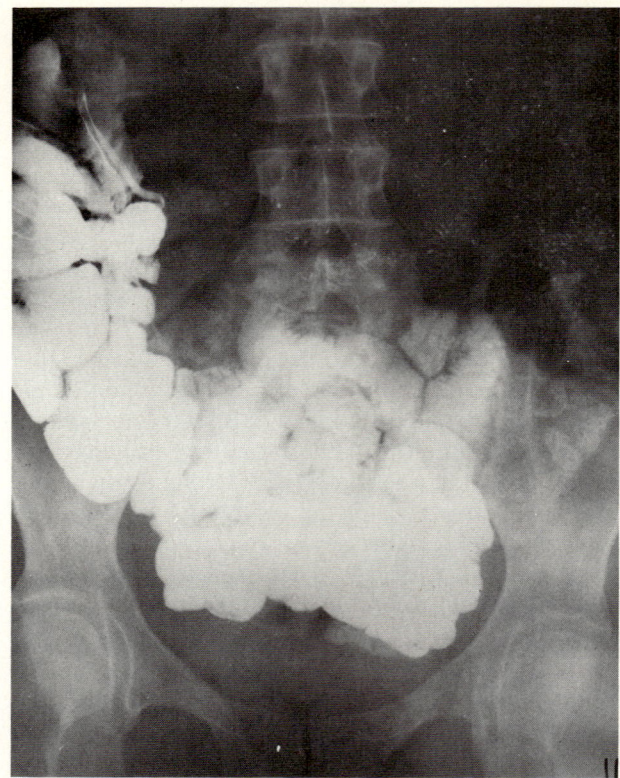

A

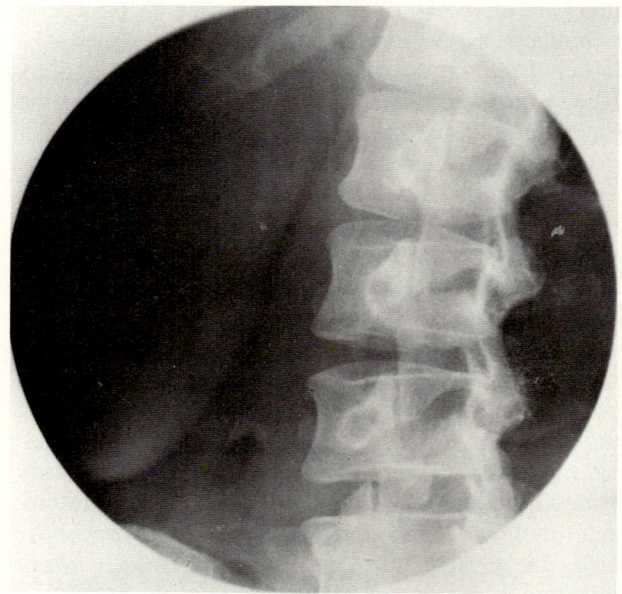

B

FIGURE 26-11   In the X ray (A), a portion of the small intestine is outlined by ingested barium; X ray (B) shows the gall bladder outlined by a radioopaque dye.

of the dye from the blood and its excretion in the bile), tests for bilirubin in the blood, plasma protein concentrations, and cholesterol assays. X-ray-opaque dyes are used to outline the gallbladder and test its emptying function.

SUMMARY

Ingested foods must be broken down into fragments small enough to pass through cell membranes.

Mechanical actions of the digestive organs:

Move foods along

Moisten and liquefy them

Pulverize them, increasing surface area

Chemical actions of the digestive organs convert large, complicated molecules of foodstuffs to smaller, simpler units in hydrolytic reactions catalyzed by enzymes.

Digestive actions in the mouth are mastication (chewing) and the chemical action of saliva.

Saliva contains:

Salivary amylase

Mucin

Lysozyme

Inorganic salts

Water

The functions of saliva are:

Solvent

Hydrolysis of starches to maltose

Lubricant

Germicide

The act of swallowing includes voluntary and involuntary phases.

Food is conveyed from the pharynx down the esophagus to the stomach by peristalsis, normally aided by gravity.

When the pressure inside the esophagus is greater than that in the stomach, the cardiac sphincter relaxes.

The functions of the stomach in digestion are storage of food, formation of chyme by mixing food with gastric secretions, and slow, controlled emptying of chyme into the duodenum.

The stomach can accommodate itself to increases in contents.

Movements of the stomach include mixing waves and peristaltic waves.

Emptying of the stomach is determined by the fluidity of the chyme and the receptivity of the duodenum.

The duodenum exerts feedback control over the stomach by the enterogastric reflex and the hormone enterogastrone.

Gastric juice has a pH close to 1 and contains:

Hydrochloric acid

Mucin

Pepsin

Rennin

Gastric lipase

Secretion of gastric juice occurs in three phases:

Cephalic phase (mental stimuli)

Gastric phase (presence of food in the stomach)

Intestinal phase (presence of chyme in the intestine)

The enzyme pepsin is secreted in an inactive form, pepsinogen. After activation, it hydrolyzes proteins to proteoses, peptones, and polypeptides.

Vomiting is a reflex act, coordinated by the vomiting center in the medulla, and includes spasmodic contractions of the abdominal muscles and diaphragm with the stomach, esophagus, and cardiac sphincter relaxed.

Digestive processes in the small intestine include mechanical mixing and hydrolytic action of enzymes on carbohydrates, proteins, fats, and nucleic acids.

Chemical action is produced by pancreatic juice, intestinal juice, and bile (a liver secretion).

Absorption of nutrients into the blood and lymph circulation occurs mainly in the small intestine.

Mechanical actions of the small intestine include:

Segmentation contractions

Pendular movements

Contractions of villi

Peristalsis

Pancreatic juice is alkaline and contains:

Sodium bicarbonate

Trypsin (secreted as trypsinogen)

Chymotrypsin (secreted as chymotrypsinogen)

Carboxypeptidase

Amylase

Lipase

Nucleases

Secretion of pancreatic juice is regulated by hormones (secretin and pancreozymin) and nervous stimulation.

Bile is secreted by the liver and temporarily stored in the gallbladder.

It contains:

Water

Cholesterol

Bile salts

Bile pigments (bilirubin, biliverdin)

Inorganic salts

Bile salts are reabsorbed and carried to the liver, where they stimulate new bile secretion.

Bile salts lower surface tension and emulsify fats and also facilitate their absorption.

Contraction of the gallbladder, releasing bile, is stimulated by cholecystokinin, a hormone secreted by the intestine.

Intestinal juice contains:

Enterokinase

Intestinal amylase

Intestinal epithelial cells also contain enzymes, which digest food materials while they are being absorbed:

Peptidases (e.g., erepsin)

Lipase

Maltase

Sucrase

Lactase

Nucleases

The hormone enterocrinin, secreted by the intestinal mucosa, is believed to stimulate secretion of intestinal juice.

The large intestine stores undigested food materials until periodic evacuations, absorbs excess water from fecal matter, and harbors microflora.

Movements of the large intestine include:

Segmenting movements

Kneading movements

Haustral churning

Mass movements

They are stimulated by a diet high in fibrous foods, irritation of the intestinal lining, and the gastrocolic reflex.

The large intestine secretes an alkaline juice containing mucus.

Distension of the rectum by feces initiates a reflex relaxing the internal anal sphincter and producing an urge to defecate.

The defecation reflex can be overcome voluntarily by constriction of the external anal sphincter.

Habitual delay of defecation may result in chronic constipation.

Movement of food through the alimentary canal normally takes about 10 to 12 hours.

Feces normally contain:

Water

Fatty acids and lecithin

Mucus

Bile pigments

Bacteria

Undigested cellulose

Sloughed off epithelial cells

Minerals

The basic digestive reactions are:

$$\text{Polysaccharides} \xrightarrow[\text{amylase}]{\text{salivary amylase,}} \text{disaccharides}$$
(starch)   (maltose)

$$\text{Disaccharides} \xrightarrow[\text{lactase}]{\text{sucrase, maltase,}} \text{monosaccharides}$$
(glucose, fructose, galactose)

$$\text{Proteins} \xrightarrow[\text{chymotrypsin}]{\text{pepsin, trypsin,}} \text{proteoses, peptones, polypeptides}$$

$$\text{Polypeptides} \xrightarrow[\text{peptidases}]{\text{carboxypeptidose,}} \text{amino acids}$$

$$\text{Fats} \xrightarrow{\text{lipases}} \text{triglycerides, diglycerides, fatty acids,}$$
glycerol

$$\text{Nucleic acids} \xrightarrow{\text{nucleases}} \text{nucleotides}$$

$$\text{Nucleotides} \xrightarrow{\text{nucleotidases}} \text{nucleosides} +$$
phosphoric acid

$$\text{Nucleosides} \xrightarrow{\text{nucleosidases}} \text{purines, pyrimidines,}$$
pentose

Disorders of digestive function include:

Indigestion: a variety of disorders caused by esophageal spasm, gastritis, peptic ulcer, cancer, gallbladder disease, intestinal disorders, or emotional upset.

Food poisoning, due to eating foods contaminated with bacteria or their toxins, metals, pesticides, and so on.

Malabsorption (celiac disease, sprue): inadequate absorption of nutrients in the small intestine even though digestive function and diet may be adequate.

Constipation: slow movement of feces through the large intestine, usually associated with large quantities of dry, hard feces.

Diarrhea: excessive elimination of semifluid feces.

Barium solutions (administered by mouth or enema) are used in conjunction with X rays to evaluate the state of the gastrointestinal tract.

QUESTIONS FOR REVIEW AND THOUGHT

1 Describe the stages of digestion of the following meal as it passes through the digestive tract: steak, french fries, green salad, apple pie, and coffee. What effect would be produced by eating ice cream for dessert?

2 Describe the mechanical actions of the mouth, esophagus, stomach, small intestine, and large intestine during the process of digestion.

3 List the glands that secrete digestive juices and the site of action of each.

4 Discuss the role of hormones in digestion.

5 What enzymes act on: (a) carbohydrates; (b) proteins; (c) fats; (d) nucleic acids?

6 Define: bolus; chyme; feces; peristalsis.

7 Describe the successive pH changes in sequence through the digestive tract.

8 Discuss the advantages of: (a) chewing foods thoroughly; (b) eating a diet high in natural fibers; (c) drinking ample amounts of fluids; (d) acting promptly on urges to defecate.

9 Discuss the role of nervous reflexes in digestion.

10 Discuss the functioning of the gallbladder and the roles of bile in digestion.

11 Outline the principal chemical reactions in the digestion of foods.

12 Describe a vicious cycle resulting in chronic constipation.

ABSORPTION AND UTILIZATION OF FOOD

27

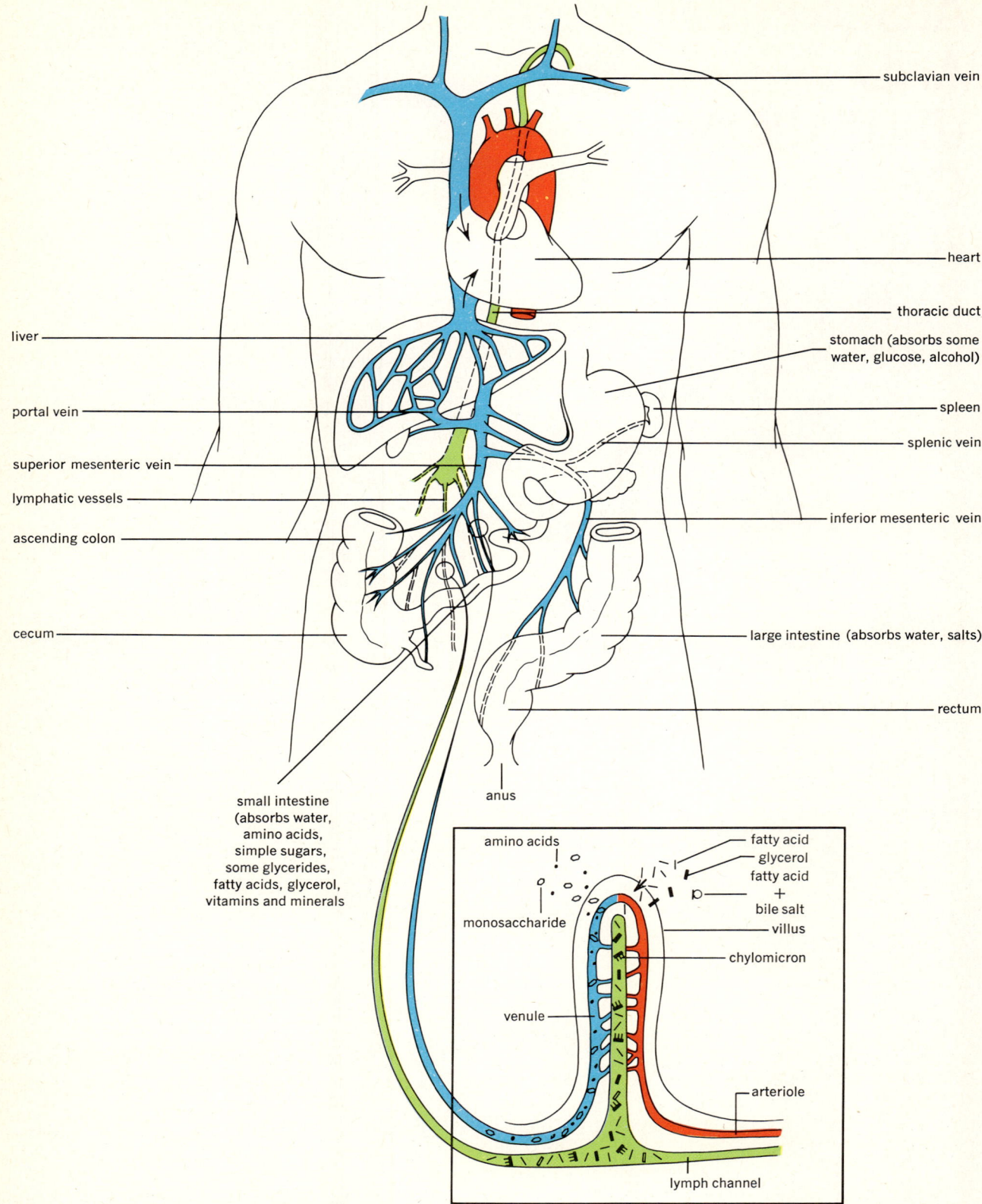

subclavian vein

heart

thoracic duct

liver

portal vein

superior mesenteric vein

lymphatic vessels

ascending colon

cecum

stomach (absorbs some
water, glucose, alcohol)

spleen

splenic vein

inferior mesenteric vein

large intestine (absorbs water, salts)

rectum

small intestine
(absorbs water,
amino acids,
simple sugars,
some glycerides,
fatty acids, glycerol,
vitamins and minerals)

anus

amino acids

monosaccharide

venule

fatty acid
glycerol
fatty acid
+
bile salt

villus

chylomicron

arteriole

lymph channel

FIGURE 27-1   The digestive tract. Absorption occurs mainly in the small intestine, but certain substances are absorbed from the stomach and large intestine. Absorbed nutrients pass into the blood and lymph circulation.

If you dip the corner of a paper towel into a glass of water, the moisture will gradually spread upward until the entire towel is saturated. After a dry spell, the soil can absorb enormous quantities of rainfall. In each case water works its way into numerous microscopic pores and is literally soaked up. The concept of absorption of food materials in the digestive tract is more complex, since it involves more than a "soaking up" of the products of digestion by the lining of the digestive tract. After the nutrients, which have been broken down into small and relatively simple components, pass through the cell membranes, they are carried by the blood and lymph circulation to the liver and other organs and tissues. There they may be oxidized to release their chemical energy, stored away for future needs, or **assimilated** into the body, where they are used as building blocks for growth and repair of tissues.

To a large extent, the absorption of food materials from the digestive tract occurs by the usual physical processes of diffusion and osmosis, as molecules move down concentration and pressure gradients. However, various types of active transport are also involved. The fact that the intestinal wall performs work in absorption is supported by observations that the intestine consumes more oxygen while absorption is going on than when it is inactive. More direct evidence is the fact that substances can be absorbed even from hypotonic solutions, that is, when their concentration in the intestines is lower than in the blood.

The enormous surface area provided by the villi and microvilli is an important factor in absorption of food, providing for greatly increased contact between the intestinal lining and the intestinal contents. The incessant churning and mixing movements of the intestine continually bring new portions of the semifluid mass in contact with the lining of the wall, increasing opportunities for the passage of materials through the cell membranes. The rich capillary and lymphatic networks within the villi provide a maximized surface for collecting nutrients and transporting them throughout the body.

SITES OF ABSORPTION

The main work of absorption occurs in the small intestine. But some absorption also occurs in other parts of the alimentary tract: the stomach and large intestine (Figure 27-1).

Absorption in the Stomach

Within minutes after taking an alcoholic beverage, the drinker begins to experience a feeling of relaxation and warmth. He or she may be laughing convivially and talking more freely than normal. The depressing effects of alcohol on control centers in the central nervous system are already being felt. Yet there has not been time for significant amounts of the drink to be emptied into the duodenum. About a fifth of the alcohol ingested is absorbed rapidly through the stomach lining and penetrates immediately into the bloodstream.

The stomach is not very well equipped for absorption. Only a few substances can be absorbed directly through the stomach lining. These are generally very simple substances, which do not need further digestion—for example, water, simple salts, and simple sugars—and lipid-soluble substances, such as alcohol and various drugs. The orange that an athlete may suck for "quick energy" provides a lift through the sugar that is absorbed in the stomach. The prompt action of alcohol and drugs that are taken by mouth is made possible because they do not have to wait to be absorbed from the small intestine. The presence or absence of food in the stomach when the drug is taken greatly influences the speed of its effect. An experienced drinker who wants to slow down the absorption of alcohol to avoid getting drunk coats the stomach beforehand with milk or some other food rich in proteins and fats.

Absorption in the Small Intestine

A view of a living segment of the lining of the small intestine under a microscope would be very much like a view of the community of bottom dwellers in an ocean reef. The ocean bottom is carpeted with the waving fronds and tentacles of sessile filter-feeders, which continually sweep in nutrients from the fluid medium of seawater that bathes them. When the intestine is filled with churning, semifluid chyme, the villi are also in constant motion, bending to and fro, contracting and straightening up again, as they take in nutrients from the chyme (Figure 27-2).

Most of the absorption of food for the body takes place in the small intestine, which is the organ best equipped for this function. Each tiny villus, with its own surface area magnified by a border of microvilli, encloses a capillary network and a collecting lymph vessel called a lacteal. The movements of the villi not only help to churn up the contents of the intestine, but also keep the blood flowing briskly through the capillary circulation. Thus, new portions of food-laden chyme are continually being exposed to fresh portions of flowing blood, maintaining a favorable concentration gradient for absorption. The intestinal hormone villikinin is believed to stimulate movements of the villi.

Digested food materials pass from the lumen of the intestine through the cells of the villi and into the network of capillaries and lymph vessels. An estimated 30 percent of the cardiac output flows through

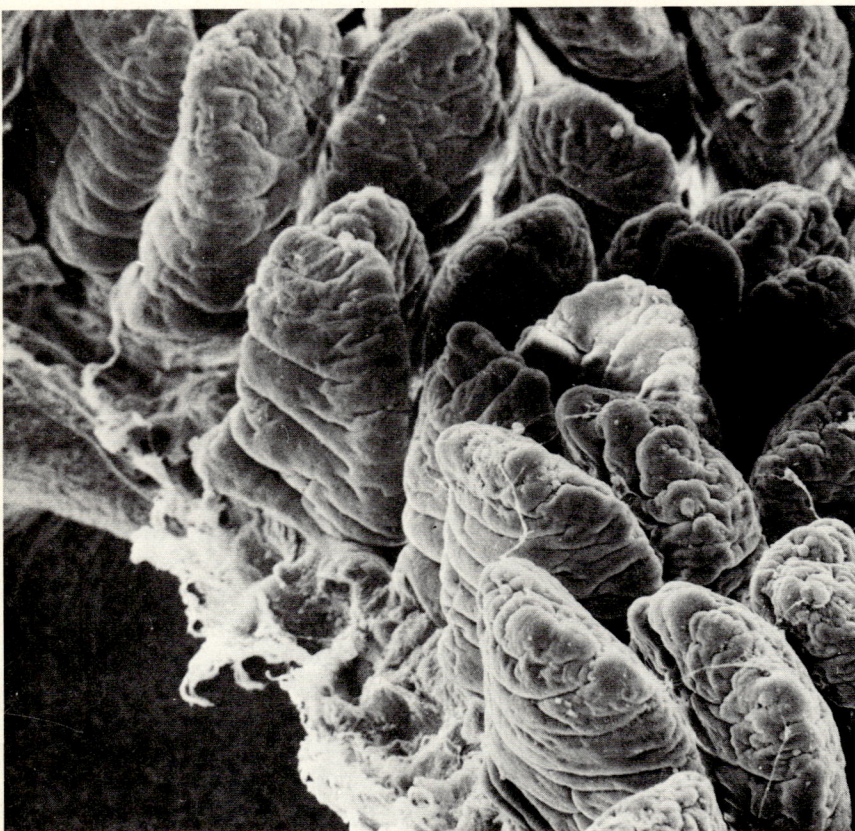

FIGURE 27-2 This isn't an undersea-scape—it's a scanning electron micrograph of villi on the lining of the small intestine.

the intestines. The capillaries of the small intestine lead into veins that connect with the hepatic portal vein, which carries blood to the liver, the body's major chemical processing center. Lymph from the lacteals is filtered by lymph nodes in the mesenteries before flowing into the thoracic duct.

The prodigious amounts of food substances absorbed into the bloodstream from the small intestine include 8 to 10 liters of water each day, 50 to 100 grams of inorganic ions, several hundred grams of carbohydrates (in the form of monosaccharides or simple sugars), and 50 to 100 grams of amino acids. About 100 grams of fatty substances are also absorbed from the small intestine: glycerol and very small fatty acid molecules directly into the bloodstream and larger fatty acids and other lipids such as cholesterol through the lacteals into the lymphatic system.

Absorption in the Large Intestine

In terms of volume, considerable absorption occurs in the large intestine—between 500 and 1000 ml of chyme enters it each day, and only 100 to 200 ml is excreted. But the types of material absorbed are very limited.

The material that enters the large intestine from the ileum still contains a small amount of incompletely digested food material, mixed with digestive enzymes. Digestion of these residues continues, but the amount is very minimal. Since the lining of the large intestine is entirely devoid of villi, absorption occurs mainly by diffusion.* Thus, the large intestine plays only a slight role in the absorption of nutrients. But it plays the major role in regulating the amount of water lost by the body in the feces. Normally, water is progressively withdrawn from the fecal matter as it passes through the large intestine. By the time the feces are expelled, they are semisolid or even hard (if their stay in the large intestine has been protracted by constipation). When an inflammation or some other irritation hurries the fecal matter through the large intestine, and the absorptive function is not fully effective, diarrhea is the result.

ABSORPTION OF CARBOHYDRATES

In the developed countries today, obesity is a major health problem. One of the contributing factors to this problem is the high content of carbohydrates in the diet. Typical "snack foods" and desserts, which

---

* Sodium is actively absorbed from the feces, while the colon actively transports potassium out into the feces.

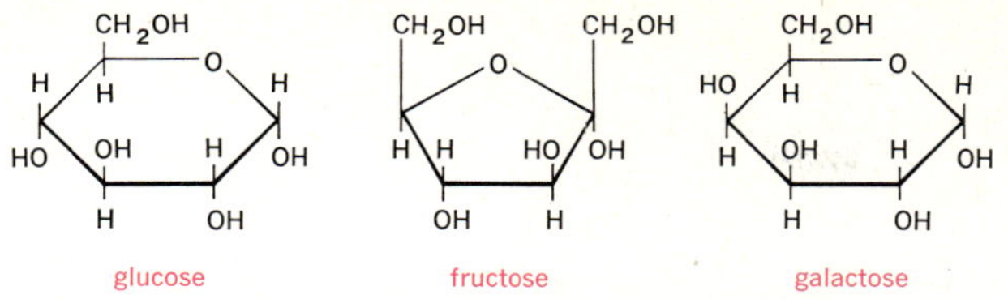

FIGURE 27-3 The monosaccharides glucose, fructose, and galactose.

have an element of emotional reward for many people, are particularly high in carbohydrates. Carbohydrates are efficient substrates for energy metabolism, but when they are consumed in excess they are stored in the body for future needs, producing an all too obvious increase in girth and weight. One of the newest research approaches to the obesity problem is the development of substances that combine chemically with carbohydrates and prevent their absorption in the intestine. Such "no-fat pills" would permit those lacking in willpower to enjoy carbohydrate-rich foods without having to regret them later when they step on the scale.

Monosaccharides are such small molecules, biologically speaking, that they might be expected to be absorbed through the intestinal membrane by simple diffusion. But there is considerable evidence to indicate that the process is not so simple. Sugars can be absorbed against a concentration gradient. Metabolic inhibitors, such as cyanides and iodoacetic acid, can block the absorption of monosaccharides. These simple sugars are absorbed at different rates, which would not occur if they merely diffused through the membrane, and they compete with one another for absorption. Galactose is most rapidly transported through the membrane, with glucose a close second and fructose absorbed less than half as rapidly as either galactose or glucose. (The rather minor structural differences of these monosaccharides can be seen in their chemical formulas in Figure 27-3.) Evidently, monosaccharides are carried through the intestinal membrane by a mechanism of active transport, involving a carrier molecule that combines with the sugar temporarily and then releases it after it has been transported across the membrane.

After absorption, monosaccharides pass into the hepatic portal blood system and are transported to the liver.

ABSORPTION OF PROTEINS

The end products of protein digestion are amino acids, small molecules that can be readily absorbed through cell membranes. But some proteins are digested only to dipeptides. Minute quantities of dipeptides and even smaller amounts of whole proteins are sometimes absorbed whole, by a process of pinocyto-

sis, in which a portion of the cell membrane forms a tiny funnel and "drinks" the large molecule, closing over it and discharging it inside the cell. Such absorbed protein molecules enter the lacteals.

The more typical absorption of amino acids is very similar to that of monosaccharides; it occurs by a form of active transport, with some amino acids being absorbed more rapidly than others. The absorption of amino acids in the intestines is much more rapid than the processes of digestion, and hence the rate of their absorption is determined by how rapidly they are provided by the hydrolysis of proteins and polypeptides. During digestion, there are never any free amino acids to be found in the small intestine—they are absorbed as soon as they are formed. The amino acids absorbed through the intestinal mucosa enter the blood capillaries and are carried into the portal blood system.

ABSORPTION OF FATS

One of the early symptoms of sprue, a condition of malabsorption in the intestine, is the appearance of large quantities of soapy fats in the feces. Fats present one of the most difficult digestive problems for the body, and their absorption also presents special problems. Unlike sugars and amino acids, fatty acids are insoluble in water. They are highly lipid-soluble, and thus may dissolve in the membrane of the epithelial cells and diffuse into the cell. Bile salts also promote the absorption of fats: fatty acids and monoglycerides released by digestion combine with the bile salts, forming a **micelle** (a colloidal particle), which can penetrate the microvilli. Meanwhile, the glycerol component of the fats, which is highly water-soluble, is quickly absorbed into the blood system.

Once in the cells, fatty acids and monoglycerides are transformed back into triglycerides under the action of the endoplasmic reticulum; then they are coated with protein and transported as microscopic fat particles called **chylomicrons** into the lacteals, from which they are carried by the lymphatic system to the blood circulation.

ABSORPTION OF VITAMINS

Vitamins are all organic chemicals, but they are a varied group, with a wide variety of properties. Some are water-soluble, while others (notably A, D, E, and K) are lipid-soluble. The water-soluble vitamins are quickly absorbed into the capillary network. But the fat-soluble vitamins must be carried in with fats. If there is insufficient fat in the diet, or if the digestion or absorption of fats is impaired (e.g., in liver or gallbladder disease), the absorption of the fat-soluble vitamins will be correspondingly reduced, and a vitamin deficiency may result even when the dietary supplies are adequate.

Vitamin B_{12} is a special case. Like the other B vitamins, it is water-soluble, but its molecule is very large—too large for simple diffusion to take place. A mucoprotein, called the **intrinsic factor** and secreted by the stomach, is needed for the absorption of vitamin B_{12}. (The actual site of absorption, however, is the lower half of the small intestine, rather than the stomach.) The vitamin apparently forms a temporary complex with the intrinsic factor, which is absorbed if sufficient calcium is present.

ABSORPTION OF ELECTROLYTES

Although salts make up a rather small percentage of the body's weight, they play a disproportionately large role in its metabolism. Large quantities of salts are lost each day in the body's excretions—urine, feces, sweat—and must be replaced through food and drink. They need not be digested, but they must be absorbed to be of use to the body. Electrolytes (salts) are absorbed both in the small and in the large intestines, but the major part of the absorption occurs in the upper portions of the small intestine because of its enormous surface area and great membrane permeability.

Electrolytes move across cell membranes by diffusion down concentration and electrical gradients and by processes of active transport (e.g., the "sodium pump"). Monovalent ions, such as sodium (Na^+), potassium (K^+), ammonium (NH_4^+), chloride (Cl^-), and bicarbonate (HCO_3^-), are absorbed more rapidly and readily than polyvalent ions, such as calcium (Ca^{++}), magnesium (Mg^{++}), iron (Fe^{++}, Fe^{+++}), tartrate ($C_4H_4O_6^-$), citrate ($C_6H_5O_7^-$), and sulfate (SO_4^-). In general, the monovalent ions are needed by the body in larger quantities than the less readily absorbed polyvalent ions. Special mechanisms exist for the absorption of the much-needed polyvalent ions calcium and iron.

Calcium is absorbed by a process of active transport, which is facilitated by dietary protein and vitamin D. Parathyroid hormone is an important controlling factor in the activation of vitamin D and thus in the absorption of calcium in the small intestine.

Iron in the diet occurs mostly in organic, ferric forms (Fe^{+++}), but iron is most readily absorbed in its insoluble inorganic, ferrous form (Fe^{++}). Organic ferric iron is usually changed to the ferrous form in the stomach by the interaction with HCl. An acceptor protein called **apoferritin** in the duodenal mucosa combines with iron after it has crossed the membrane, forming **ferritin,** which enters the blood. The acceptor mechanism is in equilibrium with the plasma iron, thus regulating the replacement of iron that has been lost by the body.

ABSORPTION OF WATER

The most obvious absorption of water occurs in the large intestine, but actually the major absorption of water occurs in the small intestine—about 10 liters a day. This rate can readily be increased, to a liter an hour or more. The contents of the small intestine remain semifluid because of the substantial water content in the digestive juices that are poured into the lumen and because water moves through the intestinal mucosa in both directions—both into and out of the lumen. Normally, there is a net flow out of the lumen, but if the fluid content of the food is particularly low or solute absorption is impaired, there may be a net addition of water to the intestinal contents.

Both in the small intestine and in the large intestine (and to some extent in the stomach as well), the absorption of water occurs by the simple physical process of osmosis, establishing and maintaining isotonicity between the fluid in the cells and the fluid in the intestinal lumen.

THE METABOLISM OF FOOD

Scientists have speculated that there may be planets in space housing exotic life forms totally different from any we have ever encountered or could imagine—perhaps slow-moving stone-like beings whose bodies are made of silicon compounds, or even incorporeal creatures made up of organized energy patterns. Though we can conceive of other possibilities of organization, we humans, like the other living things on planet Earth, are chemical beings, whose bodies are made up mainly of carbon compounds. We are active organisms, and we get the energy to power our activities from chemical compounds contained in the foods and beverages we consume. Building materials for growth and repair are also obtained from foods, but they rarely come in ready-to-use forms. Carbohydrates, proteins, and fats in the foods we eat must first be broken down into components in order to pass through cell membranes and enter the body cell; within the cells the products of digestion are subjected to further chemical reactions. In **catabolic** reactions, food materials are torn down into smaller units or oxidized to release the energy stored in their chemical bonds. In **anabolic** reactions, substances are built up into more complicated chemical compounds, the characteristic chemicals of the body. Both catabolism—breakdown reactions—and anabolism—building-up or synthetic reactions—go on constantly in the body cells. The term **metabolism** refers to the sum total of all the anabolic and catabolic reactions that go on in the body.

The chemical reactions in plants are primarily anabolic, building up complex new organic chemicals from simple raw materials such as carbon dioxide and water. In animals the emphasis is on catabolic reactions, but here, too, many anabolic reactions occur, contributing to growth and repair of body tissues.

The catabolic reactions in the human body supply energy for synthetic processes and for specialized activities such as muscle contraction, the transmission of nerve impulses, and ciliary movement. The chemical energy stored in foodstuffs is used in the formation of new chemical bonds and also converted to other energy forms, such as heat and electricity.

The body's stores of building materials and energy substrates must be continually replenished by taking in food. Otherwise, the body tissues themselves will be metabolized, for metabolic reactions must go on continually, as long as life continues. The carbohydrates and fats in foods are used in the body mainly for energy supply, although they may also be used in the synthesis of such substances as glycoproteins and cholesterol. The amino acids from proteins are used mainly as building materials, although if other energy substrates are in insufficient supply, amino acids can also be used as energy sources. In the body's priorities, catabolism takes first place; anabolic processes are deferred if there are not sufficient materials available for both.

The energy released in catabolic reactions is temporarily stored in convenient units in the energy-rich bonds of adenosine triphosphate (ATP) molecules. The use of this "energy currency" permits a controlled release of energy as it is needed for the body's reactions; if the energy stored in foodstuffs were released all at once, as in a fire, it might destroy the cells.

Carbohydrate Metabolism

A person who is feeling tired and in need of some "quick energy" is likely to reach for a candy bar or a piece of fruit. Some of the sugar in the food, in the form of glucose, is quickly absorbed through the stomach lining and passes into the bloodstream, where it is carried to the brain and does indeed produce a livelier feeling. Disaccharides and starches make their effect felt less rapidly, but they too contribute to the body's energy reserves. Except immediately after a meal, virtually all the sugar in the blood is in the form of glucose. This monosaccharide is the main product of starch digestion, and the small amounts of galactose and fructose present in foods are quickly converted to glucose in the cells. (Indeed, galactose and fructose are actually isomers of glucose, differing merely in the arrangement of the -H and -OH groups.)

All of the monosaccharides absorbed from the digestive tract, whether they started out as simple sugars or were products of digestion, have only a limited number of major alternatives in the body (Figure 27-4).

1 They may pass into the circulation as blood sugar

2 They may be carried to the liver and converted to glycogen and stored there

3 They may be converted to glycogen in skeletal muscles and used in processes of muscle contraction

4 They may be converted to lipids and stored in fat deposits

5 They may be converted to amino acids by the addition of $-NH_2$

6 They may be oxidized in the tissues as energy sources

7 They may be used in the synthesis of tissue glycolipids, glycoproteins, and mucopolysaccharides

8 They may be synthesized to lactose in the mammary glands

9 They may be excreted in the urine. (Normally sugar is not excreted in the urine; its presence is a sign that something is wrong with the body's systems for metabolic regulation, as in the endocrine disorder diabetes mellitus.)

Blood Sugar   About five hours after a meal, the blood normally contains 80 to 90 mg percent glucose. When food is eaten, the blood sugar level rises to a peak and then falls slowly. A typical mixed diet will raise the blood sugar to over 100 mg percent. But in normal people, even a high-carbohydrate meal will not increase the blood sugar level above about 140 mg percent. A high blood glucose concentration (**hyperglycemia**) triggers an automatic regulatory mechanism, in which the beta cells of the pancreas pour out the hormone **insulin.** Insulin lowers the blood sugar level by promoting the transport of glucose into the tissue cells. As the blood sugar level drops, the secretion of insulin correspondingly decreases. When the blood sugar level falls below normal (**hypoglycemia**), other regulatory mechanisms come into play. Sympathetic centers in the hypothalamus are stimulated, and **epinephrine** is secreted by the adrenal medulla, promoting the breakdown of glycogen in the liver and the release of glucose into the blood. **Glucocorticoids** of the adrenal cortex work to raise the blood sugar level by decreasing glucose utilization and promoting the synthesis of glucose from other substances. **Glucagon,** secreted by the alpha cells of the pancreas, promotes the breakdown of glycogen in the liver, while the thyroid hormone **thyroxine** produces a general speedup of metabolism, mobilizing lipids from the cells, and enhances glucose absorption from the intestine.

Role of the Liver   The liver plays a pivotal role in the body's carbohydrate metabolism. Food-laden portal blood is delivered to the liver, and here much of the glucose is removed and synthesized into glycogen ("animal starch"), a complex polysaccharide. The production of glycogen from glucose is called **glycogenesis.** When the supply of carbohydrate is particularly abundant, the liver can convert some of the glu-

metabolism of carbohydrates

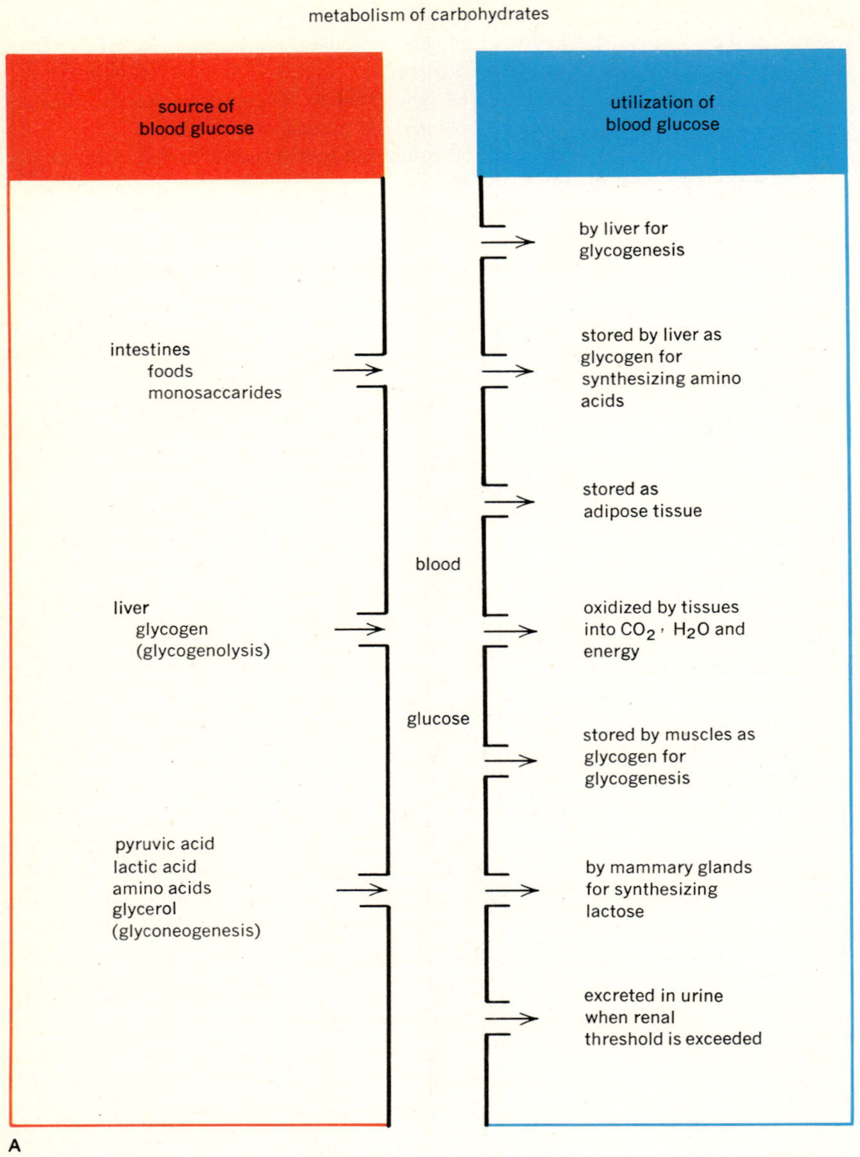

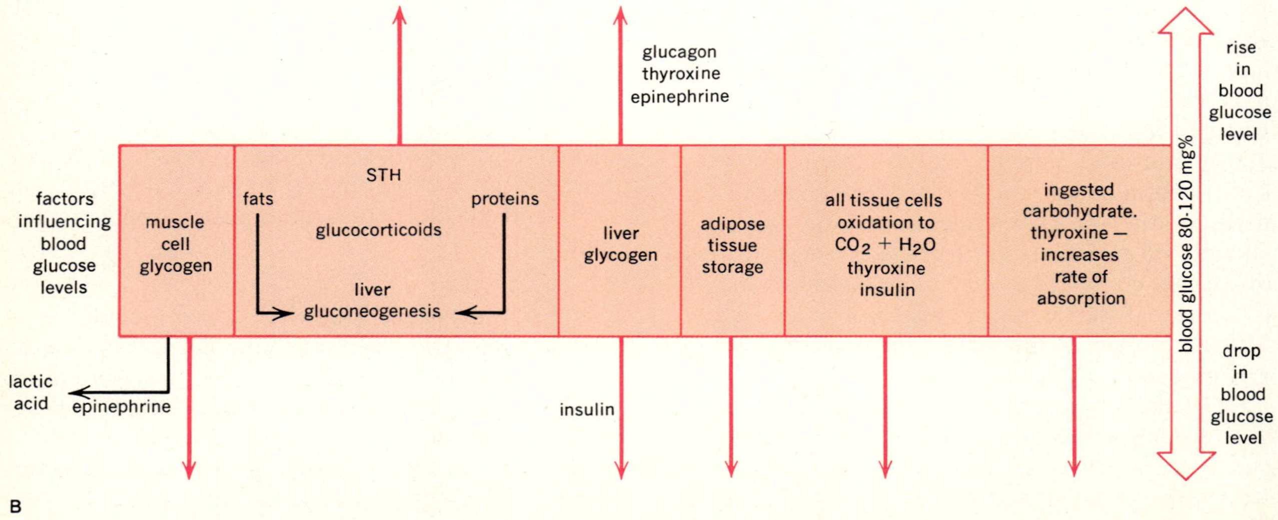

FIGURE 27-4 (A) Carbohydrate metabolism; (B) factors influencing the blood glucose level.

source of blood glucose

intestines
  foods
  monosaccarides

liver
  glycogen
  (glycogenolysis)

pyruvic acid
lactic acid
amino acids
glycerol
(glyconeogenesis)

blood

glucose

utilization of blood glucose

by liver for glycogenesis

stored by liver as glycogen for synthesizing amino acids

stored as adipose tissue

oxidized by tissues into $CO_2 \cdot H_2O$ and energy

stored by muscles as glycogen for glycogenesis

by mammary glands for synthesizing lactose

excreted in urine when renal threshold is exceeded

A

glucagon
thyroxine
epinephrine

rise in blood glucose level

factors influencing blood glucose levels

muscle cell glycogen

STH
fats   proteins
glucocorticoids
liver
gluconeogenesis

liver glycogen

adipose tissue storage

all tissue cells oxidation to $CO_2 + H_2O$ thyroxine insulin

ingested carbohydrate. thyroxine — increases rate of absorption

blood glucose 80-120 mg%

drop in blood glucose level

lactic acid
epinephrine

insulin

B

cose to fat, which is stored in various depots in the mesenteries and at characteristic sites under the skin. When the glucose supply is low, the liver breaks down glycogen to glucose, which enters the blood. This breakdown of glycogen, called **glycogenolysis,** involves a successive splitting away of glucose molecules, one by one, by a process of phosphorylation (adding phosphate groups, PO_4). Under stimulation by glucocorticoids, the liver is able to synthesize glucose from noncarbohydrate sources. For example, amino acids may be deaminated (i.e., a $-NH_2$ group removed) to keto acids, which are then converted to glucose. This process, called **gluconeogenesis,** is an important source of liver glycogen. During starvation, when there is not an adequate supply of incoming food materials, the tissue materials themselves are metabolized. First the glycogen reserves are exhausted. Then the fat depots are called on. Finally the tissue proteins are broken down, and their amino acids used for gluconeogenesis.

Muscle Glycogen   The liver is the main reservoir for the regulation of blood sugar. But actually, on a total weight basis, the muscles of the body contain more glycogen than the liver. In the muscles glycogen serves a different function: it is a source of energy for muscle contraction. The glycogen in muscles is formed from blood glucose, in basically the same kind of reactions (glycogenesis) as in the liver. But the release of glucose from stored glycogen does not occur in the muscles, since it requires a special enzyme to remove phosphate groups (a phosphatase) that is present in liver cells but not present in muscle cells. If oxygen is available, the glucose phosphate formed in the glycogenolysis of muscle glycogen is converted to pyruvic acid (Figure 27-5), and this intermediate in turn is completely oxidized to water and carbon dioxide. If sufficient oxygen is not available, the breakdown of glycogen during muscle contraction yields lactic acid, which may be oxidized to pyruvic acid when oxygen becomes available (and then resynthesized to muscle glycogen) or may diffuse into the blood and be carried to the liver, where it is synthesized to glycogen.

Energy Metabolism   More than half the energy needs of the body are normally supplied by the oxidation of glucose, and in the brain glucose is the major source of energy. The oxidation of 1 gram of glucose yields 4 Calories of heat. The release of the energy stored in glucose involves a series of chemical steps. The glucose molecule is successively split into smaller fragments, and these are oxidized; at each stage the energy liberated is stored in high-energy bonds of ATP. The process begins with a sequence of reactions called **glycolysis,** which does not require oxygen and splits the original six-carbon sugar glucose into two molecules of the three-carbon acid, pyruvic acid. Pyruvic acid is a pivotal compound in the body's metabolism. It can be used to produce amino acids or fats, or it can be oxidized to yield energy in a sequence of reactions called the **Krebs cycle,** or the **citric acid cycle.** The reactions of energy metabolism are discussed in more detail later in the chapter.

Disorders of Carbohydrate Metabolism   The enzymes that catalyze the various reactions of glycogen synthesis and breakdown, like the other enzymes in the body, are products of genes. A mutation in one of these genes can result in the formation of an abnormal enzyme, which may be unable to perform its function, or a mutation may prevent the formation of the enzyme altogether. A number of rather rare hereditary metabolic diseases involving deficiencies of phosphatases, phosphorylases, and other enzymes of glycogenolysis and glycogenesis have been discovered. Depending on which metabolic reaction is thwarted, these enzyme defects may lead to accumulations of glycogen in the liver, muscles, or other cells, or a lack of glycogen reserves. In one type, **myophosphorylase deficiency glycogenesis,** an inability to break down glycogen in the muscles results in a lack of usable energy substrates, so that the muscles are unable to do useful work.

Protein Metabolism

It seems as though the body goes to a great deal of wasted effort. Proteins taken in as food constituents are broken down to amino acids, absorbed into the bloodstream, delivered to the body cells, and there many of them are built back up into proteins again. This roundabout procedure is necessary for two important reasons: first, the protein molecules of foods are generally too large to pass through cell membranes (except in minute amounts by pinocytosis), and second, the proteins of foods are not the right proteins for the *human* body. Each organism has its own characteristic assortment of proteins, some of which may even differ slightly from proteins of other individuals of the same species, and far more from the proteins of other species. Yet all the proteins of earth's organisms are made up of the same basic set of building materials, about twenty different amino acids. Thus, after the food proteins have been broken down into their amino acid components, no matter what organism they originally came from—even a plant—they can be used to synthesize human proteins.

In contrast to the carbohydrates, in protein metabolism, anabolism usually predominates over ca-

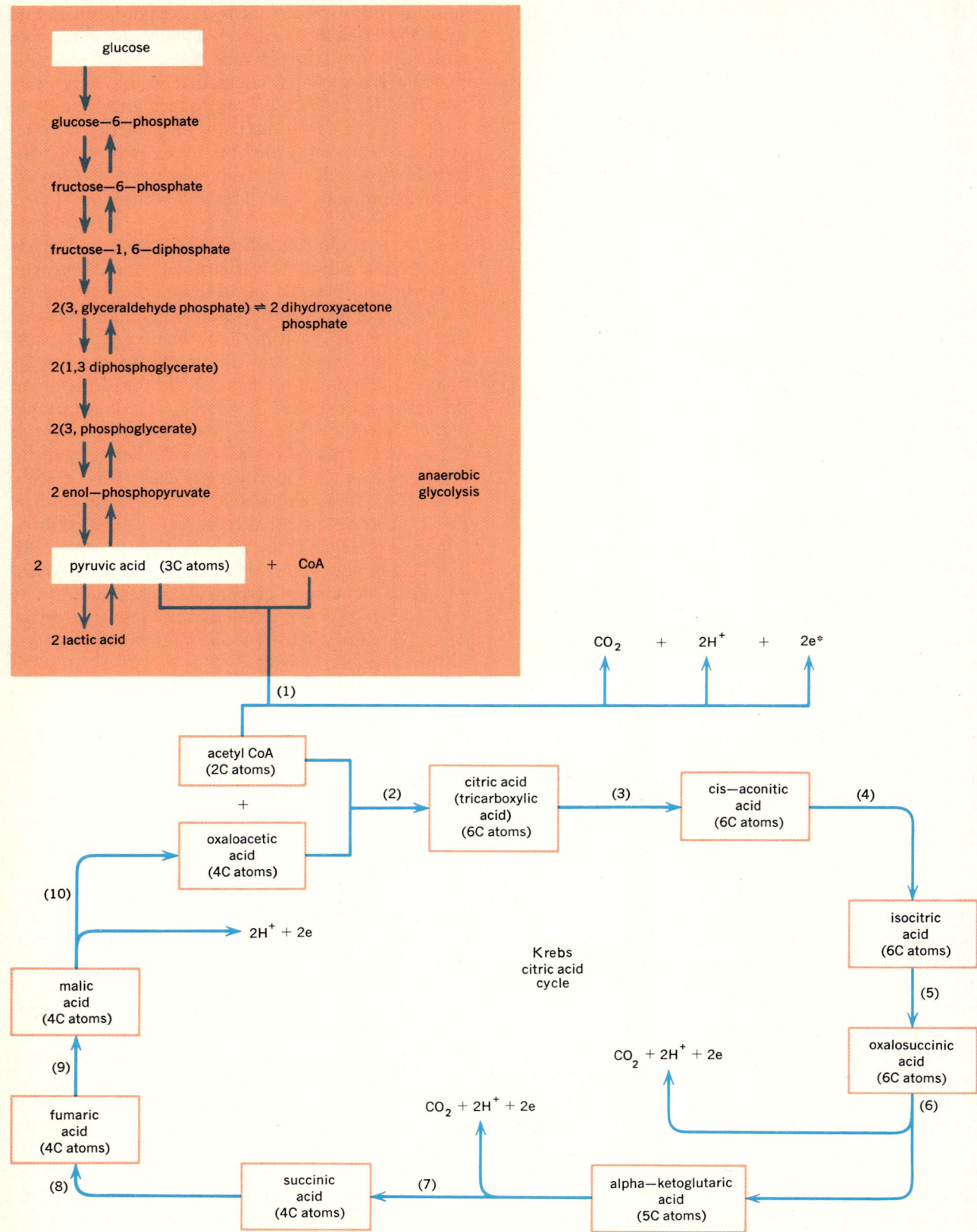

FIGURE 27-5 Energy metabolism. Energy is generated by a sequence of reactions involving anaerobic splitting of glucose (glycolysis) and aerobic oxidation of the fragments (Krebs citric acid cycle).

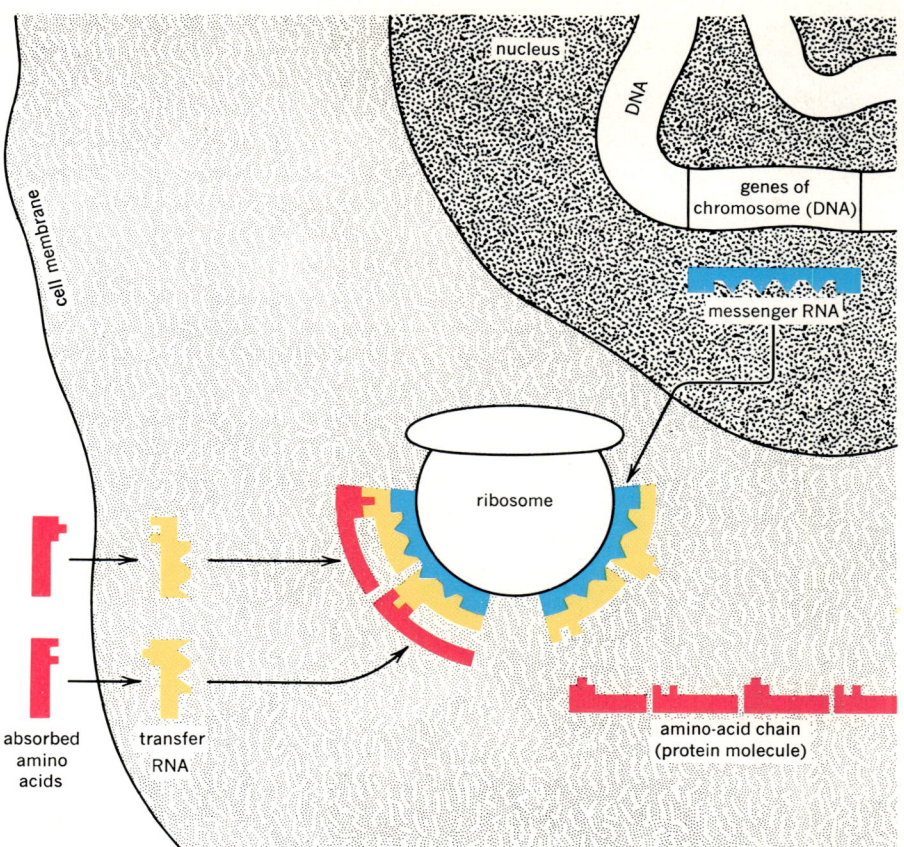

FIGURE 27-6 Protein synthesis in the cell. According to the current theory, messenger RNA carries a copy of the DNA blueprint of the genes out into the cytoplasm. Smaller transfer RNA molecules deliver amino acids to the ribosomes, where they are assembled into protein chains according to the messenger RNA template.

tabolism. In **protein synthesis,** each type of amino acid molecule is picked up by its own specific transfer RNA in the cell cytoplasm and carried to the ribosomes, where long chains of amino acids are joined together in carefully coded sequences, spelled out on "templates" of messenger RNA, which in turn are copies of portions of the DNA molecules in the chromosomes (Figure 27-6).

A large fraction of the protein in the diet is not used for tissue protein synthesis, but instead its components may be used for a variety of other purposes in the body (Figure 27-7). Amino acids are used to synthesize various nonprotein nitrogen-containing substances. These include creatine, creatinine, pyrimidines, purines, and porphyrins.

Protein catabolism occurs in the liver, to which the food-laden blood is first transported. Amino acids in excess of the body's synthetic needs may be converted to keto acids by **deamination,** that is, the removal of an amino group. Deamination of amino acids can occur in several different ways, two of which are especially important for the body. In **oxidative deamination,** catalyzed by enzymes called **amino acid oxidases,** the amino acid is oxidized at the place where the amino group is joined, and the $-NH_2$ group is re-

leased, forming ammonia. Two molecules of ammonia are then joined with a molecule of carbon dioxide to form urea, which is excreted in the urine and sweat:

$$2NH_3 + CO_2 \rightarrow H_2N\overset{\displaystyle O}{\overset{\|}{-C}}-NH_2 + H_2O$$
$$\text{urea}$$

More often deamination occurs by a reaction of **transamination,** the transfer of an amino group from an amino acid to a keto acid. The nonessential amino acids (those that do not need to be taken in as food) are formed in the body by transamination reactions. Such reactions are catalyzed by enzymes called **transaminases,** which are all derivatives of pyridoxine, one of the B vitamins. If there is a lack of this vitamin in the diet, the amino acid and protein metabolism will be affected.

The keto acids formed in both oxidative deamination and transamination reactions may be utilized directly as energy sources, or they may be converted to glucose or to fat for storage. When amino acids are used as energy substrates, a gram of protein releases

metabolism of protein

FIGURE 27-7   Protein metabolism.

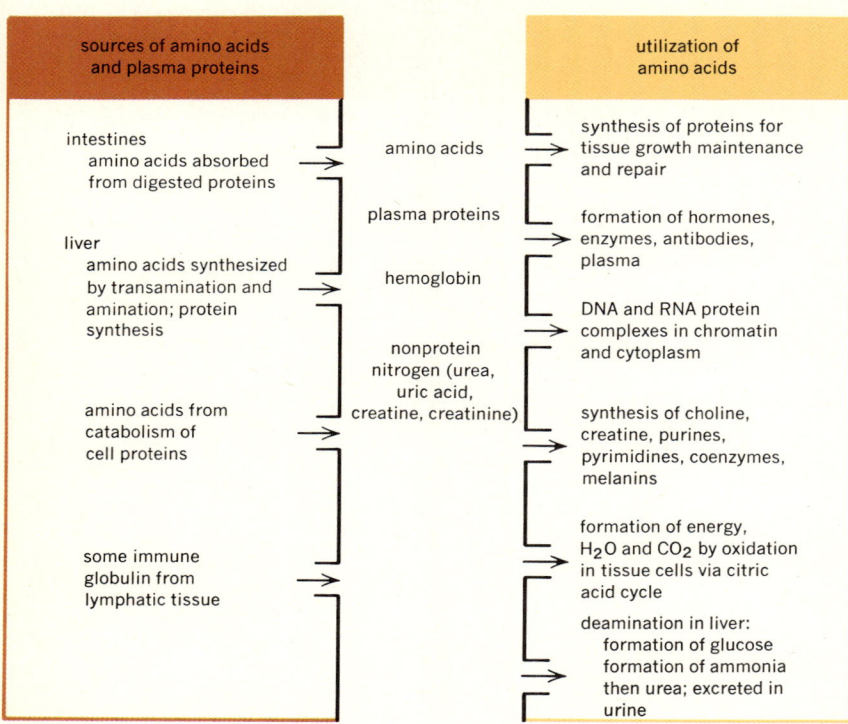

sources of amino acids and plasma proteins

intestines
  amino acids absorbed
  from digested proteins

liver
  amino acids synthesized
  by transamination and
  amination; protein
  synthesis

amino acids from
catabolism of
cell proteins

some immune
globulin from
lymphatic tissue

amino acids

plasma proteins

hemoglobin

nonprotein
nitrogen (urea,
uric acid,
creatine, creatinine)

utilization of amino acids

synthesis of proteins for
tissue growth maintenance
and repair

formation of hormones,
enzymes, antibodies,
plasma

DNA and RNA protein
complexes in chromatin
and cytoplasm

synthesis of choline,
creatine, purines,
pyrimidines, coenzymes,
melanins

formation of energy,
H_2O and CO_2 by oxidation
in tissue cells via citric
acid cycle

deamination in liver:
  formation of glucose
  formation of ammonia
  then urea; excreted in
  urine

about 4 Calories of heat, the same as a gram of carbohydrate.

Normally the blood contains between 35 and 65 mg percent amino acids, an average of about 2 mg percent for each kind of amino acid. (Actually, some are present in much larger concentrations than others.) After a meal, the amino acid concentration in the blood rises, but only by a few mg percent. Protein digestion is a long, drawn-out process, and only small amounts of amino acids are absorbed from the digestive tract at a time; these amino acids are rapidly transported through the body, where they are quickly synthesized into proteins. The various body cells can store proteins, which can be rapidly decomposed into amino acids under the influence of intracellular enzymes called **cathepsins,** and the amino acids can be transported out into the blood again. Tissues with a high metabolic rate, especially the liver, participate to the greatest degree in the storage of proteins. But each type of tissue has an upper limit to the amount of protein it can store, and the excess amino acids are then catabolized. Excess amino acids may also be excreted in the urine.

Protein synthesis is an important factor in growth and tissue formation, and protein metabolism is influenced by many endocrine hormones. Growth hormone stimulates cell and tissue formation. Androgens (especially testosterone) have a similar effect, which is most pronounced at puberty, when there is an explosive growth of the body in general and the muscles in particular. Thyroxin has an indirect action through its stimulation of cell metabolism in general. Adrenal cortical hormones have a catabolic effect, decreasing protein deposition and increasing the level of amino acids in the blood.

Disorders of Protein Metabolism   Routine testing of infants' urine shortly after birth can avert later tragedies. Defects of genes that produce key enzymes in amino acid metabolism cause the amino acids from foods or their metabolic products to build up in the body, instead of being further converted in the interrelated chains of the normal metabolic reactions. In the most publicized disorder of this kind, **phenylkenoturia** (PKU), a deficiency of the enzyme phenylalanine hydroxylase causes the amino acid phenylalanine to accumulate; it ultimately interferes with the development of the nervous system, and irreversible mental retardation may result. The condition can be detected by urine tests—before the mental damage has occurred—because some of the excess amino acid spills over into the urine. Another group of metabolic disorders, involving a deficiency of a decarboxylase enzyme that works on the amino acids leucine, isoleucine, and valine, is referred to as **maple sugar urine disease,** because the accumulated amino acids give the urine a maple sugar odor. If disorders of amino acid metabolism are detected early, the infant can be

metabolism of blood lipids

FIGURE 27-8 Fat metabolism.

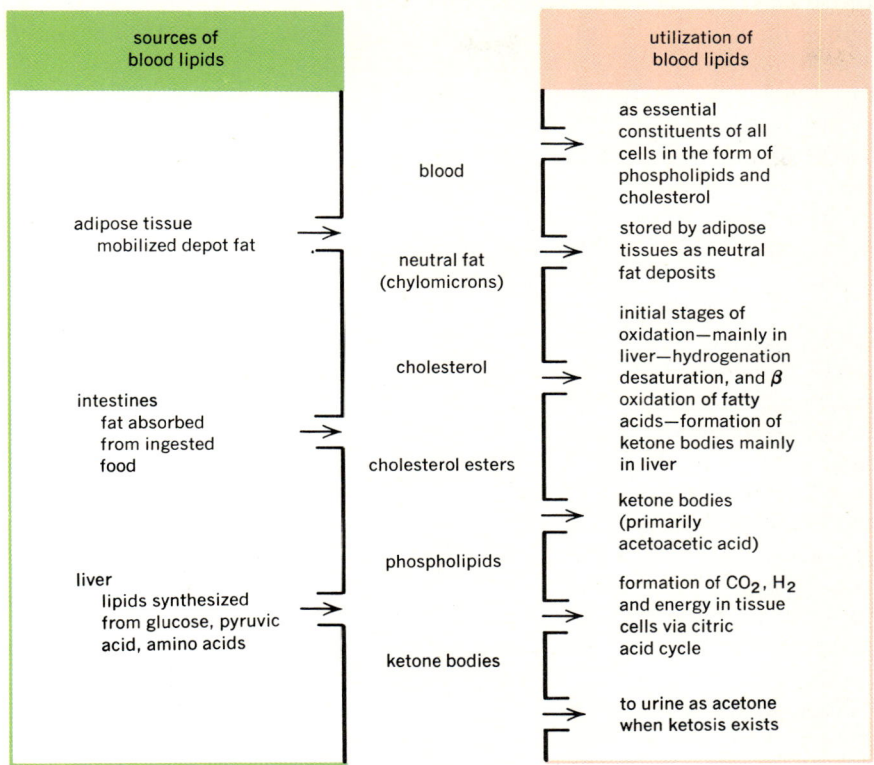

fed a specially devised diet, low in the particular amino acid or acids that its body cannot handle, and then the child will be able to grow and develop normally.

Lipid Metabolism

The modern sedentary way of life, combined with a diet that often provides more calories than the body uses each day, has turned one of the strong points of human metabolism into a negative factor. Excess fats, above what the body needs for the production of phospholipids, steroids, and other vital substances, are deposited in characteristic depots in the mesenteries and subcutaneous tissues as a reserve, which can be used for energy if insufficient food is available at some future time. Excess carbohydrate and even protein can be converted to fat and stored as well. Fat is the most efficient energy source, yielding 9 Calories of heat per gram.

Following a meal, the fat concentration in the blood may rise to as high as 1 to 2 percent, as chylomicrons are emptied by the thoracic duct of the lymphatic system into the left subclavian vein. Within a few hours, however, the chylomicrons are gradually removed from the blood. As the fat-laden blood passes through certain tissues of the body, especially adipose tissue, heart muscle, and skeletal muscle, the triglycerides in the chylomicrons are hydrolyzed to glycerol and fatty acids by an enzyme, **lipoprotein lipase,** which enters the capillaries from the tissues. The glycerol is metabolized in much the same way as glucose, while the lipid-soluble fatty acids diffuse through the capillary and cell membranes into the local cells or are transported to other parts of the body in combination with albumin. The fatty acids can be oxidized for energy (except in nerve tissue, which uses only glucose for energy) or can be used by the fat cells of adipose tissue to resynthesize triglycerides, which are stored. Fat is also a vital constituent of tissue and cell components, such as myelin in the nerve tissue (Figure 27-8).

After the chylomicrons have been removed from the blood, most of the plasma lipids are in the form of lipoproteins, which are mixtures of triglycerides (about 160 mg/100 ml of plasma), phospholipids (160 mg), cholesterol (180 mg), and protein (200 mg).

Though the fat deposits scattered through the body often seem all too permanent, actually they are in a dynamic state, with a constant breakdown **(lipolysis),** resynthesis **(lipogenesis),** and exchange with the plasma lipids. It has been found that as much as half of the total body fat reserve changes position each day, and even in the most obese person the fat stored in the tissues is not the same fat that was stored there two or three weeks before.

The liver plays a key role in fat metabolism. It synthesizes fatty acids from carbohydrate intermediates, lengthens and shortens the chains of fatty acids, saturates and unsaturates them, and oxidizes them in a process called **beta oxidation.** This type of oxidation proceeds in successive steps, in each of which a molecule of acetic acid is split off and the fatty acid molecule is shortened by two carbon atoms. The two-carbon fragments removed are combined with coenzyme A, in the form of **acetyl-CoA.** This beta-oxidation product is shunted into the citric acid cycle and subjected to further oxidation, until finally carbon dioxide and water are formed. Two molecules of acetyl-CoA can be condensed to form acetoacetic acid. This substance in turn can be converted to beta-hydroxybutyric acid and acetone. These three products, belonging to the chemical class of ketones, are called **ketone bodies** and are normally catabolized as rapidly as they are formed. However, when carbohydrate metabolism is abnormally low, as in starvation or diabetes mellitus, increased amounts of fatty acids are utilized for energy, and ketone bodies accumulate faster than catabolic reactions can dispose of them. The ketones accumulate in the tissues and body fluids, a condition called **ketosis.** Excess ketone bodies are excreted in the urine **(ketonuria),** and the volatile acetone can be detected in the person's breath, giving it a characteristic "fruity" odor.

The role of **cholesterol** in human metabolism is still cloaked in controversy. Cholesterol in the diet is absorbed from the intestine together with the neutral fats, but even on a cholesterol-free diet the body synthesizes its own cholesterol from acetyl-CoA. Cholesterol is a constituent of bile salts and is used in the formation of several hormones, including cortisol and progesterone. Some people suffer from a hereditary disorder in which abnormally large amounts of low-density lipoproteins are produced in the blood, promoting the deposition of cholesterol in the artery walls. Such people have a much greater than normal risk of early heart disease and may die of myocardial infarction in their thirties or forties.

Insulin is the main regulator of fatty acid mobilization, facilitating the transport of fatty acids into the cells. (The levels of blood glucose and fatty acids are inversely related—when the glucose is high, the fatty acid level is low, and vice versa.) The catecholamines, such as epinephrine, stimulate lipolysis and thus aid in the mobilization of fats from the depots into the blood; sympathetic innervation of the adipose tissue has a similar effect. Adrenal cortical hormones, growth hormone, and the thyroid hormone directly or indirectly increase fat mobilization as well.

Water Metabolism

The Mongolian gerbil can live comfortably on a diet consisting only of dry foods. Yet the gerbil, just like humans, needs water for various purposes: as a solvent for chemical reactions, as a circulatory fluid, as a heat transfer agent, lubricant, and so on. The gerbil gets all the water it needs by the metabolism of fats and other substances in its diet. Humans lack the gerbil's high degree of adaptation to desert survival, but we, too, produce a great deal of **metabolic water.** The oxidation of one mole (180 grams) of glucose yields six moles (108 grams) of water, and water is also formed in the oxidation of proteins and lipids. A total of about 375 ml of water is produced by oxidation of foods in the human body each day; but in order to maintain homeostasis we need about ten times that amount. For water not only participates in reactions such as the hydrolytic reactions of digestion, but is also lost in urine, feces, sweat, and expired breath. Food and drinks make up the difference of our daily fluid needs. (Though we normally think only of juices and other beverages as supplying dietary water, most "solid" foods also contain substantial amounts of water.)

The Common Metabolic Pool

If we followed a particular molecule around in the body—for example, a glucose molecule—its path might be bewilderingly complex. Perhaps it might be oxidized, yielding energy, and in the process degraded to three-carbon compounds, or finally to carbon dioxide and water. Or instead, it might be converted to an entirely different kind of compound—an amino acid or a fatty acid. Proteins, lipids, and carbohydrates all contain the three basic elements, C, H, and O, and they can be readily interconverted in the body. (Proteins contain nitrogen in addition, and the interconversions between amino acids and other substances involve addition or removal of an amino group, $-NH_2$.) A pivotal compound in the metabolism of proteins, carbohydrates, and fats is **pyruvic acid,** a keto acid (Figure 27-9), which provides a connecting link for the varied metabolic reaction pathways (Figure 27-10).

Carbohydrates, proteins, and lipids are important components of the **metabolic pool,** which includes all the substances in the body that enter into metabolic reactions. The metabolic pool also includes a variety of other substances, from nucleic acids to water and inorganic ions. Even substances such as calcium, which is stored in the bones, are part of the metabolic pool, since storage in the body is generally a dynamic

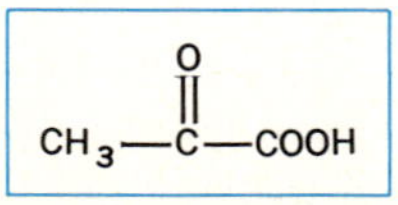

$$CH_3-\overset{\overset{\textstyle O}{\|}}{C}-COOH$$

FIGURE 27-9 Pyruvic acid.

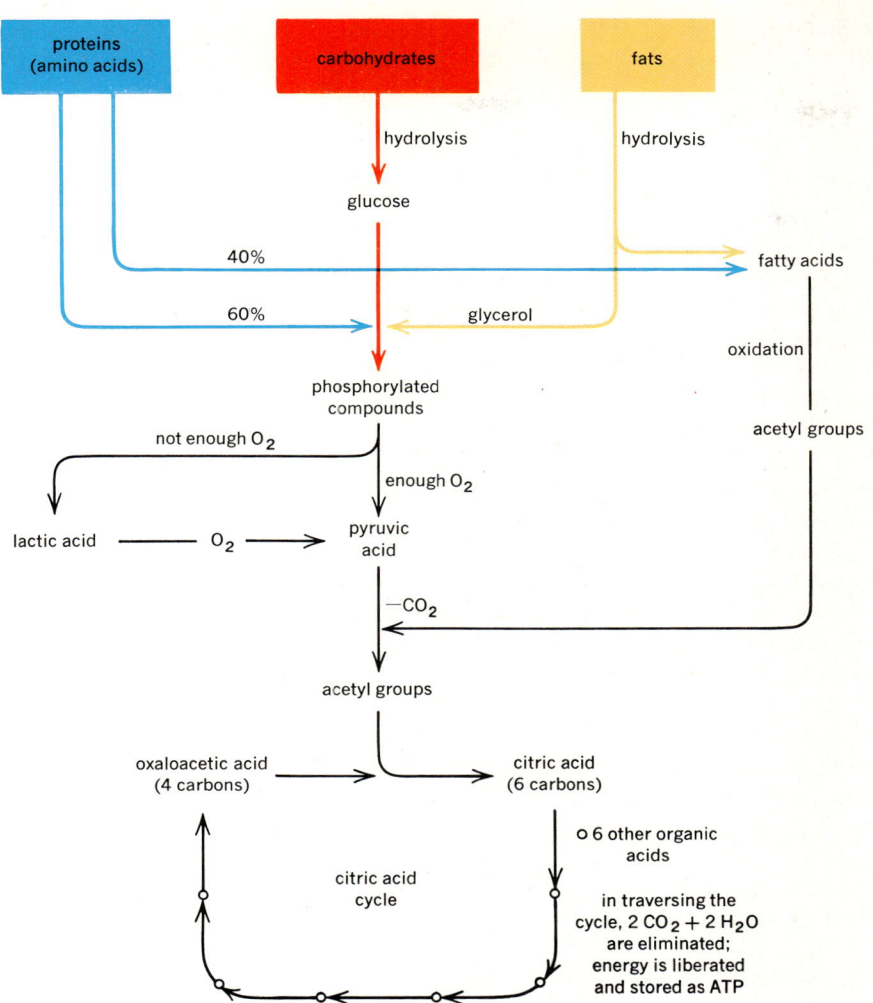

FIGURE 27-10 Interrelationship of carbohydrate, fat, and protein metabolism.

rather than a static phenomenon: there is a constant mobilization and redeposition of substances in the body's storage depots.

ENERGY METABOLISM

Virtually all the processes and activities that go on in the human body require a continual supply of energy. The vital importance of the energy-supplying reactions of metabolism is emphasized by the effect of a whiff of hydrogen cyanide gas or a pinch of cyanide crystals added to an unwary victim's drink. Death is almost instantaneous. Cyanide acts as an enzyme poison, preventing the operation of the enzyme cytochrome oxidase, which is a key catalyst in the reactions of energy metabolism.

The energy that powers the human body is chemical energy, derived from the compounds of the metabolic pool, which is in turn continually replenished by the ingestion, digestion, and absorption of food. Chemical energy is used in the body to do work. It may be converted to mechanical energy, as in the contraction of muscles to lift a load. It may be converted to electrical energy, as in the transmission of nerve impulses. Or work may be done in the form of chemical energy, as complex body chemicals are built up at the expense of the breaking of chemical bonds in other compounds.

Like most machines, the human body achieves far from a complete conversion of chemical energy to work. In fact, this conversion is only about 20 percent efficient; the rest of the stored chemical energy is given off as heat. During the performance of the work, further energy is lost as heat; for example, the heart does mechanical work in pumping blood, but some of its effort is lost in overcoming friction as the blood flows through the blood vessels. Ultimately, all the chemical energy of the body is directly or indirectly converted to heat.

All this heat production is not entirely useless: it helps to maintain body temperature at the optimum level for enzyme-catalyzed reactions. But often the heat produced by the body is in excess of its needs, and special mechanisms must be provided to get rid of the excess heat.

Reactions of Energy Metabolism: Glycolysis and the Krebs Cycle

The energy metabolism of the body consists of a sequence of reactions that has much in common with the burning of a bonfire. Chemical "fuel" is oxidized by oxygen in both cases, releasing the energy locked inside the chemical bonds and yielding simpler compounds as oxidation products. But there are a number of important distinctions. A fire burns rapidly, and the energy released is given off all at once in the form of heat and light. The oxidation reactions of the body's energy metabolism, on the other hand, proceed in a series of small, controlled steps; much of the energy released in each step is recaptured and stored in the high-energy phosphate bonds of ATP. Only a part of the energy released in metabolic reactions is given off as heat.

The energy metabolism begins with a sequence of reactions collectively termed **glycolysis** (Figure 27-11). The six-carbon sugar glucose is combined with phosphate and subjected to a series of more than a dozen conversions, ultimately yielding the three-carbon compound pyruvic acid. (Each molecule of glucose yields two molecules of pyruvic acid.) Two hydrogen atoms are eliminated in the process; they are taken up by an intermediate hydrogen acceptor, and the energy released is stored in the form of ATP.

The reactions of glycolysis do not require the presence of oxygen, and thus glycolysis is referred to as the **anaerobic** ("airless") **pathway.** Glycolysis is not a very efficient process for energy generation, since the entire reaction sequence nets only two molecules of ATP. In normal body cells, this inefficiency does not matter too much, since the pyruvic acid produced in glycolysis is then metabolized in a sequence of **aerobic** (oxygen-requiring) oxidative reactions with a much higher energy yield. But cancer cells apparently lack the appropriate enzymes for the aerobic pathway and rely on glycolysis for their energy metabolism. Their energy-squandering metabolism is one of the factors that places a great strain on the body systems when cancerous growth is present.

In the aerobic pathway, comprising the **Krebs citric acid cycle** and the **cytochrome chain** (Figure 27-11), the pyruvic acid and hydrogens yielded by glycolysis are metabolized in a series of oxygen-requiring steps linked into closely interrelated cycles, ultimately yielding carbon dioxide, water, and a number of energy-rich ATP molecules.

The reaction sequences comprising glycolysis, the Krebs cycle, and the cytochrome chain are collectively terms **cell respiration.** The overall yield of energy from the original glucose molecules is surpris-

ingly large, on the order of 40 percent (the remaining 60 percent of the energy released from glucose is dissipated as heat). This efficiency compares favorably with the conversion of the stored energy of coal to electrical energy in the best modern power plants.

Calorimetry

Diet watchers are constantly counting their calories. Although the energy of food is not used directly as heat, it is customarily measured in heat units. Actually, the unit most commonly used in physiology should properly be spelled with a capital C: a **Calorie** is the amount of heat required to raise the temperature of 1 kilogram of water 1°C. (A calorie is the amount of heat required to raise the temperature of 1 gram of water 1°C. Food energy contents expressed in calories would be inconveniently large and unwieldy.)

Food energy is released in the body by oxidation reactions. If carefully weighed amounts of the major types of food are placed in a bomb calorimeter (a reaction chamber equipped for precise measurements of heat liberated and absorbed) and ignited, the following values are obtained for the amount of heat liberated by one gram of food:

Carbohydrate, 1 g	4.3 Cal
Protein, 1 g	5.3 Cal
Fat, 1 g	9.5 Cal

The energy obtained by the oxidation of foods in the body can also be measured, either directly by placing the subject in a closed chamber through which water circulates and measuring the amount of heat taken up by the water, or indirectly by measurements of the oxygen consumption. The energy values of foods obtained from metabolism in the body are found to be:

Carbohydrate, 1 g	4.1 Cal
Protein, 1 g	4.1 Cal
Fat, 1 g	9.3 Cal

The values for carbohydrates and fats, obtained by chemical oxidation and by metabolism, check fairly well. (The small difference in each case is due to losses in digestion.) But there is a rather substantial discrepancy for protein. This difference can be explained by the fact that in the body the oxidation of protein is never complete. Urea, creatinine, uric acid, and other nitrogen compounds are excreted in the urine and still contain some chemical energy, which is not made available to the body cells.

Respiratory Quotient

One can deduce a person's diet from the air he or she exhales. The oxidation of each type of food is a

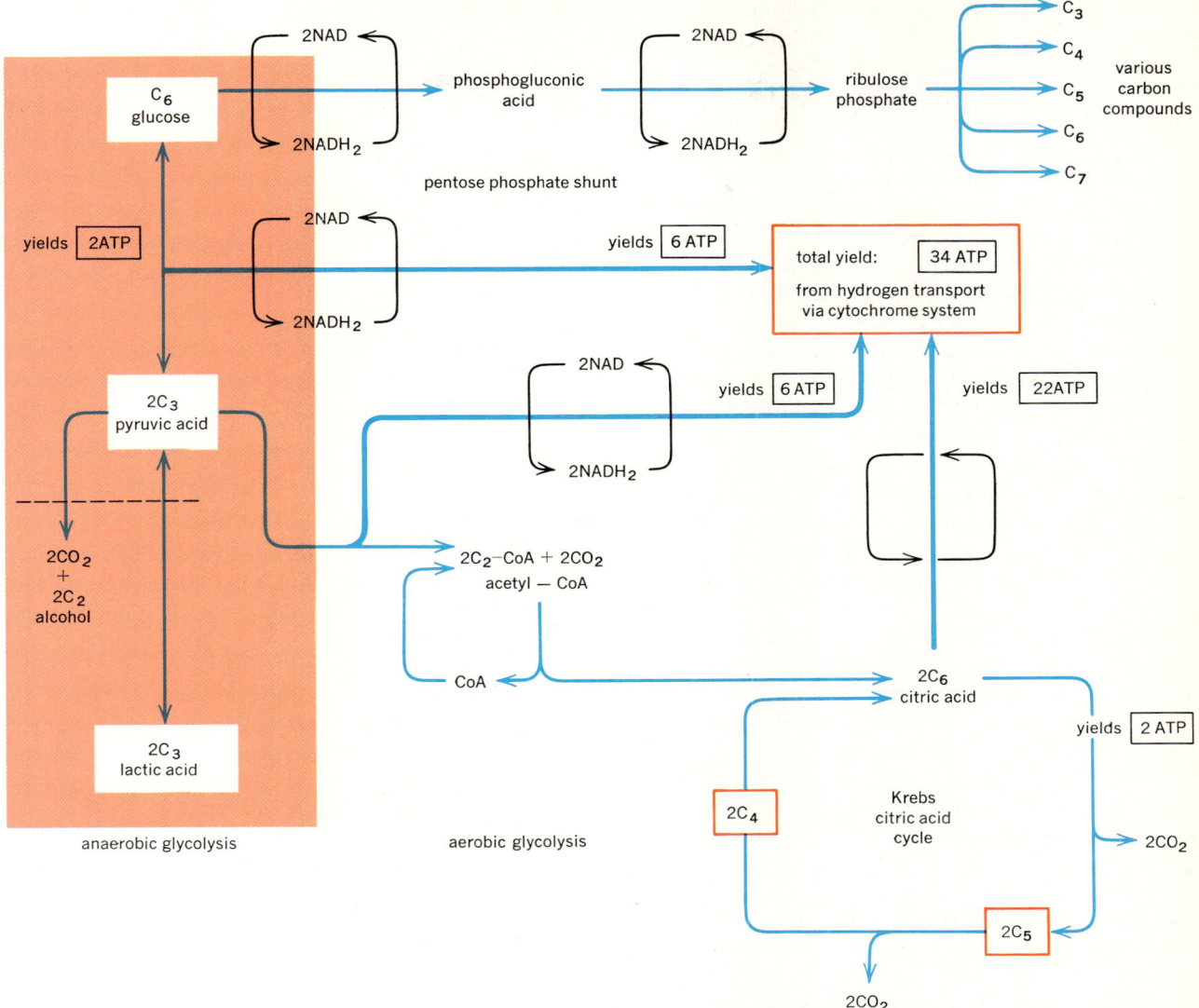

FIGURE 27-11 Reactions of cell respiration. The energy stored in sugars is converted to the more readily available form of ATP, and the sugars are ultimately degraded to carbon dioxide and water. The oxygen-consuming reactions of aerobic respiration yield a combined total of 36 molecules of ATP, as contrasted with a yield of only 2 molecules of ATP from anaerobic respiration.

chemical reaction, whether it occurs in a calorimetric bomb or in the body, and it can be described by the usual kind of chemical equation. For example, for glucose:

$$C_6H_{12}O_6 + 6O_2 + 6H_2O$$

According to this equation, for each six molecules of oxygen consumed, six molecules of carbon dioxide are produced. Thus, the ratio of carbon dioxide produced to oxygen consumed is equal to 1. This ratio is called the respiratory quotient (RQ):

$$RQ = \frac{\text{Volume of } CO_2 \text{ eliminated from body}}{\text{Volume of } O_2 \text{ absorbed by body.}}$$

For carbohydrates, RQ = 1. Proteins are in a more reduced state than carbohydrates—that is, they contain proportionately less oxygen per molecule. Therefore, more oxygen is required to oxidize a given amount of protein to carbon dioxide and water than for an equivalent amount of carbohydrate. Hence, the RQ for proteins is lower than for carbohydrates, about 0.8. Fats are in an even more reduced state, and their RQ is lower still, about 0.7. The actual RQ observed therefore depends on the composition of the diet; on the usual mixed diet, the RQ is about 0.82.

Under certain conditions, the RQ may vary widely. It can even rise above 1.0, when large amounts of carbohydrate are force-fed in experiments. (The excess carbohydrate is converted to fat, a reaction that liberates oxygen, which is used metabolically; hence less oxygen is taken into the body for the conversion of the food.) Shortly after a meal high in carbohydrates, the RQ approaches 1.0, but by about 10 hours later it approaches 0.7, the value for pure fat metabolism. After the body has consumed its ready source of carbohydrate, it begins to use its fat reserves for energy. During starvation, while the fat depots are being drawn upon for energy metabolism, the RQ hovers around 0.7, but when the fat reserves are exhausted it approaches 0.8, indicating that the proteins of the body are now being metabolized.

Exercise can also change the RQ markedly. During exercise, there is a high production of carbon dioxide and hyperventilation, while an oxygen debt is being accumulated and the oxygen intake does not keep pace. The RQ may rise to 2.0 or even higher under such circumstances, regardless of the composition of the diet. Following exercise, the production of CO_2 rapidly returns to normal, but the increased O_2 consumption continues for a time, and the RQ may drop to 0.5.

The respiratory quotients measured for specific body tissues also show a correlation with their characteristic type of energy metabolism. The RQ for brain tissue is about 1.0, indicating that carbohydrates are used almost exclusively in brain tissue metabolism. For most other tissues, the RQ is about 0.82, indicating a more balanced use of carbohydrates, fats, and proteins.

REGULATION OF BODY TEMPERATURE

On a cold day a snake is immobilized, for its body temperature tends to rise and fall with the temperature of its surroundings. When it becomes too cold, its enzyme-catalyzed body reactions slow down drastically. The human body, by contrast, maintains a remarkably constant temperature whether we are out on a cold winter day or tanning in the hot August sun.

Snakes are classed among the group of **poikilothermic** animals, whose body temperature varies greatly depending on the temperature of the surrounding medium. This group, which includes invertebrates, reptiles, frogs, and fish, is commonly referred to as "cold-blooded," which is actually a misnomer—a poikilothermic animal's body does indeed become cold in cold weather, but in hot weather its body becomes quite hot.

Humans belong to the group of **homoiothermic** animals, which maintain a relatively constant body temperature through widely fluctuating extremes of environmental temperatures. A nude person can be exposed to temperatures as low as 55° to 60°F or as high as 150°F, and still maintain a relatively constant

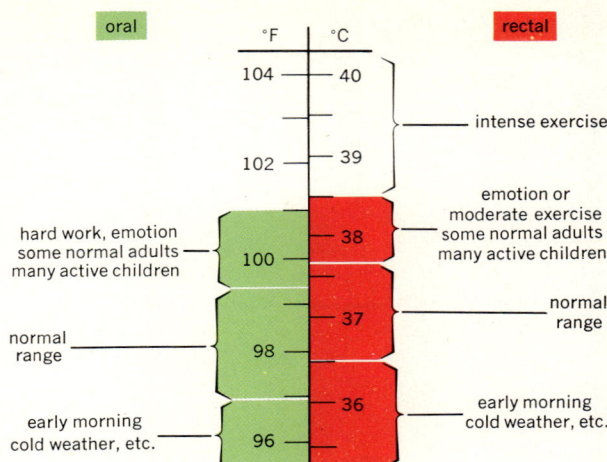

FIGURE 27-12 The "normal" body temperature is actually a range of temperatures, which can be influenced by various external and internal conditions.

internal body temperature. Only birds and mammals possess temperature-control systems, and indeed, some of them belong to a special group of **heterothermic**, or hibernating animals. These animals, such as woodchucks, dormice, and hamsters, escape the winter cold by going into a dormant state, in which all their body processes (heartbeat, respiration rate, metabolism) slow down dramatically, and the body temperature falls, though it may still remain somewhat above the environmental temperature.

The maintenance of a relatively constant body temperature is a dynamic process, in which heat is constantly being produced and dissipated. Heat is generated in the body by the catabolism of foods. The muscles and glands, which are the most active metabolically, generate the largest amounts of heat. Part of the heat produced—some 25 percent—is normally used to maintain the body temperature at the optimum level for the action of the cell enzymes and other body processes; the other 75 percent is given off into the atmosphere. Homeostasis of the body temperature is maintained by a combination of physical and physiological processes, which keep heat production and heat loss in balance.

The Normal Body Temperature

The normal human body temperature is usually quoted as 98.6°F (or 37°C), a practice that has probably caused considerable unnecessary worry. Actually, perfectly normal, healthy people show some variation from this average value (Figure 27-12). The normal range is from about 97° to 99°F (for temperatures taken orally; rectal temperatures are about 1°F higher because of the more effective insulation of the thermometer in that position). Each person has a characteristic pattern of temperature variation during the day, with differences of as much as 1° to 3°F between the low and high points. The body temperature is typically lowest in the very early morning, after several hours of sleep, when one is inactive and not digesting food. After arising, the body temperature rises to a peak and begins to fall again. "Larks"—people who find they are most lively and effective early in the day—have their body temperature peak at mid-morning or midday. "Owls"—people who feel as though they are just getting into gear as evening approaches and work best late at night—have their body temperature peak in the evening. Individual temperature curves, plotted by taking the temperature every hour over a 24-hour period, may also show various intermediate patterns, including one with two peaks, in morning and evening, with an "afternoon low" in between.

In addition to the circadian (daily) rhythm, body temperature may be affected by a variety of factors. In very cold weather, the body temperature may fall somewhat below normal. (Severe chilling may produce a catastrophic drop, which can prove fatal unless promptly treated.) Digestion of food, physical exercise, and strong emotions can make the body temperature rise. At rest the skeletal muscles, which comprise about 50 percent of the entire body mass, contribute about 40 percent of the total body heat production through the mild contractions that maintain muscle tonus. During strenuous physical activity, the heat production by the muscles accounts for as much as 80 percent of the total.

Women experience a regular rise and fall of the body temperature correlated with the menstrual cycle. This phenomenon is used as the basis of a method of determining the time of ovulation—the optimum time of the month for conception. The woman takes her temperature immediately after arising every day and plots the values throughout the month; a temperature rise is a signal of ovulation. But this method has some inherent drawbacks, since the monthly temperature variation may only be a fraction of a degree, and the rise may be masked by extraneous factors such as a mild illness or variations of the time of awakening.

Physical Factors in Body Temperature Regulation

Small animals, such as the hummingbird, must eat constantly to provide enough fuel to keep their bodies warm. Their surface-to-volume ratio is very large, and since most of the heat is lost from the body surface, their rate of heat loss is astronomical.

Several physical factors contribute to heat loss from the body. These are radiation, conduction, convection, and evaporation.

Radiation is the transfer of heat from the surface of one object to another by the emission of infrared heat rays, without actual contact between the two objects. Heat always flows from warmer objects to cooler objects. If a person is in a cool room, heat will radiate outward from the surface of his or her body. But in very hot weather, the surroundings become hotter than the body, and various objects may radiate more heat to the body than the body radiates outward. The human body absorbs heat readily, either in the form of infrared rays (e.g., from a stove) or in the form of sunlight, which is transformed into heat when it is absorbed. Dark and light skin absorb about equal amounts of infrared rays, but dark skin is more absorbent for light energy. (White skin reflects about 35 percent of the rays of sunlight, while black skin reflects very little sunlight.) In cool surroundings, radiation accounts for a large fraction of the heat loss from the body surface.

Conduction is the transfer of heat from an object to another with which it is in contact. If a person sits down on a cold chair, at first there is a brisk transfer of heat from the body to the chair by conduction. But after a few minutes, the temperature of the chair rises to almost equal to that of the body (the "benchwarmer" on a football team does exactly that), so that no further heat exchange takes place; indeed, after that the chair serves as an insulator, preventing further loss of heat from the body. Conduction of heat to objects thus plays only a minor role in heat loss from the body. However, heat loss by conduction to the surrounding air plays a more significant role. If the air is static, then as the air molecules become heated they will form an insulating layer around the body, preventing further heat loss. But when the air medium is moving, another physical factor comes into play to enhance heat loss.

Convection is a transfer of heat away from a surface by the movement of heated air or fluid. The heat transferred by the body surface to the adjacent air molecules increases their kinetic energy; they move faster and tend to spread out, that is, become less dense. Under the action of gravity, the warmer, less dense air tends to be displaced upward by denser, cool air. The convection currents that are established bring a continual supply of new cooler air in contact with the body. The further transfer of heat by conduction sets up new convection currents and continues the process. Wind, which moves air more rapidly, greatly enhances the cooling effect by continually bringing new layers of cool air in contact with the body.

Water, which has a much greater ability to absorb heat than air, does not form as effective an insulating layer around the body even when the fluid is not mov-

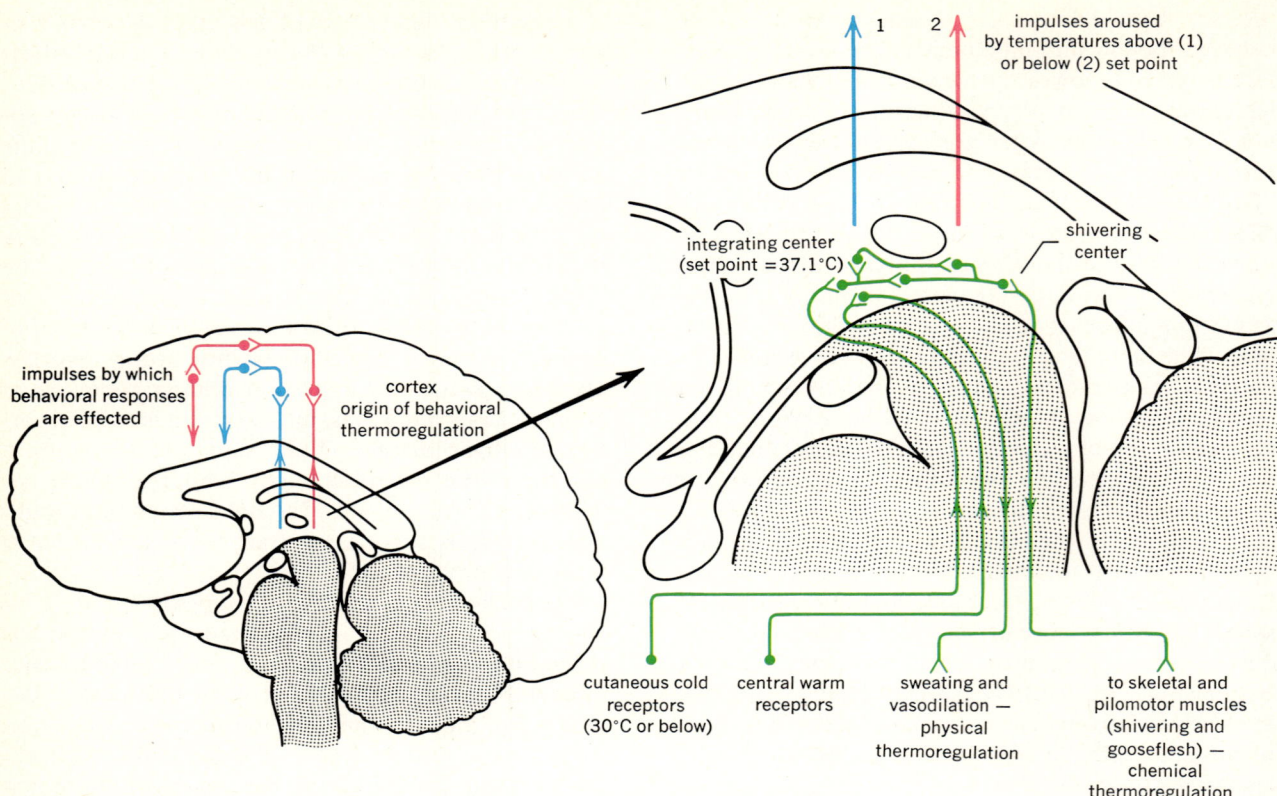

FIGURE 27-13 The hypothalamus plays a central role in body temperature regulation. Temperature adjustments are produced both by automatic reflex mechanisms and by conscious behavior mediated by the cerebral cortex.

ing. Thus, the rate of heat loss by conduction to water of moderate temperatures is far greater than the rate of heat loss to air of the same temperature.

Evaporation

When the external temperatures are high, heat cannot be transferred from the body to its surroundings by radiation, conduction, or convection. (Remember that heat cannot flow "uphill.") Yet heat continues to be produced within the body by catabolism, and heat is being transferred to the body from the hot surroundings. If the body temperature is to be maintained constant, some other mechanism of heat loss must be available. This mechanism is evaporation, a change of state from liquid to gas. The evaporation of water from the body surface and from the sweat glands carries off 0.58 Calorie of heat for each gram of water that evaporates. At moderate temperatures, evaporation accounts for a little under half as much heat loss as radiation; but at high environmental temperatures, evaporation is the only method of heat loss from the skin. A breeze, bringing new air to replace the layer of water-laden air next to the body surface, increases the effectiveness of evaporation in cooling the body. But when the atmospheric humidity is high, and the air is already saturated with water,

even a breeze is not much help. As a result, the same temperature seems much hotter in a humid climate than in a dry one.

Physiological Factors: the Body Thermostat

The hypothalamus plays such a dominant role in controlling so many aspects of our lives: appetite, sleep, emotions, growth, and so on, that it would be surprising if it did not also have a control center for regulating the body temperature. Indeed, the hypothalamus plays a central role in body temperature control. It has been found that a small area in the anterior hypothalamus responds to changes in body temperature by stimulating the body's mechanisms for heat production or heat loss (Figure 27-13). This is the body's "thermostat" or **temperature regulating center.** It contains specialized heat-sensitive neurons, which help to assess the temperature of the blood flowing through the brain. It also receives nerve impulses from the warmth and cold receptors of the skin, transmitted via the spinal cord.

The **heat-dissipating mechanism** comes into play when the body is overheated. The control center in the hypothalamus sends impulses to the sweat glands, stimulating them to evaporate water. Meanwhile, the sympathetic centers in the posterior hypothalamus are inhibited, removing the normal vasoconstrictor tone of the skin blood vessels. The superficial blood vessels dilate, greatly increasing the surface from which heat can be lost by radiation. When these mechanisms take effect and the body temperature falls, the thermostat in the hypothalamus ceases stimulating the heat-dissipating systems.

The **heat-gaining mechanism** goes into effect when the external environment is cold and the body temperature is falling. Sympathetic stimulation produces vasoconstriction in the skin, reducing the surface area for heat loss by radiation. The "goosebumps" that are observed on the skin when it is cold are another effect of the sympathetic stimulation. In humans, this part of the mechanism does not have much practical effect, but in hairier animals piloerection causes the hairs to stand on end and form a thicker blanket over the body surface, increasing the insulating qualities of the fur. When the hypothalamic thermostat is cooled below 37°C, sweating stops entirely. Meanwhile, heat production is increased in several ways. Impulses transmitted from the hypothalamus to the skeletal muscles progressively increase their tone, ultimately resulting in shivering. The increased muscle metabolism increases body heat production, to as much as 200 to 400 percent of normal. Sympathetic stimulation and thyroxin secretion (stimulated by a hypothalamic releasing factor) also produce a general increase in cell metabolism, which enhances heat production.

Impulses from the warmth and cold receptors in the skin are relayed not only to the hypothalamus, but also to the sensory area of the cerebral cortex. The sensations of skin temperature that they produce may initiate conscious actions that help to adjust the body temperature. If you feel hot, you may fan yourself, or take off excess clothing, or go swimming. When you feel cold, you will put on heavier clothes. Even during sleep, you may retain enough awareness to pull up a blanket that has been accidentally thrown off.

Practical Considerations

Before birth, a baby has no need of a finely tuned temperature control mechanism, for it lives in a perfectly regulated environment. Its mother's temperature-regulating system keeps the amniotic fluid that bathes it at a constant body temperature. When the infant is propelled abruptly out into the world, it is greeted by a number of rude shocks, not the least of which is the substantial drop in temperature. It takes a while for an infant's temperature control mechanism to become established. It must be dressed more warmly than an adult, and a fit of crying may produce a marked temperature rise. The problems of faulty temperature control are even more pronounced in premature babies. The most important function of the incubator is to maintain a relatively constant temperature for the premature baby until its own temperature control mechanism begins functioning reliably. (It may take several weeks to become established.) In emergency situations, when an incubator is not available, the simple expedient of swaddling the infant in aluminum foil has proved effective in helping to conserve body heat.

Even in an adult, the body's temperature control mechanisms sometimes go awry, or are unable to cope with environmental temperature extremes.

Fever

Some physicians tend to encourage a fever, although this approach might be looked on as "playing with fire." The rationale is that fever is a defense mechanism, and the higher body temperatures tend to inactivate the invading organisms causing the illness.

An elevation of the body temperature above the normal range, persisting for more than a few minutes, is called fever or **pyrexia.** Fever is most commonly caused by an infection, but it may also be caused by a lesion of the brain or upper spinal cord, dehydration, diathermy, or an allergic reaction to drugs or foreign proteins. The body temperature of a patient with fever may typically rise to 102°F, 103°F, or even 104°F. A temperature above 106°F (41°C) is extremely dangerous, for at this level the delicate enzymes of the body begin to be inactivated.

Paradoxically, the onset of a fever due to an infectious disease often begins with a sensation of cold. The patient cannot feel comfortable, even if wrapped in blankets and heating pads. The severe **chill** builds and precipitates an attack of uncontrollable shivering. During the chill, the patient's oxygen use is about three times as great as normal; yet in spite of the increased heat production, the feeling of cold persists. The excess heat that is being produced is stored in the body, first within the deeper portions (making the peripheral parts of the body feel cold in comparison), and finally there is an overall temperature rise of 3°F or more. The chill is over, and now the patient feels hot, and the skin is dry and flushed.

During a fever, the body's heat production is higher than normal, but the heat loss is also increased; it seems that the body's thermostat is "reset" at a higher level. It is thought that bacterial toxins or protein breakdown products, which are referred to as **pyrogens,** act on the hypothalamus to reset the temperature control mechanisms. **Aspirin** and other **antipyretic** drugs lower the body temperature during a fever by acting on the hypothalamus. Interestingly, when aspirin is taken for other purposes (e.g., for its analgesic effect) when the body temperature is normal, it does not affect the body's thermostat.

The old folk saying "starve a cold and feed a fever" has some grains of wisdom. During a fever there is a specific destruction of body protein and a higher-than-normal catabolism in general; an increased nitrogen intake (via proteins) is required to replace the nitrogen lost, and a high-calorie diet, about 4000 Calories a day, with a high percentage of carbohydrates (to make up the energy consumed in heat loss and chemical reactions) is recommended. (According to current views, however, the other half of the saying is not valid, since it is now felt that the food intake should also be kept up during a cold.)

If a fever is permitted to run its course, the body temperature may drop suddenly back to normal. This rapid fall is called a **crisis,** and it is typically accompanied by profuse sweating. If the return of the body temperature to normal is slow, it is called **lysis.** An alcohol rub helps to lower body temperature because of the extreme volatility of alcohol—it evaporates more readily than water, and in doing so carries heat away from the body surface.

Heat Stroke

During a recent summer, newspaper headlines told a cautionary tale. A young husband came home from work one hot, humid day and found his wife apparently asleep sunbathing, with an aluminized reflector spread out beneath her. Not wanting to disturb her, he fixed dinner and then went to call her, only to discover that—she was dead!

High external temperatures place a strain on the body's temperature-regulating mechanisms. If the air is dry, and sweating can occur freely, a person can withstand high temperatures, even as high as 200°F, without any apparent ill effects. But when the air is saturated with moisture, so that evaporation cannot occur, the body temperature begins to rise if the surrounding temperature is above 94°F; if the person is doing heavy physical work, even external temperatures of 85° to 90°F may produce a rise in the body temperature. As the body temperature rises, the metabolic rate increases (about 6 percent for each degree F temperature rise), and as the hypothalamus is warmed, its temperature-regulating ability becomes depressed. As a result, a vicious cycle is established, and the body temperature continues to rise. Meanwhile, the profuse sweating causes a loss of salt and water, decreasing the plasma volume, and ultimately resulting in circulatory collapse. If the body temperature rises above 110°F, the proteins of the body begin to coagulate, inactivating enzymes and irreversibly damaging cells. (The nervous system is particularly vulnerable, since nerve cells once destroyed cannot be replaced.) If the body temperature is not rapidly brought down to the normal range, for example, by bathing the victim in ice water or sponging with alcohol, death will result within a few hours.

Several degrees of reaction to excessively high external temperatures can be distinguished. **Heat cramp** is a mild reaction, in which the patient sweats profusely and the skin is warm, but body temperature is normal or only slightly elevated. The cardiovascular and thermoregulatory mechanisms still function normally. **Heat exhaustion** or **heat collapse** is more serious. The patient sweats profusely, has a lowered blood pressure and rapid pulse; muscle cramps, pallor, vertigo, nausea, vomiting, weakness, and fainting may be observed. The symptoms are due to salt and water depletion, and the treatment consists of replacing these losses as quickly as possible. In **heat stroke,** a vicious cycle has been established, and as the decreased plasma volume cuts down the blood flow through the skin and the thermoregulatory functions of the hypothalamus are impaired, sweating ceases. With the main avenue of heat loss removed, the body temperature rises rapidly. The patient's skin is dry and flushed, and he or she lapses into a coma. If the body temperature is not lowered immediately by artificial means, the victim will die.

It is possible to acclimatize the body to extreme heat, by exposing the person to heat for several hours each day while working fairly heavily. Within a week the person will be better able to tolerate hot and humid conditions, showing such physiological adaptations as an increase in plasma volume and reduced loss of salt in the sweat and urine, due to an increased secretion of aldosterone. Such acclimatization is especially valuable in preparing soldiers for duty in tropical zones and miners for work in the gold mines of South Africa, where the temperature approaches body temperature and the humidity is nearly 100 percent.

Subnormal Temperatures

When boats capsize, plunging their passengers into the water, death frequently results not from drowning, but from exposure. The body's heat-producing mechanisms cannot keep pace with the heat loss that occurs when environmental temperatures are extremely low, and the body temperature falls. Exposure to ice water for just half an hour causes the internal body temperature to fall to about 77°F, and if the person is not warmed rapidly, death will result. (The optimum temperature for the warming bath or hot packs is 110°F, which is warm enough to provide an effective heat transfer but not high enough to damage the skin.) Below 85°F, the hypothalamus entirely loses its ability to regulate body temperature; cell enzyme activity slows down, the breathing rate slows, and the oxygen supply to the cells is decreased. An overpowering desire for sleep develops, and the victim may lapse into a coma and die.

Exposure to extremely low temperatures may also cause surface areas of the body (especially the fingers, toes, and earlobes) to freeze. Such **frostbite** may cause tissue damage and permanent circulatory impairment, resulting in gangrene, and the frost-bitten areas are lost. But if the frozen areas are promptly thawed with warm water (about 110°F), permanent damage may be avoided.

Hypothermia, an artificial lowering of the body temperature below 90°F, can be performed safely by giving the person a sedative to depress the hypothalamic thermostat and then packing him in ice until the temperature falls. This device is used in heart surgery, so that the heart can be stopped for an extended period. No apparent harmful effects result from the stoppage of circulation, since the metabolic rate and oxygen requirement are greatly lowered.

There has been speculation that deep hypothermia, actually freezing the body, might be used in the future to preserve the lives of terminally ill patients until a cure for their disease has been found, or by astronauts going into a sort of "suspended animation" during long space voyages. But at the present state of cryogenics research, many unsolved problems remain. A major stumbling block is the formation of intracellular ice crystals, which can damage delicate tissues. A small number of people have been frozen after death, but there is as yet no guarantee that they could ever be thawed successfully without irreversible tissue damage.

SUMMARY

Absorption of food materials from the digestive tract occurs by diffusion, osmosis, and active transport.
Sites of absorption are:
Stomach (water, salts, sugars, alcohol, and drugs)
Small intestine (water, salts, sugars, amino acids, and fatty substances)
Large intestine (water, salts)
Monosaccharides are absorbed through the intestinal membrane by active transport, in the preferential sequence: galactose>glucose>fructose.
Amino acids are rapidly absorbed by active transport.
Small amounts of dipeptides and proteins may be absorbed by pinocytosis.
Glycerol is absorbed into the blood system, while fatty acids and monoglycerides are carried through the cell membrane, resynthesized into triglycerides by the endoplasmic reticulum, and transported as chylomicrons into the lacteals.
Vitamins include water-soluble and fat-soluble substances.
Fat-soluble vitamins are absorbed together with dietary fats.
Electrolytes are absorbed by diffusion down concentration and electrical gradients and by active transport.
Water can flow in or out of the lumen of the intestines, by osmosis.

Metabolism is the sum total of all the chemical reactions in the body.
Anabolism refers to synthetic reactions.
Catabolism refers to breakdown reactions, with a release of stored chemical energy.
Carbohydrates and fats are metabolized mainly for energy (catabolism); proteins are used mainly as building materials (anabolism).
The energy released in catabolic reactions is temporarily stored in ATP molecules.
Carbohydrates are digested to monosaccharides, which may:
(1) pass into the circulation (blood sugar)
(2) be carried to the liver and stored as glycogen
(3) be converted to glycogen in skeletal muscles and used in muscle contraction
(4) be converted to lipids and stored in fat deposits
(5) be converted to amino acids by amination reactions
(6) be oxidized as energy sources in the tissues
(7) be used to synthesize glycolipids, glycoproteins, and mucopolysaccharides
(8) be synthesized to lactose in the mammary glands
(9) be excreted in the urine (in metabolic disorders such as diabetes mellitus)
The blood sugar level is regulated by interaction of hormones: insulin, glucagon, epinephrine, glucocorticoids, thyroxine.
The liver is a key site of carbohydrate metabolism:
Glycogenesis: production of glycogen from glucose
Glycogenolysis: breakdown of glycogen to glucose
Gluconeogenesis: synthesis of glucose from noncarbohydrate sources
Amino acids are used in the synthesis of proteins and nonprotein nitrogen-containing substances such as creatine, creatinine, pyrimidines, purines, and porphyrins.
Protein catabolism occurs in the liver by oxidative deamination or transamination.
Body cells can reversibly store proteins, which are digested to amino acids by intracellular enzymes (cathepsins).
Fats may be metabolized as energy sources or stored in fat depots.
Fat deposits are dynamic, with constant lipolysis, lipogenesis, and exchange with plasma lipids.
The liver synthesizes fatty acids from carbohydrates, lengthens and shortens fatty acid chains, saturates and unsaturates them, and conducts beta oxidation, producing ketone bodies.
A continual intake of water is needed in addition to the amount produced by metabolic reactions.
Carbohydrates, proteins, and lipids are major components of the common metabolic pool and can be interconverted through intermediate keto acids (especially pyruvic acid).
Chemical energy is used in the body to do work but is ultimately converted to heat.
The reactions of energy metabolism (cell respiration) include:
Glycolysis
Krebs citric acid cycle
Cytochrome chain
Glycolysis is anaerobic and yields pyruvic acid and a small amount of energy stored in ATP.
The Krebs and cytochrome cycles are aerobic and result in complete oxidation of substrates to carbon dioxide and water, with a large yield of ATP.
The energy content of foods is measured in Calories:
Carbohydrate: 4 Cal/g
Protein: 4 Cal/g
Fat: 9 Cal/g
The respiratory quotient is the ratio of carbon dioxide produced to oxygen consumed.
The RQ differs for different diets:

Carbohydrate 1.0
Protein 0.8
Fat 0.7
Mixed diet 0.82
The RQ rises during exercise.

Animals are classed according to ability to regulate body temperature as:
Poikilothermic (body temperature varies with surroundings)
Homoiothermic (relatively constant body temperature)
Heterothermic (hibernating animals)

Homeostasis of body temperature is a dynamic process, in which heat production and heat loss are kept in balance.

The normal body temperature is about 98.6°F (37°C) but shows individual fluctuations, circadian rhythms, and is affected by extreme environmental temperatures, physical exercise, digestion of food, and strong emotions.

Heat is produced in the body by catabolism of foods.

Heat is lost by the body by:
Radiation
Conduction
Convection
Evaporation

A temperature control center in the hypothalamus acts as a thermostat, stimulating the heat-dissipating or heat-gaining mechanisms to maintain temperature homeostasis.
Heat-dissipating mechanisms include:
Sweat secretion
Dilation of superficial blood vessels
Heat-gaining mechanisms include:
Vasoconstriction in the skin
Piloerection
Shivering
Increased cell metabolism due to thyroxin and sympathetic stimulation.

An infant's temperature control mechanisms do not work reliably.

Fever is an elevation of body temperature above the normal range.
It may be caused by infection, lesion of the brain or spinal cord, dehydration, diathermy, or allergic reaction.
Pyrogens reset the hypothalamic thermostate at a higher level.
Aspirin lowers fever by normalizing the hypothalamic thermostat setting.

Fever may be a protective mechanism, inactivating invading microorganisms.

Exposure to extremely high external temperatures (especially with high humidity) can cause:
Heat cramp
Heat exhaustion
Heat stroke

Exposure to extremely low external temperatures can cause:
Fall of body temperature, leading to death
Frostbite of superficial areas

Artificial hypothermia is used in surgical operations.

QUESTIONS FOR REVIEW AND THOUGHT

1 What substances are absorbed in the: (a) stomach; (b) small intestine; (c) large intestine?

2 Describe the roles of the following in absorption of food substances: (a) villikinin; (b) intrinsic factor; (c) parathyroid hormone.

3 Discuss the relative roles of anabolism and catabolism in the human body.

4 What are the metabolic alternatives for carbohydrates in the body?

5 Describe the mechanisms that regulate the blood sugar level.

6 Distinguish among glycogenesis, glycogenolysis, and gluconeogenesis.

7 Why must ingested proteins be broken down before use in the body? What are the principal metabolic pathways for amino acids?

8 Describe the absorption of fats and their uses in the body.

9 Describe the reactions of deamination, transamination, and beta oxidation.

10 Discuss interconversions of energy as applied to the body.

11 What is the relationship between glycolysis and the Krebs cycle? Between the Krebs cycle and the cytochrome chain?

12 Lions are carnivores and live almost exclusively on meat, rich in protein and fat; herbivores such as cattle eat carbohydrate-rich plants. What would you expect the RQ's for these animals to be?

13 What factors make the charting of body temperature a somewhat unrealiable method of determining the time of ovulation?

14 Describe the effects on body temperature control mechanisms of the following circumstances: (a) bacterial infection; (b) sun bathing on the beach; (c) being lost in a snowstorm.

NUTRITION

28

For many years, courses on nutrition did not play a prominent role in the education of physicians. Today this has changed, as research is revealing more and more truth in the adage "you are what you eat."

Like other animals, humans need continual supplies of foods to provide energy for body activities and building materials for growth and repair. Some animals (**herbivores**) subsist entirely on plant foods; others (**carnivores**) get nearly all their nutrients from animal food sources. Humans share with a few other species, including the pig and the rat, the distinction of being **omnivores,** capable of living on almost any kind of food, animal or vegetable.

Though people have subsisted on a wide variety of diets, some of them extremely restricted (e.g., the potato diet of Irish farmers before the mid-nineteenth century potato famine), optimum growth, development, and health require a balance of nutrients. An adequate diet must contain not only proteins, carbohydrates, and fats, but also vitamins, minerals, and water, as well as a certain amount of indigestible fiber to keep the intestinal peristalsis stimulated. A variety of flavoring agents, spices, and other condiments contribute to making foods attractive and palatable.

Average Americans get about 15 percent of their calories from protein, 40 percent from fat, and 45 percent from carbohydrate. But this "affluent diet" is a relatively recent phenomenon and is not characteristic of most other parts of the world, where carbohydrates typically make up a far greater proportion of the diet—as much as 80 percent or more.

WATER

If suddenly *all* of the water were to vanish from your body, a dusty heap—not much more than would fit into a gallon milk jug—would cover the floor where

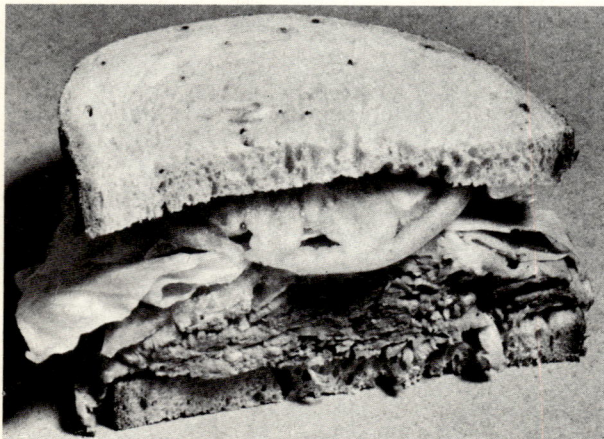

FIGURE 28-1 This roast beef sandwich contains a variety of nutrients, including protein, carbohydrate, fat, vitamins, minerals, and water.

you once stood. About two-thirds of the total body weight is water, which acts as a solvent for chemical reactions, a carrier fluid in the body's circulatory systems, a participant in hydrolytic reactions, and plays key roles in the body's heating and cooling systems. A prodigious amount of water is lost from the body each day, in urine, feces, sweat, and even in the exhaled air. All this water must be replaced, partly through metabolic reactions and partly in the daily food intake. More than two-thirds of the material ingested daily is water. The most obvious source is the water in beverages, but solid foods also contain substantial amounts of fluid, especially fruits and vegetables.

MINERALS

Probably more than 40 elements are critical for the proper functioning of the human body. Some, such as the calcium and phosphorus of bones, are present in sizeable amounts; others are needed only in minute quantities, to contribute to the functioning of enzymes. The latter minerals are often referred to as **trace elements** or **micronutrients,** emphasizing their small amounts. Altogether, minerals constitute about 4 percent of the body weight, and the major portion is found in the skeleton. Inorganic salts help to maintain osmotic relationships and the acid–base balance in the body fluids and participate in such functions as excitability, conductivity, contractility, and the coagulation of blood. Minerals are lost daily in the urine, feces, and sweat and must be replaced by the intake of foods. Marked variations of the concentrations of mineral salts in the body tissues and fluids can produce deficiency diseases or toxemia (poisoning).

Calcium is the most abundant cation in the body. Ninety-nine percent of it is found in the bones and teeth, yet the other one percent is vital for cell activities. Calcium is involved in muscle contraction (including the work of the heart), in nerve conduction, and it participates in blood clotting. A daily intake of 1 gram of calcium is needed to maintain an optimum concentration in the body fluids, but children (who are building bones and teeth) and pregnant and lactating women have increased calcium requirements. Milk and milk products are the best food sources of this mineral, but calcium is also supplied by leafy vegetables. Because of the constant turnover of the calcium stored in bones and teeth, these structures will be demineralized if the diet is deficient in calcium. This sometimes occurs during pregnancy.

Phosphorus is another abundant and vital element in the human body. About 80 percent of the phosphorus is combined with calcium in the bones and teeth; phosphorus is also an essential constituent of the nu-

TABLE 28-1 Some Important Minerals

MINERAL	FOOD SOURCES	RECOMMENDED DAILY ALLOWANCE	FUNCTIONS	RESULT OF DEFICIENCY
Calcium	Milk, cheese, eggs, leafy vegetables	1 g	Formation of bones and teeth, blood clotting, muscle contraction, nerve conduction	Tetany, rickets, bone demineralization
Phosphorus	Milk, cheese, eggs, beef	1.5 g	Formation of bones and teeth; energy metabolism; constituent of nucleic acids	Bone demineralization, metabolic disorders
Potassium	Most foods	1-2 g	Nerve and muscle action	Abnormalities of heart action, nerve disorders
Sodium	Most foods, table salt	2.5 g	Acid-base balance, fluid balance	Weakness, cramps, nausea, diarrhea, dehydration
Chlorine	Most foods, table salt	3.5 g	Chloride shift; HCl of gastric juice	Disturbance of fluid and electrolyte balance
Iodine	Seafood, iodized salt	0.25 mg	Formation of thyroid hormones	Hypothyroidism
Iron	Meat, eggs, spinach, prunes, beans, peas, whole wheat	18 mg	Constituent of hemoglobin, myoglobin, and cytochrome enzymes	Anemia, digestive disorders, dry skin
Magnesium	Green vegetables	400 mg	Neuromuscular transmission; cofactor in metabolism of glucose, pyruvic acid, and ATP	Vasodilation, arrhythmia, hyperirritability, spasticity. Excesses block nerve conduction and muscle contraction
Copper	Most foods	2 mg	Constituent of ceruloplasmin and cytochrome oxidase; synthesis of hemoglobin	Anemia
Manganese	Liver, kidneys	unknown	Activates enzymes (including arginase and cholinesterase)	Infertility, menstrual irregularities
Zinc	Most foods	15 mg	Part of enzymes (including carbonic anhydrase, lactic dehydrogenase, and peptidases); participates in CO_2 transport, energy metabolism, and digestion	Retarded growth and sexual maturation, alopecia (loss of hair), dermatitis, anorexia, vomiting
Cobalt	Most foods, tap water	1 mg	Constituent of vitamin B_{12}	Anemia
Fluorine	Drinking water	unknown	Strengthens teeth and bones	Dental caries, weak bones

cleic acids, ATP, phospholipids, phosphocreatine, and phosphorylated intermediates of carbohydrate metabolism. Increased amounts of phosphorus (equal to the amount of calcium) are needed by growing children and pregnant and lactating women; for other adults the daily requirement is about 1.5 grams. Usually the same foods that are rich in calcium (e.g., milk) provide good supplies of phorphorus as well; it is also found in beef, beans, and nuts.

Potassium is found mainly in the body cells. It plays a role in nerve and muscle activity and also influences the body water balance. Either high or low serum potassium levels produce abnormalities of the heart action. (The normal concentration is from 3.8 to 5.1 mEq/liter.) Most foods contain potassium, and thus dietary deficiencies of this element are extremely rare.

Sodium, in contrast to potassium, is found mainly in the extracellular fluid (136 to 144 mEq/liter), with only traces inside the cells. It plays a major role in determining the acid-base balance and osmotic pressure. Sodium chloride, table salt, is probably the most commonly used food additive and is routinely added to many foods. But most of this oversalting is unnecessary, from the nutritional standpoint, since the average diet provides ample amounts of sodium even without salting. Indeed, the high sodium content of the typical American diet is believed to be contributing to the development of hypertension, and persons with heart disease must severely restrict their salt intake. Some sodium is normally excreted in the urine, but the kidneys are capable of reabsorbing this mineral to maintain optimum levels in the body fluids. However, under conditions when sweating is copious, the increased amounts of sodium lost in the sweat must be promptly replaced; otherwise weakness, cramps, nausea, and diarrhea may result.

Chlorine is the other element supplied by table salt. It is distributed throughout the body in the form of chloride ions and participates in the chloride shift, in which chloride ions diffuse into red blood cells to maintain ionic equilibrium. Chlorine is also a part of the hydrogen chloride of gastric juice.

Iodine belongs to the same chemical family as chlorine. In the body it is found mainly in the thyroid gland, where it is used in the synthesis of the hormone thyroxine. Seafood is a major source of this element, but in inland areas the food and water supply tend to be iodine deficient, resulting in goiter and other thyroid malfunctions. Adequate supplies of dietary iodine can be provided by the use of iodized salt.

Iron is a key mineral in the body, since it is a constituent of the hemoglobin of red blood cells, the myoglobin of skeletal muscles, and various enzymes, including those of the cytochrome system. There is a common impression that iron is one of the more abundant mineral elements in the body, but actually the adult body contains only about 4.5 grams of iron altogether (compared with 125 grams of potassium and about 25 grams of magnesium). About half of the body iron is contained in hemoglobin. Iron is stored in the body in the form of ferritin, a protein-bound form, but the storage is limited, and a regular iron intake in the diet is necessary. Women, who lose significant amounts of iron each month in the menstrual flow, have increased requirements for this mineral and often suffer from iron deficiency. Meat, eggs, beans, peas, whole wheat, spinach, and prunes supply abundant amounts of iron.

Magnesium is widely distributed in the body; most of it is found in the bones, but it is also present in the body cells and blood serum. Magnesium is a key cofactor in the metabolism of glucose, pyruvic acid, and ATP. Excess concentrations of magnesium in the extracellular fluid depress the conduction of nerve impulses and the contraction of muscles; the latter effect can be blocked by the administration of calcium, to which magnesium is rather similar chemically. Magnesium is widely distributed in foods; green vegetables are especially good sources.

Copper is a constituent of certain enzymes, including ceruloplasmin and cytochrome oxidase. It participates in the formation of hemoglobin, although it is not an actual part of the molecule. The entire body contains only about 100 mg of copper, and yet if insufficient supplies of this element are available (as may occur in infants on an exclusive milk diet) anemia and other serious consequences will develop.

Manganese is another trace element that is vital to the body. It activates a number of metabolic enzymes, including arginase and cholinesterase, and seems to be necessary for normal reproductive function: in the presence of manganese deficiencies created in experimental animals, the testes of the males atrophy, and the females are unable to suckle their young. Since few cases of manganese deficiency are reported, the normal diet presumably provides adequate amounts of this mineral; an excess of manganese is toxic.

Zinc is an integral part of numerous enzymes, including carbonic anhydrase, lactic dehydrogenase, and peptidases, and thus is involved in such vital body reactions as the transport of carbon dioxide in the blood, energy metabolism, and digestion. In experimental animals, zinc deficiency causes retarded growth, loss of hair, dermatitis, and vomiting. It is found in most foods.

Cobalt is an essential constituent of vitamin B_{12}, which is necessary for the maturation of red blood cells. It is found in most foods, and in tap water.

Fluorine, chemically similar to chlorine, is a natural constituent of drinking water in certain localities and is deposited in teeth and bones. It is not certain whether this element is needed in the diet, but it is now commonly used to prevent tooth decay. In excess it can produce mottling of teeth and skeletal deformities.

Various other mineral elements are also essential for normal body functions, including **sulfur** (a constituent of proteins), **chromium** (participates in glucose metabolism), **molybdenum** (plays a role in enzyme activity), **selenium** (important in liver function), and **vanadium** (necessary for growth).

Some trace minerals that find their way into food or drinking water can be a danger to health; industrial water pollution has been adding to the problem. **Mercury** residues, which can cause severe neurological damage, can be a major hazard if they are concentrated from polluted waters in the bodies of seafood, such as tuna. **Cadmium,** which may leach out of water pipes into drinking water, has been implicated in the development of heart disease. Cadmium is also present naturally in wheat; but the wheat grain also con-

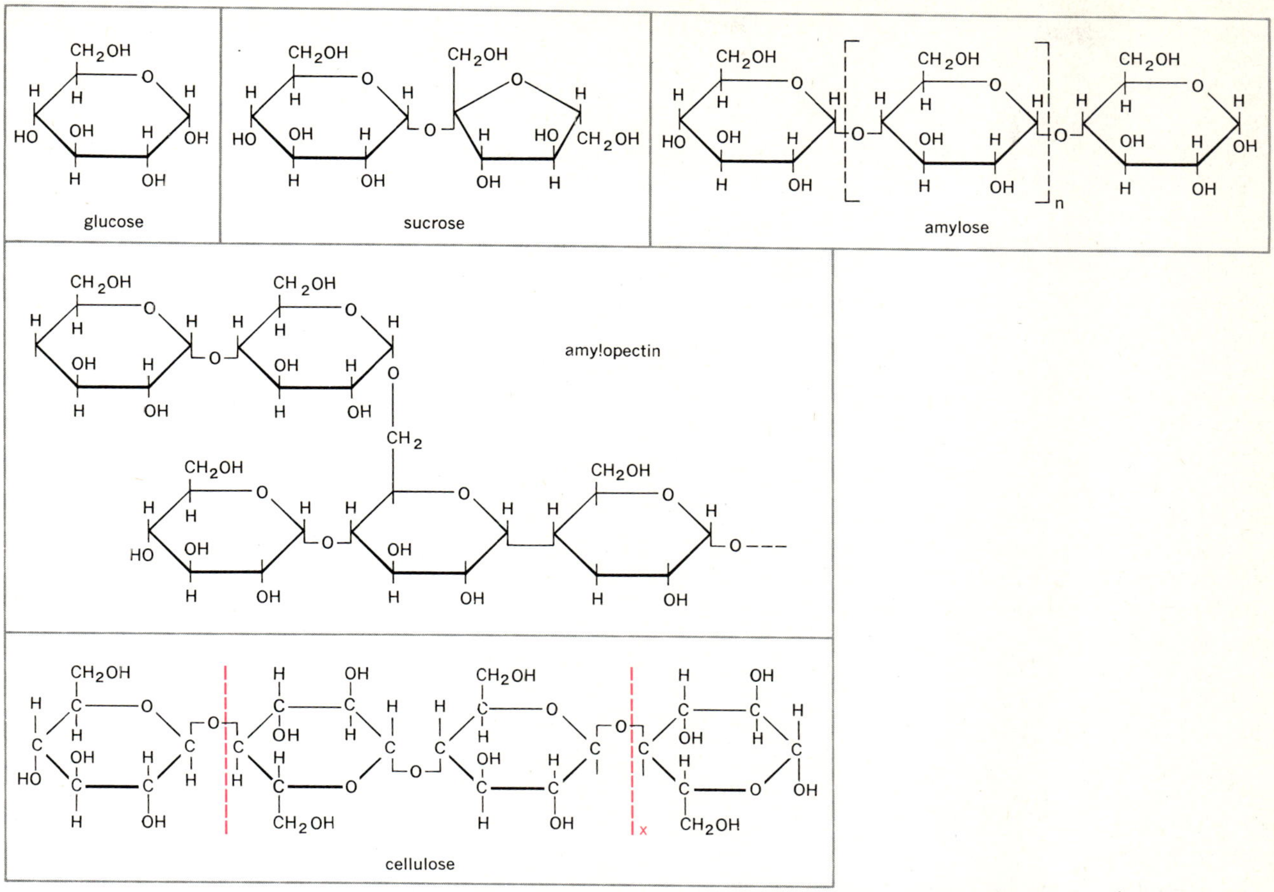

FIGURE 28-2 Chemical formulas of some common carbohydrates. Starch and cellulose are polymers consisting of long chains of glucose units, linked together. (The constituents of starch, amylose and amylopectin, differ in the arrangement of the basic glucose units, in straight or branched chains.)

tains zinc, which prevents the absorption of cadmium by the body. When wheat is refined to white flour, most of the zinc is removed, altering the mineral balance and leaving the cadmium. Meanwhile, dietary zinc and copper have been found to compete for absorption and utilization in the body, and there is some evidence that too high a zinc-to-copper ratio may promote the development of heart disease. A growing knowledge of such complex interactions of nutrients may help in devising more effective methods of food processing and in fostering the development of better nutrition.

CARBOHYDRATES

It would be difficult to find a processed food in the supermarket to which sugar was not added. Starches, too, are usually present in abundance, and carbohydrates overall generally predominate greatly in breads, crackers, cereal products, pasta, and in vegetables as well. (Take a look at the percentage breakdowns of carbohydrate, protein, and fat on the package labels next time you are in the kitchen or food

store.) Carbohydrates—sugars and starches—make up the largest single component of our diet, and an even larger fraction in many parts of the world. Carbohydrates are often regarded as prime culprits in causing obesity. Some reducing diets emphasize a high-protein diet, which provides so little carbohydrate that the body fats are mobilized, and the person actually goes into ketosis, excreting ketone bodies. In a normal diet, however, a fairly large proportion of carbohydrate is a necessary constituent, since carbohydrate is the body's preferred energy source. Any available glucose is metabolized first, before fats or proteins, and thus carbohydrates are considered to be fat-sparing and protein-sparing foods. Without sufficient carbohydrates in the diet, proteins will be metabolized for energy, and there may be an actual wasting of body proteins.

All carbohydrates contain only the three elements, C, H, and O, combined in the ratio $C_xH_{2y}O_y$—in other words, a carbohydrate molecule always contains exactly twice as many hydrogen atoms as oxygen atoms, the same proportion as in water (Figure 28-2).

In simple sugars (**monosaccharides**) the number of carbon atoms is equal to the number of oxygen atoms. Nearly all the sugars in foodstuffs are six-carbon sugars—glucose and its isomers (variant forms), all with the overall chemical formula $C_6H_{12}O_6$. In the body the five-carbon sugars ribose and deoxyribose are key constituents of the nucleic acids.

You have already been introduced to several **disaccharides,** which are combinations of two monosaccharide molecules, joined by eliminating one molecule of water. Sucrose (a combination of glucose and fructose), maltose (two molecules of glucose), and lactose (glucose and galactose) all have the overall chemical formula $C_{12}H_{22}O_{11}$; they differ only in the arrangement of some of the hydrogen and hydroxyl (OH) groups. In the body, disaccharides are digested to monosaccharides by the insertion of water.

Starches are an example of the group of **polysaccharides,** which consist of many monosaccharide residues linked together, with a water molecule eliminated at each bond. Starch is a combination of amylose, in which between three hundred and two thousand glucose units are linked together in a long chain, and amylopectin, in which up to five thousand glucose molecules are joined into a complex branching network. Glycogen, "animal starch," is another example of a polysaccharide. The most abundant polysaccharide in the vegetable kingdom, cellulose, is a major constituent of the diet but is not available to the human body as a nutrient, since we lack the appropriate cellulose-digesting enzymes. The cellulose fibers from fruits and vegetables and whole cereal grains pass through the digestive tract essentially unchanged, but the "bulk" that they add to the diet helps to satisfy hunger and is important for stimulating bowel function.

The modern diet, consisting largely of processed foods, is considerably lower in bulk than the typical diet was in the past. Recent research is prompting a reappreciation of the value of a substantial proportion of "fiber" in the diet. Not only does dietary fiber relieve problems of chronic constipation, but it can be used to advantage by dieters (indigestible cellulose is filling without being fattening). Evidence is also accumulating to indicate that a high-fiber diet may help to lower the rates both of cancer (by speeding the passage of potential carcinogens out of the body) and of heart disease. (Bran and other fibers promote the excretion of excess cholesterol.)

LIPIDS

The fats in the diet are deceptive—from the standpoint of calories, a little fat goes an extraordinarily long way. Not only are fats more economical energy sources for the body (9 Cal/gram, versus 4 Cal/gram

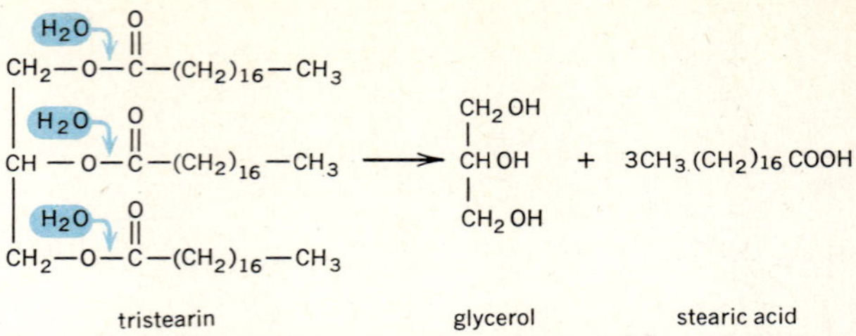

FIGURE 28-3 Tristearin, a typical fat, is digested to glycerol and a fatty acid.

for carbohydrates and proteins), but in their food forms they are far more concentrated. In most foods, proteins and carbohydrates represent less than 25 percent of the weight of the food (the rest is water). But fat is 100 percent fat, undiluted by other substances. Thus, a pat of butter melted into a baked potato contains as many calories as the whole potato.

Lipids are a heterogeneous group of substances, including fats, oils, and waxes, as well as more chemically complicated substances such as phospholipids, glycolipids, and sterols.

Neutral fats or triglycerides are water-insoluble compounds, consisting of a glycerol residue combined with three fatty acid residues (Figure 28-3). The fatty acids generally contain from 10 to 20 carbon atoms, with 14, 16, and 18 the most common. (Curiously, the naturally occurring fatty acids contain an even number of carbon atoms.) Tristearin, the major constituent of beef tallow, is a typical example, formed from glycerol and three molecules of stearic acid, $CH_3(CH_2)_{16}COOH$ or $HC_{18}H_{35}O_2$. There has been a great deal of controversy about the possible implication of saturated fats in the development of heart disease. Current research seems to indicate that the "prudent diet" should include a certain proportion of unsaturated fats, the fatty acids of which contain reactive $-CH=CH-$ bonds. (In saturated fats, all the carbon-carbon bonds in the chains of the fatty acids are saturated $-CH_2-CH_2-$ bonds.) The main naturally occurring unsaturated fatty acids are oleic, linoleic, and linolenic acids, which are all 18-carbon fatty acids with one, two, and three unsaturated bonds, respectively. Oleic acid is found both in animal tallow and in vegetable oils. (Olive oil, for which the compound is named, is a rich source.) Linoleic and linolenic acids are plant substances, found in seed oils. Unfortunately, as a result of the high chemical reactivity of the unsaturated bonds, polyunsaturated oils containing linoleic and linolenic acid residues are readily oxidized and thus tend to turn rancid during storage. As a result, polyunsaturated oils are sometimes partially or entirely hydrogenated ("hardened") to improve their keeping qualities—which eliminates their unsaturation.

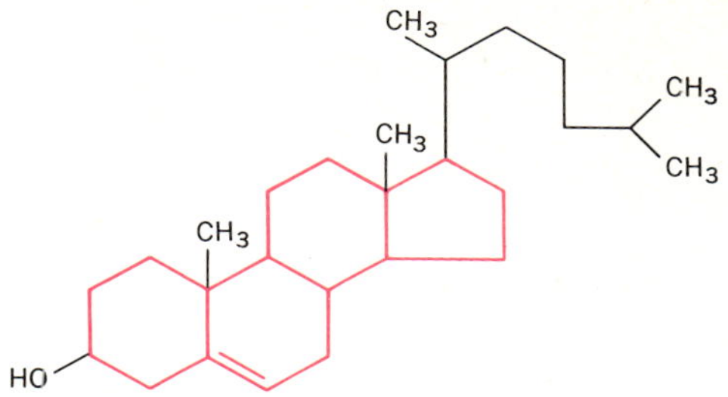

FIGURE 28-4 Cholesterol: a typical sterol. Other sterols share the same basic condensed ring structure (color) and differ in substituents.

Phospholipids or **phosphatides** are compound lipids, which contain phosphorus and nitrogen in addition to carbon, hydrogen, and oxygen. Lecithin, which is abundant in egg yolk, is an important phospholipid in the human body, occurring in all the fluids and tissues and especially in the white matter of the nervous system. Cephalins and sphingomyelin are other examples of phospholipids.

Glycolipids or **cerebrosides** are combinations of fatty acids with a carbohydrate and also contain nitrogen, but they do not contain phosphorus. They are found in the myelin sheaths of nerve fibers, together with lecithin.

Sterols are complex fatlike compounds in which the carbon atoms are linked together in an intricate system of fused rings (Figure 28-4), to various points of which alcohol —OH groups or other groups are attached. The most prominent sterol in the diet is cholesterol, which is richly supplied by egg yolks and meat. For some time cholesterol was regarded as the prime villain in the development of atherosclerosis, the formation of fatty deposits in the artery walls. Heart disease patients were strongly urged to drastically limit their cholesterol intake, and a cholesterol test became a standard item of medical screening. But gradually it was realized that the serum cholesterol level is not always correlated with the condition of the artery walls, and even on a cholesterol-free diet the body is capable of synthesizing abundant amounts. Indeed, cholesterol is a vital substance for the body. It is found in the coverings of nerve fibers, in the blood, in the bile, in the sebum secreted by the sebaceous glands of the skin, and indeed in all the cells and fluids of the body. Cholesterol protects the erythrocytes against the action of hemolytic substances, protects the skin as a constituent of sebum, aids in fat digestion as a constituent of bile, and in addition is a precursor of various steroid hormones.

The lipoproteins that transport neutral fats (triglycerides) and cholesterol in the blood are now believed to be a more reliable predictor of heart-attack risk than the total triglyceride or cholesterol levels. A diet high in saturated fats and/or cholesterol promotes high levels of very low-density lipoproteins (VLDL) and low-density lipoproteins (LDL), which contribute to obesity and atherosclerosis (the buildup of fatty cholesterol deposits inside artery walls). Polyunsaturated fats promote the transport of cholesterol by high-density lipoproteins (HDL), which prevents cholesterol deposition and actively removes it from the artery walls.

PROTEINS

The news is constantly filled with stories about the "energy shortage." Another shortage frequently mentioned is the "protein shortage." Although most Americans are able to obtain a diet that supplies all their basic nutritional needs, the inhabitants of many parts of the world subsist on a diet consisting mainly of carbohydrates of vegetable origin. Plant foods are generally rather low in protein, and in addition, their proteins are often incomplete, lacking sufficient amounts of one or more amino acids.

A human being does not really need to take in all of the twenty-three or so amino acids that occur naturally in proteins. Actually, our bodies can convert certain amino acids to others, and even build up amino acids from keto acids derived from nonprotein sources—for example, from carbohydrates or lipids. But the human body is unable to synthesize eight of the amino acids commonly found in proteins: valine, leucine, isoleucine, phenylalanine, threonine, methionine, lysine, and tryptophan. These eight are often referred to as **essential amino acids,** since they must be supplied by the diet to maintain health. Two other amino acids, arginine and histidine, are synthesized in such small amounts that they cannot keep up with the body's needs (especially during growth), and they are sometimes included in the "essential" list. The "nonessential" amino acids are not nonessential to the body—they are important constituents of proteins. But they are not essential in the diet, since they can be synthesized in the body.

The proteins of foods differ widely in the assortment of amino acids (no one protein contains *all* of the naturally occurring amino acids), in the proportions of the various types, and in the order in which they are linked together. (Imagine for a moment the infinite number of necklaces you could make by stringing together beads selected in any proportions and order you chose from an assortment of twenty-three different kinds of beads. Since proteins are not simple long chains, but are intricately coiled and folded in addition, with various parts held together by cross-links, the possibilities for variation are further multiplied.) Proteins supplied by meat, milk, and eggs are classified as **adequate proteins,** since they supply all the amino acids needed for growth and maintenance of the body. (Remember that digestion splits the protein molecules of foods into their constituent amino acids; thus it makes no difference to the body how the amino acids were originally arranged in the food proteins, but the assortment and amounts of the amino acids are matters of importance.) Some vegetables, notably the legumes (peas, beans, lentils, and peanuts), also supply substantial amounts of high-quality protein. But the protein of many plant products, in addition to being in short supply, is inadequate because it lacks one or more of the essential amino acids. Corn, for example, is lacking in lysine. It is possible to live healthfully on a vegetarian diet by stressing legumes and by using combinations of inadequate-protein foods that mutually supplement each others' deficiencies. Since the body's capacity for storage of amino acids is very limited, unless sufficient amounts of adequate protein are provided regularly, even if the diet is quite adequate for caloric requirements, a protein-deficiency syndrome called **kwashiorkor** will develop. In children, protein lack results in a retardation of growth, lethargy, and mental retardation.

The proteins found in foods, and in the body, may be classified in two main groups: simple proteins and conjugated proteins.

Simple proteins contain only amino acids, linked together by peptide bonds. Examples are serum albumin and globulins; glutenin and gliadin, proteins of wheat; zein of corn; legumin of peas; and scleroproteins such as keratins of hair, horn, and hoofs, elastin of connective tissue and ligaments, and collagen of bones, cartilage, and tendons.

In **conjugated proteins,** simple proteins are combined with some nonprotein substance. Nucleoproteins consist of simple basic proteins (protamine or histone) combined with nucleic acids. In mucoproteins, simple proteins are combined with mucopolysaccharides such as hyaluronic acid; some are found in egg white. Glycoproteins contain small amounts of carbohydrates. Phosphoproteins, which contain phosphate residues, include such common substances as casein of milk and vitellin of egg yolk. In lipoproteins, protein is combined with lecithin, cephalin, a fatty acid, or some other lipid component. Phospholipid-protein complexes occur widely in milk, egg yolk, blood, cell nuclei and cell membranes, and the chloroplasts of plants. Metalloproteins contain metallic elements, such as iron, copper, manganese, cobalt, zinc, or magnesium; this class includes numerous enzymes, as well as the hemoglobin of red blood cells.

VITAMINS

If you ask your doctor, "Do I need vitamin pills?" the answer will very likely be, "No, not if you eat a balanced diet." But study after study has clearly demonstrated that many Americans do *not* eat a balanced diet. In addition to the millions who are unaware of the foods that should be included in a good diet, and those who are living on such low incomes that they subsist on the cheapest and most filling items available, there are many who know better and can afford the best but still do not eat adequately. Perhaps they may be following the latest diet fad or opting too often for overrefined, sugar-heavy "convenience foods."

Even if the conscientious homemaker makes a determined effort to provide the family with a "well-balanced diet," they still may not receive the proper proportions of the essential vitamins. Modern techniques of processing, shipping, and storing foods often tend to remove or destroy vitamin constituents. For example, the pasteurization of milk provides protection against tuberculosis, but destroys the milk's natural vitamin C content. The manufacture of flour, involving the removal of the hulls from the grains, strips off many of their vital ingredients, especially the B-complex vitamins. Grain-product manufacturers reintroduce perhaps a dozen of the scores of vital nutrients that have been removed and call their product "enriched." Meanwhile, the discarded hulls provide a highly nutritious fodder for livestock.

The efforts of manufacturers to supplement processed food with vitamins introduce still another factor, which may further confuse the question of a balanced diet. Milk, bread, cereals, and numerous other food products are commonly enriched with various vitamins in varying amounts. On the whole, this is probably a beneficial practice; but each manufacturer considers only his own product, not the total assortment of foods a person consumes. (This, of course, varies greatly from consumer to consumer.) Since some vitamins, especially A and D, are stored in the body for long periods and may be harmful in excess, the cumulative effect of the vitamins provided by natural foods, those added to artificially "enriched" foods, and possibly vitamin pills in addition may be a cause for alarm.

Vitamins are organic substances that are needed in very small amounts for the normal metabolic processes and cannot be manufactured by the body itself. Most of the vitamins act as cofactors or prosthetic groups for enzymes in the body.

The various animal species differ widely in their vitamin requirements. Rats and mice, for example, like most animals, can synthesize all the vitamin C they need, whereas humans and guinea pigs need a regular dietary intake of this vitamin. Plants do not need to take in any vitamins; they synthesize all that they need, and indeed plant substances provide major sources of vitamins in the human diet. Little more than a dozen vitamins have been definitely established as needed in human nutrition, though numerous others are suspected to be essential to good health.

The existence of vitamins was not realized until the beginning of the twentieth century, although the **deficiency diseases** resulting from their lack had been observed for thousands of years. In general, vitamin deficiencies may be caused by a number of factors, including: (1) inadequate intake, which may be associated with an overall reduction of food intake (as in a poverty-level diet or in a reducing diet), or may be due to an overemphasis of certain kinds of foods at the expense of others; (2) inadequate absorption, as in prolonged vomiting or diarrhea or the use of mineral oil as a laxative (it dissolves fat-soluble vitamins and carries them out in the feces); (3) liver disease, resulting in a failure to convert vitamin precursors to active vitamins or a failure to store the vitamins; (4) increased body demands for vitamins, as during pregnancy, lactation, or fever.

Individual vitamin requirements vary. Growing children have different nutritional needs from adults. Body size is an important determining factor, as is the degree of physical activity. Illness and individual metabolic idiosyncrasies may also have an effect on the amounts of various vitamins needed at various times.

The problem is further clouded because the minimal requirement, necessary to prevent deficiency diseases, and the optimal intake, promoting good health, may be quite different. Conflicting claims and acrimonious epithets are hurled back and forth by food faddists and anti-food faddists. Indeed, for certain vitamins there is still controversy over whether they are needed in the diet at all. It is often rather difficult to establish human vitamin requirements, since long-term rigorously controlled diet experiments would be difficult or unethical; moreover, some vitamins (e.g., vitamin E) are normally required in such small quantities and are so widespread among common foods that cases of deficiency are extremely rare.

Vitamins are grouped into two basic categories according to their solubility. Vitamins A, D, E, and K are soluble in fats and oils, and are therefore called the **fat-soluble vitamins.** They require the presence of bile in the intestines to be absorbed; a defect of fat absorption thus leads to deficiencies of these vitamins. The fat-soluble vitamins tend to be stored in the body for relatively long periods, and thus a steady intake is not vital. But accumulation may become a factor if the levels of intake are high.

Vitamin C and the varied group that make up the B complex are **water-soluble vitamins.** The vitamins of this group are not stored in the body; excesses are excreted rapidly. As a result, cumulative overdoses do not present a problem, but a steady daily source of the water-soluble vitamins must be ensured.

Information on various known vitamins, their food sources, their role in the body, daily dietary requirements, and conditions caused by deficiencies, is summarized in Table 28-2.

Vitamin A

Bugs Bunny has probably done more for the popularization of carrots than any ad campaign could accomplish. Carrots are a rich source of **beta-carotene,** a yellow pigment that is a precursor of vitamin A. The actual vitamin, **retinol,** is produced from the precursor in the body, mainly in the liver and in the wall of the small intestine. Fish liver oils provide an abundant supply not only of vitamin A precursors (carotenoid pigments), but also of the vitamin itself.

As might be guessed from the name retinol, vitamin A plays an important role in the chemistry of vision. **Rhodopsin** (visual purple) is formed from a carotenoid substance, and a deficiency of vitamin A results in night blindness, due to the failure of visual purple to be resynthesized after it has been broken down by exposure to light. Vitamin A is also involved in growth processes and the maintenance of the skin and mucous membranes. Deficiency produces dry, rough skin and keratinized epithelium of the mucous membranes, an increased susceptibility to respiratory infections, and xerophthalmia, an eye condition that can lead to blindness. Massive doses, for example, 500,000 IU per day (compared with the minimum daily requirement of 5000 IU), produce toxic effects, including headache, nausea, lethargy, and calcium deposits in the ligaments and joint capsules.

The B Complex

The members of the B complex group are not similar chemically, nor are their effects similar. Their grouping together was essentially an accident of history. When the concept of vitamins was first formulated, very little was known about their chemical nature of their functions in the body. As a result, they were simply arbitrarily designated by letters of the alphabet as they were discovered. The B-complex vitamins are all water-soluble and are found together in various foods; when a new "vital factor" was extracted and named vitamin B, it was not realized at first that it was a mixture. As one component after another was isolated and found to have quite different properties and effects, they were distinguished by numerical subscripts (B_1, B_2, etc.) and only later, as their chemical nature was established, called by appropriate chemical names.

Thiamine (Vitamin B_1)

Serendipity—shrewdly taking advantage of lucky accidents—has traditionally played a major role in sci-

TABLE 28-2 Some Important Vitamins

VITAMIN	FOOD SOURCES	RECOMMENDED DAILY ALLOWANCE	FUNCTIONS	RESULT OF DEFICIENCY
A (retinol)	Fish liver oils; fruits, vegetables (beta-carotene)	5,000 I.U.* (3 mg)	Synthesis of visual pigments	Night blindness, xerophthalmia, epithelial changes
B₁ (thiamine)	Yeast, whole-grain cereals, liver, meat, milk, legumes, nuts	1.5 mg	Coenzyme in carbohydrate and energy metabolism	Anorexia, indigestion, polyneuritis, beriberi
B₂ (riboflavin)	Milk, cheese, liver, meat, yeast, wheat germ, leafy vegetables	1.7 mg	Constituent of flavin enzymes in electron transport system	Cheilosis, dermatitis, glossitis, keratitis of the cornea
Niacin	Liver, meat, chicken, fish, yeast, peanuts, wheat germ, legumes, milk	20 mg	Constituent of NAD and NADP, coenzymes in cell respiration	Pellagra (dermatitis, dementia, diarrhea, death)
Pantothenic acid	Yeast, liver, eggs	10 mg	Constituent of coenzyme A	Stunted growth, dermatitis, gray hiar, personality changes, numbness, pain in feet
B₆ (pyridoxine)	Yeast, wheat germ, liver, fish, milk, eggs	2 mg	Coenzyme in amino acid and protein metabolism	Anemia, dermatitis, convulsions, gastrointestinal disturbances, atrophy of lymphoid tissue and susceptibility to infection
Biotin	Liver, yeast, milk, eggs, vegetables, nuts, grains	0.3 mg	Constituent of coenzymes in reactions combining CO_2 with other compounds	Dermatitis, listlessness, gastrointestinal disorders, muscle pains, incoordination
Folic acid	Vegetables, eggs, liver, cereals	0.4 mg	Promotion of growth and coenzyme in red blood cell maturation	Anemia, sprue, growth retardation
B₁₂ (cyanocobalamin)	Liver, meat, eggs, milk	6 μg	Maturation of red blood cells	Pernicious anemia
C (ascorbic acid)	Citrus fruits, tomatoes, green pepper, leafy vegetables	60 mg	Oxidation–reduction reactions; aids in production of collagen and cartilage; maintenance of capillary integrity; wound healing	Scurvy (capillary fragility, weight loss, weakness, dyspnea, subcutaneous hemorrhages, loosened teeth, fragile bones, swollen joints)
D₂ (calciferol) D₃ (7-dehydrocholesterol)	Fish, milk, butter, egg yolk	400 I.U.* (20 μg)	Intestinal absorption of calcium, control of bone formation and resorption	Rickets and osteomalacia: soft and fragile bones, deformation of skeleton. Effect of overdose: demineralization of bone, elevation of plasma calcium, kidney stones, calcium deposits in soft tissues
E (alpha-tocopherol)	Wheat germ oil, meat, milk, butter	30 I.U.*	Antioxidant; protection against radiation and pollutants	In animals: infertility, degeneration of muscles and nerves, renal tubular changes
K	Leafy vegetables, tomatoes	unkown	Synthesis of prothrombin and other blood clotting factors	Slow blood clotting and hemorrhage

*I.U. = international units.

entific discoveries. An example was the discovery of the first of the B vitamins. In the late nineteenth century, a disease called **beriberi** was raging in the Dutch East Indies. In this disease the nerves and muscles degenerate, leading to paralysis. A Dutch physician, Christiaan Eijkman, was sent as a member of a medical team to study the disease. At the time the germ theory of disease was still quite recent and had excited the imagination of medical researchers. Eijkman vainly tried to isolate the microorganism that must be responsible for beriberi. Then suddenly similar symptoms developed in a flock of chickens being used at the hospital for bacteriological research. Eijkman redoubled his efforts, trying to isolate the causative germ or transfer the disease from a sick chicken to a healthy one. Neither approach gave results, and then, as mysteriously as it had appeared, the disease suddenly disappeared, and all the sick chickens recovered dramatically. Some medical detective work revealed the answer. The patients at the hospital were fed only the highest quality polished rice, while the experimental chickens were normally fed unpolished (whole-grain) rice. Then the cook ran out of the commercial chicken feed and substituted some polished rice from the hospital stores. That was when the chickens fell ill. Later the cook was transferred, and his successor thought it highly improper to use fine quality food fit for humans on chickens. He went back to feeding the chickens unpolished rice, and they quickly recovered. Following up this finding in 1896, Eijkman discovered that he could produce the disease at will by feeding the chickens polished rice, and then cure them by switching to unpolished rice. Although Eijkman himself did not appreciate the true significance of his findings, during the following decade several researchers suggested that the rice hulls contained some essential nutrient, which was ultimately found to be thiamine (vitamin B_1).

The richest food sources of thiamine are yeast and whole-grain cereals. Meat, milk, legumes, and nuts also provide good supplies of this vitamin. The minimum daily requirement varies with the body size and number of calories utilized per day; for adults the MDR is about 0.5 mg per 1000 Cal. A vitamin B_1 deficiency initially causes anorexia (loss of appetite) and indigestion, then an involvement of the nervous system, loss of motor function, and ultimately the full beriberi syndrome, including enlargement of the heart and dyspnea along with the neurological symptoms.

In the body thiamine combines with phosphate to form cocarboxylase, which plays a vital role in the oxidation of carbohydrates in reactions of cellular respiration. Since the nervous system and cardiac muscle rely almost exclusively on carbohydrate metabolism for their energy supply, they are particularly vulnerable to a thiamine deficiency.

Riboflavin (Vitamin B_2)

Bacteria inhabiting the intestines normally produce enough riboflavin to give people a head start toward filling their bodies' requirements for this vitamin, but an additional 1.5 to 2.0 mg each day should be consumed in food.

Riboflavin was originally isolated from milk; other food sources for vitamin B_2 include peanuts, meat, eggs, yeast, wheat germ, and such vegetables as broccoli and spinach.

In the body riboflavin combines with phosphate to form two enzymes, flavin mononucleotide (FMN) and flavin adenine dinucleotide (FAD), which function in the electron transport systems that are coupled with the cycles of energy metabolism. Riboflavin deficiencies in humans are usually mild and result in such symptoms as cheilosis (an inflammation and cracking in the corners of the mouth), dermatitis, glossitis (inflammation of the tongue), and keratitis of the cornea. Often riboflavin deficiency occurs together with a deficiency of other B vitamins such as thiamine or niacin; deficiency syndromes such as pellagra, beriberi, sprue, and kwashiorkor may well be due to a combined deficiency of a number of vitamins, as well as other aspects of malnutrition. Severe riboflavin deficiencies produced experimentally in animals caused impaired growth, weakness, bradycardia, and respiratory failure.

Niacin

A controversial treatment for schizophrenia involves the administration of megadoses (grams, rather than milligrams) of the B vitamin niacin. Normally an intake of about 20 mg of niacin is required daily to prevent the deficiency syndrome **pellagra.** Pellagra is sometimes called the "disease of D's," since it can result in dermatitis, dementia (due to nervous lesions with myelin degeneration), diarrhea (due to gastrointestinal lesions and fatty degenerations of the liver), and death. A deficiency of other B-complex vitamins usually contributes to the syndrome.

Niacin, also called nicotinic acid, is a constituent of two important coenzymes of cellular respiration: nicotinamide adenine dinucleotide (NAD) and nicotinamide adenine dinucleotide phosphate (NADP). Niacin can be formed in the body in limited amounts from the amino acid tryptophan. Good food sources of the vitamin are meat, chicken, fish, yeast, peanuts, wheat germ, legumes, and milk. Niacin is also synthesized by bacteria in the colon.

Pantothenic Acid

Coenzyme A plays many critical roles in the body's metabolism, participating in carbohydrate, fat, and protein metabolism and energy transfer. Pantothenic acid is a key constituent of this coenzyme.

FIGURE 28-5 These pigs were littermates. They were fed the same diet except that the pig on the left received adequate supplies of the B-vitamin nicotinic acid, and the pig on the right did not.

The amount of pantothenic acid required in the human diet has not been established, since a deficiency of this B vitamin does not normally occur in humans. But experiments have shown that some at least is essential. Volunteers on a diet that restricted the pantothenic acid intake developed alarming symptoms: personality changes, alternating periods of sleepiness and insomnia, extreme fatigue after mild exercise, staggering, and gastrointestinal symptoms. In other studies, the "burning feet syndrome" observed among prisoners of war was relieved by daily injections of calcium pantothenate.

Pantothenic acid is distributed widely in nearly all foods, especially in yeast, liver, and eggs. It is also synthesized by intestinal bacteria.

Pyridoxine (Vitamin B₆)

It is fortunate that pyridoxine deficiency is rare, since it can cause anemia, dermatitis, convulsions, and gastrointestinal disturbances.

In the cells, pyridoxine exists in the form of pyridoxal phosphate and acts as a coenzyme for a variety of chemical reactions relating to amino acid and protein metabolism. These reactions include transamination, decarboxylation (removal of a —COOH group), synthesis of tryptophan, conversion of amino acids into other substances needed by the cells, and transport of amino acids across cell membranes, as well as the desaturation of fats in the liver to form unsaturated fats.

The richest sources of pyridoxine are the same foods that provide abundant supplies of the other B-complex vitamins: yeast, wheat germ, liver, fish, milk, and eggs. Pyridoxine is also synthesized by intestinal bacteria.

Biotin

Eating raw eggs is unwise, for they contain a protein, avidin, which ties up biotin and prevents its absorption. Cooking the eggs destroys avidin.

In experiments on humans, biotin deficiency has been shown to cause a mild dermatitis, listlessness, gastrointestinal symptoms, and muscle pains and incoordination.

The precise amounts of biotin needed by the body have not been determined; they are probably in the microgram range. This B vitamin is synthesized by colon bacteria and also widely distributed in both plant and animal foods, such as liver, yeast, milk, egg yolk, vegetables, nuts, and grains.

In the body biotin serves as a prosthetic group in several different coenzymes that cause carbon dioxide to combine with organic compounds, forming such products as oxaloacetic acid, urea, purines, and fatty acids.

Folic Acid

The term *folic* literally means "leafy," and this vitamin is supplied by fresh leafy, green vegetables. It is also found in liver, beef, eggs, yeast, and cereals, and is produced in considerable amounts by intestinal bacteria.

Folic acid is involved in the chemical reactions that produce certain amino acids, purines, and thymine. It is a potent growth promoter and is also important in the maturation of red blood cells. Thus, a folic acid deficiency can produce anemia, along with diarrhea, gastrointestinal lesions, and glossitis.

Vitamin B₁₂

A total gastrectomy (removal of the stomach) will result in pernicious anemia. The cells of the stomach lining secrete an "intrinsic factor," which combines with vitamin B₁₂, protecting it from attack by the digestive enzymes and promoting its absorption in the intestines. Like folic acid, vitamin B₁₂ is necessary for the growth and maturation of red blood cells (though the two B vitamins act separately and affect different steps of the process). Vitamin B₁₂ does its work in amazingly small amounts—just micrograms each day are needed.

The usual active form of vitamin B₁₂ is **cyanocobalamin,** a metal-containing compound that has an atom of cobalt held in coordination in a manner similar to the iron in hemoglobin.

Vitamin B₁₂ is supplied by liver, meat, eggs, and milk. A deficiency of the vitamin causes macrocytic anemia and degenerative changes in the central nervous system, resulting in weakness and numbness of the limbs, and finally in a complete loss of ability to control them. Pernicious anemia may be caused either by inadequate intake of vitamin B_{12} itself or by a lack of intrinsic factor, which prevents the absorption of the vitamin. It can be successfully treated in either case by the injection of vitamin B_{12} or liver extracts containing the vitamin.

Choline and Inositol

In multiple vitamin supplements, some of the members of the B complex, such as choline and inositol, are included in a special category under a disclaimer such as "naturally occurring factors for which no special dietary values are claimed because their presence is without nutritional significance." This is not to say that choline and inositol are not significant for the body—quite the contrary! But their status as vitamins is currently in doubt.

Inositol is synthesized by the body, and a normal diet supplies about a gram of it each day (in such foods as nuts, fruits, and meats), so that inositol deficiency generally does not occur. Inositol is essential for growth and prevents the accumulation of fat and cholesterol in the liver.

Choline, unlike true vitamins, is not a constituent of enzymes. It is contained in lecithins and concerned in fat metabolism; in the form of acetylcholine it acts as a mediator of nerve impulses.

Vitamin C

Nobel Prizewinner Linus Pauling put his international reputation on the line some years ago when he proposed the use of megadoses of vitamin C as a preventative for the common cold. His proposal was greeted with near-universal derision by the scientific community; meanwhile, the general public plunged by the millions into one of the most massive uncontrolled experiments in medical history. It did seem unbelievable that the regular ingestion of gram quantities (from one to ten grams daily) of a vitamin could be physiologically harmless and could confer such benefits. Yet there was some suggestive evidence in support of Pauling's thesis. Humans are one of the few animal species that require a dietary supply of vitamin C. (Of the common laboratory animals, only the guinea pig shares our inability to synthesize this substance.) It has been found that rats and mice, for example, synthesize far larger amounts of this vitamin than would correspond to what was considered the normal human intake, and under stress they synthesize even greater amounts of vitamin C. After a time, corroboratory studies began to trickle in. According to the latest evidence, it seems that taking vitamin C in the doses suggested by Pauling does indeed reduce the average incidence of colds and lessens the severity of the symptoms of those that occur. In addition, it seems to be helpful in detoxifying carcinogenic environmental pollutants and has been found to exert a cholesterol-clearing action on atherosclerotic arteries. Some questions of possible long-term toxicity still remain to be resolved—in particular, the question recently raised of deterioration of vitamin C tablets during storage, forming potentially harmful products, and some studies indicating that megadoses of vitamin C, when taken in conjunction with the trace mineral copper, might be carcinogenic. Meanwhile, in 1976 Linus Pauling started a new vitamin C controversy by reporting the results of studies indicating an anticancer activity of the vitamin: large doses of vitamin C have significantly prolonged the lives of terminal cancer patients.

Beneficial effects of vitamin C were being utilized long before the concepts of vitamins or deficiency diseases were known. Centuries ago, many of the sailors who sailed on long voyages were stricken by a mysterious disease called **scurvy**. After the ship had been out of port for a few months, the crewmen began to suffer from bleeding gums and loosened teeth. Their bones became fragile, and the joints were swollen and painful. Many of them died. In the mid-eighteenth century, a British navy physician, James Lind, experimented on treating scurvy victims with various foods and found that fresh citrus fruit cleared up the condition. Through Lind's efforts, the practice of stocking citrus fruits or juices on sea voyages gradually spread, and in 1795 the British Navy officially adopted the practice of giving its sailors a regular ration of lime juice. (British sailors have been called "limeys" ever since.) The actual vitamin involved in preventing scurvy was isolated and studied by Albert Szent-Gyorgyi and others in the early 1930s, and was named **ascorbic acid.**

In the body, ascorbic acid undergoes reversible oxidation–reduction reactions, between ascorbic acid and dehydroascorbic acid. Its metabolic roles are not clear, but it seems to aid in the production of collagen and cartilage and contributes to the soundness of teeth and their supporting bones and gums. It is liberally present in the adrenal cortex, which suggests that it may be used in the synthesis of steroid hormones. A vitamin C deficiency interferes with the healing of wounds, promotes capillary fragility, and produces weight loss, weakness, dyspnea, numerous subcutaneous hemorrhages, and the other symptoms of scurvy mentioned.

The best sources of vitamin C are fresh fruits and vegetables, especially the citrus fruits (oranges, lemons, limes, grapefruit), tomatoes, and strawberries. Leafy green vegetables are also a good source, provided there is not too great a loss of the vitamin in cooking. (Heat, combined with exposure to light, causes a breakdown of the vitamin, and large quantities of water used in cooking may dissolve it out of foods.)

Vitamin D

Vitamin D is actually manufactured in the body. Why then does it qualify as a vitamin? The production of vitamin D in the body occurs only under special conditions: in skin exposed to sunlight. People who are outdoors a great deal and have a large portion of their skin surface exposed to sunlight produce more of the vitamin and thus need only minimal amounts in the diet. In the winter, when the sunlight is weaker and people tend to stay indoors or go out wrapped in heavy layers of clothing, a deficiency of the vitamin may develop unless the dietary supply is sufficient. (People who live in equatorial regions, who might be expected to produce extraordinary amounts of vitamin D, have another factor to contend with: although they are usually scantily clothed, they tend to be rather dark-skinned, and the deposits of melanin in their skin screen out a large fraction of the sun's rays.)

The form of vitamin D produced in irradiated animal skin is activated **7-dehydrocholesterol** and is denoted as vitamin D_3. The plant substance **ergosterol,** when irradiated, produces **calciferol** (vitamin D_2), which has a similar effect in the body and is the commercial form of vitamin D.

Vitamin D increases calcium absorption from the gastrointestinal tract and also helps to control bone formation and resorption. A deficiency of the vitamin in children causes the disorder called **rickets**—because of faulty calcium deposition, the bones are soft and fragile, and the skeleton becomes malformed. The weight of the body causes the legs to bow outward and the joints are enlarged. In adults, vitamin D deficiency leads to **osteomalacia,** characterized by a softening of the bones, various skeletal deformities, and frequent fractures. Symptoms of vitamin D deficiency may occur, even if the intake or manufacture of the vitamin is sufficient, in cases of kidney damage. The active form of the vitamin is believed to be 1,25-dihydrocholecalciferol, which is produced in the kidney from vitamin D.

As a typical fat-soluble vitamin, vitamin D is stored in the body for long periods. This property had evolutionary advantages, since stores of the vitamin built up in the sunny summer could help to tide a person over the winter. But excessive intake of the vitamin can prove toxic, producing demineralization of bone, elevation of plasma calcium, the formation of kidney stones, and deposition of calcium in soft tissues. Since vitamin D is one of the vitamins most commonly added to foods, contained in vitamin supplements, and of course contained in foods and manufactured in the body, the question of a possible overdose is of more than academic interest.

The main food sources of vitamin D are fish (especially oily fish such as salmon, sardines, and herring) and milk that has been irradiated with ultraviolet light or fortified with added vitamin D.

Vitamin E

Like vitamin C, vitamin E has been a medical cause célèbre in recent years. Does vitamin E really help to prevent heart disease? The controversy continues to rage. A recent attempt at an epidemiological study that might have resolved the question had to be abandoned when the researcher was unable to find enough elderly people who were *not* taking the vitamin to serve as a control group. Meanwhile, each month seems to bring some new and miraculous claim for the powers of vitamin E. (The claims are so improbably varied and hysterically espoused that they tend to excite skepticism and may be blinding serious researchers to the possible real benefits of the substance.)

Vitamin E is so widespread in foods that actual deficiencies of this vitamin are virtually unknown. It is believed that children with cystic fibrosis may have a vitamin E deficiency as a result of malabsorption in the intestines. Otherwise, the research on deficiency symptoms has been done mainly on animals placed on artificial vitamin E-deficient diets. In such animals, insufficient vitamin E intake has produced infertility, anemia, and muscular dystrophy, as well as defective fat absorption.

The active form of vitamin E has been identified as alpha-tocopherol. (It occurs naturally in a group of tocopherols; what value, if any, the other forms may have in the diet has not been established.) Vitamin E acts as an antioxidant, preventing the oxidation of unsaturated fats, and it provides protection against free radicals and other highly reactive chemical forms produced by the action of radiations and environmental pollutants. The vitamin has also been reported to inhibit the action of some of the prostaglandins.

The richest food source of vitamin E is wheat-germ oil. Whole wheat products, lettuce, meat, milk, and butter also provide the vitamin.

Vitamin K

Taking an antibiotic may have undesirable side effects. One of these is to kill the population of normal intestinal flora, along with the pathogens that have invaded the body. Temporarily at least, the body is without its normal supply of vitamins produced by the intestinal bacteria. A similar situation occurs in newborn infants for the first few days after birth, before the characteristic microflora have had time to be established. At such times a dietary supply of vitamin K, which is normally produced in sufficient amounts within the body, becomes important. This vitamin is present in most foods, especially spinach and other leafy vegetables and tomatoes.

Vitamin K is essential in blood clotting, functioning in the synthesis of prothrombin and in the synthesis or preservation of other factors involved in coagulation. In the presence of vitamin K deficiency (which may also be produced by liver disease, which interferes with the absorption of fats), blood clotting is slowed and hemorrhage occurs readily. Vitamin K is often given routinely before surgery and to expectant mothers before delivery to control possible hemorrhages.

A BALANCED DIET

The average person can now choose from a far greater variety of foods than ever before in our history. Supermarkets stock frozen chow mein, lasagne, blintzes, and numerous other ethnic delicacies; fresh fruits and vegetables are shipped in from all parts of the country and even from overseas; processed foods of various kinds can be stored on the pantry shelf for long periods without spoiling or losing their nutritive value. Choices grow ever more confusing. In addition, modern food processing methods have introduced new problems, since they may remove valuable nutrients from foods.

Whatever the diet, it should be designed to provide adequate calories to supply the body's energy needs (mainly in the form of carbohydrates, with some fat) and enough protein to provide for tissue repair (a minimum of 65 to 100 grams of protein daily is recommended for adults). All the necessary vitamins and minerals must be applied, and the adequate diet should also provide sufficient water and enough fiber to promote good bowel function.

Eating a variety of foods helps to ensure that all the body's dietary needs will be met. Representatives should be chosen from each of the major food groups (Figure 28-6): meat, fish, poultry, eggs, or legumes; fruits and vegetables; milk and milk products; and cereal and grain products.

BASAL METABOLIC RATE

Just lying in bed asleep requires a considerable amount of energy. Though you are not making any conscious efforts, and may not even be moving, your heart is beating, you are drawing air into and out of your lungs, automatic systems are maintaining your body temperature, and a variety of chemical reactions are going on in your cells. If you awake and begin to move around, eat and digest food, and do physical

A

B

C

D

FIGURE 28-6 The major food groups: meat, fish, poultry, eggs, and legumes (A); fruits and vegetables (B); milk and milk products (C); cereal and grain products (D).

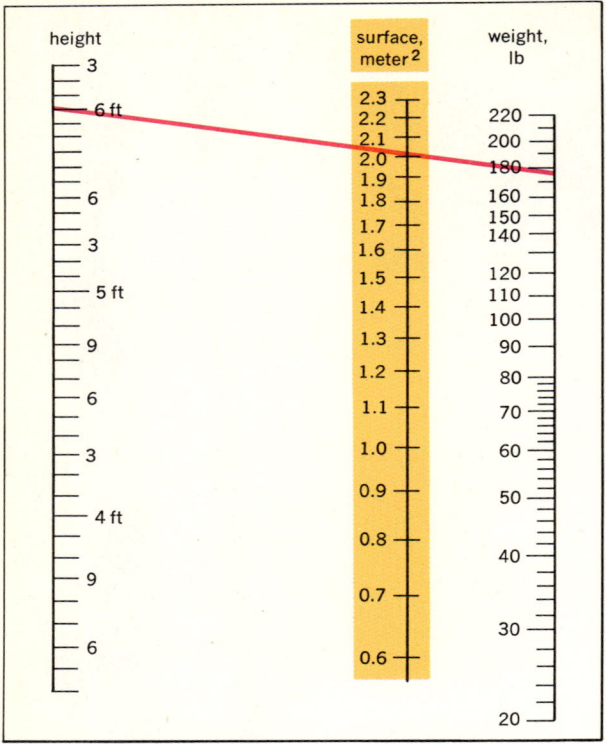

FIGURE 28-7 Nomogram from determining body surface area from height and weight.

work, obviously your energy consumption will rise sharply. But no matter how inactive you may be, your rate of energy expenditure will not fall below a certain basic value. This is the **basal metabolic rate (BMR),** the minimal level of energy expenditure required to maintain the basic cell and body functions. This quantity can be a considerable diagnostic aid in indicating the condition of various body systems, especially the function of the thyroid gland, which is a major factor in regulating the body's rate of metabolism.

The basal metabolic rate is measured clinically by an indirect method—measuring the amount of oxygen used per unit time. The value obtained is expressed in heat units and related to the total body surface (which is found from statistical charts correlating height and weight with total body surface). Of course, the true low point of metabolism, which occurs during sleep, cannot be reproduced at will in the clinical laboratory. But as close an approximation as possible is obtained by having the person eat a light meal at least 12 hours before the test, get a night's sleep of at least 8 hours, then rest for 30 minutes in a semidark room with a minimum of physical activity and psychological distractions. Only then is the BMR determined, while the subject lies still and relaxed.

The basal metabolic rate is measured as Calories per square meter of body surface area per hour (Fig-ure 28-7), but it is often expressed as a percentage of the normal value. (The norms are compiled statistically from large samples of people of each age group.) A BMR of +10 would denote a value 10 percent above the average for the person's age group; −7 would be 7 percent below the norm. Variations of up to 10 percent above or below normal are common. Thus, the normal range for men is about 36 to 44 Cal/m²/hour, and for women (who tend to be smaller and less active) about 32 to 40 Cal/m²/hour. Converted to a full day's energy expenditure, in men the BMR accounts for about 1600 to 1800 Calories, and in women 1300 to 1500 Calories.

A variety of factors can affect the basal metabolic rate. Age is one of the most significant. Rapid growth processes and high levels of physical activity during the first two years of life cause the BMR to be extremely high; it levels off rapidly during childhood and puberty and continues to decrease steadily until old age, when the atrophy of muscle tissue brings a further abrupt drop. Sex is another significant factor: women usually have a lower BMR than men. Racial variations exist, but are not very substantial. Malnutrition lowers the BMR, while fever is an indication of an extremely high BMR. Secretions of the adrenal glands, especially during stress, can temporarily elevate the BMR. Malfunction of the thyroid gland is a major determining factor of abnormal basal metabolic rates—oversecretion (hyperthyroidism) elevates the BMR, while undersecretion (hypothyroidism) produces a subnormal BMR. More direct and reliable indications of thyroid function are given by newer clinical tests, such as the determination of protein-bound iodine in blood serum and the rate of uptake of radioiodide by the thyroid gland.

CALORIC REQUIREMENT

Weight watchers find lists of calorie contents of foods helpful in keeping their energy intake and expenditure balanced. (A small sample of such calorie counts is given in Table 28-3.) The idea of counting calories to determine one's appropriate food intake is based on the premise that each person has a caloric requirement that remains relatively constant from day to day. If the food intake does not meet this requirement, weight will be lost as the body's reserves are mobilized; if more calories are taken in than are used, the residue will be stored as fat and weight will be gained.

We have seen that just existing at a minimal level uses up a certain basal number of calories—about 1600 to 1800 a day for a man on the average, and 1300 to 1500 for a woman. The slightest exertion above this minimal level—sitting up, standing, walking, exercising—uses up additional calories (Figure

TABLE 28-3 Calorie Contents of Some Foods and Beverages

FOOD OR BEVERAGE	SIZE OF PORTION	CALORIES
Apple	1 medium	80
Banana	1 medium	100
Beans, green	1 cup	125
Beer	8 oz	114
Bread, white	1 slice	65
Butter	1 thin pat	50
Cheese, cheddar	1 ounce	115
Chicken, broiled	½ breast	106
Coffee or tea, no sugar or cream	1 cup	0
Coffee or tea, sugar and cream	1 cup	100
Egg, boiled	1 medium	78
Frankfurter	1 (⅛ pound)	170
Hamburger	1 (3 oz)	185
Lamb chop	5 oz	400
Lettuce	2 large leaves	5
Martini	1 average	150
Milk, whole	8 oz	160
Milk, nonfat (skim)	8 oz	90
Orange	1 medium	70
Orange juice	4 oz	50
Peanut butter	1 tablespoon	95
Peas	1 cup	115
Pizza	⅛ of 14" pie	185
Potato, baked	1 medium	90
Shrimp	6 medium	90
Spaghetti in tomato sauce with cheese	1 cup	190
Steak, sirloin	6 oz	660
Tomato	1 medium	25
Tomato juice	4 oz	30
Tuna, canned in oil	3 oz	170
Watermelon	1 wedge, 4 × 8"	115

sleeping		60 cal/hr
basal		70 cal/hr
standing		100 cal/hr
walking		200 cal/hr
swimming		500 cal/hr
running		600 cal/hr

FIGURE 28-8 Effects of activity on metabolic rate.

tributed to their increased muscle activity as they wrote on their papers. (When mental activity is performed under conditions of emotional stress, such as a final examination or a tense chess match, stimulation of the sympathetic nervous system does cause some increase in Calorie expenditure through a speeded-up heart rate, increased breathing rate, etc.)

Physical activity is a primary factor, but not the only one determining caloric requirements. Body size is an important factor. Age is another; growing children need far more calories in proportion to their size than adults, and the caloric requirement gradually decreases throughout adulthood. Thus, if a person continues to eat the same diet throughout his life, in middle age he will find himself gradually putting on weight. The very process of digesting food uses up a certain amount of energy and thus contributes to the caloric requirement. This energy expenditure is called the **specific dynamic action** (S.D.A.) of food and accounts for about 6 to 10 percent of the total. The S.D.A. of protein is higher than that for fat or carbohydrate, which is one reason why reducing diets are often high in protein. The environmental temperature also plays a role in determining caloric requirements, since part of the energy is expended for maintaining a constant body temperature. The lumberjack's caloric requirement is so high not only because of the heavy physical labor the job involves, but also because the body constantly loses heat in the frosty weather, and more heat must be generated by the oxidation of food materials in the tissues.

OBESITY

Young mothers often tend to worry about whether their babies' weight gain is rapid enough, and plumpness in the baby is commonly considered a sign of glowing health. But it is now believed by medical researchers that children who are overfed as youngsters develop more fat cells and are doomed to have weight problems when they are adults.

28-8). Thus, the amount of physical exercise a person normally engages in is an important determinant of his or her caloric requirement. For example, a person weighing about 150 pounds would require only about 2000 Calories a day if confined to bed. A sedentary worker (e.g., a student, office clerk, or typist) would need from 2200 to 2500 Calories a day. A person engaged in more strenuous activity (e.g., a metalworker or furniture painter) has a daily energy expenditure of between 2800 and 3200 Calories. Lumberjacks working in cold weather may use as many as 8000 Calories in a day.

Mental exertion, no matter how intense and tiring, does not use up very many Calories. In one experiment, students were given very difficult mathematical problems to work out while their metabolic rate was measured. During the test, their metabolic rate rose only a few percent, and most of the increase was at-

FIGURE 28-9 Obesity is a major health problem in the affluent nations today. Fortunately, few cases are as extreme as this (the twins weighed more than 700 pounds each).

Obesity or overweight (Figure 28-9) is a major health problem in the affluent nations today. It is a chronic problem, caused by consistently taking in more calories than one uses. The excess is converted to fat in the body and stored in the characteristic fat depots. One tends to think of a grossly fat person as gluttonously self-indulgent and lacking in will-power; yet overweight can develop gradually and insidiously. As small an "overindulgence" as one extra pat of butter or slice of bread a day can add up to a weight gain of nearly a pound a month.

Many factors have contributed to our "national disease" of obesity. An increasingly sedentary way of life has been combined with an unprecedented abundance of food. "Snack foods" and "treats" typically are heavy in fats and carbohydrates, and are often consumed in large quantities in a rather absent-minded way, as an accompaniment to other activities.

In a minority of cases, obesity may have a specific organic cause—usually a glandular disorder involving the thyroid, pituitary, adrenals, or gonads. Obesity tends to run in families, which suggests that a hereditary factor may be involved. (Of course, the familial tendency may simply be due to the learning of faulty eating habits by example.) It has been suggested that an as yet undetermined abnormality of the hypothalamus may be involved in many cases of obesity, since food intake is regulated to a large extent by the hunger and satiety centers in the hypothalamus. Perhaps fat people's "appestat" is set too high, causing them to take in more food than they need.

For many obese people, the strongest motivation to lose weight is provided by the desire to be more physically attractive. But there is a far more compelling reason to avoid overweight: obesity greatly increases the probability of dying at an early age. Excess body weight puts a strain on the heart in several ways. The heart must pump harder to supply enough blood to the muscles, which must work harder to move the extra weight. The adipose deposits require a copious blood supply; for each extra pound of fat, millions of extra capillaries are formed and add to the peripheral resistance, raising the blood pressure. Obese persons are also more prone to atherosclerosis, as well as to gallstone formation and infectious diseases such as nephritis (kidney inflammation) and pneumonia.

A bizarre form of obesity that has recently been recognized is the **Prader–Willi syndrome,** which affects young children, usually between two and five years of age. Prader–Willi children have an insatiable desire for food and will indiscriminately eat anything that is available—frozen or rotten food, raw meat, sticks of butter, jars of vitamin pills, pet food, as well as gluttonous portions of more normal fare. Ironically, the caloric requirement of such children is usually lower than normal, so that they become extremely obese. The syndrome is usually linked with a mild mental retardation. It is not hereditary or caused by emotional problems; the current view is that it may be due to a neurological disturbance involving the hypothalamus.

DIETING

A pound of body fat contains about 3500 Calories. To lose a pound of weight (a permanent loss of body mass, not a transitory loss of water), a person must use up 3500 more Calories than he or she takes in. Some thought about caloric requirements and calorie contents of foods should convince you that unless the person is a lumberjack, such a weight loss cannot be accomplished in a day or two, and it will require a substantial reduction of food intake, plenty of hard work, or a combination of the two. But most people do not like hard work, and those who have allowed themselves to become obese are often rather short on will-power—hence the continuing popularity of fad diets, which promise a quick weight loss with minimum effort.

Such fad diets, which may involve a severe cutback of total calories or a restriction of food intake to just one or a few specific foods, seem to show results at first, as the dieter's weight plummets encouragingly. But this initial weight loss is mainly a loss of water, and soon the dieter reaches a plateau. By this time, the dieter is chronically hungry, out of sorts, and will probably become so discouraged that he or she goes off the diet, quickly regains the weight that was lost so laboriously, and soon plunges enthusiastically into a new "crash" diet.

The most reliable way to lose weight and to keep it off is to make a permanent change in eating habits, incorporating a small reduction in total caloric intake—enough to produce a small but steady weight loss (perhaps a pound or two a week) and stabilize the body weight at the desired level. An increase in physical activity (again as a permanent change in habits, rather than a sudden "crash" program of strenuous exercises that may put too great a strain on an unconditioned heart) can also contribute to the weight loss program by increasing the energy expenditure. (Exercise has also been found to lower low-density lipoproteins and increase HDL, thus lowering the heart-attack risk.) But it usually is not practical to achieve any significant weight loss by exercise alone, as seen from Table 28-4, which lists the amounts of various kinds of exercise and portions of foods equivalent to 100 Calories. (Indeed, strenuous exercise may make the dieter so hungry that he or she eats extra food and more than makes up the calories lost.)

One important factor to be considered in any reducing diet is that a reduction of the total food intake reduces not only the total number of calories but also the intake of vitamins, minerals, and water. The dieter may need to drink more water than usual and take a vitamin and mineral supplement. The diet should be balanced in the basic nutrients and should supply sufficient protein (at least 65 to 100 grams daily). Leafy vegetables are a special help to the dieter, since they are usually relatively low in calories, high in vitamins and minerals, and supply roughage that helps to satisfy hunger and promote good bowel function.

Appetite depressants and metabolic stimulators are sometimes prescribed to aid the dieter.* Such drugs can have potent side effects, and should be taken only under strict medical supervision. Some people are "compulsive eaters" and use food as a solace and escape from emotional problems. Such individuals may need psychological counseling to aid them in overcoming their overeating.

A different eating problem is **anorexia nervosa,** a condition in which the person refuses food or eats such minimal amounts that, if untreated, she literally starves herself to death. Anorexia nervosa occurs most often in adolescent girls and is believed often to be psychological in origin.

MALNUTRITION

While inhabitants of the affluent nations seek "no-calorie" foods and beverages to curb their growing

TABLE 28-4 Energy Equivalents of Food and Exercise

100-CALORIE FOOD PORTIONS	MINUTES OF ACTIVITIES NEEDED TO CONSUME 100 CALORIES
1 cup coffee with cream	
and sugar	7 running
1 pancake	9 bicycling
1 fried egg	14 tennis
5 ounces milk	20 golf
1 ounce cheese	20 gardening
8 ounces cola drink	20 walking
1 ounce Scotch	22 bowling
6 potato chips	
1 ¼ apples	
2 ounces ground beef	

obesity, in many parts of the world people are not getting enough to eat. Malnutrition is believed to affect as many as 1.5 *billion* people today. It may be caused by a lack of essential nutrients or an inability of the body to utilize nutrients when they are supplied by the diet (due to malabsorption or metabolic disorders).

Droughts, floods, and disasters created by humans such as wars bring famine. People of the affected regions are unable to obtain enough food, and the lack of sufficient calories and protein leads to a condition called **marasmus,** taken from a Greek word meaning "to waste away." The starving person's limbs are shriveled sticks, the belly bloated, the skin hanging in wrinkles and drawn tight over bones. Anemia, diarrhea, and dehydration result, along with a generally debilitated condition that leaves the victim easy prey to infectious diseases. Children, whose growing bodies have increased protein requirements, are most severely affected (Figure 28-10).

In many regions people subsist on a diet high in carbohydrates, which supplies enough total calories but not enough protein for growth. In areas where corn is the major item of the diet, a lack of the essential amino acid lysine makes whatever protein is supplied inadequate.* The condition that results from a protein deficiency is called **kwashiorkor,** from African words meaning "first-second." (It is the disease the firstborn child gets when a second child is born, and the first child can no longer drink mother's milk.) The child suffering from kwashiorkor seems incongruously plump, but the deceptive plumpness is actually bloating caused by accumulated fluids pushing against wasted muscles. Kwashiorkor can lead to mental retardation, irritability, and apathy, along with anemia, diarrhea, and a loss of appetite.

---

* The use of amphetamines as an aid to weight reduction is now restricted because of the dangers of habituation and abuse.

* A hybrid corn with adequate amounts of lysine has been developed, but it is sometimes difficult to get people to make even slight changes in dietary habits and farming practices.

FIGURE 28-10 These Nigerian children were suffering from extreme malnutrition in the aftermath of war.

SUMMARY

Humans are omnivores, eating both plant and animal foods.

An adequate diet must contain proteins, carbohydrates, and fats in balanced amounts, together with vitamins, minerals, water, and indigestible fiber.

Minerals needed in human nutrition include:
- Calcium
- Phosphorus
- Potassium
- Sodium
- Chlorine
- Iodine
- Iron
- Magnesium
- Copper
- Manganese
- Zinc
- Cobalt
- Sulfur
- Molybdenum
- Vanadium

Some trace minerals in the diet are harmful: for example, mercury and cadmium.

Carbohydrates include:
- Monosaccharides (simple sugars)
- Disaccharides (two monosaccharide residues)
- Polysaccharides
  - Starch
  - Glycogen
  - Cellulose

Lipids include:
- Neutral fats (glycerol + fatty acids)
- Phospholipids
- Glycolipids
- Sterols

Proteins in the diet are composed of about 23 amino acids, 8 of which cannot be synthesized in the human body (essential amino acids).

Adequate proteins supply all the amino acids needed for growth and maintenance of the body.

Proteins can be classified as:
- Simple proteins
- Conjugated proteins

Vitamins are organic substances that are needed in very small amounts for normal metabolic processes and cannot be manufactured by the body.

Most vitamins act as cofactors or prosthetic groups for enzymes.

Deficiency diseases result from the lack of vitamins.

Fat-soluble vitamins are A, D, E, and K.

Water-soluble vitamins include the B-complex and C.

Vitamin A (retinol) plays a role in the chemistry of vision; a deficiency produces night blindness and skin disorders.

Vitamin B_1 (thiamine) participates in cell respiration; a deficiency produces beriberi.

Vitamin B_2 (riboflavin) functions in energy metabolism; a deficiency causes cheilosis, dermatitis, glossitis, and keratitis of the cornea.

Niacin is a constituent of NAD and NADP, coenzymes of cellular respiration; a deficiency results in pellagra.

Pantothenic acid is a constituent of coenzyme A.

Vitamin B_6 (pyridoxine) participates in amino acid and protein metabolism.

Biotin functions in coenzymes involved in the combination of carbon dioxide with organic compounds.

Folic acid is involved in the production of amino acids, purines, and thymine; a deficiency can cause anemia.

Vitamin B_{12} (cyanocobalamin) is necessary for maturation of red blood cells; a deficiency results in pernicious anemia; intrinsic factor produced by the stomach is necessary for its absorption.

Vitamin C (ascorbic acid) participates in oxidation-reduction reactions; a deficiency can cause scurvy; large doses may help to prevent the common cold.

Vitamin D is produced in irradiated skin (7-dehydrocholesterol, D_3) or by irradiation of plant ergosterol (calciferol, D_2); a deficiency results in rickets.

Vitamin E (tocopherol) acts as an antioxidant; various effects have been claimed, but actual deficiencies in humans are rare.

Vitamin K is essential in blood clotting.

A balanced diet should include representatives of the food groups: meat, fish, poultry, eggs, or legumes; fruits and vegetables; milk and milk products; cereal and grain products.

The basal metabolic rate (BMR) is the minimal level of energy expenditure required to maintain the basic cell and body functions.

The BMR depends on body size (surface area), age, sex, and glandular secretions.

For men the BMR is about 1600 to 1800 Cal/day, for women 1300 to 1500 Cal/day.

The daily caloric requirement is made up of the basal metabolism plus energy expenditure for physical activity, digestion of food, and maintenance of body temperature.

Obesity or overweight results from an intake of food exceeding the energy expenditure.

Endocrine disorders and psychological problems may contribute to obesity.

A malfunction of the hypothalamus may be involved, especially in the Prader-Willi syndrome.

Effective dieting should produce a gradual weight loss by a combination of reduced food intake and increased physical activity.

Anorexia nervosa is a pathological condition of self-starvation believed to have emotional causes.

Malnutrition may be caused by a lack of essential nutrients or inability of the body to utilize nutrients supplied by the diet. Forms include:

Marasmus: due to a lack of calories and protein.

Kwashiorkor: due to a lack of protein (or of adequate protein).

QUESTIONS FOR REVIEW AND THOUGHT

1 Why is a knowledge of nutrition important for physicians and allied health personnel? Discuss.

2 Discuss the roles of five minerals in the body. Is it advisable, nutritionally, to take massive supplements of minerals?

3 True or false: carbohydrates are unnecessary and fattening. Discuss.

4 Discuss the roles of dietary fiber.

5 A pat of butter may have as many Calories as the baked potato on which it is placed. Why?

6 Would the substitution of a hydrogenated margarine for butter in the diet help in reducing heart attack risk? What about a completely cholesterol-free diet? Discuss.

7 What are the essential amino acids? Are they adequately supplied by a vegetarian diet? Discuss.

8 Deficiencies of what vitamins cause the following conditions: (a) beriberi; (b) pellagra; (c) xerophthalmia; (d) scurvy; (e) pernicious anemia; (f) rickets?

9 Does eating a variety of foods automatically ensure that nutritional needs will be met?

10 What factors affect the basal metabolic rate?

11 What is the best way to lose excess weight?

12 Distinguish between marasmus and kwashiorkor. Why are children most severely affected?

ANATOMY OF THE URINARY SYSTEM

29

Like the macro-world in which we live, the micro-cosm of the human body has its pollution problems. Nutrients taken in through the digestive system and oxygen supplied by the inhaled air are utilized to synthesize a variety of enzymes, hormones, building materials and other substances and are metabolized to provide the energy needed to power the body's activities. But these metabolic processes, like the processes in huge factory-complexes, generate byproducts and wastes. Carbon dioxide and water, ammonia and various other nitrogenous products, and inorganic salts are continuously produced in the cells, pass into the tissue fluid, and then enter the bloodstream. If allowed to build up in the body, they would disturb the delicate balance of the interrelated chemical reactions of the body. To maintain homeostasis and prevent the body from polluting itself with its own waste products, these wastes must be eliminated continuously, as they are produced.

EXCRETORY ORGANS

The development of reasonably reliable birth control pills and intrauterine contraceptive devices has brought a revolution of attitudes, not only toward sexual practices, but also toward frankness of speaking about sexual matters. But other taboos remain in force—those relating to the organs and functions of excretion. Significantly, some of the "four-letter words" not used in polite company pertain to this area of human experience, and explicit descriptions of excretory functions generally arouse feelings of disgust. Yet the functions of the excretory organs are just as essential to the well-being of the body as those of the other body systems. Indeed, the human body has more avenues of excretion than the average person is aware of.

Gaseous substances, such as carbon dioxide and water vapor, pass out of the body mainly through the lungs, via the exhaled air. The lungs can to some degree serve as excretory organs for other wastes and poisons as well, as can be attested by anyone who has ever smelled the alcohol-laced breath of a drinker or the "acetone" breath of a diabetic.

The sweat glands of the skin help to eliminate excess water, salts, and urea, and also play a major role in ridding the body of excess heat, another by-product of metabolism. Even the mammary glands can perform some minor excretory functions, passing on to the hapless infant a share of any drugs or pollutants its mother has taken in.

Undigested food materials, secretions, and a variety of other solid wastes are eliminated through the alimentary canal, in the feces. But the major excretory organs, especially for the elimination of nitrogenous wastes, are the kidneys, which produce urine.

TABLE 29-1   Organs of Excretion

EXCRETORY ORGAN	SUBSTANCES EXCRETED
Lungs	Gaseous wastes: carbon dioxide, water vapor
Skin (sweat glands)	Water, carbon dioxide, salts, nitrogenous wastes
Alimentary canal (large intestine)	Solid wastes of digestion; secretions water, carbon dioxide, salts
Kidneys	Water, nitrogenous wastes, soluble salts, bacterial toxins, ingested drugs and poisons, etc.

The basic excretory organs and the major substances that they eliminate are summarized in Table 29-1. Since the excretory functions of the lungs, skin, and large intestine have already been discussed in other chapters, we will focus here on the kidneys and the other organs of the urinary system. Their structure is described in this chapter; in the following chapter the functions of the urinary system and some potential disorders of the urinary organs are explored; Chapter 31 treats the key role of the kidneys in regulating the fluid, electrolyte, and acid–base balances of the body.

THE URINARY SYSTEM

One of the popular reducing diets requires that the dieter drink ten or more glasses of water a day. Dedicated dieters who try this regimen find themselves spending an inordinate amount of time in the bathroom. The organs of the urinary system, depicted in Figure 29-1, are linked into an effective feedback system with the hypothalamus and pituitary gland and maintain a precise balance of the tissue fluids. If excess fluid is taken into the body, it will be eliminated in fairly short order, mainly in the form of urine.

Urine is produced in a pair of bean-shaped organs, the **kidneys.** A pair of narrow tubes, the **ureters,** carry the urine from the kidneys to the expandable baglike **urinary bladder,** in which the urine is stored temporarily. At convenient intervals, the urine is voided through a single muscular tube, the **urethra,** which leads to the exterior.

THE KIDNEYS

The kidneys are among the hardest working organs in the body. They filter about 180 quarts of fluid each day, though they excrete a net of only a quart or two of urine a day. Water, electrolytes, and other substances are selectively reabsorbed and thus reclaimed for the body's use.

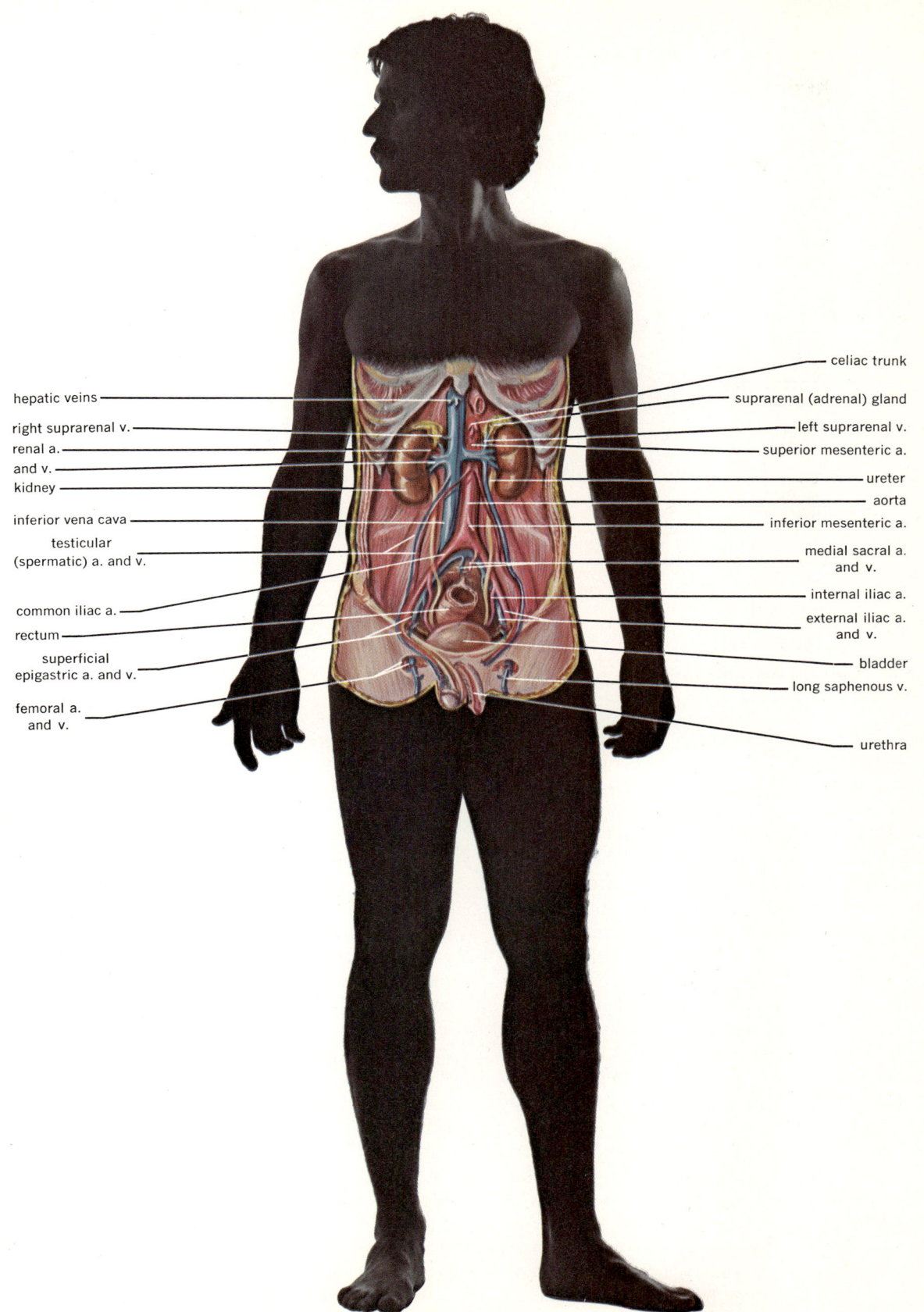

hepatic veins

right suprarenal v.

renal a.

and v.

kidney

inferior vena cava

testicular
(spermatic) a. and v.

common iliac a.

rectum

superficial
epigastric a. and v.

femoral a.
and v.

celiac trunk

suprarenal (adrenal) gland

left suprarenal v.

superior mesenteric a.

ureter

aorta

inferior mesenteric a.

medial sacral a.
and v.

internal iliac a.

external iliac a.
and v.

bladder

long saphenous v.

urethra

FIGURE 29-1   Organs of the urinary system, shown in relation to the genital system and major vessels.

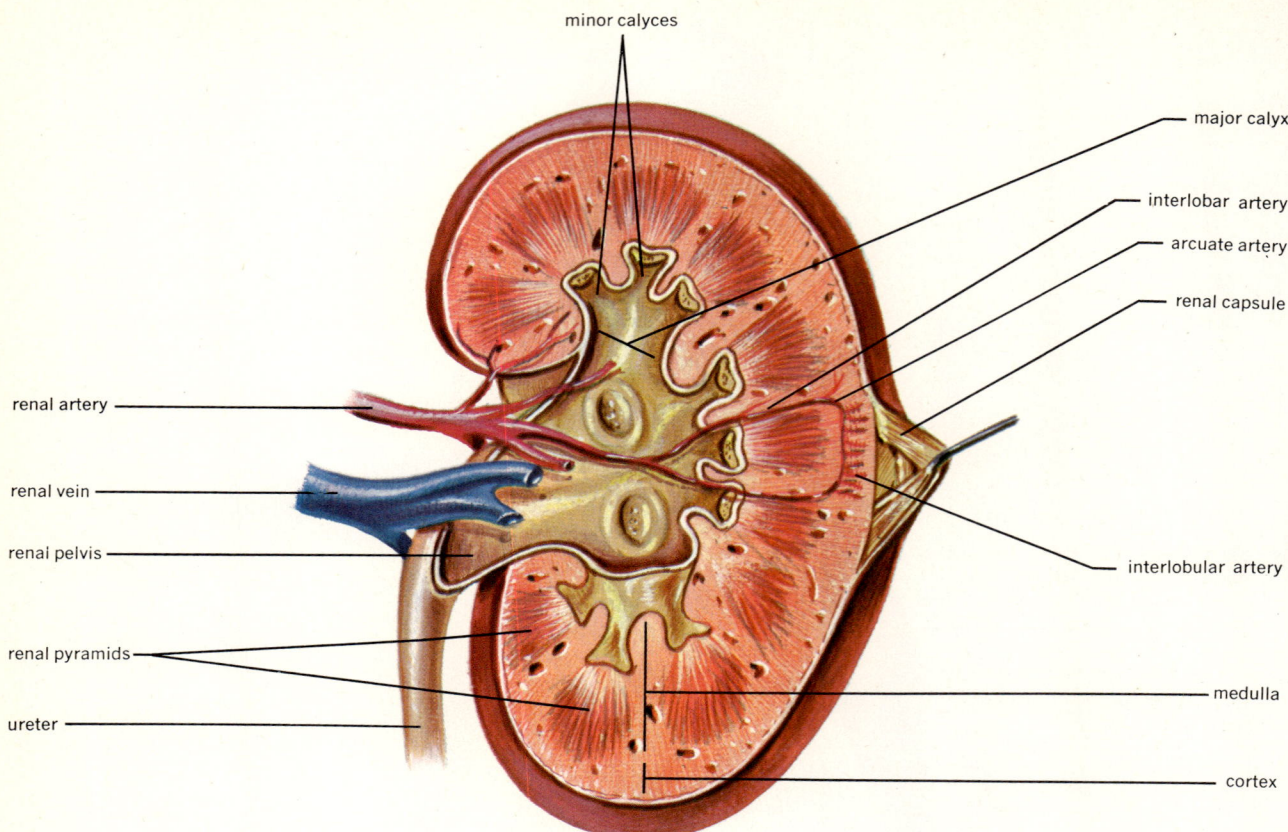

minor calyces

major calyx

interlobar artery

arcuate artery

renal capsule

renal artery

renal vein

renal pelvis

interlobular artery

renal pyramids

medulla

ureter

cortex

FIGURE 29-2 The kidney in longitudinal section.

Location and Structure

One of the early things a boxer learns is the location of the kidneys, for a kidney punch is potentially so dangerous that the rules of the ring do not permit it.

The kidneys are a pair of reddish structures, with a distinctly beanlike shape. (Kidney beans were named for their resemblance to kidneys.) The normal adult kidney is about 10 to 12 cm long, 5 to 6 cm wide, and about 3 to 4 cm thick. Like other paired organs, the kidneys are arranged one on each side of the midline of the body against the posterior body wall. As Figure 29-1 shows, they are located under the diaphragm, at the level of the last thoracic and first three lumbar vertebrae—just above the waistline. The kidneys are actually outside the peritoneal cavity, fitting snugly between the parietal peritoneum and the posterior abdominal wall. Unlike most of the other abdominal organs, the kidneys are not held in place by mesenteries. They are embedded in a heavy cushion of fat, which both protects and supports them, and each kidney is anchored to surrounding structures by a layer of fibrous connective tissues called the **renal fascia.**

Pressures of adjacent organs in the abdominal cavity do not permit a perfect symmetry of the paired kidneys. The left kidney is usually slightly larger than the right; moreover, the right kidney is displaced somewhat downward by the liver. (The bulk of the spleen lies above the left kidney.) Each kidney is capped by a mass of glandular tissue, the adrenal glands, which play a key role in the endocrine system.

Like the bean that is named for it, each kidney has a concave indentation on its medial surface, called the **hilus.** All the structures that enter or leave the kidney pass through the hilus: a renal artery, the renal vein, and the renal pelvis, which is actually the enlarged proximal portion of the ureter. The kidney is covered with a thin but tough, transparent fibrous membrane called the **renal capsule,** which normally can be easily stripped off in dissection. (If the kidney becomes inflamed, the renal tissue adheres to the capsule, and it cannot be removed without tearing the kidney.)

Figure 29-2 shows a kidney sliced open longitudinally. Within the renal capsule, the body of the kidney can be seen to be composed of two distinct regions. The outer region, the **cortex,** presents a granular appearance on the cut surface. Extensions of the cortex, the **renal columns,** project inward, alternating with a dozen or so pyramid-shaped wedges with a streaked appearance. These are the **renal pyr-**

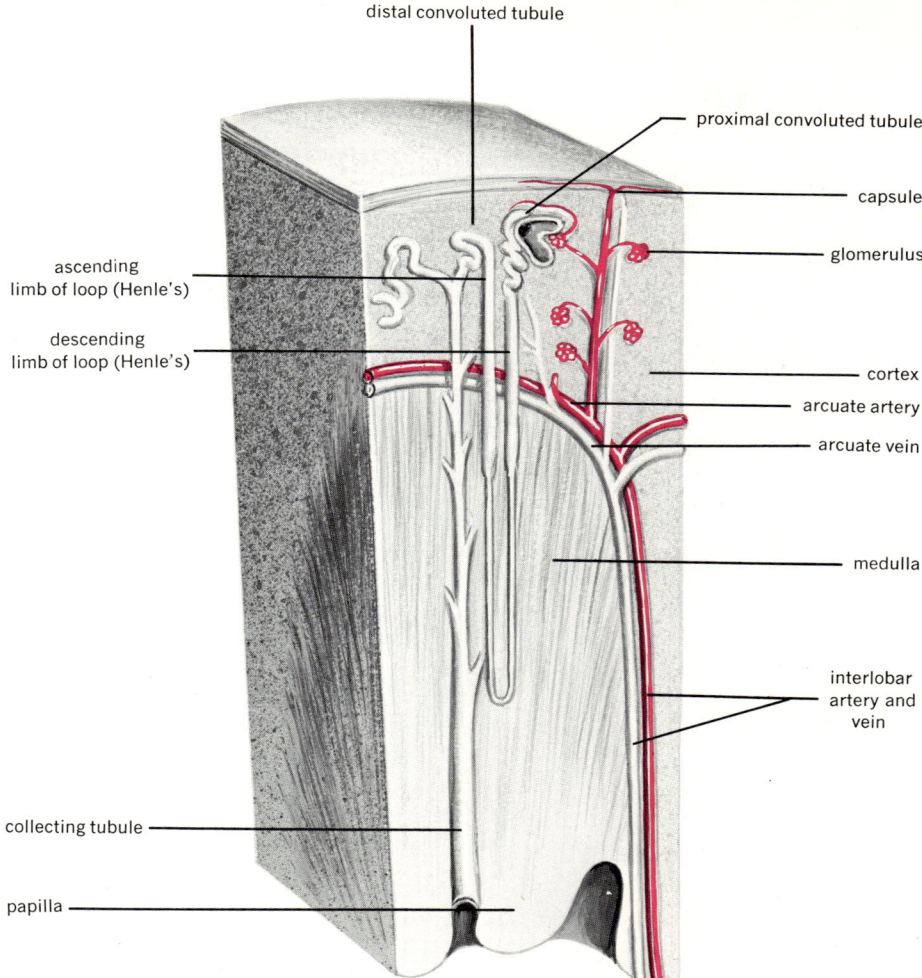

distal convoluted tubule

proximal convoluted tubule

capsule

glomerulus

ascending
limb of loop (Henle's)

descending
limb of loop (Henle's)

cortex

arcuate artery

arcuate vein

medulla

interlobar
artery and
vein

collecting tubule

papilla

FIGURE 29-3 Schematic depiction of
the structural components of the nephron.

amids, which comprise the inner layer of the kidney, the medulla. The bases of the pyramids are turned toward the exterior of the kidney, while their apices (the **renal papillae**) are pointed in toward the center of the kidney. There are a dozen or more renal pyramids in each kidney, each of which empties urine into a cup-shaped tube called a **minor calyx** through minute openings in the top of the papilla. The minor calyces are branches of about three larger tubes, the **major calyces.** The major calyces, together with a funnel-shaped sac, the **renal pelvis,** lie in a central cavity of the kidney, the **renal sinus.** At the hilus, the major calyces and renal pelvis unite with the upper end of the ureter.

Microscopic Anatomy: the Nephron

The structural and functional unit of the kidney—the nephron—is too small to be seen with the naked eye. In fact, each kidney contains at least a million nephrons. Not all of them function at once, so there is considerable reserve capacity. The nephrons are also

capable of enlarging to increase their capacity. Thus, if one kidney is removed, it is found that the remaining kidney shows a 50 percent increase in mass within two months.

Under a microscope, each nephron is found to consist of two main parts (Figure 29-3): a renal corpuscle and renal tubules. The **renal corpuscle,** located in the granular area (cortex), is formed by a twisted knot of capillaries, the **glomerules,** enclosed in a double-walled cup, the **Bowman's capsule.** Extending from the Bowman's capsule is a **renal tubule,** consisting of several sections. First comes a coiled and twisting portion, called the **proximal convoluted tubule** ("proximal" because it is nearest to the Bowman's capsule and "convoluted" because of its tortuous path). The tubule then straightens out and dips down into the medulla. This portion is referred to as the **descending limb of the loop of Henle.** The tubule makes a hairpin turn and returns toward the glomerulus as the **ascending limb of the loop of Henle,** then soon begins to twist and turn. (This twisting region

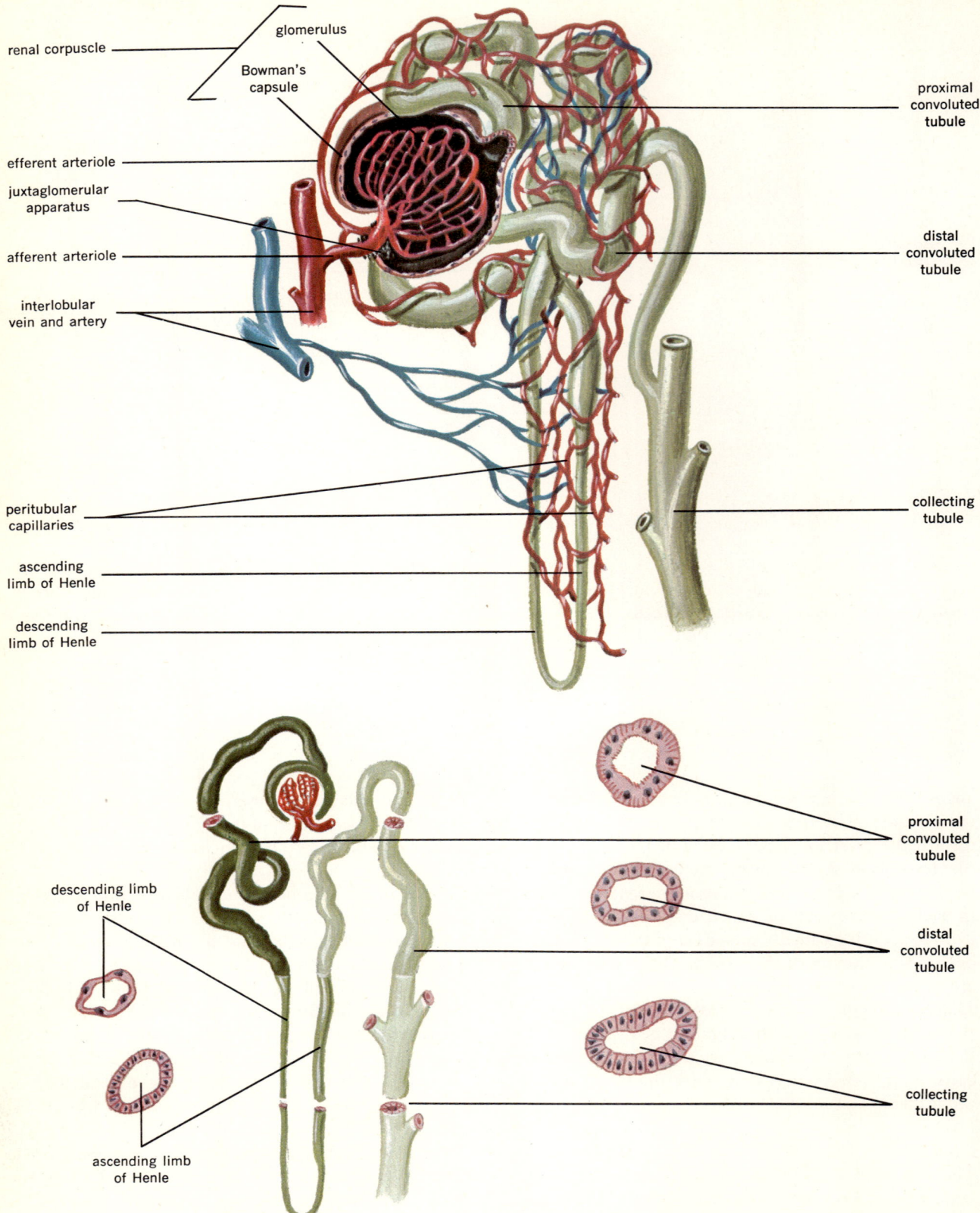

renal corpuscle

glomerulus

Bowman's capsule

efferent arteriole

juxtaglomerular apparatus

afferent arteriole

interlobular vein and artery

peritubular capillaries

ascending limb of Henle

descending limb of Henle

proximal convoluted tubule

distal convoluted tubule

collecting tubule

descending limb of Henle

ascending limb of Henle

proximal convoluted tubule

distal convoluted tubule

collecting tubule

FIGURE 29-4 **The nephron. Major cell types of different parts of the tubules are shown below.**

forms the **distal convoluted tubule.**) The renal tubule finally ends in a **collecting tubule,** which empties by way of **papillary ducts** into one of the minor calyces of the pelvis. The loops of Henle and collecting tubules, extending down into the medulla, give the medullary pyramids their striated appearance.

The "typical" nephron described here is a **juxta-medullary nephron,** whose glomerulus lies close to the medulla. **Cortical nephrons,** whose glomeruli lie close to the surface of the kidney, generally lack the thin portions of the loop of Henle, and the loop does not penetrate all the way into the medulla.

The microscopic structure of the nephron is highly specialized for its functions in urine formation (Figure 29-4). A major operation of filtration occurs in the renal corpuscle, as fluid from the capillary tufts of the glomerulus passes into the system of renal tubules. The **filtering membrane** consists of three main parts. First the fluid must pass through the **endothelium of the glomeruli,** which is thin and sievelike, perforated by "windows" about 750 Å in diameter. Then comes a **basement membrane** of connective tissue, which is continually renewed. The final barrier that the initial filtrate from the blood must pass is the **visceral layer of the Bowman's capsule,** which is formed by specialized cells called **podocytes.** These cells have a highly branched cytoplasm, with extensions of many different shapes and sizes. The cytoplasmic processes interdigitate, leaving narrow gaps called slit pores. The three parts of the glomerular filtration membrane together provide for selective permeability, holding back formed elements of the blood and proteins larger than a molecular weight of 70,000. The epithelial cells of the proximal convoluted tubules are equipped with a **brush border** of microvilli, which provide a greatly enhanced surface for absorption. (The total surface area of the proximal convoluted tubules is estimated at more than 50 square meters.)

Blood Supply

Since a major function of the kidneys is to remove metabolic wastes from the blood, it is not surprising that these organs have a particularly rich blood supply, with blood vessels in intimate association with the kidney structures. (Indeed, the glomerulus, which is a key part of the nephron, the functioning unit of the kidneys, is actually part of the blood vessel system.)

Blood is supplied to the kidneys via the **renal arteries,** which are branches of the abdominal aorta (Figure 29-5). Usually one renal artery supplies each kidney, subdividing at the hilus into dorsal and ventral branches, which separately enter different areas of the kidney tissue. These branches give rise to the **interlo-**

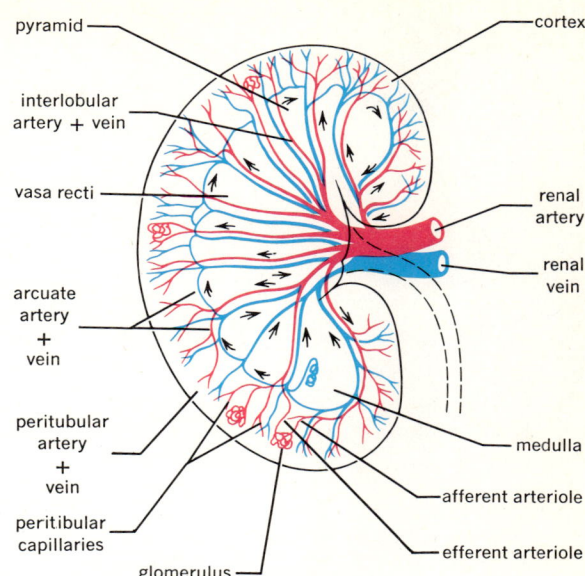

FIGURE 29-5 Blood vessels of the kidney.

bar arteries, which travel up the renal columns. At the boundary zone between the cortex and medulla, the interlobar arteries branch laterally to form the **arcuate arteries,** then enter the cortex as **interlobular arteries,** dividing at intervals to form **afferent arterioles,** each of which supplies a glomerulus.

As might be expected from the special status of the glomerulus as part of the functioning unit of the kidney, the blood-vessel connections of this twisted knot of capillaries are somewhat out of the ordinary. Instead of the usual arteriole-capillary-venule sequence, blood is carried out of the glomerulus in another arteriole, the **efferent arteriole,** which is much smaller than the afferent arteriole. This size differential results mainly because there is about a 20 percent reduction of fluid volume of the blood flowing out of the glomerulus, because of the fluid filtered into the renal tubule.

The efferent arterioles from juxtamedullary nephrons become **arterial vasa recta,** which pass to varying levels of the medulla, then turn back as **venous vasa recta** and drain into the **arcuate veins** at the junction of the cortex and medulla. The blood vessels of the cortical nephrons have a different structure: the efferent arterioles break up into a fine mesh of capillaries, closely associated with the convoluted tubules and the loop of Henle. These capillaries unite to form **interlobular veins,** which empty into the arcuate veins. The arcuate veins in turn merge into **interlobar veins,** which join to form the **renal vein,** which emerges at the hilus and parallels the path of the renal artery. Blood from the two renal veins is ultimately returned to the heart via the inferior vena cava.

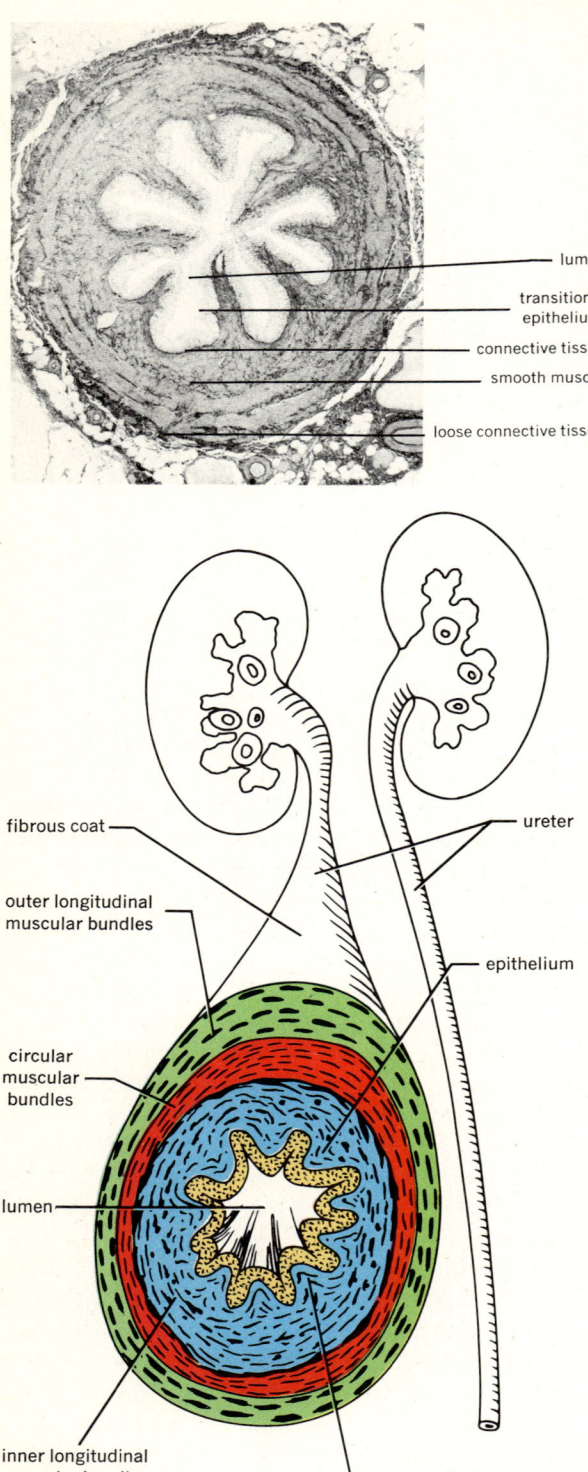

lumen

transitional epithelium

connective tissue

smooth muscle

loose connective tissue

fibrous coat

outer longitudinal muscular bundles

circular muscular bundles

lumen

inner longitudinal muscular bundles

ureter

epithelium

mucosa in longitudinal folds

FIGURE 29-6 **The ureter in cross section, showing the typical three muscular layers.**

A special modification of the nephron's blood-vessel system occurs at the point where a portion of the distal convoluted tubule comes in contact with the afferent arteriole. This is the **juxtaglomerular complex,** in which specially modified juxtaglomerular cells containing prominent granules are found among the smooth muscle cells of the afferent arteriole. The juxtaglomerular cells secrete **renin,** a substance that acts on other blood-borne agents to produce angiotensin II, a hormone that helps to regulate blood pressure.

In addition to its blood vessels, the kidney is also supplied with lymphatic vessels, which form networks around the tubules. Like the blood vessels, the larger lymphatic vessels exit at the hilus and ultimately drain into the thoracic duct.

The blood vessels of the kidneys are accompanied by a network of autonomic nerves, which help to control the circulation of blood in the kidneys by regulating the diameters of the small blood vessels.

THE URETERS

Considering the relative infrequency with which a person has to urinate, it may seem surprising that urine is actually produced continuously, 24 hours a day. The urine that is formed continuously in each kidney trickles out through the ureter, which beings at the renal pelvis and narrows into a long, muscular tube leading to the bladder. In the adult, each ureter is about 25 to 30 cm long and 4 to 5 cm in diameter. Its wall is three-layered (Figure 29-6): an outer fibrous coat, a middle muscular coat containing layers of longitudinal and smooth muscle fibers, and an inner lining of mucous membrane. Contractions of the muscular coat of the ureters produce peristaltic waves, which begin at the kidney end and travel downward toward the bladder. (When the muscles are contracted, the lumen of the ureter becomes star-shaped.)

There are three constricted areas along the course of the ureter: at the junction of the renal pelvis and the tubelike portion of the ureter, where the ureter crosses the iliac artery, and at the point where the ureter enters the bladder wall. These three "bottle-necks" have no particular effect on the flow of urine, but they may become trouble spots if stones are formed in the kidneys and pass into the ureters. Such stones, or renal calculi, may become lodged in the constricted portions of the ureters, producing excruciating pain and a blockage of urine flow.

THE URINARY BLADDER

Without the urinary bladder, urine would be eliminated continuously, in an incessant trickle. The bladder is an expandable baglike structure, situated mainly in the pelvic cavity, directly behind the symphysis pubis, and covered by the parietal peritoneum. (As it fills with urine, however, the bladder expands upward into the abdomen.) In males the rectum is

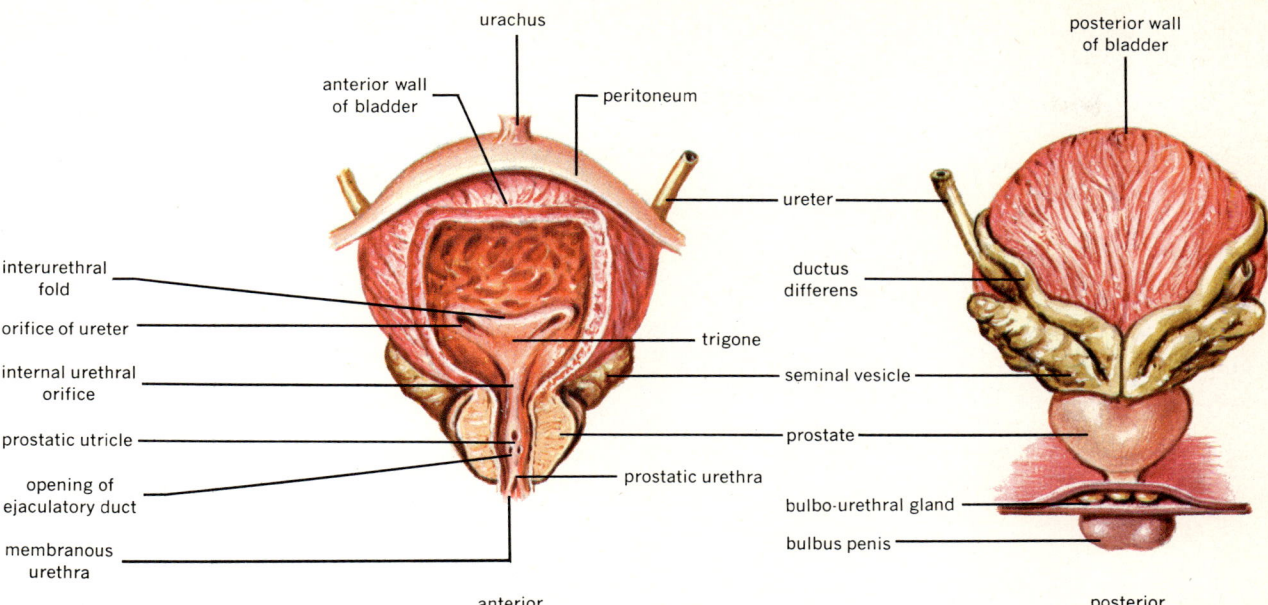

FIGURE 29-7 The urinary bladder and associated structures.

directly behind the bladder; in females, the uterus and vagina lie posterior to the bladder.

The thick, strong walls of the bladder contain three heavy layers of smooth muscle (longitudinal, circular, and longitudinal), which are collectively known as the **detrusor muscle.** Like the ureters and urethra, the bladder is lined with a unique **transitional epithelium.** The cells of this mucous lining are piled up on top of one another in folds or **rugae** in a random fashion and can slip over one another as the bladder expands. (When the bladder expands to a volume of about half a liter—one pint—an intense desire to urinate is felt. But under special circumstances, such as after a spinal block for surgery, the bladder can store up to 1.5 liters of fluid.) An exception to this expandable inner structure is a smooth, triangular area at the bottom of the bladder, called the **trigone** (Figure 29-7).

The two ureters enter the bladder at the upper corners of the trigone, each about a centimeter from the midline. The end of the ureter enters the bladder at an oblique angle, slanting downward and toward the midline, and traveling for a few centimeters under the bladder epithelium. This arrangement helps to prevent a backflow of urine, since contractions of the bladder compress the ends of the ureters, but it does not prevent the spread of infection from the bladder to the kidneys.

At the bottom of the trigone is the internal urethral orifice, through which the urine flows out into the urethra. A dense mass of circular muscle around the urethral openings forms the **internal sphincter** of the bladder. The spincter muscle is normally in a state of

contraction; its relaxation, under the control of the parasympathetic nervous system, occurs when an accumulation of urine in the bladder makes voiding necessary and is coordinated with reflex contractions of the bladder wall. (The presence of an additional, **external urethral sphincter,** composed of striated muscles, permits voluntary control over voiding, and the voiding reflex can be consciously suppressed by keeping the external sphincter contracted.)

The bladder has a rich supply of blood and lymph vessels. Branches of the internal iliac arteries carry blood to the bladder; venous blood drains into the internal iliac veins. There are also numerous links with the nervous system: sensory nerve fibers carry impulses from stretch receptors in the bladder wall, while autonomic fibers (both parasympathetic and sympathetic) play key roles in the functioning of the bladder.

THE URETHRA

A cystoscopy, the inspection of the interior of the bladder with a lighted tubular instrument, is a relatively simple procedure in a woman, while for a man it is far more complicated and painful—so much so that it is commonly performed under general anesthesia. This dramatic difference is due to the fundamental difference in the structures of the male and female urogenital tracts (Figure 29-8). In both sexes, urine is emptied from the bladder through a small tube, the **urethra,** which emerges at the exterior surface of the body in an opening called the **urinary meatus.** In both sexes, there is a typical smooth muscle

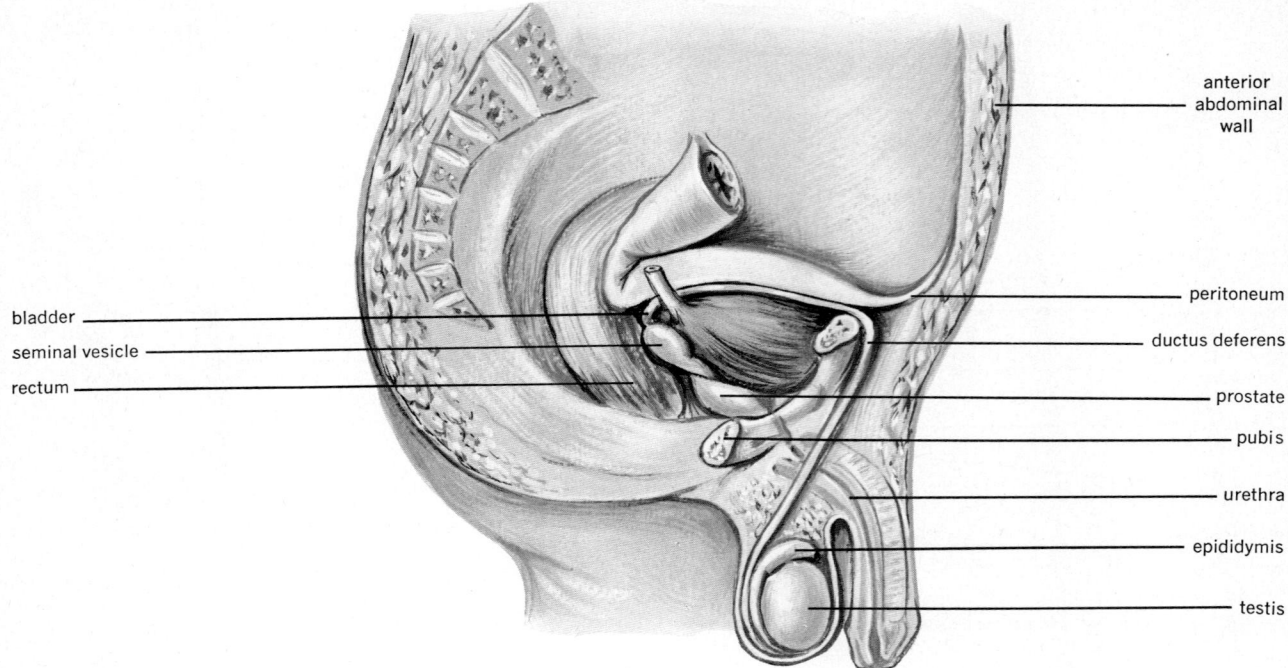

bladder

seminal vesicle

rectum

anterior
abdominal
wall

peritoneum

ductus deferens

prostate

pubis

urethra

epididymis

testis

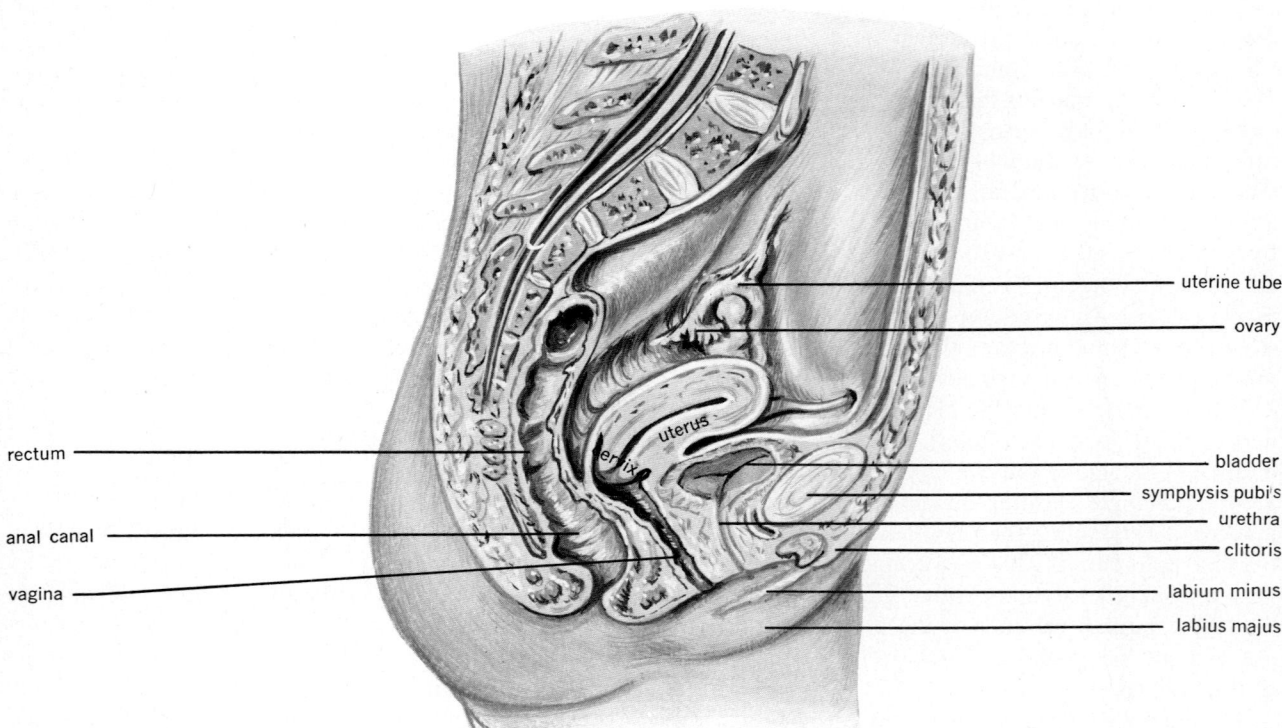

rectum

anal canal

vagina

cervix

uterus

uterine tube

ovary

bladder

symphysis pubis

urethra

clitoris

labium minus

labius majus

FIGURE 29-8   The male urethra travels a much longer path than the female urethra.

structure of the walls, with a mucous membrane lining, and an external sphincter of striated muscle surrounds the urethra a short distance below the internal sphincter. But there the resemblance ends.

In females the urethra is a short tube, about 2.5 to 3 cm long, situated behind the symphysis pubis and supported by the anterior wall of the vagina. The meatus appears as a small slit, between the clitoris and the opening of the vagina. The female urethra is surrounded by a complex network of glands and ducts, which are often foci for chronic infection.

The male urethra takes a much longer, tortuous course. Below the bladder, it threads its way through the prostate gland, then between two sheets of fibrous tissue connecting the pubic bones, and finally out through the penis, with a total length of about 20 cm. The three portions of the male urethra are known as the **prostatic portion,** the **membranous portion,** and the **cavernous** or **penile portion.**

In females, the urinary and reproductive passages are completely separate. In males, however, the urethra serves the double function of carrying either urine or seminal fluid. The intimate association of the urethra with the prostate gland sometimes causes problems in older men: if the prostate gland enlarges, it compresses the prostatic portion of the urethra and makes micturition (urination) difficult and painful.

SUMMARY

Metabolic processes generate waste products, which must be eliminated from the body to maintain hemostasis.

Metabolic wastes are eliminated through:
  The lungs
  The skin (sweat glands)
  The alimentary tract (large intestine)
  The urinary system

The urinary system is the main avenue of excretion of nitrogenous wastes, water, and salts. It consists of:
  2 kidneys (produce urine; regulate blood composition and acid-base balance)
  2 ureters (convey urine from kidneys to bladder)
  1 urinary bladder (stores urine temporarily)
  1 urethra (conveys urine from bladder to exterior)

The kidneys are a pair of bean-shaped abdominal organs.
  Blood vessels and nerves enter and leave through a concave indentation, the hilus.
  Within the renal capsule are an outer layer, the cortex, and an inner layer, the medulla.
  The nephron, the structural and functional unit of the kidney, consists of:
    glomerulus

Bowman's capsule
proximal convoluted tubule
loop of Henle
distal convoluted tubule
collecting tubule
papillary ducts
  The papillary ducts empty into the minor calyces of the renal pelvis.
  There are at least one million nephrons in each kidney.
  The kidneys have a rich blood supply. An unusual feature is the fact that blood is carried both to and from the glomeruli in arterioles.

The ureters are a pair of narrow, muscular tubes that carry urine from the kidneys to the urinary bladder.
  Each ureter begins in an enlarged region called the renal pelvis.
  Muscular contractions in the ureters produce peristaltic waves that travel from the kidneys to the bladder.

The urinary bladder is a muscular, baglike structure that can expand to store urine.
  The muscle layers of the bladder are collectively called the detrusor muscle, which contracts to force urine out of the bladder.
  The bladder and other urinary passageways are lined with a transitional epithelium, which permits considerable expansion.
  The trigone is a triangular area at the bottom of the bladder, outlined by the openings of the ureters and urethra.
  Urine is held in the bladder by an internal sphincter under parasympathetic control and an external sphincter of striated muscles around the urethra, under voluntary control.

The urethra is a small tube leading from the bladder and terminating in an opening called the urinary meatus.
  The female urethra is a short tube, 2.5 to 3 cm long, anterior to the vagina.
  The male urethra, about 20 cm long, passes through the prostate gland, the pelvic floor, and along the length of the penis (prostatic, membranous, and penile portions).
  Unlike the female urethra (which is entirely separate from the vagina), the male urethra serves both excretory and reproductive functions, carrying either urine or semen.

QUESTIONS FOR REVIEW AND THOUGHT

1 What are the main body structures involved in the excretion of: (a) excess water; (b) carbon dioxide; (c) nitrogenous wastes; (d) drugs, toxins, and so on; (e) inorganic salts?

2 List the structures of the urinary system and their functions.

3 What are the structural distinctions between the kidney cortex and medulla?

4 Describe the structure of the nephron, with special emphasis on the glomerulus and the filtering membrane.

5 Compare the intimate association of the urinary system with the circulatory system to the association of respiratory and circulatory system components in the lungs.

6 What special structural adaptations does the urinary bladder have for its function of temporary storage of urine?

7 Contrast the male and female urinary systems. What effects on urinary function might be expected in pregnancy, when the uterus expands to accommodate the growing fetus?

FUNCTIONS OF THE URINARY SYSTEM

30

A traveler lost in the desert continues to produce urine, even after drinking water supplies are exhausted and the body is becoming dangerously dehydrated. His urine is far more concentrated than usual, but still precious water continues to be lost, and the only hope of survival may lie in actually drinking his own urine.

Under such extreme conditions, the major functions of the kidneys—to maintain the balances of body fluids, electrolytes, and pH and to eliminate metabolic wastes—are at war with one another. The wastes must be diluted with water, yet the body has no water to spare if there is no continuing fluid intake. However, under more normal conditions the functions of the kidneys mesh harmoniously, and they serve as a major link in the body's "quality control" system.

The kidneys show remarkable versatility in their ability to regulate the volume and composition of the extracellular fluid. They are far more than simple filters, since they can also selectively reabsorb substances needed by the body and selectively secrete substances for elimination. The urine produced varies greatly in amount and concentration, depending on the dynamics of the body's needs. A certain amount of water must be used to dissolve and dilute potentially toxic wastes, but the kidneys also act as a spillway for any excess water not needed by the body. The amount of inorganic salts excreted by the kidneys also varies widely, so that the kidneys indirectly control the osmotic pressure and electrolyte composition of the extracellular fluids (ECF). They may even regulate the pH of the ECF by controlling the amounts of hydrogen ions and electrolytes excreted. (The kidneys have the ability to manufacture ammonia and substitute it for sodium, further contributing to the maintenance of the body's acid–base balance.)

In addition to these crucial homeostatic functions, the kidneys are the major avenue of excretion of nitrogenous wastes, such as urea, uric acid, creatinine, and ammonia. They also have an indirect endocrine function; through the hormone-activating substance **renin** produced in the cells of the juxtaglomerular complex, the kidneys help to regulate their own functioning.

The kidneys are not entirely autonomous, however. They are part of a feedback circuit involving the hypothalamus, which continuously monitors the composition of the extracellular fluid and secretes a hormone, **ADH (antidiuretic hormone),** that regulates the kidney function.

CHARACTERISTICS OF URINE

In many parts of the world urine has been considered a useful substance. The ancients used it as a soap for washing. Eskimos gave a guest the honor of providing the urine to be used for washing up after the greasy evening meal. Some American Indians used urine as a mouthwash; and some South American natives have even used it as a refreshing drink.

Urine is a watery solution of nitrogenous wastes and salts. Its characteristics vary greatly depending on the time of day, the food and fluid intake, the amount of physical exercise, the general health, and various other factors. Urine is usually a transparent liquid with an amber or light yellow color, but the first urine produced after awakening is usually much more concentrated and darker in color. Cloudy urine may be a sign of illness, or may simply be due to mucin secreted by the mucous membrane lining the urinary tract or to the presence of phosphates and carbonates. (When a urine specimen stands at room temperature, it turns cloudy as a result of the action of bacteria, producing phosphate precipitates. But fresh urine is normally sterile and has even been used an emergency antiseptic under battlefield conditions.)

Urine is usually slightly acid, but its pH may vary between 4.5 and 8.0. The composition of the diet affects the pH of urine: a high-protein diet tends to make the urine more acid, while a vegetable diet makes urine slightly alkaline. After a heavy meal, the pH of urine tends to rise, as large quantities of hydrochloric acid are secreted for digestion, producing a rise in the alkalinity of the blood and a consequent increase in the excretion of alkali as the kidneys act to adjust the body's acid-base balance.

The specific gravity* of urine can vary from 1.002 to 1.040 under normal conditions, depending on how dilute or concentrated the urine is. (Increased amounts of dissolved solids increase the specific gravity.) A large fluid intake will normally result in the production of large amounts of rather dilute urine, while restricted fluid intake will result in more concentrated urine. Exercise also affects the amount and concentration of urine, since during heavy physical exertion large quantities of water are lost from the body by sweating and the kidneys secrete a more concentrated urine to compensate. (Exercise also lowers the pH of urine, since acid metabolic products enter the blood during physical exertion.)

Urine is normally about 96 percent water. The solutes that form the remaining 4 percent are organic and inorganic waste products. They include **sodium chloride** and other inorganic salts and a variety of nitrogen compounds such as **urea** (nearly half of all the solids excreted in the urine), **ammonia, uric acid,**

---

* The specific gravity of a substance is its density compared to the density of water. Thus, urine is slightly denser than pure water.

TABLE 30-1 Average Composition of Urine Excreted Daily (Grams in 24 hours)

WATER	1500 ml
Inorganic constituents	
Sodium	4
Potassium	3
Calcium	0.2
Magnesium	0.1
Iron	0.005
Chloride	9.5
Sulfate	2
Phosphate	2
Bicarbonate	1.5
Ammonia	1
Organic constituents	
Urea	25
Creatinine	1.5
Uric acid	0.8

and **creatinine.** Some of the wastes excreted in the urine are derived from the body's metabolism, and others are unused constituents of the diet. Table 30-1 presents the average values of some common constituents of urine excreted in 24 hours by an adult man on a mixed diet.

The average amount of urine excreted daily is about 1500 ml, containing about 60 grams of solutes (25 grams inorganic salts and 35 grams organic wastes). The amount can vary considerably under normal conditions, and even more in various pathological states. A persistent increase in the daily urine output is referred to as **polyuria,** a temporary increase is called **diuresis,** and a decrease below the average values is referred to as **oliguria.**

In addition to the normal constitutents mentioned, urine may also contain a variety of abnormal constituents. Appreciable amounts of **glucose** or **ketone bodies** in the urine may indicate diabetes mellitus. **Albumin** is a normal constituent of blood plasma that normally is not filtered into the renal capsule; its presence in urine (referred to as **albuminuria**) is usually due to increased permeability of the glomerular membrane. **Blood** may be present in the urine (hematuria) when any of the organs of the urinary tract are injured or inflamed; **pus** in the urine indicates an infection somewhere in the urinary tract (or possibly in the reproductive tract). **Bile pigments** in the urine may be due to obstructive jaundice or hemolytic diseases and give the urine a greenish-yellow or golden-brown color. **Calculi** or stones are formed by the precipitation of mineral salts somewhere in the urinary tract.

Some unusual constituents of urine may indicate unusual but not necessarily pathological states. Various poisons, bacterial toxins, and drugs are excreted through the kidneys. (Oral medications for urinary tract infections are often dyes, which impart vivid and unexpected colors to the urine.) Endocrine hormones may be excreted in the urine; the excretion of gonadotropic hormones produced by the placenta during pregnancy forms the basis of a pregnancy test. **Urinalysis,** or the laboratory examination of urine, provides valuable diagnostic indications of the functioning of the body.

URINE PRODUCTION

At this very moment, urine is being formed in your kidneys from the copious blood flow that passes through them. Urine production is not a simple process, but occurs in a series of steps, in which the concentrations of various constituents seesaw back and forth until they are finally adjusted to the optimum values that will provide for satisfactory elimination of wastes while leaving the volume and composition of the body fluids in proper balance. These optimum values are continually adjusted to correspond to the changing needs and activities of the body.

Three main processes contribute to the formation of urine (Figure 30-1). First blood plasma from the glomerulus is filtered through the membrane of the glomerular capsule into the renal tubules. As the fluid then moves through the nephron, water and solutes are transported out of the tubules into the peritubular capillaries, and thus selectively reabsorbed for the use of the body. A few substances are secreted into the tubules from the peritubular capillaries. Thus, the fluid that finally trickles into the renal pelvis and down the ureters has a quite different composition from the initial filtrate, and all the more from the blood from which it was formed.

Glomerular Filtration

If glomerular filtration were the only process involved in urine formation, our lives would be much more complicated than they are now. Each day the kidneys of a normal adult filter about 170 to 180 liters of fluid—about 18 buckets full! If all this fluid were excreted as urine, we would lose (and have to replace by drinking) about 400 pounds of fluid each day!

Glomerular filtration is a passive process, and it is rather unselective. Fluid passes out of the tuft of capillaries that forms the glomerulus, successively passing through the capillary membrane, the basement membrane, and the visceral layer of the Bowman's capsule to enter the renal tubule. This combined filtering membrane acts as a sievelike ultrafilter, retaining large particles and any molecules with a molecular weight greater than about 70,000 (i.e., the formed elements of the blood and nearly all of the plasma proteins). Thus, the filtrate contains essentially every-

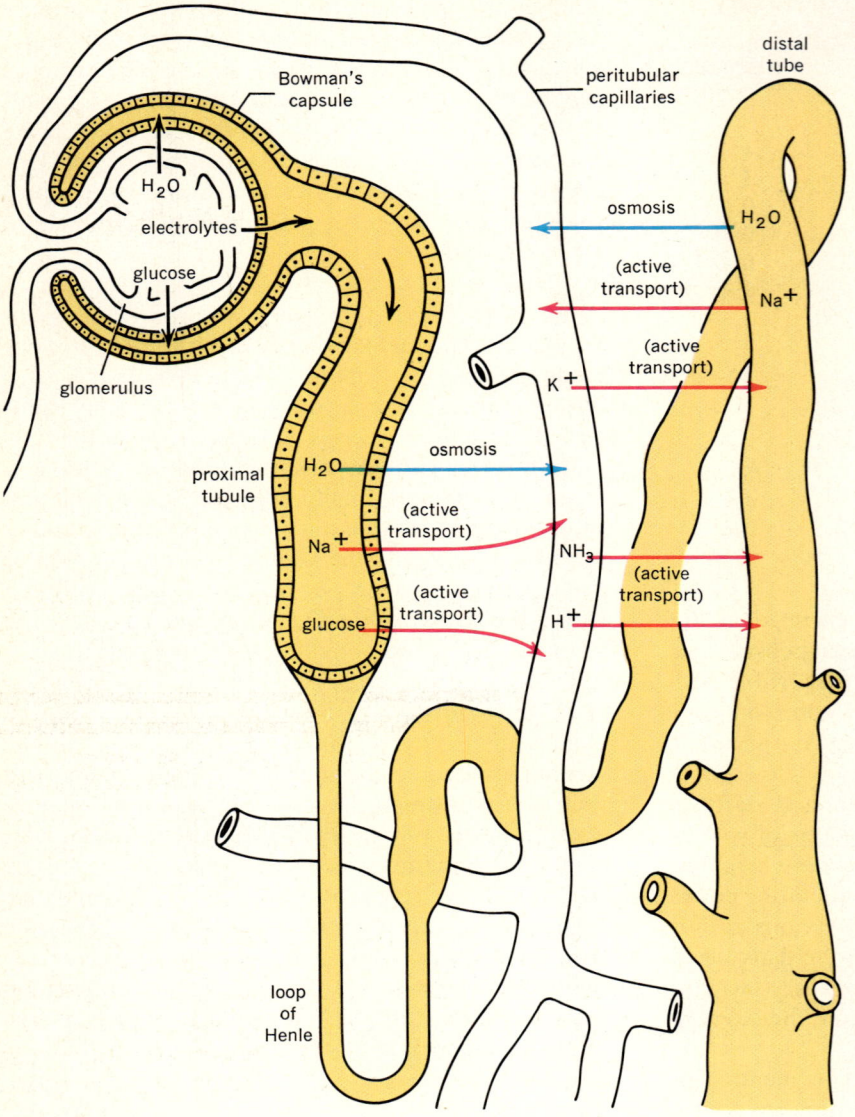

FIGURE 30-1 Mechanisms of urine formation in the nephron: glomerular filtration, tubular reabsorption, and tubular secretion.

thing that plasma does except for the protein. (Blood plasma contains about 7 g percent protein, while the glomerular filtrate contains less than 0.03 g percent. The small amounts of low-molecular-weight plasma proteins that filter through the glomerular membrane are reabsorbed in the tubules by pinocytosis.)

The driving force for glomerular filtration is the blood pressure in the glomerulus, together with the resistance provided by the narrow efferent arteriole. The blood pressure in the glomerular capillary is about 65 mm Hg. It is opposed by the osmotic pressure of the plasma (about 30 mm Hg) and the pressure of the filtrate outside the glomerulus (12 mm Hg), giving a net or "effective" glomerular filtration pressure of about 23 mm Hg.

Various factors affect the filtration rate. An increase in the blood pressure in the glomerulus, for example, caused by constriction of the efferent arteriole, will increase the filtration rate, while a decrease in glomerular blood pressure (e.g., due to constriction of the afferent arteriole) will decrease the rate of filtration. (Sympathetic stimulation produces a strong constriction of the afferent arteriole and thus a substantial drop in glomerular filtration.) If the arterial blood pressure falls very low, as in circulatory shock, the effective glomerular filtration pressure will approach zero, and filtration will stop. Drinking large amounts of liquids results in a dilution of the plasma, so that the osmotic pressure is decreased and the filtration rate is increased. Dehydration, on the other hand, concentrates the plasma proteins, thus increasing the osmotic pressure and decreasing the filtration rate.

About 1200 ml of blood (24 percent of the total

125 ml/min.

cardiac output) passes through the kidneys each minute. Of this amount, a total of about 125 ml of fluid is filtered out of all the glomeruli of the kidneys each minute.

Tubular Reabsorption

The glomerular filtrate contains many substances that the body cannot afford to lose. First there are the huge volumes of water. (Even 90 percent reabsorption of the water filtered through the glomerular capsules would not be efficient enough to save us from severe and dangerous dehydration, since we still would be urinating about 18 liters of fluid a day. The actual reabsorption of water in the renal tubules is closer to 99 percent.) In addition, the glomerular filtrate contains glucose, vitamins, proteins, amino acids, and various inorganic salts, all of which can be profitably reserved for the body's use.

Of the 125 ml of glomerular filtrate formed each minute, about 100 ml is removed from the proximal tubules, another 7 ml in the loops of Henle, an additional 12 ml from the distal tubules, and 5 ml more from the collecting ducts. Only 1 ml/min flows into the renal pelvis.

The reabsorption of water apparently occurs by a passive process of osmosis. Glucose, amino acids, vitamins, and any protein that has leaked through are reabsorbed by processes of active transport. These substances are normally completely reabsorbed from the glomerular filtrate. Inorganic ions, such as sodium, potassium, calcium, magnesium, bicarbonate, phosphate, and chloride ions, are reabsorbed in variable amounts, depending on the needs of the body. The movement of these ions occurs partly by active transport and partly by passive diffusion.

A good explanation for some of the mysteries of tubular reabsorption is provided by the **countercurrent mechanism.** According to this hypothesis, sodium and other substances are actively transported out of the filtrate in the proximal tubule, establishing an osmotic gradient so that water also moves out into the interstitial fluid by passive diffusion. In the descending limb of the loop of Henle, sodium passively diffuses into the filtrate, while water diffuses out, further reducing the volume of the filtrate and making it quite concentrated. In the ascending limb of the loop of Henle and most of the distal tubule, sodium is actively transported out of the filtrate, but the tubule is impermeable to water, so that there is no movement of water either in or out. The filtrate gradually becomes less concentrated and finally hypotonic until, in the last part of the distal convoluted tubule, the membrane is permeable to water, and additional water diffuses out into the interstitial fluid. In the collecting duct, there is some additional active transport

of sodium, but because the interstitial fluid is hypertonic, there is a rapid diffusion of water out of the filtrate, concentrating it even further.

Because of the active transport of sodium out of the ascending tubules, without an accompanying transport of water, the interstitial fluid becomes increasingly hypertonic deep within the medulla, promoting the diffusion of water out of the filtrate both in the descending limbs of the loops of Henle and in the collecting tubules. This countercurrent mechanism thus explains the progressive concentration of the filtrate without any need to assume active transport of water. The concentration of the interstitial fluid is maintained by the slow blood flow in the vasa recta, which lie close to the loops of Henle and also act as countercurrent systems (Figure 30-2).

Tubular Secretion

Heroin addicts in drug rehabilitation programs are often required to take periodic urine tests to determine whether they have been using the drug. Various drugs and other substances get into the urine by processes of active transport from the vascular to the tubular side of the epithelial cells of the renal tubules. Many of the substances secreted by the tubular cells are foreign to the body—ingested drugs, for example, such as penicillin, Diodrast (used for X rays of the kidneys), and para-aminohippuric acid (PAH). Some, however, are normal body products, such as potassium, creatinine, NH_4^+, and H^+. The proximal tubules secrete large quantities of hydrogen ions, helping to maintain the acid–base balance.

The processes of tubular secretion are opposite in effect to those of tubular reabsorption, serving to selectively increase the concentrations of certain substances in the urine and enhance their elimination from the body.

REGULATION OF RENAL FUNCTION

A baby wets its diaper round the clock. But after a year or two, at about the same time the child learns to control urination, the kidneys begin to show a regular daily pattern of variation of selective reabsorption. At night, during sleep, the reabsorption of water is greatly increased, and smaller amounts of more concentrated urine are produced. As a result, the bladder is usually able to cope with a night's urine production without undue distension, and the person can sleep undisturbed.

Unlike the control over urination, the control of selective reabsorption and the other mechanisms that contribute to urine formation is not voluntary. The amount of water excreted by the kidneys is controlled mainly by the hormone **ADH** (antidiuretic hormone), produced by the hypothalamus and secreted by the

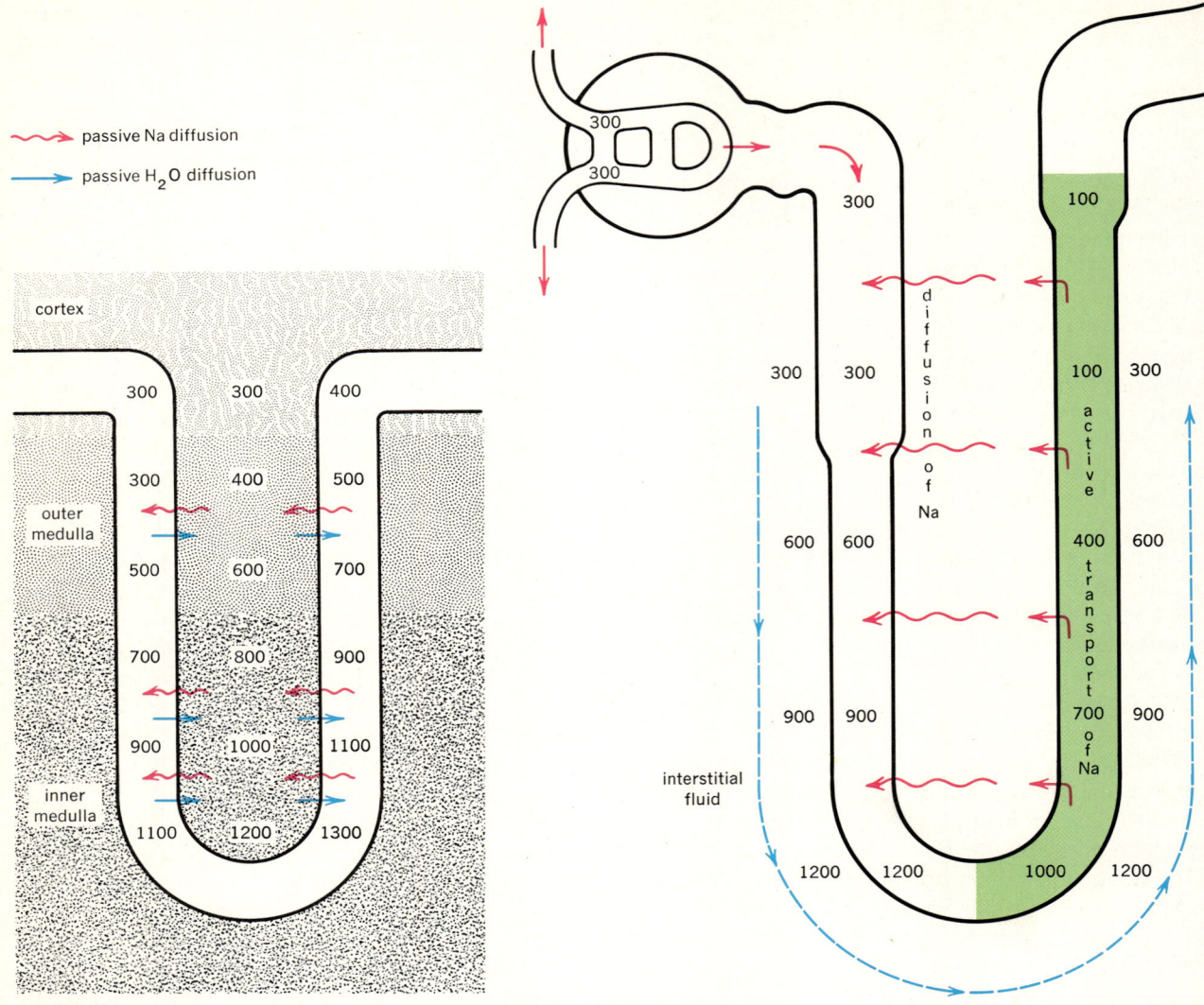

FIGURE 30-2 Countercurrent mechanisms in the vasa recta (A) and tubules of the nephron (B).

posterior pituitary (Figure 30-3). The hypothalamus, one of the most important regulatory centers in the body's control systems, continuously monitors the body fluids. Osmoreceptors in the anterior hypothalamus signal a rise in the plasma osmotic pressure (as a result of dehydration). The hypothalamus also receives impulses from volume receptors in the vascular system, which signal a decrease in the volume of circulating blood (e.g., due to hemorrhage). Such signs of dehydration stimulate the liberation of ADH, which is carried in the bloodstream to the kidneys. Its main effect is to increase the size of the pores in the epithelial cells of the distal tubule and collecting ducts, making them permeable to water and thus markedly increasing the reabsorption of water. In the complete absence of ADH, the urine output can rise to as high as 15 to 18 ml per min; under the influence

of the hormone, the urine output may be reduced to 0.35 ml/min.

The secretion of ADH is controlled by a feedback mechanism. When enough water has been reabsorbed, the volume of the blood rises and the plasma osmotic pressure falls. The appropriate receptors stop sending out their signals, the control center in the hypothalamus is no longer stimulated, and the secretion of ADH ceases. Thus, the hypothalamus-pituitary-kidney link serves a homeostatic function, conserving water for the body when it is in short supply and returning the concentrations of the body fluids to the optimum values.

ADH secretion is stimulated not only by dehydration of the tissues, but also by trauma and pain, anxiety, and certain drugs (e.g., morphine and some tranquilizers) and anesthetics. Ethyl alcohol, on the other

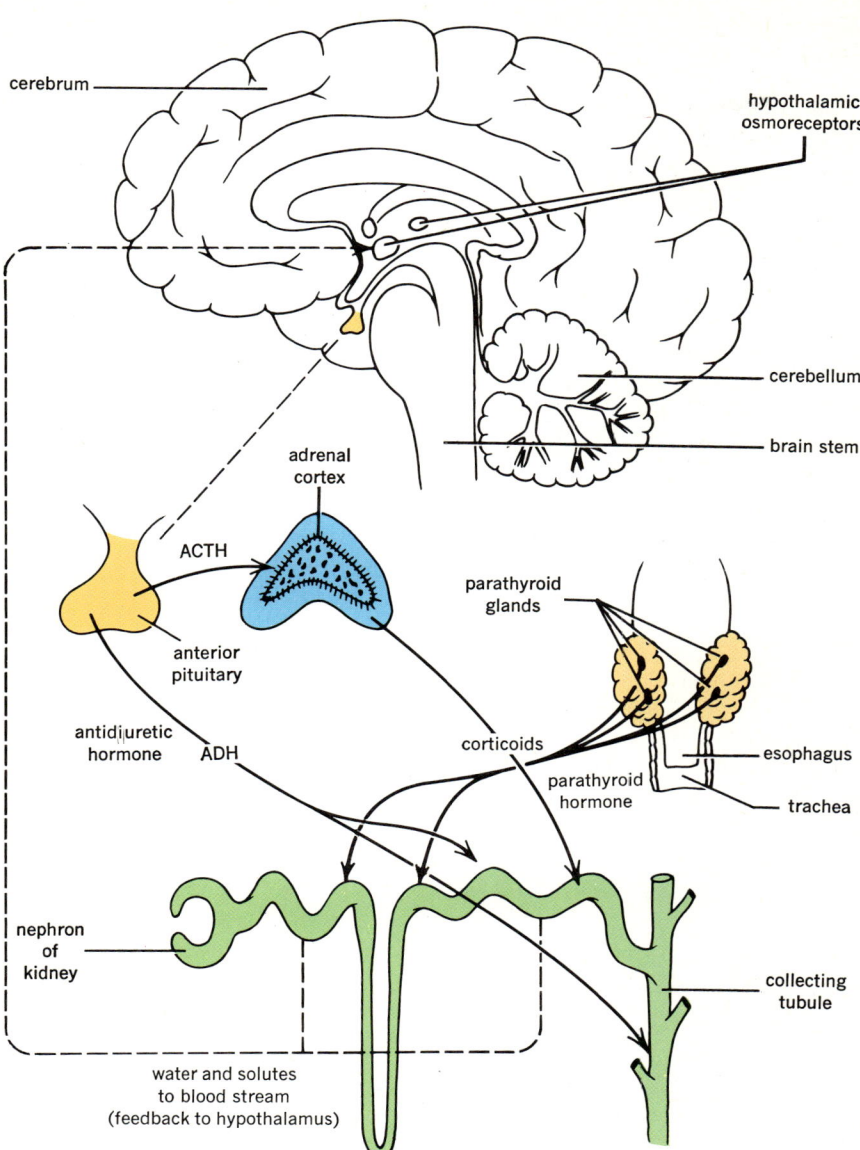

FIGURE 30-3 ADH and other hormones regulate kidney function.

hand, suppresses ADH secretion and also augments glomerular filtration by dilating the afferent arteriole. A heavy drinker makes frequent trips to the bathroom. If he or she is drinking concentrated drinks, such as straight whiskey, urine production may far exceed fluid intake, and considerable dehydration may result. The caffeine in coffee, tea, and cola drinks also has a diuretic effect, increasing urine production by decreasing tubular reabsorption of water.

The work of the kidneys is also controlled indirectly by other endocrine hormones. Aldosterone, produced by the adrenal cortex, increases the reabsorption of sodium and increases the excretion of potassium. When more sodium is reabsorbed, the osmolality of the extracellular fluid around the renal tubules is increased, and, as a result, more water is reabsorbed as well, diffusing down the increased osmotic gradient. The excretion of calcium and phosphate is controlled by the hormone of the parathyroid glands, which increases calcium reabsorption and decreases phosphate reabsorption.

The kidneys themselves play an indirect role in the hormonal regulation of their own functioning. An enzyme substance called **renin** is produced in the cells of the juxtaglomerular complex. This proteolytic enzyme enters the blood and activates a plasma globulin known as **angiotensin** to form angiotensin I. Under the influence of another plasma enzyme, angiotensin I loses two amino acid residues and is converted to the hormone **angiotensin II.** This hormone is a potent va-

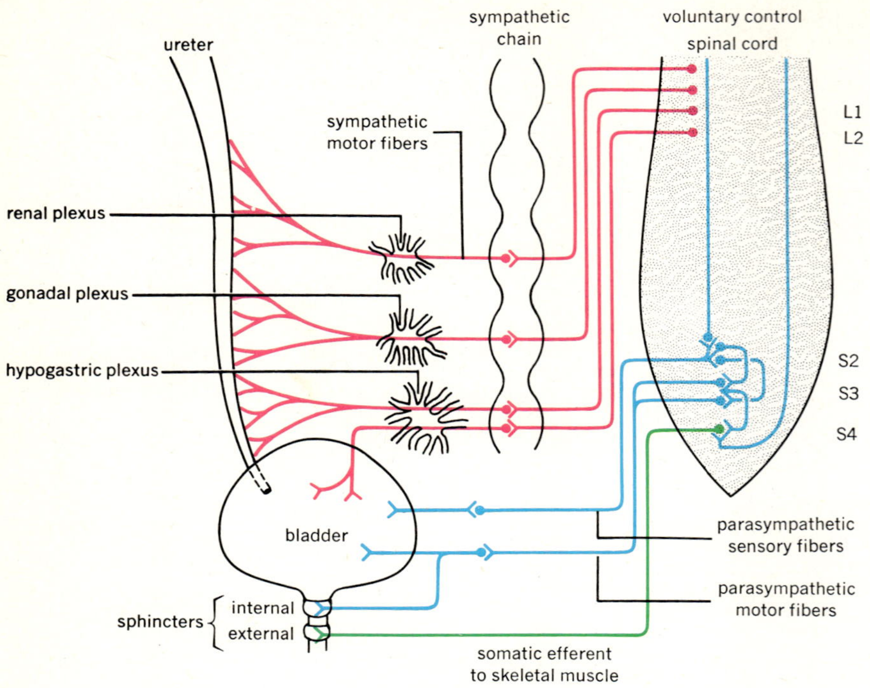

FIGURE 30-4 Innervation of the bladder, ureter, and urethra.

soconstrictor, which can directly raise the blood pressure throughout the body. In addition, angiotensin II stimulates the adrenal cortex to secrete aldosterone, the action of which causes the kidney to retain salts and water and indirectly increases arterial blood pressure.

MICTURITION (URINATION)

The question of toilet training has been a burning issue among parents and physicians for some time. Some cultures have viewed the problem tolerantly, dressing infants and young children in a minimum of clothing and permitting them to relieve themselves whenever and wherever the urge takes them. The development of more stringent standards of sanitation has imposed greater pressure to get even the youngest members of the community to conform, but at first the possibilities for cooperation are limited. In the very young child, urination, or micturition is a completely reflex action. As urine builds up in the bladder, pressure is exerted on the detrusor muscle of the bladder wall. Impulses are carried to the sacral region of the spinal cord, and parasympathetic neurons are activated (Figure 30-4). Eventually the muscle is reflexly stimulated to contract, and simultaneously the internal sphincter relaxes. The reflex continues to operate until the bladder is completely empty, after which the sphincter closes and the bladder begins to fill again as urine continues to trickle down from the kidneys.

There is some debate about the exact age at which control over the external urethral sphincter is learned, and the child gains the ability to start and stop urination at will. Probably there is considerable individual variation, but the expectations of parents and physicians also vary greatly depending on the culture. In the Soviet Union, babies of a few months are commonly placed on a potty before they are even able to sit up unaided. Some of the more permissive practitioners in the West advise letting the child learn to control bladder and bowel functions himself, by imitation of his elders, when he or she is ready. According to some psychoanalytical theories, tense confrontations between parent and child over toilet training may be a source of lifelong psychological trauma. At any rate, by the age of three most children have learned to inhibit the voiding reflex if it comes at an inconvenient time and to initiate urination voluntarily, by relaxing the external sphincter and increasing the intraabdominal pressure. By this age or a little after, most children are also able to inhibit urination during sleep (or at least to wake up in time to go to the bathroom). But some continue to bedwet.

Bedwetting or **nocturnal enuresis** is a more common problem among older children than is generally realized. (Indeed, some young men in the armed forces suffer from the problem and may be assigned to a "skunk squad" of others who share their difficulty.) Medical researchers are divided in their opinions on the causes and best treatment of bedwetting. Drugs such as imipramine may be used to control enuresis. Buzzer systems activiated by the wetting of the bedclothes have also been used. Some doctors believe that bedwetting in older children is caused mainly by deep-seated emotional problems; others hold that a limited bladder capacity or a slowness of maturation of the nervous system is the main cause. Studies in sleep laboratories have shown that bedwetting usually starts in the deepest phase of sleep, when dreaming is rare.

Normally in an adult, the presence of about 300 ml of urine in the bladder will stimulate a desire to urinate. The reflex stimulation can be inhibited, and urine will continue to accumulate. (Like the stomach, the bladder accomodates to its contents, with very little variation of internal pressure—up to a definite limit.) When the volume of urine in the bladder reaches about 700 ml, the average person will experience real pain and have difficulty in controlling the urination reflex.

Spinal cord injuries may result in a loss of voluntary control over urination, so that the act of voiding becomes a purely reflex action. Involuntary micturition, or **incontinence,** may also result from unconsciousness, irritation of the bladder (due to an infection or the presence of irritants in the urine), or a loss of muscle tone in the bladder or urethral sphincter muscles in the aged. A desire to urinate may be produced, even when the bladder is not full, by visual or auditory stimuli, such as the sight and sound of running water. Emotional stress may prevent the bladder from relaxing and thus stimulate an urge to urinate.

Retention of urine may be caused by an obstruction in the urethra or neck of the bladder, by a nervous contraction of the urethra, or by a lack of the urge to void. This complication may be experienced after childbirth. If urine retention continues, the bladder becomes painfully distended and may need to be relieved by catheterization (the insertion of a tube through the urethra into the bladder). If distension of the bladder is not relieved, there may be a continual dribbling of urine (overflow incontinence). Distention may cause the muscular wall of the bladder to lose its tone, so that the bladder cannot contract. Large volumes of urine are then retained for a long tine, and infections **(cystitis)** may develop.

A failure to urinate may be due to a far more serious condition: a failure of the kidneys to produce urine. Such a shutdown of kidney function is referred to as **anuria** and can lead to a severe toxic condition called **uremia.**

PRACTICAL CONSIDERATIONS

Kidney failure can be a death sentence. Without the excretory functions of the kidneys, toxic wastes build up in the blood and tissues and ultimately poison the body. In 1972, the United States government took a historic position on the value of life, initiating a billion dollar program for public support of dialysis treatments to maintain the lives of people whose own kidneys had ceased to function.

Kidney failure can be due to a variety of causes. A hereditary abnormality called **polycystic kidneys** involves a failure of the collecting tubules to fuse with the tubules of the nephron during early development, resulting in many cystlike structures. In severe forms, this condition results in death in infancy; in milder cases there is enough functional kidney tissue to maintain life until middle age. **Nephritis,** an acute inflammation of the kidneys, sometimes develops 10 to 20 days after an acute infection. It usually occurs during the first two decades of life. Most patients recover spontaneously, but in about 2 percent the condition becomes chronic. Hypertension and uremia (a buildup of urea and other wastes in the blood due to renal failure) may result. In **pyelonephritis,** there is an actual invasion of the kidney tissue by bacteria. Kidney failure may also result from circulatory failure and is often a contributing factor in death after a myocardial infarction.

There are a number of clinical tests for evaluating kidney function. The simplest are studies of the urine, which can reveal much about the work of the kidneys. The volume of the daily urine output and its specific gravity may be determined. If the urine output falls below 500 ml per day, this is a sign of renal insufficiency. A failure of the specific gravity of urine to rise when the output decreases also indicates a kidney malfunction. Urinalysis includes tests for such substances as glucose, protein (albumin), ketone bodies, blood, and other abnormal constituents. Tests of **clearance** can also monitor kidney function. Renal clearance is defined as the volume of blood plasma that is completely cleared (emptied) of a substance in a unit time, and can be calculated as:

$$Clearance = \frac{UV}{P}$$

where U is the concentration of the substance in the urine, P is the concentration of the same substance in the plasma, and V is the rate of urine flow. The polysaccharide inulin is often used in clearance tests to determine the glomerular filtration rate, since it passes freely through the glomerular membrane but is not reabsorbed or actively secreted to any significant degree. If the renal clearance of a particular substance is greater than that of inulin, this is an indication that the substance is actively secreted by the kidneys. A renal clearance less than the value for inulin indicates reabsorption of the substance.

If both kidneys have ceased to function adequately, the patient's life can be prolonged by the use of an

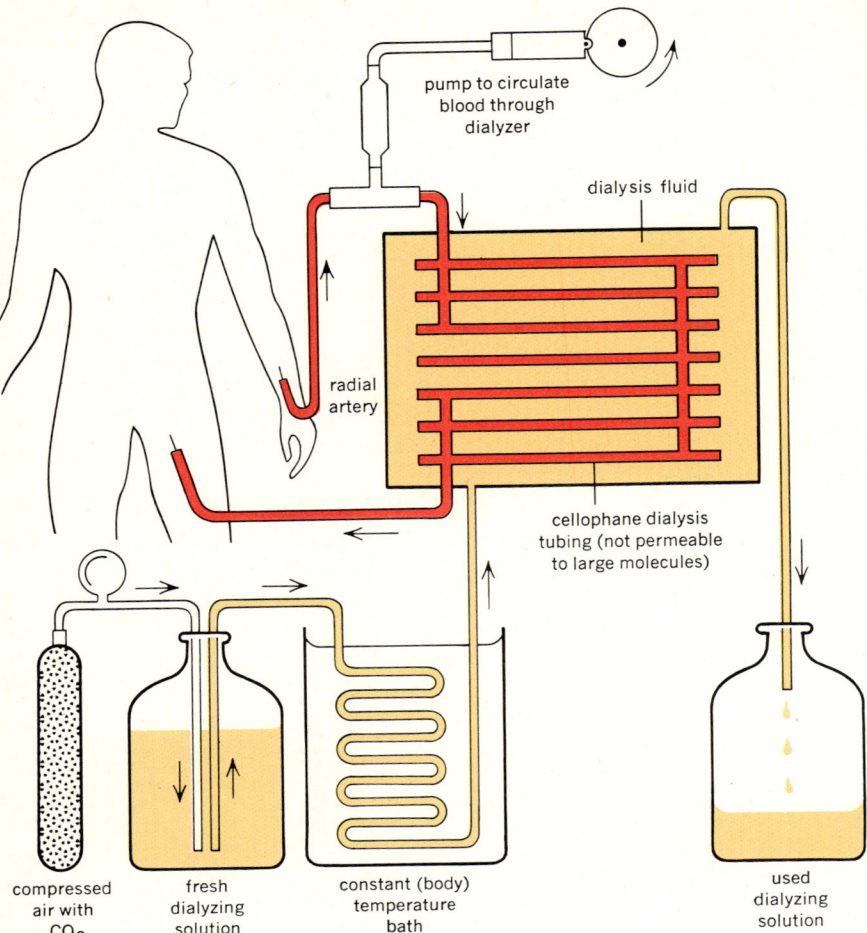

pump to circulate
blood through
dialyzer

dialysis fluid

radial
artery

cellophane dialysis
tubing (not permeable
to large molecules)

compressed
air with
CO_2

fresh
dialyzing
solution

constant (body)
temperature
bath

used
dialyzing
solution

FIGURE 30-5 Hemodialysis: schematic diagram of the operation of the artificial kidney. Modern portable dialysis units work according to the same basic principles.

artificial kidney, utilizing the principle of dialysis (Figure 30-5). The patient's blood is passed through a coiled tube of selectively permeable material, such as cellophane, immersed in a tank of a synthetic bathing fluid (the dialyzing solution), maintained at normal body temperature. (Since it is blood that is being subjected to dialysis, the procedure is often referred to as **hemodialysis.**) As the blood passes through the tube, formed elements and proteins remain in the blood, while urea, potassium, phosphate, and other substances present in toxic amounts diffuse out through the semipermeable membrane into the dialyzing solution. Two to three treatments a week are required, and each treatment takes five to twelve hours. The first dialysis machines available could be used only in hospitals by highly trained personnel; now home dialysis units that can be run by a member of the patient's family are available.

Dialysis treatments are a reprieve from death, but they can be a great strain on the patient and his or her family, and may have varous side effects (pain, itching, depression) and dangers such as the risk of bleeding to death if the tubes accidentally pull loose.

Whenever possible, patients with irreversible kidney failure are given a kidney transplant. A relative of the patient may donate one of his or her functioning kidneys, or a donor kidney may be obtained from a cadaver. Careful cross-matching of blood and tissue antigens and the use of immunosuppressive drugs are needed to avoid rejection. (The problems of organ transplantation are discussed in more detail in Chapter 37.) In general, kidney transplants have been among the most successful types of organ transplantation, and thousands of such operations have been performed.

SUMMARY

The functions of the kidneys are:
Regulation of the volume, composition, and pH of body fluids.
Excretion of nitrogenous wastes, inorganic salts, and excess water.
Secretion of renin, which catalyzes a conversion of a plasma globulin ultimately resulting in the hormone angiotensin II, which acts as a vasoconstrictor and stimulates aldosterone secretion.
Urine is a watery solution of nitrogenous wastes and salts of variable composition, pH 5.5 to 7.5, specific gravity 1.002 to 1.040.

The average 1500 ml of urine excreted daily by an adult contains about 60 grams of solutes (25 grams inorganic constituents, 35 grams organic constituents, mainly urea).

Abnormal constituents such as glucose, ketone bodies, albumin, blood, pus, bile pigments, and calculi may indicate pathological states of various body systems.

Poisons, drugs, and hormones are also excreted through the kidneys.

Urine is produced in the nephrons by processes of:

Glomerular filtration (diffusion of water and molecules smaller than M.W. 70,000 through the sievelike glomerular membrane, due to the pressure of blood in the glomerulus).

Tubular reabsorption (removal of water, glucose, amino acids, vitamins, and inorganic ions from the glomerular filtrate in the renal tubules by diffusion and active transport).

The countercurrent mechanism accounts for the progressive concentration of the filtrate without the need to assume active transport of water.

Tubular secretion (selective secretion of drugs, hydrogen ions, potassium, creatinine, etc. into the tubules by active transport).

The functions of the kidneys are regulated by hormones:

ADH (antidiuretic hormone): produced by hypothalamus, secreted by posterior pituitary; increases tubular reabsorption of water, results in more concentrated urine.

Aldosterone: secreted by adrenal cortex, increases reabsorption of sodium and excretion of potassium; increases reabsorption of water.

Renin-angiotensin I-angiotensin II system: renin secreted by juxtaglomerular complex in kidneys acts on plasma globulin, which is subsequently converted to angiotensin II; this hormone raises blood pressure and stimulates aldosterone secretion.

Parathyroid hormone: secreted by parathyroid glands, controls excretion of calcium (increases reabsorption) and phosphate (decreases reabsorption).

Micturition or urination involves an involuntary parasympathetic reflex (stretching of bladder detrusor muscle stimulates contraction of bladder and relaxation of internal sphincter) and voluntary relaxation of the external urethral sphincter.

An urge to urinate is felt when the bladder contains about 300 ml of urine, but the reflex can be inhibited.

The bladder expands and accommodates to its contents without any significant change in internal pressure, up to a limit.

Pain and involuntary urination may occur when the bladder contains about 700 ml of urine.

Voluntary control over urination is usually learned by the age of three.

Bedwetting (nocturnal enuresis) sometimes continues for years.

Incontinence (involuntary urination) may result from:

Spinal cord injuries

Irritation of the bladder

Loss of muscle tone in the bladder or urethral sphincters in the aged

Retention of urine may result from:

Obstruction of the urethra or neck of the bladder

Nervous contraction of the urethra

Lack of the urge to void (common just after childbirth)

Retention of urine may result in painful distension, overflow incontinence, loss of bladder muscle tone, and infection.

Anuria is a failure of the kidneys to produce urine and can lead to uremia (buildup of urea and other toxins in the blood).

Kidney failure may be caused by:

Polycystic kidneys

Nephritis

Pyelonephritis

Circulatory failure

Kidney function is evaluated by:

Measurement of daily urine output

Determination of specific gravity of urine

Tests for abnormal constituents such as glucose, albumin

Clearance tests

An artificial kidney utilizes the principle of dialysis (the passage of small solute molecules through a semipermeable membrane) to cleanse the blood of a patient with nonfunctioning kidneys of accumulated toxic wates.

A kidney transplant from a live or cadaver donor can restore kidney function.

QUESTIONS FOR REVIEW AND THOUGHT

1 Discuss the homeostatic functions of the kidneys.

2 Describe the processes of glomerular filtration, selective reabsorption, and tubular secretion. Compare their effects on: (a) the amount of water excreted and (b) the amount and nature of solids excreted.

3 What are the normal and abnormal constituents of urine?

4 What is the countercurrent mechanism?

5 Describe the nervous and endocrine mechanisms regulating: (a) urine formation and (b) micturition.

6 What conditions can produce incontinence?

7 Describe the operation of the artificial kidney. Does kidney dialysis perform the same functions as the work of a normal kidney?

THE BODY FLUIDS

31

Most scientists believe that the early life forms evolved in the waters of the earth's oceans, and that the original water creatures retained an intracellular fluid very similar to the watery medium in which they lived. As higher forms of life developed, and some invaded the dry lands, there were various changes in body structures, and structural components such as shell or bone and adipose tissue reduced the overall fluid content of the body.

Each human being passes through a similar evolution as he or she develops: an early human embryo is about 97 percent water, a newborn infant 77 percent water, and an adult man only about 60 percent water. (In a woman, because of the larger proportion of essentially water-free adipose tissue, water constitutes only about 54 percent of the body weight.)

Through all the vicissitudes of daily living, the composition of the fluid media of the body remains relatively constant. This constancy is maintained through a dynamic equilibrium, to which the complexly interacting respiratory, circulatory, digestive, excretory, endocrine, and nervous systems of the body all contribute. The dynamic equilibrium of the body fluids is one of the most important aspects of homeostasis.

Seawater is merely a mixture, in which various solids and gases are dissolved and suspended in a fluid medium, water. But in living organisms, even those whose gross composition does not differ very much from seawater, there is a high degree of internal organization. Even a single-celled ameba is not a mere suspension of solids in a membrane-bounded fluid medium. In higher organisms, such as humans, there is a correspondingly greater degree of internal organization, structural differentiation and compartmentalization. Even the body fluids can be thought of as compartmentalized (Figure 31-1). The largest portion—about two-thirds of the total body fluids—is found within the cells and is termed the **intracellular fluid.** The remaining one-third is the **extracellular fluid,** which includes the fluids in the blood and lymph vessels, the cerebrospinal fluid, synovial fluid, special fluids such as the intraocular fluid in the eyes, and the **interstitial fluid,** which bathes the cells.

Water enters the body through the digestive tract, in the form of beverages and food constituents. Water leaves the body through the lungs, the kidneys, the large intestine, and the skin. In order for the fluid balance to be maintained, the water intake must precisely balance the water output. The dynamic equilibrium is maintained by continual adjustments both of intake (through the thirst mechanism) and of output (mainly by variations of urine output).

Within the body there is a continual interchange of water and other materials among the fluid compart-

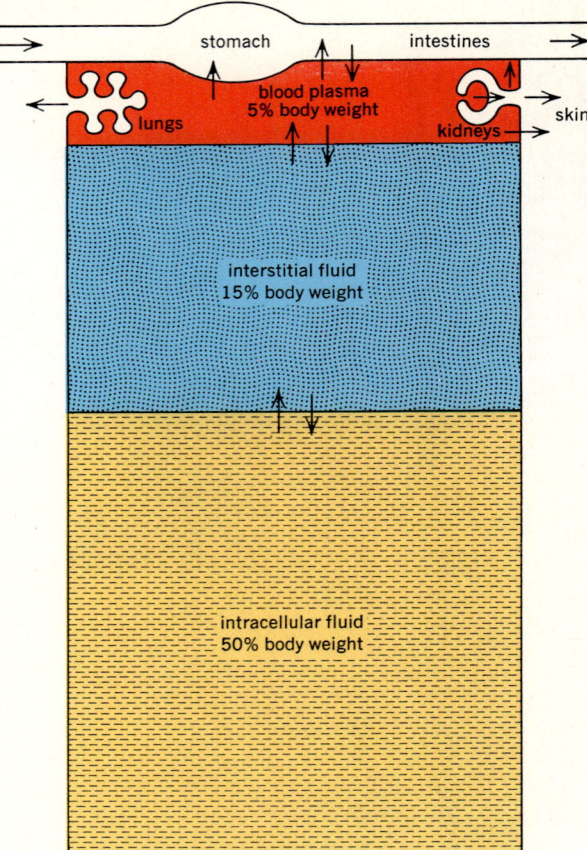

FIGURE 31-1   The fluid compartments of the body.

ments. Water diffuses freely in and out of the membranes of blood vessels and of the individual cells. Other constituents of the body fluids may move from one compartment to another by diffusion or by energy-consuming processes of active transport. In passing from the vascular compartment to the individual cells and the reverse, substances must pass through the interstitial fluid, which plays an important role in the body's fluid dynamics. Both the plasma volume and the cell volume are kept relatively constant by temporary increases and decreases in the amount of fluid in the interstitial compartment. The selective permeability of the cell membranes promotes distinct differences in composition of the fluids in the major compartments of the body. Maintaining these differences requires constant work in the form of active transport.

COMPOSITION OF THE BODY FLUIDS

Values of the total body water and the amounts contained in the various fluid compartments cited in different texts vary greatly. There are a number of reasons for the discrepancies. First of all, the values are averages, and there is a great deal of individual variation in amounts of fluid. Age is an important factor that can influence the amount of body water. In addition to the progression already mentioned, from 97 percent water in the early embryo to about 60 percent in an average adult man, there is a further dehydration in old age, so that people over 65 usually are less than 50 percent water. Sex can also make a difference: women tend to be less muscular and have relatively more adipose tissue than men; both factors contribute to a lower relative water content in women. Even in the same sex, a fat man will have less body water than a thin one. As a result, values of total body fluid are often expressed in terms of "fat-free tissue" or "lean body mass." (In an average adult man, water is about 70 of the fat-free tissue.)

Further variations are introduced by methods of measuring body water. The most direct method would be to weigh the body, then to dry it thoroughly and then reweigh it. For obvious reasons, the direct method is not suitable for living subjects, although it has been used for experimental animals and, at one time, for executed criminals. An indirect method of determining fluid volumes is to inject a substance that will be rapidly distributed through the body fluids, and then take a sample of fluid and measure the dilution of the test substance. If substances can be found that are distributed only to one particular compartment—for example, the extracellular fluid—then differential fluid volumes can be determined. There are many problems in choosing suitable substances for such dilution studies, since they must be nontoxic and must be distributed to the appropriate body fluids. A number of substances have been used, including radioactive sodium, radioactive chloride, radioactive bromide, thiosulfate ion, thicyanate ion, inulin (a plant polysaccharide), and sucrose. These substances are injected into the bloodstream and are rapidly distributed to the extracellular compartment, without penetrating appreciably into the cells. The values obtained thus give the volume of the extracellular compartment, and the intracellular fluid volume is obtained by substracting this volume from the total body fluid. Unfortunately, because of variations of behavior and distribution of the different test substances, the values they give vary, and none of them exactly measures the real extracellular space.

The constituents of the body fluid comparments are summarized in Table 31-1. In terms of mass, proteins and nonelectrolytes actually constitute about 90 percent of the dissolved constituents in the plasma, about 60 percent in the interstitial fluid, and about 97 percent in the intracellular fluid. But the electrolytes, which dissociate into ions, make a disproportionately large contribution to the osmolality of the body fluids. As Table 31-1 emphasizes, there are substantial dif-

TABLE 31-1   Composition of Body Fluids (milliosmols per liter)

SUBSTANCE	BLOOD PLASMA	INTER-STITIAL FLUID	INTRA-CELLULAR FLUID
Sodium	144	137	10
Potassium	5	4.7	141
Calcium	2.5	2.4	0
Magnesium	1.5	1.4	31
Chloride	107	113	4
Bicarbonate	27	28	10
Phosphate	2	2	11
Sulfate	0.5	0.5	1
Glucose	5.6	5.6	
Amino acids	2	2	8
Lactate	1.2	1.2	1.5
Protein	1.2	0.2	4
Urea	4	4	4

ferences in the fluid compositions of the major compartments.

Vascular Compartment   The water of the blood plasma accounts for about 5 percent of the total body weight. The fluid in the blood vessels circulates rapidly through the body and is under pressure. The membrane of the capillary wall is permeable to water and all the plasma solutes except the proteins, and the blood pressure provides a filtering force that continually moves fluid out of the vascular compartment into the interstitial fluid compartment. The osmotic force of the plasma proteins continually draws water back into the vascular compartment. The lymph vessels that drain the intercellular spaces and transport the collected fluid back to the cardiovascular system also contribute to the continual interchange of materials between the vascular and interstitial compartments, which together make up the extracellular fluid.

Interstitial Fluid Compartment   The fluid that bathes the individual body cells, together with the lymph, aqueous humor of the eye, synovial fluid of the joints, bile, water in the urinary tract, pericardial, pleural, and peritoneal fluid, and cerebrospinal fluid, constitutes about 17 percent of the total body weight. The main difference between interstitial fluid and plasma is in the protein content; proteins are a major constituent of blood plasma, but there is very little protein in the interstitial fluid, since a free exchange of proteins is barred by the capillary and cell membranes.

The selective permeability of the capillary membranes accounts for the substantial difference in protein content between the plasma and interstitial fluid. But there are also small but significant differences in

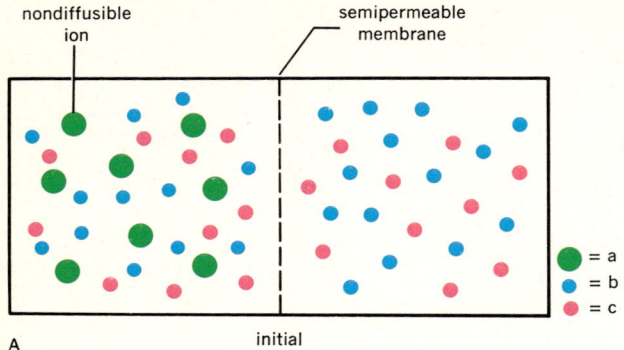

nondiffusible ion

semipermeable membrane

= a
= b
= c

A   initial

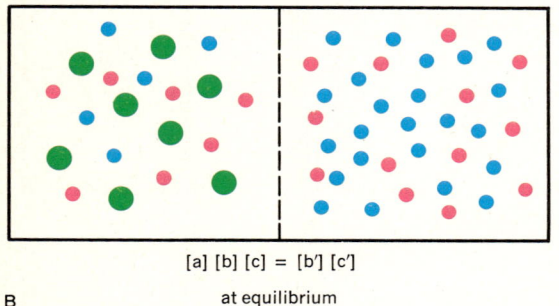

[a] [b] [c] = [b'] [c']

B   at equilibrium

FIGURE 31-2 **The principle of Donnan equilibrium can account for unequal concentrations of diffusible substances without active transport when a nondiffusible substance is present on one side of a semipermeable membrane.**

the concentrations of various electrolytes—small ions that can readily pass through the membranes. However, it is not necessary to assume processes of active transport to account for these differences. They are readily explained by a principle called **Donnan equilibrium** (Figure 31-2). Donnan showed that when a membrane separates two solutions of electrolytes, one of which contains an ion that cannot diffuse through the membrane, the final distribution of the diffusible ions in the solutions is unequal. At equilibrium, the product of the concentrations of the ions on one side of the membrane equals the product of the ion concentrations on the other. In this case, proteins remain inside the vascular compartment, and diffusible ions pass through into the interstitial space.

Intracellular Fluid Compartment Physiologists find it convenient to speak of the "intracellular fluid compartment," with a water content about 37 percent of the total body weight. But actually the cells of the body form 100 trillion tiny individual fluid compartments, each bounded by its own cell membrane. Each cell is bathed in interstitial fluid, and there is a continual interchange of substances through the cell membrane. As in the blood vessels, water diffuses freely in both directions, but the cell membrane is highly selective in the ions and other solutes that it permits to

pass through. Energy-consuming processes of active transport maintain quite substantial differences between the interstitial and intracellular fluids. For example, both sodium and chloride are present in much higher concentrations in the interstitial fluid than in the intracellular fluid, while the cells contain more potassium and phosphates than the fluids that surround them. Protein, a major cell product, is much more abundant in the intracellular fluid than in the interstitial fluid.

REGULATION OF TOTAL BODY FLUID

A baseball pitcher can lose more than ten pounds during a ballgame. Virtually all of this weight loss is fluid, poured out by the sweat glands as the body works to dissipate the excess heat generated by muscle contraction during the strenuous exercise. In the more sedentary activities that characterize the average person's daily life, the fluid loss due to sweating is far more modest, but still appreciable, and fluid is also lost continually through the other main channels of excretion. If this lost fluid were not replaced promptly, the person would rapidly become dehydrated, placing an increasing strain on the workings of body systems, until circulatory failure ultimately led to death. On the other hand, if fluid intake exceeded output, edema would result, placing a strain on the cardiovascular system. Normally, fluid intake precisely equals fluid output, and a dynamic equilibrium of the body fluids is maintained (Figure 31-3).

Fluid Intake

In past ages, forced drinking has been used as a simple but effective method of torture. Today, adhering to the regimen of drinking four to six glasses of fluids each day sometimes seems to resemble a refined form of "water torture," if one attempts to drink when not thirsty. Actually, left to its own devices, the healthy body is remarkably able to adjust its fluid intake to an appropriate level to balance the daily fluid loss. Not all the fluid that enters the body is taken in as beverages. Most foods contain at least 50 percent water, and meat and vegetables usually contain far more. On an average mixed diet, the food eaten contributes from 700 to 1200 ml of fluid daily. The chemical reactions of metabolism also contribute a certain amount of water to the body's fluid balance, amounting to about 300 ml a day. The actual intake of fluids as such is normally governed partly by habit (for example, the customary glass of juice in the morning, cups of coffee with meals, a glass of milk at bedtime) and partly by the sense of thirst.

The mechanism of thirst is seemingly simple, but actually rather complicated and still not entirely understood. Local effects—a drying of the mucous

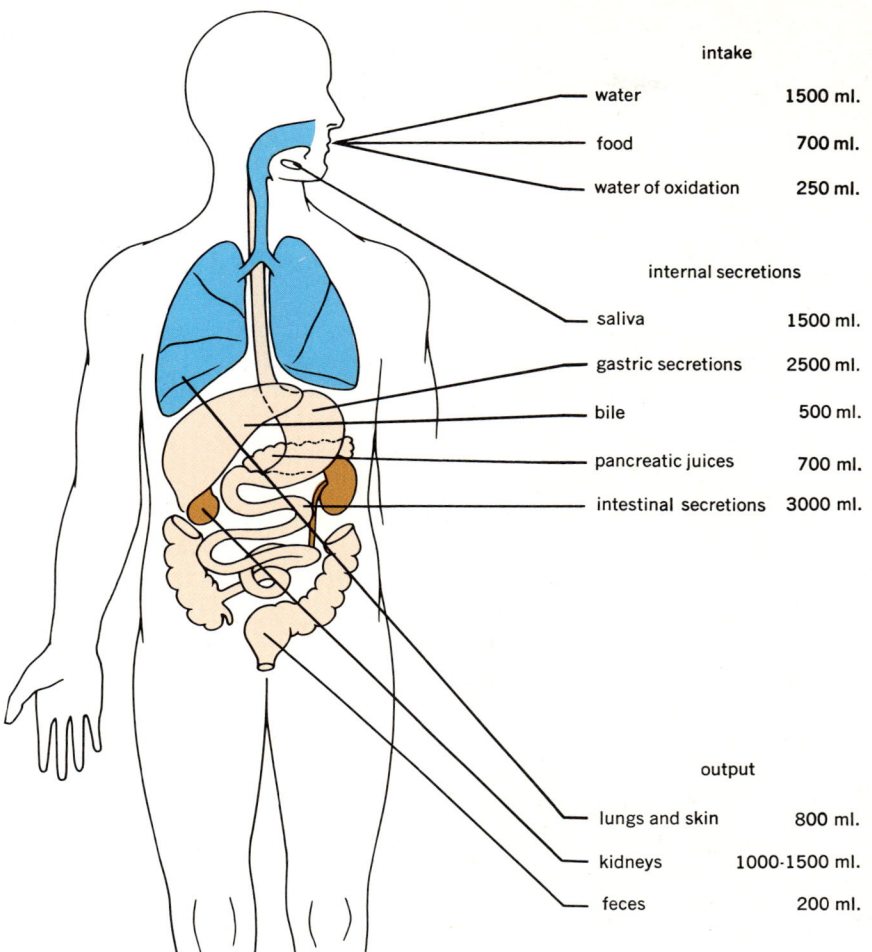

intake

water	1500 ml.
food	700 ml.
water of oxidation	250 ml.

internal secretions

saliva	1500 ml.
gastric secretions	2500 ml.
bile	500 ml.
pancreatic juices	700 ml.
intestinal secretions	3000 ml.

output

lungs and skin	800 ml.
kidneys	1000-1500 ml.
feces	200 ml.

FIGURE 31-3 Fluid intake and output are balanced in a dynamic equilibrium. Values indicated are normal averages. An increase or decrease in intake due to environmental conditions sets off feedback mechanisms via the hypothalamus that adjust the output correspondingly. Increased output (e.g., sweating on a hot day) similarly stimulates an increased intake.

membranes of the oral cavity and pharynx and a cessation of saliva flow—play an important role in the immediate sensations of thirst, which serve as a stimulus for drinking. But these sensations are closely linked into a nervous mechanism controlled by the thirst center in the hypothalamus. When osmoreceptors in the hypothalamus signal that the extracellular fluids are becoming too concentrated, impulses from the control center somehow give rise to the sensation of thirst. This feedback system is very sensitively tuned to conditions of excess fluid loss—hot summer weather and participation in sports, for example, send people flocking to the drinking fountains and refreshment stands. But strangely thirst is satisfied almost immediately by the act of drinking, before the new fluid intake has had time to be absorbed into the bloodstream. The moistening of the mouth and pharynx and the distention of the stomach apparently initiate feedback impulses, which turn off the stimulation of the hypothalamic thirst center. (If it were not

for these feedback mechanisms, and thirst continued until the tissues were fully rehydrated, you would continue to drink until your stomach burst!) Under the influence of these controlling mechanisms, fluid intake varies greatly from individual to individual, and in the same individual at different times, depending on the person's size, weight, and activities, and on enviromental conditions.

When fluids are taken by mouth, water is rapidly absorbed from the intestinal tract into the plasma compartment. If large amounts of water are taken without accompanying food, absorption is complete in about 30 to 40 minutes. Both the blood volume and the cardiac output may be temporarily increased. But soon the body adjusts. Capillary networks open to increase the vascular bed, and the sinusoids of the liver and spleen expand, serving as reservoirs. Fluid passes rapidly into the interstitial compartment, and the kidneys step up their elimination of water. Balance is restored within two to three hours.

Fluid Output

One of the main reasons doctors generally recommend drinking large quantities of fluids is to soften the feces and aid bowel function. But many people who try to follow the advice find that the extra water serves instead to augment the kidney function. The body has four main avenues of fluid output: through the lungs, skin, large intestine, and urinary tract. The first three are influenced mainly by environmental factors, but the last can be varied within broad limits to control the body's fluid balance. The urinary system is the single most important mechanism in the homeostasis of body fluid.

Lungs

A dog pants on a hot day as a means of losing excess heat through the evaporation of water. Unlike dogs, humans have an efficient system of sweat glands to serve that function, but the exhaled air is still laden with moisture. The amount of water lost through the lungs varies with the humidity and temperature of the inspired air and with the depth and rate of breathing; on the average, it comes to about 300 ml per day.

Skin

Even on a cool day, when we are resting comfortably, we continually lose water that diffuses through the skin and evaporates without a trace. This water loss, which we do not even notice, is referred to as **insensible perspiration.** High temperatures and physical exertion bring the mechanism of sweating into play, and some of the fluid excreted by the sweat glands may form visible drops or trickles of water on the surface of the skin. This mechanism, referred to as **sensible perspiration,** is an important part of the body's temperature control system, but may be a threat to the body's fluid balance if fluid intake is limited. Under normal conditions, the fluid loss through the skin is about 500 ml per day, but high temperatures and physical exertion can drastically increase this amount. Under extreme conditions, water loss through the skin and expired air may reach as much as 20 liters a day. If environmental temperatures are high, this fluid loss cannot be reduced, even if the body is becoming dehydrated, until severe dehydration causes the body's temperature-control mechanisms to break down entirely.

Large Intestine

Dietary fiber makes bowel function more rapid and effective mainly by absorbing large quantities of water. The feces produced are softer and more bulky; they are moved more rapidly through the intestines and eliminated more easily from the body. A lack of fiber in the diet and an insufficient fluid intake may result in excessive resorption of water in the large intestine. The feces become hard and difficult to pass, setting up a vicious cycle of constipation, often accompanied by hemorrhoids and anal fissures. Normally about 200 ml of water is lost in the feces each day. In diarrhea, however, the water losses are much greater, and if fluid intake is not correspondingly increased, severe dehydration may result.

Kidneys

The kidneys are the main spillway for the body's excess water. This avenue of excretion is the only one that provides wide latitude for regulation of fluid output. The average fluid output in the urine is about 1500 ml, but this amount can vary greatly, depending on the fluid intake and the amounts of water lost through the other channels of excretion. If fluid intake is restricted, or large amounts of water are being lost in sweating or diarrhea, the kidneys can reabsorb more water than usual and put out small amounts of rather concentrated urine; if water intake is excessive, the kidneys get rid of the excess by producing large quantities of highly dilute urine. Regardless of fluid intake, however, a certain minimum amount of urine must be produced, containing sufficient water to keep the excreted wastes in solution. The role of ADH and other hormones in regulating kidney function was discussed in the last chapter.

Body Water Reserves

Through natural calamities, accidents, and wars, humans have been forced through the ages to suffer a variety of hardships. Under severe deprivations, some survive but others die. One type of stress that the body is sometimes called on to bear is a loss of water. Few suffer such exotic misfortunes as being stranded on the desert or pinned on a lonely mountainside by a plane crash. But prolonged vomiting or diarrhea can place equally strenuous demands on the body's water reserves. Under such conditions, as well as situations when there is no drinking water available, people with the largest percentage of body water stand the best chance for survival. Obesity is one factor that reduces the body's fluid reserves, since adipose tissue is essentially water-free. The progressive tissue dehydration that occurs in old age produces a great depletion of water reserves. Typically, dysentery-like diseases take their greatest toll from the very old and the very young. That babies should be particularly susceptible to dehydration due to diarrhea or vomiting at first seems paradoxical, since infants have proportionately more body water than adults. But they also lose proportionately more fluid in urinary output, and as a result their water reserves are poor. Normally this large output is balanced by an equally large fluid intake (a baby perhaps a tenth of your body weight may drink nearly as much fluid each day as you do), but an additional fluid loss may place too great a stress on the infant's system.

ELECTROLYTES

The fluids of the body can conduct electricity. This property is imparted by the presence of electrolytes, substances which can dissociate into electrically charged ions. Various inorganic salts are taken into the body as constituents of foods; they are excreted by the kidneys, large intestine, and skin.

In the body, electrolytes serve many general and specific functions. They participate in the maintenance of osmotic relationships, acid-base balance, the conductivity of nerves, the contraction of muscles, the transport of gases, and the clotting of blood.

Sodium and potassium are the most important electrolytes involved in the homeostasis of body water. The differential permeability of the cell membranes maintains a differential distribution of these two cations: the concentration of sodium inside the cells is low, while its concentration in the extracellular fluid is high; for potassium the situation is just the reverse, and it is found mainly in the intracellular fluid compartment.

Electrolytes contribute to the movement of water from one fluid compartment to another by creating osmotic pressure gradients. When excess table salt (sodium chloride) is taken in, for example, the osmotic pressure of the interstitial fluid and plasma is increased, promoting reabsorption of water from the kidney tubules; thus extra water is retained in the body. Profuse sweating causes a loss of both water and sodium chloride. If enough sodium is lost from the extracellular fluids, they become hypotonic to the intracellular fluid. Water moves down the osmotic pressure gradient, from the interstitial fluid into the cells, ultimately producing a decrease in the blood volume. Potassium loss may similarly cause fluid to move out of the body cells into the extracellular fluid and ultimately to be excreted in the urine.

Sodium, potassium, and other positively charged ions are often spoken of as though they existed and moved in isolation. But it should be recalled that wherever there are positive ions, there are also negative ions such as chloride, bicarbonate, sulfate, and phosphate in amounts to precisely balance the electrical charges of the positive ions, leading to electrical neutrality. Even in regions where there is a local separation of charges, such as the polarized cell membrane of the neuron, there is a mutual attraction between the sodium ions outside the membrane and negative ions clustered on the inner surface of the membrane.

Interactions of electrical charges and the maintenance of electrical neutrality play a key role in the transport of electrolytes through membranes. Negative ions such as chloride or bicarbonate may move with positive ions; or one type of positive ion may be exchanged for another. For example, the polarization, depolarization, and repolarization of the nerve cell membrane involve exchange of sodium and potassium ions; when sodium ions move out of the kidney tubules into the interstitial fluid, they may be exchanged for hydrogen ions, thus participating in the maintenance of the body's acid-base balance.

ACID-BASE BALANCE

The range of pH in the body is extremely narrow or rather wide, depending on the definition of "in" the body. In the digestive tract, the hydrogen ion concentration varies ten millionfold, from pH 1 to pH 8. But in some respects, the digestive tract is effectively "outside" the body proper. In the extracellular fluids, the pH is normally maintained with phenomenal constancy, at about 7.4 in arterial blood and about 7.35 in venous blood and interstitial fluids.* Variation of just a few tenths of a pH unit from these values can have lethal results for the body: pH values of the extracellular fluids below 7.0 or above 7.8 are incompatible with life. Generally speaking, pH values of the arterial blood below 7.4 are classified as **acidosis,** while a person with a pH of the arterial blood above 7.4 is said to have **alkalosis** (Figure 31-4). (Remember that the pH scale is a negative logarithmic scale, in which each unit represents a power of ten, and the hydrogen ion concentration is high when the pH is low, and vice versa.)

Like the other equilibria in the body, the acid-base balance is a dynamic equilibrium. Acids and bases are taken in with food, and acids are produced in metabolic processes. The output side of the ledger includes excretion through the lungs and kidneys, as well as losses of acid in vomiting.

Three main mechanisms operate to control the pH in the body fluids:

1 The action of chemical buffer systems, which soak up excess amounts of acid or base
2 Respiration, which drains off carbon dioxide
3 Renal excretion of acid and base

Buffer Systems

If you were to add a portion of some acid material, such as orange juice, to a sample of blood, you would find that the pH of the blood remained fairly constant. Obviously, the physiological mechanisms of respiration and renal excretion do not operate in a

---

* The pH of the intracellular fluids has never been measured directly, but is believed from indirect evidence to range from 4.5 to 8.0 in different cells, averaging about 7.0

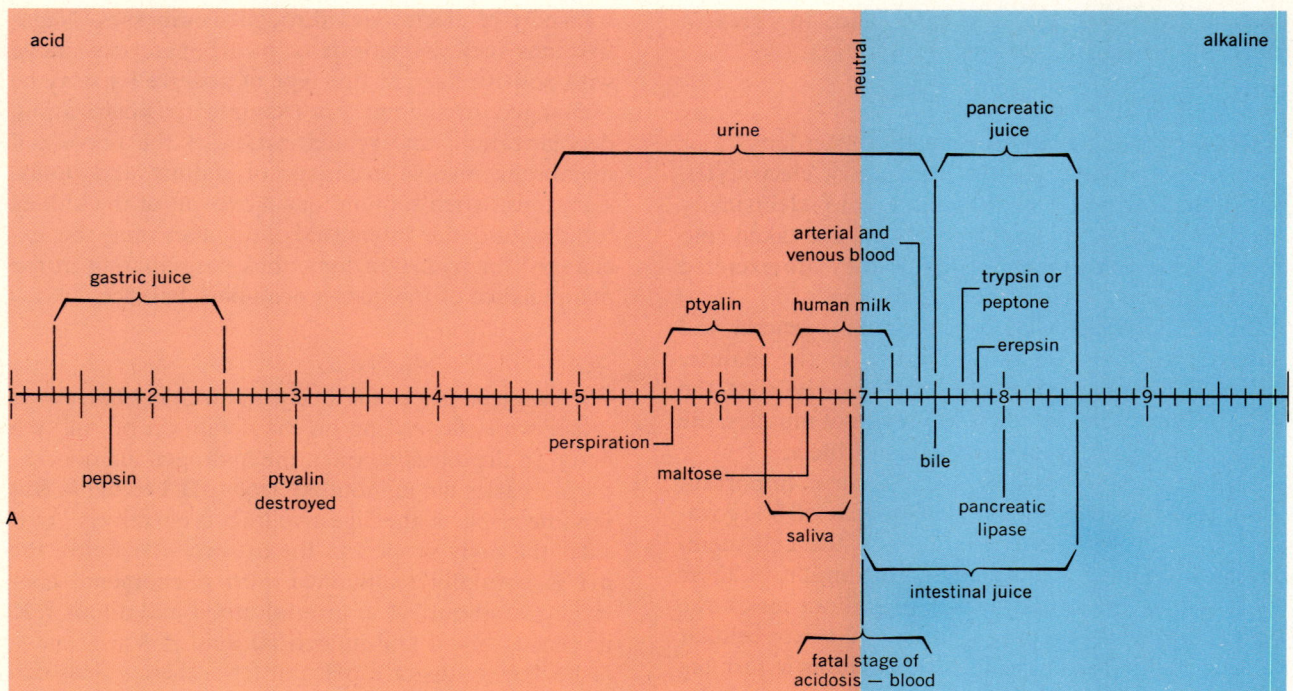

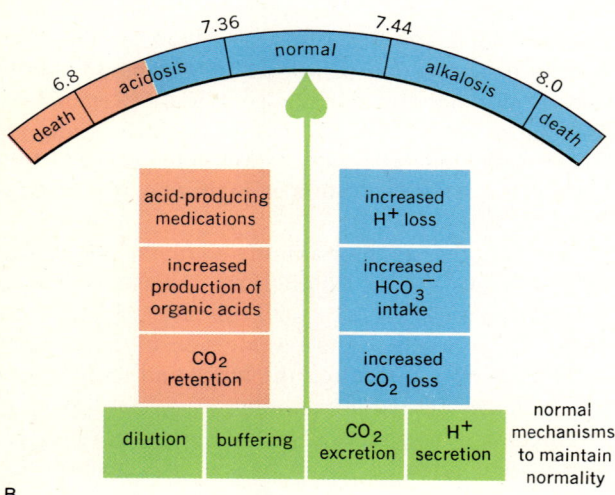

FIGURE 31-4   The pH scale runs from 1 to 14. Some values of physiological significance are indicated in (A); factors affecting body fluid pH are shown in (B).

test tube; the excess acid is absorbed in this case by the blood buffer systems, which act as a sort of a "chemical sponge." The buffer systems of the body fluids are so effective that they could successfully neutralize a liter of 1 N hydrochloric acid, infused into the bloodstream, without permitting the blood pH to fall below the critical value of 7.0. The daily challenges that the body faces are usually far more modest, involving mainly the gas CO_2, produced in cell respiration.

The buffer systems operating in the body consist of a weak acid and its sodium or potassium salt. The three most important buffer systems of the body are:

$$\frac{\text{Carbonic acid (H}_2\text{CO}_3)}{\text{Sodium bicarbonate (NaHCO}_3)}$$

$$\frac{\text{Sodium dihydrogen phosphate (NaH}_2\text{PO}_4)}{\text{Disodium hydrogen phosphate (Na}_2\text{HPO}_4)}$$

Protein buffer systems

A strong acid or base dissociates rapidly and completely in aqueous (water) solution, producing hydrogen or hydroxyl ions. A weak acid or base, on the other hand, dissociates only partially, leaving part of the hydrogen or hydroxyl ions it contains bound in undissociated acid molecules. Thus, if the strong acid hydrochloric acid, which exists in aqueous solutions entirely in the form of H^+ and Cl^- ions, is added to the bicarbonate buffer system, the following reaction occurs:

$$HCl + NaHCO_3 = H_2CO_3 + NaCl$$

Few of the H_2CO_3 molecules dissociate into $H^+ + HCO_3^-$ ions, and thus the excess hydrogen ions are effectively tied up. In addition, the carbonic acid tends to undergo a further reaction, dissociating into carbon dioxide and water:

$$H_2CO_3 = H_2O + CO_2$$

The carbon dioxide formed stimulates the respiratory center, and excess carbon dioxide is blown off in the lungs.

If a base, NaOH, is added to the same buffer system, the following reaction occurs:

$$NaOH + H_2CO_3 = NaHCO_3 + H_2O$$

neatly removing the excess hydroxyl ions.

A buffer system can be effective in keeping the pH of the medium unchanged only as long as both components of the buffer system are present. Extreme excesses of acid or base might overpower the buffer system by using up all of one component (i.e., the weak acid or its salt). The bicarbonate buffer system in the blood is not as powerful as it might be, for a pH 7.4 there are about 20 molecules of bicarbonate for each molecule of carbonic acid; thus, it is better equipped to handle an excess of acid than an excess of base. Despite its limited capacity, the bicarbonate system is an important buffer system in the body because of its plentiful supply, and, most important, because it is backed up by physiological mechanisms: the concentration of carbon dioxide can be regulated by the respiratory system, and the bicarbonate ion concentration can be regulated by the kidneys.

In the phosphate buffer system, NaH_2PO_4 is a weak acid, while Na_2HPO_4 is a very weak base. Like the carbonic acid–bicarbonate system, this system can take up either hydrogen or hydroxyl ions. It functions most effectively in the kidney tubules, where the phosphate concentration is increased and the tubular fluid is usually more acidic than the extracellular fluids. (Like the bicarbonate buffer system, the phosphate system has a greater buffering capacity in a slightly acidic medium).

The proteins of the cells and plasma are the most plentiful buffer systems of the body. Proteins are formed from amino acids, whose acid ($-COOH$) and basic ($-NH_2$) groups are bound together by peptide linkages. But proteins also have some free acid and amino groups, which can react with bases or acids, respectively. The protein buffers inside the cells act as a first line of defense against gross shifts of the acid-base balance. Since carbon dioxide can diffuse readily through cell membranes, and hydrogen ions and bicarbonate ions can also diffuse to some extent, the buffer systems inside the cells help to regulate the pH of the extracellular fluids as well.

Respiratory Regulation

If you breathe in and out very deeply and rapidly (hyperventilation), you may induce alkalosis in your body fluids. The rapid, deep breaths drive off larger than normal amounts of carbon dioxide in the expired air, producing an increase in the proportion of bicarbonate ion in the body fluid and causing the pH to rise. Fortunately, this voluntarily induced condition is self-limiting—before you have had a chance to come to serious harm, the decrease in carbon dioxide content (and carbonic acid level) of the blood produces a depression of the breathing center. A brief period of apnea follows, during which the carbon dioxide level rises to normal again, and a normal blood pH is restored.

The respiratory system is a key link in the body's mechanisms for regulating the acid-base balance. An excess of carbon dioxide, which could produce acidosis, stimulates the breathing center, increasing the rate and depth of breathing. The excess carbon dioxide is blown off, and the pH of the body fluids returns to normal.

The pH regulation by the respiratory system can not only handle the carbon dioxide produced in cell respiration, but also indirectly takes care of other acid products that enter the blood, such as acid products of digestion or the lactic acid produced by muscle metabolism. Such acids react with the bicarbonate buffer system, generating CO_2, which is then carried to the lungs and removed from the body. If the normal ventilation is not sufficient to cope with the amount of CO_2 being formed, the concentration of CO_2 in the arterial blood will rise and stimulate the respiratory center, which in turn stimulates respiratory activity to a higher level until the excess carbon dioxide is eliminated.

Renal Regulation

The pH of urine varies from day to day (in the range from about 4.5 to 8.0), depending on the composition of the body fluids, which in turn is determined by the general health and diet. The kidneys have several different mechanisms for compensating for excess alkalinity or acidity in the body fluids.

First, both NaH_2PO_4, which is acidic, and Na_2HPO_4, which is alkaline, can be excreted in the urine. If there is a tendency toward acidity of the extracellular fluids (which is often the case, since normal metabolism produces an excess of acids), sodium ions are reabsorbed and exchanged for hydrogen ions, and the more acid NaH_2PO_4 is excreted. This exchange occurs according to the reaction:

$$\underset{\text{(excreted)}}{Na_2HPO_4} + 2H_2CO_3 \rightarrow \overset{\text{(reabsorbed)}}{NaH_2PO_4} + 2NaHCO_3$$

Thus, bicarbonate ions are conserved for the body in the process, further contributing to a rise in the pH of the body fluids, and the urine is usually somewhat acid.

If there is a tendency toward alkalinity, the more alkaline form, Na_2HPO_4, will be excreted, and bicarbonate ions may also be eliminated in the urine. (Normally, this does not occur, and more than 99.9 percent of the filtered bicarbonate is reabsorbed. Bicarbonate appears in the urine when the level of bicarbonate in the blood exceeds 28 millimoles per liter.)

The kidneys are also capable of producing ammonia from the breakdown of the amino acid glutamine in the presence of the enzyme glutaminase. In the tubules, the free ammonia (NH_3) combines with hydrogen ions and is excreted as ammonium (NH_4^+) salts. This mechanism permits a further compensation for excess acidity in the extracellular fluids. The ammonium ions are exchanged for sodium ions, which are retained in the body. The secretion of ammonia in the kidney tubules does not occur unless the body fluids are tending toward acidosis, and the excretion of ammonium salts is coupled with a retention of bicarbonate ions.

In contrast to the respiratory mechanism, which brings a prompt adjustment of the pH of body fluids, the regulatory mechanisms of the kidneys are slower acting. But they play an extremely important role in the maintenance of the body's acid–base balance.

PRACTICAL CONSIDERATIONS

A pregnant woman is usually advised to cut down on salt in her diet to avoid troublesome swelling of feet and ankles. Fluid retention may also be a problem around the time of the menstrual periods. These common practical situations emphasize the intimate relationship between the body electrolytes and fluids, as well as the influence of endocrine hormones on the fluid balance of the body.

An excess of fluid in the interstitial space is called **edema.** This condition may result from (1) an increase in the blood pressure in the capillaries; (2) a drop in the plasma protein and hence a low plasma colloid osmotic pressure; (3) obstruction of the lymphatic drainage; (4) an increase in capillary permeability; or (5) fluid retention by the kidneys. Obstruction of the venous system may raise the capillary blood pressure, causing fluid to leak out into the interstitial spaces; a rise in capillary pressure may also be caused by heart failure, or by a local dilation of arterioles. (In allergic reactions, histamine relaxes the smooth muscle of the arterioles and constricts the venules, producing localized edematous swellings such as hives.) In certain types of kidney disease, the capillary membrane of the glomerular tuft becomes abnormally permeable, permitting large quantities of albumin to leak out into the renal tubules. The loss of protein from the blood plasma lowers the osmotic pressure in the vascular compartment; as a result, water diffuses out of the capillaries and accumulates in the interstitial space. Lymphatic drainage may be blocked by a tumor or inflammation, causing excess fluid to build up in the tissue spaces. Bacterial toxins may increase capillary permeability, resulting in an escape of proteins. When the kidneys fail to put out enough urine to balance the fluid intake, the excess fluid accumulates in the extracellular compartment. The plasma volume increases, elevating the capillary pressure, which in turn gives rise to edema. An imbalance of electrolytes commonly produces a disturbance of the fluid balance, and vice versa.

Deprivation of water, profuse sweating, diarrhea, or prolonged vomiting can result in a decrease in the extracellular fluid volume (dehydration). Circulation is impaired, and the blood flow to the kidneys is reduced. Without a sufficient blood supply, the kidneys cannot function properly, and waste products accumulate in the body. Fluids must be replaced promptly, either by mouth or by direct infusion into the bloodstream, in order to prevent permanent damage to the body systems or death.

Hospitalized patients often need fluid and electrolyte therapy. Injuries and surgical operations often involve a substantial loss of blood, and the fluid lost must be promptly replaced. Burns over large areas of the body present special problems of fluid replacement, since the burned areas exude large quantities of plasma. When patients cannot take in sufficient amounts of fluid and food by mouth, carbohydrate solutions, providing a ready source of energy, may be infused directly into the bloodstream (Figure 31-5). Care must be taken not to create electrolyte imbalances in treatments involving fluids. If water is used to irrigate a gastric tube, for example, ions can be

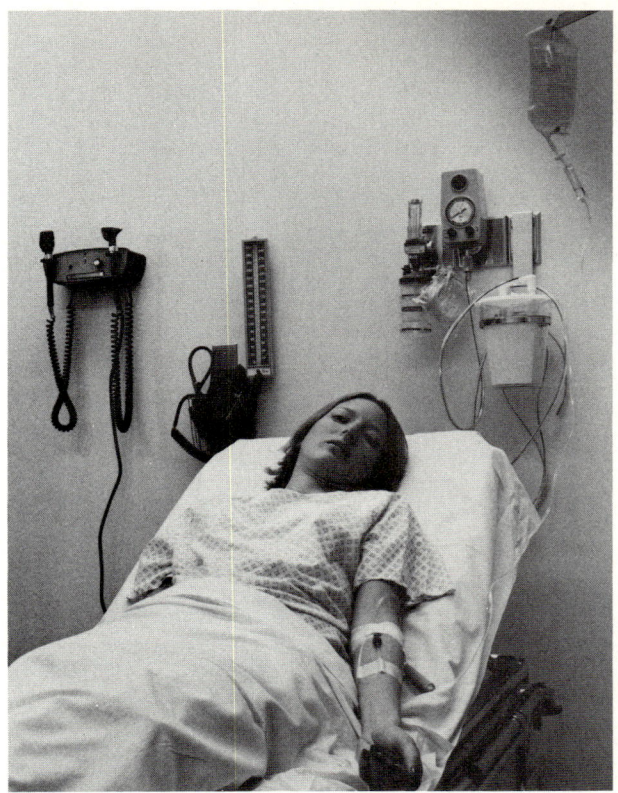

FIGURE 31-5 Intravenous infusion permits effective replacement of fluids and nutrients, to maintain to restore homeostasis.

washed out. Repeated enemas can similarly produce an electrolyte imbalance. Thus, it is preferable to use an isotonic sodium chloride solution (0.85 percent) or a balanced salt solution (containing other ions in addition to NaCl) for such procedures.

Severe diarrhea can result not only in dehydration, but also in acidosis, since large quantities of alkaline digestive juices, containing bicarbonate ions, are eliminated before they have had a chance to be reabsorbed. Vomiting may give rise either to alkalosis (if mainly acid stomach contents are vomited) or to acidosis (if contents from deeper in the gastrointestinal tract are vomited). Kidney disease, in which the kidneys are unable to rid the body of the excess acid products of metabolism; damage to the respiratory center or obstruction of the respiratory tract, resulting in a buildup of carbon dioxide in the body; and diseases such as diabetes mellitus, in which abnormal fat metabolism yields acid products, are all potential causes of acidosis. Alkalosis is a less common condition and is most often caused by the excessive intake of alkaline substances such as sodium bicarbonate for the treatment of indigestion or peptic ulcers.

The use of the terms acidosis and alkalosis is often confusingly imprecise. To clarify the situation, the terms compensated and uncompensated acidosis or alkalosis are introduced. In **compensated alkalosis,** the bicarbonate content of the blood increases, but the bicarbonate buffer system, backed up by the respiratory and excretory functions, manages to cope with the rise of a compensatory increase in H_2CO_3, without any change in the blood pH. If, however, the excess of bicarbonate (due, perhaps, to the ingestion of "antacids" or to excessive vomiting) is so great that the regulatory mechanisms are overwhelmed, the blood pH rises, and **uncompensated alkalosis** exists. Correspondingly, **compensated acidosis** refers to a condition in which there is a decrease in bicarbonate with a compensatory reduction of the H_2CO_3 content of the blood, keeping the pH unchanged; in **uncompensated acidosis,** the plasma bicarbonate is so depleted that the pH falls.

SUMMARY

The body of an adult man is about 60 percent water; 54 percent for an adult woman.

The body fluids are divided into compartments:

Intracellular fluid

Extracellular fluid

Vascular fluid (blood plasma)

Interstitial fluid

Special fluids (lymph, synovial, cerebrospinal, intraocular, etc.)

There is a continual interchange of materials among the fluid compartments, by diffusion and active transport.

Water enters the body through the digestive tract (food and beverages; reabsorption of water of metabolism) and leaves the body through the lungs, kidneys, large intestine, and skin.

Maintenance of fluid balance requires that water intake precisely equal water output.

The total amount of body fluid depends on age, sex, and amount of adipose tissue.

Water is about 70 percent of the fat-free tissue in an adult man.

The composition of the main fluid compartments differs:

Blood plasma and intracellular fluid have a much higher content of protein and nonelectrolytes than interstitial fluid.

Most of the sodium is in the extracellular fluid; most of the potassium is in the intracellular fluid.

The exchange of materials between the vascular and interstitial compartments is produced by diffusion, determined by the capillary blood pressure and the osmotic pressure gradient due to the plasma proteins.

Composition differences between the intracellular and interstitial fluids are maintained by energy-consuming processes of active transport.

Fluid intake is regulated by habit and the thirst mechanism and includes:

Beverages (variable amount)

Fluid content of foods (700 to 1200 ml daily)

Water of metabolism (about 300 ml daily)

Fluid output occurs through the:

Lungs (saturation of expired air with water) (about 300 ml daily)

Skin (insensible and sensible perspiration) (about 500 ml daily or more)

Large intestine (water in feces) (about 200 ml daily)

Kidneys (urine) (about 1500 ml daily)
  Fluid output through the lungs, skin, and large intestine is influenced mainly by environmental factors; excretion through the kidneys can be regulated within wide limits to control the body's fluid balance.
Electrolytes can dissociate into electrically charged ions.
  Sodium and potassium are the most important electrolytes involved in the homeostasis of body water.
  Electrolytes contribute to the movement of fluids from one compartment to another by creating osmotic pressure gradients.
  Movements of ions are governed not only by concentration gradients, but also by forces of electrical attraction between positive and negative ions and the maintenance of overall electrical neutrality.
The pH of the extracellular fluids must be maintained in the narrow range from 7.0 to 7.8 to be compatible with life.
  The normal pH of arterial blood is about 7.4, and venous blood 7.35.
  Arterial blood pH values below 7.4 are classified as acidosis, above 7.4 as alkalosis.
  Acids and bases are taken in with foods and produced in metabolism; acid-base balance is preserved by:
    Chemical buffer systems
    Respiration
    Renal excretion
The major buffer systems of the body are:
  Carbonic acid (H_2CO_3) + sodium bicarbonate ($NaHCO_3$)
  Sodium dihydrogen phosphate (NaH_2PO_4) + disodium hydrogen phosphate (Na_2HPO_4)
  Protein buffer systems
Buffers can take up excess hydrogen or hydroxyl ions without any appreciable change in pH.
  The bicarbonate buffer system of the blood is backed up by the respiratory system, which blows off excess carbon dioxide, and the kidneys, which regulate bicarbonate concentration.
  The phosphate buffer system functions mainly in the kidney tubules.
  Protein buffer systems are especially important in intracellular fluids, which indirectly regulate the acid-base balance of extracellular fluids.
An excess of carbon dioxide (product of cell respiration), producing acidosis, stimulates the respiratory center in the medulla, increasing the rate and depth of breathing and eliminating additional carbon dioxide in the expired air, correcting the acidosis.
  Alkalosis, in which the carbon dioxide level of the extracellular fluids is reduced, depresses the respiratory center, causing temporary apnea that restores the body fluid pH to normal.
The kidneys regulate the pH of body fluids by:
  Excreting NaH_2PO_4 (in acidosis) or Na_2HPO_4 (in alkalosis)
  Reabsorbing bicarbonate ($NaHCO_3$) in acidosis
  Producing ammonia from glutamine breakdown and excreting it

as ammonium ($NH_4{}^+$) salts (in acidosis)
Edema is an excess of fluid in the interstitial space. It may result from:
  An increase in capillary blood pressure
  A drop in plasma protein (colloid osmotic pressure)
  Obstruction of lymphatic drainage
  Increase in capillary permeability
  Fluid retention of the kidneys
Dehydration (a decrease of fluid in the interstitial space) impairs the circulation and kidney function.
Fluid and electrolyte therapy is used to replace losses or provide for current needs if normal intake is prevented.
Acidosis and alkalosis are disturbances of the acid-base balance:
  Compensated alkalosis: bicarbonate content increased but pH unchanged.
  Uncompensated alkalosis: bicarbonate content increased, pH rises.
  Compensated acidosis: bicarbonate content decreased but pH unchanged.
  Uncompensated acidosis: bicarbonate depleted, pH falls.

QUESTIONS FOR REVIEW AND THOUGHT

1 Describe the fluid compartments of the body.

2 What mechanisms operate to keep the fluid composition of the body relatively constant?

3 What are the major sources of fluid intake?

4 What are the major mechanisms of fluid output?

5 Describe the operation of the thirst mechanism in fluid homeostasis.

6 A plane has crash-landed in the desert. Days may pass before rescuers locate it, and the water supplies were destroyed in the crash. Which of the passengers and crew stand the best chances for survival: the pilot, a 35-year-old man; the stewardess, a 24-year-old woman; a six-month-old baby; a 70-year-old man; a 40-year-old female passenger who was badly burned in the crash.

7 It is 95° F and you are working in the sun and sweating profusely. Whenever you feel thirsty, you drink water from the gallon jug you brought along. Are you taking in all you need to maintain constancy of body fluids?

8 Describe the mechanisms that regulate the body's acid-base balance.

9 How can an imbalance of electrolytes produce a disturbance of the fluid balance?

10 Giving nourishment by intravenous infusion introduces larger amounts of fluid into the body than normal eating does. Describe the adjustments necessary in the patient's body to maintain homeostasis.

11 What are the dangers in regularly taking bicarbonate for indigestion?

THE ENDOCRINE SYSTEM

32

Endocrinology is one of the fastest developing areas of biomedical research. The past two decades have seen a proliferation of newly discovered hormones, releasing factors that control the secretion of long known hormones, and even inhibiting factors that further regulate their secretion.

The nervous system and the endocrine system are the two major control systems of the body. The coordinating effects of the nervous system are transmitted nearly instantaneously by electrochemical impulses; the endocrine glands secrete chemical regulators, which are carried through the body by the bloodstream. The action of these chemical regulators—hormones—is more slowly established and longer-lasting than that of nerve impulses. Nerve action is measured in milliseconds. Some hormones exert their effects in seconds; others need several days to get started, and then last for weeks, months, or even years. Nerve impulses control the functions only of muscles and glands, while hormones may act on all the cells of the body.

A **hormone** may be defined as a chemical substance that is secreted into the body fluids by one cell or a group of cells and controls and regulates the functions of other cells in the body. Chemically, the hormones are a varied group, but all can be classified in two main subdivisions: (1) proteins or derivatives of proteins and amino acids (e.g., amines) and (2) steroids. They are synthesized in the endocrine glands by anabolic reactions and secreted into the extracellular fluids around the secretory cells, from which they are absorbed into the bloodstream. (Endocrine glands are sometimes referred to as ductless glands, in contrast to exocrine glands such as sweat glands and the glands that secrete digestive juices, which pour their secretions into ducts leading to the outside of the body or to specific body cavities.)

Some hormones may be considered as **local hormones:** they function at or close to the point where they are secreted and are usually destroyed rapidly. Secretin and cholecystokinin, which are secreted in the small intestine and transported to the nearby pancreas and gallbladder to aid in digestion, are among the hormones with specific local effects; acetylcholine and norepinephrine, secreted at the synapses of neurons and acting there, have even more narrowly local effects. The nerve transmitter substances secreted by neurons are now commonly referred to as **neurohumors,** to distinguish them from the more general hormones secreted by the endocrine glands. (Norepinephrine is also secreted by the adrenal medulla and carried through the body to exert more far-reaching effects; in that role it is a true hormone.) **General hormones** are carried through the body and have effects on distant organs. Some, such as the thyroid hormone, affect the functioning of literally all the cells of the body. Others act only on specific types of cells or tissues—for example, the pituitary hormone ACTH, which specifically stimulates the adrenal cortex. The tissues that are specifically affected by hormones in this way are called **target tissues.**

The action of endocrine hormones pervades every aspect of body function. Hormones regulate metabolism, growth and development, and reproduction. They play many vital roles in homeostasis, the maintenance of a constant internal environment, controlling the metabolism of carbohydrates, fats, and proteins, the electrolyte and water balance, and the blood-sugar level. Working in conjunction with the nervous system, hormones integrate the responses of diverse organs and tissues of the body to internal and external stimuli.

MECHANISMS OF HORMONE ACTION

For decades hormone actions were explained at the organ level, or perhaps the tissue level. But now explanations are being found at the cellular and molecular levels. With this more complete understanding, we can soon expect to have spectacular payoffs—the ability for intervention into body processes at a level never before thought possible.

Exactly how hormones exert their action in the body has been a subject of lively conjecture and speculation. There is evidence to indicate that hormone action is mediated through the sequence of specific DNA activation (or inhibition of protein suppressors of specific genes), RNA synthesis, and ultimate enzyme production. But increasingly, attention has been focused on events that take place at the cell membrane.

When hormones reach their target cells, do they actually enter the cells to produce their effects? It is thought that the steroid hormones, such as the sex hormones, may actually do so, possibly penetrating through the cell membrane in combination with a special receptor chemical. But protein and polypeptide hormones have very large molecules. Human growth hormone, for example, consists of a chain of 188 amino acids and has a molecular weight of 21,500. Studies by Earl W. Sutherland in the late 1950s revealed a new aspect of body chemistry and suggested how such hormones may exert their effect; these studies won Sutherland a Nobel Prize in 1971.

Sutherland isolated and studied a compound called **cyclic AMP** (an abbreviation for adenosine 3′,4′-monophosphate), which is closely related to ATP (adenosine triphosphate), the "energy currency" of living cells. Inside the cell, ATP can be converted to cyclic AMP by the action of an enzyme, **adenyl cyclase,** which seems to be fixed in the cell membrane.

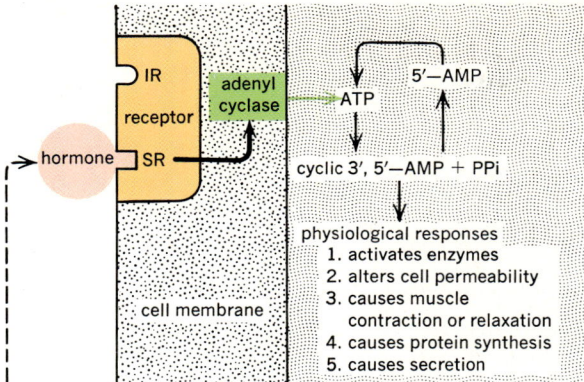

FIGURE 32-1 Two-messenger mechanism of hormone action. The hormone (first messenger) reacts at the surface of the cell membrane with a specific stimulatory (SR) or inhibitory (IR) receptor site. In the case of stimulation, the enzyme adenyl cyclase then catalyzes the synthesis of cyclic AMP within the cell. cAMP, the second messenger, then stimulates characteristic physiological responses of the cell. Reaction at an inhibitory site inhibits the action of adenyl cyclase and causes a drop in cAMP levels within the cell.

According to Sutherland's elegant hypothesis, a protein or proteinlike hormone does not actually enter the cell on which it acts, but instead reacts at the surface of the cell membrane with a specific receptor site. This reaction may stimulate the enzyme adenyl cyclase on the inner surface of the membrane, sparking an increase in cyclic AMP synthesis, which in turn provides the starting signal for the specific effect on the cell that the hormone produces. Or the reaction with the receptor site may inhibit another enzyme, **phosphodiesterase,** which normally breaks down cyclic AMP. This effect also results in a net increase in the amount of cyclic AMP in the cell. Still another type of specific receptor site may be involved in a reaction with a hormone at the cell membrane. This type of reaction may inhibit adenyl cyclase and reduce the amount of cyclic AMP in the cell.

In each case the hormone acts as a "first messenger," which must have its message translated by a "second messenger," cyclic AMP, which works inside the cell to produce the ultimate effect (Figure 32-1). The variety of specific receptor sites and the chemical makeup of the cell itself help to ensure that each hormone will act precisely on the appropriate cells and produce its own characteristic effect.

The secretion of hormones is controlled by feedback mechanisms, which frequently involve the interrelated action of other hormones. Some hormones stimulate the secretion of a second hormone or reinforce its action. Others inhibit the synthesis, secretion, or activity of a second hormone. Thus, both positive and negative feedback mechanisms are important in hormone action. These mechanisms are so finely tuned that normally the amount of hormones circulating in the blood remains remarkably constant: the rate of their production keeps pace with the rate of their utilization and destruction.

The nervous system also has a profound effect on endocrine secretions. Sympathetic impulses to the adrenal medulla stimulate the secretion of the hormones epinephrine and norepinephrine, which reinforce the effects of sympathetic stimulation. The hypothalamus, a portion of the brain, has been found to produce not only hormones, but also releasing factors, which stimulate the secretions of hormones of the anterior lobe of the pituitary, as well as inhibitory factors, which inhibit the secretion of pituitary hormones.

Some of the complex interrelationships between the nervous system and the endocrine glands and among the individual endocrine hormones are pointed out in the following discussions of the endocrine glands.

THE ENDOCRINE GLANDS

Most of the systems of the body form continuous anatomical structures. The heart and blood vessels of the circulatory system are linked together into a continuous network. Starting at the distal end of one of the nerves of the peripheral nervous system, it would be possible to trace a pathway to the spinal cord, brain, or any nerve in the body, without ever leaving nerve tissue. The bones of the skeleton are articulated into a single structure, and the digestive system and respiratory system each form continuous tracts. The glands of the endocrine system, on the other hand, are scattered through the body like islands. Anatomically many of the glands are composed of modified epithelial tissue, but during the early development of the body they lose their connection with the rest of the epithelium and sink into the mass of other tissues. Possessing no structural connection, they still are unified into a system functionally, interacting in a marvelously harmonious fashion to coordinate and control the activities of the body.

The major endocrine glands, shown in Figure 32-2, are the hypophysis (or pituitary), the thyroid, the parathyroids, the thymus, the pancreas, the adrenal glands, and the gonads (testes in the male and ovaries in the female, with the placenta functioning as an additional endocrine organ during pregnancy). The hypothalamus and pineal body, portions of the brain, also have been found to have endocrine functions, and hormones are also secreted by individual cells or groups of cells in the linings of the stomach and duodenum and in the liver and kidneys.

The endocrine glands and their secretions are summarized in Table 32-1.

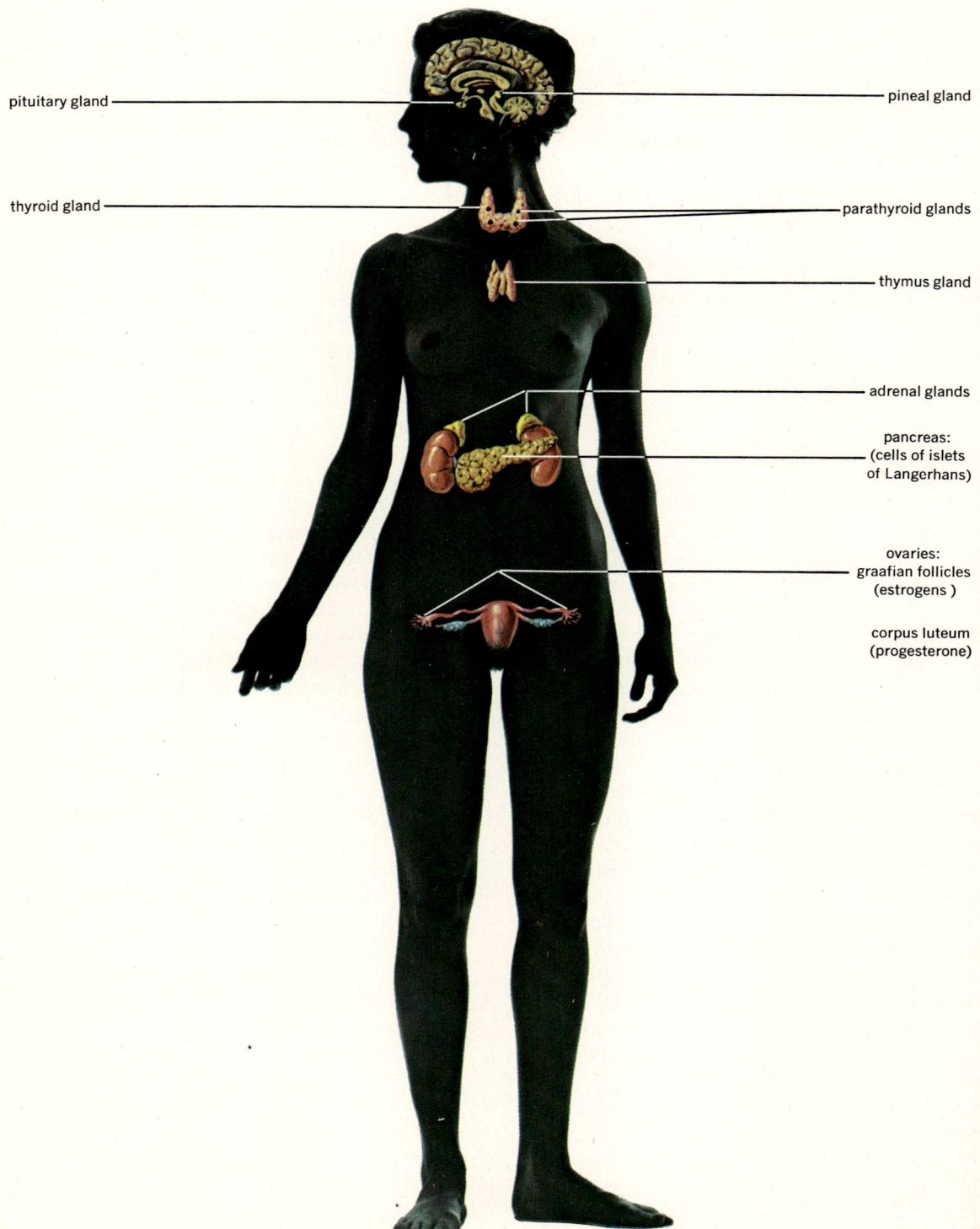

pituitary gland ———————————————————————— pineal gland

thyroid gland ———————————————————— parathyroid glands

———————————————————— thymus gland

———————————————————— adrenal glands

pancreas:
(cells of islets
of Langerhans)

ovaries:
graafian follicles
(estrogens)

corpus luteum
(progesterone)

FIGURE 32-2   The endocrine glands.

TABLE 32-1 Major Hormones and Hormonelike Substances

GLAND	HORMONE	MAIN EFFECTS
Adenohypophysis	Growth hormone (somatotropin, STH)	Stimulates liver to secrete somatomedin, which stimulates growth, increases protein synthesis
	Prolactin (LTH)	Stimulates milk production by mammary glands; maintains corpora lutea and secretion of progesterone
	Thyrotropic hormone (TSH)	Stimulates thyroid hormone synthesis and secretion
	Adrenocorticotropic hormone (ACTH)	Stimulates secretion of glucocorticoids by adrenal cortex
	Follicle-stimulating hormone (FSH)	Stimulates growth of follicles in ovary and of seminiferous tubules in testes, ovum and sperm production
	Luteinizing hormone (LH); Interstitial cell-stimulating hormone (ICSH)	Stimulates ovulation and secretion of sex hormones by ovaries and testes
Adenohypophysis (pars intermedia)	Melanocyte-stimulating hormone (intermedin, MSH)	Controls skin pigmentation
Hypothalamus	Releasing factors	Release of tropic hormones by adenohypophysis
Hypothalamus (stored in neurohypophysis)	Vasopressin (antidiuretic hormone, ADH)	Stimulates contraction of smooth muscles, constriction of blood vessels, and reabsorption of water by kidneys
	Oxytocin	Stimulates uterine contractions and release of milk by mammary glands
Pineal gland	Melatonin	Inhibits ovaries; may help to regulate pituitary
Thyroid	Thyroxine	Stimulates oxidative metabolism (increases BMR)
	Calcitonin	Regulates calcium metabolism (antagonist of parathormone): lowers serum Ca^{++}
Parathyroids	Parathormone	Regulates calcium and phosphorus metabolism: raises serum Ca^{++}, lowers serum $PO_4^{\equiv}$
Thymus	Thymosin	Stimulates maturation of immunologically competent lymphocytes
Liver	Somatomedin	Stimulates growth, increases protein synthesis
Stomach mucosa	Gastrin	Stimulates secretion of gastric juice
Duodenal mucosa	Secretin	Stimulates secretion of pancreatic juice rich in $NaHCO_3$ and of bile and intestinal juice
	Pancreozymin	Stimulates secretion of pancreatic juice rich in enzymes
	Cholecystokinin	Stimulates contraction of gallbladder and release of bile
	Enterogastrone	Inhibits mobility and secretion of stomach
	Enterocrinin	Stimulates secretion of intestinal juice
	Villikinin	Stimulates motility of villi
Pancreas (alpha cells)	Glucagon	Stimulates conversion of liver glycogen to blood glucose; raises blood sugar level
Pancreas (beta cells)	Insulin	Stimulates glycogen storage and glucose utilization; lowers blood sugar level
Kidneys	Erythropoietin	Stimulates erythropoiesis

TABLE 32-1 (Continued)

GLAND	HORMONE	MAIN EFFECTS
Blood (under action of renin from kidneys)	Angiotensin	Stimulates vasoconstriction, causing blood pressure rise
Adrenal medulla	Epinephrine	Reinforces action of sympathetic nerves; stimulates glycogen breakdown, raising blood sugar; increases cardiac output; elevates BMR
	Norepinephine	Similar to epinephrine; constricts blood vessels
Adrenal cortex	Glucocorticoids (cortisol, cortisone, hydrocortisone, etc.)	Inhibit incorporation of amino acids into proteins; stimulate conversion of proteins to carbohydrates; help maintain normal blood sugar level; antistress, antiallergy
	Mineralocorticoids (aldosterone, deoxycorticosterone, etc.)	Regulate sodium-potassium metabolism (increase blood Na^+, decrease blood K^+), increase body fluid
	Sex hormones (adrenosterone, dehydroepiandrosterone, etc.)	Stimulate development of secondary sex characteristics, especially male
Ovaries	Estrogens	Stimulate development and maintenance of female sex characteristics and behavior
	Progesterone	Stimulates female sex characteristics; maintains pregnancy; stimulates development of mammary glands
Placenta	Chorionic gonadotropin	Acts with other hormones to maintain pregnancy (detected in pregnancy tests)
	Placental lactogen	Mimics growth hormone and prolactin
Testes	Testosterone	Stimulates development and maintenance of male sex characteristics and behavior
Seminal vesicles (and others)	Prostaglandins	Variety of effects including stimulation of uterine contractions, vasoconstriction, raising and lowering of blood pressure
Damaged tissues	Histamine	Increases capillary permeability
Various body cells	Chalones	Work with epinephrine to inhibit cell division
Various specialized glands	Pheromones	Produce effects on other members of the same species (sex attractants, etc.)

THE HYPOPHYSIS (PITUITARY GLAND)

Few other structures in the body have such a profound and pervasive influence as the pituitary gland. This pea-sized mass of glandular tissue, weighing little more than half a gram, indirectly controls such critical body functions as growth, metabolism, sexual development, reproduction, lactation, blood vessel tone, and the maintenance of the body's fluid balance.

As befits its importance, the pituitary (also called the hypophysis) has a protected position, at the base of the brain. It lies in a small deep fossa, the sella turcica, in the floor of the cranial cavity. The round body of the gland is surrounded by a capsule of fibrous connective tissue, and a slender stalk, the **infun-** **dibulum,** passes upward, penetrates the dura mater, and connects the pituitary to the hypothalamus, which lies above it (Figure 32-3).

The hypophysis consists of two distinct parts, or lobes, which have a somewhat different internal structure, embryological origin, and different functions. The larger, anterior lobe, called the **adenohypophysis,** forms from an outpouching from the roof of the oral cavity, while the smaller, posterior lobe, the **neurophypophysis,** develops from an outpouching from the forebrain.

The adenohypophysis, the glandular portion of the pituitary, consists of three parts: the **pars distalis,** containing most of the functional cells of the gland; the **pars tuberalis,** a thin epithelial plate surrounding the

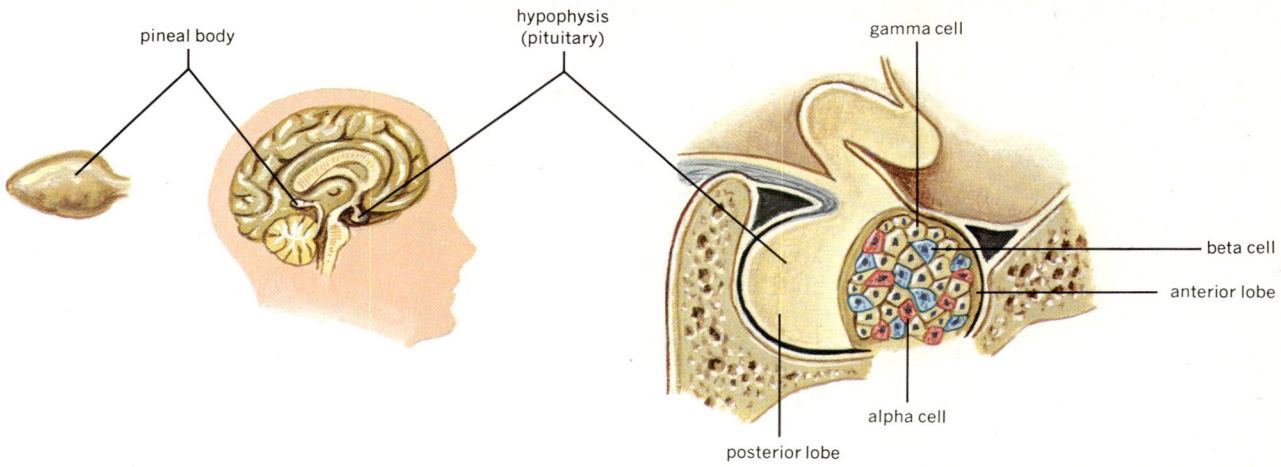

FIGURE 32-3 The pituitary gland. The micrograph shows a section of the adenohypophysis, ×340.

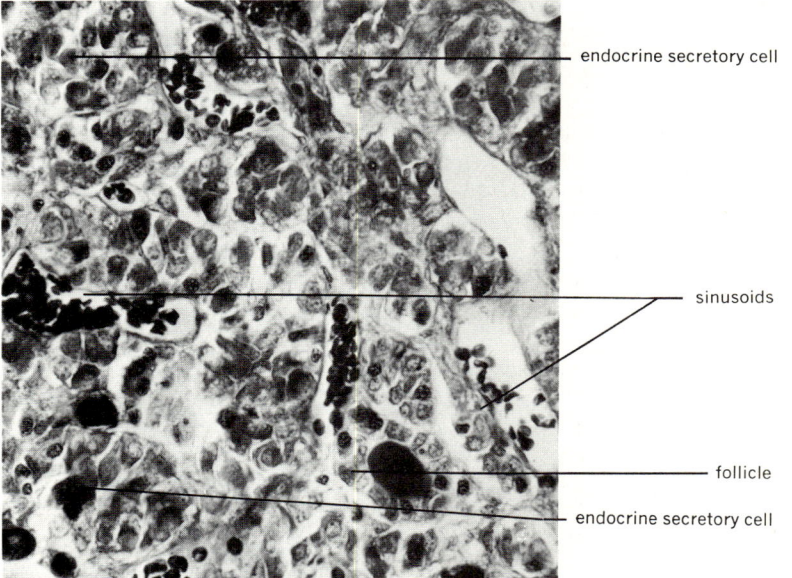

infundibular stalk; and the **pars intermedia,** or intermediate lobe, which has an active hormone-producing role in many animals but does not seem to have much importance in man. Three major cell types can be recognized in the adenohypophysis by simple staining techniques: **basophils,** which accept basic dyes (about 15 percent), **acidophils,** which accept acid dyes (about 35 percent), and **chromophobes,** which stain only faintly (about 50 percent). The cells are arranged in blocks or cords around thin-walled sinusoidal blood vessels. A rich vascular plexus in the infundibular stalk, forming the **hypophyseal portal system,** carries the products of neurosecretory cells down to the pituitary from the hypothalamus.

The neurohypophysis, the nervous portion of the pituitary, consists mainly of the **pars nervosa,** together with the infundibulum, which includes the infundibular stalk and the medial eminence. It is composed of numerous branching nerve fibers and tiny neuroglialike cells called **pituicytes.** Connective tissue from the capsule penetrates the neurohypophysis, bringing with it an abundant blood supply. Venous blood from both the anterior and the posterior lobes is drained by veins that communicate with the cavernous venous sinuses, eventually emptying into the internal jugular veins. Neurons from the hypothalamic nuclei pass through the infundibular stalk and terminate in the posterior lobe. The hormones released by the neurohypophysis are actually produced in the hypothalamus and trickle down the nerve fibers into the posterior lobe of the pituitary. There they are stored in the pituicytes or pass directly out into the bloodstream.

Role of the Hypothalamus

Until the late 1960s, the pituitary was regarded as the "master gland" of the body, directly or indirectly controlling the functions of the other endocrine glands. One of the most important recent advances in endocrinology has been the growing realization that the true role of "master gland" belongs to the hypothalamus, with the pituitary as its humble servant. First researchers were surprised to discover that the neurohypophysis does not manufacture its two hormones, but only receives them from the hypothalamus and stores them temporarily. Then it was learned that the adenohypophysis secretes its hormones not on its own initiative, but at the bidding of the hypothalamus, transmitted through chemical releasing factors and inhibiting factors. These new discoveries open up promising new possibilities for intervening when endocrine function has gone awry. Thyrotropin, for example, is a complicated glycoprotein, far too large a molecule to synthesize economically. Yet its releasing factor, TRF, is a polypeptide consisting of only three amino acids, which can be synthesized readily.

The hypothalamus functions as a complicated control center, continually receiving information on the current status of the body systems via nerve impulses and by monitoring the composition and temperature of the circulating blood. All these incoming messages are interpreted, evaluated, and outgoing messages are dispatched via nerves or through the hormones of the endocrine system. If a person is under stress, for example, the hypothalamus is informed, produces corticotropin releasing factor (CRF), the releasing factor for ACTH, and sends it down the hypophyseal portal system to the adenohypophysis, which is stimulated to produce ACTH. This pituitary hormone passes out into the bloodstream and is carried to the adrenal cortex, which in turn is stimulated to produce its own hormones, glucocorticoids, which aid the body in combatting the stress. The hypothalamus plays a key role in the intricate feedback systems that govern the secretion of the endocrine hormones.

Hormones of the Adenohypophysis

The hormones of the adenohypophysis have a most profound effect on the body, affecting almost every aspect of its physiology. For the most part, these effects are not exerted directly, but rather by influencing the secretion of hormones by other glands of the endocrine system.

The hormones isolated from the secretions of the adenohypophysis include: growth hormone (GH; also called somatotropin, or STH); adrenocorticotropic hormone (or corticotropin; ACTH); thyrotropin (TSH); lactogenic hormone (prolactin, or luteotropic hormone, LTH); follicle-stimulating hormone (FSH); luteinizing hormone (LH) in the female and interstitial cell-stimulating hormone (ICSH) in the male; melanocyte-stimulating hormone (MSH); and β-lipo-

tropic hormone (β-lipotropin or β-LPH). All of these hormones are proteins, and three of them (FSH, LH, and TSH) are glycoproteins, containing a carbohydrate component in addition to the amino acids. Growth hormone and lactogenic hormone are secreted by the acidophils; the other anterior pituitary hormones are secreted by the basophils.

The adenohypophysis secretes its hormones at the bidding of the hypothalamus. Neurons of the hypothalamus are believed to release substances into the blood that flows through the capillary plexus of the hypophyseal portal system; these releasing factors are carried to the adenohypophysis and stimulate the secretion of the appropriate hormones.

Growth Hormone Those who are blessed with normal stature seldom pause to think of how amazingly well-regulated the process of human growth is. Growth begins at conception, first explosively and then gradually slowing, with a brief spurt at puberty; finally, at a preset time somehow built into the body's "clock," growth ceases at a total height and mass determined by the person's heredity and nutrition.

For some, however, the fine tuning of the growth processes breaks down, and dwarfism or giantism may result. Through the years, these victims of endocrine malfunction have been regarded with pity or derision, displayed as sideshow freaks or kept as pampered pets in decadent royal courts. Nothing could be done to help them until quite recently.

The main hormone controlling growth of the body is the **growth hormone (GH)** secreted by the anterior pituitary. The effect of this hormone (also called **somatotropin, STH**) is to cause all tissues capable of growing to grow. It increases the rate of protein synthesis in all the body cells, both by enhancing amino acid transport through the cell membrane and by increasing the formation or activity of RNA. Growth hormone also decreases the rate of carbohydrate utilization throughout the body and increases the mobilization and energy metabolism of fats.

For a time the position of growth hormone seemed somewhat anomalous: all the other hormones of the adenohypophysis act upon another endocrine organ, causing it to secrete its own hormone in turn and thus producing their effects on the body indirectly. But growth hormone seemed to affect all the body cells generally, rather than acting on some particular endocrine target organ. However, it was found in 1957 that growth hormone, too, acts through a hormone intermediary. In 1967 Judson van Wyk at the University of North Carolina isolated the elusive intermediary, a hormone named **somatomedin,** which is secreted by the liver. It is small wonder that its existence was not suspected earlier, for somatomedin exerts its effects in exceedingly small amounts. Only one part of somatomedin is present in 10 million parts of blood. It is now believed that somatomedin is the true "growth hormone," acting on the body cells, while the function of growth hormone (somatotropin) is to stimulate the secretion of somatomedin by the liver.

The effects of under- or oversecretion of the pituitary growth hormone are dramatic (Figure 32-4). Such malfunction may be caused by a tumor of the pituitary; if the tumor is glandular, too much of the pituitary hormones will be produced, while if the tumor is composed of nonsecreting cells, the working part of the gland will be crowded and inhibited.

If too little somatotropin is secreted during childhood, **pituitary dwarfism** will result, producing a **midget.** The person's body parts are all in appropriate proportions, but the overall stature is much smaller than normal.* The condition is commonly associated with a retardation of sexual development, and the person's sex organs remain infantile. Sexual development can be stimulated in such cases by administering sex hormones, but care must be taken not to begin the treatment too soon, for the sex hormones produce not only sexual development but also a stoppage of body growth.

If growth hormone, like insulin, varied little from one species to another, the slaughterhouses would provide an amply supply of beef and hog pituitaries for treating pituitary dwarfs during childhood and aiding them to achieve normal growth and development. Unfortunately, the growth hormones of other species (except for the primates) have little effect on humans. A small number of children have been successfully treated with human pituitary extracts, but these must be obtained from human cadavers, and 150 pituitaries are needed to treat just one child for a year. The human growth hormone molecule is a good-sized protein, 188 amino acids long. In 1970, Choh Hao Li at the University of California in San Francisco announced a stunning feat: he synthesized a small amount of pure human growth hormone. However, it will be some time before industrial synthesis on a scale that would help children destined to grow into midgets is feasible. Now it is hoped that somatomedin will prove to be a simpler substance, more readily synthesized, and can be used for the treatment of dwarfism.

Underproduction of somatotropin in adult life produces a condition called **Simmonds' disease,** or **hypophyseal cachexia,** in which there is a severe atrophy of

---

* **Achondroplasia,** a form of dwarfism in which the head and trunk are of normal size but the arms and legs are unnaturally short, is a different condition, resulting from a defect in the transformation of cartilage into bone. The condition is hereditary, usually inherited as a dominant.

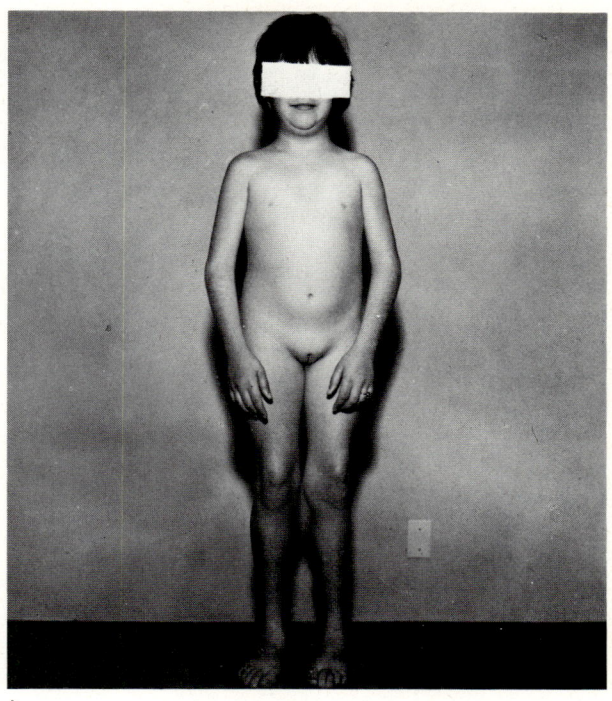

A

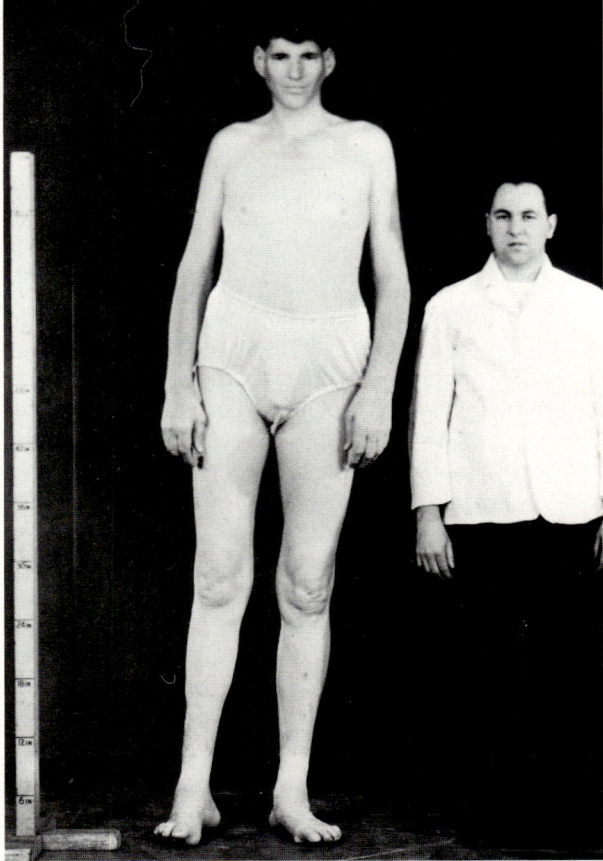

B

FIGURE 32-4   A pituitary dwarf (A) and a pituitary giant (B, shown with a normal-sized man) both suffer from malfunction of the pituitary gland.

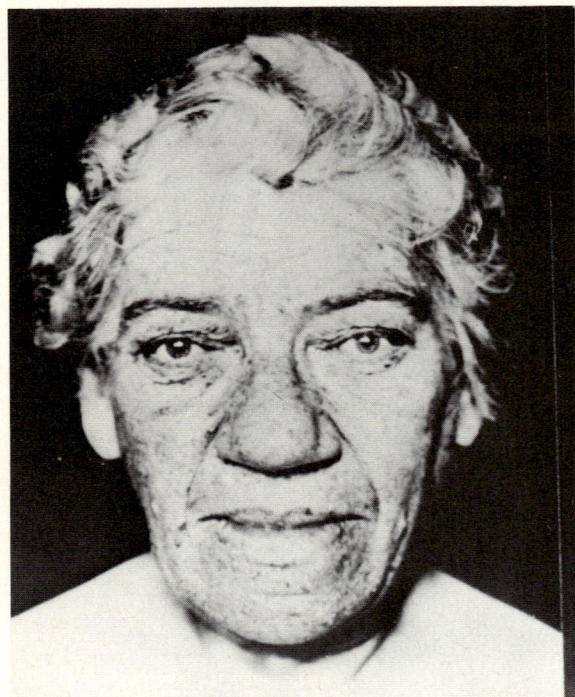

FIGURE 32-5 Acromegaly results from hypersecretion of pituitary growth hormone after growth is complete.

body tissues, producing emaciation, muscular debility, loss of sexual function, and premature aging.

Oversecretion of the pituitary growth hormone produces quite different conditions. If it occurs during childhood, before the epiphyses of the long bones close, **giantism** results, and the person may grow to a height of seven or eight feet. If pituitary oversecretion occurs in adulthood, the long bones are no longer capable of elongation, so there is no increase in height. But the excess growth hormone can stimulate the bones to increase in thickness, producing gross distortions (Figure 32-5). The hands and feet become large and spadelike, while the bones of the face and skull thicken and the lower jaw protrudes. Soft-tissue organs, such as the tongue, liver, and kidneys, also become enlarged. This condition is called **acromegaly.**

The recently discovered hypothalamic inhibitor of growth hormone secretion, **somatostatin (GR–IH),** is showing promising results in the treatment both of giantism and of acromegaly. Somatostatin also counters the blood-sugar-elevating action of growth hormone, apparently by inhibiting both the alpha- and the beta-cells of the pancreas.

In addition to the inhibiting factor, the secretion of growth hormone is also regulated by a releasing hormone, secreted by the hypothalamus and transported to the adenohypophysis via the hypophyseal portal system.

Prolactin A bird brooding the eggs in her nest, a mother mouse laboriously carrying her young in her mouth away from a threatened burrow, and a human mother breast-feeding her baby are all acting under the influence of the same hormone: the anterior pituitary hormone **prolactin.** This hormone has been shown to function not only in the stimulation of the mammary glands, promoting the secretion of milk, but also in fostering the "maternal instinct," even in animals such as birds that do not produce milk.

Prolactin is believed to be identical with **luteotropin (LTH),** which stimulates the corpus luteum of the ovary to secrete its own hormone, progesterone. Prolactin is present in the blood of children and of adult men, although it is not known what function it served there. (Elevated prolactin levels in men depress sperm count and libido, but in both men and women prolactin levels increase sharply during sexual excitement, reaching a peak at orgasm.) In the woman, prolactin levels begin to rise early in pregnancy, leveling off just before delivery. (The normal prolactin level in a non-pregnant woman is about 10 μg/liter of blood plasma and rises to 200 just before delivery; in men the normal level is about 6μg/liter.) Lactation does not occur during pregnancy to any significant extent, despite the high prolactin levels; it is thought that its end-effect is blocked by the high levels of female sex hormones, estrogen and progesterone, that exist during pregnancy. After the baby is born, prolactin secretion is stimulated by a nervous reflex, initiated by the act of suckling. Like the other anterior pituitary hormones, the secretion of prolactin appears to be controlled by a releasing hormone and an inhibiting hormone secreted by the hypothalamus.

Thyrotropin It took the hypothalamuses of 5 million sheep to produce 1 milligram of thyrotropin-releasing factor, which was enough to identify its amino acid composition. It was found to be surprisingly simple, consisting of only three different amino acids—histidine, glutamic acid, and proline—in equal amounts. But there was not enough of the substance to determine the sequence of the amino acids. Researchers synthesized the six possible tripeptides containing these three amino acids and tested them for physiological activity. None of them was active until an acetyl group was added to the N-end. Minor chemical modifications yielded a synthetic substance identical with the natural releasing factor: pglu-his-pro-NH$_2$. (*pglu* stands for pyroglutamic acid.) This achievement opened the way for a relatively cheap, simple way of regulating the activity of the thyroid gland.

The pituitary hormone thyrotropin, or thyroid-stimulating hormone (TSH), influences both the

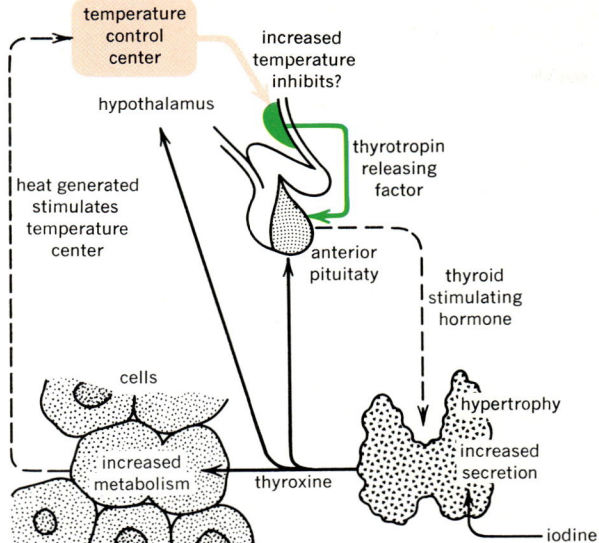

FIGURE 32-6 Feedback mechanisms involving the hypothalamus and pituitary control the secretion of the thyroid hormone thryroxine.

structure and the secretory activity of the thyroid gland. The secretion of thyroid hormone and thyrotropin is regulated by a feedback mechanism involving the hypothalamic releasing factor (Figure 32-6). High concentrations of thyroid hormones in the body fluids inhibit the secretion of TSH. As the level of the pituitary hormone falls, stimulation of the thyroid gland ceases, and it in turn stops secreting its own hormones. As the concentration of thyroid hormones in the body fluids falls, the inhibition on the secretion of thyrotropin is lifted, and the cycle of secretion begins again. Thus, both over- and undersecretion of the thyroid hormones are neatly prevented.

The secretion of TRF and therefore of TSH is influenced by a number of external factors. Exposure to cold increases secretion and ultimately raises the basal metabolic rate, thus contributing to homeostasis. Various emotional states can produce either an increase or a decrease in secretion.

Adrenocorticotropin   Within minutes, stress can produce a 20-fold rise in the secretion of **adrenocorticotropin (ACTH).** This hormone in turn stimulates the adrenal cortex to pour out its hormones: greatly increased quantities of glucocorticoids, cortisol, and corticosterone, and slightly increased amounts of aldosterone and adrenal androgens. A variety of stresses can stimulate ACTH secretion, for example, pain, extreme heat or cold, hypoxia, debilitating diseases, or emotional trauma. As in the case of thyrotropin, ACTH secretion is controlled by feedback mechanisms and is inhibited when the levels of cortisol and other adrenal cortical hormones are high.

This feedback regulation appears to operate not only at the level of the adenohypophysis, but also through the hypothalamus, which stimulates ACTH secretion by producing **corticotropin releasing factor (CRF).** It is believed that the adrenal hormones themselves do not act on the hypothalamus and hypophysis; instead, the feedback inhibition is produced by some alteration of the body conditions produced by the adrenal hormones.

ACTH is a polypeptide consisting of a chain of 39 amino acids. It is essential for the growth and maintenance of the adrenal cortex, which atrophies if the ACTH secretion is insufficient. (ACTH can be given by injection to correct adrenal insufficiency.) ACTH also has a lipolytic effect, promoting a mobilization of fats and raising the fatty acid levels in the blood.

Follicle-Stimulating Hormone   Several decades ago, the birth of quintuplets was a rare event, greeted by worldwide publicity. Today so many quintuplets are being born that they often go unnoticed by the press. The difference has been caused by drugs such as Perganol, used in the treatment of infertility. Normally, one follicle in one of the ovaries of a woman matures each month and releases its ovum. A factor in many cases of infertility is a failure of this ripening of the follicles to occur on schedule. Perganol corrects this defect, but sometimes it overcorrects, stimulating several ovarian follicles to mature simultaneously. Several ova are released and may all be separately fertilized. (Perganol-induced multiple births are all fraternal, rather than identical.)

The hormone that stimulates the ovarian follicles to develop is **follicle-stimulating hormone (FSH).** FSH and another hormone secreted by the adenohypophysis, **luteinizing hormone (LH),** are called **gonadotropic hormones,** since they act on the gonads. The secretion of both these gonadotropins is controlled by a hypothalamic releasing factor, **LRF–FRF.** There is still great confusion about how these hormones, together with the sex hormones, interact to produce the periodic changes of the menstrual cycle. In addition to the regular cyclic variations of secretion, there is evidence that a center in the hypothalamus permits the psychic attitude to increase or decrease the secretion of the gonadotropin releasing factor.

In addition to stimulating the ovarian follicles to develop, FSH also stimulates the secretion of estrogen by the ovaries. This pituitary hormone is also present in men, in whom it stimulates the development of the seminiferous tubules and maintains spermatogenesis.

Luteinizing Hormone   In recent years there has been a revolution in the status and expectations of women. It is no longer considered "natural and proper" for a woman to marry, have children, and spend the major part of her life as a contented housewife. Along with these changing attitudes, birth control has become an important factor in our society. Attention has been focused upon the hormones that regulate the menstrual cycle and promote and maintain pregnancy. The use of synthetic sex hormones as birth control pills has already provided a means of intervening in the process. As more is learned about various aspects of hormonal control, other stages of the cycle amenable to intervention are being discovered. For example, the releasing hormone that controls the secretion of the gonadotropic hormones, FSH and LH, may be a key factor in future approaches to birth control.

Luteinizing hormone (LH) acts in conjunction with FSH in influencing the maturation of the ovarian follicles. Its action occurs in the final stages of maturation, and it initiates the rupture of the ripe follicle (i.e., ovulation), and stimulates the formation of the corpus luteum and the production of progesterone.

A comparable hormone is found in males and is called **interstitial cell-stimulating hormone (ICSH).** It acts on the interstitial cells of the testes to promote the production of the male sex hormone, testosterone. Testosterone in turn inhibits ICSH secretion, in a feedback mechanism presumably involving the hypothalamic releasing hormone LRH.

Melanocyte-Stimulating Hormone

If a solution of human **melanocyte-stimulating hormone (MSH)** is injected into a frog, its skin darkens dramatically, within seconds. In amphibians, MSH causes the melanin-containing granules in the pigmented skin cells (melanocytes) to disperse, so that the entire cell becomes almost black. In humans, this hormone, secreted by the pars intermedia of the pituitary, also causes the skin to darken. (The effect is greater in persons with genetically dark skin than in those who have inherited a naturally light skin.) The mechanism seems to be somewhat different, however, since much of the melanin actually leaves the melanocytes and becomes dispersed through the epidermis.

ACTH has a similar skin-darkening effect, although to a lesser degree (about one-thirtieth that of MSH). Interestingly, MSH has exactly the same structure as the first 13 amino acids in the 39-amino-acid chain of ACTH. The two hormones are often secreted in high concentrations together. In Addison's disease, for example, in which the adrenal cortex is damaged and the ACTH secretion increases in a vain attempt to compensate for the lack of adrenal cortical hormones, MSH secretion also rises, producing a characteristic darkening of the skin.

Beta-Lipotropin

The newest in the family of anterior pituitary hormones, β-lipotropin, was discovered in 1964 by C. H. Li of the University of California in San Francisco. This hormone helps to mobilize lipids from the body's fat depots, but another of its roles seems to be even more important: it serves as a prohormone for a number of smaller fragments, which exert powerful effects on the nervous system. A number of segments of the β-lipotropin molecule have been isolated from the pituitary and studied. One segment, corresponding to the amino acids 47 through 53 in its protein chain, has been named MSH/ACTH 4-10, because this seven-amino-acid sequence is also identical with portions of the MSH and ACTH molecules. Tests have shown that this small peptide has dramatic effects on the brain, helping mentally healthy subjects to remember and concentrate better, increasing the comprehension of the mentally retarded, and improving the memory of senile subjects. The amino-acid sequence 61 through 91 corresponds to β-endorphin, a natural pain killer that has a powerful analgesic and tranquillizing effect and is showing promise in the treatment of depression and schizophrenia. Smaller segments of the β-lipotropin chain, all starting with amino acid 61, correspond to other endorphins and to one of the enkephalins. Researchers studying these hormones are discovering a variety of effects, from analgesic effects to the stimulation of violence and irritability, from mental stimulation to sensations of pleasure and even the triggering of epileptic seizures. This research may ultimately provide new insights into the functioning of the limbic system of the brain, which is the seat of the emotions.

Hormones of the Neurohypophysis

The posterior pituitary is not really an endocrine gland, but merely a storage depot. The hormones that it releases into the bloodstream are actually secreted by the hypothalamus and travel along axons terminating in the neurohypophysis. The two hormones that are temporarily stored here are oxytocin and vasopressin.

Oxytocin

Before the invention of anesthetics, when "natural childbirth" was the only option available, the newborn infant was usually placed immediately at its mother's breast to suckle. This practice had a valuable result: the act of suckling initiates a nervous reflex producing the secretion of **oxytocin,** a hormone that produces powerful contractions of the smooth muscle of the uterus. The effects of the hormone help to expel the placenta rapidly, minimize the danger of hemorrhage, and help to get the uterus back to its nonpregnant size more promptly.

Oxytocin affects the smooth muscle of the pregnant (and postpartum) uterus, but does not cause contractions of the nonpregnant uterus. Its secretion rises sharply at the end of pregnancy and helps to expel the fetus from its mother's uterus during parturition. Injections of the hormone are sometimes given to speed up the delivery; it may be given prophylactically immediately after birth to prevent possible complications. (Nowadays, both mother and baby are usually too groggy from the anesthetic to be in the mood for immediate suckling, and the majority of mothers do not plan to breastfeed their babies anyway, so the natural stimulation does not operate.)

The other major function of oxytocin occurs during the process of lactation: it causes the ejection of milk from the alveoli of the mammary glands into the ducts so that the infant can obtain it by suckling. Oxytocin secretion is stimulated not only by the reflex arc triggered by the act of suckling, but also by psychological stimuli. A breast-feeding mother often feels her milk "let down" when she hears her baby cry, or even when she thinks about feeding the baby.

Stimulation of the breasts and other erogenous areas during sexual intercourse produces a rise in the oxytocin levels in the blood, which contributes to the uterine contractions during orgasm.

Vasopressin (Antidiuretic Hormone)

The second hormone of the posterior pituitary goes by several "aliases," which describe its several distinct functions. **Vasopressin** relates to its pressor effect (raising the arterial blood pressure), due to vasoconstriction of all the arterioles. (It is sometimes called **pitressin,** emphasizing its relationship to the pituitary.) The name **antidiuretic hormone (ADH)** is used in referring to another major effect of the hormone—it stimulates the reabsorption of water by the cells of the distal convoluted tubules and collecting tubules of the kidney. A lack of antidiuretic hormone would create a rather embarrassing situation: the person would have to void more than 15 liters of urine a day! The well-known diuretic effect of drinking alcoholic beverages is due to a depression of ADH secretion. Urination may be so copious that more fluid is eliminated than is taken in (especially when straight liquor is consumed, rather than beer or other more dilute drinks), and the resultant dehydration may partially account for the hangover that is suffered later.

The antidiuretic effect of ADH is produced by far lower concentrations of the hormone than its pressor effect; thus ADH probably plays a minor role in circulation dynamics.

Osmoreceptors in the supraoptic nuclei of the hypothalamus continually report on the concentration of solutes in the plasma. A rise in osmotic pressure causes the neurons to fire, releasing ADH. The secretion of the hormone results in more water being retained in the body, effectively diluting the body fluids, in a self-regulating feedback system. Hemorrhage is a powerful stimulus for ADH secretion; trauma, pain, and anxiety can also stimulate its release.

Lesions of the posterior pituitary or the supraoptic nuclei of the hypothalamus can cause a disease called **diabetes insipidus,** in which copious amounts of very dilute urine are produced. (Unlike diabetes mellitus, due to a pancreatic insufficiency, there is no sugar in the urine, and the blood-sugar level is not elevated.)

THE THYROID GLAND

Years ago, people suffering from obesity were commonly diagnosed as "hypothyroid" and treated with thyroid extract. An insufficiency of thyroid function can indeed cause a gain of weight, but it is now recognized that the causes of obesity are far more complex and unfortunately not universally amenable to such a simple treatment.

The thyroid gland is found in the middle anterior portion of the neck. It is butterfly-shaped, consisting of two lobes, one on each side of the trachea, connected by a thin strand of tissue called the isthmus, which passes over the anterior surface of the trachea (Figure 32-7). In an adult the gland weighs about 30 g, but this may vary by as much as 10 g, depending on age, sex, diet, and climate. During puberty and pregnancy the thyroid increases in size and becomes more active; physiological stress can also produce an increase in both size and activity.

The thyroid gland is covered with a double capsule: an outer capsule continuous with the deep cervical fascia and an inner fibroelastic capsule adhering to the surface of the gland. Septa from the inner capsule extend into the gland.

Each lobe of the thyroid gland is composed of numerous follicles, each about the size of a pinhead. These follicles, called **acini,** are the structural and functional units of the thyroid gland. Each follicle consists of a single layer of cuboidal cells, forming a sac surrounding a cavity filled with a substance called **colloid** (Figure 32-8). Colloid is a homogeneous substance, containing the products of the secretory epithelium. Normally the follicles are of uniform size. But in iodine deficiency the follicles become distended with colloid, and the cells lining the acini become flattened. If the thyroid is overactive, on the other hand, the reserves of colloid become depleted, and the epithelial cells become columnar in shape.

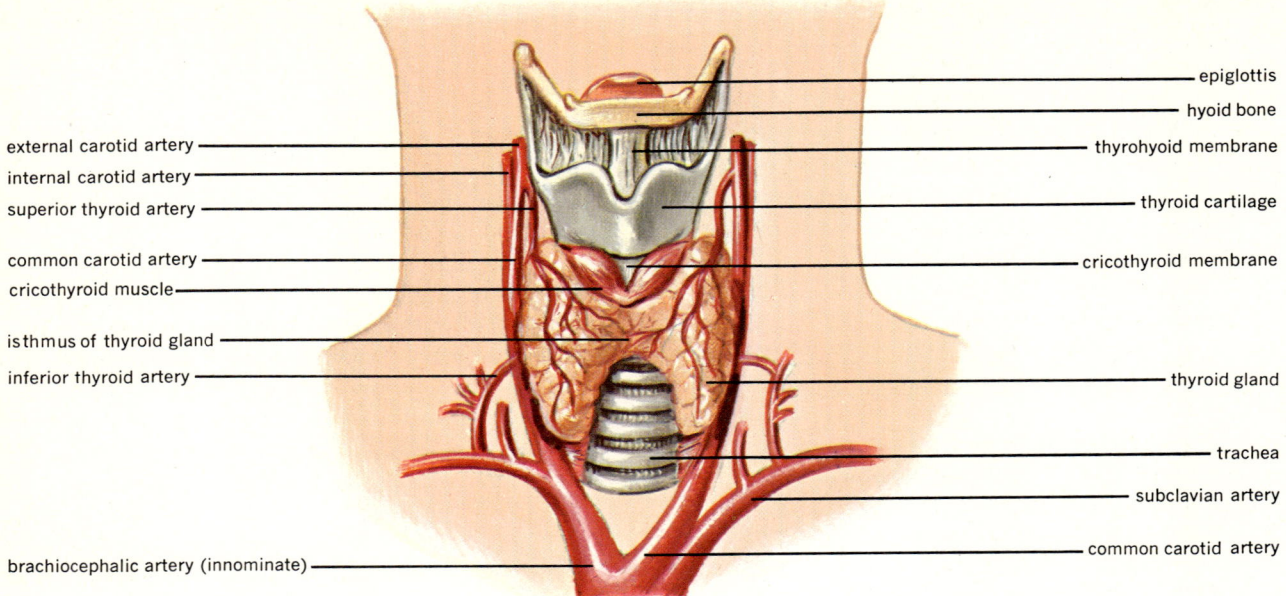

external carotid artery

internal carotid artery

superior thyroid artery

common carotid artery

cricothyroid muscle

isthmus of thyroid gland

inferior thyroid artery

brachiocephalic artery (innominate)

epiglottis

hyoid bone

thyrohyoid membrane

thyroid cartilage

cricothyroid membrane

thyroid gland

trachea

subclavian artery

common carotid artery

FIGURE 32-7   The thyroid gland and its blood supply.

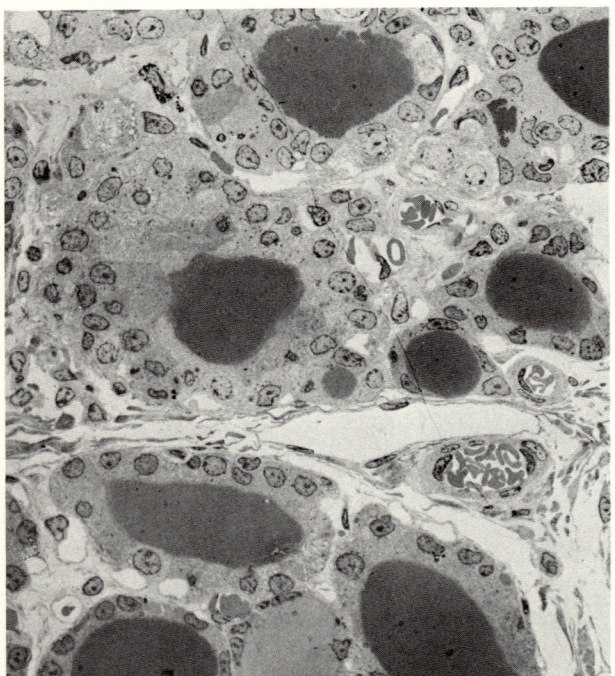

FIGURE 32-8   This section of thyroid tissue (×450) shows large colloid-filled follicles, with walls of epithelial cells.

The acini of the thyroid gland are surrounded by abundant networks of blood and lymph vessels, which bring fresh supplies of nutrients (including the iodine the gland needs for its secretions) and carrying away the thyroid hormones.

The thyroid gland has an astonishing ability to take up and concentrate iodine. Iodide ions are removed from the circulating blood by an active transport mechanism (an "iodide pump") so effectively that the iodide concentration in the gland is 50 to as much as 300 times greater than that in the blood.

The thyroid gland uses this iodine to produce several iodinated derivatives of the amino acid tyrosine (thyroid hormones), which are combined into a protein form, **thyroglobulin,** and stored in the follicles. When these hormones enter the blood and are carried through the body, they help to regulate the rate of metabolism.

The thyroid gland also secretes another hormone, **calcitonin,** which does not contain iodine and is concerned in the body's calcium metabolism.

Thyroglobulin

Iodine is an essential element in the diet. The body's need for this nutrient is very specialized: all of the iodine used by the body is incorporated into the complex of thyroid hormones.

The iodide that is absorbed from the blood by the thyroid gland is first oxidized to elemental iodine, then combined with the amino acid **tyrosine** (Figure 32-9). If one iodine atom is added to the tyrosine molecule, **monoiodotyrosine** is formed; the addition of two atoms of iodine produces **diiodotyrosine.** Monoiodotyrosine and diiodotyrosine molecules then combine to form the two hormones, **3,5,3'-triiodothyronine** (T_3) and **thyroxine** (T_4). These hormones are then combined into the storage form, **thyroglobulin,** which is a protein with a molecular weight of 680,000.

Proteinases produced by the thyroid cells hydrolyze thyroglobulin and split out T_3 and T_4, which diffuse

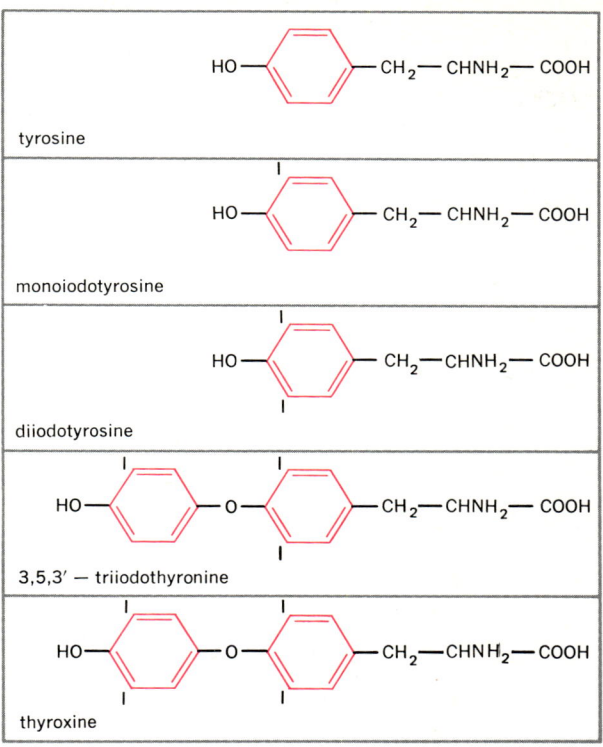

FIGURE 32-9 Structures of the thyroid hormones triiodothyronine and thyroxine and their chemical precursors.

out into the blood. There they are promptly bound to the plasma globulin. As the blood circulates through the body, the thyroid hormones are slowly freed from this combination and diffuse into the body cells.

The anterior pituitary hormone TSH regulates all aspects of thyroid activity, from iodide uptake and the synthesis of thyroglobulin to the synthesis of the proteinases that permit the release of T_3 and T_4 into the bloodstream. The circulating iodothyronines, in turn, control the secretion of TSH through a feedback circuit involving the thyrotropin releasing factor (TRF) of the hypothalamus.

Thyroxine and triiodothyronine have a profound effect on the body as a whole. They act in general to speed up metabolic processes. They have been found to function in at least 20 enzyme systems. The thyroid hormones stimulate almost all aspects of carbohydrate metabolism, both directly and by promoting an increased secretion of insulin; they also enhance the mobilization and oxidation of fats and stimulate an increase in protein synthesis in nearly all the tissues of the body. According to one theory, thyroxine affects the permeability of the mitochondrial membrane, enhances electron transfer, and stimulates the body's oxidative enzymes.

The thyroid hormones are essential for growth and mental development. Through their effect on metabolism, they influence circulation, water and electrolyte balance, and protein, carbohydrate, and fat metabolism.

Calcitonin

The discovery of calcitonin was rather embarrassing for endocrinologists. For many years the thyroid gland had been one of the best studied and supposedly best known of the endocrine glands. Then belatedly, around 1960, it was suddenly discovered that in addition to the iodothyronines, this gland produces another hormone with an entirely different function. Indeed, there was some confusion at first, and it was thought that the hormone was synthesized by the parathyroid glands, which secrete another hormone involved in calcium metabolism. But finally things were straightened out, and it was found that calcitonin is indeed a thyroid hormone, secreted by the parafollicular cells between the follicles. It was found to be a polypeptide consisting of a single chain of 32 amino acids; its sequence has been determined, and it has been synthesized.

Calcitonin acts on the bones to inhibit resorption. The effect is manifested within minutes: calcium stops passing out of the bones into the extracellular fluid, and the blood calcium level falls. This hormone is secreted in response to increased concentrations of calcium in the blood and thus helps to regulate the blood calcium level. Its action is exactly opposite to that of the parathyroid hormone, and thus the body has a double system for regulating calcium metabolism. Calcitonin seems to act as a short-term regulator, preventing acute excesses of calcium in the body fluids, while the parathyroid hormone, which is slower acting, sets the long-term level of calcium ions in the body fluids.

Disorders of the Thyroid Gland

In some ancient cultures it was believed that a goiter beautified the neck. This gross swelling, however, is in reality a signal of a nutritional deficiency or of a serious glandular disorder.

Simple goiter is an enlargement of the thyroid gland, due to a lack of sufficient iodine in the diet. The body of an adult man contains about 14 mg of iodine. But a total dietary intake of only about 35 to 50 mg of iodine is needed each year (i.e., about 1 mg a week) for the formation of adequate amounts of thyroxine. In some inland regions, particularly in the Great Lakes region of the United States and in the Swiss Alps, the soil does not contain enough iodine for foods to supply even this small amount of the mineral. Years ago, endemic goiter was common in these regions, especially in adolescent girls, whose needs for thyroid hormones are increased. When the diet does not supply sufficient iodine, insufficient

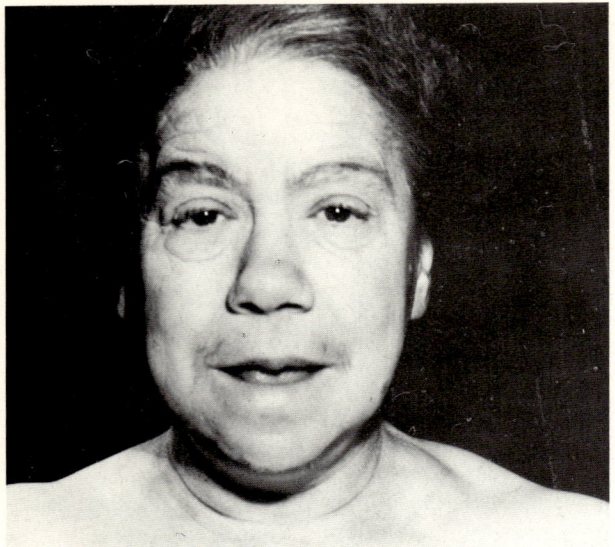

A

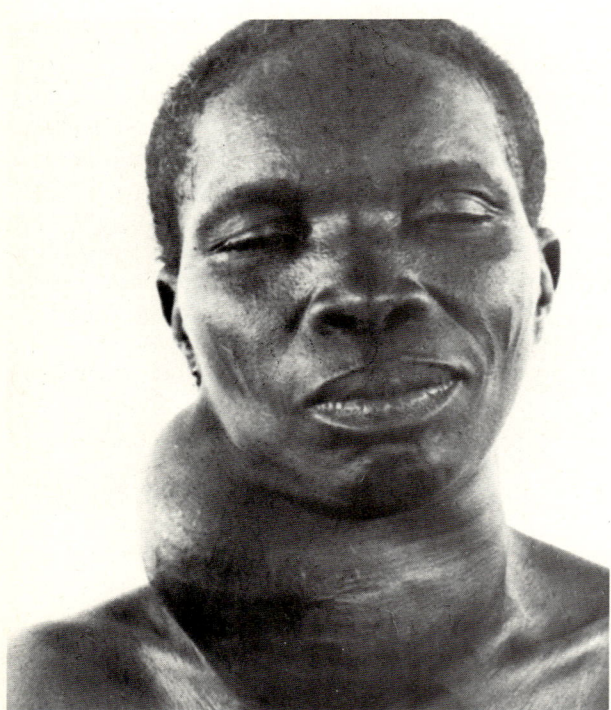

B

FIGURE 32-10 Thyroid disorders: (A) myxedema (this 55-year-old woman, hospitalized for depression and dementia, recovered completely after thyroid treatment); (B) iodine deficiency produced a giant multinodular goiter on the neck of this Nigerian woman.

amounts of thyroxine are secreted, removing the inhibition on the hypothalamus and hypophysis. Increased thyrotropin secretion causes the thyroid gland to hypertrophy and secrete large amounts of colloid. Sometimes the enlarged thyroid gland is able to produce enough thyroxine for the body's needs. But if there is too little iodine available, the vicious cycle

continues, and the gland may grow as large as 300 to 500 grams or more and may press on the trachea, producing choking sensations. In the early stages, this type of colloid goiter can be treated successfully by administering iodine, but if the enlargement is too great, surgical removal of part of the gland may be necessary. The popularization of iodized table salt has now virtually eliminated endemic goiter as a health problem.

The effects of hypofunction of the thyroid gland (Figure 32-10) vividly reveal the crucial importance of thyroxine to the body's metabolism. **Hypothyroidism** may be caused by endemic colloid goiter, by destruction of the thyroid gland by diseases or by irradiation, or by surgical removal of the gland. If undersecretion of thyroxine occurs during infancy, a condition called **cretinism** develops. Every aspect of the child's development is greatly retarded; if untreated, the child will ultimately grow to be a dwarf, sexually undeveloped, with the mentality of an idiot. A cretin's teeth and bones are poorly developed, and the body poorly proportioned, with a large head, protruding abdomen, and weak muscles. The body temperature and blood pressure are low, heart rate slow, basal metabolic rate about 25 percent below normal. Treatment of a cretin at any time with thyroid extract usually returns physical growth to normal, but unless the treatment is begun within a few months after birth, mental development will be permanently retarded.

Atrophy or removal of the thyroid gland in adulthood results in **myxedema.** As might be expected, the lack of thyroid hormone causes a general slowdown of mental and physical processes. The person suffers from extreme sleepiness, sleeping as much as 14 to 16 hours a day, lethargy, mental sluggishness, a decreased cardiac output and blood volume, obesity, constipation, depressed growth of hair, and scaly skin. Edematous swelling of the face and bagginess under the eyes are typical of this condition. An increase in the blood lipids caused by the lack of thyroid hormone often leads to severe arteriosclerosis, which can result in deafness, cardiovascular disease, and an early death. Treatment with desiccated thyroid or thyroid extract produces a dramatic improvement.

Most cases of **hyperthyroidism** are believed to be the result of excessive secretion of thyrotropin by the adenohypophysis, the cause of which is unknown at present. (It is often hereditary, frequently follows severe physical or emotional disturbances, and is much more common in cold climates than in hot climates.) In a person whose thyroid gland is secreting too much thyroxine, the body processes are speeded up. The appetite is increased, but the person loses weight

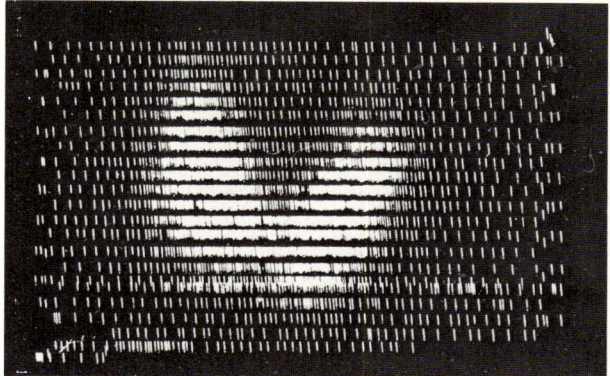

FIGURE 32-11 In this scintigram, the thyroid gland is clearly outlined by radioactive iodine.

(sometimes as much as 100 pounds), has a high metabolic rate (+100 percent), is nervous and emotional, and the skin is flushed and moist. Tachycardia and palpitation, diarrhea, and tremors of the hands are common. The thyroid gland is usually enlarged to two to three times the normal size, but within the gland there is an even greater increase in follicular cells, so that the thyroxine secretion is 5 to 15 times the normal rate. Often the eyeballs of the patient protrude, sometimes so severely that the eyes are damaged because the eyelids do not close completely during blinking and sleep, and the epithelial surfaces dry out and become ulcerated. This type of hyperthyroidism is commonly known as **exophthalmic goiter,** referring to the typical bulging eyes and enlarged thyroid gland. The increased thyroxine secretion causes an elevation of the levels of protein-bound iodine in the blood and low levels of serum cholesterol. Exophthalmic goiter may be treated with thyroid-inhibiting drugs such as propylthiouracil, thiocyanate, thioureas, and mercaptoimidazoles, which inhibit the uptake of iodine by the thyroid gland and limit or pervent the production of thyroxine. Surgical removal of the thyroid gland is often performed in severe cases, or injections of radioactive iodine may be given to destroy secretory cells of the gland internally. (The radioisotope is taken up selectively by the thyroid gland (Figure 32-11) and thus does not act on other organs of the body.)

A less common type of hyperthyroidism is caused by an **adenoma** of the thyroid gland, a localized tumor that may secrete large quantities of thyroid hormone, independent of the feedback control by the hypothalamus and hypophysis.

Tests of Thyroid Function

The past few decades have witnessed the development of increasingly sophisticated methods of assaying thyroid function. The oldest and simplest procedure for determining thyroid activity was the determination of the **basal metabolic rate BMR.** A variation of more than 15 percent above or below the normal value is a strong suggestion that the thyroid gland may be over- or underactive. (In myxedema, typical values are -40 to -50, in hyperthyroidism $+40$ to $+60$.) But since other factors may influence the BMR, this test is not entirely specific for thyroid function.

The combination of the iodothyronines with plasma globulin when they enter the blood provides the basis for a chemical test: the protein-bound thyroid hormones are precipitated out of a sample of the patient's blood plasma, and the amount of **protein-bound iodine (PBI)** is determined chemically. The normal PBI concentration is from 4 to 8 micrograms per 100 ml of plasma. This procedure gives a measure of the amount of circulating thyroid hormones.

Another type of test involves the use of radioiodine (^{131}I). The radioisotope is administered intravenously in minute quantities (much smaller than the doses used for the clinical treatment of hyperthyroidism). The rate of iodine uptake is then measured by means of a calibrated radioactive detector placed over the neck. In a normal person, an average of 4 percent of the injected radioiodine is taken up by the thyroid gland per hour. In hyperthyroidism, the uptake is as much as 20 to 25 percent per hour, while in myxedema the uptake is less than 1 percent per hour. Sophisticated detection and camera equipment can also show the intensity and distribution of the radioactive tracer (see Figure 32-11), pinpointing the site of the problem.

THE PARATHYROID GLANDS

Years ago, the surgical treatment of hyperthyroidism had puzzling and often tragic results. Sometimes the patients recovered uneventfully after the thyroid gland was removed and lived a normal and healthy life thereafter, taking thyroid extract. But sometimes the patients died in agonizing pain with tetanuslike fits. Finally, it was discovered that in the unsuccessful cases the surgeon had removed not only the thyroid gland, but also the parathyroids.

The error was understandable. The parathyroid glands are four minute, yellow-brown ovoid bodies, about 6 mm long and 3 mm thick, embedded in the lobes of the thyroid gland (two in each lobe). Each parathyroid gland is covered by a thin connective tissue capsule and penetrated by septa carrying a rich supply of blood and lymph vessels and nerves. The cells of the gland are arranged in clusters and irregular cords and include two types of epithelial cells (Figure 32-12): **chief cells,** which are polygonal in shape, and larger but less numerous **oxyphil cells,**

back of larynx

FIGURE 32-12 The parathyroid glands. In the painting their relation to the thyroid gland, larynx, and trachea can be seen. The micrograph shows a section of parathyroid tissue (×260).

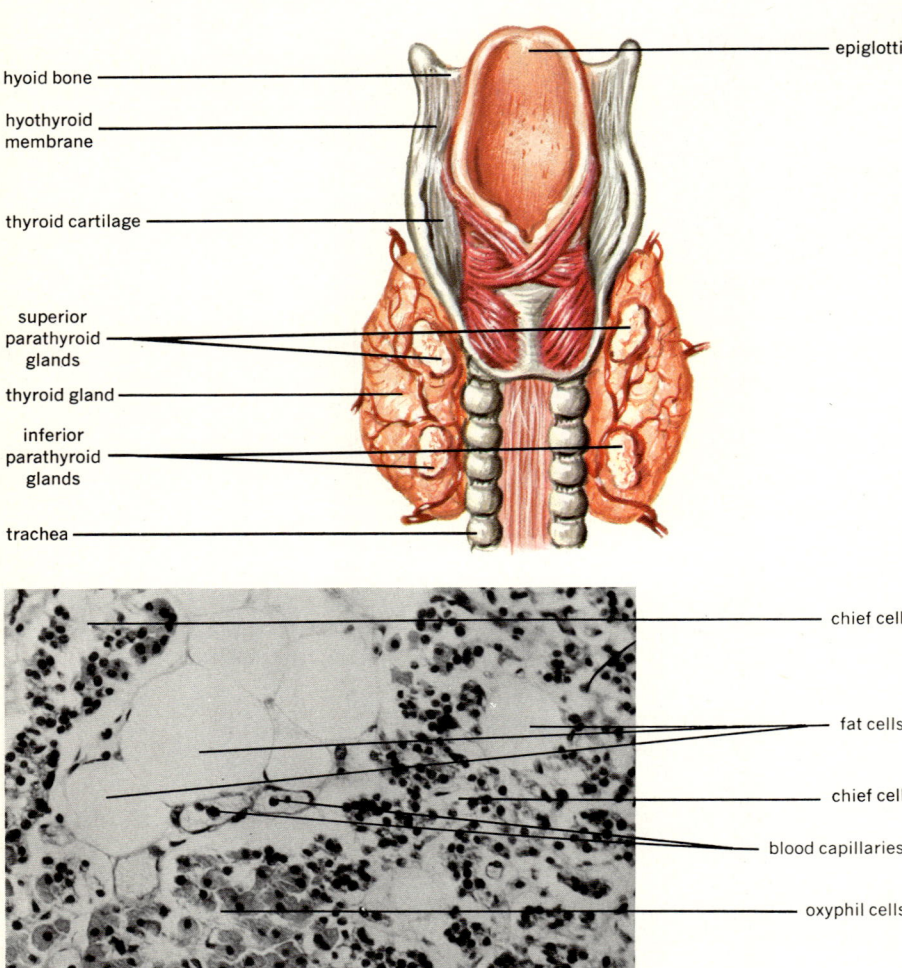

epiglottis

hyoid bone

hyothyroid membrane

thyroid cartilage

superior parathyroid glands

thyroid gland

inferior parathyroid glands

trachea

chief cell

fat cells

chief cell

blood capillaries

oxyphil cells

which are cuboidal and are scattered singly or in small groups throughout the gland. The chief cells have a large, vesicular nucleus, embedded in the center of a faintly staining cytoplasm that contains granules of glycogen. The chief cells secrete the parathyroid hormone. The function of the oxyphil cells, which appear after puberty, is not yet known.

Parathyroid Hormone

Ninety-nine percent of all the calcium in the body is deposited in the bones. But as we have seen, storage of minerals in the bones is not a static situation; instead, there is a constant dynamic exchange, as calcium continually passes out of the bones into the extracellular fluid and out of the ECF into the bones. The bones thus not only support the body, but act as a reservoir for the circulating calcium needed in nerve conduction, muscle contraction, and other body activities. One of the hormones governing the rate of

resorption of calcium from bones is calcitonin, secreted by the thyroid gland. But the action of this hormone is relatively transitory; the long-term calcium levels are set by the action of the parathyroid hormone, which is also referred to as **parathormone (PTH).**

Parathormone has been isolated in pure form, and the amino acid sequence of the biologically active portion of the molecule has been worked out. It has a molecular weight of about 9000 and consists of 84 amino acids, but apparently all the hormonal activity is contained in the first 34 amino acids.

The overall effects of parathyroid hormone are to increase the calcium levels in the extracellular fluids and decrease the phosphate concentration. The hormone is secreted by the parathyroids in response to lowered calcium levels in the ECF, in a self-regulating feedback system independent of pituitary control. It exerts its effects in three major sites: (1) in the

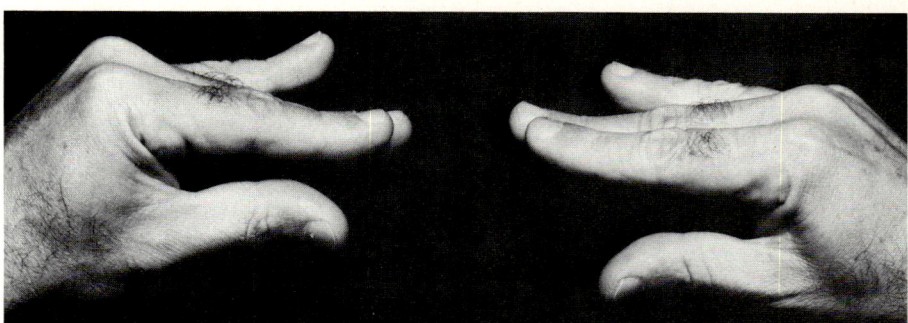

FIGURE 32-13 Carpopedal spasm—Trousseau's sign in hypoparathyroidism.

bones, where it promotes resorption of calcium and phosphate into the extracellular fluids by increasing the number and activity of the osteoclasts; (2) in the intestine, where it enhances the absorption of calcium and phosphate; and (3) in the kidneys, where it increases the reabsorption of calcium but enhances the excretion of phosphate with the urine.

The functioning of parathyroid hormone is dependent on adequate supplies of vitamin D, with which it is linked in a complex feedback circuit. Recent studies have shown that vitamin D, synthesized in the skin, is subjected to a series of conversions in the body—first in the liver to an intermediate product, 25-hydroxy-vitamin D_3, and then in the kidneys to the active form, **1,25-dihydroxy-vitamin D_3.** The latter functions as a hormone, stimulating the production of a protein that enhances the functions of PTH. Parathyroid hormone or a low level of calcium in the blood stimulates the synthesis of this active form of vitamin D, while the thyroid hormone calcitonin inhibits it.

The magnesium level also appears to play a key role in PTH functioning: low magnesium levels lead to impaired synthesis or release of parathormone, resulting in hypocalcemia (reduced calcium levels in the blood).

Disorders of the Parathyroid Glands

Many aspects of the body's metabolism resemble a tightrope walker proceeding across a high wire. A precise balance must be maintained at all times; tipping too far to either side can result in dire—even fatal—consequences. The calcium metabolism, which is kept in balance mainly by the parathyroid hormone, is no exception.

Hypofunction of the parathyroid glands results in a drop in the level of calcium ions in the blood below normal. With the lack of calcium, the nervous system becomes highly excitable, and the skeletal muscles in turn are affected. The condition called **tetany** develops as the blood calcium level falls, with twitching, spasms, and convulsions (Figure 32-13). Tetany results when the parathyroids are accidentally damaged or removed during the surgical removal of the thy-

roid. The treatment includes both acute and chronic phases. In the acute phase, the physician must cope with the medical emergency during the postoperative period, injecting calcium salts intravenously to raise the serum calcium level and prevent spasms and convulsions. Then in the chronic stage, the major goal of treatment is to maintain a normal serum calcium level, through the administration of vitamin D and calcium salts.

Hyperfunction of the parathyroid glands has almost as harmful effects. The excretion of both calcium and phosphorus in the urine is greatly increased. The blood calcium level rises so high that kidney stones form, and the muscle tone is weakened. Enhanced resorption of calcium from the bones results in their demineralization, and they become fragile and deformed, with fluid-filled cysts, and are prone to spontaneous fractures; the teeth fall out. Hyperparathyroidism may result from an enlargement or tumor of one or more of the glands; surgical removal of part of the enlarged gland helps to restore the balance of the calcium-phosphate metabolism. Parathyroid hyperfunction may also result from disorders of vitamin D metabolism or renal insufficiency, in which sufficient amounts of the active form of vitamin D are not synthesized in the kidneys and the blood calcium level falls. Removing the malfunctioning kidneys and placing the patient on hemodialysis may aggravate the disturbance of calcium homeostasis; in such cases (as well as vitamin D-resistant forms of rickets), promising results have been obtained from treatment with synthetic vitamin D derivatives such as 1α-hydroxy-vitamin D, which help to normalize the calcium metabolism.

THE ADRENAL GLANDS

The adrenal glands resemble an admiral's cocked hat in shape and are perched one atop each kidney (Figure 32-14). Each adrenal gland is really two endocrine glands in one, for its outer **cortex** and inner **medulla** have different embryonic origins, structure, and secrete quite different hormones.

The adrenal glands, which are sometimes called the

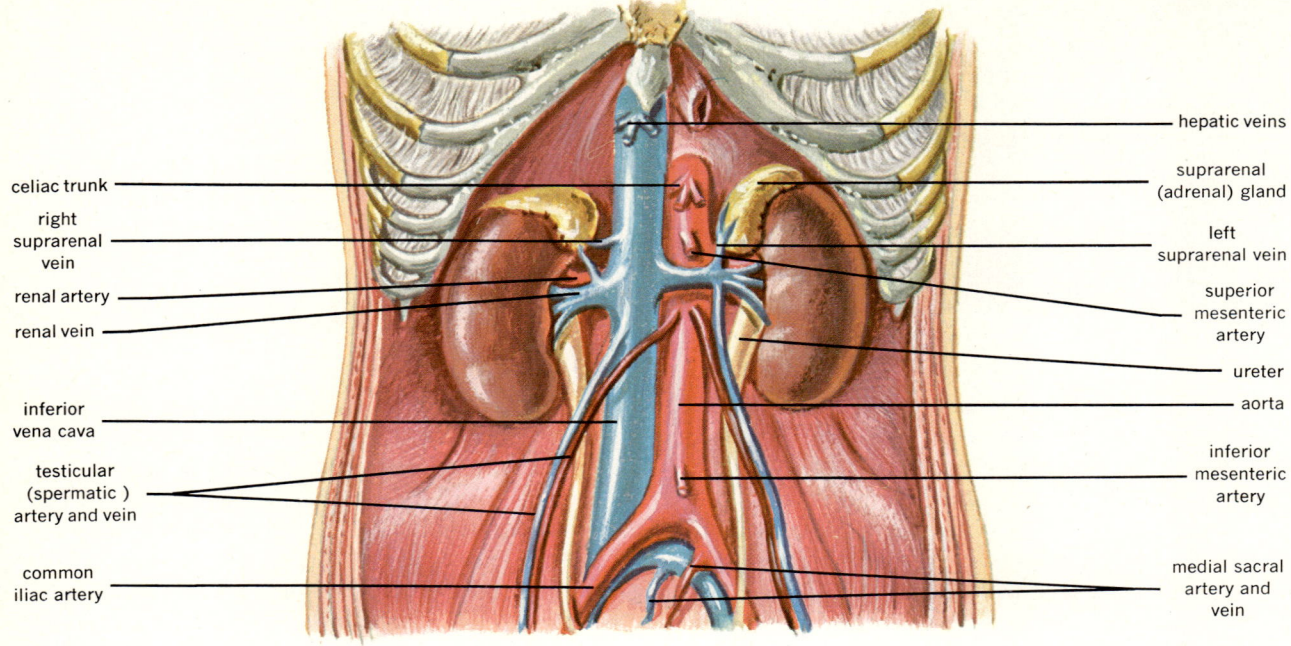

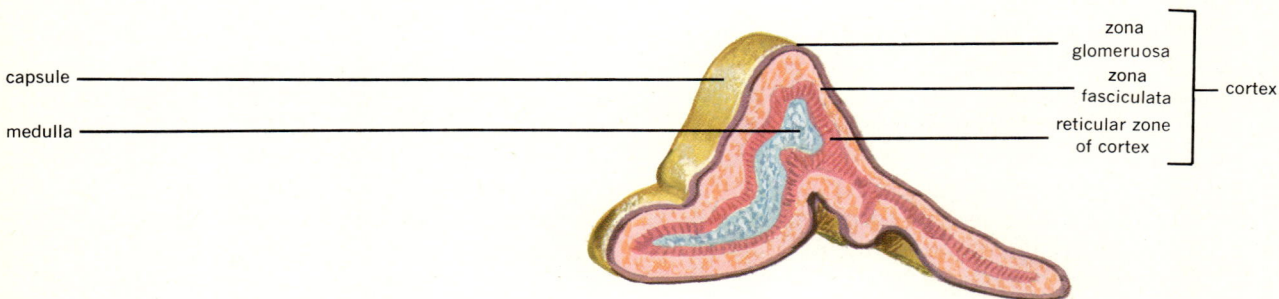

FIGURE 32-14   The adrenal glands, in situ and internal structure.

suprarenal glands (literally, "above the kidneys"), are each about an inch and a half long and half an inch in diameter, with an average weight of 4 grams. They are loosely attached to their respective kidneys by connective tissue and fat, but each adrenal has its own fibrous connective-tissue capsule. The outer cortex makes up the bulk of the gland. It is bright yellow outside and reddish brown inside. The medulla is much thinner and gray in color.

Cords of cells, separated by blood vessels, compose the adrenal cortex, which is divided into three poorly defined zones: a narrow outer **zona glomerulosa,** a heavier, middle **zona fasciculata,** and an inner, irregular **zona reticularis.** Within the last zone lies the medulla, which is composed of groups of irregular epithelioid cells. The gland as a whole is highly

vascular—it is estimated that an amount of blood equal to six times the weight of the gland passes through it each minute. Preganglionic sympathetic nerve fibers from the splanchnic nerves penetrate the capsule of the adrenal glands, pass through the cortex, and terminate in the medulla, which is especially responsive to autonomic impulses.

Embryologically, the adrenal cortex develops from the mesoderm, in close association with the gonads. The medulla is an outgrowth from the neural ectoderm, with the same origin as the sympathetic nervous system.

Adrenal Cortex
Probably more hormones are produced by the adrenal cortex than any other endocrine gland of the

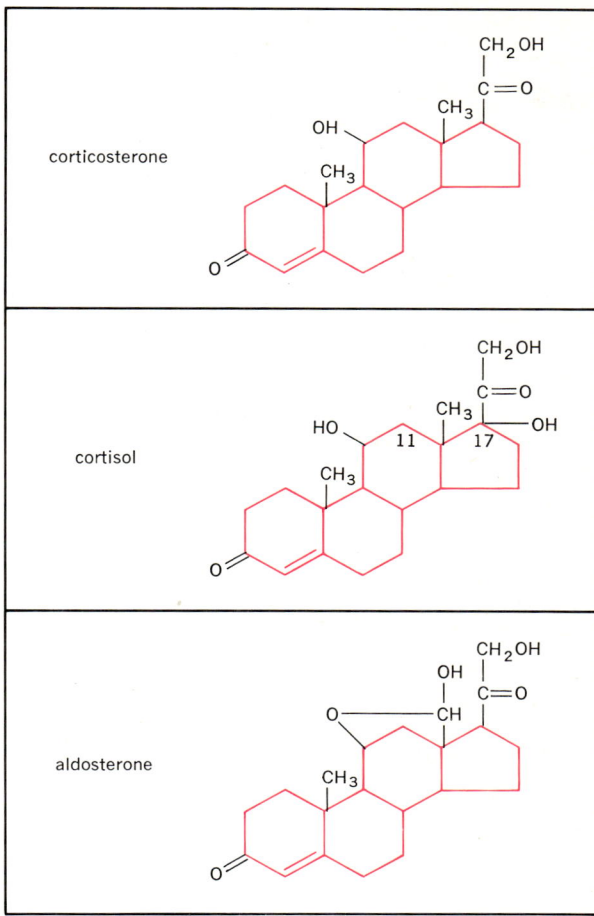

FIGURE 32-15 Chemical structure of corticosterone, cortisol, and aldosterone. All share the same basic steroid ring system, with minor differences in substituents.

electrolytes in the extracellular fluid, their reabsorption in the kidney tubules, and blood pressure.

The principal mineralocorticoid secreted by the adrenal cortex is **aldosterone,** which accounts for at least 95 percent of the mineralocorticoid activity. Normally from 70 to 200 micrograms of aldosterone is secreted each day, but the secretion can rise to 900 micrograms per day if the diet is severely restricted in sodium content. **Deoxycorticosterone** has a similar action but is only one-thirtieth as potent as aldosterone; **corticosterone** has both mineralo- and glucocorticoid effects.

The main physiological effect of aldosterone is to increase the reabsorption of sodium ions in the renal tubules, raising the sodium concentration and osmotic pressure of the extracellular fluid. For each sodium ion that is reabsorbed, the kidney excretes a potassium or hydrogen ion, so that the mineralocorticoid also helps to regulate the potassium level and pH in the body fluids. Further effects follow from aldosterone's main action. As positive sodium ions are reabsorbed, negative ions (bicarbonate or chloride) accompany them, attracted by the opposite electrical charge of the sodium ions. The increase in osmotic pressure caused by the reabsorption of sodium ions also causes a net diffusion of water back into the blood and tissue fluids. If too much aldosterone is secreted, excessive reabsorption of sodium ions can thus lead to an excessive retention of water in the body, producing elevated blood pressure and edema. Diuretics administered in such cases either inhibit tubular reabsorption of sodium in the kidneys or block the action of aldosterone.

Aldosterone secretion is normally regulated by feedback mechanisms (Figure 32-16). It is stimulated by (1) a decreased sodium concentration in the extracellular fluids; (2) an increased extracellular potassium concentration; (3) a decreased extracellular fluid or blood volume. There is experimental evidence to indicate that both decreased sodium and increased potassium concentrations in the blood and ECF have a direct stimulating action on the adrenal cortex. Yet this does not seem to be the whole story. A diminished blood flow to the kidneys stimulates the release of the enzyme **renin,** which catalyzes the formation of **angiotensin** in the blood. Angiotensin, in turn, not only stimulates vasoconstriction and raises blood pressure, but also produces an increase in aldosterone secretion by the adrenal cortex. ACTH also increases aldosterone secretion to some degree, although its principal effect is on the glucocorticoids.

body. More than three dozen hormones have been found to be produced by this gland. All of them belong to a single chemical class, the **steroids** (Figure 32-15).

Functionally, the adrenal cortical hormones can be grouped into three major classes:

1 **Mineralocorticoids,** which influence primarily the electrolytes of the extracellular fluids, especially sodium, potassium, and chloride; these are secreted mainly by the zona glomerulosa
2 **Glucocorticoids,** which act primarily on the carbohydrate metabolism and are secreted mainly by the zona faciculata
3 **Androgens** (male sex hormones), secreted by the zona reticularis.

Mineralocorticoids Americans eat too much salt. Small amounts of sodium chloride are vital to life and health; but an excessive salt intake may lead, in many cases, to high blood pressure. The mineralocorticoids secreted by the adrenal cortex are an important link in the mechanisms regulating the concentrations of

Glucocorticoids If the adrenal cortices are removed, the volume of the extracellular fluid and blood will fall rapidly, resulting in a reduced cardiac

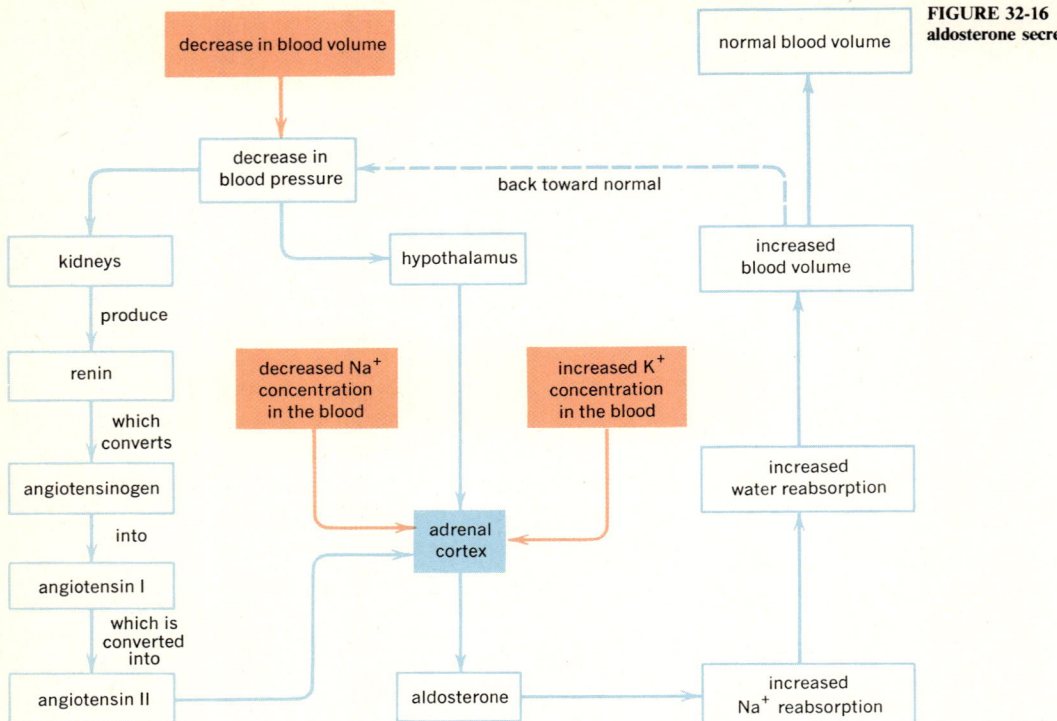

FIGURE 32-16 Mechanisms regulating aldosterone secretion.

output. The person, if untreated, sinks into a shock-like state and will die within a few days. Mineralocorticoid therapy dramatically saves the patient's life; but even with these hormones, the patient is by no means normal. The patient's systems of carbohydrate, protein, and fat metabolism are deranged, and he or she is unable to respond adequately to physical and mental stress. Even a minor illness, such as a respiratory tract infection, can lead to death. Though the effects of a lack of mineralocorticoids are more immediately evident, a lack of glucocorticoids can be equally devastating.

The main glucocorticoid secreted by the adrenal cortex is **cortisol** (also known as **hydrocortisone**), which accounts for at least 95 percent of the glucocorticoid activity. Small amounts of glucocorticoid activity are also provided by **corticosterone** and **cortisone.**

The secretion of glucocorticoids is controlled by the pituitary hormone ACTH, the secretion of which is in turn stimulated by CRF (corticotropin releasing factor), produced by the hypothalamus and sent down to the adenohypophysis via the hypophyseal portal system. The glucocorticoids in turn inhibit the secretion of both ACTH and CRF, to complete the circuit of a typical self-regulating feedback system.

The glucocorticoids have a variety of important effects in the body.

1 Glucocorticoids act in several ways to raise the blood sugar level. They decrease the utilization of glucose, accelerate the breakdown of proteins to amino acids (except in the liver), facilitate the transport of amino acids through the cell membranes into the liver cells, and stimulate increased gluconeogenesis in the liver (i.e., the chemical conversion of amino acids to glucose). Thus, prolonged high levels of glucocorticoids in the blood result in a net loss of tissue proteins (i.e., a negative balance) and can lead to diabetes as the elevated blood glucose levels continually challenge and finally exhaust the insulin production of the pancreas.

2 Glucocorticoids promote the mobilization of fats from adipose cells, the catabolism of fats, their use in gluconeogenesis, and the deposition of fats. The net result is a redistribution of the body fat.

3 Glucocorticoids work with the hormones of the adrenal medulla to produce vasoconstriction and maintain normal blood pressure.

4 The secretion of glucocorticoids increases dramatically during stress, especially in cases in anxiety or severe injury. In some way, which has not yet been satisfactorily determined, these hormones of the adrenal cortex help the body to cope successfully with adverse and threatening conditions of the external environment.

5 The antiinflammatory properties of cortisol and the other glucocorticoids have long been known and used therapeutically. The hormones are thought to combat inflammation in two ways: by decreasing capillary permeability and thus helping to prevent movement of fluid into the inflamed area; and by stabilizing the lysosome membrane, preventing the release of lytic enzymes by these organelles. Glucocorticoids are used to relieve the pain and inflammation of rheumatoid arthritis and other inflammatory conditions. But the physician must proceed with caution in treating inflammations with corticosteroids when there is a possibility of an accompanying bacterial infection, because of the following property of the glucocorticoids.

6 High concentrations of glucocorticoids decrease the number of circulating eosinophils and cause the lymphoid tissues to atrophy, sharply reducing or entirely blocking antibody formation. Because of this action, an oral antibiotic is often used in conjunction with topical corticosteroids in treating an inflammatory condition.

Adrenal Sex Hormones

The bearded lady in the circus may be suffering from overactive adrenal glands. In both sexes, the adrenal cortex normally secretes physiologically significant amounts of male sex hormones (androgens) and insignificant amounts of female sex hormones (estrogens). The adrenal androgens increase retention of nitrogen in the body and cause an increase in the growth of tissues and muscular strength. Exactly what role the adrenal sex hormones play in the normal body is still unclear. They may supplement the action of the gonadal hormones; recent studies suggest that the adrenal androgens increase the libido in women.

Normally the role of the adrenal sex hormones is minor. But when an adrenal tumor produces excessive amounts of androgens, the result is masculinization. A woman grows a beard, her voice deepens, her muscular strength increases, and her clitoris may grow to resemble a penis. An adrenal tumor in a small child may result in precocious sexual development.

The Adrenal Medulla

Hyperfunction of the adrenal glands seems to be one of the prices we must pay for our modern stress-oriented society. The pressure of deadlines, the sudden jarring noises of passing jet planes or jackhammers in the street, worries about overdue bills, unemployment, crime, and other modern concerns continually stimulate both the sympathetic nervous system and its endocrine backup mechanism, the hormones of the adrenal medulla.

The adrenal medulla secretes two hormones: **epinephrine** (adrenaline) and **norepinephrine** (noradrenaline). Unlike the steroid hormones of the adrenal cortex, the hormones of the medulla are **catecholamines** (Figure 32-17). They are sometimes called **sympathomimetic amines,** for they mimic the effects of the sympathtetic nervous system. They are secreted in response to impulses from sympathetic nerves and serve to reinforce and prolong the effects of sympathetic stimulation. Pain, exposure to cold, hypotension, hypoxia, hypoglycemia, emotional upsets, and certain anesthetics stimulate the release of catecholamines.

The two hormones are synthesized together (first norepinephrine, which is converted to epinephrine) and accumulate in the adrenal medulla in a mixture

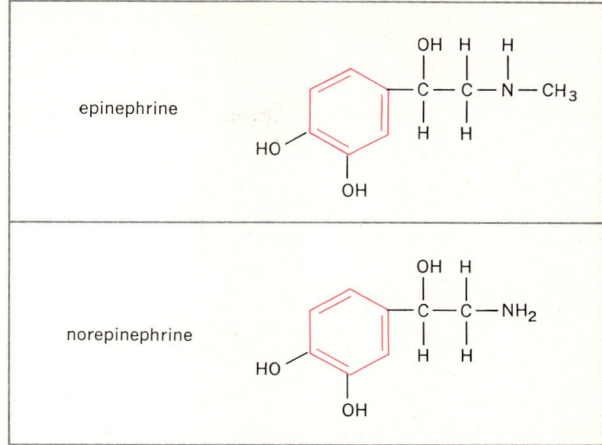

FIGURE 32-17 Chemical structure of catecholamines epinephrine and norepinephrine.

usually containing 80 to 90 percent epinephrine and 10 to 20 percent norepinephrine. Their effects are basically similar, but there are some key differences. Both epinephrine and norepinephrine dilate the coronary arteries and stimulate the heart; both cause peripheral vasoconstriction. (Epinephrine, however, produces a much stronger stimulation of heart action and a weaker constriction of the blood vessels in the skeletal muscles than norepinephrine.) Both produce a rise of the systolic pressure, but norepinephrine causes a rise in the diastolic pressure also. Both dilate the bronchi, widen the pupils, inhibit the intestinal muscle, and close the sphincters. In addition, epinephrine excites the central nervous system, affects the carbohydrate metabolism in striated muscle and liver, promotes recovery from fatigue in striated muscle, and produces hyperglycemia. Norepinephrine, in addition to being produced by the adrenal gland, is also the neurotransmitter released at the ends of postganglionic sympathetic nerve fibers and is present in the brain and spinal cord.

The functioning of the adrenal medulla is intimately linked with the sympathetic nervous system. Both the release of stored hormones (an energy-consuming process) and the resynthesis of the hormones are triggered by nerve impulses. After the hormones have produced their effect, they are inactivated, either rapidly by the enzyme O-methyl-transferase or more slowly by monoamine oxidase.

Epinephrine has been called the "emergency hormone," since it helps the body to cope with emergency situations. But the adrenal medulla is not essential to life, in contrast to the adrenal cortex. Epinephrine preparations are used in medicine as a heart stimulant, to relax the bronchioles in asthma, and to constrict the arterioles of the mucous membranes and skin, reducing the loss of blood in minor

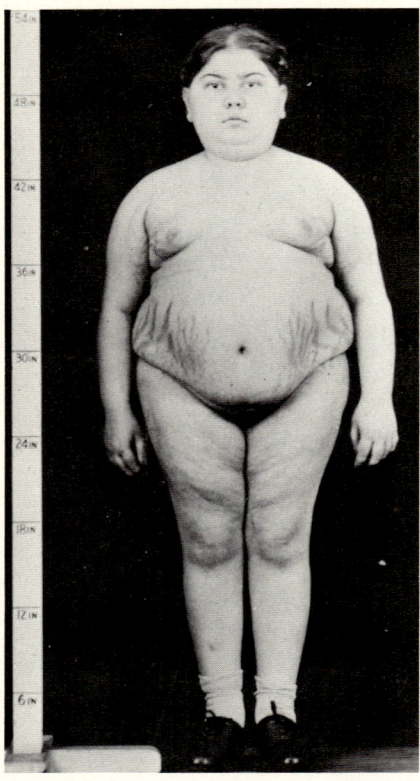

FIGURE 32-18 This 12-year-old girl suffered from Cushing's syndrome.

operations. Actually the commercial preparations of epinephrine are really combinations of epinephrine and norepinephrine, so that the effects resulting from an injection of epinephrine are a combination of the effects of the two hormones.

Disorders of the Adrenal Glands

One of the many dangers in following "crash diet" fads without medical supervision in the attempt to lose unwanted pounds is the possibility that the obesity may not be due to simple overeating, and a true glandular disorder may remain undetected. Hypofunction of the thyroid gland can lead to obesity. Another characteristic form may be the result of hyperfunction of the adrenal cortex, which may be caused by an adrenal or pituitary tumor.

The complex of symptoms called **Cushing's syndrome** (Figure 32-18) is due mainly to an oversecretion of cortisol and to a lesser extent of aldosterone and possibly the adrenal androgens as well. There is a mobilization of fat and a wasting of muscles in the arms and legs, while fat is deposited in the face, neck, and trunk. The face becomes round and puffy (a "moon face") with slitlike eyes; fat deposits in the neck and shoulders produce a characteristic "buffalo hump." Blood sugar levels are raised, to as high as 140 to 200 mg percent; this "adrenal diabetes" may

exhaust the overstimulated beta cells of the pancreas and lead to diabetes mellitus. Changes in fluid and electrolyte balance produce edema and hypertension. The wasting of tissue proteins causes such diverse effects as muscular weakness, osteoprosis with a weakening of the bones, and large purplish streaks visible on the skin, which are the result of tears in the subcutaneous tissues. Oversecretion of adrenal androgens may accompany the oversecretion of gluco- and mineralocorticoids, causing an increased growth of facial and body hair and signs of masculinization. Cushing's syndrome is treated by irradiation or surgical removal of a hypertrophied pituitary gland or ACTH-secreting tumor, if that is causing the condition, or by partial or total adrenalectomy (removal of the adrenal glands) with the administration of adrenal steroids to make up for any deficiency that develops.

In **primary aldosteronism,** a tumor produces excessive secretion of aldosterone. The patient has all the symptoms of Cushing's syndrome due to the disturbance of mineral metabolism (e.g., high sodium level, low potassium, edema, hypertension) without the other symptoms.

In the **adrenogenital syndrome,** which has already been described, an excessive secretion of adrenal sex hormones (usually due to a tumor of the adrenal cortex) produces a masculinizing effect. In an adult male, the effects of this malfunction are masked by the virilizing effects of the gonadal testosterone, so that an adrenal cortical tumor is difficult to diagnose. (Exceptions are the rare cases when an adrenal tumor produces an excessive secretion of female sex hormones, causing a feminine-like growth of the breast tissue.) In a woman the masculinizing effects are more obvious, and in a male child an adrenal tumor can stimulate full development of the sex organs, secondary sex characteristics, and adult sexual desires at an age as young as two to four years.

Hypofunction of the adrenal cortex leads to a condition known as **Addison's disease.** There are disturbances of the electrolyte and water balance, with a rise in potassium, a fall in sodium, chloride, and bicarbonate, severe dehydration, and a fall in blood pressure, which can lead to kidney failure. The carbohydrate metabolism is also disturbed, with hypoglycemia and low liver glycogen reserves. A characteristic bronzing of the skin is due to a deposition of melanin. If a patient with Addison's disease is untreated, he or she will die within a few days as a result of the electrolyte disturbances. But full treatment necessitates not only mineralocorticoid administration, but also the use of glucocorticoids to bolster the body's resources in coping with stress.

Rare tumors called **pheochromocytomas** can cause hyperfunction of the adrenal medulla, which pro-

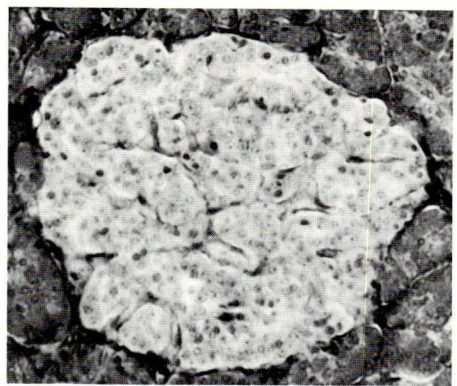

FIGURE 32-19 Section of human pancreas, × 190, showing an islet of Langerhans surrounded by acini of the exocrine portion of the gland.

duces excessive amounts of catecholamines (up to 500 times the normal amounts). Hypertension, hyperglycemia, excretion of catecholamines and glucose in the urine, and an elevated BMR are symptoms of this condition.

THE PANCREAS

The modern "sweet tooth" is probably causing more harm than many a dangerous drug such as heroin. The diet of our distant ancestors contained relatively small amounts of sugars, supplied mainly by fruits. Refined cane sugar—sucrose—did not become a significant factor in the human diet until about 200 years ago; since then sugar consumption has risen steadily, until now each person in the United States consumes an average of more than 100 pounds of sucrose a year. According to some researchers, sugar may be the major culprit in the development of atherosclerosis. For those who have not been fortunate enough to inherit a strong pancreas, continual high intake of sugar can "burn out" glandular cells of this organ, leaving it unable to regulate the body's carbohydrate metabolism.

We have already seen that the pancreas is really two unrelated organs in one. The bulk of the organ produces exocrine secretions, which are carried by ducts into the intestines and aid in the digestion of food. Scattered through the exocrine glandular tissue

are "islands" of endocrine cells, which secrete hormones that regulate carbohydrate metabolism. The number of these **islets of Langerhans** has been estimated at from 200,000 to 1,800,000 in the adult pancreas. The islets are not encapsulated; only a thin layer of reticular connective tissue separates them from the surrounding acinar tissue. Reticular fibers associated with the capillaries in the islets provide internal support. Two types of secretory cells are found in the islets, differing in their structure, staining properties, and in the hormones they secrete (Figure 32-19). The first type, **alpha cells,** are found around the periphery of the islets. They contain large numbers of dense, membrane-enclosed spherical granules, and they secrete the hormone **glucagon.** The **beta cells** of the islets are smaller and more numerous. They are situated in the interior of the islets and secrete the hormone **insulin.**

Both insulin and glucagon are concerned with the regulation of the body's carbohydrate metabolism, but their effects are opposite. (Yet the two hormones do not antagonize or block one another; they work independently.) When the blood sugar level rises—after a meal, for example, or when growth hormone or glucocorticoids produce hyperglycemia—the secretion of insulin is stimulated, and it causes the blood sugar level to fall. When the blood sugar level falls below the normal value, glucagon is secreted and acts to raise the glucose level of the blood. Like the interaction of parathyroid hormone and calcitonin in regulating the blood calcium level, insulin and glucagon together keep the blood sugar level within a relatively narrow range.

Insulin

Insulin represents a historic landmark in biochemistry: it was the first protein whose complete amino acid sequence was delineated. This feat was accomplished by the English biochemist Frederick Sanger in 1954 and won him a Nobel Prize.

Insulin is actually rather small protein, containing 51 amino acids arranged in two polypeptide chains, held together by disulfide (-S-S-) bridges (Figure 32-20). It is made in the beta cells of the pancreas, in

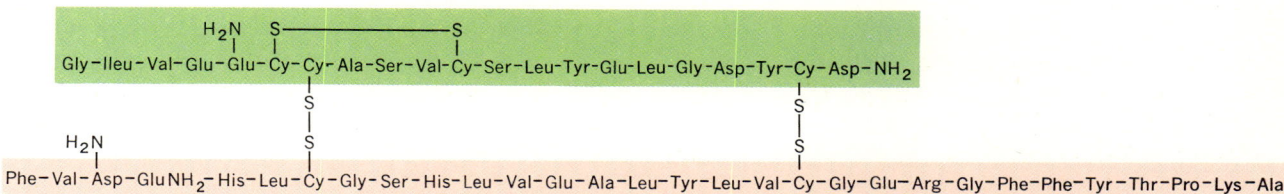

FIGURE 32-20 The amino acid sequence of insulin. The two chains of amino acid residues are held together by disulfide (-S-S-) bonds. (The sequence is printed in linear fashion for clarity; the actual molecule is curled and folded into an intricate and characteristic three-dimensional structure.)

the region of the Golgi apparatus. Initially an 84-amino-acid polypeptide, proinsulin, is synthesized and then split by a trypsinlike enzyme at two points. The larger unit formed is the active hormone, insulin, which is then stored in packets in granules. When the beta cells are activated by a rise in the blood glucose level, the granules move toward the cell membrane, fuse with it, and open, discharging their contents. Insulin then enters the blood and is carried by the portal vein into the main circulation.

When the blood sugar rises—either after the ingestion of a meal high in carbohydrates or, in an assay of pancreatic function, after an injection of glucose—there is an initial peak of insulin secretion. The concentration of the hormone in the blood then falls, only to show a secondary rise after perhaps half an hour. It is thought that the first peak represents the secretion of stored insulin, while the second rise is due to new synthesis of the hormone.

Insulin acts in several ways to lower the blood sugar level. It facilitates the transport of glucose through cell membranes; since the rate at which a cell utilizes glucose is determined to a large extent by the rate at which it enters the cell, insulin thus speeds up the rate of glucose metabolism. Insulin acts on the cellular enzymes that catalyze the conversion of glucose to glycogen and thus helps to take glucose out of circulation by storing it away in starch form. Insulin also stimulates lipogenesis, the synthesis of fatty acids from glucose. In addition insulin also speeds the transport of amino acids into cells and promotes their incorporation into peptides, while inhibiting the conversion of amino acids and fatty acids to glucose in the liver.

Precise regulation of the blood sugar level is crucial to life. A lack of insulin can lead to coma and eventual death. But before considering disorders of the endocrine functions of the pancreas, let us briefly discuss the other half of the "balancing act," glucagon.

Glucagon

The average person in the street has probably heard of insulin and may have a rough idea of what it does; but few people have ever heard of glucagon or realize that the pancreas secretes a second hormone.

Glucagon is a polypeptide, containing only 29 amino acids arranged in a straight chain. Glucagon is secreted by the alpha cells of the pancreas in response to hypoglycemia, a fall in the blood sugar level. It works mainly in the liver, stimulating glycogenolysis (the breakdown of glycogen to glucose) and gluconeogenesis (the synthesis of glucose from noncarbohydrate materials). The rapid mobilization of glucose from the liver sparked by glucagon raises the blood sugar level. (If purified glucagon is injected in a dose of only 1 microgram per kg of weight, its hyperglycemic effects are observed within ten minutes.) Glucagon has no effect on muscle glycogen. But it has recently been found to increase heart rate and stroke volume and thus cardiac output, like digitalis and the catecholamines. Though large doses must be used to produce the effect, there seem to be few if any side effects; so glucagon may be useful in the treatment of patients in acute heart failure.

Disorders of the Pancreas

In recent years, medical controversy has swirled about the subject of **hypoglycemia.** A syndrome has been described in which the blood sugar level is below the normal limits; the rise produced by glucose loading is rapidly followed by a sharp drop to the low level again, apparently due to an overreaction of the pancreas, producing too much insulin. In addition to the expected symptoms caused by the low blood sugar, such as chronic tiredness and fainting spells, a confusing variety of other symptoms has been described, including some mimicking other conditions, such as gastrointestinal disorders and mental illness. Some medical workers claim that this type of hypoglycemia is an extremely rare condition, usually due to a tumor of the pancreas that results in hypersecretion of insulin. But others say that chronic overindulgence in sweets can overstimulate a hypersensitive pancreas and ultimately "burn out" its beta cells, so that hypoglycemia can ultimately lead to diabetes. They suggest that the condition can be controlled by a high-protein diet, which leads to a lower, steadier stimulation of the pancreas and thus helps to normalize the blood sugar level. Unfortunately, a note of hysteria has been injected into the controversy by the invasion of numerous quacks, who have found "low blood sugar" a happy hunting ground and combine dietary counsels with expensive injections of adrenal cortical extracts.

Whether or not hypoglycemia is as widespread a problem as some researchers claim, there is no question that another disorder of the beta cells, **diabetes mellitus,** is a major health problem, currently ranked as the third largest killer in the U.S. *Mellitus* literally means "sweet" and refers to the fact that when the blood glucose level rises above about 180 mg percent, the excess sugar spills over into the urine and is excreted. (Some intrepid medical researcher of bygone days, noticing that flies were attracted to the urine of a diabetic patient, tasted the specimen and discovered it was sugary.)

The pancreas of a diabetic patient often contains beta cells, but they do not have secretory granules and do not give the typical staining reactions for insulin—they have become nonfunctional. Diabetics also typically have elevated levels of the blood-sugar-raising hormone, glucagon. Exactly why these abnormalities occur is not certain, but a tendency for diabetes seems to be hereditary, transmitted through recessive genes carried by about 20 percent of the population. Recent research indicates that juvenile-onset diabetes, a form that begins in childhood, may be a delayed effect of a viral infection, such as mumps or rubella. (It is believed that after the initial acute infection the virus remains in the body and, in susceptible persons, invades the beta cells and destroys them or possibly triggers an autoimmune reaction, causing the body to attack its own beta cells.) About 4 percent of the population develop some degree of diabetes mellitus at some stage of life, the majority of them in middle or old age (maturity-onset diabetes).

A failure of the pancreas to secrete insulin results in a variety of effects: (1) hyperglycemia—a rise in the blood sugar level to as high as 300 to 1200 mg percent (in comparison with the normal 100 mg percent); (2) glycosuria, an excretion of glucose in the urine; (3) dehydration—the elevated glucose concentration in the extracellular fluids causes a diffusion of water out of the body cells, and the high glucose level in the urine in turn causes diuresis; (4) polydipsia, an extreme thirst and inordinate drinking; (5) excessive eating, yet a loss of weight, due to the excretion of glucose and changes in metabolism; (6) disturbances of fat metabolism, leading to the formation of ketone bodies, which build up in the blood and are excreted in the urine; if unchecked, they can result in (7) acidosis, (8) coma, and (9) death. Even if the case of diabetes is mild enough not to lead to coma or death, it may increase the risk of disability and death in other ways. The alterations of fat metabolism result in atherosclerosis, greatly increased susceptibility to infection, cataracts, hypertension, and chronic kidney disease. Indeed, people who have had poorly controlled diabetes during childhood are likely to die of heart disease in their twenties.

Tests for diabetes include a test for glucose in the urine and the glucose tolerance test, in which the fasting blood sugar is determined, and then a definite amount of glucose is given and the blood sugar determined at intervals for about two hours. A five- or six-hour glucose tolerance test is used to diagnose hypoglycemia.) The "acetone breath" of a diabetic, due to ketone bodies, is another typical sign.

Mild cases of diabetes may be controlled by diet alone, adjusting the amounts of carbohydrates so as to avoid putting a strain on a pancreas that has lost part of its functional ability. Various oral drugs, such as tolbutamide (Orinase), can be used to stimulate the function of the pancreas when there are still some functional beta cells capable of responding. If these measures cannot control the condition, the patient takes carefully determined doses of insulin each day. (The hormone must be injected, for if taken orally it would be destroyed by the digestive enzymes.) Fortunately, although there are minor species differences in insulin molecules, beef and hog insulin are sufficiently effective in humans, and thus there is no shortage of the hormone.

A diabetic's insulin requirements vary, depending on the amount of carbohydrate ingested and the degree of physical activity. (Exercise has an insulinlike effect and reduces the insulin requirement.) It is therefore possible for a diabetic to accidentially administer an overdose of the hormone. If this happens, the glucose level of the blood falls catastrophically, and the brain is deprived of sufficient supplies of its energy substrate. The syndrome called **insulin shock** results, and the patient experiences convulsions, loss of consciousness, and finally coma. (In fact, it is sometimes difficult to distinguish between a diabetic coma, which must be treated with insulin, and insulin shock, which requires immediate intravenous injection of glucose.) Insulin shock is sometimes induced purposely in the treatment of certain mental disorders; after the jolt to the central nervous system caused by the therapy, some patients show an improvement of their mental activity.

Somatostatin, the hypothalamic hormone that depresses growth hormone activity, has been found to lower insulin levels in the blood, but it lowers glucagon secretion even more, producing a net lowering of the blood glucose level. Researchers are attempting to modify the somatostatin molecule to produce a longer-acting form of the hormone, which may be used in the future, either alone or in conjunction with insulin, for the treatment of diabetes.

Medical attention has been focused mainly on the beta cells of the pancreas, though an appreciation of the role of glucagon in diabetes is growing. Certain rare cases of **idiopathic hypoglycemia,** on the other hand, seem to be caused by a lack of alpha cells and a consequent failure to secrete glucagon.

THE GONADS

The term *gonad* literally means "seed," and the male and female sex organs—the gonads—produce the "seeds" of the new generation. The principal function of the gonads—testes in the male and ovaries in the female—is to produce the germ cells (sperm and ova) that can unite with germ cells of the opposite sex to produce a new life. But both the testes and the ovaries double as potent endocrine glands, whose hormones have profound influences not only on the sex organs, but also on a number of other body organs and functions.

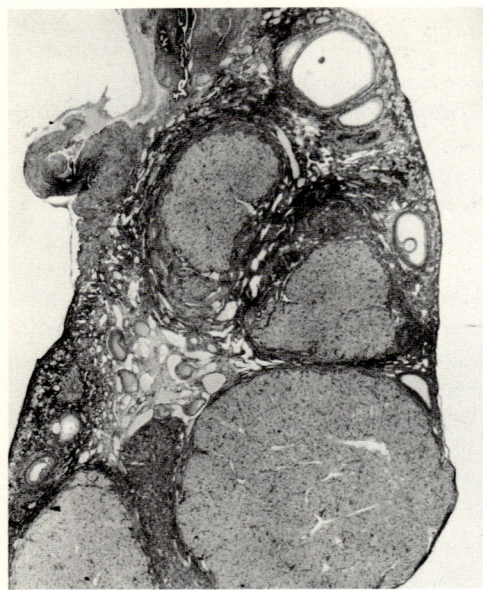

FIGURE 32-21 Section of a cat ovary, ×11. Note the developing ovum in a follicle. The large gray areas are corpora lutea.

The role of the gonads in reproduction is discussed in the following chapters. Here we shall focus on their endocrine functions.

The Ovaries

The "surface" characteristics that distinguish a woman from a man—rounded body contours, breasts, smooth skin, and high-pitched voice—are due in large measure to the secretion of her sex hormones. Whether sex differences go deeper, and extend to differences in mental abilities and emotional make-up, or whether the observed differences are merely the result of cultural conditioning, is currently the focus of lively and often strident debate.

Female sex hormones are secreted mainly by the ovaries. These are two small glands found in the pelvic portion of the female abdomen and attached to the broad ligament. Specialized epithelium in the outer layer of each ovary produces the ova (Figure 32-21). At birth, the ovaries of a baby girl contain about 400,000 immature follicles, most of which are doomed never to develop. At puberty, these primary follicles begin to ripen, usually one each month, developing into a mature form called a **graafian follicle.** Each graafian follicle contains an ovum. When it is ripe, the follicle bursts, expelling the ovum, which is carried to the uterus by one of the fallopian tubes. The empty follicle develops into a body called the **corpus luteum,** which during its brief existence is a vigorous hormone secreter.

The monthly cycle of ripening of follicles and formation of the corpus luteum, together with the corresponding changes that occur in the uterus as it first prepares for the possible reception of a fertilized ovum and then sheds its highly vascular lining in the menstrual flow, is regulated by an interplay of hormones: both the hormones of the gonads themselves and gonadotropic hormones of the anterior pituitary. If pregnancy is established, the placenta, too, becomes a temporary endocrine gland, producing its own sex hormones.

The major hormones produced by the ovaries are **estrogens** and **progesterone.** In addition to these female sex hormones, small quantities of **androgen** (a masculinizing hormone) are produced, although little is known about its function in the female. During pregnancy, a group of polypeptides referred to as **relaxin** is also secreted; they act to relax the symphysis pubis and uterus and soften the cervix and may potentiate the effect of estrogen and progesterone on the endometrium (the lining of the uterus).

The Ovarian Hormones

Up to the age of ten or so, if the actual genital organs were covered, there would be little to distinguish a girl from a boy. But then a biological clock in the girl's body seems to set off an alarm that rouses the hypothalamus. A releasing factor is sent down to the adenohypophysis, and the secretion of follicle-stimulating hormone (FSH) begins. Now the dormant ovaries awaken, and their follicles begin to grow and to secrete their own hormones, the **estrogens.**

There are three main estrogens produced by the ovaries: β-**estradiol, estrone,** and **estriol,** the most potent of which is β-estradiol. The estrogens are all steroids (Figure 32-22), and they are chemically rather similar to one another—and indeed, to the male sex hormone testosterone as well (Figure 32-24). The estrogens have a variety of effects on the body. They stimulate an explosive development of the female sexual organs, as the uterus, fallopian tubes, and vagina enlarge and the labia and mons pubis take on their adult contours. The breasts begin to develop under the prompting of estrogens, and the body rounds out into feminine curves, as fat is deposited in the subcutaneous tissues. The strengthening flow of estrogens sparks a growth spurt, causing the pelvis to broaden and the long bones to lengthen. But at the same time, estrogens cause the epiphyses of the long bones to close, so that the rapid growth soon comes to an end. (Usually a girl achieves her full height within a year after she begins to menstruate. If she were lacking in female sex hormones, her growth would be slower but would continue longer, reaching a greater overall height.) Estrogens increase the general metabolism slightly and create a slight positive nitrogen balance (that is, they increase the amount of body protein).

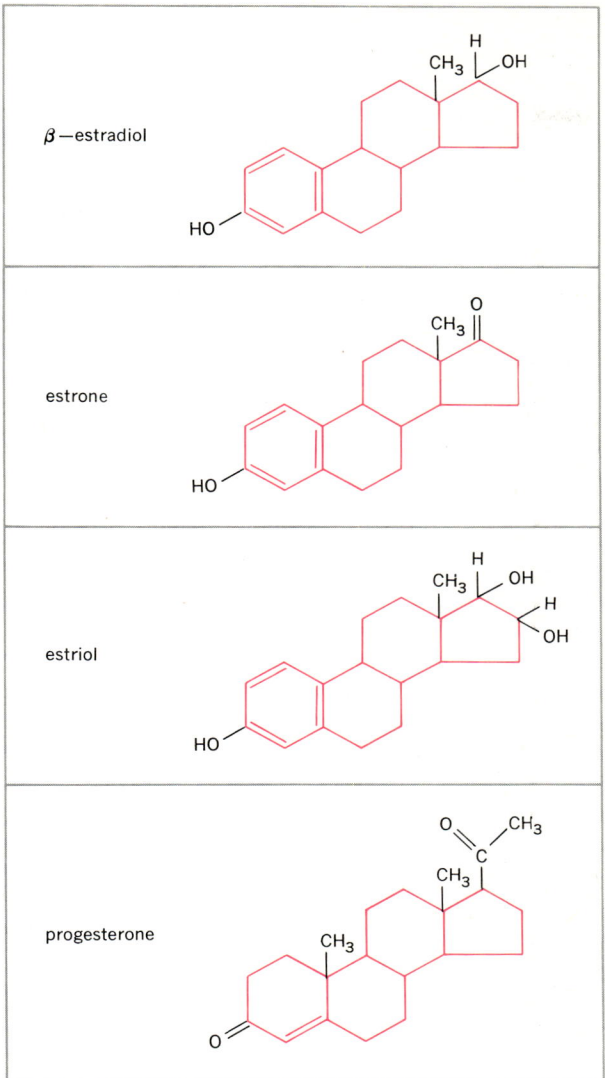

FIGURE 32-22 **Chemical structures of estrogens (β-estradiol, estrone, and estriol) and progesterone.**

β—estradiol

estrone

estriol

progesterone

They promote the development of a soft, smooth, and highly vascular skin. Estrogens cause retention of sodium, chloride, and water by the kidneys, but this effect is normally slight and becomes significant only during pregnancy (or sometimes in the pregnancylike state produced by birth control pills).

When the female sexual organs are ready to function, the hypothalamus stimulates the adenohypophysis to secrete another gonadotropic hormone, luteinizing hormone (LH), which causes a ripened ovarian follicle to rupture and release the ovum it contains (ovulation) and develop into a corpus luteum. Another anterior pituitary hormone, luteotropic hormone (LTH, also called prolactin), now maintains the activity of the corpus luteum, which begins to secrete the other female sex hormone, **progesterone.**

Progesterone, another member of the steroid family, has its main effect on the uterus. Acting in sequence with estrogen, it prepares the endometrium, the lining of the uterus, for the possible reception and nourishment of a fertilized ovum. Progesterone also decreases uterine contractions, helping to prevent expulsion of the implanted ovum, and fosters the development of the breasts into functional milk-secreting organs. The actual milk secretion, however, is stimulated by the anterior pituitary hormone prolactin (LTH). Like estrogen, progesterone enhances the retention of Na^+, Cl^-, and water by the kidneys, although its effect is far less potent than that of aldosterone.

The waxing and waning of the female sex hormones during the menstrual cycle and their special effects during pregnancy are discussed in later chapters. The secretion of the ovarian hormones is controlled by gonadotropins of the adenohypophysis, but the estrogens and progesterone, in turn, help to regulate the secretion of the pituitary hormones through feedback mechanisms. In addition to the ovarian sex hormones, both male and female sex hormones are secreted by the adrenal cortex, and during pregnancy the placenta acts as a powerful auxiliary endocrine organ.

The Placenta

The powerful uterine contractions of parturition do not cease with the delivery of the baby; after a few minutes, the placenta that has nourished it during its prenatal life breaks away from the uterine lining and is expelled from the mother's body. Human mothers generally have no further contact with the placenta, which in modern hospitals is whisked away to serve as a source of valuable biochemicals. But in most mammalian species, the new mother is more practical: even if she happens to be a herbivore, she promptly eats the placenta. This instinctive act helps to bolster her strength after the ordeal of labor, and may also provide a reinfusion of useful hormones.

During pregnancy, the placenta secretes large quantities of sex hormones. Estrogens and progesterone are produced, along with some hormones unique to this temporary endocrine gland: chorionic gonadotropin and placental lactogen.

Chorionic gonadotropin begins to be secreted soon after an ovum is fertilized, rises to a peak about seven weeks after ovulation, and then drops to a low value after about 16 weeks. Because of this pattern of secretion, this hormone has provided the basis for a rapid and early test for detecting pregnancy. Unlike the estrogens and progesterone, chorionic gonadotropin is a glycoprotein. Its functions are much like those of the pituitary hormone, luteinizing hormone. It prevents the corpus luteum from shriveling up at the end of the monthly cycle and enhances its secretion of progesterone and estrogens. The increased levels of these sex hormones cause the endometrium to continue growing instead of being sloughed off. Up to about the eleventh week of pregnancy, the hormones produced by the enlarged corpus luteum maintain the pregnancy (removal of the ovary up to this time provokes a spontaneous abortion), but then the placenta produces sufficient sex hormones to take over.

Human **placental lactogen,** a recently discovered placental hormone, has two types of effects: it mimics the effects of growth hormone, and it also exhibits an action on the breasts similar to that of prolactin.

Disorders of the Ovaries

Puberty has always been a time of identity crisis, and the emphasis on sex in modern advertising has made adolescence an even more painful time for many a young girl. She wonders despairingly whether her straight, flat torso will ever resemble the pneumatic excesses of the models in the ads. The advent of the menses, which marks her "coming of age," is met with mixed feelings. In some cases, however, the development of secondary sex characteristics and the establishment of the menstrual cycle may be delayed long past the usual time or even prevented entirely.

Amenorrhea, the complete absence of menstruation, may result from a variety of causes. If the menstrual cycle has never begun at all, one of the links in the chain of endocrine glands is probably malfunctioning: either the hypothalamus is failing to produce its releasing factors, or the adenohypophysis is not producing gonadotropins, or the ovaries themselves are not secreting sufficient sex hormones. Such hormonal imbalances are usually accompanied not only by an absence of menstrual periods, but also by a lack of development of the breasts and other secondary sex characteristics. If the menstrual cycles cease after they have been well established, the most likely cause is pregnancy. However, inadequate secretion of estrogens by the ovaries can produce irregular menstrual periods, or their complete cessation. (Here, too, it may not be the ovaries that are defective; they may secrete smaller than normal amounts of estrogens in such conditions as hypothyroidism.) Removal of the ovaries in a fully developed woman causes the sexual organs to regress to some extent, so that the uterus and vagina become small and the lining of the vagina becomes thin and easily damaged. The breasts atrophy, and the pubic hair thins. (These changes are similar to those that normally occur at menopause.) Because of these undesirable side effects, an effort is often made to leave the ovaries in place if possible when the uterus must be removed in a hysterectomy;

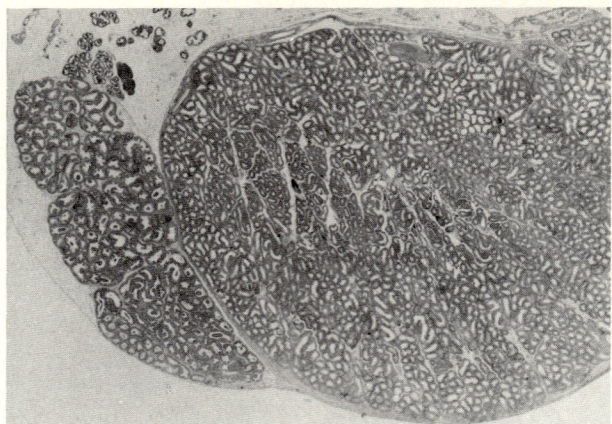

FIGURE 32-23 Section of a rabbit testis, ×5.

or estrogen therapy may be used to replace the secretions of ovaries that have been removed. The value of estrogen therapy in menopause is still a matter of some debate; recent studies have suggested that taking birth control pills or other female sex hormones after the age of 40 may increase the risk of cancer.

One of the most frequent complaints that a high school nurse hears is of **dysmenorrhea,** a difficult or painful menstruation. Cramps, low abdominal pain, headache, nausea, and emotional lability may accompany the menstrual flow. The use of birth control pills often relieves the symptoms, and the condition often disappears after a full-term pregnancy.

Hypersecretion by the ovaries is a rare condition, generally due to an ovarian tumor. In such cases there is generally an oversecretion of estrogens, rather than progesterone, Hypertrophy of the endometrium, with irregular bleeding, may result.

The Testes

During the Middle Ages and Renaissance, the harems of Arab rulers were commonly guarded by eunuchs, men who had been castrated to eliminate their sexual desires and capacity. Meanwhile, in Europe, castration was sometimes performed for a different reason: to preserve the pure boyish sopranos of choir boys.

The removal of the testes can produce all these effects because, like the ovaries in the female, the male gonads have two major functions: they produce the germ cells that act in reproduction and they also are powerful endocrine organs, secreting male sex hormones. The testes are small, ovoid structures, suspended in the scrotum by the spermatic cord, which passes down from the inguinal region. Two major types of specialized cells are found in the testes (Figure 32-23): tubules containing germinal epithelium, which function in the production of sperm, and **interstitial cells of Leydig,** clustered among the seminifer-

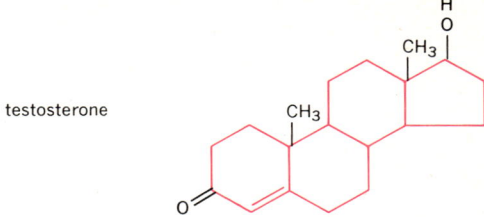

FIGURE 32-24 Chemical structure of testosterone.

FIGURE 32-25 Pattern baldness develops under the influence of testosterone.

ous tubules, which secrete **androgens** (male sex hormones).

The major androgen produced by the testes is **testosterone,** which belongs to the group of steroids (Figure 32-24). Small quantities of another androgen, Δ^4-androstene-3,17-dione, are also secreted by the testes, and the adrenal gland secretes at least five different androgens, but the effects of all of these are slight in comparison with testosterone.

Hormones of the adenohypophysis play just as profound a role in controlling the functions of the testes in men as they do in controlling the functions of the ovaries in women. Spermatogenesis in the testes is controlled by FSH, while the anterior pituitary hormone interstitial cell-stimulating hormone (ICSH), which is identical with LH in the female, controls the secretion of testosterone.

Testosterone Women's liberation extremists hold that the typical behavioral and personality differences between men and women are culturally conditioned, rather than innate. Yet there is evidence to indicate a structural basis for at least some differences between the sexes. The greater aggressiveness of men, for example, seems to be linked to some degree with the secretion of the male sex hormone testosterone.

The secretion of testosterone begins early in life—in the male fetus, in fact. In the absence of this hormone (e.g., if the testes are removed early in development), female sexual organs will develop, even if the fetus is genetically male. On the contrary, injections of testosterone during pregnancy cause a female fetus to develop male sexual organs. Testosterone is responsible both for the development of the male external genitalia and for the descent of the testes into the scrotum, which occurs during the eighth or ninth month of prenatal life.

Small quantities of testosterone continue to be secreted during childhood, but there is a dramatic increase in secretion at puberty. Like estrogens, testosterone sparks a furious growth spurt, along with the development of mature sexual organs and secondary sexual characteristics such as the appearance of hair in the pubic and axillary regions, on the face and chest. (Testosterone also contributes to the develop-

ment of pattern baldness such as that shown in Figure 32-25, in men who are genetically disposed to it. Eunuchs do not become bald.) Enlargement of the larynx at this time causes an abrupt lowering of the voice. Like estrogens, testosterone promotes bone growth, but at the same time causes the epiphyses of the long bones to close, so that the rapid growth spurt soon ceases. Testosterone has an especially strong enhancing effect on muscular development.

Testosterone is responsible to some degree for sexual interest and sex drive. But in humans, an intricate complex of psychological factors is superimposed on this underlying endocrine mechanism.

Disorders of the Testes

In our day, castration is no longer practiced for such frivolous reasons as preserving a soprano singing voice. But testes may occasionally have to be removed surgically because of disease. Male children sometimes are born lacking functional testes, or the testes may fail to descend from the abdominal cavity into the scrotum. In the latter condition, called **cryptorchidism,** the higher body temperatures prevailing in the protected abdomen, in comparison with the free-hanging scrotal sac, prevent the testes from producing viable sperm at sexual maturity, although they may secrete a normal complement of androgens. (Sometimes, however, partial or complete degeneration of undescended testes occurs.) If cryptorchidism is corrected early—by surgery or by an injection of testosterone, which usually stimulates the testes to descend through the inguinal canal—normal sexual development will occur.

In cases when the testes are nonfunctional or re-

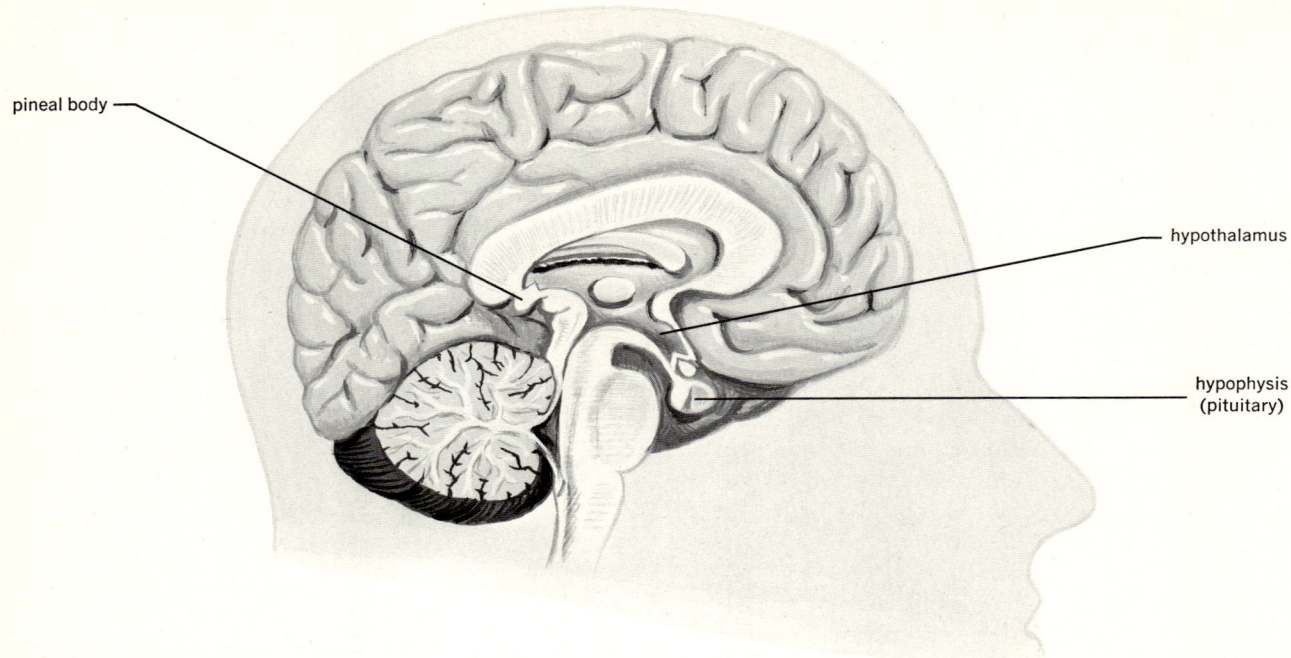

FIGURE 32-26 Medial view of the brain showing the pineal body in relation to the hypothalamus and hypophysis.

moved before puberty, the person will be a **eunuch,** possessing neuter sexual characteristics throughout his life. His external genitalia remain child-sized, he does not develop the normal masculine distribution of hair (nor will he become bald, even if he has inherited baldness genes), his voice is high, his muscles are weaker than those of a normal man, and his bones are thin, although he may grow quite tall. (Recall that testosterone stimulates bone growth, but causes the ephiphyses to close early.) Similar symptoms can be produced by damage to the hypothalamus, preventing the secretion of adequate amounts of gonadotropic hormones. This hypothalamic type of eunuchism is often accompanied by extreme obesity due to overeating, because of damage to the satiety center in the hypothalamus; the condition therefore is also referred to as the **adiposogenital syndrome.**

If the testes are removed after puberty, some of the sexual characteristics revert to a juvenile state, but others remain relatively unchanged. The sex organs decrease in size only slightly, and the voice becomes only a little higher; but there is a loss of the masculine hair production, the muscles become weaker, and the bones thinner. Sexual desires are decreased but not entirely lost, if sexual activities had been practiced before castration. Erection and even ejaculation can still occur, although with less ease.

Hypergonadism occasionally occurs, due to tumors of the interstitial cells. Up to 100 times the normal amount of testosterone may be secreted by such a tumor. In a young child, precocious sexual develop-

ment and a short stature result. But cases of hypergonadism are rarely diagnosed in adult men—the extra testosterone merely produces a moderate enlargement of the sex organs and a heightening of the masculine characteristics that are already present—a combination that is hardly likely to send a man complaining to his doctor. Tumors of the germinative epithelium occur more often, sometimes producing bizarre **teratomas,** which contain a variety of differentiated tissues such as placental tissue, hair, teeth, and bone. Often such tumors secrete no hormones, but if large quantities of placental tissue are present they may secrete chorionic gonadotropin; such tumors may also secrete estrogens, which cause an overgrowth of the breasts.

THE PINEAL GLAND

You have a "third eye," located deep within your brain. This is the pineal gland, a small conical body, less than 1 cm long, attached by a stalk to the posterior wall of the third ventricle, above the superior colliculi of the midbrain (Figure 32-26). Until recently, the status of the pineal gland as an endocrine organ was highly controversial, and despite greatly increased interest, many mysteries of its functions still remain to be unraveled.

Although it is located within the brain, the pineal gland is innervated exclusively by the peripheral autonomic nervous system. It responds to changes in environmental lighting, information about which is carried to it over nerve pathways that have not yet

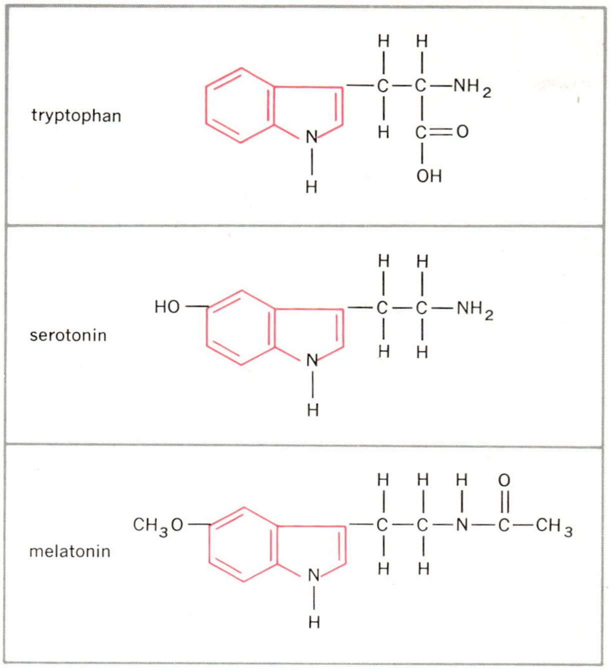

FIGURE 32-27 Chemical structures of tryptophan, serotonin, and melatonin.

been entirely worked out, leading from the retina to the superior cervical ganglia, and from there to the pineal gland via postganglionic sympathetic fibers. When light strikes the retina, impulses from these sympathetic fibers, transmitted to the pineal gland by the neurotransmitter norepinephrine, stimulate the secretion of the pineal hormone **melatonin.** (There is still some question whether melatonin is the only hormone secreted by the pineal gland or other hormones are also produced.)

Melatonin is a derivative of the amino acid tryptophan (Figure 32-27), and its synthesis proceeds through an intermediate stage of serotonin, which is an important neurotransmitter substance in its own right. Melatonin synthesis waxes and wanes each day, in correlation with the alternation of light and darkness. In frogs melatonin causes the pigment granules in the melanocytes of the skin to concentrate near the nuclei, so that the overall skin color becomes lighter. This function is the basis for the hormone's name, but it does not seem to be its function in mammals.

An important effect of the pineal secretions is to inhibit the gonads. Ovulation is blocked, and puberty is delayed (both in males and in females) when melatonin production is high. Melatonin is believed to act through the hypothalamus, modulating its secretion of releasing factors, resulting in an inhibition of LH secretion by the adenohypophysis. (Another pineal substance has been found to decrease the secretion of

FSH.) Thus, the pineal gland is believed to be the seat of the body's "biological clock," which signals the onset of maturation and regulates the menstrual cycle.

The pineal hormone also seems to be involved in the normal daily fluctuations of the body temperature, since these fluctuations cease in animals if the pineal gland is removed. Other experimental evidence indicates that pineal hormones inhibit ACTH secretion and thus indirectly help to regulate the secretions of the adrenal glands.

Many mysteries persist regarding the role of the pineal gland in the human body, intensified by the observation that this gland often becomes completely calcified in adults, without any significant physiological effects on the body.

THE THYMUS

If the thymus of a young animal is removed, it will be able to accept tissue transplants from unrelated animals, without any problems of rejection. Long regarded as a mystery gland, which is prominent in the child but tends to atrophy in adulthood, the thymus is now firmly ensconced as a working member of the lymphatic system. (Its anatomy and functions were described in Chapter 22.) Its major contribution is to stimulate the lymphoid organs to produce immunocompetent lymphocytes. The thymus can also be regarded as an endocrine gland, since it performs its function by means of hormones.

Certain diseases, including rheumatoid arthritis, hemolytic anemia, and myasthenia gravis, are now believed to be autoimmune diseases, in which the body's defenders mistakenly consider some of the body's own cells as "foreign" and form antibodies against them. Significantly, in such diseases the thymus is found to be greatly enlarged, and presumably secreting excessive hormones.

Thymic Hormones

Heather was born with a poorly developed thymus gland. By the time she was four, in 1974, she was near death from infections that her inadequate immune system was unable to fight off. Fortunately for Heather, her physician decided to try a radical new treatment, using a recently isolated hormone fraction from beef thymus glands. Heather responded dramatically, producing immunologically competent T lymphocytes in sufficient numbers to conquer the infections that raged in her body. Gradually she regained her strength and became a normal, healthy little girl—kept that way by regular injections of thymic hormones.

The thymus fraction used to treat Heather and subsequent patients has been named **thymosin** and is actually a mixture of more than two dozen polypeptides, with molecular weights from 900 to 14,000. It is not yet certain how many of the components contribute to the hormonal action; a 108-amino-acid polypeptide from the mixture was purified and found to be active, but not as active as the complete mixture. Thymosin appears to work on immature T lymphocytes, converting them to mature forms.

Two polypeptides, **thymopoietin I** and **II,** have been isolated from a different fraction of beef thymus and found to work on bone marrow cells that have not yet differentiated into T cells, causing them to develop into immunocompetent T lymphocytes. Still another thymic polypeptide that induces T cell differentiation has also been isolated; but this hormone is not specific, since it also stimulates the maturation of B cells (another type of lymphocytes) and is found not only in the thymus but in every kind of cell, including plant cells. This widely occurring substance has been named **ubiquitous immunopoietic polypeptide (UBIP).**

An encouraging property of thymic hormones is the fact that they are not species-specific. Like the insulin used by millions of diabetics to control their disease, thymic hormones isolated from beef and pig glands work effectively on humans. It is hoped that they will eventually prove useful not only for patients like Heather, born with defects of the immune system, but also for cancer patients, who suffer from a variety of immunodeficiencies. It probably is no mere coincidence that the incidence of cancer and infections increases with age, as the size of the thymus gland decreases; thymic hormones may ultimately prove to be effective anti-aging agents as well.

PROSTAGLANDINS

Prostaglandins may some day help us to routinely heal ulcers, reduce high blood pressure, clear stuffed noses, induce safe abortions, and perform dozens of other medical functions.

The prostaglandins received their name as a result of a misunderstanding. One of these hormonelike substances was originally found in human semen, and was thought to be produced by the prostate gland. (This prostaglandin is actually produced in the seminal vesicles.) Later a number of other closely related substances, present in many body fluids and tissues, were discovered.

Prostaglandins are derivatives of the polyunsaturated fatty acid arachidonic acid (Figure 32-28). They are thought to be formed in the cell membrane and may act through an interaction with adenyl cyclase, modulating cyclic AMP formation. They exert their effects in extremely small concentrations. At least 15 natural prostaglandins have been found, and more than a thousand synthetic prostaglandin ana-

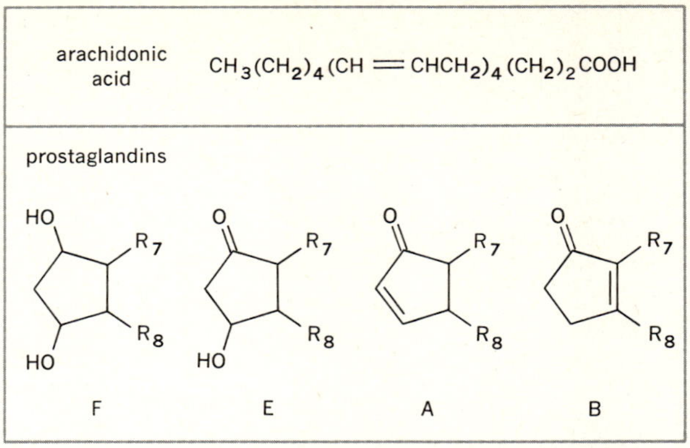

FIGURE 32-28 Prostaglandins are derivatives of the fatty acid arachidonic acid (top) and occur in four basic ring structures (bottom). (Modified from N. Anderson and H. Benson, *Annals, N.Y. Acad. Sci., 180:* 15, Fig. 1.)

logs are being tested for drug activity. Various prostaglandins affect the lipolysis of fat depots and the blood level of fatty acids, the activity of smooth muscle of the digestive tract, cardiovascular system, and respiratory system, and organs of the reproductive tract. Prostaglandins have been used to induce second-trimester abortions, to induce ovulation in cattle and horses, to speed the healing of stomach ulcers, to improve the blood flow in cases of peripheral arteriosclerosis, to relieve asthma by relaxing the bronchioles, and to lower high blood pressure.

Prostaglandin research has cast light on the functioning of a common drug, which has been used widely for many years without much knowledge of how it works: aspirin. Aspirin has been found to produce its pain-relieving effects by inhibiting the synthesis of certain prostaglandins. The enzyme that converts fatty acids to prostaglandin precursors has three active sites: an oxygen-binding site, a fatty acid-binding site, and a site where an activator of the enzyme binds. Aspirin attaches itself to the fatty acid-binding site, blocking the action of the enzyme. The aspirin substitute Tylenol (acetaminophen) also works on the same enzyme, but binds to the activator site.

Very unstable substances called prostaglandin endoperoxides and thromboxanes have recently been discovered and found to be even more active than the corresponding prostaglandin. Research efforts are focusing on unraveling the interconversions and roles of these three types of compounds.

CHALONES

The mysterious tissue extracts called chalones have been known for decades, yet no one has yet been able to isolate and identify the exact structure of one. Some researchers doubt that they exist at all, attempting to explain their effects by other mechanisms. But there is considerable evidence to support the existence of these substances, and it is hoped that they may one day be used in the treatment of such diverse problems as cancer, aging, psoriasis, and organ rejection.

Chalones are hormonelike substances that are apparently produced by cells undergoing differentiation. They act as mitotic inhibitors, preventing other cells of the same type from embarking on mitosis. They are water-soluble compounds and act in the living body, as well as the test tube, inhibiting proliferation without any apparent toxic effects. An unusual feature of the chalones is that they are not species specific, but they are tissue specific: a chalone from fish skin will work on skin from a mouse or a human but has no effect on liver, kidneys, or blood cells. Chalones are hormonelike in that they help to control cell activities, but they are local products, produced on the spot rather than carried to distant areas of the body through the bloodstream.

Chalones are believed to work with epinephrine to inhibit mitosis. (Growth and repair of body tissues is believed to occur mainly during sleep, when the adrenal glands secrete less epinephrine, and thus the chalones are ineffective.)

The major hopes for clinical applications of chalones are centered on conditions characterized by uncontrolled cell multiplication, such as cancer and psoriasis (a skin condition). In animal experiments chalones have caused cancerous tumors to break down and disappear. In clinical trials on humans, they have also been used to suppress rejection reactions in skin and bone marrow grafts.

SUMMARY

Endocrine glands secrete chemical regulators (hormones) that are carried through the body by the bloodstream and control and regulate the functions of other cells in the body.
> The action of hormones is slower and longer lasting than nerve action.
> Hormones are all (1) proteins or protein and amino acid derivatives, or (2) steroids.
> Hormones may be local (e.g., digestive hormones, neurohumors) or general.
>> Some act on body cells in general, others on narrowly specific target tissues.
The mechanism of action of protein and polypeptide hormones includes a regulation of cyclic AMP formation in the cell, produced by an interaction of the hormone at a receptor site on the cell surface with adenyl cyclase or phosphodiesterase.
> The hormone acts as the "first messenger," and cyclic AMP as the "second messenger."
> Steroid hormones act differently, actually entering the cells.
> Hormone secretion is regulated by feedback mechanisms, often involving other hormones and nervous influences.
The major endocrine glands are:
> Hypothalamus
> Hypophysis (pituitary)
> Thyroid
> Parathyroids
> Pancreas
> Adrenal glands
> Gonads (ovaries, testes)
> Pineal gland
> Thymus
The hypophysis consists of two lobes, anterior (adenohypophysis) and posterior (neurohypophysis).
> The adenohypophysis secretes hormones under the control of releasing factors of the hypothalamus.
>> Hormones secreted are:
>> Growth hormone (GH, somatotropin, STH)
>> Adrenocorticotropin (ACTH)
>> Thyrotropin (TSH)
>> Lactogenic hormone (prolactin, luteotropic hormone, LTH)
>>> Follicle-stimulating hormone (FSH) in female and interstitial cell-stimulating hormone (ICSH) in the male
>> Melanocyte-stimulating hormone (MSH)
> The neurohypophysis stores and releases into the bloodstream hormones secreted by the hypothalamus:
>> Vasopressin (antidiuretic hormone, ADH)
>> Oxytocin
Somatotropin stimulates the secretion of somatomedin by the liver.
> Hyposecretion of pituitary growth hormone can result in:
>> Dwarfism
>> Simmond's disease (hypophyseal cachexia)
> Hypersecretion of pituitary growth hormone can result in:
>> Giantism
>> Acromegaly
> Somatotropin secretion is regulated by a hypothalamic releasing hormone and a hypothalamic inhibitor (somatostatin).
Prolactin (LTH) stimulates secretion by the corpus luteum of the ovary and promotes milk secretion.
Thyrotropin stimulates secretion by the thyroid gland.
Adrenocorticotropin (ACTH) stimulates secretion of glucocorticoids and to some extent of aldosterone and androgens by the adrenal cortex.
Follicle-stimulating hormone and luteinizing hormone are gonadotropins, both controlled by the hypothalamic releasing hormone LRH.
Follicle-stimulating hormone stimulates the ovarian follicles to develop.
Luteinizing hormone initiates ovulation and stimulates the formation of the corpus luteum and secretion of progesterone.
> Interstitial cell-stimulating hormone stimulates secretion of testosterone by the interstitial cells of the testes.
Melanocyte-stimulating hormone is secreted by the pars intermedia and has a skin-darkening effect.
Oxytocin secretion is stimulated by suckling through a nervous reflex.
> It produces uterine contractions and ejection of milk from the alveoli of the mammary glands.
Vasopressin (ADH) has a vasoconstrictive effect and stimulates reabsorption of water by the kidneys.
> Lesions preventing ADH secretion result in diabetes insipidus.
The thyroid gland secretes iodine-containing hormones (thyroxine and triiodothyronine) that speed up metabolic processes and calcitonin, which inhibits resorption of calcium from bones, lowering blood calcium levels.
> Simple goiter results from a lack of iodine in the diet.
> Hyposecretion of thyroxine can result in:
>> Cretinism
>> Myxedema
> Hypersecretion of thyroxine can result in:
>> Exophthalmic goiter

Thyroid function is tested by determinations of:
BMR
Protein-bound iodine (PBI)
Radioiodine uptake

The parathyroid glands secrete parathyroid hormone, which stimulates resorption of calcium from bones, raises the calcium level in blood and extracellular fluids, and lowers the phosphate level.

The adrenal glands consist of an outer cortex and inner medulla, with different structure and functions.

Hormones secreted by the adrenal cortex are steroids:
Mineralocorticoids (aldosterone, deoxycorticosterone)
Glucocorticoids (cortisol, corticosterone, cortisone)
Androgens

Hormones secreted by the adrenal medulla are catecholamines:
Epinephrine (adrenaline)
Norepinephrine (noradrenaline)

Mineralocorticoids increase reabsorption of sodium ions in the kidneys, regulating the water and electrolyte balance, osmotic pressure, and pH of body fluids.

Glucocorticoids raise blood sugar level, promote redistribution of fat, produce vasoconstriction, protect the body against stress, and have an antiinflammatory effect.

Adrenal sex hormones are mainly androgens, with small amounts of estrogens.

Excess secretion, caused by a tumor, produces masculinization.

Epinephrine and norepinephrine are sympathomimetic amines, secreted in response to stimulation by sympathetic nerves and reinforcing the effects of sympathetic stimulation.

Disorders of the adrenal cortex include:
Hyperfunction
Cushing's syndrome
Primary aldosteronism
Adrenogenital syndrome
Hypofunction
Addison's disease

The pancreas functions as an exocrine gland and an endocrine gland.

Endocrine secretions are produced by islets of Langerhans, scattered among the acini.

Alpha cells secrete glucagon; beta cells secrete insulin.

Insulin secretion is stimulated by a rise in blood sugar level. It lowers the blood sugar level by speeding up glucose metabolism, promoting conversion of glucose to glycogen, stimulating lipogenesis, and inhibiting gluconeogenesis.

Glucagon raises the blood sugar level, by stimulating glycogenolysis and gluconeogenesis.

Disorders of the pancreas include:
Hypoglycemia (hyperfunction of beta cells)
Diabetes mellitus (hypofunction of beta cells)

The ovaries produce germ cells (ova) and secrete hormones that stimulate development and maintenance of sex organs and secondary sex characteristics and function in the menstrual cycle:
Estrogens (β-estradiol, estrone, estriol)
Progesterone

During pregnancy the placenta is supplementary endocrine gland, secreting:
Progesterone
Estrogen
Chorionic gonadotropin
Placental lactogen

The testes produce germ cells (sperm) and secrete hormones (androgens) that stimulate development and maintenance of sex organs and secondary sex characteristics and muscular development:

Testosterone
Δ^4-Androstene-3,17-dione

Removal of the testes can result in eunuchism.

The pineal gland is stimulated by environmental light and secretes the hormone melatonin.

It is believed to act as a "biological clock," governing body rhythms such as the menstrual cycle.

The thymus gland stimulates the production of immunocompetent cells by the lymphoid organs, through hormones: thymosin, thymopoietin I and II.

Prostaglandins are produced in seminal vesicles and other tissues and have varied effects on fat metabolism, activity of smooth muscle, and reproductive organs.

Aspirin works by inhibiting prostaglandin synthesis.

Chalones are mitotic inhibitors produced by differentiating cells and are tissue specific but not species specific.

QUESTIONS FOR REVIEW AND THOUGHT

1 What are the major differences between nerve and hormone action?

2 Distinguish between endocrine and exocrine glands.

3 List the endocrine glands, the hormones they secrete, and their main effects.

4 Describe an example of a feedback mechanism in the regulation of hormone secretion.

5 Discuss the releasing factors of the hypothalamus. Why has it been said that their discovery has produced a revolution in endocrinology?

6 You are a family doctor and a series of patients have come to you with complaints that you think may be due to endocrine disorders. What are your tentative diagnoses in each case, what corroboratory tests might you request, and what treatments might you suggest?

(a) A child, six years old, is the size of a normal three-year-old, but well proportioned and of normal intelligence.

(b) A woman, age 50, is 5'4" tall but weighs only 98 pounds. She is highly nervous and excitable, complains of insomnia, and her eyes are somewhat protruding.

(c) A woman, age 50, is 5'4" tall and weighs 170 pounds. She has a round, puffy face with heavy facial hair and a heavy torso, but her arms and legs are thin. She claims she has not been eating excessively, but has gained 30 pounds in the past six months.

(d) A man, age 55, has been losing weight recently and has been plagued by constant thirst and frequent urination. His breath has a fruity odor.

(e) A woman, age 26, has not menstruated for the past four months. She is about 20 pounds overweight and complains of frequent tiredness and lethargy.

7 What hormones control: (a) the blood sugar level; (b) the calcium level; (c) growth; (d) the female reproductive cycle; (e) immunity mechanisms; (f) blood pressure? List *all* the hormones affecting each item and give their effects and the gland secreting them.

8 What advantage is provided by the transport of thyroid hormones in the blood by globulin?

9 What do glucocorticoids do? Why can the use of cortical steroids to treat inflammation be dangerous?

10 Compare the effects of epinephrine, norepinephrine, and sympathetic stimulation.

11 What are prostaglandins and chalones? Should they be classified as hormones?

THE MALE REPRODUCTIVE SYSTEM

33

Are two sexes really necessary? All-female societies envisioned by speculative fiction writers do not seem too farfetched from the scientific standpoint. Eggs of a number of species, even mammals, have already been successfully stimulated to develop parthenogenically, without benefit of fertilization, into fully viable adult individuals. Techniques of cloning, in which an exact genetic duplicate of an individual can be grown by implanting a skin or intestinal cell into a denucleated ovum, will probably ultimately be feasible for humans. Such types of single-parent reproduction have a number of inherent disadvantages, including the perpetuation of the parent's genetic deficiencies along with strengths and a restriction of the variability that sexual matings introduce by providing a combination of traits from two individuals in the offspring. The diversity provided by sexual reproduction furnishes a valuable reservoir of talents and abilities, some of which can be of crucial importance in adaptation to changing environmental conditions. Fortunately for the future adaptability of the human race, it does not seem likely that people will be giving up their favorite "indoor sport," no matter what reproductive alternatives scientific advances provide, and the separate male and female reproductive systems will continue to perform their traditional functions.

The male reproductive system is adapted for one specific sequence of functions: the production of genetic "blueprints" for the new generation and their delivery to a female of the species with appropriate paraphernalia for effecting a union with her corresponding DNA set to start off the new life. The male organs that perform these functions include: **testes,** in which the germ cells **(sperm)** are produced; **glands** that produce auxiliary secretions which, together with the sperm, make up the fluid **semen** that is transferred to the female in the act of copulation; **ducts** for carrying the various fluids; and a copulatory organ, the **penis,** which greatly reduces the potential uncertainties of mating by delivering the semen to an appropriately shaped receptacle inside the female's body. The basic structures of the male reproductive system are depicted in Figure 33-1.

Some of the structures shown in Figure 33-1 and the discussion of them in the following pages will sound familiar because precisely the same structures were described in Chapter 29. In the male, the penis is a structure shared by two different body systems, the excretory and reproductive systems, and the urethra provides a common pathway out of the body both for semen and for urine.

The main anatomical distinction between the human male and female is the presence of conspicuous external genitalia in the male. In the female, the major reproductive organs—uterus, ovaries, fallopian tubes—are all located within the pelvic cavity. In the male, the pelvic cavity contains only the seminal vesicles, prostate, and a portion of the vas deferens. The testes are suspended in a pouch (the scrotum), and the penis is an external appendage attached to the urogential diaphragm, a musculomembranous partition below the pelvic cavity.

THE SCROTUM

The design of the human body is for the most part a model of efficiency. But at first thought it seems as though evolution had a momentary lapse when it came to developing the scrotum. The testes, containing a man's entire genetic heritage, seem shockingly vulnerable, suspended in a dangling pouch of skin. This inherent vulnerability is compensated for by an important advantage. Spermatozoa are delicate cells. The high temperatures prevailing inside the body cavity could produce large numbers of mutations in the sperm DNA or even damage the sperm so much as to make them nonviable. But heat retention in the scrotal sac is not as efficient as in the rest of the body, and as a result the temperature in the testes averages about 3 to 5° F below normal body temperature. Some modern practices have eliminated part of this natural advantage. It has been computed that the temperature rise due to the wearing of trousers has produced a definite increase in the human mutation rate. Hot baths have been suggested as a method of birth control. (Unfortunately the production of temporary sterility in this way is not too reliable, and, moreover, is rather risky from the mutational standpoint.)

The scrotum is a continuation of the abdominal wall and is suspended from the pubis. It is divided by a septum into two sacs, each of which contains and supports one of the testes, together with its connecting tube, the **epididymis.** The scrotum consists of skin, arranged in folds (rugae), and an incomplete layer of smooth muscles, called the **dartos muscle.** If the scrotum is exposed to cold temperatures, the fibers of the dartos layer contract reflexly, producing a wrinkled appearance and raising the testes closer to the warmth radiated by the pelvis. This automatic thermostat further protects the sperm from potentially harmful temperature variations, since they are sensitive to cold as well as excessive heat.

THE TESTES

The external genitals, the complex of body characteristics and even behavior that constitute maleness, and the myriads of tiny wiggling sperm that can fertilize an ovum, all owe their development to the testes, a pair of oval white bodies about the size and shape of pigeon eggs, suspended in the scrotum. The male go-

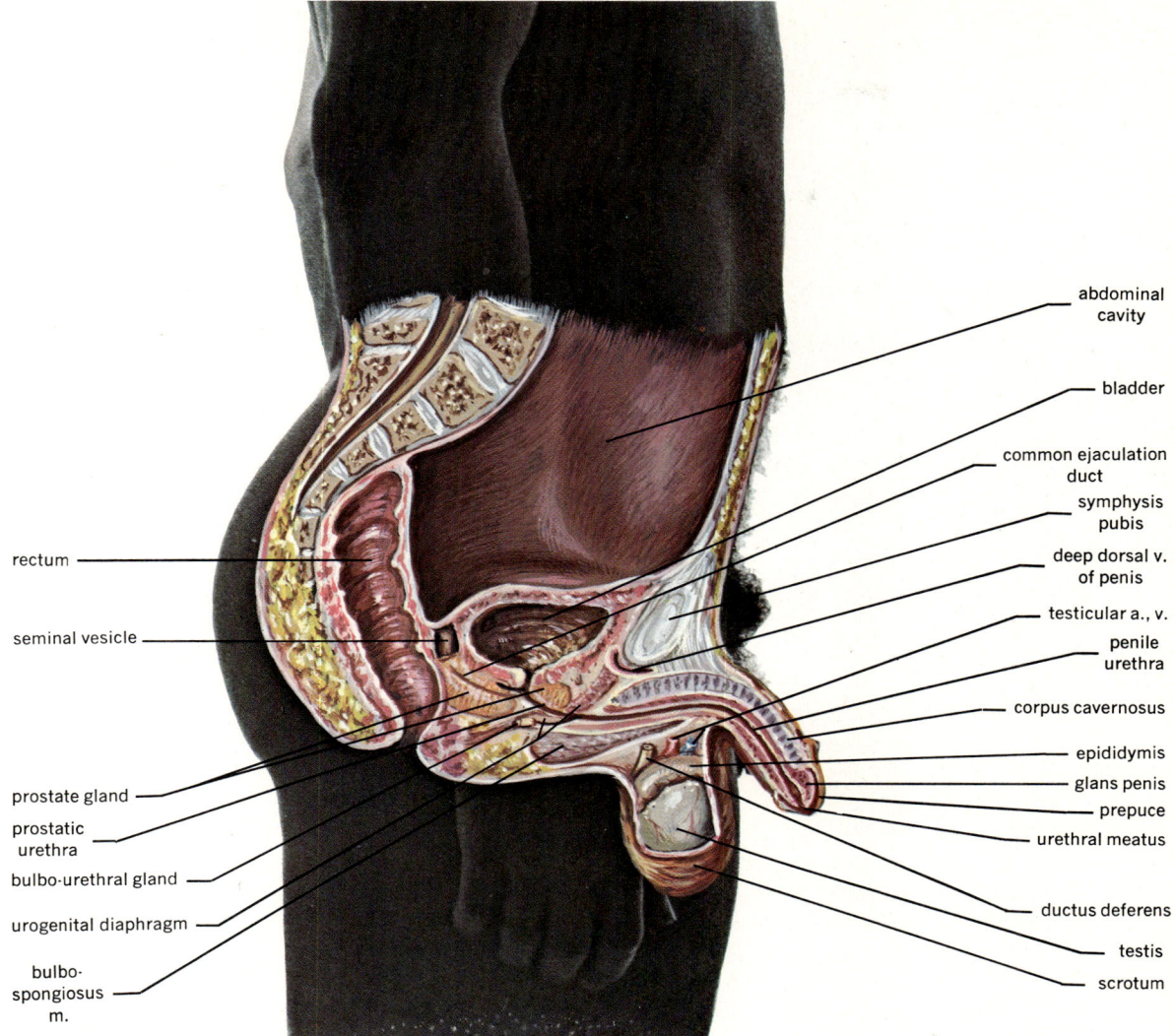

rectum

seminal vesicle

prostate gland

prostatic
urethra

bulbo-urethral gland

urogenital diaphragm

bulbo-
spongiosus
m.

abdominal
cavity

bladder

common ejaculation
duct

symphysis
pubis

deep dorsal v.
of penis

testicular a., v.

penile
urethra

corpus cavernosus

epididymis

glans penis

prepuce

urethral meatus

ductus deferens

testis

scrotum

FIGURE 33-1   Organs of the male reproductive system, shown in midsagittal section of the pelvis and external genitalia.

nads—the testes—not only produce spermatozoa, but also secrete copious amounts of **testosterone,** the male sex hormone. As we have seen, testosterone stimulates the development of the male sex organs, promotes the formation of the male secondary sexual characteristics, and contributes to the sex drive.

Each egg-shaped testis (Figure 33-2) is enclosed in an outer layer of dense white fibrous tissue, the **tunica albuginea.** At its posterior border, it extends inward, forming an incomplete vertical septum, the **mediastinum testis.** Extensions from this septum divide the testis into 250 to 400 wedge-shaped lobules. Each of these lobules contains one to three tightly packed coiled tubules, the **seminiferous tubules.** (If one of these slender tubules were uncoiled and stretched out, it would be about two feet long! Yet the entire testis is only 3 to 4 cm long.) The tubules contain sperm cells in various stages of development, arranged in layers.

The cells in the center of the tubule are maturing spermatozoa, while those at the periphery, closest to the **germinal epithelium** (the tissue from which the testes developed during prenatal life), are round spermatogonia. **Sertoli's cells,** embedded among the various germ cells, support and nourish the reproductive cells. **Interstititial cells of Leydig,** which secrete androgens, are scattered in clusters among the tubules.

The seminiferous tubules join to form a series of straight ducts, **tubuli recti,** which in turn form a network of anastomosing tubules called the **rete testis** at the posterior upper margin of the testis. The spermatozoa are emptied from the seminiferous tubules into the rete testis.

Descent of the Testes

Up to the seventh month of fetal life, both the male and female gonads are small egg-shaped bodies lying

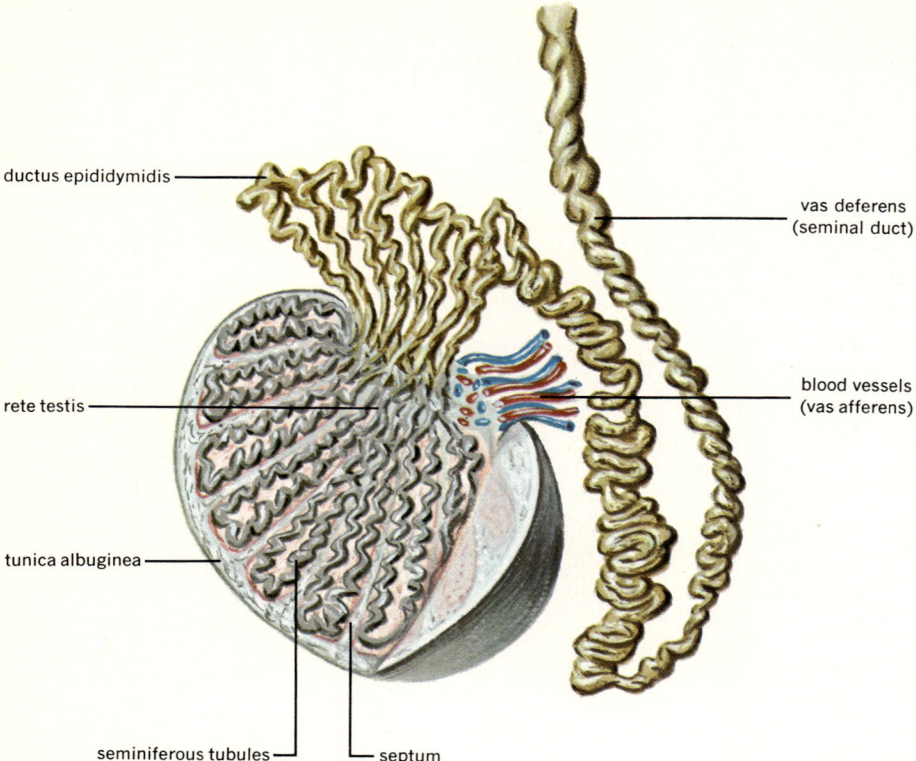

FIGURE 33-2 The testis, partially dissected to show details of the seminiferous tubules.

ductus epididymidis

rete testis

tunica albuginea

seminiferous tubules — septum

vas deferens (seminal duct)

blood vessels (vas afferens)

within the abdominal cavity. The ovaries in the female remain in this position throughout life. But about two months before birth, the testes of a male fetus normally leave the abdominal cavity, passing down through the inguinal canal into the scrotum. The exact cause of the descent of the testes is not known, but pituitary hormones and testosterone initiate the process. A ligament called the gubernaculum testis seems to play a key role. This ligament extends through the inguinal canal, attaching the testis to the floor of the scrotum. As the body of the fetus grows explosively, the growth of the gubernaculum does not keep pace; it even shortens, gradually pulling the testis into the scrotum. Its function complete, the gubernaculum atrophies and disappears.

Occasionally one or both of the testes fails to descend on schedule. Descent may be prevented by a hormonal deficiency or some physical obstruction. If the condition, called cryptorchidism, is discovered before puberty, it can be corrected by simple surgery. If it is uncorrected, the higher intraabdominal temperatures will depress spermatogenesis (the formation of sperm). Eventually the undescended testes begin to atrophy, and no viable sperm are produced.

The inguinal canal remains a weak point in the abdominal wall. Straining while lifting a heavy object may cause a loop of intestine to protrude through the inguinal canal into the scrotum, producing an inguinal hernia.

Spermatogenesis

The male reproductive cells—sperm—must be able to do three things. They must be able to reach the female reproductive cell—the ovum—and breach its formidable defenses, and they must also carry exactly half a set of human genetic information, capable of combining with the half-set carried by the ovum to provide to full set of genetic instructions for the offspring. The first task requires some sort of device for locomotion, since the sperm must swim upstream through the fluids of the female reproductive tract to reach the egg. The second task involves piercing the thick protective covering (the corona radiata) that surrounds the ovum. The third requires a reduction of the normal chromosome complement to exactly half, including one representative of each type of chromosome pair. The process of spermatogenesis satisfies all three requirements, yielding microscopic tadpolelike cells (Figure 33-3) that are little more than a head containing a packet of chromosomes, a lashing, undulating tail, and a small sac like a grenade at the tip of the head, containing a charge of the enzyme hyaluronidase. (This sac bursts on contact with the ovum, releasing the enzyme, which attacks the hyaluronic acid in the protective covering of the ovum.)

Spermatogenesis begins at about the age of 13 and may continue throughout the rest of the man's life. Germ cells called **spermatogonia,** which were formed during fetal life, begin to differentiate, passing

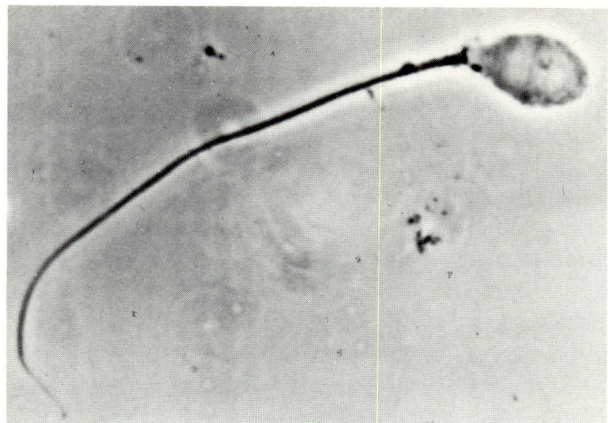

FIGURE 33-3   In the micrograph, a human sperm is shown magnified 1800×. Structural details are shown in the diagram.

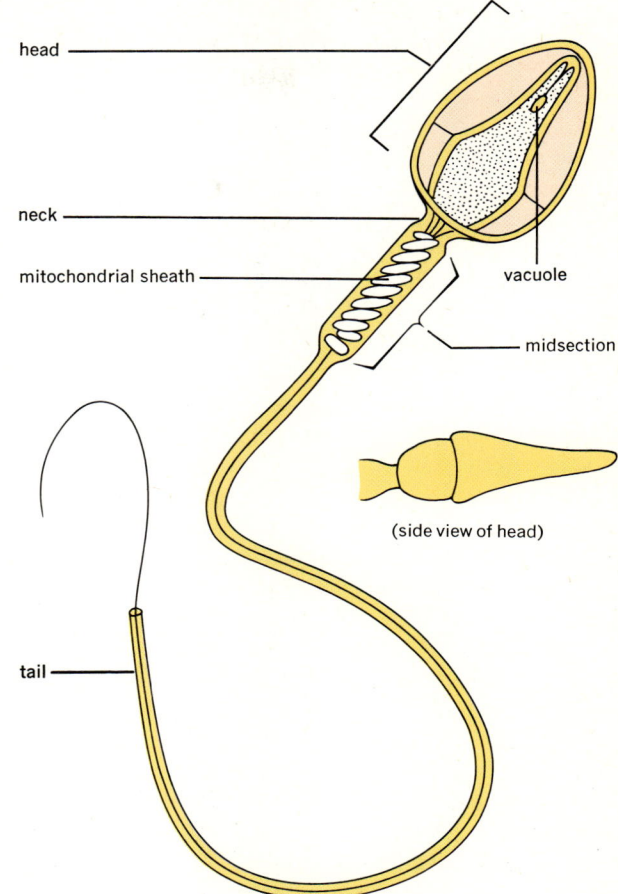

head

neck

mitochondrial sheath

vacuole

midsection

(side view of head)

tail

through a sequence of stages (Figure 33-4). The spermatogonia each contain the normal complement of 46 chromosomes. As they increase in size, they become primary spermatocytes. At this stage they undergo a special type of cell division, called **meiosis,** in which the cells divide twice in succession, while the chromosomes are duplicated only once. In this **reduction division,** a single primary spermatocyte divides to form two **secondary spermatocytes;** these in turn promptly divide again, without a second duplication of the chromosomes, and a total of four **spermatids** is formed, each containing only 23 chromosomes. The chromosomes assort themselves during the cell divisions so that each spermatid receives only one of each chromosome pair.

The normal human complement of 46 chromosomes includes 22 pairs of autosomes and a single pair of sex chromosomes, XX in the female and XY in the male. At the end of the reduction division, each spermatid has received one of each pair of autosomes, and only one sex chromosome. Thus, a single primary spermatocyte with XY sex chromosomes yields four

spermatids, two with an X chromosome and two with a Y chromosome.

The spermatids still do not look very much like mature sperm. They are transformed into **spermatozoa** in a process called **spermiogenesis.** A tail (flagellum) is formed, and the cell membrane contracts around the cell nucleus to form the head. (Much of the cytoplasm is lost.) The neck and body, found between the head and tail, contain many mitochondria

FIGURE 33-4   Spermatogenesis: one spermatogonium gives rise to four spermatozoa via meiotic division.

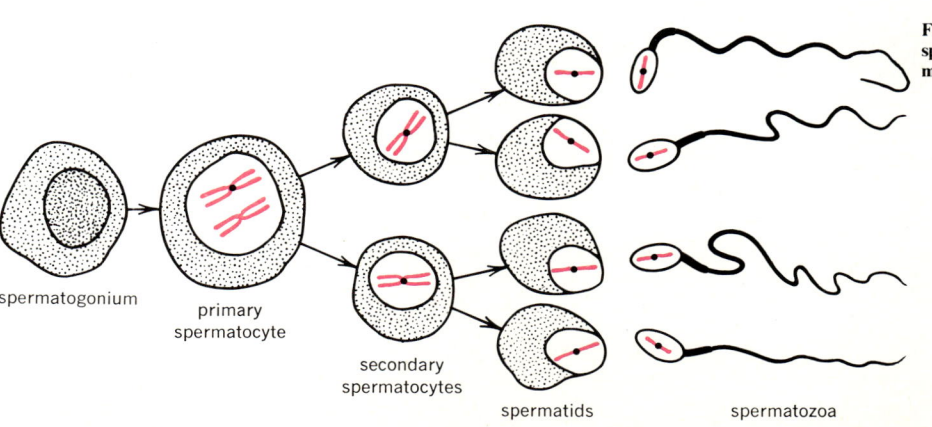

spermatogonium

primary spermatocyte

secondary spermatocytes

spermatids

spermatozoa

that act as the "engine" for the miniature projectile that is the sperm, since they produce large amounts of ATP, providing energy for the lashing of the flagellum. Spermatozoa can "swim" at a respectable rate, considering their size: about 2 to 3 mm per minute.

The process of development from spermatogonium to spermatozoon takes about 74 days. Even after release from the testis, spermatozoa are not capable of fertilizing an ovum. They remain in the duct system for a time, undergoing a process called ripening, before they are ejected. Meanwhile, only a small fraction of the original spermatogonia embark on the differentiation into spermatozoa at any particular time. The remainder continue to reproduce themselves as spermatogonia, serving as undifferentiated stem cells.

Spermatogenesis is influenced by the follicle-stimulating hormone of the adenohypophysis. Adequate levels of testosterone also seem to be necessary for sperm production. Infectious diseases, alcoholism, dietary deficiencies, injury, inflammation, X rays, and high temperatures can affect spermatogenesis. With advancing age, the seminiferous tubules undergo a gradual involution, but apparently never entirely cease to function.

THE DUCT SYSTEM

With growing concern about overpopulation, vasectomy has become a popular surgical procedure for men who feel they have completed their families and do not wish to risk fathering additional children. The operation consists of cutting and tying off each vas deferens, one of the ducts that carry sperm on the way out of the body. After a vasectomy, sperm continue to be produced but reach a dead end and are resorbed by the body. Meanwhile, sexual activity can go on as usual, since normal amounts of hormones and other secretions are produced—only the ejaculate does not contain sperm.

The male genital duct system consists of a sequence of ducts leading from the testes up into the abdominal cavity, and then down again, through the penis and out of the body. From the rete testis, 10 to 15 long spiral tubes lined with ciliated epithelium, the **ductuli efferentes,** carry the sperm out of the testis and into the **epididymis.** This is a long tube—actually some 4 to 5 meters long—coiled into a comma-shaped body posterior to the testis. Here the spermatozoa mature and may be stored to some extent. Smooth muscle in the wall of the epididymis propels the sperm toward the urethra during ejaculation.

In the "tail" of the comma, the epididymis is less coiled, and its wall is thickened, as it merges into the **vas deferens.** This tube has a heavy coat of circular smooth muscle, which moves the sperm along by peristaltic contractions. Sperm are stored in the vas defe-

rens without losing their fertility for periods from several hours to as long as 42 days, depending on the degree of sexual activity. The vas deferens from each testis leads up through the inguinal canal and into the pelvic cavity, where it eventually joins with the duct of a seminal vesicle to form an **ejaculatory duct.** The vas deferens, together with nerves, blood vessels, and lymphatics, form a structure called the **spermatic cord.**

THE SEMINAL VESICLES

The name of the seminal vesicles arose from a misunderstanding. Early anatomical studies of these two membranous pouches seemed to indicate that their function is to store sperm. In fact, as it was later discovered, sperm are stored mainly in the vasa deferentia, and the function of the seminal vesicles is quite different.

The seminal vesicles, which lie on the posterior surface of the bladder, near its base (Figure 33-5), each consist of a single tube, coiled upon itself. They function as secretory organs, producing slightly alkaline mucoid secretions that contain abundant amounts of fructose, along with smaller amounts of vitamins (ascorbic acid and inositol), five amino acids, ergothioneine, phosphorylcholine, and prostaglandin. During ejaculation, the secretions of the seminal vesicles are emptied into the ejaculatory ducts at the same time that the vasa deferentia empty sperm. The secretions of the seminal vesicles add bulk to the semen and help to nourish and protect the delicate spermatozoa. The prostaglandin may provoke uterine contractions that help to propel the sperm on their way to the fallopian tubes.

Each seminal vesicle joins with the corresponding vas deferens to form a narrow **ejaculatory duct,** about an inch long. The ejaculatory ducts pass through the prostate gland to empty into the urethra, into which they squirt their contents during ejaculation.

THE PROSTATE GLAND

Two out of every three men over the age of 70 suffer from prostate problems. Not only is this gland a frequent site of cancer and bacterial infections, but even more often—for unexplained reasons—it enlarges. Since the prostate surrounds the urethra, enlargement of the gland obstructs the urethra and can cause difficult and painful urination. Surgical removal of the prostate may be necessary to correct the condition.

The prostate is about the size and shape of a chestnut (See Figure 33-5). It is encased in a musculofibrous capsule, extensions from which divide the gland into lobules. Each lobule is lined with a secretory epithelium and equipped with a duct to carry its secretions into the urethra. The prostate secretes a thin,

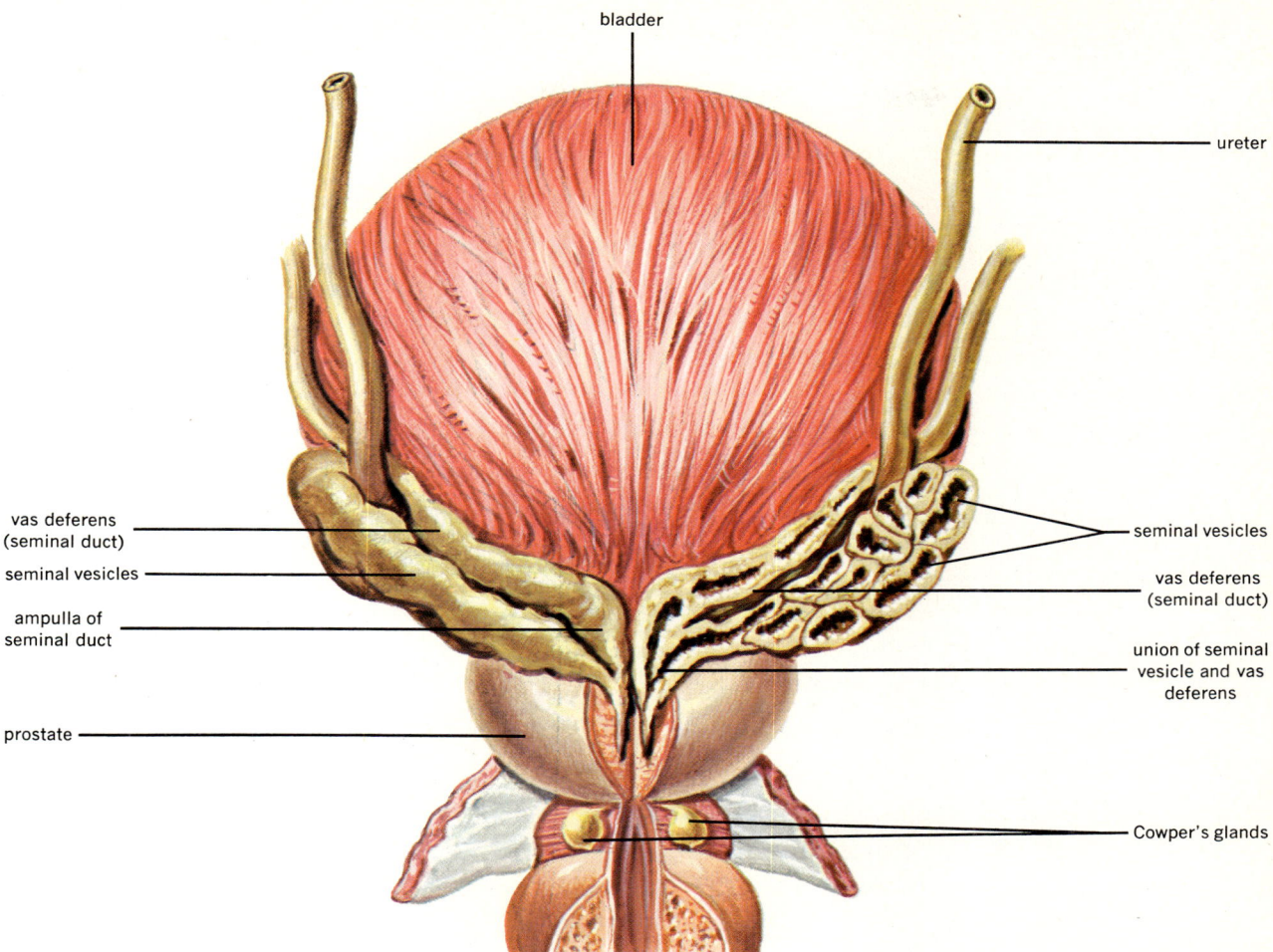

FIGURE 33-5   Male reproductive organs in relation to the bladder, viewed from behind.

milky alkaline fluid that adds to the bulk of the semen and aids the mobility of the sperm. When the vasa deferentia and seminal vesicles contract during ejaculation, pouring their contents through the ejaculatory ducts into the urethra, the prostate contracts simultaneously, adding its secretions to the semen. The alkalinity of the prostate secretions help to neutralize the acid metabolic products of the sperm in the fluid from the vas deferens, and in the body of the female serves to neutralize the acidic vaginal secretions, which normally have a pH from 3.5 to 4.0. This neutralizing function is crucial to successful fertilization, since spermatozoa do not achieve their optimum motility until the pH of the surrounding fluids rises to about 6 to 6.5.

THE BULBOURETHRAL GLANDS (COWPER'S GLANDS)

During sexual stimulation, even before intercourse has taken place, a viscid secretion appears at the tip

of the penis. This fluid is produced by the **bulbourethral** or **Cowper's glands,** two teardrop-shaped structures, each the size of a pea, situated on either side of the urethra, inferior to the prostate. The mucous fluid that the bulbourethral glands secrete into the urethra is viscid and alkaline, and it serves two important functions. First, it washes out the urethra in preparation for ejaculation, neutralizing any lingering traces of acid urine, which could kill the delicate sperm. Then it serves as a lubricant for the penis.

THE URETHRA

The presence of urine would destroy sperm. Yet the male urethra serves as a conduit for both urine and semen. Fortunately the products of the urinary and genital systems never pass through the urethra simultaneously; the nervous reflexes involved in the act of ejaculation automatically inhibit urination.

The male urethra is an S-shaped tube, lined with mucous membrane, about 17.5 cm long. It extends

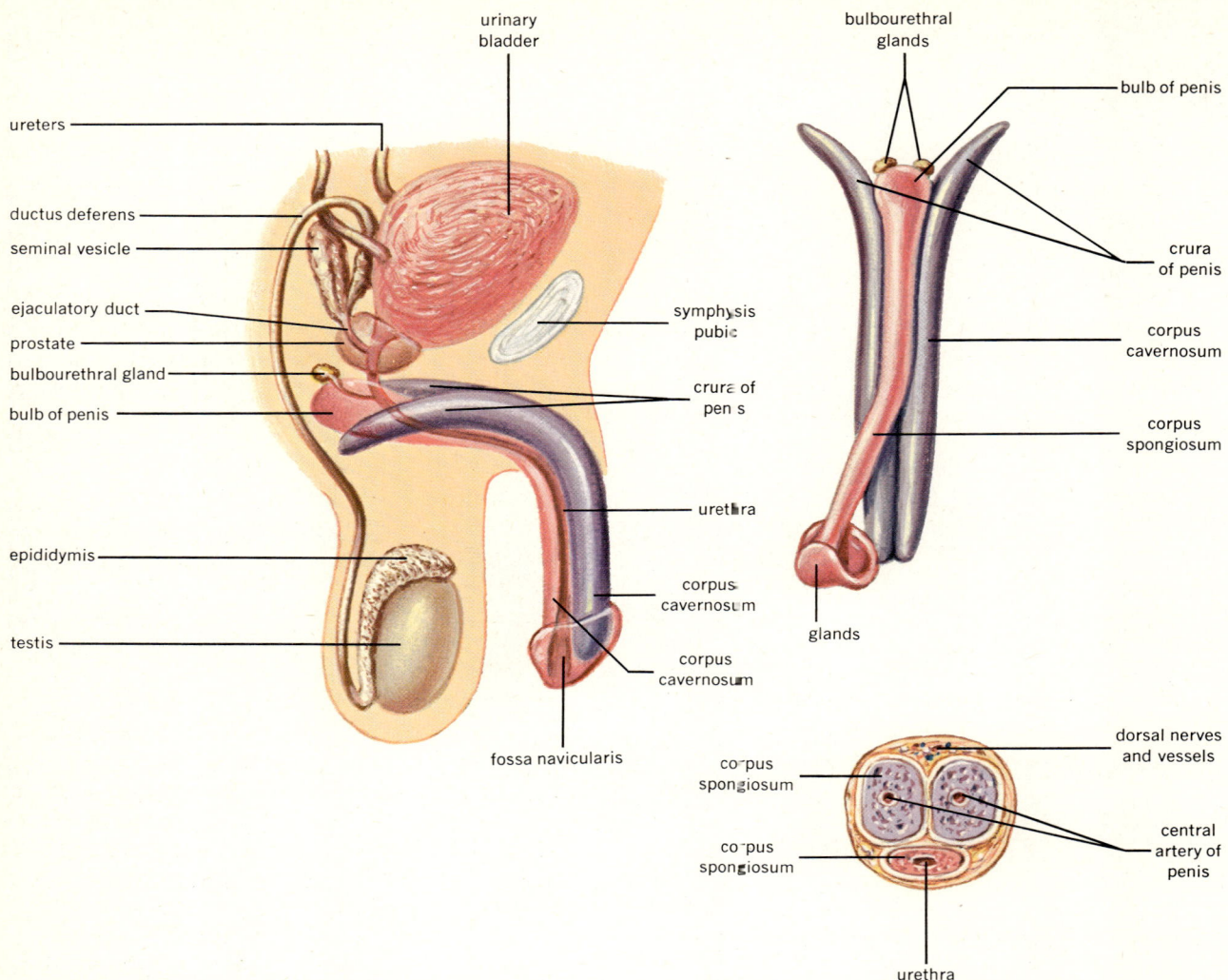

FIGURE 33-6 Structure of the penis and its relation to other structures of the male reproductive system. Upper right: a dissected penis; lower right: cross section.

from the outlet of the bladder out of the pelvic cavity and down the length of the penis, ending at the external urethral orifice at the top of the penis. The urethra is sometimes arbitrarily divided into three successive parts: the **prostatic, membranous,** and **cavernous** or **spongy** portions.

THE PENIS

A rod-shaped copulatory organ, which fits neatly into a suitably adapted sheath within the body of the female, was a structural innovation that arose relatively early in the evolution of life on earth, and has been repeated again and again in such diverse animals as worms, insects, and mammals. (Curiously, birds do not have penises, although they are far more closely related to us than many lower species that do have copulatory organs; birds transfer their sperm from male to female by a sort of suction mechanism.)

The human penis is a cylindrical structure, attached to the anterior and lateral walls of the pubic arch in front of the scrotum (Figure 33-6). It is composed of three cylindrical masses of erectile tissue, arranged longitudinally and bound together by fibrous bands and covered with skin. (The skin of the penis, like that of the scrotum, is more deeply pigmented than that of the rest of the body and has a very thin epithelium. Only the upper end of the shaft is covered with hair.) Two of the cylindrical masses that form the penis, called the **corpora cavernosa penis,** are arranged laterally. The third, the **corpus cavernosum urethrae** or **corpus spongiosum,** forms the ventral surface and contains the urethra. All three masses are truly "cavernous," since they contain extensive venous sinuses. Usually the penis is small and flaccid and hangs limply. But during sexual excitement, arterial blood under pressure flows into the venous sinuses and distends them, so that the penis stands out stiffly and enlarges to more than twice its flaccid size. (Despite locker-room comparisons and boasts, there is remarkably little variation in size of penises—far less than the typical variation among men in overall height and body mass.)

At the distal end of the penis, the corpus spongiosum expands to form the **glans penis,** which terminates in a longitudinal slit at the external urethral meatus. A fold of skin called the **prepuce** or foreskin loosely covers the glans. A cheeselike sebaceous secretion of the glans, called smegma, may accumulate under the foreskin if it is not regularly drawn back and scrupulously cleaned. The accumulations can foster the multiplication of microbes and cause infection. This problem is commonly avoided by removing the foreskin surgically shortly after birth, in the operation of circumcision. There is some evidence of an additional benefit, in a reduced incidence of cervical cancer in wives of circumcised men.

A rich supply of tactile receptors makes the penis extremely sensitive during copulation. In addition, this organ is supplied with efferent fibers from both the parasympathetic and the sympathetic nervous system. Autonomic impulses play an important role both in erection and in ejaculation.

SEMEN

If every sperm in a single drop of semen fertilized an egg, enough children would be produced to populate an entire city the size of Chicago. The fluid that is ejaculated during the male sexual act—semen—contains about 120,00,000 spermatozoa per milliliter, and 2 to 5 ml of semen is usually ejaculated in a single sexual act.

Semen is a milky white, viscid fluid, containing not only spermatozoa, but also the secretions of the epididymis, seminal vesicles, prostate gland, and bulbourethral glands. The various components that are added to the fluid from the testes combine to create optimum conditions for the survival and functioning of the sperm. The alkaline secretions of the prostate neutralize acids and create a pH of about 7.5. Fructose, contributed by the seminal vesicles, provides an energy source for the spermatozoa. Mucus from the seminal vesicles and bulbourethral glands furnishes lubrication, but initially makes the semen so viscid that the spermatozoa are relatively immobile. Within about half an hour after ejaculation, however, proteolytic enzymes in the fluid dissolve the mucus, and the sperm become highly motile.

The spermatozoa are the most important ingredients of semen; if the sperm count falls below a certain critical value, fertilization cannot occur. (The reason for the apparent profligacy of discharging hundreds of millions of spermatozoa in a single ejaculation is discussed in Chapter 35.) The other components of semen are essential to the proper functioning of the sperm. If sperm are washed clear of the other components, they rapidly become infertile. Then, if the other components of semen are added to such infertile sperm, they regain their fertility within an hour or so.

ERECTION AND EJACULATION

An adolescent boy's first erections are often a source of embarrassment. Without any conscious wish or control, stray erotic thoughts are promptly translated into an all too visible physical manifestation. He may also worry about the erections he notices when he wakes up in the morning, before he empties his bladder, wondering if he is "normal."

Erection of the penis is provoked by sexual stimulation, either physical or psychological. Watching an erotic scene in a movie, or even thinking an erotic thought may be enough to stimulate an erection. Impulses are transmitted from the hypothalamus to the penis by parasympathetic nerves arising from the sacral portion of the portion cord. An artery with a thick, muscular wall courses through each of the columns of cavernous tissue in the penis, and the numerous terminal branches of these arteries open directly into the venous sinuses in the cavernous tissue. Parasympathetic impulses cause the muscular artery walls to relax, and blood flows out into the sinuses, inflating them like balloons. The penis becomes firm and erect, facilitating its penetration into the female vagina during sexual intercourse.

The erection that results from a postponement of urination is produced by a different set of stimuli. It is due to a reflex initiated by pressure of the distended urinary bladder on the prostate gland.

The rhythmic friction on the skin of the penis that occurs during intercourse stimulates the numerous nerve endings in the glans, and impulses are carried up to the thalamus and cerebral cortex. The sexual stimulation gradually builds in intensity, until it stimulates a second reflex mechanism, involving the sympathetic nervous system. Impulses travel downward over sympathetic nerves passing through the hypogastric plexus to the genital organs and initiate **ejaculation.** First peristaltic waves move along the tubes leading from the testes. Rhythmic contraction of the smooth muscle layers of the testes, epididymides, seminal vesicles, and prostate gland expel their contents—the constituents of semen—into the urethra. The bulbourethral glands discharge additional amounts of mucus at this time. The process up to this point are referred to as **emission.** Ejaculation proper occurs when parasympathetic impulses traveling over the pudendal nerves stimulate the skeletal muscles encasing the base of the erectile tissue of the penis to contract rhythmically, increasing the pressure in the urethra and propelling the semen outward in spurts. The act of ejaculation, together with the feelings of intense pleasure associated with it, comprise the male **orgasm.**

PRACTICAL CONSIDERATIONS

Since the landmark work of Masters and Johnson, the subject of sexual dysfunction has been increasingly recognized as a legitimate area of medical concern. At the same time, many unqualified "sex therapists" have set themselves up in practice, often doing more harm than good. The treatment of sexual dysfunction is a complicated mixture of science and art, since the sexual organs are not only subject to a variety of physical malfunctions, but can also be greatly influenced by psychological factors.

The effects of castration and underdevelopment of the testes were described in the last chapter. Hyposecretion of androgens can result in a lack of development of the male sexual organs, with effects reaching far beyond the inability to function sexually.

True **hermaphroditism**—the presence of both male and female gonads—is a rare anomaly, although several kinds of pseudohermaphroditism may occur as a result of hormonal influences during prenatal development. The development of the male genitalia occurs in response to stimulation by androgens, secreted by the testes of the fetus. But if the mother is suffering from a masculinizing tumor of the adrenals, a genetic female fetus may receive a sufficient dose of androgens to stimulate the development of male external genitalia. A genetic male, on the other hand, may develop female genitalia if his testes are defective and do not secrete sufficient androgens at the appropriate time. Such pseudohermaphrodites have an apparent sex that does not correspond to their genetic constitution and gonads. These individuals may never realize their mixed-up state and may marry and live a normal life (though of course they are sterile). Or they may suffer from sexual dysfunction or psychological maladjustment. In such cases treatment with hormonal therapy and plastic surgery can produce an apparent sex reversal that actually reinstates the original genetic sex.

Chromosomal anomalies resulting from nondisjunction (failure of the chromosomes to separate properly during meiosis) can lead to anomalies of sexual development. Nondisjunction during spermatogenesis can lead to such abnormal chromosome sets as 44/XO, 44/XXY, or 44/XYY of the offspring. (The 44/XXX genotype can be produced by similar nondisjunction in oogenesis, the formation of the ova.) XO individuals are apparent females, but their gonads are rudi-

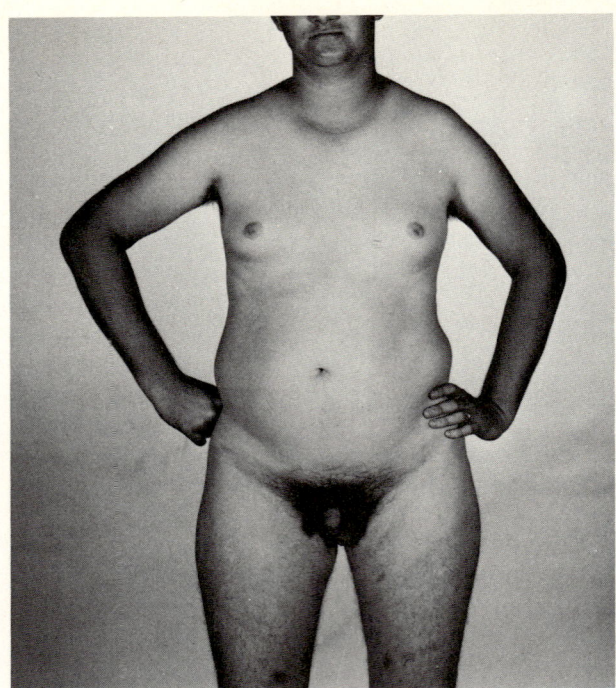

FIGURE 33-7 Klinefelter's syndrome, an XXY condition.

mentary or absent, and maturation does not occur at puberty. This condition is referred to as **Turner's syndrome.** In **Klinefelter's syndrome** (Figure 33-7), an XXY individual has male genitalia and develops male characteristics, but his seminiferous tubules are abnormal, and he is likely to be mentally retarded. A flurry of publicity greeted the discovery that a number of criminals convicted of violent crimes have an XYY genotype. It was theorized that the extra Y chromosome increases testosterone production and stimulates aggression. But the significance of this finding is tempered by the fact that many normal, law-abiding men also have an XYY genotype.

Several developmental anomalies may affect the penis (Figure 33-8). In **phimosis,** the prepuce fits too tightly over the glans penis and cannot be retracted. This condition is corrected by circumcision. **Hypospadias** is a condition in which the undersurface of the penis fails to close completely, leaving an abnormal opening of the urethra. In **epispadias,** on the other hand, there is an abnormal opening of the urethra on the dorsal surface of the penis.

In many cases of **infertility,** when a couple has tried unsuccessfully for years to have a child, it is found that the man is not producing enough sperm, or is producing a large proportion of abnormal sperm. A sperm count below 35 million per milliliter or the production of more than 25 percent abnormal sperm greatly reduces fertility. Reduced fertility or even total sterility in the male can be caused by a number of

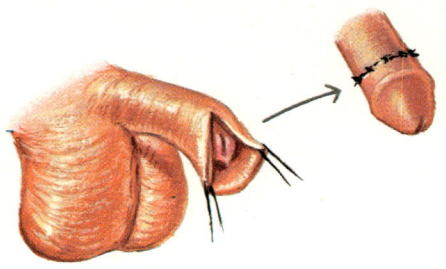

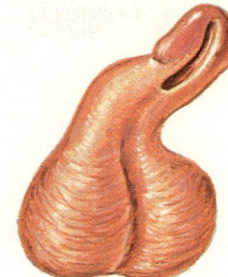
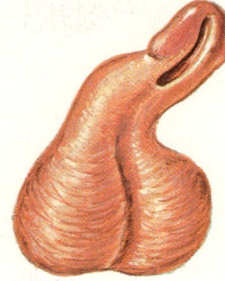

FIGURE 33-8 In circumcision the prepuce is removed. The other illustrations show some congenital anomalies of the penis: hypospadias, epispadias, and phimosis.

circumcision

hypospadias

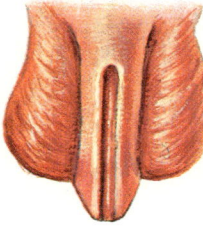

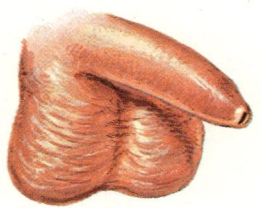

epispadias

phimosis

factors that cause degenerative changes in the seminiferous tubules, such as infectious diseases (e.g., a case of mumps suffered after puberty), alcoholism, dietary deficiencies, local injury, inflammation, or exposure to X rays. Sometimes infertility due to a reduced sperm count can be overcome by combining the semen from several ejaculations and using the mixture for artificial insemination. Conditions that prevent the production of other constituents of semen—for example, inflammation of the seminal vesicles due to gonorrhea or tuberculosis—may also result in infertility even if the sperm production is normal.

The terms "sterility" and "impotence" are sometimes confused in common speech, although actually they refer to entirely different phenomena. **Sterility** is an inability to produce viable offspring. **Impotence** refers to an inability to achieve erection or ejaculation. Its causes may be physical (e.g., due to an injury severing the autonomic innervation of the penis) but often are psychological and require skilled counseling by the sex therapist.

The question of what is "normal" sexual functioning in the older man is still in dispute. Often there is a decline in sexual activity in old age, associated with a reduced production of testosterone by the Leydig cells of the testes. But the **male climacteric,** if it does exist, does not seem to be the same sort of abrupt transition as the female menopause, in which changes in endocrine activity produce not only a cessation of ovulation, but also a variety of symptoms and changes affecting many body systems.

SUMMARY

The male reproductive system includes:
  Testes (produce sperm and androgens)
  Seminal vesicles, prostate, bulbourethral glands (auxiliary secretions)
  Ducts (ductuli efferentes, epididymis, vas deferens, urethra)
  Penis (copulatory organ)
The testes are suspended in the scrotum, which maintains an appropriate temperature for spermatogenesis.
The testes contain seminiferous tubules, in which germinal epithelium differentiates into spermatozoa.
  Sertoli's cells support and nourish the reproductive cells.
  Interstitial cells of Leydig secrete androgens.
  The seminiferous tubules join to from tubuli recti, which form a network, the rete testis.
  About two months before birth, the testes descend from the abdominal cavity through the inguinal canal into the scrotum.
In spermatogenesis, the formation of sperm, germ cells pass through the sequence of stages: spermatogonia—primary spermatocytes—secondary spermatocytes—spermatids—spermatozoa.
Spermatogenesis involves a type of reduction division called meiosis.
Spermiogenesis is the conversion of spermatids to spermatozoa.
Spermatozoa have a haploid chromosome set (23 chromosomes), a reduced amount of cytoplasm, and are divided into a distinct head, body, and tail (flagellum).
After release from the testes, spermatozoa pass into the epididymis, where they remain for a time, ripening.
The male genital duct system consists of:

Ductuli efferentes, which carry sperm out of the testis into the epididymis

Epididymis, a long coiled tube in which sperm mature

Vas deferens, a tube leading up through the inguinal canal and into the pelvic cavity

Ejaculatory duct, formed by the union of the vas deferens and the duct from a seminal vesicle

Urethra, common passageway for urine and semen, leading through the penis to the exterior

Auxiliary secretions are contributed by:

Seminal vesicles (alkaline mucoid secretions containing fructose, vitamins, amino acids, and prostaglandin)

Prostate gland (thin, milky alkaline fluid that neutralizes acid and adds to sperm motility)

Bulbourethral glands (Cowper's glands) (viscid alkaline fluid that neutralizes acid urine and lubricates; secreted both before and during ejaculation)

The penis is composed of three cylindrical masses of erectile tissue (corpora cavernosa penis and corpus spongiosum) with a bulbous end (glans penis) covered by a fold of skin (prepuce) that is removed in circumcision.

Semen consists of the combined secretions of the testes (sperm), epididymis, seminal vesicles, prostate gland, and bulbourethral glands.

Normal semen contains about 120 million spermatozoa per ml, with 2 to 5 ml emitted in each ejaculation.

Erection of the penis is produced by sexual stimulation, initiating a parasympathetic reflex resulting in engorgement of the venous sinuses in the cavernous tissue of the penis with blood.

Ejaculation, the ejection of sperm, is stimulated by another autonomic reflex, provoked by stimulation of sensory receptors on the glans penis.

Rhythmic contraction of smooth muscle of the testes, epididymides, seminal vesicles, prostate gland, and bulbourethral glands expel their secretions into the urethra (emission); ejaculation is produced by contraction of skeletal muscles encasing the base of the erective tissue.

Male sexual disorders include:

Cryptorchidism
Eunuchism
Enlargement and disease of the prostate
Hermaphroditism
Chromosomal anomalies (Turner's syndrome, Klinefelter's syndrome)
Developmental anomalies of the penis
  Phimosis
  Hypospadias
  Epispadias
Infertility (sometimes due to reduced sperm count)
Impotence

QUESTIONS FOR REVIEW AND THOUGHT

1 What are the advantages of sexual reproduction?

2 List the principal structures of the male reproductive system and describe how the anatomy of each is adapted to its particular function(s).

3 If you were designing an improved model of *Homo sapiens,* would you retain the scrotum in its present position? Discuss.

4 What determines the development of testes or ovaries in a fetus, what can go wrong with the process, and what abnormal conditions result?

5 Through what stages are spermatozoa formed, and how is their structure adapted to their functions?

6 What structures contribute to the production of semen? List the substances they produce and describe their functioning.

7 What mechanisms protect sperm from contact with urine despite the dual function of the urethra?

8 Describe the process of erection of the penis and the stimuli that can induce it.

9 Diagram the errors of meiosis that lead to XO, XXY, and XYY genotypes. What conditions result from each type of nondisjunction?

10 What is the difference between sterility and impotence? Discuss possible causes of each.

THE FEMALE REPRODUCTIVE SYSTEM

34

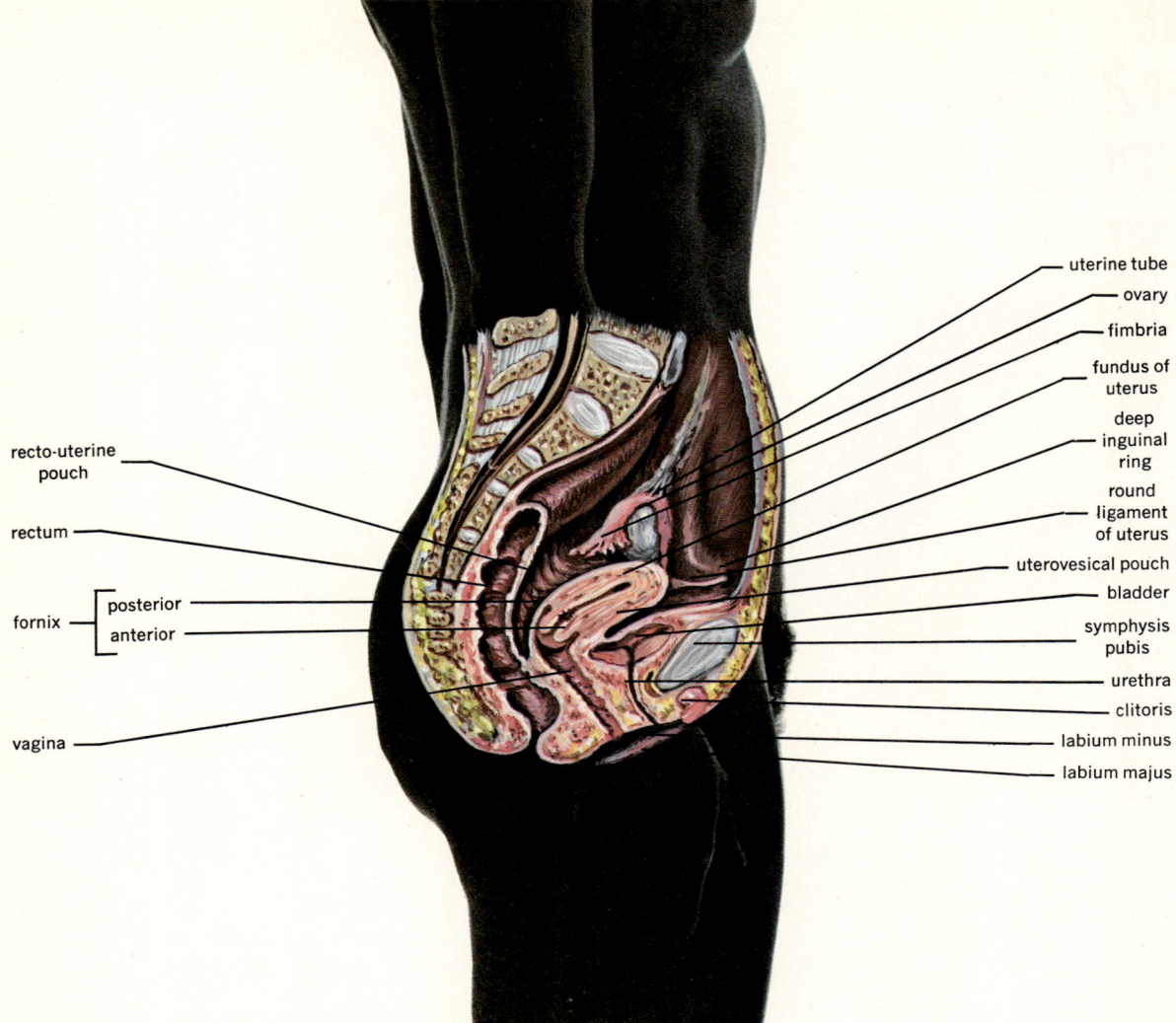

recto-uterine
pouch

rectum

fornix
posterior
anterior

vagina

uterine tube

ovary

fimbria

fundus of
uterus

deep
inguinal
ring

round
ligament
of uterus

uterovesical pouch

bladder

symphysis
pubis

urethra

clitoris

labium minus

labium majus

FIGURE 34-1   Organs of the female reproductive system, shown in midsagittal section of the pelvis.

The female body has been a favored subject for artistic creations ever since man learned to express himself in clay, wood, and other artistic media. Primitive carved or molded female figures probably had a religious significance even more important than their aesthetic value, symbolizing fertility. They often depicted an obviously pregnant figure, with exaggerated emphasis on the breasts, bulging abdomen, and genitals. Through the ages, art has reflected varying standards of ideal feminine beauty. A comparison of the opulent nudes of a century or two ago with the latest *Playboy* centerfolds, for example, indicates that the current ideal is somewhat thinner than her great-great grandmother.

With the current emphasis on sexual pleasure and the controversy over the role of women (and men) as sex objects, it is often easy to lose sight of the fact that a large part of a woman's body is adapted specifically for the functions of conceiving, bearing, and nurturing children. The menstrual periods are regular reminders of the physiological aspects of the feminine condition.

The structures of the female reproductive system (Figure 34-1) consist of a pair of female gonads, the **ovaries;** a pair of **uterine (fallopian) tubes,** which transport ova to the pouchlike **uterus,** within which a fetus can develop; a passageway, the **vagina,** communicating with the exterior; and associated external structures, the **external genitalia.** The **mammary glands** of the breasts may be considered as accessory organs of the reproductive system—although they do not contribute directly to the conception and early development of the child, after birth their exocrine secretion (milk) provides nourishment for the infant.

EXTERNAL STRUCTURES

The theme of a successful masquerade as a person of the opposite sex has long been a popular literary de-

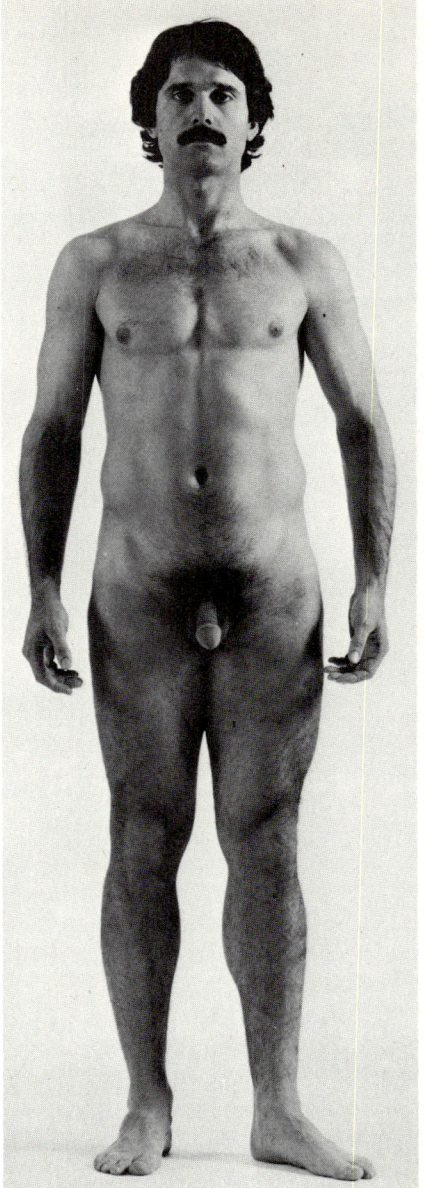
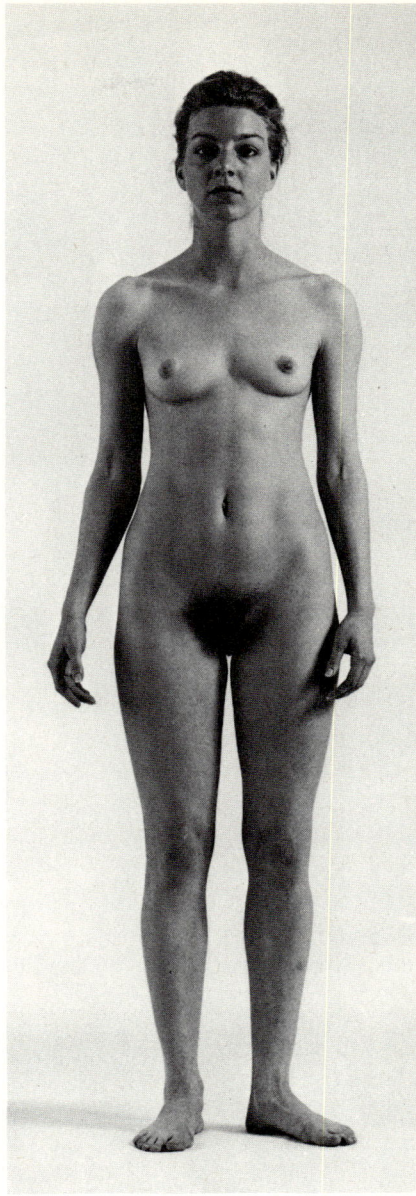

FIGURE 34-2 The human male and female show pronounced anatomical similarities. Structural differences are associated mainly with the reproductive function.

vice, and modern transvestites often produce startlingly convincing effects. But such masquerades are successful only as long as the person is clothed. Nude, the differences between the sexes are unmistakable. With the striking contrast between male and female external genitalia (Figure 34-2), it may seem surprising that the external reproductive structures in both sexes are derived from the same embryonic origins.

Viewed from the front, little is revealed of the female genitalia, other than a mound of fatty tissue over the symphysis pubis, the **mons pubis.** This structure is sometimes referred to as the mons veneris, the "mound of Venus," and it is often an erogenous area, capable of sexual stimulation. After puberty the mons pubis is covered with coarse pubic hair, like the corresponding area of the male perineum.

A perineal view reveals more details of the female genital anatomy. The perineum is the area of the inferior pelvic outlet, between the pubis and the coccyx. It contains all of the external female genitalia, which are often referred to as the **vulva.** In addition to the mons pubis, the vulva includes the labia majora, labia minora, clitoris, and the vestibule (Figure 34-3).

Labia majora literally means "large lips." The labia majora are large, fleshy, liplike structures, composed of folds of adipose tissue with overlying skin. They extend from the mons pubis downward and backward to within an inch of the anus. The labia majora are homologous to the scrotum in the male (i.e., they have a similar embryonic origin). Like the scrotum, the labia majora become pigmented after puberty. The outer surfaces of the labia majora are hairy, but

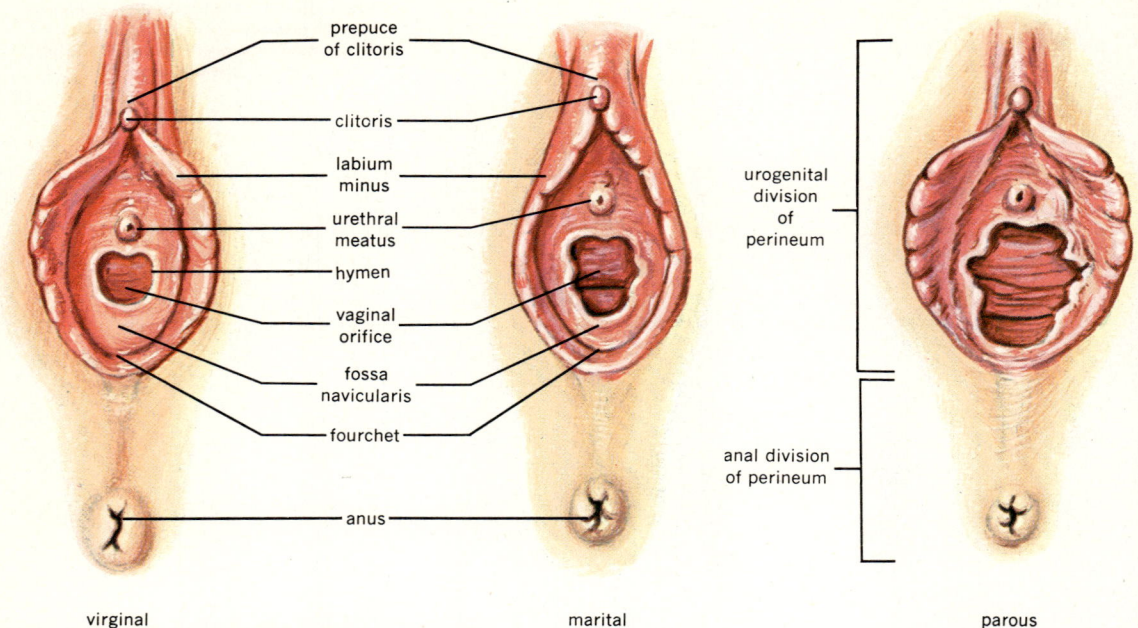

prepuce
of clitoris

clitoris

labium
minus

urethral
meatus

hymen

vaginal
orifice

fossa
navicularis

fourchet

anus

urogenital
division
of
perineum

anal division
of perineum

virginal   marital   parous

FIGURE 34-3 The vulva: virginal, marital, and parous states.

the inner surfaces of the folds are smooth and moist and contain sebaceous and sweat glands.

Within the encircling folds of the labia majora lie two more folds of skin, the **labia minora** ("small lips"), which border the vestibule, into which the urethra and vagina open. The labia minora are thin, highly vascular folds of delicate skin. They contain sebaceous glands, but no hair or sweat glands. Anteriorly, folds of the labia minora form a prepuce for the clitoris.

The **clitoris** is a small protuberance, at the apex of the triangle formed by the junction of the labia minora. It is homologous to the penis in the male, and it also contains erectile tissue, with venous cavernous spaces and specialized nerve endings that are highly sensitive to tactile stimulation. Unlike the penis, however, the clitoris does not contain the urethra, and it is much smaller than the penis. (Normally it is more or less hidden in the folds of the labia minora.) The clitoris is one of the most important regions of sexual stimulation in the female and has become something of a *cause célèbre* for feminists rebelling against the "myth of the vaginal orgasm."

In many animals the urethra and vagina open into a common chamber, the urogenital sinus. This is not the case in the human female; the urethra and vagina are entirely separate throughout their course, but their openings to the exterior are situated rather close together, in a region of the vulva called the **vestibule.** This is the region between the labia minora, posterior to the clitoris. The urethral orifice is an opening about

4 to 6 mm in diameter, about an inch posterior to the clitoris. Small **paraurethral glands,** homologous to the prostate in the male, are clustered around the orifice and open via a pair of ducts at the orifice.

If the labia are like "lips," then the prominent "mouth" they surround is the **orifice of the vagina,** the passageway leading to the uterus. A pair of **greater vestibular glands (Bartholin's glands)** is found deep within the perineal tissues, one on each side of the vaginal orifice. These glands are homologous to the bulbourethral glands in the male and secrete a mucous substance that moistens and lubricates the vestibule and vagina. A similar function is also served by the paraurethral glands and a smaller pair of vestibular glands, the **lesser vestibular glands.** All of these glands can become infected with microorganisms, including the gonococcus, which causes the venereal disease gonorrhea.

Initially, a thin mucous membrane stretches across the opening of the vagina. This is the **hymen,** which has long been considered a sign of virginity. This small sheet of tissue has probably caused a great deal of unnecessary worry and heartache through the centuries. Usually it is broken in a female's first copulation, but there is a great deal of individual variation in hymens, just as in most other physical characteristics. A virgin may have a complete or imperforate hymen, or it may be incomplete or partial, or even entirely absent. The hymen may be such a thin delicate membrane that it ruptures during childhood, in the course of normal exercise. It may be so elastic and yielding that it survives undamaged through many copulations. Or the hymen may be so tough and unyielding that it causes severe pain in an attempt at copulation and must be removed surgically to make intercourse possible.

The term **obstetrical perineum** is used in clinical practice to denote the portion of the perineum between the vagina and anus. During childbirth the tissues of the perineum stretch to a remarkable degree, but they may tear, potentially undermining the support for the bladder and bowel and possibly damaging the anal sphincters. To minimize the damage and permit easier surgical repair, an incision called an **episiotomy** is commonly made in the obstetrical perineum just before the passage of the fetus through the vagina and neatly sutured afterward.

INTERNAL ORGANS

Unlike the male, the working organs of the female reproductive system are hidden away inside the body, protected within the pelvic cavity. These organs are the vagina, the uterus, the uterine tubes, and the ovaries.

The Vagina

The vagina plays a key role both in the beginning and in the end of the reproductive process. It is the organ of copulation, receiving the penis of the male during copulation, and it also serves as a birth canal during parturition, or childbirth.

The vagina is a muscular tube, about 4 to 6 inches long, extending from the vestibule to the uterus. It passes upward and backward, between the bladder and the rectum. Its walls are smooth muscle and fibroelastic connective tissue, lined with a mucous membrane of stratified squamous epithelium, thrown into transverse folds (rugae). The vaginal wall is capable of constriction and enormous dilation. Normally, it is folded in to form a collapsed tube; during intercourse, the wall of the vagina adapts itself to fit snugly about the thrusting penis; and during childbirth the vagina expands to form a canal 10 cm or more in diameter, permitting the passage of the head and body of the infant. (After childbirth, the orifice of the vagina remains permanently enlarged, about three to four times the size of the orifice of the virgin vagina.)

At its superior end, the vagina is continuous with the **cervix,** the lower part of the uterus, which projects into the vault of the vagina. Recesses known as the **anterior, posterior,** and **lateral fornices** are formed around the projecting cervix. The lining of the vagina does not contain any glandular cells, but it is moistened by secretions of the cervix and those of the glands of the vestibule. The mucus secreted by the cervix is acidified to a pH between 4 to 6 by the action of vaginal bacteria, mainly lactobacilli, acting on glycogen from the cells of the vaginal epithelium. This acidic environment inhibits the growth of microorganisms and thus helps to safeguard the pelvic organs from infection.

During the menstrual cycle, there are cyclic changes in the cells of the vaginal lining, and vaginal smears are sometimes used to determine the time of ovulation. Vaginal smears are of greater clinical importance in the **Pap test,** a cytological examination originated by George Papanicolaou as a screening test for cancer of the cervix and uterus.

The Uterus

It seems extraordinary that a 7- or 8-pound human infant, measuring perhaps 20 inches or more in length, can be accommodated inside an organ that, in its normal nonpregnant state, is no bigger than a small pear.

The pear-shaped uterus is about 3 inches long and 2 inches across its widest part. In the nonpregnant state, its muscular walls are very thick, and its cavity is a mere slit; in pregnancy the walls expand, producing a cavity large enough to hold not only the fetus but also the sac of fluid in which it floats. The nonpregnant uterus is flattened somewhat from front to back and is normally tilted forward to an angle of about 90° to the vagina. The upper, larger portion is the **body** of the uterus, with the bulging upper surface known as the **fundus.** The lower, narrow section is the **cervix,** which is pierced by a short cervical canal that extends from the **internal orifice** (or **os**) in the interior of the uterus, to the **external os,** the opening into the vagina. The uterine wall is pierced by two additional openings, on the upper part of the body of the uterus, communicating with the uterine tubes (Figure 34-4).

The uterus is firmly anchored and supported in its position in the pelvic cavity, above the bladder and in front of the rectum. **Broad ligaments,** which are extensions of the outer, serous layer of the uterine wall and consist of a double sheet of peritoneum, extend laterally and are attached to the sides of the pelvic cavity. The uterine arteries course through the broad ligaments. The **cardinal ligaments,** the principal supports of the uterus, lie in the base of the broad ligaments. Two **round ligaments,** attached to either side of the uterus near the uterine tubes, extend anteriorly. Two fibrous bands, the **uterosacral ligaments,** curve along the floor of the pelvic cavity and help to support the uterus. Although the uterus is securely supported, it is freely movable, and its position varies, depending on the degree of distension of the bladder and rectum.

The uterus has a three-layered wall. The outer layer is a peritoneal covering that closely hugs the fun-

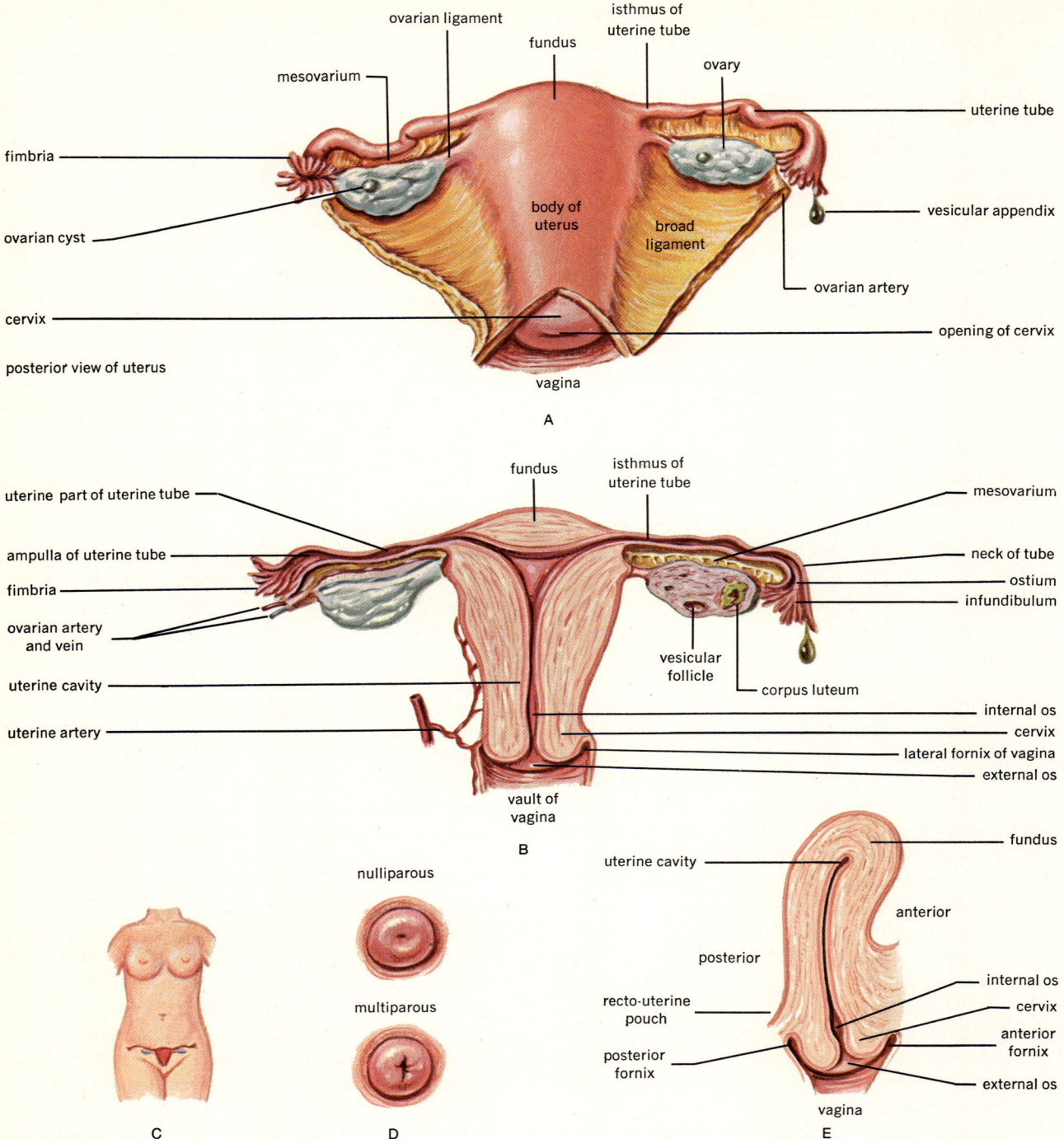

FIGURE 34-4 **The female reproductive system: (A) uterus, posterior view; (B) uterus in section; (C) position of the reproductive organs in the body; (D) cervix before and after childbirth; (E) sagittal sections of uterus.**

dus and body of the uterus and is continuous with the peritoneum of the broad ligament. The middle layer is a thick muscular layer called the **myometrium.** It consists of bundles of interlaced smooth muscle fibers embedded in connective tissue and forming three poorly defined, intertwined layers of circularly, longi-

tudinally, and spirally arranged smooth muscle. The intertwined arrangement of the muscles is important in preventing hemorrhage after childbirth; the contracting muscles press on the blood vessels of the uterine wall and stop them from bleeding.

The inner surface of the uterus is lined with a

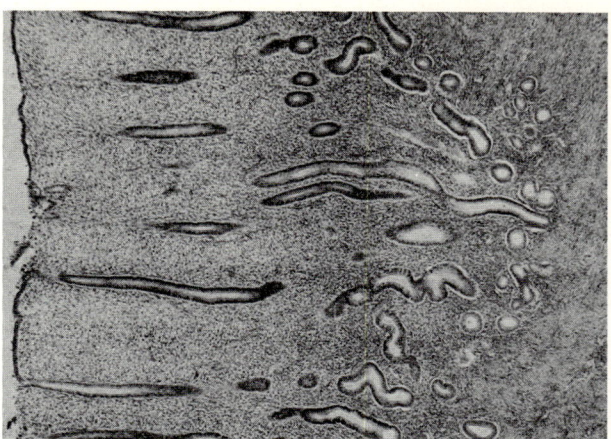

FIGURE 34-5 Section through the human endometrium in the proliferative phase, ×30.

highly vascular mucous membrane called the **endometrium** (Figure 34-5). The connective tissue stroma of the endometrium supports tubular epithelial glands, opening into the lumen of the uterus. During the menstrual cycle, the endometrium undergoes cyclic changes, characterized by three distinct phases: first the growth phase; then the secretory phase, in which the endometrial glands are highly active; and finally the menstrual or sloughing-off phase, initiated by a sudden constriction of the coiled arteries supplying the superficial layers, shutting off the blood flow to the endometrium and causing death of the endometrial tissue. An equally sudden relaxation of the arteries then floods the damaged capillary beds with blood, and the weakened mucosa ruptures and the endometrium is sloughed off. After the heavy flow subsides, the epithelium regenerates to cover the raw surface, and the cycle begins again.

The Uterine Tubes

In men sterilization can be produced by a relatively simple surgical procedure of cutting the vasa deferentia, preventing sperm from passing from the testes to the urethra. In women a somewhat more complicated but analogous method can be used, by tying off the uterine tubes, which conduct the ova from the ovaries to the uterus.

The two uterine tubes, also called **fallopian tubes** or **oviducts,** extend laterally from the body of the uterus, between the layers of the broad ligament. Curiously, the uterine tubes do not form a completely continuous conduit from ovaries to uterus (see Figure 34-4). Each uterine tube, about 10 cm long, ends in a funnel-shaped lateral end, the **infundibulum,** the opening **(ostium)** of which is surrounded by a fringe of finger-like processes, the **fimbriae.** The longest of the fimbriae may actually touch the ovary. When an ovum is released from an ovary, it must cross a small gap

before entering the uterine tube. Occasionally, an ovum loses its way and wanders about the abdominal cavity instead of entering the uterine tube. Trouble can result if sperm happen to travel up the tubes at such a time, and fertilize the ovum in the abdominal cavity. The embryo then begins to develop outside the uterus, in an **ectopic pregnancy.** Fortunately this is an extremely rare event; the infundibulum is believed to move toward the ovary at the time of ovulation, lessening the possibility of an ovum straying. The opening of the uterine tubes into the abdominal cavity does provide another trouble source, however, since it furnishes a route for the spread of infection into the peritoneal cavity.

The muscular tunic of the uterine tubes consists of a well-developed inner circular smooth muscle layer, which becomes progressively thicker toward the uterus, and a thinner outer longitudinal layer. The tubes are lined with a mucosa arranged in longitudinal folds, covered with a single layer of columnar epithelium. Some of the epithelial cells are ciliated, and some are secretory. Peristaltic movements produced by contraction of the muscular layers of the tubes and the ciliary action of the epithelium help to conduct the ovum to the uterus. The journey takes from three to four days, and fertilization, if it is going to occur, usually occurs on the way, while the ovum is still within the tube. If fertilization does not occur, the unfertilized ovum begins to disintegrate on the final stages of its journey to the uterus.

The Ovaries

Each girl is born with ovaries containing about a quarter of a million follicles, each of which contains a **primary oocyte** that could develop into an ovum. But in the course of her lifetime, only 400 to 500 of these primary oocytes will actually develop to the secondary oocyte stage and be released from the ovaries, and few of these will actually be fertilized.

The multitude of potential ova—enough, if fertilized, to populate a good-sized city—is contained in two small ovoid structures, about 3 cm long in the adult female. These two ovaries lie near the lateral walls of the pelvis, connected by folds of peritoneum (the **mesovarium**) with the posterior surface of the broad ligament of the uterus and attached to the sides of the uterus by the **ovarian ligament,** a fibrous cord within the broad ligament.

The substance of the ovary is divided into a thin outer cortex and an inner **medulla.** Within the peritoneal covering of the ovary is a thin **germinal epithelium,** consisting of a single layer of cuboidal cells. Below it is a dense connective tissue layer, the **tunica albuginea,** and beneath this are the **ovarian follicles,** in which the ova develop. The medulla of the ovary con-

FIGURE 34-6   The female breast.

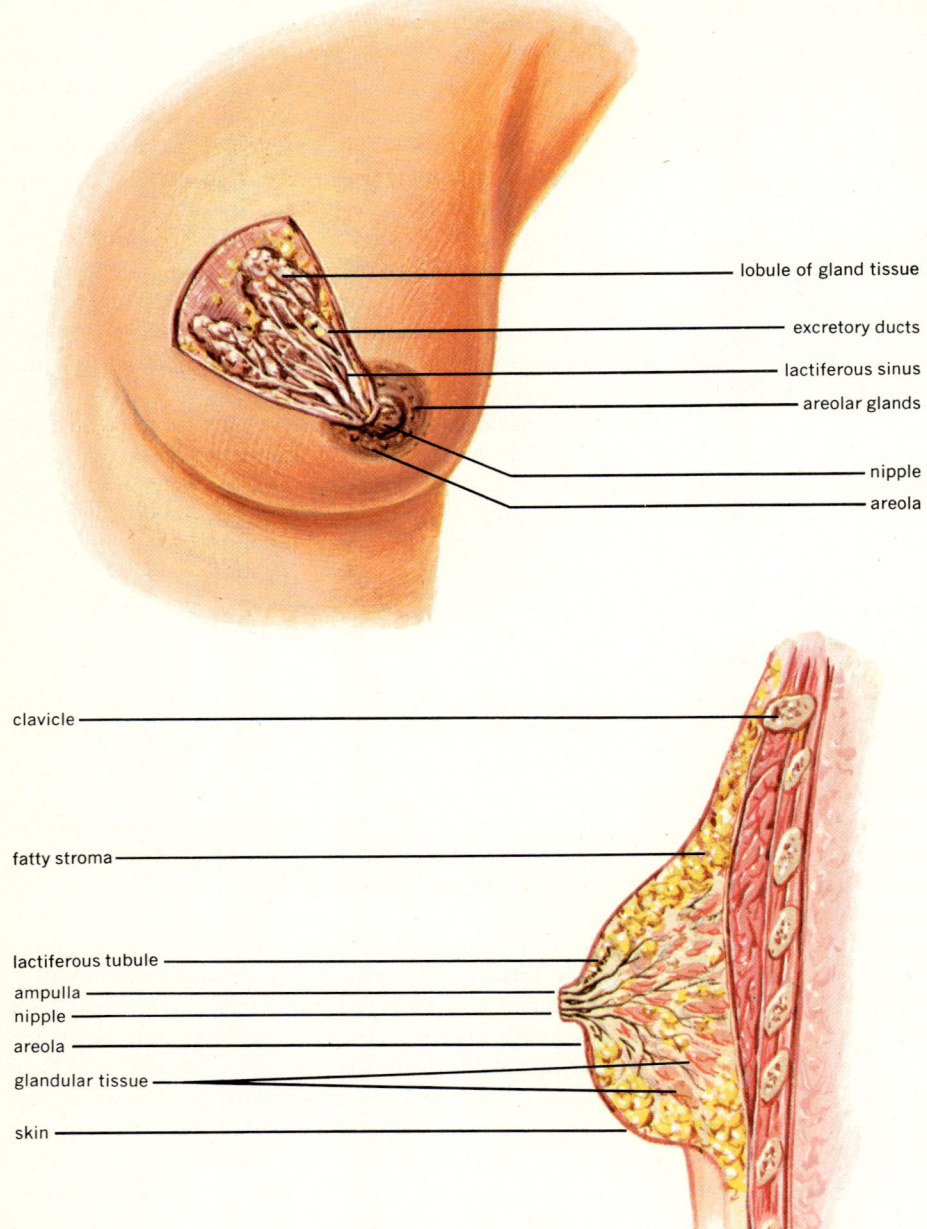

lobule of gland tissue

excretory ducts

lactiferous sinus

areolar glands

nipple

areola

clavicle

fatty stroma

lactiferous tubule
ampulla
nipple
areola
glandular tissue
skin

tains nerves, large coiled blood vessels, lymph vessels, and a less dense connective tissue.

THE MAMMARY GLANDS

Appearances can be deceiving. It seems obvious that a woman with larger breasts would produce more milk than a woman with smaller breasts. But this is not necessarily true, since the size of the breasts is determined more by the amount of fat around the glandular tissue than by the amount of glandular tissue itself.

The breasts of a modern woman very likely will never perform their function, since small families have become fashionable and breast feeding has become unfashionable. But the female breasts are adapted specifically for the nourishment of children. The breasts, or **mammary glands,** are a pair of convex structures, anterior to the pectoral muscles, and extending from the lateral margin of the sternum to the anterior border of the axilla (Figure 34-6). Each is actually a modified sweat gland, consisting of about 15 to 20 glandular tissue **lobes,** divided by connective-tissue bands and arranged radially about a central cylindrical **nipple.** Each lobe is embedded in fat and connective tissue and has its own excretory duct; the ducts converge toward the nipple like the spokes of a wheel. Just before they reach the nipple, each duct enlarges into a small reservoir or **ampulla,** then terminates in a tiny opening at the surface of the nipple. The nipple is surrounded by a circular pigmented area of skin known as the **areola,** which in light-complexioned women is initially pink but acquires a brown pigmentation during pregnancy. The areola contains numerous sebaceous glands that appear as small nodules under the skin. Their secretions lubricate the nipple.

At puberty, ovarian hormones stimulate an extensive growth and branching of the duct system of the mammary glands, along with deposition of fat. After puberty, the breasts may vary slightly in size according to the phase of the menstrual cycle. During pregnancy, further development of the breasts prepares them for their active function: the duct system branches profusely and the terminal branches end in secretory alveoli. Actual milk secretion begins after parturition, under the control of the hormones prolactin (which initiates and maintains milk secretion) and oxytocin (which stimulates milk release). At menopause, breast tissue atrophies somewhat.

The breasts have a rich blood supply, which is even more abundant during lactation. Longitudinal bundles of smooth muscle fibers accompany the ducts, and circular smooth muscle fibers are present within the nipple and around its base. The breasts are often an erogenous area, and the nipples contain erectile tissue. (Erection of the nipples is commonly produced not only by sexual stimulation—mental or physical—but also by suckling of an infant and by such extraneous stimuli as cold environmental temperatures.)

THE OVARIAN CYCLE

Why does each woman have hundreds of thousands of follicles in her ovaries, when only about 400 will ever develop into mature germ cells within her entire lifetime? What determines which particular follicle will develop next and which are doomed to degenerate? These are still unsolved mysteries. But the actual events that occur in the ovaries have been well studied, and they have been found to follow a monthly cycle.

Follicular Development

Once each month, on about the first day of menstruation, several primitive graafian follicles and the primary oocytes that they contain begin to grow and develop. The follicular cells begin to proliferate and secrete estrogens, along with minute amounts of pro-

gesterone. Meanwhile, the primary oocyte passes through a sequence of divisions involving reduction of the chromosome number (meiosis), and it is ultimately transformed into a secondary oocyte. (At this secondary oocyte stage, the ovum contains 23 unpaired chromosomes.) Usually only one follicle comes to full maturity and migrates to the surface of the ovary. If more than one follicle matures simultaneously, and fertilization occurs, a multiple birth will result. (The twins, triplets, or higher multiples formed in such cases are fraternal, rather than identical.) Follicles that become active and then regress are called **atretic follicles.** A cross section of an ovary usually reveals follicles in various stages of development and regression (Figure 34-7).

When the follicle begins to develop, a clear membrane, the **zona pellucida,** forms around the ovum. The follicular cells grow in number and size and arrange themselves in layers around the ovum, and a fluid collects inside the follicle. During this time the ovum increases in diameter from about 35 to 150 μ, and the follicle grows from 120 to 6000 μ.

Oogenesis

Looking at a human sperm and egg, it seems hard to believe that they come from the same species. The sperm is a tiny tadpolelike cell, with a long flagellum; the ovum is thousands of times larger than the sperm, and it is a spherical cell, without any flagellum or other projections. These vast differences represent adaptations to different functions. Both ovum and sperm must contribute half a chromosome set to the new offspring, and each contains precisely a haploid number of chromosomes; but the sperm must travel to reach its destination, and its job is finished when it meets and joins with the ovum. Thus, a sperm needs a means of propulsion (the flagellum), enough energy to take it up the female reproductive tract, enzymes to attack the outer covering of the ovum—and little else. The ovum, on the other hand, travels passively, propelled by the peristaltic movements of the uterine tubes. Its journey from ovary to uterus is a leisurely one, and if it happens to be fertilized, as much as 10 days may elapse between its propulsion out of the ovary and the settling down of the developing egg in the lining of the uterus. Thus the ovum needs not only an appropriate supply of chromosomes, but also a food supply that will last for 8 to 10 days, until the embryo can begin drawing nourishment from the mother's body.

It would be difficult to pack such a large food supply into one ordinary cell. But oogenesis, the formation of a mature ovum, differs somewhat from spermatogenesis, the formation of sperm. Instead of four tiny, identical products, oogenesis yields only one, ab-

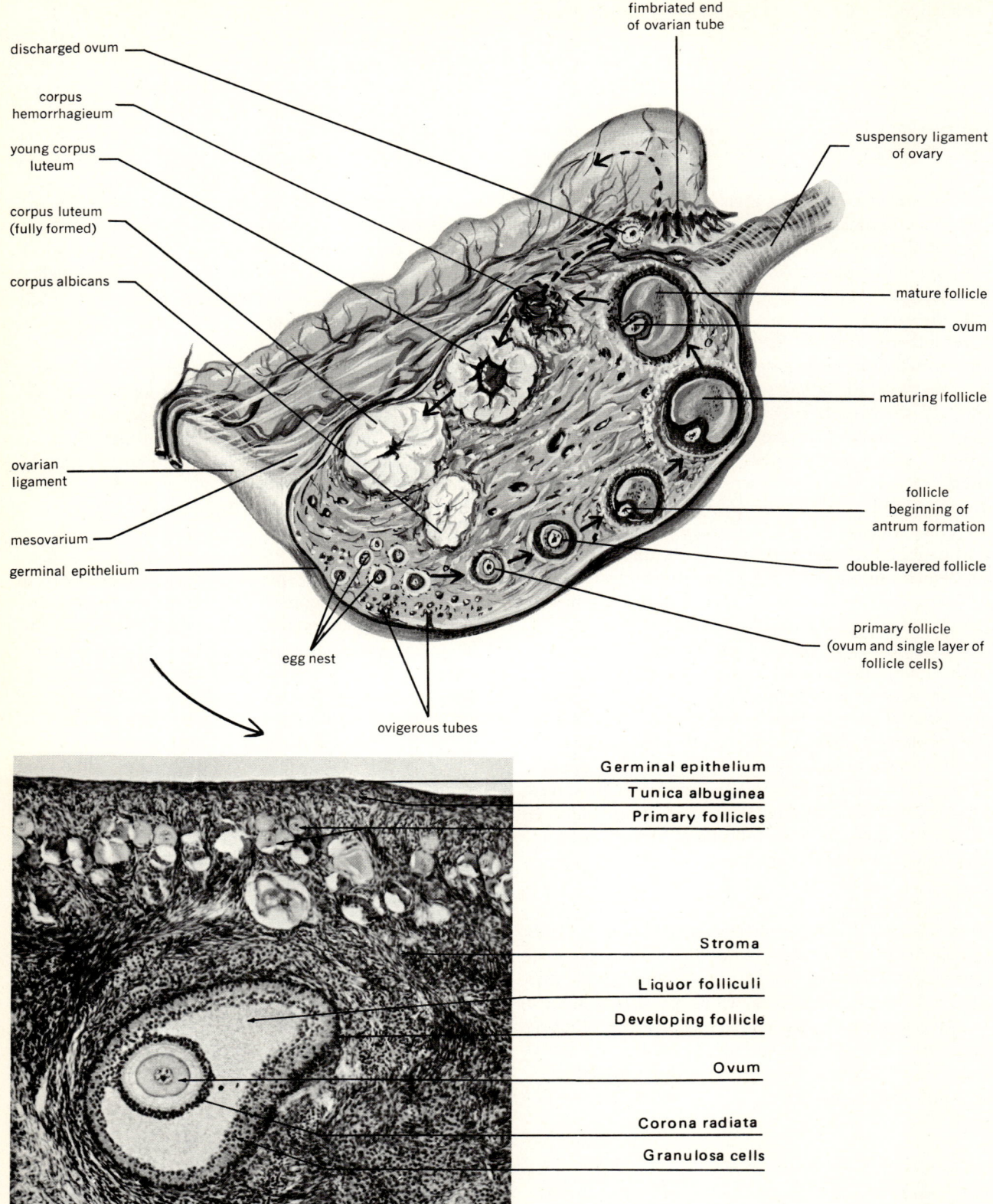

discharged ovum

corpus hemorrhagieum

young corpus luteum

corpus luteum (fully formed)

corpus albicans

ovarian ligament

mesovarium

germinal epithelium

egg nest

ovigerous tubes

fimbriated end of ovarian tube

suspensory ligament of ovary

mature follicle

ovum

maturing follicle

follicle beginning of antrum formation

double-layered follicle

primary follicle (ovum and single layer of follicle cells)

Germinal epithelium
Tunica albuginea
Primary follicles

Stroma
Liquor folliculi
Developing follicle
Ovum
Corona radiata
Granulosa cells

FIGURE 34-7   The ovary. Successive stages of development of the ovarian follicle and ovum are shown counterclockwise, beginning at the lower left (egg nest). The micrograph shows a section of the cortex of an ovary, with primary and maturing follicles ($\times 88$). Corpora lutea, not shown in this micrograph, can be seen in Figure 32-23.

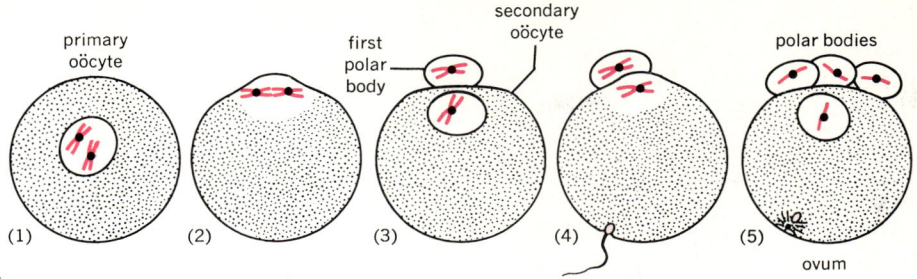

primary
oöcyte

first
polar
body

secondary
oöcyte

polar bodies

(1)　　　(2)　　　(3)　　　(4)　　　(5)

ovum

A

B

FIGURE 34-8 Oogenesis: (A) diagramatic sequence from primary oocyte (1) to an ovum and three polar bodies (5). Note that the second division of meiosis does not occur unless triggered by the penetration of a sperm (4), the nuclear material of which forms the male pronucleus. The micrographs show a fertilized human ovum with two polar bodies (B) and a fertilized ovum with three polar bodies, the first having divided (C).

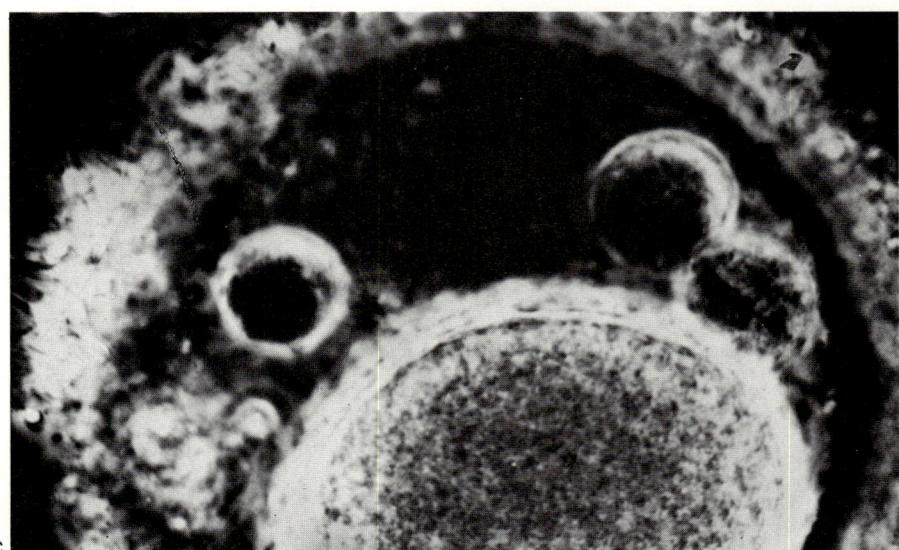

C

normally large ovum, and three tiny cells called **polar bodies** or **polocytes** (Figure 34-8). By the time a female child is born, the oogonia in her ovaries have divided and redivided mitotically, eventually forming **primary oocytes** analogous to the primary spermatocytes in the male. The germ cells remain at this primary oocyte stage until puberty when, each month, a few follicles begin to develop. In each developing follicle, the primary oocyte begins the divisions of meiosis, the first of which yields a **secondary oocyte** and a

polar body. In this division, the chromosomes in the nucleus are apportioned equally between the two daughter cells. But the division of the cytoplasm is quite unequal—the secondary oocyte takes nearly all of it, leaving the polar body with just a thin envelope of cytoplasm around its nucleus. In the second division of meiosis, which does not occur unless fertilization occurs, the secondary oocyte throws off a second polar body, again keeping the lion's share of the cytoplasm for itself although the polar body receives half the chromosomes. (Meanwhile, the first polar body divides also, producing two tiny polar bodies.) As in spermatogenesis, the meiotic divisions of oogenesis occur with only one duplication of the chromosomes. The ovum and the three polar bodies that result each have a set of 23 chromosomes (one from each pair of autosomes and one sex chromosome), but the ovum has nearly four times its "fair" share of cytoplasm. In this way it receives the extra food supply it will need if fertilization occurs.

Ovulation

One of the first attempts to teach birth control methods in India involved a string of beads that was given to each woman. It contained a number of green beads and five black ones. The woman was supposed to count a bead each day, starting at the appropriate part of her menstrual cycle, and refrain from intercourse on the days she counted a black bead. Many women misunderstood the instructions and thought that merely counting the beads would protect them from becoming pregnant—with predictable results.

But even when rhythm methods of birth control are followed properly, they are far from foolproof. There is a great deal of variation in the female sexual cycles, both from woman to woman, and in the same woman depending on the time of year, illness, emotional upsets, and various other factors. If the exact time of ovulation—the release of the mature ovum from the ovary—could be pinpointed, the rhythm methods could be made a much more effective means of contraception. Numerous attempts have been made to determine times of ovulation, by charting daily temperature fluctuations, taking vaginal smears, and so forth. All of these methods have drawbacks. Some women experience a sharp pain at the time of ovulation, which doctors call *mittelschmerz* (a German word for "middle pain"), apparently due to irritation of the peritoneum by hemorrhage from the ruptured follicle. But many women never have any indication at all.

The ovum is mature and ready for release after about 10 to 14 days of growth. The mature follicle, called a graafian follicle, is at the surface of the ovary at this point, and it is distended with fluid. Suddenly it ruptures, and the ovum oozes out in a stream of follicular fluid. This event usually occurs about midway in the menstrual cycle, which averages from 28 to 30 days. The ovum is swept up by the infundibulum into the uterine tube, the peristaltic contractions of which are creating currents in the fluid.

The Corpus Luteum

It would seem that with the release of the ovum, the ruptured ovarian follicle has completed its function.

But its story is not yet over; after discharging the ovum, the deserted follicle will develop into a new entity, the corpus luteum, and for a brief time will function as an important endocrine gland in its own right.

After ovulation, the ruptured follicle collapses, fills with blood and serous fluid, and a clot forms. The clot is invaded and reabsorbed by follicular cells, and gradually capillaries and connective tissue grow into the mass. At this point the entire structure has become a **corpus luteum,** literally a "yellow body" (named for its yellow-pigmented lipid inclusions), which secretes estrogens and progesterone. Its subsequent fate is determined by events occurring elsewhere in the reproductive tract, and it in turn plays a major role in these events. If the ovum is not fertilized, the corpus luteum reaches its maximum development in about a week, then degenerates into a white fibrous scar, the **corpus albicans** ("white body"). If fertilization occurs, the corpus luteum continues to grow and secrete its hormones, reaching a maximum development in the second month of pregnancy. After that, it gradually regresses, although it continues to function actively as an endocrine gland during the first three months of pregnancy. During this time the corpus luteum is crucial to the fate of the developing embryo: if the ovaries are removed at any time up to about the 11th week of pregnancy, spontaneous abortion will result; afterward, the hormones secreted by the placenta are sufficient to maintain the pregnancy. After childbirth the corpus luteum is rapidly transformed into a corpus albicans.

THE MENSTRUAL CYCLE

The first menstrual flow is an important landmark in a girl's life, signaling her physiological entry into womanhood. During the next 35 years or more, its monthly recurrence will be met with a variety of mixed feelings—annoyance because of the need to resort to chafing pads or potentially leaky tampons; relief, if a child was not wanted, or disappointment if an attempt to become pregnant has failed; and satisfaction at this obvious sign that her reproductive system is in good working order. But probably it will seldom occur to her just how curious a process the menstrual cycle is. George Corner of Princeton University has described menstruation as "an unexplained turmoil in the otherwise serenely coordinated process of uterine function, a puzzling paradox whereby a normal function regularly displays itself by the destruction of tissues."

The ovarian cycle is closely coordinated with a complementary cycle of changes in the uterus, which prepares itself for the possible implantation of an embryo and then, if this event does not occur, sloughs off

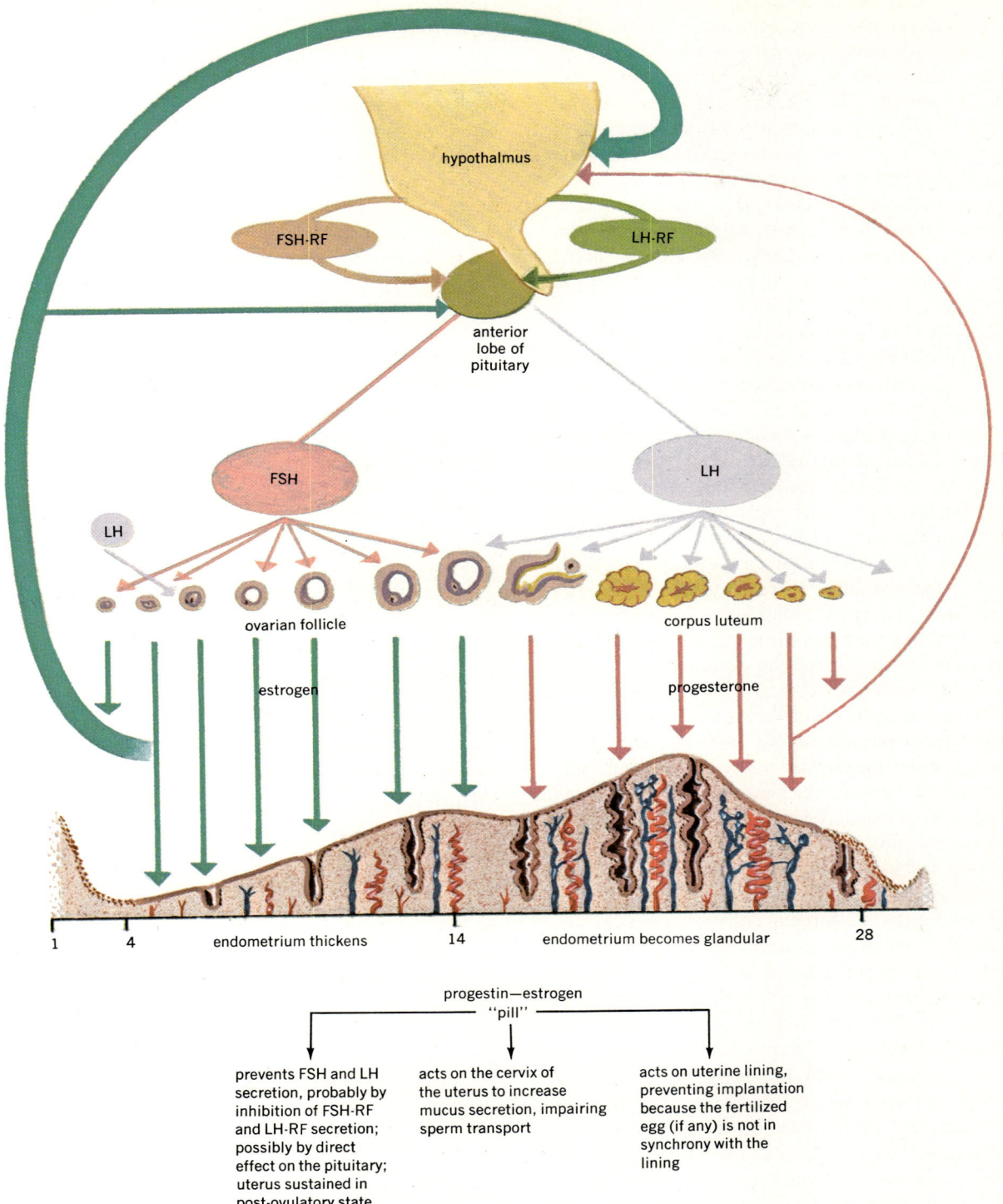

FIGURE 34-9 The female reproductive cycle is normally controlled in a complex feedback interrelationship with the hypothalamus and endocrine glands. The "pill" artificially regulates hormone levels, resulting in a feedback inhibition of ovulation.

its lining and starts over again (Figure 34-9). This cycle of buildup and breakdown is repeated over and over again, at intervals that average 28 to 30 days. (In different women, the normal "monthly" cycle may vary from as little as 19 days to as much as 37 days, and there may be considerable variation from month to month, although generally fertility and regularity seem to be correlated.)

During the **menses,** the menstrual blood flow, patches of the endometrium become necrotic as a result of a sudden shutoff of their blood supply, and slough off, leaving raw bleeding areas. Fortunately, the entire endometrium does not become necrotic at once, and the blood flow remains relatively moderate and controlled. Normally the menstrual flow lasts for about four or five days. During this **menstrual phase,** the superficial functional layer of the endometrium disintegrates and is sloughed off, and there is bleeding into the uterine cavity; the blood is discharged through the vagina. (Menstrual blood is unique in that it is nonclotting.) Even before the menstrual flow ceases, repair of the raw areas begins, and a new superficial layer of the endometrium begins to be regenerated.

On about the fifth day of the cycle, the **proliferative phase** begins. The endometrium thickens, with a rapid proliferation of glands and stroma, restoring the structure of the superficial layer and its rich blood supply. By the time of ovulation, the endometrium is about 2 to 3 mm thick. In the case of an average 28-day cycle, the proliferative phase extends through about the 14th day; if the menstrual cycle is irregular, this is the phase that is shorter or longer than the average, and the length of the postovulatory phase remains relatively constant.

The following two weeks comprise the **postovulatory** or **premenstrual phase,** which is also called the **secretory phase.** During this phase of the cycle, the endometrium grows still thicker, reaching as much as 6 mm. The superficial layer becomes vascular and edematous, as fluid accumulates; the glands become increasingly coiled and begin to secrete. But then, if the ovum is not fertilized and (or) implantation does not occur, the corpus luteum regresses, and the diminishing flow of ovarian hormones triggers a constriction of the coiled arteries in the endometrium, producing the degenerative changes that result in the menstrual flow. The cycle begins again.

If a woman never becomes pregnant, she will experience an average of about 440 menstruations during her lifetime, from the age of about 12 or 13 to perhaps 45. The menstrual cycles cease during pregnancy and do not resume until about six weeks after childbirth; if the mother is breast feeding her baby, the resumption of menstruation may be delayed for as much as six months after the birth. (Lactation is not a foolproof method of birth control, however.) Some irregularity of the menstrual cycles during the first year after puberty is common, and, indeed, menstrual flow may occur initially without actual ovulation. Soon, however, a regular pattern is usually established.

For many women "that time of the month" has little to distinguish it from the rest of the cycle, other than the actual flow of blood. But, for many, menstruation is preceded by a variety of symptoms that have been called the **premenstrual syndrome** or **premenstrual tension.** Complaints include headaches, irritability, tiredness, nausea, aching joints, and feelings of heaviness or pain in the breasts. Some statistical studies have indicated that women are more prone to have accidents during the premenstrual phase, and the majority of crimes by women seem to be committed at this time. The main cause for the discomforts of the premenstrual syndrome seems to be an increased retention of fluid (which may amount to as much as 6 to 7 pounds), due to the increased secretion of progesterone at this time of the cycle. **Dysmenorrhea,** or cramping pains during the menstrual flow, is another common complaint associated with the menstrual period; its cause is unknown, but it commonly disappears spontaneously after a pregnancy.

ENDOCRINE CONTROL OF THE FEMALE SEXUAL CYCLES

The growth and regression of the ovarian follicles, the waxing and waning of the endometrium, and all the other cyclic events of the female sexual cycle are closely controlled by an intricate interplay of hormones that is much like a musical piece played by an orchestra. One after another, the different musicians take their turn carrying the melody, and then fade back into a blending with the other instruments of the orchestra or even stop playing altogether.

Hormones of the anterior pituitary play an important role in the control of the sexual cycles. **Follicle-stimulating hormone (FSH)** stimulates the ovarian follicles to develop and stimulates the secretion of **estrogen** by the ovaries. For the first few days of the proliferative phase of the menstrual cycle, the estrogen levels rise gradually (see Figure 34-9). Then suddenly, on about the 12th day of the cycle,* there is an abrupt "estrogen surge," as the level of the hormone rises to a peak. About 12 hours after the estrogen surge, there is a similar peak secretion of the anterior pituitary hormone **LH (luteinizing hormone),** which works with FSH to bring about the final maturation of the follicle and triggers its rupture a day or two later. Another anterior pituitary hormone, **LTH (luteotropic hormone)** stimulates hormone secretion by the corpus luteum.

The ovarian sex hormones, **estrogen** and **progesterone,** also play key roles in the regulation of the sexual cycle. During the postmenstrual phase, there is at first a rise in the estrogen levels, producing a proliferation of endometrial cells, growth of the endometrial glands

---

* Days of the menstrual cycle are counted from the first day of menstrual flow.

and arteries, an increase in the water content of the endometrium, and increased contractions of the myometrium. Then, as the corpus luteum begins to secrete actively, the progesterone level rises. This hormone has its own effects on the uterus: secretion by the endometrial glands, an increase in the water content of the endometrium, and a decrease in myometrial contractions. The rise in progesterone levels after ovulation also produces a rise in the body temperature, by about 1° F, which can be used as an indication of the day of ovulation.

Both positive and negative feedback mechanisms link the pituitary gonadotropins, the hypothalamic releasing hormones that regulate their secretion, and the ovarian sex hormones. The establishment of these relationships made it possible to develop birth control pills, which contain synthetic estrogenlike or progesteronelike hormones (or both), producing a feedback inhibition of ovulation. The artificial hormones prevent an ovarian follicle from maturing, but menstruation does occur, since the pills are stopped near the end of the cycle each month.

MENOPAUSE

A wave of concern was produced by the announcement that estrogen therapy, widely used to relieve the symptoms accompanying menopause, seems to have resulted in an increased incidence of uterine cancer.

The abrupt cessation of function of the reproductive system in the human female, which commonly occurs some time in the forties, has no true parallel in the male. In addition to a cessation of menstrual periods, which may be gradual or abrupt, this time of physiological change in women, menopause, may be accompanied by a variety of unpleasant symptoms. Flushes involving the head, neck, and upper thorax, and so-called "flashes," hot tingling sensations over the whole body, are common complaints. Headache, dizziness, excessive sweating, weakness, an elevation of blood pressure, itching, nervousness, and emotional depression may also occur. In about 20 percent of women, the symptoms are severe enough to need medical treatment. The internal physical changes that occur at menopause consist of a gradual atrophy of the reproductive organs, with a concomitant cessation of secretion of the ovarian sex hormones. The ovaries, uterine tubes, and uterus become smaller; the ovarian follicles are replaced by fibrous tissue; and the vagina shortens, narrows, and loses some of its elasticity.

Estrogen therapy does not maintain the reproductive function, but can alleviate many of the secondary symptoms. The risk of developing uterine cancer can be minimized by using low doses of estrogen and by frequent monitoring of samples of endometrial cells. (If estrogen therapy is stopped at the first sign of pre-cancerous changes in the endometrium, the uterus returns to normal.)

PRACTICAL CONSIDERATIONS

Many lives have been needlessly lost because of the mistaken impression that a resumption of bleeding months after the regular monthly periods have ceased is merely another inconvenient symptom of menopause. Such bleeding is not a symptom of menopause, and in a large proportion of cases it has a far more serious cause: cancer.

The organs of the female reproductive system—ovaries, uterus, breasts—are frequent sites for tumors, cysts, polyps, and other growths. Many such tumors are benign and never cause any trouble to the patient unless they grow to such large size that they press on the bladder, rectum, or other structures. But malignant tumors are also common, particularly in women over forty. If cancer of the reproductive organs is detected in the early stages, while it is still confined to the organ in which it started—breast, ovary, uterus—the prospects for survival are very good. If the woman fails to notice or respond to early symptoms, such as lumps in the breasts, unusual bleeding, or excessive discharges from the vagina, the cancer may spread rapidly, invading other organs, beyond any hope of cure. Regular self-examinations of the breasts (Figure 34-10) and widespread Pap test screening can do much to lower the cancer mortality rates among women.

It has been estimated that about half the women over the age of forty will be advised at some time to have a **hysterectomy,** the surgical removal of the uterus. In cases of uterine cancer, this operation is often the only treatment offering hope of saving the patient's life. (In a hysterectomy for uterine cancer, often the uterus, uterine tubes, ovaries, and associated lymph nodes are all removed to minimize chances of leaving a bit of cancerous tissue that might continue its malignant growth.) But hysterectomies have also been performed as a means of sterilization (instead of the far less radical procedure of tubal ligation) or even for such frivolous reasons as "might as well have it out now to save trouble later." Responsible physicians have raised serious questions about the frequency of hysterectomies, citing this procedure as one of the most common types of unnecessary operations performed by their less scrupulous colleagues.

Dilation and curettage (D & C) is a surgical procedure in which the cervix is dilated with instruments and the walls of the cervix or uterus proper are carefully scraped. This procedure can be used to remove uterine polyps, soft benign growths, to obtain tissue for laboratory examinations, and also for abortions.

Endometriosis is a bizarre disorder of the female

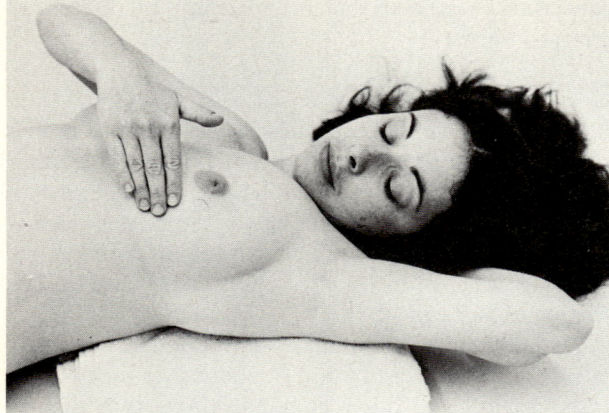

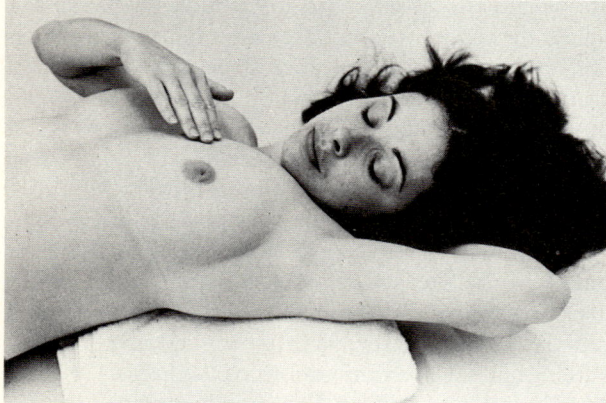

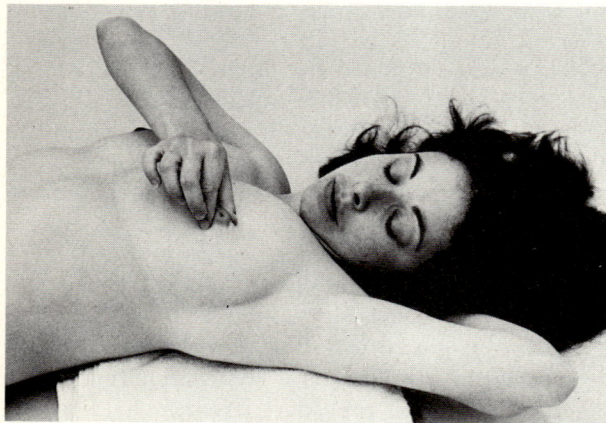

FIGURE 34-10 Regular self-examination of the breasts can detect suspicious lumps while they are still small.

breakdown products, which may build up from month to month, producing pain and serving as a possible focus of infection. Surgical treatment may be necessary to correct the condition.

Childbirth places great strains on the uterus and its supports, and may result in a displacement of the uterus from its normal position, for example, **retroversion** (tipping backward) or **retroflexion** (bending backward of the body of the uterus). An abnormal position of the uterus may be corrected by the insertion of a mechanical support called a **pessary** (Figure 34-11). The stretching of the uterine supports during childbirth may also produce a **prolapse** of the uterus, in which the uterus falls from its normal position so that the cervix protrudes far into the vagina or even protrudes from its orifice. Pressure of the prolapsed uterus on the bladder may cause incontinence. The condition may be corrected with a special type of pessary or by surgical repair of the supports.

Like many regions of the body, the vagina has its characteristic microflora. If conditions are favorable, disease-producing organisms may become dominant in the microcommunity, causing vaginal infections. Various bacteria, *Trichomonas vaginalis* (a parasitic protozoan), and *Candida albicans* (a yeast fungus) are the most common culprits; typical symptoms of vaginal infections include a copious and sometimes foul-smelling discharge and a maddening itch. Local applications of bactericides, fungicides or other chemical preparations in the form of tablets, jellies, or suppositories are usually effective treatments.

With the complicated interplay of hormones and structures involved in the female sexual cycles, there are numerous opportunities for things to go wrong, resulting in **infertility**—the inability to conceive. One of the most frequent causes of infertility in women is a failure to ovulate, which may be diagnosed by tests for the presence of progesterone breakdown products in the urine. Blockage of the uterine tubes is another common disorder leading to infertility. Possible causes of infertility in men have already been discussed; in some cases when attempts at conception have been unsuccessful, the cause may lie in a chemical incompatibility between husband and wife.

reproductive system, in which bits of endometrial tissue become detached from the uterine lining and settle down to grow elsewhere in the body—for example, on other organs of the pelvic cavity. These displaced bits of endometrium respond to the same hormonal influences that produce the cyclic changes in the uterine lining, proliferating and then sloughing and bleeding in turn. If this occurs in the peritoneal cavity, there is no outlet for the discharge of blood and tissue

SUMMARY
The structures of the female reproductive system are:
  2 Ovaries (gonads)
  2 Uterine (fallopian) tubes
  1 Uterus
  1 Vagina
  Vulva (external genitalia)
  2 Breasts (mammary glands)
The female external genitalia (vulva) include:
  Mons pubis (mons veneris)
  Labia majora

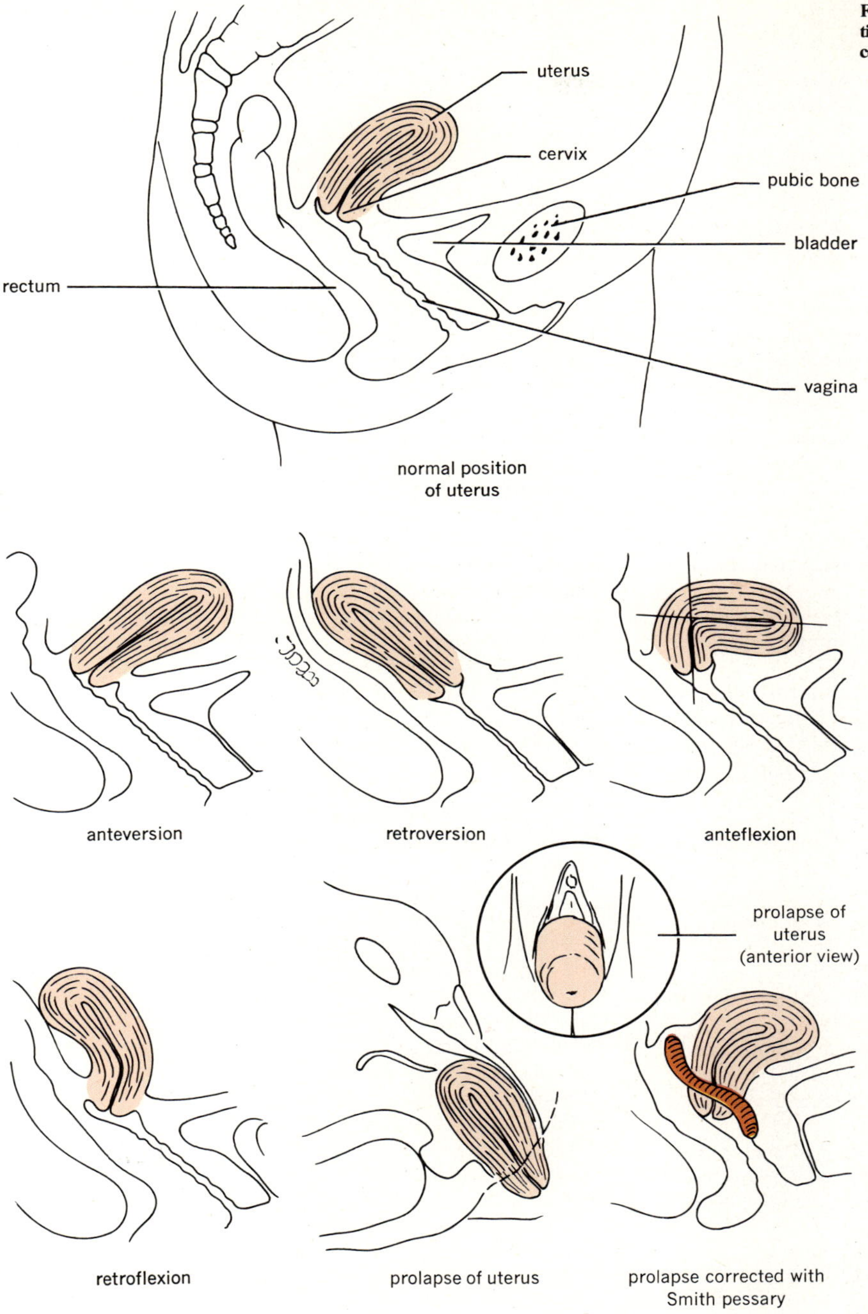

FIGURE 34-11 Normal and abnormal positions of the uterus. A pessary can be inserted to correct prolapse of the uterus.

uterus

cervix

pubic bone

bladder

rectum

vagina

normal position
of uterus

anteversion

retroversion

anteflexion

prolapse of
uterus
(anterior view)

retroflexion

prolapse of uterus

prolapse corrected with
Smith pessary

Labia minora
Clitoris
Vestibule
    Orifice of Vagina
    Paraurethral glands
    Greater vestibular glands (Bartholin's glands)
    Lesser vestibular glands
    Hymen
The vagina is a muscular tube extending from the vestibule to the uterus. It is the female organ of copulation and serves as the birth canal.
The uterus is a pear-shaped organ that expands to accommodate the growing fetus.

It consists of a body (including the fundus) and cervix.
Openings in the uterine wall communicate with the uterine tubes (2) and the vagina (through the cervix).
The uterus is freely movable but anchored in the pelvic cavity by ligaments.
The three-layered wall of the uterus includes:
    Outer peritoneal covering
    Myometrium (muscular layer)
    Endometrium (higher vascular lining)
The uterine tubes extend laterally from the uterus to the ovaries, ending in the funnel-shaped infundibulum, the opening of which is surrounded by fingerlike fimbriae.
After ovulation, the ovum enters the infundibulum and is carried

by peristalsis of the uterine tubes to the uterus.

The ovaries are two ovoid structures containing follicles, each enclosing a potential ovum.

The breasts consist of 15 to 20 glandular tissue lobes, arranged around a central cylindrical nipple, through which the secretions (milk) pass via excretory ducts.

The shape of the breasts is determined mainly by deposits of adipose tissue.

Hormones control breast development, cyclic changes, milk secretion, and milk release.

The ovarian cycle consists of:

Development of graafian follicle with oogenesis

Migration of the follicle to the surface of the ovary

Rupture of the follicle, discharging the ovum (ovulation)

Formation of the corpus luteum and its secretion of hormones

Regression of the corpus luteum and formation of the corpus albicans

Oogenesis is the formation of a mature ovum, containing a haploid chromosome set and an extra large amount of cytoplasm (food sypply). It includes the steps

Oogonium

Primary oocyte

Secondary oocyte and polar body (which subsequently divides)

Secondary oocyte and second polar body

The menstrual cycle consists of the phases:

Menstrual phase (superficial layer of endometrium breaks down in patches and is sloughed off, with bleeding)

Proliferative phase (from end of menstrual flow to ovulation; endometrium thickens and superficial layer is reconstructed)

Postovulatory, premenstrual, or secretory phase (endometrium thickens further, endometrial glands begin to secrete; ends with constriction of coiled arteries, necrosis of endometrial tissue)

Menstruation (menstrual blood flow) may be accompanied by pain (dysmenorrhea) and/or preceded by fluid retention, headaches, irritability, and so on (premenstrual syndrome)

The ovarian and menstrual cycles are regulated by an interplay of pituitary and gonadal hormones:

FSH (follicle-stimulating hormone, from anterior pituitary) stimulates development of ovarian follicles and secretion of estrogen by ovaries.

LH (luteinizing hormone, from anterior pituitary) brings about final maturation of follicle and triggers ovulation.

LTH (luteotropic hormone, from anterior pituitary) stimulates hormone secretion by the corpus luteum.

Estrogen (from ovaries) produces proliferation of endometrial cells, growth of endometrial glands and arteries, increase in water content of endometrium, and contractions of myometrium.

Progesterone (from corpus luteum) produces secretion by the endometrial glands, increase in water content of endometrium, and decrease in myometrial contractions.

The pituitary gonadotropins, hypothalamic releasing hormones, and ovarian sex hormones are interlinked by positive and negative feedback mechanisms.

Menopause is an abrupt cessation of reproductive functioning in the female, occurring at about age 45, involving atrophy of the reproductive organs and a cessation of secretion of sex hormones.

In some cases, menopause is accompanied by unpleasant symptoms such as flushes, hot flashes, sweating, headache, weakness, and emotional depression.

Disorders of the female reproductive organs include:

Benign and malignant growths (cysts, polyps, tumors, etc.)

Endometriosis

Abnormal position of the uterus (retroversion, retroflexion, prolapse, etc.)

Vaginal infections

Infertility (failure to ovulate, obstruction of uterine tubes, etc.)

The Pap test is a cytological examination of vaginal smears for precancerous and cancerous changes in cells.

Hysterectomy is the removal of the uterus (sometimes with uterine tubes and ovaries).

Dilation and curettage is a dilation of the cervix and scraping of the uterine lining.

QUESTIONS FOR REVIEW AND THOUGHT

1 List the structures of the female reproductive system and their functions.

2 Describe the anatomical similarities and differences of the male and female reproductive organs.

3 Is it valid to consider an unbroken hymen as a criterion of virginity?

4 How is the structure of the vagina adapted to its functions?

5 Describe the female reproductive cycle in the following aspects: (a) changes in the ovary; (b) changes in the uterus; (c) secretion of hormones; (d) development and migration of the ovum.

6 If you were redesigning the female *Homo sapiens,* would you retain the menstrual cycle? Discuss.

7 Define: ectopic pregnancy; areola; fimbriae; endometrium; dilation and curettage; dysmenorrhea.

8 Outline the process of oogenesis, mentioning all the stages in the formation of the mature ovum. What further steps occur after fertilization?

9 Compare and contrast spermatogenesis and oogenesis.

10 What is the premenstrual syndrome, and what causes it?

11 What is menopause? Is there a comparable condition in men?

CONCEPTION, PRENATAL DEVELOPMENT, AND BIRTH

35

The odds against your having been born were staggering. First of all, your parents had to have chosen each other, out of all the other billions of humans on the planet. They had to be in reasonably good health at the time of your conception, and they had to have sexual intercourse within a rather narrow time span—perhaps as little as 24 hours—in which viable sperm would be available to fertilize a viable egg. A particular ovum, formed by the random assortment of chromosomes in meiosis during the maturation of a particular follicle among the hundreds of thousands in your mother's ovaries, contributed to your conception. Millions of spermatozoa started out on the journey from your father's testes into your mother's reproductive tract. Some went astray or died on the way to the uterine tube where the ovum was making its leisurely way to the uterus. But there were still millions left to bombard the ovum, each sperm with a slightly different chromosome set from its companions. One by one the spermatozoa exhausted themselves battering against the resistant outer coating of the ovum; pure chance selected the ultimate victor, which entered the ovum and merged its chromosome set with the one provided by your mother. If any of the circumstances of your conception had varied—even, perhaps, a second's difference in the time of orgasm—another child might have been conceived instead of you. Even after sperm and ovum joined and your hereditary legacy was set, there were many chances for mishaps: you might have been aborted before your development was far along, or you might have developed some gross malformation; or you might have been twins. The improbable sequence of events that occur before birth, resulting so frequently in the formation of a perfect human being, is one of the most amazing parts of the human life story.

SEXUAL INTERCOURSE

The development of effective methods of birth control has brought a revolution in attitudes toward the proper function of sexual intercourse. Before, any act of intercourse had a high possibility of resulting in pregnancy; now sex and procreation can be effectively separated, and there is a widespread groping for new values and standards, for workable definitions of what the role of sexual activities in modern life should be—an adjunct of the pursuit of pleasure, a symbol of a deeper emotional commitment, or different things in different circumstances.

The schism between sex and procreation has been further widened by the development of techniques in which conception can be produced without an actual act of intercourse—the penetration of the penis of the male into the vagina of the female with the release of ejaculate. Through artificial insemination, a woman can be impregnated merely by the insertion of a specimen of semen deep into her vagina. Medical researchers have worked out techniques for fertilizing human ova in a culture dish and inserting the developing early embryo into the mother's uterus; the first such "test-tube baby" was born in 1978. Techniques of cloning, the reproduction of an individual from a single cell, which would permit "one-parent reproduction" no longer seem to be mere science fantasy. Yet even if the procreative function of intercourse becomes unnecessary or undesirable, it is likely that copulation will continue to be a favored activity because of the intensely pleasurable sensations generated by the act.

During sexual excitement, the penis of the male, which normally hangs down limply, becomes erect and hardened as the erectile tissue becomes engorged with blood. Psychological factors play an important role in the building of such sexual excitement, which is reinforced by autonomic nervous mechanisms, as described in Chapter 33. Similar mechanisms operate in the body of the female, producing an engorgement of the clitoris and labia with blood.

Insertion of the penis into the vagina of the female, followed by rhythmic movements, eventually brings on a response of intense excitement, accompanied by widespread sensations and reflex contractions of the epididymis, vas deferens, seminal vesicles, prostate gland, and the skeletal muscles at the base of the penis, resulting in the forcible expulsion of about 3 to 4 ml of semen from the penis into the vagina. The expulsion of semen is termed **ejaculation,** and the total response, psychic and physiological, is known as an **orgasm.**

During copulation, the action of the penis against the clitoris and vaginal walls, together with stimulation of other erogenous areas of the body, greatly enhances the sexual excitement of the female, stimulating the flow of lubricating secretions and adaptation of the muscular vagina to the shape of the penis. Ultimately, the female may experience an orgasm comparable to that of the male. During the female orgasm, the uterine tubes and the vaginal and uterine walls undergo rhythmic contractions, but there is no comparable production and expulsion of fluid. It is thought that the rhythmic contractions of the female reproductive tract aid in the movement of sperm in the direction of the uterus and uterine tubes, but the female orgasm is not a necessary prerequisite for fertilization; indeed, conception is possible even if the female plays an entirely passive role in intercourse.

FERTILIZATION

The question of whether abortions should be permitted raises a corollary that is still being heatedly debated: exactly when does "life" begin, and when should the product of conception be considered as an entity in its own right, separate from its mother? From the biological standpoint it can be argued that a new being comes into existence at the instant of conception, because when the sperm fuses with the ovum, the resultant zygote contains the complete set of genetic blueprints for all of its subsequent development into a human being. But at this stage the fertilized egg is still only a *potential* human being, incapable of existence outside its mother's body. In the aftermath of the historic Supreme Court decision on abortion, the fetus has essentially been considered as a legal entity only when it reaches the stage when it has a possibility of survival outside the womb.

Fertilization, when it occurs, takes place in the upper third of the uterine tube. It rarely takes place in the uterus, for by the time an unfertilized egg reaches the uterus—about four days after ovulation—it has already degenerated. In fact, the human egg is normally fertilizable for only about a 24-hour period after ovulation, after which it begins to break down. Human sperm are equally delicate: although they may survive in the female genital tract for up to 72 hours, they are healthy and highly fertile for only about 24 hours. Thus, if fertilization is to occur, copulation must take place within a very narrow "window" of time, within a day or less of the actual moment of ovulation.

If only one ovum is normally released at a time, what advantages can there be for so many sperm—300 to 500 million of them—to be provided by a single ejaculation? This apparent wastefulness actually provides a number of adaptive advantages. First of all, many of the sperm go astray and do not enter the uterine tubes at all, and approximately half of those that do find their way into the tubes enter the tube that does not contain an ovum. Even when the sperm actually encounter a mature ovum, it takes many sperm to bring about fertilization, although only one can participate in the actual act of union.

In the race up the female reproductive tract, the prize does not go to the swiftest. The sperm that reach the ovum first find it surrounded by a seemingly impregnable barrier: a jagged covering of cells called the **corona radiata,** named for its resemblance to the corona of the sun (Figure 35-1). The first sperm to reach the ovum batter themselves futilely against its outer covering. The head of each sperm is equipped with a small structure that literally explodes like a miniature bomb when it hits the egg, releasing a tiny charge of the enzyme **hyaluronidase.** This enzyme hydrolyzes hyaluronic acid polymers, which are a major component of the cementing material that binds the cells of the corona radiata together. Each sperm carries such a minute amount of hyaluronidase that an estimated 35 million sperm are needed to impact with the egg before a large enough hole is breached in the corona radiata. When this is accomplished at last, the next sperm to reach the egg fuses with it. As soon as the head and neck of the sperm penetrate into the ovum, the outer membrane of the ovum immediately thickens, effectively preventing the entrance of additional sperm. Now the head of the sperm rapidly swells, forming a **male pronucleus.** Some physiologists believe that the final division of meiosis in the ovum, throwing off the second polar body and producing a **female pronucleus** with 23 chromosomes, does not occur until it is stimulated by the actual penetration of the sperm. Ultimately, the chromosomes of the male and female pronuclei align themselves to form the full complement of 46 chromosomes of the fertilized ovum, or **zygote.** A new individual life has been conceived, and the female is now pregnant.

Sex Determination

Theoretically, the chances of any new baby being a boy or a girl are exactly equal. In humans, sex is determined by the sex chromosomes: a female has an XX genotype, and a male has an XY genotype. The fertilized ovum receives one sex chromosome from its mother (via the ovum) and one from its father (via the sperm). The ovum can contribute only an X chromosome, since the mother has the female XX genotype. But the sperm may contribute either an X chromosome or a Y chromosome, since the father's genotype is XY. Thus, half the sperms contain a Y chromosome and half contain an X chromosome. If a sperm containing a Y chromosome fertilizes the ovum, the product will be male (XY); if a sperm containing an X chromosome fertilizes the ovum, the product will be female (XX).

Mathematically, it all seems very simple and clearcut: the sex of the children is determined by the father's sperm, and on the average half will be male and half female. However, there is considerable evidence to indicate that things are not so simple. First of all, we all know families in which *all* the children are boys, or all girls. Perhaps these isolated cases are merely the result of the small samples involved, since the laws of probability work more reliably the larger the sample involved. But statistically it is found that about 106 boys are born for every 100 girls, and it has been estimated that at fertilization the disparity is even higher: about 130 males for each 100 females. A disproportionately higher mortality rate for males at all ages gradually lowers the ratio, so that by 14 to 18 years, the beginning of the reproductive age, it has evened out to 1:1. What could be causing the disproportion at conception?

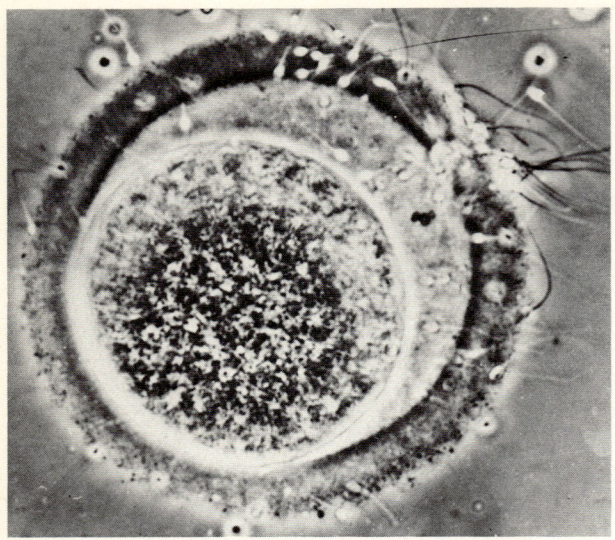

There have been reports that Y sperm swim faster than X sperm. Thus, Y sperm would reach the ovum first and stand a better chance of fertilizing the ovum, especially if copulation occurred on the day of ovulation. There may also be differences in fragility of the sperm and chemical differences that could be influenced by the intrauterine environment. There is also a small difference in weight, because of the greater bulk of the X chromosome, in comparison with the Y chromosome. In recent experiments it has proved possible to separate X and Y sperm by sensitive methods of ultracentrifugation, and it is expected that in the future it may be possible for a couple to decide on the sex of their child in advance by using a sex-separated sample of the husband's sperm for artificial insemination. Experimental techniques for purposely deter-

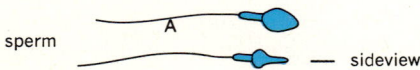

sperm

FIGURE 35-1 Sperm can be seen bombarding a human ovum in the micrograph. The diagram shows the sequence of stages in fertilization, joining of the male and female pronuclei, and division into two blastomeres.

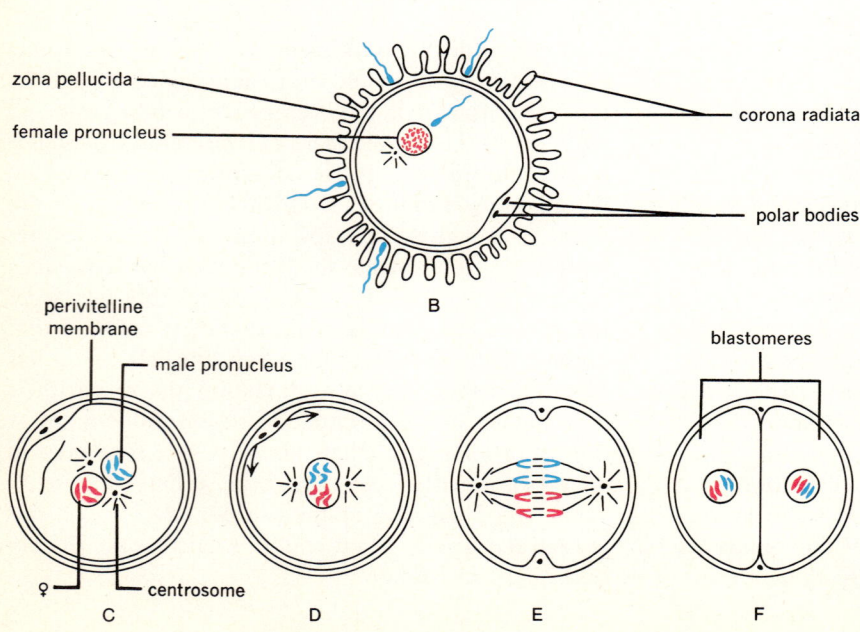

mining the sex of children by carefully timing intercourse to the appropriate part of the wife's ovarian cycle, to take advantage of the difference in sperm motility, are also being developed.

Infertility

About one in every ten married couples is unable to have children. In two out of three cases in which both persons have been examined, infertility of the wife has been found to be responsible for the failure to conceive. Failure to ovulate, the production of abnormal ova, and malformations of some portion of the female reproductive tract are common causes of infertility in women. Drugs such as Perganol have proved helpful in correcting endocrine imbalances that have prevented ovulation. Obstruction of the uterine tubes and various other disorders of the reproductive organs can sometimes be corrected surgically. When surgical repair is not possible, fertilization in vitro may offer a hope of normal childbirth. Careful timing is necessary to obtain a ripened ovum and to insert the developing embryo into the uterus at the optimum phase for implantation; the mother's ovarian cycle may be artificially regulated with hormones for this purpose.

In men a common cause of infertility is insufficient production of sperm by the germinal epithelium of the testes, or the production of abnormal sperm. In such cases, conception can sometimes be produced by combining several ejaculates and using them for a single artificial insemination. A failure of the prostate or other glands to add their secretions to the semen may also produce infertility, even when the sperm count is adequate: the acid secretions of the female reproductive tract are inimical to sperm and must be neutralized if the sperm are to remain viable. In cases where male infertility is complete, the couple may choose to have the wife impregnated by artificial insemination with donor sperm. In such cases the child will receive half its genetic heritage from its mother, and half from the anonymous donor.

Contraception

It has been estimated that if the world population continued to increase at its present rate, in about 600 years there would be one person for every square foot of land area on the earth. Advances in medicine and sanitation have greatly reduced the death rate from disease; unless the other Malthusian spectres of famine and war are to be permitted to adjust the world's population growth to more manageable proportions, the only workable alternative is to voluntarily limit the birth rate. Fortunately, greater knowledge of the functioning of the male and female reproductive systems has permitted the development of effective methods of **contraception,** the prevention of births.

One of the oldest methods of contraception is **coitus interruptus,** the removal of the penis from the vagina before ejaculation. Though widely practiced at least since Biblical times (it is mentioned in Genesis 38), coitus interruptus is a rather ineffective and highly psychologically unsatisfying method of contraception.

Mechanical barriers to the passage of sperm have been an important approach to contraception (Figure 35-2). A **condom** is a sheath, now commonly made of rubber, which is placed over the penis. It not only prevents the entrance of semen into the vagina, but also provides protection against venereal disease and was originally used for that purpose. The diaphragm, a cup-shaped device that covers the cervix, was designed about a century ago and was one of the most widely used approaches before more effective modern contraceptives were designed. The effectiveness of a

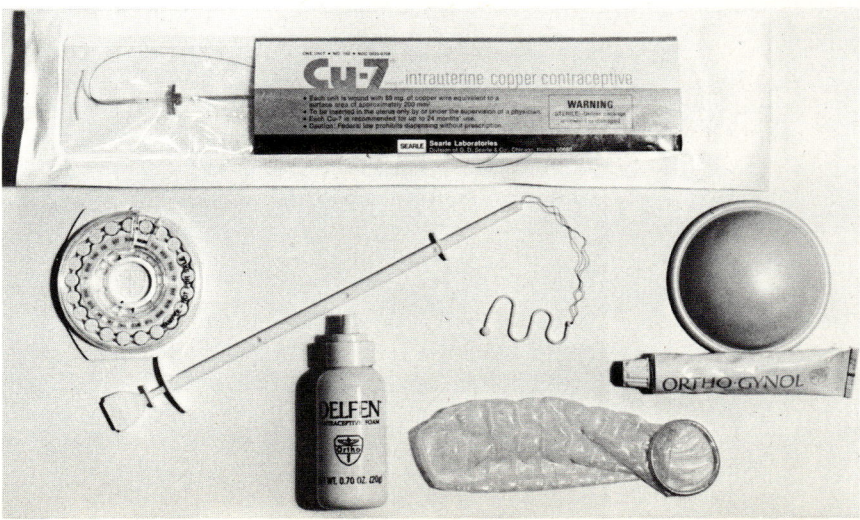

FIGURE 35-2 A variety of contraceptive devices: IUDs, pills, foam, condom, diaphragm, and jelly.

diaphragm is increased when it is used in conjunction with spermicidal jellies, creams, or foams.

A variety of **chemicals** and **douches** have been used before or after intercourse, to wash out the semen or kill sperm (e.g., by the creation of a low pH).

The **rhythm method** attempts to utilize a calculation of the natural female menstrual cycle to minimize chances of conception. Since ova and sperm each have an effective lifetime of only a day or two, it would be expected that only copulations occurring at or near the time of ovulation will result in conception. Allowing a few days on either side of the probable ovulation date to take various irregularities into account, this still leaves a substantial portion of the month comprising a theoretical "safe period," in which sexual intercourse should not result in pregnancy. Unfortunately, some women tend to be so irregular in their monthly cycles (some may even ovulate twice or more in a month) that the rhythm method is not very effective. Charting the monthly variations of the woman's body temperature somewhat improves the contraceptive effectiveness of the rhythm method, but the ambiguities of interpreting temperature charts still leave considerable margin for error.

One of the major contraceptive efforts has centered on attempts to artificially regulate the monthly cycle by administering hormone preparations in a sequence that maintains the body in a pregnancy-like state for most of the month, suppressing ovulation, then stopping the pills to stimulate a menstrual flow. This is the basis of **"the pill,"** probably the most reliable contraceptive device yet devised. The question of long-term side effects, however, has not been definitely resolved. Some statistical evidence indicates that birth control pills may increase the risk of thrombophlebitis, an inflammation of the veins combined with blood clotting within the blood vessels, and pulmonary embolism, the formation of blood clots within the lungs. The question of the risks of cancer is still being debated. Diabetes and other hormonal imbalances may also be triggered by "the pill." (Of course, pregnancy and childbirth can also result in these and other equally dangerous side effects, so it is often a question of weighing the relative potential hazards.)

Intrauterine devices (IUDs) are another major contraceptive approach (Figure 35-2). Coils, loops, rings, and other devices made of stainless steel, copper, or plastic, are inserted into the uterus and left there. For some reason that is not yet entirely understood, the presence of such a foreign body in the uterus prevents implantation of an embryo in the uterine wall, and thus pregnancy cannot result even if an egg is fertilized. Combinations of intrauterine devices with sex hormones, which are very slowly released in minute amounts, seem very promising. Since the hormones can act directly on the uterus, rather than through the bloodstream, the dose can be greatly reduced, with a corresponding reduction of side effects.

Prostaglandins have been found to induce uterine contractions, strong enough to prevent implantation, expel a newly implanted ovum, or induce abortions. Other approaches to a "morning after" pill and drugs to produce temporary male sterility are under intensive study. In recent tests, daily oral doses of the drug danazol, combined with a monthly injection of testosterone to ensure normal sex drive, have proven 85 percent successful in rendering male volunteers infertile.

Another technique, still experimental, is to immunize the wife against her husband's sperm, so that her body defenses will actively attack them and prevent fertilization. An even more ingenious **immunological approach,** recently developed in India, is to immunize the woman against human chorionic gonadotropin (HCG). Antibodies produced in response to the HCG vaccine block the action of the hormone, which is secreted by a fertilized egg and would normally stimulate the secretion of progesterone; as a result, the immunized woman menstruates on schedule, and the ovum is expelled. Immunized women could still bear children if they wished by taking doses of progesterone.

Surgical **sterilization** has been gaining in popularity in recent years. In the male it is accomplished by **vasectomy,** a simple surgical procedure consisting of cutting and tying the vasa deferentia, so that sperm cannot enter the ejaculate. The comparable operation in women, **tubal ligation,** is a major operation, but is equally effective and permanent.

Since the Supreme Court ruling, **abortion** has become a legal means of terminating unwanted pregnancies. This surgical procedure is simplest and safest when performed within a month or so after the onset of pregnancy. Early in pregnancy, abortion can be produced by applying suction to the uterine cavity, bringing on expulsion of the implanted embryo and a menstrual-like bleeding. Dilation and curettage can also be performed. Abortion carries a definite risk of complications (though lower than the risk of complications with a full-term pregnancy), and its moral and legal implications are still controversial.

PREGNANCY

Aldous Huxley's novel, *Brave New World,* shocked the public in the 1930s with visions of a future world in which children would be reproduced by cloning, after rigorous genetic selection, nurtured through their fetal growth in glass wombs, and not born but decanted into a narrowly regimented life. With the advances in research that more than a generation has brought, Huxley's speculations now seem far less shocking and quite within the realm of possibility—perhaps in the not too distant future. For the most part, however, women must still conceive their children in the normal manner and go through the trials, tribulations, and joys of a full-term pregnancy. To be sure, today's woman in the developed countries can likely look forward to only about two pregnancies in her entire reproductive lifetime—a far cry from her counterpart a few generations ago, when each pregnancy was rapidly followed by another. (Some physiologists have even argued that for women in the childbearing years, pregnancy and lactation are actually the normal physiological states.)

Important events of pregnancy occur before the mother has the slightest suspicion that she may be pregnant. The fertilized ovum continues its leisurely journey through the uterine tube, taking a day or two to reach the uterus. It begins to divide and divide again, forming first a cluster of cells, and then a fluid-filled ball. During this time the dividing cells live on the supply of food provided by the quadruple-sized share of cytoplasm from the original ovum. But that food reserve is limited and will soon run out. After the tiny embryo has spent four or five days in the uterus—that is, on about the seventh to ninth day after conception, the ball of cells settles down into the endometrium, and the placenta, which will provide for a transport of materials back and forth between mother and fetus, begins to form.

A few days later, the mother has the first hint of the new life growing within her, when the expected menstrual flow does not appear on schedule. A week or two later, as the hormone levels rise, she may experience the nausea of "morning sickness," and at this time a more definitive establishment of pregnancy becomes possible. The mother's urine contains gonadotropins, which can be detected by injecting a urine specimen into a female animal and examining its ovaries some time later for signs of maturation (corpora lutea and hemorrhagic foci indicating ruptured follicles), or by more rapid laboratory tests.

When a human baby is born, it is already about nine months old. It has spent these nine months of life since conception living as a parasite within the body of its mother, drawing nourishment from her tissues and dependent for its well-being on her physical state. The normal period of pregnancy, or **gestation period** (i.e., the time from the fertilization of the ovum to the birth of the child) is 266 days for humans. In comparison with other mammals, this is a medium-length gestation period, as befits the human body weight and the degree of development undergone by the young before birth. Rats and mice, for example, are born in an extremely immature state after a gestation period of only three weeks, while an elephant has a pregnancy lasting neary two full years.

During its nine months of prenatal development, the human embryo undergoes an incredible increase in size and complexity—from a microscopic single cell to a six- to nine-pound mass of protoplasm composed of nearly 10 trillion cells, integrated into functional systems ready to cope with such tasks as respiration, circulation, digestion, and excretion. The mother's uterus undergoes a correspondingly startling increase in size: from a capacity of about 2 to 3 ml in the virgin uterus to about 5 to 7 liters at the time of childbirth.

EMBRYONIC DEVELOPMENT

The early development of the embryo is surprisingly similar among a variety of animal species—so similar, in fact, that valuable insights into human development have been gained through studies of fertilized eggs of such diverse species as frogs, chickens, and even sea urchins. In the late nineteenth century, the German anatomist Ernst Haeckel proposed the hypothesis: "ontogeny recapitulates phylogeny"—in other words, the embryonic development of an individual (ontogeny) repeats or mirrors the evolutionary development of its ancestors (phylogeny). Later studies have shown that Haeckel's hypothesis is correct only in broad outline, since the recapitulation is far from precise and complete. However, the embryological development of higher organisms, including humans, does include various aspects of the embryological development of their ancestors, and early embryos of various vertebrates show a startling resemblance to one another.

Our knowledge of the stages of early human development comes largely from observations of embryos taken from pregnant uteruses removed for medical reasons in hysterectomies, and from aborted embryos and fetuses. Efforts have been made to maintain human embryos under artificial conditions for varying periods of time (usually a few weeks at most), but the "test tube babies" envisioned by Huxley are still an achievement for the future. Indeed, it was not until 1968 that researchers actually brought about a fertilization of a human ovum in vitro. In 1978 British doctors announced the birth of the first child born as a result of fertilization outside the body. But this "test-tube baby" completed her embryonic development in the womb of a real mother.

In the broad sense, the science of embryology deals with the entire development of the young animal from conception to birth (or hatching from the egg in species that do not develop inside the mother's body). In humans it is customary to reserve the term **embryo**

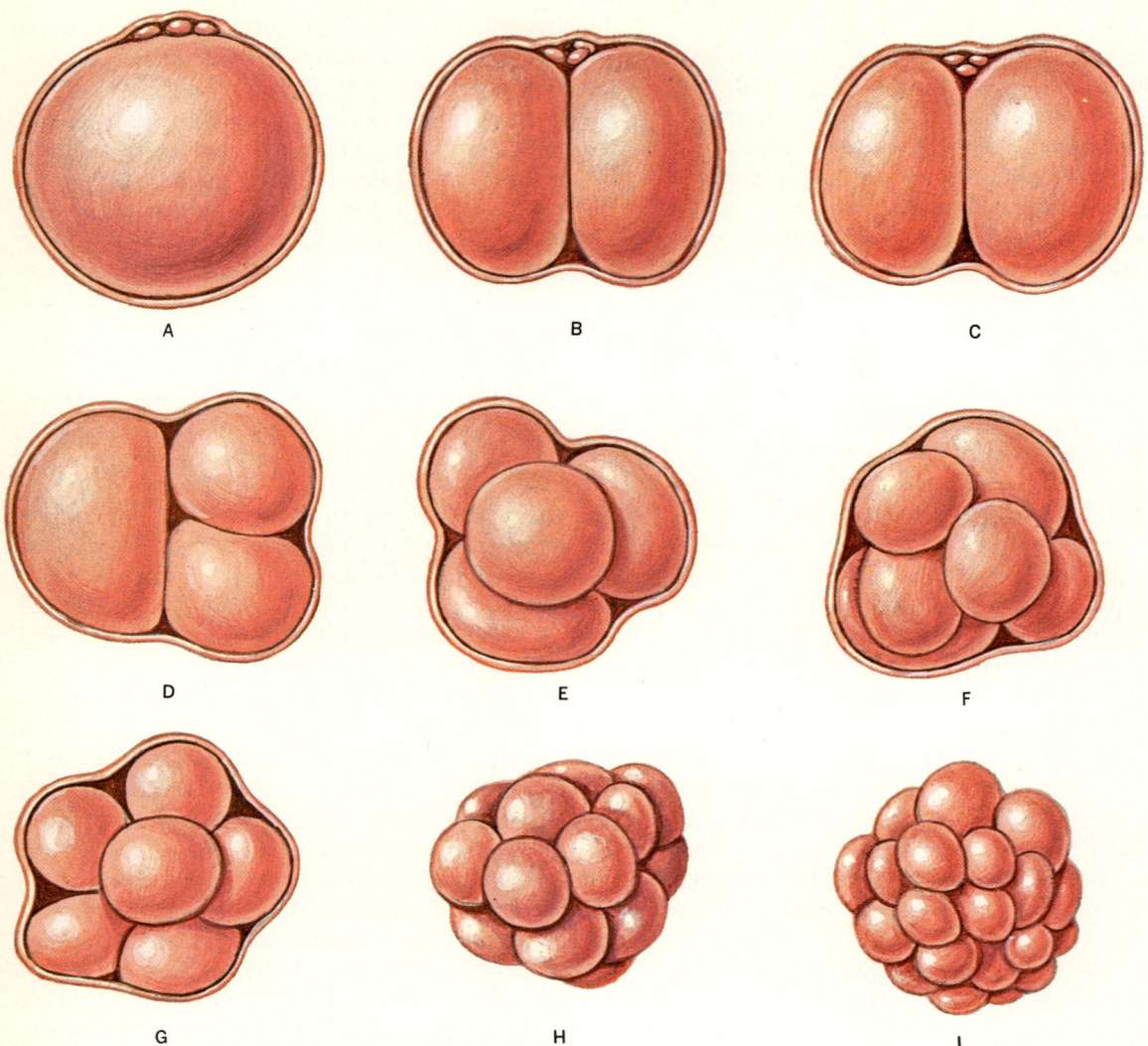

FIGURE 35-3   Cleavage of the fertilized ovum. Successive divisions produce a berrylike cluster, the morula (I). Note that there is no increase in overall mass, despite the increase in number of cells, as each division produces smaller cells.

for the developing young only up to about 10 to 12 weeks, when all the basic organs have been formed and the embryo is recognizably human. After this time, until birth, the human embryo is referred to as a fetus.

Cleavage and Implantation

After the nuclei of sperm and ovum have fused, joining their chromosomes to form a full set of 46, for a time there is no apparent activity. But the zygote is doubtless a center of considerable behind-the-scenes biochemical activity, for then a furrow appears, and the single cell divides into two smaller duplicates of itself. This is a mitotic division, and it is the first in a series of divisions referred to as **cleavage** (Figure 35-3). The cells of the embryo divide again and again, at a quickening pace. Unlike the usual mitosis, there is not a period of cell growth between successive divi-

sions. Instead, for a time the individual cells become smaller and smaller, and the overall size of the embryo remains approximately unchanged. (Remember that the original ovum is an unusually large cell, and that its food supply is limited. The developing embryo has little energy to spare, and expends its food reserves on mitosis.) The progressively smaller cells formed in the divisions of cleavage are called **blastomeres.** Ultimately they form a berrylike solid mass of cells, called a **morula** (which literally means "mulberry").

The divisions of cleavage are the beginning of a long process of development in which many changes occur in a precise sequence, following a harmoniously regulated time schedule, all spelled out in the DNA blueprints contained in the nucleus of the fertilized ovum.

The morula reaches the uterine cavity about three

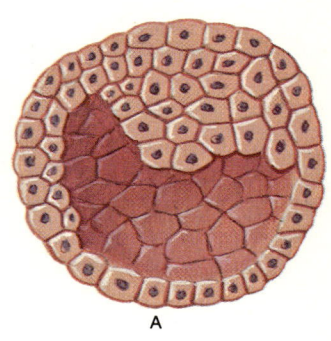

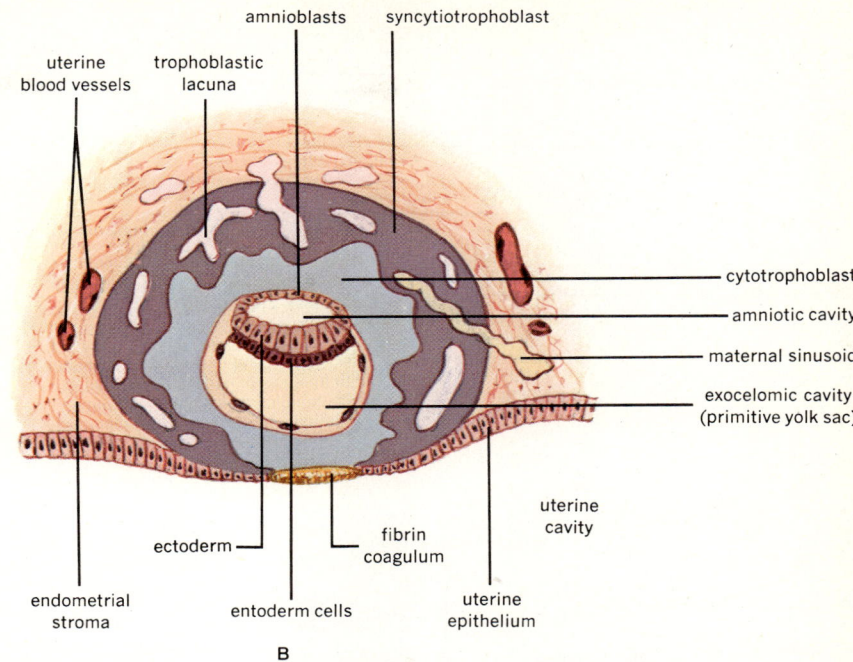

FIGURE 35-4 The blastocyst (A) is a hollow ball of trophoblast cells and an inner cell mass; after implantation of the blastocyst in the uterine wall (B), differentiation of cell layers and cavities proceeds.

to four days after ovulation and proceeds into the next stage of development. As the cells continue to divide, they gradually group themselves to form a hollow, fluid-filled ball, the **blastocyst** (Figure 35-4). By the seventh day, the cells of the blastocyst have differentiated into an outer layer, called the **trophoblast,** and a cluster of cells inside the ball, called the **inner cell mass.**

Now the blastocyst secretes proteolytic enzymes that eat a hole in a spot on the endometrium of the body of the uterus. The embryo begins to sink into the endometrium. Fingerlike projections called chorionic villi grow out into the uterine mucosa. Blood vessels and glands in the penetrated area are disrupted, and the fluid that leaks out provides nourishment for the developing embryo. The epithelium heals over, entirely enclosing the embryo, which is now **implanted** in the tissues of the uterine wall. During pregnancy, the endometrium is greatly thickened and highly modified; it is referred to at this time as the **decidua** (from a Latin word meaning "to shed," since the entire modified endometrium will be discarded after the birth of the child). The portion of the endometrium on which the implanted embryo rests is called the **decidua basalis,** and the mucosa covering it is the **decidua capsularis.**

During the second to third weeks after fertilization, the blastocyst becomes firmly embedded in the uterine mucosa, and the trophoblast and inner cell mass begin to grow and differentiate. Curiously, at this stage the majority of the cells of the developing blastocyst are not destined to form the actual embryo, but instead will develop into the encircling membranes and other structures that will protect and nourish the embryo and provide for its respiration and elimination of wastes.

Further Embryonic Development

The early stages of embryonic development consist mainly of cell division. The cells that are formed by mitosis are all basically similar, but by the time the blastocyst is implanting itself in the endometrium, other changes are beginning to occur, and the first signs of differentiation appear. Growth is only part of the amazing nine-month transformation of zygote into baby. **Differentiation**—the gradual modification of cells and groups of cells for specific functions—is an even more important part of the story.

At about two weeks after fertilization, the developing blastocyst consists of a hollow ball of cells surrounding two cavities, separated by a double-layered plate of cells known as the **embryonic disk** (Figure 35-5). One cavity will become the **amniotic cavity,** which will surround the developing embryo and fetus with a cushion of shock-absorbing fluid. The other cavity is the primitive **yolk sac,** which is not as significant in humans as it is in lower vertebrates, such as birds and reptiles. Only the cells of the embryonic disk will actually form the embryo. One layer of cells is called the **ectoderm,** the other the **entoderm.** A third layer of cells, called **mesoderm,** develops between the ectoderm and entoderm. These three layers of cells are called the **primary germ layers;** each of them will give rise to definite structures in the developing body of

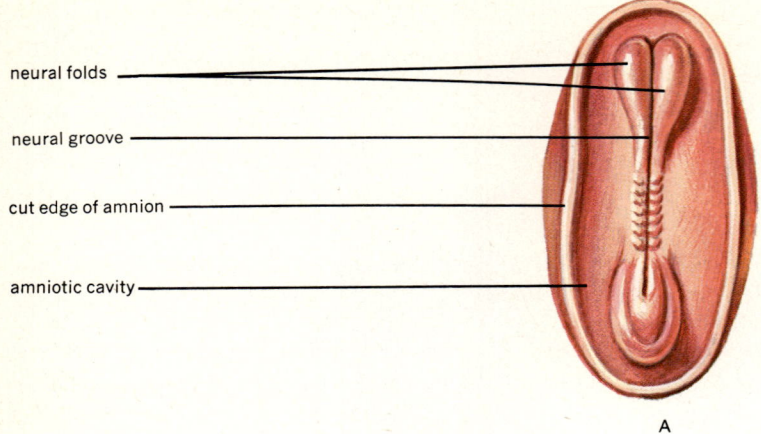

neural folds

neural groove

cut edge of amnion

amniotic cavity

A

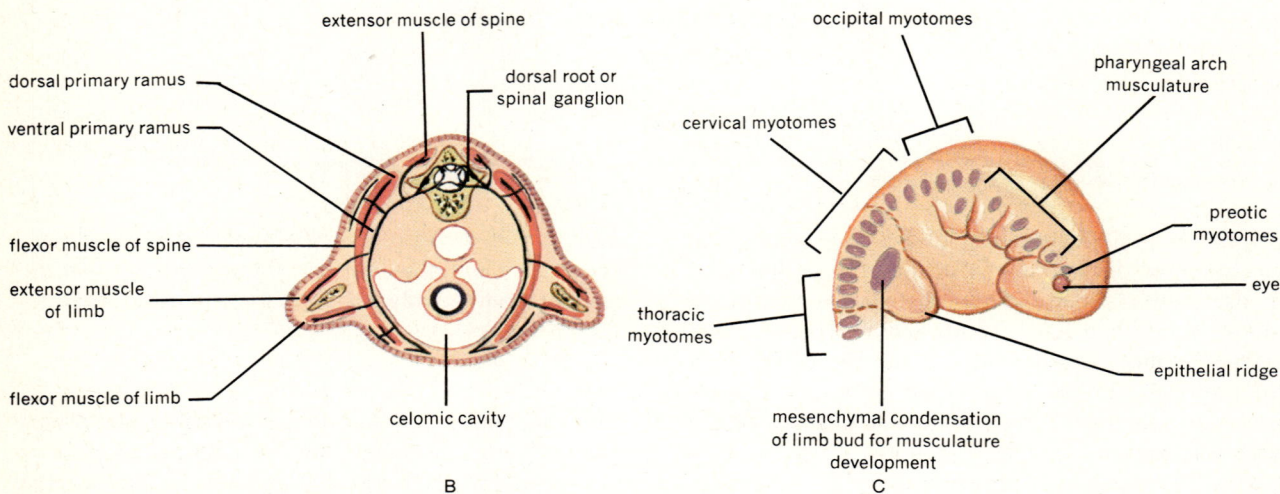

extensor muscle of spine

dorsal primary ramus

dorsal root or
spinal ganglion

ventral primary ramus

flexor muscle of spine

extensor muscle
of limb

flexor muscle of limb

celomic cavity

B

occipital myotomes

pharyngeal arch
musculature

cervical myotomes

preotic
myotomes

thoracic
myotomes

eye

epithelial ridge

mesenchymal condensation
of limb bud for musculature
development

C

FIGURE 35-5   Early embryonic development: (A) embryonic disk, showing neural folds and the neural groove; (B) limb bud stage (cross section through embryo); (C) longitudinal view of head, neck, and thorax of embryo at seven weeks.

the embryo. The ectoderm will develop into the epidermis and its appendages (nails, hair, etc.) and the nerve tissues. The entoderm will give rise to the epithelial lining of the digestive tract and the structures derived from it. A large proportion of the body—connective tissue, muscles, bone, and tissues of the blood and lymph vessels—will be derived from the mesoderm.

Gradually the embryonic disk begins to take on new shapes. A band of cells, called the **primitive streak,** forms in the posterior part of the longitudinal axis of the embryonic disk. In front of the primitive streak, cells multiply to form a knot or node, which will participate in the formation of the **notochord,** the foundation of the backbone.

The flat embryonic disk begins to be transformed into a cylinder. The portion near what will be the head grows more rapidly than the other portions and folds over, forming a cylinder with ectoderm on the

outside and entoderm on the inside. The cavity inside the cylinder will become the gastrointestinal tract.

Ectoderm along the midline of the embryonic disk thickens to form the **neural plate,** the lateral edges of which rise to form the longitudinal **neural folds** (see Figure 35-5). These folds fuse along the midline, forming the **neural tube,** from which the brain, spinal cord, neurohypophysis, retinas, and optic nerves will develop.

The embryo still does not look remotely like a human being at this point, but the basic systems of the body are developing. Toward the end of the third week, when the mother has just about realized that her menstrual period is overdue and may soon suffer the first symptoms of "morning sickness," the primitive heart of the embryo is already beginning to beat. At this time, the embryo itself is a little longer than 1.5 mm, or the height of the letter *e* in this sentence. A little over a week later, at about the end of a month, the embryo has spurted to about 5 mm in length. The heart is large in proportion to the size of the body and is now divided into four chambers. Around this time a pair of little buds appear on the sides of the body, followed in a day or two by another pair farther back from the already well-distinguished head region. In another day or two, eyes can be discerned. At about this time the embryo also has a prominent tail and gill pouches! By the sixth week, the embryo has grown to about 13 mm (about half an inch). The arms and legs have lengthened considerably, hands and feet can be distinguished, and the features of the face are beginning to emerge.

At the end of the second month, when the embryo is about an inch long, its face is definitely humanoid, with distinct eyes, ears, and nose (see Figure 35-8 on page 770). The embryo is now able to respond to stimuli, such as touch, by the contraction of voluntary muscles, and it is beginning to exhibit spontaneous movements. (But the embryo is still so tiny and weak that its mother cannot yet feel even the faintest flutters of movement within her womb. She will not feel the "quickening" of life until about the fourth or fifth month of pregnancy.) The tail of the embryo is disappearing, as the rapidly growing buttocks cover it. At this time the general plan of organs and organ systems has been essentially completed. Virtually all that remains is an increase in size and a "finishing off" of the details of development.

Toward the end of the third month, when the embryo is about three inches long, its sex can be distinguished, and now that it has all the basic human structures it is designated a fetus. Considering all the major developments that are crowded into the first few months of intrauterine life, it is not surprising that this period is particularly sensitive to all sorts of adverse influences upon the mother—effects of drugs (such as the infamous thalidomide), poor nutrition, and diseases such as German measles. Such influences may result in gross abnormalities or even death of the embryo.

The growing embryo is attached, first by a stalk and then by a ropelike umbilical cord, to the placenta, a structure formed jointly by the outer membranes encasing the embryo and the tissues of the mother's uterus. The embryo receives nourishment from the placenta via its umbilical "lifeline."

THE PLACENTA

If "test tubes babies" are ever to be a reality, the functions of the placenta will have to be carefully duplicated. This amazing organ provides for an exchange of materials between the embryonic and maternal bloodstreams, *without* any actual intermingling of blood from the mother and embryo. Oxygen and nutrients are supplied to the embryo, and its waste products are removed, to be disposed of by the mother's excretory system.

Shortly after the blastocyst burrows into the uterine lining, the placenta begins to form. Villi from the chorion, the outermost membrane surrounding the embryo, penetrate into the decidua basalis (the portion of the endometrium beneath the implanted embryo). The villi enlarge, multiply, and branch, and capillaries from the embryonic vascular system grow into them, as extensions of the umbilical arteries and vein. Meanwhile, in the decidua basalis, sinuses form around the chorionic villi and fill with maternal blood. Thus, the villi are bathed in maternal blood, and a variety of gases and nutrients can diffuse freely across the membranes separating them. (The mature placenta has a total surface area of about 16 square meters.) Hormones and antibodies also pass through the placental barrier, perhaps by pinocytosis. The fetus thus receives a supply of antibodies that its mother's body has manufactured against various disease pathogens, such as the germs of smallpox, diphtheria, scarlet fever, measles, and polio. These antibodies will provide temporary protection in the first few months after birth, before the infant's own immunological system has begun to work properly. The placental barrier normally bars the passage of bacteria, but viruses and syphilis spirochetes can slip through and affect the fetus. Drugs taken by the mother can also pass through the barrier.

When it is fully formed, the placenta is a sizeable structure (Figure 35-6): a circular disc 8 inches in diameter and nearly an inch thick, taking up a quarter to a half of the inner surface of the uterus and weighing about 1 pound. After the birth of the fetus, the placenta becomes detached from the uterus and is

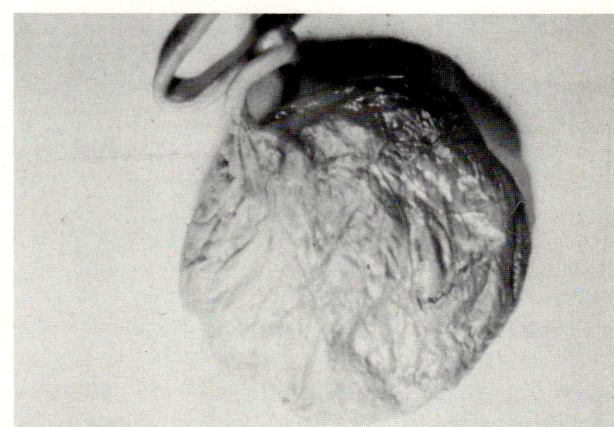

FIGURE 35-6 **The afterbirth: placenta shown from the fetal surface, with umbilical cord attached.**

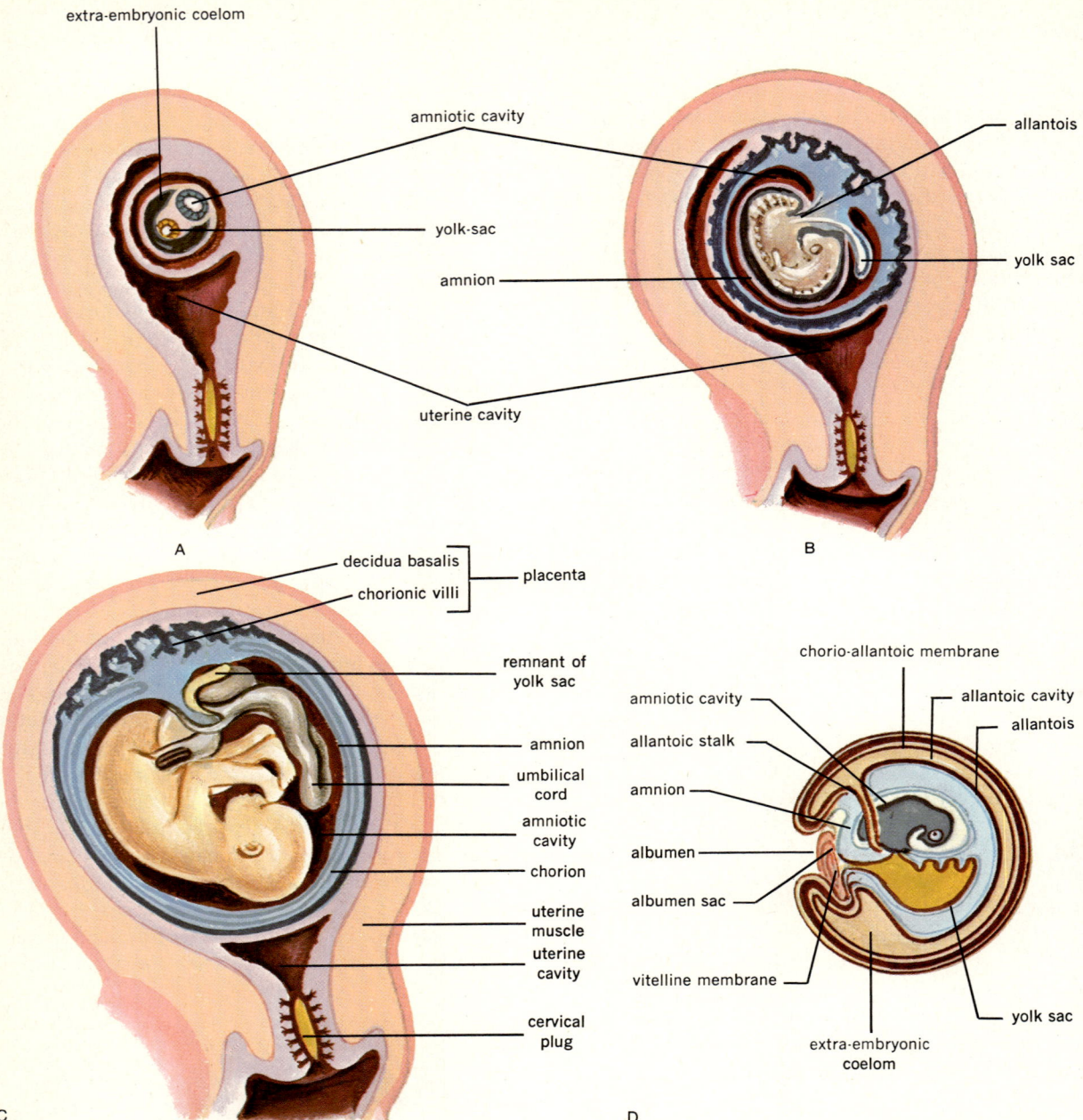

FIGURE 35-7 Development of the human embryo and its extraembryonic membranes (A,B,C); note the difference in relative size of the yolk sac and allantois of a developing chick (D). The chick utilizes the yolk as a source of nutrients throughout development, and the allantois is a receptacle for its urinary wastes; the fused chorioallantoic membrane is a site of gas exchange. In the developing human, the functions of food supply, gas exchange, and waste removal are performed by the placenta. The yolk sac is insignificant, and the remnants of the allantois are incorporated into the umbilical cord.

expelled by a series of uterine contractions. It is commonly called the "afterbirth."

In addition to its life-support functions for the fetus, the placenta is an important endocrine organ. During the early months of pregnancy, the placenta secretes chorionic gonadotropins, which maintain the corpus luteum until the placenta is secreting enough female sex hormones on its own. The chorionic gonadotropin level peaks at about the third month and then rapidly decreases. Meanwhile, the levels of estrogen and progesterone secreted by the placenta rise steadily until the time of birth.

EXTRAEMBRYONIC MEMBRANES

Before birth, every human being is a water animal, floating in a chamber entirely filled with fluid. This fluid is called **amniotic fluid,** since it is contained within a membrane called the **amnion.** The amnion is a thin, tough, transparent membrane, derived from the inner layer of the trophoblast, reinforced with mesoderm. At first it is a small sac with a cavity covering only the dorsal part of the embryo, but gradually it enlarges to surround the embryo completely and continues to grow as the embryo grows (Figure 35-7). The amniotic fluid is isotonic and protects the embryo and fetus from mechanical shocks and jars, temperature fluctuations, and other influences of the outside environment.

The **chorion,** the outermost membrane surrounding the embryo, is relatively thick; its villi aid in the nutrition and excretion of the embryo. Like the amnion, the chorion is derived from the trophoblast portion of the blastocyst.

A third extraembryonic membrane, the **allantois,** is derived from the digestive tract of the embryo. In egg-laying animals, the allantois is a large sac that serves as a receptacle for wastes and functions as a breathing organ. In the early human embryo, the allantois aids in the excretion of wastes, but by the fourth month only remnants of it are left. The main significance of the allantois in human development is that it becomes incorporated into the umbilical cord, and its blood vessels become the two umbilical arteries and the umbilical vein.

The **yolk sac** is a fourth extraembryonic membrane that is far more important in egg-laying animals than in humans. It is a dilation of the primitive gut, and its blood vessels aid in the early nutrition of the embryo. (Unlike the eggs of birds and reptiles, the human egg does not have a store of yolk as a major food supply.) The yolk sac of the human embryo soon degenerates, and its remnants are incorporated into the umbilical cord.

The **umbilical cord** is formed during the sixth week of development, by a wrapping of amnion around the remnants of the yolk sac, the body stalk, and the allantois. This lifeline, which connects the abdomen of the fetus to the placenta, grows to about 23 inches long and half an inch in diameter and contains a large umbilical vein with two umbilical arteries wrapped around it in a spiral. At birth, after the placenta is expelled from the uterus, the umbilical cord is ligated and cut a short distance from its attachment to the infant's abdomen. With the umbilical supply lines cut, the infant's circulatory system undergoes the major reorganizations that were described in Chapter 21, and the umbilical cord itself shrivels and drops off after a few days. The scar that remains is the **umbilicus,** or "belly button."

THE FETAL PERIOD

By the time the developing embryo enters the fetal period, which is often considered to date from the beginning of the third month of development, it is already beginning to look like a miniature human (Figure 35-8). It is still tiny—perhaps 5 cm long—but it already has the footprints and fingerprints it will carry for life, eyelids that close over its eyes, and tiny fingernails beginning to grow. Differences between male and female sex organs can now be distinguished externally. The head of the fetus is quite large in proportion to its body, about half the total length from crown to rump. Spontaneous movements occur, and reflexes such as squinting and gripping are becoming established.

During the third month, the growth of the trunk and limbs is more rapid than that of the head. The eyes, which until this time looked laterally (as in most animals), now are on the ventral aspect of the face, and the ears reach their final position. The two halves of the palate fuse together, the vocal cords are completed, and bone begins to form in centers throughout the body. The external genitalia have developed, and germ cells are present. By the end of the third month, the fetus still weighs less than an ounce, but it can swallow, frown, and withdraw its leg if its foot is tickled; it urinates into the amniotic fluid and can digest any fluid that is swallowed.

During the fourth month, the fetus acquires a truly human appearance. Its eyes, ears, nose, and mouth are well formed. Hair begins to grow on its head, and eyelashes and eyebrows appear. Its fingernails harden, and nipples appear. At this stage the fetal heartbeat can be heard with a stethoscope applied to the mother's abdomen, and the mother may be beginning to feel faint flutterings of movement. The fetus is lengthening rapidly—by the end of the fourth month, its total length reaches about 23 cm (9 inches), and its head is only about a third of the crown-to-rump length.

In the fifth month, the entire body of the fetus becomes covered with a coat of fine hair called **lanugo.** Its face is red and wrinkled, and its eyelids open and close. Bone marrow develops. The fetus grows to about 30 cm (12 inches) in total length, and weighs more than a pound.

By the end of the sixth month, the fetus has completed the second trimester (third) of its development. It is now about 14 inches long, and weighs more than two and a half pounds. It may have a full head of hair, but the lanugo has largely disappeared. Its body, though still wrinkled, has advanced further toward infant proportions. It may frequently suck its thumb. The fetus is now reaching a critical stage. If it were born prematurely at the end of the sixth month, even with modern techniques of incubator care, it might not survive for more than a few hours. But by the twenty-eighth week the surface-active agent in the liquid film lining the alveoli of the lungs is formed, and this seems to be the turning point: a fetus born at

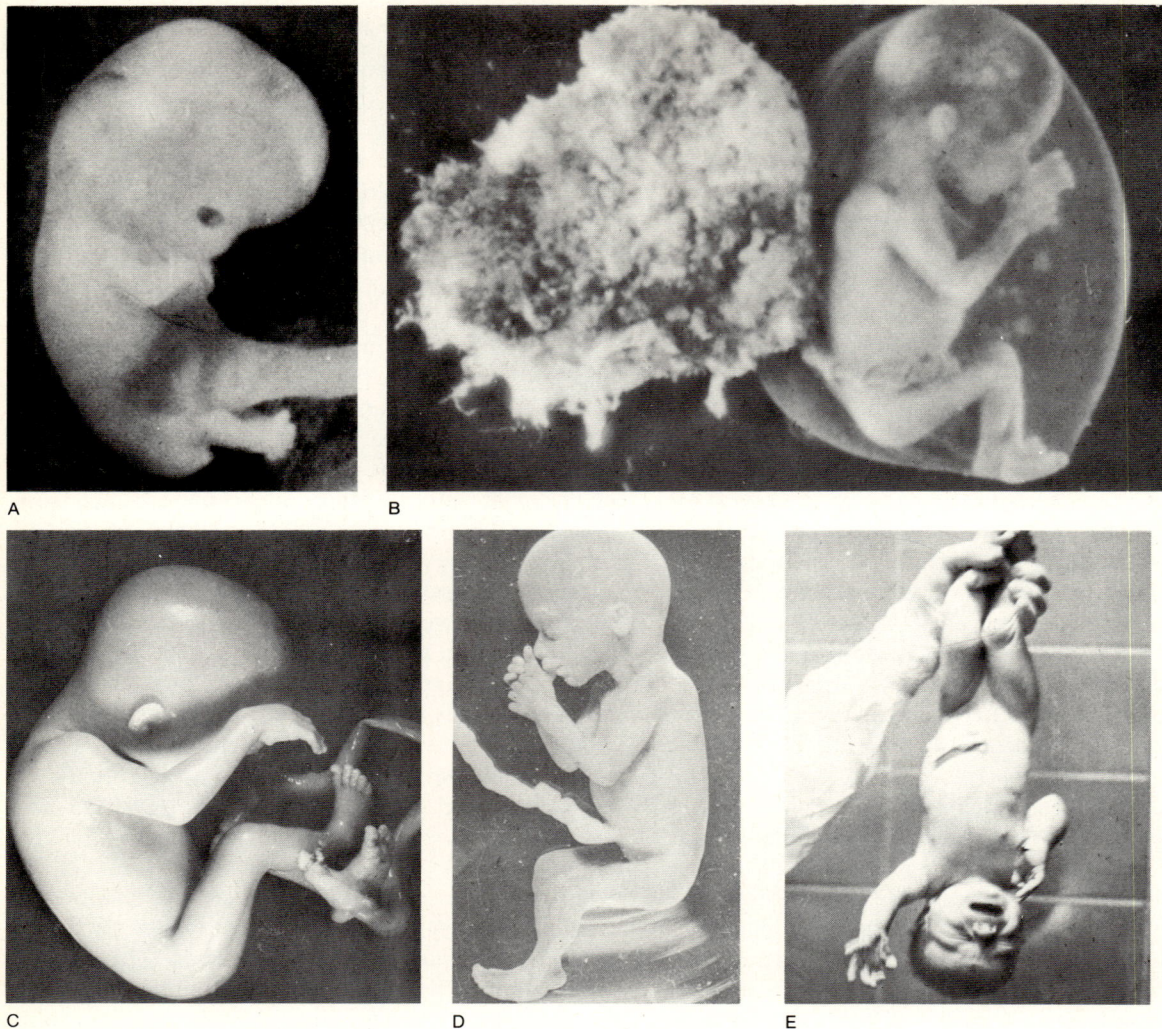

FIGURE 35-8   Human fetal development: (A) 8 weeks. Note the vestige of a tail. **(B) 10 weeks.** In the amniotic sac. **(C) 18 weeks.** Unmistakably human and beginning to make its movements felt. **(D) 28 weeks.** Old enough for a chance at survival if born prematurely. **(E) Birth at term.** The end and the beginning.

this time, usually weighing about three pounds or so, may survive with proper care and develop into a normal adult.

The final three months of pregnancy are a "finishing off" period. The wrinkled skin of the fetus is firmed out as subcutaneous fat deposits are laid down. In males, the testes descend into the scrotum during the eighth month. The fetus sleeps and wakes up, kicks, startles, and sucks its thumb. It may turn many times before settling down into the head-down position in which it will be propelled into the world. If born prematurely during the eighth month, the fetus can usually survive without incubation or special care. At the end of the ninth month (actually a little short of nine full months—approximately 266 days from conception), the fetus has reached full term. It weighs about seven pounds, measures about 20 inches long, and is ready to be born.

CHANGES IN THE MOTHER DURING PREGNANCY

A continuing debate is raging over whether it is legal and fair to restrict a pregnant woman from working in various occupations during the late stages of pregnancy. There is considerable disagreement among legislators, business executives, physicians, and working women about just how incapacitating the condition of pregnancy is and how much protection a pregnant woman requires. There are definite changes in the maternal body during pregnancy (Figure 35-9).

One of the first signs of pregnancy is an enlargement of the breasts. They will continue to grow during the pregnancy, gaining a pound or more in weight, and may become engorged and painful. The nipples become enlarged, erect, and acquire a deep pigmentation.

By the fourth month, the expanding uterus can no

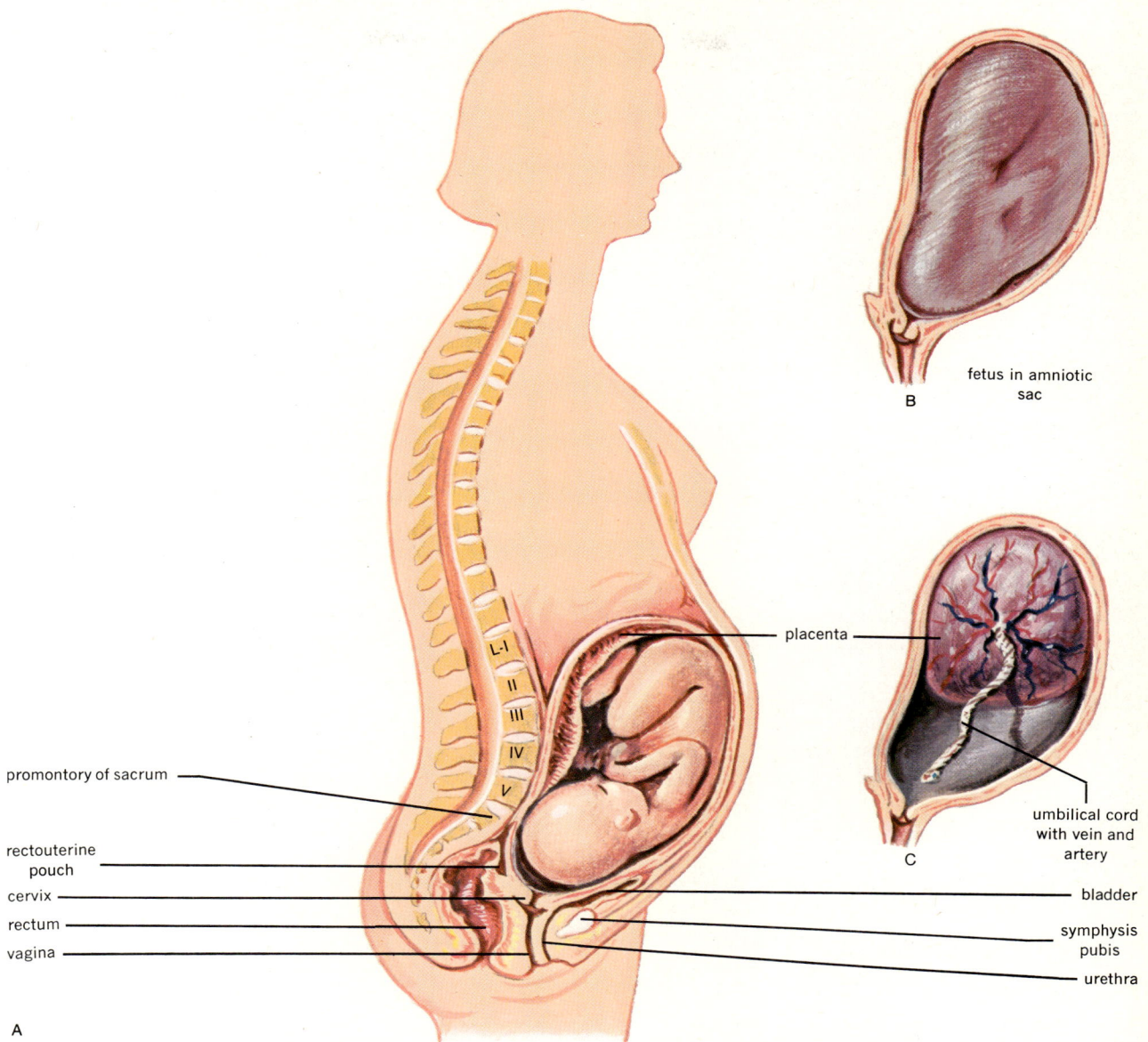

promontory of sacrum

rectouterine pouch

cervix

rectum

vagina

A

placenta

fetus in amniotic sac

B

umbilical cord with vein and artery

C

bladder

symphysis pubis

urethra

L-I

II

III

IV

V

FIGURE 35-9   (A) Pregnant woman, mid-sagittal section; (B) fetus in amniotic sac; (C) placenta in the uterus with fetus removed.

longer fit into the pelvic cavity and expands upward into the abdominal cavity. The anterior abdominal wall becomes stretched and protrudes progressively as the uterus continues to expand. The resultant shift of the center of gravity requires compensation, and the mother may lean backward when she stands and walks. (High-heeled shoes, which tend to throw the body forward, require even greater compensation during pregnancy.)

During the early months of pregnancy, there may be little or no weight gain, or even a loss of weight if the nausea and vomiting of morning sickness are severe. But morning sickness usually disappears after the third month, and a steady weight gain ensues,

amounting to an average of about 20 to 25 pounds. Obstetrical fashions have fluctuated; at one time doctors had their pregnant patients watch their diet strictly to limit the weight gain to 14 pounds or less. Now it is felt that if the weight gain is that small the fetus may not be well enough nourished; but weight gains much in excess of 25 pounds usually mean that the mother is overeating and laying down deposits of adipose tissue. The fetus at term accounts for only a portion of the mother's total weight gain. The amniotic fluid and membranes account for perhaps two-thirds of the weight of the fetus. The enlargement of the uterus and breasts contribute to the weight gain, and a substantial fraction is due to retention of fluid, probably as a result of the increased levels of steroid hormones during pregnancy. After birth, when the hormone levels drop, an increased urine output rapidly returns the body fluid to normal values.

By the end of pregnancy, the mother's blood volume is about 30 percent greater than normal, and her cardiac output is correspondingly increased. Her blood pressure may tend to rise, and should be checked regularly. Respiration is increased, due to the increased size and speeded-up metabolism, but pressure of the uterus on the diaphragm decreases the vital capacity. Feelings of dyspnea may be experienced. The thyroid and parathyroid glands become hyperactive, producing an increased mobilization of calcium and phosphorus for the needs of the fetus. The diet must be adequate to meet the increased demands for these minerals, as well as nitrogen, iron, and other substances; otherwise the mother's body will suffer, since the fetus has first call on the available resources.

The pregnant woman must not only eat for two, but also excrete for two. The kidneys increase their activity to excrete the increased amounts of nitrogenous wastes. Pressure of the uterus on the bladder may produce a frequent need to urinate. Fluid retention may cause the feet and ankles to swell, and the face and eyes may become puffy.

Drugs, alcohol, and other substances taken in by the mother (including the nicotine and other substances in cigarette smoke) can pass through the placental barrier and affect the fetus. But tales of frightening events experienced by the mother producing birthmarks on the child or esthetic experiences of the mother developing the child's musical or artistic talent are merely tales and have no basis in fact.

PARTURITION (CHILDBIRTH)

One of the newest exploratory trends in obstetrics is a return to a more "natural" childbirth, in which the mother gives birth to her child without the sedation, bright lights, stirrups, and other paraphernalia of the modern hospital delivery room. This approach, pioneered in France, is an effort to reduce the physical and emotional trauma associated with each human being's entry into the world. Yet birth inevitably brings a certain amount of trauma. Picture the fetus, sheltered inside its mother's womb. For nine months it has rested in gently supporting fluids. No sharp chills or sudden flushes disturb its equanimity. Darkness reigns. Sounds are muted, and shocks and pressures are dissipated by the surrounding fluid. It moves and stretches, grasping with a hand, kicking a leg, sucking a thumb that chances to find its mouth. Toward the end of its stay, conditions have become increasingly crowded as it nearly fills the confining uterine cavity. But life is serene and undemanding.

This serenity comes to an abrupt end for the fetus when the very walls of its world begin to heave and contract. At first the contractions are mild and infrequent. Then they become progressively more frequent and severe, culminating at least in a series of violent upheavals which forcibly propel the infant out into a world of light, noise, and endless problems. The warm, sheltering environment is suddenly replaced by a strange, thin medium: air. At the same time the oxygen supply from the mother is cut off. With a convulsive gasp the infant draws in this strange new mixture of gases and fills its lungs for the first time. Intricate and vital changes now occur within the circulatory system of the newborn, as the old pathways of circulation through the umbilical cord are shut off, the arc of pulmonary circulation is established as a major link, and the heart must adjust itself to the new blood flows. With the temperature shield removed, the infant's body must learn to operate its system of thermostatic controls. At first this is rather erratic, but it improves with time.

After nine months of comparative calm, what precipitates this sudden upheaval? It is thought that mechanical and hormonal influences are interlinked into a positive feedback mechanism which, at the appropriate time, suddenly precipitates the violent expulsion of the fetus from the mother's body. During pregnancy, the levels of **estrogen** and **progesterone,** secreted by the placenta, rise steadily. Progesterone inhibits uterine contractions, and thus helps to maintain the pregnancy, while estrogens tend to increase the contractility of the myometrium. In the last few months of pregnancy, the estrogen levels rise more rapidly than the progesterone level, and signs of heightened myometrial irritability become increasingly evident as the term of pregnancy approaches. (Normally **parturition,** or childbirth, occurs around the 280th day after the onset of the last menstrual period, or about 266 days after conception.) Meanwhile, the fetus has been growing larger and increasingly pressing on the walls of the uterus and stretching the cervix with its head. At some point the pressure and stretching, combined with the influence of estrogens, become sufficient to excite reflex contractions in the body of the uterus. Stretching and irritation of the cervix produce a reflex stimulation of the neurohypophysis, causing the hormone **oxytocin** to be secreted. The muscular wall of the uterus responds to this hormone with vigorous contractions, initiating the process of **labor** that will result in the expulsion of the fetus.

A vaginal discharge of blood-tinged mucus, referred to as "show," is a common sign of impending labor. It represents the mucous plug that had filled

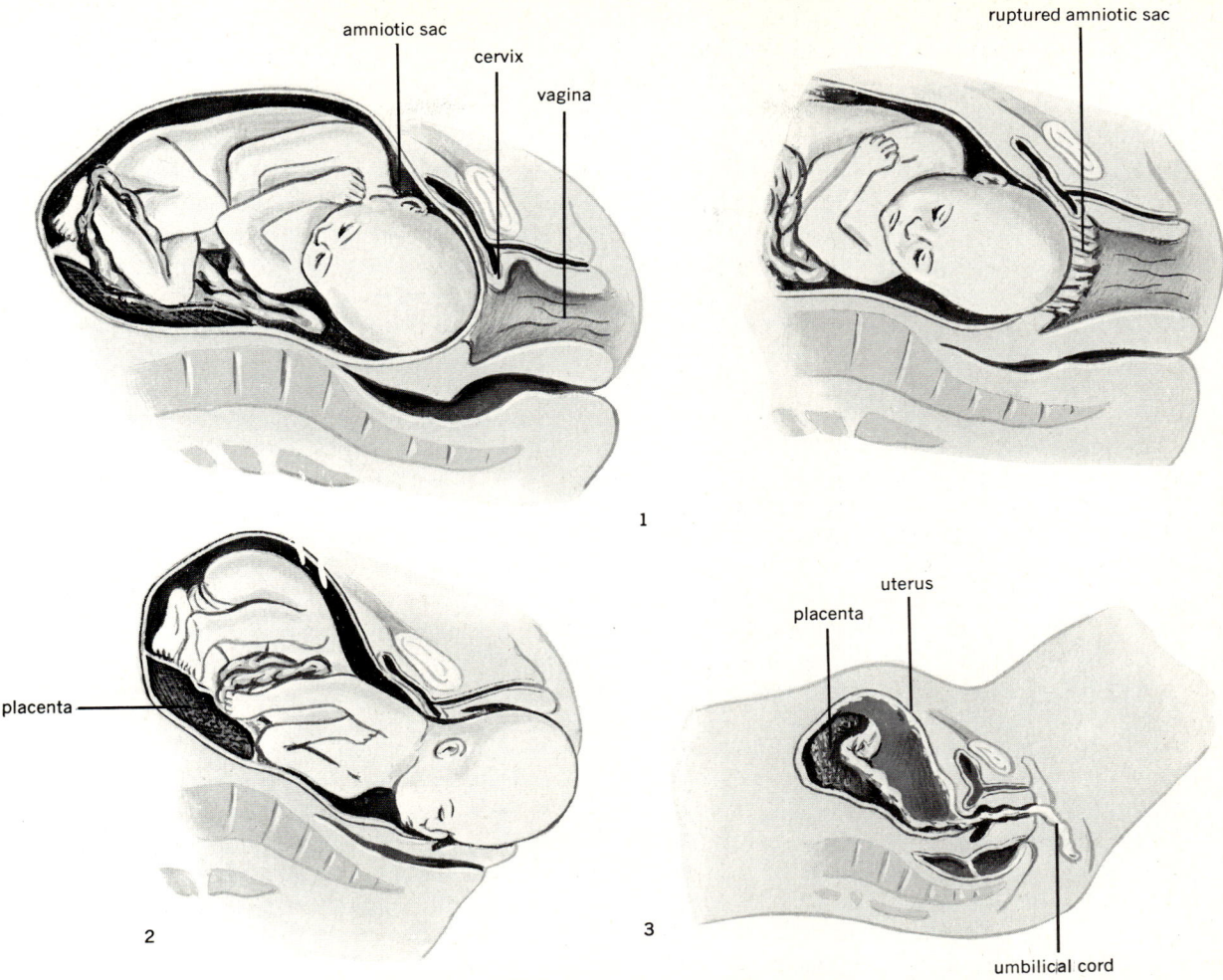

FIGURE 35-10 Parturition: position of the fetus before birth and the three stages of labor: (1) dilation of cervix and rupture of amniotic sac; (2) delivery; (3) expulsion of the placenta.

the cervical canal during pregnancy. Labor itself, which usually follows within 24 hours, is commonly divided into three stages (Figure 35-10). In the **first stage of labor**, regular contractions of the uterus gradually move the fetus downward (usually head first) toward the cervix. At the same time, the cervix softens and dilates, and the pubic ligaments relax, permitting the head of the fetus to move into the birth canal. These effects are believed to be produced by estrogens and progesterone; the ovarian hormone relaxin may also play a role. Cervical dilation continues until the opening is about 10 cm across, large enough to permit the passage of the baby's head (which at this point of its development has the greatest circumference of any part of its body). The amnion, stretched by the downward movement of the fetus, finally bursts, sending a flood of amniotic fluid streaming out through the birth canal.

The **second stage of labor** extends from the time of complete dilation of the cervix to the delivery of the baby. Uterine contractions become more and more frequent and severe, propelling the fetus out through the birth canal. The mother may be asked at this stage to assist the process by "bearing down," tensing her abdominal muscles as though she were attempting to defecate.

The entire process, from the first "labor pain" to the emergence of the infant from the greatly dilated opening of the vagina, usually lasts from 8 to 24 hours in a first pregnancy. In subsequent pregnancies the time of labor is usually shorter; sometimes the actual labor pains may last only minutes.

The emergence of the baby does not quite complete the process of birth. In the **third stage of labor,** which follows a brief lull after the birth of the baby, the uterus resumes its contractions, expelling the placenta (the "afterbirth") and constricting the uterine blood vessels, preventing hemorrhage. This stage normally takes from 10 to 45 minutes.

LACTATION

Breast feeding has largely gone "out of style," not only in the affluent countries, but indeed throughout the world. The substitution of bottle for breast may make women less "tied down" after the birth of the baby, but it has unfortunate physiological and psychological effects for both mother and child. The suckling of the child stimulates the secretion of oxytocin, which produces uterine contractions that bring the postpartum uterus back to its nonpregnant size and tone far more rapidly than when the mother does not breastfeed her child. The close body contact that is automatically provided during breastfeeding is emotionally rewarding for both mother and child and is believed by many psychologists to lay the foundation for greater emotional stability in the child's later life. (Cuddling and fondling can also be provided during bottle feeding, but it is often a temptation to prop the bottle and make the feeding a more impersonal activity.) In addition, mother's milk provides benefits for the child that cannot be provided as well by cow's milk. Cow's milk may indeed be "nature's most perfect food"—for calves, but there are considerable differences between cow's milk and human milk. Human milk contains about 50 percent more lactose than cow's milk, while cow's milk contains more than twice as much protein as human milk. (Calves grow faster than human babies.) Hence, in preparing formula for human infants from cow's milk, the milk must be diluted with water to lower the protein content, and sugar is frequently added. Despite the lower protein content, human milk has significantly higher levels of the amino acid cystine, necessary for the development of the central nervous system, and taurine, an amino acid important in the transmission of nerve impulses. Human milk has a larger variety and amount of nucleotides than cow's milk. The level of fats in human milk is also higher; its fatty acid composition parallels that of human brain tissue, and the abundant cholesterol in human milk contributes to the development of nerve tissue. It has also been suggested that early exposure to cholesterol makes the body better able to handle it later in life. Cow's milk has a higher ash (mineral) content than human milk, but it is deficient in certain nutrients that are adequately supplied by human milk: for example, iron and vitamins C and D. Modern bottle-fed babies are more likely to suffer from obesity at all stages of life than breast-fed babies, and some studies indicate that bottle-feeding may increase the vulnerability to heart disease in later life.

Curiously enough, the human breasts do not produce true milk until two or three days after birth. During pregnancy the secretion of prolactin by the anterior pituitary and the production of milk by the breasts are inhibited by the high levels of estrogens and progesterone in the blood. After parturition, the levels of sex hormones drop and the feedback inhibition is lifted. Prolactin secretion increases rapidly, but it takes a couple of days for a copious milk production to become established. The baby does not go completely unrewarded for its early efforts, however. During the first few days after birth, the breasts secrete a few milliliters of a watery, yellowish fluid called **colostrum,** which contains basically the same amounts of protein and lactose as milk, but almost no fat. Colostrum is rich in antibodies to diseases to which the mother is immune.

Milk is secreted continuously into the alveoli of the breasts, but it does not flow readily into the ducts. The release of milk from the nipples requires the action of another hormone, oxytocin, which produces a "let-down" or ejection response. Suckling by the infant stimulates sensory neurons that carry impulses to the hypothalamus, triggering a reflex secretion of oxytocin. Emotional factors can also stimulate—or inhibit—this "let-down" reflex and may play a major role in many instances of failure to breast feed. The continual removal of milk from the breasts stimulates a continued secretion of prolactin, which in turn maintains milk secretion in a positive feedback mechanism. (If breast feeding is stopped, the breasts stop secreting milk within a week or two.) With continued stimulation, a woman can continue to produce milk for several years, although the rate of secretion usually decreases markedly after 7 to 9 months. During the period of maximum secretion, the daily output of milk is usually about 1 liter, although with greater demand (e.g., if the mother is nursing twins) it can be increased to 2 to 3 liters.

CONGENITAL ABNORMALITIES

One of the first things a mother usually asks about her newborn baby is, "Is it all right? Does it have all its fingers and toes?" For nearly nine months she has wondered and worried about the "surprise package" growing inside her abdomen, speculating on the possibility that it may turn out to be malformed in some way. Her fears are not entirely groundless. About two children in every hundred are born with some severe and obvious malformation (Figure 35-11). Another three or so are born with less severe defects, or defects that do not show up until some time after birth.

Birth defects may affect various systems of the body, depending on the developmental stage at which the injurious influence—perhaps a defective gene, a

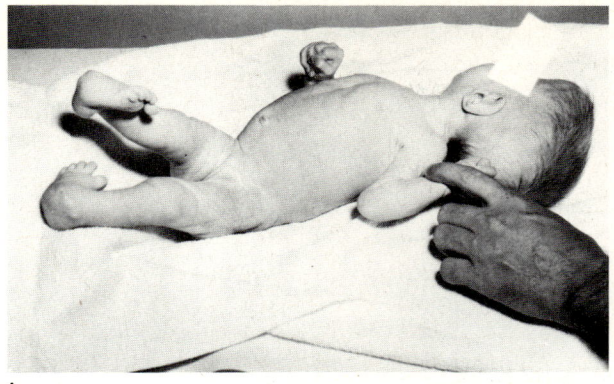

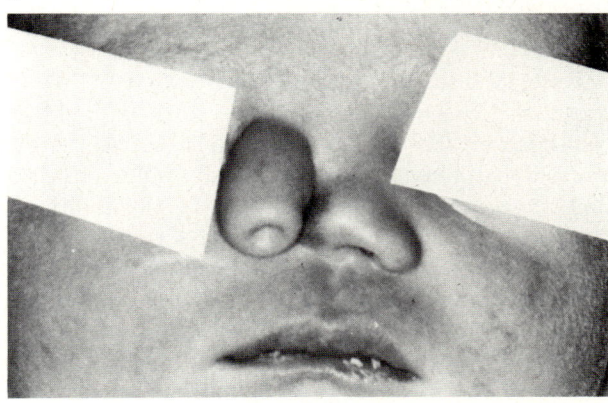

FIGURE 35-11   Birth defects: congenital clubfoot (A), cleft nose (B).

disease such as German measles, or a drug such as thalidomide—acted on the fetus. Malformations of the nervous system include mental retardation, anencephaly (absence of a major portion of brain tissue), spina bifida (a malformation at the base of the spinal cord), and hydrocephalus ("water on the brain"). Children may be born with heart and circulatory defects, including holes in the heart wall and malformed valves or major blood vessels. Harelip and cleft palate are common birth defects; clubfoot (talipes), congenital dislocation of the hip, and extra fingers or toes may also be observed. Pyloric stenosis, a blockage of the stomach outlet, is fatal without surgical correction. Congenital cataracts and congenital deafness frequently follow German measles suffered by the mother during the first three months of pregnancy. Often several different birth defects occur in the same child.

Some congenital abnormalities are due entirely to environmental factors, such as drugs taken by the mother. An influence that causes birth defects when it acts on the mother during pregnancy is referred to as a **teratogen.** After the thalidomide tragedy, physicians became much more cautious about prescribing *any*

drugs for a pregnant woman, especially during the first three months of pregnancy, when major organ systems are developing. New drugs are routinely screened for teratogenic potential, and old drugs have been reexamined. Antibiotics such as tetracyclines and antinomycin can cause deafness, growth retardation, and other fetal abnormalities; even aspirin has been implicated in some birth defects. Smoking, heavy drinking, and the abuse of drugs such as LSD can also adversely affect the developing embryo or fetus. (Smoking produces vasoconstriction in the mother's body, which cuts down the oxygen and nutrients delivered by her blood to the fetus. Nicotine passing through the placental barrier also produces direct effects on the fetus, such as a speedup of the fetal heart rate immediately detectible when the mother smokes a cigarette. Babies of heavy-smoking mothers are more likely than average to be born prematurely and to have a low birth weight, which is often associated with developmental defects.)

Other environmental factors that can affect embryonic and fetal development are maternal diseases such as rubella (German measles), herpes, and syphilis, as well as radiations—routine chest X rays in early pregnancy are *not* advisable, and even dental X rays should not be taken unless the abdomen is protected with a lead apron.

Some birth defects have a genetic cause. For example, Down's syndrome, characterized by a "mongoloid" appearance of the eyes, mental retardation, and often abnormalities of the internal organs, has been found to be linked with the presence of an extra chromosome 21, due to nondisjunction. Probably most congenital malformations are produced by a combination of genetic and environmental influences.

Fortunately for the peace of mind of prospective parents, the techniques of **amniocentesis,** in which a sample of amniotic fluid is withdrawn and examined, can detect a number of serious fetal abnormalities such as Down's syndrome early enough so that the parents can, if they wish, have the defective fetus aborted and try again to conceive a normal child. Amniocentesis is usually used in high-risk groups, such as expectant mothers in their forties, who have a much higher probability of producing a Down's child. In practice, this procedure has saved the lives of many more fetuses than it has caused to be aborted, since in the majority of cases the results show that the fetus is normal.

TWINS AND MULTIPLE BIRTHS

The armadillo invariably gives birth to four identical offspring. In humans, multiple births are a far rarer event. It has been calculated that twins occur in approximately one out of 88 births, triplets in one out of

FIGURE 35-12 Identical twins—two individuals from a single zygote.

88 × 88 births, quadruplets in one out of 88 × 88 × 88 births, and so forth. (These odds have been changed dramatically by the use of fertility drugs such as Perganol, which may stimulate the simultaneous maturation of several ova, resulting in multiple births.)

There are two different types of twins (or higher multiples). If the cell mass of the developing embryo somehow becomes separated into two parts during one of the earliest divisions of cleavage, before the individual cells have begun to differentiate, each part can develop into a complete human being. Both were formed from the same zygote and have exactly the same heredity; hence twins produced in this way are **identical** or **monozygotic twins** (Figure 35-12). If two or more ova mature at the same time and each is fertilized by a different sperm, the resultant twins are **fraternal** or **dizygotic twins.** They resemble one another no more than siblings conceived and born in the more usual manner, one at a time. Twins of opposite sex are always fraternal, rather than identical.

Multiple births place a greater stress on both mother and fetuses. Nutrition of the fetuses is poorer, crowding may produce various abnormalities, and because of the large combined weight and mass of the growing fetuses, they are commonly born prematurely. (The Anderson quintuplets, one of the recent multiple births, were born two months before term and were all under three pounds. Although all the infants survived with incubator care, the most stressed quint had severe heart defects that had to be repaired surgically.) The record for human multiple births is nine (a Perganol case); none of the babies survived.

PRACTICAL CONSIDERATIONS

The widespread use of birth control pills as a contraceptive has led to a pervasive change in sexual mores, which in turn has produced two epidemics among young people: venereal disease and—paradoxically—illegitimate pregnancies.

Venereal diseases are caused by a variety of microorganisms; their only similarity is in their mode of transmission: through sexual contacts such as kissing and sexual intercourse. (The latest studies indicate that there may be some truth to the possibility of contracting a venereal disease from a contaminated toilet seat or other article, but such cases are rare.)

One common type of venereal disease, **syphilis,** is caused by a corkscrew-shaped microorganism, *Treponema pallidum* (Figure 35-13A). This spirochete penetrates the skin or mucous membrane and enters the bloodstream and tissues. A few weeks after infection, the characteristic sore or "hard chancre" commonly appears on the genitals or in the mouth. During this primary stage of syphilis, the fluid in the chancre is extremely infectious. Even if no treatment is given, the chancres usually disappear spontaneously after 10 to 40 days; two to six months later the secondary stage appears, characterized by small raised red areas on the skin or mucous patches in the mouth or reproductive organs. The lesions of secondary syphilis also heal spontaneously, but the infection has merely gone underground. At some later time, possibly delayed by many years, the tertiary stage of syphilis develops. Draining sores appear on the skin, nodules appear in the subcutaneous tissue; the heart and blood vessels, lungs, and central nervous system may be badly damaged. Deterioration of mental faculties (paresis) and paralysis of limbs result. Untreated syphilis in a pregnant woman can affect her unborn child, producing abortion, stillbirth, or an infant with an advanced tertiary stage of infection. Fortunately, antibiotics such as penicillin are highly effective in treating syphilis. Blood tests called the Wasserman test and VDRL (Venereal Disease Research Lab) test are used to detect syphilitic infection and are commonly required as part of the procedure for obtaining a marriage license.

Gonorrhea is an even more common venereal disease than syphilis. This is a pus-producing inflammation of the genital mucosa, caused by a bacterium,

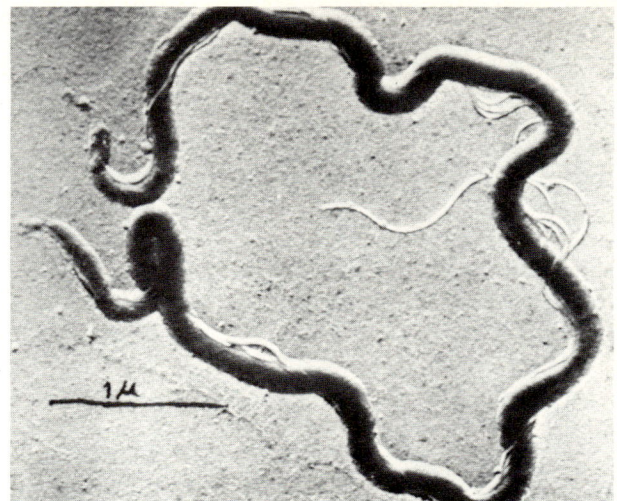

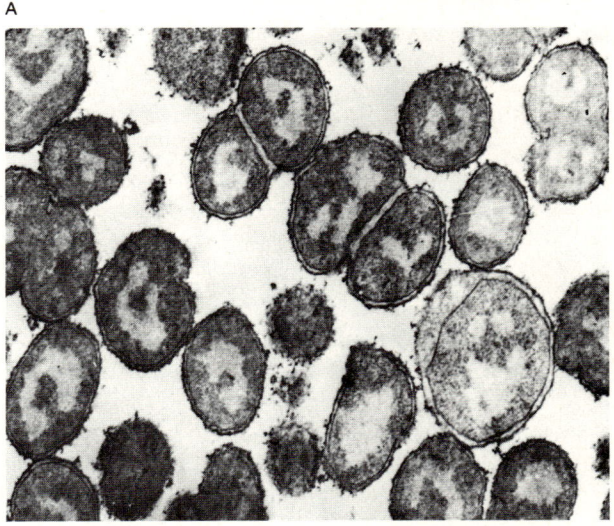

FIGURE 35-13 Venereal disease pathogens: (A) *Treponema pallidum,* the syphilis spirochete, and (B) *Neisseria gonorrhoeae,* the gonococcus.

Neisseria gonorrhoeae (Figure 35-13B), commonly called the gonococcus. If untreated, the infection can spread through the reproductive tract, causing sterility by sealing off the tubes that carry sperm or ova. Other complications include inflammations of the bladder, rectum, mouth, joints, kidneys, bones, heart valves, meninges, and peritoneum. Although the gonococcus cannot pass through the placental barrier, infection of the infant may occur during its passage through the infected birth canal. At one time, nearly a third of all cases of blindness in children were due to gonorrheal infection of the eyes at birth; now silver nitrate or an antibiotic solution is routinely dropped into the eyes of newborn infants to prevent possible infection. Various antibiotics and sulfonamides are used in the treatment of gonorrhea, but careful supervision by a physician is required, since an apparent cure may leave the patient still capable of transmitting the infection, and penicillin treatments may cure gonorrhea while masking an unsuspected case of syphilis (which requires larger doses of the drug for a cure). Recently physicians have been concerned by reports of penicillin-resistant strains of gonorrhea pathogens, which must be treated with other, more expensive antibiotics. Meanwhile, there have been promising reports on progress in research on the development of vaccines to provide immunity against syphilis and gonorrhea. (An actual case of the disease, even if successfully treated, does not confer any lasting immunity to the pathogens, and thus the same person may become infected repeatedly, especially if sexual partners are not also examined and treated when a case of VD is discovered.)

Another venereal disease that is causing growing concern is a viral disease, referred to as **herpes simplex virus Type 2.** Similar to the herpes simplex virus Type 1 that produces cold sores, eye infections, and superficial skin disorders on the upper body, the venereal herpes produces painful blisters on the reproductive organs. The lesions heal, but can recur periodically for years. It is believed that herpes simplex virus Type 2 is the second most common venereal disease, a disturbing statistic since the virus has been found to produce serious malformations of children born to infected mothers and has also been implicated as a causative agent in cervical cancer.

The other major side effect of early or promiscuous sexual activity, illegitimate pregnancy, may be the result of failure of contraceptive techniques (even the best forms of contraception are not 100 percent effective) or simply a neglect to use them.

For most women, pregnancy has a smooth and relatively uneventful course. But a variety of complications can occur.

Ectopic Pregnancy   Considering the path the ovum must travel before and after fertilization, it seems amazing that it nearly always reaches the uterus and implants in the normal place. However, exceptions do occasionally occur. When implantation of the fertilized ovum occurs somewhere other than the uterus, the resulting pregnancy is termed an ectopic pregnancy. The secondary oocyte may remain attached to the ovary and be fertilized there (an ovarian ectopic pregnancy). Or it may fail to enter the uterine tube, be fertilized in the abdominal cavity, and implant on the broad ligament or one of the abdominal organs (an abdominal ectopic pregnancy). If a past infection has roughened the wall of the uterine tube, the fertilized ovum may settle down in the tube, producing a tubal ectopic pregnancy. All these cases pose a serious threat both to the developing embryo and to its mother. Only the uterus is specially adapted to provide sufficient nourishment and support for a growing fetus; an ectopic pregnancy may result in fatal hemorrhage.

Abortion and Miscarriage

With all the controversy about the morality of induced abortions, it is easy to lose sight of the fact that this term is also used for any premature termination of pregnancy in which the fetus is expelled during the first three months of pregnancy. Such spontaneous abortions occur most often in the tenth week, at the time of the third missed menstrual period, or in the sixth week, at the time of the second missed period. A high percentage of spontaneously aborted embryos are found to be grossly malformed; thus spontaneous abortions seem to be a natural mechanism for correcting reproductive errors. Various factors, including serious maternal illness, the presence of multiple fetuses, and a softening of the cervix after a large number of successive births, may cause premature termination of pregnancy at later periods. If the fetus is expelled during the fourth to sixth months, it generally cannot survive, and the event is termed a miscarriage. Premature labor after the sixth month can produce an infant capable of surviving, with suitable special care that may include precise temperature regulation, administration of oxygen as needed, and feeding through a tube directly into the stomach. A premature infant stands a better chance at survival, the closer it is to term at birth; a child born at any time during the ninth month of pregnancy usually does not need special incubator care.

Toxemia of Pregnancy

In some women, the stresses of pregnancy may prove too great for the kidneys, and the excretory function may break down. Fluid retention, rapid weight gain, the appearance of albumin in the urine, and a rise in blood pressure are danger signals pointing to the development of toxemia. If corrective measures are not taken, a more serious condition called **eclampsia** may develop. Convulsions commonly occur, and it may be necessary to induce labor prematurely to save the life of either the fetus or the mother.

Induction of Labor

Sometimes for medical or other reasons it is desirable to induce labor, rather than waiting for it to occur without warning in its own good time. Labor may be induced with injections of oxytocin. (But this technique cannot be used safely and effectively unless the cervix has already begun to soften and the pubic ligaments to relax; otherwise the vigorous uterine contractions induced by the hormone may kill the fetus and rupture the uterus.) When the head of the fetus is well settled into the pelvic canal and the cervix has already begun to di-

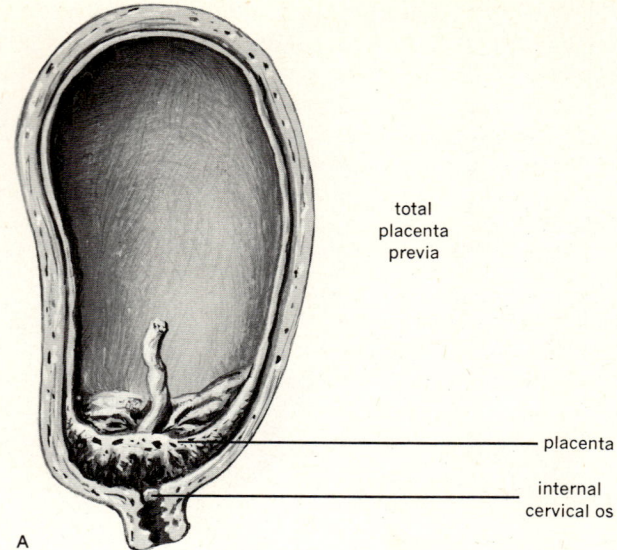

total placenta previa

placenta

internal cervical os

A

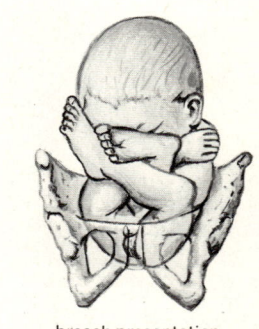

B   breech presentation

FIGURE 35-14 Abnormalities of pregnancy: placenta previa and breech presentation.

late, simple rupturing of the membranes may be sufficient to induce labor through the normal positive feedback mechanisms.

Placenta Previa

Normally the fertilized ovum implants in the body of the uterus, but occasionally it implants close to the cervix, and the growing placenta partially or entirely covers the internal os (Figure 35-14A). This condition, called placenta previa, can produce serious complications in the early stages of labor, when a portion of the placenta may detach itself prematurely from the uterine wall, leading to dangerous hemorrhage and possible death or brain damage of the fetus due to anoxia when the placental supply lines are cut off.

Abnormal Deliveries

Normally a child enters the world head first. Occasionally, however, the fetus fails to orient itself in the proper head-down position in the pelvis. Instead of the head, the face, arm, buttocks, or some other part of the fetus may enter the birth canal first. (A buttocks-first birth is called a **breech presentation;** see Figure 35-14B.) Such abnormal presentations usually result in a more difficult birth than usual. An obstetrician who knows in advance that a child is not in the correct position may manipulate the mother's abdomen so as to turn the fetus and avoid the problem.

Caesarean Section
If pelvic measurements indicate that the mother probably will not be able to deliver her child in the normal manner, or if labor has proceeded nonproductively for a long time, the obstetrician may elect to remove the baby from the uterus by Caesarean section, through an incision in the abdominal wall. With modern surgical techniques, there is no truth to the notion that a woman cannot safely have more than three Caesarean births, and indeed, it is possible for a woman to deliver a child by the normal vaginal route after a previous Caesarean operation.

Puerperal Sepsis (Childbed Fever)
Until about a century ago, maternal death in childbirth was very common. The cause was usually an infection, due to microbes introduced into the reproductive tract by the attending physician or midwife. The Viennese physician Ignaz Semmelweis pioneered the practice (at that time revolutionary) of having the physicians and attendants wash their hands in a disinfectant solution before assisting at a birth. This simple precaution dramatically reduced the death toll from this unnecessary scourge; the modern aseptic delivery room is an extension of Semmelweis's work.

THE POSTNATAL PERIOD
The first year of a baby's life is crowded with major events and accomplishments. After its abrupt expulsion from its mother's sheltering womb, it must rapidly acquire the ability to breathe, suckle, and regulate its body temperature. Gradually it begins to relate to its environment, responding first to its mother's touch and voice, and later to other humans and objects. Steadily the infant masters its own body, learning to focus its eyes, to reach and grasp with its hands, to turn over, sit, creep, stand, and finally to walk. It learns to communicate, first merely by crying, but then shaping its experimental babblings into recognizable words. These developmental accomplishments are accompanied by a steady physical growth, as the baby roughly triples its birth weight.

After the end of the first year, growth and development continue, with the mastery of increasingly complex motor and intellectual skills. Life after birth is commonly divided into five major periods:

1 **The period of the newborn,** or **neonatal period,** lasts from birth through the first few weeks of life. Crucial circulatory and other physiological adjustments occur; this is one of the most vulnerable periods of life.

2 **The period of infancy** begins at the end of the neonatal period and continues approximately to the end of the first year, when the infant can stand alone and walk.

3 **The period of childhood** lasts from the end of infancy to the time of sexual maturation, or puberty, usually at about 12 to 14 years in girls and 14 to 16 years in boys.

4 **The period of adolescence** begins with sexual maturation and extends through the teen years, as intellectual and emotional maturity is gradually acquired. This period is considered to end at about 19 in girls and 21 in boys. It is ironic that the physical ability to reproduce is developed some years before full maturity is reached.

5 **The period of maturity** extends from the completion of adolescence until old age, when retrogressive and degenerative changes may occur.

There are no sharp demarcations between the successive stages of life, as one blends imperceptibly into another. Individuals show a great deal of variation in the ages at which they reach various developmental landmarks, and in the same individual different phases of development may proceed more rapidly or slowly than others.

SUMMARY
Copulation or sexual intercourse includes erection of the penis of the male, its insertion into the vagina of the female, with rhythmic movements producing ejaculation.

The male orgasm includes ejaculation and psychic stimulation; a female orgasm may also occur but is not necessary to fertilization.

Fertilization requires delivery of at least 35 million sperm to the uterine tube containing a viable ovum.

Hyaluronidase carried by the sperm dissolves the cementing material of the corona radiata, permitting the entrance of a spermatozoon.

Immediately after one sperm has entered, the ovum becomes impermeable to penetration by others.

The male and female pronuclei join to form a full chromosome set of 46.

Sex is determined by the sex chromosomes: each ovum carries one X chromosome, and each sperm carries either an X or a Y chromosome.

Contraceptive techniques include:
Coitus interruptus
Mechanical barriers
Condom
Diaphragm
Spermicidal jellies, creams, foams, and douches
Rhythm method
Birth control pills (estrogens and progesterone)
Intrauterine devices
Prostaglandins
Immunization
Sterilization
Vasectomy
Tubal ligation
Abortion

The human gestation period is 266 days from fertilization (280 days from the onset of the last menstrual period).

The zygote (fertilized ovum) undergoes cleavage, dividing to form first a morula, then a blastocyst.

The ovum travels through the uterine tube, reaching the uterus at the morula stage, then implanting in the uterine lining at the blastocyst stage.

After implantation, differentiation proceeds, with the formation of extraembryonic membranes and the three primary germ layers of the embryo:

Ectoderm (develops into epidermis and nerve tissues)

Entoderm (develops into epithelial lining of digestive tract and derived structures)

Mesoderm (develops into connective tissue, muscles, bone, blood and lymph vessels)

Significant stages of embryonic development are the primitive streak, notochord, neural plate, neural tube.

During early development the human embryo has gill pouches and a tail.

The placenta is formed from embryonic and maternal tissues. Chorionic villi of the embryo are surrounded by venous sinuses of the decidua.

The placenta provides for an interchange of materials (oxygen, nutrients, wastes) between the maternal and fetal circulation, by diffusion, without any intermingling of blood.

The extraembryonic membranes of the embryo are:

Chorion: outer membrane; functions in nutrition and excretion of the embryo.

Amnion: thin, transparent membrane inside the chorion, surrounding the embryo and containing isotonic amniotic fluid in which it is suspended.

Allantois: in humans, incorporated into the umbilical cord.

Yolk sac: in humans, incorporated into the umbilical cord.

The umbilical cord connects the abdomen of the embryo with the placenta and contains two umbilical arteries and an umbilical vein.

The embryonic period extends approximately to the end of the tenth week of intrauterine development; the remaining period is the fetal period.

Basic structures are completed by the end of the embryonic period; during the fetal period details are completed and weight and flesh are gained.

The surfactant film in the alveoli is formed at about the 28th week, after which viable birth is possible.

During pregnancy the mother gains weight as breasts and uterus enlarge and increased fluid is retained.

There are increased nutritional requirements and increases stress on the vascular, respiratory, and kidney systems.

Parturition is initiated by mechanical stimulation of the uterus (especially the cervix) by the fetus and hormonal effects of estrogen and oxytocin.

First stage of labor: regular contractions of the uterus propel the fetus down into the birth canal; cervix dilates to 10 cm; pubic ligaments relax; membranes rupture.

Second stage of labor: severe uterine contractions propel the baby out through the birth canal, aided by contractions of the abdominal muscles.

Third stage of labor: expulsion of the placenta (afterbirth).

Lactation is mutually beneficial to mother and child, stimulating more rapid normalization of the mother's uterus and providing ideal nourishment for the infant.

Milk secretion is stimulated and maintained by prolactin.

Milk release is stimulated by oxytocin, secreted in response to mechanical stimulation of the nipples by suckling.

Colostrum is secreted during the first few days after birth.

Congenital abnormalities can be caused by environmental factors (teratogens: maternal disease, drugs, anoxia) or genetic factors (e.g., Down's syndrome).

Identical twins are produced by the separation of cell masses from one zygote during an early stage of cleavage.

Fraternal twins result from the fertilization of two different ova by two different sperm.

Multiple births place a greater strain on the mother and more often result in death or abnormalities of the fetuses.

Veneral diseases are infectious diseases transmitted by sexual activities:

Syphilis

Gonorrhea

Herpes simplex virus Type 2

Abnormalities of pregnancy and childbirth include:

Ectopic pregnancy (implantation outside the uterus)

Abortion and miscarriage (premature termination of pregnancy)

Toxemia and eclampsia

Placenta previa

Breech presentation and other abnormal presentations

Puerperal sepsis (childbed fever)

The major periods of life after birth are:

Period of the newborn

Period of infancy

Period of childhood

Period of adolescence

Period of maturity

QUESTIONS FOR REVIEW AND THOUGHT

1 Since ova are viable for only about 24 hours after ovulation, and Y sperm swim faster than X sperm, what is the best time of the month for a couple to have intercourse if they wish to conceive a baby boy? When will conception of a girl be most likely?

2 Why are so many sperm per ejaculation needed for fertilization?

3 Discuss currently used and experimental means of contraception. What are their advantages and drawbacks?

4 A major stumbling block thus far in attempts to maintain embryos in vitro has been the lack of an effective artificial placenta. What functions would such a device have to perform?

5 Are the membranes that surround the developing embryo derived from the body of the embryo or the mother? What about the placenta?

6 Describe the process of human embryonic development and the corresponding changes in the mother's body during pregnancy.

7 Define: orgasm; coitus interruptus; condom; blastomere; morula; blastocyst; trophoblast; amnion; chorion; allantois; eclampsia; parturition; colostrum.

8 When does the human embryo begin to move spontaneously and respond to stimuli? When does it have a recognizably humanoid appearance? When can the sex of the embryo be distinguished? When is it capable of surviving outside its mother's womb?

9 Describe the stages of labor. Under what conditions is the injection of oxytocin advisable? inadvisable?

10 What is the difference between identical and fraternal twins?

11 Discuss the three major types of veneral disease.

GROWTH AND AGING

36

Nothing in our world is constant. Throughout the history of the earth, great mountain chains have been thrown up, and then gradually worn away. The seasons of the year bring changing conditions of life for the earth's animals and plants. But few changes in the physical world are as rapid and dramatic as those that occur within the life of an individual organism.

The early life of an animal or plant is a period of rapid growth. Many plants go on growing throughout their lifetime. A few animals, such as fish and some turtles, share this ability for indeterminate growth. But in most animals—including humans—growth gradually slows down and ceases entirely. Ultimately, a period of senescence sets in, in which the body structures and functions gradually become less efficient, and there may even be a net decrease in body size. Death comes as the end of life, either by accident or disease, or simply from the accumulated effects of the general deterioration of aging.

Thus, the life of a human, from conception to death, may be viewed as a continuous process, a series of events that follow one another in a programmed sequence, varying in details but leading to the same ultimate conclusion.

In the previous chapter we traced the exciting sequence of events that transforms a single cell, the zygote, into a complex being, the newborn baby. In this chapter we follow the rest of the sequence of development, from birth through adulthood to death.

PATTERNS OF GROWTH

If a tiny crystal of copper sulfate is placed in a saturated solution and left carefully undisturbed, it can be seen to grow in size, day by day. A snowball rolling down a hill also grows, as it gathers more snow from the hillside. But growth in the nonliving world differs from the growth of living organisms in a number of vital respects.

A copper sulfate crystal or a rolling snowball grows by a process called **accretion,** an addition of material to the outside. This is a passive process—a crystal does not purposely gather new building materials. By contrast, a living organism grows by **intussusception,** the intake of simple building materials, which are modified, built up into more complicated structural materials, and incorporated into the living substance of the cells. For humans and other animals, the basic building materials are taken in as food, which must be broken down to its constituent amino acids, sugars, fatty acids and glycerol, and other simpler substances, which are then assembled into the specific proteins, carbohydrates, and fats needed by the organism. There is some "waste" of raw materials, as some food constituents are processed to yield energy or excreted in the form of various waste products. But the concept of growth implies a net gain: the total of the food materials taken in exceeds the amount returned to the environment, and there is a net increase in size and weight of the organism.

Growth in size can result from an increase in the size of the individual cells, by cell division increasing the total number of cells, or by the deposition of material outside the cells. Often all three processes are involved in the growth of an organism. But growth in size is not the whole story. The dramatic growth of a zygote to a human baby and the growth of a baby to an adult involve another important process: differentiation, an increasing specialization of individual cells for specific functions.

During the whole period of development there is a shifting balance between the increase in the number of cells and the differentiation of these cells. In the early embryo, cell division proceeds at a rapid pace. But quickly, cells begin to differentiate, to form tissues, organs, and organ systems. If this did not occur, an embryo would grow into a mass of undifferentiated cells rather than a baby. After birth the processes of cell division and maturation continue, as the body and its parts not only grow in size but are continually modified and reshaped, permitting the mastery of new skills. Sometimes the growth of the child may even involve actual destruction of existing material, which has served its functions and must make way for new and different structures.

During adult life, a new phase of development begins. Active growth has ceased, and the activities of the body are directed toward the maintenance of function. Cells that wear out or are destroyed by accident or disease are replaced, and a dynamic equilibrium is maintained. But ultimately the repair processes become less efficient and cannot adequately replace the day-to-day losses. Slowly various body functions deteriorate.

Rates of Growth

A small child seems to grow amazingly rapidly. In the first year after birth, it triples its weight and adds about 50 percent in height. Yet in comparison with the explosive growth that occurred before birth, a newborn baby is already a has-been. In the nine months from conception to birth, a human fetus increases its size and weight about 10 *billion*fold!

In comparison with other animals, the growth of a human child seems even more modest. A blue whale, with a gestation period little more than the human nine months, grows from a single cell to a two-ton infant by the time of birth. Even after birth, many animals grow far more rapidly than humans: a pig, for example, weighing only 3 pounds at birth, reaches a weight of 200 pounds by six months. The develop-

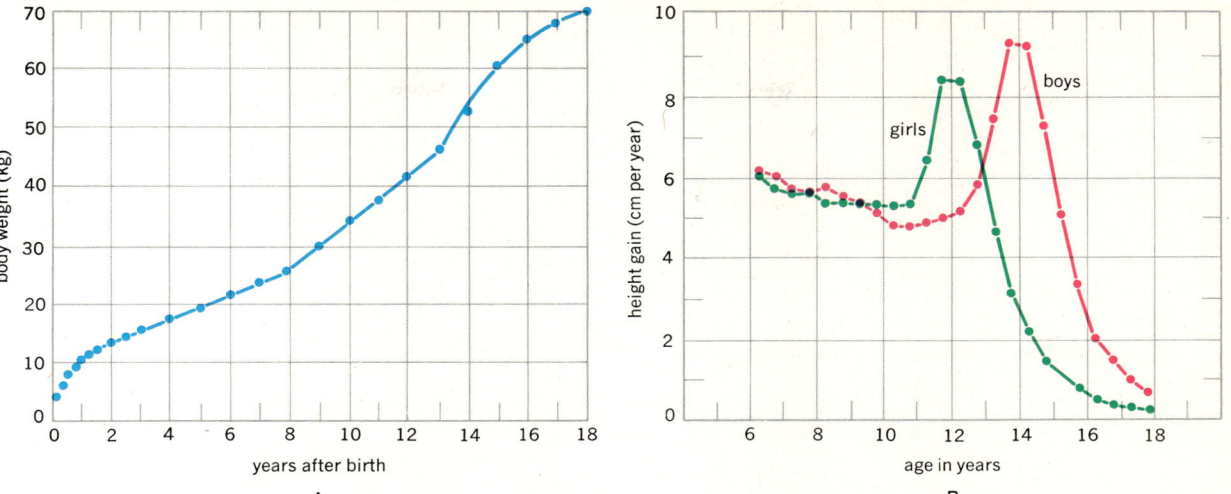

FIGURE 36-1 (A) The human growth curve. (From A. K. Laird, "Evolution of the Human Growth Curve," *Growth*, Vol. 31, 1967, p. 345.) (B) The adolescent growth spurt in girls and boys (ages are averages of a much wider normal range in each case). (From J. M. Tanner, *Growth and Adolescence*, 2nd edition, Blackwell Scientific Pubs., Oxford, 1962. Used with permission.)

ment of human body structures and skills is correspondingly slower than that of nearly any other animal of comparable size. A colt or a calf is able to stand and walk within minutes after birth; a newborn human baby cannot even hold its head up, and nearly a full year will pass before it is able to walk unassisted. At an age when many large mammals are already fully grown and rearing their own young, the human child is still quite immature and completely dependent on the care of adults.

Human growth is not a steady process (Figure 36-1). Dropping steadily throughout prenatal life, the rate of growth continues to fall after birth. The first doubling of the birth weight comes in about six months, while in the next six months there is only a 50 percent increase. Then follows a period of consolidation, as the "baby fat" is lost and muscle is gained, with a very slow apparent rate of overall growth. In the second year of life, the weight gain is approximately half the 200 percent increment of the first year, and the gain in height is correspondingly halved. Then growth settles down for a time to a steady 5 or 6 pounds and 2 to 3 inches a year. (With these steady gains, the *relative* rate of growth, in proportion of the total body size, is still slowing down.) A new phase is ushered in by the flow of sex hormones that occurs during adolescence and sparks a sudden "growth spurt," adding as much as 7 inches in a year.

Children vary greatly in rates of growth and development. Thus, any particular child might be considerably behind or ahead of the averages for his or her chronological age. A more objective evaluation of a child's degree of development is skeletal age, found by X-ray measurements of the wrist region. Clues to

development are also provided by studies of the eruption and development of the teeth (dental age), the manipulative ability (neural age), and the development of secondary sex characteristics (sexual age).

Despite this variation, measurements of a child's height and weight provide a fairly good basis for predicting its adult height and weight. As a general rule of thumb, a two-year-old boy will double his height and quintuple his weight by adulthood. For a girl, the adult values are the corresponding multiples of her height and weight at 18 months. Statistical tables have been drawn up, relating the height and weight at various ages to the probable adult values. The predictions become much more reliable after about 10 years of age.

It is a commonplace observation that children in the U.S. today are growing faster and larger than they did in the past, and they are also achieving their full growth earlier. This acceleration of growth and maturation is believed to be due mainly to improved living conditions, particularly diet.

Body Proportions

The cherubs in paintings by some of the old masters have a disturbingly "wrong" look. Each detail is painstakingly perfect, yet somehow they do not look like the young children they are supposed to depict. The answer lies in the proportions: the heads are too small. Part of an artist's training is in observation of the structure of the body, which instills a feel for its relative proportions. The total height of an adult, for example, is about seven and half times the height of the head. But what some of the old-time artists did not realize is that this is not true of a child. A new-

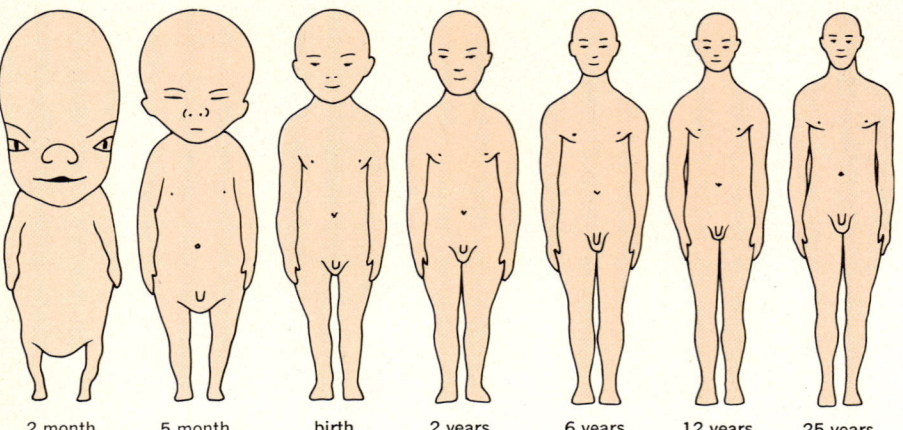

FIGURE 36-2 **Growth is a differential process, resulting in a gradual change in body proportions.**

2 month embryo   5 month fetus   birth   2 years   6 years   12 years   25 years

born baby's head is about a quarter of its total length, reflecting the relatively large and well-developed brain that the skull contains. If you measured the circumference of a three-year-old's head and compared it with that of an adult, the result would be an astonishing 90 percent.

Obviously, with the dramatic changes in body proportions that occur from birth to adulthood, some parts of the body grow far more rapidly than others (Figure 36-2). The shape of the head alters greatly, as the cranium grows very little and the face, particularly the jaws, enlarge greatly. The arms at birth are fairly well developed, but the legs are spindly little things that make up only about a third of the total body length; in the adult, the legs account for fully a half. The pelvis, too, is relatively small in an infant. In girls, the shape of the pelvis becomes greatly modified at puberty, in preparation for childbearing.

The genitals of a newborn baby seem disproportionately large. For a number of years they grow much more slowly than the rest of the body. Then, at the time of the adolescent growth spurt, there is an explosive growth of the external reproductive organs, during which they reach approximately their adult size.

The internal organs, too, grow at varying rates and proportions. The characteristic potbelly of a small child, for example, is due mainly to the large liver, which ceases to protrude in about the fourth year as the growth of the rest of the body outstrips it. (The potbelly that may develop in middle age, on the other hand, consists mainly of fat deposits.)

Cessation of Growth

A fish or a tortoise can go on growing throughout its entire life, but human beings cease to grow when they have completed less than a third of their lifespan. After the adolescent growth spurt, there is a rapid

deceleration; then the epiphyses of the long bones close, and growth in height stops entirely. In boys this cessation of growth usually occurs by the age of 18 to 21; girls reach their full adult height earlier, by about 16 to 18. The onset of maturity may be delayed by undernourishment, but growth eventually ceases. Why this occurs remains a mystery, but it is being actively researched since the seemingly programmed sequence of growth and its completion may hold important keys to the prolongation of vigorous life. A discovery of the "off switches" of human growth may also provide clues to the conquest of cancer, a form of growth run wild.

Hormones of the adrenals and pituitary play an important role in determining the closure of the epiphyses. Their interactions with other hormones and with control centers in the brain may be key factors in the working of the built-in clocks that determine human growth and development. But researchers are looking for secrets of growth even deeper, at the level of the cells and of the genes within them.

It has been found that cells, too, seem to have a built-in clock that determines their specific life span. If cells from a human embryo are suspended in a tissue culture, they will grow and divide. But there is a limit to this tissue growth: Stanford University microbiologist Leonard Hayflick has found that after cultured fibroblasts from the skin of aborted fetuses have divided an average of about 50 times, they cease dividing and ultimately die. Cells from adult humans double their population in a tissue culture only an average of 20 times; the total number of divisions in the culture decreases with increasing age of the person whose cells were taken. Liver cells and others show a similar **Hayflick limit** of about 50 divisions, which correspond approximately to the number of divisions such cells would undergo in the human body in a lifetime of about 110 to 115 years. (There are some exceptions to this limited cell life span. The HeLa line of cancer cells, for example, has been maintained in tissue cultures for many years, and it seems likely that such cells can go on dividing indefinitely.)

Some researchers believe that growth ceases when the hormonal processes that trigger DNA synthesis and cell division somehow break down in aging cells. In one series of experiments, mammary cells from a mouse were transplanted into a series of other mice. After four such transplantations over a 12-month period, the cells gradually lost their ability to proliferate. But growth of the transplanted cells could be restarted if the recipient mouse was bred and became pregnant. Apparently the reproductive hormones produced by the pregnant mouse sparked a resumption of DNA synthesis and division of the transplanted cells.

Although growth in height ceases at adulthood, there may be a net increase in weight in later years. Indeed, excessive weight gain is one of the major problems in the industrially developed countries, and diet books, diet pills, and weight-reducing devices chalk up extremely lucrative sales each year. The tendency to gain weight in middle age occurs because there is usually a decrease in physical activity and a general decrease in metabolism but no comparable reduction of appetite. As a result, the sedentary adult takes in more calories than the body can use up, and the excess is stored as fat.

Pregnancy usually adds 20 to 30 pounds to a woman's weight. Although the birth of a child may well be the ultimate in a "crash" weight-loss program for its mother, a certain residue of the added weight remains and may persist unless a careful program of diet and exercise is pursued.

GROWTH AND DEVELOPMENT OF THE CHILD

A newborn baby needs much more food, pound for pound, than you do, because your growth is probably already completed or nearly so; you need provide only for the daily energy expenditures of keeping your organs running smoothly and materials for keeping them in good repair. A baby's food not only must provide for these needs but also must support a tremendous increase in size and weight.

A baby's growth in size is accompanied by striking changes in many body structures. The soft bones of the skull, which may have been distorted during birth, become symmetrical and harden as the cartilaginous portions of the skeleton are gradually filled in with bone. The rapid initial growth of the brain slows down and is ultimately limited as the fontanels and sutures of the skull close. (The fontanels are usually closed by the end of the second year; fusion of the sutures is not complete until the twenties.) Two curves that were not present at birth appear in the vertebral column: the cervical curve when the infant begins lifting up its head at about three months of age, and the lumbar curve when the child begins to stand, toward the end of the first year.

From infancy to maturity, the heart grows twelvefold. It beats rapidly at first—an average of 140 beats per minute in a newborn baby. The rate drops steadily, to 115 for a one-year-old, 110 at two years, 95 at eight years, and the rate is ultimately about halved by adulthood. The blood pressure, on the contrary, approximately doubles from a systolic pressure of 70 mm Hg in infants. The breathing rate, like the heart rate, is rapid at first and gradually falls, from 30 to 80 times a minute in an infant to 15 to 20 times in an adult.

The physical growth and development of a child is paralleled by the development of motor and intellectual skills. It is believed that physical and behavioral development are closely linked: even intensive training cannot teach a child a particular skill until it has reached the development stage of readiness for it.

Mothers and fathers often compare the progress of their children with that of the children of neighbors and relatives. Such comparisons can cause a great deal of unnecessary unhappiness. Children develop and mature at greatly differing rates, and a child may be ahead in some respects and behind the average in others. One child, for example, may crawl at 5 months and walk at 10, but not begin to talk until 18 months; another child, forming intelligible words well before the end of the first year, may not walk until 13 months.

Although a newborn baby is totally dependent on the care of adults, it does come into the world with a set of working reflexes that help fit it for survival. It can blink and sneeze. A light touch on the cheek will initiate the rooting reflex, as the baby turns its head toward the stimulus. The presence of a nipple elicits quite competent sucking movements. A touch on the palm of the hand produces a grasping reflex; a newborn baby's grip can be strong enough to support its weight if it is lifted in this fashion. (This reflex is lost in a couple of months, and subsequently an ability for voluntary grasping is developed.) Another characteristic infant reflex is the startle reflex: a rapid change in position or a sudden noise can cause an infant to fling its arms outward suddenly.

As the body, and especially the nervous system, develops, the child acquires a repertoire of skills. Some landmarks of the first year are charted in Figure 36-3. An individual child may show considerable variations from these norms and still be quite normal.

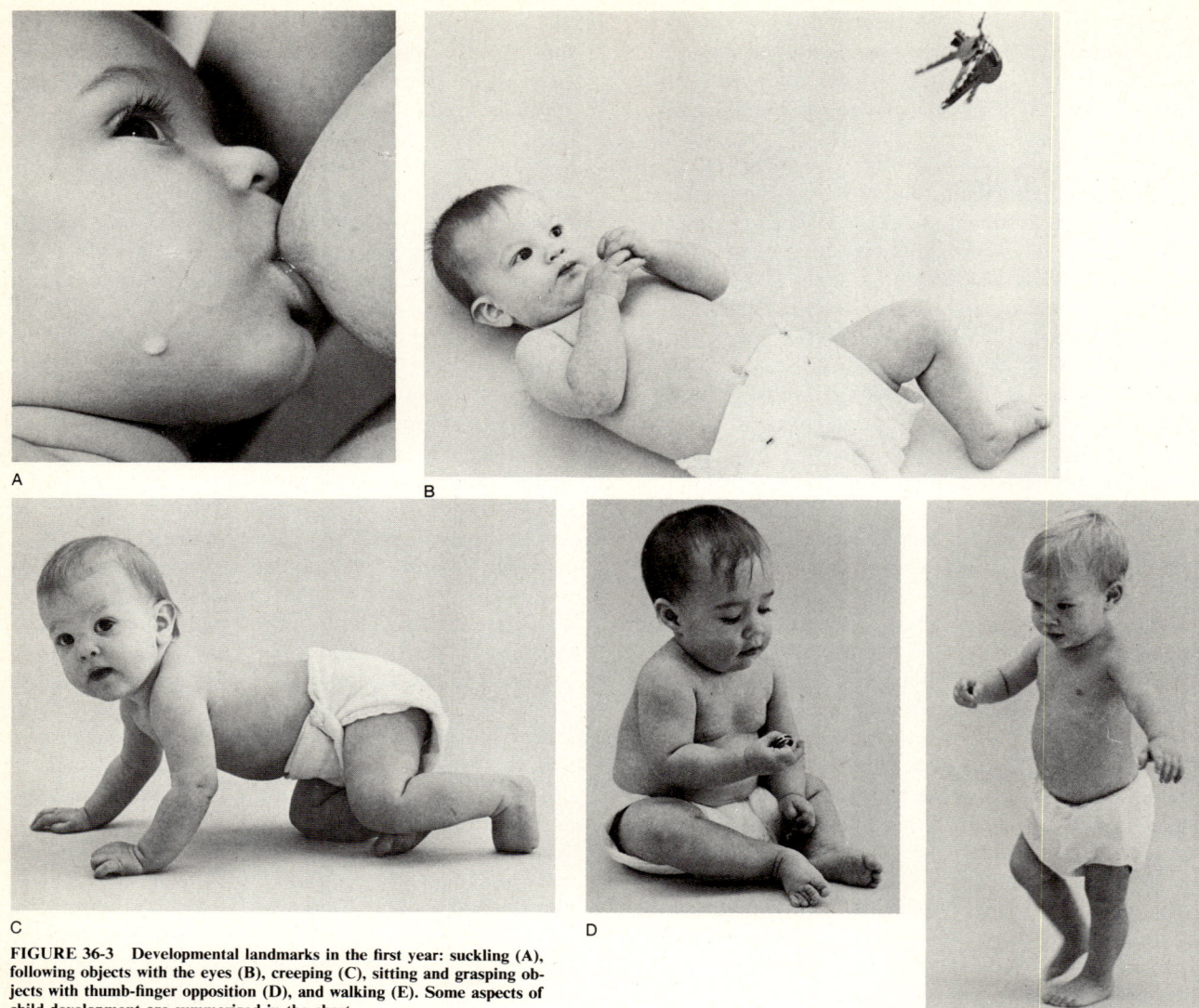

FIGURE 36-3 Developmental landmarks in the first year: suckling (A), following objects with the eyes (B), creeping (C), sitting and grasping objects with thumb-finger opposition (D), and walking (E). Some aspects of child development are summarized in the chart.

A consistent lag in all areas, which increases progressively, however, may signal some degree of mental deficiency.

As the years pass, the child acquires increasing motor coordination and skill and is capable of increasing mental discrimination, reasoning, and learning.

ADOLESCENCE

Few periods in the life of an individual are as potentially traumatic as adolescence. The rapid physical and physiological changes of puberty may disturb or even frighten an uninformed child. The wide variation of the time of onset of puberty and rate of development may leave a child "out of phase" with the majority of his or her classmates, which may give rise to feelings of inadequacy that can persist into later life.

Sex hormones begin to appear in the body in signif-

icant amounts by about the 10th year in girls and the 11th year in boys. These hormones promote an explosive growth and maturation of the reproductive organs and a sweeping series of changes that produce the secondary sex characteristics.

In girls, the first sign of adolescent development is the appearance of breast buds. Development of the breasts commonly begins between the ages of 9 and 11, but the breasts are not fully mature for another eight years or so. Pubic hair begins to grow around age 11 on the average; axillary or armpit hair develops a year or two later. **Menarche,** the first menstruation, occurs on the average around 13 years of age; however, a great range is observed, from 9 to 17.

The onset of puberty in boys is just as variable as in girls. Usually the first sign is an accelerated growth of the testes, beginning at 12 on the average (sometimes as early as 10) and extending over a period of four

DENVER DEVELOPMENTAL SCREENING TEST

STO. = STOMACH
SIT = SITTING

Date

Name

Birthdate

Hosp. No.

PERCENT OF CHILDREN PASSING

25 50 75 90

May pass by report →

Footnote No. →
see back of form

R

Test Item

PERSONAL-SOCIAL

- REGARDS FACE
- R SMILES RESPONSIVELY 1
- SMILES SPONTANEOUSLY
- R INITIALLY SHY WITH STRANGERS
- R PLAYS PAT-A-CAKE
- FEEDS SELF CRACKERS
- R FEEDS SELF CRACKERS
- RESISTS TOY PULL 2
- PLAYS PEEK-A-BOO
- WORKS FOR TOY OUT OF REACH
- R DRINKS FROM CUP
- PLAYS BALL WITH EXAMINER
- R INDICATES WANTS (NOT CRY)
- R IMITATES HOUSEWORK
- R USES SPOON, SPILLING LITTLE
- HELPS IN HOUSE – SIMPLE TASKS
- R PUTS ON CLOTHING
- R WASHES & DRIES HANDS
- R DRESSES 3 WITH SUPERVISION
- SEPARATES FROM MOTHER EASILY
- PLAYS INTERACTIVE R GAMES e.g. TAG
- R REMOVES GARMENT
- BUTTONS UP
- R DRESSES WITHOUT 3 SUPERVISION

50%

FINE MOTOR-ADAPTIVE

- FOLLOWS TO MIDLINE 4
- EQUAL MOVEMENTS *
- FOLLOWS PAST MIDLINE 4
- GRASPS RATTLE 5
- REGARDS RAISIN
- REACHES FOR OBJECT
- FOLLOWS 180° 4
- HANDS TOGETHER
- SIT, LOOKS FOR YARN 6
- R SIT, TAKES 2 CUBES
- RAKES RAISIN ATTAINS
- NEAT PINCER GRASP 8 OF RAISIN
- R THUMB-FINGER GRASP 7
- PASSES CUBE R HAND TO HAND
- R BANGS 2 CUBES HELD IN HANDS
- R SCRIBBLES SPONTANEOUSLY
- TOWER OF 2 CUBES
- TOWER OF 4 CUBES
- DUMPS RAISIN FROM BOTTLE-SPONT.
- DUMPS RAISIN FROM BOTTLE-DEMONSTR
- IMITATES VERTICAL LINE WITHIN 30°
- TOWER OF 8 CUBES
- R IMITATES BRIDGE
- PICKS LONGER LINE 10 3 of 3
- 9 COPIES O
- 11 COPIES +
- 12 COPIES ☐
- IMITATES ⌐ DEMONSTR
- R DRAWS MAN 3 PARTS 13
- DRAWS 13 MAN 6 PARTS

* 100% pass at birth

LANGUAGE

- RESPONDS TO BELL
- VOCALIZES – NOT CRYING
- R LAUGHS
- R SQUEALS
- TURNS TO VOICE
- R IMITATES SPEECH SOUNDS
- DADA OR MAMA, NONSPECIFIC
- R 3 WORDS OTHER THAN MAMA, DADA
- DADA OR MAMA, SPECIFIC
- R COMBINES 2 DIFFERENT WORDS
- POINTS TO 1 NAMED R BODY PART
- R NAMES 1 PICTURE 14
- R FOLLOWS DIRECTIONS/2 of 3 15
- R USES PLURALS
- GIVES 1ST & R LAST NAME
- COMPREHENDS 16 COLD, TIRED, HUNGRY/2 of 3
- COMPREHENDS 17 PREPOSITIONS/3 of 4
- R RECOGNIZES COLORS/3 of 4
- OPPOSITE ANALOGIES 18 2 of 3
- 19 DEFINES WORDS/6 of 9   87%
- 20 COMPOSITION OF/3 of 3   87%

GROSS MOTOR

- STO LIFTS R HEAD
- STO HEAD UP 45°
- STO HEAD UP 90°
- SIT-HEAD STEADY
- R ROLLS OVER
- STO CHEST UP 21 ARM SUPPORT
- BEAR SOME WEIGHT ON LEGS
- PULL TO SIT 22 NO HEAD LAG
- SITS WITHOUT SUPPORT
- R STANDS HOLDING ON
- R PULLS SELF TO STAND
- R GETS TO SITTING
- R STANDS MOMENTARILY
- R WALKS HOLDING ON FURNITURE
- R STANDS ALONE WELL
- R STOOPS & RECOVERS
- R WALKS WELL
- R WALKS BACKWARDS
- R WALKS UP STEPS 23
- R KICKS BALL FORWARD
- 24 THROWS BALL OVERHAND
- BALANCE ON 1 FOOT 1 SECOND
- JUMPS IN PLACE
- R PEDALS TRICYCLE
- BROAD JUMP 25
- BALANCE ON 1 FOOT 5 SECONDS/2 of 3
- BALANCE ON 1 FOOT 10 SECONDS/2 of 3
- HOPS ON 1 FOOT
- CATCHES BOUNCED 27 BALL/2 of 3
- 26 HEEL TO TOE WALK/2 of 3
- BACKWARD HEEL-TOE/2 of 3 28

MONTHS 1 2 3 4 5 6 7 8 9 10 11 12 13 14 15 16 17 18 19 20 21 22 23 24

YEARS 2½ 3 3½ 4 4½ 5 5½ 6

years or more. Development of the penis begins on the average at 13 and lasts about two years. Pubic hair first appears between 10 and 15; axillary hair usually begins to grow a couple of years later, but it may precede the growth of pubic hair. Mature sperm usually are not produced until 14 to 16 years of age.

Adolescence is a time of growth spurt and of substantial changes in body proportions. In girls, subcutaneous fat deposits are laid down, and the pelvis is broadened. In both sexes, there is a growth spurt in the larynx, resulting in a deepening of the voice. In boys, however, this change is much greater; the harsh squeaks and croaks that may sometimes result when an adolescent boy speaks are caused by his incompletely developed muscular control over his growing larynx.

Adolescence is also a time of heightened activity of the sebaceous glands, which are susceptible to plugging and infection. Annoying and sometimes disfiguring acne is the frequent result.

Physical growth and intellectual maturation continue for some years after sexual maturity is reached.

FACTORS AFFECTING GROWTH

Today millions of people in various parts of the world are at the point of starvation. Most of them are children. For them, the normal patterns of growth will be upset because one of the most important factors affecting growth is the supply of raw materials and energy in the form of food. Undernourishment can slow the rate of growth and reduce the ultimate stature attained.

Not only the quantity of food in the diet, but also its quality is important. An adequate supply of protein is essential for growth; protein deficiency can lead to stunting and mental retardation. Vitamins are also crucial. Vitamin A controls the activities of the osteoclasts and thus helps to regulate the shape of the bones. Vitamin D is a key factor in the calcification of bones. A deficiency of it leads to rickets, in which the bones, poorly calcified, become distorted and bent. Vitamins of the B group are necessary for normal growth of other tissues. A vitamin C deficiency results in an inadequate content of collagen in the developing bones and other tissues.

Disease can interfere with growth; after recovery, there is often a growth spurt that partially or wholly compensates for the lag.

An important factor affecting growth is heredity. Tall parents tend to have tall children. Short parents often have short children, but may have children taller than either of them. (Shortness seems to be dominant, tallness recessive.) Marriages of short and tall people produce children who show great variation in size. The hereditary determination of body size and growth is rather complicated. Some genes appear to control total size, while others control the size of specific body parts, such as the legs or spinal column; still others control rate and duration of growth. (Some children achieve a greater height by growing longer than the average, while others have a greater growth spurt during adolescence.)

Sex is another important factor affecting growth. Before adolescence, girls are usually smaller than boys, but they are well ahead in the rate of maturation of all tissues. Girls are correspondingly advanced in nearly all motor skills, as well as in verbal expression. Because puberty sets in earlier in girls, they enter the growth spurt phase before boys of the same age. Thus, at 11 or so, girls are taller and heavier on the average than boys. But when the boys enter their own adolescent growth spurt, they quickly catch up. Not only do boys grow faster than girls, but they continue to grow for a longer time and thus end with a somewhat greater stature.

The control of growth is mediated through the endocrine hormones. Human growth hormone, secreted by the pituitary, is a major growth-stimulating factor. Thyroid hormone also stimulates growth, especially of the skeleton and nervous system, through a general stimulation of metabolism. During the adolescent growth spurt, sex hormones produced by the gonads and adrenal cortex further stimulate growth.

ABNORMALITIES OF GROWTH AND DEVELOPMENT

The legends of many peoples tell of giants as tall as mountains who once walked the earth and "little people" with magical powers, only as large as a normal person's thumb. Perhaps such tales have grown in the telling. The tallest man whose height has been reliably recorded was only 8 feet 11 inches tall, while the tiniest midget ever reliably measured had an adult height of about 23 inches.

Although there are some tribes of seven-foot "giants" and four-foot pygmies, among the more genetically heterogeneous general population, dwarfs and giants are often the result of some malfunction of the pituitary gland (pituitary giants and midgets), thyroid gland (cretins), or a hereditary defect of bone formation (achondroplastic dwarfs). The disproportionate growth of acromegaly, which growth hormone stimulates when it is secreted in excess after the epiphyses have closed, was depicted in Figure 32-5 on page 700.

Localized **neoplasms,** in which cells multiply wildly without regard to the needs of the body, may occur at any stage of development, from the embryo through adulthood. The growth of such tumors may be stimulated by a variety of influences, including chemical irritation of the skin, infection by viruses, genetic factors, and hormonal influences. A tumor may be an undifferentiated mass of tissue, or inappropriate differentiation may occur; some tumors have been found to contain such bizarre items as fully formed teeth. **Benign neoplasms** grow slowly and are enclosed in connective-tissue capsules that clearly delimit them from surrounding tissues; they generally do not pose a serious threat to life unless they occur in a critical organ such as the brain, where mechanical pressure from a growing tumor mass can damage vital tissues. **Malignant neoplasms (cancers)** grow rapidly, are not bounded by capsules, and invade surrounding tissues. They may shed cells into the blood and lymph vessels and spread to other sites of the body, where secondary neoplasms develop. Cancer, the second leading cause of death in the U.S., is discussed in Chapter 37.

An extremely curious and tragic growth disorder is a rare disease called **progeria.** For a person with this disease, the clocks of life are speeded up. The person begins to age while still a child and quickly shows such signs of senescence as arthritis, cataracts, wrinkled skin, loss of bone, muscle, and nervous tissue, memory impairment, heart and vascular deterioration, and sterility. Death from "old age" occurs before the age of 30. Progeria is believed to be the result of a genetic defect, with affects a key enzyme system involved in the timing mechanisms of metabolism. The rare cases of the disease are of great interest to researchers studying aging, since they permit the observation of a process that normally is spread out over a full lifetime.

AGING

The Greek goddess Eos, the rosy-fingered dawn, once fell in love with a mortal, Tithonus. They were married, but Eos was tormented by the thought that her husband would one day die and leave her. Eos begged Zeus to give Tithonus immortality, and her request was granted. But she carelessly neglected to ask for eternal youth for her husband. As the years went by, Tithonus became a withered old man, so pitiful that the gods eventually had compassion and changed him into a cicada.

This myth symbolizes some basic attitudes that have been held by people of all ages: a longing for immortal life, but a dread of the ravages of age.

Aging or **senescence** is a biological process characterized by a gradual deterioration of the structures and functions of the organism, resulting in an increased susceptibility to accident and disease. Many scientists regard aging as an integral part of the long developmental process that begins with the fertilized egg and ends with death. Indeed, some aspects of aging are observed at an early age, when vigorous growth is still taking place. The healing of wounds,

FIGURE 36-4 The face of age.

for example, is most efficient in a newborn baby and declines steadily thereafter.

Aging seems to be one of the great tragedies of life. Just when people have accumulated a lifetime of knowledge and experience, they find their minds dulling, their bodies withering and adding a continuing roster of aches, pains, and minor and major crises to burden their existence. Is aging an inevitable part of life? Or may researchers uncover ways to delay, prevent, and even reverse the inexorable deterioration? As medical research gains mastery over one killer disease after another, the life expectancy of the population has been rising steadily. It is paradoxical that in our youth-oriented culture, the average age of the population is actually increasing, as more and more people are living to old age. Murmurs of "gray power" are only one of the many indications that it is past time for a reevaluation of our attitudes toward the old and of society's provisions for the life and care of the aged. Such questions should be of personal significance to each of us. Medical advances have granted us an increasing expectation of living our allotted "three score years and ten" or beyond, and thus the question of the quality of life in our later years holds growing urgency.

CHANGES IN THE AGING BODY

Except for rare superstars like Hank Aaron, baseball players at 35 are already "over the hill." Their reflexes and stamina have been reduced to a point where they can no longer compete effectively with the younger players around them. A movie star at 35 eyes the telltale wrinkles in the mirror and turns hopefully to creams, diets, and special exercises that promise to return some of the glow of youth.

No sooner has maturity been reached than a pro-

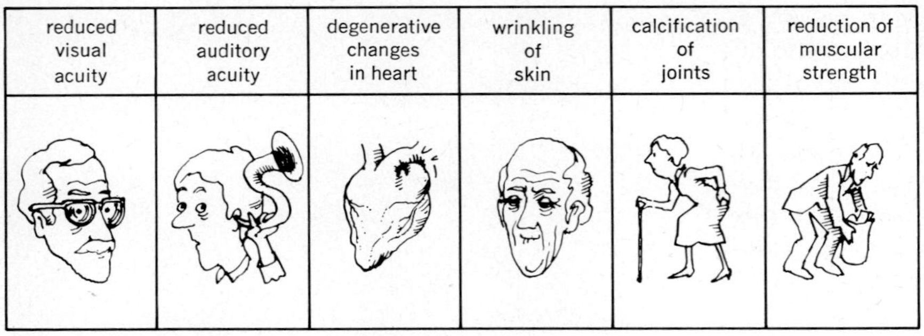

reduced visual acuity	reduced auditory acuity	degenerative changes in heart	wrinkling of skin	calcification of joints	reduction of muscular strength

FIGURE 36-5 Characteristic changes in the aging body.

gressive decline in the body's efficiency begins. Different organs and tissues of the body age at different rates. Nerve and muscle cells, which lose the ability for cell division at an early age, show a correspondingly earlier decline in their functional capabilities than tissues such as those of the liver and pancreas, in which active cell division continues.

Some of the characteristic changes in the aging body are summarized in Figure 36-5. Some of the most striking—and most tragic—changes are observed in the central nervous system. A combination of loss of nerve cells, which are not replaced in the adult body, a slowing of the nerve conduction, and a reduction of circulation to the brain results in a progressive decline of mental efficiency that actually begins at the age of 20 or so. For some time the effects of this decline are masked by the continuing acquisition of knowledge and skills, but ultimately a lengthening of the reaction time and growing lapses of memory become apparent. Learning is more difficult for older people, partly because of the reduced mental efficiency and partly because of interference from previously acquired knowledge.

The senses of the aging person become less acute. There is a progressive hearing loss, particularly of higher tones, which can make it difficult to distinguish the sounds of speech. The eyes become prone to various degenerative diseases, and a reduction of the ability of the eye muscles to accommodate the lens results in farsightedness. Taste is dulled as taste buds are progressively lost. (At 75, a person has lost up to 64 percent of the taste buds.)

Various degenerative changes occur in the circulatory system. The heart muscle may be partially replaced by fibrous or fatty material. A progressive stretching and deterioration of the elastic fibers stiffen the artery walls, and calcified fatty deposits within them (arteriosclerosis) may weaken them so that they burst when the blood pressure is raised by emotion or straining, or may lead to circulation-blocking blood clots.

The deterioration of the elastic fibers is a cause of wrinkling of the skin. Meanwhile, the collagen fibers increase in number with age, invade other tissues, and

become cross-linked into inflexible masses. Often calcium salts are deposited around the fibers. The loss of resiliency of the chest and the stiffness of movement of the joints in old people are due to these factors. (Another contributing factor in joint stiffness is an increase in the viscosity of the lubricating synovial fluid.)

While calcium is creating problems by being deposited in places where it should not be, it is being dissolved out of the bones, weakening them and making them more susceptible to fractures (osteoporosis).

Aging upsets the fluid balance of the human organism. There is a gradual loss of tissue fluid throughout life, causing the tissues to dry up. The glomerular filtration rate in the kidneys drops, as many of the glomeruli are lost and not replaced (as much as 44 percent in a 75-year-old). Meanwhile, a loss of control over the smooth muscles may result in incontinence.

Complex hormonal changes occur in the aging body. In women the drop in the production of female sex hormones brings a dramatic cessation of menstruation at menopause. In men the deterioration of gonad activity is more gradual. Sexual activity usually declines and may cease entirely.

Are all of these aging changes a necessary accompaniment to growing older?

There is a growing realization that some of the changes generally regarded as a normal part of the aging process are actually avoidable effects of modern conditions and attitudes. In primitive regions, for example, away from the barrage of noise that continuously assails the ears of modern city dwellers, a high degree of hearing acuity is retained even into extreme age. The inactivity resulting from the attitude that older people should "take it easy" and not exert themselves may be a significant factor in the loss of calcium from their bones. (The resultant weakness and fragility of the bones compel further inactivity, thus perpetuating a vicious cycle.) In one study conducted in the USSR, a group of 60-year-olds was placed on a supervised program of rigorous exercises. Tests, 10 years later, revealed them to be physiologically younger than they were at 60.

The decline of sexual activity, too, seems to a large

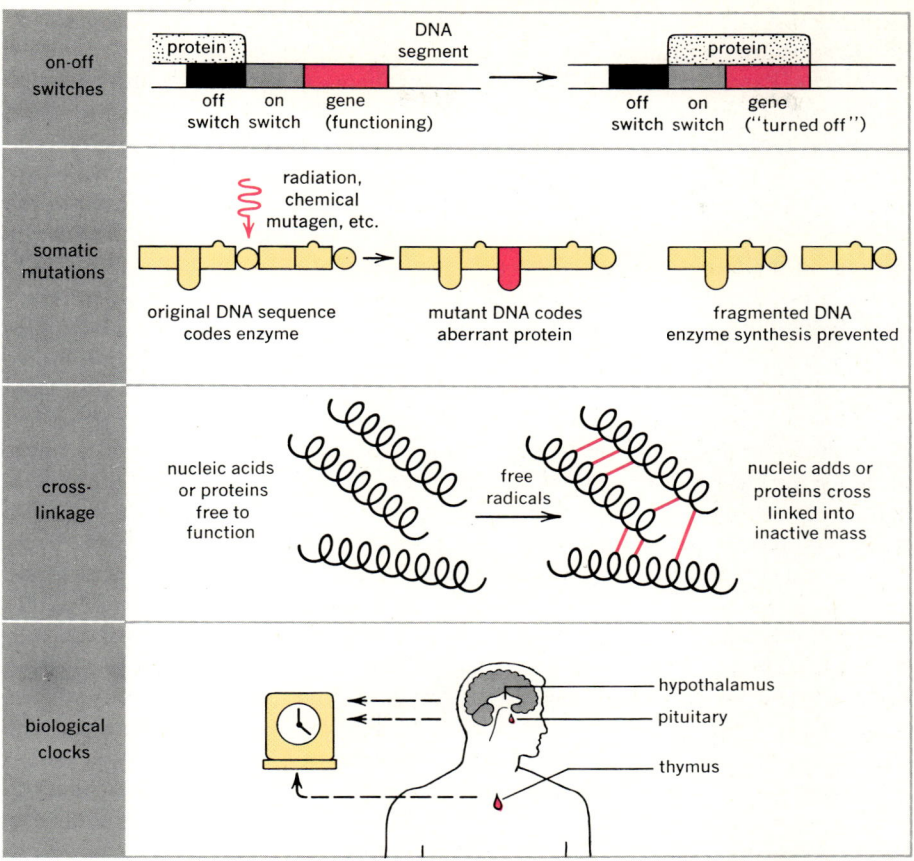

FIGURE 36-6 Some current hypotheses on the mechanisms of aging.

extent to be the result of a feeling that this is what is expected of older people. Recent studies have highlighted the fact that sexual activity can continue throughout adult life, and there is a growing feeling that nursing homes and other centers for the aged should make provisions for greater privacy and opportunities for sexual relationships.

THEORIES ON SENESCENCE

The discouraging catalog of changes in the aging body outlined in the preceding section is a spectre that awaits all of us, if we are fortunate enough to avoid the pitfalls of accident and disease along the way to extreme age. Yet if we knew precisely how the body ages, we might be able to modify and perhaps prevent or even reverse the aging process. Aging research is now an actively growing field, and a number of theories have been advanced in attempts to explain senescence (Figure 36-6).

Many scientists are inclined to believe that aging is an integral part of the development of the organism that proceeds in programmed sequence throughout the lifetime, controlled by the genes. Aging and death, they argue, actually have an adaptive value for the species, since they remove one generation to make room for the next. There is some evidence to support

some sort of **genetic control of the aging process.** For example, children of long-lived parents in turn tend to live longer than those whose parents died young. The "Hayflick limit" of cells in tissue culture also seems to agree with the concept of an inherently finite lifespan, with an upper limit for humans of about 110 to 115 years.

USC gerontologist Bernard Strehler has suggested that the aging process may be programmed by the **on-off switches** contained in the genes. In the course of development, numerous genes are successively turned on, contribute their part to the building of the organism, and then are turned off, never to function again. Other genes, involved in the day-to-day maintenance of the body, continue to function. The deterioration of aging may occur when key genes are turned off, either accidentally or as part of the body's programmed instructions for the life cycle. Strehler believes that faulty translation of the genetic information relayed by messenger RNA may lie at the basis of this switching off of genes, which ultimately leaves the cells unable to perform their normal functions.

Various body systems are being scrutinized as possible **biological clocks** that govern aging and the lifespan. The **thymus,** for example, reaches its zenith of development in adolescence and then gradually atrophies. Fewer and less efficient T-cells are produced, and at the same time there is a drop in the number of circulating antibodies produced by B-cells. Paradoxically, as the body's immunological defenses against the disease decline, around the age of 50 an increase in circulating gamma globulins is observed; enlargement of the spleen and a proliferation of the plasma cells involved in antibody production, which also occur at this time, indicate intense activity in the immunological system. This increased activity is associated with autoimmune responses, as faulty lymphocytes begin to make errors in their recognition of self and non-self cells, mistaking some of the "self" cells for enemy invaders. Mutations in body cells, changing their antigenic properties, may be a contributing factor in these autoimmune reactions, which are believed to be a significant factor in the aging process.

The **hypothalamus** is another candidate for the body's biological clock. The various control centers of the hypothalamus and its hormones, which work through the pituitary to control and coordinate the glands of the endocrine system, have been implicated in the functioning of various cyclic processes in the body. Gerontologist W. Donner Denckla believes that the key to the aging process lies in an "aging hormone" secreted by the **pituitary,** which blocks the action of thyroxin.

While some aging researchers are searching the body for built-in time clocks that govern the human lifespan, others are looking for clues to the aging process in environmental influences on the body and its cells. They view the major causes of aging as lying in the "wear and tear" resulting from the continual insults of radiations, chemical mutagens, and temperature influences upon the body, its cells and biomolecules. Leslie Orgel of the Salk Institute postulates an "error catastrophe" resulting from **somatic mutations.** Radiations and chemical mutagens continually cause changes in the genes. The genes of a human being represent the end product of a long process of selection, weeding out the less efficient alternatives and allowing the best adapted to survive. Any particular mutation, or change in a gene will almost certainly be a negative change; the information molecules of the cell gradually become blurred with errors, which reduce the efficiency of the protein-synthesizing apparatus. The faulty enzymes produced may then cause a further deterioration of the templates, compounding the damages that ultimately result in aging and death. Although any particular mutation will affect only one cell, growing numbers of mutation-damaged cells are gradually accumulated. The accumulation of enough nonfunctional or abnormal cells in an organ will impair its functioning, and since the organs of the body are intricately interrelated, the deterioration of one organ may produce a spreading wave of damage to others.

Another current theory of senescence attributes the major effects of aging to **free-radical reactions,** which can produce damage at random in a biological system. Free radicals are highly reactive chemical substances, which are continually being generated in the media of the body. Free-radical reactions commonly occur in cells, especially when oxygen combines with unsaturated fats. Such reactions may result in **cross-linking** of biomolecules, immobilizing them and preventing them from functioning. Cross-linking of DNA in the genes might stop them from transmitting their information; a similar effect might be produced by cross-linking of the proteins that normally cover most of the DNA in the chromosomes, or the formation of cross-links between the proteins and DNA, preventing key genes from being turned on. Free-radical reactions producing cross-linkage of collagen fibers, which account for more than a third of all the body proteins, can have far-reaching effects, contributing to arteriosclerosis and hypertension, reduced lung activity, and a decline in muscle activity. Dense barriers of cross-linked collagen can interfere with the diffusion and active transport of substances across cell membranes, cutting off the flow of nutrients to the tissues. Cross-linking of other protein molecules can interfere with their normal metabolic reactions and may jam key enzyme systems of the body. Free-radical reactions might also contribute to the formation of a variety of inert chemical "gunk," which gradually builds up to clog the cell and interfere with its functioning. Insoluble particles of a yellowish "age pigment," **lipofuscin,** have been observed to accumulate in some cells with age. This waste product occupies 6 to 7 percent of the total volume of heart muscle cells by the age of 90, and in some types of cells it may occupy as much as 30 percent of the total volume. But whether the accumulation of senility pigments is a cause of aging or merely an accompanying effect is still uncertain.

The various theories of aging that have been advanced are not necessarily mutually exclusive. Many gerontologists, such as Nathan Shock, believe that aging is a complex process, with many contributing factors. Aging researchers are now testing hypotheses and exploring ways of actively intervening to slow or reverse the aging process.

RESEARCH ON PROLONGING LIFE

The medical advances of the past century have produced a steady increase in the average life expectancy of the population. Yet the actual life span of humans has remained unchanged. The dramatic increases in life expectancy have been the result of reductions of the probability of dying in younger age groups. Research on specific killer diseases has been aimed at permitting increasing numbers of people to live to the full length of the human life span. Studies of the aging process have had more exciting goals: to extend the period of vigorous life and, perhaps, to permit people to live beyond the normal span, to 120, 150, or even longer.

Some of the early aging studies bordered on what would now be regarded as quackery. Monkey testes were implanted in aging men, for example, in the hope that the introduced sex hormones would have a rejuvenating effect. Yet even such approaches have been fruitful to some degree: synthetic sex hormones now appear to help elderly men and menopausal women, delaying the onset of such degenerative diseases as arthritis and high blood pressure.

The role of nutrition in the aging process has been a fruitful subject of aging research. Deficiencies of vitamin C and B vitamins appear to accelerate in aging process, although excesses of these vitamins have not been found to lengthen the life span.

Many aging experiments have been conducted not on humans but on animals. In addition to the advantage of being able to manipulate the animal subjects at will and to control conditions to a greater degree than would be possible with humans, animals provide another crucial advantage as experimental models of aging. The life span of a mouse, for example, is far shorter than that of a man, and thus the entire sequence of development, from birth to death, can be studied within a reasonable time.

One of the "landmark" aging experiments was that of Clive McCay, back in 1932. McCay fed very young rats a diet sharply reduced in calories and found that some of them lived 50 percent longer than normal. Similar effects have since been demonstrated in a variety of other species. There is some evidence that underfeeding in early life can also extend the lives of humans: studies of extremely old people frequently disclose a history of undernutrition in childhood. However, it should be kept in mind that drastic underfeeding of both young animals and children produces a marked stunting of growth and also dramatically increases susceptibility to disease.

In efforts to eliminate the undesirable effects of underfeeding while still lengthening lifetime, later researchers have attempted to find specific factors that limit growth and aging. In experiments in the early 1960s at Monsanto Chemical Company, young chicks and weanling mice were fed a diet deficient in the essential amino acid tryptophan. Normal growth and development apparently ceased as long as this amino acid was withheld. After a year on the experimental diet, the animals were placed on a normal diet. Nor-

mal growth was resumed, and the year of "suspended development" was reflected in a year added to their lifetimes.

There is some evidence that restricting the diet of young animals may delay the onset of aging by operating through the immune system. UCLA researchers Roy Walford and Richard Liu have found that a low-calorie, low-protein diet delays maturation of the immune system in young mice, so that their immune responses seem low; but when the animals get older, their immune system actually works more effectively than in mice fed a normal diet. Walford suggests that this suppression of the immune system in early life may delay the appearance of autoantibodies that are believed to contribute to the aging process. Similar results, both in lengthening of the life span and in suppression of immune responses, have been obtained by lowering the body temperature of fish and other experimental animals.

The falling levels of thymosin in the blood observed with increasing age, and the concomitant decrease in the efficiency of immune surveillance by the T-cell, have prompted experiments on the rejuvenating effects of thymus transplants and thymus hormones, under way at the National Institute on Aging.

Other researchers are focusing their efforts on the problem of free-radical reactions and cross-linking of biomolecules. University of Nebraska researcher Denham Harman and other gerontologists have extended the life span of a variety of experimental animals, from fruit flies and roundworms to mice, by the addition of antioxidants, such as BHT (a common food additive) and vitamin E, to their diet. (Antioxidants block free-radical reactions between oxygen and unsaturated fats.) Enzymes that dissolve cross-linked biomolecules and substances such as β-aminopropionitrile (a substance occurring naturally in the chick pea), which prevent cross-linking of collagen, are being studied for antiaging potential.

Most of the current aging research has centered on the degenerative changes in the brain, attempting to prevent or reverse the impairments of mental function that are among the most pitiful aspects of senility. A drug called centrophenoxine, which retards the formation of lipofuscin, has been used experimentally to improve symptoms of senility in human patients. Another blocker of lipofuscin accumulation, dimethylaminoethanol (DMAE), produced a 27 percent increase in the life span of experimental mice. DMAE is a natural body chemical, which is normally converted to choline; it acts as a stabilizer of the lysosome membrane. (According to some aging researchers, leakage of lytic enzymes into the cell through the lysosome membrane is a key factor in aging.) Isoprinosine, which stimulates a renewal of the ribosomes and thus improves the effectiveness of protein synthesis, has been found to improve the brain functioning of aged animals and is also being tested as an antiviral agent.

DEATH

People have always tried to shield themselves from the thought of personal death. Throughout the ages, in society after society, some form of life after death has been held to exist. Yet from the TV newscasts to the cells within our own bodies, death is a constant presence in our lives.

All the animal species have been found to have a characteristic life span. Its length is roughly correlated with the size of the animal and its age at sexual maturity; the life span of an animal is inversely related to its metabolic rate. In natural communities, few organisms live out their full span and die a "natural" death—predators, accidents, and disease take a high toll. Until the revolution brought about by modern medical advances, this was true for humans also. Even now, no one really dies directly of "old age," but the deterioration of the bodies of extremely aged people leaves them easy prey to accidents and disease that would bring only minor discomfort to a younger person.

What is death? It may be defined as the cessation of all metabolic processes. In a multicellular organism such as a human being, death usually results from the failure of some vital organ to continue carrying on its vital functions, due to accident, disease, or degeneration. When one vital organ fails, the effects of this failure spread throughout the interrelated systems of the body. Regardless of which organ was the first to fail, the effects of this failure ultimately reach the circulatory system, and the heart stops. Deprived of the oxygen and nutrients delivered by the circulatory system, the cells of the body begin to die off. Nerve cells are the most vulnerable: irreparable brain damage sets in about four or five minutes after a person's heart has stopped. Other types of cells and tissues are slower to die, but eventually all succumb. Death of the cells is accompanied by rapid and irreversible changes in the structure of the cell, and ultimately a lysis of its membrane and contents. The organizing influence is gone.

The definition of death given above was simple, but death itself can sometimes be difficult to determine. At one time, stoppage of the heart was the accepted definition of "clinical death." Yet now it is often possible to resuscitate a person who has seemingly "died," by electrical stimulation or even mere manipulation of the heart and lungs. The growing practice of organ transplants has focused attention on the need for a reliable definition of death: an essential organ to be used for a transplant should be removed as quickly as possible after death, so that it will not deteriorate. Yet, it would be morally wrong to remove such an organ if there were any possibility that its original owner could still be resuscitated. Full agreement has not yet been reached on a firm definition of death, but several criteria are now commonly used as guidelines: an absence of heartbeat; an absence of respiration; and a flat EEG for several hours. Recent studies by French researchers may ultimately bring firmer assurance to diagnoses of clinical death: certain enzyme levels in the cerebrospinal fluid have been found to be correlated with the true status of the body. In cases when the enzyme levels were normal, even with a flat EEG, the patients ultimately recovered.

Even after clinical death, the body still continues for a time with some of its normal functions. Hair continues to grow for several hours, the liver converts glucose to glycogen, and the muscles contract. **Rigor mortis,** a rigid stiffening of the body that sets in about two hours after death, is due to an irreversible conversion of ATP to ADP. The stored ATP in the muscles provides the energy for muscle contraction, but then the muscles remain contracted because there is no resynthesis of the ATP needed to power muscle relaxation. Rigor mortis persists for about 30 hours, at which time the muscle cells themselves break down and become flaccid.

Medical science has now acquired skills that permit the prolongation of life far beyond the point where death once would have been considered inevitable. Medical ethics often seem to compel heroic efforts to prevent a patient from dying even when the prospects for eventual full recovery have become hopeless. In recent years there has been a growing concern over whether it is rational and humane to keep a terminally ill patient lingering in a drug-dulled agony. Questions have even been raised of whether **euthanasia,** the active taking of the life of a hopelessly ill person (as opposed to passively allowing the person to die), might be justified under certain conditions. Yet to sanction the taking of lives runs counter to the code of ethics on which our society is based. Such questions are not easily resolved. Recently the U.S. Supreme Court stated, "We need not resolve the difficult question of when life begins and ends. When those trained in the respective disciplines of medicine, philosophy, and theology are unable to arrive at any consensus, the judiciary is not in a position to speculate as to the answer."

SUMMARY

Growth in the inorganic world occurs by accretion; in living organisms growth occurs by intussusception.

Growth in size can result from an increase in cell size, cell division, and/or the deposition of material outside cells.
Growth of living organisms also includes differentiation.
The development of human body structures and skills is slower than that of nearly any other animal of comparable size.
Human growth shows periods of acceleration, deceleration, and consolidation, with considerable individual variation.
From fetus to infant to adult, the relative proportion of the head decreases steadily as legs and other body parts grow disproportionately.
In humans growth ceases by about 18 to 21 in boys, 16 to 18 in girls.
During childhood, growth in size is accompanied by modifications of body structures (e.g., calcification of bones) and development of motor and intellectual skills.
In adolescence the primary and secondary sexual characteristics are developed.
Growth is affected by:
Quantity and quality of food
Disease
Heredity
Sex
Endocrine function
Growth abnormalities include:
Giantism
Dwarfism (midgets, achondroplastic dwarfs, cretins)
Neoplasms
Progeria
Aging or senescence is characterized by a gradual deterioration of structures and functions, resulting in an increased susceptibility to accident and disease.
A progressive decline in the body's efficiency begins after maturity is reached.
Aging changes include:
Loss of nerve cells
Lessening of sensory acuity
Degenerative changes in the circulatory system
Deterioration of elastic fibers, cross-linkage of collagen, and deposition of salts (wrinkling and stiffness)
Decalcification of bones
Gradual loss of fluid, drop in glomerular filtration rate
Hormonal changes (menopause)

Theories of senescence include:
Genetic control of aging process by "on-off switches" of genes or the action of biological clocks in the thymus, hypothalamus, pituitary, and so on
Somatic mutations resulting in "error catastrophe"
Cross-linkage of biomolecules via free-radical reactions
Death is the cessation of all metabolic processes.
In higher organisms, death usually results from the failure of some vital organ to continue its vital functions, due to accident, disease, or degeneration.
The effects of failure of a vital organ spread to other body systems, ultimately leading to heart stoppage and irreversible brain damage.
With modern techniques, persons can sometimes be successfully resuscitated after heart stoppage.
Lack of electrical activity in the brain is now an important criterion of death.
Rigor mortis is a result of irreversible conversion of ATP to ADP; muscles remain contracted for about 30 hours until muscle cells degenerate.
Euthanasia is the taking of the life of a hopelessly ill person.

QUESTIONS FOR REVIEW AND THOUGHT

1 In what ways does growth of living organisms differ from growth in the nonliving world?
2 Compare human growth to that of other animals.
3 Give examples of the differential growth of parts of the body.
4 What is the Hayflick limit? How does it accord with the theories of a built-in time clock of aging and death?
5 What factors affect growth?
6 Distinguish between benign and malignant neoplasms.
7 What is progeria?
8 Which of the changes that typically accompany aging do you think are normal parts of the aging process, and which could be avoided by a change in life style?
9 Discuss the major theories of aging. Are any of them mutually contradictory?
10 What experimental approaches to the prolongation of life are now being pursued?
11 What criteria do you think would form a valid definition of death?

DISEASE AND THE BODY'S DEFENSES

37

Throughout life, a human being is constantly at war. Enemies lurk both without and within. Potentially pathogenic microbes swarm in air, water, food, and on the surfaces of objects; they congregate at the major entrances into the body, ready to slip inside if there is a breach in the defenses, and some may even exist inside the body in an uneasy truce with the body defenders, ready to multiply and spread if exposure, malnutrition, or mental stress temporarily lowers the resistance.

We have already encountered a number of homeostatic mechanisms, involving the nervous and endocrine systems, the circulatory system, the excretory system, and others, which normally function to maintain the dynamic equilibrium of body processes. These homeostatic mechanisms are a major protection against disease and death. But one weak link—for example, a liver damaged by cancer, a heart rendered less efficient by degenerative changes, lungs filled with fluid due to a bacterial infection—can lead to a chain reaction of physiological catastrophe. Even the body itself can sometimes become its own enemy, attacking its own cells instead of invaders.

In this chapter the major types of pathogens and other assaults on the body's integrity are described, along with the body's powerful defenses against them.

SOME HISTORICAL PERSPECTIVE

People often sigh longingly for a return of the "good old days." Their rosy thoughts of the past bear little resemblance of the actual reality. Pollution? Picture drinking water polluted with raw sewage, and air redolent of the smell of smoky lamps or the stench of mass bonfires burning the bodies of plague victims. Overpopulation? Hardly a problem in a time when large families were actively sought because so few of the children born survived beyond infancy and childhood. Always the spectre of disease hovered, making a mockery of human ambitions. Even the causes of disease were unknown, and were imagined to lie in the malign influence of evil spirits or mysterious imbalances of "body humors." Some folk remedies were effective and represented the results of shrewd empirical observations; but many treatments, even those used by physicians, were of little avail and frequently killed more patients than they cured. Since the causes of diseases were unknown, there was no scientific basis for searching for means of prevention and cure.

The pioneering efforts of such scientists as Pasteur and Lister riveted the attention of the scientific community on the microbial world. Here were the villains. Contagious diseases were caused by germs, microscopic parasites that were transmitted from one infected organism to another.

With the passage of time, disease after disease was associated with a particular microbe or group of microbes, and mechanisms of its transmission and action were worked out. The advent of sulfa drugs, and then penicillin and the other antibiotics, brought marked advances in the control of bacterial diseases. Improved techniques of vaccination led to equally dramatic advances in the prevention of viral diseases. Advances in controlling parasitic diseases have often been achieved through the avenue of tracing the life cycles of the parasites and discovering vulnerable stages in which the chain of infection can be broken.

Medical advances and improved standards of sanitation have dramatically increased the average life span. Today, especially in the developed nations, degenerative diseases and cancer have replaced infectious diseases as the major killers (Figure 37-1).

DISEASES

A complete categorization of the diseases and afflictions that can beset humanity would be enought to make one blanche. There are literally thousands of them. Most fit under one of a few basic categories: bacterial, viral, fungus and other parasitic diseases, cancer, and degenerative diseases. The causes of some diseases that afflict us have not yet been determined.

Bacterial Diseases

More than 250,000 bacteria can fit comfortably on the head of a pin. Under ideal conditions, a single bacterium can give rise to this number of descendants in a matter of hours. In part, it is their potential to multiply to staggering proportions that makes pathogenic bacteria so dangerous.

Bacteria are microscopic single-celled organisms with a rather primitive structure: they lack a distinct nucleus (although they do have chromosomes) and the typical cell organelles; the bacterial cell is enclosed in a cell wall, but unlike a plant cell wall, the bacterial cell wall is made of a complex of proteins, polysaccharides, and sometimes lipids. Under unfavorable conditions some bacteria can convert themselves to a resistant form called a **spore,** which can withstand the effects of even such extreme influences as detergents and high temperatures. (But spores can be killed by sterilizing with steam under pressure.)

Bacteria can be classified in three main types (Figure 37-2): rod-shaped **bacilli,** spherical **cocci,** and corkscrew-shaped **spirilla.** They may occur singly or in chains or clumps of two, three, or more.

Far from all bacteria are pathogenic (i.e., cause diseases). Decay bacteria in the soil return the materials of dead organisms to the pool of usable substances; nitorgen-fixing bacteria convert atmospheric nitrogen to forms usable by plants and ultimately by animals and humans. Bacteria living in the human intestinal tract not only do not cause disease, but contribute vitamins to the nutrition of their host.

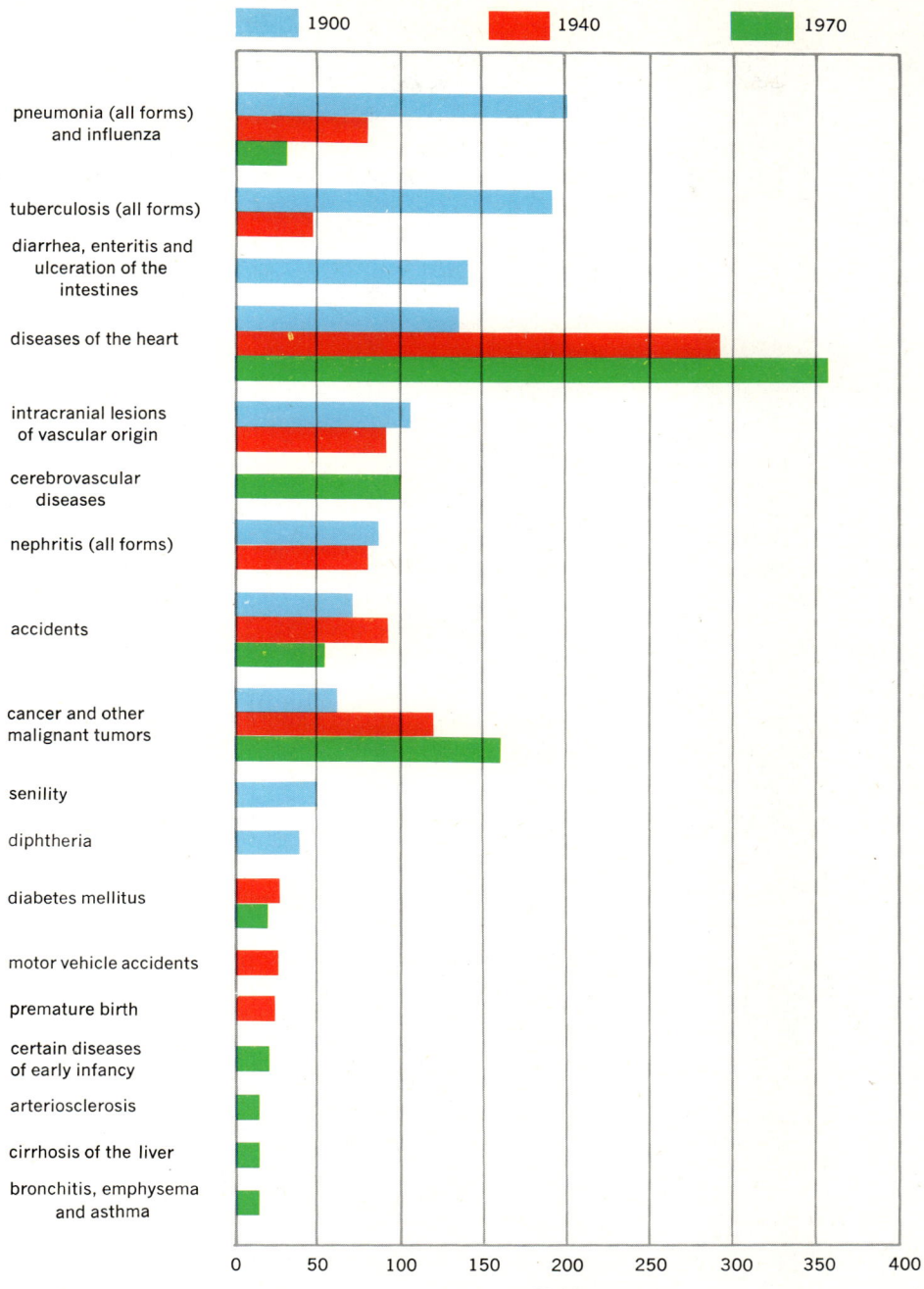

FIGURE 37-1 The increase in life-span from 1900 to the present has been accompanied by dramatic changes in the major causes of death.

The legion of disease-causing bacteria, however, includes such notables as the pathogens of typhoid fever *(Salmonella typhosa),* tuberculosis *(Mycobacterium tuberculosis),* cholera *(Vibrio comma),* syphilis *(Treponema pallidum),* pneumonia *(Diplococcus pneumoniae),* scarlet fever and rheumatic fever *(Streptococcus pyogenes),* and food poisoning (species of the genus *Salmonella).*

The causes and means of transmission of these and other diseases that had plagued humanity through the ages remained obscure until the nineteenth century.

The epic work of Pasteur in 1865 in the isolation of the tiny parasite causing a disease that was killing silkworms and threatening the existence of the French silk industry led to the **germ theory of disease.** According to this theory, communicable diseases are caused by microscopic parasites that are transmitted (directly or indirectly) from one infected organism to another.

That this theory is also pertinent to diseases in humans was definitively established through the experiments of Robert Koch, a German physician who first

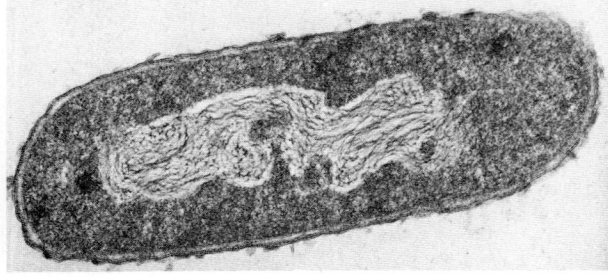

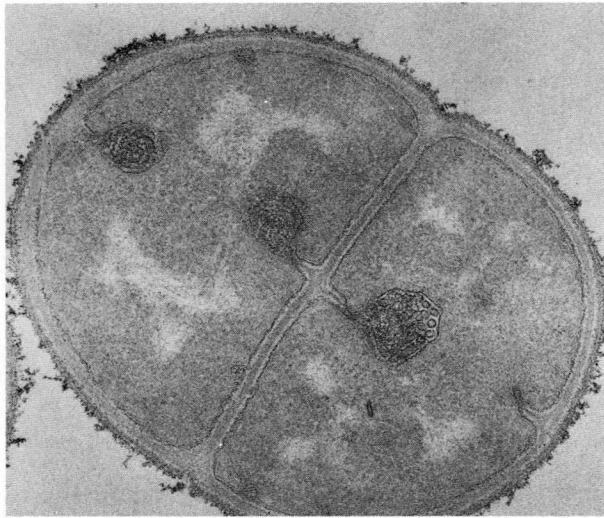

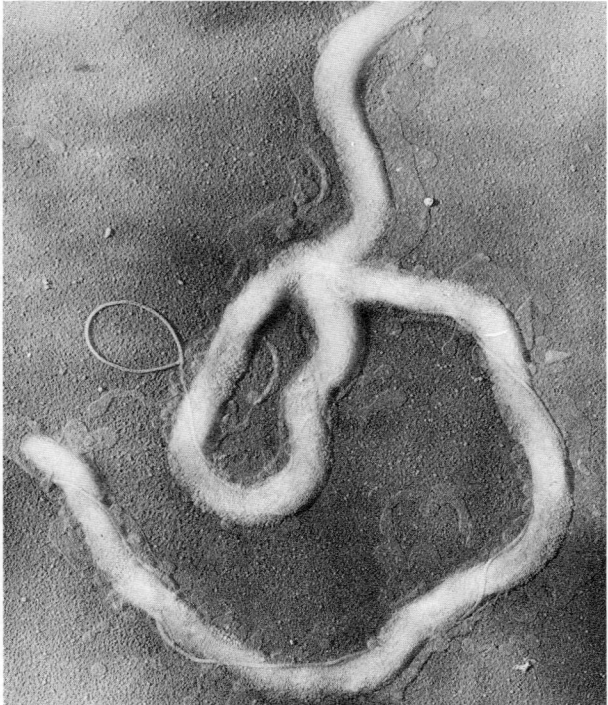

FIGURE 37-2 Typical bacteria: (A) bacillus (*E. coli* B); (B) coccus (*Sarcina urea,* dividing); (C) spirillum (a spirochete with an axial filament).

isolated the bacterium responsible for the cattle disease anthrax and then focused his attention on the dread human disease tuberculosis. In 1882 he discovered the causative factor in tuberculosis, the tubercle bacillus, *Mycobacterium tuberculosis,* and formulated rules for identifying the causative agent of a disease that are still used today. According to this set of rules, called **Koch's postulates,** (1) the organism must be found to be *always* present in the diseased organism; (2) the suspected organism must be isolated from the diseased plant or animal and grown in pure culture; (3) the isolated organisms, after growth in pure culture, must produce the symptoms characteristic of the disease when reinoculated into healthy animals or plants; and (4) the newly diseased animals or plants must yield the same microorganisms as those found originally.

Following the pioneering work of Pasteur and Koch, the causative agents of many bacterial diseases were identified, and the means by which they were transmitted were determined.

Pathogens of infectious diseases may be transferred by direct contact, as may occur while cleaning or feeding a sick person, in handshaking, kissing, or sexual intercourse. Transmission may also occur by less direct routes. Bacteria may be breathed into the respiratory tract, either carried on minute dust particles or borne on the droplets expelled by a sneeze. They may be taken into the alimentary tract, sometimes in milk from cows whose udders are infected with pathogens (such as the tubercle bacillus), but more often by a chain of contamination involving various numbers of steps. A parent thriftily finishing off the partly eaten food left by a sick child may catch a cold as a reward. Money has been found to swarm with bacteria, which could be transferred to the mouth in nailbiting or other nervous habits. Food handlers who do not take appropriate sanitary measures after excretion can spread disease; if they are ill or are **carriers** of a disease (i.e., harboring active colonies of disease-producing bacteria without themselves showing signs of the disease), their feces will contain disease bacteria, which can be transferred from hands to food, and from there to the eaters of the food. Flies that alight on excrement and then on food can spread bacteria; biting insects can deposit or inject disease germs into their victims.

After the infectious agent has gained access into the body by one means or another, an **incubation period** characteristically follows. During this time there are no outward signs of infection, but within the body the invading pathogens are multiplying at the expense of their host. Eventually, after a period that varies from a few hours to a matter of weeks or months, depending on the disease, the numbers of the pathogens are so great that they cause a disturbance of the normal life processes of the host, and the outward signs of disease become manifest. Then follows a series of pitched battles within the body, with the body defenses pitted against the invaders.

The harm to the host organism caused by pathogenic bacteria is usually produced by **toxins,** poisons manufactured by the invading bacteria. These are of two types, exotoxins and endotoxins.

Exotoxins diffuse out from the living bacterial cell into the surrounding medium—either culture medium (when the bacteria are grown artificially) or tissues of the host organism. A filtrate from a medium in which exotoxin-producing bacteria have been growing will cause the same symptoms as a culture of the bacteria themselves. In fact, the rapid lethal effects of eating foods contaminated with *Clostridium botulinum* are due not to multiplication of the bacteria within the host, but rather to the action of exotoxins accumulated during anaerobic multiplication of the bacteria within the stored food before it is eaten. Exotoxins are proteins and include some of the most powerful poisons known. The exotoxins of tetanus and botulism are far more powerful than any snake venom. A single ounce of *Clostridium botulinum* toxin would be enough to kill 400 million people!

Endotoxins, on the other hand, are produced within the bacterial cell and are not released until the cell dies and disintegrates. They are less toxic than the exotoxins, and are lipoprotein-polysaccharide complexes. The bacteria that cause typhoid fever and Asiatic cholera are among those that produce endotoxins. (Generally, bacteria produce either exotoxins or endotoxins, but not both.)

Viral Diseases

Viruses lie at the very borderline of life. Though bacteria are primitive, viruses are so rudimentary that many scientists do not consider them to be truly alive. Ranging in size from about 10 mμ (e.g., the influenza virus) to about 500 mμ (e.g., ornithosis virus), viruses are little more than nucleic acids, enclosed within an outer protein coat. Some viruses that infect humans have an inner core of RNA (e.g., poliomyelitis, influenza, and mumps viruses), while others have a DNA core (e.g., smallpox and yellow fever viruses). Like living organisms, viruses reproduce according to their nucleic acid-encoded blueprints, but they can do so *only* within a living host, utilizing the host's nucleic acid- and protein-synthesizing facilities to manufacture virus particles.

Structurally, viruses are classified according to their basic symmetry: spherical or cubic (e.g., adenovirus, chicken pox), helical or screw (e.g., influenza), or complex (e.g., vaccinia). Some common pathogenic

A

B

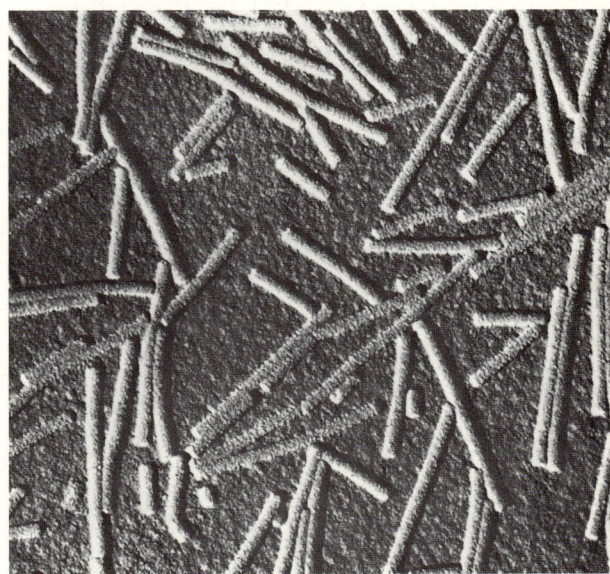

C

FIGURE 37-3   Some typical viruses: poliovirus (A); T5 bacteriophage, showing polyhedral head (B); tobacco mosaic virus (C).

viruses are shown in Figure 37-3.

Yellow fever was one of the first human diseases to be attributed to a **filterable virus,** a microorganism so

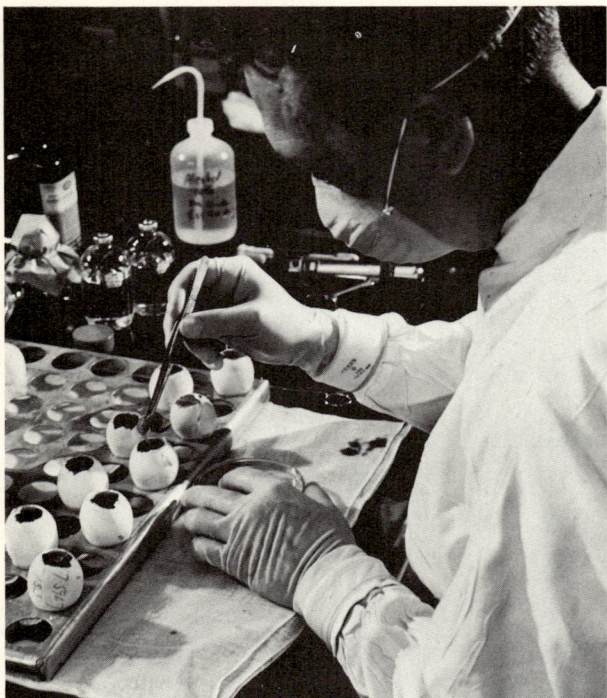

FIGURE 37-4 Viruses for vaccines are typically cultured in chick embryos.

tiny that it cannot be seen with the most powerful optical microscope and passes through a filter fine enough to trap the smallest bacteria. This discovery was made in a heroic series of studies, in which a medical research team headed by Walter Reed in Cuba deliberately infected themselves with the yellow fever pathogen through bites of the *Aedes* mosquito. (One of the researchers died.)

Paradoxically, virus research was conducted many years before scientists realized that such organisms existed. At the end of the eighteenth century, the English physician Edward Jenner performed his epoch-making experiments establishing that inoculation with material from the blisters of a person suffering from the mild disease cowpox (vaccinia) conferred immunity to the dreaded scourge smallpox. Nearly a century later, Pasteur used similar techniques of inoculation to provide immunity to rabies, dramatically saving the life of a boy bitten by a mad dog in 1885. In this case, since there was no naturally occurring mild form of the disease to use in making up a vaccine, Pasteur made his own by passing a rabies infection through a series of different animals until its virulence was attenuated. Pasteur was unable to isolate the germ responsible, but the technique worked.

As the years went by, more and more diseases, including poliomyelitis, influenza, measles, and the common cold were traced to viruses. Progress in the study of virus diseases was slow until techniques were developed for growing the viruses outside the living organism, first in chick embryos, and then in mashes of tissues, bathed in blood (with the addition of penicillin to stop the growth of bacteria in the cultures). The latter innovation, for which the American microbiologist J. F. Enders and his colleagues T. H. Weller and F. C. Robbins shared a Nobel Prize, made the polio virus readily accessible to scientific study for the first time. (Prior to Enders' discovery, the polio virus could be grown only in living human or monkey nerve tissue.) This discovery paved the way for the development of successful antipolio vaccines by Salk and Sabin.

The demonstrable mutability (i.e., genetic change) of viruses has been an important factor in the efforts of scientists to derive vaccines against virus-caused diseases. On the positive side of the ledger, a virus strain can be readily adapted to a new host, such as a tissue culture or chick embryo (Figure 37-4); in the process it often loses most of its virulence for its original host, but may still retain enough similarity to the original form to produce immunity to the original disease. Such an "attenuated" virus can then be used as a vaccine. On the negative side, the mutability of viruses sometimes results in the appearance of a new, more virulent strain, to which a person vaccinated against the original form has no immunity. During the major Asian flu epidemics of 1957 and 1968, the United States had splendid demonstrations of the speed with which concerted efforts of medical researchers and drug companies produced and distributed a new vaccine to counter a new strain of the influenza virus, which was reaching epidemic proportions.

In addition to the numerous disease-causing viruses that afflict humanity, there are also viruses that cause diseases in other vertebrates, in insects, in plants, and even in bacteria. The latter viruses, called **bacteriophages** ("bacteria eaters"), have become extremely valuable subjects of study for researchers in genetics.

Fungus Diseases

From the familiar bread mold to penicillin to billions of dollars of crop losses, the effects of fungi on our lives are far greater than we realize. Air, soil, and water teem not only with microbes, but with microscopic spores of fungi. Many of these fungi are harmless, others produce economic losses by infection of crop plants or spoilage of food and materials; still others are dangerous parasites that may attack plants, animals, and even humans.

Fungus diseases of humans range from common skin infections such as ringworm and athlete's foot to severe and sometimes fatal systemic **mycoses,** caused by less "well-adapted" parasites that are not normally found in living organisms. These fungi normally live a quiet saprophytic life, feeding on decomposing matter in the soil, and they may wreak havoc on the human system if they are accidentally introduced by inhalation or through a wound.

On the positive side of the ledger are the yeasts that produce alcoholic beverages and make dough rise, and numerous antibiotic-producing fungi such as the *Penicillium* mold (Figure 37-5).

Other Parasitic Diseases

That 20-foot-long tapeworms might be feeding inside one's intestinal tract is not a pleasant thought. Yet millions of people are infested with tapeworms and other parasites.

A well-adapted parasite does not kill its host, or even sicken it very severely—for if all the hosts were killed by their parasites, or made too ill to feed and reproduce, the parasites would soon disappear also. Trouble arises when a new host moves into the area, one to which the parasite has not adapted through long ages of mutual evolution. Such is the case in vast areas of tropical Africa, infested by tsetse flies carrying the trypanosomes that cause sleeping sickness. Trypanosome infestation is endemic among the native fauna, but for these African animals it is only a minor inconvenience at most. In humans and their livestock, trypanosomes run wild. Multiplying explosively in the bloodstream, they destroy blood cells and produce anemia, then move on to the nervous system, destroying tissues of the brain and spinal cord, producing profound lethargy and often death.

Parasites that afflict humans for the most part belong to several major groups of organisms: protozoa, such as the trypanosomes of sleeping sickness, the amebas responsible for amebic dysentery, and the plasmodia that produce malaria; and various flatworms (e.g., tapeworms and trematodes) and roundworms (e.g., pinworms, trichina worms, and filarial worms).

Often the parasite has a rather complicated life cycle, living successively in a series of hosts (Figure 37-6). The malaria parasite, for example, is transmitted to humans and other animals (principally apes, monkeys, birds, and reptiles) by the bite of an infested mosquito, which has drawn blood from an infested person or animal. Tapeworms develop in the digestive tract and shed segments, bearing fertilized eggs, in the feces. If the feces are eaten, as by a rooting hog, the eggs hatch in the intestines; the worm larvae burrow through the intestinal wall, and migrate to the muscles, where they encyst. A person eating improperly cooked meat containing encysted tapeworm eggs becomes infested in turn when gastric

FIGURE 37-5 A colony of *Penicillium chrysogenum,* a mutant form of which now produces nearly all the world's penicillin.

juices free the larvae from their cysts and they develop into adult worms in the person's intestines. Schistosomiasis, the second most prevalent disease in the world (the first is malaria), is caused by parasitic blood flukes (schistosomes), which mate in the victim's blood vessels. Their eggs pass out through the urine and feces and contaminate rivers and streams, developing successively into two different types of larvae, one of which infests snails (an intermediate host) and the other that penetrates the skin of humans swimming or bathing in the infested water.

Advances against parasitic diseases have been achieved through two major approaches, necessitating a thorough knowledge of the parasite's life cycle: first, through drugs that kill the parasites, and, second, through environmental control of intermediate hosts—for example, extermination of mosquitoes to control malaria and sleeping sickness and the development of molluscicides to kill the intermediate host snails that carry schistosome larvae.

Many parasites, particularly the various worms, generally do not kill their victims. But in living off their victims' tissues and body products, the parasites sap the energies of the hosts, leaving them in a debilitated state. Then the host can fall prey much more easily to bacterial and viral infections that may in turn prove fatal.

Cancer

Heart disease is by far the biggest killer in America today. Yet if you ask people what disease they fear

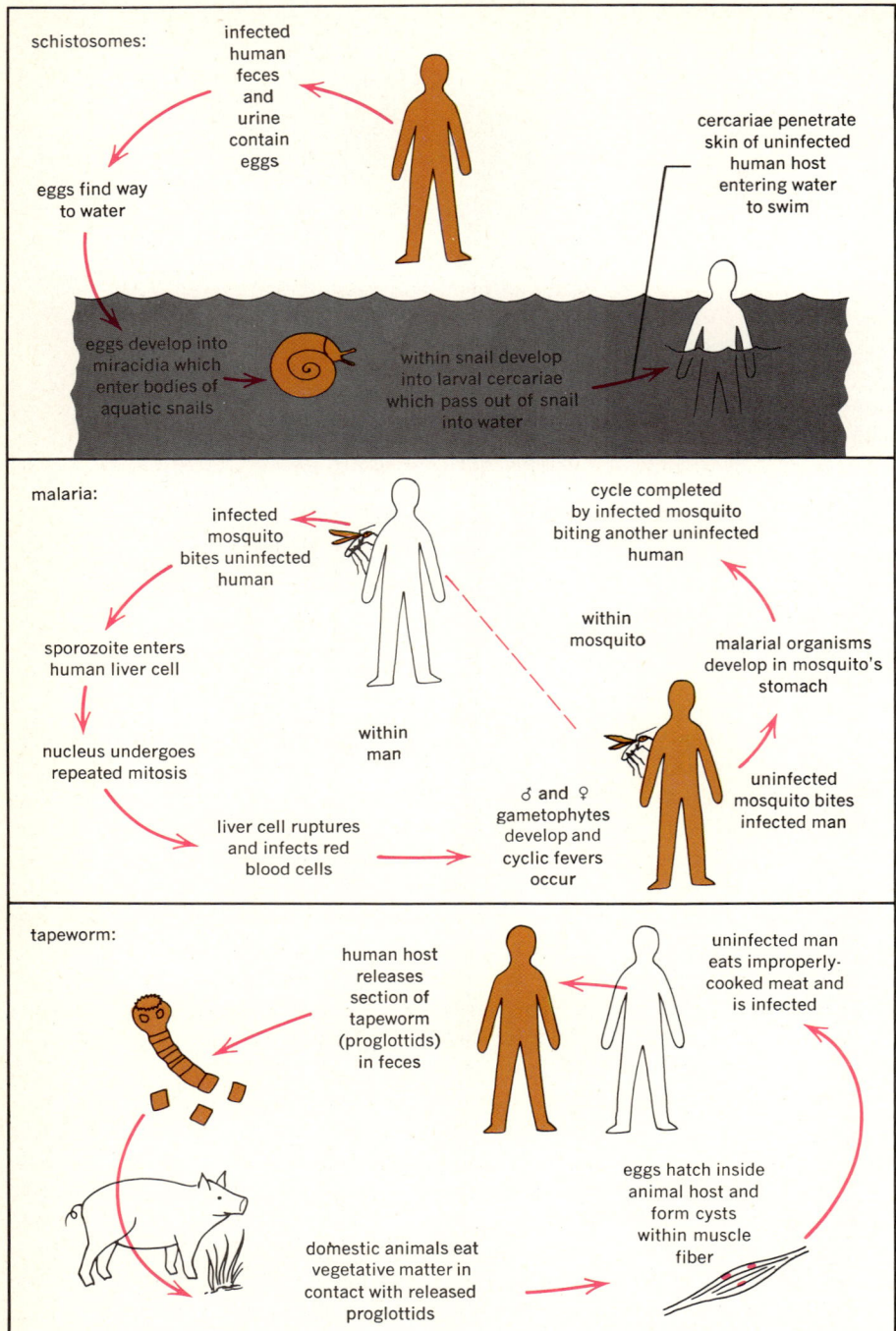

FIGURE 37-6 Life cycles of some common parasites: schistosome, malaria plasmodia, and tapeworm.

schistosomes:

infected human feces and urine contain eggs

cercariae penetrate skin of uninfected human host entering water to swim

eggs find way to water

eggs develop into miracidia which enter bodies of aquatic snails

within snail develop into larval cercariae which pass out of snail into water

malaria:

infected mosquito bites uninfected human

cycle completed by infected mosquito biting another uninfected human

sporozoite enters human liver cell

within mosquito

malarial organisms develop in mosquito's stomach

nucleus undergoes repeated mitosis

within man

uninfected mosquito bites infected man

liver cell ruptures and infects red blood cells

♂ and ♀ gametophytes develop and cyclic fevers occur

tapeworm:

human host releases section of tapeworm (proglottids) in feces

uninfected man eats improperly-cooked meat and is infected

eggs hatch inside animal host and form cysts within muscle fiber

domestic animals eat vegetative matter in contact with released proglottids

most, the answer will invariably be cancer. Cancer is a major killer in its own right, taking the lives of more than 360,000 Americans each year. But numbers alone are not the reason for the dread cancer evokes. Cancer is an insidious disease, in which body tissues suddenly turn traitor, multiplying uncontrollably and invading and choking off healthy tissues. Why do cells suddenly run wild, and how can the process be controlled or reversed? Despite billions of dollars already invested in cancer research, the field still holds more questions than answers. Encouraging progress is being made, however, and several promising approaches may be just on the threshold of providing cancer cures.

It has been suggested that cancer is not a single disease, but rather a hundred or more different diseases. Cancer strikes the young as well as the old, although it becomes far more prevalent in middle and old age. It may affect virtually any tissue of the body: lung, brain, breast, skin, bone, blood, reproductive, intestinal, liver, and so on. But in essentially all cases there is at least a single basic common characteristic: the cells exhibit a wild, uncontrolled growth. Whereas normal cells "recognize" their neighbors and cease growing upon contact with them, cancer cells show no such recognition and contact inhibition. Instead, cancer cells continue wild growth, piling over one another in a disorderly array. They literally choke out their normal neighbors.

Another common characteristic of cancerous tissue, and a critical factor in the deadliness of this disease, is the phenomenon of **metastasis.** Cancer cells are capable of dislodging from their original site of growth, entering the bloodstream or lymph channels, and being dispersed to other regions of the body. At these new sites, the metastasizing cancer cells continue the growth patterns characteristic of the original cancerous tissue.

Cancers are commonly classified according to the types of tissues in which they arise: for example, **carcinoma,** arising in epithelial tissues; **sarcomas,** which begin in connective tissue; and **leukemias,** the blood cancers. Neoplasms may also be classified according to the degree of spread, in four graduated stages: a stage I cancer is limited to its site of origin, while stage IV denotes widespread metastasis.

The experimental evidence seems to indicate that in some manner DNA plays a fundamental role in cancer. The nature of this role is obscure. Some have theorized that a mutation in the genetic code causes a cell to continue multiplying without regard either to normal replacement requirements or to the normal mechanism of contact inhibition. Others have suggested that the off-switches that gradually slow down the growth of the rapidly multiplying cells of the embryo somehow malfunction in cancer cells. Still others have speculated (without necessarily contradicting the preceding theories) that a virus plays a strategic role in the onset of cancer. There is considerable evidence implicating viruses in at least some human cancers, but whether viruses are causative factors in all cancers is not known. It is thought that the viral nucleic acid may become incorporated into the cell DNA.

Further evidence seems to indicate that viral invasion (or DNA mutation) will not result in cancer unless certain contributing factors—chemicals called **carcinogens**—are present at the same time. Certain aromatic hydrocarbons, aromatic amines, azo dyes, nitrosamines, and mycotoxins (poisons produced by fungi, such as the molds that grow on peanuts) have been shown to be carcinogens. Exactly how these chemicals act is still unclear; Nobel Prize-winning cancer researcher C. B. Huggins has suggested that carcinogens may act directly on the cellular DNA, inducing changes in the genetic material.

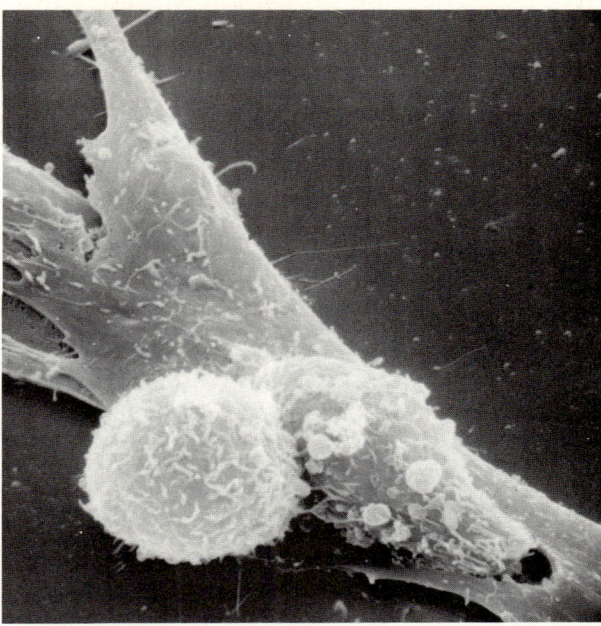

FIGURE 37-7 Scanning electron micrograph of three human cancer cells (malignant melanoma), grown in culture, ×3000.

The immune system is also involved in the prevention and development of cancer. Cancer cells start out as normal body cells but are modified in various ways, enough so that they should be recognized as "foreign" by the body's defenders. It is believed that this is precisely what occurs—that little cancers are continually getting started and then being killed by the body's defense mechanisms before they can cause trouble. In a cancer victim, somehow the immunity mechanism has failed to recognize the cancer cells as "foreign" and has allowed them to multiply unhindered.

For years the standard treatments for cancer have been surgery, radiation therapy, and chemotherapy. If the cancer is caught early, before metastasis, frequently a cure can be effected by cutting out the cancerous tissues and any surrounding tissues suspected of harboring cancer cells. Many cancers, particularly deep-seated cancers that are not readily accessible to surgery, may be destroyed by exposure to radiation. Finely focused beams of X rays, rods of radioactive cobalt, needles or beads of radioactive gold, and other radiation sources are used. For cancer cells that originated in the thyroid gland and have metastasized, a solution of radioactive iodine can seek out and destroy the widespread foci of cancerous growth. (Cancer cells retain some of the physiological characteristics of the normal tissue from which they originated, though they do tend to dedifferentiate, reverting to more primitive, generalized forms.)

Modern technology has brought exciting new advances into the field of surgery. Laser beams, which can be focused far more sharply than a beam of X rays, have been used to destroy pigmented cancer cells known as melanoma, which absorb the laser beams selectively. Techniques are being developed for introducing dyes into nonpigmented cancer cells that would permit a similar selective destruction. Cryosurgery, the use of ultracold probes to kill cells, has also proved valuable in treating cancer. Cryosurgery permits a bloodless excision, minimizing the chance that stray cancer cells will be carried off by the bloodstream into other areas where they might settle down and form new tumors.

Many of the drugs currently being used in cancer chemotherapy were discovered empirically, in mass screening trials in which any chemicals that were found to kill cells were tested on cancer cells, and the most promising ones used in animal and then clinical trials. One of the problems with such drugs is that they typically kill not only cancer cells, but normal cells as well. They may be so toxic to the body as a whole that doses sufficient to eradicate the cancer also kill the patient. In recent years encouraging results have been obtained by using small doses of anticancer drugs such as adriamycin and methotrexate in combinations or in sequence, achieving a therapeutic effect at doses that still can be tolerated by the patient. Especially promising results in **combination chemotherapy** of cancer were reported by Italian researcher Gianni Bonadonna, who used a combination called CMF (cyclophosphamide, methotrexate, and fluorouracil) after mastectomy in a large-scale study of breast cancer sponsored by the U.S. National Cancer Institute. Long-term results in the treatment of leukemia and Hodgkins disease (a cancer of the lymph nodes) have also indicated the effectiveness of combinations of drugs. In another approach, the **drug rescue technique,** a toxic dose of an anticancer drug is given, and then, after a brief interval, a specific antidote to the drug. Because cancer cells metabolize much more actively than normal cells, they are more rapidly vulnerable to the drugs than the body as a whole and can be destroyed before the body has been seriously damaged. The antidote then "rescues" the patient from the drug's toxic effects.

Empirical gropings have provided some valuable ammunition for the fight against cancer. But a much surer approach to the goal of curing cancer would be to discover specific ways in which cancer cells differ from normal cells and tailor-make drugs to capitalize on such differences. Intensive research is currently focused on the search for specific metabolites that might be needed by cancer cells and not (or not as much) by normal cells. Asparaginase, which has shown some success against leukemia, works on this principle, because the cancerous cells are more dependent on supplies of the amino acid asparagine (which is destroyed by the enzyme) than normal cells. The cell membrane is another focus of intense interest among cancer researchers, since it is here that the crucial reaction of contact inhibition occurs in normal cells, and also here that the interaction with the body's immunity system takes place.

Perhaps the most promising approaches against cancer are those that involve a bolstering or stimulation of the body's own defense mechanisms. Recent approaches include the use of human interferon, isolated from donor blood; injections of BCG (a bacillus long used in Europe for immunization against tuberculosis) and other immunostimulators such as levamisole to mobilize the body's defenses; and the use of a tumor-specific "transfer factor" isolated from the blood of donors who have developed resistance to the particular type of cancer to provide passive immunity in cancer patients.

Degenerative Diseases

Anyone who has owned or used an old car knows that after a time it begins to require increasingly frequent and expensive trips to the service station as one part after another wears out or breaks down. It seems that some key parts and systems of the human body also do not come equipped with a "lifetime guarantee," but gradually deteriorate with age; unfortunately, unlike a car, bodies are strictly one to a customer, and there is no option of deciding to junk the old wreck and trade it in for a newer model.

The medical advances of the past century have brought a revolution in the patterns of human mortality. Infectious diseases used to be the major killers, claiming a large proportion of their victims among the very young. The development of effective drugs and immunizations has greatly reduced the mortality from infectious diseases, permitting vastly increased numbers of people to live to middle and old age, when they fall prey to a progressive deterioration of the structure and function of major organs and systems of the body. Degenerative diseases and cancer (which itself may be caused partly by a deterioration of the body's defense mechanisms) have become the major killers.

Some of the degenerative changes that accompany the aging process—such as the progressive loss of nerve cells, the deterioration of elastic fibers, cross-linkage of collagen, decalcification of bones, loss of working muscle tissue, and the deposition of salts, "aging pigment," and other nonfunctional elements in various organs—were noted in Chapter 36. One of the most crucial and vulnerable body systems is the circulatory system. Degenerative diseases of the heart and blood vessels are not only the number one killer in the developed countries, but also contribute to senility (through a less efficient supply of blood to the brain), deafness, kidney failure, and malfunctions of other organs and systems. Atherosclerosis, the build-up of fat deposits in the artery walls, narrows the blood-vessel lumen, raising the blood pressure, forcing the heart to work harder against the increased peripheral resistance, and increasing the possibility of thrombosis, which can cause catastrophic damage to heart, brain, or other vital structures. Even without the massive damage of a "cerebral accident" or myocardial infarction, hardening of the arteries (arteriosclerosis) can force a gradual slowdown and restriction of activities and a blunting of mental acuity.

What causes degenerative diseases? Are they a necessary concomitant of aging, a natural slowing down of the body's built-in "clock," or are they pathological processes, which could be arrested or reversed if we could only find the keys to their causes and mechanisms? Some conditions that were previously regarded as degenerative diseases, such as Parkinson's disease, are now believed to be the delayed results of slow-acting viruses, from an infection suffered much earlier in life. Other degenerative diseases, such as arthritis and multiple sclerosis, are thought to be autoimmune diseases, in which the body's defense mechanisms somehow become sensitized against specific types of the body's own cells and attack them. In multiple sclerosis, for example, one of the most common neurological diseases in Europe and North America, it is thought that circulating antibodies attack the nerve cell junctions and destroy the myelin sheaths of the nerve fibers, with destruction of white matter in spots scattered throughout the nervous system. Sensitization is believed to occur through a virus infection (possibly the measles virus), 10 to 15 years before the first symptoms of MS develop; a genetically determined susceptibility to such virus-induced sensitization of the immune system is believed to be involved. As the degeneration proceeds, mild blurring of vision, slurred speech, and muscular incoordination eventually develop into incapacitating disabilities.

Infectious agents and autoimmune responses may ultimately be found to play a role in heart disease as well, but the current feeling among the medical community is that this degenerative disease is produced by the combined factors of a whole life style. Overconsumption of carbohydrates and saturated fats, an oversedentary life, and the constant stress of deadlines and responsibilities are believed to contribute to atherosclerosis. There is also a hereditary factor, in that some people are more predisposed to develop circulatory problems in response to these contributory factors than others.

The modern treatment and management of heart disease is aimed along several basic lines. Prevention is important: stressing a prudent diet, establishing a regular program of exercise carefully geared to the individual's physical condition, and seeking a lifestyle that cuts down unnecessary tension and stress are approaches that can reduce the risk of heart attack and stroke. Patients who have been found to suffer from atherosclerosis may be given carefully regulated doses of an anticoagulant, to minimize the dangers of clot formation inside the narrowed blood vessels. Artery-clearing techniques are being explored. With the use of heart-lung machines, surgery can be performed on the heart itself, repairing heart defects, replacing damaged valves and portions of blood vessels, and grafting collateral blood vessels into place to bypass a dangerously blocked coronary artery.

THE BODY'S DEFENSES

"Be on guard"—this is the watchword of the body's defenses, which operate 24 hours a day, throughout our lives. If these defenses are breached, illness and even death may follow.

Like an old-time fortified city, the body has several lines of defense to fall back on. The first line of defense, analogous to the outer wall of the fort, consists of the physical barriers to the entry of microbes. Few microorganisms can penetrate through unbroken skin, and chemical substances secreted by the sweat, sebaceous, and lacrimal glands are highly toxic to certain types of bacteria. There are, however, several portals of entry into the body: the orifices of the respiratory, digestive, and urogenital tracts. These entry routes are supplied with backup defenses: the mucous membranes that line the oral and nasopharyngeal cavities are covered with a sticky mucus that catches and immobilizes microbes and other particles, permitting them to be swept out by ciliary action or engulfed by phagocytic cells. Antimicrobial secretions add to the defenses of these and other portals into the body. Microbes that reach as far as the stomach are subjected to a sterilizing acid bath. Auxiliary "troups" in the body's defending army are the swarms of microflora that normally inhabit the skin and linings of the body; these harmless microbes, by their presence, inhibit the growth of potentially pathogenic forms.

Formidable as these defenses are, they can be breached and frequently are. A cut finger may provide an extra, insufficiently defended entryway into the body. A portion of spoiled food may contain more microbes than the defenses of the digestive tract can cope with. Microbes can slip past the protective mechanisms of the respiratory tract and penetrate

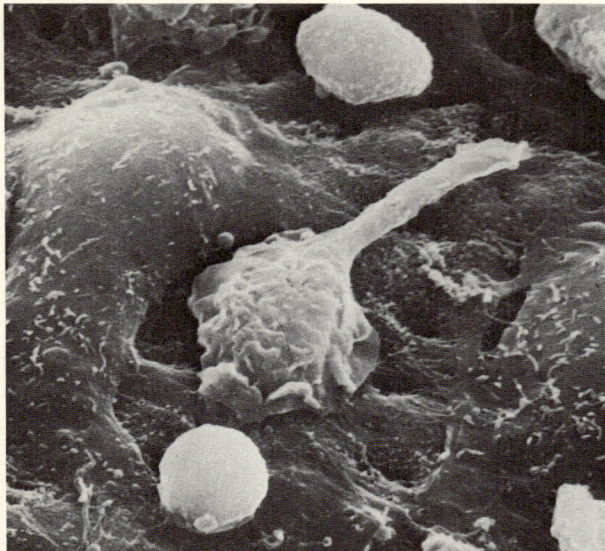

FIGURE 37-8 Scanning electron micrograph of an angry macrophage in pursuit of a small lymphocyte.

into the lungs. When infection occurs, the body has a number of additional defenses to call on. These include both nonspecific defense mechanisms, such as inflammation and interferon (a general defense against viruses) and specific immune responses, which deal with the precise type of microbial invader.

Inflammation

If you have ever suffered from acne, you were undoubtedly warned by parents, doctors, and others not to squeeze the pimples. If you succumbed to the temptation and did so anyway, there were probably a number of occasions when instead of healing promptly, the lesion grew into an angry red, pus-filled swelling, far more unsightly and painful than the original pimple. What happened was that bacteria were introduced into the wound (probably by your own fingers—even freshly washed hands usually have many microbes clining to the skin) and triggered a sequence of events, most of which were designed to aid the body in coping with the invaders. First the tissue damage caused by the bacteria stimulated the release of **histamine** and a group of polypeptides called **kinins.** The effect of these chemical mediators was to dilate the blood vessels of the microcirculation and increase the permeability of the vessels to protein. Fluid accumulated in the tissue spaces, producing edema. Meanwhile, the kinins and substances released by the bacteria themselves exerted a powerful **chemotaxic effect,** attracting phagocytic leukocytes. Neutrophils were first on the scene. Within minutes, leukocytes were adhering to the capillary walls in the region of the inflammation, and gradually they slipped through the gaps between cells and migrated out into the tissues. There they began to engulf bacteria. Meanwhile, tissue macrophages (Figure 37-8) were stimulated to multiply and add their efforts to the fight. Later monocytes migrated in from the bloodstream, became macrophages, and joined the battle. Plasma proteins that leaked out into the tissues through the permeable vessels added their specific effects, described later in the chapter. The pus, consisting of the bodies of white blood cells killed in the battle, bacteria, and bits of cell debris, was eventually cleaned up by the macrophages, preparing the way for tissue repair. Or—if the body's defenders were unequal to the fight—the area became walled off in an abscess, which had to be drained before it could heal.

The typical local manifestations of the inflammatory response are redness, heat, pain, and swelling. (The pain is caused both by distension of the tissues and by stimulation of pain nerve endings by chemicals released in the battle.) A common systemic sign of infection is fever. A protein released by the neutrophils participating in the inflammatory response appears to act on the hypothalamus, resetting its thermostat. It has been theorized that the increased body temperature in fever makes conditions less favorable for the growth and reproduction of invading microbes. But in many cases fever is even more undesirable for the body, speeding up metabolism, placing a burden on the circulatory system, and sometimes leading to convulsions.

Interferon

One day soon we will have the "cure" for the common cold. We will also have cures for measles, mumps, smallpox, rubella, and hundreds of other viral diseases—all with the same chemical. This miracle drug is not a new one, however; nature devised it millions of years ago. It is one of the body's own defenses, interferon.

Interferon was not discovered until 1957, although it had been known for several decades that infection with one virus may produce a temporary, generalized immunity against infection by other, unrelated viruses. The effect is called the interference phenomenon. Then it was found that a small protein, interferon, is produced by virus-infected cells and protects other cells of the body from virus infection. Its production seems to be stimulated in the following way (Figure 37-9): When the viral nucleic acid penetrates into a cell, it uses the cell's facilities to replicate, producing a double-stranded RNA (or in the case of a DNA virus, a double-stranded DNA-RNA hybrid). The new RNA acts as a messenger RNA, attaching to the host cell's ribosomes and directing the formation

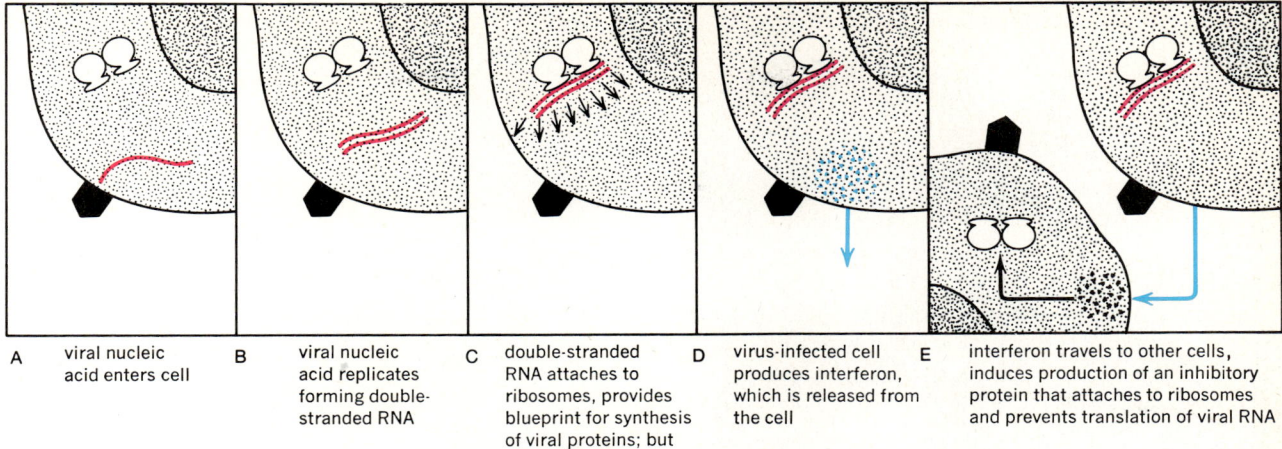

| A | viral nucleic acid enters cell | B | viral nucleic acid replicates forming double-stranded RNA | C | double-stranded RNA attaches to ribosomes, provides blueprint for synthesis of viral proteins; but sets off "alarm" in cell | D | virus-infected cell produces interferon, which is released from the cell | E | interferon travels to other cells, induces production of an inhibitory protein that attaches to ribosomes and prevents translation of viral RNA |

FIGURE 37-9 Induction of interferon by an invading virus.

of viral protein, instead of the host cell's own proteins. But the double-stranded RNA is thought to act as an "alarm" stimulus for the cell, causing it to produce interferon. The interferon is released and travels to other cells of the body, where it induces the formation of a special translation inhibitory protein. The latter attaches to the ribosomes and prevents translation of the viral RNA messages (i.e., it "interferes" with the virus reproduction) while permitting the synthesis of the host cell's proteins to proceed normally. Thus, the viral infection is effectively contained.

If interferon is produced in the body and works so effectively against viruses, why does anyone ever get sick with viral diseases? First of all, some viruses apparently manage to avoid stimulating interferon production or are very weak interferon stimulators. When such viruses invade, this important body defense never gets properly mobilized. Second, although the interferon mechanism is more rapid acting than the more specific defense of antibody production (interferon synthesis begins within hours after viral infection), it takes time for the interferon levels to build up. Meanwhile, the invading viruses have been busy directing their enslaved host cells to manufacture huge numbers of new virus particles—so many that the cell bursts, spewing out hordes of infectious viruses that can infect other cells and repeat the process. Interferon acts only to contain the viral infection; it does not help the cells that are already being forced to replicate viruses, and by the time the body has produced significant amounts of interferon, many body cells have already been damaged or killed.

Since interferon provides general protection against all viruses, not just the specific one that induced its production, it would be possible to help a person under viral attack by administering a substantial dose of interferon. Unfortunately, interferon is highly species-

specific. Interferon from a guinea pig or cow will not work on humans. Thus, any interferon to be used to treat humans would have to be produced in human cells. However, interferon is normally produced and exerts its action in extremely minute amounts. Large volumes of donor blood would have to be processed to get enough interferon to cure just one cold.

Another possible approach would be to administer a substance that boosts the person's own interferon production. Various bacteria, viruses, and chemical substances have been tried as interferon inducers. Double-stranded RNAs have proved most effective, especially a synthetic cytidylic acid complex called poly I:C. Work on these substances has had to proceed cautiously, because most of them have toxic side effects.

Thus far, the most promising results have been obtained with human interferon extracted from donor blood: it has cured colds and other virus diseases and also has been found to be effective against certain types of cancer. But human interferon is still so fantastically expensive that it can be used only on a very limited experimental basis. New techniques of genetic engineering, which are discussed in Chapter 38, may some day make it possible to synthesize large quantities of interferon cheaply and effectively.

Specific Immune Responses

The field of immunology is in the throes of a revolution. Theories that were generally accepted five or ten years ago are rapidly becoming obsolete. Floods of new information are pouring in. Some of it neatly fills in gaps in our knowledge and rounds out the growing picture; other new findings, at present, seem more to confuse than to illuminate.

It had been known for a long time that the body is capable of producing proteins, called **antibodies,**

FIGURE 37-10 Gerald Edelman is shown here with a model of an antibody whose complete structure he delineated.

which react very specifically with invading microbes and other foreign particles, inactivating or killing them. The first time the body is exposed to a particular antigen (i.e., the "foreign" substance), it takes some time for specific antibodies to that antigen to be produced. Then, if a second exposure later occurs, large quantities of the appropriate antibodies appear in the blood far more rapidly, indicating that the body somehow "remembered" the antigen, or perhaps kept a copy of the antibody on file for future use. Indeed, a variety of antibodies are found in the circulating blood even in a healthy person. They are all proteins (Figure 37-10), belonging to the class of gamma globulins, and are called **immunoglobulins.**

Five groups of immunoglobulins have been found, differing in chemical properties and biological function; they are denoted as IgA, IgD, IgE, IgG, and IgM. The IgG (normally about 75 percent of all the antibodies) and IgM antibodies provide most of the specific immunity against microbes. IgA antibodies, secreted by lymphoid tissue lining the gastrointestinal, respiratory, and genitourinary tracts, are part of the body's first line of defense. IgE antibodies are involved in allergic reactions; the function of the IgD antibodies is unknown at present. Immunoglobulins may be found either free in the blood plasma or bound to the surface of lymphocytes.

Gradually it was learned that antibodies are produced by lymphocyte-like **plasma cells** in the lymph nodes. Recent research has indicated that the total picture of antibody production and the action of the immunity system as a whole is far more complex.

B Cells, T Cells, and Antibody Formation

When you think about it, it seems rathers astonishing that shortly after your body is introduced to a new chemical for the first time, it can turn out antibody molecules so precisely tailor-made to the contours and reactive sites of the new antigen that antigen and antibody can interact, fitting together as smoothly and precisely as a key fits a lock.

When researchers wondered at first how this specific antibody production occurs, they assumed that somehow the antigen was used as a model, and the antibody was shaped to its specifications. But now most immunologists accept the **clonal selection theory** of antibody formation. According to this theory, during embryonic development, a variety of random mutations occur in the DNA of millions of lymphocytes, so that each becomes capable of making one—and only one—type of antibody. Many of these potential antibodies will never be made; but when the body is exposed to a new antigen, a lymphocyte capable of producing just the right kind of antibody for it will begin to multiply, giving rise to a whole clone* of plasma cells, all producing the same new antibody. Some of these plasma cells will participate in active antibody synthesis, meeting the current challenge. Others will be kept on file in the immunity system's "memory bank," ready to respond more rapidly to a new visit by the same kind of antigen.

This theory was very self-consistent and satisfying,

---

* A clone is a population of cells, all derived from a common parent cell and sharing the same heredity.

but it failed to explain some findings on patients and experimental animals with immunological deficiencies, as well as some facets of hypersensitivity and the rejection of grafts. New light was cast on the situation when it was realized that lymphocytes are not all alike. Two major classes have been discovered and named **B lymphocytes** and **T lymphocytes.**

Precursors of both the B cells and the T cells are originally formed in the bone marrow. Some of these lymphocyte precursors migrate to the thymus, where they are transformed into T lymphocytes. Some are exported into the bloodstream, where they join the pool of circulating long-lived lymphocytes. Some settle down in the lymph nodes; other travel back and forth between the bloodstream and the lymph circulation.

Meanwhile, the precursors of the B cells take a different route. In chickens and other birds, the transformation of precursors into B lymphocytes occurs in a gastrointestinal structure called the bursa of Fabricius (hence the name "B" cell, in contrast to the "T" for thymus). Humans do not have a bursa, and although it is believed that a comparable site exists, it is not yet known where or what it is.

Electron microscopy has revealed structural differences between the B cells and T cells: the B cells have numerous fingerlike projections on the cell surface, while the T cells usually have very few. This distinction corresponds to the readily detectable surface immunoglobulins on B cells; T cells also have been found to contain some surface immunoglobulins, but they are more difficult to detect.

The functional differences between the two types of lymphocytes are even more striking. The B cells are the potential antibody producers, which are involved in the development of immunity against specific diseases. T cells have a number of important functions. They secrete a number of chemicals called **lymphokines** that affect the behavior of macrophages: these T-cell secretions attract macrophages, impair the ability of macrophages to migrate, thus causing them to accumulate in an area of inflammation, and also activate the macrophages, causing them to swell up and become extremely active phagocytes. (The "angry" macrophage shown in Figure 39-8 was stimulated artificially with oil, but a similar effect would be produced by T-cell secretions.) T cells somehow help B cells to become active antibody producers. But T cells also can suppress B-cell activity. The latter role is believed to be important in the recognition of "self" cells and chemicals that keeps our antibody systems from destroying our own body tissues. T cells can also act directly as "killers," becoming sensitized to a specific antigen and then releasing a powerful battery of chemicals on it if the same antigen is ever encoun-

tered again. This type of response is referred to as **cell-mediated immunity** (as opposed to the antibodies, which are proteins released by B lymphocytes); as in the case of antibody production, some of the sensitized T cells do not participate in the local reaction, but are kept on file in the body's "memory bank." Cell-mediated immunity is the mechanism that operates in hypersensitivity and in the rejection of transplants. At this writing, it is still controversial whether the same T cell can, under different circumstances, serve as a helper, a suppressor, or a killer, or whether several different kinds of T cells are involved.

Another important function of the T cells is to conduct an **immune surveillance.** When a body cell becomes a malignant cancer cell, it undergoes various changes, including changes in the cell surface. If patrolling T cells encounter such a changed cell, they perceive it as foreign, are sensitized, and attack it, along with any other cells like it. It is believed that body cells become cancerous as often as one each day, but are promptly killed off by T cells, which are thus an important defense against cancer.

An important distinction between T cells and B cells is that T cells travel through the body and exert their effects locally. B cells, on the other hand, mainly remain in the lymph nodes (about 80 percent of the circulating lymphocytes are T cells). Antibody synthesis occurs there, after sensitization by antigen carried by the lymphatic system, and the antibodies are sent out through the bloodstream to the site where they are needed.

Antibody Action

Not every foreign chemical stimulates antibody production. The principal antigens are proteins and polysaccharides. Molecules with a molecular weight below about 10,000 usually escape the notice of the B cells and do not serve as antigens unless they are combined with a larger molecule such as a protein. The B cell progeny then form antibodies that fit both the protein and the attached small molecule, which is called a **hapten.** If the hapten and protein later become separated, or the hapten is encountered alone, the specific antibodies will also respond to it (Figure 37-11). A hapten might also provoke an antibody response because it happens to "match" a portion of an antigen for which antibodies are already on file. These two variations explain why small molecules can sometimes trigger a violent allergic response.

Antibodies fight invading microbes in several ways. They may combine with viruses, preventing their attachment to the host cell membranes and thus preventing them from multiplying. (Remember that viruses can complete their life cycle only within a living host cell.) Antibodies may be formed against bacterial

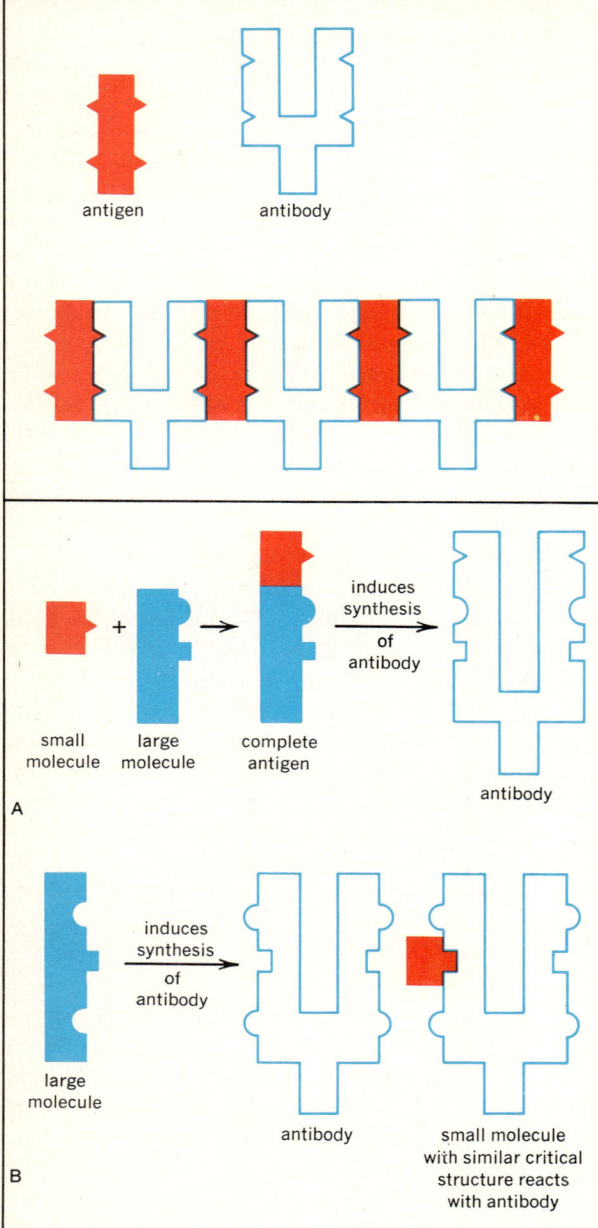

FIGURE 37-11 Antigens and antibodies fit together like a key in a lock. Since antibodies have more than one potential binding site for the corresponding antigen, an interlocking chain or clump of antigen-antibody complexes may be formed. The scheme below shows two ways that a small molecule can form an antigen-antibody complex, either participating in the induction of antibody synthesis (A) or being mistaken for a larger antigen with a similar reactive group (B).

One of the most important mechanisms of antibody action involves the activation of a complex system of blood proteins that are collectively referred to as **complement.** Precursors of the complement proteins normally circulate in the blood in an inactive form and are activated by a sequence of chemical reactions initiated by the presence of antigen-antibody complexes. Some of the activated complement proteins enhance the inflammatory response by stimulating the secretion of histamine and formation of kinins, by acting directly on blood vessels to produce dilation, and by coating the antigen in such a way as to permit the phagocytes to engulf it more effectively. Some complement proteins attack microbes directly by catalyzing breakdown of the bacterial cell wall. These reactions occur only with microbes that are already combined with antibodies; thus the antibodies provide the specificity in the response and are said to "fix" complement to the cell surface.

IMMUNITY

You have a lifetime protection against many diseases. Some of the antibodies on file in your body were acquired when you suffered an illness—perhaps a particular kind of cold, or flu, or measles. Others were deliberately stimulated by giving you vaccines—specially inactivated or attenuated forms of the pathogens of more serious diseases. The antibodies produced against these specially modified viruses or bacteria will effectively act against the naturally occurring forms as well. In each case, you may be said to have acquired an **active immunity** to the disease, since your own body has produced the antibodies and is keeping the blueprints on file for future needs.

The development of vaccines has dramatically changed our lives. In past years, everyone caught the measles sooner or later; for most it was a minor inconveience, requiring some tedious days in bed, but some suffered serious complications that brought lifetime disability, and some died. Diphtheria was a major childhood killer before vaccines; now many doctors never see a single case in all their years of practice. The control of smallpox through vaccines has been so successful that smallpox vaccination generally is no longer required. After a vigorously pursued vaccination program in the last remaining endemic areas, the World Health Organization reported in 1977 that this disease had finally disappeared entirely from the face of the earth.

Developing active immunity, either stimulated by an actual attack of a disease or provoked by vaccines, takes time. In a first contact with an antigen, the antibody response develops slowly, over a period of several days, and it may take even longer for effective levels to build up. If you suddenly discover that you have been exposed to a disease to which you had not

toxins and combine chemically with them, preventing them from interacting with the susceptible sites on cell membranes. Since antibodies generally have more than one potential reaction site, they can link together in a chain or clump of antigen-antibody complexes, collecting the antigens into convenient groups that can be phagocytized.

been foresighted enough to develop an active immunity, it is generally too late to get yourself vaccinated. The rapidly multiplying microbes in your body would win the race with antibodies. But there may be some hope for protection by an injection of antibodies that someone else has produced against the disease. An injection of gamma globulin is sometimes given to an unprotected teenage boy who has been exposed to mumps. In the case of tetanus, a specific **antiserum,** produced by injecting an animal such as a horse with tetanus toxin and later extracting antibody-containing serum, can be used to provide emergency protection after a possible exposure. The protection provided by such measures is referred to as **passive immunity.** In each case, after the emergency is over, it is wise to obtain a vaccination to develop active immunity, since the introduced antibodies that provided protection are rapidly lost from the body, and there are no copies of them in the "memory bank." Indeed, the presence of antibodies serves as a feedback inhibitor for the production of similar antibodies by the body's own immunity system. This principle is the basis for the RhoGAM vaccine that protects Rh negative mothers who have just given birth to an Rh positive child from becoming sensitized to the foreign blood antigen. Paradoxically, the mother is given a dose of anti-Rh antibodies, which prevent her own system from manufacturing any.

The antibodies that are transferred to the fetus through the placenta and then to the infant in its mother's milk confer passive immunity to any diseases for which the mother possesses antibodies and provide valuable protection during the time when the infant's own immunity system is not yet functioning effectively.

AUTOIMMUNE DISEASES

Sometimes, during wartime, friendly soldiers are accidentally killed. The body is constantly at war. Its defenders are dedicated to the task of killing all foreign invaders. But sometimes they seem to get their identification signals mixed up and attack and kill some of the very "natives" they have been entrusted to defend. The results are disastrous for the body.

The T lymphocytes have the job of patrolling the body and inspecting each cell and particle they meet for "foreignness." Yet how can a single cell—even such a versatile cell as a T lymphocyte—distinguish between "self" and "other," especially when there are many thousands of different types of proteins and other potentially antigenic chemicals in the normal human body? The clonal selection theory of the origin of lymphocytes provides a plausible answer: as the original lymphocytes are traveling out from the thymus and bone marrow, on the way to seeding the lymph nodes, many of them meet body proteins that

exactly match their own immunological specifications. At this stage in the development of the young organism, these lymphocytes are still unique, and they are tied up by the body proteins and inactivated before they have a chance to reach the lymph nodes and give rise to clones of plasma cells or immunologically competent T cells. By the time the child's immunological mechanism has become fully established, all the lymphocytes capable of forming immunity against the body's own chemicals have been weeded out.

How then can autoimmune reactions occur? A failure of the body to recognize its own cells can result from a number of causes, for example: (1) drugs or pollutants from the environment may act as haptens, combining with normal body proteins to form complexes that are considered foreign; later both constituents of the complex may act as foreign antigens; (2) a body cell may be infected by a virus whose DNA or RNA causes the production of a new protein (antigen); (3) genetic mutations may alter body cells, changing their antigenic properties; (4) the body may be invaded by a microbe that superficially resembles some normal body constituent; later the lymphocytes sensitized against that microbe may give a cross reaction against the self-antigen it resembles; (5) death or damage of cells might release some intracellular proteins that the lymphocytes have not encountered before and therefore regard as foreign; (6) mutation or deterioration of lymphocytes might change their immunological properties. These and other events may result in the production of antibodies or sensitized lymphocytes against the body's own cells. Autoimmune damage may also occur even when the immune system is working properly, if the release of complement and other chemicals damages not only the invading microbes but also nearly normal cells—the "innocent bystanders."

Some forms of arthritis, anemia, myasthenia gravis, multiple sclerosis, and other diseases are believed to be caused by the development of autoimmune reactions, and this mechanism is continually being implicated in additional diseases. However, in some cases the autoimmune mechanism is a normal part of body functioning: the T lymphocytes continually inspect the body cells for "fitness," in an immune surveillance that not only weeds out incipient cancers but also eliminates old or damaged erythrocytes and other body cells that have outlived their usefulness.

TISSUE TRANSPLANTS

Each of us is unique—and the body knows it. The constant surveillance by the immune system, distinguishing "self" from "other" and ruthlessly eradicating all foreigners, normally works to the body's benefit. But sometimes an organ is irreparably damaged by disease or injury, and the loss of its function

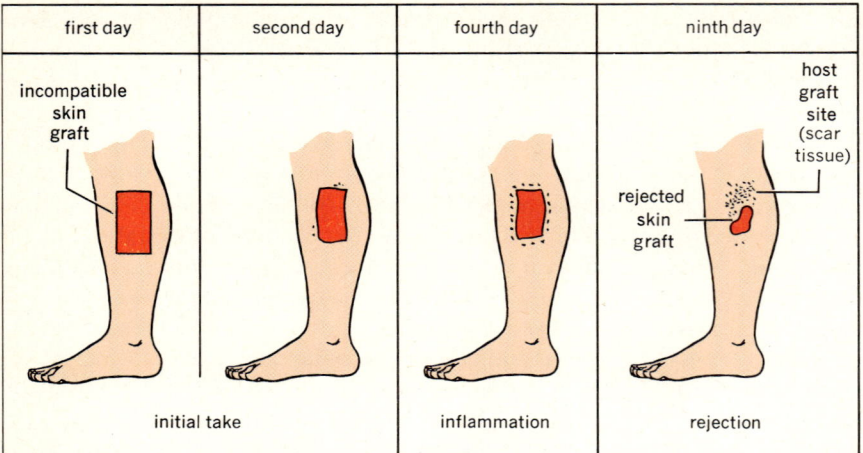

first day	second day	fourth day	ninth day
incompatible skin graft			host graft site (scar tissue)
			rejected skin graft
initial take		inflammation	rejection

FIGURE 37-12 An incompatible transplant stimulates the body's immune system, triggering a series of reactions that culminates in rejection of the transplanted tissue.

threatens the life of the body as a whole. In recent years, physicians have tried to solve such problems by transplanting healthy organs—from a living donor or a person who has just died from an accident—into patients whose own organs have been hopelessly damaged. The field of transplant surgery was making modest progress, with skin grafts and successful transplants of corneas and kidneys, when the first human heart transplant, performed by the South African surgeon Christiaan Barnard in 1967, suddenly focused world attention on the field; the flood of heart transplants that followed quickly pointed up both the promise and the problems of tissue transplantation. Although the operations were brilliant technical successes, and the transplanted hearts took up their life-sustaining function in the new bodies, in nearly every case within a year or two the patients were dead—their own bodies had killed their new hearts.

The problems of **transplant rejection** is an immune problem (Figure 37-12). Each person has many proteins that differ from those of every other person in the world—except perhaps an identical twin. A transplanted heart or kidney or skin graft obtained from another person contains numerous foreign antigens, and the patient's body reacts vigorously against them, attacking the foreign cells so fiercely that the transplanted tissue shrivels and dies. (Corneal transplants are an exception, since the poor blood supply does not give the immune system a chance to operate on a foreign cornea.)

Several different approaches have been used in attempts to overcome the rejection problem. The first successful kidney transplants were performed between identical twins. (Since kidneys conveniently come in pairs, a living doner can give up one kidney and still survive.) For less closely related donor-recipient pairs, histocompatibility tests were worked out, so that the prospective recipient could be matched as closely as possible with prospective donors according to various tissue antigens. However, good matches are often hard to find. Soon transplant surgeons turned to avenues of immunosuppression. Exposure to radiation or drugs that selectively kill actively dividing lymphocytes have been used to temporarily knock out the recipient's immunity system just before and for some time after the transplant. Specific antilymphocyte sera are being developed to inactiviate precisely the T cells responsible for the rejection of foreign tissues.

But the use of immunosuppressives carries with it a whole new set of problems. If too low a dose is used, the transplanted organ will be rejected. If too high a dose is used, the patient will be helpless before the onslaught of invading microbes; indeed, many of the transplant patients who do not survive die of postoperative pneumonia. As transplant surgeons have learned to successfully walk the tightrope of immunosuppressive therapy, and more patients have survived, another discouraging effect has emerged: transplant patients have been found to have a higher than average risk of developing malignant tumors. Without the immune surveillance of the T cells, the transplant patient is more vulnerable not only to infectious diseases, but also to cancer.

Despite the problems and risks, organ transplants are saving the lives of growing numbers of patients. Thus far, kidney transplants have been the most successful. Already hundreds of patients are in their second decade of life after a successful kidney transplant. Several thousand of these operations are now performed each year. If a transplanted kidney is rejected, it can often be successfully replaced with another.

After the wave of disillusion that followed the initial surge of heart transplants, the operations continued at a greatly reduced rate. Now that some heart transplant patients have survived for more than five years, the technique is again growing in acceptance. In addition to kidneys and hearts, lungs, spleens, livers, and other organs have been transplanted, with varying degrees of success.

HYPERSENSITIVITY AND ALLERGY

Hayfever sufferers do not need a calendar to know when the middle of August has rolled around. Their eyes begin to water; their nasal membranes swell and produce a watery discharge; and they are periodically swept by paroxysms of uncontrollable sneezing. They are victims of a hypersensitive immunity system, which reacts to environmental antigens—in the case of hayfever, usually the airborne microscopic pollen grains of the ragweed plant—to an inappropriately extreme degree, as though they were major threats to life.

Allergens (environmental antigens that produce the complex of immune responses classified as allergy) may be carried in the air and inhaled—for example, pollen grains, dust particles, or mold spores; they may be natural or artificial constituents of foods, or substances that come in contact with the skin (e.g., the "enzyme" ingredients in some modern laundry detergents leave residues on clothes that produce itching and contact dermatitis in susceptible individuals). In susceptible individuals, allergens stimulate the production of a special class of antibodies, the IgE type. These antibodies attach themselves to receptor sites on mast cells and basophils and stimulate the cells to release histamine and other vasoactive chemicals. Local inflammatory responses result, producing such symptoms as watery eyes and sneezing, bronchial spasm, or skin rashes, depending on the particular **shock organ** that contains the sensitized receptors. In the case of extreme sensitization, large quantities of histamine, serotonin, and other amines are released into the bloodstream, producing hypotension, spasms of the laryngeal muscles, and bronchiolar spasm. Such an extreme systemic response, called **anaphylaxis,** can result from a single bee sting in a sensitized individual and can lead to death if therapeutic measures are not taken immediately. People who know they have been sensitized to the venom of bees or hornets often carry an emergency kit with antihistamines and a prefilled syringe of epinephrine (to produce bronchodilation).

An allergy victim can be helped by a series of **desensitizing** injections, which paradoxically utilize the immunity system to bring the problem under control. Minute amounts of the allergen to which the person is sensitized are injected in gradually increasing doses. Such injections stimulate the formation of IgG antibodies, which will subsequently tie up any antigen introduced in the normal manner, blocking the reaction of the IgE antibodies and thus preventing the inflammatory response. In a new experimental approach to allergy treatment developed at the University of California at San Diego, a pentapeptide analog of the binding group of the IgE molecules has been synthesized. When it is injected into an allergy victim, the pentapeptide ties up the binding site on the mast cells, preventing the IgE antibodies from triggering the allergic response.

CHEMOTHERAPY

A living organism is in essence a complex chemical "factory," in which literally thousands of different chemical reactions take place simultaneously. Thus, it seems logical that if something goes wrong with the body, chemical reactions must be involved, and suitable chemicals added to the system might help to set things right again. Perhaps a missing metabolite could be supplied, or the reactions vital to an invading microbe could be thwarted. The approach of chemotherapy attempts to devise and use drugs to achieve these goals.

The field of chemotherapy was launched in the researches of the German bacteriologist Paul Ehrlich at the beginning of this century. Ehrlich had done some valuable work on the development of stains for the microscopy of bacteria and white blood cells and then moved into the field of immunity and serum therapy. Ehrlich theorized that since stains for bacteria colored them specifically, they must react with some substance in the bacterium and therefore might very likely damage or kill it. He set out on a dogged search for a "magic bullet," which would selectively kill a pathogen without killing the host organism that it invaded. He chose trypanosomes, for this microorganism is not only large and easy to observe, but also destroys one of its victims, the mouse, in 100 percent of the cases. So if Ehrlich could save just a single mouse, he would know that he was on the right track.

For eight years Ehrlich struggled, testing hundreds of compounds. He had some success with the 606th compound, dihydroxydiamino-arseno-benzene hydrochloride. But he continued the search, trying to find a better compound. Then, in 1909, a curious coincidence occurred. Ehrlich noticed a published report describing the syphilis spirochete and commenting on its "relationship" to trypanosomes. This resemblance is actually quite superficial, but it was fortunate that this bit of misinformation happened to reach Ehrlich at that particular time. He and his associates were already up into the 900s, but they decided to try compound 606 on spirochetes. In preliminary tests on animals, the results were dramatic, and in trials on human syphilis sufferers in 1910, compound 606 proved

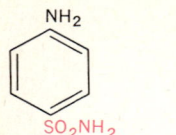 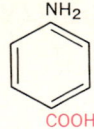

FIGURE 37-13 The strong chemical resemblance between sulfanilamide (left) and PABA (right) leads bacteria to mistake the drug for their normal metabolite.

equally effective. Salvarsan, the first of the "miracle drugs," was born.

The next major landmark in the history of chemotherapy occurred in 1932. Gerhard Domagk, a German biochemist, was testing dyes produced by I. G. Farbenindustrie for possible antibacterial activity. He had just obtained promising results with the orange-red dye Prontosil on mice when his young daughter fell ill with a serious streptococcal infection. She did not respond to any conventional treatments. In desperation, Domagk tried his experimental compound—and his child recovered dramatically. Further tests of Prontosil revealed that a small portion of the molecule is just as effective as the whole compound. This active portion was sulfanilamide, the first of the sulfa drugs. Sulfanilamide bears a striking chemical resemblance to para-aminobenzoic acid (PABA), a compound needed by bacteria for their metabolic activities (Figure 37-13). Bacterial enzymes that normally combine with PABA may join with sulfanilamide by mistake and then be unable to complete their normal reactions. Sulfanilamide is thus a selective agent—a "magic bullet" that strikes at the bacterium through its special metabolic requirements, while leaving the host organism unharmed.

Another important milestone in chemotherapy was the rediscovery of penicillin, the first of the antibiotics. This substance was first discovered accidentally in 1928 by a British microbiologist, Alexander Fleming, who noticed one day that one of his bacterial culture dishes was contaminated with a bluegreen mold. Instead of merely discarding the spoiled specimen, Fleming took a closer look and noticed that a circular region around the mold was entirely free of bacterial growth. He prepared extracts from the mold, which also exhibited antibacterial properties, even in extreme dilutions. Fleming named the active substance penicillin and published his findings in a medical journal the following year, but no one took much notice at the time. It was not until a concerted effort was launched to find an effective way of treating the wounded in World War II that the true potential of this new antibiotic was realized and fully developed.

Other antiobiotics were subsequently discovered among the metabolic by-products of various bacteria and fungi. Their production, both by chemical syn-

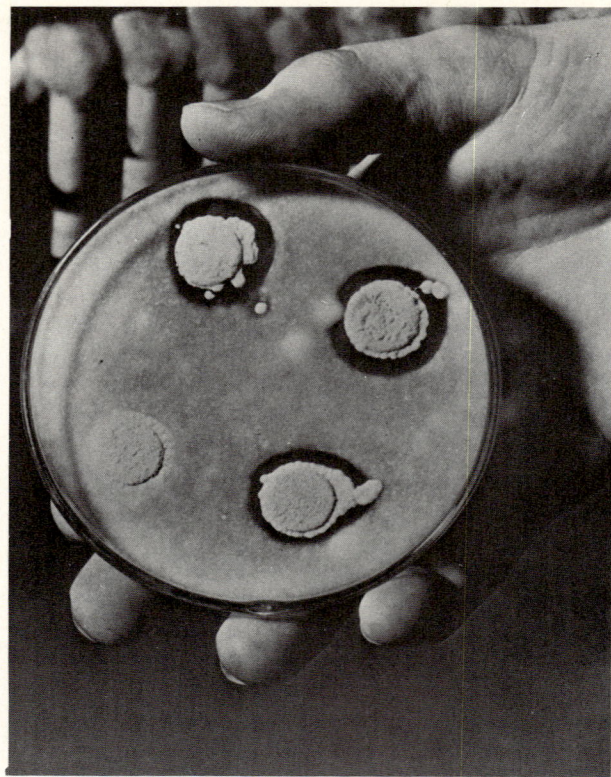

FIGURE 37-14 Small disks of blotting paper soaked with antibiotic solutions were placed on the surface of a petri dish inoculated with bacteria. The size of the clear rings around the disks, representing areas of inhibition of bacterial growth, indicates the potency of the antibiotics.

thesis and by large-scale culturing of carefully selected strains of microorganisms, is now an important aspect of the drug industry (Figure 37-14).

Despite the large number of effective antibiotics already developed, drug research continues actively. In addition to the search for more effective and less toxic agents (few drugs leave normal cells *completely* untouched), a continually expanding arsenal of new drugs is needed to keep one step ahead of the bacteria. Like all living things, bacteria have the ability to mutate, so that a bacterial population shows considerable variation. Often a drug will kill nearly all the bacteria in a population; but the few that remain, protected by a resistance to the action of the drug, can rapidly multiply and form the nucleus for a new population of drug-resistant bacteria—which, however, might succumb readily to another drug that works by a somewhat different mechanism. It is feared that the too-common prescribing of antibiotics for relatively minor illnesses and the use of antibiotic-treated feeds in raising meat animals may be contributing to the development of drug-resistant bacterial populations.

For a long time, all the antibiotics developed were

effective only against bacteria, not against viruses. In recent years, however, some progress has at last been made on developing effective antiviral agents. One of these, rifampicin, was initially used against bacteria. Then it was discovered that the drug works by selectively inhibiting the bacterial RNA polymerase, while leaving mammalian RNA polymerase relatively untouched. Meanwhile, it was found that the vaccinia virus, a large DNA-containing virus, contains its own RNA polymerase in addition to its DNA and protein coat. Scientists in several laboratories put the two pieces of information together and tried rifampicin against vaccinia and other viruses that contain RNA polymerase. It proved effective against such viruses as vaccinia, smallpox, and an adenovirus. Other antiviral drugs now under development or already in use are 5-iodo-2-deoxyuridine, Vira-A, and phosphonacetic acid (against herpes simplex type 1, a viral disease of the eye), amantadine hydrochloride (used to prevent Asian A influenza in persons exposed to the virus), inosiplex (found effective against rhinoviruses that cause the common cold), ribavirin (a broad-spectrum antiviral, which is effective against both DNA and RNA viruses and works by selectively inhibiting replication of the viral protein), and levamisole (an immunity stimulator that is also being tested in the treatment of cancer).

Chemotherapeutic approaches are also being used in the areas of cancer, allergy, and metabolic diseases. An encouraging trend is typified by the development of rifampicin and the pentapeptide now being tested against allergies. In the past, the development of new drugs was mainly a trial-and-error process. Researchers laboriously screened hundreds of thousands of chemicals, trying to find one or two that would have some activity; if a promising substance was found, various chemical modifications were introduced, to see what changes in the effect would be produced and, if possible, deduce some information about the way the drug acted. Now, increasingly, knowledge gained about the molecular mechanisms of biological processes is suggesting approaches to the development of new drugs.

SUMMARY

Types of diseases include:
  Bacterial diseases
  Viral diseases
  Fungus diseases
  Other parasitic diseases (protozoa, worms)
  Cancer
  Degenerative diseases
Pathogenic bacteria invade the host organism and multiply, producing toxins: exotoxins or endotoxins. Some bacteria are neutral or helpful.
Viruses are inherently parasitic, since they can complete their life cycle only within the cells of a living host, utilizing its protein- and nucleic acid-synthesizing facilities.
  Vaccines have been developed to provide immunity against many virus diseases.
Fungus diseases may produce local lesions or serious systemic mycoses.
Parasitic diseases affect millions of people, especially in tropical countries.
  Common parasites belong to the groups of protozoa, flatworms, and roundworms.
  Many parasites have complicated life cycles, involving intermediate hosts.
In cancer, body cells suddenly begin to multiply uncontrollably, invading and choking off healthy tissues.
  Cancer is characterized by uncontrolled growth, a failure of contact inhibition, and metastasis.
    Types of cancer include:
      Carcinoma
      Sarcoma
      Leukemia
  Contributory factors may be virus infection, environmental carcinogens, and a failure of the immunity system.
  Approaches to the treatment of cancer include:
    Surgery
    Radiation therapy
    Chemotherapy
    Stimulation of immune mechanisms
Degenerative diseases are produced by a gradual deterioration of structure and function of major body organs and systems.
  They include cariovascular diseases, arthritis, and various nervous system disorders such as multiple sclerosis.
The body's defenses against disease include:
  Skin and mucous membranes
  Antibacterial secretions
  Normal microflora
  Inflammation
  Interferon
  Specific immune responses
Bacterial infection produces localized inflammation, including the sequence: release of histamine and kinins, vasodilation and increased permeability of blood vessels, edema, chemotaxis, phagocytosis, and specific immune responses, followed by tissue repair.
  Fever is a common systemic effect of infection.
Viral double-stranded RNA stimulates synthesis of interferon, which prevents virus protein synthesis in other cells—a generalized response, producing temporarily increased immunity to all viruses.
The introduction of a foreign antigen into the body stimulates the production of specific antibodies, which attack the antigen and are kept on file for future appearances.
  Antibodies are proteins (immunoglobulins), produced by plasma cells in the lymph nodes.
  The clonal selection theory states that during embryonic development random mutations occur in the DNA of lymphocytes, so that each becomes capable of making only one type of antibody.
There are two major types of lymphocytes, T cells and B cells.
  T-cell precursors travel to the thymus, where they develop into lymphocytes and then seed the lymph nodes or circulate in the blood and lymph systems, exerting their effects locally.
    T cells:
      Secrete lymphokines, attracting, retaining, and exciting macrophages
      Help B cells to become active antibody producers
      Suppress B-cell activity

Act as killers, becoming specifically sensitized to antigens

Conduct immune surveillance, eliminating incipient cancers and worn-out body cells

B-cell precursors travel from the bone marrow to some analog of the bursa, where they acquire the capability to produce antibodies.

B cells mainly remain in the lymph nodes, where they are sensitized by antigens and give rise to clones of antibody-producing plasma cells.

Antibodies attack microbes by:

Combining with viruses, preventing their attachment to host cell membranes

Combining with bacterial toxins, preventing them from interacting with susceptible sites on cell membranes

Clumping antigens into complexes that can be phagocytized

Stimulating the activation of complement and fixing complement to the microbe cell surface

Complement proteins enhance the inflammatory response, coat the antigen to make phagocytosis more effective, and catalyze breakdown of the bacterial wall.

Haptens are small molecules that stimulate antibody formation by combining with proteins, or react with antibodies for antigens whose reactive sites they fortuitously resemble.

Active immunity is stimulated by an actual exposure to a disease pathogen or disease, producing the formation of specific antibodies that are kept on file.

Passive immunity is produced by administering preformed antibodies and provides temporary protection but prevents mobilization of the immune mechanisms.

Autoimmune diseases result from a breakdown of the "self-recognition" mechanism of the T cells, resulting in the production of antibodies or sensitized lymphocytes to the body's own cells.

Sensitization may be caused by viral infection; modification of normal body proteins, by mutation or the action of haptens; cross reactions after sensitization by a foreign antigen; release of intracellular proteins due to cell damage or death; modification of lymphocytes.

Immune surveillance results in rejection of transplants of tissues and organs unless the immune mechanisms are suppressed by radiation, drugs, or antilymphocyte sera.

Immunosuppressive treatment lowers the patient's defenses against infectious diseases and cancer.

Allergens stimulate the formation of IgE antibodies, producing an inflammatory response, or in severe cases systemic anaphylaxis. Desensitization stimulates the formation of IgG blocking antibodies.

Chemotherapy is now used against bacterial, viral, and parasitic disease, cancer, allergies, and metabolic disease.

QUESTIONS FOR REVIEW AND THOUGHT

1 Under optimum conditions, bacteria such as *Salmonella* can go through a complete cell generation in 20 minutes, with each cell growing and dividing to form two new ones. In view of this, discuss the possible effects of such common careless practices as: (a) preparing foods without thorough hand washing beforehand; (b) finishing off a portion of food left partly eaten by a sick person; (c) taking unrefrigerated foods on picnics or in bag lunches to school or work; (d) allowing cooked foods to cool down to room temperature over a period of several hours before refrigerating.

2 Why do you think researchers have had so much difficulty in proving that viruses are implicated in human cancers? Discuss in the light of Koch's postulates.

3 What are the principal approaches to treating or preventing: (a) bacterial diseases; (b) viral diseases; (c) parasitic diseases; (d) heart disease; (e) cancer?

4 How is a vaccine produced, and how does it work?

5 Describe the various lines of defense of the body against invading pathogens.

6 Describe the processes of inflammation. Is this response positive or negative for the body?

7 How does interferon work? Why is it not yet being widely used in the treatment of viral diseases?

8 Compare T lymphocytes and B lymphocytes.

9 Describe the formation and functioning of antibodies.

10 Distinguish between active and passive immunity.

11 Do you believe organ transplants are a practical approach to the treatment of degenerative diseases? Discuss.

12 How do desensitizing injections help allergy sufferers?

BIOMEDICAL FRONTIERS

38

MEDICAL ELECTRONICS
PROSTHETICS
GERMFREE RESEARCH
BIOCHEMICAL ENGINEERING
GENETIC ENGINEERING

For generations humans have been able to redirect their fate by modifying their environment—they have built canals for their commerce, cleared forests for their agriculture, rechanneled rivers and created huge lakes. But now we are gaining the capability of redirecting our fate in a far more difficult way: by changing ourselves. Errors of heredity and accidents of life are at last yielding to corrective measures such as artificial limbs and organs, chemical correction of processes that have gone awry, and even the insertion of new genetic information.

Many of the achievements and work in progress at the frontiers of biomedical science have already been described; some other important trends are discussed in this chapter. A recurring theme in all these studies is the accelerated progress that has been made possible by a cross-fertilization of the health sciences and technology. Electronics, in particular, is making exceptionally valuable contributions to medical advances.

MEDICAL ELECTRONICS

In the past, there was very little communication between physicians and engineers. In recent years, however, the invasion of medicine by electronics has produced a vast array of instrumentation that has greatly enhanced the physician's effectiveness. Each year hundreds of millions of dollars worth of medical electronic instruments are sold. Thousands of items are included—electronic and electromechanical instruments that are used on patients by doctors and nurses; devices used in biomedical research on experimental animals or human volunteers; devices used for diagnosis, treatment, or to monitor the patient's condition. Since 1960, scores of universities have set up graduate programs in bioengineering, to keep up with this fast-growing field and make the communication between physicians and engineers even more fruitful.

The need for instrumentation and automatic analysis is growing by leaps and bounds. Each year about 5 billion tests are performed in clinical laboratories in the United States. Already the nation faces a shortage of a hundred thousand medical laboratory technicians, and each year the shortage grows worse. Automatic instruments help to fill this gap by reducing the needs for specially trained personnel and dramatically increasing the number of analyses that a single technician can turn out in a working day. The Autoanalyzer, for example, permits twelve different analyses to be performed simultaneously on a single sample. A single blood specimen, can be analyzed simultaneously for its content of sodium, potassium, chloride, carbon dioxide, calcium, alkaline phosphatase, glutamic oxaloacetic transaminase, bilirubin, total protein, albumin, urea, and glucose. Using tradi-

tional methods, a technician might have performed perhaps a dozen analyses in a workday. But a single machine of the type described, operated by a single technician, can perform more than 2500 tests in a single day!

Progress in microminiaturization has played an important role in the development of medical electronics and biomedical engineering. Compact monitoring devices have been designed that are so small that they can easily be worn on the body during normal activities. (Some can even be implanted within the body.) Many of these devices are designed to report their readings to radio receivers, which may be some distance away. Heart rates, nerve impulses, and various secretions of experimental animals and human volunteers have been monitored during the performance of a variety of activities, from sleep to strenuous athletics. Such microminiaturized instruments can even transmit their reports from spacecraft to receiving stations back on earth, permitting continuous monitoring of the physiological condition of orbiting astronauts.

Computers are playing a growing role in modern medical research and practice. Many hospitals routinely store medical records, including X rays, other diagnostic data, and family medical histories, in computer systems, where they are available for instant retrieval. Computer-controlled monitoring devices are used in intensive-care units of a number of hospitals to monitor the heartbeat, blood pressure, respiration rate, and other indicators (Figure 38-1) that are constantly compared with data on normal recovery cycles stored in the computer memory bank. Any deviation beyond present limits results in an alarm or warning flash that will be observed by a nurse at a central monitoring station. A single device can monitor the progress of a number of patients.

Other computers have been utilized in routine medical examinations. One computer is regularly used to process automated tests on as many as 4000 patients a month. The computer method is two to three times faster than the standard procedure, and four times as many tests can be performed on the patient for the same cost. A central computer in Washington, D. C., analyzes electrocardiogram recordings, sent to it over a special telephone line. Within fifteen seconds, the analysis is sent back to the hospital that submitted the query. Computer programs are even being worked out to serve as a sort of "superconsultant," containing a comprehensive compendium of medical knowledge that may be useful in the diagnosis and treatment of disease, in a readily retrievable form.

One of the most exciting recent blends of sophisticated medical instrumentation and computer technol-

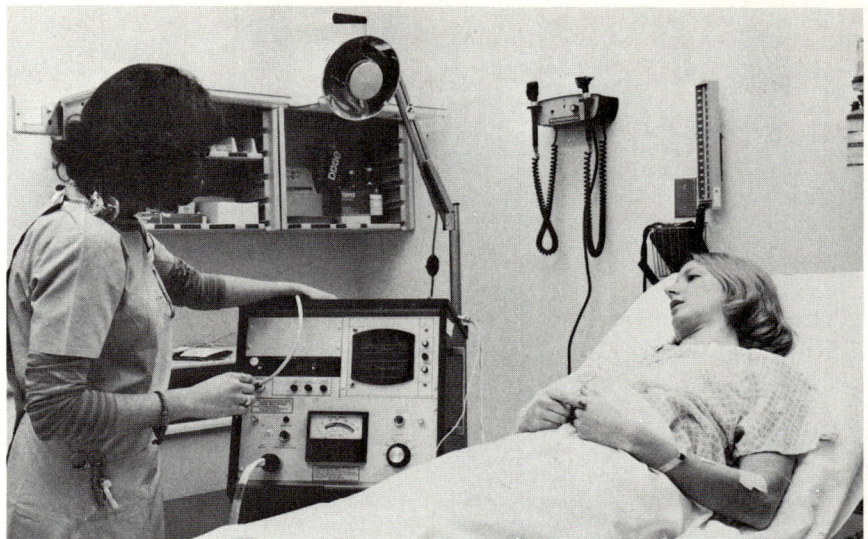

FIGURE 38-1 In a modern hospital, bedside monitors keep a continuous check on the patients' vital functions.

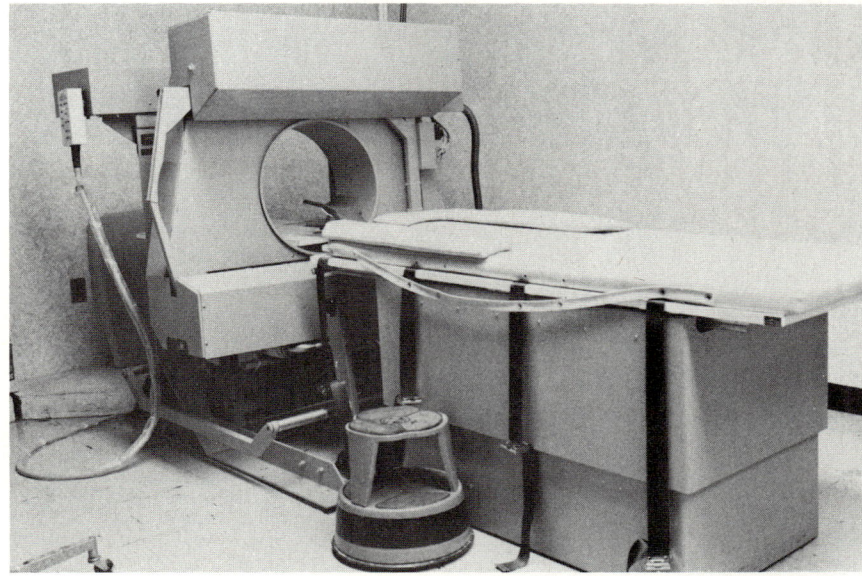

FIGURE 38-2 A new tool for medicine: the CAT-scanner (A) and one of its results (B).

A

ogy is the **CAT-scanner.** (The abbreviation stands for "computerized axial tomography.") Among the normally conservative medical community, this new advance in diagnosis is freely being called a "revolution." Narrow beams of X rays are passed through the patient's body and recorded by an electronic detector. By rotating the frame that holds the X-ray source and detector, gradually a full picture of a "slice" of the patient is built up (Figure 38-2). The readings are temporarily stored in a computer and then reconstructed into a vivid image that can reveal tumors, cysts, infarcts, hemorrhage, atrophy, and other lesions. The CAT-scanner can successfully replace other, potentially more dangerous or less accurate diagnostic techniques, such as angiography, pneumoencephalography, and radionuclide scanning.

B

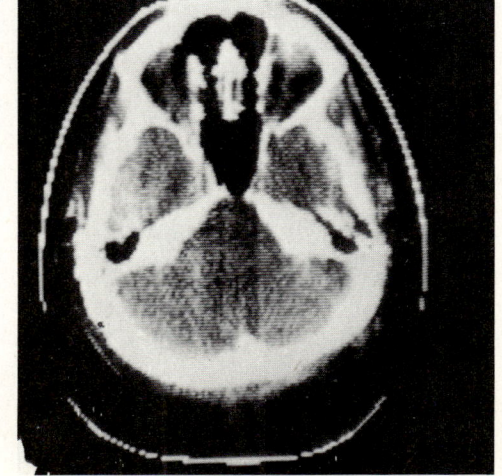

A

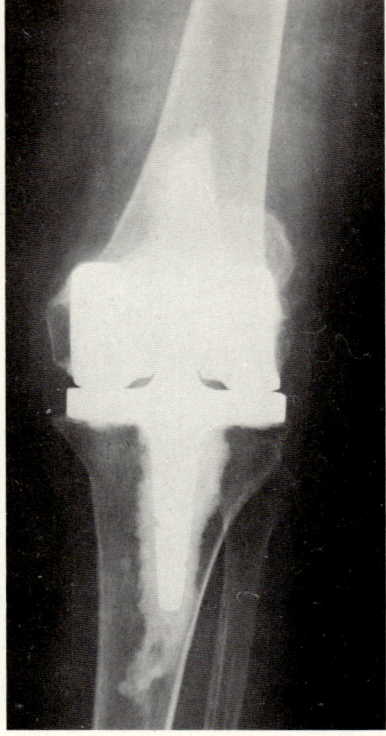

B

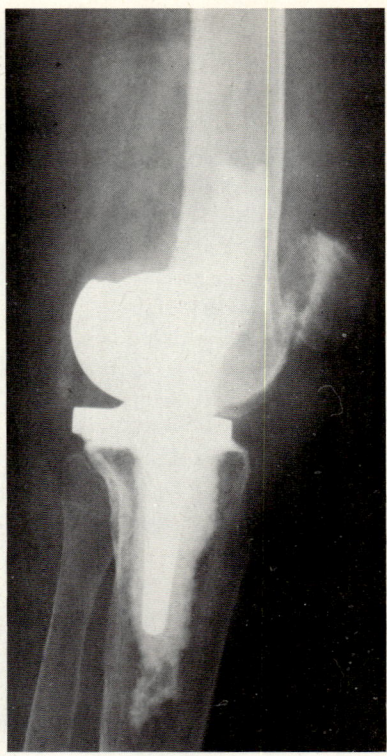

C

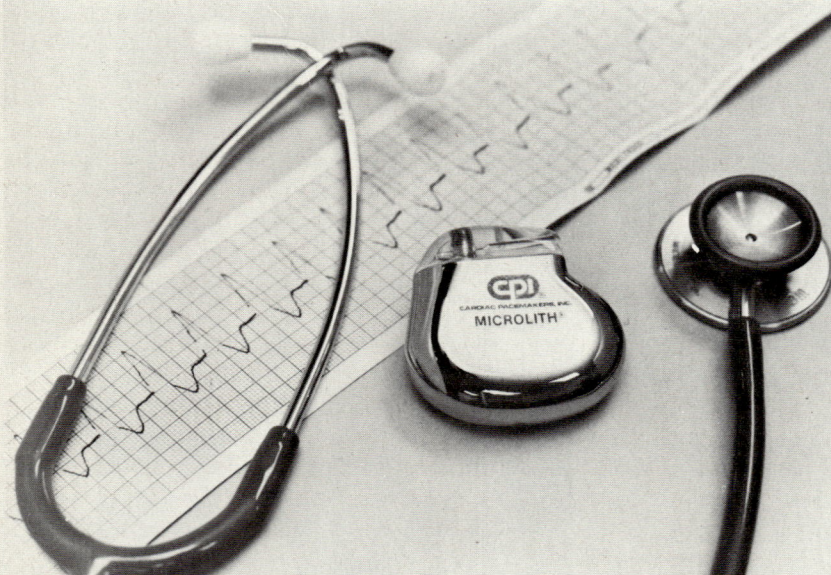

D

FIGURE 38-3 Prosthetics researchers are working to make artificial limbs approximate the natural functions as closely as possible. Prototypes of a myoelectric arm (A), controlled by impulses from nerves in the stump and providing feedback for a sense of touch, are being developed with the aid of patients carefully selected for courage and motivation. Advanced metal-and-plastic knee prostheses (shown in anterior and lateral views in B and C) simulate the complex motions of the human knee joint. Cardiac pacemakers regulate the heart rhythm artificially, either at a programmed rate or on "demand," when the heart activity falls below a predetermined level. The model shown (D) weighs 75 grams (2.6 ounces) and is shaped for physiologically compatible implantation.

PROSTHETICS

The idea of replacing lost or damaged body parts with artificial substitutes has alternately intrigued and appalled people through the ages. The earliest prosthetic devices—crude wooden "peglegs" to replace a missing lower leg and metal hooks in place of a missing hand—restored lost functions only to the most rudimentary degree. In recent years, with a growing knowledge of body functions and increasing sophistication of instrumentation, dramatic progress has been made in the field of prosthetics—so much so that extrapolations of current trends have been used to create popular TV series characters such as the "Six Million Dollar Man" and "Bionic Woman," whose numerous prosthetic devices, incorporating bionic principles, are actually improvements on the limbs, eyes, and other body parts that are standard equipment for normal humans.

Thousands of people are able to live and work today because of implanted electronic pacemakers that control the rhythm of their heartbeats. Damaged heart valves and portions of arteries can be successfully replaced with synthetic substitutes. Hip joint prostheses are bringing new mobility to people crippled with arthritis. Progress is being made toward the development of artificial hearts, lungs, kidneys, and other major organs. Prototypes of artificial limbs that operate powered by the body's own electricity and provide a certain amount of neural feedback have already been built (see Figure 38-3). Artificial eyes—miniature TV cameras that can actually be implanted into the orbits and linked up with the appropriate analyzing areas of the brain—are on the drawing board, and simple prototypes are already being tested.

Ultimately, we can envision the development of effective prostheses for all of the major body organs and parts. But if we gain the technological know-how to produce adequate replacements for the human heart, lungs, kidneys, liver, and ultimately perhaps even the human brain, then we will have the capacity to build a truly artifical human: a robot. Such a robot would be able to think and move and perhaps to experience emotions such as love and hate, much as we do. But would such robots be truly *alive?* And what would their relationship be to their human creators—slaves, equals, or ultimately masters?

GERMFREE RESEARCH

We are accustomed to thinking of microbes—"germs"—as enemies. Bacteria, viruses, and other microorganisms cause countless diseases that plague humans and their domestic animals and cultivated plants. Yet the microbes that are a constant part of our environment also include numerous neutral and even helpful species. If somehow we were able to eradicate all germs, what would our life be like? Would it even be possible?

The first person to raise such questions and suggest that they be tested experimentally was Louis Pasteur. The experiment that he suggested, back in 1885, was ingeniously simple. A chick develops within its shell in a sterile—that is, germfree—environment. Pasteur suggested that if a hatching chick were protected from contact with germs, fed sterilized food, and raised in a sterilized environment, it would be possible to determine whether microbes were necessary to its survival. Pasteur thought that animals could not survive without microbes, but he did not have the time or energy to conduct the experiments himself. Sporadic attempts to raise animals under germfree

conditions were made during the decades that followed, but various technical difficulties kept cropping up. Finally, in the 1930s, J. A. Reyniers and his associates at Notre Dame University designed workable stainless steel germfree isolators (Figure 38-4A). Later, cheap and convenient plastic isolators such as the one shown in Figure 38-4B were devised. Problems of diet and rearing were laboriously solved, and a variety of animals were eventually born, reared, and kept through many successive generations without any contact with microorganisms. (Germfree mammals can be obtained by delivering young by caesarian section directly into the sterile environment, since the smbryonic mammal within its membranes, like the chick in its shell, is in a "germfree chamber" before birth.) It was definitely established at last that life in a germfree world is possible for virtually any higher animal, as long as sufficient nutrients are provided. (Germfree experiments helped to establish definitively that normal microflora contribute various vitamins to the nutrition of their hosts.) Germfree animals have been found to be relatively normal. They mature at the same rate as their conventional counterparts, are healthy and vigorous, and produce the same numbers of offspring. But the weight of the reticuloendothelial system, lymphatic tissue, and the connective tissue in organs normally in contact with the microflora is somewhat reduced. The feces of germfree animals are practically odorless, and when such animals die there is no decay.

The field of **gnotobiology** includes not only studies of the germfree state, but also investigations in which germfree animals have been deliberately exposed to one or more strains of microorganisms, the identity of which is strictly known. Such studies have revealed the role of bacteria in tooth decay and have disclosed a link between amebic dysentery and the presence of certain bacteria.

In studies of the immunological apparatus, the toxicity and fate of new drugs, the origin and growth of tumors, the effects of irradiation, and nutritional studies, germfree animals provide unique advantages as "controls," since studies can be conducted with them without distortion of the results produced by the effects of extraneous microorganisms. Germfree animals were also used to assay specimens of moon rocks for the possible presence of microorganisms.

Germfree research has numerous medical applications. Human infants expected to suffer from hereditary immunological deficiencies have been delivered by caesarian section into sterile isolettes and raised under germfree conditions until transplants of immunogenic tissue could be administered and sufficient immunocompetence could be developed to make them able to survive in our germ-filled world. Pro-

FIGURE 38-4 The original stainless steel germfree isolator units have now largely given way to inexpensive plastic isolators, which have placed germfree research within the budget of nearly every research lab.

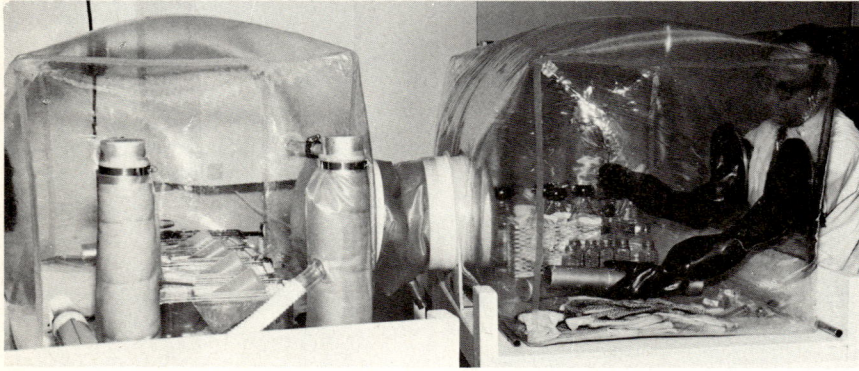

longed rearing in such conditions, with a plastic barrier between the child and the rest of the world, seems to have no adverse effects on mental, physical, and psychological development.

Germfree techniques are also used in the postoperative management of transplant patients who are being given immunosuppressive treatments.

The knowledge gained in gnotobiological studies will also be of vital importance in the future, if humans undertake long space voyages and establish domed settlements on alien satellites and planets.

BIOCHEMICAL ENGINEERING

Virtually every individual is born defective in some way. Some enzyme or other protein may be made in insufficient quantities, or not at all. In most of us

these minor defects do not affect key steps in vital processes. But in some, the genetic deficiency is translated into gross malformations or malfunctions of the body mechanisms.

It seems logical that a disorder due to a chemical deficiency could be corrected by introducing the appropriate chemical into the body. This approach is not new. For decades, diabetics have been enabled to lead a normal life by regular injections of insulin, which their own pancreas is unable to manufacture in sufficient quantities to regulate the blood sugar level. Thyroid extract similarly replaces the lacking secretions of an underactive thyroid gland.

However, the correction of physiological disorders by the introduction of suitable biochemicals—which might be called biochemical engineering—has certain inherent difficulties. First of all, the chemical introduced must produce the desired effect in the human body. Many proteins are quite species-specific; thus far, it has not been possible to treat growth disorders with injections of growth hormone, for example, as readily as diabetes is treated with insulin, because only human growth hormone works sufficiently well on humans, and it is extremely expensive and can be obtained only in limited amounts. In addition, the chemical introduced must be delivered to the appropriate place to exert its action. Insulin, like other hormones, is carried through the bloodstream. Diabetics must inject their insulin, rather than taking it by mouth, because the protein would be digested before it could pass out of the gastrointestinal tract into the blood. In the case of defects of enzymes that act inside cells, the problem is even more complicated—how can the missing enzyme be delivered to the cell organelles where it will exert its effect?

Recent studies in the field of biochemical engineering have been centered on a group of hereditary metabolic diseases characterized by deficiencies of enzymes that catalyze the breakdown of lipids. Without the key enzymes, lipids accumulate in the cells; mental retardation and enlargement of the spleen and liver may result. In one type, Tay-Sachs disease, lipid buildup in brain cells causes young children to deteriorate progressively, both physically and mentally, and finally die after a few years. Fabry's disease, a sex-linked conditioned carried on the X chromosome, is found more often in men than in women; the condition produces severe pains in the arms and legs during the teen years, and usually death in the early forties from the clogging of the kidneys with fat deposits. Roscoe Brady and his team at the National Institute of Neurological Diseases and Stroke have achieved promising results in replacing the lacking enzymes in patients with such diseases of the lipid metabolism. Injections of alpha galactosidase, the enzyme lacking in Fabry's disease patients, have dramatically reduced the fats transported from the bloodstream to the kidneys. In victims of another lipid storage disease, Gaucher's disease, injections of the enzyme glucocerebrosidase eliminated much of the patient's accumulated fat. Thus far, enzyme treatments of Tay-Sach's disease have been unsuccessful, since the enzyme does not pass the blood-brain barrier and thus cannot get to the brain cells where it is needed. Methods of bypassing the difficulty are being explored.

A new advance called **microencapsulation** is revolutionizing many fields of industry and medicine and offers great promise in biochemical engineering. Enzymes are immobilized within microscopic globules of lipid membranes (Figure 38-5). Pores in the membranes are too small to let the eyzymes out, but they permit the substrate molecules to diffuse in. (The molecules of an enzyme's substrate are usually much smaller than those of the enzyme.) In preliminary experiments, phagocytes in a culture have been induced to take up these tiny enzmye packets, called liposomes, by coating the liposomes with aggregated IgM antibodies, making them seem like foreign particles that have stimulated an immune response. The enzymes used were peroxidases, which are lacking in certain genetic diseases. In normal cells peroxidases are found in the lysosomes, the intracellular digestive organelles. The researchers were encouraged to note that a substantial amount of the enzyme entered the lysosomes of the cells that had phagocytized the liposomes, indicating that this technique may be useful in combatting the effects of the genetic deficiencies.

Such techniques of biochemical engineering, however, can only control genetic diseases; they cannot cure them. A diabetic must go on taking insulin for the rest of his or her life, and the patients with Fabry's and Gaucher's diseases will need repeated injections of enzymes to keep the accumulation of fats under control. Enzyme-deficiency diseases cannot be truly cured unless the defective genes themselves are repaired or replaced. The rapidly growing field of genetic engineering offers hopes of doing precisely that.

GENETIC ENGINEERING
We are rapidly gaining the power to remake ourselves. Techniques of genetic engineering are providing avenues for manipulating the genetic apparatus of life.

At a meeting of the American Association for the Advancement of Science at the end of 1968, noted geneticist Robert Sinsheimer spoke about the prospects for genetic engineering: "All that seems needed is the technique to transfer what we already know to be feasible in bacteria, carrot cells, or frogs to man. I feel strangely akin to the physicists who pointed out in the 1930's that the principles required for the release of the energy locked in the atomic nucleus were understood. Here, too, the principles seem in hand. All that seems really needed is optimism, sustained effort, and support commensurate with the importance of the problem."

If we could make genes to order, and introduce them into the body, or if we could learn to manipulate the on-off switches that determine whether a particular gene in the body will function or be repressed, we would have ways to intervene in a variety of biochemical diseases and in the aging process as well. Research in the rapidly growing field of genetic engineering is providing means of doing precisely these things.

Genes have already been synthesized in a test tube,

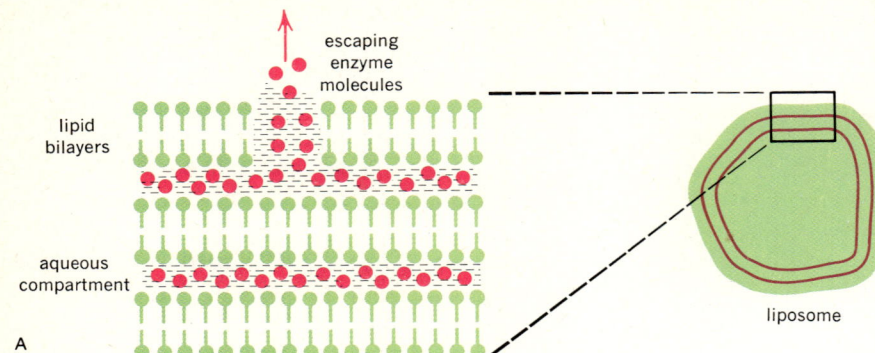

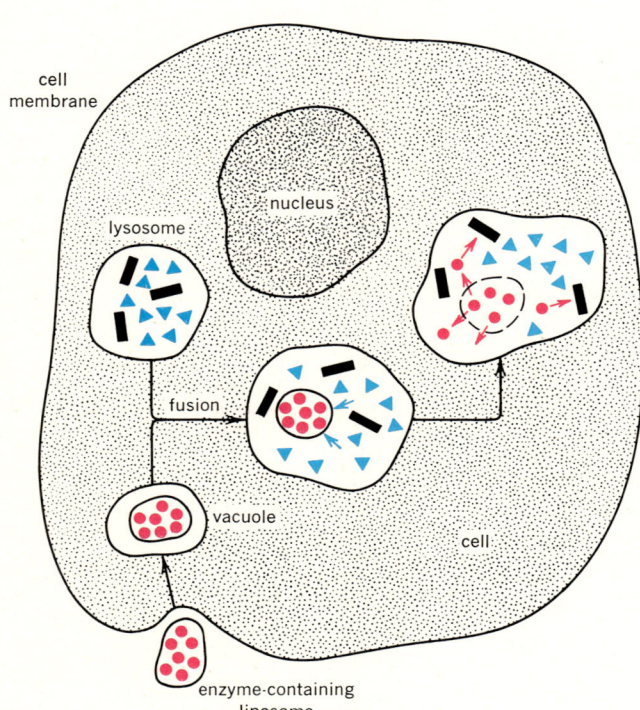

FIGURE 38-5 Microencapsulation: (A) Structure of a liposome: lipid layers alternate with layers of entrapped enzyme (dots) and water. Degrading enzymes produce breaks in the membrane through which entrapped molecules can escape. (B) A liposome, taken into the cell by endocytosis, fuses with a lysosome containing substrate molecules (bars). Lysosomal enzymes (triangles) release the entrapped enzyme, which acts on the substrate. (Modified from *New Scientist*, 27 December 1973, pp. 891–892.)

without the participation of living cells. In one approach, pioneered by Nobel Prize winner Har Gobind Khorana, DNA molecules are built up by laboriously assembling short segments, nucleotide by nucleotide, and alternately adding these segments to one strand of the growing DNA chain or the other, each time leaving a "sticky end" to which the next segment can be jointed (Figure 38-6A). In this technique, the blueprint of the gene is strictly followed—which means that the nucleotide sequence of a gene must be precisely known before it can be synthesized. In a newer method, developed by a team of Harvard University biochemists (Figure 38-6B), genes can be copied without knowing their detailed structure, by isolating the messenger RNA that directs the production of the gene's protein product, then combining this RNA with DNA raw materials and an enzyme, reverse transcriptase, which reverses the normal sequence and catalyzes the synthesis of the corresponding DNA from an RNA template. (RNA viruses use reverse transcriptase in their takeover of the host cell's protein-synthesizing machinery.)

If we are rapidly gaining the ability to make genes to order, what about means for introducing them into cells? One method that has been proposed is the use of viruses. When a virsus enters a cell, it can attach itself to the host's own genes; in experiments on bacteria, viruses have also been shown to carry some of

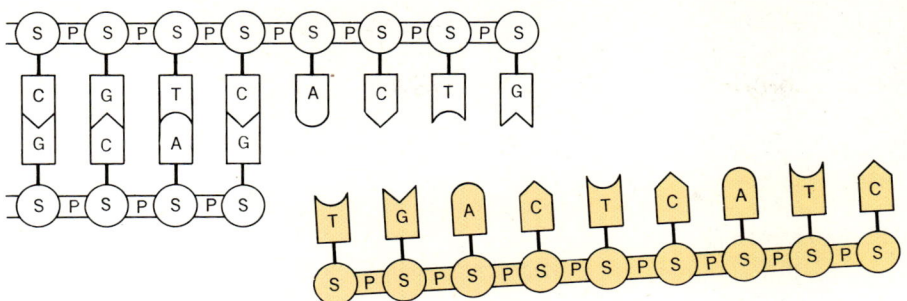

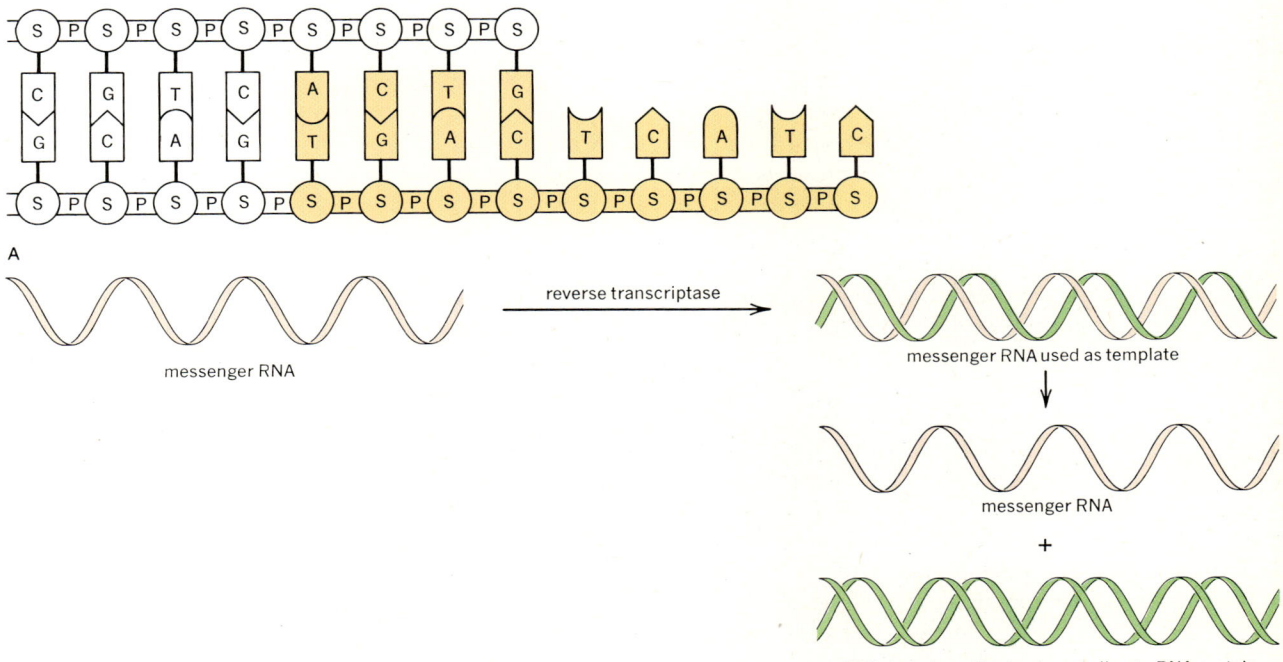

FIGURE 38-6   Gene synthesis: (A)Khorana's "sticky end" technique. In each step the complementary strand added is longer than the space being filled, leaving a dangling "sticky end" free for further reaction. (B) Reverse transcriptase permits the synthesis of DNA on an RNA template.

A

reverse transcriptase

messenger RNA

messenger RNA used as template

messenger RNA

+

DNA (gene) synthesized according to RNA protein

B

the genes of a former host along with them and transfer them to a new cell. Thus, viruses specially bred for desirable characteristics, such as the ability to induce the synthesis of a key enzyme, could be used to introduce such genes into deficient cells. Desirable genes, either obtained from normally functioning cells or synthesized artificially, could also be "tacked onto" the normal virus genes and then sent into the body via vaccination.

Exciting progress has been made along this line. Viruses have been used to introduce specific genes into plant and mammalian cells. Indeed, a similar transfer into living humans was made accidentally. A research team at Oak Ridge National Laboratory, directed by Stanfield Rogers, was working with the Shope papilloma virus, which produces tumors in

rabbits but is not pathogenic in man. The virus induces the production of the eyzyme arginase (which breaks down the amino acid arginine) in rabbits, in addition to producing tumors. Routine blood tests of researchers who had been working with the virus revealed a significant drop in the level of arginine in their blood, apparently as a result of increased arginase production. Thus, the typical question that arises in the study of any new biological phenomenon, "Is it applicable to humans?" seems to have been answered almost before it was raised.

Other studies have pointed up further avenues for introducing genetic changes into human cells. Techniques have been devised for fusing different types of cells grown together in a culture. The hybrid cells generally retain some of the chromosomes of each parent. The variety of hybrids produced has even included interspecies hybrids, such as mouse-rat, mouse-hamster, and mouse-human combinations. Such exotic hybrids probably could not be used in genetic engineering, since they would likely be rejected by the patient's immune system. The use of red blood cells as gene donors seems more feasible, since red cells do not contribute any of their membranes to the surface of the new cell when they form hybrids. Similar techniques have also been applied to the fusion of spermatozoa with cells in culture. In one experiment, the fusion of normal mouse sperm with cultured mouse fibroblasts lacking an enzyme needed for DNA synthesis and normal cell division corrected the enzyme deficiency. It is believed that cells fused with sperm would be recognized as "self" and would not be rejected, since the sperm chromosomes are fragmented, and most of their genes are lost in the progeny of the fused cells. (About one of every million cell clones obtained from the fusion in the mouse experiments produced the needed enzyme.) In the treatment of a genetic disease, cells could be extracted from the patient, grown in culture with sperm from a normal individual, and then the cells that had incorporated the appropriate genes could be reinjected into the patient, where it is hoped they would multiply.

One of the newest areas of genetic engineering, **recombinant DNA** research, has excited an unparalleled furor. Recombinant DNA techniques involve the introduction of specific genes from other organisms into microorganisms, which can then be cultured in quantity to obtain genetic material for study or to produce useful proteins. Such techniques were made possible by several key developments. One was the discovery of **plasmids,** tiny ring-shaped chains of genes that are reproduced independently of the chromosomes in bacteria. The other crucial developments were the discoveries of two classes of enzymes: **restriction enzymes,** which recognize specific sequences of DNA bases and neatly snip both strands of the DNA molecule at that spot, and **DNA ligases,** which can join sticky ends of DNA, producing an unbroken strand. The combination of these separate discoveries yielded an elegantly simple and potent technique: isolate a gene of interest—even a human gene—cut open a plasmid with restriction enzymes, insert the foreign gene, binding it with ligases, and then reintroduce the expanded plasmid into bacteria and let them reproduce it. Then, after means were devised to turn on the genes and have the bacteria translate them into proteins, such techniques would permit large-scale production of human enzymes, hormones, and other substances that could be used in biochemical engineering. For example, the gene for human growth hormone could be isolated, introduced into a microbe

by means of plasmids, and then the microbe, now capable of synthesizing human growth hormone, could be cultured in huge vats, producing tons of the hormone that is now so scarce and costly.

In addition to direct clinical applications, recombinant DNA techniques could bring a revolution in biochemical research. One of the main limitations on research on the human body at the molecular level has been the lack of sufficient material to work with. Hormones, enzymes, and other key biomolecules are typically present in the body media in amounts that are barely detectable. Nobel Prize winner Gerald Edelman was able to delineate the complete structure of an antibody only because a bizarre tumor of a cancer patient happened to produce abnormally large quantities of it. Such lucky accidents are rare in the normal course of events, but recombinant DNA techniques would provide virtually limitless quantities of biomolecules. Such techniques would permit researchers to determine the complete genetic structure of the body, and the results of that achievement—both in knowledge and in practical applications—would be overwhelming and beyond our capacity to imagine at present.

At first, geneticists plunged eagerly into the new field. The repertoire of restriction enzymes and plasmids was expanded, and genes from such diverse creatures as clawed toads, fruit flies, and ultimately mammals were inserted into bacteria, using both plasmids and viruses as vehicles. But gradually voices of alarm began to be raised, and eventually genetics researchers voluntarily imposed a temporary moratorium on certain types of recombinant DNA research, until potential risks could be properly assessed and guidelines drawn up for research techniques to minimize the risks.

Several potential problems were causes for concern. It was feared that transfers of genes among microorganisms and especially of human genes to microorganisms might give rise to new pathogens, whoch would produce virulent diseases that could sweep through the population because we would have no evolutionarily developed defenses against them. A particular fear was that cancer genes or oncogenic viruses might inadvertently be transferred to the coliform bacillus *E. coli,* a favorite subject of genetics experiments, which might then escape from the laboratory and spread through the population. The commonly used recombinant DNA technique of "shotgunning," in which whole chromosomes are digested with restriction enzymes, the fragments incorporated into plasmids, transferred to bacteria, and the cell progeny cloned to see what new properties turned up, could indeed conceivably result in some unpredictable new microorganisms. Particularly disturbing was the simplicity of recombinant DNA techniques—experiments could be conducted with the equipment available in a typical high school laboratory, and they were often being conducted carelessly, by persons inexperienced in the proper precautions to be taken in microbiological work.

Some recombinant DNA researchers pointed to thousands of experiments, in which there was no indication that any virulent microorganisms had escaped. They further noted that microorganisms have been coexisting with humans and our prehuman ancestors for many millions of years, and thus nature has had ample time and facilities for experimentation. Any possible transfers of genetic material must undoubtedly have already occurred, many times. Yet the question remained: how much risk is acceptable in the search for biomedical knowledge?

During the moratorium, guidelines were drawn up, classifying types of recombinant DNA experiments according to their degree of potential risk, and standards were established for precautionary measures to contain them. Particularly sensitive experiments must be conducted in escape-proof "P4 facilities," very similar to those used for germfree and gnotobiological studies. In addition, geneticists tinkered with *E. coli* and developed new strains unable to survive outside the pampered conditions of the microbiological laboratory, to be used expressly for recombinant DNA experiments. These experiments are already bearing fruit; recombinant DNA synthesis of human insulin was announced in 1978, and pharmaceutical manufacturers are using recombinant DNA techniques for large-scale production of somatostatin, human growth hormone, and other valuable biomolecules.

The recombinant DNA controversy is the latest skirmish in a continuing dialogue that has been going on since the whole concept of genetic engineering was proposed. It has even been suggested that research in this field should be deliberately slowed down or suppressed until we acquire the maturity to use our knowledge wisely. But geneticists such as Nobel Prize winners Arthur Kornberg and Joshua Lederberg contend that the idea of applying new genetic knowledge to modify human characteristics is neither so new nor so horrifying as its opponents imply. Their view is aptly summed up in the words of geneticist Robert Sinsheimer: "I would suggest that those who feel this way are not among the losers in that chromosomal lottery that so firmly channels our human destinies. This response does not come from the 250,000 children born each year in this country with structural or functional defects. . . . It does not include, for example, the 50 million 'normal' Americans with an I.Q. of less than 90."

SUMMARY

Medical electronic instruments are used for diagnosis, treatment, monitoring of patient's condition, and in biomedical research. Computers are used to store and retrieve records and "consult" in diagnoses.
CAT-scanners use computer integration of readings from narrowbeam X-ray scanning to produce a detailed picture that can detect tumors and other lesions.
Prosthetic devices have been developed for heart pacemakers, valves, and arteries, bones and joints, limbs, and eyes.
Animals raised in a germfree environment are essentially normal but have an undeveloped reticuloendothelial system and require nutrients supplied by microflora in conventional animals. Germfree techniques have been applied in the postoperative management of transplant patients and in the treatment of infants with hereditary immune deficiencies.
Biochemical engineering is the correction of physiological disorders by the introduction of suitable biochemicals—for example, hormones or enzymes.
Microencapsulation may permit more effective introduction of deficient enzymes.
Genetic engineering is the alteration of genes of body cells to correct physiological disorders.
Genes have been synthesized in vitro.
Techniques that might be used to introduce genes into human cells are infection with nonpathogenic viruses and cell fusion (possibly with sperm).
Plasmids can be used to transfer mammalian genes to bacteria and may permit large-scale production of human enzymes, hormones, and other substances that could be used in biochemical enginnering.

QUESTIONS FOR REVIEW AND THOUGHT

1 In what areas of biomedical research and clinical practice have electronic devices provided valuable new tools and approaches? Give examples.
2 Recently some medical experts have questioned the desirability of so many hospitals investing in CAT-scanners. Discuss the pros and cons you would consider if you were a hospital administrator deciding whether to order one for your hospital.
3 Considering the underdevelopment of the RES in germfree animals, what do you think the effect on them would be if they were suddenly exposed to a normal, germ-filled environment? Do you think it will ever be feasible and/or desirable to make our environment germfree?
4 Distinguish between biochemical engineering and genetic engineering. How could the two approaches be applied to the treatment of Tay-Sachs disease?
5 What advantages are offered by microencapsulation?
6 Describe the Khorana and reverse transcriptase methods of gene synthesis. What advantage would the use of genes obtained by such methods have over "shotgunning" in recombinant DNA research?
7 What are plasmids? What do restriction enzymes and DNA ligases do?
8 Do you think recombinant DNA research should be encouraged, restricted, or suppressed? Who do you think should make such decisions?

THE
HEALTH
SCIENCES
AND
SOCIETY

39

The health sciences are the number two industry in the nation. In fiscal 1979, close to $200 billion was spent for medicine. This was more than the amount spent for defense. As our knowledge of the body increases and our ability to heal improves, the health sciences will continue to expand and assume a larger and larger fraction of our national economy.

As our ability to intervene into life processes and our control over the human body grow, a host of ethical problems is acquiring new urgency. Are there any circumstances in which the fruits of biomedical advances should *not* be used? Many of the new instruments and techniques are expensive and scarce. If we have the capability for saving lives, who is to decide which lives should be saved? And if *all* possible lives should be saved, who will pay the bill?

The scientific research on which modern biomedical advances are based often requires painstaking work of testing and development on human subjects. Who should the guinea pigs be, and what safeguards should be provided for their protection? What element of risk should be permitted against the benefits of a new drug? What about people who knowingly or unknowingly abuse their own bodies? What about the effects of human activities on our planet and on our health?

In this chapter the background of some of the ethical dilemmas that characterize the interaction of the modern health sciences and society is explored.

THE FDA

How do you strike an appropriate balance between benefit and risk?

It is estimated that in the United States alone, more than three thousand different chemicals are added to the foods we eat, and more than four thousand drugs are currently in use. Food additives produce various beneficial effects: some are coloring or flavoring agents; some are used to change the texture of foods, to make dough rise, to make whipped toppings foam; some keep foods from spoiling, or caking, or turning liquid. The variety of modern foods and the mass marketing processes needed to feed a largely urbanized nation of more than two hundred million people would be impossible without the use of food additives. Drugs also play crucial roles, improving health and saving lives.

Yet few of these benefits come unalloyed with unfavorable side effects. During the early days of the chemical industry, food and drug manufacturers plunged enthusiastically into the use of chemicals, often with only rudimentary screening for harmful effects. The nation at large served as the guinea pigs—if a new food additive turned out to be making people ill, then after a public outcry it was withdrawn. In-

FIGURE 39-1 The array of foods offered by the modern supermarket would be impossible without food additives.

stances of corporate irresponsibility prompted the establishment of the federal Food and Drug Administration (FDA) in 1906, and subsequent legislation has gradually broadened its powers. Today the FDA oversees the testing of new food additives and drugs and is gradually reviewing a number of food additives that had previously been classified on the "GRAS" ("generally regarded as safe") list.

There are many inherent problems in the testing of food additives and drugs. First of all, though there are many basic similarities between animals and humans, animal tests may not be fully applicable to humans because of metabolic differences between species; indeed, even individual humans show many metabolic idiosyncrasies that can confuse test findings. For example, many people metabolize about 1 percent of the artificial sweetener cyclamate to a toxic product, cyclohexylamine; but other, equally "normal" people convert as much as 40 percent of ingested cyclamate to cyclohexylamine. Animal tests and initial human trials indicated that the drug thalidomide was a safe and effective tranquilizer and anti-nausea agent. Only when the drug was in widespread use in Europe, and an epidemic of cases of a rare birth defect called phocomelia (Figure 39-2) began to show up among children born to mothers who had taken the drug during early pregnancy, was it realized that a tragic mistake had been made. (By the

FIGURE 39-2 **This three-year-old boy, born without arms to a German mother who took thalidomide during pregnancy, uses a power-driven artificial arm to make mud-pies.**

time the story broke, the FDA still had not approved thalidomide for general use in the United States, and thus an even more widespread tragedy was averted.)

Food additives are commonly approved if they are shown to be safe "at the intended levels of use." This practice makes sense, since virtually any chemical can be harmful if it is consumed in large enough amounts. A number of babies die each year because their mothers accidentally substituted salt for sugar in their formula, and indeed, for persons with special metabolic problems, even a "normal" intake of either salt or sugar can be harmful. But modern humans in our affluent society take in a great variety of foods in their diet. Often several foods may contain the same food additive, all at the "safe" level; or different food additives may interact with one another, with body chemicals, or with drugs being taken for an illness. How can the true "safe" level be determined under such confusing conditions?

The question of cancer raises special problems. It is believed that many carcinogens take years—even decades—to manifest their effects. Heavy reliance is therefore placed on animal studies. Technically, according to a legislative regulation referred to as the Delaney amendment, any substance that has been shown to produce cancer in experimental animals, at any level of dosage, must be prohibited. This was the basis on which cyclamates were banned. (Ironically, later evidence seems to indicate that cyclamate itself may actually be innocent of that particular charge.) But this restriction is difficult to apply in practice. If the Delaney amendment were strictly enforced, many common foods—egg, for example—would have to be banned, since they have also been shown to produce cancer in experimental animals when given in abnormally large doses.

Drugs are tested not only for safety, but also for effectiveness. However, the evaluation of drug effectiveness is sometimes a subjective matter. To further confuse the issue, there is a common **placebo effect:** If sick people *think* they have been given a drug, they may show dramatic improvement, even though they may actually have received only sugar pills. Spontaneous recoveries are also common, and a drug may receive the credit when actually it was the patient's own body defenses that coincidentally triumphed over the disease. To avoid these potentially confusing factors, elaborate **double blind** studies must be set up, in which not only patients, but also physicians are unaware of which patients are receiving the drug being evaluated and which are serving as controls.

Some consumerists charge that the FDA, chronically overworked and underfinanced, is not vigilant enough in protecting the public interests and tends to rely too heavily on tests performed by the food and drug industries themselves—hardly disinterested parties. Yet many researchers level opposite charges—that excessively cautious and restrictive FDA attitudes and cumbersome procedures tend to discourage research and delay the introduction of potentially valuable drugs, many of which indeed have already been in general use in Europe for years. Probably there is some validity to both complaints. The ethical question remains: how much risk is justified in the pursuit of potential benefits?

DRUG ABUSE

It is said that we live in particularly troubled times. Yet there have been troubled times all through human history. Even in times of peace for the community in general, there is always the potential for numerous personal tragedies and problems that sometimes seem too great to bear. Through the ages, various mood-altering drugs have been discovered and experimented with, using them as chemical aids to forget one's troubles—at least temporarily—or to heighten pleasure or seek mystical insights.

Unfortunately, we have yet to discover or devise a mood-altering drug that is free of any harmful side effects. Many such drugs are **physically addictive:** after the user has taken the drug for awhile, body metabolism is altered, and he or she comes to depend on

TABLE 39-1 Commonly Used Mood-Altering Drugs and Their Effects

TYPE OF DRUG	NAME	ORIGIN	EFFECTS
Depressants			
Alcohol	Beer	Grain	Relaxation, breakdown of inhibitions, euphoria, depression, decreased alertness and impairment of coordination; *large doses:* nausea, unconsciousness, hangover, death; *long-term abuse:* malnutrition, psychosis, liver and brain damage, delerium tremens, death
	Liquor	Grain	
	Wine	Fruit	
Barbiturates	Chloral hydrate		Relaxation, euphoria, decreased alertness, drowsiness, impaired coordination, sleep; *large doses:* slurred speech, stupor, hangover, death; *long-term abuse:* sleepiness, confusion, irritability, withdrawal sickness
	Nembutal	Synthetic	
	Phenobarbital		
	Seconal		
Inhalants	Aerosols (Freon)		Relaxation, euphoria, impaired coordination; *large doses:* stupor, death; *long-tern abuse:* hallucinations, damage to liver, kidneys, bone marrow, and brain; death
	Airplane glue	Synthetic	
	Amyl nitrate		
	Nitrous oxide		
Narcotics	Codeine	Opium poppy	Relaxation, relief of pain and anxiety, decreased alertness, euphoria, drowsiness, hallucinations; *large doses:* stupor, death; *long-term abuse:* lethargy, weight loss, temporary impotence, withdrawal sickness
	Demerol	Synthetic	
	Heroin	Opium poppy	
	Methadone	Synthetic	
	Morphine	Opium poppy	
	Opium	Opium poppy	
Tranquilizers	Librium		Relief of anxiety and tension, suppression of hallucinations and aggression, sleep; *large doses:* drowsiness, blurred vision, dizziness, stupor; *long-term abuse:* destruction of blood cells, jaundice, coma; death
	Miltown	Synthetic	
	Thorazine		
Stimulants			
Amphetamines	Benzedrine		Increased alertness. excitement, euphoria, decreased appetite; *large doses:* restlessness, rapid speech, irritability, insomnia, convulsions; *long-term abuse:* insomnia, excitability, delusions, hallucinations, psychosis
	Dexedrine	Synthetic	
	Methedrine		
Antidepressants	Elavil		Relief of anxiety and depression; *large doses:* nausea, hypertension, weight loss, insomnia; *long-term abuse:* stupor, coma, convulsions, heart failure, damage to liver and white blood cells, death
	Ritalin	Synthetic	
	Tofranil		
Caffeine	Coffee	Coffee bean	Increased alertness; *large doses:* restlessness, insomnia, upset stomach; *long term abuse:* may contribute to heart disease and cancer
	Cola	Kola nut	
	No-Doz	Synthetic	
	Tea	Tea leaves	
Cocaine	Cocaine	Cocoa leaves	Exhilaration, excitation, talkativeness, tremors; *large doses:* irritability, depression, psychosis; *long-term abuse:* damage to blood vessels, convulsions, psychosis
Nicotine	Cigarettes		Relaxation, constriction of blood vessels; *large doses:* headache, loss of appetite, nausea; *long-term abuse:* impairment of breathing, heart and lung diseases, cancer, death
	Cigars		
	Pipes	Tobacco leaves	
	Snuff		
Psychedelics			
Cannabis	Hashish	Cannabis plant	Relaxation, breakdown of inhibitions, euphoria, alteration of perception and judgment; *large doses:* panic, stupor; *long-term abuse:* fatigue, psychosis
	Marijuana	Cannabis plant	
	THC (tetrahydro-cannabinol)	Synthetic	
Hallucinogens	DMT	Synthetic	Perceptual changes, excitation, hallucinations, exhilaration, panic; *large doses:* anxiety, exhaustion, comiting, psychosis; *long-term abuse:* delusions, panic, psychosis
	LSD	Synthetic	
	Mescaline	Cactus, peyote	
	Nutmeg	Nutmeg tree	
	Psilocybin	Psilocybe mushroom	
	Scopolamine	Henbane plant or synthetic	
	STP	Synthetic	

a steady supply of the drug. If the use of the drug is suddenly stopped, painful **withdrawal symptoms** or even death may result. Even if there is not an actual physical addiction, there is still the danger of developing a **psychological dependence** on the drug—the user loses the habit of facing the world without the chemical "crutch," and may ultimately withdraw from facing life's problems entirely, "dropping out" of the struggle. Many of the commonly used mood-altering drugs damage vital body organs, such as the liver or brain, or may produce mutations in germ cells, endangering the health of future generations. A preoccupation with the inner world of the mind, which seems heightened by the drug, may lead the drug user to neglect more mundane concerns, such as eating regular, balanced meals, and thus further contribute to the deterioration of health. Impaired coordination produced by some drugs can make the drug user dangerously accident-prone—and our technological world of fast-moving cars and industrial machinery is notably intolerant of mistakes.

Despite all these potential pitfalls, growing numbers of people are using—and abusing—a variety of drugs (both legal and illegal) as mood changers, to produce a feeling of relaxation, or stimulation, or a breakdown of inhibitions, a "trip" of hallucinations, or a euphoric "high." The drugs that are most widely abused today fall into three main classes: **depressants, stimulants,** and **psychedelics** (Table 39-1).

When the subject of drug abuse is raised, the drugs people usually think of first are the central nervous system depressants that belong to the group of **narcotics.** The first of the narcotics, **opium,** has been a problem for centuries. Derived from the opium poppy, this depressant drug can bring dreamy relief from pain or anxiety and can produce euphoria and hallucinations. But it is highly physically addictive: the withdrawal symptoms include severe convulsions. Ironically, when **heroin** was first produced, it was touted as a safe, nonaddictive painkiller that could be substituted for opium or for **morphine,** an opium derivative. But heroin was soon found to be extremely addictive and dangerous. (An overdose can kill.) The narcotic **methadone** can produce a "high" similar to that of heroin, and it is also an addictive drug. However, it has been found that regular administration of methadone to a heroin addict, in doses too small to produce a "high," blocks the effects of heroin and helps to control the addict's craving for it. It has been objected that addition-control programs based on methadone maintenance simply substitute one addiction for another. However, such programs have shown some success in enabling addicts to lead relatively normal, productive lives and have probably helped to lower crime rates. (Illegal narcotics are gen-

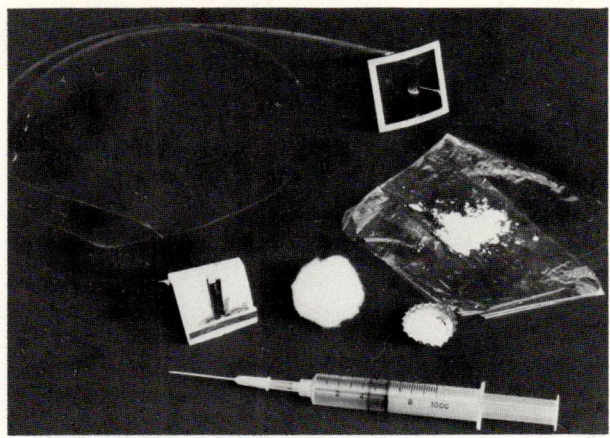

FIGURE 39-3 Paraphernalia of the heroin user.

erally so expensive that addicts are driven to crime to support their habit.)

With all the current concern about drug addiction, people rarely think of alcohol as a drug. Yet it is estimated that drinking is a problem for as many as ten percent of drinkers—and about 95 million people drink! Alcoholism is the number one drug problem in the United States today, and it is currently considered the third ranking health problem in general, after heart disease and cancer. Ethyl alcohol is a depressant drug, one that interacts with the metabolism of the brain and can damage the tissues of the brain and liver. (Recall that the liver plays a major role in detoxifying poisons that have entered the body.) A large proportion of automobile accidents are caused because drivers' coordination, reflexes, and judgment were impaired by a few drinks taken before driving. Alcohol is another drug characterized by the development of both psychological dependence and physical addiction. As with narcotics and many other drugs, a phenomenon of **tolerance** is observed with alcohol: the user finds he or she must take progressively larger doses to achieve the same effect.

The most commonly used stimulants are **caffeine** (occurring in coffee, tea, cola beverages, and chocolate) and **nicotine** (in cigarettes and other tobacco products). Both have a powerful effect on the central nervous system, but also have harmful side effects (both caffeine and nicotine may be contributing factors in heart disease; excessive use of caffeine may produce irritability and insomnia, while smoking has been implicated in premature birth, lung disease, and cancer). Both caffeine and nicotine are characterized by strong psychological dependence (the question of actual physical addiction is in dispute) and tolerance.

The abuse of **amphetamines** and other "pep pills" is an area of growing concern on the drug front. For a time they were prescribed in weight-control programs

FIGURE 39-4   A patch of marijuana growing wild.

to curb appetite, but medical use is now closely restricted. Amphetamines can produce feelings of euphoria and mental alertness, but objective tests indicate that the user's intelligence and creativity have not really been stimulated as much as the person believes they have. Amphetamines work by increasing the release of a natural brain stimulant, norepinephrine. Overexcitation may occur, to the point where the user cannot sleep, and euphoria alternates with periods of deep despair. Tolerance to the drug builds up quickly, and long use of amphetamines may lead to hallucinations, delusions, and violent behavior.

At this writing, one of the most hotly debated drug topics is whether the use of marijuana should be legalized. Some claim that this psychedelic drug is no more dangerous than alcohol (hardly a recommendation) and not addictive (though it does produce some psychological dependence). Opponents of the drug argue that its use promotes a withdrawal from active participation in life. The effects of the drug (from relaxation through euphoria and alternation of perceptions to panic—a "bad trip"—and even psychosis) seem to vary among users, and even in the same user depending on the external circumstances. Very little about the drug's effects is yet known with certainty, but some studies with marijuana and its active principle, **tetrahydrocannabinol (THC),** indicate that THC and its conversion products persist in the brain for days after it has been taken in.

Regardless of the status of marijuana, there is little doubt of the potential dangers of another "consciousness-expanding" drug, **LSD (lysergic acid diethyla-** **mide).** LSD is an extremely potent substance—a single ounce would provide enough doses for 300,000 people. Indeed, it has been estimated that a few pounds of this drug, distributed in the water supply of New York City, could affect the mental acuity of the entire population of the city. The LSD molecule is chemically very similar to the neurotransmitter serotonin, and it is believed to interfere with the normal workings of brain cells. The drug produces hallucinations that may be extremely pleasant fantasies or frightening nightmares. An unfortunate by-product of the use of this and other psychedelic agents is that during the "experience" the user's judgment may be distorted, and they may do harm to themselves or others. Serious and sometimes permanent after-effects have been noted: the LSD user may experience recurrences of hallucinations weeks or months after stopping use of the drug, susceptible individuals may develop a full-blown psychosis, and there are some indications that the drug can cause chromosome breaks that might result in birth defects in the user's children.

POLLUTION

Buckminster Fuller and other modern thinkers have pioneered a new view of the world, as Spaceship Earth—a closed, carefully balanced, and limited system, hurtling through space with us humans as its passengers and crew. What we do today, to and for our planet, may vitally affect our survival as a species. Our Spaceship Earth has so far shown a marvelous ability for self-adjustment and repair, an almost life-

FIGURE 39-5 A smoggy day in New York.

like homeostasis, but we may be reaching the limits of its capacity—and if we foul our nest irreversibly, we may not get another chance.

Through most of the development of technology, humans have been relatively heedless of consequences for our planet. In addition to useful products, human activities invariably generate wastes, which we have for the most part discarded thoughtlessly—into the air, waters, and lands. The result has been a growing pollution, which often offends our eyes, assaults our noses, and may undermine our health.

Industry and automobiles spew a devil's brew of pollutants into the air, including potentially carcinogenic hydrocarbons, carbon dioxide, carbon monoxide, oxides of sulfur and nitrogen, lead compounds, fluorine compounds, and a variety of "particulates." When weather conditions combine to concentrate air pollutants close to the ground level (Figure 39-5), the "smog" that results can kill, taking a toll mainly from the very young and the very old, as well as people with respiratory problems. Even without such glaring instances, our lungs are insidiously subjected to the caustic and debilitating effects of air pollutants every moment of every day and night. The lungs of the modern city dweller are characteristically blackened with soot deposits. The incidence of respiratory diseases of all kinds, especially emphysema, is rising.

A variety of chemicals pollute the waters of our planet. Industrial wastes contribute heavy metals such as mercury and cadmium, caustics, solvents and other organic compounds. Pesticides sprayed on croplands are washed by the rain into rivers and streams. Even individual citizens contribute to the pollution of

our waterways, with nitrogen- and phosphorus-rich organic wastes, detergents, and other chemicals that are washed and flushed down our drains every day. Wastes that are flushed away do not conveniently disappear. They may be taken up by microscopic water life and then increasingly concentrated by animals that feed on it, until these pollutants enter the human diet. (Remember the sudden scare back in 1970, when a high school chemistry teacher found mercury contamination in canned tuna?)

Radiation is another type of pollution that is causing concern. A certain amount of "background" radiation, produced by radioactive minerals and cosmic rays, is natural to our planet, but the natural radiation levels have been increased by the lingering effects of atmospheric explosions of nuclear weapons. The expansion of atomic power plants is adding concern, both because of the possibility of an accident that might result in a release of radiations and because such plants generate a certain amount of radioactive wastes, which must somehow be safely disposed of. Radiations can damage tissues and are powerful mutagenic agents; they can produce somatic mutations that may lead to illness or premature aging, or genetic mutations that may affect future generations.

Still another area of pollution has been growing and apparently will continue to grow in intensity and seriousness: noise pollution. Physicians have long been aware of the dangers of prolonged exposure to high noise intensities within factories and in other industrial surroundings. They are only now becoming aware of the role that noise plays in the daily life of

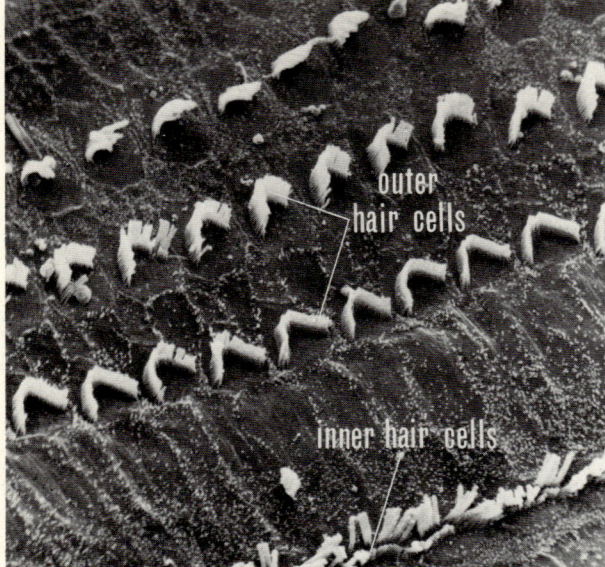

A

B

FIGURE 39-6 Noise can cause actual physical damage to the sound receptors of the ears. (A) Normal organ of Corti of a guinea pig; (B) organ of Corti after 24-hour exposure to noise levels typical of loud rock music (120 dB).

the average citizen. A recent surprising finding is that the noise level in urban communities frequently exceeds the accepted standards of tolerance in industry. Special circumstances, such as those created in discotheques and by rock-and-roll bands, produce an even greater assault on our eardrums. Even in the supposedly peaceful countryside, tractors and other powered machinery can produce a deafening roar. Deleterious psychological and physiological changes have been found to result from prolonged exposure to high noise levels. In addition to the obvious result of irreversible

loss of hearing acuity (Figure 13-6), more pervasive effects on the major body systems have already been discovered. Exposure to annoyingly high noise levels triggers a general stress reaction involving the adrenal hormones and their effects on other organs and systems of the body. In one series of studies, men exposed to noise levels greater than 75 decibels (about the level heard close to a high-speed highway) were found to develop permanent constriction of the blood vessels. Other studies revealed that noise levels in the 90 to 95-decibel range (about the level heard 25 feet from a motorcycle and slightly less than that of a jet plane flying overhead at a thousand feet) produced high blood pressure, which could not be normalized even with drugs. Studies of animals have revealed rises in blood cholesterol levels and sharp increases in birth defects resulting from prolonged exposure to high noise levels.

The growing public concern about pollution of all kinds is an important step toward the solution of the problem. Already controls are being imposed and pollution control devices are being developed. Perhaps the most promising approach is the development of ways to recycle wastes, to turn them into valuable resources rather than pollutants. As we gradually learn to use and reuse, rather than to use and throw away, we are moving toward a more efficient operation of our Spaceship Earth.

A RIGHT TO DIE?

In 1976 a tragic dilemma touched the hearts of Americans and raised a host of unresolved medical and ethical questions. A young woman named Karen Ann Quinlan lay in a bed in a New Jersey hospital. Her wasted body was just a wraith of her former self, festooned with life-sustaining tubes and curled tightly into a fetal position. Doctors said that Karen was unaware of her surroundings, her brain irreparably damaged; she had not roused since she sank into a coma following the ingestion of a mixture of barbiturates and alcohol. Her parents asked first the doctors, then the courts to grant permission to turn off the respirator that was sustaining Karen's life, since there was no hope that she could ever recover. At first the request was denied, since by all the presently accepted criteria—even the modern definition of "brain death"—Karen was still alive. To turn off the life-support devices, it was said, would be murder. For months Karen Ann Quinlan lingered on in her strange twilight state, at a cost of more than $100,000 a year to the taxpayers and uncountable anguish to her grieving parents. Ultimately, a judge granted the Quinlans the authority to withdraw the "extraordinary" means that were artificially prolonging their daughter's life. Karen was moved to a nursing home, her respirator was turned off, and surprisingly her lungs resumed the work of breathing on their own. But she remained in an apparently hopeless vegetative state. As Karen's case faded from the headlines, the medical and moral questions it raised continued to spark a moral and legal reevaluation of our attitudes toward life and death.

Does a person have an inherent right to die? Must physicians continue to exert extraordinary efforts to maintain the life of a terminally ill patient, who may be in intolerable pain or—like Karen—in an "irreversible vegetative state"? Does anyone have the right to say that someone else should die? Is quality of life a major concern? Should a mentally defective child, suffering from an intestinal blockage, be given the operation that will save its life and doom its parents—or the community—to support it in the decades to come? Is it morally justified to allow it to slowly starve to death? Is euthanasia more humane in such circumstances? And if a passive or active procurement of death is permissible in some circumstances, who is to decide where to draw the line?

One man once thought he had the answers to such questions. Adolf Hitler classified whole groups of people as subhuman vermin, who could be exterminated with impunity, to preserve the "purity" of the higher races. The atrocities that were committed at Hitler's orders have left a searing memory that makes people shrink from the thought of ever taking such a path again. Would even a partial retreat from a firm stand on the sanctity of human life—all human life—open the way to a return of Hitlerism, of genocide in the name of eugenics?

This is one of the most poignant moral dilemmas facing the medical community—and the community at large.

PRIORITIES IN OUR SOCIETY: THE DOLLAR VALUE OF LIFE

The resources of Spaceship Earth are limited—not only resources of materials and energy, but resources of human skills as well. Many noble goals have been proposed—the elimination of poverty and hunger, the elevation of all mankind to a life of ease and plenty, the conquest of disease, and thousands of others of more limited scope. It would be wonderful if all these goals could be pursued simultaneously. But we cannot afford it—we do not have sufficient resources. Therefore, choices must be made; we must determine our priorities.

In recent years, within the field of health sciences, there has been a decrease in emphasis on basic research into the causes of diseases and an increased emphasis on spending for health care delivery. In 1972, for example, the United States Congress passed

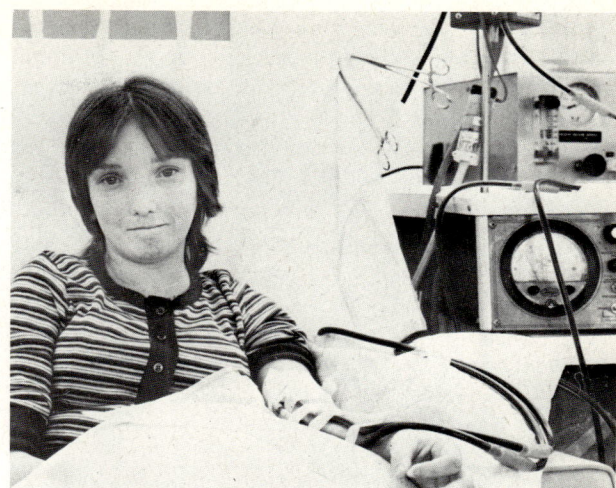

FIGURE 39-7   What is the price of a life? A multimillion dollar kidney dialysis program is saving the lives of thousands.

a bill that would effectively make available the use of kidney dialysis machines to all who could benefit from them. It is estimated that this program, which is saving thousands of lives, may cost more than a billion dollars a year by 1980. But there has been no corresponding increase in research funds for determining the fundamental causes of and cures for various kidney diseases. This disproportionate emphasis is shortsighted. A relatively small investment in basic research may lead to a huge payoff in the saving of lives.

Just what is a human life worth? In one sense, this is a question that cannot be answered. However, in determining priorities of funding—both within the sphere of the health sciences and in balancing expenditures for the health sciences against those in other areas of public endeavor, such as defense, road building, and various educational and social programs— some means of setting dollar values can be useful.

Immunologist Hugh Fudenberg has made extensive studies on the **cost effectiveness** of basic biological research, comparing the cost of medical advances with the cost of the disease to society. In the case of polio, for example, the development and testing of vaccines cost about $41 million, and their use in the first seven years after licensing cost another $612 million. If this money had not been spent, and effective polio vaccines had not been developed, during those seven years an estimated 154,000 persons would have suffered paralytic cases of polio, and 12,500 of them would have died. The cost of hospitalization and care for those polio victims would have come to $327 million, and the lost income of the dead and disabled would be $6.4 billion. The total $6.7 billion saved because all those people did *not* have polio is more than ten times the $653 million investment in the vaccines. And the savings go on and on, as additional years go by. Similar figures can be cited for other medical advances. The development of new clinical tests that shorten the hospital stays of patients yields savings in the multimillions. The annual bill for heart disease is currently $40 billion. Any significant decrease in the incidence of heart disease would pay huge dividends.

It would seem obvious that a greatly increased program—a national commitment—to research toward the conquest of disease would not only be highly cost-effective, but would ultimately lead to a major reduction of human suffering and death.

SUMMARY
The federal Food and Drug Administration (FDA) oversees the testing of new food additives and drugs for safety and effectiveness.
  Problems of testing of food additives and drugs include:
    Limited applicability of animal tests to humans
    Individual metabolic idiosyncrasies
    Multiple sources of the substances in actual use and their interaction with other ingested chemicals
    Delayed development of cancer and other effects
    Placebo effect
Commonly abused mood-altering drugs are classified as:
  Depressants (e.g., alcohol, opium, heroin)
  Stimulants (e.g., caffeine, nicotine, amphetamines)
  Psychedelics (e.g., marijuana, LSD)
Problems of drug abuse include:
  Physical addiction (with withdrawal symptoms and increasing tolerance)

Psychological dependence and "dropping out" of life
  Physical and mental impairment
Types of pollution include:
  Air pollution (by industrial products, automobile exhausts, etc.)
  Water pollution (by industrial and domestic wastes)
  Radiation (from nuclear weapons detonations and possibly from nuclear power plants or their wastes)
  Noise pollution
The growing ability to prolong life has raised unresolved ethical questions about the quality of life and the right to die.
There is a need for a reassessment of priorities in the health sciences; a disproportionate emphasis on health care delivery instead of research can be more costly in the long run.

QUESTIONS FOR REVIEW AND THOUGHT
1 Who should make decisions in the areas of medical ethics and the allocation of priorities in our nation's investments and expenditures affecting the health sciences?
2 Are food additives necessary?
3 Present regulations require that a new drug may not be approved for marketing unless its safety and efficacy have been established. Are there circumstances in which such restrictions should be relaxed, for example, in the treatment of terminal cancer patients?
4 How can a double blind study compensate for misleading results due to the placebo effect?
5 Give examples of the main classes of abused mood-altering drugs and characterize them with respect to mental and physical effects and the potential for physical addiction, psychological dependence, and tolerance.
6 Do you think marijuana use should be legalized? Give reasons for your answer.
7 Describe the major types of pollution and their effects on the body.
8 Discuss the concept of cost effectiveness as applied to the allocation of funds to biomedical research and health care delivery. Do you think this is a valid approach to determining priorities?

GLOSSARY

Prefixes

a-, an- without, not, away from
ab- away from
ad- to, toward
adeno- glandular
amphi- on both sides
ante- before, forward
anti- against
bi- two, twice, double
brady- slow
circum- around, about
contra- opposite, against
cyto- cell
de- down, from
di- two, twice, double
dys- difficult, bad, improper
ecto- outside
endo- in, within
entero- pert. to intestines
ento- inside, within
epi- on, upon, outside of
erythro- red
eu- good, normal
ex- out of, from
extra- outside, beyond, in addition
hemi- half
hyper- over, excessive, above
hypo- under, deficient
infra- underneath, below
inter- between, among
intra- within, on the side
iso- equal to
juxta- next to
leuco-, leuko- white
macro- large, long
mal- bad, poor, abnormal
mega- large, one million
micro- tiny, one millionth
mono- one
multi- many, much
myelo- pert. to spinal cord or bone marrow
myo- pert. to muscle
oto- pert. to ear
para- beside, beyond
peri- around, beyond
pneumo- pert. to lungs or air
poly- many, much
post- after, behind
pre- before, in front of
pro- before, in front of
pseudo- false
pulmo- pert. to lungs
pyelo- pert. to pelvis
re- again, back
retro- backward, behind
rhin-, rhino- pert. to nose

semi- half
sub- under, beneath
super- above, over
supra- above, on upper side
syn- with, together
tachy- fast
trans- across, beyond
tri- three
un- not, back
uni- one

Suffixes

-algia pain
-ase enzyme ending
-blast immature or primitive
-cele swelling
-cyte cell
-ectomy surgical removal of an organ or part
-emia blood
-gram record drawn by a machine (e.g., electrocardiogram)
-itis inflammation of
-mimetic simulating a process or function
-oid like, resembling
-ology study of, science of
-osis process, esp. disease process
-otomy surgical opening or repair of an organ without its removal
-phil having an affinity for
-plasia change or development
-plasm fluid substance of a cell
-pnea pert. to breathing
-pod foot
-tome a cutting instrument (e.g., microtome)
-trophic pert. to nutrition
-tropic turning toward, changing
-uria urine

abdomen body region between diaphragm and pelvis
abduction movement away from midline; opposite of adduction
absorption uptake of substances into or across tissues
acetabulum cup-shaped socket in hip bone into which head of femur fits
acetylcholine neurotransmitter active at synapses and myoneural junctions
acidosis condition in which there is an excess of acid (lowered pH) in the blood
acinus a saclike group of secretory cells surrounding a cavity
actin contractile protein of thin myofibrils
action potential difference in electri-

cal charges on inner and outer surfaces of cell membrane during conduction of nerve impulse or contraction of muscle
adduction movement toward midline; opposite of abduction
adenohypophysis anterior pituitary gland
adenoid glandular; especially pert. to the nasophyarngeal tonsils
adenosine triphosphate (ATP) a nucleotide compound occurring in all cells and serving as a form of energy storage
adipose fatty
adrenal endocrine gland located above the kidney (suprarenal)
adrenergic activated by, or secreting epinephrine (adrenaline); sympathomimetic
adventitia outermost covering of a structure
aerobic having molecular oxygen present or growing only in the presence of molecular oxygen
afferent conveying toward a center (e.g., afferent nerves and blood vessels)
agglutination clumping of cells (e.g., bacteria, blood cells) distributed in a fluid
agglutinin antibody that clumps a particular antigen
agglutinogen antigen that stimulates the production of a specific agglutinin
albumin one of a group of proteins found in animal and vegetable tissues and fluids
aldosterone mineralocorticoid hormone secreted by the adrenal cortex
alimentary pert. to food or to organs of digestion
alkalosis condition in which there is an excessive proportion of alkali in the blood; opposite of acidosis
allele one of two or more alternative forms of a gene occupying corresponding positions on a specific pair of chromosomes and controlling the expression of a given characteristic
allergy a hypersensitive state of altered reactivity acquired through exposure to a particular allergen, which stimulates the production of IgE antibodies
alveolus a small cavity (e.g., alveoli of lungs)

ameboid movement movement characteristic of ameba, by protrusion of footlike pseudopods

amenorrhea absence or abnormal stoppage of the menses

amino acid an organic compound with an amino (NH_2) and a carboxyl (COOH) group in its molecule; amino acids are the structural units of proteins

amniocentesis surgical perforation of the uterus through the abdominal wall to obtain amniotic fluid, which is tested for fetal abnormalities

amnion the thin but tough membrane that contains the fetus and the amniotic fluid that surrounds it

amphiarthrosis slightly movable joint

ampulla saclike dilation of a tube or duct

anabolism constructive processes by which living cells convert simple substances to more complex compounds; opposite of catabolism

anaerobic lacking molecular oxygen or growing in the absence of molecular oxygen

anaphylaxis an unusual or exaggerated allergic reaction to a foreign substance

anastomosis a connection between vessels or parts of a tube

androgen a substance producing masculinizing effects, male sex hormone

anemia a reduction below normal of the number of red blood cells or amount of hemoglobin

anesthesia loss of sensation

aneurysm a blood-filled sac formed by dilation of the wall of an artery, vein, or the heart

angina a spasmodic, choking pain, especially angina pectoris (resulting from oxygen starvation of the heart wall)

angstrom (Å) unit of length equal to 10^{-10} meter

anion a negatively charged ion

anoxia reduction of oxygen in body tissues below physiologic levels

antagonist a muscle that acts in opposition to the action of another muscle

anterior in front of, or in the forward part; ventral; opposite of posterior

antibody a specific immunoglobulin produced by the body in response to an antigen that has entered the body; it reacts with the antigen and inactivates or destroys it

antigen a substance that, when introduced into the body, stimulates the formation of specific antibodies

antrum a cavity or chamber, especially in a bone

anus distal end and outlet of the alimentary canal

aorta the largest artery of the body, arising from the left ventricle of the heart and branching off into numerous smaller arteries

apex the top or pointed end of a conical structure

aphasia loss of the power of speech or the ability to use or understand words

apnea temporary cessation of breathing

aponeurosis a flat sheet of white fibrous tissue serving as a muscle attachment

aqueduct a channel or passage in a body structure, especially a channel for the conduction of liquid

arachnoid thin, weblike middle membrane of the coverings of the brain (meninges)

areola a small cavity; the ringlike pigmented area around the nipple

arrhythmia a variation from the normal rhythm of heart contraction

arteriole a small arterial branch, leading into a capillary

arteriosclerosis hardening of the arteries; formation of calcified fatty deposits in the artery walls that narrow the channel for blood flow

artery a blood vessel carrying blood away from the heart

articular pertaining to a joint

asphyxia a condition resulting from a lack of oxygen in respired air, which can lead to unconsciousness or death

aspirate to remove fluids or gases from a cavity by suction

astrocytes star-shaped cells of the neuroglia

atherosclerosis deposition of fatty plaques in the lining of the artery walls

atrium a chamber of cavity; upper chamber of the heart

atrophy wasting away or decrease in size of tissue or structure

autoimmune disease an illness caused by the mistaken formation of antibodies against the body's own cells or cell products

autonomic self-controlling, independent

axilla the armpit

axon nerve cell process transmitting impulses away from the cell body

bacillus rod-shaped bacterium

bacteriophage a virus that infects bacteria; also called *phage*

basophil type of white blood cell that strains readily with basic dyes

benign not malignant; not life-threatening

biceps a muscle with two heads

bilateral pertaining to both sides

bile fluid secreted by the liver that aids in fat digestion in the intestines

bilirubin red pigment in bile

blastocyst stage in embryonic development following the morula, when the cells are arranged in a single layer to form a hollow sphere

BMR basal metabolic rate

bolus a soft, rounded mass of chewed food

brachial pertaining to the arm

bronchiole small branch of a bronchus

bronchus one of the two main branches of the trachea

buccal pertaining to the cheek

buffer a chemical system that can combine with either added acid or base, thus tending to maintain a constant pH of the solution

bursa a fluid-filled sac or cavity that lessens friction in a joint

calcification deposition of calcium salts in tissues

calculus a "stone" composed of mineral salts, formed in the body

calorie the amount of heat required to raise the temperature of 1 gram of water 1°C. Calorie contents of foods are usully expressed in large calories (Calories), equal to 1000 calories

canaliculus a small canal or channel

cancellous of a reticular, lattice-like, or spongy structure

capillary a very thin tube; the smallest of the blood and lymph vessels

carbohydrate a class of organic compounds containing carbon, hydrogen, and oxygen in specific proportions

carcinogen a substance or influence (chemical, radiation, etc.) that causes cancer

carcinoma a malignant tumor made of epithelial cells and tending to infiltrate surrounding tissues and give rise to metastases

cardiac pertaining to the heart

caries tooth or bone decay

carotid principal arteries of the neck

carpal pertaining to the wrist

cartilage a firm and elastic type of dense connective tissue

catabolism breakdown of complex chemical compounds into simpler substances by living cells, usually with a release of energy; opposite of anabolism

catalyst a substance that alters the rate of chemical reactions without itself being consumed or altered in the reaction

cataract opacity of the lens of the eye

catecholamines a class of compounds with sympathomimetic action, including epinephrine, norepinephrine, and dopamine

cation a positively charged ion

caudal pertaining to or toward the tail; opposite of cephalic

cecum a blind pouch; the first part of the large intestine

celiac pertaining to the abdomen

cellulose a polysaccharide found in plant structures; the major constituent of dietary fiber

centimeter unit of length equal to 0.01 meter, about 2/5 of an inch

centriole cell organelle that forms a spindle during cell division

cephalic pertaining to the head or toward the head end; opposite of caudal

cerebellum division of the brain involved in the coordination of movements

cerebrum the forebrain; contains sensory and motor areas and involved in higher mental faculties

cerumen ear wax

cervical pertaining to the neck region, or to the neck of an organ (e.g., cervix uteri)

chalone a hormone-like substance that inhibits cell proliferation

chemoreceptor a receptor adapted for chemical stimulation

chemotherapy the treatment of cancer or other diseases with drugs

chiasm an X-shaped crossing, especially the crossing of the optic nerves

cholesterol a fatty alcohol found in animal fats and oils, bile, blood, and various tissues, including brain and nerves

cholinergic stimulated, activated, or transmitted by acetylcholine; applied to nerve fibers that liberate acetylcholine at a synapse; parasympathomimetic

cholinesterase an enzyme that hydrolyzes acetylcholine

choroid skinlike; the thin, pigmented vascular coat of the eyeball

chromatid newly formed chromosome

chromatin a network of readily stained nucleoprotein fibers in the cell nucleus that forms the chromosomes during mitosis and meiosis

chromosome a deeply staining body in the nucleus, consisting of a linear thread of DNA associated with RNA and protein, which carries hereditary information

chyle milky fluid taken up by lacteals in the intestines after digestion of food

chylomicron a stable droplet of emulsified fat transported in lymph and blood

chyme semifluid, partly digested food material leaving the stomach

cilium tiny vibratile hairlike process attached to the free surface of cells

circadian daily; occurring periodically with a 24-hour cycle

circumduction circular movement of a limb or of the eye

clone a cell culture, organism, or group of organisms all derived from a single parent cell and sharing the same heredity

coagulation clot formation; solidification into a gelatinous mass

coccyx "tailbone," small bone distal to the sacrum at the caudal end of the spinal column

cochlea anterior portion of the labyrinth of the inner ear, shaped like a snail shell, containing the receptors for hearing

codon sequence of three nucleotides in RNA specifying a particular amino acid to be incorporated into a protein

coenzyme a nonprotein substance that activates an enzyme

collagen principal supportive protein of skin, tendon, bone, cartilage, and connective tissue

collateral secondary or accessory; a small side branch

colloid a stable dispersion of matter (particle size 1 to 100 mμ); gelatinous substance that does not diffuse readily through membranes

coma profound unconsciousness from which the person cannot be roused even by powerful stimulation

commissure a site of joining of corresponding parts; bundle of nerve fibers passing from one side of the brain or spinal cord to the other

concha shell-shaped structure; bony projection into the nasal cavity

condyle rounded projection on a bone, usually for articulation with another bone

congenital present at birth

contraceptive device or technique used to prevent conception or implantation

contraction a shortening, e.g., of muscles

contralateral on or pertaining to the opposite side

convoluted rolled together or coiled

corium true skin or dermis

coronal pertaining to the crown of the head; situated in the direction of the coronal suture, in a longitudinal plane perpendicular to the median plane

coronary encircling in the manner of a crown

corpus body

corpuscle a small body or particle

cortex the outer layer of an organ

costal pertaining to the ribs

crenation shriveling of a cell due to passage of fluid out into the surrounding medium

cretinism condition of dwarfism and mental retardation resulting from congenital lack of thyroid secretion

cribriform sievelike; part of ethmoid bone

cricoid ring-shaped; cartilage of larnyx

cruciate cross-shaped

crypt a pit or tube-shaped depression on a free surface

cubital pertaining to the elbow, ulna, or forearm

cutaneous pertaining to the skin

cyanosis bluish color of the skin and mucous membranes resulting from deficient oxygenation of the blood

cyst a closed cavity or sac, especially containing a liquid or semisolid material

cytokinesis division of the cytoplasm to form two cells in mitosis or meiosis

cytology the study of cells

cytoplasm the protoplasm of a cell exclusive of the nucleus

deamination removal of an amino group (NH_2) from a compound (e.g., from an amino acid)

decussation a crossing over

defecation elimination of fecal matter from the intestines

deferens carrying away

deglutition swallowing

dehydration removal of water; the condition resulting from excess loss of water from the body

deltoid triangular-shaped

dendrite branched nerve cell process that transmits impulses toward the cell body

dentate having toothlike projections

deoxyribonucleic acid (DNA) the nucleic acid present in the chromosomes, in which the hereditary information is encoded; a high-molecular-weight compound consisting of nucleotides, linked together in a double helix and each containing deoxyribose, phosphate, and a nitrogen base (adenine, cytosine, guanine, or thymine)

depolarization loss or neutralization of polarity

dermatome area of skin supplied by sensory fibers of a single dorsal root

dermis the true skin, corium; layer under the epidermis

dialysis separation of crystalloids and colloids in a solution by their differential diffusion through a semipermeable membrane

diapedesis movement of white blood cells through intact blood vessel walls

diaphragm a separating membrane or partition; the musculomembranous partition separating the thoracic and abdominal cavities

diaphysis the shaft of a long bone

diarthrosis a freely movable joint

diastole the relaxation phase of heart contraction, in which the ventricles are dilated

diencephalon the "tween" brain, between the cerebral hemispheres and midbrain; includes the hypothalamus and thalamus

diffusion the process of spreading, scattering, dispersion; spontaneous intermingling of the molecules of two fluids resulting from random kinetic movements

digit a finger or toe

diplopia double vision; the perception of two images of a single object

disaccharide a sugar composed of two simple sugars (monosaccharides)

dissect to cut apart, separate; to expose body structures for anatomic study

distal farther from a point of reference; toward the end of a structure; opposite of proximal

diuretic increasing the secretion of urine

diverticulum a pouch or outpocketing from a main cavity or tube

dizygotic derived from two separate zygotes, e.g., dizygotic (fraternal) twins

dominant in genetics, capable of expression when carried by only one of a pair of homologous chromosomes

dorsal pertaining to the back; toward the back or posterior; opposite of ventral

duct a tube or passage, especially for secretions or excretions

dura mater the tough, fibrous, outermost membrane covering the brain

dyspnea difficult or labored breathing

dystrophy degeneration of an organ resulting from faulty nutrition, abnormal development, infection, or other causes

ectoderm the outermost germ layer of an embryo, from which the epidermis, nervous system, external sense organs, and certain endocrine glands develop

ectopic displaced, out of the normal position, e.g., ectopic pregnancy

edema presence of excessive fluid in the tissues

effector a muscle or gland that responds to nerve impulses

efferent carrying from a center (e.g., efferent nerves and blood vessels)

electrocardiogram (ECG) graphic record of the electrical activity of the heart

electroencephalogram (EEG) graphic record of the electrical activity of the brain

electrolyte a substance that dissociates into ions in solution, becoming capable of carrying an electric current

electron a minute particle with a negative electric charge

elimination expulsion of wastes from the body

embolus a clot or other plug carried through the blood to lodge in a vessel and obstruct circulation

embryo early stage of development of an organism (in humans, in the first two months after conception)

emesis vomiting

encephalon the brain

endocrine secreting into the blood or tissue fluid instead of into ducts

endoderm the innermost germ layer of an embryo, from which the epithelium of the respiratory tract, digestive tract, bladder, and urethra are derived

endoplasmic reticulum network of tubules and vesicles in the cytoplasm

endorphin natural opiate produced in the brain

energy the capacity for doing work

enzyme a protein that acts as a catalyst in living systems

eosinophil type of white blood cell readily stained by the red dye eosin

epidermis outermost, nonvascular layer of the skin

epinephrine hormone secreted by the adrenal medulla; adrenaline

epiphysis end of a long bone; a center for ossification of the long bone

epithelium covering or lining tissue

erythrocyte red blood cell

estrogen female sex hormone

ethmoid sievelike

eupnea normal respiration

evagination outpocketing

eversion a turning inside out

exocrine secreting into a duct

extrinsic originating outside; opposite of intrinsic

exudate material that has escaped from blood vessels and been deposited in or on tissues

facilitation increased ease of passage of a nerve impulse across a synapse

fascia a sheet of fibrous connective tissue

fetus developing young in later stages of development (in humans from the third month of intrauterine development until birth)

fiber threadlike structure

fibrillation spontaneous contraction of individual muscle fibers, uncontrolled by motor neurons; spasmodic contraction of the heart muscle

fibrin insoluble protein forming an essential part of a blood clot

fibrinogen soluble protein that is converted to fibrin during clotting

fibroblast connective tissue cell that forms fibrous tissues

filiform threadlike

filtration the passage of liquid through a filter under the action of gravity, pressure, or vacuum

fimbria fringelike structure

fissure a cleft or groove

fistula an abnormal passage between two internal organs or from an organ to the surface of the body

flaccid limp, weak, soft

follicle a small sac or gland

foramen small opening, hole, or passage

fossa a pit, hollow, or depression

fundus base of a hollow organ; the part farthest from its outlet

fusiform spindle-shaped

gamete male or female reproductive cell (i.e., sperm or ovum)

ganglion a knot or knotlike mass; group of nerve cell bodies; a nerve center outside the central nervous system

gastric pertaining to the stomach

gene the functional unit of heredity; a portion of the DNA on the chromosome that directs the production of a specific protein and/or expression of a specific trait

genitalia the reproductive organs

genotype the genetic constitution of an individual; the alleles present at a specific locus

germ cells reproductive cells

germ layer one of the three basic tissue layers (ectoderm, endoderm, mesoderm) of the embryo from which the tissues and organs develop

gestation pregnancy; period of development of the young from conception to birth

gland secreting structure

glomerulus a cluster, e.g., of blood vessels or nerve fibers

glossal pertaining to the tongue

glucagon pancreatic hormone that raises blood sugar level

glucocorticoid class of hormones of the adrenal cortex that protect against stress and affect protein and carbohydrate metabolism

gluconeogenesis formation of carbohydrates from protein or fat

glucose a six-carbon simple sugar (monosaccharide); the principal blood sugar

gluteal pertaining to the buttocks

glycerol the alcohol component of fats

glycogen animal starch; the main polysaccharide stored in animal cells

glycogenesis formation of glycogen

glycogenolysis splitting up (hydrolysis) of glycogen, yielding glucose

goblet cell a goblet-shaped epithelial cell containing mucin

gonad ovary or testis

gradient a slope or difference between two levels, e.g., of concentration, electrical potential, etc.

gram a metric unit of weight equal to 0.035 ounce

gustatory pertaining to taste

gyrus a convoluted ridge

hallucination a false sense perception with no basis in reality

hapten a substance that can interact with specific combining groups on an antibody but elicits an immune response only when combined with a carrier protein

helix a coiled structure, spiral

hematocrit volume percentage of erythrocytes in whole blood

hemiplegia paralysis of one side of the body

hemoglobin the oxygen-carrying red pigment (an iron-containing protein) in red blood cells

hemolysis destruction of red blood cells with liberation of hemoglobin

hemopoiesis the formation and development of red blood cells

hemorrhage bleeding

hemostasis stoppage of bleeding; interruption of the blood flow through a blood vessel or body part; stagnation of blood

heparin a substance produced by the liver that inhibits blood coagulation

hepatic pertaining to the liver

heredity transmission of characteristics from parent to child

hernia "rupture"; protrusion of a loop of an organ through an abnormal opening

hilus, hilum depression where vessels and nerves enter an organ

histology study of the detailed structure of tissues

homeostasis a tendency toward stability of the internal environment of the organism; maintenance of equilibrium between the organism and the environment

homologous corresponding, similar in origin, structure, position

hormone secetion of an endocrine gland that regulates the functions of other organs

hyaline glasslike, transparent

hydrolysis chemical decomposition reaction involving insertion of water and splitting of a compound

hymen a membrane that may partially or entirely occlude the vaginal outlet

hyoid shaped like the letter U; a bone at the base of the tongue

hypercapnia abnormally high CO_2 concentration in the blood

hyperglycemia higher than normal blood glucose level

hypermetropia farsightedness, inability to focus on near objects

hyperplasia overgrowth; increase in size of a part due to abnormal increase in the number of cells

hyperpnea abnormal increase in the depth and rate of respiration; panting

hypertension abnormally high blood pressure

hypertonic possessing excessive tone, tension, or activity; possessing a concentration greater than isotonic

hypertrophy enlargement of an organ or part because of an increase in the size of its cells

hypodermic applied beneath the skin

hypoglycemia lower than normal blood glucose level

hypophysis the pituitary gland

hypothalamus a portion of the diencephalon, forming the floor and part of the lateral wall of the third ventricle, and containing numerous control centers for body functions

hypotonic possessing a concentration less than isotonic

hypoxia oxygen deficiency; low oxygen content in the inspired air

idiopathic of unknown or spontaneous origin

immune highly resistant to a particular disease; pertaining to the development of antibodies or cellular immunity

immunoglobulins proteins with antibody activity

implantation attachment of the blastocyst to the epithelial lining of the uterus

inclusion a particle or foreign substance contained in a cell

incubation period time interval between entrance of infecting organisms into the body and the appearance of the first symptoms of disease

infarct, infarction an area of coagulation necrosis in a tissue due to local ischemia resulting from obstruction of circulation

inferior situated below or directed downward; opposite of superior

inflammation protective response to tissue damage, characterized by pain, heat, redness, swelling, and loss of function

inguinal pertaining to the groin

inhibition restraint of a process

insertion place of attachment of a muscle

insulin pancreatic hormone that lowers the blood sugar level

in situ in the normal place; confined to the site of origin

integument covering; the skin

intercellular between cells; interstitial

intercostal between the ribs

interneuron, internuncial neuron connector neuron, situated between the primary afferent neuron and the final motor neuron in a chain of neurons

interstitial pertaining to or situated in the spaces or gaps of a tissue; intercellular

intima innermost

intrinsic inherent; situated or originating entirely within a structure; opposite of extrinsic

invagination inpocketing

inversion turning inward

in vitro observable in a test tube, culture dish, or artificial environment

in vivo within the living body

involuntary independent of conscious control, not willed

involution return of an organ to its normal size after enlargement; also retrograde or degenerative change

ion an electrically charged atom or group of atoms

ipsilateral on the same side

irritability excitability; responsiveness to stimuli

ischemia temporary lack of blood supply to an area

isotonic having the same concentration, tension, or pressure

jaundice condition characterized by yellowness of the skin, membranes, and body fluids resulting from deposition of bile pigments

karyotype a grouping or arrangement of the set of 46 human chromosomes according to size and shape

keratin a protein that is the principal constituent of hair and nails

ketone a compound (e.g., acetone) containing the carbonyl group, CO

ketosis accumulation of ketone bodies (acid products of fat catabolism) in the blood

kilogram a metric unit of weight equal to 1000 grams or approximately 2.2 pounds

kinesthesia "muscle sense"; sense of position and movement of body parts

labia lips

lacrimal pertaining to tears

lactation secretion of milk

lacteal lymphatic vessel of the small intestine that takes up chyle

lacuna a small pit or hollow cavity

lamella a thin leaf or plate, e.g., of bone

lamina a thin, flat plate or layer

lateral of or toward the side; opposite of medial

lemniscus a longitudinal band of sensory nerve fibers in the brain stem

lesion a wound, injury, or infected area

leukocyte white blood cell

ligament a tough, fibrous band connecting bones or visceral organs

limbic system a group of structures of the diencephalon and cerebrum concerned in aspects of emotion and behavior

lipid fat and fatlike compounds

liter a unit of volume in the metric system, equal to 1.0567 quart; the volume occupied by 1 kilogram of pure water at its temperature of maximum density and under standard atmospheric pressure

lobe a well-defined portion of an organ

locus place; in genetics, the position of a gene on a chromosome

lumbar pertaining to the loins; the part of the back between the ribs and the hip bones

lumen the cavity or channel within a tubular organ or structure

lymph colorless, watery fluid contained in lymphatic vessels

lymphocyte a type of white blood cell produced in the reticular tissue of lymph glands

lysis destruction (e.g., of blood cells) by a specific antibody; destruction of a chemical compound by an enzyme or other agent

lysosome a cell organelle containing lytic (decomposing) enzymes

macrophage a large phagocytic cell

macula a spot

malignant virulent; tending to become progressively worse and to result in death

mammary pertaining to the breast

manometer an instrument used to measure the pressure of liquids or gases

mastication chewing

matrix the ground substance in which cells are embedded

meatus a passage or channel

medial of or toward the middle; opposite of lateral

mediastinum the tissues and organs of the thorax situated between the two lungs

medulla inner or central part of an organ, as contrasted with the cortex

meiosis a type of cell division in maturation of the sex cells, in which the chromosome number is reduced to half its original value (from diploid to haploid)

membrane a thin layer or sheet of tissue

meninges the membranes covering the brain and spinal cord (dura mater, arachnoid, and pia mater)

menopause cessation of menstruation in the human female

menstruation monthly discharge of blood from the uterus

mesencephalon midbrain

mesentery a fold of the peritoneum attaching the intestine to the posterior abdominal wall

mesoderm the middle of the three primary germ layers of the embryo, from which the connective tissue, muscle, blood, and parts of many organs develop

metabolism the sum of all the chemical processes in the living organism

metastasis the transfer of disease (e.g., cancer) from one organ or part to another not directly connected with it

meter a metric unit of length equal to 39.371 inches

microflora bacteria, yeasts, and other microorganisms inhabiting a particular area (e.g., the human skin or intestine)

microglia a type of neuroglia; small phagocytic cells in the central nervous system

micron a metric unit of length equal to 1 millionth of a meter (10^{-6} meter or 10^{-3} millimeter), about 1/25,000 of an inch

micturition urination

milliliter a metric unit of volume equal to 1/1000 of a liter, 0.033815 of a fluid ounce; interchangeable with cubic centimeter (cc)

millimeter a metric unit of length equal to 1/1000 of a meter, or about 0.04 inch

mineralocorticoid hormone of the adrenal cortex causing retention of sodium and loss of potassium

mitosis a mode of cell division in which a constant number and quality of chromosomes is maintained from one cell generation to the next

mitral shaped like a miter; pertaining to the mitral (bicuspid) valve

mole the molecular weight of a compound, expressed in grams

monosaccharide a simple sugar

monozygotic formed from a single zygote, e.g., monozygotic (identical) twins

morphology study of the shape and structure of organisms

motor neuron, motoneuron a nerve cell that transmits nerve impulses away from the brain or spinal cord; efferent neuron

mucosa mucous membrane

myelin fatty material forming a sheath around nerve fibers

myocardium the heart muscle

myopia nearsightedness; inability to focus on distant objects

myosin a muscle globin that acts as an enzyme in initiating muscle contraction

nares nostrils

necrosis death of tissue, usually in small, localized areas

nephron structural and functional unit of the kidney, consisting of the renal capsule, the proximal convoluted tubule, the descending and ascending limbs of Henle's loop, and the distal convoluted tubule

neurilemma the thin, membranous outer covering of a nerve cell

neuroglia supporting tissue of the central nervous system

nuerohypophysis posterior pituitary gland

neuron nerve cell

neutrophil a type of white blood cell easily stained by neutral dyes

nucleotide an organic compound consisting of a five-carbon sugar (ribose or deoxyribose), a phosphate residue, and a nitrogen base (adenine, cytosine, guanine, thymine, or uracil); the nucleotides are the structural units of nucleic acids

nucleus a dense, spheroid structure within cells, which acts as a control center for cell activities and contains the hereditary information of the organism; the central core of an atom, containing protons and neutrons; a group of neuron cell bodies in the brain or spinal cord

occiput back of the head

occlusion blocking or obstruction

olecranon elbow

olfactory pertaining to the sense of smell

oligodendroglia a type of neuroglia

oogenesis formation of the female gametes (ova)

ophthalmic pertaining to the eye

orbit the bony socket that contains the eyeball

organelle a small functional structure within a cell, e.g., the mitochondria, Golgi complex, lysosomes, ribosomes

os bone; mouth (adjectival forms are osseous and oral, respectively)

osmosis diffusion of a solvent through a semipermeable membrane that selectively holds back solute particles

ossification formation of bone from fibrous tissue or cartilage

ovum the female gamete, egg cell

oxidation chemical combination with oxygen or loss of electrons

oxyhemoglobin oxidized form of hemoglobin, a compound of Hb with two atoms of oxygen

palate the roof of the mouth

papilla a small nipple-shaped elevation

paralysis loss of motor function or impairment of sensory function

paraplegia paralysis of the legs or lower part of the body

parasympathetic pertaining to the craniosacral division of the autonomic nervous system, controlling normal body functions

parenchyma the essential, functional elements of an organ

paresthesia abnormal or perverted sensation

parietal of or pertaining to the walls of a cavity or organ

parotid located near the ear

parous having given birth

parturition the act of giving birth

pathogen disease-producing agent

pathology study of the essential nature of disease, especially the structural and functional changes in tissues and organs caused by disease

pectineal pertaining to the pubic bone

pectoral pertaining to the chest or breast

peduncle a band of nerve fibers connecting different parts of the central nervous system

pelvis a basin-shaped structure, especially the lower portion of the trunk of the body, bounded by the hip bones, sacrum, and coccyx

pennate shaped like a feather

peptide a compound consisting of two or more amino acids (of lower molecular weight than a protein)

pericardium the fibrous sac surrounding the heart

perineum the region of the pelvic outlet

periosteum the tough fibrous membrane surrounding a bone

peripheral pertaining to or situated near the outer surface; away from the center

peristalsis progressive waves of muscular contraction that travel along a tube, moving its contents along

peritoneum the serous membrane lining the abdominopelvic cavity and surrounding the viscera

peroneal pertaining to the fibula or the outer side of the leg

petrous rocklike

pH the negative logarithm of the hydrogen ion concentration; a measure of acidity (the lower the pH, the more acid)

phagocytosis the engulfing of cells (e.g., microorganisms) or foreign particles by an ameboid cell

phalanges bones of the fingers or toes

phenotype the outward expression of a hereditary trait, or the entire physical, biochemical, and physiological makeup of an individual, determined genetically and environmentally

phrenic pertaining to the diaphragm

pia mater the vascular innermost covering (meninx) of the brain and spinal cord

pilomotor causing movement of a hair

pineal shaped like a pine cone

pinocytosis ingestion of liquid droplets by a cell via minute invaginations of the cell surface

piriform pear-shaped

pisiform pea-shaped

placebo an inactive substance that produces the same effect as a potent drug because the subject thinks it is really a drug

plantar pertaining to the sole of the foot

plaque a fatty deposit in the lining of an artery wall

plasma the fluid portion of the blood

plasma membrane the cell membrane

plasmid a small circular form of DNA found in some bacteria, which carries hereditary information outside the bacterial chromosome and can be transferred from one bacterium to another

plasmolysis contraction or shrinking of a cell because of water loss by osmosis

platelet a disk-shaped structure found in the blood, which participates in coagulation

pleura a serous membrane lining in the thoracic cavity and enclosing the lungs

plexus a network, e.g., of nerves or blood vessels

plica a fold or ridge

polyp a protruding growth from mucous membrane

polysaccharide a carbohydrate composed of more than ten monosaccharide residues

pons a bridge; tissue connecting two or more parts; the portion of the brain between the medulla oblongata and the mesencephalon

popliteal behind the knee

portal a gateway or entrance to an organ, especially that of the liver

posterior situated behind or toward the rear; opposite of anterior

precursor something that precedes; a substance from which another, usually more active substance is formed

presbyopia farsightedness of old age

process a prominence or projection, e.g., of a bone or nerve; a sequence of operations or events

progesterone a hormone secreted by the corpus luteum, adrenal cortex, and placenta that prepares the uterus for the reception and development of a fertilized ovum

prognosis prediction of the probable outcome of a disease

prolapse the falling down or sinking of an organ or part

proprioceptors sensory nerve endings in the muscles, tendons, and joints that provide information on the movement and position of body parts

prosthesis, prosthetic device an artificial substitute for a natural body part (e.g., arm, leg, eye, pancreas, heart valve)

proton an atomic particle with a positive electric charge; a hydrogen ion

protoplasm the living substance of cells

proximal nearest; closest to the center or a point of reference; opposite of distal

psoas pertaining to the loin, the part of the back between the ribs and hip bones

psychosis a severe mental disorder in which contact with reality is lost

psychosomatic pertaining to the mind-body relationship, especially applied to physical disorders believed to have emotional causes

pterygoid wing-shaped

puberty adolescence; the period during which the secondary sex characteristics are developed and the capacity for reproduction is attained

pyruvic acid a three-carbon organic acid that is a pivotal compound in the Krebs cycle and in the metabolism of carbohydrates, fats, and amino acids

racemose like a cluster of grapes

radial proceeding outward from a center, like the spokes of a wheel

ramus branch

receptor peripheral ending of a sensory neuron; a chemically reactive site on the cell surface that reacts specifically with a hormone, neurotransmitter, or other substance

recessive in genetics, expressed only when present on both of a pair of homologous chromosomes

recombinant DNA the transfer of genes from one species to another by cutting and splicing of DNA

reduction chemical combination with hydrogen, loss of oxygen, or gain of electrons; restoration of a broken bone to normal relationships

reflex an involuntary response to a stimulus

refraction bending of a light ray as it passes from one medium to another of a different density

renal pertaining to the kidneys

resting potential difference in electrical charges on outer and inner surfaces of the membrane of a normal cell at rest

resuscitation the restoration to life or consciousness of one apparently dead

reticular netlike

reticulocyte a young red blood cell that shows a basophil reticulum when stained

reticulum a network

reverse transcriptase an enzyme that synthesizes DNA from an RNA template

rhinencephalon olfactory portions of the brain; the limbic system

ribonucleic acid (RNA) a nucleic acid functioning in protein synthesis; a high-molecular-weight compound consisting of nucleotides, linked together in a single helix and each containing ribose, phosphate, and a nitrogen base (adenine, cytosine, guanine, or uracil); types include messenger RNA, transfer RNA, and ribosomal RNA

ribosome spherical granule of ribonucleoprotein that serves as the organelle of protein synthesis. Ribosomes may be bound to the membranes of the endoplasmic reticulum or lie free in the cytoplasm and may occur singly or in clusters (polysomes)

ruga a wrinkle or fold

saccule a little sac

sagittal like an arrow; pertaining to a plane or section parallel to the long axis of the body

sarcoma a cancerous tumor arising from muscle, bone, or connective tissue

sarcoplasm the cytoplasm of muscle cells

sciatic pertaining to the ischium (the inferior dorsal part of the hip bone)

sclera the tough, opaque, fibrous coat of the eyeball

sebum secretion of the sebaceous (oil) glands

semen the thick, whitish fluid secreted by the male reproductive organs and containing the spermatozoa

semilunar half-moon-shaped

senescence aging, old age

sensory neuron a nerve cell that transmits nerve impulses from the periphery to the central brain or spinal cord; afferent neuron

septum a dividing wall or partition

serous producing or containing serum

serratus saw-toothed

serum a watery animal fluid; plasma without the clotting factors

sesamoid shaped like a sesame seed

sigmoid shaped like the letter S

sinus a cavity

soleus pertaining to the sole; a leg muscle shaped like the sole of a shoe

somatic pertaining to the body framework or walls, as distinguished from the viscera; in genetics, pertaining to body cells rather than germ cells

spastic contracted or in a state of continuous contraction; hypertonic, so that the muscles are stiff and movements awkward

specific gravity the density of a substance compared to that of pure water, which is assigned a value of one

sperm, spermatozoa the male gametes

spermatogenesis formation of the male gametes (sperm)

sphenoid wedge-shaped

sphincter a ring-shaped muscle enclosing an orifice

sphygmomanometer an instrument for measuring arterial blood pressure

spirometer an instrument for measuring inhaled and exhaled air

splanchnic visceral

sputum matter ejected from the respiratory tract through the mouth

squamous scalelike or platelike

stasis a stoppage or diminution of flow of blood or other body fluid

stenosis narrowing of a duct or canal

stimulus an agent that causes a reaction in an organism or any of its parts

stratum layer

striated striped, banded, marked with parallel streaks or lines

stroma the framework or matrix of a structure

subcutaneous beneath the skin

sulcus a groove or furrow

superior above, higher, directed upward; opposite of inferior

surfactant surface-active substance, which lowers surface tension

suture seam, a type of fibrous joint in which the opposed surfaces are closely united; stitches made to close a surgical or accidental wound

sympathetic pertaining to the thoracolumbar division of the autonomic nervous system, controlling responses to stressful conditions

symphysis a line of junction and fusion of two bones originally separate; a type of joint in which bone surfaces are firmly united by a plate of fibrocartilage

synapse the region of contact between two nerve processes, where a nerve impulse is transmitted from one neuron to another

synarthrosis an immovable joint

syndrome a complex of symptoms

synergist a muscle or organ acting in cooperation with another

synovial pertaining to or secreting the fluid of the joint capsules

synthesis the putting together or parts to form a more complex whole

systemic pertaining to or affecting the body as a whole

systole the contraction phase of the heart cycle

talus the ankle bone

tarsus the instep; region of articulation of the foot with the leg

tegmentum a covering

tendon a fibrous cord of connective tissue that attaches a muscle to a bone or other structure

testosterone male sex hormone secreted by the testis

thorax the chest

threshold the lowest strength stimulus that results in a detectable response

thrombocyte blood platelet

thrombus a blood clot obstructing a blood vessel

tonus a partial, steady contraction of muscle

toxic poisonous, harmful

tract a bundle of nerve fibers within the central nervous system; a group of organs forming a continuous pathway (e.g., digestive tract, respiratory tract)

transamination transfer of an amino group (NH_2) from one compound to another (e.g., from an amino acid to a keto acid)

trauma a wound or injury

treppe increase in height of contractions when a muscle is stimulated rapidly at regular intervals

trochlear like a pulley

trophic pertaining to nutrition; pertaining to hormones that control the activity of other endocrine structures

tubercle a nodule or small eminence

tumor a swelling; a new growth or tissue in which cell multiplication is uncontrolled (a neoplasm)

tunica covering

turbinate shaped like a top or cone; the nasal concha

tympanum drum; the cavity of the middle ear

ulcer an open sore or lesion of the skin or mucous membrane, produced by the sloughing of inflammatory necrotic tissue

umbilicus the navel

unilateral pertaining to only one side of the body

urea the chief organic constituent of urine; product of protein decomposition

utricle a little sac

uvula a small fleshy projection hanging from the soft palate

vaccine a suspension of killed or attenuated microorganisms administered for the prevention or treatment of disease by stimulation of the body's immune mechanisms

vagina a sheath-like structure, especially the canal leading from the vulva to the uterus

vagus "wandering"; the tenth cranial nerve

valve a structure that permits flow of a fluid in one direction only

vas a vessel or duct

vascular pertaining to or having blood vessels

vasoconstriction narrowing of blood vessels, especially of arterioles, leading to a diminution of blood flow to a part

vasodilation increase in the diameter of blood vessels, especially of arterioles, leading to an increase in blood supply to a part

vasomotor pertaining to nerves controlling the activity of smooth muscle in blood vessels

vastus wide, large

vein a vessel carrying blood toward the heart

ventral pertaining to the belly; toward the belly or anterior; opposite of dorsal

ventricle a small cavity or chamber, as in the brain or heart

venule a small vein, collecting blood from the capillary beds

vermiform worm-shaped

vestibule a space or cavity at the entrance to a canal

villus a minute fingerlike projection of the mucosa into the lumen of the intestine

viscera internal organs

vitamin a group of organic compounds (not proteins, carbohydrates, or fats) that occur in foods in small amounts and are essential for metabolism

vitreous glassy

volar pertaining to the palm of the hand or the sole of the foot

voluntary under willful or conscious control

Wallerian degeneration destructive changes occurring in an axon severed from the cell body

xiphoid sword-shaped

yolk sac a membranous sac surrounding the yolk of an embryo; in humans a transitory structure incorporated into the gut

zygote the fertilized egg; cell formed by the union of two gametes

zymogen an inactive precursor that is converted to an enzyme by the action of acid, another enzyme, or other agent

CREDITS

Chapter 1
Figure 1-1(A, B, and C): Nina Leake. *Figure 1-1(D):* Courtesy Lotz, MD, Vienna, Virginia, Nina Leake, photographer. *Figure 1-2:* The Bettmann Archive.

CHAPTER 2
Figure 2-3 (all): United Nations.

CHAPTER 4
Figure 4-1(A): Merck and Co., Inc. *Figure 4-1(B):* Carolina Biological Supply. *Figure 4-1(C):* Lee V. Leak, Ph.D., Howard University College of Medicine. *Figure 4-3:* Dr. Richard L. Wood, University of Miami School of Medicine. *Figure 4-4:* From J. Rhodin, *Histology*, Oxford University Press, 1974. *Figure 4-5:* Keith Porter. *Figure 4-6(A):* From J. Rhodin, *Histology*, Oxford University Press, 1974. *Figure 4-6(B):* D. W. Fawcett. *Figures 4-7 and 4-8:* From J. Rhodin, *Histology*, Oxford University Press, 1974. *Figure 4-10(A):* George Palade. *Figure 4-10(B):* Donald F. Parsons. *Figure 4-11:* Courtesy Dr. G. Albrecht-Buehle, Cold Spring Harbor Laboratory, New York (Scientific American April 1978) *Figure 4-12(A):* From J. Rhodin, *Histology*, Oxford University Press, 1974. *Figure 4-12(B):* Landrum B. Shettles.

CHAPTER 5
Figure 5-2 (all): Carolina Biological Supply. *Figures 5-5 (all), 5-7(A and B), 5-8 (all), 5-9, 5-10, 5-12, 5-13, 5-14(A and B):* From J. Rhodin, *Histology*, Oxford University Press, 1974. *Figure 5-15:* Carolina Biological Supply.

CHAPTER 6
Figure 6-3 (all): Eric V. Gravé. *Figure 6-5:* James G. Hirsch. *Figure 6-9 (all):* Eric V. Gravé. *Figure 6-11 (all):* Grace M. Donnelly, Arnold Sparrow, Robert F. Smith, Brookhaven National Laboratory. *Figure 6-14 (both):* From L. S. Penrose, *Recent Advances in Human Genetics*, Little, Brown, 1961. *Figure 6-16(A):* Courtesy of Irene A. Uchida. *Figure 6-16(B):* D. H. Carr, M. L. Barr.

CHAPTER 7
Figure 7-1: From J. Rhodin, *Histology*, Oxford University Press, 1974. *Figure 7-2(A):* Nina Leake. *Figure 7-2(B):* Lisa Berg. *Figure 7-2(C):* Nina Leake. *Figure 7-3 (both):* Fairfax County Police, Virginia. *Figure 7-4(A):* From J. Rhodin, *Histology*, Oxford University Press, 1974. *Figures 7-4(B) and 7-6(B):* Camera M. D. Studios. *Figure 7-11:* H. Harlan Stone.

CHAPTER 8
Figure 8-2: From J. Rhodin, *Histology*, Oxford University Press, 1974. *Figure 8-3:* Carolina Biological Supply. *Figure 8-5 (both):* From J. Rhodin, *Histology*, Oxford University Press, 1974. *Figure 8-8 (both):* American Museum of Natural History. *Figure 8-16:* Courtesy of Radiography Markets Division, Eastman Kodak Company. *Figure 8-21:* R. W. Carlin. *Figure 8-25:* Lester V. Bergman & Associates, Inc. *Figure 8-27(A and B):* Armed Forces Institute of Pathology. *Figure 8-27(C):* Elizabeth Wilcox.

CHAPTER 9
Figure 9-7(A): Armed Forces Institute of Pathology. *Figure 9-7(B):* Photo courtesy Pfizer, Inc.

CHAPTER 10
Figure 10-2 (all): From J. Rhodin, *Histology*, Oxford University Press, 1974. *Figure 10-4:* H. E. Huxley, MRC Lab of Molecular Biology, Cambridge, England. *Figure 10-18:* Katherine Bendo.

CHAPTER 11
Figure 11-1: From J. Rhodin, *Histology*, Oxford University Press, 1974. *Figure 11-3:* From E. M. Greisheimer and M. P. Wiedeman, *Physiology and Anatomy*, J. B. Lippincott Co., 1972. *Figure 11-4:* H. E. Huxley, MRC Lab of Molecular Biology, Cambridge, England. *Figure 11-7:* Wide World Photos. *Figure 11-8:* Courtesy Phipps & Bird, Inc. *Figure 11-15:* Wide World Photos. *Figure 11-22 (both):* Nina Leake. *Figure 11-24:* Wide World Photos.

CHAPTER 12
Figure 12-3 (both): From J. Rhodin, *Histology*, Oxford University Press, 1974. *Figure 12-5:* Don Silberberg, MD, University of Pennsylvania Hospital. *Figure 12-14:* From J. Rhodin, *Histology*, Oxford University Press, 1974.

CHAPTER 13
Figure 13-15: Stanley Krippner, Maimondes Hospital. *Figure 13-26:* From Frederic A. Gibbs, "Influence of Blood Sugar Level in Wave and Spike Formation in Petit Mal Epilepsy", *Archives of Neurology* Vol. 41, pp. 1111–1116, 1939.

CHAPTER 14
Figure 14-9: Nina Leake.

CHAPTER 15
Figure 15-1(A): From J. Rhodin, *Histology*, Oxford University Press, 1974. *Figure 15-4:* Philip Daly.

CHAPTER 16
Figure 16-11: Lee V. Leak, Ph.D., Howard University College of Medicine. *Figure 16-12:* Nina Leake.

CHAPTER 17
Figure 17-3(A): Katherine Bendo. *Figure 17-3(B):* Nina Leake. *Figure 17-11:* Richard Schlecht. *Figures 17-19 and 17-20:* Nina Leake. *Figure 17-21:* Courtesy Graham-Field Surgical Co., Inc. *Figure 17-22 (both):* Courtesy Eye Clinic, The Hennepin County Medical Center, Minneapolis. *Figure 17-23:* Nina Leake.

CHAPTER 18
Figure 18-4(A and B): Nina Leake. *Figure 18-4(C):* Katherine Bendo. *Figure 18-12 (all):* R. A. Buckingham, MD, Clinical Professor Otolaryngology, Abraham Lincoln School of Medicine, University of Illinois, Chicago.

CHAPTER 19
Figure 19-1: Carolina Biological Supply. *Figure 19-3:* Armed Forces Institute of Pathology. *Figure 19-4:* Dr. R. F. Baker, University of Southern California. *Figure 19-5:* Lester V. Bergman & Associates, Inc. *Figure 19-8:* Eric V. Gravé. *Figure 19-10(A, B, and C):* From J. Rhodin, *His-*

tology, Oxford University Press, 1974. *Figure 19-10(D):* Lester V. Bergman & Associates, Inc. *Figure 19-13:* Armed Forces Institute of Pathology. *Figure 19-14:* SEM Courtesy of Thomas L. Hayes and Lawrence-Berkeley Laboratory, University of California. *Figure 19-18:* Nina Leake. *Figure 19-20:* From Langley, Telford, Christensen, *Dynamic Anatomy and Physiology,* 1974, courtesy McGraw-Hill Book Company.

CHAPTER 20
Figure 20-3: Lester V. Bergman & Associates, Inc. *Figure 20-5:* Charles L. McIntosh, MD, National Heart and Lung Institute, National Institute of Health. *Figures 20-8, 20-10, 20-12:* From J. Rhodin, *Histology,* Oxford University Press, 1974. *Figure 20-33:* Bruce Roberts/Photo Researchers.

CHAPTER 21
Figure 21-4: David R. Redwood, MD, National Heart and Lung Institute, National Institute of Health. *Figures 21-8 and 21-10 (both):* Nina Leake. *Figure 21-13:* National Heart and Lung Institute, National Institute of Health. *Figure 21-14:* Armed Forces Institute of Pathology. *Figure 21-15:* Courtesy New York Hospital, EKG Department.

CHAPTER 22
Figures 22-3 and 22-5: From J. Rhodin, *Histology,* Oxford University Press, 1974. *Figures 22-8(C) and 22-9:* Armed Forces Institute of Pathology.

CHAPTER 23
Figure 23-2 (all): Katherine Bendo. *Figure 23-7 (both):* Nina Leake. *Figure 23-9:* Elizabeth Wilcox. *Figure 23-12:* From J. Rhodin, *Histology,* Oxford University Press, 1974.

CHAPTER 24
Figure 24-2(B): Nina Leake. *Figure 24-8 (all):* Nina Leake. *Figure 24-9 (both):* American Cancer Society. *Figures 24-10 and 24-11:* Nina Leake.

CHAPTER 25
Figure 25-6: Courtesy Columbia Dentoform Corp., photograph by Katherine Bendo. *Figures 25-10 and 25-14(B and C):* From J. Rhodin, *Histology,* Oxford University Press, 1974. *Figure 25-16:* From Lanhley, Telford, Christensen, *Dynamic Anatomy and Physiology,* 1974, courtesy McGraw-Hill Book Company. *Figure 25-19 (all):* Armed Forces Institute of Pathology.

CHAPTER 26
Figure 26-11: Elizabeth Wilcox.

CHAPTER 27
Figure 27-2: Lee V. Leak, Ph.D., Howard University College of Medicine.

CHAPTER 28
Figure 28-1: Katherine Bendo. *Figure 28-5:* USDA. *Figure 28-6 (all):* Nina Leake. *Figure 28-9:* Dale Wittner, People Weekly, © 1978 Time, Inc. *Figure 28-10:* UNICEF photo by Paul Larsen.

CHAPTER 29
Figure 29-6: From J. Rhodin, *Histology,* Oxford University Press, 1974.

CHAPTER 31
Figure 31-5: Nina Leake.

CHAPTER 32
Figure 32-3: Micrograph, From J. Rhodin, *Histology,* Oxford University Press, 1974. *Figure 32-4(A);* Armed Forces Institute of Pathology. *Figure 32-4(B):* From the teaching collection of the late Dr. Fuller Albright, courtesy of the Endocrine Unit and Department of Medicine, Massachusetts General Hospital. *Figure 32-5:* Armed Forces Institute of Pathology. *Figure 32-8:* From J. Rhodin, *Histology,* Oxford University Press, 1974. *Figure 32-10(A):* From the teaching collection of the late Dr. Fuller Albright, courtesy of the Endocrine Unit and Department of Medicine, Massachusetts General Hospital. *Figure 32-10(B):* The Center for Disease Control, Atlanta. *Figure 32-11:* Armed Forces Institute of Pathology. *Figure 32-12:* From J. Rhodin, *Histology,* Oxford University Press, 1974. *Figure 32-13:* Camera MD Studios. *Figure 32-18:* From the teaching collection of the late Dr. Fuller Albright, courtesy of the Endocrine Unit and Department of Medicine, Masachusetts General Hospital. *Figures 32-19, 32-21, and 32-23:* From J. Rhodin, *Histology,* Oxford University Press, 1974. *Figure 32-25:* Lisa Berg.

CHAPTER 33
Figure 33-3: Lester V. Bergman & Associates, Inc. *Figure 33-7:* Armed Forces Institute of Pathology.

CHAPTER 34
Figure 34-5: From J. Rhodin, *Histology,* Oxford University Press, 1974. *Figure 34-7:* From Langley, Telford, Christensen, *Dynamic Anatomy and Physiology,* 1974, courtesy McGraw-Hill Book Company. *Figure 34-8(B and C):* Landrum B. Shettles. *Figure 34-10:* Nina Leake.

CHAPTER 35
Figure 35-1: Landrum B. Shettles. *Figure 35-2:* Ron Nelson. *Figures 35-6 and 35-8 (all):* Landrum B. Shettles. *Figure 35-11 (both):* Armed Forces Institute of Pathology. *Figure 35-12:* Stella Kupferberg. *Figure 35-13 (both):* HEW, Public Health Service, Center for Disease Control.

CHAPTER 36
Figure 36-3 (all): Nina Leake. *Figure 36-4:* Hella Hammid/Rapho-Photo Researchers.

CHAPTER 37
Figure 37-2(A): G. Cohen-Bazire. *Figure 37-2(B and C):* Stanley Holt. *Figure 37-3(A and B):* R. C. Williams. *Figure 37-3(C):* Carl Zeiss Co. *Figure 37-4:* Merck and Co., Inc. *Figure 37-5:* Photo courtesy Pfizer, Inc. *Figure 37-7:* S. Mims and T. Triche, MD, Ph.D., National Institute of Health. *Figure 37-8:* Lee V. Leak, Ph.D., Howard University College of Medicine. *Figure 37-10:* New York Times Pictures. *Figure 37-14:* Photo courtesy Pfizer, Inc.

CHAPTER 38
Figures 38-1 and 38-2(A): Nina Leake. *Figure 38-2(B):* Georgetown University. *Figure 38-3(A):* Jim Collison.

INDEX†

† References to figures are italicized.